MICROBIOLOGY

DAVID T. SMITH, M. D.
Professor of Microbiology
Associate Professor of Medicine
Duke University School of Medicine

NORMAN F. CONANT, Ph. D.
Chairman and Professor
Department of Microbiology
Duke University School of Medicine

JOHN R. OVERMAN, M. D.
Professor of Microbiology
Assistant Professor of Medicine
Duke University School of Medicine

JOSEPH W. BEARD, M. D.
Professor of Surgery
In Charge of Experimental Surgery
Duke University School of Medicine

HILDA POPE WILLETT, Ph. D.
Professor of Microbiology
Duke University School of Medicine

JOHN E. LARSH, JR., Sc. D.
Professor of Parasitology
School of Public Health and School of Medicine
University of North Carolina and
Duke University School of Medicine

D. BERNARD AMOS, M. D.
Professor of Immunology
Associate Professor of Experimental Surgery
Duke University School of Medicine

CHESTER M. ZMIJEWSKI, Ph. D.
Assistant Professor of Immunology
Duke University School of Medicine

EDWARD GLASSMAN, Ph. D.
Professor of Biochemistry
University of North Carolina School of Medicine

SUYDAM OSTERHOUT, M. D., Ph. D.
Assistant Professor of Microbiology
Associate in Medicine
Duke University School of Medicine

D. GORDON SHARP, Ph. D.
Professor of Biophysics
University of North Carolina School of Medicine

APPLETON-CENTURY-CROFTS
Division of Meredith Publishing Company
NEW YORK

MICROBIOLOGY

To the memory of
PHILIP HANSON HISS, JR.
HANS ZINSSER
and to
STANHOPE BAYNE-JONES

whose labors over more than one third of a
century have made this textbook a favorite
with students of medicine and public health.

Preface

The combination of new ideas, trained investigators, and research grants has resulted in a literal explosion of new discoveries in practically all divisions of microbiology since the last edition. This development necessitated the addition of four new authors and the inclusion of five new chapters. The new chapters include bacterial genetics, transplantation of tissue, the unclassified species of *Mycobacterium, Serratia marcescens,* and enteroviruses. The chapters on bacterial physiology and immunology have been increased both in length and in scope. The chapter on the *Staphylococcus* has been expanded, but the other chapters on bacterial and spirochetal diseases have been condensed somewhat to compensate for an increase in other areas.

In the preface to the first edition of this text, written in 1910, the authors emphasized the importance of a basic approach which would include not only the biologic characteristics of the organisms but also the reactions of the living tissues to the bacteria and their products. This approach made the volume of equal value to the microbiologist and to the student of public health and clinical medicine. This same point of view has been retained in this edition and extends to the divisions of virology, mycology, and parasitology. The chapters dealing with infections have an introductory paragraph which emphasizes the public health aspect of the disease. The more important biologic and cultural characteristics have been emphasized by printing in boldface type. Highly technical sections and descriptions of disease of minor importance have been printed in small type.

In general the text has been written for the student, and the bibliographies collected for the graduate students and the teacher. The bibliographies are longer than before and include over 2,500 references from the current literature of 1960-64.

There are 257 new illustrations in this edition which brings the total to 606 including the three full-page color plates in the section on parasitology.

We wish to thank our many colleagues and students for their critical advice and generous help in the preparation of this revision; especially those who have supplied us with new illustrative material.

We are indebted to Elon H. Clark, Robert L. Blake, Robert King, Stephen Honeycutt, and Henry F. Pickett for the preparation of new illustrations. We wish to acknowledge the valuable assistance of our secretaries, Miss Hope Smith, Mrs. Elizabeth Smith, Mrs. Carlotta Kale, Mrs. Helen Sullivan, Mrs. Bonnie Freitas, Mrs. Barrie Wallace, Mrs. Judy Kenan, and Mrs. Edith Black Kristoff who have cheerfully typed and retyped the manuscript many times.

We also wish to express our appreciation to Appleton-Century-Crofts for many helpful suggestions in the preparation of the manuscript.

DAVID T. SMITH
NORMAN F. CONANT
JOHN R. OVERMAN

Preface to the First Edition

The volume here presented is primarily a treatise on the fundamental laws and technic of bacteriology, as illustrated by their application to the study of pathogenic bacteria.

So ubiquitous are the bacteria and so manifold their activities that bacteriology, although one of the youngest of sciences, has already been divided into special fields—medical, sanitary, agricultural, and industrial—having little in common, except problems of general bacterial physiology and certain fundamental technical procedures.

From no other point of approach, however, is such a breadth of conception attainable, as through the study of bacteria in their relation to disease processes in man and animals. Through such a study one must become familiar not only with the growth characteristics and products of the bacteria apart from the animal body, thus gaining a knowledge of methods and procedures common to the study of pathogenic and non-pathogenic organisms, but also with those complicated reactions taking place between the bacteria and their products on the one hand and the cells and fluids of the animal body on the other—reactions which often manifest themselves as symptoms and lesions of disease or by visible changes in the test tube.

Through a study and comprehension of the processes underlying these reactions, our knowledge of cell physiology has been broadened, and facts of inestimable value have been discovered, which have thrown light upon some of the most obscure problems of infection and immunity and have led to hitherto unsuspected methods of treatment and diagnosis. Thus, through medical bacteriology—that highly specialized offshoot of general biology and pathology—have been given back to the parent sciences and to medicine in general methods and knowledge of the widest application.

It has been our endeavor, therefore, to present this phase of our subject in as broad and critical a manner as possible in the sections dealing with infection and immunity and with methods of biological diagnosis and treatment of disease, so that the student and practitioner of medicine, by becoming familiar with underlying laws and principles, may not only be in a position to realize the meaning and scope of some of these newer discoveries and methods, but may be in better position to decide for themselves their proper application and limitation.

We have not hesitated, whenever necessary for a proper understanding of processes of bacterial nutrition or physiology, or for breadth of view in considering problems of the relation of bacteria to our food supply and environment, to make free use of illustrations from the more special fields of agricultural and sanitary bacteriology, and some special methods of the bacteriology of sanitation are given in the last division of the book, dealing with the bacteria in relation to our food and environment.

In conclusion it may be said that the scope and arrangement of subjects treated of in this book are the direct outcome of many years of experience in the instruction of students in medical and in advanced university courses in bacteriology, and that it is our hope that this volume may not only meet the needs of such students but may prove of value to the practitioner of medicine for whom it has also been written.

It is a pleasure to acknowledge the courtesy of those who furnished us with illustrations for use in the text, and our indebtedness to Dr. Gardner Hopkins and Professor Francis Carter Wood for a number of the photomicrographs taken especially for this work.

P. H. Hiss, Jr.
H. Zinsser

Contents

Contents

Contents

MEDICAL PARASITOLOGY

MICROBIOLOGY

THE GENERAL BIOLOGY OF BACTERIA AND THE GENERAL METHODS OF BACTERIOLOGY

1

Outline of the History and Scope of Bacteriology

The history of many concepts now embodied in the doctrines of bacteriology is an account of attempts to solve the problems of the origin of life, the putrefaction of dead organic materials, and the nature of communicable changes in the bodies of living men and animals. The visible aspects of these phenomena were as apparent and as interesting to ancient observers as they are to modern biologists. In the past, notions of ultimate causes were derived from the available factual knowledge colored by the theologic and philosophic tenets of the time. The early history of what has become the science of microbiology is to be found, therefore, in the writings of the priests, philosophers, and scientists who studied and pondered these basic biologic problems.

Fortunately for the student of medical bacteriology, Bulloch (8) published in 1938 a small concisely written book entitled *The History of Bacteriology,* containing the results of his extensive studies.

Among ancient peoples epidemic and even endemic diseases were regarded as supernatural in origin and sent by the gods as punishment for the sins of man. The treatment and, more important, the prevention of these diseases were sought by sacrifices and lustrations to appease the anger of the gods. Since man is willful, wanton and sinful by nature there was never any difficulty in finding a particular set of sins to justify a specific epidemic.

The Egyptians apparently had a vague notion that disease could be transmitted by touch; certainly the Hebrews at the time of Moses believed that leprosy was contagious.

They thought it could be contracted by personal contact from the clothes of the patient and even by living in the home of a former leper (Leviticus 13 and 14). Although recognizing that leprosy could be transmitted by direct contact, the Hebrews also believed it could be created de novo as in the case of Miriam who angered the Lord by speaking against Moses (Numbers 12:9). The establishment of quarantine by Marseilles and Venice in the fourteenth century was perhaps influenced as much by the religious feelings that a period of purification was needed as by the pragmatic idea that such a period of isolation would prevent the spread of disease.

At the time of the siege of Troy the Greeks believed in the divine origin of epidemic diseases, but as they lost faith in their gods they also lost faith in the divine origin of disease. By 430 B.C. Thucydides had concluded that certain plagues were contagious.

Hippocrates rejected the theory of divine origin but did not consider the possibility of contagion. He recognized two factors that were involved in the development of disease —an intrinsic factor of "constitution" of the patient, and an extrinsic factor, or "miasm," air modified in some unknown way so that the air itself became deleterious. The belief in the disease-producing effect of bad air thrived in the Middle Ages and has persisted to modern times as shown by the medical words "influenza" and "malaria."

Although the Middle Ages were characterized by a series of destructive epidemics the belief that disease is caused by a living contagious agent grew slowly. A knowledge of the natural history of syphilis influenced

Fracastorius, who clearly stated the theory that the agent of communicable diseases was living, a "contagium vivum." In his book on contagious diseases, published in 1546, Fracastorius (32) described the transmission of disease by direct contact, by intermediary inanimate fomites, and through the air "ad distans." He called the agents of disease "seminaria morbi," living germs, and expressed the opinion that the seeds of these agents, passing from one infected animal, produced the same disease in another which received them. These essentially true statements were unconvincing because they were not based upon a demonstration of the physical reality of the hypothetical invisible organisms. Even after the discovery of bacteria, confirmation of the theories of Fracastorius was long delayed.

Although Fracastorius, as we now know, had indeed proposed the true germ theory of disease, no further progress could be made until microscopes were invented to visualize these germs and until the question of spontaneous generation of bacteria was settled.

According to Singer (69) and Disney (18) the compound microscope was invented independently by Zaccharias Jansen in Holland and Galileo in Italy about 1609 (33).

Bacteria were discovered by Antony van Leeuwenhoek (1632-1723) in 1676. This statement has been placed beyond refutation through available historical records by the great biography of van Leeuwenhoek published by Dobell (19) in 1932. In addition to translations from the "Nether-Dutch" of all of the important parts of the letters of Leeuwenhoek in which bacteria and protozoa are described, this book contains convincing evidence that Leeuwenhoek was in fact the "father of protozoology and bacteriology."

The "microscope" with which he saw bacteria was a simple biconvex lens, of short focal length, clamped between two metal plates. The preparation under examination in a drop of fluid or thin glass tube was fixed upon a metal point and moved into focus by means of screws. One type of the instrument is shown in Figure 1, copied from a drawing made by Dobell. It is probable that Leeuwenhoek's best glasses gave a magnification of 300 diameters. He never disclosed the secrets of all his methods, and it is not known with certainty how he obtained the necessary illumination of his preparations. Dobell suggests that Leeuwenhoek probably hit upon some simple means of dark ground illumination. The first written descriptions of bacteria are in his letter to the Royal Society of London, dated October 9, 1676 (Dobell's No. 18). Here he gives recognizable descriptions of bacteria in various waters and in "pepper water" in which he was searching with his magnifying glass for the cause of the hotness of pepper. Clearer descriptions of several forms of bacteria are given in his letter to the Royal Society, dated September 17, 1683 (Dobell's No. 39). In this he described the animalcules he found in the feces of man and animals and in the tartar from his teeth. A drawing of bacteria accompanied this letter. The original has been lost, but the record has been preserved in the plate illustrating the Latin translation of this letter published in 1695 (78). We reproduce a photograph of this famous drawing here, as Figure 2. It shows beyond question that Leeuwenhoek saw the chief forms of bacteria—cocci, rods, filaments and spirochetes (14). Leeuwenhoek believed that the air was the source of his

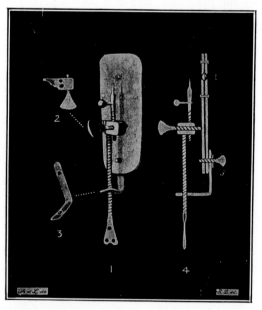

Fig. 1. Leeuwenhoek's "microscope." (From Dobell. *Antony van Leeuwenhoek and His "Little Animals."* Courtesy of Harcourt, Brace & World, Inc.)

microscopic creatures and that they existed in this medium in the form of seed or germs. It is doubtful if he ever heard of Fracastorius' book which was published 137 years before, and certainly neither he nor any of his immediate successors associated these "seed" with the "seed" which caused disease.

In 1678 Hooke confirmed Leeuwenhoek's discovery, and during the early part of the eighteenth century the "little animals" were seen and described by a number of microscopists. The difficulties of assigning them a place and giving them a name are exemplified in Linnaeus' creation in 1758 of the genus *Vermes* which he called "Chaos" (44). A few years later, Wrisberg named these organisms *Infusoria*. No doubt this helped Linnaeus to give them a name, for in the eleventh edition of his *Systema naturae* (44), in 1767, according to Bulloch (8), he formed a class called *Chaos infusorium*. That he was still confused as to the nature of bacteria and protozoa is indicated by his listing them with "the ethereal nimbus floating in the month of flowering." In some respects the classification of bacteria is chaotic even now.

The first important classification of the *Infusoria* was made by O. F. Müller (50) in 1773 and 1786. The terms *Vibrio* and *Monas* were introduced by Müller. Some 50 years later, Ehrenberg (25), without really understanding the nature of bacteria, began to publish classifications of them. In 1829 he established the genus *Bacterium,* using a term formed from the Greek word Βακτήριον, the diminutive of Βάκτρον, signifying a staff. The whole subject of bacteriology has taken its common name from the prominence of the rod forms.

The transference of the bacteria to the plant kingdom was first proposed by Ferdinand Cohn in 1854. Cohn's (15) publications after 1872 marked a great advance in the systematic study of bacteria. His personal influence as a teacher and director of investigators equalled that of his written works. Under Cohn's guidance, the botanic point of view became dominant in bacteriology. In 1857 Nägeli had noted the relationship of bacteria to fungi and had introduced the term *Schizomycetes,* a term which has remained for the scientific designation of these organisms.

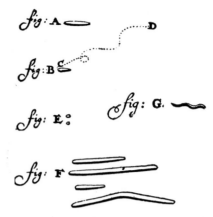

Fig. 2. Leeuwenhoek's picture of bacteria from the human mouth. Dobell's identifications are as follows: A, a motile *Bacillus.* B, *Selenomonas sputigena.* E, micrococci. F, *Leptothrix buccans.* G, probably *Spirochaeta buccalis.* (From van Leeuwenhoek.)

Primitive classifications of bacteria were established and accepted before they were associated with disease. One early concept of the origin of disease, however, involved a belief in a communicable agent such as that responsible for the leavening of bread, the making of wine and the brewing of beer. Robert Boyle suggested in 1663 that some diseases such as "Feavers and others" might be a kind of fermentation. But fermentations and putrefactions often occurred without any known cause and were, therefore, attributed to spontaneous generation.

The problem of spontaneous generation is one facet of the larger problem of the origin of life. That phase of the problem which deals with small animals, worms, and insects could be studied without the aid of a microscope but, backed by Aristotle's authority, this conception of spontaneous generation, or abiogenesis, dominated thought throughout the Middle Ages. Samson's riddle relating to the production of bees and honey from the carcass of a lion (Judges 14:8, 14) was matched in 1648 by van Helmont's directions for generating mice from pieces of dirty cloth and fermenting grain. What appeared to be particularly astonishing to van Helmont was that the mice generating from rags and grain were sexually mature and capable of copulating with mice descended from natural parents (77). Similar fanciful notions of the generation of insects were put to experimental test by Francesco Redi shortly after the middle of the seventeenth century. Redi proved conclusively that the maggots which appeared in decomposing meat were developed from the eggs of flies and showed by experiments that when meat was screened by gauze so that flies could not deposit their eggs in it no visible worms or insects were generated, although the meat putrefied. Redi's conclusion that life comes from life, supported by experiments which anyone could repeat, should have decided the issue.

The work of Redi and his followers (61) finally disposed of the theory of spontaneous generation of living things of macroscopic size, yet its advocates did not surrender but continued to believe in spontaneous generation at the microscopic level. The old controversy about spontaneous generation, now transferred to the microscopic level, had to be settled before acceptable conclusions could be reached regarding other problems.

Needham, the Welshman (52), found bacteria in his infusion of animal and vegetable materials even after boiling and excluding air from the vessels. Needham and Buffon were assailed by the great Italian naturalist, Abbé Spallanzani (70) who pointed out the technical errors in their work (1765-1776). He also discovered bacteria which grew in the absence of air, and forms which resisted boiling which we now know as spores. His work would have settled the question of spontaneous generation had Needham not shifted the grounds for the controversy by claiming that the excessive heating produced chemical changes in the solutions which made spontaneous generation impossible. Schulze (67), Schwann (68), Schröder and von Dusch (66) supported Spallanzani with numerous new experiments including the introduction of cotton stoppers to filter bacteria from the air.

The question was not definitely settled until the years immediately following 1860 when Pasteur conducted a series of experiments which were important not only in incontrovertibly refuting the doctrine of spontaneous generation of bacteria, but also in establishing the principles of scientific investigation which have influenced bacteriologic research since his time.

Pasteur attacked the problem from two points of view. In the first instance he demonstrated that when air was filtered through cotton wool innumerable microorganisms were deposited upon the filter. A single shred of such a contaminated filter dropped into a flask of previously sterilized nutritive fluid sufficed to initiate a rapid and luxuriant growth of microorganisms. In the second experiment he succeeded in showing that similar sterilized "putrescible" liquids, when left in contact with air, would remain uncontaminated provided the entrance of dust particles was prevented. This he accomplished by devising flasks, the necks of which had been drawn out into fine tubes bent in the form of a U. The ends of these U-tubes, being left open, permitted the sedimentation of dust from the air as far as the lowest angle of the tube, but, in the absence of an air current, no dust was carried up the second arm into the liquid. In such flasks he showed that no contamination occurred but that it could be immediately induced by slanting the entire apparatus until the liquid was allowed to run into the bent arm of the U-tube. Finally, by exposing a series of flasks containing sterile yeast infusion at different atmospheric levels, in places in which the air was subject to varying degrees of dust contamination, he showed an inverse relationship between the purity of the air and the contamination of his flasks with microorganisms (56, 57, 58) (Fig. 3).

The doctrine of spontaneous generation of bacteria had thus received its final refutation, except in one particular. It was still puzzling why complete sterility was sometimes not obtained by the application of definite degrees of heat. In England, as in France, the chief opponent of the doctrine of spontaneous generation was a man of ideas, great experimental skill, keen insight and exact method. This was John Tyndall (75) who, starting from experiments to remove motes from air, made many important discoveries in bacteriology. He demonstrated independently the great heat-resistance of spores previously discovered by Cohn in 1871 (15), and devised the method of fractional sterilization. By means of lectures and demonstrations, and by a notable book published in 1882, Tyndall, as Bulloch states, "gave the final blow to the doctrine of spontaneous generation" and opened the road for the advancement of the germ theory of disease (8).

Meanwhile Pasteur, while investigating spontaneous generation, had been carrying on experiments on the subject of fermentation along the lines suggested by Cagniard-Latour (10). As a result of these experiments, he not only confirmed the opinions both of this author and of Schwann concerning the fermentation of beer and wine by yeast, but also showed that a number of other fermentations, such as those of lactic and butyric acid, as well as the putrefactive decomposition of organic matter were directly due to the action of microorganisms. The importance of his contribution to bacteriology can hardly be overemphasized; indeed, as René Dubos (22) has so aptly said in his *Louis Pasteur, Free Lance of Science* (1950) the domestication of microbial life began with Pasteur.

Proof that putrefaction is caused by living agents stimulated Lister (34, 45), who was a bacteriologist as well as a surgeon, to apply carbolic acid dressings to operative wounds. Thus were instituted the antiseptic principles later largely replaced by aseptic methods which have made modern surgery possible. The history of bacteriology in surgery from the time of Lister to the present era has been reviewed by Meleney (48).

Almost 150 years passed after Leeuwenhoek's discovery of bacteria and protozoa before any definite applications of this new knowledge were made in the study of the cause of disease. In a remarkable series of investigations during the first quarter of the nineteenth century Agostino Bassi proved almost conclusively that a fungus, later named in his honor *Botrytis bassiana,* was the cause of a disease of silkworms called "mal segno" in Italy and "muscardine" in France. Bassi's biographer, Calandruccio (11), called Bassi the founder of the theory of parasitism.

In 1839 Schoenlein (65) found the causative fungus in the lesions of favus, and in 1846 Eichstedt (28) discovered a fungus in the skin-scrapings from patients with pityriasis versicolor and noted the contagiousness of the disease. Rayer and Davaine had seen rod-shaped organisms in the blood of animals dead of anthrax in 1850. Rayer (60) recalled experiments made by Barthélemy in

Fig. 3. One of Pasteur's original flasks. (From Bulloch. *The History of Bacteriology,* Oxford University Press.)

1825 showing that anthrax was inoculable in series in sheep. By 1863 Davaine (16) had proved experimentally that the disease could be transmitted by blood and the sediment of laked blood containing these rods, but could not be transmitted by blood from which the rods were absent. Between 1868 and 1872 Obermeier (55) at the Charité in Berlin, under Virchow's eye, was carefully confirming his discovery of the relationship of a spirillum to relapsing fever. He demonstrated for the first time the presence of a pathogenic microorganism in the blood of man.

It must be remembered that during these early years of etiologic research investigators had pure cultures to work with only by accident and did not know when contaminants were present in the materials they used. There was much speculation and loose thinking and a considerable amount of equivocal work that hindered the development of bacteriology.

Henle (36), the future teacher of Robert Koch, affirmed his belief in the animate nature and specific action of the agents of contagion. He insisted on the proof that an organism causing a disease must be accompanied by demonstration of its constant presence in the lesions, the isolation of this microorganism and the reproduction of the disease by inoculation. With much the same point of view in 1865 Villemin (79) proved by experiments on rabbits that the tubercle was inoculable. Villemin interpreted his experiments as evidence that tuberculosis was the effect of a virus. He thought that the virus must be present in the morbid products and when introduced into a susceptible animal must be able to reproduce itself and at the same time reproduce the disease.

In 1876 Robert Koch, who had been a pupil of Jacob Henle, came to Breslau at the invitation of Cohn to demonstrate the results of his studies on anthrax. In Cohn's laboratory, Koch exhibited his culture methods, showed the life cycle of the anthrax bacillus from spore to spore, and proved beyond doubt the ability of cultures of this organism to produce the disease. Koch's classic paper on the etiology of anthrax, published in 1876, was the first of a great series of enlightening contributions by him and his pupils. It inaugurated a new era of research in bacteriology (40).

Koch realized the importance of method and technic and was not long in introducing many of the procedures which are now everyday, indispensable practices in laboratories of bacteriology. From Weigert, Ehrlich and Salomonsen he learned methods of staining bacteria with aniline dyes (27). In his work on anthrax his chief culture medium had been sterile aqueous humor from the eyes of animals. He had seen the advantages of the older opaque solid media made from potato, beets, starch, bread, egg-white and flesh, but

realized that they were incapable of giving all the desired information about bacterial colonies. In order to separate one species of bacterium from another, in 1881 Koch devised a transparent solid medium by mixing gelatin with Löffler's peptone solution. During a period of 13 years, from about 1870 to 1883, and especially during the seven years after 1876, fundamental discoveries went hand in hand with advances in technic, and improvements in apparatus (41, 42).

The period of great technical advance, 1871 to 1884, saw the gradual introduction of methods of filtration of fluids containing bacteria. It was desirable to test the possible toxicity of filtrates, freed from cells of the organisms. When it became apparent that filter papers, porous clay cups, and packed asbestos fibers would not retain bacteria, the logical step of making tighter filters was taken. Chamberland (13) devised a successful filter from a cup of unglazed porcelain in 1884. The Berkefeld type of filter, made of *Kieselguhr,* was introduced by Nordtmeyer (53) in 1891. The Chamberland-Pasteur filters made possible the immediately realized discovery of bacterial toxins. There seems to have been no suspicion at that time that these filters would later appear to be sieves capable of separating visible from invisible forms of life and to be a sort of dividing partition between biologic concepts.

It was found, unexpectedly, that the agents of some of the communicable diseases passed through these filters in invisible forms. In 1892 Iwanowski (37) showed that the ultramicroscopic agent of mosaic disease of tobacco plants was present in the filtered juice of diseased leaves. In 1899 Beijerinck independently confirmed this discovery. He conceived of the invisible self-perpetuating agent of mosaic disease as a contagium fluidum vivum. A few years later Löffler and Frosch showed that foot and mouth disease also was due to a filterable virus. Since then many diseases of animals and plants have been added to this list by the demonstration of the filterability of their etiologic agents (71).

By means of filters a remarkable material causing transmissible lysis of bacteria was discovered by Twort (74) in 1915 and independently by d'Herelle (17) in 1917. This material, called "bacteriophage" by d'Herelle, is now recognized as a virus of bacteria.

While Koch and his students were concentrating on more precise technical methods and describing the etiologic agents of infection, Pasteur and his associates were laying the foundation for modern immunology. Immunology, like bacteriology, has an ancient history, a preliminary period of approximate realization and, after a lapse of many years, a rapid advancement through scientific experimentation upon animals. Many ancient peoples immunized themselves against the venom of serpents by introducing small quantities of the poison into cuts or scratches in the skin. Variolization, the inoculation against smallpox with dried material from dermal lesions, was discovered in China over 20 centuries ago, and from there it spread along the trade routes throughout Asia.

It is the achievement of Edward Jenner that a practice of the people was converted by controlled observations into a scientific principle of prophylaxis. About 1778 Jenner began his study of the immunity to smallpox which seemed to exist in milkmaids who had been infected with cowpox. He published his observations and experiments in 1798, establishing a method of protection against smallpox and a generally applicable principle of active immunization by the use of attenuated virus (4, 38, 62).

Almost 100 years passed between the period of Jenner's investigations and the effective foundation of the science of immunology by Pasteur. In 1877 Pasteur became interested in the recovery of animals from infection. He found that fowls inoculated with old cultures of the bacterium of chicken cholera recovered after a mild illness and were subsequently refractory to infection with virulent organisms. He penetrated at once to the core of this phenomenon. Referring to these old cultures as "attenuated virus," he recognized the relationship of his discovery to the immunity against smallpox consequent upon jennerian vaccination, and gave the general term "vaccine" to the various attenuated organisms he later used to induce immunity to several bacterial diseases.

After his studies on chicken cholera Pasteur began his investigation of anthrax, using as a prophylactic a vaccine made from cultures of the anthrax bacillus attenuated by growth at 42° to 43° C. In 1881, at the dramatic demonstration of the power of his vaccine to protect sheep against anthrax at Pouilly-le-Fort, Pasteur gained an extraordinary triumph (22, 23, 76).

Living, attenuated virus, however, was not without its dangers. A new advance upon a safer, but possibly less effective, line was made in this country between 1884 and 1886 by D. E. Salmon and Theobald Smith (63), who showed that immunity could be produced by injections of heat-killed cultures of the hog cholera bacillus.

From successes in immunization against bacterial diseases Pasteur transferred his interest to the study of rabies. He recognized that rabies was due to an ultramicroscopic virus whose incubation period could be shortened by passage through rabbits and virulence further attenuated by desiccation of the spinal cords of experimentally infected animals. Results were achieved rapidly, and by 1886 several thousand victims of the bites of dogs and wolves had received the Pasteur treatment. In commemoration of this triumph, the Pasteur Institute was erected in Paris in 1888.

The success of Pasteur in immunizing against rabies provided a pattern of approach which, with many modifications, has resulted in effective vaccination against typhus fever, yellow fever, and poliomyelitis.

During these years Pasteur had noted the differences in resistance exhibited by different species of animals, had seen that lowering the body temperature decreased the resistance of an animal to infection, and had conceived of immunity as being a sort of exhaustion process which, by depletion of certain essential materials, rendered the body unfavorable as a medium for the growth of microorganisms. Little, however, had been accomplished in the search for a specific explanation of the mechanism of immunity (54).

During the last decade of the nineteenth century phenomenal progress was made in the study of specific serologic reactions and their interpretation. Two schools of immunologic doctrine grew up. In one, protection was attributed wholly to the action of the blood and tissue fluids. In the other, certain cells of the body were regarded as the agents of defense against infection. Bordet (7) attempted to explain the serologic reaction in terms of physical chemistry while Ehrlich supported a chemical explanation for both the immunizing process and the mechanism of reactions of antigens with the products of immunization (26, 56). Ehrlich's famous side-chain or receptor theory (27) dominated immunologic thought for the next 25 years. Both Bordet and Ehrlich supported the humoral theory of immunity (7), and they were soon in conflict with the cellular and phagocytic theory of immunity which Metchnikoff had been developing since 1881 (49). It is now apparent that there was much truth in both points of view, but since blood and tissue fluids are the products of cells, the distinctions drawn were somewhat artificial.

The first decade of the twentieth century witnessed the development of a new phase of immunology, one that deals with states of specific hypersensitivity, referred to sometimes as anaphylaxis and sometimes as allergy. The study of hypersensitivity in man actually began with Jenner's observation of the accelerated vaccinal reaction in certain previously vaccinated persons. In 1837 the physiologist Magendie (46) described the sudden death of dogs which had been repeatedly injected with egg albumin, and in 1894 Flexner reported that animals which were apparently uninjured by an initial dose of dog serum would succumb to a second dose administered after a lapse of some days or weeks. The first systematic study of anaphylaxis was undertaken by Richet and Portier (59) in 1902. The publication of Arthus (1) in 1903 and the "phenomenon of Theobald Smith" communicated to Ehrlich in 1904 served to focus attention upon the curious state of hypersensitivity which develops after a certain interval of time following the parenteral injection of proteins. Koch's tuberculin stimulated interest in the tuberculin-like type of allergy. But the effective development of this field of investigation in relation to man took place after 1905 when von Pirquet and Schick (80) published their observations on serum sickness. Since that time there has been an enormous accumulation of knowledge on the numerous causes of hypersensitiveness, the protean manifestations of hypersensitiveness, and the relationship of allergy and anaphylaxis to immunity and other features of infection.

The discovery in 1949 by Hench and Kendall (35) that cortisone and the adrenocorticotrophic hormone (ACTH) rapidly and completely inhibit allergic reactions of various kinds opened new fields for investigation and supplied new therapeutic agents for the control of a variety of diseases which were formerly partially or completely resistant to all forms of therapy.

The history of immunology has been summarized briefly here because this science sprang from bacteriology and is still intimately connected with it. It is becoming more and more apparent, however, that immunology and serology have an independent status. While they are inseparably associated with bacteriology, they are important subdivisions of the fields of biochemistry and physiology. One direction of this independent destiny has been clearly indicated in Landsteiner's and Heidelberger's work on the chemical basis of the specificity of immune reactions (5).

Domagk's (20) report in 1935 on the dramatic effect of prontosil on streptococcic infections was soon confirmed by Levaditi and Vaisman (43) in France and Colebrook and Kenny in England. In 1936 Tréfouël, Tréfouël, Nitti and Dovet (73) from France; and Buttle, Gray and Stephenson (9) in England discovered independently that prontosil (20) was converted in the body to sulfanilamide, the active chemical agent.

The success of the sulfonamides catalyzed new interest in chemotherapeutic agents and has resulted in the discovery of the sulfones, which are partially effective in the treatment of leprosy, and in para-aminosalicylic acid and isonicotinic acid, which are remarkably effective against the tubercle bacillus.

The long tortuous story of the antibiotics reviewed by Waksman (81, 82) in 1941 and 1944 can be divided into the fruitless period, beginning with Pasteur and ending with Blum in 1925, and the fruitful period, beginning with Fleming's discovery of test tube penicillin in 1929 (30) (Fig. 4).

Finally, as a result of the stimulus of World War II, Chain and Florey and their associates (12, 31) revived Fleming's peni-

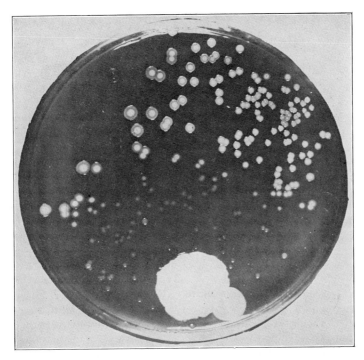

Fig. 4. Photograph of Fleming's original culture which was accidentally contaminated by *Penicillium notatum*. (From Fleming. *Brit. J. Exper. Path.*, 10:226, 1929.)

cillin and demonstrated its practical clinical value. As the result of millions of tests with thousands of organisms, we now have Waksman's streptomycin (81, 82), Meleney's bacitracin (47), Burkholder's chloromycetin (25a), Duggar's aureomycin (24), and Finlay's terramycin (29).

There is every reason for believing that newer, more specific and potent chemotherapeutic and antibiotic drugs will be discovered in the coming years. However, the new therapy has created new problems, such as resistance of the organisms, sensitization of the patient to the drugs, modifications of the clinical syndromes, and the creation of new syndromes by disturbance in the normal ecologic flora of the body.

The biochemical approach to the problem of infectious disease which began as a trickle 30 years ago has now reached flood tide. Studies on both saprophytic and pathogenic bacteria have revealed with monotonous regularity that bacteria, with few exceptions, employ the same enzyme systems and metabolic pathways as the cells of animals. In Dubos' stimulating monograph on *Biochemi-*

cal Determinants of Microbial Diseases (21), the path for the future is defined as a search for "a combination of minor and subtle peculiarities of the infective agents which permit them to survive, multiply, and cause damage in specific *in vivo* environments." The peculiar and specific reactions of the host, both chemical and immunologic, must receive simultaneous and equal attention. The importance of the unsolved biologic problems in infectious disease was reviewed by the philosopher-bacteriologist E. G. D. Murray in 1955 (51).

The 1954 Nobel prize winners Enders, Weller, and Robbins, perfected the tissue culture methods for virus cultivation which has revolutionized the study of viruses. This was followed by the 1958 Nobel prize winners Lederberg, Beadle, and Tatum, whose new technics have catalyzed the study of microbial genetics, and the 1960 Nobel prize winners Macfarlane Burnet and Peter Brian Medawar, whose studies have laid a foundation for a partial understanding of the immunological control of transplanted tissue (Table 1).

Table 1. The Nobel Prize Winners in the General Field of Microbiology

1901	Emil von Behring	Diphtheria antitoxin
1902	Ronald Ross	Malaria
1905	Robert Koch	Tuberculosis and other diseases
1907	Charles L. A. Laveran	Protozoa causing diseases
1908	Elie Metchnikoff Paul Ehrlich	Antibodies and phagocytosis
1913	Charles Richet	Anaphylaxis
1919	Jules Bordet	Complement fixation and immunity
1928	Charles Nicolle	Typhus fever
1930	Karl Landsteiner	Blood groups
1939	Gerhard Domagk	Antibacterial effects of prontosil
1945	Alexander Fleming Ernst Boris Chain Howard Walter Florey	Penicillin
1951	Max Theiler	Yellow fever vaccine
1952	Selman Abraham Waksman	Streptomycin
1954	John F. Enders Thomas H. Weller Frederick C. Robbins	Tissue culture method for growing polio and other viruses
1958	Joshua Lederberg George Wells Beadle Edward Lawrie Tatum	Microbial genetics
1960	Marfarlane Burnet Peter Brian Medawar	Immunological control of transplanted tissues

Bacterial genetics has become a major division of microbiology. The phenomenon of antigenic relationships between species and general bacteria, as well as the more practical problem of varying degrees of virulence, depends upon the bacterial gene. An extension of these studies to the viruses has brought hope that chemical compounds might be found and synthesized which would block some essential enzymatic reactions in the virus (72) without injuring the cells of the host. The genetic material of a virus obviously has to possess the information for the synthesis of the protein coat of the virus, and there is now evidence that the enzymes which are responsible for the synthesis of nucleic acids of animal viruses may, at least in some instances, be new virus-controlled proteins (3). Tamm and Eggers (72) have reported their success in demonstrating inhibition of virus multiplication in the cell of certain picornaviruses. The two substances used were guanidine hydrochloride and 2-(α hydroxybenzyl) benzimidazole (HBB). The first practical application of this type of investigation was made by Kaufman, Martola, and Dohlman in 1962 (39), when they succeeded in curing spontaneous viral induced herpetic keratitis in man by the application of 5-iodo-2'-de-oxyuridine.

In the more general field of genetics, Wilkins (83) has demonstrated that bacteria are the tools which the biochemists are utilizing to learn the structure and the method of controlling the synthesis of the chromosome itself.

Many of the most beneficial applications of microbiology have been made in public health and hygiene. The aim of these activities has been the control and eradication of infectious diseases. Except for those diseases transmitted through the respiratory tract (2), most of the pestilential afflictions of mankind have been brought under control by application of the principles of microbiology and immunology. It is not an exaggeration to state that modern ways of life owe their security to the guardianship of microbiologists.

REFERENCES

1. Arthus, M. M. Compt. rend. Soc. de biol., 55:817, 1903.
2. Austrain, R. Bact. Rev., 24:261, 1960.
3. Baltimore, D., and others. Proc. Natl. Acad. Sci. & Dis., 49:843, 1963.
4. Baron, J. The Life of Edward Jenner, M.D., London, H. Colburn, 1827.
5. Bayne-Jones, S. Science, 73:599, 1931.
6. Behring, E. Deutsche med. Wchnschr., 16: 1145, 1890.
7. Bordet, J. Studies in Immunity, translated by F. P. Gay, New York, 1909.
8. Bulloch, W. The History of Bacteriology, London, Oxford University Press, 1938.
9. Buttle, G. A. H., and others. Lancet, 1:1286, 1936.
10. Cagniard-Latour. Compt. rend. Acad. d. sc., 4:905, 1837.
11. Calandruccio, S. Agostino Bassi, di Lodi, II Fondatore della Teoria Parasitaria, Catania, 1892.
12. Chain, E. Lancet, 2:177, 1941.
13. Chamberland, C. Compt. rend. Acad. d. sc., 99:247, 1884.
14. Cohen, B. The Leeuwenhoek Letter. A photographic copy of the letter of the 9th of October, 1676 sent by Antony van Leeuwenhoek to Henry Oldenberg, Secretary of the Royal Society of London. Published by the Society of American Bacteriologists, Baltimore, 1937.
15. Cohn, F. Beitr. z. Biol. d. Pflanz., 1, 2:127-224, 1872; 2, 2:249, 1876.
16. Davaine, C. J. L'Œuvre de C.-J. Davaine, Paris, 1889, pp. 1-93, 490-575.
17. d'Herelle, F. Compt. rend. Acad. d. sc., 165: 373, 1917.
18. Disney, A. N. Origin and Development of the Microscope, London, 1928.
19. Dobell, C. Antony van Leeuwenhoek and His "Little Animals," New York, Harcourt, Brace and Co., 1932.
20. Domagk, G. Deutsche med. Wchnschr., 61: 250, 1935.
21. Dubos, R. J. Biochemical Determinants of Microbial Diseases, Cambridge, Mass., Harvard University Press, 1954.
22. ——— Louis Pasteur, Free Lance of Science, Boston, Little, Brown and Co., 1950.
23. Duclaux, E. Pasteur, the History of a Mind, translated by Erwin F. Smith, Philadelphia, 1920.
24. Duggar, B. M. Ann. New York Acad. Sc., 51:177, 1948.
25. Ehrenberg, C. G. Die Infusionsthierchen als vollkommene Organismen, Leipzig, 1838.
25a. Ehrlich, J., and others. Science, 106:417, 1947.
26. Ehrlich, P. Klin. Jahrb., 6:299, 1897.
27. ——— Collected Studies on Immunity, translated by C. Bolduan, New York, 1906.
28. Eichstedt. Neue Notiz. a. d. geb. d. Natur. u. Heilkunde, 39:270, 1846.
29. Finlay, A. C., and others. Science, 111:85, 1950.
30. Fleming, A. Brit. J. Exper. Path., 10:226, 1929.
31. Florey, H. W., and others. Antibiotics, London, Oxford University Press, 1949.
32. Fracastorius, H. De contagionibus et contagiosis morbis et eorum curatione, libri tres, Venice, 1546. Consulted in the German translation by Viktor Fossel, in the Klassiker der Medizin series, 1910.
33. Gage, S. H. The Microscope, 15th ed., Ithaca, N.Y., 1932.
34. Godlee, J. Lord Lister, London, 1917.
35. Hench, P. S., and others. Proc. Staff Meet., Mayo Clin., 24:181, 1949.
36. Henle, J. Pathologische Untersuchungen, Berlin, 1840.
37. Iwanowski, D. Bull. d. Acad. imp. d. Sci. d. St. Petersbourg, 13:237, 1892. Quoted from Centralbl. f. Bakt., 5:250, 1899.
38. Jenner, E. An Inquiry into the Causes and Effects of the Variolae Vaccinae, London, 1798, p. 13.
39. Kaufman, H. E., and others. Arch. Ophthal., 68:235, 1962.
40. Koch, R. Beitr. z. Biol. d. Pflanz., 2, 2:277-308, 1876.
41. ——— Gesammelte Werke. ed. by G. Gaffky and E. Pfuhl, Leipzig, 1912.
42. ——— Zur Züchtung von pathogenen Mikroorganismen, Mitt. a. d. Kaiserlichen Gesundheitsamte, 1:1-48, 1881.
43. Levaditi, C., and Vaisman, A. Compt. rend. Soc. de biol., 119:946, 1935.
44. Linnaeus, C. Systema naturae, 10th ed., Holmiae, 1758, 820-821.
45. Lister, J. The Collected Papers of Joseph, Baron Lister, 2 vols., Oxford, 1909.
46. Magendie, F. Lectures on the Blood. Translation, Philadelphia, 1839.
47. Meleney, F. L., and Johnson, B. J.A.M.A., 133:675, 1947.
48. ——— Treatise on Surgical Infections, New York, Oxford University Press, 1948.
49. Metchnikoff, E. L'Immunité dans les maladies infectieuses, Paris, 1901. Translated by F. G. Binnie, Cambridge, 1905.
50. Müller, O. F. Animalcula infusoria, Hauniae, 1786.
51. Murray, E. G. D. Tr. Roy. Soc. Canada, 49: Series III, 1955.
52. Needham, T. Philosoph. Trans., 490:615, 1749. Quoted by Bulloch.
53. Nordtmeyer, H. Ztschr. f. Hyg., 10:145, 1891.
54. Nuttall, G. H. F. Parasitology, 16:214, 1924.
55. Obermeier, O. H. F. Centralbl. f. d. med. Wissensch., 11:145, 1873.
56. Pasteur, L. Ann. de chim. et phys., 64:5-110, 1862.
57. ——— Œuvres de Pasteur, Paris, 1922-1928.
58. Porter, J. L. Bact. Rev., 25:389, 1961.
59. Portier, and Richet, C. Compt. rend. Soc. de biol., 54:170, 1902.
60. Rayer. Compt. rend. Soc. de biol., 2:141-144, 1850.
61. Redi, F. Esperienze intorno alla generazione degl'insetti, 5th ed., Florence, 1688. A translation of this book was published by M. Bigelow, Chicago, 1909.
62. Roddis, L. H. Edward Jenner and the Discovery of Smallpox Vaccination, Menasha, Wisconsin, 1930.
63. Salmon, D. E., and Smith, T. Proc. Biol. Soc., Washington, 3:29, 1886.

64. Schatz, A., and others. Proc. Soc. Exper. Biol. & Med., 55:66, 1944.
65. Schoenlein. Arch. f. Anat. Physiol. u. Wissensch. Med., 82, 1839.
66. Schröder, H., and von Dusch, T. Ann. d. Chem. u. Pharmacie, 89:232, 1854.
67. Schulze, F. Ann. d. Phys. u. Chem., 39:487, 1836.
68. Schwann, T. Ann. d. Phys. u. Chem., 41:184, 1837.
69. Singer, C. The dawn of microscopical discovery, J. Roy. Micr. Soc., 317-340, 1915.
70. Spallanzani, L. Saggio di osservazioni microscopiche, Modena, 1765. This reference is quoted from Bulloch.
71. Stanley, W. M. The isolation and properties of tobacco mosaic and other virus proteins, Harvey Lect., 1938, Ser. XXXIII, p. 170.
72. Tamm, I., and Eggers, H. J. Science, 142:24, 1963.
73. Tréfouël, J., and others. Compt. rend. Soc. de biol., 120:756, 1936.
74. Twort, F. W. Lancet, 2:1241, 1915.
75. Tyndall, J. Essays on the Floating-Matter of the Air in Relation to Putrefaction and Infection, New York, 1882.
76. Vallery-Radot, R. The Life of Pasteur, translated by R. L. Devonshire, New York, 1926.
77. van Helmont, J. B. Ortus medicinae id est initia physicae inaudita, Tract 21, Imago fermenti impraegnat massam semine, Amsterdam, Elzivir, 1648, Part 9, p. 113.
78. van Leeuwenhoek, Antony. Arcana naturae detecta, Delft, 1695, p. 42.
79. Villemin, J. A. Compt. rend. Acad. d. sc., 61:1012-1015, 1865.
80. von Pirquet, C. F., and Schick, B. Die Serumkrankheit, Leipzig, 1905.
81. Waksman, S. A. Bact. Rev., 5:231, 1941.
82. ———— Proc. Soc. Exper. Biol. & Med., 57:244, 1944.
83. Wilkins, M. H. F. Science, 140:941, 1963.

2

Classification of Bacteria

It is not surprising that Linnaeus, Müller, Ferdinand Cohn and those who have followed encountered difficulties in classifying bacteria, since these microorganisms lack definitive morphologic characteristics and the usual sexual methods of reproduction which form the basis for classification in the botanic and zoologic sciences (3, 4). The morphology of the individual organism with its recognizable internal and external structures, specific staining reactions, and colony formations does indeed form the basis for classification; but alone these characteristics are inadequate and must be supplemented by other properties such as biochemical activity, antigenic structure, and pathogenicity.

Bacteria are minute, unicellular plant-like organisms without chlorophyll, which usually multiply by binary division. The individual cells in colonies are physiologically independent, although they are influenced by environmental changes produced by neighboring cells. The individual cells which are spheres are called **cocci,** the straight rods **bacilli,** and the curved rods **spirilla** (Fig. 1).

The **cocci** are, when fully developed and free, perfectly spherical but when two or more are in apposition, may be slightly flattened along the tangential surface, giving an oval appearance. The **bacilli** are straight rods whose length varies from 2 to 10 times their width and with ends which may be gently rounded like those of *Salmonella typhosa,* or squared like *Bacillus anthracis.* The **spirilla** vary from small comma-shaped organisms with a single curve, to longer sinuous forms with from 4 to 20 curves which suggest the appearance of an animated corkscrew. The turns in typical spirilla are always in three planes and are best described as helicoidal. Among the known microorganisms the bacilli outnumber by far the other forms.

Many variations from these fundamental types occur even under normal conditions and will be discussed in subsequent chapters.

Size of Microorganisms. There is considerable variation in the size of different microorganisms. Cocci may vary from 0.15 μ to 2 μ in diameter, although the usual coccal forms found in pus are in the range of 0.8 μ to 1.2 μ. A graphic illustration of the size of the *Staphylococcus* which causes boils is shown by the calculation that a drop with a volume of 1 ml. can easily contain two billion organisms. There is even greater varia-

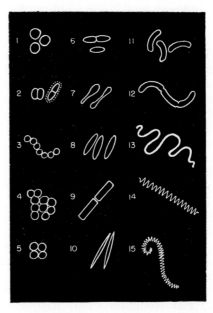

Fig. 1. Morphology. 1, single cocci. 2, cocci in pairs. 3, cocci in chains. 4, cocci in clusters. 5, cocci in tetrads. 6, coccobacilli. 7, club-shaped bacilli. 8, bacilli with rounded ends. 9, bacilli with square ends. 10, fusiform bacilli. 11, vibrios. 12, *Spirilla.* 13, *Borrelia.* 14, *Treponema.* 15, *Leptospira.*

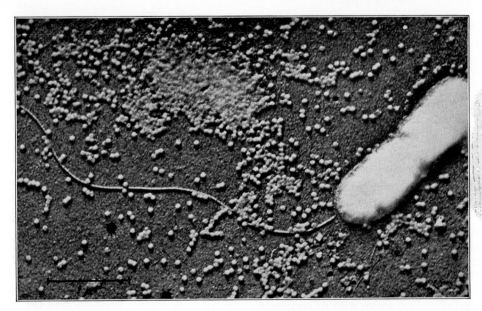

Fig. 2. Electron micrograph showing a small bacillus with polar flagellum in a field filled with rabbit papilloma virus. X 22,100 (Electron micrograph by Dr. D. G. Sharp.)

tion in the size of bacilli which vary from the small *Haemophilus influenzae* which may be 0.5 μ in length by 0.2 μ in width, to *Bacillus anthracis* which is 5 to 10 μ in length and 1 to 3 μ in width.

When properly stained, the rickettsias are definitely visible with the ordinary microscope. The viruses vary from the relatively large forms like the virus of mouse pneumonitis (0.45 μ) to the minute virus of poliomyelitis (0.027 μ). Even the larger viruses cannot be properly studied by the ordinary light or darkfield microscopes although they can be photographed by ultraviolet light. The discovery of the electron microscope by Kroll and Ruska, in 1931 (7), opened up a new dimension for the study of the morphology of the bacterial cell and provided, for the first time, a glimpse of the size, shape, and structure of viruses (Fig. 2). The early studies by Marton (14) and Krause (13) were followed by the more detailed explorations of Mudd and Anderson (16), Knaysi (12), Wyckoff (21), and Johnson (10) (Fig. 2). Magnifications up to 100,000 have been obtained and particles as small as 10 mμ have been photographed.

The smallest free-living microorganisms must be somewhat larger than the small viruses because they must have a complement of enzymes and genes for growth and reproduction, while the viruses use a part of the host's-cells enzymes for growth. The smallest independent organisms probably occur in the *Mycoplasmatales* order, where the individual organism may be as small as medium-sized viruses. Morowitz and Tourtellotte (15) have calculated that the smallest self-duplicating unit would have to be 500 angstrom units and contain 150 large molecules (Fig. 3). The smallest living organism actually observed is *M. laidlaw,* which has twice the diameter (1,000 angstroms) and eight times the volume with 1,200 large molecules. *M. gallisepticum,* with a large diameter of 2,500 angstroms, has 20,000 large molecules and encompasses an automatic metabolic and reproductive system.

Staining Reactions. Certain differential stains such as the gram stain and the acid-fast stain are of aid in classification. After staining by Gram's method some organisms are found to be violet and some red. All of the stainable spiral organisms, about one third of the cocci and one half of the bacilli appear red. Gram's more or less fortuitous

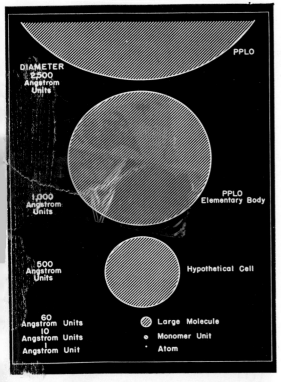

DIAMETER
2,500
Angstrom
Units

PPLO

1,000
Angstrom
Units

PPLO
Elementary Body

500
Angstrom
Units

Hypothetical Cell

60 Angstrom Units
10 Angstrom Units
1 Angstrom Unit

◩ Large Molecule
◦ Monomer Unit
· Atom

Fig. 3. Relative size of pleuropneumonia-like organism, PPLO elementary body, and smallest hypothetical living cell. (From Morowitz and Tourtellotte. *Scientific American*, 206:117, 1962.)

empirical discovery that some organisms ... be stained violet and others red fur- ... s one of the simplest and most useful ... nics in all microbiology (1).

A thin film of organisms on a glass slide is fixed with heat, and then treated with gentian or crystal violet for one minute, rinsed quickly with water, and covered with Gram's iodine solution for one minute. Following another quick rinse in water the slide is decolorized with alcohol or a mixture of acetone and ether, washed thoroughly, and counterstained with safranin for 10 seconds, washed with water and dried.

In the first step all organisms are stained violet, and all assume a dirty bluish brown color after treatment with the iodine solution. The iodides serve as a mordant to fix the violet dye in certain types of organisms so it is not washed out by the alcohol or ether-acetone decolorizing agents. The safranin stains red those organisms which have been decolorized. A little practice and judgment are required in applying the de-

colorizing solution to prevent inadequate or excessive decolorization.

The organisms which retain the violet dye are referred to as **gram-positive** and those which are decolorized and counterstained with the red dye are called **gram-negative**. The physiochemical reactions which produce the differential staining are not completely explained.

An intact cell wall is essential for retaining the crystal violet stain. Gerhardt and his associates (8) have shown that crushed cells and protoplasts of cells, which were originally gram-positive, stain gram-negative after damage or destruction of the cell wall. Spontaneous autolysis of a portion of the cell wall probably explains the frequent occurrences of gram-negative organisms in pure cultures of gram-positive organisms (Fig. 4). These increase rapidly as the culture ages. The various theories purporting to explain the mechanism by which gram-positive organisms retain the crystal violet have been reviewed and criticized by Salton (17). Although lipids, polysaccharides, RNA, and certain proteins can all retain the crystal violet-iodine-complex, these are not sufficiently different in number and amount to explain the binding of the blue stain by the gram-positive organism; the predominance of mucopeptides in the gram-positives and lipids in the gram-negatives might play an accessory role, however (17). Later work by Salton (18) shows that the gram-positiveness of organisms corresponds to a decreased leakage of P_{32} compounds.

The studies of Bartholomew and Finkelstein (2), shown in Figure 4, demonstrate that crystal violet stains the cell wall as well as the protoplasm of both gram-positive and gram-negative bacilli (Fig. 4 A-E). The *E. coli* cells, which are gram-negative, can actually bind more crystal violet per gram of cell weight than *B. subtilis*, a typical gram-positive organism (2). The organisms remain the same size after treatment with the iodine (Fig. 4 B), unless there is excessive washing with water between the crystal violet and the iodine reagent. With moderate washing the blue dye is washed from the cell wall but not from the protoplasm; with excessive washing of the cell, the dye is washed out and the organism appears gram-negative. With brief decolorization with alcohol, the blue dye is removed from the gram-negative organism but not from the gram-positive one (Fig. 4 C). On counterstaining with safranin the gram-negative organism stains red. Brief washing with water does not wash the red stain from the organism, but prolonged washing will do so with the bacilli appearing thinner and thinner

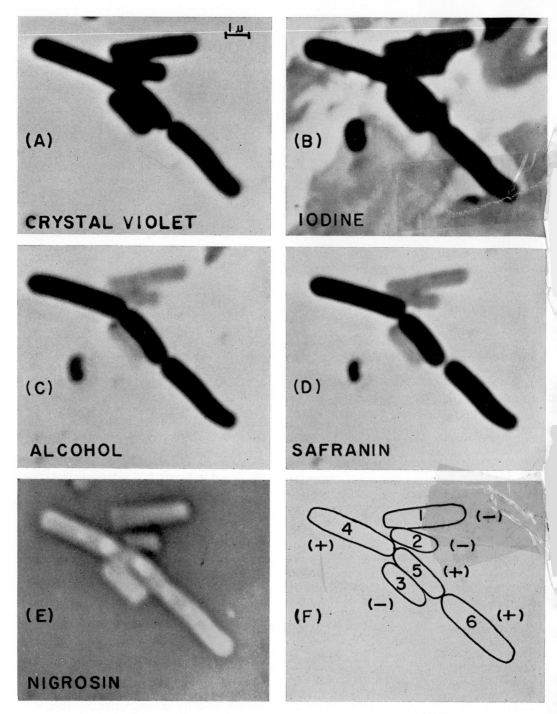

Fig. 4. Gram stain of *Bacillus subtilis*. The appearance of a group of cells following each step of the gram procedure (A-D) and nigrosin-negative staining (E). This group contained both gram-positive and gram-negative cells. The dark-appearing cells were gram-positive and the light-appearing cells were gram-negative. (From Bartholomew and Finkelstein. *J. Bact.,* 75:77, 1958.)

(2). Even the brief washing necessary to clear the slide of excessive safranin has apparently removed the safranin from the cell wall, so the gram-negative cell in Figure D is not as wide as that in Figures A and B. Finkelstein and Bartholomew (5) have found that the binding of crystal violet by both gram-positive and gram-negative microorganisms can be interpreted as obeying the Freundlich and Langmuir laws of absorption.

Treatment with iodine produces a crystal violet-iodine-complex in both gram-positive and gram-negative organisms. Salton (17) visualized the differential decolorization as depending upon changes in the cell wall pores during the process of dehydration with alcohol. The alcohol wash, after treatment with iodine, dissolves away much of the lipid from the cell wall of the gram-negative bacteria, after which the crystal violet-iodine-complex easily escapes. In contrast, the dehydration by alcohol of the cell wall of the gram-positive organism reduces the size and the pores in the cell wall and makes the decolorization of the cells much more difficult.

The gram reaction is indicative of a more profound difference between gram-positive and gram-negative bacteria than their physio-chemical reactions to dyes, as shown by certain immunologic properties and variations in susceptibility to sulfonamide and antibiotic therapy. With the exception of gram-negative cocci, the sulfonamides are more effective in the treatment of infection caused by gram-positive organisms. Again, with the exception of gram-negative cocci, penicillin is even more restricted in its action against gram-positive bacteria while streptomycin is in general more effective against gram-negative bacilli.

Colony Formations. Microscopic unicellular bacteria multiply rapidly and form macroscopic colonies in 24 to 48 hours when supplied with adequate food, temperature, moisture, and a solid or semisolid supporting base. With some species, such as *Mycobacterium tuberculosis,* a longer period of incubation is required, and some form colonies which are so small that a hand lens or even the low power of the microscope is required for visualization. Theoretically a colony is composed of the descendants of a single cell, but it may develop from a clump of cells or from two or more unrelated organisms. Even a colony with a gross characteristic appearance may contain a contaminating species which has been overgrown by the dominant organism. The gelatin plate was introduced by Koch in 1881 and the agar plate by Frau Hesse a few years later. By repeated replating of single colonies pure cultures can be obtained.

The gross appearance of colonies, when grown under standardized conditions, is of considerable aid in classification, since they differ in configuration, texture, size, shape, color, odor, and degree of adherence to the medium. The morphology of a colony is related primarily to the postfission movements of the bacteria composing it. These movements have been classified by Graham-Smith

Table 1. Thallophyta

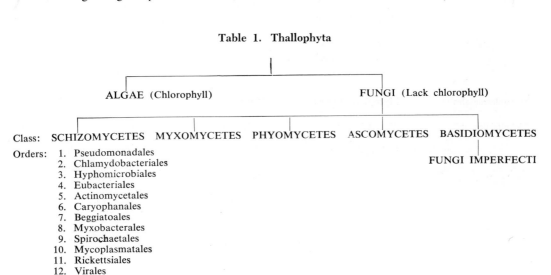

Table 2. Class: Schizomycetes

ORDER	FAMILY	GENUS	SPECIES
Eubacteriales	Micrococcaceae	*Staphylococcus*	*S. aureus*
		Micrococcus	*M. species*
		Gaffkya	*G. tetragena*
		Sarcina	*S. lutea*
	Enterobacteriaceae	*Escherichia*	*E. coli*
		Salmonella	*S. typhosa*
		Shigella	Dysentery group
		Paracolobacterium	Paracolon group
		Proteus	Proteus group
		Aerobacter	Aerogenes group
		Klebsiella	Friedländer group
		Serratia	*S. marcescens*
	Brucellaceae	*Pasteurella*	*P. species*
		Brucella	*B. species*
		Haemophilus	*H. species*
		Moraxella	*M. lacunata*
		Bordetella	*B. pertussis*
		Actinobacillus	*A. lignieresii*
	Bacteroidaceae	*Bacteroides*	*B. species*
		Fusobacterium	*F. fusiforme*
		Streptobacillus	*S. moniliformis*
		Dialister	*D. pneumosintes*
	Achromobacteraceae	*Alcaligenes*	*A. faecalis*
	Neisseriaceae	*Neisseria*	Meningococcus
			Gonococcus
		Veillonella	Anaerobic cocci
	Lactobacillaceae	*Diplococcus*	*D. pneumoniae*
		Streptococcus	*S. species*
		Lactobacillus	Acidophilus group
	Corynebacteriaceae	*Corynebacterium*	*C. diphtheriae*
		Listeria	*L. monocytogenes*
		Erysipelothrix	*E. insidiosa*
	Bacillaceae	*Bacillus*	*B. anthracis* (aerobic**)**
		Clostridium	*C. tetani* (anerobic)
Pseudomonadales	Spirillaceae	*Vibrio*	Cholera group
		Spirillum	*S. minus*
	Pseudomonadaceae	*Pseudomonas*	Pyocyaneus group
Actinomycetales	Mycobacteriaceae	*Mycobacterium*	*M. tuberculosis*
	Actinomycetaceae	*Actinomyces*	*A. bovis* (anaerobic)
		Nocardia	*N. asteroides* (aerobic)
	Streptomycetaceae	*Streptomyces*	*S. species* (soil)
Spirochaetales	Spirochaetaceae	*Spirochaeta*	Saprophytes
	Treponemataceae	*Treponema*	*T. pallidum*
		Borrelia	*B. recurrentis*
		Leptospira	*L. icterohaemorrhagiae*
Mycoplasmatales	Mycoplasmataceae	*Mycoplasma*	Pleuropneumonia group
Rickettsiales	Rickettsiaceae	*Rickettsia*	*R. species*
		Coxiella	*C. burnetii*
	Chlamydiaceae	*Chlamydia*	*C. trachomatis*
		Miyagawanella	*M. psittacii*
			M. lymphogranulomatis
		Colesiota	*C. species*
	Bartonellaceae	*Bartonella*	*B. bacilliformis*
		Haemobartonella	*H. species*
		Grahamella	*G. species*
		Eperythrozoon	*E. species*
	Anaplasmataceae	*Anaplasma*	*A. species*
Virales	**Virus agents of disease**		

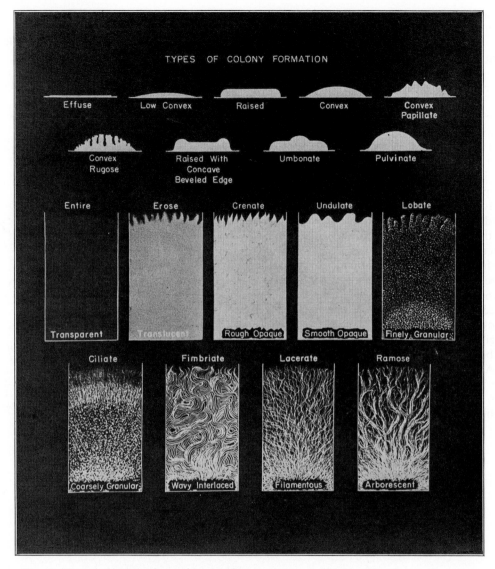

Fig. 5. Types of colony formation showing structure of colonies, elevation, and nature at edges.

(9) as loop-forming, folding, snapping and slipping. Colonies of organisms of the loop-forming group usually have wavy edges (*B. anthracis*). Those of the folding and snapping group (*Past. pestis, C. diphtheriae*) have serrated or crenated edges, and those of the slipping group (*E. coli, Proteus vulgaris*) have smooth or lobate edges with a spreading growth (Fig. 5). Motile organisms in fluid media give a smooth homogeneous growth, but nonmotile forms may at times produce definite colonies in undisturbed fluid media.

Other solid media, such as potatoes, bread, coagulated serum, silica gel and tissue from animals, may form the base for the development of definite colonies. It is important to remember that the same microorganism will produce colonies which very greatly in morphology depending upon their location in a dish of poured medium, whether on the surface, in the depth of the medium, or between the medium and the bottom of the dish.

The position of bacteria among other living things is still indefinite, since these organisms have characteristics which relate them to the blue-green algae, to the fungi, and to the protozoa. The bacteria do not contain chlorophyll but since they have, on the whole, a predominance of plant-like characteristics, they are generally placed in the plant kingdom. The relationship of the bacteria to simple plants may be graphically represented by Table 1.

There is no entirely satisfactory classification for bacteria, and none has been accepted for international use. New systems are being proposed from time to time (6, 11, 19, 20). Throughout this book an attempt has been made to follow the terminology proposed in the seventh edition of Bergey's Manual. Recognizing that this classification is not perfect and that changes will be made in succeeding editions it seems wiser to use a recorded terminology rather than to introduce new names for old organisms. The well known common names such as the tubercle bacillus and the typhoid bacillus will be used as before in the body of the text.

A diagrammatic presentation of some of the groupings occurring in the seventh edition of Bergey's Manual is outlined in Table 2.

REFERENCES

1. Bartholomew, J. W., and Mittwer, T.   Bact. Rev., 16:1, 1952.
2. ———— and Finkelstein, H.   J. Bact., 75:77, 1958.
3. Buchanan, R. E.   Bact. Rev., 22:204, 1958.
4. Bulloch, W.   History of Bacteriology, London, Medical Research Council, 1930.
5. Finkelstein, H., and Bartholomew, J. W.   J. Bact., 80:14, 1960.
6. Floodgate, G. D.   Bact. Rev., 26:277, 1962.
7. Freundlich, M. M.   Science, 142:183, 1963.
8. Gerhardt, P., and others.   J. Bact., 72:721, 1956.
9. Graham-Smith, G. S.   Parasitology, 3:17, 1910.
10. Johnson, F. H., and others.   J. Bact., 46:167, 1943.
11. Kluyver, A. J., and Van Neil, C. B.   Zentralbl. f. Bakt., II Abt., 94:369, 1936.
12. Knaysi, G., and others.   J. Bact., 53:525, 1947.
13. Krause, F.   Naturwiss., 25:817, 1937.
14. Marton, L.   Bull. Acad. Belg. Classe des Sci., 23:672, 1937.
15. Morowitz, H. J., and Tourtellotte, M. E.   Sci. Am., 206:117, 1962.
16. Mudd, S., and Anderson, T. F.   J. Immunol., 42:251, 1941.
17. Salton, M. R. M.   Bact. Rev., 25:77, 1961.
18. ————   J. Gen. Microbiol., 30:223, 1963.
19. Skerman, V. B. D.   Bact. Rev., 13:175, 1949.
20. Van Neil, C. B.   Cold Spring Harbor Symposia on Quantitative Biology, 11:285, 1946.
21. Wyckoff, R. W. G.   Electron Microscopy, New York, Interscience Publishers, 1949.

3

General Morphology and Reproduction of Bacteria

When unstained, most bacteria are transparent, colorless, homogeneous or granular bodies with a low refractive index, approximately that of water. The bacterial cell consists of four morphologically distinct structures—protoplasm, cytoplasmic membrane, cell wall, and capsule—each varying in chemical, physiologic and antigenic constituents (Fig. 1). The protoplasm of the organism is a fluid, or potentially fluid, colloid which is surrounded by an extremely thin, ductile, cytoplasmic membrane. The intact cytoplasmic membrane with its contents is usually referred to as a **protoplast.** The **cytoplasmic membrane,** which varies from 5 to 10 mμ in thickness, is composed mainly of lipid and protein (89) and contains cyto-

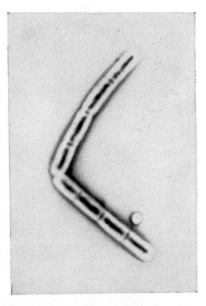

Fig. 2. *Bacillus cereus,* crystal violet nuclear stain showing cell plates but not cell wall. (From Clark, Webb, and Chance. *J. Bact.,* 73:72, 1957.)

chrome (135, 136). It is physiologically active, permitting in a selective manner the entrance and exit of small molecules. By the usual staining methods this membrane stains more deeply than the cytoplasm and resists decolorization longer. When the cell is plasmolyzed, the membrane contracts with the cytoplasm, draws away from the cell wall, and can be photographed readily with the electron microscope. It has been identified in thin sections of bacteria (99) and isolated from ruptured protoplasts by differential centrifugation (135, 136).

Cell Wall. The cell wall under normal conditions encloses and is in direct contact with the cytoplasmic membrane. This wall represents 20 per cent of the dry weight of

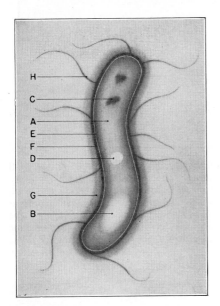

Fig. 1. Morphologic structure of a bacillus. A, cytoplasm. B, nucleus. C, cytoplasmic granules. D, vacuole. E, cytoplasmic membrane. F, cell wall. G, slime layer or capsule. H, flagellum.

21

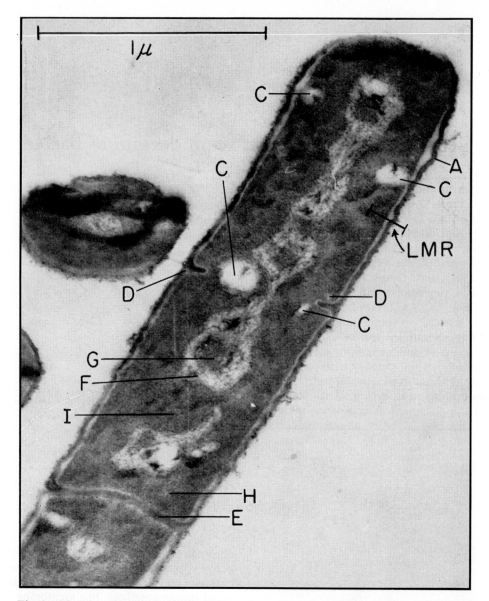

Fig. 3.   Electron micrograph of ultra-thin section of *Bacillus cereus.* X 60,000. A, cell wall showing evidence of shrinking of cytoplasm. C, four peripheral bodies cut at different levels. D, beginning of centripetally growing transverse cell wall. E, completed transverse cell wall. F, low-density fibrous component of nuclear apparatus. G, dense body in nuclear apparatus which may be inclusions of cytoplasmic material. H, small dense particles which appear to be main constituent of cytoplasm. I, unidentified cytoplasm inclusions. LMR, scale indicating the *limit* of resolution of light microscope using visible light. (From Chapman and Hillier. *J. Bact.,* 66:362, 1953.)

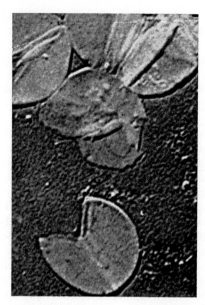

Fig. 4. Electron micrograph of cell wall of *Streptococcus faecalis*. (After Bibb and Straughn. *J. Bact.*, 84:1094, 1962.)

Fig. 5. Electron micrograph of cell walls of *Salmonella enteritidis*. (From Ribi, Milner, and Perrine. *J. Immunol.*, 82:75, 1959.)

The cell wall is not stained by ordinary bacterial stains unless previously treated with the proper mordant (70, 115) (Fig. 2) and is not visible when living cells are examined in the darkfield; but it is delineated clearly in electron micrographs (23) (Fig. 3). In completely plasmolyzed cells the tough cell wall remains as a "ghost." After mechanical (97) or enzymatic disruption, the cell walls of cocci resemble grape hulls (Fig. 4) (5, 8, 88), as do the cell walls of organisms from the psittacosis and rickettsial groups of organisms (63). In contrast, the cell walls of bacilli break up into irregular plates (113, 114) (Fig. 5), which sometimes seem to be composed of fibrous structures (121, 128) (Fig. 6). The cell wall encloses the cytoplasmic membrane (Fig. 7).

Purified cell wall fractions contain very high molecular weight components, usually in the form of complexes of proteins, lipids, and polysaccharides (37, 108, 109, 113, 114, 119, 120, 121). The cell wall of gram-positive organisms is rigid and maintains the shape of the organism. The cell walls of gram-negative organisms are much more complex than those of gram-positive organisms. They consist of two or perhaps three

Fig. 6. Fragment of envelope of *L. hyalina* after tryptic digestion showing fibrous structure. X 160,000. (Courtesy of J. A. Chapman and M. R. J. Salton.)

the organism (108) and varies in thickness from 10 to 25 mμ. It contains pores of approximately 1 mμ in diameter which admit small molecules to the cytoplasmic membrane. It is rigid and relatively nonelastic but highly ductile like a cellophane bag.

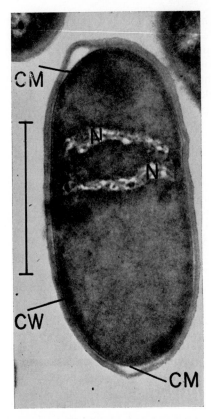

Fig. 7. Electron micrograph of ultra-thin sections showing N = nucleus, CW = cell wall, CM = cytoplasmic membrane. (From Chapman. *J. Bact.,* 78:96, 1959.)

whole body of the organism as an immunizing antigen. The cell wall of Group A streptococci contains the specific M protein (5), and there are several immunizing antigens in the cell wall of *Past. tularensis* (105). The cell walls of most fungi are composed of chitin (3), although a few contain cellulose.

Growth of Cell Wall. It was assumed for generations that the cell wall grew in a uniform manner about its entire circumference until Bisset (11, 13) demonstrated that cell wall growth in septate bacilli is immediately adjacent to the septum. These observations have been confirmed by Bisset and Pease (15) for spirilla, and by Cole and Hahn (33) for *Streptococcus pyogenes.* The latter demonstrated this mode of growth by direct and indirect fluorescent staining (Fig. 8), but when the same technic was applied to the growth of *S. typhosa,* growth was found not to be localized but a general ultramicroscopic intercalation (34).

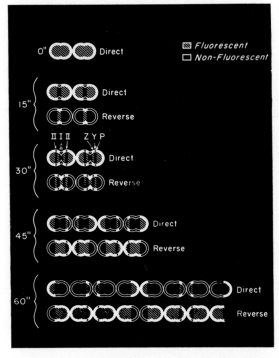

Fig. 8. Growth of cell wall of *Streptococcus pyogenes* demonstrated by direct and indirect immunofluorescence. Growth is not uniform but limited to two actively growing areas for each coccus. (From Cole and Hahn. *Science,* 135:722, 1962.)

distinct layers (111), the inner layer being analogous to the cell wall of the gram-positive forms in chemical structure and rigidity. The cell walls of *Mycobacterium* also show three distinct layers (62, 94, 131). In this instance the third or innermost layer provides the mechanical support for the bacillary shape of the organism.

A number of chemical entities are found in the cell walls of bacteria which do not exist in the tissues of man and animals, and this makes possible the blocking of certain specific enzyme systems in bacteria by antibiotics without injuring the cells of the host. The chemical structures and enzyme systems of the cell walls will be discussed in detail in Chapter 4.

The antigens of the cell wall are as important and as unique as its biochemical constituents and in the future may replace the

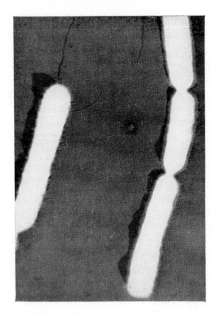

Fig. 9. Electron micrograph of *Bacillus megaterium*. No capsule is visible after the addition of nonspecific *B. cereus* immune serum. (From Baumann-Grace and Tomcsik. *Schweiz. Ztschr. f. Path. u. Bakt.,* 21:906, 1958.)

Slime Layer or Capsule. Under normal conditions the cell wall is surrounded by a loosely attached slime layer consisting of mucoid substances of high molecular weight which are diffusing constantly into the medium. When viscous material is produced in sufficient amounts and remains concentrated at the surface of the cell wall, it is called a capsule and is the substance which gives a stringy texture to fluid cultures and a moist, glistening surface to colonies grown on solid media. Bacteria are prolific in the production of polysaccharides. Under favorable conditions they may synthesize as much as 60 per cent of their dry weight as intracellular polysaccharides and many times their cellular dry weight as extracellular polysaccharides (139). Both capsule and slime layer are visualized readily with the wet film India ink method (48). Using specific antiserums Tomcsik (6, 53) and his associates have studied capsules of certain species of bacilli in which the major component, a polypeptide, is enclosed in a polysaccharide framework which has septa that join the cell wall (Figs. 9, 10, 11).

The capsular material apparently is produced by the living cell wall. Similar chemical and antigenic substances often can be extracted from bacteria which have no demonstrable capsule or from bacterial cells whose capsules have been removed previously by mechanical means (46).

Encapsulated organisms are phagocytized with difficulty by the normal leukocytes of the body, and the virulence of the pneumococci, Friedländer's bacillus, and the influenza bacillus is associated with the presence of well-developed capsules. However, many nonpathogenic organisms have equally well developed capsules, and capsule formation may be induced in nonencapsulated strains in the mucoid phase of dissociation. Some pathogenic bacteria, such as those which cause anthrax and plague, are nonencapsulated when grown on ordinary artificial media but readily acquire capsules within the infected animal body. In other species, such as the pneumococcus, the loss of the capsule is accompanied by a diminution or complete loss of virulence. The ability to produce the capsular material is a hereditary

Fig. 10. Electron micrograph of *Bacillus megaterium*. Polysaccharide capsule with transverse septum was visible after the addition of homologous polysaccharide immunoserum. (From Baumann-Grace and Tomcsik. *Schweiz. Ztschr. f. Path. u, Bakt.,* 21:906, 1958.)

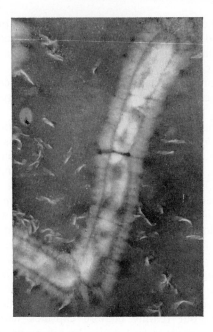

Fig. 11. Electron micrograph of *Bacillus mega-terium*. Polypeptide capsule with radial striations was visible after the addition of anthrax polypeptide immunoserum. Note absence of material in the region of the transverse septa. (From Baumann-Grace and Tomcsik. *Schweiz. Ztschr. f. Path. u. Bakt.,* 21:906, 1958.)

characteristic which is lost only when the culture undergoes phase variation or dissociation, but its expression is determined by environmental factors.

Bovarnick (17) found that the capsule of the anthrax bacillus was a polypeptide of *d*-glutamic acid. The capsular substances of other bacterial species studied up to the present time consist essentially or exclusively of high **molecular weight polysaccharides,** usually acidic in nature and often possessing acetyl and amino groups (46). The capsular substance is not essential for the life of the organisms. The capsule of the type III pneumococcus can be readily hydrolyzed by an adaptive enzyme (47), and the capsules of other organisms may be washed off with neutral aqueous solvents without affecting the viability of the bacteria (46).

Organs of Locomotion. When suspended in a drop of fluid, many bacteria are seen to be actively motile. It is important,

however, in all cases to distinguish between actual motility and the so-called Brownian or molecular movement which takes place whenever small particles, such as carmine granules, are held in suspension in a fluid. The motion consists of a rapid to-and-fro vacillation during which there is actually no permanent change in position of the moving particles except as they are influenced by currents in the drop.

The true motility of bacteria, on the other hand, is active motion due to impulses originating in the bacteria themselves (91), resulting in a permanent change in the actual position of the bacterium in the field.

Motility is a characteristic of practically all species of vibrios, spirilla and spirochetes, some bacilli and an occasional nonpathogenic coccus (56, 76). In 1890 Messea classified motile bacteria according to the number and location of their flagella. Those with a single flagellum at one pole were called **monotrichous;** with one flagellum at each pole **amphitrichous;** with a tuft of flagella at one pole **lophotrichous;** with flagella completely surrounding the bacterial body **peritrichous.** Bacteria without flagella are **atrichous.** Knaysi (70) prefers to classify motile bacteria into two groups: those which carry only lateral flagella and those which have only terminal flagella. Leifson (81) has employed the wave length and amplitude of the flagella in the classification of motile bacilli (Fig. 12).

Bacterial flagella are thin hair-like appendages 10 to 13 mμ in diameter (Fig. 13) and many times the length of the mother cell. In young, well nourished cells they appear to be anchored to the cell wall (Fig. 13), but in old cells or partially digested cells they may be seen to penetrate the cell wall and cytoplasmic membrane and end in a small granule (Ch. 18, Fig. 5). This arrangement was demonstrated in 1950 by Houwink and van Iterson (61) in a series of beautiful electron micrographs. Bacterial flagella have a helical structure when viewed at a magnification of 77,000. The chemical studies of Astbury and Weibull (2) and Weibull (135) have shown that these structures belong to the keratin-myosin-epidermin-fibrinogen group of proteins with a molecular

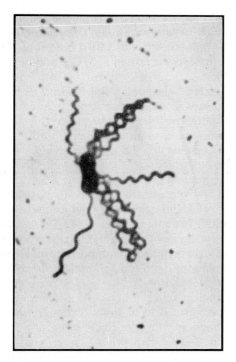

Fig. 12. Flagella of *Proteus*. Stained by Leifson's method. One normal and several wavy forms. (From Leifson and others. *J. Bact.,* 69:73, 1955.)

weight of about 41,000. Koffler and his associates suggest that each flagellin molecule consists of two units, each containing an n-terminal alanine (74). The same investigators have shown that DNA from flagellated *B. subtilis* would induce flagellation in non-flagellated strains of *B. subtilis* (101).

Vibrio comma has a single terminal flagellum which is somewhat thicker than that of bacillary flagella. It arises from a relatively larger granule, 150 to 220 mμ, which is imbedded deep in the cytoplasm (96, 130). Grace (52) reports a single blepharoplast in a spirillum from which one or several flagella originate (141).

The electron micrographs of Czekalowski and Eaves (38) and Swain (126) show the absence of external flagella in species of *Leptospira*, *Borrelia* and *Treponema*. The contractile material occurs in a band, composed of individual fibers, which is wrapped around the body of the *Leptospira* (Ch. 52, Fig. 2) and buried in the body of the *Borrelia*

(Ch. 51, Fig. 1) and the *Treponema* (Ch. 50, Fig. 4). After partial digestion of the organism, the individual fibers unravel and may give the picture in an electron micrograph of external flagella.

The current interest in the nature and function of flagella was stimulated by the observations of Pijper (110), who studied the motion of *Salmonella typhosa* by his special darkfield technic which utilized direct sunlight as the source of illumination.

Pilated or Fimbriated Bacilli. These hairlike appendages project from the cell walls of certain strains of colon bacilli, *Salmonella* and *Shigella*. They were recognized by Duguid and his associates in 1955 (49) and named fimbriae (Fig. 14). The author also noted that organisms with fimbriae caused hemagglutination (50). Brinton (22) introduced the name pili to describe these hairlike structures. The structures are composed entirely of protein and have no power of mobility (143). They are antigenically different from all other antigens of the cells. Brinton and his associates (23) have found that the pilation character can be transferred genetically from pilated (p+) to non-pilated (p−) strains of *Enterobacteriaceae*.

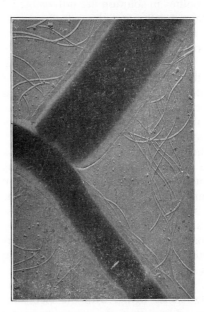

Fig. 13. Electron micrograph showing flagella arising from cell wall. (From Knaysi. *Elements of Bacterial Cytology,* Comstock Publishing Co.)

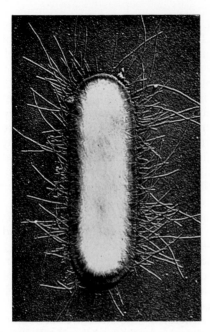

Fig. 14. Electron micrograph of fimbriae or pili of *Sh. flexneri* type la. (From Duguid and Gilles. *J. Path. & Bact.,* 74:397, 1957.)

Cytoplasmic Granules. The cytoplasm is the major site for cellular metabolism. The metabolites in solution are not visible in fresh or stained cells, and the cytoplasm may appear remarkably homogenous. Visible granules do appear; however, in older cells they vary in amount with the type of medium and the functional state of the cells. Accumulation of food reserves, such as polysaccharides, starch lipids, and lipid containing complexes, can be identified by appropriate methods of staining (24, 104, 138).

The mitochondria of animal cells are as large as small bacteria, contributing, no doubt, to the denial for many years of the presence of mitochondria in bacteria. The long series of studies by Mudd and his associates and others (95, 96) have shown that all bacteria have granules which are the functional, if not the morphological, equivalents of definite mitochondria.

A study of thin sections of bacteria, such as *Azobacter agilis,* with the electronmicroscope, shows that the respiratory enzymes are contained in tubular intracytoplasmic membranes which originate in, and are attached to, the peripheral cytoplasmic membrane (107) (Fig. 15). These internal membranous structures are less complex in cocci and some other bacilli (106) but more complex in *Mycobacterium* (35, 62) and in yeast (35).

The metachromatic, Babes-Ernst or volutin granules, which are present in abundance in diphtheria, plague, and all mycobacterial species and in smaller numbers in other bacteria, appear to be polyphosphate which plays an active role in cellular metabolism. The granules (138) accumulate when grown in a polyphosphate accumulative medium (Fig. 16) and are sharply reduced when the medium is changed (Fig. 17). There seems to be a reciprocal relationship between nucleic acid synthesis and polyphosphate accumulation, with polyphosphate furnishing both phosphorus and the energy requirement for nucleic acid synthesis (95). This concept was confirmed by a study of *C. diphtheriae* in which synchronized cell division was induced (118). Knaysi (73) believes that the volutin granules contain both ribonucleic acid and metaphosphate.

Protoplasts and Spheroplasts. The bacterial protoplast has been defined as the cytoplasmic membrane and its contents. This is a proper definition for an organism which, because of a genetic defect, cannot synthesize even a trace of a cell wall or whose cell wall has been completely removed by lysozyme (65, 134, 136). The organisms which cause the disease pleuropneumonia in animals, the pleuropneumonia-like organisms and the mutant L forms of bacteria, have no detectable cell walls and could be properly described as protoplasts. However, organisms which have the genetic machinery for forming cell walls, but whose enzymes are inhibited by growth in penicillin or in cycloserine (133), should be called spheroplasts (Fig. 18). These structures usually have enough cell wall left to permit the attachment of specific bacteriophages (85) and immediately produce normal cell walls when the inhibiting substance is removed (59, 127). The pleuropneumonia-like organisms and the stable L type bacterial mutants have an excessive amount of lipid in the cytoplasmic membrane (123).

Cell walls that are composed largely of acetyl aminopolysaccharides are readily dis-

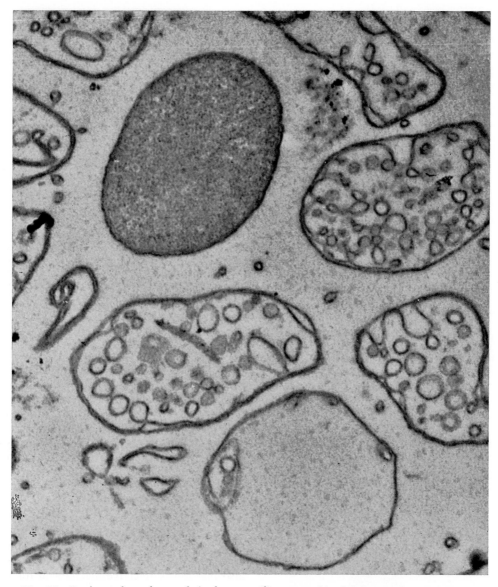

Fig. 15. Sections of envelopes of *Azobacter agilis* prepared by brief two-minute ballistic disintegration. The solid cell near the top was not ruptured, and internal structures were destroyed in the cell at the bottom. Other cells show numerous internal membranes. (From Pangborn, Marr, and Robrish. *J. Bact.,* 84:669, 1962.)

solved by treatment with lysozyme, after which the cytoplasmic membrane ruptures and spills out its contents. In 1953 Weibull (136) carried out this procedure in a solution made hypertonic by M/3 sucrose and M/100 Mg++. Under these conditions the protoplasts were not injured and continued to metabolize in a normal manner. The flagella remained attached to the protoplasts but no longer induced motility (Fig. 18). Spheroplasts can be produced in cells not sensitive to lysozyme but sensitive to penicillin by growing them in a sucrose medium containing 800 units of penicillin per ml. When penicillin is eliminated the cell walls regenerate. A normal human serum fraction also may inhibit the synthesis of cell wall and give rise to protoplasts (86). All protoplasts

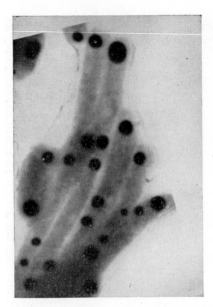

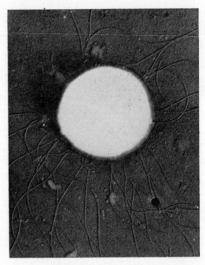

Fig. 16. *Mycobacterium thamnopheos* after growth on polyphosphate (metaphosphate) accumulation medium. Note accumulation of cytoplasmic granules. (From Mudd, Yoshida, and Koike. *J. Bact.,* 75:224, 1958.)

Fig. 18. Electron micrograph of a spheroplast of *Bacillus megaterium* showing flagella coming through the cytoplasmic membrane. (From Kawata, Asaki, and Takagi. *J. Bact.,* 81:160, 1961.)

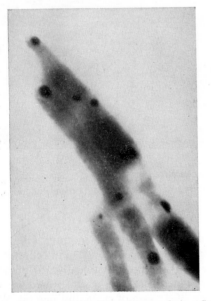

Fig. 17. *Mycobacterium thamnopheos.* Same culture as shown in Figure 16 after growth for 24 hours in Dubos medium and glucose. Note reduction in cytoplasmic granules. (From Mudd, Yoshida, and Koike. *J. Bact.,* 75:224, 1958.)

assume a spherical shape even when derived form a rod-shaped organism (136).

Lederberg and St. Clair (80) have induced protoplasts to grow into colonies by planting them in a suitable medium containing 1 per cent agar. These colonies are very similar, if not identical, to the L colonies of the pleuropneumonia-like organisms which have been studied by Dienes (45) and Klieneberger-Nobel (68). The colonies contained both the **large bodies** (125) of Dienes (Fig. 19) and the minute, filter-passing forms discussed in Chapter 54. In most instances the penicillin in the medium simply blocks the synthesis of the cell wall, but it also provides a selective mechanism for mutants which cannot synthesize a cell wall even in the absence of penicillin. One such genetic defect has been identified by Davis and by McQuillen (84) as an inability to synthesize diaminopymelic acid. The metabolic defects in other mutants are not known.

Bacterial Spores. Endospore formation is a distinguishing feature of the organisms of the family *Bacillaceae,* of which the aerobic genus is called *Bacillus* and the anaerobic genus, *Clostridium.* Organisms in these groups occur chiefly in the intestinal contents of man and animals, in soil, water and air. Most of them are saprophytic. Others

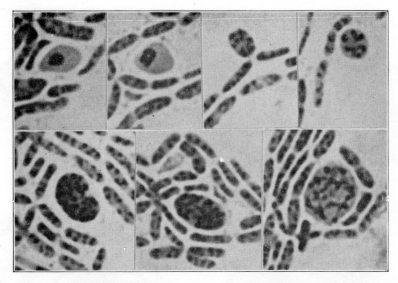

Fig. 19. Photograph of bacteria. Stained to show nuclear structure of "large bodies." (From Stempen. *J. Bact.,* 61:341, 1951.)

produce their effects only when a medium of dead or injured tissue affords them a nidus for growth in the animal body.

The true endospore is a highly refractile body formed within the bacterial cell at a certain stage of growth (7) (Fig. 20). The size, shape, and position of the spore are relatively constant characteristics of species and are therefore of some value in distinguishing one kind of bacillus from another. The position of the spore in the cell may be central, subterminal, or terminal. It may be of the same diameter as that of the cell or smaller, or may be larger, causing a swelling of the cell. Even the surface of the spore, as revealed by electron micrographs, may be characteristic of the species (18), and in the spores appear new antigens which are different from those in the vegetative bacilli (102).

Evidence is accumulating that spore formation may be a generative process in which there is fusion of nuclei followed by reduction of nuclear material (77). Certainly some nuclear material and a considerable part of the cytoplasm disappear after the fertile part of the organism has been enclosed in a dense spore wall.

The beautiful electron micrographs made from thin sections of *Bacillus cereus* and *Bacillus megaterium* by Chapman (26, 27)

and Robinow (115, 116) reveal the complexity of spore formation (Fig. 21). *B. megaterium* has two spore coats, while *B. cereus* has three.

When the spores of any microorganism are brought into an environment with suit-

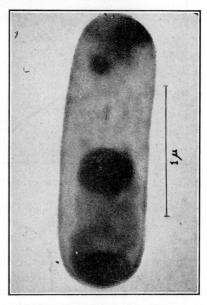

Fig. 20. Nucleus in spore formation. Electron micrograph showing a pair of nuclear bodies which are in the process of being enclosed in a spore. (From Knaysi and Baker. *J. Bact.,* 53:539, 1947.)

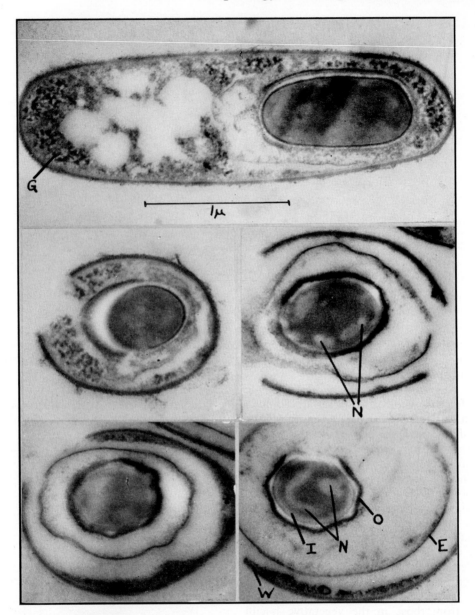

Fig. 21.   Electron micrographs of ultra-thin sections of *Bacillus cereus*. X 38,600. The figures show cells in late stages of sporulation and just prior to liberation from the sporangium wall. E, exosporium; O, outer coat; I, inner coat; N, nuclear element; W, sporangium wall; G, dense granule. (From Chapman. *J. Bact.*, 71:348, 1956.)

able temperature, moisture and nutrition for bacterial growth, the spores develop into vegetative forms. This process varies according to species. In general it consists of an elongation of the spore body with a loss of its highly refractile character and resistance to ordinary methods of staining. The de-veloping vegetative cell may now rupture and slip out of the spore membrane at one of its poles, leaving the empty spore capsule still visible and attached to the bacillary body (72). Again, a similar process may take place equatorially instead of at the pole. Occasionally the two halves of the spore coat are completely severed and each remains as a cap about one end of the germ cell.

In other species there may be no rupture of the spore membrane at all, the vegetative form arising by gradual elongation of the spore and an absorption or solution of the membrane. Division in the ordinary way then ensues. The process of spore formation with *Clostridium pectinovorum* is essentially the same as the genus *Bacillus* (51).

Halvorson (58) has found that dipicolinic acid determines both the dormancy and the heat resistance of spores, and endogenous dipicolinic acid regulates the L-alanine-triggered germination (66). It is obvious that the germination of spores is controlled by a complex system of stimulators and inhibitors (58, 140).

Cyst Formation. Some species of *Myxobacteriales, Chlamydobacteriales,* and *Eubacteriales* produce cysts rather than endospores. The process of forming cysts was studied in some detail by Bisset in 1955, who found that cysts were much more resistant to drying (12, 87) than the negative cells and somewhat more resistant to heat. Cyst formation has been studied in *Myxococcus xanthus* by Voelz and Dworkin (132), *Azobacter agilis* and *Azobacter vinelandii* by Socolofsky and Wyss (124), and Wyss and others (145). The cysts of these species were resistant to drying but not to heat.

Cell Nucleus. The development of special staining technics for deoxyribonucleic acid (116) and the invention of the phase and electron microscopes have shown without question that bacterial cells do have particulate nuclei analogous to those in higher plants and animals (28, 29, 30, 31, 71, 100).

There is no disagreement about the fact that nuclear division occurs prior to cellular division, but considerable difference of opinion exists about the type of division employed by bacteria—whether amitotic or mitotic. Bisset (10, 11) favors amitotic division, and Robinow (116) and his associates interpret the complex figures of chromatin material as evidence of nonchromosomal division analogous to that shown by the dividing nucleus in the schizonts of the avian malarial parasite, *Plasmodium elongatum.*

Chance has used an acid fuchsin stain to

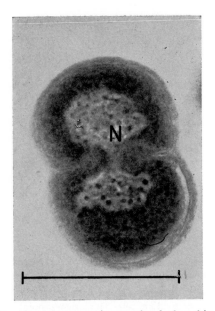

Fig. 22. Electron micrograph of ultra-thin section of a cell in amitotic division. Note the appearance of granules in the nuclear zone and the beginning of ingrowth of the cytoplasmic membrane. (From Chapman. *J. Bact.,* 78:96, 1959.)

study nuclear division in fresh cells (25). In some cells the nuclear material was apparently divided directly by a cross-wall and did not recede from the partition until cell division was well advanced.

Amitotic division can be seen in Figure 22; the process is nearly complete and the beginning of the cross septum is apparent. Figure 23 shows nuclear division completed and the cytoplasmic membrane has nearly separated the cytoplasm. Chapman's observations (28, 29) on the mechanics of cell division with the centripetal growth of the cell wall have been confirmed by the studies of Conti and Gettner (36).

Reproduction of Bacteria. Binary division into two equal parts is the usual and predominant mode of reproduction of bacteria under standardized conditions of cultivation in the laboratory. Knaysi (70) has emphasized that the process is not the simple constrictive maneuver implied by the term "fission" but consists of three regular consecutive steps. Near the middle of the organism the cytoplasmic membrane grows inward, dividing the cytoplasm into two sister cells. This new end cytoplasmic membrane

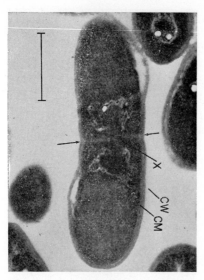

Fig. 23. Electron micrograph of ultra-thin section of a dividing cell. The arrows point to the centripetal growth of the cytoplasmic membrane. X designates a rarely observed fibrillar arrangement in the cytoplasm. (From Chapman. *J. Biophys. & Biochem. Cytol.,* 6:221, 1959.)

is split, and each sister cell then lays down its own cell wall, thus furnishing a continuous cell wall enclosing a cytoplasmic membrane and cytoplasm. An increase in turgor of the growing cells eventually forces a complete separation.

Spherical cells may or may not elongate before division. The planes of cleavage of spherical forms determine the conformation of the aggregate of cells. Division in one plane produces diplococci or cocci in chains (*Streptococcus*) while cleavage in two or more planes gives rise to grape-like clusters (*Staphylococcus*) or to arrangement in packets or cubes (*Sarcina*). The cylindrical or curved forms may at time remain attached end-to-end in chains or spirals.

Although **budding** is considered a rare and unusual form of reproduction, Bisset (14) and his associates have studied cell division in a series of flagellated bacilli and in one motile coccus (56). The bacilli grew out of one end by a process resembling budding. Division in the motile coccus left the old cell with the flagellum; the new cell later developed its own flagellum.

A **branching** type of reproduction has been observed in many species, particularly

when subjected to abnormal conditions, and has its beginning in the formation of a bud (70). An unusual type of branching has been described by Murray and Douglas (97) in the new photoheterotrophic organism, *Rhodomicrobium vannielii*. Branching is the characteristic method of reproduction among the *Streptomycetaceae*. In Figure 24 a portion of the nucleus is seen leaving the main stem and migrating into the branch (90). The internal structure of the anaerobic *Actinomyces* has been investigated by Overman and Pine who employed thin sections and the electron microscope (106).

Filamentous growth is characterized by the appearance of long, unsegmented, multinucleated filaments under conditions of ordinary cultivation in many organisms. Certain strains of the influenza bacillus, the typhoid bacillus and aerobic spore-forming organisms produce filaments in abundance during rapid growth on moist media.

A polyploid strain of *E. coli* has been produced by exposing the culture to the fumes of natural camphor (103).

Reproduction by **conidia** or asexual spore formation is common among the fungi, but it is doubtful whether this mode of multiplication occurs in bacteria.

Sexual reproduction in bacteria is unusual but it does occur. Indirect evidence for this phenomenon was furnished by Tatum and Lederberg in 1947 (129) and by Lederberg in 1950 (78). When mutant strains of *E. coli* requiring various amino acids for growth and *E. coli* strains resistant to streptomycin or azide were grown together in a selective medium, some of the isolates were found to have metabolic abilities characteristic of both parents. To these observations should also be added the hybridization between *E. coli* and *Sh. dysenteriae* (83), *E. coli* and *S. typhosa* (4), and *E. coli* and *S. typhimurium* (122). Direct evidence for sexual reproduction was furnished by Lederberg in 1956 (79) when he photographed side-by-side pairing or conjugation of intact cells which was accompanied by a transfer of a nucleus from one cell to another followed by separation of the conjugants. In some strains of *Bacteriodes,* a long conjugation tube forms which transports material from one cell to another (Ch. 5, Fig. 7) (16).

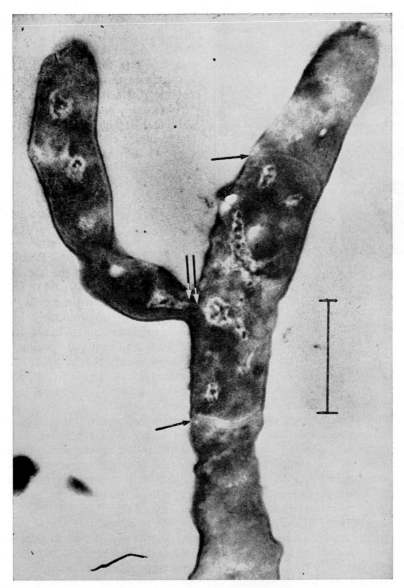

Fig. 24. Electron micrograph of ultra-thin section of a streptomycete. Complete transverse cell walls are indicated by single arrows. The double arrows show a nucleus migrating into the newly formed branch. (From Moore and Chapman. *J. Bact.*, 78:878, 1959.)

Mutants with Altered Colonial Morphology, Antigenicity, and Virulence. In Arkwright's (1) and de Kruif's (40) original studies and in much subsequent work concerned with variations associated with pathogenic bacteria, attention has been focused on the high degree of correlation between changes in colony form, antigenic structure and virulence (54, 55). These changes result from mutations, and the new forms are,

in general, as stable as the ones from which they were derived (Fig. 25).

THE S—R TYPE OF DISSOCIATION. Organisms belonging to the coli-typhoid-paratyphoid-dysentery group usually are in the smooth (S) phase when isolated from the patient. The colonies are smooth, soft, and composed of short, plump rods which show little variation in size. The organisms make homogenous suspensions in physiologic saline

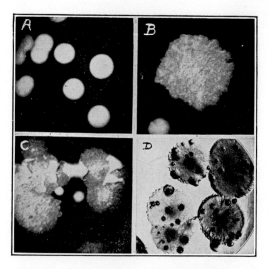

Fig. 25. Types of bacterial colonies. A, smooth. B, rough. C, smooth developing from rough colonies. A, B, and C are from a culture of an acid-fact bacterium. D, colonies of the cholera vibrio with secondary daughter colonies. (From Eisenberg.)

and agglutinate readily in specific serum or in the serum of the convalescing patient. The smooth character of the colony and its specific antigenicity depend upon the presence of surface antigens which have been identified as gluco-lipid-protein complexes. After growing for some time on artificial media, rough type (R) colonies appear which are larger, but flatter, and have rough or corrugated surfaces (Fig. 25). These colonies are not soft and do not make homogenous suspensions in physiologic saline. They are agglutinated spontaneously by an increase in salt content and and will not agglutinate, or agglutinate poorly, in a specific serum prepared by immunization with organisms from S colonies. The R forms have lost their virulence and are phagocytized easily by the cells of normal animals. Microscopically the cells from the R colonies are pleomorphic, varying from very short rods to long filaments which may show branching. Such changes in colony form and microscopic appearance are associated with the loss of the surface gluco-lipid-protein complexes. With this loss, another polysaccharide antigen complex is uncovered which is group specific for enteric organisms (137). However, even

the latter surface layer may be lost by further dissociation.

The change from S to R may occur suddenly in one step; or by a series of steps, resulting in the appearance of **intermediate colonies,** which both in morphology and virulence are intermediate between the typical S and R. The S and R types are relatively stable under standard conditions of cultivation but the intermediates are unstable and revert, on replating, either to the typical S or the typical R forms. These intermediate forms have been designated as Sr, SR or sR depending upon their resemblance to the S or R forms.

The rather dramatic changes seen in the appearance of the S and R colonies depend upon the behavior of the bacilli immediately after cell division (9, 64). In the smooth forms the short daughter cells "slip by" each other to line up uniformly in the colony, while in the rough cultures cell division is delayed, long forms are produced, and when division occurs the "slipping" process is incomplete.

The possibility of the so-called mutants being present in a mixture of organisms, even in apparently pure cultures, has been eliminated by the recovery of variants in strains called **clones,** which are the descendants of a single organism selected directly from a microscopic preparation (20). Working with an unstable S type strain of *S. typhimurium,* Zelle (146) separated each daughter cell as division occurred, and established the occurrence of one R form for each 148 cell divisions. Braun (20, 21) observed a spontaneous mutation rate of 1×10^{-7} for S—R changes in a strain of *Br. abortus.*

Under conditions of artificial cultivation the direction of dissociation is from the S to the R, presumably because the R forms are better adapted for growth on the relatively poorer diet afforded by lifeless media; and the characteristics which originally gave the organism virulence for animals no longer have any survival value. When a culture containing a mixture of S and R forms is injected into an animal, the conditions are reversed and the R forms, lacking defensive and offensive weapons, soon are eliminated by the phagocytic cells while the S forms survive and multiply.

Virulence is commonly, but not always, associated with the S type colony. With some organisms, such as the anthrax bacilli and the human and bovine types of tubercle bacilli, the R forms are more virulent.

In the gram-positive and gram-negative groups of cocci the smooth and rough characteristics of the colonies depend upon the presence or absence of certain surface antigens and not upon variations in the mechanism of cell division, as observed in the group of enteric bacilli.

THE MUCOID COLONY. Organisms with well developed capsules such as *D. pneumoniae, H. influenzae, K. pneumoniae,* and *Cryptococcus neoformans,* produce mucoid colonies (39). Mucoid (M) colonies also are produced by *Past. pestis* and some dissociates of *Brucella, Salmonella, Shigella,* and *Vibrio comma.* In the latter group the polysaccharide material often is referred to as a "slime layer" rather than a true capsule (46). The capsular material usually is specific and antigenic for mice and men but not for rabbits. The capsule functions as a defense mechanism against phagocytosis and encapsulated organisms usually, but not always, are more virulent than the unencapsulated forms.

In some nonpathogenic organisms such as *Serratia marcescens* one may observe a complete cycle of changes from M—S—R—M with an independent and unrelated variation in the color of the colonies (112).

THE DWARF COLONY. Other types of dissociation such as the appearance of **dwarf** (D) colonies, **gonidial** (G) (54), and **pleuropneumonia-like colonies** (L) (67) occur less frequently, or else our methods of detection are less efficient.

Organisms from the dwarf colonies usually are diphtheroid in form and gram-positive, regardless of the reaction of the original strain to staining by Gram's method. They have poorly developed enzyme systems, grow slowly, have little or no virulence, and revert slowly under favorable conditions to the original parent type. D colonies have been isolated from patients with chronic gonorrhea (93) and frequently are isolated from bacterial populations which have been exposed to penicillin or streptomycin.

THE G COLONY. The G colonies average about 0.5 mm. in diameter and are composed of minute coccoid and bacillary forms. They resemble the D type in that they always are gram-positive, biochemically inert, and nonpathogenic. Hadley originally thought these forms represented the gonidial stage in the life cycle of bacteria. They have been studied in some detail in cultures of staphylococci (57, 60). The G forms pass through filters which retain ordinary bacteria. Although their reversion to the normal type cell is slow and difficult, we agree with Morton (92) that this should be accomplished before accepting a particular G form as specific.

THE L COLONIES. The pleuropneumonia-like colonies (L) are associated almost constantly with *Streptobacillus moniliformis* (*Actinomyces muris ratti*) (41, 42, 43, 44, 67, 68, 69, 117).

They also have been isolated from strains of *H. influenzae* (43), *S. typhosa* (44, 75) and other intestinal bacteria. Dienes has found that exposure to high concentrations of penicillin accelerates the development of L colonies or at least facilitates their detection and isolation (77). In microscopic preparations minute coccoid and filamentous forms are seen and also relatively large, globoid bodies which contain the minute forms. Subcultures have been maintained for many generations on solid media but reversion to the original stock type may occur in liquid media. The true pleuropneumonia organisms are pathogenic for certain animals and never revert to a large form.

METHODS OF INDUCING DISSOCIATION. Dissociation occurs as a natural process, but the phenomenon can be induced by a variety of methods. Dissociation is more frequent in liquid media and in old cultures after prolonged incubation. The addition of small amounts of lithium chloride or phenol results in the appearance of more variants. Dissociates appear most frequently after exposing a large population of bacteria to sulfonamides, penicillin, streptomycin, ultraviolet light, x-rays, radium emanation, nitrogen mustard gas, or bacteriophage (82). Under these conditions, 99 per cent of the organisms are killed and some of the survivors show characteristics which differ in one way or another from the parent strain.

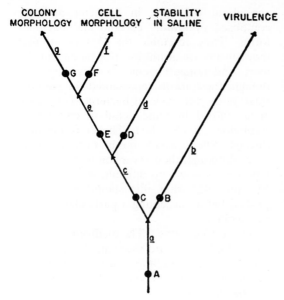

Fig. 26. Diagram illustrating a mechanism for the production of linked and nonlinked variations. (From Braun. *Bact. Rev.,* 11:75, 1947.)

organisms in media containing the anti-R serum. As previously noted, the R form has an advantage over the S form when the organisms are grown on an artificial medium, but when specific antibodies directed against its surface, antigens are added to the medium, this advantage disappears, and the balance of forces favors the growth of the S forms.

THE NATURE OF DISSOCIATION. Most of the changes in colonial morphology, antigenicity, and virulence are of the nature of a biochemical mutation. Although we know little about the steps involved in the biosynthesis of surface antigens, we may assume that loss of an antigenic component represents failure to carry out a step in the series of biosynthetic reactions. The loss of a certain combination of characteristics as a unit is not inconsistent with the single gene-single enzyme theory because if the missing enzyme produced an intermediate substance necessary for several reactions, then all of them would be affected (Fig. 26). Furthermore, the loss of a single property, such as the ability to synthesize a specific capsule, results in such varied changes as loss of capsule, loss of specific agglutinability, loss of virulence, and change from M to S in colony form, because all of these different properties are dependent upon the presence of the capsule. Unfortunately, however, not all the facts connected with changes in virulence can be explained by a simple change in colony form or a change in known antigens.

In extensive studies on population changes due to mutations Braun (19, 20) has demonstrated that the accumulation of a specific metabolite, alanine, limits the increase in smooth cells and creates an environment suitable for the establishment of rough cells with greater resistance to alanine. Similar effects of metabolites on population changes have been observed in vivo as well as in other species.

In the animal body the virulent M and S forms have an advantage over the R and other forms in the early stages of the infection because of their offensive and defensive weapons. As the patient recovers, however, the bacteria are subjected to the action of the antibodies specifically manufactured against their surface antigens. This favors the development of the R form which is not affected by the specific anti-S antibodies. R forms frequently are isolated from patients during convalescence and from patients studied near the end of an epidemic (141). The same phenomenon can be observed in the test tube. Cultures grown in media containing antiserums, prepared by immunization with M or S phase organisms, soon show a predominance of R forms. Also R forms can be reverted to S forms by growing the R type

REFERENCES

1. Arkwright, J. A.   J. Path. & Bact., 24:36, 1921.
2. Astbury, W. T., and Weibull, C.   Nature, London, 163:280, 1949.
3. Avery, R. J., and Blank, F.   Canad. J. Microbiol., 1:140, 1954.
4. Baron, L. S., and others.   J. Exper. Med., 112:361, 1960.
5. Barkulis, S. S., and others.   J. Bact., 74:207, 1957; 77:177, 1959.
6. Baumann-Grace, J. B., and Tomcsik, J.   Schweiz. Ztschr. f. Path. u. Bakt., 21:906, 1958.
7. Bayne-Jones, S., and Petrilli, A.   J. Bact., 25:261, 1933.
8. Bibb, W. B., and Straughn, W. R.   J. Bact., 84:1094, 1962.
9. Bisset, K. A.   J. Path. & Bact., 47:223, 1939.
10. —— J. Bact., 67:41, 1954.

11. ———— The Cytology and Life History of Bacteria, 2nd ed., Baltimore, Williams & Wilkins, 1955.
12. ———— J. Gen. Microbiol., 13:442, 1955.
13. ———— in Symposium. Soc. Gen. Microbiol. 6th, 1956, p. 1.
14. ———— and Pease, P. E. J. Gen. Microbiol., 16:382, 1957.
15. ———— and Pease, P. E. J. Bact., 79:612, 1960.
16. Bladen, H. A., Jr. J. Bact., 85:250, 1963.
17. Bovarnick, M. J. Biol. Chem., 145:415, 1942.
18. Bradley, D. E., and Franklin, J. G. J. Bact., 76:618, 1958.
19. Braun, W. Bact. Rev., 11:75, 1947.
20. ———— Bacterial Genetics, Philadelphia, W. B. Saunders Co., 1953.
21. ———— and Ciaccio, E. Bact. Proc., p. 41, 1952.
22. Brinton, C. C. Nature, 183:782, 1959.
23. ———— and others. Biochem. & Biophys. Comm., 5:293, 1961.
24. Burdon, K. L. J. Bact., 52:665, 1946.
25. Chance, H. L. J. Bact., 74:67, 1957.
26. Chapman, G. B., and Hillier, J. J. Bact., 66:362, 1953.
27. ———— J. Bact., 71:348, 1956.
28. ———— J. Biophys. and Biochem. Cytol., 6:221, 1959.
29. ———— J. Bact., 78:96, 1959.
30. ———— J. Bact., 84:169, 180, 1962.
31. Chatterjee, B. R., and Williams, R. P. J. Bact., 83:1112, 1962.
32. Clark, J. B., and others. J. Bact., 73:72, 1957.
33. Cole, R. M., and Hahn, J. J. Science, 135:722, 1962.
34. ———— Bact. Proc., p. 26, 1963.
35. Conti, S. F., and Naylor, H. B. J. Bact., 79:331, 417, 1960.
36. ———— and Gettner, M. E. J. Bact., 83:544, 1962.
37. Cummins, C. S. Internat. Rev. Cytol., 5:25, 1956.
38. Czekalowski, J. W., and Eaves, G. J. Path. & Bact., 69:129, 1955.
39. Dawson, M. H., and others. J. Infect. Dis., 62:138, 1938.
40. De Kruif, P. J. Exper. Med., 33:773, 1921; 35:561, 621, 1922.
41. Dienes, L. J. Bact., 50:441, 1945.
42. ———— Complex Reproductive Processes in Bacteria, Cold Spring Harbor Symposia on Quantitative Biology, 11:51, 1946.
43. ———— Proc. Soc. Exper. Biol. & Med., 64:165, 166, 1947.
44. ———— and others. J. Bact., 59:755, 1950.
45. ———— and Weinberger, H. J. Bact. Rev., 15:245, 1951.
46. Dubos, R. J. The Bacterial Cell, Cambridge, Mass., Harvard University Press, 1945.
47. ———— and Avery, O. T. J. Exper. Med., 54:51, 1931.
48. Duguid, J. P. J. Path. & Bact., 63:673, 1951.
49. ———— and others. J. Path. & Bact., 70:335, 1955.
50. ———— and Gillies, R. R. J. Path. & Bact., 74:397, 1957.
51. Fitz-James, P. C. J. Bact., 84:104, 1962.
52. Grace, J. B. J. Gen. Microbiol., 10:325, 1954.
53. Guex-Holzer, S., and Tomcsik, J. J. Gen. Microbiol., 14:1, 1956.
54. Hadley, P. J. Infect. Dis., 40:1-312, 1927; 60:129, 1937.
55. ———— and Wetzel, V. J. Bact., 45:529, 1943.
56. Hale, C. M. F., and Bisset, K. A. J. Gen. Microbiol., 18:668, 1958.
57. Hale, J. H. Brit. J. Exper. Path., 28:202, 1947.
58. Halvorson, H. O. Spores, Minneapolis, Minn., Burgess Publ. Co., 1961.
59. Hirokawa, H. J. Bact., 84:1161, 1962.
60. Hoffstadt, R. E., and Youmans, G. P. J. Infect. Dis., 51:316, 1932.
61. Houwink, A., and Van Iterson, W. Biochem. et Biophys. Acta, 5:10, 1950.
62. Imaeda, T., and Ogura, M. J. Bact., 85:150, 1963.
63. Jenkins, H. M. J. Bact., 80:639, 1960.
64. Kahn, M. C. Third Internat. Congr. Microbiol., New York, 1939, p. 160.
65. Kawata, T., and others. J. Bact., 81:160, 1961.
66. Keynan, A., and Halvorson, H. O. J. Bact., 83:100, 395, 1962.
67. Klieneberger, E. J. Path. & Bact., 40:93, 1935.
68. ———— -Nobel, E. Bact. Rev., 15:77, 1951.
69. ———— Biol. Rev., 29:154, 1954.
70. Knaysi, G. Elements of Bacterial Cytology, 2nd ed., Ithaca, New York, Comstock Publishing Co., 1951.
71. ———— and Baker, R. F. J. Bact., 53:539, 1947.
72. ———— and others. J. Bact., 53:525, 1947.
73. ———— J. Bact., 77:532, 1959.
74. Koffler, H., and others. Arch. Biochem. & Biophysics, 67:509, 1956.
75. Landman, O. E., and Ginoza, H. S. J. Bact., 81:875, 1961.
76. Langston, C. W., and others. J. Bact., 80:714, 1960.
77. Lederberg, J., and Zinder, N. J. Am. Chem. Soc., 70:4267, 1948.
78. ———— J. Bact., 59:211, 1950.
79. ———— J. Bact., 71:497, 1956.
80. ———— and St. Clair, J. J. Bact., 75:143, 1958.
81. Leifson, E., and others. J. Bact., 69:73, 1955.
82. Luria, S. E. Science, 111:507, 1950.
83. ———— and Burrous, J. W. J. Bact., 74:461, 1957.
84. McQuillen, K. Biochem. et Biophys. Acta, 27:410, 1958.
85. Mahler, H. R., and Fraser, D. Biochem. et Biophys. Acta, 22:197, 1956.
86. Michael, J. G., and Braun, W. Proc. Soc. Exper. Biol. & Med., 100:422, 1959.
87. Miller, R. E., and Simons, L. A. J. Bact., 84:1111, 1962.
88. Mitchell, P., and Moyle, J. J. Gen. Microbiol., 16:184, 1957.
89. ———— Ann. Rev. Microbiol., 13:407, 1959.
90. Moore, R. T., and Chapman, G. B. J. Bact., 78:878, 1959.
91. Morowitz, A. J. Science, 119:286, 1954.

92. Morton, H. E.   Bact. Rev., 4:177, 1940.
93. ——— and Shoemaker, J.   J. Bact., 50:585, 1945.
94. Mudd, S.   Am. Rev. Resp. Dis., 85:272, 1962.
95. ——— and others.   J. Bact., 75:224, 1958.
96. ——— Ann. Rev. Microbiol., 8:1, 1954.
97. Murray, R. G. E., and Douglas, H. C.   J. Bact., 59:157, 1950.
98. ——— and Robinow, C. F.   J. Bact., 63:298, 1952.
99. ——— Canad. J. Microbiol., 3:531, 1957.
100. ——— The Bacteria, Vol. VI, New York, Academic Press, 1960, p. 35.
101. Nasser, D., and Koffler, H.   Bact. Proc., p. 35, 1963.
102. Norris, J. R.   J. Gen. Microbiol., 28:393, 1962.
103. Ogg, J. E., and Zelle, M. R.   J. Bact., 74:477, 1957.
104. O'Leary, W. M.   J. Bact. Rev., 26:421, 1962.
105. Ormabee, R. A., and others.   J. Immunol., 74:351, 359, 1955.
106. Overman, J. R., and Pine, L.   J. Bact., 86:656, 1963.
107. Pangborn, J., and others.   J. Bact., 84:669, 1962.
108. Park, J. T.   Symposia of Soc. for Gen. Microbiol. No. 8, The Strategy of Chemotherapy, 1958, p. 49.
109. Perkins, H. R.   Bact. Rev., 27:18, 1963.
110. Pijper, A., and others.   J. Bact., 65:628, 636, 1953; 69:151, 1955.
111. Primosigh, J., and others.   Biochem. et Biophys. Acta, 46:68, 1961.
112. Reed, G. B.   J. Bact., 34:255, 1937.
113. Ribi, E., and others.   J. Immunol., 82:75, 1959.
114. ——— and others.   Proc. Soc. Exper. Biol. & Med., 100:647, 1959.
115. Robinow, C. F.   J. Bact., 66:300, 1953.
116. ——— Symposia of Soc. of Gen. Microbiol., 6:181, 1956.
117. Sabin, A. B.   Bact. Rev., 5:1, 1941.
118. Sall, T., and others.   J. Bact., 76:640, 1958.

119. Salton, M. R. J.   Biochem. et Biophys. Acta, 45:364, 1960.
120. ——— Microbial Cell Walls, New York, John Wiley & Sons, 1961.
121. ——— Bact. Rev., 25:77, 1961.
122. Schneider, H., and others.   J. Exper. Med., 114:141, 1961.
123. Smith, P. F., and Rothblat, G. H.   J. Bact., 83:500, 1962.
124. Socolofsky, M. D., and Wyss, O.   J. Bact., 84:119, 1962.
125. Stempen, H.   J. Bact., 61:341, 1951; 70:177, 1955.
126. Swain, R. H. A.   J. Path. & Bact., 69:117, 1955.
127. Tabor, C. W.   J. Bact., 83:1101, 1962.
128. Takeya, K., and Hisatsune, K.   J. Bact., 85:17, 1963.
129. Tatum, E. L., and Lederberg, J.   J. Bact., 53:673, 1947.
130. Tawara, J.   J. Bact., 73:89, 1957.
131. Toda, T., and others.   Proc. Jap. Acad., 36:372, 430, 432, 1960.
132. Voelz, H., and Dworkin, M.   J. Bact., 84:943, 1962.
133. Ward, J. R., and Martin, C. H.   Proc. Soc. Exper. Biol. and Med., 111:156, 1962.
134. Weibull, C., and Beckman, H.   J. Bact., 79:638, 1960.
135. ——— Ann. Rev. Microbiol., 12:1, 1958.
136. ——— J. Bact., 66:688, 696, 1953.
137. White, P. B.   J. Path. & Bact., 50:160, 1940.
138. Widra, A.   J. Bact., 71:689, 1956; 78:664, 1959.
139. Wilkinson, J. F.   Bact. Rev., 22:46, 1958.
140. Williams, O. B., and others.   Bact. Rev., 16:89, 1952.
141. Williams, M. A., and Chapman, G. B.   J. Bact., 81:195, 1961.
142. Williams, R. E. O.   Bact. Rev., 27:56, 1963.
143. Wohlhieter, J. A., and others.   J. Bact., 84:416, 1962.
144. Work, E.   Nature, 179:841, 1957.
145. Wyss, O., and others.   J. Biophys. & Biochem. Cytol., 10:555, 1961.
146. Zelle, M. R.   Genetics, 26:174, 1941.

4

The Composition and Organization of a Bacterial Cell

The bacterial cell appears to be formed on the same general chemical pattern as the cells of other living organisms. Variations induced by changes in the environmental conditions under which a given bacterial specimen is grown make it difficult to obtain an exact picture of its chemical composition. The problem is further complicated by the appearance in any given species or strain of mutants which differ from the parental type. There are, however, certain chemical constituents which, although varying markedly from one bacterium to another, are basic components of all bacterial cells.

Bacteria, in common with all other living cells, contain a high proportion of water. It is the major component of the cell and represents 75 to 85 per cent of the total weight. Bacterial spores often have 10 to 20 per cent less water than the vegetative forms, and a large percentage of this water is present in a bound form. Unlike free water, bound water does not act as a solvent or play a role in osmotic phenomena.

The carbon content ranges from 45 to 55 per cent of the dry weight, and nitrogen from 8 to 15 per cent. The ash content is highly variable, reflecting growth conditions and nature of the medium. It accounts for 1.3 to 13.9 per cent and consists of elements which after incineration are found in the ash as oxides. Phosphorus constitutes from 10 to 45 per cent of the ash content, being present in the cell in a number of important molecules such as nucleic acids, phospholipids, and coenzymes. Other mineral components which have been identified are potassium, sodium, magnesium, calcium, iron, sulfur, chlorine, manganese, and traces of copper, aluminum, zinc, and molybdenum.

The organic fraction of the dry matter may be separated into the macromolecular frac-

tion, including the proteins, nucleic acids, carbohydrates, and lipids, and the low-molecular weight constituents, which are acid soluble. The latter are usually separated by extraction with 5 per cent trichloroacetic acid or perchloric acid and include such substances as amino acids, sugars, organic acids, nucleotides, various phosphate esters, vitamins, and coenzymes. Although the total amount of this fraction is low, it constitutes a very important and characteristic milieu, reflecting the ability of the organism to concentrate such metabolites as amino acids to a level much higher than that found in the external environment.

The protein content as estimated roughly from nitrogen values is approximately 50 per cent of the dry weight but varies considerably with the age of the culture. The amino acids which make up bacterial protein are the same as those which make up proteins of other living cells.

The nucleic acid content of bacteria is high and includes both the ribose and deoxyribose types of the same base composition as that from other sources. The relative amounts of the bases of the DNA vary, however, from species to species. Molar ratios of adenine to guanine of 0.5 to 2.5 have been reported in different bacteria by Lee (22), who first recognized the importance of DNA base analyses as a taxonomic aid. It has been shown in general that organisms which are very closely related genetically or by the criteria of numerical taxonomy have similar DNA base compositions (25).

The lipid content ranges from 1 to 40 per cent of the dry weight, but in most bacteria that do not deposit lipid inclusions the lipid content is less than 8 per cent of the dry substance. In *Mycobacterium* the lipid content may reach 40 per cent. The lipid may be free, or it may be bound with protein or carbohydrate. Bacterial lipid, extracted from the cell, consists of free fatty acids, phospholipids, neutral fats, and waxes. The fats of the acid-fast bacteria are unique in that they are fatty acid esters of trehalose rather than esters of glycerol, and their phosphatides do not contain choline and ethanolamine. In bacteria lipids are stored as granules of poly-β-hydroxybutyrate, a metabolite less rich in energy but more readily available than chains of fully reduced saturated fatty acids (31, 49).

The carbohydrate content varies from about 4 to 24 per cent, the concentration being markedly dependent on carbon excess in the medium (31). In addition to starch and glycogen (6), a variety of polysaccharide gums are formed, and complex polysaccharides, either free or associated with proteins and lipids, are commonly present in the surface layers of the cells. These polysaccharides, which are in the form of highly polymerized units, are of considerable practical importance, conferring immunologic specificity to the cell (8). Some polysaccharides have also been shown to be antigenic.

Although the tremendous amount of data which has accumulated on the chemical composition of the bacterial cell is most impressive, it tells us little about how these simple molecules are joined together to form macromolecules of lipoprotein, lipopolysaccharide, and nucleoprotein as they exist in the cell. In order to understand the relationship between chemical composition and cellular function, the location of the various components of the cell must be found. In spite of the problems encountered in working with organisms of the size of bacteria, considerable advances have been made in the isolation and chemical identification of microscopically recognizable structural components.

Between the external environment of the bacterial cell and the internal protoplasm are a number of surface components: surface appendages, surface adherents, cell wall, and protoplasmic membrane. Because of the high ratio of surface area to volume of a bacterium, it is not surprising that surface phenomena play an important part in bacterial actions. An electric charge resides at the bacterial surface in aqueous suspensions. This charge plays a prominent role in adsorption, especially during filtration, in agglutination phenomena, and in electrophoresis. In neutral solutions the charge is negative. Mutual repulsion between these charged bodies accounts in part for their ability to remain in suspension for long periods.

Surface Appendages (46).   The main surface appendage of bacterial cells is the flagellum, an organelle of locomotion. Flagella may be easily removed from the organism by vigorous shaking without destroying the viability of the cell or its ability to produce new flagella. Chemically the flagella belong to the fibrous group of proteins and consist of at least 99 per cent protein (20). Most of the amino acids generally found in protein have been detected with the exception of histidine, tryptophan, proline, and hydroxyproline. The x-ray patterns of the flagella of *Proteus vulgaris* and *Bacillus subtilis* are similar to that of the actomyosin complex of skeletal muscle, but the flagella are unlike muscle in that they do not contain measurable amounts of phosphorus, nucleotides, and certain amino acids. Fine structures have been demonstrated in electron micrographs of some bacterial flagella in support of Weibull's hypothesis that each flagellum consists of a bundle of helically wound subfibrils (46). No enzymatic activity has been demonstrated in flagella preparations, and it is not clear whether flagella produce the necessary energy themselves or whether it is derived from the cell body. The synthesis of bacterial flagella and the effects of various environmental conditions on their formation have been discussed by Kerridge (19).

Surface Adherents (39).   Many bacteria are surrounded by layers of material that are external to the rigid cell wall. This material is either organized into a thick capsular gel, cytologically demonstrable, or as a diffuse layer of loose slime easily washed from the surface. Surface adherents may be dispensed with by the cell without affecting its viability or ability to synthesize new capsular material. They have a low affinity for dyes and are probably formed by the accumulation of polymers of high viscosity outside the cell wall. The environment and conditions of culture markedly influence the expression of an organism's ability to produce capsular material.

Bacterial capsules are polymeric materials, either polysaccharide or polypeptide in nature. The capsule of the pneumococcus is polysaccharide and is responsible for the virulence and type specificity of the organism. Almost 80 different types of this organism have been defined on the basis of their immunologically distinct capsular polysaccharides. The monosaccharide units shown to be present in various pneumococcal capsular polysaccharides are glucose, galactose, rhamnose, glucuronic acid, galacturonic acid, N-acetylglucosamine, N-acetylgalactosamine, fucosamine, ribitol-P, and glycerol-P. Various pneumococcal types can utilize a wide variety of carbohydrates as a source of carbon and, by interconversions probably via glucose-1-phosphate, synthesize the component monosaccharides of the capsular polysaccharide. When encapsulated pneumococci are grown to the resting phase, nucleoside diphosphoglycosyl compounds accumulate in considerable amounts due to exhaustion of energy sources. Mills and Smith (27) have studied the role of these nucleoside diphosphoglycosyl compounds as glycosyl precursors for capsular polysaccharide production.

The capsule of Lancefield's A and C groups of *Streptococcus* is hyaluronic acid, a polymer of N-acetylglucosamine and glucuronic acid. Since some strains of streptococci produce hyaluronidase, however, the capsule can be seen only during the very early phases of growth.

One of the most interesting bacterial capsules is that of *Bacillus anthracis,* which is a polypeptide composed of d-glutamic acid, linked largely, if not entirely through the gamma carboxyl groups (45). In *Bacillus subtilis,* however, 50 to 55 per cent of its polypeptide glutamic acid is present as the l-isomer. In this organism an enzyme prevents accumulation of the peptide as a capsular gel. The nutritional requirements and enzyme systems involved in the biosynthesis

of these homopolymers have been extensively investigated (16).

The Cell Wall (35, 39, 40, 50). Beneath the capsule and other surface adherents is the major structural component, the bacterial cell wall. This is a rigid structure accounting for about 10 to 25 per cent of the dry weight of the cell. It is responsible for the cell's constant form and allows it to withstand osmotic pressures up to 20 atmospheres. The complexity of the cell wall is demonstrated by the finding with the electron microscope of a fine structure in many preparations, together with a highly complex chemical makeup. A number of methods are now available for the preparation of cell walls, free of other cellular components (35).

GRAM-POSITIVE BACTERIA. The walls of gram-negative bacteria are chemically more complex than those of gram-positive species. The walls of gram-positive bacteria contain a small variety of amino acids, amino sugars, and sugar components polymerized to form mucopeptides, polysaccharides or oligosaccharides, and the teichoic acids. Hydrolysis of these materials reveals several substances not generally encountered in cells of higher organisms. The mucopeptide contains glucosamine, and its 3-0-carboxyethyl substituent, **muramic acid,** first discovered in spore peptides (Fig. 1). The peptide of gram-positive bacteria is composed of three, four, or five principal amino acids. Alanine and glutamic acid are invariably present

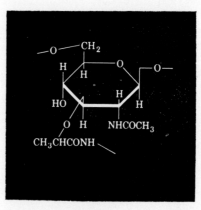

Fig. 1.   Structure of muramic acid.

along with either 1-lysine or diaminopimelic acid. The glutamic acid and part of the alanine are present as the d-isomer. In addition, glycine and aspartic acid have been observed in some species. Our knowledge of how these components are linked together to function as a rigid structure is incomplete. The amino sugars, N-acetylglucosamine, and N-acetylmuramic acid form the backbone structure, being alternately linked with a 1-4, 1-6 linkage. Peptides are linked to this repeating structure through the COOH group of muramic acid. By analysis of fragments liberated by lysozyme treatment of isolated walls of *M. lysodeikticus,* a cross-linking of peptide chains through the ε-amino group of one of the lysine molecules is suggested (11). There is additional evidence that cross-linking may be a general feature of mucopeptide structure (35). A tentative model of a mucopeptide subunit is shown in Figure 2.

In addition to the mucopeptide, the cell walls of some gram-positive organisms possess polysaccharides or oligosaccharide residues. Upon hydrolysis monosaccharide components are obtained which are characteristic of certain taxonomic groups (Fig. 3). Rhamnose is the distinctive sugar of the streptococci, arabinose of the walls of *Mycobacterium* and *Corynebacterium.* Glycine is found in the walls of the staphylococcus (29). Such sugars have been isolated in lysozyme digests of walls.

Another interesting group of compounds found in the walls of some gram-positive species is the **teichoic acids.** They are phosphate polymers, containing either glycerol or ribitol residues and labile ester-linked d-alanine. Detailed investigations of the distribution and composition of the teichoic acids have been carried out by Baddiley and his group (2, 3, 48). Not all of the teichoic acid is confined to the cell wall, since small amounts have also been found in underlying regions of all or nearly all of the gram-positive bacteria examined. The "intracellular" teichoic acid is probably located in the region between the wall and the protoplast membrane (14). Both wall and "intracellular" teichoic acids are of importance because of their serologic properties. The group-specific antigen of *Staphylococcus aureus* is serologically identical with the wall teichoic acid derived from that organism, the serologic specificity probably being due to the α-N-acetylglucosaminyl residues (13, 42). The teichoic acid of the *S. aureus* walls studied

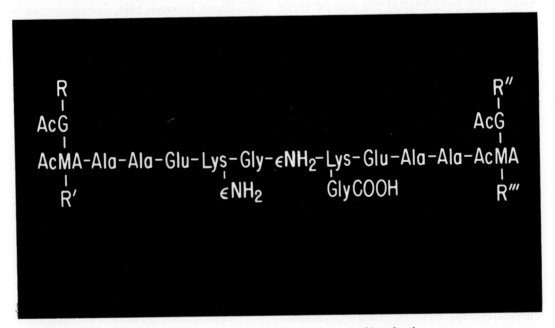

Fig. 2.   Tentative model of cell wall mucopeptide subunit.

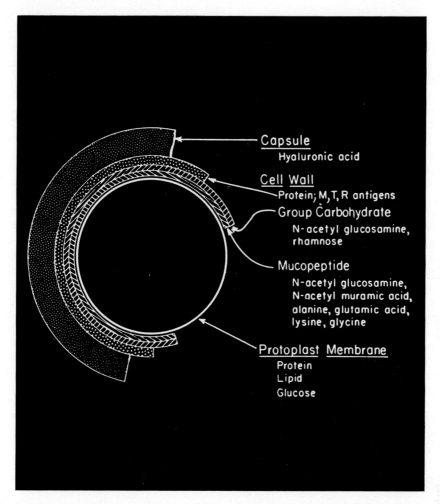

Fig. 3. Diagrammatic representation of the subcellular components of hemolytic strepto-cocci. The monosaccharides listed for the carbohydrate are those of group A streptococci. (From Krause. *Bact. Rev.,* 27:369, 1963.)

by Baddiley's group is a ribitol phosphate polymer (Fig. 4), but that of the closely re-lated *albus* species contains glycerol teichoic acids (10). In streptococci the group D anti-gen has been identified as the intracellular teichoic acid and is of the glycerol phosphate type (48). In L-phase variants of these organisms, the group-specific and the cell-wall polysaccharide antigen is absent (15).

GRAM-NEGATIVE BACTERIA. The cell walls of gram-negative bacteria are chemi-cally and physically more complex than those of gram-positive species. A rigid muco-peptide layer chemically similar to that found in gram-positive bacteria is present in these organisms, as demonstrated by Weidel and his associates (47) but accounts for only 10 to 20 per cent of the weight of the cell wall. A quantitative analysis of the muco-peptide component prepared from various gram-negative species has been made (24). Large amounts of protein, lipid, and poly-saccharide components are present as a macro-molecular complex. The protein con-tains a complete range of amino acids, and the lipid content may be as high as 22 per cent. The polysaccharides, extractable by relatively gentle procedures, are character-istic of the rough and smooth antigens of the organism and upon hydrolysis will give two or more of the following sugars: glucose, galactose, fucose, rhamnose, mannose, and tyvelose (9). Weidel (47) visualizes the cell wall of gram-negative organisms as consisting of three layers of which the innermost is the rigid mucopeptide and the middle lipopolysaccharide, with lipoprotein forming the outermost layer. This structure is consistent with the layers observed in electron micrographs of thin sections of various gram-negative species (30). A more complete coverage of the cell walls of bacteria can be found in the reviews of Salton (39, 40), Perkins (35), and Rogers (38).

FUNCTION OF THE CELL WALL. The major function of the cell wall in maintaining the morphology of the cell may be attributed to the mucopeptide lattice. The presence of the wall is essential in the usual biological or cultural environment in order to protect the delicate cytoplasmic membrane against an osmotic pressure within the cytoplasm many times greater than that from without. Anything which prevents the formation of new cell wall material for a growing protoplast, or which destroys the existing wall, will lead to lysis of the cell. There are widely distributed in nature a number of lytic enzymes that have a direct action on the cell wall. The most widely studied of these is lysozyme, which promotes the hydrolysis of β (1-4) glycosidic linkages between N-acetylmuramic acid and N-acetylglucosamine. Lysozyme acts most readily on certain gram-positive organisms but under the proper conditions will also attack gram-negative species (36, 51). A number of other enzymes lytic for bacteria have been isolated from mammalian tissue, various microorganisms, and bacteriophages (35).

The presence in cell walls of structural components unique in that they are not found in tissues of higher forms makes the bacterial cell wall an excellent target for chemotherapeutic agents. There is considerable evidence that penicillin owes its antibacterial effects to an interference with the formation of the cell wall. Much of this work was stimulated by Park's observation (33) that growth of staphylococci in the presence of penicillin leads to the accumulation of uridine nucleotides combined with muramic acid and peptides of the same composition as those found in the walls of staphylococci. These nucleotides are probably precursors of cell wall material accumulating when penicillin inhibits cell wall synthesis (34). The mode of action of penicillin and other chemotherapeutic agents which attack the cell-wall synthesizing systems is discussed further in Chapter 8.

The Cytoplasmic Membrane. Beneath the cell wall and in close association with it is the delicate cytoplasmic membrane, vitally

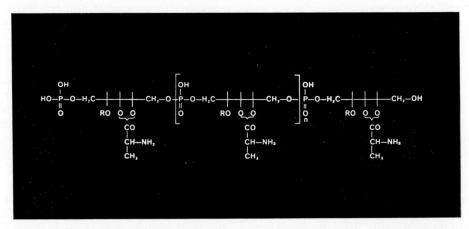

Fig. 4. Ribitol teichoic acids from cell walls. *Bacillus subtilis:* R $= \beta$-glucosyl; n $= 7$. *Staphylococcus aureus* H: R $=$ α- and β- N-acetylglucosaminyl; n $= 6$. *Lactobacillus arabinosus* 17-5: R $=$ a-glucosyl, and alternate ribitol residues also have α-glucosyl at the 3-position; n $= 4$-5. (From Baddiley. *Endeavour,* 23:33, 1964.)

important to the cell. Although bacteria are normally regarded as extremely tolerant to osmotic changes in their external environment, some species, especially gram-negative ones, readily undergo either plasmolysis or plasmoptysis when placed in media containing varying salt concentration. During plasmolysis there is a shrinkage of the cytoplasm away from the cell wall, which may be observed both with the light and electron microscope (7). The presence of an osmotic barrier in bacteria is also indicated by their ability to concentrate certain amino acids within the cell against concentration gradients. In gram-positive bacteria a gradient of 300 to 400 times may exist across the surface layers. Such substances as phosphates, phosphate esters, purines, pyrimidines, and other soluble materials may be present within the cell in a highly concentrated state, thus contributing to the high internal osmotic pressure of the cell. Osmotic activity is also indicated by their selective permeability towards various compounds, especially organic acids (1).

If an organism such as *Bacillus megaterium* or *Micrococcus lysodeikticus* is treated with lysozyme, the organism is converted to a spherical protoplast. In these organisms wall degradation may be complete and leave none of the characteristic wall compounds. If these protoplasts are then liberated in a hypotonic medium, lysis takes place and the protoplasts rupture, leaving "ghosts" or broken membrane fragments which can then be separated from the lysate by high-speed centrifugation. Such membranes have been very useful in enzymatic and chemical analyses. The membrane fraction has been shown to account for 10 to 20 per cent of the dry weight of the cell. Its most constant feature is a high concentration of lipid (15 to 30 per cent), which is mostly present as phospholipid. Fifty to sixty-five per cent of the membrane is protein. The membrane protein presents a characteristic and constant but not unusual pattern (43). It appears similar to cell protein and is unlike that of the wall peptide in that it contains all the common l-amino acids and no d-amino acids. Unfortunately, not all organisms are equally susceptible to lysozyme action, and it has not been possible to prepare sufficiently pure membrane fractions of gram-negative organisms for study. Much of the difficulty is associated with the presence of large amounts of the protein-lipid-polysaccharide complexes remaining after attack on the mucopeptide, and a union between the cell wall and cytoplasmic membrane that is so strong that separation of these two structures may be incomplete during plasmolysis (37).

The cytoplasmic membrane has been established as the site of respiratory enzymes and cytochrome-linked electron transport in a number of aerobic organisms (17). The extent to which enzymes may be localized in the membrane is shown in Table 1. It is probable that those functions, which in the cells of higher organisms are performed by mitochondria, are dealt with in bacteria by

Table 1. **Enzyme Activities at 25° C. of Dialyzed Fractions of *Staphylococcus aureus***
(Mitchell, 1963)

| | mμ mole substrate/g. sec. | | % TOTAL ACTIVITY |
ENZYME	MEMBRANE	CYTOPLASM	IN MEMBRANE
Glucose-6-phosphatase	4.3	39.8	10
α-Glycerophosphate dehydrogenase	10.3	9.8	51
Glucose-6-PO$_4$ dehydrogenase	3.9	68.0	5.4
Lactic dehydrogenase	64.2	3.2	96
Acid phosphatase	25.2	2.0	93
Glucose dehydrogenase	1.6	<0.3	>85
Succinic dehydrogenase	4.7	<0.3	>94
Formic dehydrogenase	16.6	<0.3	>93
Malic dehydrogenase	19.8	<0.5	98
Malic enzyme	0	26.6	0
Isocitric dehydrogenase	1.64	45.2	3.5

the cytoplasmic membrane (26). The finding by electron microscopy of systems of concentric intracytoplasmic membranes or lamellae in some bacteria (32) and their relationship with the membrane are regarded by some as the bacterial equivalent of mitochondria (12). In addition to these enzymatic functions, the cytoplasmic membrane probably has biosynthetic abilities, such as that of synthesizing capsular polysaccharides and other large molecules found on the external side of it.

Cytoplasm (4). Many types of inclusions may be observed within the bacterial cytoplasm of both living and stained preparations. In most cases the presence of vacuoles and inclusions is conditioned by the environment and physiologic state of the cell. Many appear to be absent during the most active phases of growth and to increase in prominence during the latter phases of the growth cycle. The metachromatic granules which stain red with such dyes as toluidine blue and methylene blue are found in many different types of microorganisms. The chief chemical component of these granules is polymetaphosphate of very high molecular weight. Lipid globules, glycogen, and other polysaccharide inclusions may also be detected by specific cytochemical technics.

In addition to the granules and inclusions which may be seen in stained preparations, the use of the electron microscope with a resolving power of 20 Å. and the development of technics for sectioning has enabled us to gain further knowledge of the internal structure of the cell. Within the cell wall and membrane layers of the cell two types of somewhat amorphous material may be seen in thin sections (Fig. 5). The transparent material seen in and around the core of the cell corresponds in distribution to the chromatin material described by cytologists, while the outer electrondense material consists of closely packed granules, 100 to 200 Å. in diameter. The bulk of the ribonucleic acid appears to be associated with these granules. Relatively pure preparations of granules of similar dimensions may be obtained by high-speed centrifugation of lysed protoplasts or disrupted cells. Wide variations have been observed in the sedimentation pattern of these granules, the **ribosomes,** obtained from different sources. Not only does the magnesium concentration markedly affect the sedimentation coefficient, but both the metabolic state of the cell at the time of breaking the cells and the method of breaking the cells alter the pattern. Because of these wide variations which have been observed under

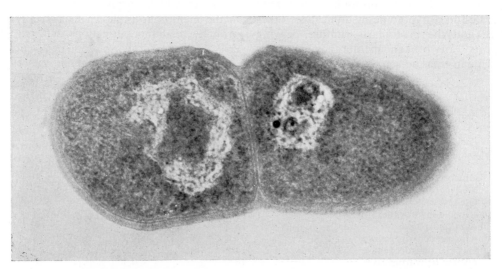

Fig. 5. A dividing cell in the process of laying down a septum between the two daughter cells. Fairly deep projections of cytoplasm into the nuclear region and of nuclear region into cytoplasm can be observed. The bacterial cytoplasm appears to consist largely of 200 Å granules. (From Chapman. *J. Biophys. & Biochem. Cytol.,* 6:221, 1959.)

different conditions, it is difficult to compare the ribosomes from different sources. Those which have been most extensively studied, however, show in common particle groups of 70-100 S. which dissociate in low concentrations of magnesium into two groups of 24-40 S. and 40-60 S. (23).

At present the most precisely formulated theory of the role of ribosomes is that they provide the sites for protein synthesis. According to the messenger hypothesis of Jacob and Monod (18), an unstable messenger RNA is produced by the gene and associates temporarily with the ribosomes to act as template for protein synthesis. The details of this hypothesis are presented in Chapter 7.

The Nucleus (4). The central area of lesser electron density visualized in thin sections of bacteria with the electron microscope has been shown to occupy a position corresponding to the chromatinic bodies. Structures observed in bacterial cells and suspected of being nuclear elements or their equivalent, can only be identified by a positive Feulgen reaction. It is difficult to demonstrate chromatin bodies by direct staining because of the high concentration of ribonucleic acid. Pretreatment, however, with hot 1 N HCl or with ribonuclease will remove all or nearly all of the RNA in a few minutes, allowing the chromatin bodies to be seen in any stage of the growth cycle of the organism. Although the Feulgen reaction identifies the chromatin material as deoxyribonucleic acid, staining of the chromatin bodies of bacteria is not directly equivalent to the staining of chromosomes of higher cells (30).

Much of the controversy that has existed among cytologists concerning the nature and structure of the bacterial nucleus may be due to the absence of a limiting nuclear membrane and a resulting intimate association between cytoplasm and "nucleus." In a preparation of lipase-treated protoplasts of *Bacillus megaterium,* the isolated bodies were found to be composed of strands of deoxyribonucleic acid coiled around a ribonucleoprotein core (44). In accordance with existing biological tenets, this DNA provides the mechanism for the transmission of hereditary characteristics from one bacterial cell to another.

REFERENCES

1. Ajl, S. J. Proc. 4th Int. Congr. Biochem., 13:215, 1959.
2. Baddiley, J. Fed. Proc., 21:1084, 1962.
3. ——— Endeavour, 23:33, 1964.
4. Brieger, E. M. Structure and Ultrastructure of Microorganisms, New York, Academic Press, 1963.
5. Caro, L. G. J. Biophys. Biochem. Cytology, 9:539, 1961.
6. Cedergren, B., and Holme, T. J. Ultrastruct. Res., 3:70, 1959.
7. Cota-Robles, E. H. J. Bact., 85:499, 1963.
8. Cummins, C. S. Microbial Classification, 12th Symp. Soc. Gen. Microbiol., Cambridge University Press, 1962, p. 212.
9. Davies, D. A. L. Advan. Carbohydrate Chem., 15:271, 1960.
10. Ellwood, D. C., and others. Biochem. J., 86:213, 1963.
11. Ghuysen, J. M. Biochim. et Biophys. Acta 47:561, 1961.
12. Glauert, A. M., and Hopwood, D. A. J. Biophys. Biochem. Cytol., 6:515, 1959.
13. Haukenes, G., and others. Biochim. et Biophys. Acta, 53:425, 1961.
14. Hay, J. B., and others. Biochim. et Biophys. Acta, 71:188, 1963.
15. Hijmans, W. J. Gen. Microbiol., 28:177, 1962.
16. Housewright, R. D. Chap. 9 in The Bacteria, I. C. Gunsalus and R. Y. Stanier, eds., Vol. III, New York, Academic Press, 1962.
17. Hughes, D. E. J. Gen. Microbiol., 29:39, 1962.
18. Jacob, F., and Monod, J. J. Molec. Biol., 3:318, 1961.
19. Kerridge, D. In Microbial Reaction to Environment, 11th Sym. Soc. Gen. Microbiology, Cambridge University Press, 1961, p. 41.
20. Koffler, H., and others. Arch. Biochem. Biophys., 64:509, 1956.
21. Krause, R. M. Bact. Rev., 27:369, 1963.
22. Lee, K. Y., and others. Ann. Inst. Pasteur, 91:212, 1956.
23. McCarthy, B. J. Carnegie Inst. Wash. Yearbook, 58:281, 1959.
24. Mandelstam, J. Biochem. J., 84:294, 1962.
25. Marmur, J., and others. Ann. Rev. Microbiol., 17:329, 1963.
26. Marr, H. G. Ann. Rev. Microbiol., 14:241, 1960.
27. Mills, G. T., and Smith, E. E. B. Fed. Proc., 21:1089, 1962.
28. Mitchell, P. Membranes and Surfaces of Cells, Biochem. Soc. Symposia, 22:142, 1963, University Press, Cambridge.
29. Morse, S. I. J. Exp. Med., 116:229, 1962.
30. Murray, R. G. E. 12th Symp. Soc. Gen. Microbiol., 12:119, 1962.
31. Neidhardt, F. C. Ann. Rev. Microbiol., 17:61, 1963.
32. Pangborn, J., and others. J. Bact., 84:669, 1962.
33. Park, J. T. J. Biol. Chem., 194:877, 1952.
34. ——— and Strominger, J. L. Science, 125:99, 1957.
35. Perkins, H. R. Bact. Rev., 27:18, 1963.
36. Repaske, R. Biochim. et Biophys. Acta, 30:225, 1958.

37. Robinow, C. F. Outline of the Visible Organization of Bacteria, in The Cell, 4:45, New York, Academic Press, 1960.
38. Rogers, H. J. Biochem. Soc. Symp., 22:55, Cambridge University Press, 1963.
39. Salton, M. R. J. Chap. 3 in The Bacteria, Vol. I, I. C. Gunsalus and R. Y. Stanier, eds., New York, Academic Press, 1960, p. 97.
40. ——— Microbial Cell Walls, New York, John Wiley & Sons, Inc., 1961.
41. ——— J. Gen. Microbiol., 29:15, 1962.
42. Sanderson, A. R., and others. Biochem. Biophys. Res. Comm., 5:472, 1961.
43. Shockman, G. D., and others. J. Bact., 85:168, 1963.
44. Spiegelman, S., and others. J. Bact., 75:102, 1958.
45. Toru, M. J. Biochem. (Osaka), 46:189, 1959.
46. Weibull, C. Chap. 4 in The Bacteria, Vol. I, I. C. Gunsalus and R. Y. Stanier, eds., New York, Academic Press, 1960, p. 153.
47. Weidel, W., and others. J. Gen. Microbiol., 22:158, 1960.
48. Wicken, A. J., and Baddiley, J. Biochem. J., 87:54, 1963.
49. Wilkinson, J. F. J. Gen. Microbiol., 32:171, 1963.
50. Work, E. J. Gen. Microbiol., 25:167, 1961.
51. Zinder, N. D., and Arndt, W. F. Proc. Nat. Acad. Sci., 42:586, 1956.

5

The Genetics of Bacteria

Although man has speculated for centuries on the mechanism of heredity, the science of genetics dates from the rediscovery of Mendel's paper in 1900. However, it was not until 1946 (67, 68, 69) that mating and recombination were shown to exist in the bacteria. Prior to that time, the inability to make crosses between bacterial strains made the interpretation of variations in bacterial populations very difficult. This was especially true before the advent of technics which permitted the isolation of pure clones, when it was thought that all bacteria belonged to a single species with a tremendous capacity for variation (pleomorphism). General acceptance of the occurrence of variation in fixed species of bacteria (monomorphism) did not come about until much later (1920-30). There is no doubt today that mutation and selection account for most, if not all, of bacterial variation.

The continuity of bacterial characteristics from generation to generation is made possible only by the fact that cells have a definite organization which is duplicated with each division. In higher organisms the visible nucleus is organized into thread-like structures, the chromosomes, which maintain their integrity from generation to generation and are in large part responsible for the transmission of characteristics. Cytologic studies in bacteria have established beyond doubt the presence of nuclear bodies in bacteria (Chapter 3), and it seems likely that in bacteria, as well as in higher organisms, there is a similar material basis for the inheritance of genetic determinants (59).

Operationally a **gene** is defined as a factor which can change or **mutate** to alternative forms, called **alleles,** which result in a permanent detectable change. This new characteristic is transmitted to progeny cells and is distributed to other strains according to precise mechanisms when gene transfer occurs. Collectively all the genes of an organism are known as the **genome,** and the particular assortment of normal and mutant genes in any strain is called the **genotype.** The biochemical or morphological appearance is called the **phenotype.** The phenotype is the result of the interaction between the genotype and the environment both inside and outside the cell.

The normal or standard strain is usually called the wild type (designated $+$). In bacteria the original strain, whether it contains mutant genes or not, is called the **prototroph,** while the mutant strains derived from it which require additional nutrients in the medium are called **auxotrophs.** Auxotrophic genes are indicated with a minus sign ($-$).

In bacteria, e.g., *Escherichia coli* and *Salmonella typhimurium,* the genes are thought to be **linked together** on a circular **chromosome** (see Fig. 9) composed of DNA (deoxyribonucleic acid) and to exert their influences by controlling the type and amount of protein made by the cell. Genes can also be defined as that unit of DNA which controls the synthesis of a single protein or a single polypeptide chain. However, the recognition of a specific molecule of DNA as a specific gene has not been achieved.

BACTERIAL MUTATIONS

Few, if any, genes are completely stable. Indeed, the production of new genes by mutation provides the raw material for evolution through natural selection. A **mutation** is a change in a gene that results in an altered morphological or biochemical phenotype which is inherited. Mutations occur spontaneously in all organisms (Table 1)

51

Table 1. Spontaneous Mutation Rates in Different Organisms

(From Sager and Ryan. *Cell Heredity,* John Wiley & Sons)

Organism	Character	Rate	Units
Bacteriophage: *T2*	lysis inhibition, $r \rightarrow r^+$ host range, $h^+ \rightarrow h$	1×10^{-8} 3×10^{-9}	per gene* per replication
Bacteria: *Escherichia* *coli*	lactose fermentation, $lac^- \rightarrow lac^+$ phage $T1$ sensitivity, $T1\text{-}s \rightarrow T1\text{-}r$ histidine requirement, $his^- \rightarrow his^+$ $his^+ \rightarrow his^-$ streptomycin sensitivity, $str\text{-}s \rightarrow str\text{-}d$ $str\text{-}d \rightarrow str\text{-}s$	2×10^{-7} 2×10^{-8} 4×10^{-8} 2×10^{-6} 1×10^{-9} 1×10^{-8}	per cell per division
Algae: *Chlamydomonas* *reinhardi*	streptomycin sensitivity, $str\text{-}s \rightarrow str\text{-}r$	1×10^{-6}	
Fungi: *Neurospora* *crassa*	inositol requirement, $inos^- \rightarrow inos^+$ adenine requirement, $ade^- \rightarrow ade^+$	8×10^{-8} 4×10^{-8}	mutant frequency among asexual spores
Corn: *Zea mays*	shrunken seeds, $Sh \rightarrow sh$ purple, $P \rightarrow p$	1×10^{-5} 1×10^{-6}	
Fruit fly: *Drosophila* *melanogaster*	yellow body, $Y \rightarrow y$, in males $Y \rightarrow y$, in females white eye, $W \rightarrow w$ brown eye, $Bw \rightarrow bw$	1×10^{-4} 1×10^{-5} 4×10^{-5} 3×10^{-5}	mutant frequency per gamete per sexual generation
Mouse: *Mus musculus*	piebald coat color, $S \rightarrow s$ dilute coat color, $D \rightarrow d$	3×10^{-5} 3×10^{-5}	
Man: *Homo sapiens*	normal $\rightarrow$ hemophilic normal $\rightarrow$ albino	3×10^{-5} 3×10^{-5}	
Human bone marrow cells in tissue culture	normal $\rightarrow$ 8-azoguanine resistant normal $\rightarrow$ 8-azoguanosine resistant	7×10^{-4} 1×10^{-6}	per cell per division

* Correction of the other mutation rates in this table to a per-gene basis would not change their order of magnitude.

and can have very mild or very severe effects, depending upon the cellular process which is affected. If plated on an agar medium, a mutant bacterium will give rise to a clone of cells all of which are mutant. These mutant cells will breed true with respect to the new phenotype but with low frequency may mutate further to new mutant types or backmutate to the original parental type (Table 1). The mutation rate is usually expressed as the probability of any one bacterium or gene changing during a defined unit of time, usually one generation or one division time. Although the spontaneous mutation rate is relatively constant for a specific gene in a given strain, mutation rates vary for different characteristics and for similar characteristics from strain to strain (7, 42, 60, 81, 118). Indeed, it can be seen in

Table 1 that the rate in the forward direction (i.e., from wild type to mutant) need not coincide with the rate in the backward or reverse direction (i.e., from mutant to wild type); some mutants are quite stable and do not show backmutation to wild type.

Theoretically, if each gene tends to mutate at a rate of about 10^{-8} bacteria per division, and if there are only 100 genes per bacterium (there are probably many more), then in a culture of 10^8 bacteria per ml., there will be 100 new mutant genes in the 2×10^8 cells per ml. found after the next division. Most of these mutations, however, will be deleterious, and the cells containing them will die. This potential genetic variability even in pure cultures should be kept in mind at all times.

Mutations of different genes occur independently of one another. This is one reason why two or more antibiotics are supplied together during drug therapy. The probability of a single bacterium having a mutation in two separate genes so that it is resistant to two or more drugs at the same time is the product of the probabilities that a mutation for resistance in each gene will occur. Thus, if the rate of mutation to streptomycin resistance is 10^{-6} bacteria per generation and that to penicillin resistance is 10^{-5} bacteria per generation, then the probability that a single bacterial cell will mutate to resistance for both is 10^{-5} times 10^{-6} or 10^{-11} bacteria per generation, an extremely small probability (see Chapter 8).

The spontaneous rate of mutation of a gene can be raised 10- to 100-fold by the use of **mutagens.** These are very diverse and include x-rays, gamma rays, ultraviolet light, neutrons, alpha particles, various chemicals (nitrous acid, acridine dyes, nitrogen mustards, purine, and pyrimidine analogs), and many other agents. Their mechanism of action is not known with certainty, and we shall discuss various hypotheses after we have considered the chemical nature of the gene.

Morphologic Mutants. One method for detecting morphologic mutants consists of plating normal bacteria which may have been treated with a mutagen on an agar plate in such a way as to cause the growth of many nonoverlapping colonies. These colonies are examined at intervals for morphologic variations differing from the normal. Morphologic mutations are named for the trait affected. These include colony size, shape, texture, and color, where color is a part of the colony morphology (63). Many of these, such as the R, S, M, G and L forms, have been discussed in Chapter 3. It should be noted that not all morphologic changes have been analyzed genetically to determine whether they are in fact due to true gene mutations or to some other agency.

Biochemical Mutants. While morphologic mutations have use as gene markers, the mutations more useful to bacterial geneticists are those which affect the nutrition of the bacterium. Many microorganisms, such as the enteric coliform, *Escherichia coli*, can grow very well on a medium containing a

simple carbohydrate (e.g., glucose) as a carbon and energy source, ammonium salts or nitrates as a nitrogen source, and additional salts and minerals. From this simple **minimal** medium these organisms can synthesize all of the organic compounds which they must have to grow and reproduce. Since genes control chemical pathways by specifying the amount and the structure of the proteins of the cell (see Chapter 7), it is possible to produce a mutant strain in which there is an absence of an enzyme catalyzing a reaction in the pathway leading to the synthesis of a vital compound (e.g., tryptophan) which the cell can usually manufacture. This compound (tryptophan) is now required as a supplement to the minimal medium or the cell will die.

The early methods used to detect biochemical mutations in bacteria were very similar to those originally developed by Beadle and Tatum (11) for the detection of biochemical mutations in the bread mold *Neurospora crassa*. Although there are differences in technic due to the differences between the biology of molds and bacteria, this basic method can be summarized as follows (Fig. 1): one stage in the cell cycle of normal cells is exposed to a mutagenic agent, such as ultraviolet light, x-rays, or chemical mutagens. The treated cells are then plated

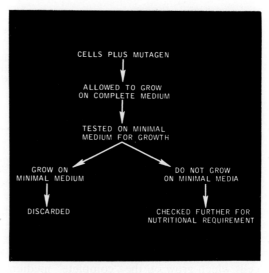

Fig. 1. General method for detecting nutritional mutants.

Table 2. **Methods Used to Select Some Types of Bacterial Mutants**

(From Stanier, Doudoroff, and Adelberg. *The Microbial World*, Prentice-Hall, Inc.)

Type of mutant	*Selection methods*	*Detection*
Able to use as carbon source a compound not utilizable by "wild-type."	Plate on agar containing the compound in question as the only available carbon source.	
Resistant to inhibitory chemical agents, such as penicillin, streptomycin, sulfonamides, dyes.	Plate on agar containing the inhibitor.	Plating method is absolutely selective; only the desired type will form colonies.
Resistant to bacteriophage.	Plate on agar previously spread with heavy phage suspension.	
Resistant to ultraviolet irradiation.	Successive enrichment for UV-resistant cells by alternating light doses of irradiation with incubation periods.	Colony streaked on agar, irradiated with UV, examined under microscope 3 hours later. Normal cells will have formed filaments; UV-resistant cells appear as microcolonies.
Auxotrophic (requirement for one or more growth factor not required by wild-type cells).	*Penicillin-sensitive bacteria:* Incubate in growth medium lacking the growth factor in question, but containing penicillin. Wild-type cells multiply and are killed; auxotrophic mutants are unable to multiply without the growth factor and survive (penicillin kills only actively growing cells).	Plate in agar lacking the growth factor. Mark wild-type colonies that appear, then add layer of agar containing growth factor. Auxotrophs form colonies only after addition of growth factor ("delayed enrichment method").
Unable to ferment a given sugar.	*Penicillin-sensitive bacteria:* Apply penicillin technique as above, using sugar in question as only fermentable carbon source.	Plate on agar containing sugar in question, plus chemical indicator that changes color in the presence of fermenting cells (e.g., acid-base indicator). Mutant colonies appear a contrasting color.
Increased virulence for host.	Serial passage through susceptible host organisms.	Individual isolates must be separately tested.
Changed flagellar antigens.	Plate on dilute agar containing antibody against specific flagellar antigen.	Normal type forms dense colonies; mutants form spreading colonies as the result of flagellar motility.
Pigmentation and colony morphology variations.	None.	Direct inspection of colonies.

on a **"complete"** medium—that is, a minimal medium which is supplemented with extracts derived from yeast cells, mammalian liver, plants, as well as with mixtures of compounds, such as many of the known biochemicals, vitamins, amino acids, nucleic acid derivatives, etc. Each of the colonies of cells which grow on the "complete" medium are tested on the minimal medium, and any colony which can grow on the minimal medium is discarded. These are not deficient in a synthetic pathway. Those bacteria which grow on the complete medium but which do not grow on the minimal medium are saved for further study. Many of these are mutants in which the synthesis of a specific compound present in the complete medium does not take place. Tests are then carried out to discover the nature of this compound, and the mutant is named for the required nutrient. For example, a strain which required tryptophan is designated **try⁻** (tryptophan-requiring) while a strain which requires adenine is **ade⁻** (adenine-requiring) (51, 55).

Other types of biochemical mutations are those which, unlike the wild type, cannot use various sugars, such as lactose, maltose, or galactose, as carbon sources. These mutants usually lack the ability to carry out a step in the pathway leading to the conversion of these sugars into intermediates in glycolysis. These mutations are named according to the sugar which cannot be fermented. For example, a strain which cannot utilize maltose is maltose-negative **(mal⁻)** while a strain which cannot utilize lactose is lactose-negative **(lac⁻).** Note that here the mutant is named for the substrate which cannot be metabolized, while those discussed above were named for the particular product which could not be synthesized.

In the absence of special technics (Table 2) morphologic mutants are more easily recognized than biochemical mutants. However, selection technics can be devised so that biochemical mutations can be detected with much greater ease than is ever achieved with mutations that primarily affect morphology. Even so, many inherited changes occur which remain overlooked because methods for detecting them directly are not available. This is especially true of genes which modify the chemistry of the organism so greatly that these mutants cannot be kept alive by some external manipulation, such as supplying a necessary chemical or changing the pH or temperature. Such mutant genes do irreparable damage to the cell, and the cell dies. The mutants which we will discuss in this chapter are mainly those in which a change in the gene has resulted in a biochemical deficiency which is reparable; these mutations are lethal only in the absence of a special environment. For example, the mutant bacterial strains which can no longer synthesize tryptophan grow on a medium supplemented with tryptophan. They die if the tryptophan is omitted.

The method described above for selecting biochemical mutations in microorganisms is very tedious, mainly because the frequency of mutations is very low even when a very effective mutagenic agent is used. The problem is even more complicated if one is looking for mutations blocked in a specific pathway. However, several technics have been perfected which help to select for the right type of biochemical mutations. These take advantage of the fact that various toxic agents, such as penicillin, will kill only growing cells (25, 70). Thus, if the treated cells are incubated in a minimal medium and then exposed to penicillin, a large majority of the nonmutated prototrophs will grow and be killed. After an appropriate length of time, the cells are plated on a complete medium, and the colonies which grow are then tested for their ability to grow on the minimal medium as described above. The surviving cells are found to be greatly enriched with bacteria containing biochemical mutations. One can also **select for mutants with specific requirements** by exposing the bacteria, not to penicillin in the minimal medium, but to penicillin in a minimal medium supplemented with various nutrients which will allow unwanted mutants to grow and be killed. Thus, bacteria can be exposed to penicillin in a **complete medium** lacking histidine. In addition to the prototrophs, most biochemical mutants except those involving histidine synthesis will also grow and be killed. This results in an enrichment of histidine mutants in the surviving cells. All sorts of variations of the penicillin-killing technic have been developed (3).

Another method for selecting for the newly formed mutant cells was developed by Lederberg and Tatum (69) in which treated bacteria are spread on minimal medium and colonies are allowed to form. These are the prototrophs, and their locations are recorded by marking the glass petri plate. The agar is then overlayed with a complete medium. Colonies which now appear on the plate after further incubation are probably auxotrophs which are saved and analyzed.

Mutants Resistant to Inhibitory Agents. A wide variety of mutants can be obtained with increased resistance to toxic environments provided by the presence of antibiotics and other lethal compounds, ultraviolet radiation, or bacteriophages (see Chapter 8). The mutants can be selected by exposing cells to the toxic treatment and selecting those which survive. In addition to **resist-**

ance, actual **dependence** upon some inhibitors has been observed. For example, it has been shown that the sulfonamides are toxic because they interfere with the metabolism of para-aminobenzoic acid. Such interference is counteracted in the resistant mutants by an increased synthesis of para-aminobenzoic acid (26). Occasionally, mutations occur which increase the rate of synthesis of para-aminobenzoic acid to such a high level that this normal metabolite now becomes toxic. This toxicity can be eliminated by the sulfa drugs, and a dependence upon sulfa drugs is a result. Mutation to **dependence** upon streptomycin, in addition to resistance, can also occur, but the exact mechanisms are not fully agreed upon (16, 41, 43a, 49, 63a).

These mutants are named for the toxic agent with a superscript **r, s,** or **d** to indicate resistance, sensitivity, or dependence, respectively. Thus, a strain sensitive to streptomycin or T_1 phage would be represented as Sm^s or T_1^s, respectively, while a mutant resistant to these agents would be designated Sm^r or T_1^r, respectively. There are some very interesting genetic aspects to chemotherapy (80).

Color Reactions for Specific Enzyme Deficient Mutants. Strains which are deficient in a particular enzyme can sometimes be detected by plating the cells after treatment with a mutagen and then spraying the colonies which form with various reagents that reveal enzymatic deficiencies. Mutants deficient in alkaline phosphatase can be detected by spraying the colonies with a substrate (para-nitrophenyl phosphate) which is colorless and which becomes yellow when hydrolyzed by this enzyme. Those colonies which remain white after spraying are deficient or completely lacking alkaline phosphatase. Alternatively, chemicals can be put into the agar. As an example, mutants which cannot metabolize lactose can be easily detected on EMB agar.

Replica Plating. One of the most useful technics for detecting biochemical mutations either with or without enrichment procedures, as well as for easily testing the nutritional requirements of large numbers of colonies after gene transfer, is called **replica plating** (65). When colonies have grown suffi-

ciently on agar plates, a piece of sterile velvet is pressed gently against them so that the fine hairs of the fabric will pick up some cells of each colony. Thus, an impression of the colonies is imprinted on the velvet. When the cloth is now pressed against fresh agar plates, an identical imprint of colonies will be made. However, only those cells which can grow on the new medium will contribute toward reproducing the old pattern. These can be scored very easily. One can thus test the growth requirements, the resistance to toxic substances, or the ability to ferment various sugars of large numbers of bacterial clones with great ease. It should be noted that this technic was used to show that mutants resistant to streptomycin were not produced in response to streptomycin treatment but were present prior to streptomycin treatment and were merely selected out by this antibiotic (66). This demonstrated that mutations to streptomycin resistance, as well as most other mutations, occur spontaneously at all times. Luria and Delbruck (74) demonstrated this earlier with the **statistical fluctuation test.**

THE CHEMICAL NATURE OF THE GENE

It is only through the analysis of gene mutations that we can gain any insight into the nature of the hereditary material itself, since a gene can be detected only after it has mutated from normal to new forms. By studying the behavior of the mutant gene during crosses to the prototroph or to other auxotrophs, the geneticist can follow the transmission of hereditary material from generation to generation. Thus, the mutant gene acts as a marker of the hereditary material very much like a radioactive element, such as C^{14}, acts as a marker or tracer of the chemical in which it is located.

In addition to having the limited capacity to mutate or change, the chemicals comprising the gene must be sufficiently complicated to store the chemical information which is transmitted from one cell generation to the next. Very few molecules in the cell have sufficient structural diversity. Glycogen and starch can be eliminated from consideration even though they are large molecules because they are made up of identical subunits (i.e., glucose). However, proteins and nucleic acids do have sufficient variation in arrangements of different subunits (amino acids or nucleotides, respectively) to allow consideration as the storers of the genetic information of an organism.

In 1944 Avery, McLeod, and McCarthy (6) showed that the substance which could transform R-type pneumococcus into S-type cells had the properties of DNA. The transformed cells are truly altered in their heredity because (1) the change is permanent for many generations and (2) extracts of S-type cells which have been derived from R-type cells by a transformation now can transform other R-type cells into S-type cells. The finding that the transforming principle was DNA was most unexpected at that time. First, it was anticipated that the transformation principle would be the polysaccharide capsule itself. Secondly, the prevailing opinion among geneticists at that time was that the gene was made up of protein, since it was thought that only proteins had sufficient structural diversity required of the gene. DNA, though large, had been reported to be very simple in structure and to consist of identical repeating tetranucleotide subunits (72). We now know that this was incorrect, that the structure of DNA is very complex, and that it has certain unique properties which make it ideally suited to be the repository of genetic information.

Hershey and Chase (53) first provided evidence that the hereditary information in the bacterial phage, which is made up of DNA and protein, resides solely in the DNA. By labeling either the DNA or the protein of the phage with radioactive phosphorus (P^{32}) or sulfur (S^{35}), respectively, and determining the fate of the label during phage infection, these investigators were able to show that only the DNA enters the bacterium. All but 3 per cent of the phage protein remains outside, and the protein which does enter is a very special type and probably does not represent the hereditary material. More recently it has been reported that phage nucleic acid which is free of protein can by itself infect bacterial cells under certain conditions (57).

We conclude from these and many other experiments that in phage and bacteria DNA is the hereditary material. Does this generalization apply to higher forms? Unfortunately it is not possible to carry out such critical experiments in multicellular organisms. However, several lines of evidence indicate that even in higher organisms the genetic material is DNA. First, DNA is associated exclusively with the chromosomes in which the genes are located. Secondly, the haploid amount of DNA per cell is constant for a species. Finally, the sperm heads, or that part of the sperm which carries the entire hereditary contribution of the male parent, is approximately 50 per cent DNA (dry weight) and contains no detectable amounts of RNA. The protein of the sperm is probably not the bearer of hereditary information, since it is protamine, a unique type not found in other cells. Thus there is much to suggest that the role of DNA is the same in bacteria, phage, and higher organisms (97).

The Structure of DNA. The basic unit of the DNA molecule is the nucleotide. This consists of either a purine or pyrimidine base (such as adenine, guanine, thymine, or cytosine or its derivatives, hydroxycytosine or methylhydroxycytosine) attached to deoxyribose which is linked to a phosphate group (Fig. 2). The molecule as a whole is composed of two long strands wrapped around one another to form a double helix. Because the long molecule is easily sheared into small fragments, (48, 52, 85), the molecular weight of DNA in vivo is not known, but it has been possible to isolate DNA molecules with a molecular weight in excess of 100 million (18). The basic structural continuity of each strand depends upon a backbone consisting of alternating deoxyribose and phosphate moieties, while the purines and pyrimidines are attached to the sugar. Based on x-ray diffraction studies by Wilkins and Stokes (113, 114), Watson and Crick (112) proposed that the double helical molecule is held together by hydrogen bonds between a purine and pyrimidine, each on a separate chain. Further, the specificity between the bonding is such that the adenine on one chain is always paired with thymine on the other, while the guanine is always paired with cytosine (Fig. 2b). The fact

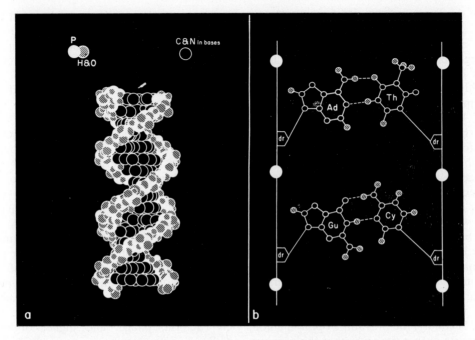

Fig. 2. The structure of DNA. a, the double helix of DNA (after Feughelman et al. *Nature,* 175:834, 1955); b, schematic diagram of the ladder of DNA. The backbone of the helix, represented by the side of the ladder, consists of phosphate (white circles) alternating with deoxyribose molecules (designated dr). The rungs of the ladder consist of the complementary base pairs held together by hydrogen bonds (dotted lines).

that on a molar basis the adenine content equals the thymine content and the guanine content equals the cytosine content is in good agreement with this model (Table 3).

This molecular interpretation of the DNA molecule has some very interesting theoretical consequences in terms of the replication

Table 3. Base Ratio of Some DNA's and RNA's

(From Sager and Ryan. *Cell Heredity,* John Wiley & Sons)

	DNA				RNA			
Organism	A/T	G/C	$\frac{A+T}{G+C}$	$\frac{\text{6-Amino}}{\text{6-Keto}}$	A/U	G/C	$\frac{A+U}{G+C}$	$\frac{\text{6-Amino}}{\text{6-Keto}}$
1. Tobacco mosaic virus					1.14	1.37	1.28	0.94
2. Phage T2	1.00	1.09	1.87	0.97				
3. Phage φX174 (single-stranded DNA)	0.75	1.31	1.35	0.76				
4. E. coli	1.09	0.99	1.00	1.05	1.38	1.18	0.83	1.06
5. Serratia marcescens	1.03	0.85	0.69	1.15	0.84	1.28	0.80	0.81
6. Pneumococcus	0.945	1.14	1.59	0.92				
7. Yeast	0.964	1.08	1.80	0.95	0.93	1.087	1.12	0.927
8. Sea urchin	1.02	1.01	1.85	1.01	1.086	1.085	0.767	0.992
9. Starfish oocyte nucleoli					1.47	1.34	0.575	0.962
10. Salmon sperm	1.02	1.01	1.43	1.00				
11. Ox liver	0.99	1.00	1.37	1.00	0.79	0.80	0.63	1.04
12. Ox liver nuclei					0.805	0.865	0.795	0.990
13. Calf thymus	0.985	1.15	1.28	0.938				
14. Man—sperm	0.98	1.03	1.67	0.976				
15. Man—thymus	1.05	1.00	1.54	1.03				
16. Man—liver	1.00	1.00	1.54	1.00				

of DNA. One of the primary requirements of the genetic material is that it be self-replicating; that is, the chemical information stored in its own structure must be transferred exactly to daughter molecules. The complementary nature of the Watson-Crick model of DNA provides a source of specificity which maintains the continuity of nucleotide sequence during replication; each strand is the **template** upon which the new strands are synthesized. DNA replication can thus be imagined as a separation of the two chains, followed by the synthesis of new chains on each of the old chains. Since adenine and thymine pair only with each other, and since guanine and cytosine do likewise, two double helices arise from a single one without the loss of the specificity or of the information stored in the original molecule. That DNA replication occurs via this mechanism is strongly suggested by the **density gradient centrifugation experiments** of Meselson and Stahl (78) using *E. coli,* of Sueyoka (103) using Chlamydamonas, of Simon (96) using human cells in tissue culture, and by the action of the enzyme **DNA polymerase,** which catalyzes the synthesis of DNA very similar to a **DNA primer molecule** which must be added to the system (15).

The Molecular Basis of Mutation. If DNA is the genetic material, the chemical basis of mutation must reside in changes in its structure. More specifically, mutations are probably changes in the nucleotide sequence of the DNA molecule. Thus, if a given nucleotide sequence is altered, the chemical specificity that resides in that sequence will change, and altered chemical patterns in the cell will result. This change in nucleotide sequence can be a **substitution** of one base pair for another (e.g., adenine-thymine for guanine-cytosine), a **deletion** or an **addition** of one or more base pairs, an **inversion** of a sequence of base pairs, or a combination of these and other more extreme changes. Theoretically, the greater the damage to the DNA, the less one would expect a reversion or backmutation to occur. Indeed, one might never expect a deletion to backmutate, and only rarely would an inversion be expected to do so. As mentioned above, there are mutant strains which have not been observed to backmutate. Genetic analysis reveals that these usually constitute **multisite** mutations; that is, these mutations involve either deletions or inversions affecting many adjacent nucleotide pairs (28, 87).

Mutations can probably take place in many ways. For example, a wrong base might be substituted for another during replication. Figure 3a indicates how adenine might occasionally undergo a rare tautomeric shift in its structure so that it now pairs with cytosine instead of thymine. This will cause a **transition** of the adenine-thymine base pair to a guanine-cytosine base pair in subsequent replication of the DNA Fig. 3b). Some chemical mutagens (the purine and pyrimidine analogs) are thought to operate in a similar way, first by being incorporated into the DNA instead of the normal base and then by causing a higher rate of **transitions** because they themselves have a higher frequency of tautomer formation and subsequent incorrect pairing. Thus, bromouracil, a very effective mutagen (14),

does replace its analog, thymine, in the DNA. This, however, does not cause mutations by itself, since up to 90 per cent of the thymine in the DNA can be replaced by bromouracil. However, if bromouracil tautomerizes more frequently than thymine because of the greater electronegativity of the bromine (and this has not yet been conclusively demonstrated), it could cause the shift of adenine-thymine base pairs of guanine-cytosine base pairs (and vice versa) at a higher frequency than would occur spontaneously (Fig. 4). Bromouracil seems to be more effective as a mutagen when it is **being incorporated** than after it has been incorporated into the DNA. This is probably due to the reduction of the electronegativity of the bromine when the bromouracil is a member of the DNA chain. This would suggest that bromouracil converts guanine-cytosine pairs to adenine-thymine pairs more frequently than the reverse (38a). In agreement with this, the base analog, 2-aminopurine, which would be expected to do the opposite, i.e., convert adenine-thymine to guanine-cytosine pairs, does cause more reversions of bromouracil-induced mutations than does bromouracil itself.

Mutations might also be produced by chemically converting one base to another in the DNA chain. Hydroxylamine, an effective mutagen for phage and other viruses, is thought to act by changing cytosine so that the product pairs with adenine instead of guanine (39, 40). The result is a shift of a guanine-cytosine pair to an adenine-thymine pair. If bromouracil converts adenine-thymine pairs to guanine-cytosine pairs, and if hydroxylamine carries out the same process, one would expect that mutations caused by bromouracil would not be readily reversed by hydroxylamine and vice versa. Indeed, there seems to be evidence for this (40, 51). As would be expected, 2-aminopurine, which carries out the reverse transition, readily reverts mutants produced by either bromouracil or hydroxylamine (38a).

Not all mutagens act in this way, however. Acridine dyes are thought to cause mutations "by sliding between adjacent base-pairs forcing them 6.8Å. apart, instead of 3.4Å. (24, 89). If this happened at one point in one chain and not in the other, it

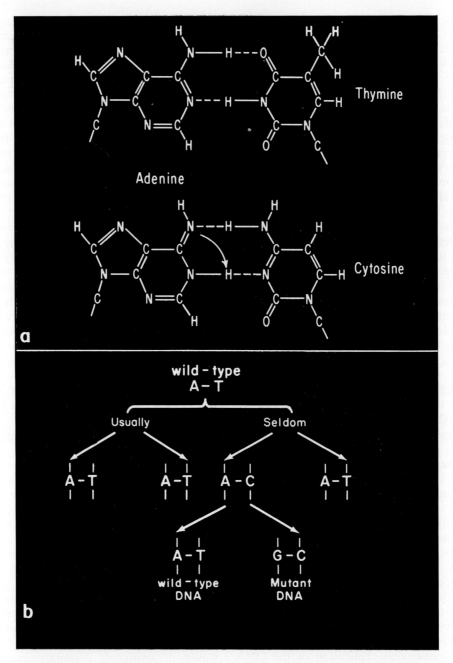

Fig. 3. Possible mechanism for mutation formation. a, the pairing possibilities of adenine in its two tautomeric states. b, the conversion of an A-T base pair to a G-C base pair due to incorrect pairing of adenine with cytosine during DNA replication. (After Sager and Ryan. *Cell Heredity,* John Wiley & Sons.)

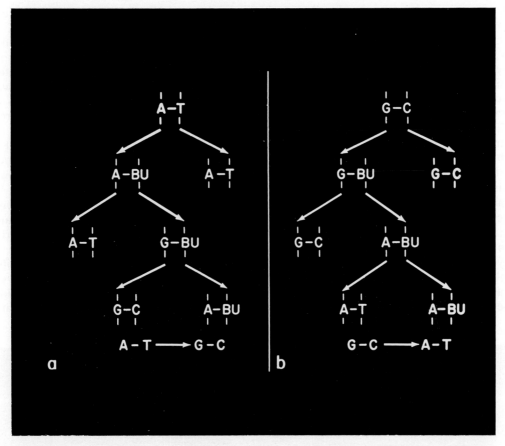

Fig. 4. Possible changes in base pairs brought about by 5-bromouracil. (After Levine. *Genetics,* Holt, Rinehart & Winston, Inc.) a, the conversion of an adenine-thymine (A-T) base pair to a guanine-cytosine (G-C) base pair by the incorporation of 5-bromouracil (BU) into the DNA followed by an erroneous pairing of the 5-bromouracil with guanine instead of adenine during a subsequent replication of the DNA; b, the conversion of a G-C base pair to an A-T base pair by an erroneous pairing of BU with guanine instead of adenine while the BU is being incorporated into the DNA.

could lead to an addition or a subtraction of a nucleotide pair during subsequent replication. This change would be manifest as a mutation. Ultraviolet light is thought to be a mutagen because it causes the formation of thymine dimers, which, if too numerous, can interfere with DNA replication so that death occurs (95). X-rays are thought to be an effective mutagen because the ionizations which are produced can alter the DNA chemically. One would not expect mutations caused by acridine or ultraviolet light to be easily reversed by the base-analog mutagens, and vice versa, since the changes induced by these mutagens are different from one an-other. This seems to be true (24). However, caution in accepting these hypotheses must be emphasized, since direct proof is lacking and the evidence is entirely circumstantial (51, 102).

THE TRANSMISSION OF GENETIC MATERIAL

It was noted that the true insights into the nature of bacterial variation did not come about until it was possible to transfer genes from one bacterial cell to another. These genes, of course, are marked by mutations and can be followed either by the movement of mutant genes into normal cells, or the reverse. By using strains which cannot grow on a minimal medium, or which are resistant to various inhibitory agents, such as streptomycin, it is possible to set up selection systems in which parental cells die and only the progeny derived from a mating can live. For example, genes can be transferred to a strain which requires histidine and which is resistant to streptomycin **(his⁻ Sʳ)** from a strain which can grow in the absence of histidine but which is sensitive to streptomycin **(his⁺ Sˢ).** The cells which result from a **transfer** and a **recombination** of genes with the production of a new type **(his⁺ Sʳ)** can be detected by plating out on a medium which lacks histidine and contains streptomycin. Only this new type can grow. Since millions of bacteria can be spread on an agar plate, one can detect such events even if they have a frequency of 10^{-6}. As we shall see, the analysis of gene transfer in bacteria required such sensitive selective technics.

Transformation. Historically, the first evidence of the transfer of genes from one bacterium to another was via transformation (6). DNA from a donor strain is mixed with cells of a recipient strain which supplies all of the parental genetic material to the progeny except for the few molecules of the donor DNA which are incorporated (Fig. 5a). One can utilize the selection procedures described above to prevent the growth of the parental recipient in order to select for the rare transformed cell. In most cases, genes on the bacterial chromosomes will be transferred independently of each other during transformation, indicating that the size of the DNA molecule which is integrated into the recipient cell does not comprise a very large part of the donor's genome. Occasionally, however, when two genes are located

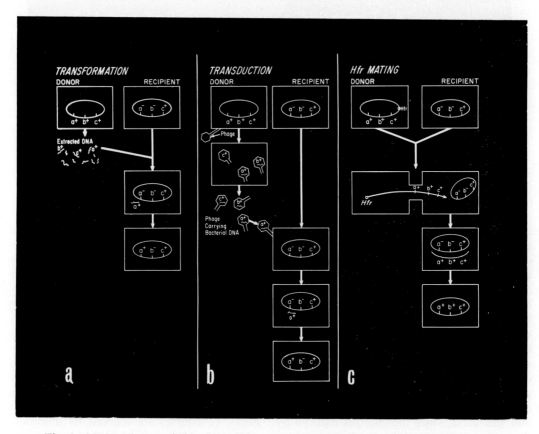

Fig. 5. Modes of transmission of genetic material in bacteria. a, transformation; b, transduction; c, HFR mating.

very close to one another on the bacterial chromosome, they are transformed at the same time simultaneously (43).

Since the experiments of Avery, McLeod, and McCarthy (6) were performed, it has been possible to transfer many genes via the process of transformation. In *Pneumococcus* and *Haemophilus,* which do not grow on a simple minimal medium, mutants involving morphology, the ability to utilize sugars other than glucose, or the resistance to various drugs have been particularly useful. In *Bacillus subtilis* which can be grown on a simple minimal medium, many types of mutations involving simple nutritional mutants have been transformed (34, 86, 115). The available evidence suggests that the incorporation of the small donor DNA molecule involves a breakage of the recipient's DNA at two places so that the piece of donor's DNA is incorporated intact (36, 106).

Transduction. Another method by which small parts of the genetic material can be transferred between bacteria involves bacterial viruses rather than extracts containing DNA (Fig. 5b). This type of transfer, called **transduction,** was discovered by Zinder and Lederberg (120) during a search for recombination in *Salmonella typhimurium,* a bacterial species closely related to *E. coli.* As in transformation, any given bacteriophage is likely to transfer only a very small segment of the chromosome from the donor strain. This segment is probably DNA (88); its size depends upon the phage used (51). The phages which function in transduction are called **temperate phages.** These lyse only a fraction of the cells which they infect; surviving cells become **lysogenized.** Lysogenic bacteria perpetuate and transmit the power to produce the temperate bacterial phage in the form of a non-infectious particle called the **prophage.** Lysogenic bacteria are immune to infection by phage genetically related to the prophage. Transduction has also been recorded in *E. coli,* and mating experiments such as those described below have shown that the prophage is actually located on a specific site on the bacterial chromosome; it is transmitted as a single gene to the recipient bacteria during conjugation. This prophage can remain undetected indefinitely, but occasionally as a result of some treatment (such as ultraviolet light), the prophage becomes detached from its specific chromosomal locus and initiates the vegetative stage of phage development. It is postulated that fragments of the DNA of the host bacteria are then incorporated into the maturing phage particles and are transported by them into a second host bacterial cell. The implantation of such DNA fragments into the genetic structure of the new hosts completes the transduction cycle.

Some phages will transduce only one specific region of the chromosome. Thus the temperate *E. coli* phage, λ, segregates in the prophage state as a genetic unit exhibiting linkage to the galactose marker and transduces the major part of the galactose locus. However, some phages, such as P1, do not seem to have any one specific location and will transduce many different areas of the genetic chromosome in *E. coli.* Transduction has been reported in many bacterial species (4, 23, 27, 29, 30, 54, 61, 71, 82, 104).

Of great interest to the bacterial taxonomist are studies on transduction in the *Salmonella* concerning the transfer of antigenic characters, the somatic O, and the flagellar H antigens. Serotyping in this genus is very complicated because of the multiplicity of types, which is largely due to numerous permutations of a set of antigens. Applying the technic of transduction to the investigation of the recurrent pattern of antigenic combinations, a number of workers have succeeded in demonstrating the transfer of antigens through the agency of phage lysates. Zinder and Lederberg (120) demonstrated that a flagellar antigen of *S. typhimurium* could be transduced to *S. typhosa* to produce a previously unrecognized serotype and that an exchange of flagellar antigens among various serotypes of *Salmonella* constructed several known serotypes as well as new antigenic combinations not previously described. Transductions of antigenic characters were unaccompanied by detectable changes in biochemical properties. The finding that numerous antigenic recombinations can be produced through the action of phage lysates has led to considerable speculation on the importance of this phenomenon in the production of new serotypes in nature.

Mating and Chromosomal Transfer. In 1946, Lederberg and Tatum (67, 68) reported the first evidence for sexual reproduction in *E. coli*. They utilized two mutant strains which Tatum had obtained by successive use of x-rays or ultraviolet light. One strain **(Y-10)** required threonine, leucine, and thiamine for growth **(thre⁻ leu⁻ B₁⁻ phenal⁺ cyst⁺ biot⁺).** The other strain **(Y-24)** required phenylalanine, cysteine, and biotin **(thre⁺ leu⁺ B₁⁺ phenal⁻ cyst⁻ biot⁻).** These two strains therefore differed from each other at six gene loci. Both could not survive on minimal media. Lederberg and Tatum grew mixed cultures of strain **Y-10** and **Y-24,** and were able to select out new types that were able to grow on minimal medium. These colonies were <u>prototroph</u> for all six of the mutants originally present in both parents **(thre⁺ leu⁺ B₁⁺ phenal⁺ cyst⁺ biot⁺).** In addition, it was possible to select for colonies that had only a single requirement as well as various combinations of the six mutant types. This eliminated the possibility that symbiotic aggregates between **Y-10** and **Y-24** had formed. The frequency of occurrence of the new gene combination

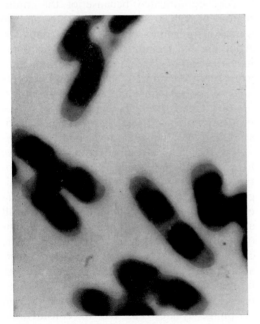

Fig. 6. Conjugation in *E. coli* as seen using the light microscope. (From Lederberg. *J. Bact.,* 71: 497, 1956.)

or recombinants was of the order of one per million cells. This was much higher than the backmutation rate of these genes, and rules out the origin of the new types by simultaneous reverse mutation of all genes. In addition, by the use of sintered glass filters it was possible to show that actual contact between the parental types was absolutely necessary. Lederberg and Tatum concluded therefore that the new types arising from mixed cultures were the result of a process that permitted a **recombination** of genetic material through a sexual process of *E. coli*.

It was soon shown that there are several mating types in *E. coli* (50, 51, 55), the basis of which is presence or absence of a **fertility factor (F).** **F⁻ cells,** which lack the F factor, will acquire it when in contact with **F⁺ cells,** which contain it. Cells in which the F factor is attached to the bacterial chromosome will show a high frequency of recombination **(HFR)** with F⁺ or F⁻ cells with which they come into contact (10⁻³ to 10⁻¹ recombinants per parent). Analysis of such HFR matings has indicated that there is actual chromosomal transfer of large amounts of genetic material from the HFR cell to the F⁻ recipient (Fig. 5c). Both of the strains which Lederberg and Tatum used, Y-10 and Y-24, were subsequently shown to be F⁺. The low frequency of recombination (10⁻⁶ to 10⁻⁵ recombinants per parent) which these authors observed is thought to be due to the attachment of the F factor to the chromosome in occasional cells, converting these cells from F⁺ to HFR and enabling them to transfer their genetic material to other F⁺ cells, which do seem capable of being recipients while in the stationary phase of growth (65).

Chromosomal Transfer from HFR Strains. The initial step in genetic transmission from HFR strains involves effective contact between cells of opposite mating types (Fig. 6). The donor and the recipient cells appear to be connected by a protoplasmic bridge as shown in Figure 7. Effective contact is established quite rapidly and in most cases, the mating process is completed in 90 minutes or less (64).

The second step in HFR transmission is the transfer of the chromosome from the HFR donor to the F⁻ recipient in an oriented

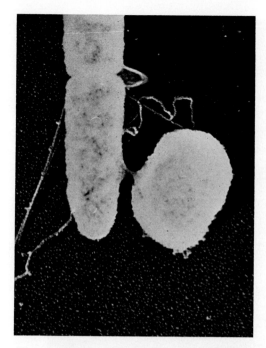

Fig. 7. Electron microscope photograph of conjugating HFR K12 and F⁻ C bacteria. The bacteria are connected by a thin bridge. The HFR K12 is elongated and is in division, while the cell from strain C is spherical. The HFR K12 bacterium also has a few long flagella. (From Anderson, Wollman, and Jacob. *Ann. Inst. Pasteur*, 93:450, 1957.)

fashion. This is evident in a cross where HFR strain, **thre⁺ leu⁺ azi^s T$_1^s$ lac⁺ gal⁺ mal⁺ xyl⁺ man⁺ Sm^s** λ^s **T$_3^s$ B$_1^+$ meth⁺** is mixed with F⁻ cells containing the complementing genotype, **thre⁻ leu⁻ azi^r T$_1^r$ lac⁻ gal⁻ mal⁻ xyl⁻ man⁻ Sm^r** λ^r **T$_3^r$ B$_1^-$ meth⁻**, F⁻ (55). After about 60 minutes, the cells are plated onto a minimal medium containing streptomycin. The HFR parent will be killed on the medium containing streptomycin and the F⁻ parent will be unable to grow since threonine and leucine are absent. Cells capable of forming colonies will have a new recombinant genotype, **thre⁺ leu⁺ Sm^r**. The **thre⁺** and **leu⁺** are from the HFR parent, and the **Sm^r** is from the F⁻ parent. This new type must be specifically selected because their frequency is much lower than either parental type (about 10 per cent). By replica plating the recombinant **thre⁺ leu⁺ Sm^r** colonies onto various media, one can determine the genotype for the **azi, T$_1$, lac, gal, mal, xyl, man,** λ, **T$_3$, B$_1$** and **meth** loci. Results

typical of such crosses have been reported by Jacob and Wollman (55). In spite of the fact that all the surviving recombinant progeny (**thre⁺ leu⁺ Sm^r**) received **thre⁺** and **leu⁺** from the HFR donor parent, only 90 per cent carried the **azi^s** marker of the HFR donor, only 70 per cent had **T$_1^s$**, only 40 per cent had **lac⁺** and only 25 per cent had **gal⁺** (Fig. 8A) while less than 1 per cent had **mal⁺, xyl⁺, man⁺, meth⁺ or B$_1^+$**. This is interpreted to mean that the transfer of genetic material from HFR to F⁻ begins with the **thre⁺** and **leu⁺** markers and that the other marker genes are not transferred all the time. This indicates that a complete chromosome is rarely transferred and that the zygote is an incomplete diploid (**merozygote**). The breaking point of the chromosome varies so that the probability of transfer of any gene is proportional to its distance from the **origin** of the leading point.

The oriented nature of the genetic transmission from HFR to F⁻ has been confirmed by experiments in which the mating process was interrupted at different times (55, 98). This interruption can be accomplished with a blendor which shears apart the conjugating cells. The analysis of such data clearly show that with the HFR strain used above, the **thre⁺ leu⁺** markers are transferred first at about eight minutes after mixing, the **azi^s** at nine minutes, the **T$_1^s$** at 11 minutes, the **lac⁺** at 18 minutes, the **gal⁺** at 25 minutes, and the **Sm^s** at 90 minutes. These results are diagrammatically represented in Figure 8B.

It will be noted that the order of the genes on the chromosome as depicted in Figure 8A and 8B are the same even though widely different technics were used to obtain these data. A similar ordering of these genes is also revealed by yet a third technic. Radioactive P^{32} can be incorporated into DNA of the bacterial chromosome. If the bacteria are now stored in the cold, the P^{32} will disintegrate to S^{32}, and the chromosome will break. By varying the length of cold storage and then carrying out an HFR mating, one can, in principle, repeat the interrupted mating experiments, since the longer the P^{32} is allowed to disintegrate, the more likely is the occurrence of a chromosome break that will prevent the transfer of genes distal to it. The relative rates of loss of the individual marker

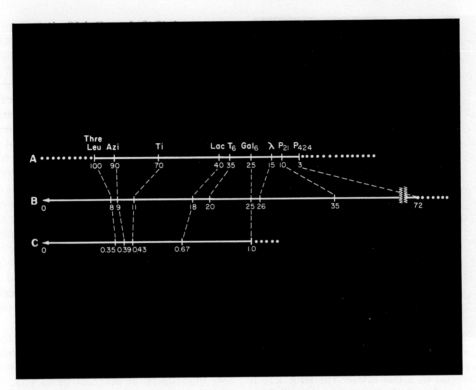

Fig. 8. Comparison of the genetic map of the proximal portion of the chromosome in *E. coli* HFR H obtained by various methods. A, gradient of simultaneous transfer when **Thre+ Leu+** progeny are selected; B, time of entry after mating (minutes); C, relative rate of loss after p³² disintegration. (Data compiled from Jacob and Wollman. *Sexuality and the Genetics of the Bacteria*, Academic Press.)

genes in such an experiment (Fig. 8C) is strikingly similar to the relative time of entry of these genes in a normal cross (Fig. 8B). It has been estimated from evidence such as this that it would take 100 to 110 minutes for the entire chromosome to be transferred at 37° C. (provided it did not break), and that one minute of transfer corresponds to about 10^5 nucleotides or to 34 μ of a Watson-Crick helix (55, p. 234). The physical model to explain these data is diagrammed in Figure 5c. The HFR strain slowly transfers its chromosome to the recipient strain in an oriented manner; i.e., one end also goes first, the rest of the chromosome trailing behind. Genetic analysis of different types of HFR strains (Fig. 9) as well as radioautographs of DNA labeled with tritiated thymidine (Fig. 10) have revealed that the bacterial chromosome is circular (19, 20). Circular genomes of viruses and phage have also been reported (17, 31, 35) but it

is clear that in higher organisms most chromosomes are not circular (59).

The third step in the transmission of genetic material in HFR *E. coli* is the actual series of recombinational events that result in the integration of the transferred HFR markers into the genome of the recipient. A number of hypotheses have been suggested. One possibility is that there is actual breakage of the host DNA molecule to permit the insertion of the donor DNA molecules into the recipient chromosome. This breakage must occur at two points with a refusion of the old and new ends (**breakage-fusion model**). The second possibility is that during replication the new chain of DNA first copies the recipient's chromosomal strand and then at various points switches and copies the donor's strands (**copy-choice model**). Whichever model is correct, the result is the formation of a recombinant bacterial cell which has genes derived from both

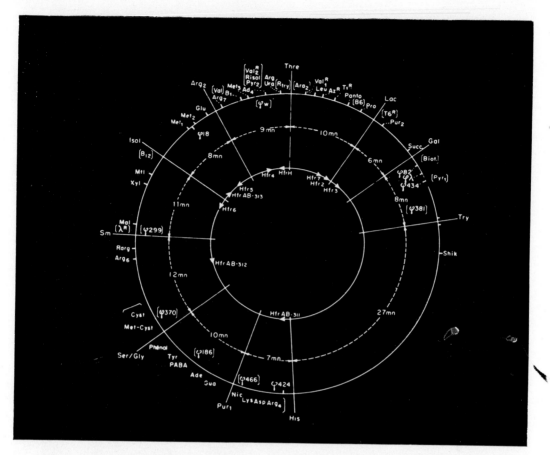

Fig. 9. The circular genetic chromosome of *E coli*. Schematic representation of the linkage group of *E. coli* K12. The outer line represents the order of the characters. The dotted lines represent the time intervals of penetration between pairs of markers corresponding to the radial lines. The inner line represents the order of transfer of different HFR types. Each arrow corresponds to the origin of the corresponding HFR strain.

Symbols correspond to synthesis of threonine (Thre), leucine (Leu), pantothenate (Panto), proline (Pro), purines (Pur), biotin (Biot), pyrimidines (Pyr), tryptophan (Try), shikimic (Shik), histidine (His), arginine (Arg), lysine (Lys), nicotinamide (Nic), guanine (Gua), adenine (Ade), para-aminobenzoic acid (PABA), tyrosine (Tyr), phenylalanine (Phenal), glycine (Gly), serine (Ser), cystein (Cyst), methionine (Met), vitamin B_{21} (B_{12}), isoleucine (Isol), thiamine (B_1), valine (Val); the fermentation of arabinose (Ara), lactose (Lac), galactose (Gal), maltose (Mal), xylose (Xyl), mannitol (Mtl); requirement for succinate (Succ), aspartate (Asp), glutamate (Glu); resistance to valine (Val^r), to sodium azide (Az^r), to phages T_1 ($T_1{}^r$), λ (λ^r); repression for arginine (R_{arg}), isoleucine (R_{isol}), tryptophan (R_{try}), location of inducible prophages 82, λ, 434, 381, 21, 424, 466, and of noninducible prophages 186, 370, 299, 18, and W. Symbols in brackets indicate that the location of the marker with respect to neighboring markers has not been exactly determined. (From Jacob and Wollman. *Sexuality and the Genetics of the Bacteria,* Academic Press.)

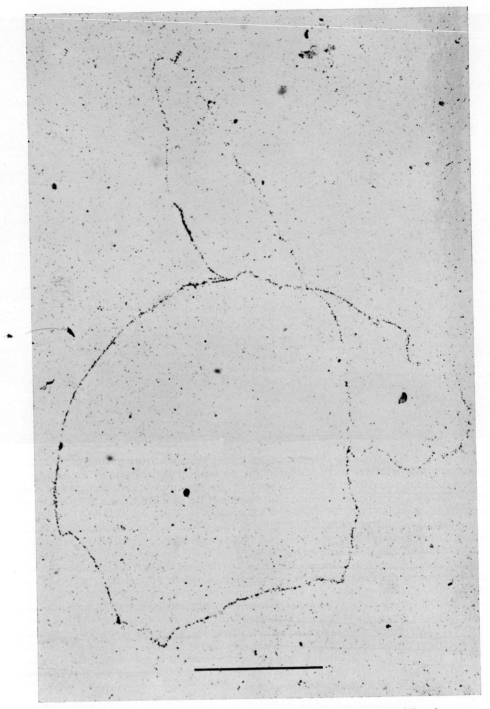

Fig. 10. The chromosome of *E. coli,* K12 HFR, labeled with H$_3$-thymidine for two generations. This chromosome is replicating while in the form of a circle. The loops are the replicated region. The scale shows 0.1 mm. (From Cairns. *Cold Spring Harbor Symp. Quant. Biol.,* 28:43, 1963.)

parents. There are data to indicate that the breakage-fusion mechanism is operating to produce the bulk of recombinants in phage (58, 79) and in bacterial transformation (36, 106).

The fourth step in the transmission of genetic material in *E. coli* is the phenotypic expression of the markers that have been integrated. These will depend upon the integration of the HFR genes into the host genome and their separation from the F⁻ genetic material. In many cases, it takes up to 9 or 10 divisions of the bacteria before the various genes are sorted out and are expressed. In addition, it must be remembered that the cytoplasm may have a store of the products of the gene which has been replaced, and many divisions may be necessary before this cytoplasmic storehouse is diluted out (5).

Recombination. Figure 8 represents three methods of ordering genes along an HFR chromosome. These are based on the likeli-

hood that longer chromosome segments break more frequently than shorter ones. The frequency of breakage is thus a measure of distance. Another method of ordering genes along a chromosome and obtaining an estimate of physical distance between them is based on the probability of **recombination** or **crossing over** between two genes. This is also proportional to the physical distance between them and, since the distances measured are additive, will lead to ordering in a linear fashion. When two different mutants with the same nutritional requirement are crossed (e.g., Lac_1^- × Lac_2^-) one can detect **lac⁺ recombinants** by plating the cells on minimal medium containing lactose as sole carbon source. The frequency with which **lac⁺** cells form is a measure of the **crossover distance** between Lac_1 and Lac_2. If the two mutant sites lie within the functional unit that codes for one polypeptide chain (see Chapter 7), then the recombination rate will be very low. By

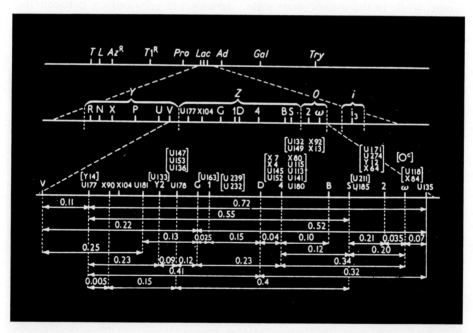

Fig. 11.   Diagrammatic map of the lactose region of *E. coli* K12. The **upper line** represents the position of the *Lac* region with respect to other known markers. The **middle line** represents an enlargement of the *Lac* region with the four loci, *y, z, o,* and *i,* all of which are involved in the utilization of lactose as a carbon source. The **lower line** represents an enlargement of the *z* and *o* loci. Recombination frequencies (given at the bottom) are obtained in two factor crosses of the type **HFR Lac⁻_A ad⁺ Sˢ × F⁻ Lac⁻_B ad⁻ Sʳ**, from the ratios "recombinants **Lac⁺ ad⁺ Sʳ / recombinants ad⁺ Sʳ.**" (From Jacob and Monod. *Molec. Biol.*, 3:318, 1961.)

measuring the crossover distances between many genes within this unit, one can deduce a linear order such as that shown in Figure 11. Each of these represents a mutant site along the nucleotide chain of the DNA (13, 21). The smallest unit which can mutate and still produce a detectable change in the phenotype is called a **muton** (13). The smallest unit of recombination is called a **recon** (13), while the unit of function of the hereditary material has been called the **cistron** (13). The muton and the recon probably correspond to a single nucleotide pair, while the cistron probably corresponds to that length of DNA which codes for a single polypeptide chain (13).

The Episome. Jacob and Wollman (55) define the episome as "a genetic structure which is added to the genome of a cell and which inside this cell may exist in two distinct, and even mutually exclusive states: the **autonomous** state and the **integrated** state" (Fig. 12). In the integrated state the episome is on but not part of the bacterial chromosome, while in the autonomous state it is in the cytoplasm of the cell and multiplies independently of the bacterium. Epi-

somes can alternate between the integrated and the autonomous state. Most episomes contain nucleic acid which is probably DNA (21). They can be eliminated by treatment with acridine dyes (101). Once lost, a cell can regain an episome only by contact with a bacterium containing that episome. There are several interesting phenomena in higher organisms which might be due to the episomal-like particles (55). Examples of episomes in bacteria include (1) the temperate bacteriophages, (2) the sex factor of *E. coli,* (3) colicinogenic factors, (4) the multiple drug resistance transfer factor in Shigella.

1. THE TEMPERATE BACTERIOPHAGES. As discussed above, these are bacterial viruses which when they infect a bacterial cell may either enter vegetative growth **(the autonomous state)** and eventually lyse the cell or become prophages and attach to the bacterial chromosome **(the integrated state).** One can convert the prophage to the vegetative phage with a brief treatment of ultraviolet light or by other means (33). This remarkable relationship between the phage and its host is not unique and is also true of other episomes.

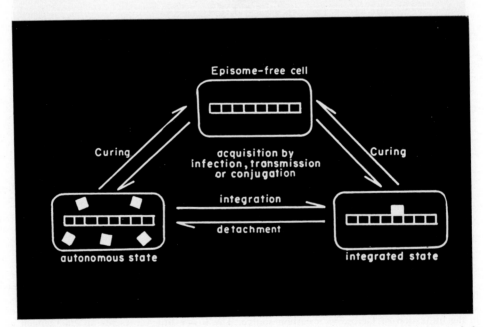

Fig. 12. The alternative states of an episome. (From Jacob and Wollman. *Sexuality and the Genetics of the Bacteria,* Academic Press.)

An example of the importance of the bacteriophage episome has been described in *Corynebacterium diphtheriae,* where the active and continued participation of a lysogenized bacteriophage is necessary for the conversion of nontoxin-producing strains to toxin producers. A reversion of the toxigenic cells to the nonlysogenic state results in a return to the nontoxigenic condition (45, 46, 47).

2. THE SEX FACTOR. It will be recalled that in addition to HFR and F⁻ cells of *E. coli,* F⁺ bacteria exist which contain the F cytoplasmic particles. These F particles are infective and can be transferred to F⁻ cells of related species (76). Cells containing F particles can also transmit their chromosomes to other bacteria with a very low frequency. This is thought to occur when the F factor occasionally becomes attached to the bacterial chromosome, which is thus converted to HFR (51, 55). This represents the **integrated** state of the F particle. The **autonomous** F particle is highly infective and will convert over 90 per cent of the F⁻ cells which come into contact with F⁺ cells during mating. HFR is unstable and can revert back to F⁺ regularly. It is of interest that no F particles exist free in an HFR cell and that the recombinant progeny from an F⁻ × HFR cross are F⁻ unless the entire chromosome is transmitted. If this occurs, the progeny will contain the HFR locus, which is transmitted last during chromosomal transfer. Occasionally recombination will take place between the F particle and the bacterial chromosome so that an F particle carrying bacterial genes is produced. Such F particles carrying genes for the lac region and for the gal region have been reported (2, 32, 55, 56, 92, 93).

3. THE COLICINOGENIC FACTORS. These are **bacteriocidins** which are produced by the colicinogenic bacteria and which kill *E. coli.* As is the case during bacteriophage growth, the production of a colicin is lethal for the synthesizing bacteria. Acquisition of colicinogeny can come about only by contact with colicinogenic bacteria and is transmitted independently of all other genes. It is thus analogous to the autonomous F particle. There are also indications that the colicinogenic factors can exist **integrated** with the bacterial chromosome (99) so that it probably is correct to consider these units as episomes. Indeed, it has been reported that colicinogenic factors can confer fertility somewhat like the F factor (99).

4. THE RESISTANCE TRANSFER FACTOR (RTF). Decreasing effectiveness of sulfonamide in the treatment of bacillary dysentery in Japan after World War II led to the isolation of *Shigella* strains with resistance not only to the sulfa drugs but also to streptomycin, chloramphenicol, and tetracycline. It was soon found that this multiple drug resistance was easily transferred from *Shigella* to *E. coli* (107) and other bacteria. Usually this resistance transfer factor (RTF) is found in the autonomous state but Watanabe and Fukasawa (107) were able to show that RTF could integrate with the chromosome of *E. coli.* Like the F factor and most bacterial phages, RTF is composed of nucleic acid, presumably DNA (109).

The Significance of Gene Transfer in Bacteria. The over-all importance of genetic exchange in bacteria by mating, transformation, transduction, or episomal transfer is difficult to assess (94). The recombining of useful mutations with other useful mutations is the basis of evolution in higher organisms, and it is probable that these phenomena have played some role in the evolution of bacteria and have yielded new genotypes with different combinations of bacterial characteristics. It is difficult to show that such phenomena take place in a natural population, but recently it has been shown that DNA transformation of bacteria can occur in a normal environment (90, 91), and that the transfer of the episome RTF can occur in vivo. The transfer of F⁺ and HFR chromosomes from *E. coli* to *Salmonella* and other enteric bacteria has been accomplished (8, 9, 10). However, the extent to which gene transfer in bacteria has influenced the evolution of various species of bacteria is not known (75).

It should be emphasized that when compared with higher organisms, the genetic mechanisms found in bacteria seem primitive; certainly they represent a unique process. The precise distribution of genetic material observed as a result of meiosis in higher animals and plants has not been shown to occur in bacteria. The student should consult other texts for the details of the genetic mechanisms in higher forms (59, 73).

REFERENCES

1. Adelberg, E. A. J. Bact., 65:348, 1953.
2. ——— J. Bact., 79:321, 1960.
3. ——— and Myers, J. W. J. Bact., 65:343, 1953.
4. Allen, L. K., and others. J. Dairy Res., 30: 351, 1963.
5. Anderson, T. F. Cold Spring Harbor Symposia on Quantitative Biology, 23:47, 1958.
6. Avery, O. T., and others. J. Exp. Med., 79: 137, 1944.
7. Bacon, D. F. J. Bact., 81:786, 1961.
8. Baron, L. S., and others. Proc. Nat. Acad. Sci., 45: 976, 1959.
9. ——— and others. Proc. Nat. Acad. Sci., 45: 1752, 1959.
10. ——— and others. Science, 130:566, 1959.
11. Beadle, G. W., and Tatum, E. L. Proc. Nat. Acad. Sci. (U.S.), 27:499, 1941.
12. Ben-Gurion, R. J. Gen. Microbiol., 30:173, 1963.
13. Benzer, S. The Chemical Basis of Heredity, W. D. McElroy and B. Glass, eds., Baltimore, The Johns Hopkins Press, 1957.
14. ——— and Freese, E. Proc. Nat. Acad. Sci., 44:112, 1958.
15. Bollum, F. J. Progress in Nucleic Acid Research, 1:1, 1963.
16. Bryan, B. E. J. Bact., 82:461, 1961.
17. Burton, A., and Sinsheimer, R. L. Science, 142:961, 1963.
18. Cairns, J. J. Mol. Biol., 4:407, 1962.
19. ——— J. Mol. Biol., 6:208, 1963.
20. ——— Cold Spring Harbor Symposia on Quantitative Biology, 28:43, 1963.
21. Campbell, A. M. Adv. in Genetics, 11:101, 1962.
22. ——— Ann. Rev. of Microbiol., 17:49, 1963.
23. Coetzee, J. M., and Sachs, T. G. Nature, 185:869, 1960.
24. Crick, F. H. C., and others. Nature, 192: 1227, 1961.
25. Davis, B. D. J. Amer. Chem. Soc., 70:4267, 1948.
26. ——— Public Health Reports, 67:376, 1952.
27. Demerec, M. Cold Spring Harbor Symposia on Quantitative Biology, 23:59, 1958.
28. ——— Proc. Nat. Acad. Sci., 46:1075, 1960.
29. DeWitt, S. K. J. Bact., 83:693, 1962.
30. Dowell, C. E. J. Bact., 84:1071, 1962.
31. Dulbecco, R., and Vogt, M. Proc. Nat. Acad. Sci., 50:236, 1963.
32. Echols, H. J. Bact., 85:262, 1962.
33. Endo, H., and others. Biochem. Biophys. Res. Comm., 11:477, 1963.
34. Ephrati-Elizur, E., and others. Proc. Nat. Acad. Sci., 47:56, 1961.
35. Foss, H. M., and Stahl, F. W. Genetics, 48: 1659, 1963.
36. Fox, M. S. Nature, 187:1004, 1960.
37. Freese, E. J. Mol. Biol., 1:87, 1959.
38. ——— Genetics, 45:623, 1959.
38a. ——— Molecular mechanism of mutation, in Molecular Genetics, Part I, ed. by J. H. Taylor, New York, Academic Press, Inc., 1963.
39. ——— and others. Proc. Nat. Acad. Sci., 47:845, 1961.
40. ——— and others. J. Mol. Biol., 3:133, 1961.
41. Goldschmidt, E. P., and others. Genetics, 47:1475, 1962.
42. Goldstein, A. J. Bact., 70:588, 1955.
43. Goodgal, S. H. J. Gen. Physiol., 45:205, 1961.
43a. Gorini, L., and Kataja, E. Proc. Nat. Acad. Sc., 51:487, 1964.
44. Greer, S., and Zamenhof, S. J. Mol. Biol., 4:123, 1962.
45. Groman, N. B. J. Bact., 69:9, 1955.
46. ——— and Eaton, M. J. Bact., 70:637, 1955.
47. ——— Ann. Rev. Microbiol., 15:153, 1961.
48. Guild, W. R. J. Mol. Biol., 6:214, 1963.
49. Hashimoto, K. Genetics, 45:49, 1960.
50. Hayes, W. British Medical Bulletin, 18:36, 1962.
51. ——— The Genetics of Bacteria and Their Viruses, Oxford, Blackwell Scientific Publications, 1964.
52. Hershey, A. D., and others. J. Mol. Biol., 6:230, 1963.
53. ——— and Chase, M. J. Gen. Physiol., 36:39, 1952.
54. Hollaway, B. W., and Monk, M. Nature, 184:1426, 1960.
55. Jacob, F., and Wollman, E. L. Sexuality and the Genetics of Bacteria, New York, Academic Press, 1961.
56. ——— and Monod, J. J. Mol. Biol., 3:318, 1961.
57. Kaiser, A. D., and Hogness, D. S. J. Mol. Biol., 2:392, 1960.
58. Kellenberger, G., and others. Proc. Nat. Acad. Sci., 47:869, 1961.
59. King, R. C. Genetics, New York, Oxford University Press, 1962.
60. Kirchner, C. E. J. J. Mol. Biol., 2:331, 1960.
61. Korman, R. Z. J. Bact., 84:228, 1962.
62. Kornberg, A. The Chemical Basis of Heredity, W. D. McElroy and B. Glass, eds., Baltimore, Johns Hopkins Press, 1957.
63. Labrum, E. L. J. Bact., 65:394, 1953.
63a. Lederberberg, E. M., and others. Proc. Nat. Acad. Sc., 51:678, 1964.
64. Lederberg, J. J. Bact., 71:497, 1956.
65. ——— and others. Genetics, 37:720, 1952.
66. ——— and Lederberg, E. M. J. Bact., 63: 399, 1952.
67. ——— and Tatum, E. L. Cold Spring Harbor Symposia on Quantitative Biology, 11: 113, 1946.
68. ——— and Tatum, E. L. Nature, 158:558, 1946.
69. ——— and Tatum, E. L. J. Biol. Chem., 165:381, 1946.
70. ——— and Zinder, N. J. Amer. Chem. Soc., 10:4267, 1943.
71. Lennox, E. S. Virology, 1:190, 1955.

72. Levene, P. A., and Bass, L. W. Nucleic Acids, New York, The Chemical Catalog Co., 1931.
73. Levine, R. P. Genetics, State, Holt, Reinhart and Winston, Inc., 1962.
74. Luria, S. E., and Delbruck, M. Genetics, 28:491, 1943.
75. Marmur, J., and others. Ann. Rev. of Microbiol., 17:329, 1963.
76. ———— and others. Proc. Nat. Acad. Sci., 47:972, 1961.
77. Meselson, M. Cold Spring Harbor Symposia on Quantitative Biology, 23:9, 1958.
78. ———— and Stahl, F. W. Proc. Nat. Acad. Sci., 44:671, 1958.
79. ———— and Weigle, J. J. Proc. Nat. Acad. Sci., 47:857, 1961.
80. Mitchison, D. A. British Medical Bulletin, 18:74, 1962.
81. Miyake, T. Genetics, 45:11, 1960.
82. Morse, M. L. Proc. Nat. Acad. Sci., 45:722, 1959.
83. ———— J. Bact., 83:775, 1962.
84. ———— and others. Genetics, 41:142, 1956.
85. Nester, E. W., and others. Proc. Nat. Acad. Sci., 49:61, 1963.
86. ———— and Lederberg, J. Proc. Nat. Acad. Sci., 47:52, 1961.
87. Nomura, M., and Benzer, S. J. Mol. Biol., 3:684, 1961.
88. Okubo, S., and others. Proc. Nat. Acad. Sci., 50:679, 1963.
89. Orgel, A., and Brenner, S. J. Mol. Biol., 3:762, 1963.
90. Ottolenghi, E., and Hotchkiss, R. D. Science, 132:1257, 1960.
91. ———— and MacLeod, C. M. Proc. Nat. Acad. Sci., 50:417, 1963.
92. Pittard, J., and Adelberg, E. A. J. Bact., 85:1402, 1963.
93. ———— and others. J. Bact., 85:1394, 1963.
94. Ravin, A. W. Bact. Review, 24:201, 1960.
95. Setlow, R., and Setlow, J. K. Proc. Nat. Acad. Sci., 48:1250, 1962.
96. Simon, E. H. J. Mol. Biol., 3:101, 1961.
97. Sinsheimer, R. L. Science, 125:1123, 1957.
98. Skaar, P. D., and Garen, A. Proc. Nat. Acad. Sci., 42:519, 1956.
99. Smith, S. M., and Stocker, B. A. D. British Medical Bulletin, 18:46, 1962.
100. Stainer, R. Y., Doudoroff, M., and Adelberg, E. A. The Microbial World, Englewood Cliffs, N.J., Prentice-Hall, Inc., 1957.
101. Stouthamer, A. H., and others. Genetic Res. Camb., 4:305, 1963.
102. Streizoff, E. Biochem. Biophys. Res. Comm., 5:384, 1961.
103. Sueoka, N. Proc. Nat. Acad. Sci., 46:83, 1960.
104. Takahashi, I. Biochem. Biophys. Res. Comm., 5:171, 1961.
105. Terzaghi, B. E., and others. Proc. Nat. Acad. Sci., 48:1519, 1961.
106. Voll, M. J., and Goodgal, S. H. Proc. Nat. Acad. Sci., 47:505, 1961.
107. Watanabe, T., and Fukasawa, T. J. Bact., 81:669, 1961.
108. ———— J. Bact., 82:202, 1961.
109. ———— Bacteriol. Rev., 27:87, 1963.
110. ———— J. Bact., 85:788, 1963.
111. ———— and Lyang, K. W. J. Bact., 84:422, 1962.
112. Watson, J. D., and Crick, F. H. C. Nature, 171:737, 1953.
113. Wilkins, M. H. F. Science, 140:941, 1963.
114. ———— and Stokes, A. R. Nature, 171:1, 1953.
115. Young, F. E., and Spizizen, J. J. Biol. Chem., 238:3126, 1963.
116. ———— and others. J. Biol. Chem., 238:3119, 1963.
117. Zamenhof, P. D. The Bacteria, New York, Academic Press, Inc., 1964, vol. 5.
118. Zamenhof, S., and others. Proc. Nat. Acad. Sci., 48:944, 1962.
119. Zinder, N. D. Science, 131:924, 1960.
120. ———— and Lederberg, J. J. Bact., 64:679, 1952.

6

Nutrition and Growth of Bacteria

A wide diversity of nutritional habits is represented among the bacteria. Some organisms can synthesize all of their protoplasmic constituents from simple components such as ammonia and carbon dioxide; others, however, require an organic source of nitrogen and carbon as well as certain growth factors before they will grow. In spite of this marked variation from organism to organism in respect to carbon, nitrogen, or energy source, an examination of the basic nutritional requirements of microorganisms demonstrates the essential similarity of bacterial protoplasm. These requirements reflect common physiologic and biochemical mechanisms. Also, many bacterial requirements are held in common with those of higher animals, so that information obtained at either level has proved invaluable to both.

During growth of a given bacterium the nutrients of the medium are converted into bacterial protoplasm, consisting of a group of very complex materials. Whereas gross analyses of the bacterial cell will provide a general orientation to the problems of bacterial nutrition, such fundamental questions as what constitutes an adequate usable supply for a particular organism can be answered only by direct experimentation. In order for synthesis to occur, the bacterium must be furnished with all the substances essential in the synthesis and maintenance of its protoplasm, a source of energy, and suitable environmental conditions. These comprise the nutritional requirements of a given organism. Nutrients must be present in the environment in a form available to the bacterial cell. Such compounds must be capable of penetrating the external boundaries of the cell and must be of such a nature

that they can then be utilized by the cell in performing one of its vital functions.

Universally Required Nutrients. In spite of the marked differences in the nutritional requirements of the various species of bacteria, there are a few nutrients which appear to be required by all bacteria.

WATER. Bacteria require high concentrations of water in their immediate environment for growth and multiplication. Water is the vehicle by which all essential nutrients are brought into the cell and all waste products are taken away. Not only is it a reactant in metabolic reactions, but it also forms an integral part of the organism's protoplasm.

INORGANIC SALTS. Like all other organisms, bacteria require the presence of certain inorganic salts for growth. These inorganic substances have three principal roles: (1) the maintenance of a proper colloidal state and osmotic pressure, (2) the maintenance of acid-base balance which, although perhaps not as critical as in the mammal, must occur, and (3) to function as a part of enzymes or as activators of enzymatic reactions.

Little is known about the actual inorganic requirements of bacteria and their role in the living cell. This is because of the minute amount required by the organism and the fact that such traces as are present as contaminants in the constituents of the media usually satisfy the cell's needs. The use of chelating agents which combine with the metal to form an inactive compound has been helpful in preparing mineral-free media for such studies. Among the most essential of the inorganic elements for bacteria are sulfur, iron, magnesium, and phosphorus. The need for others is more difficult to assess, but, on the basis of known physiologic functions and the demonstration of a requirement by certain organisms, potassium, calcium, manganese, zinc, copper, and cobalt are also essential for most bacteria (58).

Sulfur is a constituent of such substances as cystine, methionine, and thiamine. It may be supplied to some organisms in the form of sulfate; others require an organic source such as methionine. Iron is essential for the functioning of several enzymes, as shown by the suppressed activity of catalase, peroxidase, formic hydrogenlyase, and cytochrome in iron-deficient cells. Magnesium participates in phosphorylation and other enzymatic reactions. A number of bacteria form long chains in a magnesium-deficient medium but readily revert to the normal state upon the addition of magnesium. Phosphate plays an important role in energy transfer. Its uptake is linked with metabolism, is negligible in the absence of nutrient, and is markedly inhibited by cyanide, dinitrophenol, or azide, which depress metabolic activities. The uptake and loss of phosphate as demonstrated by the use of P^{32} is poisoned by the heavy metals.

Most of the studies on the inorganic requirements of bacteria have been oriented primarily toward the determination of those which are strictly indispensable. Other ions, however, are of great importance for under natural conditions these elements can, when present, partly fulfill the requirement for some of the essential ions. Likewise, a number of antagonistic relationships between individual ions have been observed and have emphasized the importance of maintaining the proper ratio of ions. Such antagonism has been explained as resulting from competition between structural analogs for an essential enzyme site (31).

CARBON DIOXIDE. Bacteria will not grow when completely deprived of carbon dioxide. This inability to grow is due to an interruption of synthetic processes whereby carbon dioxide is assimilated in the cell. It is impossible to evaluate directly the true importance of the heterotrophic assimilation of carbon dioxide, but the use of isotopically labeled CO_2 and subsequent demonstration of its incorporation into cell constituents,

has provided convincing proof that this is an essential physiologic function for all forms of life. Carbon dioxide has been shown to be assimilated in heterotrophic organisms by at least 12 different primary reactions. These reactions are of major importance in the over-all metabolism of the cell, and include such key reactions as fatty acid synthesis, the reversal of glycolysis starting from pyruvate, the de novo synthesis of purines, and the maintenance of the supply of the C_4 dicarboxylic acids for syntheses occurring via the tricarboxylic acid cycle (57).

The Organic Requirements (52). Although bacteria vary markedly in their energy requirements, there are several basic patterns of nutrition which help to characterize the different types. The least exacting group of organisms are the **autotrophic** bacteria, which are able to live in a strictly inorganic environment, utilizing carbon dioxide or carbonates as a sole source of carbon. The **chemosynthetic autotrophs** (39) obtain their energy by the oxidation of an inorganic substrate (iron, sulfur, ammonia, nitrite), the nature of which is specific for that particular organism. The nitrification of ammonia in the soil is brought about by certain of these organisms. The genus *Nitrosomonas* initiates the conversion by the oxidation of ammonia to nitrite. The nitrite is then oxidized to nitrate by *Nitrobacter*. Another autotroph of particular interest, *Thiobacillus thiooxidans,* oxidizes inorganic sulfur to sulfate in order to meet its energy requirement. This organism has an exceptionally high tolerance of acid and is unaffected by a pH value as low as 0.6 or a sulfuric acid content greater than 5 per cent. In order to live in such a system, the organism possesses a permeability system that prevents the toxic environment from entering and enables the organism to grow in an environment in which competition from other forms has been eliminated. A similar explanation may account for the ability of certain other organisms to exist under adverse conditions.

Also included with the chemoautotrophs are the hydrogen bacteria, which derive energy from the oxidation of hydrogen, and the iron bacteria, which oxidize ferrous salts to ferric hydroxide. In all of these organisms, however, the energy source is absolutely specific and is confined to one substance or to a few closely related substances (56).

The **photosynthetic autotrophs** are pigmented anaerobic organisms that obtain energy for their synthetic activities by the utilization of radiant energy. The photosynthesizing pigment is a magnesium porphyrin, closely related to chlorophyll *a* of green plants. In some of these organisms the green color is evident; in others it is masked by carotenoid pigments of unknown function. The pigments have been shown to occur in well-defined structures, the "chromatophores" (Fig. 1) (45). Isolated chromatophores are 300 to 500 Å. in diameter and contain proteins, phospholipids, and respiratory pigments in addition to the chlorophyll and carotenoids.

There are three main kinds of photosynthetic bacteria: (1) **purple sulfur bacteria** (*Thiorhodaceae*), which reduce CO_2 at the ultimate expense of H_2S; (2) **purple nonsulfur bacteria** (*Athiorhodaceae*), which reduce CO_2 at the ultimate expense of organic compounds, require growth factors and cannot use H_2S as a hydrogen donor; (3) **green sulfur bacteria** (*Chlorobacteriaceae*) which reduce CO_2 at the ultimate expense of H_2S.

The dependence of CO_2 assimilation on a supply of radiant energy characterizes these organisms as photosynthetic. Bacterial photosynthesis, however, differs from the process in green plants in that molecular oxygen is not produced. The primary reaction in bacterial photosynthesis as advanced by Van Niel (54, 55) involves the photochemical activation of water with its splitting into H and OH free radicals. The energy required for this split is furnished by the light energy absorbed by chlorophyll. The highly unsaturated resonating structure of chlorophyll enables it to absorb successive quanta of radiant energy and thereby effect the characteristic reduction of the product resulting from the fixation of CO_2 by some constituent of the plant. In green plants the hydroxyl groups formed from the activated water molecules appear as peroxides, which are then broken down to water and molecular oxygen. Bacteria, however, depend for

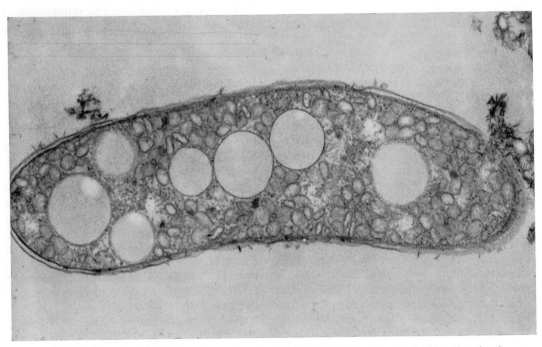

Fig. 1. Section of a photosynthetic bacterium, *Rhodospirillum rubrum,* showing the circular profiles of the chromatophores and seven large granules. (From Boatman. *J. Cell. Biology,* 20:297, 1964.)

this reduction on an external hydrogen donor.

A general over-all reaction to represent the process of photosynthesis is expressed in the equation

$$nCO_2 + 2nH_2A \longrightarrow (CH_2O) + nH_2O + 2nA$$

where H_2A is a specific hydrogen donor.

In the over-all photosynthetic process, only the activation of water is photochemical in nature; the remainder is not dependent on light energy and is considered as a series of "dark" reactions. The findings obtained in studies employing isotopically labeled CO_2 suggest that many of the intermediates in the Krebs cycle and in the anaerobic breakdown of the hexoses are also important in the process of photosynthesis. Phosphoglyceric acid is the form in which carbon dioxide is reduced.

An alternate hypothesis proposed by Arnon (1) suggests that radiant energy is used solely for the synthesis of ATP by cyclic photophosphorylation and that the substrate acts as the electron donor in the assimilatory process (Fig. 2). In this scheme the photolysis of water is not considered to be the primary light reaction. Stanier's observations support the latter hypothesis (50). A more complete discussion of this important group of organisms and of the mechanisms of bacterial photosynthesis may be found in the excellent reviews of Van Niel (54, 55), Stanier (51), Geller (15), Ormerod and Gest (38), and Clayton (7).

Whereas the autotrophic bacteria are more closely related to plants in their general pattern of metabolism, the heterotrophic organisms are related to animals. These bacteria, which include all those pathogenic for man, require a more complex source of carbon than CO_2 and obtain their energy by the degradation of organic matter. Considerable variation occurs among this group in respect to utilizable nitrogen sources and the need for accessory growth factors. Some, such as the genus *Azotobacter*, are able to transform atmospheric nitrogen into nitrogenous compounds within the cell; some grow readily when supplied with ammonia or nitrate as a source of nitrogen and glucose as the carbon source; others are more fastidious

in their requirements, needing one or more amino acids or vitamins in order to perform its synthetic functions.

Lwoff and others (29) have suggested an additional group, the **hypotrophic** organisms, whose relationship with the host is so intimate that the parasite has no developed metabolic system of its own and derives its energy from the host cell, as in the case of the viruses.

Although it is convenient to divide bacteria into different groups on the basis of their nutritional requirements, there are no clear-cut boundaries of separation between these groups but rather a gradual transition from one to another. In general, however, the specialization and differentiation encountered as one progresses from the autotrophic to the heterotrophic and more fastidious organisms is indicative of the organism's response to environmental conditions, with the consequent loss of various synthetic abilities as a result of assuming a more fastidious or parasitic existence. Fildes' (11) hypothesis that parasitism is caused by the loss of enzymes necessary to synthesize

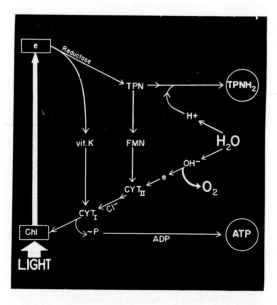

Fig. 2. Proposed scheme of photosynthesis. A chlorophyll unit absorbs light and produces a high-energy electron which is returned by pathways that are coupled with phosphorylation. One pathway provides for the reduction of TPN together with the evolution of O_2 from water. (From Arnon. *Nature*, 184:10, 1959.)

cellular components is now well recognized. Such a theory pictures the autotrophic organisms as the more primitive ancestors from which the heterotrophs have evolved by a series of mutations resulting in gaps in their metabolic pathways.

Growth Factor Requirements. Many of the bacteria among the heterotrophic group are unable to grow even when supplied with an adequate source of carbon, nitrogen, and essential mineral salts. In addition, these organisms require **accessory growth factors** or **vitamins** which may be provided in the form of yeast extract or blood serum. Most of these vitamins are members of the B-complex group, every member of which has been found essential for some nutritionally exacting organism. And in every instance in which an organism does not require an exogenous source of any member in the B-complex group, it can be shown capable of synthesizing its own supply. This fact points to an underlying similarity in metabolic need between the animal and microbic worlds. Several of the vitamins were first discovered as growth factors for bacteria, and their importance in animal and plant nutrition became apparent later.

In most instances these vitamins function as the prosthetic group or a part of the prosthetic group of essential enzyme systems. The synthetic disability may refer to the whole prosthetic group, or to only a part of the essential molecule. Nicotinic acid is the active group in the nicotinamide adenine nucleotides (NAD and NADP), the prosthetic group of several dehydrogenases important in fermentation and respiration reactions. Many bacteria, such as the staphylococci and diphtheria bacilli, require nicotinic acid for growth. In *Haemophilus parainfluenzae,* however, the synthetic abilities have been further impaired, and even when supplied with nicotinic acid and the other constituents of the coenzyme molecule, it is still unable to effect the necessary group linkages. Only when the intact coenzyme molecule is furnished, does growth occur. In most cases, though, the known phosphorylated coenzyme form of the vitamin penetrates the cell with difficulty and is poorly utilized when supplied as a nutrient.

That loss of synthetic ability occurs at different points in the synthesis of a given vitamin is shown by the fulfillment of the thiamine requirements of different species. Some bacteria require the intact thiamine molecule for growth, and some grow readily if supplied with both the pyrimidine and thiazole moieties of the molecule, while others require only the pyrimidine fraction or the thiazole component from which they can complete the synthesis of thiamine.

Vitamin deficiency is not necessarily an all-or-none affair. An organism may be able to get along without a certain growth factor but grows better when it is supplied. Such a factor would be stimulatory rather than essential to the organism's nutrition and would in such cases supplement the cellular stores of metabolite produced by the organism at a rate too low to supply its full requirement.

Another interesting relationship between the B-complex vitamins which has been observed is an inhibition in growth of certain organisms by low concentrations of an essential metabolite and the subsequent restoration of growth by another vitamin (34, 43). These inhibitory effects may play an important role in the coordinated control of interwoven metabolic pathways.

THE B-COMPLEX VITAMINS. (53) **Thiamine,** the first member of the B-complex to be identified, consists of a thiazole and a pyrimidine unit. It exists in bacterial cells and in animal tissues primarily as thiamine pyrophosphate, which is the coenzyme for yeast carboxylase and enzymes important in the oxidative decarboxylation of *a*-keto acids.

Riboflavin is the active fraction of the flavin nucleotides (flavin phosphate and flavin adenine dinucleotide) which are important in biologic oxidations. They are involved in the *d*- and *l*-amino acid oxidase systems, in glycine oxidase, and in the oxidation of glucose.

Vitamin B₆ includes several closely related growth factors (pyridoxine, pyridoxamine, and pyridoxal) with widely varying activity for different microorganisms. Its functional form, pyridoxal phosphate, participates in reactions concerned with the synthesis and degradation of all of the naturally occurring *a*-amino acids. The key role of this vitamin in amino acid metabolism is emphasized by the fact that the vitamin B_6 requirement of a number of bacteria is dependent upon the amino acid content of the culture medium.

Nicotinic acid and its amide, **nicotinamide,** are important growth factors for many microorganisms. It is incorporated in the pyridine nucleotides (NAD and NADP) which function as cofactors in dehydrogenation reactions involved in the anaerobic degradation of carbohydrate, in the citric acid cycle, and in the deamination of glutamic acid.

Pantothenic acid is a component of coenzyme A, which is essential for many acetylation reactions. This relationship is illustrated in Figure 3, which shows the chain of reactions a cell may employ to form the vitamin, pantothenic acid, and its active form. Inability to complete the synthesis may occur at a number of different sites. The organisms shown in the diagram can carry on the reaction sequence from the point of entry onwards.

Biotin, which functions as a growth factor for a number of microorganisms, occurs in nature primarily in the bound form. One of these complexes, biocytin, is a conjugate of biotin and lysine. The biotin requirement of an organism is greatly influenced by the components of the culture medium as shown by the sparing action of aspartic acid and oleic acid on the biotin requirement for a number of species. The metabolic role of biotin in the activation of CO_2 for fixation into aspartate and its participation in the synthesis of fatty acids explains these requirements. Biotin is also probably involved in the deamination of amino acids (aspartic acid, serine, threonine), and the decarboxylation of oxaloacetate. The ability of pimelic acid and desthiobiotin to fulfill the biotin requirement of certain organisms suggests their role as precursors in biotin synthesis.

p-**Aminobenzoic acid (PABA)** is a component of all of the members of the folic acid group of vitamins, each of which serves as a growth factor for certain organisms. This group includes the parent vitamin **pteroylglutamic acid (folic acid)** and a number of other compounds closely resembling tetrahydropteroylglutamic acid in structure. Various organisms elicit different responses to these compounds. The main functional form of the folic acid group is coenzyme F, whose structure has not been determined. Folic acid functions in a number of reactions concerned with one-carbon transfer important in the metabolism of certain amino acids, purines, and pyrimidines. The importance of this vitamin in microbial nutrition is emphasized by the growth inhibitory effect of the sulfonamide drugs, which inhibit the incorporation of *p*-aminobenzoic acid into folic acid by those organisms with no exogenous folic acid requirement.

Vitamin B_{12} (cyanocobalamin), unlike the other B-complex vitamins, is not present in yeast and green plants. It is structurally quite complex and exists in nature in a number of different forms. The biochemical activity of this group of vitamins is closely associated with that of the folic acid group and is involved either directly or indirectly in a number of functions of importance to microbial

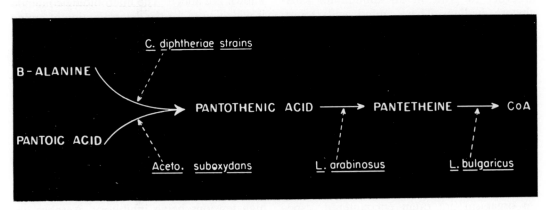

Fig. 3. Abbreviated scheme of the biosynthesis of coenzyme A.

growth. It functions in the metabolism of labile methyl groups and in the biosynthesis of purines and pyrimidines and their deoxyribosides. Vitamin B_{12} is also involved in the synthesis of serine and methionine.

OTHER GROWTH FACTORS. A number of additional substances have been shown to have growth factor activity for certain species (28, 16). **Inositol** and **choline** are sometimes included in the B-complex group, although they are required in greater amounts than true vitamins and no cofactor function has been demonstrated. Hemin is required by certain species of the genus *Haemophilus* and is incorporated in the cytochromes and iron-porphyrin-containing enzymes. **Coprogen** is another iron-containing pigment and is highly active for a number of fungi (19). Another iron-complexing compound required by some organisms, **ferrichrome,** is probably an iron carrier in the synthesis of heme and other iron-containing compounds (35).

Lipoic acid or thioctic acid occurs in natural materials largely combined in amide linkage with oxidative enzymes. It is catalytically involved in acetate synthesis and in the oxidation of pyruvate and *a*-ketoglutarate (44).

Certain organisms also have requirements for oleic acid, compounds with vitamin K activity (12, 21) and for one or more of the purine and pyrimidine bases or their derivatives (16). Asparagine, glutamine and putrescine are also essential for certain species.

AMINO ACID REQUIREMENTS. Many bacteria require one or more amino acids in order to grow in an ammonium salts-glucose medium. These amino acids represent units essential to the organism which it is unable to synthesize. In some organisms the synthetic capacity is so limited that 17 or 18 amino acids must be added to a synthetic culture medium. The gram-positive bacteria are especially limited in their ability to synthesize the amino acids and thus depend upon an exogenous source.

The requirement for a given amino acid is often influenced by the composition of the culture medium. Interrelationships between the vitamin and amino acid requirements of an organism are often encountered, especially with pyridoxal, biotin, folic acid, and vitamin B_{12}. Toxic effects may also be exerted when an amino acid is added to a medium containing only a few amino acids, although no inhibitory effect is evident when it is added to a more complex medium. Many examples of mutual competition between amino acids have been described since the discovery of this type of interference. Such relationships probably play an important role in the regulation of enzymic processes within the cell so that the proper amounts of the various products are produced at the proper time and there is no excessive accumulation of intermediates.

One of the ultimate problems of microbial nutrition is to study the relationships of microorganisms in the mixed associations in which they exist in nature. A number of bacteria have the ability to enter into, and benefit from, symbiotic relationships where each member produces nutritional growth factors helpful to the other. The chemical nature of most of these associations, however, is poorly understood.

MICROBIOLOGIC ASSAY. The finding of various bacterial species, for which the different vitamins and amino acids are essential, has led to the use of bacteria in the microbiologic assay of these substances (Table 1). Such a method employs an organism which requires the substance to be determined and is based upon the growth or metabolic response of the organism to increasing amounts of the factor when grown in a medium free of the substance. The standard curve thus obtained may be used for the calculation of results obtained when aliquots of the unknown are added. The microbiologic method is widely used for the determination of amino acids, the B-complex vitamins, and certain inorganic elements (3).

Requirements for Oxygen. On the basis of their oxygen requirements bacteria may be divided into four groups: **obligate anaerobes,** which will grow only under conditions of high reducing intensity; **facultative anaerobes,** which are capable of growth under both aerobic and anaerobic conditions; **obligate aerobes,** which require oxygen for growth; and **micro-aerophilic organisms,** which grow best at low oxygen tensions, high tensions being inhibitory. Aerobes obtain energy by the complete breakdown of

Table 1. Vitamins Required by Various Microorganisms

VITAMIN	EXAMPLE OF DEPENDENT ORGANISM	GROWTH-LIMITING CONCENTRATIONS $m\mu g/ml$
p-Aminobenzoic acid	Acetobacter suboxydans	0-1.0
Folic acid	Streptococcus faecalis	0-0.8
Biotin	Lactobacillus arabinosus	0-0.2
Nicotinic acid	Lactobacillus arabinosus	0-40
Pantothenic acid	Lactobacillus casei	0-20
Riboflavin	Lactobacillus casei	0-25
Thiamine	Lactobacillus fermenti	0-5
Pyridoxine	Saccharomyces carlsbergensis	0-40
Vitamin B_{12}	Lactobacillus leichmannii	0-.025
Inositol	Saccharomyces carlsbergensis	0-100

carbohydrates; anaerobes effect only a partial breakdown or fermentation of carbohydrate. Catalase and a complete cytochrome system which are present in aerobic bacteria are lacking in the anaerobic organisms.

The oxidation-reduction potential (Eh) of the culture media determines whether growth of an inoculum will occur when transferred to fresh media. The Eh of most media in contact with air is about $+ 0.2$ to 0.4 volt at pH 7. The strict anaerobes are unable to grow unless the Eh of the medium is at least as low as -0.2 volt. Oxygen, usually considered to be toxic to the strict anaerobes, is not inhibitory provided the Eh is sufficiently low. The Eh of the culture is depressed by the exclusion of oxygen, by the use of oxido-reduction buffer systems such as cysteine-cystine or ascorbic acid, and by the activity of the growing cells themselves. Aeration tends to provide more positive potentials.

Extracellular Enzymes (41).   Surrounded by a semipermeable membrane, bacteria, in common with all living organisms, are limited in their ability to utilize the great variety of large molecule substrates in their natural environment unless these substances are first broken down to smaller units. The need for bacteria to develop systems capable of hydrolyzing such large molecules is vital for the bacteria themselves, as well as being essential for the conservation and recycling of carbon, nitrogen, and other elements. If one looks in the right place and in the proper way, one will always find some organism which can break down any selected naturally occurring substance. This hypothesis is the basis for the **enrichment culture**

technic used in isolating organisms capable of breaking down substances of high molecular weight. A medium containing essential inorganic salts and the particular substrate under study is inoculated with a mixture of organisms derived from a source in which it is probable that destruction of that substrate has been occurring. Soils and muds are the most common sources of inoculum in the isolation of an organism capable of destroying the polysaccharide capsule of the pneumococcus.

Most extracellular enzymes are inductive and as visualized by Pollock (Fig. 4) (40) are probably formed somewhere near the cell surface and either liberated into the surrounding environment or retained at the surface. Among the substances attacked by extracellular enzymes are **polysaccharides** such as cellulose, starch, and pectins, **mucopolysaccharides,** including chitin, hyaluronic acid, and chondroitin sulfate, **proteins,** and **nucleic acids.** A number of the more invasive pathogenic bacteria including β-streptococci, staphylococci, and members of the *Clostridium* group elaborate a number of extracellular enzymes which destroy various components of the body tissues and thus contribute to the over-all pathogenesis of infection.

The Uptake of Nutrients (23).   The interchange of materials between the interior and the external environment of the bacterial cell is regulated by a selectively permeable barrier, permeable to water and selective to the passage of other substances. The movement of a substance through a membrane involves a number of factors. Some of these are due to

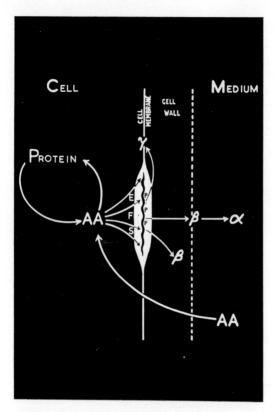

Fig. 4. A scheme illustrating the possible course of penicillinase synthesis and liberation by *Bacillus cereus* and its probable location in relation to cell structure. EFS refers to the enzyme-forming site; AA to free amino acids; and PPP to polypeptide penicillinase precursor on the EFS. (From Pollock. *Proc. Internat. Symp. on Enzyme Chemistry,* 1958.)

properties of the membrane itself, such as thermodynamic and hydrostatic forces. The direction of the movement of substances under the influence of such **factors of permeation** is in the direction tending to reduce the gradient. In biological systems, however, an **active transport** requiring an expenditure of energy of metabolism makes possible the passage of materials which otherwise would be unable to penetrate. The cytoplasmic membrane of bacteria is very poorly permeable to hydrophilic organic compounds. The entry of most organic nutrilites of this type is mediated by stereospecific permeation systems, the **permease systems.** The stereospecific component of such systems, the **permease,** is protein in nature and is functionally distinct from metabolic enzymes

involved in its utilization after entrance into the cell.

The permeases are highly specific. Mutations in a well-circumscribed locus on the chromosome result in the loss of permease activity. Such mutants are **cryptic** in that the enzyme capable of metabolizing that particular substrate remains hidden from its substrate added to the medium. When such cells are ruptured, however, the substrate may now be metabolized. Cells which are cryptic toward a given substance behave as a rule quite normally toward other substrates. The most comprehensive studies of permease systems have been with the β-galactoside system of *E. coli* (8, 23). Permease systems have now been postulated for at least 30 different substrates, including various carbohydrates, amino acids, intermediates of the Krebs cycle, and a number of organic acids.

The carrier transport model has been the most useful model for interpreting the role of the bacterial permeases in membrane transport. As visualized by Cohen and Monod (8), the bacterial cell is surrounded by an osmotic barrier highly impermeable toward polar substances but allowing slow leakage in both directions. Within this barrier, according to this hypothesis, there are permeases, protein in nature, which form stereospecific, reversible complexes with different hydrophilic compounds. This involves two chemical reactions, the first on the outside and the second on the inside of the membrane, with a diffusion step between (23).

$$S \xrightarrow{\text{outside}} S' \xrightarrow{\text{diffusion}} S' \xrightarrow{\text{inside}} S$$

S' is usually visualized as a substrate-carrier complex.

There is wide variation from one permease to another in the degree of dependence on energy-yielding metabolism, and in the case of valine and tryptophan it is not clear whether the carbon source acts upon the entry or exit reaction.

GROWTH OF BACTERIA

Growth may be defined as an increase in bacterial protoplasm and thus represents the sum of all the processes of assimilation and dissimilation in the organism. In a bacterial culture growth is a phenomenon of the individual cell, whose ability to grow and reproduce itself depends upon its ability to form new protoplasm from the nutrients available (26). The conditions under which this takes place are genetically controlled.

Bacterial growth consists of a succession of phases characterized by variations in the rate of change of the population. Since technical difficulties limit studies on the growth of individual cells, we usually examine entire populations and from the data thus obtained draw inferences with respect to the individual cells. The development of a bacterial culture is accompanied both by an increase in cell mass and in the number of organisms, with no constant relationship between the two. In quantitative studies dealing with cell growth it is therefore necessary to distinguish between **cell concentration,** or the number of cells per unit volume of culture, and **bacterial density,** defined as total protoplasm per unit volume. In most problems dealing with bacterial chemistry, physiology, and nutrition, the significant variable is bacterial density. Knowledge concerning the actual cell concentration, however, is important in problems concerning cell division.

Various technics are in general use for estimating bacterial densities and cell concentrations. Unfortunately, no single method permits the simultaneous determination of both of these properties. For the determination of bacterial density indirect methods have been substituted for the laborious determination of dry weights. The most widely used of these determines the turbidity of broth cultures by measuring the light transmitted or optical density of the culture by means of instruments fitted with photoelectric cells. In well-dispersed cultures optical density remains proportional to bacterial density throughout the positive phases of growth. A close correlation between nitrogen determinations and dry weights permits the use of total cellular nitrogen as a measure of bacterial density; methods based on the estimation of metabolic activity and the volume of packed cells after centrifugation have also proved of value.

Actual enumerations of cell concentrations are performed either by total direct counts or by indirect viable counts. Total counts may be made by means of a counting chamber such as the Petroff-Hauser counter, which is similar in principle to the hemacytometer but has a much shallower chamber and is employed with darkfield illumination. Viable counts require the plating of a sample of the culture over the surface of an agar plate; although discrepancies sometimes arise, this method is by far the most sensitive.

Since bacteria multiply by binary fission, each doubling of the number of organisms in the culture represents one **generation;** and the length of time elapsing between the formation of a cell and its division is the **generation time.** The increase in population may be expressed exponentially by the equation $b = B2^n$, where b represents the number of organisms at the end of a time period, B the number of bacteria in the inoculum, and n the number of generations. Similarly, the generation time (g) may be calculated by dividing the number of generations into the time interval elapsed (t): $g = t/n$. Complex media give rise to a greater dispersion of generation time than do simple media (42).

According to Monod (33) the growth of a bacterial culture can be characterized by three fundamental growth constants: the **growth lag,** the **growth rate,** and the **ultimate population** that can be supported by the medium.

The growth lag is the difference in the number of divisions lost to the development of the culture by this period because growth is at a slower rate than that attained during the exponential phase. The rate of division during exponential growth is measured by the slope of the growth curve. Employing the traditional equation expressed in terms of the variables of the growth curve, the growth rate (R) during the exponential or logarithmic phase of growth may be expressed as

$$R = \frac{\log_2 b_2 - \log_2 b_1}{t_2 - t_1}$$

where there are b_1 cells at time t_1 and b_2 at time t_2. Mathematical treatment of the phenomena of growth has proved of great value in permitting quantitative evaluation of the effects of given variables on growth, as well as of studying cellular components as a function of the growth rate (14, 25). Of special importance are the systematic studies which have been made of cell yields as a function of energy-yielding substrate concentration. The growth yield per mole of ATP was found to be the same for very different microorganisms growing at the expense of preformed monomers (47). The dry weight yield of cells in grams (Y_{ATP}) is approximately 1.5 per mole of ATP for various types of organisms and fermentations (4, 49).

Factors Affecting Growth. Growth is largely influenced by conditions that affect enzyme formation. The rate of growth of any bacterial culture is, therefore, a function of several variables. The various species under optimal conditions differ considerably in their maximum rates because of the limitation of their own chemical machinery. Heredity determines how the organism will respond to environmental influences and is responsible for the differences among species subject to the same environment. For each bacterium there is an optimal temperature at which the organism grows most rapidly and a range of temperature over which growth can occur. The growth rate of bacteria is probably less sensitive to the damaging effects of excessive heat than is the fission rate, since very large and bizarrely shaped living organisms are often observed in cultures grown at high temperatures, above that supporting the most rapid division rate. All bacteria can be divided roughly into three groups on the basis of the temperature ranges through which they grow: **psychrophilic,** −5° to 30° C., optimum at 10° to 20° C.; **mesophilic,** 10° to 45° C., optimum at 20° to 40° C.; and **thermophilic,** 25° to 80° C., optimum at 50° to 60° C. For most pathogenic bacteria the optimal temperature for growth is 37° C. The marine bacteria are among those which grow best at the lower temperatures, while those found in hot springs prefer high temperatures. One of the most interesting observations in respect to differences in temperature optima is the variation existing among different types of tubercle bacilli whose optimal temperatures conform with the body temperature of their host (6). The primary effect of temperature on the growth of a bacterial culture is its influence on the rate of chemical reactions. Within the biologic range this approximates a doubling of reaction rate for each 10° C. rise in temperature.

Table 2 shows the effect of temperature on the growth and respiration of *Aerobacter aerogenes*. The exponential growth rate is increased by a factor of 2.3, and the respiratory activity by a factor of 2.9, with an increase from 22 to 37° C. Above 37° C. both growth yield and growth rate decline sharply, reaching a zero value at about 42° C. The respiratory activity, however, increases with temperature rise to 42° C., followed by inhibition. The critical temperature range between optimal growth and total inhibition, during which there is no alteration of respiratory activity, corresponds to

Table 2. Influence of Temperature on Growth of *Aerobacter aerogenes*
(From Senez)

RESPIRATORY ACTIVITY OF RESTING CELLS		GROWTH		
Temperature C	$-Q_{O_2}$	Temperature	r	G
22.2	60.3	23.0	0.552	0.354
27.2	83.5	27.0	0.751	0.356
32.1	114.6	32.0	0.967	0.336
37.6	175.6	37.0	1.305	0.324
41.8	199.2	38.8	0.833	0.217
45.0	166.1	39.7	0.600	0.172
47.0	146.3	40.8	0.400	0.095
		42.0	0	0

Aerobic cultures in glucose medium.
$-Q_{O_2}$ = respiratory activity of resting cells (μl O_2 consumed per hour per mg. cells);
r = exponential growth rate; G = weight (g/g) yield from glucose.

an energy uncoupling (47). In a number of organisms an increase in temperature results in a gain of nutritional requirement (28).

The pH of the medium likewise affects the growth rate, and here also there is an optimal pH with a wider range over which growth can occur. For most pathogenic bacteria the optimal pH is a little on the alkaline side at pH 7.2 to 7.6.

The size and condition of the inoculum, the nature of available substrates, and suitable oxygen and carbon dioxide tensions also exert a marked effect upon the rate of growth and the type of growth curve that a culture will display.

The Growth Curve. When a suitable nutrient medium is inoculated with viable bacteria and the rate of growth of the culture followed, a characteristic growth curve may be obtained. The growth of a population as a function of time usually is plotted on a semilogarithmic scale, the log of the number of bacteria per milliliter being plotted against time in hours. Immediately after inoculation some little time is required for the cells to adjust to the conditions in the new environment. After this period of adjustment, the organisms begin to divide at an increasing rate until the maximum rate of multiplication is attained. Retarding influences soon come into play, accompanied by a reduction in the rate of cell division and an increase in the death rate.

Figure 5 represents a typical growth curve in which the cycle has been divided into four phases. Several workers (33), believing the life cycle of bacteria more complicated than this, have further subdivided the curve, describing seven phases of growth. These additional phases represent periods of transition and emphasize the gradual merging of phases in sequence. In this discussion, however, for the purpose of simplicity, we shall adhere to the original scheme. At zero time the medium was inoculated with viable bacteria. After a two-hour **lag period, a to b,** a constant rate of growth, the **logarithmic phase, b to c,** occurred with doubling every half-hour until the tenth hour, as shown by the linear part of the curve. This was followed by a period of declining rate and then by a **stationary period, c to d,** during which the population remained relatively constant. Finally, the stationary period gave way to one in which the population was declining. The **period of decline, d to e,** obviously is one in which death occurs at a rate greater than that of cell division, and, by the same

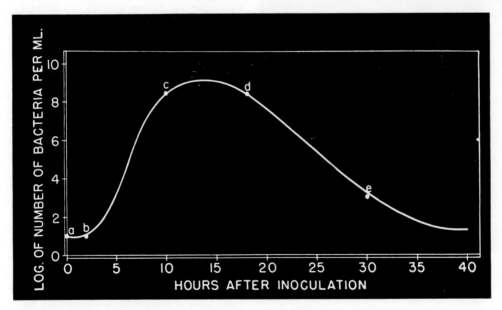

Fig. 5. The growth curve. The number of bacteria per milliliter of culture medium is plotted on a logarithmic scale as a function of time. The four phases of growth are presented: a to b, lag phase; b to c, exponential phase; c to d, stationary phase; and d to e, period of decline.

token, the stationary period involves equal death and division rates.

THE LAG PHASE. Coincident with the different phases of growth as measured by an increase in cell numbers, various changes occur in certain physiologic and morphologic characteristics of the cell. The original conception of the lag phase as a period of rest is no longer tenable, for actually this is a period of intense activity. During the early hours of culture growth the cells increase considerably in size at a time when little or no cell division is occurring. That there is no lag in the synthesis of protoplasm is also shown by the increase in total protein, ribonucleic acid, and cell phosphorus. The increased basophilic-staining properties during early growth reflect a high concentration of nucleotides. The increase in ribonucleic acid is of particular interest because of its active role in protein synthesis.

Other changes also are associated with this progressive increase in protoplasm synthesis. There is a marked increase in metabolic activity, a reduced resistance to many injurious physical and chemical agents, a decrease in electrophoretic charge, and a lowered susceptibility to spontaneous agglutination. It is because of these properties that this adjustment period is often referred to as a phase of **rejuvenescence,** a period during which the protoplasm of the old cells is acquiring the characteristics of new protoplasm which will fit them for reproduction. This phase of adjustment is necessary for the replenishing of the internal supply of intermediate metabolites and corresponds to the time required for the metabolism of the culture to build up to a steady state, which is necessary if cell synthesis is to occur at a maximum rate (27). Under suitable conditions the lag phase may be so shortened as to be imperceptible, as occurs when a large inoculum is obtained from a culture growing in its logarithmic phase. When inocula are taken from the period of decline, hours may elapse before growth is established. From these observations it has been concluded that subcultured bacteria continue to multiply at the same rate that they multiplied in the culture from which the inoculum was obtained.

The transition between two physiologic states follows a simple pattern, as shown in Figure 6. When cells are shifted to a medium providing a higher growth rate, as indicated by the altered slope of the growth curve, the low preshift rates of DNA synthesis and of cell division are maintained for a definite period of time, whereas the rate of mass increase and of RNA synthesis immediately goes up. During this transition from slow to fast growth following a change of medium, the rate of protein synthesis increases in strict proportion to the increase in number of ribosomes per nucleus (24). The main-

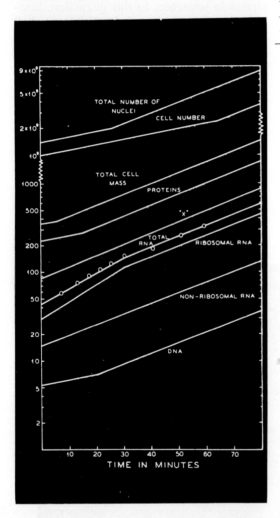

Fig. 6. Curves for individual cell constituents following the transfer of cells grown in glucose salts minimal medium to broth at 0 time. The two top curves show the increase with time of the number of cells and nuclei; the other curves show the increase of various cell constituents. (From Kjeld-gaard. *Biochim. et Biophys. Acta,* 49:64, 1961.)

tenance of the existing rates of DNA synthesis and cell division for a period of time following the shift to a new medium is suggestive of an important role for rate-controlling mechanisms in the bacterial cell.

THE EXPONENTIAL PHASE. With the onset of the exponential or logarithmic phase, during which maximum multiplication is taking place, the cells become smaller. In this phase the cells are dividing at a constant rate determined both by the inherent nature of the organism and the environmental conditions. There is a wide diversity in the rate of growth of the various microorganisms, as evidenced by marked differences in generation times. The coliform organisms are among the most rapidly growing bacteria with a generation time of about 20 minutes, while the tubercle bacillus, even under the very best conditions, requires about 15 hours. These differences among the various genera are probably due to variations both in the rate of penetration of nutrients and to differences in rate of synthesis of new protoplasm. It is not known whether the slow rate is due to a single rate-limiting reaction or whether the slower growth rate may be attributed to a gearing of the entire metabolic pattern to a lower rate. According to Monod (33), however, the maximum growth rate is controlled by a large number of different rate-determining steps rather than by the slowest reaction in the system.

During exponential growth a steady state of metabolism is temporarily achieved and **growth is balanced.** During this period all constituents of the organism are, mathematically speaking, increased by the same factor.

As bacteria are usually grown, cell division occurs at random, and it is impossible to obtain information on the dynamic growth mechanism of individual cells. In order to overcome this difficulty, technics have been introduced for inducing all the individuals of a bacterial culture to undergo division at the same time. Growth under such conditions is **synchronous,** and the population as a whole can now be treated as a single sample in order to obtain information on cellular and nuclear division in bacteria and the effect of cyclical changes on various physiologic properties (Fig. 7) (46).

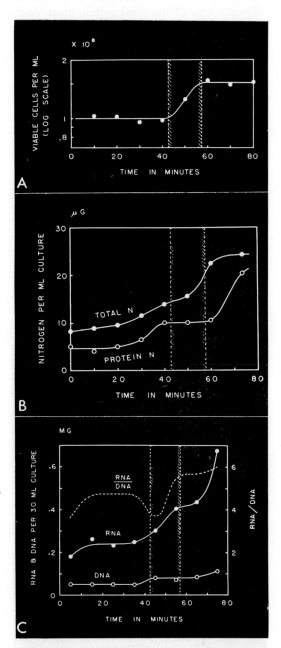

Fig. 7. A, viable growth curve of *Escherichia coli* obtained by synchronous culture. The pair of vertical broken lines indicates the time of the beginning and end of cell division. B, increase in the total and protein nitrogen of synchronized cells. C, synthesis of ribonucleic acid and deoxyribonucleic acid by synchronized cells. (From Maruyama. *J. Bact.,* 72:821, 1956.)

Synchrony may be obtained in a number of ways. One of the most widely used, originally observed by Hotchkiss (20) takes advantage of the effect of an initial low-temperature treatment, followed by shift to a higher one. If the temperature shift is wide enough, the divisions of most of the bacteria tend to become synchronized. Figure 8 shows the effect of holding an exponentially growing culture of pneumococci at 25° C. for 15 minutes before returning to 37° C. Not only was cell division of most of the cells synchronized, but after returning to 37° C., susceptibility of the cells to the transforming effect of pneumococcal DNA changed in a cyclic manner. A second type of temperature-shift system employs a multi-shift system, which gradually phases the culture after two or three cycles and enables it to maintain synchronous division. The effect of temperature changes in synchronizing cell division has been discussed by Maaløe (30), who credits the burst of DNA synthesis observed following a temperature shift from 25 to 37° C. on the excessively large capacity of the DNA-synthesizing system at 37° C. All DNA replication initiated at 25° C. runs to completion very rapidly when the temperature is raised.

In the second method for obtaining synchronous growth, small amounts of a required nutrient are added at intervals to a culture of organisms in a medium nutritionally complete except for the single nutrient to be added. Thus growth by a thymine-requiring mutant of *E. coli* is **unbalanced** in a thymine-deficient medium, since thymine appears essential only for the synthesis of DNA and in its absence many other synthetic processes continue unabated. Cell division of this organism is synchronized by the addition of thymine after a suitable period of thymine starvation (2).

Another method for synchronizing the multiplication of the individuals in a population makes use of the cyclic changes in size which accompany fission. By the use of differential centrifugation or differential filtration a population of bacilli homogeneous in size can be separated (32). A modification of this method has been introduced by Helmstetter and Cummings (17) utilizing an anion exchanger for the continuous removal of new daughter cells from a culture.

THE STATIONARY PHASE. With the ordinary methods of cultivation the accumulation of waste products, exhaustion of nutrients, change in pH, and other obscure factors exert a deleterious effect on the culture, resulting in a decreased growth rate and causing the cells to revert to a "resting type of metabolism." The factors which cause growth cessation are imperfectly understood. The importance of the combined effect of pH and products of metabolism, however, has been shown in studies with *A. aerogenes* and *E. coli* where the toxicity of the accumulated formic acid increases rapidly as the pH decreases to levels reached in unaerated media (9). Other end products of metabolism may also be toxic as an acid environment develops. The exhaustion of essential nutrients from the culture medium is considered by some workers as the major factor limiting bacterial growth (10,

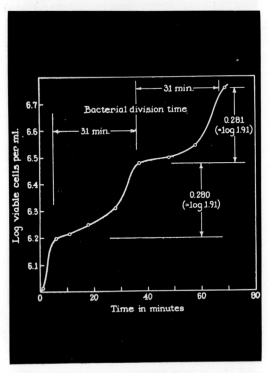

Fig. 8. Synchronization of pneumococcal growth. Curve shows the course of growth at 37° C. immediately following 15 minutes conditioning at 25° C. (From Hotchkiss. *Proc. Nat. Acad. Sc.,* 40: 49, 1954.)

13). With concentrations of glucose and $(NH_4)_2 SO_4$ frequently used in the culture of *E. coli,* chemical analyses for residual carbon, energy, and nitrogen sources in cultures after maximal growth indicate that virtually all of these nutrients are exhausted in a single growth cycle. When such media are enriched with adequate amounts of nutrients, full growth is again possible (48).

During the stationary phase the viable count remains constant at its maximum value. The length of this phase varies with the organism. In some it is very brief; in others it lasts for hours or days. Those bacteria which form spores remain viable for very long periods of time. Eventually the stationary phase is followed by a stage of decreasing population. In some cases the cells in dying cultures become quite elongated, abnormally swollen, or distorted in bizarre forms. The change to an abnormal cell form is the result of unbalanced growth.

In an attempt to prevent the onset of the stationary phase and phase of decline, technics have been introduced for the **continuous culture** of bacteria. These devices provide growing microorganisms with frequent replenishments of nutrient. One type of continuous culture apparatus, the turbidostat, is operated by adding nutrient in re-

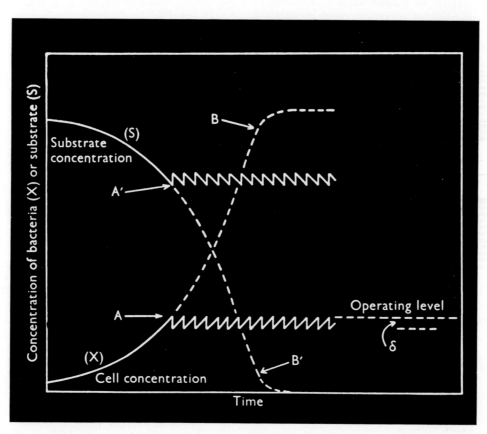

Fig. 9. Operation of a turbidostat inoculated at zero time with a low concentration of bacteria. The inoculum at first grows under batch conditions which if continued would cause the curves for cell and substrate concentrations (X and S) to follow the dotted lines, with X increasing until S had fallen to zero. At point A the cell concentration reaches a level where its turbidity causes operation of the photoelectric relay, and addition of fresh medium. This decreases the cell concentration until the relay ceases operation. The influx of fresh medium causes a simultaneous increase in substrate concentration. As growth continues, X again increases and S decreases until the relay operates again. (From Herbert. *Recent Progress in Microbiology.* Courtesy of Charles C Thomas.)

sponse to increased turbidity of the culture, thus maintaining a uniform density through dilution and wash-out of excess cells (Fig. 9). A second type includes the bactogen or chemostat, in which growth is kept at a constant level by a growth-limiting factor supplied at a fixed rate of input. This type of apparatus thus offers a means of controlling the growth rate, allowing growth to be studied at very low substrate concentrations and over a wide range of rates. Both the chemostat and the turbidostat have the advantage of providing constant environmental conditions for the study of populations over long periods of time. This advantage has permitted a variety of studies such as an accurate measurement of mutation rates in bacteria, evolutionary changes in bacterial populations, and a study of the kinetics of induction of an inducible enzyme at very low concentrations of an inducer (37). The principles and applications of continuous culture systems have been reviewed by Novick (36), Herbert (18), and James (22).

REFERENCES

1. Arnon, D. I. Nature, 184:10, 1959.
2. Barner, H. D., and Cohen. S. S. J. Bact., 72:115, 1956.
3. Barton-Wright, E. C. The Microbiological Assay of the Vitamin B-Complex and Amino Acids, New York and London, Pitman Pub. Corp., 1952.
4. Bauchop, T., and Elsden, S. R. J. Gen. Microbiol., 23:457, 1960.
5. Boatman, E. S., and Douglas, H. C. J. Biophys. Biochem. Cytology, 11:469, 1961.
6. Clark, H. F., and Shepard, C. C. J. Bact., 86:1057, 1963.
7. Clayton, R. K. Bact. Rev., 26:151, 1962.
8. Cohen, G. N., and Monod, J. Bact. Rev., 21:169, 1957.
9. Dagley, S., and others. J. Gen. Microbiol., 8:314, 1953.
10. Ecker, R. E., and Lockhart, W. R. J. Bact., 82:511, 1961.
11. Fildes, P. Proc. Roy. Soc. Med., 28 (Part 1):79, 1934.
12. Francis, J., and others. Biochem. J., 55:596, 1953.
13. Freter, R., and Ozawa, A. J. Bact., 86:904, 1963.
14. Fujimoto, Y. J. Theoretical Biol., 5:171, 1963.
15. Geller, D. M. Chap. 10 in The Bacteria, Vol. II, Gunsalus, I. C., and Stanier, R. Y., eds., New York, Academic Press, 1961.
16. Guirard, B. M., and Snell, E. E. Chap. 2 in The Bacteria, Vol. IV, Gunsalus, I. C., and Stanier, R. Y., eds., New York, Academic Press, 1962.
17. Helmstetter, C. E., and Cummings, D. J. Proc. Nat. Acad. Sci., 50:767, 1963.
18. Herbert, D. Symposium VI in Recent Progress in Microbiology, Tunevall, G., ed., Springfield, Ill., Charles C Thomas, 1959, p. 381.
19. Hesseltine, C. W., and others. Mycologia, 45:7, 1953.
20. Hotchkiss, R. D. Proc. Nat. Acad. Sc. U.S., 40:49, 1954.
21. Hutner, S. H., and Holz, G. G. Ann. Rev. Microbiol., 16:189, 1962.
22. James, T. W. Ann. Rev. Microbiol., 15:27, 1961.
23. Kepes, A., and Cohen, G. N. Chap. 5 in The Bacteria, Vol. IV, Gunsalus, I. C., and Stanier, R. Y., eds., New York, Academic Press, 1962.
24. Kjeldgaard, N. O. Biochim. et Biophys. Acta, 49:64, 1961.
25. ——— and Kurland, C. C. J. Mol. Biology, 6:341, 1963.
26. Kuempel, P. L., and Pardee, A. B. J. Cell. Comp. Phys. Supp. 1, 62:15, 1963.
27. Lamanna, C., and Mallette, M. F. Basic Bacteriology, 2nd ed., Baltimore, The Williams & Wilkins Co., 1959, p. 330.
28. Lichstein, H. C. Bact. Rev., 23:261, 1959.
29. Lwoff, A., and others. Cold Spring Harbor Symposia on Quantitative Biology, 11:139, 1946.
30. Maaløe, O. Chap. 1 in The Bacteria, Vol. IV, Gunsalus, I. C., and Stanier, R. Y., eds., New York, Academic Press, 1962.
31. MacLeod, R. A., and Snell, E. E. Ann. New York Acad. Sci., 52:1249, 1950.
32. Maruyama, Y. J. Bact., 72:821, 1956.
33. Monod, J. Ann. Rev. Microbiol., 3:371, 1949.
34. Moulder, J. W., and Woods, D. D. J. Gen. Microbiol., 9:4, 1953.
35. Neilands, J. B. Bact. Rev., 21:101, 1957.
36. Novick, A. Ann. Rev. Microbiol., 9:97, 1955.
37. ——— Symposium VI in Recent Progress in Microbiology, Tunevall, G., ed., Springfield, Ill., Charles C Thomas, 1959, p. 403.
38. Ormerod, J. G., and Gest, H. Bact. Rev., 26:51, 1962.
39. Peck, H. D., Jr. Bact. Rev., 26:67, 1962.
40. Pollock, M. R. In Proc. Intern. Symp. on Enzyme Chemistry, Tokyo and Kyoto, 1957, Ichihara, K., ed., New York, Academic Press, 1958, p. 369.
41. ——— Chap. 4 in The Bacteria, Vol. IV, Gunsalus, I. C., and Stanier, R. Y., eds., New York, Academic Press, 1962.
42. Powell, E. O., and Errington, F. P. J. Gen. Microbiol., 31:315, 1963.
43. Rabinowitz, J. C., and Snell, E. E. Arch. Biochem. Biophys., 33:472, 1951.
44. Reed, L. J. Vitamins and Hormones, 20:1, 1962.
45. Schachman, H. K., and others. Arch. Biochem. and Biophys., 38:245, 1952.
46. Scherbaum, O. H. Ann. Rev. Microbiol., 14:283, 1960.
47. Senez, J. C. Bact. Rev., 26:95, 1962.
48. Sinclair, N. A., and Stokes, J. L. J. Bact., 83:1147, 1962.

49. Sokatch, J. T., and Gunsalus, I. C. J. Bact., 73:452, 1957.
50. Stanier, R. Y., and others. Proc. Nat. Acad. Sci. U.S., 45:1246, 1959.
51. ———— Bact. Rev., 25:1, 1961.
52. Starkey, R. L. Bact. Rev., 26:142, 1962.
53. Umbreit, W., and Molitor, H., ed. Symposium XI, Vitamin Metabolism, Intern. Congr. Biochem. 4th Congr., Vienna, 1958, New York, Pergamon Press, 1960.
54. Van Niel, C. B. Bacterial Photosyntheses, Chap. 75 in The Enzymes, Sumner, J. B., and Myrback, K., eds., Vol. II, Pt. 2, New York, Academic Press, Inc., 1952, p. 1074.
55. ———— Ann. Rev. Microbiol., 8:105, 1954.
56. Vishniac, W., and Trudinger, P. A. Bact. Rev., 26:168, 1962.
57. Wood, H. G., and Stjernholm, R. L. Chap. 2 in The Bacteria, Vol. III, Gunsalus, I. C., and Stanier, R. Y., eds., New York, Academic Press, 1962.
58. Wyatt, H. V. Exptl. Cell Research, 30:56, 1963.

7

Metabolism of Bacteria

Studies of the gross chemical constitution of the bacterial cell show us the main building blocks of which the organism is made, but they fail to show the dynamic state of the organism's existence. The life of the bacterial cell is not a static situation. For the maintenance of life most of the components of the cell must be continually rebuilt, and in order for growth to occur new cellular material must be synthesized. Energy derived from the breakdown of certain foodstuffs must be properly channelled in order to drive these endergonic reactions. All of these changes which take place following the entry of a nutrient into a living organism are encompassed in the term **metabolism.** The whole process of bacterial metabolism consists of a series of overlapping and interdependent enzymic reactions. Because of this close interrelationship, in order to obtain a complete understanding of the dynamics of the processes which govern the vital activities of a cell, it is necessary to consider the metabolism of any one organism as a whole. In the following discussion emphasis is placed upon principles and main metabolic pathways rather than upon the details which have been covered in a number of excellent texts and reviews (23, 24, 41, 61, 76, 81).

Metabolism may be conveniently divided into two parts: **anabolism,** or assimilation, which includes synthetic processes; and **catabolism,** or dissimilation, describing degradative processes. Assimilation cannot occur unless accompanied by an amount of dissimilation adequate to supply the necessary energy. Syntheses thus are coupled to the energy-yielding reactions. Catabolic processes, however, apparently can occur without concurrent synthesis, as evidenced by a high rate of respiration by cells when suspended in a medium inadequate to allow growth but containing a large amount of glucose which fulfills their energy requirement.

When one examines the metabolic capabilities of bacteria, one is impressed not only with the diversity of physiologic reactions but also with the numerous fundamental metabolic systems which are essentially similar in bacteria and the higher forms of life. One thus finds in the study of bacterial metabolism evidence of differentiation as well as the basic essentials of life. All of these metabolic activities are governed by a complex system of enzymes which catalyze specific reactions.

The Nature of Enzymes. Enzymes are proteins that catalyze chemical reactions in living systems. An understanding of the mechanism whereby enzymes exert their catalytic action depends on an understanding of the details of protein structure. Enzymes are susceptible to changes in hydrogen ion concentration, temperature, and various chemical and physical agents. They are produced only by living cells and in small concentrations act as catalysts in specific reactions which normally could not proceed under biologic conditions in their absence.

The substance which is acted upon by an enzyme is known as the **substrate,** for which most enzymes usually exhibit a marked specificity. The activity of the enzyme protein is dependent upon the presence of active catalytic centers with which the substrate combines. Anything that destroys the specific configuration at these sites destroys the catalytic activity of the enzyme.

The breakdown or synthesis of a compound usually proceeds through a chain of reactions in which each step is catalyzed by a specific enzyme. If one of these enzymes is missing, the chain of reactions will stop at the substrate whose enzyme is not present.

Most enzymic-controlled reactions are of a reversible nature; i.e., the same enzymes catalyze both the dissimilation and the synthesis of compounds. In complex biochemical systems, however, such as the bacterial cell, enzyme-catalyzed reactions do not proceed alone. The product of one reaction is often the substrate in another chemical reaction and is thus removed. Practically, therefore, many enzyme-catalyzed reactions, although theoretically reversible, are irreversible because the conditions permit it to go only in one direction.

Many enzymes, especially those concerned in respiratory processes, are composed of two fractions. One part, the **apoenzyme,** is protein in nature and is responsible for substrate specificity; the other part is a smaller molecule, nonprotein in nature and referred to as the **prosthetic group.** The bond between the prosthetic group and the protein carrier varies in strength. In some cases the union is firm, whereas in others it is loose enough to permit the prosthetic group to move from one protein carrier to the other. Several of the prosthetic groups in essential enzyme systems are members of the B-complex group of vitamins. Many enzymes also require metal ions as cofactors for activity.

Localization of Enzymes in Bacteria (36, 47, 67).   Since the enzymatic capabilities of bacterial protoplasts prepared by treatment with lysozyme parallel those of intact cells of the same species, the cell wall is believed to contribute little more than mechanical strength to the bacterial cell.

When protoplasts are fractionated by differential centrifugation, three components are usually obtained: (1) membrane fragments sufficiently large to permit detection with the light microscope, which sediment at moderately low centrifugal force; (2) submicroscopic particles which require a centrifugal force of approximately 100,000 g for one hour; and (3) the soluble fraction which remains in the supernatant after removal of the submicroscopic particles. The membrane fragments resemble mammalian mitochondria in their range of enzymic activity. The cytochromes, reduced nicotinamide adenine dinucleotide (NADH) oxidase, succinic dehydrogenase, and malic dehydrogenase are among the enzymes detected in the membrane fraction of gram-positive species (94). The submicroscopic particles consist of ribonucleoprotein and in purified preparations are devoid of oxidative enzymes (11). These RNA granules, or ribosomes, appear to be similar in function to the microsomes from plant and animal tissues and to be the site of protein synthesis in the cell. Among the enzymes which have been identified with the soluble fraction are catalase, acid phosphatase, hexokinase, and several dehydrogenases.

BIOLOGIC OXIDATION

In the heterotrophic organisms energy is obtained by the oxidation of a wide variety of organic compounds; in the autotrophic bacteria it is derived from the oxidation of simple inorganic substances. Nowhere in biology does one find the variety of oxidoreduction reactions possessed by the bacteria. The variety of compounds which serve as energy and carbon sources for microorganisms is almost limitless.

In biologic oxidations as well as in chemical ones, the essential characteristic is the removal of electrons from the substance being oxidized, whether or not there is an accompanying addition of oxygen or the loss of hydrogen. Oxidation and reduction are reversibly linked, and no oxidation can be conceived without an accompanying reduction. Since the majority of biologic oxidations involve a **dehydrogenation,** or removal of hydrogen from an organic compound, biologic oxidations may be expressed more simply in terms of the transfer of hydrogen if we remember that such a transfer actually involves a loss of electrons. Biologic oxidations may be represented in a general way by the reaction

$$AH_2 + B \rightleftharpoons A \text{ (oxidized)} + BH_2 \text{ (reduced)}$$

Here the substrate AH_2 is oxidized to A, and the substance B acts as the hydrogen acceptor and is reduced to BH_2. The oxidation is catalyzed by an enzyme specific for both substrate and hydrogen acceptor. The hydrogen acceptors may be intermediate products from the breakdown of carbohydrate or protein—or, in certain instances, of molecular oxygen itself.

In the transfer of hydrogen from the substrate to a final hydrogen acceptor, reducing equivalents are removed, two at a time, and passed via a graded series of reversible oxidation-reduction systems. It is thus a chain reaction such that the derivatives en route are alternately reduced and oxidized. The occurrence of several reversible oxidation-reduction reactions between the initial substrate and final oxidant makes for a smoother release of energy, providing a system whereby oxidations involving large amounts of energy resulting from the complete oxidation of a carbohydrate are split up into several integrated partial reactions, and the energy is stored or liberated in smaller packets.

The relative tendency for two oxidation-reduction systems to act either in releasing or accepting electrons depends upon their affinity for electrons. This is termed the **oxidation-reduction potential,** which is a measure of the ability of the system to accept or donate electrons reversibly with reference to the standard hydrogen electrode. In biologic systems it is customary to refer to the normal potential at a given pH by the symbol E_0'. A knowledge of the potential of any two oxidation-reduction systems enables one to predict the direction of interaction. A system with a more positive normal oxidation-reduction potential than another system has a greater tendency to take up electrons; i.e., it is a stronger oxidizing agent. Also associated with this difference in potential is the free-energy change involving the oxidized form and the reduced form of the two systems.

Enzymes in Oxidation-Reduction Reactions. In the bacterial cell there are a number of electron transfer systems that function as carriers between two different oxidation-reduction systems. The most important of these carrier systems are (1) the **pyridine nucleotides,** (2) the **flavin nucleotides,** and (3) the **cytochromes.** Table 1 shows the relationship of the potentials of these carriers in respect to each other and their relationship to the potentials of the oxygen and hydrogen electrodes. An examination of these potentials shows that the reduced form of the pyridine nucleotides could be easily oxidized by the oxidized form of the flavin nucleotides, and the resulting reduced flavin enzymes could then be oxidized by the oxidized form of cytochrome c.

Table 1. Oxidation-Reduction Potentials
(pH 7, 30° C.)
(Fruton & Simmonds)

	E_0', VOLTS
Oxygen electrode	+0.81
Cytochrome c	+0.26
Flavin nucleotides	−0.22
Pyridine nucleotides	−0.32
Hydrogen electrode	−0.42

DEHYDROGENASES. The dehydrogenases constitute a group of enzymes which catalyze bimolecular oxidation-reduction reactions between a metabolite system and the pyridine nucleotide carrier system. Many of the pyridine-dependent dehydrogenases are specific for nicotinamide adenine dinucleotide (NAD); others are specific for the nicotinamide adenine dinucleotide phosphate (NADP) system. The structure of NAD is

$$\text{nicotinamide}^+\text{—ribose—}\overset{\overset{\displaystyle O^-}{|}}{\underset{\underset{\displaystyle O}{\|}}{P}}\text{—O—}\overset{\overset{\displaystyle OH}{|}}{\underset{\underset{\displaystyle O}{\|}}{P}}\text{—ribose—adenine}$$

NADP differs from this only in having an additional phosphate group. The reactive part of the molecule is the nicotinamide fraction, which reversibly undergoes oxidation and reduction. The bulk of hydrogen transport in main-line respiration passes through the pyridine nucleotides. Among the microbial dehydrogenases that require the pyridine nucleotide system are yeast alcohol dehydrogenase, glucose-6-phosphate dehydrogenase, and glutamic dehydrogenase. There is some evidence that the two forms of the pyridine nucleotide have different functions (35).

FLAVOPROTEINS. Riboflavin is the functional group of the catalytic flavoproteins and participates in hydrogen transport either as flavin mononucleotide (FMN) or flavin adenine dinucleotide (FAD). Many bacterial flavoproteins are now known. Some, such as the *d*-amino acid oxidase and glucose oxidase, mediate rapid electron transfer between a metabolite and molecular oxygen without the apparent participation of any other electron carrier. A second group of flavoproteins catalyzes electron transfer between reduced NAD or NADP and cytochrome c and appear to require the presence of a metal ion for electron transfer to these oxidants. A third group (e.g., succinic dehydrogenase) catalyzes the oxidation of metabolites by various electron acceptors with the participation of metal ions in the transfer. Flavoproteins have also been identified as participants in the metabolism of fatty acids and in bacterial luminescence.

THE CYTOCHROMES (73). There is little doubt that the respiration of most aerobic organisms proceeds via a cytochrome system. The cytochromes are iron-porphyrin enzymes which are widely distributed in nature in both animals and plants. All of the obligately aerobic bacteria studied have relatively high concentrations of the cytochromes, but a functional role for these has not been unequivocally demonstrated in the obligately anaerobic clostridia which have no oxidative metabolism as well as in some of the facultative anaerobes, such as streptococci and pneumococci (58).

The cytochromes consist of a number of components, each of which is readily able to undergo oxidation-reduction reactions. They function in aerobic oxidations by forming part of a chain of enzymes that transport hydrogen or electrons from the substrate being oxidized to molecular oxygen. Whereas in mammalian systems the sequence of events proceeds via cytochrome b, cytochrome c_1, cytochrome c, cytochrome a, and cytochrome a_3, this scheme is less defined in microorganisms. Numerous cytochromes of the a, b, and c types as well as the newly described cytochrome o have been described in various bacterial species. Although these bacterial cytochromes appear to function in the respiratory chain, they differ from mammalian cytochromes in their absorption spectra, physical and chemical properties, and specificity. Cytochrome-containing bacteria possess several different pigments, but there is apparently no specific combination of types required for hydrogen transport. Also, in bacteria several cytochromes can function as terminal **oxidases.** Some bacteria have only one oxidase; others may have two or three. These oxidases then react with oxygen. The antibiotic antimycin A does not inhibit the bacterial respiratory chain, although this has been found to be the site at which inhibition ocurs in mammalian systems.

Catalase and **peroxidase** are iron-porphyrin-containing enzymes that catalyze reactions involving hydrogen peroxide. Organisms which possess the enzyme catalase decompose the hydrogen peroxide formed as an end-product of certain bacterial oxidations:

$$2\ H_2O_2 \xrightarrow{\text{catalase}} 2\ H_2O + O_2$$

This substance, if allowed to accumulate, is highly toxic. The enzyme peroxidase catalyzes the oxidation of organic compounds by using hydrogen peroxide as the hydrogen acceptor:

$$A\ H_2 + H_2O_2 \xrightarrow{\text{peroxidase}} A + 2\ H_2O$$

At low peroxide concentrations, catalase also can catalyze the oxidation of a number of substrates such as formate, nitrite, and several alcohols. In general, catalase activity has been demonstrated in most cytochrome-containing aerobes and facultative anaerobes, while it is absent in the anaerobes and lactic acid bacteria.

Electron-transport Systems (15). The division of bacterial species into obligate aerobes, facultative anaerobes, and obligate anaerobes is made on the basis of physiologic differences among the organisms. Figure 1 presents a tentative scheme of some of the pathways employed by various microorganisms in electron transport.

In the obligate aerobe energy is obtained by the complete oxidation of the substrate via the pyridine nucleotides, flavoproteins, and cytochromes, with oxygen serving as the final electron acceptor. In the obligate anaerobe, however, the ultimate hydrogen acceptor is another substrate. The pathway utilized by a facultative anaerobe varies with the environmental conditions as well as with the organism itself in respect to its cytochrome content. The great diversity of met-

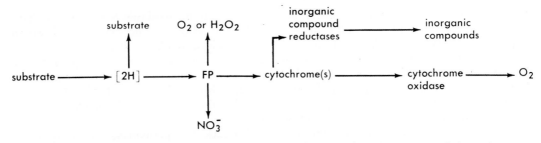

Fig. 1. Electron transport pathways. Scheme shows various systems used by micro-organisms. [2H] may represent reducing equivalents, reduced pyridine nucleotides, or reduced flavoprotein, depending upon the pathway under consideration. (Adapted from Dolin. *The Bacteria,* ed. by Gunsalus and Stanier. Academic Press.)

abolic types among bacteria thus makes for great diversity in the composition of the electron transport chain.

Transfer of Energy. In order for the energy requirements of the cell to be fulfilled, energy released in the oxido-reductive reactions must be conserved in a biologically usable form. To accomplish this, there is in the living cell a coupling between oxidation and energy-trapping reactions. For transfer of chemical bond energy to occur, the reactions must have a common reactant. The most important single common reactant in a large number of reactions is the high-energy phosphorus compound adenosine tri-phosphate (ATP):

$$\text{adenine—ribose—}\overset{\overset{O}{\parallel}}{\underset{\underset{OH}{|}}{P}}\text{—O}\sim\overset{\overset{O}{\parallel}}{\underset{\underset{OH}{|}}{P}}\text{—O}\sim\overset{\overset{O}{\parallel}}{\underset{\underset{OH}{|}}{P}}\text{—OH}$$

When phosphoric acid is linked to nitrogen, to a carboxyl group, or to another phosphate group, the energy yield upon hydrolysis is from 12,000 to 16,000 calories, as compared with the 3,000 liberated by the rupture of a simple ester bond. Such phosphate-containing linkages are referred to as energy-rich phosphate bonds and are an important source of available energy for syntheses and other energy-requiring processes. ATP is produced by substrate-level phosphorylation, in which inorganic phosphate is added to a substance that is being oxidized in an enzymatic reaction. In addition, oxidative phosphorylations occur in respiration in conjunction with the electron transport system. The yield of $\sim$ P provided by an oxido-reduction depends upon the voltage span

between substrate and final hydrogen acceptor.

The metachromatic or volutin granules commonly seen in such organisms as *A. aerogenes, C. diphtheriae,* and *Mycobacterium* have been identified as high-molecular-weight polyphosphates. They appear to be storage forms for high-energy phosphate produced by oxidative phosphorylation.

CARBOHYDRATE METABOLISM

Many different types of carbohydrates may be attacked by bacteria ranging from the simple 3-carbon compounds to the more complex polysaccharides such as starch and cellulose. These substances are the chief sources of energy for both aerobic and anaerobic life, and the numerous products formed vary from species to species.

The Cleavage of Glycosidic Bonds (65). Polysaccharides are formed through the condensation of small molecules of the hexose type to form chains of their constituent units. These units are joined together by glycosidic bonds. Cleavage of these linkages must be effected in order to make the monosaccharides available for metabolic use. In microorganisms there are two general mechanisms for breaking these glycosidic bonds: (1)· **hydrolysis** by specific enzymes, the **glycosidases** (carbohydrases), and (2) **phosphorolysis** catalyzed by enzymes known as **phosphorylases.** The glycosidases are widespread among the bacteria and include enzymes that catalyze the hydrolysis of glycosidic bonds in simple glycosides such as lactose and sucrose as well as the bonds of the more complex polysaccharides. The best-known of the enzymes attacking the poly-saccharides are the **amylases,** which act on starch. In most bacteria studied the break-down of starch, which consists essentially of glucose joined by 1-4 linkages, has been shown to be due to two enzymes. An amylase first converts the starch to maltose, which is then broken down to glucose by the enzyme maltase (95).

Cellulose, which also consists of glucose units, is more resistant to hydrolytic attack than is starch, but a number of microorgan-isms, especially the anaerobic organisms found in the soil and in the intestinal tract of herbivorous animals, have the ability to de-compose it. Cellulose is hydrolyzed in a non-specific manner until only glucose is left. The decomposition is catalyzed, at least in certain microorganisms, by two enzymes: cellulase, which breaks it down to cellobiose, and cellobiase, which attacks cellobiose with glucose production.

Whereas reactions involving the hydroly-sis of complex sugars are irreversible in na-ture and are concerned only with their breakdown, phosphorolysis mechanisms are reversible and are important in the synthesis of disaccharides and polysaccharides.

Anaerobic Breakdown of Carbohydrates (97). Glucose occupies an important posi-tion in the metabolism of most biologic forms, and its anaerobic dissimilation pro-vides a metabolic pathway common to most forms of life. Although a wide variety of substrates is fermented by microorganisms, the breakdown is effected by relatively few distinct pathways. The ability to ferment a sugar or related compound of different con-figuration from glucose is the result of the organism's ability to convert the substrate to intermediates common to the pathways for glucose fermentation.

The terms **glycolysis** and **fermentation** have been applied to the anaerobic or in-complete decomposition of carbohydrate to the level of lactic acid. The dissimilation of carbohydrate does not occur in a single step but involves a complicated series of catalyzed interactions including oxidoreductions and phosphorylations.

THE EMBDEN-MEYERHOF-PARNAS GLY-COLYTIC SCHEME. The basic concepts of glycolysis are incorporated in the Embden-Meyerhof-Parnas scheme, which provides the major pathway for glucose breakdown in many organisms. NAD and ATP play an important role in this system, in which all the intermediates are phosphorylated. A mechanism is thus provided for the trapping of energy originally present in the substrate so that it is available in usable form for cel-lular reactions requiring energy. Figure 2 shows the reactions involved in this system.

The ultimate fate of the key metabolite pyruvate depends upon the conditions pre-vailing and the nature of the organism. The final product in certain organisms is either alcohol or lactic acid; in others the lactic acid is further metabolized anaerobically to such products as butyric acid, butyl alcohol, acetone, and propionic acid; while in the aerobic species the substrate is broken down completely to carbon dioxide and water (Fig. 3).

ALTERNATE PATHWAYS. Whereas the Embden-Meyerhof system is believed to be the major pathway in many microorganisms, as well as in animal and plant tissues, it does not represent the only available pathway for carbohydrate metabolism. The pentose phos-phate pathway or "hexose-monophosphate shunt" is known to function in the fermenta-tion of hexoses, pentoses, and several other carbohydrates in a number of microorgan-isms (29). In this route glucose-6-phosphate is oxidized to 6-phosphogluconic acid, which is in turn converted to pentose phosphates. The scheme provides one important means for the metabolism of the pentoses and would permit an entrance of the pentoses into the Embden-Meyerhof pathway for those organ-isms that utilize both systems. The wide diversity of fermentation types probably re-flects the use, especially by the facultative aerobic organisms, of mechanisms of carbo-hydrate dissimilation other than the Embden-Meyerhof scheme.

Fate of Pyruvate under Anaerobic Con-ditions. Bacteria differ markedly from ani-mal tissues in the manner in which they dis-pose of the pyruvic acid formed as an inter-mediate in the breakdown of carbohydrate. In mammalian physiology the main course of respiration is such that substrates are oxidized down to CO_2 and H_2O, oxygen be-ing the ultimate hydrogen acceptor. Among

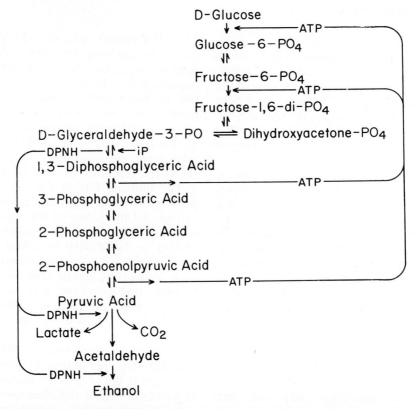

Fig. 2. Embden-Meyerhof-Parnas glycolytic scheme.

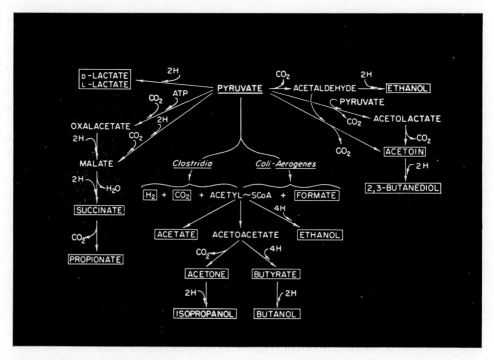

Fig. 3. Fermentation product formation from pyruvate. (From Wood. *The Bacteria,* ed. by Gunsalus and Stanier. Academic Press.)

the bacteria, however, incomplete oxidation is the rule rather than the exception, and the products of fermentation may accumulate to a remarkable degree.

The chief metabolic value of the anaerobic breakdown of carbohydrate beyond the pyruvic acid stage lies in the extra energy liberated in the process. Bacterial fermentations are of practical importance because they produce products of industrial value, and because species differences in fermentation patterns are of great benefit in identifying and differentiating bacteria.

Among the major fermentation patterns are the alcoholic, homolactic, heterolactic, butyl-butyric, propionic, and formic.

1. Alcoholic fermentation. The oldest known type of fermentation is the production of ethanol from glucose. In yeasts, which carry out an almost pure alcoholic fermentation, the alcohol arises from the decarboxylation of pyruvic acid by the enzyme carboxylase, with the formation of acetaldehyde and carbon dioxide. The acetaldehyde is then reduced by alcohol dehydrogenase to ethyl alcohol. Although some alcohol is produced by a number of bacteria, it is produced via another pathway and is the major end product in only a relatively few species (14).

2. Homolactic fermentation. All members of the genus *Streptococcus* and many lactobacilli and other microorganisms ferment glucose predominantly to lactic acid with no more than a trace accumulation of other products. In the dissimilation of glucose by the homofermenters, pyruvate is reduced to lactic acid by the enzyme **lactic dehydrogenase** with reduced NAD acting as the hydrogen donor.

Although the same enzyme, lactic dehydrogenase, is involved in the production of lactic acid by both muscle tissue and certain bacteria, a striking difference exists. In muscle tissue this fermentation normally proceeds with the accumulation of very little lactic acid, for as rapidly as it is formed it is oxidized to carbon dioxide and water while the rest is reconverted into glycogen. In mammalian physiology it is a rule that the constancy of the internal milieu must be maintained within narrow limits; consequently, homeostatic mechanisms tend to prevent the accumulation of the products of intermediary metabolism. Furthermore, the main course of respiration is such that substrates are oxidized down to carbon dioxide and water, oxygen being the ultimate hydrogen acceptor. The last requirement is so rigorous that death ensues almost immediately in the absence of oxygen. Among the bacteria, however, incomplete oxidation is the rule rather than the exception and the products of fermentation may accumulate to a remarkable degree.

3. Heterolactic fermentation. In addition to the production of lactic acid, some lactobacilli and organisms in the genus *Leuconostoc* ferment glucose with the accumulation of additional products such as ethanol, acetic acid, glycerol, and carbon dioxide. Recent evidence indicates that the heterolactic fermentation differs fundamentally from the homolactic type and that the Embden-Meyerhof pathway does not function in heterolactic fermentation. Lactic acid and alcohol arise via an alternate route, the pentose phosphate pathway in which the pentose phosphate is split into 3- and 2-carbon units, that are converted to lactate and ethanol, respectively.

4. Butyl-butyric acid fermentations. Among the characteristic products of carbohydrate fermentation of organisms in the genus *Clostridium* are butyric acid and organic solvents such as n-butanol and acetone. The key reaction in this type of fermentation is the formation of acetoacetate, catalyzed by acetyl $\sim$ Co A derived from pyruvate or acetate.

5. Propionic acid fermentation. Propionic acid bacteria are closely related to the lactobacilli and get their name from their characteristic production of propionic acid from glucose. The propionic acid appears to be formed by the decarboxylation of succinate, derived from oxalacetate following carbon dioxide fixation with pyruvate. These bacteria also form acetic and succinic acids as typical fermentation end products.

6. Formic acid fermentation. This type of fermentation is often referred to as the mixed acid fermentation, characteristic of the *Enterobacteriaceae* and certain other facultative organisms. Formic acid, acetic acid, lactic acid, succinic acid, ethanol, hydrogen, and carbon dioxide are among the end products. Organisms displaying this type of fermentation can be divided into two groups: those organisms resembling *E. coli* in that they produce volatile acids but no butanediol and a second group which produces butanediol as a major end product. Other variations within the group reflect fundamental differences in the genotype and provide a basis for taxonomic differentiation.

The formic acid arises from a phosphorolytic cleavage of pyruvate to acetyl coenzyme A and formate. In these organisms the acetyl coenzyme A generated is the source of acetate and ethanol. The formate is broken down in *E. coli* to carbon dioxide and hydrogen by the hydrogenlyase enzyme system. In organisms lacking this lyase, such as *Shigella* and *S. typhosa,* the formate accumulates, and no gas is produced in the fermentation of glucose.

Several groups of organisms, including the *Aerobacter, Bacillus,* and *Serratia,* produce butanediol in fermentations which are otherwise of the mixed acid type. Pyruvate is the precursor of acetoin (acetylmethylcarbinol), two molecules being decarboxylated in its conversion to one molecule of the neutral acetoin. 2,3-Butanediol($CH_3CHOHCHOH-CH_3$) is then produced by the reduction of acetoin ($CH_3COCHOHCH_3$). This reduction is slowly reversible in air and, when made strongly alkaline, is the basis for the Voges-Proskauer reaction, a test for acetoin. Also, since so much pyruvic acid is converted to acetoin, there is less of it to be converted into acetic acid. Because of this reduced acid production, there is no color change of the methyl red indicator by *Aerobacter,* while *E. coli* turns it red.

Aerobic Breakdown of Carbohydrates (39). The pathways of aerobic dissimilation are very complex, and many problems concerning terminal respiration in microorganisms still exist. Pyruvate and acetate may be formed under aerobic conditions and further metabolized to carbon dioxide and water. Probably the most important respiratory mechanism for terminal oxidation is the tricarboxylic acid cycle of Krebs, which, together with the known reactions of glycolysis, can account for the complete oxidation of glucose. This cycle is unique in that it provides the cell not only with an energy source

but also with carbon skeletons for the synthesis of cellular material.

Figure 4 shows the reactions in this cyclic system and the major intermediates. Pyruvate is introduced into the system by being converted to acetyl-coenzyme A, which under the influence of the "condensing enzyme" undergoes condensation with oxaloacetic acid to yield citric acid. This 6-carbon citric acid molecule is then decarboxylated and oxidized to regenerate the 4-carbon oxaloacetic acid molecule. The pyruvic acid is completely oxidized. Anything capable of generating acetyl-Co A can be oxidized via the cycle; also, important synthetic mechanisms utilize reactants of the cycle to provide a common meeting ground for carbohydrate, fat, and protein metabolism. It is of great significance that a number of the enzymes of the citric acid cycle are associated in cytoplasmic particles with the enzymes of the respiratory chain of electron transfer from reduced pyridine nucleotides to oxygen.

Although enzymes of the citric acid cycle have been demonstrated in a number of microorganisms, and it is probable that the cycle serves as a major pathway in some bacteria, alternate pathways are known in several instances to be of greater significance than the citric acid cycle (37, 96). It has been suggested that in many microorganisms the principal function of the citric acid cycle may be related to the synthesis of carbon skeletons rather than to the supply of energy (40, 63). Many gaps are still present in our knowledge of oxidative cyclic mechanisms and the metabolic sequences within the whole cell.

Oxidative Assimilation and the Synthesis of Glycosidic Bonds. In a culture of growing bacteria, all of the carbohydrate which disappears from the medium is not completely oxidized, but some is converted into bacterial carbohydrate by the process of oxidative assimilation. The energy derived from the oxidation of a portion of the substrate is used for converting the remainder into carbohydrate, in reactions catalyzed by phosphorylases.

In reactions of this type glucose-1-phosphate is formed which then reacts with another monosaccharide to form the initial glycosidic linkage. Once this bond is formed,

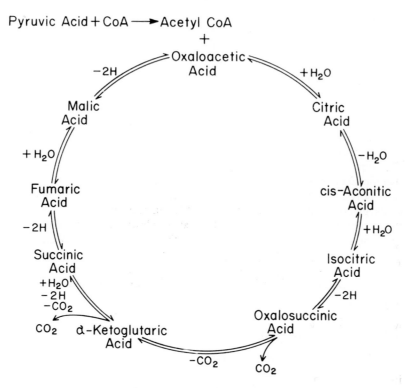

Fig. 4. The citric acid cycle.

other complex sugars can be produced in reactions catalyzed by the **transglycosidases,** enzymes that catalyze the replacement of one component of a glycosidic bond by another. Energy obtained from ATP is necessary to make the initial glycosidic bond. An example of polysaccharide formation by this method is the synthesis in *Leuconostoc mesenteroides* of dextran from sucrose. In this synthesis the fructose units of sucrose are replaced by glucose units in a series of transglucosidation reactions.

$$\text{glucose-1-PO}_4 + \text{fructose} \xrightleftharpoons{\text{phosphorylase}} \text{sucrose} + \text{H}_3\text{PO}_4$$

$$n\text{-sucrose} \xrightleftharpoons{\text{transglucosidase}} n\text{-fructose} + (\text{glucose})_n$$

Much work has been devoted to the dextrans because of their use in the production of a plasma-volume expander (57).

Although the direct synthesis of polysaccharides and other complex carbohydrates from glucose phosphate is the simplest example of reaction mechanisms by which these substances are made, a second mechanism is also of great physiologic importance (27). This type of transglycosidation employs uridine diphosphate (UDP) sugars as glycosyl donors in the reaction. Sucrose can thus be formed from uridine diphosphate glucose (UDPG) and *d*-fructose:

$$\text{UDPG} + d\text{-fructose} \rightleftharpoons \text{sucrose} + \text{UDP}$$

During recent years considerable evidence has accumulated which emphasizes the importance of the nucleoside diphosphoglycosyl compounds in many monosaccharide interconversions (77) and in the synthesis of oligosaccharides and polysaccharides (72). Much attention has been centered on the capsular material of the pneumococcus, which is responsible for the virulence and type specificity of the many pneumococcal types. In view of the ability of these various types to utilize a wide selection of carbohydrates as a source of carbon, the pathways for sugar interconversions are of special interest in studies on the biosynthesis of polysaccharides. When various capsulated pneumococcal types are grown to the resting phase, considerable amounts of nucleoside diphosphoglycosyl compounds accumulate when growth ceases, due to exhaustion of energy sources (71). Such observations indicate the presence in pneumococci of the requisite enzymic pathways for the synthesis of nucleoside diphosphate compounds of many of the monosaccharide units present in their capsular polysaccharides. These nucleosides act as glycosyl precursors for the synthesis of capsular polysaccharides in the pneumococcus (50). Nucleotide derivatives are also of importance in the synthesis of **teichoic acids,** the phosphate polymers originally isolated from the walls of a number of bacteria (4, 56).

LIPID METABOLISM

Our knowledge of how microorganisms degrade and synthesize lipids is incomplete. It is believed, however, that here as well as in other phases of bacterial metabolism there are close similarities to the metabolic pathways in higher forms of life. The β-oxidative reactions and consequent breaking of the long carbon chain by removal of successive 2-carbon fragments, have been demonstrated in various bacteria (78). This mechanism has been assumed to be a general one, operative in the bacterial degradation of fatty acids. The initial reaction involves activation of the fatty acid by combination with coenzyme A. The resultant fatty acyl-Co A is then subjected to a sequence of reactions, the over-all effect of which is to shorten the carbon skeleton by two carbon atoms, producing as one product acetyl-Co A and as the other acyl-Co A, which is susceptible to a second attack. Repetition of this process will result ultimately in the complete oxidation of a long-chain fatty acid to yield acetyl-Co A. Evidence for the formation of acetyl-Co A from the oxidation of fatty acids focuses attention again on the important metabolic role of substances closely related to acetic acid.

Recent studies on the synthesis of lipids in animal tissues and microorganisms have revealed the complexity of the reactions involved and have shown that it involves more than a mere reversal of the β-oxidation system (42, 90, 91). The chief function of the β-oxidation system in lipid synthesis is probably that of elongating existing fatty acids, while another mechanism is operative in initiating fatty acid synthesis.

Much interest has centered on the finding that the fixation of carbon dioxide is a key reaction in the synthesis of fatty acids in both animal tissues and microorganisms. In this reaction malonyl-Co A is formed by the carboxylation of acetyl-Co A in the presence of the enzyme acetyl coenzyme A carboxylase and ATP. Malonyl-Co A is then condensed with itself, acetyl-Co A, or propionyl-Co A to form long-chain fatty acids (1). One of the most pertinent findings in this area is that the B-complex vitamin biotin is the prosthetic group of the acetyl-Co A carboxylase and is tightly bound to the enzyme protein (88, 89).

NITROGEN METABOLISM

Bacteria vary widely in their ability to utilize the various sources of nitrogen for the synthesis of protein. In Chapter 6 several potential sources of nitrogen for assimilatory purposes were listed, ranging from free atmospheric nitrogen to complex proteins. Ammonia forms the key intermediate in nitrogen metabolism, and most organisms, when supplied with a usable source of energy and other indispensable nutrients, can readily use ammonia as the principal source of protein nitrogen. Even in those organisms which can utilize atmospheric nitrogen, nitrates, and nitrites, ammonia is the form of nitrogen that enters into the organic nitrogen of the cell.

The Metabolism of Inorganic Nitrogen (80). Since inorganic nitrogen is the ultimate source of nitrogen for all forms of life, its metabolism is of tremendous biologic significance. Green plants and many microorganisms can convert the nitrogen atom from various inorganic oxidized states to the more reduced forms, ammonia or amino groups. Dependent upon these organisms are all other heterotrophic forms of life, including man and most microorganisms, which are incapable of transforming the more oxidized states of inorganic nitrogen to ammonia and organic nitrogen. The basic features of inorganic nitrogen metabolism center on oxidation-reduction reactions. The nitrogen atom exists in nature in a variety of different oxidation states, each of which has been implicated in the pathways of inorganic nitrogen metabolism.

The atmosphere is the ultimate source of nitrogen for all forms of life, but because of its relative inertness, it can be metabolized by only a few microorganisms. These are the **nitrogen-fixing** bacteria that transform atmospheric nitrogen into ammonia for incorporation into organic nitrogen compounds. Among the soil bacteria in which nitrogen-fixation has been most extensively studied are species of *Azotobacter* and *Clostridium pasteurianum* (52).

The nitrate present in the soil is the principal source of nitrogen for higher plants. Its presence in the soil is the consequence of **nitrification** by bacteria capable of oxidizing the ammonia that is continually formed from nitrogen compounds by degradative processes occurring in all organisms. Autotrophic organisms of the genus *Nitrosomonas* rapidly convert ammonia to nitrite, while *Nitrobacter* species oxidize nitrite to nitrate. The reverse of the nitrification reactions, the reduction of nitrate to nitrite, hydroxylamine, ammonia, or nitrogen, has been demonstrated in a wide variety of heterotrophic microorganisms (*E. coli, Cl. perfringens, Proteus vulgaris*). In this process the nitrate may be assimilated via ammonia or the amino level into nitrogen-containing cell components, such as proteins and nucleic acids. The nitrate may also be used in some microorganisms in respiration, in which case the nitrate is used as the terminal electron acceptor instead of oxygen. The reduction products, which may include nitrite, nitric oxide, nitrous oxide, and molecular nitrogen, depending on the organism and environmental conditions, are probably not further oxidized but excreted into the surrounding medium. When the products formed are volatile, the nitrogen escapes into the atmosphere and is lost from the soil in the process referred to as **denitrification** (55).

Hydrolysis of Proteins and Peptides. For most of the heterotrophic organisms, amino acids and partially hydrolyzed proteins (peptones) provide the principal nitrogen sources. Since the native protein molecule is too large to enter the bacterial cell, in order to be utilized it must first be broken down into smaller units by extracellular proteolytic enzymes excreted into the medium. There are only a few species which are able to do this; among the most important, especially from a medical viewpoint, are certain species of clostridia, such as *Cl. histolyticum*. Organisms of this type produce very powerful proteolytic enzymes which cause considerable liquefaction of tissue around the wound. The invasiveness of *Cl. perfringens* has been accredited in part to the action of a specific proteinase, collagenase, identical with its K-toxin, which acts on muscle tissue to give a friable mass of fibrils from which the supporting tissue and sarcolemma have completely disappeared. A number of aerobic bacteria also produce extracellular proteinases. When inoculated into a medium containing protein as the sole source of nitrogen, however, even the highly proteolytic species fail to grow; they must first be supplied with some utilizable source of nitrogen from which to synthesize the extracellular proteases.

Whereas only a few bacteria are able to attack native protein, once this has been hydrolyzed to peptones the majority of heterotrophic organisms can then complete the breakdown to the constituent amino acids. A variety of peptidases have been found in microorganisms, most of which are not liberated into the medium but must be extracted from the disintegrated cells.

Amino Acid Metabolism (79, 83). The amino acids liberated by the action of the proteinases and peptidases may undergo a variety of metabolic transformations. It is unlikely that any amino acid is always metabolized by a single series or group of reactions. Most of the amino acids have several fates in metabolism and may follow diverse metabolic pathways simultaneously. Also, in the bacterial cell the metabolic transformations of amino acids are coupled and integrated with reactions of carbohydrate and lipid metabolism.

Certain of the metabolic pathways for amino acids involve an initial removal of the *a*-amino group of the molecule. This may be accomplished by (1) the process of **deamination,** which involves the initial separation of the nitrogen from the carbon chain of one amino acid and the utilization of the ammonia so formed for the synthesis of other amino acids or (2) **transamination,** in which free ammonia is not formed but the nitrogen is transferred directly.

DEAMINATION. The process of oxidative deamination whereby amino groups are removed from amino acids, results in the formation of a keto acid and ammonia. This reaction, catalyzed by a flavoprotein, may be represented as

$$\text{R-CH-COOH} + 1/2\ O_2 \xrightarrow[\text{oxidase}]{\text{amino acid}}$$
$$\text{R-C-COOH} + NH_3$$
$$\overset{\|}{O}$$

Cell-free preparations with L-amino acid oxidase activity have been obtained from several microorganisms. The *Enterobacteriaceae* have the most active deaminases, while the streptococci and staphylococci have a very limited ability to deaminate amino acids.

The oxidative deamination of glycine has also been observed, as has the presence of a number of D-amino acid oxidases in microorganisms. The oxidative deamination of glutamic acid to yield the corresponding keto acid, *a*-ketoglutaric acid, involves the participation of L-**glutamic acid dehydrogenase.** This reversible conversion of L-glutamic acid to *a*-ketoglutaric acid, which is a member of the citric acid cycle, serves also as a link between the metabolism of this amino acid and that of carbohydrates.

Some deaminations are nonoxidative in nature. One of these is the deamination of L-aspartic acid to form fumaric acid by the enzyme **aspartase** found in *E. coli* and a number of other bacteria. This reversible reaction is another point at which the metabolism of an amino acid is linked to the metabolism of carbohydrates. Other amino acids which can be deaminated by nonoxidative reactions include serine, threonine, and cysteine.

A special type of deamination is the **Strickland reaction** employed by some of the strictly anaerobic microorganisms such as *Clostridium sporogenes* and *Clostridium botulinum* (5). In this reaction some amino acids act as reducing agents, others as oxidizing agents. If one amino acid from each group is added to a cell suspension, there occurs an intermolecular oxidation-reduction reaction with the concomitant deamination of both amino acids. An example of such coupled deaminations is the over-all reaction between alanine and glycine:

$$2\ \text{glycine} + \text{alanine} \xrightarrow{2\ H_2O} 3\ \text{acetic acid} + 3\ NH_3 + CO_2$$

TRANSAMINATION REACTIONS. These reactions probably provide the chief mechanism by which amino acids are formed. In such reactions the amino group of an *a*-amino acid is transferred to the *a* position of an *a*-keto acid under the influence of specific enzymes, the **transaminases,** for which pyridoxal phosphate is a cofactor:

aspartic acid + *a*-ketoglutaric acid $\rightleftharpoons$ oxaloacetic acid + glutamic acid

alanine + *a*-ketoglutaric acid $\rightleftharpoons$ pyruvic acid + glutamic acid

The reaction is believed to be a general one of widespread occurrence. In *E. coli* transamination has been shown to involve at least three distinct enzymes, transaminase A, B, and C (66), as well as additional transaminases with greater substrate specificity (62).

DECARBOXYLATION. Bacteria also possess enzymes that attack amino acids at the carboxyl group and catalyze the decarboxylation of amino acids to yield carbon dioxide and an amine, according to the general reaction

$$\text{R-CHNH}_2\text{-COOH} \longrightarrow \text{R-CH}_2\text{NH}_2 + CO_2$$

The **decarboxylases** are highly specific, inducible enzymes formed only when the organism is grown in an acid medium in the presence of the specific substrate. Pyridoxal phosphate is the coenzyme for these reactions. A number of decarboxylases have been purified and activity has been shown for arginine, lysine, histidine, ornithine, phenylalanine, tyrosine, glutamic acid, and aspartic acid.

Some of the amines produced by bacteria from amino acids, such as histamine and tyramine, have pharmacologic activity in animals, but their physiologic significance to the cell itself is not clear. It has been suggested, however, that since decarboxylation takes place under acid conditions and causes the pH to shift to the alkaline side, whereas deamination occurs under alkaline conditions and gives rise to an acid shift, these systems achieve some degree of internal stabilization in an unfavorable environment.

Unlike these decarboxylases which are inducible, however, diaminopimelic acid decarboxylase is a constitutive enzyme important in the synthesis of lysine from diaminopimelic acid. It has been found in cell-free extracts of a wide variety of bacteria but is absent from lysine auxotrophs which accumulate diaminopimelic acid (98). The enzyme is highly specific for *meso*-diaminopimelic acid and requires pyridoxal phosphate for maximal activity.

Assimilation of Nitrogen (52). Ammonia is the simplest nitrogen source for those species of bacteria, yeasts, and molds that are capable of introducing it into organic compounds. Several mechanisms have been described for incorporating inorganic nitrogen via the ammonium ion. These include the reversible **glutamic dehydrogenase** reaction in which *a*-ketoglutarate reacts with ammonia to form glutamic acid, and the **alanine dehydrogenase** system, in which alanine is synthesized from pyruvic acid, NH_3, and NADH:

a-ketoglutaric acid $+ NH_3 + NADPH \rightleftharpoons$
L-glutamic acid $+ NADP$

pyruvic acid $+ NH_3 + NADH \rightleftharpoons$
L-alanine $+ NAD$

The reversible formation of L-aspartic acid from ammonia and fumaric acid, an unsaturated dicarboxylic acid intermediate of the Krebs cycle, has been demonstrated in extracts of a number of organisms. This reaction is catalyzed by **aspartase.**

In addition to these pathways for the introduction of ammonia into amino acids, ammonia can be converted into amide groups to form asparagine and glutamine. This latter reaction provides a means of storing ammonia within the cell and provides a device for permitting ammonia to penetrate the cell. The synthesis of carbamyl phosphate from ammonium carbonate has been demonstrated in cell-free preparations. The carbamyl phosphate is an important precursor of the pyrimidine ring and reacts with ornithine to form citrulline:

$$CO_2 + NH_3 + ATP \rightleftharpoons H_2N - \overset{\overset{\displaystyle O}{\|}}{C} - OPO_3^{--} + ADP$$

Once ammonia has been converted to *a*-amino groups, it can then enter into a number of reactions. Most significant in the synthesis of amino acids are transamination reactions (p. 104), which provide a general mechanism for the elaboration of a number of amino acids. These reactions furnish a method of forming both the amino acid when the keto acid and glutamic acid are available, and the keto acid from the amino acid, the keto acid being further metabolized by devious routes. That this is not the only mechanism available for the synthesis of amino acids, however, is shown by the demonstration of other pathways of biosynthesis of certain amino acids. Also revealed by detailed analysis of biosynthetic pathways is the importance of various products of catabolism as precursors of biosynthesis. This is especially true of such compounds as pyruvate, a key compound in a variety of dissimilatory pathways yet a vital precursor of such amino acids as alanine, valine, leucine, diaminopimelic acid, and lysine.

Although there are still significant gaps in our knowledge, most of the steps in amino acid biosynthesis have now been defined. The broad synthetic powers of numerous bacteria have led to their extensive use by biochemists as experimental material for unraveling the reaction sequence involved in the synthesis of the amino acids. The analysis of these pathways has profitably utilized several experimental approaches. Among the most useful has been the use of auxotrophic mutants, which differ from the wild-type parent in that they have a growth-factor requirement. Such a mutant lacks a single enzyme essential in the synthesis of the growth factor and, as a result of this deficiency, usually accumulates the compound preceding the blocked reaction. By identification of the accumulated precursor, a clue is thus obtained which is useful in the complete elucidation of the biosynthetic sequence. Other technics which have been invaluable, alone and when combined with studies in auxotrophic mutants, include isotope incorporation and the use of extracted enzymes and metabolite analogs. These approaches together with the availability of improved and more sensitive methods of testing have sparked the tremendous advances seen in this area in recent years.

In the biosynthesis of the amino acids certain general patterns emerge. Whereas most of the reactions in a biosynthetic sequence are reversible, the energetics are such that the reaction proceeds in the forward direction. Entirely different degradative and biosynthetic pathways are observed for a number of amino acids. Also of importance is the evidence for a high degree of unity throughout the biologic kingdom in amino acid synthesis. Comparative studies to date have revealed only two major differences in the synthesis of amino acids. In *E. coli* and the other gram-negative forms studied, ornithine arises from glutamate via a series of N-acetyl derivatives. This pathway, however, is not operative in *Neurospora* or in various members of the gram-positive *Bacillaceae* which utilize a different but unestablished route.

Another striking difference is that of lysine synthesis. In bacteria lysine arises from the 7-carbon compound diaminopimelic acid, while in the fungus *Neurospora* the synthesis is via a 6-carbon intermediate, *a*-aminoadipic acid. Diaminopimelic acid is a unique amino acid, not universally distributed throughout the biologic kingdom but present only in certain bacteria and blue-green algae. It is not a constituent of the intracellular proteins of these organisms but is confined to the mucopeptide component of the cell wall. In addition to this structural role, it is the intermediate precursor of lysine even in bacteria that do not have diaminopimelic acid in their cell walls.

Diaminopimelic acid → Lysine + CO_2

Isotopic studies have shown that aspartate and pyruvate are precursors of diaminopimelic acid. For details of this and other pathways of amino acid biosynthesis the student is referred to the discussions of Umbarger and Davis (83) and Greenberg (21).

Protein synthesis will not take place unless all of the naturally occurring amino acids are provided. Whereas the wild-type *Escherichia coli* is able to effect a rapid synthesis of all the amino acids and then incorporate them into protein, an amino-acid-requiring mutant cannot form protein unless this requirement is met. The ribosomes of the bacterial cell appear to provide the sites at which amino acids are incorporated into peptide bonds. This incorporation of the amino acids into protein requires an energy source for synthesis of the peptide bond. With intact cell preparations this is usually provided by the metabolism of utilizable carbohydrate, which provides the necessary ATP.

The first step in amino acid incorporation involves activation by specific amino acid activating enzymes, with the formation of an enzyme-bound, aminoacyl adenylate intermediate:

$$\text{Amino acid} + \text{Enzyme} + \text{ATP} \underset{}{\overset{\text{Mg}^{++}}{\rightleftharpoons}} \text{Enzyme—aminoacyl adenylate} + \text{PP}$$

Since the further incorporation of this activated amino acid involves transfer to a specialized type of ribonucleic acid, the discussion will be continued following a consideration of the vital role played by the nucleic acids.

METABOLISM OF NUCLEIC ACIDS AND PROTEINS

Each living cell reacts in a characteristic manner. The source of this biologic specificity is the chemical uniqueness of the cell's own array of nucleic acid and protein molecules. This chemical specificity is accomplished by the arrangement of a relatively small number of basic units into long chains of characteristic sequential order. The ultimate determinant, however, of all biologic specificity is contained in the substance of its genes, the deoxyribonucleic acid (DNA). Passed down from generation to generation, specific giant molecules of DNA maintain the continuity of living matter, insuring that a staphylococcus cell continues to be a staphylococcus and a bacillus a bacillus. A second type of nucleic acid, the ribonucleic acid (RNA), carries instructions from the genes to the building sites in the cytoplasm, the ribosomes, where it directs the assembly of proteins. In the structure of the DNA molecule thus resides all the vital information required for the synthesis of new DNA, RNA, and protein. Probably the most important problem in modern biology is how all of this information is coded into the nucleotide chains of DNA and then used in the synthesis of new macromolecules.

Nucleic Acids and Nucleotides. Nucleic acids, nucleotides, and their derivatives are major indispensable components of all living matter. They play a vital role not only in genetics and protein synthesis but also in coenzyme function, energy storage, and energy transfer.

All self-reproducing free-living forms possess two types of nucleic acid, ribonucleic acid (RNA) and deoxyribonucleic acid (DNA). These are macromolecules composed of four kinds of nucleotide units, linked through phosphate bridges to form polynucleotide chains. By definition a nucleotide consists of a nitrogenous base, sugar, and phosphate, while a nucleoside is comprised of a base and sugar. In RNA the sugar moiety is ribose and the bases are adenine, guanine, cytosine, and uracil. The sugar of

DNA is deoxyribose, and the bases are adenine, guanine, cytosine, and thymine (Table 2). The details of the biosynthesis of the

Table 2. Purine and Pyrimidine Derivatives

BASE	NUCLEOSIDE	NUCLEOTIDE
Adenine	Adenosine	Adenylic acid (AMP)
Guanine	Guanosine	Guanylic acid (GMP)
Cytosine	Cytidine	Cytidylic acid (CMP)
Uracil	Uridine	Uridylic acid (UMP)
Thymine	Thymidine	Thymidylic acid (TMP)

purines and pyrimidines as well as their degradation have been studied in great detail (45, 68). An interesting point of difference between the synthesis of the purine and pyrimidine ring systems is that the purine ring is not synthesized de novo from small molecule precursors but as part of a nucleotide, whereas the pyrimidine ring is synthesized as such.

DEOXYRIBONUCLEIC ACID. The structure of DNA has been established as a polymer in which the long chain is composed of repeating units of 2-deoxyribose and phosphate with a nitrogenous base attached to each deoxyribose residue. According to Watson and Crick (92, 93), DNA consists of two polynucleotide chains twisted together to form a double-stranded helix, with the sugar-phosphates on the outside to form the backbone and the bases toward the inside perpendicular to the long axis, like steps in a circular stairway. The adenine of one chain is linked to thymine of the second chain, and guanine to cytosine by hydrogen bonds. In samples of DNA the concentration of adenine always matches that of thymine, and the concentration of guanine is equal to that of cytosine. Although the relative amounts of each base may vary in preparations of DNA from different sources, the purine content always equals the pyrimidine content. The following generalization has thus been made concerning the base distribution in DNA:

$$\text{Adenine} + \text{thymine} = \text{cytosine} + \text{guanine}$$

This double-stranded helix structure provides a useful model for an explanation of the replication of DNA. Watson and Crick (92, 93) proposed that the replication of DNA involves the separation of the two strands and the polymerization of new complementary strands upon them. A daughter strand is thus formed from each parent strand. This theory received strong support from the studies of Meselson and Stahl (49) with *E. coli* in which the dilution of N^{15} in DNA was followed through successive generations.

Using a purified enzyme preparation from *E. coli,* Kornberg and his associates (38) have described a system capable of synthesizing DNA. Synthesis proceeds according to the following reaction:

$$n \, d \, ATP + n \, d \, GTP + n \, d \, CTP + n \, TTP + DNA$$
$$\rightleftharpoons (d \, ATP - d \, GTP - d \, CTP - d \, TTP)_n$$
$$- DNA + 4 \, n \, PP$$

In this reaction the four deoxyribonucleoside triphosphates are polymerized by the enzyme polymerase with the elimination of inorganic pyrophosphate. All four deoxynucleoside triphosphates are required, as well as Mg^{++} and some DNA to act as primer. When DNA is omitted, no reaction at all takes place. Evidence has been presented which strongly suggests that this added DNA functions as a template, directing the synthesis of exact copies of itself. The polymerase is unique in that it takes directions from this template, matching the particular purine or pyrimidine substrate with a base on the template to form a hydrogen-bonded pair (38).

The role of DNA as the sole carrier of genetic information together with the solution of the molecular structure of DNA provide the missing links for an adequate interpretation of Beadle and Tatum's one gene-one enzyme hypothesis (6). The linear sequence of the nucleotides in DNA conveys specific biologic information, in particular the specification of amino acid sequence in proteins.

RIBONUCLEIC ACID (74). Whereas genetic information for protein structure is encoded in DNA, the main sites of protein synthesis in cells appear to be cytoplasmic ribonucleoprotein particles, the ribosomes. Because of the spatial separation of these two entities in cells, the genetic control of protein synthesis is mediated by the transfer of information via RNA molecules, synthesized under the control of DNA, to the ribosomes. Here they act as templates controlling the assembly of amino acids. At least three different functional types of RNA are concerned with protein synthesis: **ribosomal RNA, "messenger" RNA,** and **amino acid transfer RNA.**

By differential centrifugation of disrupted cell preparations two major fractions of RNA may be obtained: the ribosomal RNA sediments at 100,000 *g,* while the soluble RNA (sRNA) remains in the supernatant. In a bacterial cell the ribosomal RNA accounts for about 85 per cent of the total RNA. It appears to exist in varying degrees of aggregation and is especially influenced by the concentration of magnesium and metabolic state of the cell at the time of breaking (64). A general similarity has been observed in the pattern of the particle size of ribosomes derived from a number of microorganisms (43). The ribosomes of *E. coli* have sedimentation constants in the ultracentrifuge of 100 S., 70 S., 50 S., and 30 S., although the nucleic acid content of all these fractions is the same, approximately 63 per cent. The 100 S. particle appears to be a dimer of two 70 S. particles, while the 70 S. particle consists of an association of two unequal units, corresponding to the 50 S. and 30 S. particles. Also of interest is the observation that bacteria of different DNA composition show a total ribosomal RNA composition which is quite constant. Tracer studies of the synthesis of the RNA portion of ribosomes suggest a three-stage model. Two sequential precursors, representing 10 per cent of the total RNA have been identified and designated as the eosome and neosome (64). The last stages in ribosomal assembly involving the addition of protein to eosome material are inhibited by chloramphenicol. In slices of bacteria that have been analyzed for distribution of radioactivity, newly synthesized RNA, unlike the bulk of the RNA, is localized in a central region of the cell, at a time corresponding to the finding of radioactivity in the eosome fraction (9).

At present the most precisely formulated theory of the role of ribosomes in information transfer is the "messenger" hypothesis advanced by Jacob and Monod (31, 32). According to this hypothesis an unstable messenger RNA is produced by the gene and associates temporarily with ribosomes to act as a template for protein synthesis. Evidence for the present concept of a "messenger" RNA has come largely from studies of induced enzyme formation and phage infection. The existence of an RNA which is rapidly labeled in intact cells, has the composition of DNA, and can form what appears to be specific hybrids with DNA has been demonstrated.

Among the best-documented studies supporting the messenger RNA concept are those of Volkin and Astrachan (86, 87) in which it was observed that in *Escherichia coli* infected with T2 bacteriophage, a minor species of RNA was synthesized whose base composition appeared to be similar to the DNA of the phage but not of the host. The newly synthesized RNA does not merely accumulate but undergoes constant breakdown and renewal, or "turnover." This turnover phenomenon appears to be part of its function. The synthesis of this RNA is essential for phage protein synthesis, and a direct stoichiometric relationship exists between the amount of RNA and protein synthesis. The function of this type of RNA as a component of the template actually making protein was indicated by the discovery of such RNA bound to ribosomes (8). No new ribosomes are synthesized after phage infection; the newly synthesized "messenger" RNA as well as newly synthesized protein are associated with ribosomes present before phage infection. This type of RNA has also been discovered in noninfected cells and other biologic systems; in this case the base composition of the RNA resembles that of the cellular DNA (22). Additional convincing evidence for the existence of a phage-specific messenger is the isolation from extracts of specific RNA-DNA hybrids where the RNA has a composition similar to the DNA.

RNA of DNA-like composition can also be synthesized in vitro with the enzyme RNA polymerase. RNA synthesized in this manner markedly activates the incorporation of amino acids into protein in cell-free systems.

The over-all reaction consists of the polymerization of the four nucleoside triphosphates to RNA with the concomitant release of pyrophosphate. The reaction is completely dependent on DNA, the presence of a divalent metal such as Mn^{++} or Mg^{++}, and all four nucleoside triphosphates. In the synthesis of RNA, both strands of the DNA are copied during the process, the composition of the DNA primer determining the composition of the RNA product. Such syntheses do not lead to the destruction of the priming DNA. The RNA polymerase provides a means for the synthesis of "messenger" RNA in biologic systems (30).

Another functional type of RNA, "transfer" RNA, has the unique property of binding amino acids. It constitutes about 10 to 15 per cent of the RNA in cells and is a major fraction of the soluble RNA that does not sediment with the ribosomes. It does not appear to be either a precursor or degradation product of RNA of larger molecular weight. The mechanism by which complexes are formed between this "transfer" RNA and an amino acid is via a specific amino-acid-activating enzyme which activates the amino acid by forming first an amino-acyl-adenylate complex and then the corresponding amino-acyl-RNA complex (7). One enzyme protein thus serves to recognize both the amino acid and its specific acceptor RNA:

$$\text{Amino acid} + \text{ATP} + \text{Enzyme} \rightleftharpoons$$
$$\text{Amino acyl} - \text{AMP} - \text{Enz} + \text{PP}$$
$$(\text{Amino acyl} - \text{AMP} - \text{Enz}) + \text{T-RNA} \rightleftharpoons$$
$$\text{Amino acyl} - \text{RNA} + \text{Enzyme} + \text{AMP}$$

Each of the naturally occurring amino acids can be linked to RNA in this way. The system catalyzing reactions of this type has been detected in every organism and tissue so far examined. The linkage of the amino acid to RNA is an ester one between the carboxyl group of the amino acid and the ribose hydroxyl of the terminal adenosine, which is essential for amino acid attachment. The known end groups of transfer RNA are pGp—RNA—pCpCpA.

Despite uniformities in structure at the ends of "transfer" RNA, specificity in the formation of amino acyl-RNA has been demonstrated. There is first a specificity in the action of activating enzymes for the formation of the enzyme-amino acyl-adenylate complex and, second, a specificity of the complex in its reaction with T-RNA. This second specificity extends to the recognition of T-RNA molecules specific for individual amino acids. The importance of amino acid-specific T-RNA stems from Crick's hypothesis (12) that the RNA of the ribosome contains a code which specifies the sequence of the amino acids of the protein being made. The key to the code lies in the sequence of nucleotides in the RNA. According to this theory, an amino acid cannot be coded for directly by RNA but requires an "adaptor" molecule which can hydrogen bond with the ribosomal template coding unit in order to transport the amino acid to its proper position in the peptide chain. This adaptor molecule is T-RNA. Each molecule carries the code or complement of the code for the single amino acid it binds. Amino acyl-RNA formation is thus a very crucial step for insuring specificity in reading the "messenger" RNA in the ribosome. A failure of one of the enzymes to discriminate among the various amino acids or among the RNA-binding sites would lead to errors in the amino acid sequence of proteins and would result in an altered or inactive protein.

The Synthesis of Proteins (69). Early studies with bacteria and a number of tissues revealed a close correlation between the rate of growth of cells and their ribonucleic acid content. This can be attributed to the linear relationship between the rate of protein synthesis and the RNA content of the cells. Accumulated evidence points to the ribosome as the site of protein synthesis in bacteria and yeast. The strongest evidence for protein synthesis in these systems employs the labeling of specific enzyme proteins in a cell-free ribosomal system. In contrast to the amino acyl-AMP, which does not separate from the enzyme, the sRNA, carrying its amino acid, goes out into the cell sap and can be isolated in appreciable amounts from fresh cells. There seems to be a fairly large cytoplasmic pool of these 20 amino acyl-s RNA's. The transfer of amino acids from amino acyl-RNA to ribosomes has been demonstrated in cell-free systems and has been shown to re-

quire guanosine triphosphate, magnesium, and probably free sulfhydryl groups. One or more enzymes are involved in the transfer reaction (Fig. 5).

A direct physical association of the transfer RNA and the ribosome is believed to occur during transfer. This initial association is very transitory, and the amino acid is transferred from the amino acyl-RNA to the ribosome very rapidly. The RNA is then free to form amino acyl-RNA once again. One of the most striking aspects of this reaction is a lack of specificity for the "transfer" RNA species, as illustrated by the finding that hemoglobin is formed by a system containing *E. coli* sRNA and a rabbit reticulocyte ribosome which carries the template for hemoglobin synthesis.

Labeling experiments are suggestive of an ordered synthesis of the polypeptide chain, starting at the N-terminal end and finishing at the C-terminal end. This ordered synthesis is presumably a function of the "code" and is accomplished by the mechanism of interaction between "messenger" RNA and amino acid-specific "transfer" RNA. There is evidence that this code can be transcribed only from a single starting point corresponding to the N-terminal amino acid (13). In order to find its proper place in the amino-acid sequence, a triplet of bases in the T-RNA is supposed to hydrogen bond to a triplet of bases in the messenger RNA. In addition, the T-RNA of the incoming amino acid must bond to the preceding molecule of T-RNA, thereby providing for sequential growth. Once the linear peptide chain has been formed, specific disulfide bond and tertiary structure formation is considered to follow spontaneously resulting in the final globular product (3).

The Genetic Code (59, 60). The "messenger" RNA is the bearer of the genetic code. The question of transfer of information from nucleic acid to the synthesis of protein involves the problem of how the sequence of only four bases in the nucleic acid determines the sequence of the twenty amino acids in the protein. The laboratories of Nirenberg (59), Ochoa (60), and others have utilized the advantages of synthetic polynucleotides prepared with polynucleotide phosphorylase as synthetic "messengers." In their system

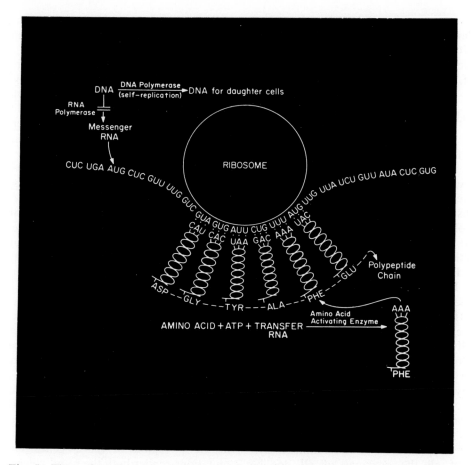

Fig. 5. The action of structural genes. Synthesis of protein begins with the genetic code embodied in DNA. It is transcribed into "messenger" RNA, which finds its way to a ribosome, the site of protein synthesis. Amino acids are carried to their proper location on the "messenger" RNA by molecules of transfer RNA. The sequence of code letters is tentative.

synthetic polymers containing only uracil (polyuridylic acid) serve as templates for the production of polyphenylalanine by a cell-free system from *E. coli* consisting of ribosomes, amino acid-activating enzymes, amino acids, "transfer" RNA, ATP, and GTP. This important finding indicated that poly U can act as "messenger" RNA and that UUU triplets presumably code for phenylalanine. Polymers containing all possible combinations of the four RNA bases have been studied in an attempt to establish nucleotide coding letters for each of the amino acids.

The minimum coding unit is a three-letter one, where 64 different sets are possible. Although many questions still exist concern-

ing this code, Crick's proposal (13), based on genetic experimentation with a bacteriophage system, suggests a nonoverlapping triplet code where selection of the correct sequence of bases depends on reading at a fixed starting point. Since there are 64 possible triplets and only 20 amino acids, there is more than one code word for each amino acid. Such a code is termed "degenerate," implying that a specific amino acid can be directed to the proper site in a protein chain by more than one code word. This degeneracy affords flexibility which is advantageous to the cell.

Most mutations correspond to the change of a single base or base pair in DNA. This change is communicated via the messenger

RNA to the protein-synthesizing site, where a mutant protein, differing from the wild-type protein only by a single amino acid replacement in the polypeptide chain of the protein, is synthesized (34, 100).

REGULATION OF BACTERIAL METABOLISM

The flow of metabolites through the various chemical pathways of the bacterial cell is exceedingly complex and is controlled by intricate processes of regulation, the over-all patterns of which still remain undescribed. Some of the control systems, however, are known; they involve genetic and nongenetic interactions.

The Regulation of Assimilative or Degradative Pathways. All bacteria are faced with the problem of sudden changes in the sources of carbon and nitrogen in their environment (54, 82). Although glucose is generally supplied to cultures grown in the laboratory, the carbon source in nature may involve lactose, acetate, an amino acid, or some hydrocarbon. The survival of each bacterial cell depends on its ability to utilize a wide variety of such carbon and nitrogen sources as soon as one source is depleted and another is presented. The continued synthesis of all the enzymes of all possible assimilative pathways, however, represents a severe drain on the metabolism of the bacterium. The bacterial cell solves this problem by synthesizing such enzyme systems only in the presence of the compounds to be utilized. Such enzymes are **inducible,** and the substances which cause the **induction** are called **inducers.** These are usually, but need not be, the substrate of the enzyme pathway. Thus, beta-galactosidase is synthesized in great amounts (5 to 10 per cent of the total protein of the cell) only if the cell is utilizing lactose as the sole carbon source, or if other beta-galactosides are present (31, 32).

The currently accepted mechanism of induction was proposed by Jacob and Monod (31, 32), who analyzed a great many mutants of *E. coli* that were defective in the induction process of beta-galactosidase. According to their hypothesis, the synthesis of most, if not all, enzymes is controlled not only by **structural genes,** which specify the amino acid sequence of an enzyme, but also by **regulatory genes,** which are concerned with the amount of enzyme produced. Regulatory genes function by coding for a repressor substance, probably a protein (51), which inhibits the transcription of structural genes to make "messenger" RNA. This inhibition is counteracted by the inducer.

This hypothesis is based upon the analysis of various types of mutants (Figure 6; see also Figure 10 in Chapter 5, p. 68) which have been observed in the lactose system. These mutants have been symbolized and defined as follows: (1) The y^- **mutants** usually lack the enzyme galactoside-acetylase, which is involved in the permeation of beta-galactosides. Penetration of lactose into the cell is low; beta-galactosidase is normal. These mutants map in the y gene. (2) The z^- **mutants** lack significant beta-galactosidase activity even in the presence of inducer but may contain material which cross-reacts with the antibodies to the normal beta-galactosidase **(CRM).** These mutants map in the z gene, which is probably contiguous to the y gene, as shown in Figure 6. The acetylase of the y gene is normal. (3) o^0 **Mutants** lack significant amounts of both the acetylase and beta-galactosidase, though these mutants map in the o region of the z gene. Thus, o^0 mutations render both the z and y genes nonfunctional. Various types of experiments indicate that only z and y genes immediately next to the o^0 mutants are affected. (4) o^c **Mutants** are mutants which also map in the o region of the z gene, but they are **intermediate constitutives,** i.e., they always contain intermediate amounts of acetylase and beta-galactosidase even in the absence of an inducer. Like the o^0 mutants, the effect of o^c is only on z and y genes which are immediately adjacent to the mutated o region. (5) i^- **mutants** are fully constitutive and always make very large amounts of the acetylase and beta-galactosidase even in the absence of the inducer. Unlike the o^c constitutive mutations, they map in the i gene and thus affect z and y genes which are not located nearby. (6) i^s **mutants** are mutants which do not make the acetylase or beta-galactosidase even in the presence of inducer. They map in the i region and affect z and y genes anywhere in the genome.

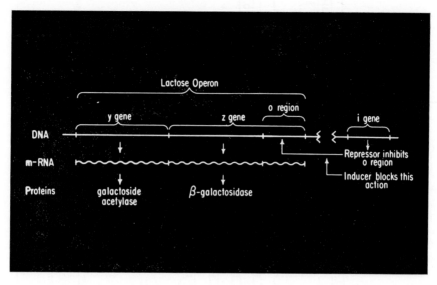

Fig. 6. Genetic control of enzyme induction at the lactose operon.

These different types of mutations can be explained on the basis of the theory of induction proposed by Jacob and Monod (Fig. 6) (31, 32). The z and y genes represent the structural genes for the acetylase and beta-galactosidase, respectively. The i gene is the regulatory gene which specifies the structure of the repressor. Because the i^- and i^s mutants can affect the action of z and y genes located some distance away, it is assumed that a cytoplasmic product, the repressor, is involved. The o region represents the area where the inhibition by the repressor takes place. Unlike the i gene mutations, the o^0 and o^c mutants do not affect z and y genes on episomes which are in the same cell and which have normal o regions. Therefore, there is probably no cytoplasmic product analogous to the repressor from the o region. This region probably represents the site where the transcription of both the z and y genes starts and is the area where the repressor acts. Thus, the $z, y,$ and o regions of the E. coli chromosome constitute an integrated functional unit, called the **operon.** It is of interest that the amounts of the acetylase and beta-galactosidase in a bacterium are coordinate, i.e., they rise and fall together depending on the environment (Fig. 7). This is a general property of enzymes coded by genes in an operon.

The inhibitory effect of the repressor on the o region is counteracted by the inducer. Thus, in the presence of lactose the repressor is not functional, the o region is not inhibited, the z and y genes can make "messenger" RNA, and galactoside-acetylase and beta-galactosidase are produced. The i^- mutants

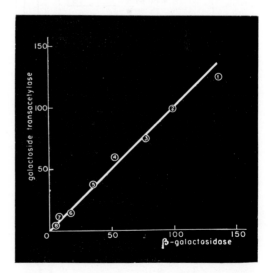

Fig. 7. Coinduction of beta-galactosidase and galactoside transacetylase. The rates of enzyme synthesis are expressed in arbitrary units. (From Jacob and Monod. Cold Spring Harbor Symposia, 26:204, 1961.)

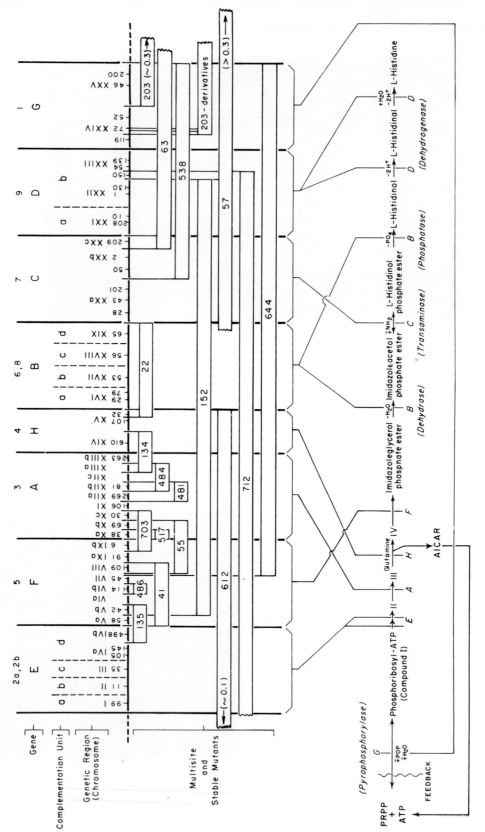

Fig. 8. The histidine operon. (Courtesy of P. E. Hartman.)

114

can be interpreted as containing defects in the i region; as a result they lack functional repressor and the z and y loci function all the time. The i^s mutants make a repressor which is insensitive to the inducer; this "super-repressor" turns off the o region all the time, and the z and y genes never work even in the presence of inducer. The o^c mutation probably represents an alteration in the operator region such that repressor is relatively ineffective, and some acetylase and beta-galactosidase is made even in the absence of inducer. The o^0 mutant represents a mutation in the operator region, which is now damaged, and transcription of the DNA never starts.

Regulation of Synthetic Pathways. Most bacteria maintain small intracellular pools of metabolites of low molecular weight, such as amino acids, purines, and pyrimidines, even when the bacteria are grown in vastly different media. This indicates that bacteria do not synthesize excess amounts of these compounds and that there is a fine balance between synthesis and utilization. Some of the processes which regulate these pools have been elucidated, and it is not surprising that some of the control mechanisms involve operons and repressors. Long-term conservation of the cell components involved in protein synthesis is achieved by **repression** and **depression** of synthetic pathways, while rapid response to immediate changes in need for metabolites is achieved by **end-product inhibition** (54, 82).

REPRESSION AND DEPRESSION. If an end product of a pathway can be obtained from the surrounding environment, the synthesis of the enzymes in this pathway usually ceases or slows down considerably. Thus, when large amounts of histidine are present in the medium, the synthesis of all of the enzymes involved in the pathway shown in Figure 8 are decreased to a very low level. This phenomenon is called **repression** (84, 85). On the other hand, if histidine is made limiting, either by growing an auxotroph blocked in the synthesis of histidine on N-formylhistidine, from which histidine is slowly released (2), or by inhibiting the first enzyme of the pathway with the histidine analog 2-thiazolealanine (53), large amounts of the histidine enzymes will be synthesized. This increased enzyme synthesis is termed **derepression.** Jacob and Monod (31, 32) have postulated the genetic interactions pictured in Figure 9 to explain these results. In their view, repression, like induction, involves the repressor product of a **regulatory gene.** Unlike the repressor of an induced enzyme pathway, the repressor in a synthetic pathway is **inactive** unless it reacts with the end products of the pathway (as a **corepressor**).

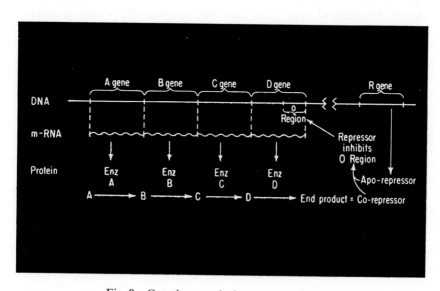

Fig. 9.   Genetic control of enzyme repression.

Only then can it inhibit the synthesis of "messenger" RNA by the structural genes at the *o* region.

Like the enzymes of the lactose operon, the levels of the various enzymes in the histidine pathway appear to be **coordinate** (2). This is of interest and indicates that the synthesis of all of these enzymes are also under a unified control. As shown in Figure 8, all of the structural genes for the histidine enzymes are located contiguously to one another and constitute an **operon.** The coordinate synthesis of all of these is thought to be due to the fact that the transcription of the DNA starts at the left end of gene G and continues until one large "messenger" RNA molecule for all the enzymes is made. By reacting with the G gene, the active repressor can stop the whole transcription process for all these structural genes.

In bacteria operons for the synthesis of leucine (46), tryptophan (99), isoleucine and valine (19), and many others have been described. It is of interest that the structural genes for the enzymes involved in arginine synthesis in *E. coli* are not closely linked to one another, and noncoordinate repression has been reported (20, 44). Although repression and derepression have little effect on short-term regulation of pathways, they do play a major role in the conservation of the protein synthesizing apparatus of the cell (54, 75, 82).

END-PRODUCT INHIBITION. It can be shown that the first enzyme of many synthetic pathways is strongly but reversibly inhibited by the end product of that pathway (82). Thus, if a given metabolite exceeds a certain concentration either by overproduction or by being supplied in the medium, the action of the first enzyme in the pathway will be inhibited, and the production of the metabolite will be decreased. This will allow the substrate of the first enzyme to be utilized elsewhere. This is true in the synthesis of histidine (Fig. 8). Not only can histidine inhibit the enzyme which catalyzes the condensation of PRPP and ATP to phosphoribosyl-ATP, but many analogs of histidine can do the same (53). These all share an alanine side chain attached to a heterocyclic

carbon atom which is adjacent to a nitrogen atom.

All of the other cases of end-product inhibition of the first enzyme in a biosynthetic pathway which are known (82) share several important properties. First, all involve inhibition of the first enzyme by the product of the pathway with little inhibition of the subsequent enzymes. Second, the end product, and not a derivative, is the inhibitor. This is especially clear in the studies using pure, crystalline aspartic transcarbamylase, which is directly inhibited by cytidine triphosphate (18). Finally, the inhibitor and the substrate of the first enzyme are competitive in their action, and the inhibition is easily reversed. This reversibility is essential for rapid adjustment to an altered environment. The result is the preferential utilization of preformed metabolites in the environment sparing the endogenous precursors of such metabolites for other pathways. There is thus strict control and very little oversynthesis of metabolites of low molecular weight.

The most puzzling feature of end-product inhibition is the lack of any structural similarity between the end-product inhibitor and the substrate of the first enzyme. Yet the substrate and inhibitor are competitive in their effects on the enzyme (51). This would indicate that the substrate and the inhibitor do not combine with the enzyme at the same site and that when the inhibitor fills its site, the substrate site is altered and the substrate is excluded. The fact that aspartic transcarbamylase (18), threonine deaminase (10), and the first enzyme in histidine synthesis (48) can be treated so as to become desensitized to its inhibitor and yet retain enzymatic activity lends credence to this view. It is of interest that Monod and coworkers (51) regard the repressor as a protein with two sites, one for reacting with the *o* region and the other with the corepressor or inducer.

For a more comprehensive discussion of the regulation of bacterial metabolism, the student is referred to the discussions of Fisher (16), Jacob and Wollman (33), Moyed and Umbarger (54, 82), and Hayes (28).

REFERENCES

1. Alberts, A. W., and others. J. Biol. Chem., 238:557, 1963.
2. Ames, B. N., and Garry, B. Proc. Nat. Acad. Sc., 45:1453, 1959.
3. Anfinsen, C. B. Basic Problems in Neoplastic Disease, Gellhorn, A., and Hirschberg, E., eds., New York, Columbia University Press, 1962, p. 113.
4. Baddiley, J. Fed. Proc., 21:1084, 1962.
5. Barker, H. A. Chap. 3 in The Bacteria, Vol. II, Gunsalus, I. C., and Stanier, R. Y., eds., New York, Academic Press, 1961.
6. Beadle, G. W. Ann. Rev. Physiol., 22:45, 1960.
7. Berg, P., and others. J. Biol. Chem., 236:1726, 1961.
8. Brenner, S., and others. Nature, 190:576, 1961.
9. Caro, L. G., and Forro, F., Jr. J. Biophys. Biochem. Cytol., 9:555, 1961.
10. Changeux, J. Cold Spring Harbor Symposia on Quantitative Biology, 26:313, 1961.
11. Cota-Robles, E. H., and others. J. Bacteriol., 75:243, 1958.
12. Crick, F. H. C. Symposia Soc. Exptl. Biology, 12:138, 1958.
13. ———— and others. Nature, 192:1227, 1961.
14. Dawes, E. A., and others. J. Gen. Microbiol., 32:151, 1963.
15. Dolin, M. I. Chap. 6 in The Bacteria, Vol. II, Gunsalus, I. C., and Stanier, R. Y., eds., New York, Academic Press, 1961.
16. Fisher, K. W. Brit. Med. Bulletin, 18:19, 1962.
17. Fruton, J. W., and Simmonds, S. General Biochemistry, 2nd ed., New York, John Wiley & Sons, Inc., 1958, p. 304.
18. Gerhardt, J. C., and Pardee, A. B. Fed. Proc., 20:224, 1961.
19. Glanville, E. V., and Demerec, M. Genetics, 45:1359, 1960.
20. Gorini, L., and others. Cold Spring Harbor Symposia on Quantitative Biology, 26:173, 1961.
21. Greenberg, D. M. Metabolic Pathways, Vol. II, Greenberg, D. M., ed., New York, Academic Press, 1961, p. 173.
22. Gros, F., and others. Cold Spring Harbor Symposia Quant. Biol., 26:111, 1961.
23. Gunsalus, I. C., and Stanier, R. Y., eds. Vol. II, The Bacteria, New York, Academic Press, 1961.
24. Gunsalus, I. C., and Stanier, R. Y., eds. Vol. III, The Bacteria, New York, Academic Press, 1962.
25. Gunsalus, I. C., and others. Bact. Rev., 19:79, 1955.
26. Hartman, P. E., and others. J. Gen. Microbiol., 22:323, 1960.
27. Hassid, W. Z. Chap. 6 in Metabolic Pathways, Vol. I, Greenberg, D. M., ed., New York, Academic Press, 1960.
28. Hayes, W. The Genetics of Bacteria and Their Viruses, Oxford, Blackwell Scientific Publications, 1964.
29. Horecker, B. L. Pentose Metabolism in Bacteria, New York, John Wiley & Sons, Inc., 1962.
30. Hurwitz, J., and others. Basic Problems in Neoplastic Disease, Gellhorn, A., and Herschberg, E., eds., New York, Columbia University Press, 1962, p. 35.
31. Jacob, F., and Monod, J. J. Mol. Biol., 3:318, 1961.
32. ———— and Monod, J. Cold Spring Harbor Symposia on Quantitative Biology, 26:193, 1961.
33. ———— and Wollman, E. L. Sexuality and the Genetics of Bacteria, New York, Academic Press, 1961.
34. Jukes, T. H. Proc. Nat. Acad. Sc., 48:1809, 1962.
35. Kaplan, N. O. Bacteriol. Rev., 27:155, 1963.
36. Kashket, E. R., and Brodie, A. F. Biochim. Biophys. Acta, 78:52, 1963.
37. Kitos, P. A., and others. J. Biol. Chem., 233:1295, 1958.
38. Kornberg, A. Enzymatic Synthesis of DNA, New York, John Wiley & Sons, Inc., 1962, p. 13.
39. Krampitz, L. O. Chap. 4 in The Bacteria, Vol. II, Gunsalus, I. C., and Stanier, R. Y., eds., New York, Academic Press, 1961.
40. Krebs, H. A., and others. Biochem. J., 51:614, 1952.
41. Lamanna, C., and Mallette, M. F. Basic Bacteriology, 2nd ed., Baltimore, Williams & Wilkins Co., 1959.
42. Lynen, F., and others. Biochem. Z., 335:123, 1961.
43. McCarthy, B. J. Carnegie Inst. Wash. Yearbook, 58:281, 1959.
44. Maas, W. K. Cold Spring Harbor Symposia on Quantitative Biology, 26:183, 1961.
45. Magasanik, B. The Bacteria, Vol. III, Gunsalus, I. C., and Stanier, R. Y., eds., New York, Academic Press, 1962, p. 295.
46. Margolin, P. Genetics, 48:441, 1963.
47. Marr, A. G. In The Bacteria, Vol. I, Gunsalus, I. C., and Stanier, R. Y., eds., New York, Academic Press, Inc., 1960, p. 443.
48. Martin, R. C., and others. Fed. Proc., 20:225, 1961.
49. Meselson, M., and Stahl, F. W. Proc. Nat. Acad., Sc. U.S., 44:671, 1958.
50. Mills, G. T., and Smith, E. E. B. Fed. Proc., 21:1089, 1962.
51. Monod, J., and others. J. Mol. Biol., 6:306, 1963.
52. Mortenson, L. E., and others. Bact. Rev., 26:42, 1962.
53. Moyed, H. S. J. Biol. Chem., 236:2261, 1961.
54. ———— and Umbarger, H. E. Physiol. Rev., 42:444, 1962.
55. Nason, A. Bact. Rev., 26:16, 1962.
56. Nathenson, S. G., and Strominger, J. L. J. Biol. Chem., 237:PC 3839, 1962.
57. Neely, W. B. Advances in Carbohydrate Chemistry, 15:341, 1960.
58. Newton, J. W., and Kamen, M. D. Chap. 8 in The Bacteria, Vol. II, Gunsalus, I. C., and Stanier, R. Y., eds., New York, Academic Press, 1961.
59. Nirenberg, M. W., and others. Fed. Proc., 22:55, 1963.
60. Ochoa, S. Fed. Proc., 22:62, 1963.
61. Oginsky, E. L., and Umbreit, W. W. An Introduction to Bacterial Physiology, 2nd

ed., San Francisco, W. H. Freeman Co., 1959.

62. Peterkofsky, B., and Gilvarg, C. J. Biol. Chem., 236:1432, 1961.

63. Roberts, R. B., and others. Proc. Nat. Acad. Sc., 39:1013, 1953.

64. ——— and others. Molecular Genetics, Part I, Taylor, J. H., ed., New York, Academic Press, 1963, p. 291.

65. Rogers, H. J. Chapter 5 in The Bacteria, Vol. II, New York, Academic Press, 1961, p. 272.

66. Rudman, D., and Meister, A. J. Biol. Chem., 200:591, 1953.

67. Salton, M. R. J. Bact. Rev., 25:77, 1961.

68. Schulman, M. P. Metabolic Pathways, Vol. II, Greenberg, D. M., ed., New York, Academic Press, 1961, p. 389.

69. Schweet, R., and Bishop, J. Molecular Genetics, Part I, Taylor, J. H., ed., New York, Academic Press, 1963, p. 353.

70. Shephardson, M., and Pardee, A. B. J. Biol. Chem., 235:3233, 1960.

71. Smith, E. E. B. Biochem. J., 76:35 P, 1960.

72. ——— and others. J. Biol. Chem., 236:2179, 1961.

73. Smith, L. Chap. 7 in The Bacteria, Vol. II, Gunsalus, I. C., and Stanier, R. Y., eds., New York, Academic Press, 1961.

74. Spiegelman, S. Fed. Proc., 22:36, 1963.

75. Stadtman, E. R. Bact. Rev., 27:170, 1963.

76. Stanier, R. Y., and others. The Microbial World, 2nd ed., Englewood Cliffs, N.J., Prentice-Hall, Inc., 1963.

77. Strominger, J. L. Physiol. Rev., 40:55, 1960.

78. Stumpf, P. K. Ann. Rev. Biochem., 29:261, 1960.

79. Symposium on Amino Acid Metabolism, McElroy, W. D., and Glass, H. B., eds., Baltimore, The Johns Hopkins Press, 1955.

80. Takahashi, H., and others. Chap 2 in Comparative Biochemistry, Vol. V, Florkin, M., ed., New York, Academic Press, 1963.

81. Thimann, K. V. The Life of Bacteria, 2nd ed., New York, The Macmillan Co., 1963.

82. Umbarger, H. E. The Control Mechanisms in Cellular Processes, Bonner, D. M., ed., New York, Ronald Press, 1962, p. 67.

83. ——— and Davis, B. D. The Bacteria, Vol. III, Gunsalus, I. C., and Stanier, R. Y., eds., New York, Academic Press, 1962, p. 167.

84. Vogel, H. J. In A Symposium on the Chemical Basis of Heredity, McElroy, W. D., and Glass, B., eds., Baltimore, The Johns Hopkins Press, 1957, p. 276.

85. ——— In Control Mechanisms in Cellular Processes, Bonner, D. M., ed., New York, Ronald Press, 1962, p. 163.

86. Volkin, E. In Molecular Genetics, Part I, Taylor, J. H., ed., New York, Academic Press, 1963, p. 271.

87. ——— and Astrachan, L. The Chemical Basis of Heredity, McElroy, W. D., and Glass, B., eds., Baltimore, The Johns Hopkins Press, 1957, p. 686.

88. Waite, M., and Wakil, S. J. J. Biol. Chem., 237:2750, 1962.

89. ——— and Wakil, S. J. J. Biol. Chem., 238:81, 1963.

90. Wakil, S. J. J. Lipid Res., 2:1, 1961.

91. ——— Comp. Biochem. and Physiol., 4:123, 1962.

92. Watson, J. D., and Crick, F. H. C. Nature, 171:737, 1953.

93. ——— and Crick, F. H. C. Cold Spring Harbor Symposia Quant. Biol., 18:123, 1953.

94. Weibull, C., and others. J. Gen. Microbiol., 20:519, 1959.

95. Whelan, W. J. Biochem. Soc. Symposia (Cambridge, England), 11:17, 1953.

96. Wood, H. G., and Katz, J. J. Biol. Chem., 233:1279, 1958.

97. Wood, W. A. Chap. 2 in The Bacteria, Vol. II, Gunsalus, I. C., and Stanier, R. Y., eds., New York, Academic Press, 1961.

98. Work, E. In Symposium on Amino Acid Metabolism, McElroy, W. D., and Glass, H. B., eds., Baltimore, The Johns Hopkins Press, 1955, p. 462.

99. Yanofsky, C. J. Bact., 24:221, 1960.

100. ——— and others. Fed. Proc., 22:75, 1963.

8

The Action of Chemical Agents and
Chemotherapeutic Drugs on Bacteria

Ages before the concept of infection was formulated, primitive man recognized that local inflammatory lesions frequently followed cuts and scratches and that prophylactic treatment with vinegar or wine was reasonably effective. As civilization advanced, each new vegetable or chemical agent was tested empirically for its antiseptic effect. With the advent of the sulfonamides and antibiotics, the simple chemical agents have become relatively less useful in therapy but have maintained their importance in the destruction of microorganisms in the nonliving environment.

Since many of the terms which have grown up around the process of killing microorganisms came into use before the nature and activities of bacteria were known, several terms with slightly different meanings are in use. The ending *-cide* is added when a killing action is implied, while *-stasis* is added when the organism is merely inhibited in growth or prevented from multiplying. A **bactericide** destroys bacteria and is practically synonymous with **germicide** or **disinfectant,** which implies an agent that kills microorganisms capable of producing an infection. A **bacteriostatic agent** is an inclusive term for those substances that prevent the growth of bacteria. An antiseptic opposes sepsis, putrefaction, or decay either by killing the microorganisms or preventing their growth; the term is commonly used for agents which are applied to living tissue. **Sterilization** refers to the killing or elimination of all forms of life. These definitions are only relative, however, since the same agent might act differently under different conditions of testing.

Factors Influencing the Rate of Destruction of Bacteria. The destruction of micro-organisms by chemical agents is primarily a chemical process, modified by the individual peculiarities of the organism and subject to the influences exerted by physical forces upon both the chemical and the organisms.

NATURE AND CONCENTRATION OF BACTERICIDAL AGENT. Many agents affect the rate of growth and death of bacteria only when used in extremely high concentrations, while others may stimulate, retard, or even kill the organism in very low concentrations. These intergradations in response have been visualized by Marshall and Hrenoff (Fig. 1) (143) in the form of a "disinfection spectrum" showing a blending of degrees of activity. There is no sharp line of separation between the different zones, and the width of the zones varies with the agent, the organism, and the method of testing. There is a marked tendency of poisonous agents to stimulate biologic processes when employed in low concentrations. It must also be emphasized that it is not the concentration of a poisonous agent which is responsible for its toxic effect but the effective concentration which accumulates at the bacterial interfaces.

TIME. When bacteria are exposed to a definite concentration of a bactericidal agent, even in excess, and though they are thoroughly mixed, all of the organisms do not die at the same time; but there is a gradual decrease in the number of living cells. Disinfection is usually considered as a process in which bacteria are killed in a reasonable length of time, but there are varying opinions about what this should be. We do know, however, that the destruction of bacteria by chemical agents is an orderly, gradual process requiring time for its completion.

pH. The hydrogen ion concentration exerts its influence on bactericidal action by affecting both the bacteria and chemical agent. When suspended in a medium of pH 7, bacteria are

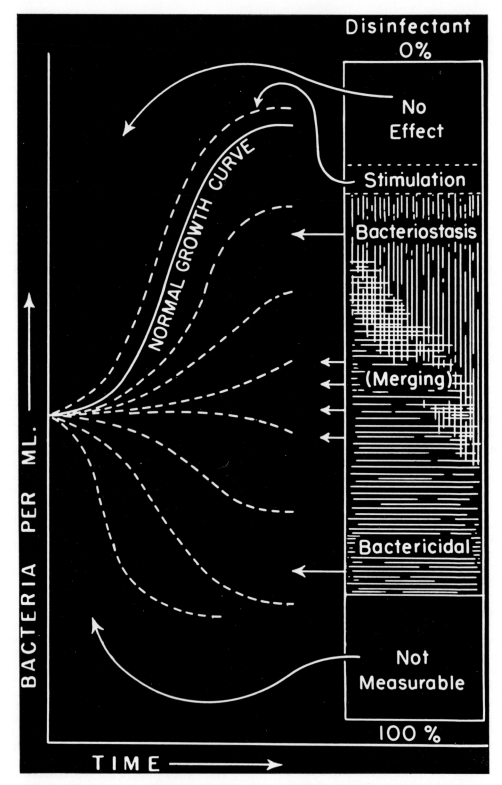

Fig. 1. The spectrum of disinfection. Assuming a normal growth curve under optimal conditions, the addition of any chemical substance in varying amounts will affect the growth to some degree. (Courtesy of Dr. Max S. Marshall.)

negatively charged. An increase of pH will result in an increased charge and may alter the effective concentration of the chemical agent at the surface of the cell. The pH also determines the degree of ionization of the bactericide. In general, the undissociated forms pass through the cell membrane more readily than the relatively inactive ionic forms.

TEMPERATURE. The killing of bacteria with chemical agents, like other chemical reactions, increases with an increase in temperature. For each 10° C. temperature increment there is, at low temperatures, a doubling of the rate of death. With some agents, such as phenol, the rate is increased five to eight times, suggesting the complexity of the reaction and the influence of other controlling variables.

NATURE OF THE ORGANISM. A number of factors relating to the organism itself exert a pronounced effect on the effectiveness of the bactericidal agent. These include the species of organism and its chemical composition, the growth phase of the culture, special structures such as spores and capsules, the previous history of the culture, and the number of bacteria in the test mixtures.

PRESENCE OF EXTRANEOUS MATERIALS. The presence of organic matter and other foreign materials often influences the activity of many agents used for disinfection and renders inert substances which show high activity in their absence. There are a number of ways in which these foreign substances may alter disinfectant activity: (1) surface adsorption by protein colloids, (2) formation of an inert or less active compound, and (3) binding of the disinfectant by active groups of foreign proteins.

The extraneous materials that interfere with disinfection also make effective neutralizing agents and may be used to stop the action of disinfectants. Activated charcoal, ferric hydroxide, and protein suspensions adsorb certain disinfectants away from the bacterial cells. Nonbactericidal concentrations of reducing agents, such as sodium sulfite, are effective against the halogens and hydrogen peroxide which act as oxidizing agents. The toxicity of the mercurials is very low in the presence of materials containing sulfhydryl groups, and organisms that are presumed to be dead may be revived by exposure to thioglycollate, glutathione, or the like. The role of antagonisms in the evaluation of antiseptics has been discussed by Klarmann (115).

Quantitative Aspects of Disinfection. When the number of surviving bacteria in contact with a unit volume of a disinfectant is plotted against time, the points tend to fall in a straight line.

Although these data seem to indicate that bacterial death is a monomolecular reaction, the process is so complex that mathematical formulation, when possible, may be very suggestive but is incapable of stating the whole sequence of events (169).

Standardization of disinfectants by comparison with the lethal action of phenol (phenol coefficient) has proved useful. The official quantitative test for evaluating antiseptics is the one of the Food and Drug Administration of the U.S. Department of Agriculture (61). This official F.D.A. method requires tests of antiseptics and disinfectants under standardized conditions against strains of S. typhosa and Staphylococcus aureus of known susceptibility to phenol. The F.D.A. test classifies agents as those that are at least equal to 2 per cent phenol and those that are not. Substances which kill bacteria by a different method or are inhibited by the presence of organic matter cannot be accurately evaluated by this method. Reddish proposes the use of a panel of testing procedures to provide more complete information on the potential value of antiseptic agents under conditions of use (172).

The increasing number of hospital-acquired staphylococcal infections has emphasized the need for re-evaluation of methods designed to control the spread of bacteria within the hospital environment (36, 98). A controlled test of certain currently used disinfectants under "in use" conditions emphasizes the importance of an effective disinfectant solution together with the proper application of isolation, nursing, and cleaning technics (178). A detailed discussion of the methods for testing disinfectants and the various types of antiseptics, disinfectants, and fungicides is found in the text edited by Reddish (173).

Mechanisms of Bactericidal and Bacteriostatic Activity. In the bacterial cell there are three major sites susceptible to attack by toxic chemical agents: the surface layers, the enzymes, and the nuclear material. The proper functioning of each of these areas is essential to the life of the organism.

PERMEABILITY CHANGES. A protoplasmic membrane, lipoprotein in nature, separates the living protoplasm from the nonliving environment and regulates the flow of solutes into and out of the cell. Membrane-like barriers also exist within the cell, restricting enzymes from contact with certain substrates.

Surface Active Agents. The group of substances known as the **surface active agents** injure the cell by damaging the membranes, resulting in an altered permeability. These substances, including such agents as the detergents and wetting agents, contain a water-soluble and a fat-soluble group in the same molecule, enabling them to orient themselves at interfaces. More than a thousand of these agents have been synthesized and tested for activity. Among the most useful are the **cationic agents,** which have a water-soluble quaternary ammonium group which dissociates to form a positively charged cation. When placed in contact with a cationic agent, bacteria lose their negative charge and assume a positive charge as result of the adsorption of the positively charged ions. This causes a loss of the semipermeability of the cell membrane, with a leakage from the cell of nitrogen, phosphorus, and other important substances, after which the agent may enter the cell and denature its active proteins (96). The pH of the medium markedly influences the toxic activity of those compounds which are most active at an alkaline pH. Most of the cationic detergents are antiseptic in a concentration of 1:3,000 and some in a 1:30,000 concentration. **Zephiran** is now used in many surgical clinics in a 1:1,000 dilution to prepare the skin before operation, and hexachlorophene in 1 per cent solution to treat the hands after washing and before drawing on the rubber gloves.

Among the **anionic detergents** are the soaps and fatty acids, agents which yield a negatively charged ion upon dissociation. These agents, most active at an acid pH, are effective against gram-positive organisms but are relatively ineffective against gram-negative forms which have near their cell surface a phospholipid that forms salts with anionic agents. The primary injury of the bile salts, long used by bacteriologists to lyse pneumococci, is a disruption of the cell membranes, permitting autolytic enzymes to act upon substrates from which they are restricted in the intact cell. The two groups of detergents neutralize each other when used together and both are inhibited by proteins. **Nonionic detergents** are relatively nontoxic, and a few, like Tween 80, facilitate bacterial growth. Additional information on these agents may be found in the reports of Glassman (77, 78) and Lawrence (130).

Phenols. The initial injury caused by the phenols is to the cell membrane, followed by interaction with and a denaturing of proteins. **Phenol** (carbolic acid, C_6H_5OH) in a 1:100 solution kills most vegetative forms of bacteria within 20 minutes and is an effective bacteriostatic agent in a 1:1,000 dilution. The 5 per cent solution which is commonly used to disinfect surgical instruments and excreta kills bacterial spores in a few hours. Its effectiveness is increased by the presence of sodium chloride, reduced considerably by ethyl alcohol, but affected very little by the presence of organic matter.

Ortho-, meta-, and **paracresol** are somewhat stronger disinfectants than phenol and are usually employed in a mixture known as tricresol. Cresols from coal tar, emulsified with green soap, are sold under the trade names of **Lysol** and **Creolin.** Lysol is about four times and Creolin about 10 times as effective as phenol. Phenol (0.5 per cent) and tricresol (0.15 per cent) are used to preserve vaccines and therapeutic serums.

Certain members of the bis-phenols have been shown to possess high bacteriostatic or fungistatic powers. These compounds, composed of two phenolic groups attached together by various linkages have been most widely used as skin antiseptics. Hexachlorophene (G-11) has been combined with soap and other detergents and has been used for the surgical preparation of hands and the field of operation (173). Additional information on the phenolic substances may be found in the discussions of Reddish (173) and Bennett (16).

DENATURATION OF PROTEINS. Proper functioning of a bacterial cell requires the maintenance of its cytoplasmic protein in an organized colloidal state. Agents which disrupt this state by coagulation or precipitation reduce the potential activity of enzymes, since enzyme reactions occur on the enzyme surface. Death is inevitable when toxic concentrations of these agents react with the nucleoproteins of the nucleus. **Acids, alkalis, alcohol, acetone,** and **other organic solvents** are among the chemical agents that act primarily by denaturing the active proteins.

Acids and Alkalis. These agents may exert their disinfectant activity through their free H^+ or OH^- ions, through the undissociated molecule, or by altering the pH of the organism's environment. The strong mineral acids and strong alkalis have disinfectant powers proportional to their degree of dissociation in solution. Some hydroxides, such as barium hydroxide, are more effective than their degree of dissociation would indicate, suggesting that the metallic cation exerts a direct toxic action on the bacteria. Boric acid in a 1 to 2 per cent solution dissociates poorly and is a very weak antiseptic; nevertheless, it is nonirritating and very useful as a mechanical cleanser for the eyes and other delicate structures.

The activity of the organic acids is apparently due to the intact molecule, since they dissociate less in solution than mineral acids but are sometimes more active as disinfectants. Benzoic acid, widely used as a food preservative, is about seven times as effective as hydrochloric acid, showing that either the whole molecule or the organic radical has a disinfecting capacity. Ethyl and methyl parahydroxybenzoic acids are more fungicidal than bactericidal (219). The accumulation of lactic acid and other organic acids during bacterial growth and metabolism slows and finally arrests the growth of many species of bacteria. The propionates have been employed for mycotic infections of the skin and vagina, and sodium and calcium propionate have proved useful as a food preservative.

Alcohols. *Ethyl alcohol* and *methyl alcohol* in a 50 to 70 per cent solution are commonly used as skin disinfectants prior to hypodermic injections. Alcohol is a very inefficient antiseptic; 100 per cent alcohol is considered inferior to a 70 per cent solution. Morton's work (149), however, reevaluates the efficacy of the various concentrations of alcohol on the moist vegetative forms, which appear quite susceptible to the higher concentrations. Ethyl alcohol enhances the bactericidal effect of mercuric chlorides but reduces the bactericidal effect of phenol and formaldehyde. Glycerol, a polyhydric alcohol, in concentrations of 50 to 70 per cent kills bacteria while preserving most viruses. Berrah and Konetzka (18) have shown that the inhibition of certain organisms by phenethyl alcohol results from a selective and reversible inhibition of the synthesis of bacterial DNA.

INTERFERENCE WITH ACTIVE GROUPS OF PROTEIN.   Enzyme proteins contain a number of reactive groups essential for activity. Among these active groups are the basic and acid groups of the nucleoproteins, carboxyl and amino groups, phenol, sulfhydryl, amide, imidazole, indole, and others. A number of agents act by direct combination with, or alteration of, these reactive groups of the protein molecules. The mercurials and arsenicals tie up the sulfhydryl groups; formaldehyde, anionic detergents, and acid dyes react with basic groups, such as the amino or imidazole groups; basic dyes, quaternary ammonium compounds, and cationic detergents attach themselves to acidic groups, such as hydroxyl groups or phosphoric acid residues. The strength of the bond with these reactive groups determines its reversibility and whether the overall effect is bacteriostatic or bactericidal. The presence of organic matter and other substances containing free reactive groups markedly reduces the effectiveness of agents whose toxic effect is due to combination with reactive groups of active proteins.

Heavy Metals.   Soluble forms of **mercury, arsenic, silver,** and other heavy metals poison enzyme activity by forming mercaptides with sulfhydryl groups. The initial reaction is reversible, and if extraneous SH groups are provided in the form of glutathione or thioglycollate, most of the cells recover. After prolonged contact with mercury, or at higher concentrations, an irreversible combination is formed which kills the organism.

Compounds of the heavy metals have a definite but limited use. The phenol coefficients of these substances are very high when measured by the routine method, but when tested in a medium containing an antidote for the excess metal, it drops to or below the level of phenol. For this reason these compounds are more effective as bacteriostatic than as bactericidal agents. Mercuric chloride under favorable conditions is a powerful germicide, which is usually employed at a concentration of 1:1,000. Many organic compounds of mercury have been prepared in the hope of finding a perfect antiseptic. Organic compounds of mercury, such as Merthiolate, Metaphen, and Mercurochrome, are relatively nonirritating and have been used as antiseptics for the skin and mucous membranes, although studies suggest that they are not as effective in the animal body as in vitro experiments indicate.

Mercury ointments, bismuth compounds, and organic arsenicals such as the arsphenamines were used in the treatment of syphilis before the introduction of penicillin. Copper sulfate prevents the growth of algae in impounded waters. Silver nitrate in a 1 per cent solution is instilled routinely in the eyes of all newborn babies to prevent the development of gonococcal ophthalmia. The antiseptic effect of silver salts is reduced by both proteins and chlorides.

Oxidizing Agents.   Chief among these agents are the **halogens, hydrogen peroxide,** and **per-**

manganate. The weak oxidizing agents convert SH groups to the oxidized S-S form, while stronger ones take it on to some nonreversible stage of oxidation and also attack phenol, indol, and amino groups.

Free chlorine, bromine, iodine, and fluorine are highly toxic to bacteria in the order listed. Chlorine is commonly used to disinfect drinking water and purify the water of swimming pools. When added to water of pH values above 2.0, it forms hydrochlorous acid and hydrochloric acid, the former being the active germicidal agent. Free chlorine may be added to water from cylinders of the gas or derived from hypochlorites, such as chloride of lime (calcium hypochlorite). Only a few parts of chlorine per million parts of water are required unless there is an excess of organic material in the water which produces irreversible reactions with chlorine. This chlorine demand of the water must be calculated and sufficient chlorine added to leave the desired amount of free chlorine. The oxidation of glucose by bacterial cells is inhibited by chlorine, and the enzyme triosephosphate dehydrogenase is reported to be particularly susceptible (121).

The cysts of *Entamoeba histolytica* are much more resistant to chlorine than *E. coli,* but the virus of poliomyelitis has about the same resistance as *E. coli.* The value of chlorine in the destruction of this virus in swimming pools is discussed by Reddish (173).

A solution of iodine contains diatomic iodine, I_2, and triiodide, I_3^-. Diatomic iodine is the important constituent, but its relative concentration is decreased by the addition of an iodide salt, usually added to bactericidal preparations to increase the solubility of the iodine. The N-halogenation of proteins is believed to be the metabolic site of attack (5).

Iodine tincture, U.S.P. contains 2 per cent metallic iodine and 2.4 per cent sodium iodide dissolved in diluted alcohol (approximately 46 per cent). This is one of the most effective agents for sterilizing catgut and is effective in the sterilization of the skin. This mild tincture has largely replaced the strong iodine tincture containing 7 per cent iodine and 5 per cent potassium iodide in 83 per cent alcohol. Since the germicidal effect of iodine is affected very little by the presence of organic materials, it has been used in preference to chlorine for the emergency treatment of small quantities of drinking water. The value of iodine as an antiseptic has been subjected to critical study by Gershenfeld and Witlin (76).

Hydrogen peroxide (H_2O_2) in a 3 per cent solution is a harmless but not very effective antiseptic. Its action is brief, limited by the presence of organic materials, and rapidly destroyed by the catalases of bacteria and tissues. Potassium permanganate in a 1:1,000 dilution or less is a standard treatment for certain types of urologic infections. It is a strong disinfectant but combines readily with inert organic materials.

Dyes. Many of the coal tar dyes not only stain bacteria but inhibit their growth in high dilutions when tested in ordinary media. At the usual pH range the basic dyes are more effective, and their affinity for the acidic phosphoric acid groups on nucleoproteins has been demonstrated by microscopic observation of their localization in the nuclear structures of tissue cells. Unfortunately, the dyes are readily absorbed and neutralized by serums and other proteins, thus limiting their use to selective agents in culture media and to treatment of local lesions on the skin and in the mouth and vagina. The triphenylmethane dyes, such as crystal violet, gentian violet, and brilliant green, have a selective effect on gram-positive organisms. The acridine, or flavine dyes, also basic dyes, have been studied in great detail by Albert and co-workers (5). The acid dyes are less effective and also less selective than are the basic dyes. Prontosil (4-sulfonamideo-2, 4-di-amino-azobenzene hydrochloride) was introduced as a therapeutic dye by Domagk in 1935 (48). The discovery that the dye was converted in the body to para-aminobenzene sulfonamide was the beginning of the intensive study and synthesis of the sulfonamides.

Formaldehyde. Formaldehyde is one of the least selective of the agents acting on proteins. At pH 9.5 and above it blocks the free amino groups; at pH 6 it attacks the nitrogen of the imidazole ring of histidine; and at pH values below 5 it is fixed mainly in amide and guanidyl groups. It also reacts with indole and sulfhydryl groups. Formaldehyde is a gas which is marketed as a 37 per cent solution called **Formalin.** Formalin is used for coagulating and preserving fresh tissues for microscopic study and is the chief ingredient of embalming fluids. When used in sufficient concentrations, it destroys all organisms including spores. By uniting with the toxic groups of bacterial toxins, such as those of diphtheria and tetanus, the toxicity of these substances is destroyed without destroying the antigenic properties. Many bacterial and rickettsial vaccines are now prepared by treatment with Formalin.

Ethylene Oxide. Ethylene oxide is an alkylating agent commonly employed in gaseous sterilization. Bacterial spores, which are hundreds of times more resistant to heat and chemical disinfectants than are vegetative bacteria, are only slightly more difficult to kill with ethylene oxide than are the vegetative cells. It appears to be effective against all microorganisms (26) if concentration of the gas, time of exposure, and temperature of exposure are well controlled. A certain minimal amount of moisture must be present for sterilization to occur. Ethylene oxide gaseous sterilization has been widely used for the decontamination of medical instruments and articles difficult to sterilize by other procedures (26) and has been suggested for the sterilization of tissue culture media (24).

INTERFERENCE WITH THE PROSTHETIC GROUP OF ENZYMES. A number of enzymes contain prosthetic groups essential for activity. Some of these contain iron and copper, and are readily inhibited by hydrogen sulfide, cyanide, hydroxylamine, and azide. Calcium-requiring enzymes are inhibited by fluoride and oxalate. These agents, however, have not had widespread use for purposes of disinfection.

METABOLITE ANTAGONISM. Competitive antagonism between inhibitor and substrate has been studied intensely since the classic finding of the competitive inhibition of succinic dehydrogenase by malonic acid.

This type of inhibition is based upon the principle that both substrate and inhibitor unite reversibly with the enzyme, but the enzyme-inhibitor union is useless and yields no product of the reaction, serving only to reduce the effective enzyme concentration:

$$E + S \rightleftharpoons ES \longrightarrow E + \text{end product}$$
$$E + I \rightleftharpoons EI$$

Such interference is brought about by antimetabolites sufficiently similar in structure to essential metabolites to be able to combine with the appropriate enzyme protein but sufficiently unrelated so that they are an inadequate substitute for the essential metabolite. The amount of inhibitor present as well as the substrate concentration determines the degree of inhibition. Products of the inhibited reaction also overcome the inhibition (noncompetitive). The sulfonamides, which compete with the essential metabolite *p*-aminobenzoic acid for space on the enzyme

surface, have been studied most intensely and are discussed in the following section (44, 221).

CHEMOTHERAPEUTIC AGENTS

Although many years have elapsed and much progress has been made since Ehrlich first introduced the term "chemotherapy," one is still impressed with the fundamental soundness of his general concepts. As used by Ehrlich the term "chemotherapy" denotes the treatment of parasitic disease by a direct chemical attack upon the invading organisms (55). Chemotherapeutics do not act primarily on the host but combine chemically with certain systems of the parasitic organisms, thus focusing attention on the parasite rather than the host. Ehrlich embodied his theories in his well-known chemoreceptor or side-chain hypothesis, and, although the representation is somewhat pictorial, his own conception of the interaction of drug with its receptor was essentially a chemical one.

Many organic and inorganic substances had been known for years to inhibit the growth of microorganisms, but their indiscriminate affinity for host proteins had limited their use in most instances to topical application and the sterilization of inanimate objects. Advance in the field of chemotherapy was slow, and it was only with the advent of the sulfonamides that a group of compounds was provided which could be tolerated in the body with minimal toxicity.

Metabolite Antagonisms. In recent years the concept of metabolite antagonisms has permeated the thinking in the field of chemotherapy. This concept is not new, since physiologists and pharmacologists for many years have employed antagonists to study the normal functions of metabolites and to determine the mode of action of drugs. It was only with the introduction of the therapeutic agent sulfanilamide that attention was focused on this biologic phenomenon of competition between metabolites and related compounds.

Bacteria are organisms potentially able to synthesize their structural and accessory components from simple compounds, though many, as a result of altered environment, have lost the power to carry out one or more stages of the essential syntheses. In such cases the product of the particular stage of synthesis which fails becomes a **growth factor** which must be added to an artificial nutrient medium. These growth factors, however, are members of a much wider class of **essential metabolites** required by a large range of microorganisms. This point is emphasized by the observation that, in all cases where examination has been made, bacteria which do not need to be supplied with one or more of the growth factors as essential nutrients do, in fact, synthesize these substances.

Sulfonamides. The theory that the bacteriostatic action of the sulfonamides is due to the blocking of an essential enzyme system or systems has been well established. Woods demonstrated that the growth-inhibiting or bacteriostatic action of sulfanilamide against certain bacteria was reversed by a factor contained in a crude concentrate from yeast cells, subsequently shown to be *p*-aminobenzoic acid. In order to reverse or prevent the bacteriostatic effect of sulfanilamide, a more or less constant molar ratio of *p*-aminobenzoic acid to sulfanilamide was required over a wide range of concentrations (221).

Woods and Fildes (222) proposed the theory that sulfonamides function by interfering with the essential metabolite, *p*-aminobenzoic acid, and thereby inhibit growth. They suggested that such inhibition requires an inhibitor closely related to the essential metabolite so that it can fit the same enzyme, but sufficiently unrelated so that it is an inadequate substitute for the essential metabolite (Fig. 2). The theory thus was based on the existence of a competition between the sulfonamide and *p*-aminobenzoic acid for a site on the enzyme surface. At the time of Woods' work *p*-aminobenzoic acid was not known to be a metabolite, but shortly after his postulation of the role of the compound in metabolism abundant proof from various sources substantiated his claim. *p*-Aminobenzoic acid was found in many living cells and was shown to be an essential nutrient for several microorganisms.

Inhibition by the sulfonamides is overcome not only by *p*-aminobenzoic acid but also by a number of secondary antagonists, including folic (pteroylglutamic) acid, methionine, serine, thymine, purines, and others. The major effect of the sulfonamides lies in their prevention of the synthesis by bacteria of pteroyl compounds, derivatives of *p*-aminobenzoic (Fig. 3). Organisms which cannot synthesize pteroylglutamic acid from *p*-aminobenzoic acid and therefore require it as a growth factor are relatively insusceptible even to large amounts of the sulfonamides. This is because the metabolic defect induced by these drugs is already present in such organisms (221). The activity of the nucleic acid derivatives, various amino acids, and vitamin B_{12} has been explained on the basis of a requirement for a coenzyme containing pteroylglutamic acid at some stage in the synthesis of these substances. Growth inhibition by sulfonamides can therefore be counteracted competitively by *p*-aminobenzoic acid or noncompetitively by pteroylglutamic acid or by products of reactions catalyzed by a pteroylglutamic acid coenzyme. The point of inhibition by the sulfonamides in the enzymic conversion of PABA to folic acid has been localized (25) and Hotchkiss and Evans, using a genetic approach, have studied the fine structure of a genetically modified enzyme in sulfonamide-resistant pneumococci (97).

Many sulfonamide derivatives have been introduced, some of which are more active and effective clinically than the original sulfanilamide. The therapeutic fitness of a chemotherapeutic remedy is difficult to assay

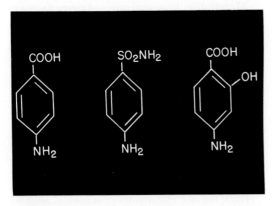

Fig. 2. Structural relationship between *p*-aminobenzoic acid (left), sulfanilamide (center), and *p*-aminosalicylic acid (right).

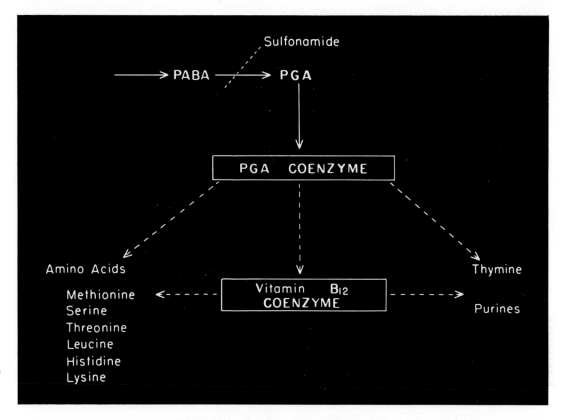

Fig. 3. Site of action of the sulfonamides.

completely on the basis of in vitro activity. Therapeutic efficacy, however, has been shown for a number of derivatives, including sulfadiazine, sulfamerazine, sulfisoxazole (Gantrisin), sulfamethoxypyridazine (Kynex), and sulfadimethoxine (Madribon) (134, 136, 153).

The sulfonamides are effective against infections caused by the β-hemolytic streptococcus, B. anthracis, E. coli, Shigella sp., V. comma, Past. pestis, H. ducreyi, and the viruses of trachoma and lymphogranuloma venereum. When sulfonamides and penicillin are equally effective, the latter is preferred because of its lower toxicity; but when sulfonamides and streptomycin are equally effective, the former are usually selected because they are less toxic. Of the many diseases once treated with sulfonamides, antibiotic therapy has largely replaced the sulfonamides in all except cholera, bacillary dysentery, chancroid, lymphogranuloma venereum, trachoma, and in uncomplicated urinary tract infections (136). In meningococcal meningitis most clinicians prefer the sulfonamides to penicillin because of their greater penetration into the cerebrospinal fluid (91).

Sulfamethoxypyridazine and sulfadimethoxine, two of the newer sulfonamides, are well absorbed from the gastrointestinal tract and are excreted slowly in the urine. They penetrate the spinal fluid well and have antibacterial activity about equal to that of sulfadiazine. Their greatest usefulness is in situations in which prolonged treatment or prophylaxis is the objective—as, for example, in the control of chronic urinary-tract infections (101).

p-AMINOSALICYLIC ACID (PAS). PAS is one of the most effective antituberculous drugs. It is a PABA analog substituted in a different part of the molecule from the sulfonamides (Fig. 2). Its primary use is in combination with either isoniazid or streptomycin.

ISONIAZID (Isonicotinic acid hydrazide). The introduction of this drug in 1952 represented a spectacular advance in the chemotherapy of tuberculosis. Isoniazid is effective in very low concentrations (0.01 to 0.25 μg/ml) and is very selective in action against *Mycobacteria*. The drug is bactericidal and is active only on growing tubercle bacilli. It penetrates well into body cavities and is effective against intracellular organisms. The most common toxic syndrome manifested clinically by isoniazid is one of vitamin B_6 deficiency seen in patients on large doses for extended periods. The peripheral neuropathy seen in such patients, however, may be prevented by the administration of vitamin B_6 (19). The only other common toxic effect of isoniazid is gastric intolerance seen in 10 per cent of patients.

Like streptomycin, bacterial resistance to isoniazid develops rapidly both in vitro and in vivo. The combination of isoniazid with streptomycin or *p*-aminosalicylic acid markedly reduces the incidence of resistance to isoniazid and at the present time represents the mainstay in the treatment of the disease.

The mechanism of action of isoniazid has been extensively studied, but despite suggestive evidence, no one mechanism can satisfactorily explain why isoniazid demonstrates such marked specificity for the mycobacteria. Structural relationships between isoniazid, niacin, and pyridoxine suggest that the drug might act as an antimetabolite against either of the vitamins (Fig. 4). Although isoniazid has been shown to be a potent inhibitor of beef spleen nicotinamide adenine dinucleotidase (NADase) catalyzing an exchange reaction between the nicotinamide moiety of NAD and analogs such as INH, there is no evidence for interference with niacin metabolism in the tubercle bacillus (81, 227).

A number of observations point to an interference by isoniazid of pyridoxal-dependent enzyme systems. Inhibition of growing tubercle bacilli by minimal concentrations of isoniazid is neutralized by pyridoxal (167, 168,) as well as by a number of amino acids. The transamination (216, 226) and decarboxylation (213, 215) of several amino acids by tubercle bacilli is inhibited by isoniazid, and the inhibition may be prevented by preincubation with pyridoxal phosphate. Certain pyridoxal-dependent enzymes from tissues and other microorganisms have also been found to be inhibited by isoniazid. Basic differences between the amino acid pools of isoniazid-sensitive and resistant tubercle bacilli when grown in the presence of the drug also reveal a derangement of amino acid metabolism, probably reflecting inhibition of various pyridoxal-requiring enzyme systems (214, 216). Davison (45, 46) has proposed that the action of isoniazid is based on the binding of pyridoxal phosphate to yield a pyridoxal-isonicotinyl hydrazone which is inactive. The more recent observation that such a binding does occur sites the locus as the ξ-NH_2-group of a lysine residue situated at the catalytic site of the apoenzyme (205).

Studies on tubercle bacilli that have become resistant to isoniazid have revealed certain important changes in their growth characteristics (65), amino acid metabolism, catalase activity, and pathogenicity (35, 120). A decrease in virulence and loss of ability to synthesize catalase has been noted in many isoniazid-resistant strains isolated from patients on isoniazid therapy (146). Although this observation has been confirmed many times, there is still no satisfac-

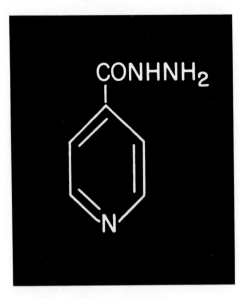

Fig. 4. Isoniazid.

tory explanation of the relation between catalase formation and isoniazid resistance (209). The papers of Toida and Saito (204), Winder (217), and Soru et al. (193) should be consulted for a more extensive discussion of the effect of isoniazid on the hemoproteins and other suggested mechanisms of action (82, 179).

Other Metabolite Analogs. The successful application of the concept of essential metabolites to the field of chemotherapy stimulated many workers to design new agents. By modifying the structure of various vitamins, for example, it was hoped to produce inhibitors which would stand in relation to the vitamin as sulfanilamide does to *p*-aminobenzoic acid. None of these has yielded a practical result as yet, but the increase in knowledge concerning metabolite-analog relationships has had other important applications (144, 220, 223). The biosynthetic incorporation of a number of analogs of vitamins, amino acids, purines, and pyrimidines has been shown, and studies of the altered macromolecule when correlated with changes in function offer much promise (44, 177).

Purine and pyrimidine analogs have been extensively studied as potential chemotherapeutic agents for virus infections and for cancer (108, 142). The effective use of 5-iodo-2-deoxyuridine (IDU) in treating eye infections induced experimentally with two DNA-containing viruses, herpes simplex and vaccinia (105) stimulated renewed interest in the search for additional compounds of this type. IDU has been successfully used in the treatment of superficial corneal disease in man caused by the herpes virus (107) and has been found to prevent the development of cytopathic effects of the varicella-zoster virus in tissue culture (171). It is an analog of thymine and inhibits the utilization of thymine compounds. IDU is incorporated into DNA. The 5-bromo derivative which is also therapeutically effective apparently acts in a similar manner; in its presence cells infected with vaccinia virus yield large amounts of noninfectious, malformed virus particles (53). The 5-fluoro derivative, however, which inhibits synthesis rather than the utilization of thymine compounds, is not clinically useful in treating herpes simplex infections. In addition to the 5-halogenated uridines, a series of substituted 5-halogenated cytidines also possesses therapeutic antiviral activity in experimental keratitis (163), and cytosine arabinoside has proved useful in clinical use both alone and in combination with IDU (106).

There is evidence that derivatives of another type of compound, isatin β-thiosemicarbazone, might also prove useful in the chemoprophylaxis and possibly in the treatment of poxvirus infections (206). This drug inhibits the maturation of vaccinia virus, a DNA virus, but has no apparent effect on the synthesis of its DNA and protein (10).

The specific inhibition of small lipid-free RNA viruses, the picornaviruses, has been under investigation by Tamm and Eggers (201), who have demonstrated an inhibition of the synthesis of viral RNA and protein by 2-(α-hydroxybenzyl)benzimidazole (HBB) and guanidine. Inhibition by these agents is believed to be due to inhibition of the production of virus-induced RNA polymerase. It is hoped that in the near future the use of metabolite analogs can be extended to the treatment of many virus infections. The present approach has already yielded some useful results and is based on the concept that selective compounds can be found or designed which will recognize and combine with a suitable virus-specific target, such as virus RNA, a virus-specific enzyme, or other virus-specific component vital to virus replication. Quantitative differences in the biosynthetic mechanisms of virus and host cells may also provide a basis for selective inhibition of virus multiplication.

Antibiotics. **An antibiotic is a chemical compound derived from or produced by living organisms, which is capable, in small concentration, of inhibiting the life processes of microorganisms.**

Antibiotic substances are distributed widely throughout nature and play an important role in regulating the microbial population of soil, water, sewage, and compost. Among the antibiotics, produced chiefly by bacteria, actinomycetes, fungi, algae, lichens, and higher plants, a number of different kinds of molecules are represented, so that chemically, biologically, or otherwise there is little or no relation between the antibiotics other than their ability to affect adversely the life processes of certain microorganisms. Several hundred antibiotics have been prepared in purified form, but only a few of these have been sufficiently nontoxic to be of use in medical practice.

The inhibition of growth of one bacterial species by the presence of another microorganism had been recognized since the latter part of the nineteenth century. The practical implications of antibiosis were probably first realized by Pasteur and Joubert (160) when they noted the antagonism between *Bacillus anthracis* and other bacteria in cultures. Emmerich and Löw (58) prepared from *Pseudomonas aeruginosa* a water-soluble antibiotic, pyocyanase which inhibited pathogenic cocci, diphtheria, cholera, typhoid, and plague organisms.

From a chronological point of view, the next potential chemotherapeutics to appear were **gramicidin** and **tyrocidin** (50). Dubos was aware of the possibilities inherent in bacterial antagonisms and began the task of searching for a clinically useful antibiotic by means of enrichment cultures. Ordinary soil contains many kinds of bacteria and in order to favor the growth and development of organisms which possibly would be antagonistic to pathogens, soil samples were "fed" cultures of living bacteria. Subsequently a gram-positive, spore-bearing bacillus capable of using micrococcal protein as a source of food, *Bacillus brevis,* was isolated. In pure culture a bactericidal substance, tyrothricin, was produced. Tyrothricin is a crude mixture of the two polypeptides, gramicidin and tyrocidine, which are active only against gram-positive forms. Although they proved to be too toxic for systemic use in man, their discovery and study was of the greatest importance in stimulating further investigation.

The vast majority of antibiotic agents which have been isolated fail to show the requisite selectivity for use in the treatment of infectious diseases. Of those which have demonstrated selective toxicity toward microorganisms, however, tremendous advances have been made toward an understanding of their mechanism of action. Several anatomic or biochemical sites have been proposed as the point of attack of various agents: the cell wall, the cell membrane, the protein and nucleic acid synthesizing systems. The primary effect of an antimicrobial agent is often difficult to distinguish from secondary changes in the physiology or anatomy of an organism, and at higher concentrations some drugs probably have multiple sites of action.

Antibiotics Affecting the Cell Wall. Several of our most effective antibiotics have been shown to affect the bacterial cell wall. These include the penicillins, cycloserine, the bacitracins, and vancomycin. Because of the peculiar characteristics of the bacterial cell wall, it is a particularly vulnerable site for selective antimicrobial activity. Not only is the bacterial wall a rigid supportive covering without which the organisms cannot survive unless placed in a medium of high tonicity, but also present in the cell wall are components unique in their absence from higher plants and from animal cells. These include muramic acid, d-alanine, d-glutamic acid, a, ξ-diaminopimelic acid, and the teichoic acids. The synthesis of these components and their incorporation into wall material provide excellent sites for selective antimicrobial action.

THE PENICILLINS. Twenty years after the introduction of penicillin into clinical medicine, it has become the most widely used antibiotic in the world, with an annual production measured in hundreds of tons. The discovery of **penicillin** in 1929 was accidental. Fleming (70) observed that cultures of *Staphylococcus aureus* which had been contaminated by a mold became transparent and underwent lysis. He ultimately identified the mold as *Penicillium notatum* and showed that a pure culture of the mold in a liquid medium produced a substance, penicillin, which, even if diluted 1:500, completely inhibited the growth of pyogenic and certain other gram-positive organisms but was inactive against gram-negative forms. Fleming also demonstrated that active filtrates were almost completely nontoxic for animals and that it would be a useful antiseptic for infected wounds. Subsequent attempts to isolate the active principle were unsuccessful because of its instability and low concentration in culture filtrates. In 1938 Chain, Florey, and their associates (1, 32) undertook the task of purifying the active principle. These workers succeeded in

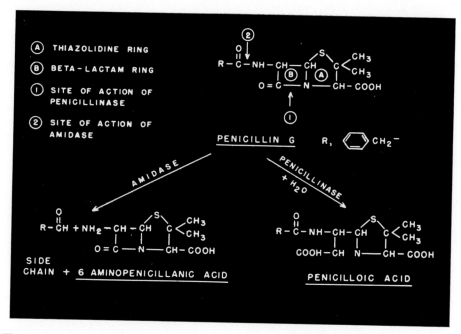

Fig. 5. Structure of penicillin G and products of its enzymatic hydrolysis. (From Klein and Finland. *New England J. Med.*, 269:1019, 1963.)

obtaining a water-soluble powder which was effective in vitro and in vivo for a number of organisms. Extensive studies of the chemistry, bacteriology, and pharmacology of the drug culminated in the production of a substance which is still the most unique and satisfactory therapeutic weapon known.

The chemistry of penicillin was worked out during the war as a result of the joint efforts of many laboratories in the United States and England. The basic structure of penicillin consists of a nucleus of a thiazolidine ring fused to a beta-lactam ring to which, in turn is attached a side chain that determines some of the specific properties of the penicillin (Fig. 5). Only a limited variety of penicillins could be prepared until total synthesis of the 6-aminopenicillanic acid nucleus was achieved in 1957 (186). As a result, three new groups of semisynthetic penicillins have been introduced for clinical use: (1) **acid-resistant penicillins** which are acid stable, well absorbed orally, and possess an antibacterial spectrum similar to that of penicillin G; (2) **penicillinase-resistant penicillins** which are effective against penicillinase-producing staphylococci; and (3)

broad-spectrum penicillins which are well absorbed orally and possess greater activity against some gram-negative species (116, 117, 118).

The introduction of penicillin revolutionized the treatment of many infectious diseases. It is effective against practically all of the gram-positive organisms as well as gram-negative cocci and spirochetes. Remarkable success has been achieved with penicillin in streptococcal and staphylococcal infections, in subacute bacterial endocarditis, gonorrhea, pneumonia, syphilis, gas gangrene, actinomycosis, and a number of surgical conditions.

Except for the appearance of penicillin-resistant staphylococci, the development of drug-resistant strains in the course of treatment with penicillin has been negligible. The incidence of strains of staphylococci highly resistant to penicillin, however, has increased at an alarming rate (13). Although staphylococcus infections responded to penicillin therapy initially, by the mid-1950's as many as 90 per cent of staphylococcal infections seen in hospital settings were associated with penicillin-resistant strains. Penicillin-resistant

Table 1. Names and Structures of Various Penicillins

R Group	Chemical Name	Generic Name	Properties
⬡—CH₂—	Benzyl P	Penicillin G	A, C, E
⬡—O—CH₂—	Alpha-phenoxy-methyl P	Penicillin V	A, C, F
⬡—O—CH— (CH₃)	Alpha-phenoxy-ethyl P	Phenethicillin	A, C, F
⬡—CH— (NH₂)	Alpha-amino-benzyl P	Ampicillin	B, C, F
⬡—O—CH₃ / —O—CH₃	Dimethoxyphenyl P	Methicillin	A, D, E
⬡—C—C— (N C—CH₃, O)	5-methyl-3-phenyl-4-isoxazolyl P	Oxacillin	A, D, F

A = Antibacterial spectrum similar to penicillin G
B = Wider antibacterial spectrum than penicillin G
C = Penicillinase-susceptible
D = Penicillinase-resistant
E = Acid-susceptible
F = Acid-resistant

staphylococci produce an enzyme, penicillinase, which splits the beta-lactam ring of the penicillin nucleus, thus rendering the antibiotic antibacterially inactive. A direct relationship has been shown between the penicillinase production and resistance of staphylococcal strains to penicillin G and to phenethicillin (4). The development of penicillinase-resistant semisynthetic penicillins has given hope to clinicians concerned with problems of staphylococcal infections. Among the penicillins resistant to hydrolysis by penicillinase are methicillin, oxacillin, cloxacillin, diphenicillin, and nafcillin (123, 151, 190). A description and clinical evaluation of these compounds is found in the review of Klein and Finland (117). Semisynthetic penicillins such as ampicillin offer promise in the handling of certain infections by gram-negative organisms (118). Against *H. influenzae, Salmonella typhosa, S. paratyphi A, S. paratyphi B* and *S. typhimurium,* ampicillin is more active than penicillin G, the tetracyclines, or chloramphenicol (122).

In general, amazing levels of penicillin can be tolerated in man. There are, however, a number of cases of adverse host reactions, usually related to hypersensitivity phenomena (34). According to recent concepts, the haptenes responsible for penicillin hypersensitivity are penicillin derivatives rather than the penicillin molecule itself (29). A penicillin derivative, penicilloyl-polylysine, has been employed as a skin-test material to determine correlation between skin reactions and systemic penicillin allergy (182). The preliminary results of this type of testing seem promising.

All of the biologically active variants of the penicillin molecule appear to function in a similar manner. Penicillin is bacteriostatic at low concentrations but bactericidal at higher ones. This inhibition occurs, however, only under conditions of growth. Bizarre forms and other morphologic abnormalities develop in cells exposed to penicillin (52). These observations provided the first suggestion for the site of action of penicillin. Lederberg (131, 133) subsequently demonstrated the production by *E. coli* of osmotically sensitive swollen forms closely resembling the protoplasts of lysozyme-sensitive organisms, when the organisms were grown in the presence of penicillin and 10 per cent sucrose. This phenomenon has since been demonstrated for a variety of microorganisms when cultured in the presence of penicillin in a hypertonic medium (140).

Biochemical evidence for the site of action of penicillin resulted from the finding that staphylococci grown in the presence of penicillin accumulate within the cells certain uridine diphosphate derivatives of a muramic acid peptide, the "Park nucleotides," the most complex of which has the structure shown in Figure 6. The content of N-acetylmuramic acid, *d*-glutamic acid, *dl*-alanine, and *l*-lysine found in the uridine nucleotide complex is the same as that found in the cell wall of the organism. The accumulation of

nucleotide when cells are grown in the presence of penicillin is believed to result from an impairment of cell wall synthesis. The lethal action of penicillin could thus be attributed to the formation of osmotically sensitive forms of the organism during growth in an unprotected medium (195, 197).

Although it is reasonable to assume that penicillin inhibits one or more enzymes involved in the synthesis of the cell wall, the mechanism of this interference is not known. Since isolated cell walls appear to be devoid of enzymatic activity, the wall substance is probably synthesized within the protoplast membrane. In *Staphylococcus aureus* radio-penicillin is fixed by a lipoprotein component, probably originating in the protoplast membrane (40) and in Salmonella the membrane has been shown to be the primary site of penicillin action (127). The most suggestive evidence of the enzymatic reaction site of penicillin is that it inhibits a process involved in the insertion of N-acetylmuramic acid into the mucopeptide polymer (73). N-acetylmuramic acid has been shown to bear a structural analogy to penicillin in the

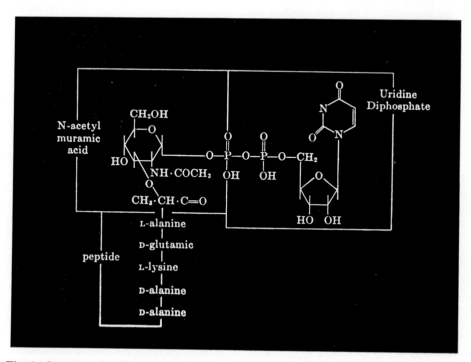

Fig. 6. Structure of a "Park nucleotide," a uridine nucleotide accumulated by *Staphylococcus aureus* when grown in the presence of penicillin. (From Gale. *Pharmacol. Rev.*, 15:481, 1963.)

location of its hydrogen-bonding groups (37). Until, however, the synthesis of wall polymer is achieved in a cell-free system by the direct demonstration of the incorporation of the muramic acid peptide moiety from the nucleotide into the wall mucopeptide, the precise nature of the chemical reaction inhibited by penicillin is unknown.

CYCLOSERINE. This antibiotic is bactericidal and has a simple structure resembling that of *d*-alanine. Its chief use has been in the treatment of tuberculosis, but severe toxicity has limited its clinical usefulness. Protoplasts are formed by culture in the presence of **cycloserine** in a hypertonic medium. This observation, together with the finding that a uridine muramic acid peptide accumulates in cycloserine-treated organisms, suggests inhibition of cell wall synthesis. The accumulated nucleotide, however, differs from that found in penicillin-treated cells in that it lacks the two terminal *d*-alanine residues in the peptide sequence. *d*-Alanine neutralizes competitively growth inhibition by cycloserine and prevents the accumulation of nucleotide. The structural similarity of cycloserine and *d*-alanine is shown in Figure 7. The enzymic basis of the antagonism between cycloserine and *d*-alanine lies in the drug's inhibition of alanine racemase and of *d*-alanyl • *d*-alanine synthetase (154, 195).

THE BACITRACINS. These are products of the "Tracey" strain of *Bacillus licheniformis*. Commercial **bacitracin** with a potency of about 50 units per milligram is a neutral water-soluble substance consisting of a mixture of peptides of low molecular weight. The drug is bactericidal, with a spectrum of activity similar to that of penicillin. It is not absorbed from the gastrointestinal tract, and its nephrotoxicity limits parenteral use. It has proved effective upon topical application in infections caused by gram-positive organisms, including those resistant to penicillin. Because of its selective activity against gram-positive organisms, bacitracin is usually combined in topical preparations with polymyxin or neomycin, which are active against gram-negative bacteria.

Bacitracin A is the main component of this group of cyclic polypeptides (3, 41). It has been reported to resemble penicillin in action, causing protoplast formation and the accumulation of mucopeptide nucleotides (2). Additional mechanisms of antibacterial action of bacitracin are discussed by Smith and Weinberg (191). The physiologic role of bacitracin to the cell which produces it appears to be in serving as a constitutive part of the spore formed in the final phase of the life cycle of the organism (17).

VANCOMYCIN. Another antibiotic which preferentially inhibits the incorporation of labeled amino acids into the cell wall is **vancomycin** (104). It also causes the accumulation in the cells of uridine nucleotides. Vancomycin and penicillin, however, appear to be bound at different sites, since pretreatment with vancomycin has no effect on the subsequent fixation of penicillin while bacitracin does (176).

Vancomycin is an antibiotic of high molecular weight derived from *Streptomyces orientalis*. Its structure is unknown. Its primary use has been in the treatment of infections due to strains of *Staphylococcus aureus* resistant to other drugs. It is one of the most potent agents for the treatment of such infections (42). Vancomycin does not show cross-resistance with other antibiotics, and staphylococci are very difficult to make resistant to vancomycin in vitro. Vancomycin is not absorbed from the intestinal tract, however, and must be administered intravenously. It has some side effects and toxic potentialities, but when it is used intelligently, such effects can be minimized (112).

Antibiotics Affecting the Cell Membrane (73). The cell membrane is a very vital

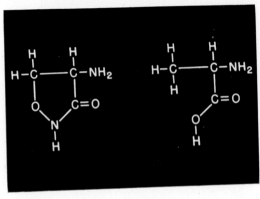

Fig. 7. Structural relationship between cycloserine and *d*-alanine.

highly organized cellular structure, distinct from the cell wall. It has three major functions: (1) to pose an osmotic barrier to free diffusion between the internal and external media, (2) to effect concentration of nutrients and metabolites within the cell, and (3) to serve as a site for various respiratory enzymes and for the biosynthesis of certain cell components. Several antibiotics have been shown to impair one or more of these functions, resulting in major disturbances in the metabolism and viability of the cell. One of the simplest and most direct tests for membrane damage is the release of purine and pyrimidine derivatives with an absorption in the ultraviolet at 260 mμ. With such agents as the polypeptide tyrocidin or the cationic detergents, there is a direct relationship between the amount of drug added and the amount of soluble materials released from the cells. The action of such agents that attack the cell membrane is independent of growth, beginning immediately when cells and antibiotic come together, and is not affected by the presence of such antibiotics as chloramphenicol that interfere with protein synthesis.

POLYMYXIN. The **polymyxins** are peptide drugs of relatively large molecular size, poor diffusibility, and significant toxicity. It is a family of drugs derived from different strains of *Bacillus polymyxa* and designated by the letters A, B, C, D, E. The polymyxins are selective antimicrobial substances specifically active against gram-negative rods. Only polymyxin B is presently used in clinical medicine. **Colistin** belongs in the group of polymyxins and is either identical with or closely related to polymyxin E (184). Although a number of toxic manifestations are observed following parenteral administration, the polymyxins have been found most useful in the treatment of various clinical conditions, especially those caused by *Pseudomonas aeruginosa*. The increasing importance of *Pseudomonas* and other gram-negative rod infections, especially in debilitated hospitalized persons, has increased the usefulness of the polymyxins during the past few years (103).

The antibiotic spectrum of colistin is identical with the polymyxins, and there is cross-resistance between these agents. On the basis of clinical testing colistin appears to be comparable to polymyxin B sulfate with regard to clinical effectiveness, and somewhat less toxic (9, 71). Clinical response is largely related to the penetrability of the infection site and the patient's own defense mechanisms.

Polymyxin brings about a disorientation of the lipoprotein membrane so that it no longer functions as an osmotic barrier. A linear relationship has been observed between the amount of antibiotic added and the proportion of cells killed, the number of cells killed being related to the amount of 260 mμ-absorbing material released. By use of a fluorescent derivative of polymyxin, the antibiotic was shown to combine specifically with the membrane underlying the cell wall (157). Sensitive cells absorb more antibiotic than resistant cells, and if cells are broken after treatment with polymyxin, the antibiotic is found in combination with small particles of lipoprotein. The interaction between the polymyxins and the membrane is believed to involve ionized phosphate groups of the lipids (157). Treatment of cells with colistin sulfate alters the morphologic appearance of the organism as demonstrated by electron microscopy of ultra-thin sections. Nuclear material disappears from its normal sites, and the cytoplasm loses its granularity and becomes homogeneous (33). Both of these effects probably result from primary damage of the cell membrane.

NOVOBIOCIN. This antibiotic is bactericidal for gram-positive organisms and has been used primarily against penicillin-resistant staphylococci. There is lack of agreement on the specific nature of its action (44, 73). A drug-induced membrane lesion is suggested by the finding that substrates for β-galactosidase are excluded from intact cells of a cryptic mutant of *E. coli*, but can enter **novobiocin** treated cells (21). Brock (23) credits the production of a membrane lesion by novobiocin to its induction of a magnesium ion deficiency. On the other hand, novobiocin causes the accumulation in *Staphylococcus aureus* of the same wall precursor nucleotides as penicillin (196). In contrast to penicillin, novobiocin inhibits the growth of penicillin-induced protoplasts. The effect on wall synthesis is believed to be a consequence of rather than a cause of the membrane damage (44).

NYSTATIN AND AMPHOTERICIN B. These two antibiotics are members of the polyene group of antimicrobial agents and are clinically effective against certain of the pathogenic fungi. Derived from species of *Streptomyces,* their structure is characterized by the presence of a large ring with a conjugated double-bond system. In both drugs there is an amino sugar, mycosamine. **Nystatin** has proved very useful in the treatment of infections caused by *Candida albicans* (93). **Amphotericin B** is effective against various systemic mycoses, such as cryptococcosis, blastomycosis, histoplasmosis, and coccidioidomycosis (14, 156). Although amphotericin B is a very valuable and potent antifungal drug, its use is frequently attended with troublesome but generally not prohibitive side effects, including various manifestations of nephrotoxicity and certain electrolyte imbalances (8, 15, 57).

These drugs have no effect on bacteria. The protoplasmic membrane of the fungus appears to be the site of action. Nystatin treatment causes a leakage of intracellular constituents (110, 141), and the drug is bound by protoplasts or membrane-containing particles of sensitive but not of resistant organisms (111). A variety of evidence has been presented to show that the binding site on the membrane contains a sterol (125). Sterols are not found in the bacterial membrane, probably accounting for the selective activity of the polyene antibiotics on fungi.

Antibiotics Affecting Protein Synthesis. There are various points in the synthesis of proteins at which inhibitors could act to produce the over-all result of inhibition of protein synthesis. Since there are many ancillary reactions—such as the synthesis of amino acids, purine and pyrimidine bases, or nucleotides and membrane transport—which will give the end result of cessation of protein synthesis, the effect of an antibiotic on such reactions must be negligible before a true role for it in protein synthesis can be sited.

CHLORAMPHENICOL (CHLOROMYCETIN) (22). The antibiotic properties of **chloramphenicol** were first described by Ehrlich in 1947. Originally obtained from *Strepto-*

myces venezuelae, it has a relatively simple structure, and is now marketed as the synthetic product (Fig. 8). The synthetic product has been shown to be equally effective and identical in every respect to the natural substance. Chloramphenicol is effective against a wide range of organisms. It is active against a number of gram-negative and gram-positive bacteria, certain rickettsiae, and the psittacosis-lymphogranuloma organisms. It is particularly useful in the treatment of typhoid fever, an infection notably resistant to most chemotherapeutics. Its indiscriminate use, however, in countries where diarrheal diseases and enteric fevers are very common has induced the appearance of many drug-resistant organisms (158). Chloramphenicol should be used only with specific indication and only when the patient is under close supervision because of the drug's inherent bone-marrow toxicity. There have been several reports of fatal chloramphenicol-induced aplastic anemia, but the more typical bone-marrow depression is related to dose and time, is reversible if the drug is stopped, and is detectable in its early stages (62).

One of the first observations relating chloramphenicol toxicity to protein synthesis was the observation by Gale and Folkes that chloramphenicol blocks protein synthesis while allowing further synthesis of nucleic acids (74). The site of inhibition has been shown to involve the transfer of amino acids from the transfer RNA component of RNA to the peptide-bond forming site in the ribosome (150, 203). The specific nature of the

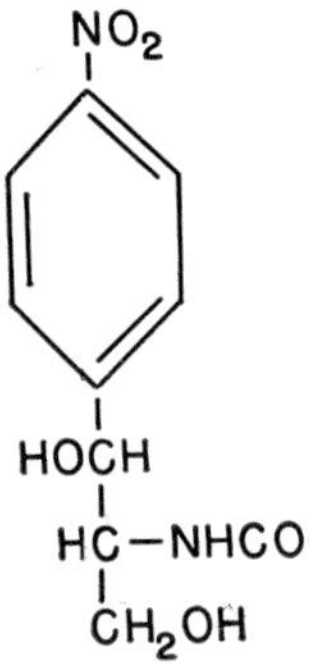

$$NO_2$$

HOCH
|
HC—NHCOCHCl_2
|
CH_2OH

Fig. 8. Chloramphenicol.

interference at this site is not known. Gale (73) and Davis and Feingold (44) give a more complete discussion of mechanisms involved in the bacteriostatic activity of the drug.

THE TETRACYCLINES. The antimicrobial spectra of the antibiotics included in this group are almost identical. They are effective against a large variety of both gram-positive and gram-negative species, rickettsiae, and the organisms of lymphogranuloma and psittacosis (94). **Tetracycline** is the parent compound; **chlortetracycline** (aureomycin) and its derivative **demethylchlortetracycline** (declomycin) substitute a chlorine atom in the basic structure, and **oxytetracycline** (terramycin) possesses an hydroxyl group in the ring (Fig. 9). There is almost complete cross-resistance between them.

Chlortetracycline is a golden yellow compound obtained by Duggar (51) from *Streptomyces aureofaciens*. Its activity appears to be about equal to that of penicillin for the gram-positive cocci and to that of streptomycin for the gram-negative bacilli. It is extensively used in the treatment of most rickettsial infections, lymphogranuloma venereum, granuloma inguinale, herpes zoster, and primary atypical pneumonia. Oxytetracycline, developed by the careful screening of a large number of fungi, possesses an antibacterial spectrum similar to that of chlortetracycline. Dozens of additional tetracycline antibiotics have been synthesized or produced by fermentation with the hope that more effective nontoxic compounds might be developed. Some of these show potential promise for clinical therapy (113, 119). Adverse side effects to the tetracyclines have been minimal, although they may cause some gastric disturbances, skin photosensitivity, or disturbances in nitrogen metabolism (187, 188). A staphylococcus enteritis resulting from the suppression of the normal microbial flora of the gastrointestinal tract has been observed in some patients.

Although investigated less intensively than chloramphenicol, the tetracyclines also interfere with protein synthesis (74). In studies with cell-free preparations of *E. coli*, oxytetracycline, like chloramphenicol, interferes with the transfer of amino acids from the amino acyl s-RNA to polypeptides (175).

The tetracyclines have been shown to inhibit the incorporation of leucine into protein of cell-free systems from rat liver, but the amount of inhibition was less and much higher drug concentrations were required than in a cell-free system from *E. coli* (72). More work is necessary to determine whether the inhibition of protein synthesis by the tetracyclines is the primary cause of bacteriostasis by this group of antibiotics. The chelating properties of the tetracycline molecule possibly influence antibiotic action (6), as has been shown by the ability of certain metals to neutralize bacteriostatic activity. Whether this chelating activity influences the integrity of active ribosomes which are dependent upon magnesium for proper functioning or whether neutralization by magnesium brings about a conversion of the free drug to an inactive complex is not known.

ERYTHROMYCIN. **Erythromycin** is the most commonly used member of the **macrolide** antibiotics, a group of antibiotics which also includes **oleoandomycin**, the **carbomycins,** and the **spiramycins.** All have a large lactone ring in their structure (84). Erythromycin, obtained from *Streptomyces erythreus,* is most active against the gram-positive cocci, including strains of penicillin-resistant staphylococci. It is also active against species of *Neisseria, Haemophilus,* and diphtheria bacilli, but it is inactive against most coliform and enteric organisms (181). Erythromycin is effective only against multiplying bacteria and may be either bacteriostatic or

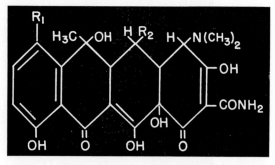

Fig. 9. General structure of the tetracyclines. Tetracycline: $R_1 = H$, $R_2 = H$; Chlortetracycline: $R_1 = Cl$, $R_2 = H$; Oxytetracycline: $R_1 = H$, $R_2 = OH$.

bactericidal, depending on the sensitivity of the organism, concentration of the drug, and population density (86, 208).

Few studies have been made on the mechanism of erythromycin action, but there is some evidence, based on kinetic studies in multiplying *E. coli* organisms, that this antibiotic interferes with protein synthesis but has little or no effect on the synthesis of nucleic acids. An explanation for lack of susceptibility of many gram-negative organisms to the macrolides may lie in the exclusion of the drug by the cell wall of the *Enterobacteriaceae* from sensitive sites within the cell. This is based on the observation that a stable L-form derived from *Proteus mirabilis* was inhibited by less than one-thousandth the concentration of erythromycin required to inhibit the parent strain from which it was derived (202).

PUROMYCIN. This antibiotic, produced by *Streptomyces alboniger,* fails to demonstrate selective toxicity and thus cannot be used in clinical medicine. Its inhibitory activity extends to the bacteria, algae, proto-zoa, and mammalian cells. **Puromycin** has been very useful in the study of various stages of protein synthesis, however, and has been found to inhibit protein syntheses by causing premature release of peptides from the ribosome before they are condensed into the newly forming protein (145, 150). The drug bears a structural resemblance to the amino acid end of aminoacyl transfer RNA, which probably accounts for its metabolic interference of amino acid incorporation (225). Puromycin differs from chloramphenicol in its action in that the latter drug interferes with the proper attachment of "messenger" RNA to ribosomes but not with its function once it is bound.

Antibiotics Inhibiting Nucleic Acid Metabolism. A number of antimicrobial agents have been shown to interfere with nucleic acid metabolism, but none of these is sufficiently nontoxic to permit clinical use. This is probably due to a near universality of the reactions involved in nucleic acid metabolism in all species. It is possible, however, that quantitative rather than qualitative

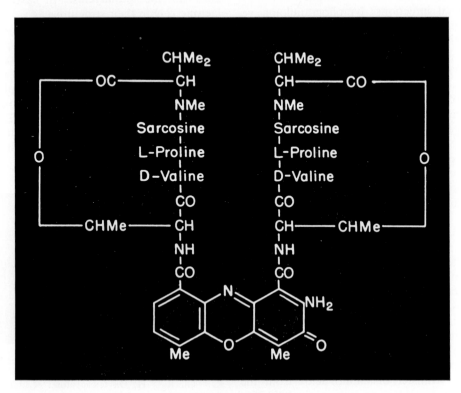

Fig. 10. Actinomycin D.

differences in the faster turnover of components such as messenger RNA or transfer RNA in the microbial system will render it more susceptible to inhibition by these substances.

The **actinomycins** have been very useful as a tool for biochemists in the unraveling of complex biosynthetic mechanisms. There are a series of actinomycins produced by various species of *Streptomyces* that consist of a common phenoxazone chromophore attached to different polypeptides (Fig. 10). Actinomycin selectively inhibits RNA synthesis; the synthesis of protein and DNA is also inhibited but only after a lag period (114). Inhibition probably results from the hydrogen-bonding of actinomycin with the guanine residues of the DNA helix, the amount bound increasing with the guanine content of the DNA polynucleotide (79, 80, 88). The actinomycins have been extremely useful in investigations concerned with DNA synthesis, DNA-dependent syntheses, "messenger" RNA, and virus multiplication (44, 73). They have also been of interest to investigators of cancer chemotherapy (39).

Mitomycin C, also derived from a *Streptomyces,* has both antitumor and antibacterial activity. It selectively affects DNA metabolism by causing a scission of DNA strands (109, 174). In nonkilling doses, mitomycin C inhibits transformation of the pneumococcus to streptomycin resistance (11).

GRISEOFULVIN (135). This is a fungistatic agent derived from cultures of *Penicillium griseofulvum* displaying selective toxicity against superficial fungi (83). The drug accumulates in the keratinized tissues of the skin, hair, and nails. Few toxic manifestations have been observed in patients on long-term therapy. There are a few observations which point to nucleic acid metabolism as the site of drug action, but there is no definitive evidence. Purine nucleotides partially reverse drug action, and there is a structural similarity between griseofulvin and a purine nucleotide (139).

The Streptomycin Group. **Streptomycin** occupies a unique position among the antibiotics because of its preferential selectivity for gram-negative and acid-fast organisms. It was isolated from *Streptomyces griseus* in the Waksman laboratories in 1943 (183) and upon crystallization shown chemically to be a glycoside, a condensation product of streptidine, streptose, and N-methyl-l-glucosamine (Fig. 11). Hydrolyzed fragments of the molecule have only negligible antibiotic activity, but reduction of the formyl group of the streptose moiety to a carbinol group yielded the medically useful drug **dihydrostreptomycin.** Several polybasic antibiotics similar to streptomycin, such as **kana-**

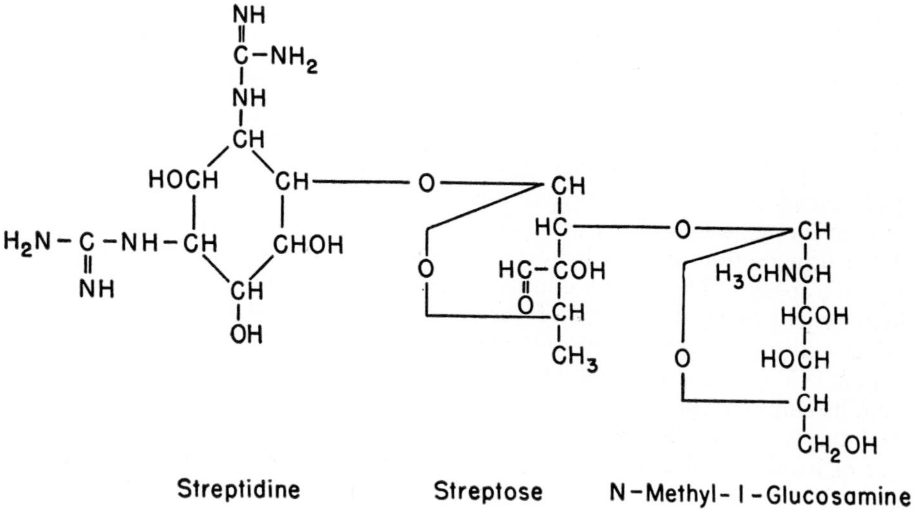

Streptidine   Streptose   N-Methyl-1-Glucosamine

Fig. 11. Streptomycin.

mycin, **neomycin,** and **paromomycin,** have been isolated from various *Streptomyces.* These agents are bactericidal for a wide range of gram-positive and gram-negative species and for the tubercle bacillus (38, 66, 75).

Streptomycin is bactericidal and requires a small amount of growth for demonstration of its lethal effect. Morphologic aberrations resulting from contact of the bacterial cell with the drug have been reported, but there is no gross lysis. In *Mycobacterium tuberculosis* death of the cell due to streptomycin is accompanied by loss of acid-fastness, increase in granulation, and lengthening of bacilli.

Bacterial resistance is a major problem in the clinical use of streptomycin. Some organisms may become resistant to phenomenal amounts almost overnight; other strains may be induced to become moderately resistant by growing them in increasing concentrations of the drug. The problem of resistance will be discussed in greater detail in a later section.

Another shortcoming of streptomycin is its toxicity in man. The most serious toxic manifestations include damage of the eighth cranial nerve and vestibular apparatus; deafness is sometimes produced.

The chief merit of streptomycin lies in its ability to attack certain organisms that are not affected by penicillin. It has proved dramatically successful in treatment of tularemia, plague, meningitis due to *Haemophilus influenzae,* and infections caused by the *Salmonella* group and *Klebsiella pneumoniae.* It has been useful in the control of *Shigella* dysentery, relapsing fever due to *Borrelia recurrentis,* and granuloma inguinale. Widespread use of streptomycin has been made in the treatment of chronic infections of the urinary tract caused by various gram-negative species. The drug has proved of decided benefit in the treatment of early progressive infiltrating pulmonary tuberculosis in man. Cures have resulted in many cases from its employment in the miliary and meningeal forms of the disease and in certain types of localized tuberculosis infection, especially when used in combination with isoniazid.

Several different types of action have been postulated for streptomycin and controversy exists concerning the major site of its lethal effect. Among the effects observed are damage to the cell membrane, cessation of protein synthesis, and the breakdown of RNA. The initial observation by Anand and Davis in 1960 (7) that streptomycin-treated sensitive organisms excrete 5'-ribonucleotides was extended by these and other workers in an attempt to show that the primary action of streptomycin is on the cell membrane. The uptake of streptomycin takes place in two stages: first, a very rapid initial uptake probably due to fixation of the drug by primary acceptors near the cell surface and, second, a larger secondary uptake which follows gradually after some minutes (7). Stimulation of net RNA synthesis and acceleration of potassium efflux, followed by loss of viability and inhibition of protein synthesis, precedes secondary uptake of the drug and subsequent events concerned with impaired respiration, decreases in RNA and DNA synthesis, and RNA breakdown and excretion (49, 207). There is evidence that the primary uptake of streptomycin is an electrostatic interaction with binding at the outer surface of the cell, while the secondary uptake occurs only after the antibiotic has gained access to intracellular binding sites of growing cells. The investigations of Landman and Burchard (126) with streptomycin-dependent *Salmonella* also suggest that the site of action of streptomycin lies in the control of septation and, therefore, in membrane function.

The first indication that streptomycin affects protein synthesis was the observation that the antibiotic inhibits the formation of inducible enzymes required for the oxidation of various aromatic compounds (67). Since this report a number of studies have shown an inhibition by streptomycin of protein synthesis in susceptible bacteria (7, 54, 59, 60, 85). Spotts and Stanier (194) proposed a unitary hypothesis to explain streptomycin activity. They visualize the bacterial ribosomes as the site of action of streptomycin and assume that association of the antibiotic with the ribosomes of streptomycin-sensitive organisms prevents the attachment of "messenger" RNA to these particles, thereby making protein synthesis impossible. This hypothesis is supported by experimental studies with streptomycin-dependent bacteria and stresses the need to explain streptomycin sensitivity, resistance, and dependency by the different reactivity toward streptomycin of one single site of action, the structure and function of which is under the control of a single genetic locus (90, 155). Impairment of ribosome function has been demonstrated directly by studies on amino acid incorporation by cell-free systems (68); ribosomes from resistant and dependent strains were about 1,000 times less sensitive to antibiotic than those from sensitive organisms (69).

There is no doubt that the production of a biochemical lesion both in the cell membrane and at the site of the ribosomes occurs when sensitive organisms are grown in the presence of streptomycin, but it is impossible to say which is the major site of its inhibitory activity. The limited studies which have been made on the mechanism of action of the polycationic antibiotics related to streptomycin indicate that it is probably similar to that of streptomycin (63).

BACTERIOCINS

Bacteriocins are bactericidal protein or polypeptide substances produced by certain strains of a particular family of microorganisms and active only on some other strains of this family. Some bacteriocins are restricted in action to only certain strains of the same species which produce them; this action is conditioned by the presence of specific receptors. Biosynthesis of bacteriocins is associated with a lethal consequence for the producing organisms (159).

Of the bacteriocins, the **colicins** have been studied in most detail (100). The colicins are produced by some strains of the family Enterobacteriaceae. Nearly 20 different colicins have been described and grouped by their bactericidal specificity. Colicin is adsorbed by specific receptors situated on the surface of sensitive organisms. Colicinogeny is a permanent hereditary trait, which may be transferred as a consequence of bacterial conjugation of bacteria of opposite mating type. Colicin agents have also been shown to induce chromosomal recombination. The

colicinogenic property, however, cannot be transferred from the donor parents to the recombinants. The colicins and other bacteriocins, because of the above and other properties, have been classified by Jacob and his coworkers (102) among the episomes, the class of genetic element which may exist in two alternative states.

Some strains of *Bacillus megaterium* produce a soluble material, a **megacin** which exhibits an iso-antagonistic effect on many other strains of this species (95, 100). Megacin appears to be a product of new protein synthesis. Unlike colicin, the mode of action is not associated with the presence of specific receptors on the cell wall of sensitive bacteria, but there is damage of the cell membrane. Other bacteriocin-like substances have been described from other genera but studies on them are incomplete.

DRUG RESISTANCE

With the advent of the sulfonamides and the introduction of bacterial chemotherapy the early recognition that bacteria can easily acquire resistance to these drugs stimulated intensive investigation into the phenomenon of drug resistance. It has now been shown that many bacteria can acquire resistance to various chemotherapeutic drugs and antibiotics, offering a serious threat to the future usefulness of several important chemotherapeutic agents.

Two alternate theories have been advanced to explain the origin of bacterial resistance: (1) adaptation, or resistance induced by some interaction of the drug and organism when together, and (2) selection, or resistance arising independently of the antibiotic by mutation. In the latter case the drug acts only as a selective agent in the isolation of the resistant mutants by the destruction of the susceptible organisms. A strongly selective environment favorable for the growth of the mutant and unfavorable for the normal parent type is required for the appearance of the mutant. Critical evidence distinguishing between the mutational and the adaptive theories has been provided by experiments aimed at deciding whether resistance arises before contact with the drug (28, 31). The fluctuation test of Luria and Delbruck (137) was the first approach and showed that the numbers of resistant colonies obtained from plating independent cultures on a drug-containing medium varied more than would be expected by chance. The best evidence in favor of the mutational origin of resistance was provided by the replica-plating procedure of Lederberg and Lederberg (132) which demonstrated that resistant cells, or cells with a high potentiality of developing resistance, existed in small numbers in the original population before contact with the drug and that resistance was heritable in their progeny. The development of resistance to the sulfonamides, penicillin, streptomycin, chloramphenicol, isoniazid, and other drugs appears to have been adequately explained on the basis of selection of mutants which arise by random mutation, the drug acting only as a selective agent to permit multiplication of the resistant variant and suppress growth of all the drug sensitive organisms.

Evidence that the mechanisms for transfer of drug resistance from parent to progeny is usually genetic has been provided by studies on recombination between resistance and known markers, and by transfer of resistance by transformation and transduction. Watanabe (210) has described more recently a multiple-drug resistance in the Enterobacteriaceae to streptomycin, chloramphenicol, tetracycline, and sulfathiazole, transmitted by "resistance transfer factors" (RTF). The factor is transferred by cell-to-cell contact in about 15 minutes, and the transferred resistance rapidly expressed in the phenotype. RTF appears to have the characteristics of an episome. It replicates faster than the host chromosomes and therefore probably exists in an autonomous state in the cytoplasm. Resistant transductants are unable to transfer RTF, indicating an integration of the episome in the chromosome.

The validity of the mutation theory has been questioned by a number of workers who believe that the distinction between genetic change and adaptation is artificial and that all modifications favoring survival under deleterious conditions should be considered as adaptive by definition, including both mutation followed by selection and induced physiologic alteration (185, 200).

A mutation rate of approximately one per billion cells characterizes mutation to streptomycin resistance (47, 99), while isoniazid has a mutation rate of one per million (199). The degree of resistance available through mutation may be fixed at a low level, subject to further increase (multistep pattern) or it may be quite variable (facultative single-step pattern) allowing full resistance to arise either by one mutation or through a series of mutations. The multistep pattern or accumulating development of resistance by successive steps is often referred to as the penicillin pattern and is also shown by the tetracyclines and chloramphenicol. The facultative single-step pattern is commonly referred to as the streptomycin pattern; it characterizes the development of resistance to streptomycin and isoniazid (27). The facility with which bacteria acquire resistance to streptomycin is unequalled in the whole field of chemotherapy and forms the main obstacle in the successful use of the drug. Resistance may develop gradually, but the change can occur rapidly and is often extreme in degree. Survival curves demonstrating the two patterns of resistance are shown in Figure 12.

Single-step mutation is controlled by a number of loci. With streptomycin the number of loci capable of controlling relatively high degrees of single-step resistance is small, so that only a few types of mutant, characterized by their degrees of resistance and growth rate, are recognized (148). Lower degrees of resistance to streptomycin are controlled by multiple loci, none of which is linked to the locus for a high degree of resistance (211). In multistep mutants additional loci are involved, leading to a pattern of resistance differing from the single-step mutants either in the variety of mutants encountered, as with streptomycin, or in the degree of resistance, as with chloramphenicol. Resistance to chloramphenicol appears to be controlled by multiple loci situated over the entire length of the chromosome investigated (30). With erythromycin, however, which also exhibits a step-by-step accretion of resistance, the mutations behave as linked factors occupying different sites of the same molecule of DNA (170).

Another interesting type of bacterial behavior is that of drug dependence, first observed by Miller and Bohnhoff (147). These workers obtained two types of meningococci following culture on streptomycin-containing media. One was highly resistant to the drug, while the other had become dependent upon streptomycin and would grow only when streptomycin was added to the culture medium. This dependence also persisted in vivo, since mice which were inoculated with dependent organisms and untreated survived while those that were treated with streptomycin died. Dependent strains have been isolated from a number of other bacteria of both gram-negative and gram-positive types, indicating that their occurrence represents a common phenomenon among microorganisms. Organisms dependent upon other antibiotics and drugs have also been demonstrated. Streptomycin-dependent mutants have proved especially useful in the study of the mechanism of action of streptomycin (68, 126).

Physiologic Mechanisms Responsible for Drug Resistance. Any theory for the mode of action of an antibacterial agent should provide an adequate explanation of the phenomena of developed resistance and the selective activity of the agent. Since many drugs have been shown to act by interference with essential enzyme systems, it is probable that the mechanism of resistance is linked in many instances with the production of an altered enzyme. A number of theoretically possible changes in the function of a cell have been suggested as possible mechanisms involved in increased resistance (43). Among these are decreased permeability of the organism to the drug, increased destruction of the inhibitor, increased synthesis of an essential metabolite or drug antagonist, and changes in the properties of an enzyme resulting in a different relative affinity of substrate and antagonist.

In some strains of bacteria it has been shown that a high degree of resistance to the sulfonamides is linked with an increased production of p-aminobenzoic acid (128, 129). Although this correlation has been confirmed

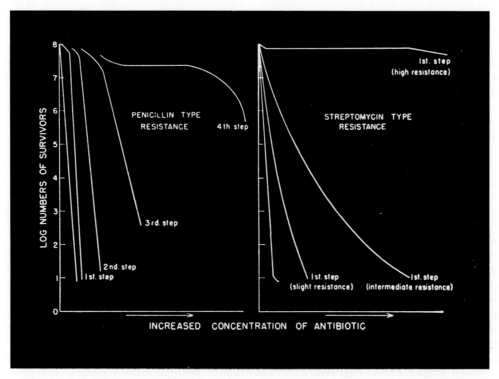

Fig. 12. Penicillin and streptomycin types of resistance pattern. (From Bryson and Demerec, *Ann. New York Acad. Sc.*, 53:285, 1950.)

by a number of workers, there are many instances in which it has been impossible to demonstrate any increased production of the vitamin by sulfonamide-resistant organisms. More recent work on mechanisms involved in resistance to the sulfonamides has focused attention on the production of altered enzymes. In the pneumococci Wolf and Hotchkiss (218) have shown that resistance to the sulfonamides can be explained by the production of enzymes with affinities for the drug that are lower than the affinity exhibited by the enzyme system from strains sensitive to the drug. Pato and Brown (161) have also been able to demonstrate in mutants resistant to sulfathiazole enzyme systems for the conversion of p-aminobenzoic acid into folic acid compounds that are different from the enzyme system of the parent strain only in that sulfonamides are less effective in inhibiting the reaction for the formation of dihydropteroic acid from p-aminobenzoic acid. The altered enzymes of the resistant mutant differ structurally from the enzyme of the parent strain in that they do not combine as readily with sulfonamides. These workers also observed, however, an additional type of mutant believed to differ in its permeability characteristics from the parent strain in such a way that sulfonamides cannot readily permeate the cells. These observations indicate that a single mechanism is not always satisfactory in explaining resistance to a single drug by all strains or species.

Studies on the mechanism of resistance to streptomycin revealed a difference between streptomycin-resistant and sensitive organisms at the ribosome level of protein formation. Cell-free extracts from a streptomycin-resistant *Mycobacterium* incorporated labeled amino acids into protein in the presence of the antibiotic, whereas an extract from sensitive cells was inhibited (59). In an extension of this approach, Flaks and his coworkers (68) have shown that streptomycin interferes with the polyuridylate (poly U) stimulated incorporation of labeled phenylalanine into acid-insoluble polypeptide, thus offering evidence in support of the theory of Spotts and Stanier (194) that the ribosomes of the various strains have different affinities

for or dependencies upon streptomycin. The production of qualitatively altered enzymes provides one of the most attractive mechanisms for the explanation of increased resistance to an antibacterial agent.

The early observation that bacteria differ markedly in their sensitivity to penicillin was followed by the discovery in a wide variety of both gram-negative and gram-positive bacteria of an enzyme, **penicillinase,** which destroys penicillin. The action of this enzyme is due to an opening of the beta-lactam ring of the penicillin molecule with the formation of the antibiotically inactive penicilloic acid. It would be preferable to call this penicillinase "penicillin-β-lactamase" to distinguish it from penicillin amidase and other possible penicillin-destroying enzymes (166). All naturally occurring penicillin-resistant staphylococcal strains as well as penicillin-resistant strains of many other species owe their resistance to the formation of this single enzyme. The action of penicillinase, however, does not give a complete answer to the problem of resistance. No penicillinase can be detected in several species of gram-negative bacteria completely resistant to penicillin. Also, artificially induced penicillin resistance in laboratory strains is not accompanied by penicillinase production. Barber (13) prefers to call this latter type of resistance in which the organism is capable of growing in the presence of unchanged antibiotic "drug-tolerance."

Penicillin-sensitive strains of *Staphylococcus aureus* do not produce any detectable penicillinase, and it has not been possible to demonstrate mutations from absolute penicillinase negativity to any degree of penicillinase positivity. Penicillin-resistance evoked by laboratory training as described by Barber (12) has nothing to do with penicillinase, but is based on the development of a mechanism for cell-wall formation which is insusceptible to inhibition by penicillin (180).

The origin of naturally occurring penicillinase-positive strains is unknown, although it has been suggested that two mutations are involved (92). Naturally occurring penicillinase positive strains possess the gene for penicillinase production, although the extent of its phenotypic expression may vary. In the wild type of all of these penicillin-resistant organisms thus far studied, the penicillinase gene expresses itself inducibly (198). Penicillinase is formed only in traces until the organisms are treated with penicillin (165). Pollock has studied in detail the properties and production of penicillinases which provide excellent models for enzyme induction and for the release of enzymes from bacterial cells (124, 164, 165, 166). Major qualitative differences have also been found to occur between penicillinases of gram-positive origin and those derived from a number of gram-negative organisms (162). Among the differences observed are their specificity patterns, lack of inducibility, possession of a marked differential permeability barrier, and difference in cellular location (89, 192).

The best clinical solution to the problem of penicillin-resistance has been afforded by the various penicillin derivatives which are only very slowly hydrolyzed, if at all, by bacterial penicillinase but still retain significant antibiotic activity. All of these are potent penicillinase inducers, but their relative insusceptibility to inactivation by the enzyme has provided a solution to the penicillinase problem.

Acquired resistance is a serious threat to the future usefulness of several important chemotherapeutic agents. Thus far there is no sure method of preventing drug fastness. Ehrlich's maxim (56), "Frapper fort et frapper vite" still constitutes our only defense, for if multiplication of the organisms is stopped immediately by prompt treatment with adequate dosage, the selection of drug-resistant mutants is not likely to occur. Combined therapy with two or more antibacterial drugs where indicated also offers promise and may be useful both in the treatment of the individual case and in discouraging the development of resistance generally. In the chemotherapy of tuberculosis this policy has been so successful that the use of two drugs is now a cardinal principle of treatment. The use of double-drug chemotherapy for non-tuberculous infections is less widespread, and the evidence that it prevents the emergence of resistance is not convincing. The problem of resistance to antimicrobial drugs is a major one, providing a clear warning against complacency in the indiscriminate and uncritical use of antimicrobial agents.

MICROBIAL PERSISTENCE. The observation has been made with many of the antibiotics that when growing cultures are exposed for several hours to the antibiotic, a small proportion of the organisms survive, although on subculture the resistance of these organisms is no greater than that of the original strain. The surviving organisms are thought to persist and exhibit phenotypic resistance because they are not multiplying. Nonmultiplying organisms have been shown not to be killed by the sulfonamides, penicillin, streptomycin, erythromycin, and isoniazid. Although the proportion of these persisters is very small in actively growing cultures, it may be much larger when growth is prevented by unfavorable conditions. In man microbial persistence is of great importance because it is probably responsible for the fact that the bactericidal activity of drugs on organisms in lesions is slower than in actively growing cultures in vitro, resulting in the need for a lengthy period of treatment. It is also probably responsible in some cases for the occurrence of relapses even after prolonged courses of chemotherapy, such as a year in the treatment of tuberculosis (138).

REFERENCES

1. Abraham, E. P., and others. Lancet, 2:177, 1941.
2. Abraham, E. P. Biochemistry of Some Peptide and Steroid Antibiotics, New York, John Wiley & Sons, Inc., 1957.
3. ——— and Newton, G. G. F. In Amino Acids and Peptides with Antimetabolic Activity, Wolstenholme, G. E. W., and O'Connor, C. M., eds., Boston, Little, Brown & Company, 1958, p. 205.
4. Abu-Nassar, H., and others. Am. J. Med. Sci., 246:569, 1963.
5. Albert, A. Symposium Growth Inhibition and Chemotherapy, Sixth Internat. Congr. Microbiol., Rome, 1953, p. 10.
6. ——— and Rees, C. W. Nature, 177:433, 1956.
7. Anand, N., and Davis, B. D. Nature, 185: 22, 1960.
8. Andriole, V. T., and Kravetz, H. M. J. Am. Med. Assoc., 180:269, 1962.
9. Asay, L. D., and Koch, R. In Antimicrobial Agents and Chemotherapy—1962, p. 466. Sylvester, J. C., ed., Ann Arbor, Mich., Am. Soc. Microbiology, 1963.

10. Bach, M. K., and Magee, W. E. Proc. Soc. Exper. Biol. & Med., 110:565, 1962.
11. Balassa, G. Ann. de l'Inst. Pasteur, 102:547, 1962.
12. Barber, M. Drug Resistance, in Microorganisms, Mechanisms of Development, Ciba Foundation Symposium, Wolstenholme, G. E. W., and O'Connor, C. M., eds., Boston, Little, Brown and Company, 1957.
13. ———— Intern. Rev. Cytology, 14:267, 1963.
14. Baum, G. L., and Schwarz, J. In Antibiotics Annual 1959-1960, Welch, H., and Marti-Ibañez, F., eds., New York, Antibiotica, Inc., 1960, p. 638.
15. Beard, H. W., and others. Am. Rev. Resp. Dis., 81:43, 1960.
16. Bennett, E. O. Ad. Applied Microbiology, 1:123, 1959.
17. Bernlohr, R. W., and Novelli, G. D. Arch. Biochem. Biophys., 103:94, 1963.
18. Berrah, G., and Konetzka, W. A. J. Bact., 83:738, 1962.
19. Biehl, J. P., and Vilter, R. W. Proc. Soc. Exper. Biol. & Med., 85:389, 1954.
20. Boone, I. U., and Woodward, K. T. Proc. Soc. Exper. Biol. & Med., 84:292, 1953.
21. Brock, T. D., and Brock, M. L. Arch. Biochem. Biophys., 85:176, 1959.
22. Brock, T. D. Bact. Rev., 25:32, 1961.
23. ———— J. Bact., 84:679, 1962.
24. Brown, B. L., and Fuerst, R. Science, 142:1654, 1963.
25. Brown, G. M. J. Biol. Chem., 237:536, 1962.
26. Bruch, C. W. Ann. Rev. Microbiol., 15:245, 1961.
27. Bryson, V., and Demerec, M. Am. J. Med., 18:723, 1955.
28. Bryson, V., and Szybalski, W. Advances in Genetics, 7:1, 1955.
29. Caron, G. A. Immunology, 6:94, 1963.
30. Cavalli, L. L., and Maccacaro, G. A. Heredity, 6:311, 1952.
31. Cavalli-Sforza, L. L., and Lederberg, J. Symposium Growth Inhibition and Chemotherapy, Sixth Internat. Congr. of Microbiol., Rome, 1953, p. 108.
32. Chain, E., and others. Lancet, 2:226, 1940.
33. Chapman, G. B. J. Bacteriol., 84:169, 1962.
34. Cohen, S. B. J. Am. Med. Assoc., 186:899, 1963.
35. Cohn, M. L., and others. Am. Rev. Tuberc., 70:465, 641, 852, 1954.
36. Colbeck, J. C. Am. J. Pub. Health, 50:468, 1960.
37. Collins, J. F., and Richmond, M. H. Nature, 195:142, 1962.
38. Conference: The Basic and Clinical Research of the New Antibiotic, Kanamycin, Ann. New York Acad. Sci., 76, Art. 2:17-408, 1958.
39. Conference: The Actinomycins and Their Importance in the Treatment of Tumors in Animals and Man, Furness, F. N., ed., Ann. N.Y. Acad. Sci., 89, Art. 2:283-486, 1960.
40. Cooper, P. D. Bact. Rev., 20:28, 1956.
41. Craig, L. C., and others. Amino Acids and Peptides with Antimetabolic Activity, Wolstenholme, G. E. W., and O'Connor, C. M., eds., Boston, Little, Brown, and Company, 1958, p. 226.

42. Dangerfield, H. G., and others. Antimicrobial Agents Annual—1960, Gray, P., Tabenkin, B., and Bradley, S. G., eds., New York, Plenum Press, 1961, p. 428.
43. Davis, B. D. Ciba Foundation Symposium on Drug Resistance in Microorganisms, Mechanisms of Development, Wolstenholme, G. E. W., and O'Connor, C. M., eds., Boston, Little, Brown, and Company, 1957, p. 165.
44. Davis, B. D., and Feingold, D. S. Chap. 9 in The Bacteria, Vol. IV, Gunsalus, I. C., and Stanier, R. Y., eds., New York, Academic Press, 1962.
45. Davison, A. N. Biochim. Biophys. Acta, 19:131, 1956.
46. Davison, A. N. Biochem. J., 67:316, 1957.
47. Demerec, M. Genetics, 36:585, 1951.
48. Domagk, G. Deutsche med. Wchnschr., 61:250, 1935.
49. Dubin, D. T., and others. Biochim. Biophys. Acta, 74:476, 1963.
50. Dubos, R. J. Exper. Med., 70:1, 11, 1939.
51. Duggar, B. M. Ann. New York Acad. Sci., 51:177, 1948.
52. Duguid, J. P. Edinburgh Med. J., 53:401, 1946.
53. Easterbrook, K. B., and Davern, C. I. Virology, 19:509, 1963.
54. Eaton, N. R., and Caffrey, R. J. Bacteriol., 81:918, 1961.
55. Ehrlich, P. Ber. d. deutsch. chem. Gesellsch., 42:17, 1909.
56. ———— Lancet, 2:445, 1913.
57. Eknoyan, G., and Roberts, A. D. Antimicrobial Agents and Chemotherapy—1962, Sylvester, J. C., ed., Am. Soc. Microbiology, Ann Arbor, Michigan, 1963, p. 497.
58. Emmerich, R., and Low, O. Ztschr. f. Hyg. u. Infectionskr., 31:1, 1889.
59. Erdös, T., and Ullmann, A. Nature, 183:618, 1959.
60. ———— and others. Acta Physiologica (Hungary), 17:229, 1960.
61. Federal Food, Drug, and Cosmetic Act of June 25, 1938. Chap. II, Sec. 201.
62. Feingold, D. S. New Eng. J. Med., 269:957, 1963.
63. Feingold, D. S., and Davis, B. D. Biochim. Biophys. Acta, 55:787, 1962.
64. Few, A. V., and Schulman, J. H. J. Gen. Microbiol., 9:454, 1953.
65. Fisher, M. W. Am. Rev. Tuberc., 69:797, 1954.
66. Fisher, M. W., and others. Antibiotics Annual 1959-1960, Welch, H., and Marti-Ibañez, F., eds., New York, Antibiotica, Inc., 1960, p. 293.
67. Fitzgerald, R. J., and others. J. Biol. Chem., 175:195, 1948.
68. Flaks, J. G., and others. Biochem. Biophys. Res. Comm., 7:385, 1962.
69. ———— Biochem. Biophys. Res. Comm., 7:390, 1962.
70. Fleming, A. Brit. J. Exper. Path., 10:226, 1929.
71. Flux, M., and others. Antimicrobial Agents and Chemotherapy—1962, Sylvester, J. C., ed., Ann Arbor, Michigan, Am. Soc. Microbiology, 1963, p. 455.
72. Franklin, T. J. Biochem. J., 87:449, 1963.
73. Gale, E. F. Pharmacological Reviews, 15:481, 1963.

74. Gale, E. F., and Folkes, J. P. Biochem. J., 53:493, 1953.

75. Gaylor, D. W., and others. In Antimicrobial Agents Annual 1960, Gray, P., Tabenkin, B., and Bradley, S. G., eds., New York, Plenum Press, 1961, p. 392.

76. Gershenfeld, L., and Witlin, B. Ann. New York Acad. Sc., 53:172, 1950.

77. Glassman, H. N. Bact. Rev., 12:105, 1948.

78. —— Ann. New York Acad. Sc., 53:91, 1950.

79. Goldberg, I. H., and others. Proc. Nat. Acad. Sci. U.S., 48:2094, 1962.

80. —— Proc. Nat. Acad. Sci. U.S., 49:226, 1963.

81. Goldman, D. S. J. Am. Chem. Soc., 76:2841, 1954.

82. —— Adv. Tuberc. Res., 11:1, 1961.

83. Goldman, L., and others. J.A.M.A., 172:532, 1960.

84. Greenberg, L., and others. Antimicrobial Agents Annual—1960, Gray, P., Tabenkin, B., and Bradley, S. G., eds., New York, Plenum Press, 1961, p. 172.

85. Hahn, F. E., and others. Biochim. Biophys. Acta, 61:741, 1962.

86. Haight, T. H., and Finland, M. Proc. Soc. Exper. Biol. & Med., 81:175, 1952.

87. —— Proc. Soc. Exper. Biol. & Med., 81:183, 1952.

88. Hamilton, L. D., and others. Nature, 198:538, 1963.

89. Hamilton-Miller, J. M. T. Biochem. J., 87:209, 1963.

90. Hashimoto, K. Genetics, 45:49, 1960.

91. Hawking, F., and Lawrence, J. S. The Sulfonamides, New York,, Grune and Stratton, 1951.

92. Hayes, W. In Drug Resistance in Microorganisms, Mechanisms of Development, Ciba Foundation Sym., Wolstenholme, G. E. W., and O'Connor, C. M., eds., Boston, Little, Brown and Company, 1957, p. 197.

93. Hazen, E. L., and Brown, R. Ann. New York Acad. Sc., 89:258, 1960.

94. Hirsch, H. A., and Finland, M. Am. J. Med. Sc., 239:288, 1960.

95. Holland, I. B. J. Gen. Microbiol., 29:603, 1962.

96. Hotchkiss, R. D. Ann. New York Acad. Sc., 46:479, 1946; 53:13, 1950.

97. Hotchkiss, R. D., and Evans, A. H. Fed. Proc., 19:912, 1960.

98. Howe, C. W., and others. New Eng. J. Med., 264:625, 1961.

99. Hsie, J., and Bryson, V. Am. Rev. Tuberc., 62:286, 1950.

100. Ivànovics, G. Bacteriol. Rev., 26:108, 1962.

101. Jackson, G. G., and Grieble, H. G. Ann. N.Y. Acad. Sc., 69, Art. 3:493, 1957.

102. Jacob, F., and others. Microbial Genetics, Tenth Symp. Soc. Gen. Microbiol., 10:67, 1960.

103. Jawetz, E. The Pediatric Clinics of North America, 8:1057, 1961.

104. Jordan, D. C. Biochem. Biophys. Research Comm., 6:167, 1961.

105. Kaufman, H. E. Perspectives in Virology, Vol. III, Pollard, M., ed., New York, Harper & Row Publishers, Inc., 1963, p. 90.

106. Kaufman, H. E., and Maloney, E. D. Arch. Ophthalmol., 69:626, 1963.

107. Kaufman, H. E., and others. Arch. Ophthalmol., 69:468, 1963.

108. Kempner, E. S. and, Miller, J. H. Biochim. Biophys. Acta, 76:341, 1963.

109. Kersten, H., and Rauen, H. M. Nature, 190:1195, 1961.

110. Kinsky, S. C. J. Bacteriol., 82:889, 1961.

111. —— Proc. Nat. Acad. Sc., 48:1049, 1962.

112. Kirby, W. M. M. Antibiotica et Chemotherapia, 11:84, 1963.

113. —— and others. Antimicrobial Agents and Chemotherapy—1961, Finland, M., and Savage, G. M., eds., Am. Soc. Microbiology, Detroit, 1962, p. 286.

114. Kirk, J. M. Biochim. et Biophys. Acta, 42:167, 1960.

115. Klarmann, E. G. Ann. New York Acad. Sc., 53:123, 1950.

116. Klein, J. O., and Finland, M. New Eng. J. Med., 269:1019, 1963.

117. —— New Eng. J. Med., 269:1074, 1963.

118. —— New Eng. J. Med., 269:1129, 1963.

119. Knothe, H. Antibiotica et Chemotherapia, 11:97, 1963.

120. Knox, R., and others. Am. Rev. Tuberc., 73:726, 1956.

121. Knox, W. E., and others. J. Bact., 55:451, 1948.

122. Knudsen, E. T. Antibiotica et Chemotherapia, 11:118, 1963.

123. —— and others. Lancet II, 632, 1962.

124. Kushner, D. J., and Pollock, M. R. J. Gen. Microbiol., 26:255, 1961.

125. Lampen, J. O., and others. J. Bacteriol., 84:1152, 1962.

126. Landman, O. E., and Burchard, W. Proc. Nat. Acad. Sc. U.S., 48:219, 1962.

127. Landman, O. E., and Ginoza, H. S. J. Bact., 81:875, 1961.

128. Landy, M., and others. Science, 97:265, 1943.

129. —— and Gerstung, R. B. J. Bact., 47:448, 1944.

130. Lawrence, C. A. Ann. New York Acad. Sc., 53:66, 1950.

131. Lederberg, J. Proc. Nat. Acad. Sc., 42:574, 1956.

132. Lederberg, J., and Lederberg, E. M. J. Bact., 63:399, 1952.

133. Lederberg, J., and St. Clair, J. J. Bacteriol., 75:143, 1958.

134. Lepper, M. H., and others. Ann. N.Y. Acad. Sc., 69, Art. 3:485, 1957.

135. Lofferer, V. O., and Riehl, G. Antibiotica et Chemotherapia, 10:335, 1962.

136. Long, P. H. Ann. N.Y. Acad. Sc., 69, Art. 3:385, 1957.

137. Luria, S. E., and Delbrück, M. Genetics, 28:491, 1943.

138. McDermott, W. Yale J. Biol. Med., 30:257, 1958.

139. McNall, E. G. Arch. Dermat., 81:657, 1960.

140. McQuillen, K. Chap. 6 in The Bacteria, Vol. I, Gunsalus, I. C., and Stanier, R. Y., eds., New York, Academic Press, 1960, p. 249.

141. Marini, F., and others. J. Gen. Microbiol., 24:51, 1961.

142. Markham, R. In The Strategy of Chemotherapy, Eighth Symp. Soc. Gen. Microbiol., p. 163, Cambridge University Press, 1958.

143. Marshall, M. S., and Hrenoff, A. K.   J. Infect. Dis., 61:42: 1937.
144. Martin, G. J.   Biological Antagonism, New York, The Blakiston Co., 1951.
145. Matthaei, J. H., and Nirenberg, M. W. Proc. Natl. Acad. Sc. U.S., 47:1580, 1961.
146. Middlebrook, G.   Am. Rev. Tuberc., 69: 471, 1954.
147. Miller, C. P., and Bohnhoff, M.   J. Bact., 54:467, 1947.
148. Mitchison, D. A.   J. Gen. Microbiol., 8:168, 1953.
149. Morton, H. E.   Ann. New York Acad. Sc., 53:191, 1950.
150. Nathans, D., and Lipmann, F.   Proc. Natl. Acad. Sc. U.S., 47:497, 1961.
151. Nayler, J. H. C., and others.   Nature, 195: 1264, 1962.
152. Neipp, L., and Mayer, R. L.   Ann. New York Acad. Sc., 69, Art. 3:448, 1957.
153. Neipp, L., and others.   Antibiotica et Chemotherapia, 9:19, 1961.
154. Neuhaus, F. C., and Lynch, J. L.   Biochem. Biophys. Research Comm., 8:377, 1962.
155. Newcombe, H. B., and Nyholm, M. H. Genetics, 35:603, 1950.
156. Newcomer, V. D., and others.   J. Chron. Dis., 9:353, 1959.
157. Newton, B. A.   Bact. Rev., 20:14, 1956.
158. Olarte, J., and others.   Antimicrobial Agents and Chemotherapy—1962, Sylvester, J. C., ed., Ann Arbor, Mich., Am. Soc. Microbiol., 1963, p. 787.
159. Ozeki, H., and others.   Nature, 184:337, 1959.
160. Pasteur, L., and Joubert, J.   Compt. rend. Acad. d. sc., 85:101, 1877.
161. Pato, M. L., and Brown, G. M.   Arch. Biochem. Biophys., 103:443, 1963.
162. Percival, A., and others.   J. Gen. Microbiol., 32:77, 1963.
163. Perkins, E. S., and others.   Nature, 194: 985, 1962.
164. Pollock, M. R.   J. Gen. Microbiol., 26:239, 267, 1961.
165. ——— In Resistance of Bacteria to the Penicillins, Ciba Foundation Study Group #13, A. V. S. De Reuck and M. P. Cameron, eds., Boston, Little, Brown, and Company, 1962, p. 56.
166. ——— Chap. 4 in The Bacteria, Vol. IV, Gunsalus, I. C., and Stanier, R. Y., eds., New York, Academic Press, 1962, p. 121.
167. Pope, H.   Am. Rev. Tuberc., 68:938, 1953.
168. ——— Am. Rev. Tuberc., 73:735, 1956.
169. Price, P. B.   Ann. New York Acad. Sc., 53:76, 1950.
170. Ravin, A. W., and Iyer, V. N.   J. Gen. Microbiol., 26:277, 1961.
171. Rawls, W. E., and others.   Proc. Soc. Exp. Biol. Med., 115:123, 1964.
172. Reddish, G. F.   Ann. New York Acad. Sc., 53:149, 1950.
173. ——— ed., Antiseptics, Disinfectants, Fungicides and Chemical and Physical Sterilization, 2nd ed., Philadelphia, Lea and Febiger, 1957.
174. Reich, E., and others.   Biochim. Biophys. Acta, 53:132, 1961.
175. Rendi, R., and Ochoa, S.   J. Biol. Chem., 237:3711, 1962.
176. Reynolds, P. E.   Biochem. J., 84:99P, 1962.
177. Richmond, M. H.   Bact. Rev., 26:398, 1962.
178. Rittenbury, M. S., and others.   Antimicrobial Agents and Chemotherapy, Finland, M., and Savage, G. M., eds., Detroit, Michigan, American Society Microbiology, 1962, p. 840.
179. Robson, J. M., and Sullivan, F. M.   Pharmacological Rev., 15:169, 1963.
180. Rogers, H. J., and Jeljaszewicz, J.   Biochem. J., 81:576, 1961.
181. Romansky, M. J., and others.   J.A.M.A., 164:1197, 1957.
182. Rytel, M. W., and others.   J. Am. Med. Assoc., 186:894, 1963.
183. Schatz, A., and others.   Proc. Soc. Exper. Biol. & Med., 55:66, 1944.
184. Schwartz, B. S., and others.   Antibiotics Annual 1959-1960, p. 41, 1960.
185. Sevag, M. G.   Symposium: Origins of Resistance to Toxic Agents, New York, Academic Press, Inc., 1955, p. 370.
186. Sheehan, J. C., and Henery-Logan, K. R. J. Am. Chem. Soc., 79:1262, 1957.
187. Shils, M. E.   Clin. Pharmacol. & Exper. Therap., 3:321, 1962.
188. ——— Ann. Int. Med., 58:389, 1963.
189. Shive, W., and others.   J. Am. Chem. Soc., 69:725, 1947.
190. Simon, H. J., and Rantz, L. A.   Ann. Int. Med., 57:335, 1962.
191. Smith, J. L., and Weinberg, E. D.   J. Gen. Microbiol., 28:559, 1962.
192. Smith, J. T., and Hamilton-Miller, J. M. T. Nature, 197:976, 1963.
193. Soru, E., and others.   Naturwissenschaften, 45:578, 1958.
194. Spotts, C. R., and Stanier, R. Y.   Nature, 192:633, 1961.
195. Strominger, J. L.   Chap. 10 in The Bacteria, Vol. III, Gunsalus, I. C., and Stanier, R. Y., eds., New York, Academic Press, 1962, p. 413.
196. ——— and Threnn, R. H.   Biochim. et Biophys. Acta, 33:280, 1959.
197. ——— and others.   J. Biol. Chem., 234: 3263, 1959.
198. Swallow, D. L., and Sneath, P. H. A.   J. Gen. Microbiol., 28:461, 1962.
199. Szybalski, W., and Bryson, V.   Am. Rev. Tuberc., 65:768, 1952.
200. ——— and Bryson, V.   Symposium: Origins of Resistance to Toxic Agents, New York, Academic Press, Inc., 1955, p. 20.
201. Tamm, I., and Eggers, H. J.   Science, 142: 24, 1963.
202. Taubeneck, U.   Nature, 196:195, 1962.
203. Tissières, A., and others.   Proc. Nat. Acad. Sc., 46:1450, 1960.
204. Toida, I., and Saito, C.   Kekkaku, 34:11, 1959.
205. Torchinsky, Yu. M.   Biochem. Biophys. Res. Comm., 10:401, 1963.
206. Turner, W., and others.   Brit. Med. J., 1962-I:1317, 1962.
207. Tzagoloff, H., and Umbreit, W. W.   J. Bact., 85:49, 1963.
208. Unger, L., and Kisch, A.   Proc. Soc. Exp. Biol. Med., 98:176, 1958.
209. Vincze, E., and others.   Acta Tuberculosea Scandinavica, 38:26, 1960.
210. Watanabe, T.   Bact. Rev., 27:87, 1963.

211. Watanabe, T., and Watanabe, M. J. Gen. Microbiol., 21:16, 1959.

212. Willett, H. P. Am. Rev. Tuberc., 68:938, 1953.

213. ——— Proc. Soc. Exper. Biol. Med., 99:177, 1958.

214. ——— Am. Rev. Resp. Dis., 80:404, 1959.

215. ——— Am. Rev. Resp. Dis., 81:653, 1960.

216. ——— Unpublished observations.

217. Winder, F. G., and Denneny, J. M. Biochem. J., 73:500, 1959.

218. Wolf, B., and Hotchkiss, R. D. Biochemistry, 2:145, 1963.

219. Wolf, F. T., and Wolf, F. A. Mycologia, 42:344, 1950.

220. Wolstenholme, G. E. W., and O'Connor, C. M., eds. Ciba Foundation Symposium on Amino Acids and Peptides with Antimetabolic Activity, Boston, Little, Brown, and Company, 1958.

221. Woods, D. D. J. Gen. Microbiol., 29:687, 1962.

222. ——— and Fildes, P. J. Soc. Chem. Indust., 59:133, 1940.

223. Woolley, D. W. Ann. New York Acad. Sc., 52:1197, 1950.

224. ——— In The Strategy of Chemotherapy, Eighth Symp. Soc. Gen. Microbiol., p. 139, Cambridge University Press, 1958.

225. Yarmolinsky, M. B., and De la Haba. Proc. Natl. Acad. Sc. U.S., 45:1721, 1959.

226. Youatt, J. Biochem. J., 68:193, 1958.

227. Zatman, L. J., and others. J. Biol. Chem., 209:453, 467, 1954.

9

Some Effects of Physical Agents upon
Bacteria and Viruses

BACTERIA

Bacteria are practically everywhere upon this planet. They have been found in the ocean waters at all latitudes from 70° south to 90° north (20) and at the bottoms of the great deeps at hydrostatic pressures as great as 13,000 pounds per square inch (31). Some live in natural hot springs at temperatures near boiling (8); others grow at temperatures near freezing. Many die in a vacuum or upon desiccation, but neither of these treatments is effective as a sterilizing process because neither kills all the organisms. In fact, vacuum desiccation from the frozen state is a process which is used for preservation of culture of some bacteria for extended periods of time. Thus there are varieties of bacteria that have adapted to the wide variety of physical conditions which exist in practically all places on earth. Perhaps the one large area most nearly approaching sterility is the surface of the sandy desert. Although the dry heat found there is destructive to most bacteria, the agent of greatest sterilizing effect is the short-wave rays from the sun in the near ultraviolet spectrum. Although there are somewhat resistant strains, even to these rays, no wide range of sensitivity has been found. The harder, ionizing rays, x-rays and the various rays from radioactive materials are destructive to all bacteria, with effectiveness roughly proportional to their ionizing power.

Among pathogenic bacteria tolerance of physical conditions is somewhat limited, but not as much as one might expect. The saprophytic varieties have rather wide tolerances compared with those of obligate parasites

which have little survival power outside the living body. We will be concerned here with both kinds of pathogens. We are probably safe in assuming that, inasmuch as they are pathogens, the physical conditions, temperature, pressure, etc., of the mammalian body are satisfactory for their growth. Much has been written in other parts of this book about conditions both chemical and physical which are optimum for bacterial growth. Let us, therefore, examine here the effects of some physical conditions which are definitely unsatisfactory. Most of these are progressively destructive, but others may be employed as means of preserving bacteria in a latent condition.

Effects of High and Low Temperatures. Exposure of pathogenic bacteria to high temperatures is of special interest because it is the method most used for sterilization. In such work we are interested in determining the number or the fraction of survivors. This fraction is called the "survival ratio" and it is usually expressed either as a negative logarithm or as a negative power of 10. For example, if 10 per cent of the individual bacteria in a culture survive some treatment, the survival ratio is said to have the logarithm -1 or to be 10^{-1}; similarly, for 1 per cent it would be -2 or 10^{-2}; etc.

Bacteria do not die instantly at high temperatures. Possibly we might regard the demise of a bacterium on a steel beam under a welding torch as instantaneous, but at lower temperatures, 100° C. or even at the somewhat higher temperatures of the steam autoclave, killing takes appreciable time. Furthermore, this time is not the same for all the individual bacteria present even in a pure culture. This is an important point to remember, because it is the reason for a well-known observation which seems, at first sight, unaccountable. The time required to sterilize an object depends, other variables remaining constant, upon the **number** of bacteria in it or upon it. It might seem that an oven or autoclave would kill 10 billion bacteria just as quickly as it would kill one, and this would indeed be true if all bacteria had exactly the same tolerance for heat; but, as we have said, this is not the case. There is little chance that any chosen individual bacterium will be one of the extremely robust resistant ones, but among the 10 billion the chance of this is much greater. Since sterilization means zero survival, if many bacteria are present, greater time must be allowed if sterilization is to be assured.

The conditions of applying heat to bacteria are generally more complex than they might appear on superficial consideration. Although the organisms may be placed in an oven at 500° C. and allowed to remain for 10 minutes, they may never experience that temperature and may survive. If they were exposed on the surface of thin glass, for example, they would attain the temperature of the oven quickly and die (Pyrex glass at 500° C. glows a dull red in a darkened place). If, however, they were buried within thick layers of glass wool, they may not become warm enough in 10 minutes to become more than uncomfortable. Another exaggerated case that may be profitably cited has to do with penetration of steam. We know that objects are brought up to high temperature much more quickly in a closed space filled with steam than in a dry oven at the same temperature. The reasons for this will appear later, but even steam does not penetrate all substances and those it does are penetrated at different rates. To take an extreme example, bacteria on glass wool inside a sealed glass ampule will survive quite a long time in an autoclave, but if the seal is broken, the rapidly penetrating steams will destroy them quickly. The different substances that are commonly sterilized vary widely with respect to the rate at which they are penetrated by steam.

Other variables which are present in all experiments involving exposure of bacteria to high temperatures are the specific heat and heat conductivity of the substance associated with the bacteria. Both of these must be considered in determining the time necessary to bring the bacteria up to the desired temperature. Organisms on a metal object which lies in contact with the heating element of an oven will be heated and killed quickly because of the high heat conductivity of metals in general. Conversely, a contaminated piece of metal lying among glass petri dishes in a dry oven will heat up much more slowly than the glass objects because of its higher specific heat; more heat is required to raise its temperature than is required by a glass object of similar size, so it takes longer to reach the elevated temperature, and any organisms on it or in cracks or holes in it will survive correspondingly longer.

For such reasons, it is necessary for experimenters to describe the conditions that they have employed in considerable detail. Many cases of controversial results have arisen because such basic physical considerations have been ignored, conditions which render seemingly similar experiments quite incomparable.

Speaking generally of the death rate of bacteria at elevated temperatures, we may observe that, let us say, half of the organisms die in a given amount of time. Half the **remainder** will die in the next time interval of equal length, etc. As this orderly rate of death continues, it is evident that the approach to sterility is via a slowly falling curve of survivors plotted against time. In fact, the approach to the final end point is usually even slower than this because of the presence of the few highly resistant individuals mentioned earlier. Thus it is apparent that determination of the exact time for killing of the last organism is rather tedious. Because of this, comparisons in the laboratory of the relative heat resistance of different kinds of bacteria are usually made at some arbitrary survival ratio, such as 10^{-1} or 10^{-2} (90 or 99 per cent killed).

We have been concerned rather much with time and rather little with temperature. This may seem to be misplaced emphasis, but it has been intentional. While it is not easy, as we have seen, to set up a readily reproducible experiment to determine the **time** of killing of bacteria at a given **constant temperature,** it is even more difficult to avoid technical pitfalls in experiments with **constant time** exposure at **different temperatures.** This is particularly true for the high temperatures, where the warm-up time becomes comparable with the killing time. Although time and temperature are inseparable in our considerations of the order of bacterial death, the larger part of published experimental results will be found expressed in the more manageable time variable under conditions of carefully maintained constant temperatures.

Practical Methods of Sterilization by Heat. The student should read the excellent review of Rahn (24) on physical methods of sterilization of microorganisms. Only a few general guide lines can be described here.

BURNING. For objects to be destroyed or which can stand incandescence, actual **burning** is a certain and easily applicable method of sterilization. Flaming by passage through a Bunsen or alcohol flame is used for transfer needles, cover slips, or other small objects which are used in handling bacteria in the laboratory.

HOT AIR. Sterilization is carried out in hot-air chambers, which are simple devices of varied construction consisting, in general, of a double-walled metallic box that are usually insulated to conserve heat and heated either by circulation of heated air from gas burners between the metal walls or by direct conduction and radiation from electric heating units placed in this space. There is a thermometer in the top and generally an automatic device to regulate the temperature is included. To insure absolute sterilization of objects in such a chamber, the temperature should be kept between 150° and 160° C. for at least an hour. Cotton cloth turns brown at 200° C. Dry heat sterilization is commonly used in laboratories for petri dishes, flasks, test tubes, syringes and pipets, and also for many articles that are injured by moisture.

MOIST HEAT. Instruments, syringes, and other suitable objects can sometimes be sterilized, in the absence of more reliable methods, by **boiling** in water. Five minutes is usually enough to destroy the vegetative forms of bacteria; spores generally require one to two hours, but spores of some saprophytic soil bacteria have survived 16 hours boiling. Addition of carbolic acid, from 2 to 5 per cent, to boiling water will usually insure the destruction of spores in 10 to 15 minutes.

PASTEURIZATION. Certain foods, particularly milk, are rid of pathogenic bacteria by this process which involves heating to about 66° C. (150° F.) for 30 minutes and then cooling quickly.

LIVE STEAM. Exposure to live steam is a commonly used method of heat sterilization. It may be carried out by simple makeshifts of the kitchen. For laboratories the original steaming device introduced by Koch has been largely displaced by devices constructed on the plan of the Arnold sterilizer, in which steam is generated by boiling a small quantity of water. This steam is circulated through the sterilizing chamber, and the excess is condensed and flows back to replenish the original water supply. Exposure to steam in such an apparatus for 15 to 30 minutes insures the death of the vegetative forms of bacteria.

Steam is a very effective agent for sterilization. When it comes in contact with relatively cold objects, it **condenses** upon them, conveying to them its latent heat (596 cal. per g.), and changing to water, which occupies very little space. More steam can enter the space vacated, to continue the process which quickly heats objects to 100° C. Hot gases such as air are not nearly so effective because they **do not** condense with the release of the heat of vaporization and **do not** make way (by condensing into small volume) for more hot gas when they have conveyed their heat to the objects to be sterilized.

STEAM UNDER PRESSURE. The use of steam under pressure is the most effective method of heat disinfection known. It is applicable to the sterilization of fomites, clothing, and any objects of a size suitable to be put in the pressure chamber and which are not injured by moisture. In laboratories this method is employed for the sterilization of contaminated apparatus, such as flasks, test tubes, and petri plates containing cultures. The device in which this is done is called an "autoclave." Of the many types that are in use, both stationary and portable, all consist fundamentally of a strong metal chamber with door or lid which fastens securely to withstand the internal steam pressure. A steam pressure gauge and safety valve are necessary. In simpler autoclaves water is placed in the bottom of the chamber and boiled there by an electric heater or by direct application of a gas flame to the bottom until the air within is replaced by steam, after which the valve is closed and heating is continued until the steam pressure and temperature attain the desired values. In more elaborate stationary models steam is supplied from the heating pipes. In any case, it is necessary to displace all air from the autoclave before closing the valve, because otherwise the result would be an application of something between dry heat and moist heat, with consequent loss in efficiency. When the sterilizing procedure is complete, it is necessary to relieve the pressure slowly; any sudden decrease of pressure by premature opening of the air vent will usually result in a sudden ebullition of any fluids in bottles or flasks, with consequent popping of plugs or stoppers.

Exposure to steam in an autoclave at 15 pounds gauge pressure (above atmospheric pressure) for 15 to 20 minutes is sufficient to kill all forms of bacterial life, including spores. Table 1 gives the temperature of the steam in an autoclave at various gauge pressures. It is not the pressure that kills the organisms, which are generally quite insensitive to such small changes in pressure. The increased pressure in the autoclave is necessary chiefly to produce steam of temperature greater than 100° C. The increased pressure gives somewhat greater penetrating power, but the greater temperature is responsible for most of the superior sterilizing effect.

DESICCATION.   By the natural process of drying in air, vegetative forms of most pathogenic bacteria are killed within a few hours. Even the tubercle bacillus, which is somewhat more resistant than other bacteria, is killed by air desiccation in a few days. Cleaning of walls and floors and natural desiccation have largely supplanted the older expensive and ineffectual processes of fumigation in the sanitation of premises previously occupied by patients with communicable disease. Irradiating such rooms with high intensity ultraviolet rays (2537 Å) has been found useful in shortening the time required for decontamination. More resistant to drying are endospores, which survive for long periods in the air, in soil, and on dry fomites.

In general it may be said that bacteria subjected to drying are greatly reduced in numbers, but it has been found also that the survivors of the initial drying, if it is properly carried out, remain viable for exceedingly long periods. So it is that desiccation, generally regarded as destructive to bacteria, is a useful method of preserving bacterial cultures free from mutation or production of variants. To achieve this result, the drying must be done quickly and from the frozen state. Flosdorf and Mudd (4) have shown that bacteria dried from the frozen state in their "lyophile" apparatus retain virulence as well as other characteristics.

RADIATIONS.   There is no longer any doubt that light and other electromagnetic rays of shorter wavelength, such as ultraviolet rays, x-rays, and gamma rays, as well as the various ionizing particle rays produced by radioactive decay and by ion accelerators, all exert a profound effect when absorbed by bacteria. Improved methods of dosimetry and a better understanding of the

Table 1. Temperature of Steam in an Autoclave at Various Gauge Pressures

POUNDS PRESSURE	TEMPERATURE, C.	POUNDS PRESSURE	TEMPERATURE, C.	POUNDS PRESSURE	TEMPERATURE, C.	POUNDS PRESSURE	TEMPERATURE, C.
1	102.3°	7	111.7°	13	119.1°	20	126.2°
2	104.2°	8	113°	14	120.2°	22	128.1°
3	105.7°	9	114.3°	15	121.3°	24	129.3°
4	107.3°	10	115.6°	16	122.4°	26	131.5°
5	108.8°	11	116.8°	17	123.3°	28	133.1°
6	110.3°	12	118°	18	124.3°	30	134.6°

properties of the various kinds of radiations have come about to a great extent through the intense study of atomic nuclear reactions and their attendant radioactive effects.

Changes of several types are experienced by bacteria when they absorb radiant energy. They may be stimulated to more rapid growth, induced to undergo mutation, killed, or inactivated and subsequently revived by absorption of rays of suitable kind and quantity. In all cases one must distinguish between energy **applied** through the medium of irradiation and energy **absorbed** from it by the organism; only the latter is effective. This basic law of photochemistry holds here as well as with the simpler chemical reactions from which it was derived. The practical value of a given kind of radiant energy for producing changes in bacteria is thus dependent on both the availability or ease of production of the rays and on the ability of the cells to absorb them. Hollaender (14) gives extensive treatments of the subject, and his books should be consulted for further information.

LIGHT. The bactericidal effect of sunlight was first measured by Downes and Blunt (2) in 1877. Later Koch demonstrated its lethal effect on tubercle bacilli by exposing them for about two hours to sunlight. Following these early observations were others showing that red and infrared rays have little, if any, effect beyond heating. With decreasing wavelength through the color range from red to violet, the effect slowly increases, as does also the absorption of the organisms. In the ultraviolet region (wavelengths less than 4,000 Å.) the rays are increasingly more effective with decreasing wavelength until a maximum is reached at 2,650 Å. Beyond this point a slight decrease in effectiveness is observed at 2,400 Å., with evidence of another maximum below 2,000 Å., which is about the practical limit of transmission for air at atmospheric pressure. A method of treating liquid bacterial cultures in vaccum in a "liquid jet" apparatus (13) has shown the great effectiveness of these ultraviolet rays of very short wavelengths. The maximum bactericidal efficiency at 2,650 Å. occurs at the same wavelength as the maximum for light absorption for the organism as a whole. This is not the same as the maximum for light absorption by protein (2,800 Å.), but it is similar to that of a small but vital part of the cell, the nucleic acid (Fig. 1).

LIGHT AS A STERILIZING AGENT. Although sunlight is germicidal at high intensity and long exposure, it contains none of the short wavelength ultraviolet rays which are most effective for the purpose. Various ultraviolet lamps are effective insofar as they produce these short waves. Arc light, and particularly a mercury arc enclosed in quartz, is highly efficient, and the cheapest source of bactericidal rays is the positive column discharge lamp containing mercury vapor and a little argon or neon at low pressure. These tubular lamps are made of glass that transmits the 2,537 Å. radiation characteristic of mercury, of which over 90 per cent of the radiant output is composed. Very little heat and visible light are generated, and this wavelength is near the 2,650 Å. maximum for lethal effect on bacteria. Such lamps, called "Sterilamps," are in general use for sterilizing air and clean metal or glassware surfaces where the low penetrating power is not a limitation. They have been placed in ducts of ventilating systems in army barracks and schoolrooms to reduce airborne infections (28). In bakeries and other food-handling establishments they serve to reduce the bacteria and mold-spore population of the air. They have come into general use in laboratory sterile rooms and hoods in which tissue cultures or other critical materials must be handled under strict aseptic conditions.

Ultraviolet lamps were introduced as an added item in sterile technic in operating rooms in 1935 by Hart (11), who found them useful in reducing the incidence of postoperative infection during the difficult winter months when upper repiratory infection among the operating personnel tends to increase the count of viable pathogens in the air. The eyes and skin of all personnel must, of course, be protected from the rays, and many surgeons feel that this added encumbrance to free and accurate movement of the operating team is more vital to patient welfare than the advantages provided by the ultraviolet rays in reducing the number of viable airborne bacteria. This is not a new dilemma: each new measure of safety in surgery has had to stand a similar period of trial.

The amount of energy (2,537 Å.) necessary to kill several kinds of bacteria suspended in air is not greatly different from that required when they are exposed on solid media. Comparison is difficult, but for *Staph. albus, Staph. aureus* (hem.), *E. coli, Serratia marcescens, Pseudomonas aeruginosa,* and *B. subtilis* the requirements averaged about one-fourth of the dose required on solid media (26).

Energy is absorbed from a beam of light by bacteria and by matter in general, not continuously, but in small amounts called "quanta." The number of quanta striking the organism in a unit of time is determined by the brightness of the light, but the size of the quanta is related to its quality or color and is related to the wavelength by the formula, $E = hc/\lambda$; where E is the quantum energy, c is the velocity of light, λ is its wavelength, and h is Planck's constant. Clearly, it is the light

of short wavelength that is delivered in large quanta. Generally speaking, reactions that require large quanta will not proceed even though many smaller quanta are supplied. This is another way of saying that an organism may be killed by a few hits by the large quanta of an ultraviolet ray but will survive many hits of the smaller quanta of red light.

The quanta of ultraviolet rays are large enough to convey sufficient energy to electrons within the organism to leave these molecules in an "excited" state. The subsequent reaction of these "excited" molecules is thought to produce the lethal event.

PHOTOREACTIVATION. When a culture of bacteria receives a given amount of lethal rays, the fraction of cells which demonstrate survival by their ability to multiply and produce colonies on an agar surface is called the "survival ratio." Kelner (19) demonstrated that this survival ratio, after exposure to ultraviolet rays (2,537 Å.), can be very greatly increased by subsequent exposure of the bacteria to rays of longer wavelength in

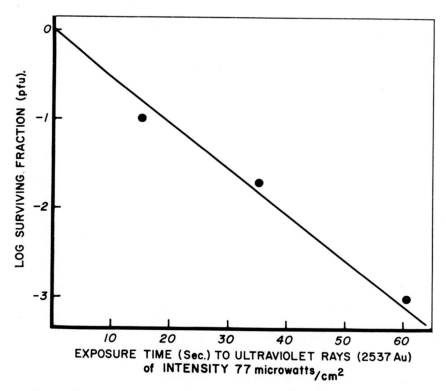

Fig. 1. Loss of infectivity of vaccinia virus under irradiation at 77 microwatts per square centimeter by 2537Å ultraviolet rays. (From Galasso and Sharp. *Virology,* 20:1, 1963.)

the near ultraviolet region of the spectrum or even visible light from a high temperature incandescent lamp. He found this photoreactivation to be greater if the reactivating light was applied soon after the initial exposure than if it was delayed. The survival ratio was increased 27,000-fold for *E. coli* and 310,000-fold for *Streptomyces griseus* by this treatment. Later work, reviewed by Jagger (16), has shown that many kinds of bacteria exhibit photoreactivation and that light of wavelength 3,800 Å. is usually the most effective. Dulbecco (3) found that bacteriophage also exhibit photoreactivation. The mechanism is still obscure; some workers hold that the effect is on the nucleic acids and others that the proteins are involved. Bacteria exposed to lethal doses of ionizing rays do not respond to photoreactivation, and some evidence (13) indicates that rays in the far ultraviolet spectrum (1,850 Å. or less) also have permanent effect.

IONIZING RAYS. X- and gamma rays are, like light and ultraviolet rays, a part of the electromagnetic spectrum, but they have very much shorter wavelengths. Soft x-rays (10 Å. to 1 Å. wavelength) are easily absorbed by matter, including bacteria, and their lethal and mutagenic properties have long been recognized for this reason. The more penetrating **hard** x-rays and gamma rays, which are of even shorter wavelength, are much less absorbed by bacteria, which accounts for many conflicting reports in the older literature regarding their effects. Although their action efficiency is low because of low absorption, they are of great interest because they give information on the mode of action of rays in general and on the structure of the cells irradiated. As a consequence of short wavelength, they act, when their large quanta are absorbed, to completely remove electrons from atoms and molecules of the bacterial substance. This is called "ionization." A single ion so produced is thought to cause mutation or death if it occurs in the vital region or target area of a cell. Several observations have led to the concept of a vital target or area in the cell much more radiosensitive than the rest. Information derived from the logarithmic nature of the survival curves of irradiated cells has further supported this theory. Early papers containing

this idea were published by Holweck (15), Lacassagne (21) and Wyckoff (30). The target theory was strongly supported by Lea (22), who explained cell death, based on this theory, as a special case of mutation, **lethal mutation.** He argued that, inasmuch as a single ionization is sufficient to bring about the action, it is only in the genetic apparatus of the cell, where giant molecules of nucleic acids are known to exist, that destruction of a single molecule could be so effective.

The target theory for inactivation of bacteria does **not** account for all the observed effects. The work, reviewed by Hollaender (14) indicates that a much more complex concept is necessary, one which takes into account such ideas as the destruction of essential enzymes, the production of poisons within and near the organisms, etc. This rapidly developing field is in such flux that current journals must be consulted constantly if the student is to be aware of latest attempts to generalize the theory of radiation effects on bacteria.

AGITATION AND TRITURATION. Trituration of bacteria by grinding them in a mortar with sand or in a vessel with glass beads will reduce some of the cells to fragments. Many are resistant to mechanical action of this sort, and it is usually necessary to freeze them and extend the grinding process. The high-speed shearing action of rotating blades in a blendor is effective on liquid suspensions of organisms.

SOUND ENERGY. Sound vibrations at high frequency, in the upper audible and supersonic range (9 to 500 kilocycles per second), are highly destructive to bacteria and other unicellular organisms in liquid suspension (9, 27).

High-frequency sound waves are produced by a mechanical vibrator driven by high-frequency electric waves generated in a suitable inductance-capacity circuit by an electronic tube. Two methods of conversion from electric to sound waves are in use. For the lower frequencies, a laminated nickel rod is made to vibrate by magnetostriction. With high frequencies (20 kilocycles and more), greater efficiency is obtained with a crystal vibrating from reversed piezoelectric effect.

Destruction of the bacteria probably results from cavitation, the rhythmic forming and collapsing of gas bubbles which occurs with explosive violence within the cells (12, 25). From Stumpf and others (27) comes Table 2, showing relative susceptibility of several types of organisms.

Table 2. Effect of Ultrasonic Vibrations on Various Bacteria

(Stumpf, Green and Smith)

Easily Disintegrated	Refractory
Haemophilus influenzae	Sarcina lutea
Salmonella	Micrococcus
typhimurium	lysodeikticus
Brucella abortus	Aerobacter suboxydans
Lactobacillus casei	Saccharomyces
Lactobacillus	cerevesiae
delbrueckii	(chloroplasts)
Proteus morganii	
Proteus vulgaris	
Clostridium welchii	
Escherichia coli	
Pseudomonas	
aeruginosa	
Pseudomonas	
fluorescens	
Staphylococcus aureus	
(erythrocytes)	

VIRUSES

The viruses are obligate parasites by definition (1). They have no life outside the living cell, and if they can be likened in any way to bacteria, the analogy would be with the bacterial spores. Both may be thought of as resting states; neither is capable of growth without change of state, which in the case of the virus particle occurs only when it enters a susceptible cell. Thus there are no physical conditions favorable for growth of isolated viruses as there are for the vegetative forms of bacteria. They may be favorable enough to preserve the virus, but in general it becomes inactivated. The rate of inactivation is usually such that the logarithm of the surviving active fraction is a straight-line function of time: in other words, if one half of the virus is inactivated in a given time, half the remainder will succumb in the next equal interval, etc. Again, like bacteria, there are resistant fractions of virus populations that survive even longer than the time predicted by the logarithmic order of decline.

Viruses resemble pathogenic bacteria in their rapid inactivation at high temperatures, but they differ basically in their response to lower temperatures. **Many bacteria die at low temperatures, but all viruses increase in stability with decrease in temperature.** They respond to electromagnetic waves with an action spectrum identical with that for bacteria, and the incident energies required to kill bacteria are approximately the same as those which inactivate virus particles. The remaining pages of this chapter deal briefly with some of the reactions of virus to physical stress.

Effects of High and Low Temperatures. High and low temperatures for pathogenic bacteria are so commonly referred to body temperature that usually the point of reference is not mentioned in a discussion such as this. For cell free virus suspensions, however, the situation is different. There is no special temperature, such as 37° C., at which growth occurs. Most viruses are rapidly inactivated at 100° C. Methods of heat sterilization, such as autoclaving, commonly used for bacteria, are suitable for viruses as well. The logarithmic inactivation rate has been demonstrated for many viruses. Such deviations as have been reported occur usually below a survival fraction of 10^{-3}. Kaplan (18) has shown that a small fraction of his vaccinia virus displayed great resistance to heat. Later Woodroofe (29) attributed this effect to the conditions of storage of samples prior to the experiments. Both Joklik et al. (17) and Hanafusa (10) have shown that vaccinia virus inactivated at 60° C. may be revived if it is mixed with closely related active virus and inoculated together into susceptible cells. Galasso and Sharp have shown (5) that titration of heated (56° C.) virus samples may be complicated by homologous interference by the inactive virus particles, with the few survivors rendering them incapable of producing plaques on tissue cultures even though residual infectivity can be detected by other means.

With decreasing temperatures the inactivation rate becomes less and less, down to 0° C. Freezing can be destructive to viruses, but this effect is minimized if it is done quickly. While the common deep freeze refrigerators which operate at about −20° C. are satisfactory for keeping most viruses for short times, prolonged storage of frozen samples is usually more satisfactory at $-70°$ C. —either in a mechanical refrigerator or in a suitably insulated cabinet containing solid CO_2 (dry ice). Frozen samples are often shipped in well-insulated containers packed with dry ice. Care must be taken, of course, to provide for escape of CO_2 from such packages, or explosion may result.

For preservation of virus samples for long periods the freeze-drying or lyophilization process has proven successful (4). The process is the same as for bacteria.

Effects of Radiant Energy. Visible and infrared light have no destructive effect on viruses other than the heat they convey to the particles, but ultraviolet rays produce rapid inactivation, especially those of wavelength in the spectral region of 2,600 to 2,800 Å. Both RNA and DNA have a maximum of absorption for ultraviolet at 2,600 Å., and the aromatic amino acids, which are present in most proteins, have their absorption maximum of 2,800 Å. Inasmuch as proteins and nucleic acids are the principal constituents of all known viruses, it is not surprising that they are all sensitive in the same spectral region (Fig. 1).

The more energetic ionizing x-rays, and the α-, beta, and gamma rays from radio-active materials and from particle accelerators are all destructive to viruses. As with bacteria, the inactivating effect is roughly proportional to the amount of ionization produced. The general finding is that the logarithm of the fraction of surviving active virus decreases as a straight line function of the time of irradiation. Figure 2 shows an example of this for vaccinia virus exposed to 2,537 Å. ultraviolet rays (7). Although some exceptions have been found, chiefly in the form of persistent survival of a small fraction of resistant virus, the general course of inactivation for all types of virus and all types of rays is the linear graph shown in the figure. Only the slope of the line is different for different viruses, for different kinds of rays, and for different intensities of energy applied. A thorough treatment of this subject will be found in Hollaender's book (14).

The inactivation of certain viruses by radiant energy, particularly ultraviolet rays, has been partially reversed by application of more rays of longer wavelength (3). This photoreactivation effect is similar to that which has been observed with bacteria, and it occurs in the same range of energy and wavelength, thus strongly suggesting that the same general reactions with nucleic acids

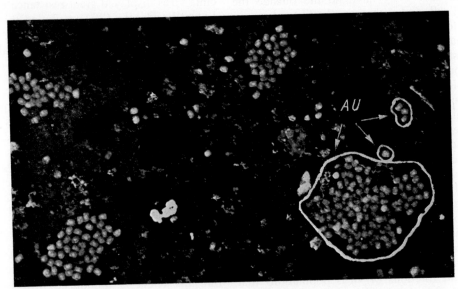

Fig. 2. Vaccinia virus particles in crude lysate of infected L. cells, sedimented preparation for electron microscopic study of aggregation. It is probable that a single particle, a small group, or a large group will infect only one cell in a titration test. Thus the number of active units (AU) is reduced by aggregation. (From Galasso and Sharp. *J. Immunol.*, 88:339, 1962.)

and/or proteins are involved with both bacteria and viruses. Simply stated, the observation is that a given dose of ultraviolet rays at wavelength 2,537 A., for example, may reduce a sample of exposed virus to 1/1000th of its original potency, but if the sample is exposed promptly to rays of about 4,000 A., the survival of virus may be 10 or 100 times greater. Many that would otherwise succumb are saved or reactivated by this process. Some photoreactivation may occur even with exposure to visible light and this must be considered in precise experimentation with radiant energy on viruses.

Photoreactivation decreases if the reactivating rays are not employed promptly after the exposure to the lethal ultraviolet. Very little reactivating effect, none in most cases, has been observed with virus treated with ionizing rays.

Effects of Grinding, Trituration, and Shock. Viruses are frequently released from infected tissues by grinding and processes of trituration which reduce the tissue structure, the cells, and sometimes even the cell organelles to small dimensions. The tissues are usually ground in a suitable buffer solution which maintains the desired pH and acts as a medium for suspension of the released virus. Mechanical devices for this purpose can be roughly divided into two categories: those that operate at slow speeds, usually for considerable time, and those that employ rapidly revolving blades at speeds of several thousand revolutions per minute. After the initial cutting up of tissue and reducing of the bits to approximately cellular dimensions, the final reduction seems to be achieved largely by **shear** in the suspending medium. The shear is present in both the high- and low-speed homogenizing devices. Shear occurs in a liquid when one part moves faster than an adjoining part. When a particle is suspended in a liquid subject to shear, it extends into regions of the fluid that are moving at different rates and experiences a corresponding twist and tearing force which is proportional to the shear in the liquid. Low-speed homogenizers usually achieve shear by forcing the fine tissue suspension to pass between glass, metal, or plastic surfaces that are close-fitting (separated by only a few thousandths of an inch). High-speed machines achieve it by passing cutting blades through the liquid so rapidly that only the liquid in actual contact with the blade moves quickly through the body of relatively stationary material. Both methods are effective, and the choice between them is often made on a basis of cost, volume of material to be treated, or time available, or, in some cases, by the facilities for keeping the material sterile and cool. Heat generated by agitation will cause a distressing temperature rise unless controlled. This is usually done by immersing the treatment chamber in a suitable cooling bath during homogenization. Some investigators believe that this is never quite as effective as the cooling that can be achieved with the slower hand-operated tissue homogenizers.

Virus particles in general are highly resistant to the mechanical forces of homogenization. They are so small that they are probably rarely caught and crushed between the upper and the nether millstone, so to speak. Their smallness probably saves them from most of the effects of liquid shear as well. They suffer, during these mechanical operations, chiefly from the effects of local and transient heating.

Effects of Sonic and Ultrasonic Waves. The effects of physical forces upon material in general are often greatly magnified if the forces are rapidly varied in magnitude. A very popular method, among virologists, for releasing virus from a suspension of infected cells is the application of high-frequency sound or ultrasonic waves. The sound, of course, is incidental, but the effect is generally one of rapid breaking of the cells with dispersion of the clumps of virus released. The mechanism is not completely understood. The effect may come about partly through shear, but some investigators believe the major effect is that of rapid formation and collapse of cavities within the liquid or perhaps within the cells. This cell **cavitation** is present whenever there is turbulent shear within a liquid and is one of the reasons for underwater noise from marine propellers.

Viruses in general are quite resistant to inactivation by sonic and ultrasonic waves. It is this quality of resistance which makes their release from infected tissues practical

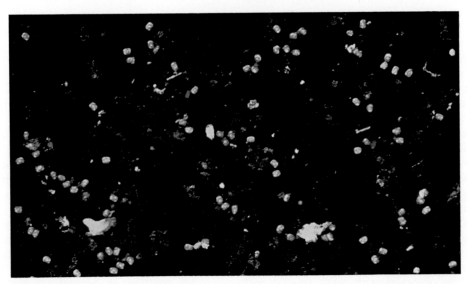

Fig. 3. Vaccinia virus particles prepared like those for Figure 2, but treated with sound waves (9,000 cycles per second). Such well-dispersed virus particles will be more effective, contain more AU, and titrate farther than aggregated virus.

by this means. The treatment can, however, be carried far enough to damage the virus. It would probably be more accurate to say that such wave energy always damages some virus, but the extent of the damage is usually tolerable and often too small to be measurable at dosages sufficient to achieve the desired release and dispersion.

Wave generators generally employed for tissue homogenization operate in the frequency range of roughly 9,000 to 100,000 cycles per second. No particular frequencies have been found to be specifically effective, no maxima of effectiveness such as the 2,600 and 2,800 Å. peak effective frequencies in the ultraviolet spectrum. Ultrasonic waves are generally more effective as the frequency is increased, but strict comparisons are difficult because with increased frequencies the technical problem of constructing a machine that is capable of conveying the energy to the material arises. Such transducers generally involve greater and greater energy losses as frequency is increased. In addition to this are the problems of dosimetry. It is relatively easy to determine the amount of ultraviolet ray or x-ray energy incident upon the virus particles in an experiment, but no such convenient methods are available for measuring the amount of vibrational energy that is ab-

sorbed by a virus particle at various frequencies. Until there is, we must be satisfied with evaluations in terms of particular designs of apparatus and their comparative performance. In the United States until recently the only widely used piece of equipment operated at 9,000 cycles per second. Much of the available data on cell disruption, virus particle dispersion, and virus particle inactivation have therefore been obtained with the Raytheon machine model S-102A. Comparative results on several bacteria are shown in Table 2. Extensive recent work with vaccinia virus has shown that this machine does inactivate the virus (23), but the time required for the destruction is great enough to allow its use for cell breakage and dispersion of virus clumps without involving measurable virus inactivation. Figure 2 shows a preparation of vaccinia virus which displays a degree of aggregation commonly encountered. Inasmuch as the effectiveness (titer) of such a preparation is dependent on the number of independent active units (AU in the figure) present (6), it is increased by a short application of sonic vibration (60 seconds in this case) which can produce a dispersion such as that shown in Figure 3.

Newer and more powerful equipment is

available now from several manufacturers, including Raytheon, but this author is not aware of any recent general compilation of comparative effects comparable with that of Table 2.

REFERENCES

1. Burnet, F. M.   The Viruses, Vol. III, Burnet, F. M., and Stanley, W. M., eds., New York, Academic Press, p. 2.
2. Downes, A., and Blunt, T. P.   Proc. Roy. Soc. London, SB., 26:488, 1877; 28:199, 1878-9.
3. Dulbecco, R.   Nature, London, 163:949, 1949.
4. Flosdorf, E. W., and Mudd, S.   J. Immunol., 29:389, 1935.
5. Galasso, G. J., and Sharp, D. G.   Virology, 15:376, 1961.
6. _____ and Sharp, D. G.   J. Immunol., 88:339, 1962.
7. _____ and Sharp, D. G.   Virology, 20:1, 1963.
8. Gaughran, E. R. L.   Bact. Revs., 11:189, 1947.
9. Gregg, E. C.   Medical Physics, Glasser, O., ed., Chicago, Yearbook Publishers, Inc. 1950, Vol. II.
10. Hanafusa, H.   Biken's Jour., 3:41, 1960.
11. Hart, D., and Nicks, J.   Archiv. of Surgery, 82:139, 1961.
12. Harvey, E. N., and Loomis, A. L.   J. Gen. Physiol., 15:147, 1931.
13. Heinmets, F., and Taylor, W. W., Jr.   Arch Biochem. and Biophys., 35:60, 1952.
14. Hollaender, A.   Chap. 10 in Radiation Biology, New York, McGraw-Hill, 1955.
15. Holweck, F.   Compt. rend. Acad. de sc., Paris, 188:197, 1929.
16. Jagger, John.   Bact. Revs., 22:99, 1958.
17. Joklik, W. K., Woodroofe, G. M., Holmes, I. H., and Fenner, F.   Virology, 11:168, 1960.
18. Kaplan, C.   J. Gen. Microbiol., 18:58, 1958.
19. Kelner, A.   J. Bact., 58:511, 1949.
20. Kriss, A. E., Abyzov, S. S., Lebedeva, M. N., Mishustina, I. E., and Mitskevich, I. N.   J. Bact., 80:731, 1960.
21. Lacassagne, A.   Compt. rend. Acad. de sc., Paris, 188:200, 1929.
22. Lea, D. E.   Actions of Radiations on Living Cells, Cambridge University Press, 1947.
23. Overman, J. R., and Sharp, D. G.   J. Exp. Med., 110:461, 1959.
24. Rahn, Otto.   Bact. Revs., 9:1, 1945.
25. Schmidt, F. O., and Uhlemeyer, B.   Proc. Soc. Exp. Biol. and Med., 27:626, 1930.
26. Sharp, D. G.   J. Bact., 39:535, 1940.
27. Stumpf, P. K., Green, D. E., and Smith, F. W., Jr.   J. Bact., 51:487, 1946.
28. Wells, W. F.   J. Franklin Inst., 229:347, 1940.
29. Woodroofe, G. M.   Virology, 10:379, 1960.
30. Wyckoff, R. W. G.   J. Exp. Med., 52:435, 1930.
31. Zobell, C. E., and Morita, R. Y.   J. Bact., 73:563, 1957.

ECOLOGY

10

Microbiologic Ecology and Flora of the Normal Human Body

Ecology is a study of the mutual relations between organisms and their environment. Disease in man and animals caused by microorganisms is only a small segment of this constantly changing balance of forces. Bacteria are ubiquitous under all conditions which permit the existence of any form of life and probably are the most primitive of all living forms (61, 86, 91). These organisms are constantly engaged in synthesizing new organic compounds and in breaking down to simpler elements the complex substances which compose plant and animal tissues. Here, as among the higher animals, there is a constant struggle for survival between individuals and species which is influenced by moisture, temperature, sunlight, composition and texture of soil, acidity and alkalinity, and other physical and chemical factors.

In the course of metabolism, the metabolic by-products formed are sometimes simple chemical compounds which are deleterious to other organisms for one reason or another, but frequently they are complex substances now called antibiotics which bacteria and fungi had been using to kill their rivals eons before man learned to employ them in the treatment of infectious diseases.

The complex relationship between the different microbial species may be classified as **neutral, antagonistic, or synergistic.** Few species are strictly neutral in their reactions because they interfere in a passive manner with the growth of other species by using up the available food supply or inadvertently poisoning their neighbors with waste products.

Many if not the majority of species exhibit the phenomenon of positive **antagonism.** Internecine warfare is common between bacteria. Pasteur and Joubert first described this phenomenon in 1877, after noting that several saprophytic species killed the pathogenic *Bacillus anthracis* in cultures. Incidentally, man profits from this basic antagonism between species, for several workers have observed the destructive effect of the nonpathogenic *Streptococcus viridans,* which is ubiquitous in the nasopharynx of man, on the pathogenic *Corynebacterium diphtheriae* (89). The antilactobacillus factor in human saliva, which is absent in newborn infants but appears after the fourth day of life and reaches the adult level by the tenth year, may be a bacterial product or a metabolic product of the salivary gland (2). The antagonism between the gram-positive cocci and gram-negative bacilli of the respiratory tract and their independent and mutual antagonism to fungi was not suspected until the introduction of antibiotics into therapy. Following treatment with penicillin, we, as well as others, have observed the replacement of an apparently pure flora of gram-positive cocci with one of gram-negative bacilli. In many instances treatment with streptomycin has produced the opposite effect, while the simultaneous administration of both antibiotics or of the administration of chloramphenicol, chlortetracycline, and oxytetracycline has resulted in the development of a flora of yeast and molds (37, 73, 78) which may produce systemic infections (48) or the emergence of strains of *Staphylococcus* (82, 83) or *Pseudomonas aeruginosa* (33) which are resistant to these antibiotics and induce a highly fatal type of pseudomembranous enterocolitis (16).

Synergism may be described as a cooperative effort by two or more microbial species which produces a result that could not be effected by the separate species alone. The ultimate result of such synergistic activity may be the synthesis of complex organic compounds, the degradation or destruction of complex organic substances, or the development of an ability of the symbionts to produce disease in man and animals which none of the participating partners possesses alone. An example of productive cooperation may be observed in the association of a fungus and an alga in the macroscopic form known as a lichen.

Frequently infections are more serious when the primary bacterial or viral agents are accompanied by secondary invaders such as diphtheria bacilli and secondary streptococci; measles or influenza virus in combination with secondary streptococci, pneumococci or influenza bacilli (20); or spore-bearing anaerobic bacilli and aerobic cocci. In these instances all of the microorganisms possess a certain degree of primary pathogenicity.

The term synergism, however, should be limited to a situation in which two or more harmless organisms acquire the ability to produce disease by a cooperative effort. Infections of this type were reviewed in some detail by Meleney in 1948 (54). The results produced by one synergistic pair are shown in Figure 1, where a mixture of a pure culture of a microaerophilic nonhemolytic streptococcus and a pure culture of an aerobic *Staphylococcus aureus* produced an extensive area of gangrene although the organisms when injected separately were unable to initiate an infection (3). Another example of true synergism was reported by Arndt and Ritts (1), where mice resistant to either *Staphylococcus aureus* or *Proteus vulgaris* developed a fulminating septicemia when both were injected simultaneously.

Examples of symbiosis between the swine influenza virus and *H. influenzae suis* will be found in Chapter 67 and of the more complicated synergism between cocci, vibrios, fusiform bacilli, and spirochetes in Chapter 51. It is probable that other as yet unrecognized instances of synergism will be found to cause sporadic infections in man.

The ecologic relationships between microorganisms and higher plants, animals or man may be described as commensalism, symbiosis, parasitism, or opportunism.

Commensalism. By this term we refer to the mutual but almost inconsequential association between bacteria and higher organisms. The bacteria normally present in the intestinal tract and on the skin may be classified as commensals, although some strains are described more accurately as opportunists.

Symbiosis. This word is applied properly to a mutually beneficial relationship between a microorganism and its more highly organized host. There are many examples of this type of relationship. Root nodules of legumes contain nitrogen-fixing bacteria which live in symbiosis with the host plant (93); cellulose-metabolizing protozoa maintain such a relationship in the intestines of termites. Intracellular microorganisms of some insects live in symbiosis with their hosts. The intracellular rickettsias of certain insects and crustaceans and some

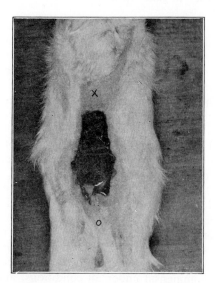

Fig. 1. Streptococcal and staphylococcal synergism. Showing 2 ml. of streptococcus culture injected at X, and 2 ml. of staphylococcus culture injected at O. In the center 1 ml. of each was injected and produced gangrene. (From Meleney. *Treatise on Surgical Infection*, Oxford University Press.)

of the filterable viruses of animals and plants seem to have established a true symbiotic existence (94). Another example is the symbiotic bacteria found in developing oocytes of the American cockroach, *Periplaneta americana* (9).

Parasitism. The microorganisms which are capable of living and multiplying within the body are **parasites,** in contrast to the **saprophytes** which make up the bulk of the microbial population and which cannot survive in a competition with living cells but require inorganic or nonliving organic matter. An illuminating discussion of parasitism as a factor in disease was published by Theobald Smith (80) in 1934. **He pointed out that the phenomenon of disease of interest to the student of medicine is largely epiphenomena in an evolving parasitism, and that the violent reactions tend to lessen and disappear as the parasitism approaches a biologic balance or equilibrium. The rapid and destructive actions of some microorganisms are the expressions of bungling parasitism. The skillful or well-adapted parasite enters its host and may produce destructive lesions only as a means of securing an exit in order to take up a new berth in another host.**

In adopting a parasitic existence, bacteria acquire some new characteristics but usually lose many others, so that parasites have fewer and less varied metabolic potentials than their saprophytic relatives.

Opportunism. Organisms which are incapable of inducing disease in a healthy host but which produce severe and even fatal infections when the resistance of the host has been reduced may be referred to as "opportunists." Certain types of *E. coli* (41) and paracolon organisms in the intestinal tract exhibit this type of parasitism. Perhaps the most dramatic example of conditional parasitism is shown by the fusospirochetal group of synergistic organisms (Chapter 51). Individually each member is a commensal under all conditions, and as a synergistic group they live as commensals in the mouths of healthy men and animals. When the host's resistance has been lowered by a vitamin C or nicotinic acid deficiency the synergistic group become opportunists and produce local infections in the gums.

But when introduced into the subcutaneous tissues of another host by a human bite or into the lungs of their own host by aspiration, they become primary pathogens and produce extensive areas of abscess and gangrene (77).

Habitat. In a broad sense the term "habitat" may properly be applied to the places of abode of microorganisms. Certain species are found most frequently and in greater numbers in soil, water, milk, air, or plants and animals.

SOIL. The soil is the great reservoir of microorganisms, containing the largest population and the greatest variety of species (79).

The most resourceful if not the most primitive of these are the autotrophic bacteria, which synthesize their complex enzyme systems and proteins from the air and the mineral elements in the rocks (86, 90, 91).

Soil is the natural habitat of *Clostridium botulinum,* whose potent toxin produces disease in man. *Cl. tetani* and other *Clostridia,* which cause gas gangrene, may be deposited in the soil in human or animal feces, but their recovery from samples of virgin soil suggests that multiplication and perpetuation may occur in the absence of fecal contamination. Pathogenic fungi, such as *Coccidioides immitis* (87) and *Histoplasma capsulatum* (23), have been grown from the soil. The spores of *Bacillus anthracis,* which definitely are of animal origin, may survive for many years in the soil. Several pathogenic organisms from the intestinal tract of man and animals live for weeks or months under favorable conditions but do not become a permanent part of the flora.

WATER. Natural waters from deep wells and from the melting snows of high mountains may be free of bacterial life. All other natural waters contain microorganisms. Some, like the fluorescent and choromogenic bacteria of fresh and salt water, have adapted themselves to a life in water. Even more specialized are the sulfur and iron bacteria (43) and the **thermophilic bacteria** of hot springs (27). At the opposite extreme are the **psychrophilic bacteria** of the Antarctic which grow at $0°$ C. (85).

Most bacteria found in surface water are

soil bacteria which have been carried into streams and ponds by surface washings of rain or by melting snow. The **heterotrophic bacteria** of the oceans are carried to these waters, along with food, by the great rivers of the world and consequently increase in number and variety from the poles to the equator (45). Of great medical importance are the relatively few highly pathogenic intestinal bacteria, such as the typhoid bacillus, the dysentery bacilli, and the cholera vibrio, which may contaminate water used for drinking and thereby initiate epidemics of major importance. Since they are extremely difficult to isolate directly from water, it is very fortunate that they are always accompanied by larger numbers of the more hardy *E. coli* which serve as an index of fecal contamination. Methods for cultivating and identifying *E. coli* will be found in Chapter 38 but for more details about the examination and sterilization of water, the student should consult the special textbooks on hygiene and sanitation and *Standard Methods for the Examination of Water and Sewage,* American Public Health and American Water Works Association, New York.

MILK. Milk from normal cows, even when drawn under aseptic conditions, usually contains from 100 to 1,000 nonpathogenic organisms per milliliter. Immediately after withdrawal saprophytes of various types are added from the dust of the air, improperly sterilized milking vessels and, finally, the hands of the milker, and droplets from his respiratory tract (32).

Streptococcus lactis of vegetative origin reaches the milk in dust particles and this organism together with staphylococci from the udder and small numbers of *Aerobacter aerogenes* and *Lactobacilli* grow in the milk and produce the characteristic acid souring by fermenting the lactose. In addition to the acid-forming bacteria, milk usually contains gas-forming organisms, proteolytic bacteria, alkali-producing organisms, and inert saprophytes.

Unpasteurized milk may contain tubercle bacilli, brucella, or hemolytic streptococci from the cow, to which man may have added diphtheria bacilli, streptococci capable of causing septic sore throat or scarlet fever as well as typhoid bacilli, other salmonella, and dysentery organisms. Staphylococci from the udder of the cow or from the hands of the milker may produce enterotoxin, which induces a specific type of food poisoning (40).

PLANTS. Plants have bacterial and mycotic diseases (8) comparable to those of animals, but so far as our knowledge extends, with the possible exception of *Sporotrichum schenckii,* plant pathogens are not pathogenic for man or animals (4).

ANIMALS. Animals are hosts for many of the most important microorganisms which produce disease in man (see Chapter 18).

AIR. While microorganisms are frequently found in the air, they do not multiply in this medium. They are either dispersed in the air along with particles of dust from the surface of the earth or they are exhaled into the air from the respiratory tract of man and animals. We shall discuss separately the **outdoor air** and the **indoor air.** The former rarely contains organisms pathogenic for man, while the latter is the vehicle of transfer for numerous important species which cause infections of the respiratory tract.

The **outdoor air** a few feet above the ground contains a great variety of chromogenic cocci and bacilli, fungus spores, and, particularly, the spores of the spore-forming aerobic bacilli.

Airplane surveys (62, 97) have shown that bacteria of the soil and water type can be found 20,000 feet above the surface of the earth and may even cross oceans in currents of air. The almost complete absence of pathogenic bacteria in outdoor air may be explained by the combined effect of desiccation and ultraviolet irradiation from the sunlight.

The **indoor air** contains smaller numbers of the same types of microorganisms found in outdoor air but supplemented by relatively large numbers of nonpathogenic as well as potentially pathogenic organisms from man, including viruses. Man constantly dispenses microorganisms into the air. Some reach the air from desquamating skin, a few from inapparent fecal contamination of the hands and clothing, but the major portion leaves the body through the upper respiratory tract. Quiet talking drives out more than 5,000 bacteria per second, although only

Fig. 2. Droplet dispersal following a sneeze. The patient had a cold; note strings of mucus. (From Jennison. *Aerobiology*, Washington, D.C., Publ. A.A.A.S., 17:102, 1947.

7.2 per cent of the expelled droplets were less than 4 μ in diameter. With gauze masks the subjects expelled only 19 bacterial contaminants, but 63 per cent of the droplets were less than 4 μ in diameter (28). Coughing drives out many more bacteria and a good healthy sneeze (Fig. 2) may disperse as many as 20,000 droplets most of which will contain bacteria or viruses (36, 39). The droplets vary in diameter from 10 μ to 2 mm., and the larger ones may travel a distance of 15 feet before reaching the ground. The larger droplets settle rapidly to the floor, adhere to particles of dust, and dry, leaving organisms attached to the dust particles. The smaller droplets remain suspended in the air but evaporate in less than one second, leaving behind "droplet nuclei" (96) of a few μ in diameter which may or may not contain one or more microorganisms. These droplet nuclei settle very slowly, and in an ordinary room filled with people they are wafted about in the air currents and remain suspended almost indefinitely.

In a closed room filled with people the sterilizing effect of ultraviolet light from the sun and the dilution factor of the vast quantities of outside air are lacking. It is obvious that under such conditions a great accumulation of potentially infective organisms will occur (49, 50, 68).

The control of airborne infectious organisms remains the most important problem in public health. The introduction of ultraviolet lights in the operating rooms has almost completely eliminated airborne infections (35, 54, 96).

BACTERIAL FLORA OF THE NORMAL HUMAN BODY

Man living in an environment of soil, air, and water is constantly bombarded by the myriads of organisms living or existing in these elements. Fortunately, man does not afford a favorable habitat for these saprophytes, and although they occasionally may be isolated in cultures, they are as a rule unable to establish themselves as a part of the normal flora in competition with the commensals which are already adapted to man as a host. Far too little is known about the effect of climate, diet, and other external and internal environmental factors on the normal microbial flora of man (70).

Normal Flora of the Skin. Most of the saprophytes from soil, water, or air may be found as transient but not as permanent residents of the skin. *Bacillus subtilis,* a gram-positive, spore-bearing, aerobic saprophyte, is not infrequently present in smears and in cultures either from normal skin or from definite lesions and must be differentiated from the closely related highly pathogenic species, *Bacillus anthracis.*

Cultures from the skin frequently grow: diphtheroids; staphylococci, both aerobic and anaerobic; sarcinae; *E. coli,* proteus, and other intestinal organisms; mycobacteria; *Staphylococcus epidermidis albus; Candida albicans;* and cryptococci (12). These organisms usually are commensals, but some become opportunists when the skin is injured. The mycobacteria are acid-fast commensals and occur most frequently in the external auditory canal and on the skin in the genital and axillary regions.

From time to time the skin of the face, neck, hands, and buttocks carries highly pathogenic hemolytic streptococci and staphylococci which have been transferred to the skin from the nose by the hands (55).

The relative freedom of the normal conjunctiva from infections may be explained by the mechanical action of the eyelids, the washing effect of the normal secretions which contain the enzyme lysozyme (24), and the production of antibiotics by the normal flora of the external eye (30, 69).

Normal Flora of the Nose, Nasopharynx, and Accessory Sinuses. Innumerable bacteria of all kinds are filtered from the air as it is breathed into the nose and passes through the nasopharynx, trachea, and bronchi. The bulk of the organisms are trapped in the mucous secretions of the nose and nasopharynx, while the few which reach the trachea and bronchi are quickly eliminated by mechanical or immunologic mechanisms. The **trachea, bronchi, lungs, accessory nasal sinuses, and mastoid sinuses are essentially sterile** in the normal individual. Certain individuals become nasal carriers of hemolytic streptococci and staphylococci and discharge these organisms in enormous numbers from the nose into the air (55). The nasopharynx might be considered the natural habitat of the common pathogenic bacteria which cause infections in the nose, throat, bronchi, and lungs, including the

pneumonias. Man is the primary host for these bacteria, and the convalescent patient and particularly the healthy carrier maintains the reservoir from which new clinical cases become infected. Some individuals carry specific pathogenic strains for years, others are apparently free of them, while the majority are best described as periodic carriers (88).

When anaerobic methods of culture are employed on filtered secretions from the nasopharynx, a flora of *Dialister pneumosintes* is revealed (59). Garrod also found gram-negative filter-passing anaerobic cocci in addition to *D. pneumosintes* (26).

Certain gram-negative organisms from the intestinal tract, such as *Pseudomonas aeruginosa, E. coli,* paracolon bacilli, and proteus, are found occasionally in normal individuals. Following penicillin therapy, these may predominate in the flora of the nasopharynx.

The nasopharynx of the infant is sterile at birth, but within two to three days after birth it has acquired the common commensal flora and the particular pathogenic flora carried by the mother and nurse. The carrier rate of pathogens may be almost 100 per cent in infants and remains higher throughout childhood than the figures previously given for adults (52).

At the present time the nasopharynx of infants is frequently colonized by penicillin resistant staphylococci derived from the nursing staff and medical staff. Berntsen and McDermott (5, 51) have noted that the elimination of penicillin-susceptible staphylococci from asymptomatic carriers by treatment with penicillin results in recolonization of the nose with penicillin-resistant strains This phenomenon suggested to Shinefield, Ribble, Boris, and Eichenwald (75) an ecologic maneuver by which a penicillin-susceptible phage-specific strain which was a good colonizer was introduced into the nose of the newborn infant to prevent the colonization of penicillin-resistant strains from the nurses. In some instances the new strain displaced the penicillin-resistant strain from the noses of the nurses.

Normal Flora of the Mouth. The normal flora contains pigmented and non-pigmented micrococci, some of which are anaerobic, gram-positive aerobic spore-bearing bacilli, coliform and proteus organisms (34), and lactobacilli (67).

The gums, pockets between the teeth, and crypts in the tonsils have an anaerobic flora which is quite unique. This includes anaerobic micrococci, microaerophilic and anaerobic streptococci, vibrios, fusiform bacilli, spirilla, borrelia, and treponema. These organisms make up the fusospirochetal synergistic group (Chapter 51). One member of this group, *Treponema microdentium,* is indistinguishable morphologically from *T. pallidum,* the cause of syphilis; consequently, dark-field examinations for suspected lesions of syphilis in the mouth should take into consideration the associated organisms (77). Students can demonstrate the abundance of this flora in their own mouths by staining or examining with the dark-field microscope a bit of material taken with the point of a toothpick from pockets which lie between the teeth at or below the gum line. Among the fungi, species of *Candida (Monilia)* (30) and *Geotrichum* are found as normal inhabitants in some 10 to 15 per cent of individuals. The natural habitat of the pathogenic species *Actinomyces bovis* is the gums (47, 70).

The mouth of the infant is not sterile at birth but in general contains the same types of organisms in about the same relative numbers as those present in the mother's vagina. This is usually a mixture of micrococci, streptococci, coliform bacilli, and Döderlein's bacillus. These organisms diminish in number during the first two to five days after birth and are replaced by the types of bacteria present in the mouth of the mother and nurse. The current literature was reviewed by Harrison in 1949 (34).

Normal Flora of the Intestinal Tract. The empty stomach of the healthy individual is usually free of microorganisms. The great number of microorganisms which reach this organ in the food are from the saliva and nasopharyngeal secretions and are either killed by the high acidity or digestive enzymes of the gastric juice or quickly passed on into the intestines. Under abnormal conditions, such as carcinoma of the stomach or obstruction from stenoses, where food is retained in the stomach, a charac-teristic flora may develop consisting of **sarcinae, yeasts,** and large gram-positive organisms formerly called the **Boas-Oppler** bacillus but now known to be a variety of *Lactobacillus acidophilus* (60). The **duodenum** usually is sterile unless there is an infection in the gallbladder when the freshly discharged bile contains the organisms present in that organ. Enterococci predominate in the small intestine. In the large bowel and in the feces, the predominate organism is not *E. coli,* as is usually stated, but various species of *Bacteroides* (46, 100). Zubrzycki and Spaulding (100) concluded from their studies that *Bacteroides,* together with enterococci, coliform bacilli, diphtheroids, and lactobacilli, account for 99 per cent of the total bacterial population. The remaining 1 per cent contains some very interesting organisms, including spore-bearing anaerobes, vibrios, fusiform bacilli, *Candida, Geotrichum, Cryptococcus, Penicillium, Aspergillus* (38, 50, 71), *Borrelia,* and *Treponema* resembling those of the mouth (77). From 2 to 5 per cent of apparently healthy individuals are carriers of pathogenic species of *Salmonella* (74). About 1 per cent of the population are carriers of *Shigella* (95), but not more than 0.0001 per cent are carriers of the typhoid bacillus.

The complete absence of colon bacilli and the almost complete absence of other bacteria from the intestinal tract of Arctic and Antarctic birds has been explained by the observations of Sieberth (76), who found that the marine algae *Phaecystes pouchetii,* which forms a considerable part of their diet, synthesizes acrylic acid which is bactericidal for both gram-positive and gram-negative bacteria. Rettger (64) concluded that bacteria, chiefly dead ones, make up nearly one third of the weight of the stool and a considerable proportion of the fecal nitrogen and fecal fat. The normal flora of the dog's nose, throat, and intestinal tract has been studied by Clapper and Meade (11).

The intestinal flora of the **newborn child** has been investigated by a number of workers. In 62 to 90 per cent of newborn infants the meconium is sterile, but in 10 to 28 per cent a few organisms, presumably acquired during labor, may be present (31, 81). In all instances within four to 24 hours after birth an intestinal flora has been established, partly from below and partly by an invasion from above. The stool of the breast fed infant is soft, light yellowish brown in color and has a faintly acid odor. **Lactobacilli,** particularly *L. bifidus,* may constitute 99 per cent of the total organisms in the feces, with the remainder consisting of enterococci, colon bacilli, and staphylococci (81). Artificially fed infants have hard, dark brown, foul-smelling stools. *L. bifidus* is uncommon, being replaced in part by *L. acidophilus* and colon bacilli and in part by **enterococci, gram-positive aerobic,** and **anaerobic bacilli,** including *Cl. capitovale, Cl. difficile,* and *Cl. lentoputrescens* (31). The flora of the artificially fed infant can be converted to that of the breast fed by adding 12 per cent lactose to whole cow's milk or lactic acid milk.

The significance of the intestinal flora has been a controversial issue since the time of Pasteur. Are the microorganisms essential for life; a natural but inevitable handicap; or an asset although not essential? Pasteur's studies on microbial fermentations suggested that the intestinal organisms might play an essential role in the metabolism of foodstuffs analogous to that of the protozoa in the gut of termites. The concept that some intestinal organisms were helpful but others harmful was suggested by Metchnikoff, who attributed the long life of the Bulgarian farmers to the consumption of buttermilk containing *L. bulgaricus.*

Reyniers and his associates at the medical school of Notre Dame have raised chickens, mice, rats, and guinea pigs in a germ-free environment (29, 65, 66). Although their animals grow to maturity and reproduce, it is not certain that they can be called "normal." Germ free rats have more albumin than normal rats, but less α_2-, β-, and γ-globulin. After an exposure to germs the α_2 fraction begins to rise in the first week, the β factor in the second week, followed by the γ-globulin after two weeks. As the globulin increases, there is a corresponding decrease of albumin (98). Germ-free guinea pigs develop fatal ulcerative enteritis in 48 hours after being fed cultures of *Sh. flexneri* dysentery bacilli. This result could be prevented by feeding *E. coli* for several weeks before

giving *Sh. flexneri.* The colon bacilli caused a remarkable reorganization of the mucosa of the intestinal tract, which presumably increased the resistance of the animal to *Sh. flexneri* (84). Freter (25) found that the characteristic vibrio, *V. comma,* and *Sh. flexneri* could be established in the intestinal tract of mice and guinea pigs if the normal flora was reduced or eliminated by previous treatment with antibiotics. In this instance, also, the feeding of *E. coli* eliminated the pathogenic organism. Later studies by Ransom (63) revealed that the elimination of the pathogenic species was due largely if not entirely to the action of enterococci. In a different type of experiment, Dubos and Schaedler (21) found that mice reared on a diet which eliminated most gram-negative organisms made the animal more susceptible to death from an intravenous injection of the Giorgio strain of *Staphylococcus aureus.*

There is only one proven instance of disease produced by a spontaneous alteration of the normal flora of the intestinal tract. When young children in hot weather develop a mild respiratory infection, the appetite fails, the fluid intake is sharply reduced, and undigested food reaches the small intestine in larger amounts, resulting in an invasion of the small intestine by *E. coli.* Organic acids produced by the metabolism of the colon bacilli irritate the gut, resulting in a syndrome of vomiting and diarrhea called in medical literature "summer diarrhea" (15).

SYNTHESIS OF VITAMINS BY INTESTINAL BACTERIA. Several methods of study, particularly those involving partial sterilization of the intestinal tract by **sulfaguanidine** and other sulfonamides (6), have shown that *E. coli, Aerobacter aerogenes* and other intestinal organisms synthesize large amounts of the B complex vitamins: **thiamin, riboflavin, nicotinic acid, pyridoxin, pantothenic acid, biotin, folic acid** and **inositol.** The fat-soluble vitamin K also is synthesized by intestinal bacteria (14, 58).

Broad-spectrum antibiotics rapidly reduce the bacteria in the intestinal tract and may precipitate acute vitamin deficiencies within a few days in patients who because of illness or poor dietary selection have low reserve stores. Bacteria in the intestinal tract may also destroy vitamins (99).

When minute amounts of chlortetracycline are added to the food of chicks and pigs, the animals grow much more rapidly than the controls. It is not known whether this effect is the result of a partial sterilization of the intestinal tract or a specific vitamin effect.

STERILIZATION OF INTESTINAL TRACT WITH ANTIBIOTICS. Efforts to sterilize the intestinal tract with various combinations of antibiotics before operations on the intestine are reasonably successful for a few days (22), but with continued therapy strains resistant to antibiotics appear.

Dearing and his associates (17) found that feeding broad-spectrum antibiotics to patients severely reduces the coliform organisms in the intestinal tract; and with the decrease of intestinal organisms, there was a decline in the amount of urobilinogen in the urine and feces, while the amount of bilirubin increased in the feces, suggesting that intestinal organisms were producing urobilinogen from bilirubin. Neomycin, alone, is very effective in temporarily sterilizing the intestinal tract of man (18). But this is not necessarily an advantage to the patient, since Dineen (19) found that mice, whose intestinal tract had been sterilized with neomycin died following small intravenous doses of the Giorgio strain of *Staphylococcus aureus,* while the control mice on a normal diet did not die of the same dose.

Normal Flora of the Genitourinary Tract. The smegma about both the male and female genitalia frequently contains *Mycobacterium smegmatis,* a harmless commensal, which may be found in voided specimens of urine and confused with the pathogenic *Mycobacterium tuberculosis.* The female urethra is either sterile or contains a few gram-positive cocci, while the anterior third of the male urethra contains gram-positive cocci, diphtheroids, and occasionally a short gram-negative bacillus which may be mistaken for *N. gonorrhoeae.*

The vulva of the newborn child is sterile, but after the first 24 hours of life it gradually acquires from the skin, vagina, and intestines a rich and varied flora of nonpathogenic organisms. The type of flora found in the vagina is dependent upon the pH reactions of its secretions and their enzyme content. At birth the vagina is sterile, but in the first 24 hours it is invaded by micrococci, enterococci, and diphtheroids. After two or three days, the estrin from the maternal circulation induces the deposition of glycogen in the vaginal epithelium. The glycogen facilitates the growth of a large gram-positive bacillus called **Döderlein's bacillus,** which is now recognized as a *Lactobacillus.* This organism produces acid from glycogen, and the flora for a few weeks is similar to that of the adult. When the passively transferred estrin is excreted through the urine, the glycogen disappears, the Döderlein bacilli disappear, the reaction becomes alkaline, and the flora then consists of micrococci: alpha and nonhemolytic streptococci, coliform and diphtheroid bacilli (13). At puberty the glycogen reappears, and the vaginal reaction again becomes acid as a result of the metabolic activity of Döderlein's bacilli, *E. coli,* and yeasts. In a study of the normal flora of 100 individuals, Carter and Jones (10) found diphtheroids present in 74 per cent, *Staphylococcus pyogenes* var. *albus* in 50 per cent, anaerobic cocci and bacilli in 48 per cent, nonhemolytic streptococci in 38 per cent, Döderlein's bacilli in 30 per cent, yeasts in 15 per cent, alpha streptococci in 9 per cent, and *E. coli* in 8 per cent. There are also occasional representatives of other members of the intestinal flora. During pregnancy there is an increase in the white staphylococci, Döderlein's bacilli, and yeasts. After menopause the flora resembles that found before puberty.

Bacteria in the Blood and Tissues. From time to time commensals from the normal flora of the mouth, nasopharynx, and intestinal tract are carried into the tissues and blood (44). They are usually eliminated promptly by the normal defense mechanisms, particularly phagocytosis (42, 53, 57). A few organisms remain for a time in lymph nodes and explain the not infrequent positive culture of diphtheroids or nonhemolytic streptococci from normal and abnormal lymph nodes. Any unusual organism of questionable pathogenicity which appears in only one of a series of blood cultures should be regarded as a contaminant from the skin or a stray transient in the blood or tissues. However, *Clostridia* capable of producing exotoxin can be found in normal organs of rabbits and dogs (7, 72).

Miller and others (56, 92) have reported that the commensals of the intestinal tract invade the blood and tissues following experimental irradiation of mice and will probably do the same in man following exposure to an atom bomb. The prompt administration of broad-spectrum antibiotics will probably prevent many of these infections.

REFERENCES

1. Arndt, W. F., and Ritts, R. E. Proc. Soc. Exper. Biol. & Med., 108:166, 1961.
2. Austin, L. B., and Zeldow, B. J. Proc. Soc. Exper. Biol. & Med., 107:406, 1961.
3. Behrend, M., and Krouse, T. B. J.A.M.A., 149:1122, 1952.
4. Benham, R. W., and Kesten, B. J. Infect. Dis., 50:437, 1932.
5. Berntsen, C. A., and McDermott, W. New Eng. J. Med., 262:637, 1960.
6. Black, S., and others. J. Biol. Chem., 145:137, 1942.
7. Boone, I. U., and others. J. Bact., 71:188, 1956.
8. Burkholder, W. H. Ann. Rev. Microbiol., 2:389, 1948.
9. Bush, G. L., and Chapman, G. B. J. Bact., 81:267, 1961.
10. Carter, B., and Jones, C. P. South, M. J., 30:298, 1937.
11. Clapper, W. E., and Meade, G. H. J. Bact., 85:643, 1963.
12. Connell, G. H., and Skinner, C. E. J. Bact., 66:627, 1953.
13. Cruckshank, R., and Sharman, A. J. Obst. & Gynec., 41:190, 1934.
14. Dam, H., and others. Naturwiss., 29:287, 1941.
15. Davison, W. C. Am. J. Dis. Child., 29:743, 1925.
16. Dearing, W. H., and Heilman, F. R. Proc. Staff Meet. Mayo Clin., 28:121, 1953.
17. ———— and others. Proc. Staff Meet. Mayo Clin., 33:646, 1958.
18. ———— and Needham, G. M. Proc. Staff Meet. Mayo Clin., 34:127, 1959.
19. Dineen, P. Proc. Soc. Exper. Biol. & Med., 104:760, 1960.
20. Dochez, A. R. Tr. A. Am. Physicians, 36:188, 1921.
21. Dubos, R. S., and Schaedler, R. W. J. Exper. Med., 111:407, 1960.
22. Duff, G. L., and Murray, E. G. D. Am. J. M. Sc., 223:301, 1952.
23. Emmons, C. W. Pub. Health Rep., 64:892, 1949.
24. Fleming, A. Lancet, 1:217, 1929.
25. Freter, R. J. Exper. Med., 104:411, 1956.
26. Garrod, L. P. Brit. J. Exper. Path., 9:155, 1928.
27. Gaughran, E. R. L. Bact. Rev., 11:189, 1947.
28. Greene, V. W., and Vesley, D. J. Bact., 83:663, 1962.
29. Gustafsson, B. Germ-Free Rearing of Rats, Acta Path. & Microbiol. Scandinavia, Supp., 73, 1948.
30. Halbert, S. P., and others. J. Immunol., 70:400, 1953; 73:169, 1954.
31. Hall, I. C., and O'Toole, E. M. Am. J. Dis. Child., 47:1279, 1934; 49:390, 1935.
32. Hammer, B. W. Dairy Bacteriology, 3rd ed., New York, John Wiley and Sons, 1948.
33. Hand, A. M. South. M. J., 47:1049, 1954.
34. Harrison, R. W. Ann. Rev. Microbiol., 3:317, 1949.
35. Hart, D. J.A.M.A., 172:1019, 1960.
36. Hatch, T. F. Aerobiology, Washington, D.C., Publ. A.A.A.S., 17:102, 1947.
37. Huppert, M., and others. J. Bact., 65:171, 1953.
38. ———— and Cazin, J., Jr. J. Bact., 70:435, 1955.
39. Jennison, M. W. Aerobiology, Washington, D.C., Publ. A.A.A.S., 17:106, 1947.
40. Jordan, E. O., and Burrows, W. J. Infect. Dis., 57:121, 1935.
41. Kauffmann, F. J. Immunol., 57:71, 1947.
42. Kerby, G. P., and others. J. Immunol., 64:123, 1950.
43. Kinsel, Norma A. J. Bact., 80:628, 1960.
44. Kotin, P. J.A.M.A., 149:1273, 1952.
45. Kriss, A. E., and others. J. Bact., 80:731, 1960.
46. Lewis, K. H., and Rettger, L. F. J. Bact., 40:287, 1940.
47. Lord, F. T., and Trevett, L. D. J. Infect. Dis., 58:115, 1936.
48. Louria, D. B. Ann. N.Y. Acad. Med., 98:617, 1962.
49. Lurie, M. B., and others. Am. Rev. Tuberc., 61:765, 1950.
50. McCoy, E. Ann. Rev. Microbiol., 8:257, 1954.
51. McDermott, W. Conference on Air Borne Infections, Bact. Rev., 25:173, 1961.
52. McFarlan, A. M. Brit. M. J., 2:939, 1938.
53. Martin, S. P., and others. Proc. Soc. Exper. Biol. & Med., 72:63, 1949.
54. Meleney, F. L. Treatise on Surgical Infection, New York, Oxford University Press, 1948, p. 81.
55. Miles, A. A., and others. J. Path. & Bact., 56:513, 1944.
56. Miller, C. P., and others. Science, 111:540, 1950.
57. Mudd, S., and others. Physiol. Rev., 14:210, 1934.
58. Najjar, V. A., and Barrett, R. Vitamins and Hormones, New York, Academic Press, 1945, Vol. III, p. 23.
59. Otlitsky, P. K., and McCartney, J. E. J. Exper. Med., 38:427, 1923.
60. Orland, F. J. J. Infect. Dis., 86:63, 1950.
61. Osborn, H. F. The Origin and Evolution of Life, New York, Scribner's, 1917, pp. 80-89.
62. Pady, S. M., and Kelly, C. D. Canad. J. Botany, 32:202, 591, 1954.
63. Ransom, T. P., and others. Proc. Soc. Exper. Biol. & Med., 107:332, 1961.
64. Rettger, L. F. Newer Knowledge of Bacteria and Immunology, Chicago, 1928, Chap. 46, p. 639.
65. Reyniers, J. A. Germ Free Life Studies, LOBUND Reports, Indiana, University of Notre Dame, 1946 through 1949.
66. ———— and others. J. Nutrition, 41:31, 1950.

67. Rogosa, M., and others. J. Bact., 65:681, 1953.
68. Rosebury, T. Experimental Airborne Disease, Baltimore, Williams & Wilkins Co., 1947.
69. ——— and others. J. Bact., 67:135, 1954.
70. ——— Microorganisms Indigenous to Man, New York, McGraw-Hill Book Co., 1962.
71. Schnoor, T. G. Am. J. Trop. Med., 19:163, 1939.
72. Schweinburg, F. B., and Sylvester, E. M. Proc. Soc. Exper. Biol. & Med., 82:527, 1953.
73. Seligmann, E. Proc. Soc. Exper. Biol. & Med., 83:778, 1953.
74. ——— and others. J. Immunol., 54:69, 1946.
75. Shinefield, H. R., and others. Am. J. Dis. Child., 105:646, 1963.
76. Sieburth, J. M. J. Bact., 82:72, 1961.
77. Smith, D. T. Oral Spirochetes and Related Organisms in Fusospirochetal Disease, Baltimore, Williams & Wilkins Co., 1932.
78. ——— Ann. Int. Med., 37:1135, 1952.
79. Smith, N. R. Ann. Rev. Microbiol., 2:453, 1948.
80. Smith, T. Parasitism and Disease, Princeton, N.J., Princeton University Press, 1934.
81. Snyder, M. L. J. Infect. Dis., 66:1, 1940.
82. Speare, G. S. Am. J. Surg., 88:523, 1954.
83. Spink, W. W. Arch. Int. Med., 94:167, 1954.
84. Sprinz, H., and others. Am. J. Path., 39:681, 1961.
85. Staka, R. P., and Stokes, J. L. J. Bact., 80:622, 1960.
86. Stanier, R. Y. Photosynthetic Mechanisms in Bacteria and Plants, Bact. Rev., 25:1, 1961.
87. Stewart, R. A., and Meyer, K. F. Proc. Soc. Exper. Biol. & Med., 29:937, 1932.
88. Straker, E., and others. Rep. Pub. Health & Med. Subj., London, No. 90.
89. Thompson, R., and Shibuya, M. J. Bact., 51:671, 1946.
90. Umbreit, W. W. Bact. Rev., 11:157, 1947.
91. ——— Symposium on Autotrophy, Bact. Rev., 26:145, 1962.
92. Vincent, J. G., and others. J. Bact., 69:38, 1955.
93. Virtanen, A. I. Ann. Rev. Microbiol., 2:485, 1948.
94. Wallin, J. E. Symbiontism and the Origin of Species, Baltimore, Williams & Wilkins Co., 1927.
95. Watt, J., and Hardy, A. V. Pub. Health Rep., 60:261, 1945.
96. Wells, W. F. Am. J. Hyg., 47:1, 11, 1948.
97. Wolf, F. T. Bull. Torrey Bot. Club, 70:1, 1943.
98. Wostmann, B. S., and Gordon, H. A. J. Immunol., 84:27, 1960.
99. Young, R. M., and Rettger, L. F. J. Bact., 46:351, 1943.
100. Zubrzycki, L., and Spaulding, E. H. J. Bact., 83:968, 1962.

11

Introduction to Immunology

Immunology deals with both the **complex invading organism** and the even more **complex reactions of the host.** It is not surprising, therefore, that the average student finds immunology more difficult than the study of cultural and biochemical reactions of bacteria in test tubes. The basic principles of immunology are presented in this section with a minimum of detail but supplemented by references to books, monographs, reviews, and recent articles for the use of the more advanced students.

New discoveries in the general field of immunology are appearing each day. Some of these confirm old theories, but many contradict the old theories. In one previous edition of this text Felton's work was presented which showed that a large dose of pneumococcal capsular polysaccharide paralyzed the antibody-producing mechanism of mice. In a later edition several reports were reviewed which suggested that the mechanism was not really paralyzed but that the newly formed antibodies were immediately neutralized by the excess of polysaccharide as soon as they were formed. In this edition still newer work indicates that the immune mechanism is indeed paralyzed, as suggested by Felton, but the paralysis need not be permanent. The apparent contradictory results reported in the previous edition are now recognized as a small part of the relatively complete picture. This brief story illustrates the rapidity of growth of the subject and the publication of contradictory results by equally competent experimenters.

The student should not be surprised to find some contradictory results reported in the following chapters. Whenever possible, we have indicated our reasons for favoring one point of view over another, but our conclusions may not be the same as those of your instructors, and only time and more investigation will prove which conclusions are correct.

The study of the altered reactivity of serum following a spontaneous or experimentally induced infection, or following the injection of harmless materials such as egg albumin or serum from another species, is known as **serology.** Serology may be defined as collection of technical laboratory procedures by which the foreign materials, **antigens,** and the specific reacting substances in the blood serum, **antibodies,** may be measured in a qualitative and quantitative manner. The quantitative measurement of these reacting substances has become an important subdivision of immunology known as **immunochemistry.** The history of its development and some idea of the exquisite exactness of its methods may be found by consulting the publications of Marrack (18, 19), Haurowitz (9), Landsteiner (16), Heidelberger (10), Kabat (14), Kabat and Mayer (15), Crowle (6), Winzler (29), Sevag (24), and Bernhart and Granboulan (1). The more general aspects of immunology are reviewed in the books by Boyd (2, 3), Cushing and Campbell (7), Raffel (23), Pappenheimer (22), Gell and Coombs (8), Humphrey and White (13). Monographs and symposia have been published by Burnet (4), Lawrence (17), Shaffer, Lo Grippo, and Chase (25), Najjar (21), Holub and Jaroskova (12), Heidelberger and Plescia (11), Taliaferro and Humphrey (28), and Simon (26). The application of immunology to preventive medicine is discussed by Maxcy (20), Smillie and Kilbourne (27), Cockburn (5), and Leavell and Clark (17a).

A discussion of the chemical and biologic nature of antigens and antibodies, their modes of interaction, and their practical use in the diagnosis of infectious diseases will be discussed in Chapter 12. In Chapter 13 the reactions of antigens with antibodies will be reviewed, and their practical use in the diagnosis of infectious diseases will be emphasized. The red blood cell groups and certain new discoveries in immunohematology will be presented in Chapter 14. Chapter 15 will introduce the problem of tissue transplantation immunity. Certain specific types of antigens, known as **toxins,** and their corresponding antibodies, known as **antitoxins,** will be presented in Chapter 16. In Chapter 17 the phenomenon of **allergy** will be introduced: it is essentially an alteration in the reactions of the tissues of man and animals subsequent to the introduction of living organisms or of originally inert harmless materials such as ragweed pollen, horse serum, and certain chemicals, drugs, and antibiotics. These segments of immunology will be brought together in Chapter 18 to explain, as far as our limited knowledge permits, the mechanisms of **infection** and **immunity** and their application to **epidemiology** (6a).

REFERENCES

1. Bernhart, W., and Granboulan, H. CIBA Symposium, Cellular Aspects of Immunity, London, Churchill, Ltd., 1960.
2. Boyd, W. C. Fundamentals of Immunology, 3rd ed., New York, Interscience Press, 1956.
3. ——— Introduction to Immunochemical Specificity, New York, Interscience Press, 1962.
4. Burnet, M. The Clonal Theory of Acquired Immunity, Nashville, Vanderbilt University Press, 1959.
5. Cockburn, A. The Evolution and Eradication of Infectious Diseases, Baltimore, Johns Hopkins Press, 1963.
6. Crowle, A. J. Immunodiffusion, New York, Academic Press, 1961.
6a. Cruickshank, R. Modern Trends in Immunology, Washington, D.C., Butterworth, Inc., 1963.
7. Cushing, J. E., and Campbell, D. H. Principles of Immunology, New York, McGraw-Hill Book Company, Inc., 1957.
8. Gell, P. G. H., and Coombs, R. R. A. Clinical Aspects of Immunology, Philadelphia, F. A. Davis Co., 1963.
9. Haurowitz, F. Chemie der Antigene und der Antikörper, in Fortischritte der Allergielehre, ed. by P. Kallos, Basel, S. Karger, 1939.
10. Heidelberger, M. Bact. Rev., 3:49, 1939.
11. ——— and Plescia, O. J. Immunochemical Approaches to Problems in Microbiology, New Brunswick, New Jersey, Rutgers University Press, 1961.
12. Holub, M., and Jaroskova, L. Mechanisms of Antibody Formation, New York, Academic Press, 1960.
13. Humphrey, J. H., and White, R. G. Immunology for Students of Medicine, Philadelphia, F. A. Davis Co., 1963.
14. Kabat, E. A. Blood Group Substances, New York, Academic Press, 1956.
15. ——— and Mayer, M. M. Experimental Immunochemistry, 2nd ed., Springfield, Ill., Charles C Thomas Co., 1961.
16. Landsteiner, K. The Specificity of Serological Reactions, 2nd ed., Cambridge, Mass., Harvard Univ. Press, 1945.
17. Lawrence, H. A. Cellular and Humoral Aspects of the Hypersensitive States, New York, Paul B. Hoeber, Inc., 1959.
17a. Leavell, H. R., and Clark, E. G. Preventive Medicine for the Doctor in His Community, New York, McGraw-Hill Book Co., 1958.
18. Marrack, J. R. The Chemistry of Antigens and Antibodies, 2nd ed., London, His Majesty's Stationery Office, 1938.
19. ——— Antibodies to Enzymes, in the Enzymes, Myrback, K., and Sumner, J. B., eds., New York, Academic Press, 1950, Vol. I.
20. Maxcy, R. F. Rosenau Preventive Medicine and Public Health, 8th ed., New York, Appleton-Century-Crofts, Inc., 1956.
21. Najjar, Y. A. Immunity and Virus Infection, New York, John Wiley & Sons, Inc., 1959.
22. Pappenheimer, A. M., Jr. The Nature and Significance of the Antibody Response. Symposium, New York, Columbia University Press, 1953.
23. Raffel, S. Immunity, 2nd ed., New York, Appleton-Century-Crofts, Inc., 1961.
24. Sevag, M. G. Immuno-Catalysis, Springfield, Ill., Charles C Thomas Co., 1951.
25. Shaffer, J. H., Lo Grippo, G. A., and Chase, M. W. Mechanisms of Hypersensitivity, Boston, Little, Brown, and Company, 1959.
26. Simon, H. J. Attenuated Infection, Philadelphia, J. B. Lippincott Company, 1960.
27. Smillie, W. G., and Kilbourne, E. D. Preventive Medicine and Public Health, 3rd ed., New York, Macmillan, 1963.
28. Taliaferro, W. H., and Humphrey, J. H. Advances in Immunology, New York, Academic Press, 1961, Vol. I.
29. Winzler, R. J. The Plasma Proteins, Putnam, F. W., ed., New York, Academic Press, 1960.

12

Antigens and Antibodies

ANTIGENS

Antigens are those substances which, following introduction into the animal body, have the property of stimulating the production of specific antibodies.

The characteristics of molecules which cause them to be antigenic depend upon (1) size, (2) presence of acid radicals in the determinant group, (3) position of determinant group in the aromatic ring, and (4) the spatial configuration in the determinant group.

Size. A molecule must have a molecular weight of approximately 10,000 or more before it can function as a complete antigen. Diphtheria toxin and serum albumins have molecular weights of about 70,000, but values as high as 6,000,000 have been found for some hemocyanins. Simple carbohydrates, polypeptides, and peptones are not antigenic, although these fragments of larger molecules may react in the test tube with antibodies formed to the complete antigen. **Lipids** of high molecular weight, such as lecithin and cholesterol, will not function as antigens in vivo when injected alone but may, under certain circumstances, become antigenic when combined with body proteins (76).

Acid Radicals. The antigenicity of a protein molecule depends not only upon size but also upon the presence of certain specific amino acids in the protein. Only a small part of the large protein molecule is really active as an antigen. Pauling (317), Campbell (55, 57), Boyd (34) and others have visualized the active areas as side chains or actual protuberances (Fig. 1).

The active areas are limited in number, size, and amino acid complexity. Yčas (442) esti-mated the number of amino acid residues occurring naturally as a little over 20, while Ogata (303) could demonstrate 30 in ovalbumin by diazotizing hapten groups. The number of different amino acids in a determinant group is apparently not greater than five. Tyrosine, tryptophane, and phenylalanine are usually present, and these must be in the right sequence with other amino acids to make a determinant group. Polymers of a single amino acid, such as glutamic acid, were not antigenic, even with molecular weights up to 100,000 (266, 267, 268, 269, 270). Most of the polymers studied by Stahmann and his associates (44, 376) were either not antigenic or only poorly antigenic, even though several amino acids were included in the polymers. Maurer (270, 271, 273, 274, 275) found that random copolymers of glutamic acid and lysine with molecular weights of 36,000 to 70,000 were weakly antigenic even though given with an adjuvant.

The order of antigenicity was $Glu_{60}Ala_{40} > Glu_{75}Ala_{25} > Glu_{90}Ala_{10} > Glu_{75}Val_{25} > Glu_{80}Leuc_{20}$ (272). Sage and his associates (349) found that complement fixation with BSA-poly-

The simple
hapten portion

A complex hapten
portion of the
functional antigen

Complete functional
antigen

Fig. 1. A conceptual representation of functional and haptenic antigens. The R group represents a single determinant of immunologic specificity and is the actual group that combines with an antibody molecule. (After Cushing and Campbell. *Principles of Immunology*, McGraw-Hill Book Co., Inc.)

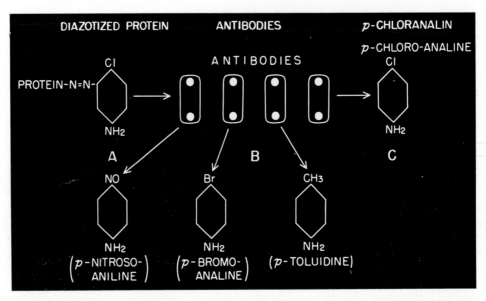

Fig. 2. Position of determinant group. *P*-chloro-aniline diazotized to a protein produces antibodies in rabbits which react with the original antigen and equally well with antigens in which the Cl group has been replaced by NO, Br, or CH$_3$. (After Raffel. *Immunity,* Appleton-Century-Crofts.)

dl-alanine increased with the chain length of the polymer. However, Maurer (274) found that polymers of *d*-amino acids were not antigenic, presumably because there are no natural enzymes to degrade them. Sela and Arnon (359, 360, 361, 362) showed that glutamic acid and tyrosin without lysine was not antigenic while Gill and Doty (146) demonstrated that the combination of glutamic acid, tyrosine and lysine was antigenic. Sela in 1962 produced multichain copolymers in which the chains of polypeptides containing L-tyrosine and L-glutamic acid were built on a multichain poly-*dl*-alanine and found these copolymers powerful and specific antigens (362). The smallest naturally antigenic polypeptide known at present is silk fibroin which was studied by Landsteiner in 1942 and restudied by Cebra in 1961 (61). The normal molecular weight of silk fibroin is from 600 to 1,000. Cebra found that tyrosine forms an important part of the antigenic determinants, but a considerable length of glycylalanyl-chain is also required for detecting specific combinations.

Position of Determinant Group in Aromatic Ring. In aromatic determinant groups lacking an acid radical the specificity is less sharply defined, and the position of the substituents in the ring becomes more important than their nature. This type of behavior is illustrated in Figure 2, where *p*-chloro-aniline is diazotized to a carrier protein and injected into a rabbit. The resulting antibodies are found to react equally well with the hapten *p*-chloro-aniline and with *p*-nitroso-aniline, *p*-bromo-aniline, and *p*-toluidine. However, if the substitution radical is changed to the ortho or meta position, or if the location of a double bond in such a determinant group is altered, the resulting antibody becomes more specific and the cross reactions less marked.

Spatial Configuration in the Determinant Groups. Spatial configuration is always important and is sometimes the sole factor in determining the specificity of the resulting antibody. In the experiment illustrated in Figure 3 Landsteiner and van der Scheer converted the tartaric isomers into levo-dextro and meso-para-aminotartranilic acids. These acids were then diazotized to horse serum protein. Rabbits injected with each of the three compounds produced antibodies which were tested with substances containing each of the three tartranilic acids but coupled this time to chicken serum protein. The data shown in Figure 3 were selected

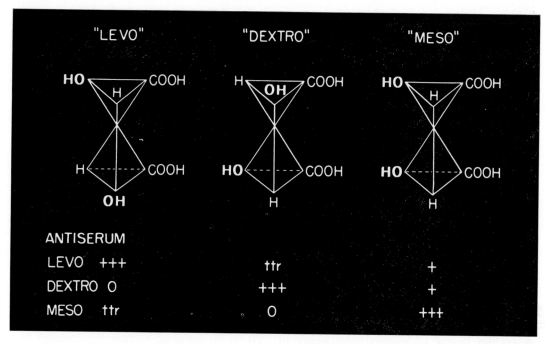

Fig. 3. Significance of spatial configuration. This figure illustrates the importance of spatial configuration in the antigen which determines the specificity of the antibody. (After Landsteiner and van der Scheer. *J. Exper. Med.*, 50:407, 1929.)

from Landsteiner and van der Scheer's table and include only the estimates of the amount of precipitate formed overnight in the icebox (0, faint trace, +, ++, +++) in mixtures containing 0.2 ml. of a 1:100 dilution of each antigen and four "capillary drops" of each serum antibody. Similar experiments have shown that the *cis* and *trans* forms of various substances can be detected by specific antibody reactions. **The antibody-producing mechanism seems to be sufficiently sensitive to distinguish between chemical compounds whose only difference is the spatial arrangements of their components.**

In the experiments illustrated in Figures 2 and 3 the testing system has been arranged so that it would appear that a single determinant group on the antigen would produce a single antibody reaction. Often pure crystalline proteins contain several determinant groups, which may induce several antibodies of somewhat different specificities, although all will be precipitated by the complete crystalline antigen. In the experiments with the diazotized proteins the naturally occurring determinants in the original protein have been largely but not completely suppressed. While all the antibody will be precipitated by the diazotized protein, only a portion of the antibody content can be precipitated by the addition of (1) the carrier protein itself and (2) the hapten group diazotized to a foreign protein. The hapten supplies the major stimulation for antibody formation, but the carrier protein also supplies subdeterminants as does the region of combination between the two components (177, 178, 307).

Rigidity in the Structure of the Determinant Group. It was assumed for many years that the absence of aromatic amino acids was the explanation for the failure of the protein gelatin to induce antibodies in rabbits, although gelatin does contain 2.3 per cent of phenylalanine, 0.7 per cent of histidine, and 0.5 per cent tyrosine. Maurer (266, 268, 269, 275) has shown that gelatin is antigenic for man and certain other animals but not antigenic for rabbits and guinea pigs unless given with adjuvants.

Gelatin is a denatured protein and is a non-rigid molecule. Sela and Arnon (361) have converted gelatin into an excellent antigen, even for rabbits, by introducing tyrosine peptides into the molecule. These experiments support the theory presented by Haurowitz in 1952 (180) that some rigidity in the structure of the determinant group is essential for antigenicity. Sela has suggested that the rigid sites in polysaccharide antigens may be the pyranose or furanose rings. However, if the molecule's structure is too rigid, such as that of polyglutamic acid or co-polyglutamyl-tyrosine peptides, it will not be a good antigen (273). Maurer (271) suggests that excess rigidity is the explanation of the observations of Levine and his associates (244) that denatured DNA from bacteriophage is more antigenic than natural DNA. The denaturing process reduces the rigidity of the determinant groups.

Complexity in the Determinant Group. A certain degree of internal complexity in the arrangement of amino acids in a protein and the sequence of sugars in a polysaccharide seems to be necessary for antigenicity. From three to five amino acids are found in the determinant groups, and, as noted above, polymers of a single amino acid such as glutamic acid are not antigenic even with molecular weights up to 100,000. Kabat and his associates (158, 215, 217) have found that the maximal determinant unit for dextran is isomaltohexose with a terminal nonreducing glucose. The terminal glucose contributes as much as 39 per cent of the total binding energy; the first five units contribute 98 per cent, leaving only 2 per cent for the sixth glucose residue (216). **In recent years antigens have been subjected to a dissection process by which additional antigenic groups have been found in the interior of the molecule.** Lapresle and Durieux (237) used extract of rabbit spleen to digest human albumin of pH 3.5 in vitro and injected the digest into rabbits. Three separate antigenic factors were detected by the appearance of three separate antibodies. The enzyme in the rabbit spleen was found to be similar to cathepsin A (238). Bovine serum albumin, after treatment with pepsin, was found by Weigle (422) to have at least four different serologic determinants. Campbell and Garvey (56, 57) have reviewed the older literature on fragmentation of foreign antigens after injection and the role of such fragments in immune responses. Additional evidence for internal determinants has been presented by Bartel and Campbell (16) and their associates (200) and by Webb and Lapresle (419).

Haptens. A single determinant group is by itself not capable of acting as an antigen in the animal body. The elegant work of Karl Landsteiner (230, 231, 232, 233, 234, 236) between 1930 and 1940, followed by that of Pauling (317), Haurowitz (178, 179, 180, 181) and Boyd (33, 34) made clear the effect of the chemical structure of the determinant group on the formation of specific antibodies. A simple chemical substance such as arsanilic acid can be converted to the diazonium salt which will then react with the aromatic amino acids in a protein to form arsanilate-azoprotein (Fig. 4). Usually 20 to 30 arsanilic groups are coupled to a protein carrier such as ovalbumin, serum albumin, or globulin. Equivalent amounts are used for more complex materials, such as the stroma of erythrocytes. These diazotized proteins, when injected into animals, induce the formation of antibodies directed specifically against the new chemical group. **Landsteiner named the chemical group which is antigenic only when coupled to a protein carrier, the hapten.** The amazing specificity of the antigen-antibody reaction is illustrated by certain classical experiments in which the hapten *p*-amino-benzene-arsenic acid (atoxyl) was diazotized in separate experiments to (a) chicken serum and (b) horse serum and then injected separately into rabbits. Antibodies formed against the atoxyl-azo-chicken serum reacted equally well with the atoxyl-azo-horse serum, and vice versa. However, when another hapten, sulfanilic acid, was diazotized to chicken serum and injected into rabbits, the resulting antibodies reacted with the sulfanilic acid-azo-chicken serum but not with the atoxyl-azo-chicken serum, showing that the specificity of the reaction depended upon the chemical hapten and not on the carrier proteins. Other studies have shown that arsenic acid (H_2AsO_4) can also neutralize the antibodies against atoxyl-azo-protein, indicating that the antigenic

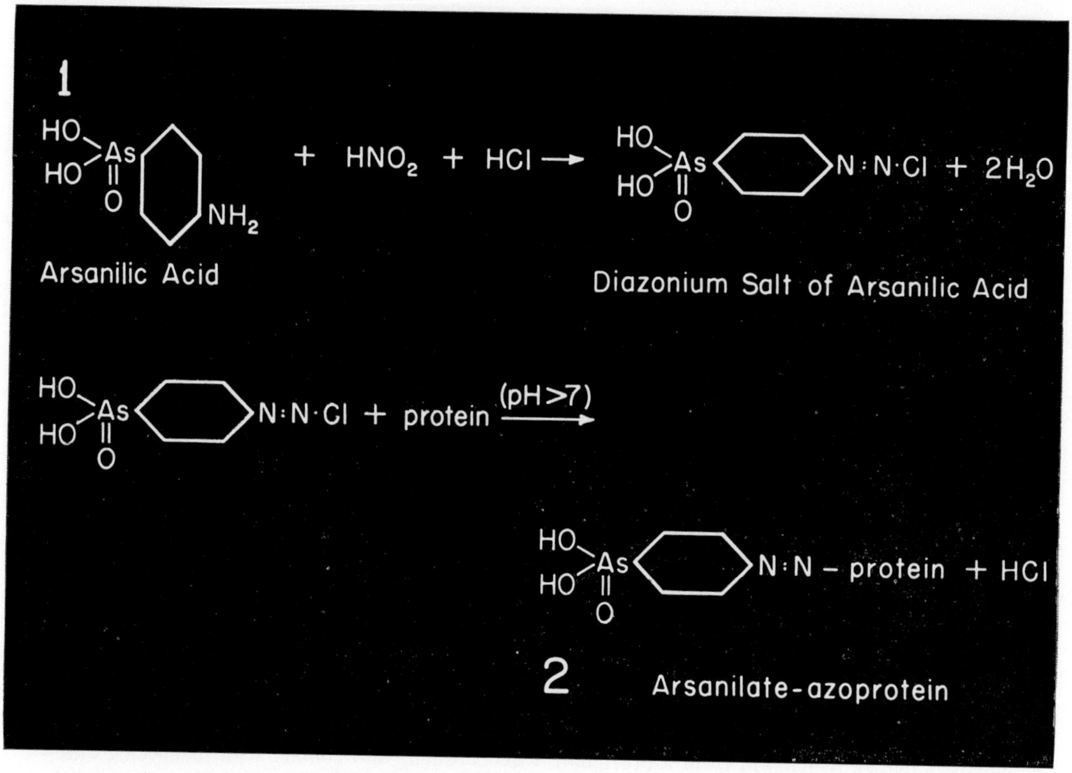

Fig. 4. Arsanilic acid diazotized to a protein carrier. (After Cushing and Campbell. *Principles of Immunology*, McGraw-Hill Book Co., Inc.)

specificity of atoxyl resides largely in the acid radical.

The arsanilate-azo-protein will be precipitated by the antibodies made in animals when solutions of the two materials are layered or mixed in a test tube. Although the antibodies are directed toward the arsanilate chemical group, arsanilic acid itself will not be precipitated but will bind the antibodies so they cannot subsequently precipitate the arsanilate-azo-protein. Arsanilic acid can be defined in this reaction as a **simple or inhibiting hapten.** If the structure of the hapten is made more complex by coupling three arsanilic acid molecules to resorcinol (Fig. 5), then a precipitate will be formed when exposed to the specific antibodies. Such a structure is defined as a complex hapten. However, **neither simple nor complex haptens will induce antibody formation.**

Spontaneous Synthesis of Hapten Antigens. It has been proved that 2-4 dinitrofluorobenzene can combine with protein in the living animal to form a complete antigen which will then stimulate antibody production (104). After the development of the antibodies, the chemical hapten alone will induce antigen-antibody reactions in the living animal. There are many reasons for believing that this is the mechanism by which individuals become sensitized to simple chemicals and drugs and subsequently develop drug eruptions and/or fever following a second exposure or dose. Sensitization of this type occurs much more frequently when sulfonamides, penicillin, or other agents are applied directly to an inflamed area of the skin or mucous membranes than when they are taken by mouth. There is some evidence that certain polysaccharides or even lipids may be adsorbed by a carrier protein and be transported to the antibody-producing cells, thus resulting in specific antibody production.

The Complete Functional Antigen. The complete functional antigen (Fig. 1) can be

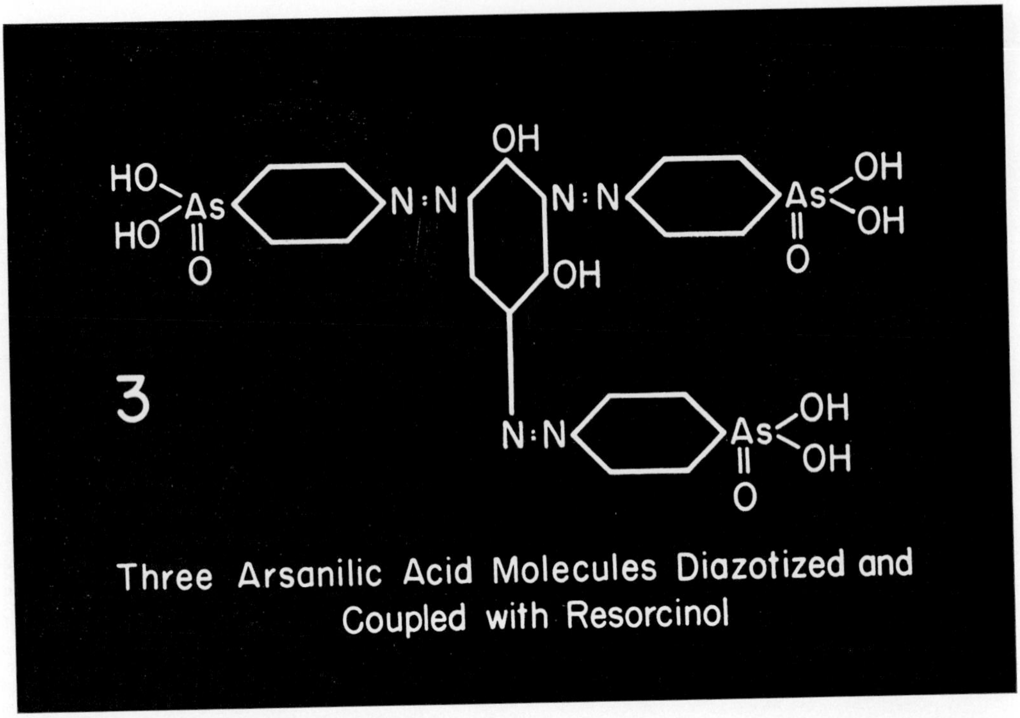

Fig. 5. Three arsanilic acid molecules diazotized and coupled with resorcinol. This makes a complex hapten which will form a precipitate when brought into contact with its specific antibody. (After Cushing and Campbell. *Principles of Immunology,* McGraw-Hill Book Co., Inc.)

visualized as a large molecule with 20 or more determinant groups, each group having a certain specific degree of internal complexity and rigidity. In natural protein antigens the determinant groups are made up of three to five amino acids, while in antigenic polysaccharides the determinant groups depend upon the sequence of the sugars and possibly the presence of branching chains (216, 361). The determinant groups of natural antigens do direct the formation of specific antibodies, but they alone are simple haptens which can combine with and inhibit precipitation but cannot stimulate the formation of antibodies or precipitate with specific antibodies. It has been shown by Campbell and Bulman (54) that certain amino acids can inhibit reactions between protein antigens and their precipitating antisera. In the artificially produced functional antigen the arsanilic acid is coupled to aromatic amino acids present in the determinant groups labeled R in Figure 1. The simple hapten portion labeled R is the functional equivalent of the arsanilic acid, while the complex hap-

ten portion of the functional unit in Figure 1 corresponds to the more complex structure shown in Figure 5.

Although antibodies which react specifically with the haptenic chemical are made in the animal body, the hapten must be attached to one of the potentially antigenic groups shown as protrusions in Figure 1. Furthermore, the entire protein "carrier" is necessary to carry the hapten to the antibody-producing cells; the complex hapten which can precipitate with the specific antibody cannot guide the hapten to the antibody-producing cells. Apparently, the amino acids in the determinant group to which the hapten has been attached must be in the antibody-producing cells to stimulate the synthesis of a new globulin molecule that has a binding site which is complementary to the original hapten.

This conception of the large protein molecule acting as a necessary carrier not only for a diazotized haptenic group but also for its own small number of reacting groups may help explain some of the puzzling observations about quantitative differences in antigenicity depending upon such mechanical factors as the method of injection. Relatively large amounts of soluble antigen, such as bovine serum albumin, ovalbumin, and serum globulin, must be injected intravenously to stimulate antibody production. Somewhat smaller amounts are effective if given subcutaneously and still smaller amounts if administered intracutaneously. Mixing the antigen with an adjuvant such as Freund's oil-water-antigen mixture, with or without accompanying heat-killed *Mycobacterium,* greatly enhances the amount of antibody production. Farr and Dixon (118) have shown that the concentration of antigen in the adjuvant is more important than the total amount of antigen. Finally, Parks and his associates (314) have found that the injection of very small amounts of antigen into the avascular structure of the eye, such as the cornea or vitreous humor, would give as good antibody rise as the use of the same amount of antigen in an adjuvant when injected intravenously. All of the observations suggest that the major portion of soluble antigen given by the intravenous or intramuscular routes is destroyed or excreted before it can come into effective contact with the cells capable of synthesizing antibodies. In contrast, particulate antigens, such as the whole bacterial cells and flagella from bacteria or even bacteriophage viruses (39), give high antibody titers after the injection of minute amounts of antigen. Particulate antigens are not excreted but readily phagocytized by polymorphonuclear or mononuclear white cells. The particulate antigens are digested by the white cells and then apparently transferred to the antibody-producing cells, although absolutely nothing is known about the mechanism of this transfer (373, 374).

Species-specific Antigens. Antigens restricted to a single species and occurring in all members of that species are called **species-specific.** These antigens do not produce antibodies when injected into the same **homologous species** but do produce antibodies when introduced into **heterologous species.**

Antibodies to species-specific antigens have a practical value in medicolegal cases in identifying the source of blood stains and the adulteration of foodstuff of protein origin, such as the addition of horse meat to beef products (424). It is also useful in ecologic studies of blood-sucking insects (400). Although these antibodies are quite specific, when the antibody containing serum is highly diluted, cross-reactions in low dilutions of serum are found between animals that are closely related phylogenetically. The cross-reactions become more marked and the serum less useful if repeated injections of the antigen are given.

Organ-specific Antigens. Antigens restricted to a particular organ of a species are called **organ-specific.** When these antigens are restricted exclusively to a single organ of a single species they are known as **"organ-specific and species-specific"** (435). The best example of this type of antigen is thyroglobulin (187, 345, 346), even though traces of cross-reacting thyroglobulin have been detected (346). In other instances the antigens are organ-specific but heterologous. The classical example of **organ-specific heterogenic antigens** is the protein of the ocular lens, where the same antigenic protein is found in species ranging from fish to man (255). Following certain types of injury to the eye in man some of this antigen is absorbed and stimulates the formation of antibodies in the serum of the patient (413). Although antibodies appear in the serum of the homologous animal the experimental studies of Ehrlich and his associates (101) suggest these antibodies are not the cause of damage to the lens. Similar organ-specific but heterogenic antigens are found in the brain, and antibodies to these antigens may result in a type of damage to the brain and spinal cord known as **demyelinating encephalomyelitis.** Under certain unexplained conditions agglutinins may be produced to the patient's own red blood cells, resulting in the development of acquired hemolytic anemia (290). These autoantibodies may play a part in congenital hemolytic anemia and other anemias (77, 439). A certain degree of organ specificity in antigens from lungs, liver, and kidneys has been demonstrated by various investigators and reviewed by Raffel (333) and Pressman (329). There is a reasonable possibility that certain chronic fatal diseases of the liver, kidneys, and connective and vascular tissues may be the result of **autoantibody formation.** These patients present symptoms which are consistent with this theory and often give a history of repeated infections or prolonged administration of drugs. For example, following sulfonamide therapy the stage might be set for a hapten to combine with a relatively specific organ antigen to produce specific antibodies, after which the hapten alone or the altered tissue protein alone could continue the damaging reactions. Recent studies have shown that the cells causing malignant tumors of man and animals are altered sufficiently to become antigenic (81, 191, 253, 399). These observations suggest that new methods may become available for diagnosis, prognosis, and therapy of malignant tumors (192).

Isoantigens. Antigens which occur in some members of a species only, such as the blood group antigens of man, are called **isoantigens.** The discovery of the four major blood groups, A, B, AB, and O by Landsteiner (229, 236) made possible the present widespread use of blood transfusions in man (430). In addition to the ABO group of antigens, certain individuals have MN and/or Rh and Hr antigens, all of which are determined by inherited genes. This inherited specificity is sufficiently exact so that a study of the isoantigens and isoagglutinins of a child and its alleged father may serve to exonerate the man (331).

Boyd's 1963 review of the genetics of the erythrocytes (36) suggests that the blood group may be a more suitable and accurate method of delineating the races of man than gross skin color or morphological features. For example, the Diego factor is confined almost exclusively to the Mongoloid races, while the Rh negative gene is completely absent from the American Indian race.

Over 80 heritable types have been found in the erythrocytes of cattle (79). Some of these are inherited in groups or complexes called **phenogroups,** which may contain as many as 12 factors. The specificity of these blood cell reactions is illustrated by the fact that the sire of a particular calf, even when pregnancy has been induced by artificial insemination can be determined with great accuracy because of the great number of different isoantigens in the cow (121, 347).

Although each of the four major isoantigens occur separately in man, several of them also occur in horses, cows, pigs, and other animals. Extensive chemical studies on these antigens from human and animal sources have been reported by Kabat (211, 212, 214) and his associates (3, 243). Substances which behave like human blood isoantigens are found widely distributed in nature in plants and in bacteria. Boyd (35) prefers the name **lectin** for cross-reacting antigens (375). Transfusion reactions and diseases caused by antibodies to these antigens will be discussed in more detail in Chapter 14.

Isoantigens are not limited to erythrocytes. Oudin (305) demonstrated seven individual antigens in rabbits' sera by the gel diffusion technic. Tullis (406) and others (141, 176, 365) have found isoantigens for the platelets, granulocytes, and lymphocytes of man. The antibodies to the isoantigens studied by Shulman could be detected by complement fixation but not by precipitation (365).

Itoh and Southam (201) inoculated nine human cancer strains and two normal cell strains into healthy human male volunteers. The malignant cells grew at first but were soon eliminated. Serologic tests showed that all volunteers developed isoantibodies which reacted with each of the malignant cells lines but not with the normal cells.

Nucleic Acids and DNA as Antigens. The clinical disease known as **lupus erythematosus** is characterized by the presence of a peculiar type of cell in the blood known as the LE cell. This cell is actually a polymorphonuclear leukocyte which has phagocytized the nuclei of other polymorphonuclear leukocytes or lymphocytes from the patient's own blood. In this instance it appears that an autoantibody prepares the subject's own cell nuclei for phagocytosis (194). Antibodies have been detected in the serum of these patients directed against (1) the whole nucleus, (2) nucleic acid, and (3) deoxyribonucleic acid (82, 135, 195, 279, 334, 387). The DNA itself, either as a hapten for the nucleic acid or independently, directs the formation of antibodies which not only react specifically with the host DNA but with DNA from other species (14, 276). In other experiments, Phillips and his associates have shown that DNA preparations from bacteria induced antibodies which cross reacted with DNA from the calf thymus and salmon sperm. Antibodies to bacteriophage DNA are directed, at least in part toward the glucosylated 5-hydroxymethylcytosine (287).

Rabbits immunized with (1) ribosomes from the liver of rats or rabbits and (2) nuclei of liver cells, develop specific antibodies (28) to RNA and DNA. Apparently the high specific antigenicity resides at the level of the purine or pyrimidine base (52, 395, 440). The marked specificity was demonstrated by hemagglutination inhibition (28). In certain instances the difference of one phosphate group was discernible. Autoantibodies of this kind may be responsible for some types of hemolytic anemia, leukopenia, and circulating autoimmune antibodies to erythrocytes, leukocytes, and ribosomes (90, 389a).

Heterogenetic, Heterophile, or Forssman Antigens. These peculiar antigens are widely distributed in nature and have been found in humans of blood groups A and AB, in bacteria and even in plants (333). Forssman (128) discovered in 1911 that the injection of emulsions of guinea pig organs into rabbits induced the formation of antibodies which would lyse sheep erythrocytes. In animal tissues the antigen seems to be a **carbohydrate-lipoprotein complex** with the carbohydrate providing specificity (236). The lipoidal substance was not antigenic but would react with antibodies formed to the complete complex. There is no lipoidal material in the Forssman antigen found in the Shiga dysentery bacillus, while in the pneumococcus the antigen seems to be a lipopolysaccharide in which the carbohydrate is the somatic carbohydrate (C substance) of the organism (21, 153). The Forssman antigen is remarkably resistant to heat, withstanding boiling and even autoclaving. The antigen is not a single entity in all biologic associations, and its specificity probably depends upon similar and not identical chemical structures (133, 333). The distribution of Forssman antigen in cells of various species of animals has been studied with fluorescein-labeled antibody (182, 394). Heterophile antibodies are present in certain human serums either normally or during the course of certain diseases. The highest titers are usually found in patients who are suffering from the disease known as "infectious mononucleosis" or in individuals who have had serum sickness from therapeutic injections of horse or rabbit serum. This fortuitous agglutination of sheep cells of serum from patients with infections mononucleosis was discovered in 1932 by Paul and Bunnell (316). More recent studies have shown that the antibodies found in infectious mononucleosis and serum sickness can be differentiated from typical Forssman antibodies and from each other (333) by selective absorption as shown in Table 1. If the sheep cell agglutinins are absorbed by guinea pig tissue, then the antibodies are of the Forssman type. If the sheep cell agglutinins are not absorbed by guinea pig tissue, but are removed by ox erythrocytes, then the antibodies are probably specific for the unknown agent which causes infectious mononucleosis. The sheep cell agglutinins which appear in serum sickness are absorbed by guinea pig tissue, rabbit, and ox erythrocytes. However, Lee (242) could not separate sheep agglutinins and beef hemolysins.

Natural Antigens in Bacteria, Fungi and Viruses. Living organisms usually contain many separate and specific antigens, some of which are very good and others poor stimulators of antibody production. Raffel (333) has suggested that we should "look upon a microbe as a bag of distinct antigens." It is probable that one or, at most, two of these antigens are essential for the virulence of the organism, and only antibodies directed against these particular antigens are of use to man and animals in their fight against the infecting agents.

The virulence-determining antigens of microorganisms may be (1) **proteins,** (2) **polysaccharides,** (3) **carbohydrate-protein complexes** with the carbohydrate acting as a hapten, or (4) the even more complex **polysaccharide-phospholipid-protein complex** found in most gram-negative organisms from the intestinal tract. The surface layer of the virulent hemolytic streptococci, the erythrogenic toxin of certain hemolytic streptococci which causes scarlet fever, and the exotoxin of *C. diphtheriae, Cl. tetani,* and *Cl. botulinum* are proteins. Certain of the toxins of *Cl. perfringens* are proteins but are also enzymes, and the corresponding antibodies are therefore both "antitoxins" and "antienzymes." Enzymes from both plant and animal sources have been found to be antigenic. The antibody induced by the enzyme will precipitate the enzyme from solution but may or may not destroy its enzymatic activity, suggesting that in some instances the chemical groups responsible for antigenicity and for the enzyme activity may be located at different points on the molecule (261, 339, 364). The antigenicity of hormones derived from another species is low, but sometimes antibodies like those to insulin (284, 441) do develop and complicate therapy (163).

The capsular polysaccharides of the pneumococci are essential for type specificity and for the virulence of the organism. They are complete antigens for man and mice and apparently owe their specific antigenicity to their high molecular weight (60,000 to 140,000), the presence of free acid groups, and the order of occurrence of certain molecular groups giving steric specificity. Polymers of basic sugar units, such as glucose, mannose, galactose, glucuronic acid, and glucosamine, are combined in various patterns to give nearly 100 distinct serologic types. Some antigenic polysaccharides identical to those found in pneumococci occur spontaneously in plant germs (186) and in many common foods.

Table 1. Occurrence of Heterogenic Antigens of Sheep Erythrocytes in Other Species
(Raffel, 1961)

ANTIGEN	OCCURRENCE OF ANTIGENS IN				
	SHEEP ERYTHROCYTES	OX ERYTHROCYTES	RABBIT ERYTHROCYTES	GUINEA PIG TISSUE	HORSE SERUM
Forssman	+	−	−	+	+
Infectious mononucleosis	+	+	−	−	−
Serum sickness	+	+	+	+	+
Protein antigen 1	+	+	..	..	..
Protein antigen 2	+	−	..	..	..
Protein antigen 3	−	+	..	..	..

The first synthesis of a naturally occurring antigen was achieved by Goebel (152) in 1940. He synthesized a polysaccharide containing glucuronic acid that induced the formation of antibodies which protected mice against large doses of Type II pneumococci. More recently E. E. B. Smith and her associates (368) have synthesized Type III capsular pneumococci polysaccharide, with the aid of enzymes in a cell-free medium.

Polysaccharide antigens have been found in every type of microorganism studied (46), and in many instances the carbohydrate seems to function as a hapten (315). The more complex polysaccharide-phospholipid-protein complex which occurs in certain gram-negative bacilli of the intestinal tract illustrates the importance of the hapten concept (32). The phospholipid fraction alone is not antigenic. The protein carrier is identical in *S. typhosa* and *Sh. dysenteriae* and induces specific antibodies when injected into animals. When, however, the polysaccharide protein complexes from *S. typhosa* and *Sh. dysenteriae* are injected separately into rabbits the antibodies are directed almost exclusively against the polysaccharide fraction, thus making possible the serologic differentiation of *S. typhosa* from *Sh. dysenteriae* (283). In the Flexner group of dysentery organisms some of the cross-reactions between members, which were formerly interpreted as the presence of two or more antigens in each organism, are now known to be due to multiple determinant groups on a single antigen molecule (321).

Common Antigens in Heterologous Organisms and Tissue. The presence of common antigens in widely separated species provides a logical basis for some of the common diagnostic tests. Examples of these are the **Paul-Bunnell** agglutination test for infectious mononucleosis, where the sheep red cell apparently shares a common antigen with the unknown etiologic agent of the disease; the **Weil-Felix** test for typhus fever, Rocky Mountain spotted fever, and scrub typhus, where Proteus OX 19 shares a common antigen with *R. prowazekii* and *R. rickettsii*, and Proteus OXK with *R. tsutsugamushi*. The Wassermann test for syphilis, certainly a common antigenic reaction, is believed by Eagle (97) and his associates to be due to the presence in the spirochete of an antigen related to an antigenic factor in normal tissue. The possibility that the proteins of *T. pallidum* act as a carrier for haptens derived from pathologically altered tissue has been discussed by Raffel (333). Regardless of the final solution of this problem, the test itself, when properly controlled, remains a very useful tool.

Unexpected, embarrassing, and even dangerous reactions may be encountered in therapy as a result of the wide dissemination of common antigens. Antipneumococcus

Type XIV antibodies produced in the horse for treating this type of pneumonia in man gave unexpectedly severe reactions (123) until it was found that the pneumococcus Type XIV specific polysaccharide contained two of the carbohydrate constituents present in human blood isoantigens A, B, AB, and O (214). Similar severe reactions were encountered occasionally when highly purified preparations of dextrans were injected into man as a blood expander in the treatment of patients in shock. Dextrans are not antigenic for rabbits and guinea pigs, but Kabat and Berg found them to be antigenic for man (213). Human contact with dextrans may occur in one of three ways: dextran is a common contaminant of commercial sugar; dextran-producing bacteria have been isolated from the intestinal tract of man; and dextrans share common polysaccharides with pneumococcal Types II, XII, and XX. A previous experience with antigens from any of these sources would explain the dangerous reactions following intravenous injection of dextran (254a).

Kaplan (219) has isolated an antigen from Group A hemolytic streptococci which produces antibodies in rabbits which would cross-react with some antigens in human heart tissue. The myofibrils and the smooth muscle of the blood vessel walls were the sites of the reactions.

Polysaccharide antigens are more likely to be duplicated in different organisms than protein antigens because of the relatively few types of sugars which make up the polymers. The more important cross-reactions will be mentioned in the chapter on specific organisms. A dramatic example was reported by Neill and his associates (293) in 1955 where an antiserum made to the fungus *Sporotrichum schenckii* gave reciprocal cross-reactions with pneumococcal Types XXXII, XXXI, XXIII, XX, and X. The pneumococcal part of the reciprocal reaction depended upon the specific capsular polysaccharide and the corresponding type-specific antiserum.

ANTIBODIES

Antibodies are globulins, modified by the animal body in response to the introduction of antigens, which have the property of reacting specifically with the particular antigen with which the animal has been injected.

Electrophoretic studies of serum reveal

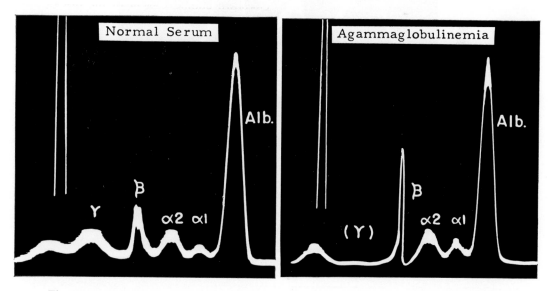

Fig. 6. Electrophoretic pattern of human serum. This figure illustrates the electrophoretic pattern found in the serum of a normal individual and in the serum of a patient with agammaglobulinemia. Note the absence of gamma (γ) globulin. (Courtesy of Dr. Wayne Rundles.)

that albumin is the largest and fastest moving element. The globulins are normally somewhat less in amount and divided by mobility into the alpha 1, alpha 2, beta, and gamma fractions (Fig. 6). The major part of the antibody content of serum is in the gamma fraction, although certain specific types of antibodies are found in other fractions or distributed throughout several fractions (84, 99, 107, 162, 164). Under antigenic stimulation the gamma globulin may increase in amount until it equals or exceeds the amount of albumin. This excess globulin may be pure antibody globulin and can be removed from the serum by precipitation with specific antigens, as illustrated in Figure 7.

Characteristics of Antibody Globulins. Purified antibody globulin is difficult and laborious to prepare but has been achieved by a variety of methods such as the salt concentration method of Heidelberger and his associates (183, 184), the acid method of Landsteiner (232) and Haurowitz (181), competition with a diazable hapten by Campbell (53), Karush and Marks (220), Bassett (17) and Farah and his associates (117), elution from a carbomethylcellulose column by Levy and Sober (246), or by 1014 exchange resins as employed by Malley and Campbell (259). In the special instance of antibodies to gelatin, Arnon and Sela (5) treated the gelatin-antigelatin precipitate with the proteolytic enzyme collagenase which digests the gelatin and frees the antibody.

Gamma globulin molecules are on the borderline of visibility with the electron microscope and pictures of them have been made by Valentine (410) and by Hall (169). **Except for their ability to react with**

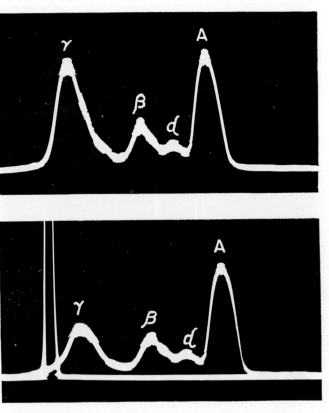

Fig. 7. Electrophoretic pattern of antiserum. Upper figure, electrophoretic pattern of a refined antipneumococcus Type I rabbit serum. Lower figure, electrophoretic pattern of the same serum after removal of antibodies by precipitation with pneumococcus Type I polysaccharide.

specific antigens, antibody globulins show no chemically recognizable differences from normal globulins. It has been assumed that the various specific antibody globulins from one species of animal, when injected into another species, would give rise to one new antiglobulin antibody which would react equally well with either an antitoxin or an antibacterial or antiviral antibody. The work of Kunkel and his associates (228) has shown this to be an error. The anti-A blood group antibodies, one antidextran and one antilevan antibody isolated from the blood of man, were injected into rabbits. Actually, antibodies specific for each "antibody" were found, which suggests that the new antibody was oriented toward the specific or unique binding site of the antibody which was used as the antigen rather than toward the general structure of the globulin molecule.

Reviews by Kabat and his associates (217), by Fudenberg and Franklin (139) and by Kunkel and Rodney (228) indicate that antibody actually is associated with at least three serum proteins identifiable by immunoelectrophoresis. These are the classical (1) γ-globulins, which usually contain most of the antibody activity and have a sedimentation coefficient of 7 Svedberg units; (2) β_2M globulin, which is usually the first type of antibody to appear after exposure to antigen and has a sedimentation coefficient of 19 S.; (3) the β_2A, which appears as a skin-sensitizing antibody and as an antibody to anti-A blood group substance (228) with a sedimentation coefficient of 7 S. The γ-7 S. globulin has in turn been split into γ_1-7 S. and γ_2-7 S. by Benacerraf and his coworker (24). Oudin (305) has identified at least seven allotypic specific types of γ-globulin in the sera of rabbits and similar but small numbers of allotypic types have been found in mice and guinea pigs (139).

The specific allotypes in the serum of rabbits are antigenic when injected into other rabbits having a different type of globulin, and induce precipitating antibodies. These allotypes of gamma globulin as well as the other types of antibody globulin mentioned above, are all under genetic control (91, 92, 139, 217).

Usually 90 to 95 per cent of the total gamma globulin has a molecular weight of about 160,000 and sedimentation coefficient of 7 S. (Fig. 8). The slow-moving heavy globulins, with molecular weight about 900,-000, have sedimentation coefficients of 19 S. (113, 115). These heavy globulins are known also as macroglobulins. There are marked variations in the amount of 19 S., globulin present in sera, dependent upon the animal species, the type of antigen, and the stage of immunization. The 19 S. antibody globulin has been found in man, mice, monkeys, horses, chickens, and rabbits (129, 403). Benedict and his associates (25) found 200 times as much 19 S. as 7 S. antibody globulin in the sera of chickens during primary immunization and for five to six days after secondary stimulation, after which the 7 S. predominated. Normally rabbits produce both 19 S. and 7 S. to primary infection with *S. paratyphi-B,* but animals given 1,000 R. in a single dose, with the spleen shielded, produce only 19 S. after primary stimulation with this organism, although 7 S. appears after a second dose (342). The presence of antigen seems to be necessary for the continual synthesis of 19 S., in contrast to 7 S., which is synthesized long after detectable amounts of antigen have disappeared (122). The somatic antigen of the typhoid bacillus stimulates primarily 19 S. antibodies (112). The "reagin" antibody in syphilis (80) and the rheumatoid factor in arthritis (112) are 19 S. antibodies. The isohemagglutinins to human red blood cells, and antibodies to the Rh factor in man, and antibodies to nucleoprotein from the liver stimulate both 19 S. and 7 S. antibodies (112). The 19 S. antibody may agglutinate human erythrocytes in saline suspension, which the 7 S. antibody does not (55, 62). The extra weight of the 19 S. antibody seems to be due to its carbohydrate content; it is not merely a polymer of the 7 S. gamma globulin (286), although it has common binding sites.

Some biologic differences have been observed in antibodies found early in the process of antibody synthesis and those found later (48, 203, 205, 227). In many instances, as noted above, the early antibodies are predominantly 19 S., and the later ones

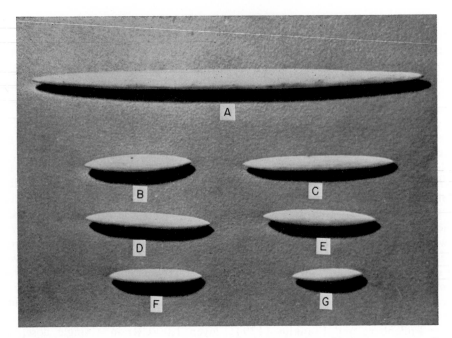

Fig. 8. Photographs of models of typical antibody molecules with human serum albumin for comparison. A, horse antipneumococcus antibody; B, horse antitoxin; C, rabbit antiovalbumin; D, human antipneumococcus; E, rabbit antipneumococcus; F, human gamma globulin; G, human serum albumin. (After Boyd. *Fundamentals of Immunology,* Interscience Publishers.)

are predominantly 7 S. (208, 382), but this may or may not be the explanation for the difference in avidity of the antibody for antigen (22, 265). **Antibodies formed later in the process bind antigens more securely but are less specific, showing more evidence of cross reaction with related antigens.**

American Indians and Negroes have a lower percentage of albumin and a higher percentage of beta and gamma globulin than do Caucasians (223). Transferrin D, a beta globulin variant, has been found to occur predominantly in Negroes, while the greatest incidence of transferrin B and C has been found in Navajo Indians (20). The gamma globulin variant Gm^{ax} has been found only in whites, and the Gm-like variant only in Negroes (381). Two genetic factors Gm(a) and Gm(b) are present in 7 S. gamma globulin molecules but absent in 19 S. molecules.

The macroglobulins are increased in the "autoimmune diseases," such as systemic lupus erythematosus (81, 341), as well as in primary macroglobulinemia as described in Waldenstrom (416). The studies of Fu-

denberg and Kunkel (138, 139) suggest that the 19 S. antibodies found in certain collagen diseases are really antibodies directed against certain genetically determined 7 S. gamma globulins.

The Life of Antibodies. The half life of antibody globulin is presumed to be the same as that of normal globulin for a particular species of animal and probably depends upon the metabolic rate of the particular animal. The half life of homologous globulin in children of six months to eight years of age is 20.3 ± 4.2 days and for adults 13.1 ± 2.8 days (85). The rate of disappearance of antibodies can be studied by (a) passively immunizing an animal with homologous antibodies, (b) passively immunizing an animal with heterologous antibodies, or (c) by internally labeling of newly formed antibody with an isotope in an actively immunized animal. Antitoxin antibodies (264) in lambs, acquired by drinking the mother's colostrum, have a half-life of approximately 30 days (Fig. 9), and Wiener's (431) studies on the persistence of placental passing Rh antibodies in infants

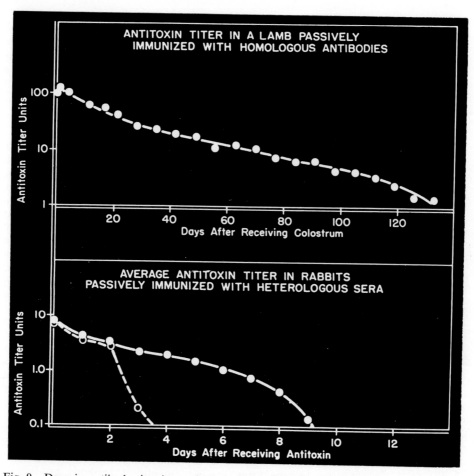

Fig. 9. Drop in antibody titer in passively immunized animals. Upper figure, antitoxin titer in lamb passively immunized with homologous antibodies in colostrum. (From Mason, Dalling, and Gordon. *J. Path. & Bact.*, 3:783, 1930.)

Lower figure, antitoxin titers in rabbits passively immunized with antitoxin from another species (horse). Solid line = average titers of three normal rabbits. Dotted line = average titers of seven rabbits which had been injected previously with horse serum. (Data from Glenny and Hopkins. *J. Hyg.*, 21:142, 1922.)

reveals a half life of 30 days. Diphtheria antitoxin in newborn infants, acquired by placental transmission, also has a half life of about 30 days (431), although the child has an effective immunity against diphtheria for three to six months. The injection of horse gamma globulin tetanus antitoxin into an infant at birth, before the development of the antibody producing mechanism, results in the slow steady type of elimination characteristic of antibodies in an homologous species (Fig. 10).

Passively transferred antibodies to a heterologous species at first disappear at the rate characteristic of the normal globulins, but with the development of antibodies the rate of disappearance is accelerated (151) and a second injection of the same type of antibodies shows a very rapid disappearance (Fig. 9).

Antibody globulins in actively immunized animals are being constantly synthesized, broken down, and resynthesized at the same rate as normal unmodified globulins. Some measurement of the speed of alteration is shown by the experiments of Schoenheimer and others (352), who fed glycine N^{15} for three days to a rabbit which had received

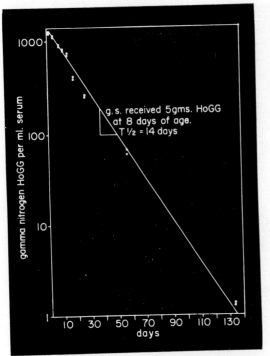

Fig. 10. Horse gamma globulin (tetanus antitoxin) injected into an infant at birth before the development of the antibody-producing mechanism. (After Smith. *Mechanisms of Antibody Formation,* Academic Press.)

the last injection of pneumococci 10 days previously. As seen in Figure 11, the total amount of antibody nitrogen was declining, but the ingested glycine isotope was incorporated in equal amounts into new globulin and new antibody globulin. The half life of a molecule of antibody globulin could be calculated as about 14 days. No glycine isotope was incorporated into antibody globulin received passively from another animal. (185). Some of the glycine isotope may have persisted in the body after the last day of feeding and subsequently have been incorporated into newly formed antibody to give the apparent half life of 14 days. Dixon and his associates (85) found that the half life of passively administered homologous gamma globulin in the rabbit was 4.6 to 5.7 days. Essentially the same rate of decline was found after active immunization following the primary injection (Fig. 12), but after the second and particularly after the third injection, antibody was produced for a

long time after the disappearance of the antigen. The initial decline had a half life of six to nine weeks, after which there was a gradual or abrupt change to a slower rate with a half life of one to two months which persisted for at least six months. This is the type of response which one might expect in man after a series of immunizing doses.

The Influence of Adjuvants on the Production of Antibodies. Certain nonantigenic substances, when mixed with antigens and injected into man or animals, cause a marked increase in antibody production (333). Aluminum potassium sulfate (alum) and aluminum hydroxide (aluminum cream) increase the antibody production to diphtheria and tetanus toxoids. Salk (350) found that calcium phosphate enhances the antibody response to influenza virus vaccines. The most widely used adjuvant in experimental work in animals and occasionally in man is a water-in-oil emulsion of the type described by Freund (131, 132). Water, lanolin, and antigen are mixed in such a manner that the antigen is contained in drops of water surrounded by oil which effectively slows and prolongs its absorption. The addition of heat-killed tubercle bacilli to this mixture enhances the adjuvant effect (235). Raffel (332) found that the active principle in the tubercle bacilli was a **lipopolysaccharide;** other lipids from the tubercle bacilli, or from a variety of other cellular sources, lacked this stimulating effect.

The amount of antibody produced by the enhancing effect of adjuvants equals or exceeds that produced by multiple injections, but cross-reacting as well as specific antibodies are formed. The cross-reacting ones, however, can be removed by the agglutinin absorption procedures, which are described in the next chapter.

The Influence of Age on Antibody Production. The ability of the tissues to form antibodies is an acquired characteristic conditioned by age. In early embryonic life this mechanism is lacking, which accounts for the observation that many viruses and bacteria will not infect the chicken but will grow readily in the embryonated egg. The age after birth at which animals begin forming antibody is not known precisely, but it is clear that (308) newborn animals respond less well to antigenic stimuli than do adult animals of the same species (309). Overman (310) studied the antibody response to mumps virus vaccine in mice one to 21 days old when vaccinated. Results indicated a weak antibody response in mice five to seven days old

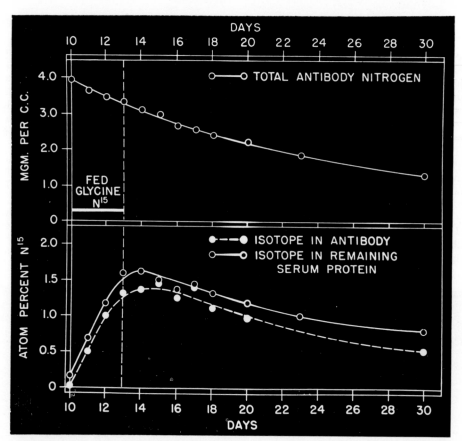

Fig. 11. Incorporation of glycine N^{15} in antibody. A rabbit was immunized against Type III pneumococcus, and glycine N^{15} was fed for three days. Although the total amount of antibody nitrogen was decreasing, the isotope was incorporated in equal amounts in both antibody and normal globulins. (From Schoenheimer, Ratner, Rittenberg, and Heidelberger. *J. Biol. Chem.,* 144:545, 1942.)

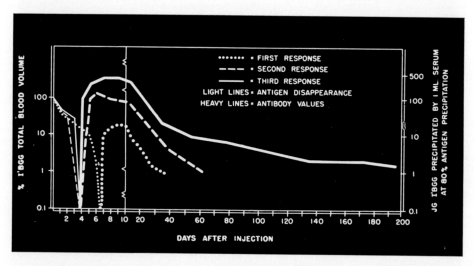

Fig. 12. First, second, and third response to antigen. The light lines show the rate of antigen disappearance and the heavy lines the rate of antibody production. With the second and third injection the antigen disappears more rapidly, the antibodies appear sooner, in larger amounts, and persist longer. (From Dixon, Maurer, and Deichmiller. 1954.)

191

when inoculated, but animals one day old failed to develop antibody. Animals 14 days old responded to the vaccine as well as did adult mice. Susceptibility of newborn or very young animals to infectious organisms is, in many instances, much greater than in adult animals. For example, hamster-adapted mumps virus produces a uniformly fatal infection in animals four days old or less, but hamsters seven days old when inoculated survive (309). The change in resistance to this virus infection appears related to the earlier onset of more effective antibody production in the older hamsters. Figure 13 shows the relation of virus growth and antibody response in hamsters of four different age groups. In other instances where

resistance to the infecting organism increases with age, some "nonspecific" mechanism may be responsible, and it may be unrelated to maturation of the antibody-forming ability of the animal. Thus, newborn mice, and mice 11 to 13 days old are quite susceptible to Coxsackie B infections, but animals 8 to 11 days old are more resistant than either the younger or older animals. The injection of S^{35} BSA in chickens showed that the neonatal chicks concentrated more antigen in their spleen and held it longer than other chickens (168).

The effect of age on antibody production probably varies with each species. An excellent study of an inbred strain of histocompatible guinea pigs by Baer and Bowser (13) showed

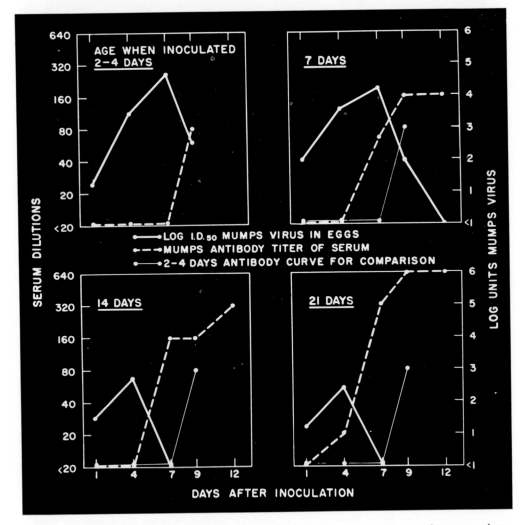

Fig. 13. Age and antibody response. Comparison of immune response and mumps virus growth in hamsters inoculated at various ages.

that two-month-old guinea pigs showed higher serum antibody titers and greater contact sensitivity than those which have reached the average life-span of two to three years. The intensity of the skin reaction to tuberculin in man seems to decrease progressively after the age of 60 years.

Species of Animal Producing the Antibody. Man, monkey, rabbit, and horse have normal gamma globulins with molecular weights up to 160,000. The first three species respond to the injection of the pneumococcal polysaccharides by the production of specific antibody globulin of about the same weight and with all the physiochemical properties of normal gamma globulin. The horse, cow, and pig respond to the same polysaccharides by the production of a heavy molecule of antibody globulin in the range of 900,000. The horse responds also with the heavy molecule of antibody when injected with the globulin of rabbit serum (404, 405). The heavy molecules, however, behave the same as smaller ones in the antigen antibody reactions (432). Some strains of mice produce complete agglutination antibodies and some incomplete or nonagglutination antibodies to polysaccharide Vi antigen (140). Hemocyanin induces 7 S. antibodies in C_3H and $C_{57}BL$ mice (114), but the 19 S. antibodies in BALB/c mice (114). Pneumococcal polysaccharide type III induces 7 S. antibodies in C_3H mice, while red blood cells from sheep produces primarily 19 S. antibodies but also some 6.5 S. antibodies (114).

When man, horse, guinea pig, and rabbit are injected with comparable amounts of the same diphtheria toxoid, the antitoxin formed by man precipitates in a narrow zone of antigen dilution, while the horse responds with an antigen with its usual broad zone of precipitation. The guinea pig and rabbit are intermediate between man and the horse (see Fig. 2 in Chapter 16).

Effect of the Antigen Used for Immunization. The horse, which makes heavy antibody globulin to pneumococcal polysaccharides and rabbit serum globulin, responds to the injection of egg albumin, albumin of rabbit serum, hemocyanin, and diphtheria toxoid with the production of a smaller molecule of antibody (184,000). These antibodies not only react specifically with their respective antigens but when injected as antigens into rabbits induce the formation of anti-antibody globulin. Antibodies of the antipneumococcal type show an extremely broad range of precipitation, with varying quantities of antigen, while the antitoxic type of antibody precipitates its antigen in the range characteristic of horse antitoxin (see Fig. 2 in Chapter 16).

The studies of Cann and Loveless (58, 59) and Kuhns (226) on human serums have shown that a part of the Rh antibody is in the alpha and beta globulins (58), and the incomplete (reagin) antibody from patients with asthma and hay fever is mainly in the beta globulin (57). The univalent nonprecipitating diphtheria antibody is in the fast moving gamma-2 globulin (213), while the blocking antibody to the univalent reagin and the classical precipitating diphtheria antitoxin migrate in the slow-moving gamma-2-globulin.

Effect of Route of Immunization. The intravenous injection of virulent pneumococci into the rabbit results primarily in the production of anticapsular antibodies, but the intracutaneous or subcutaneous injection of the same organism is followed by the appearance of predominantly antinucleoprotein antibodies and the simultaneous development of the delayed type of bacterial allergy (83). In contrast, the horse produces the standard type of diphtheria antitoxin when toxoid is injected subcutaneously or intramuscularly but not intravenously (405). Conversely, the horse makes an abundance of antibodies to pneumococci and to rabbit serum globulin when injected intravenously but not when injected subcutaneously.

Spontaneous exposure of the mucous membranes of man to pollens may result in the development of nonprecipitating antibodies which migrate with the beta globulin, while subcutaneous injection of the same pollens induces the formation of antibodies which migrate with the gamma globulin (250).

Effect of Intensity and Duration of Vaccination Period. Following injection of an antigen, there is a time interval before the antibodies appear in the blood. The duration of this lag period is a variable due to such factors as dosage and route of administration. More important, however, is the previous experience of the animal with the particular antigen: the lag period is greatly reduced in an animal whose antibody-producing cells are "trained" due to previous contact with the antigen (154).

After a **single primary injection** of a sufficient dose of an antigen, antibodies cannot be detected for at least several days. There is, then, a rise in titer which reaches its maximum usually about the end of the second week, although it may attain this peak as early as 10 days or as late as the end of the third week after inoculation. The peak is followed by a rapid decrease in the amount of circulating antibodies over a period of several weeks and then a more gradual falling off in titer which slowly approaches an undetectable level over a period of months (Fig. 12).

Following a second injection of antigen, a much more rapid rise in antibody titer is obtained, and the quantity of circulating antibodies usually is maintained at a high level for a longer period of time than occurs after a primary injection. Figure 14, redrawn from Burnet's curves, illustrates the marked differences between the primary and secondary responses. The tertiary type of response is shown in Figure 12.

The sudden but temporary drop in titer following the second injection (Fig. 14) is commonly referred to as the negative phase, and some investigators have interpreted this phenomenon as an indication that the animal during this period is less immune. Such a drop in antibody content, however, would not be surprising because some of the immune globulin would be expected to enter into combination with the newly introduced antigen. The result-

ant antibody titers, therefore, would be reduced, since only uncombined antibody would be free to react with the test antigen. The proper interpretation of the negative phase is a very practical point, since some physicians have hesitated to inject typhoid vaccine in persons exposed to typhoid fever on the theory that such an individual temporarily would be rendered more susceptible to the infection. However, it has been shown in typhoid fever that vaccine injections during the incubation period do not increase susceptibility.

The prompt and efficient production of antibodies following the secondary injections often has been referred to as the **anamnestic reaction,** and the injections of vaccines or toxoids at various intervals after primary immunizations are commonly referred to in current medical parlance as **booster injections.**

Typhoid O agglutinins are found exclusively in the 19 S. fraction of globulin in both infants and adults with primary stimulation (19). Lo

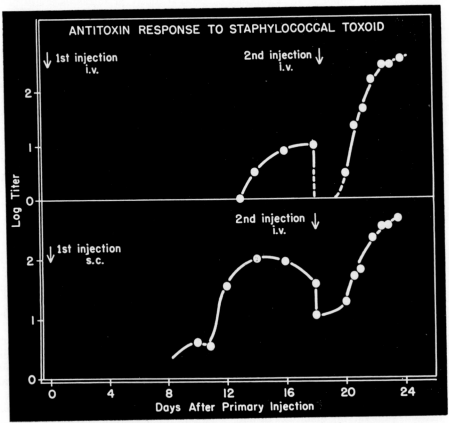

Fig. 14. Antitoxin responses to primary and secondary injections of staphylococcal toxoid. Upper figure, primary injection given intravenously. Lower figure, primary injection given subcutaneously. (After Burnet. *Production of Antibodies,* London, Macmillan & Co., Ltd.)

Spalloto and his associates (249) have found that the primary reaction of premature infants, older children, and adults to typhoid and paratyphoid antigens is the exclusive production of 19 S. antibodies. But restimulation after 13 weeks in premature infants and after six months in older children and adults results in the production of 7 S. antibodies, predominantly. In contrast to these findings, the maternally transferred antibody is always of the low molecular weight (7 S.) type and appears to inhibit active antibody synthesis for the specific antigen-antibody system for a period of many weeks (249).

Both pure antigen and pure antibody have been labeled with isotope tracers which have facilitated the study of the rate of disappearance of the antigen after injection and the appearance and disappearance of the antibody. The labeling may be accomplished either by chemical manipulation in the test tube, called **external labeling** (73, 87, 329) or by feeding the tracer material to tobacco mosaic virus (248), pneumococcus (377), or yeast. In the latter method hydrolyzed yeast is injected into rabbits, guinea pigs, or chickens, which incorporate the tracer into their newly synthesized molecules of serum albumin and serum globulin. This type of manipulation is called **internal labeling.** In the studies by Dixon, Maurer and Deichmiller (87) bovine gamma globulin and crystalline bovine serum albumin were labeled with I^{131} in the test tube and then injected into a series of rabbits. The results following three consecutive injections of I^{131} bovine gamma globulin are shown in Figure 12. In this experiment slightly less than one-half of the total antibodies produced was utilized in the elimination of the antigen. This part was catabolized and did not subsequently appear in the serum. Following the second and third consecutive injections, the antigen was eliminated more rapidly, more antibodies were produced, and they persisted longer in the serum.

The previous immunization of an animal with one antigen alters the tissue reactivity in such a manner that the injection of a different, but related, antigen results in the production of more antibodies to the original antigen than to the newly injected antigen (145). In the experiments, however, there was no increase in antibodies to the first antigen when the second was unrelated. Sometimes cross-reacting antibodies do appear in animals following the injection of apparently unrelated or even presumably nonantigenic substances. In man certain febrile diseases may cause the appearance of antibodies to salmonella, brucella, and sheep red blood cells (333), emphasizing the importance of detecting a **rising titer of antibodies** before making a final diagnosis.

This phenomenon described above for the rabbit is seen in man immunized with epidemic typhus vaccine and then spontaneously infected with murine typhus (323), in man injected with one type of influenza virus after a clinical infection with another type (188), and in rabbits injected with *Brucella abortus* followed by *P. tularensis* or vice versa (327). Francis has referred to the phenomenon as the effect of an "original antigenic sin" (188).

Dissection of Antibodies. In 1936 Parfentjev (313) treated diphtheria antitoxin made in the horse with pepsin, which reduced the size of the molecule and reduced its efficiency as an antigen without affecting its ability to neutralize diphtheria toxin. In 1942, Northrop (300) fragmented the diphtheria antibody molecule and obtained a crystalline fragment which would neutralize diphtheria toxin. Between 1941 and 1946 Petermann and his associates (322) continued the study of the physical and chemical properties of fragments of antibodies. Dramatic progress has been made in these areas since 1958 by Porter in England and by Nisonoff and his associates in this country (106, 298).

Porter (325, 326) treated purified rabbit antibody with crystalline papain which split the antibody into three fragments which then could be separated by chromatography. Each fragment had a molecular weight of approximately 50,000-60,000, as compared with 160,000 for the original untreated gamma globulin molecule. Fragment I and Fragment II would combine with the antigen but would not precipitate, while Fragment III would neither combine nor precipitate. It was apparent that the two combining sites of the original antibody molecule had been divided with one going to Fragment I and one to Fragment II. However, Fragment III seemed to be a kind of nucleus for the antibody and could be crystallized. It cannot combine with the antigen but seems to facilitate the precipitation in the region of antibody excess. Fraction III carries a number of properties characteristic of gamma globulin, including most of the antigenic determinant, the ability to fix complement, reactivity with sera from rheumatoid arthritic patients, and the capacity to be recognized as gamma globulin by homologous cells (159). Peptic digestion of Fraction III produces a variety of smaller fractions. Those which were too large to pass through a dialysis bag precipitated with antigen to rabbit gamma globulin. Fragment small enough to pass through the bag would not precipitate but inhibited the precipitation of antibody with Fraction III (159, 160).

Porter's work has been confirmed by Nisonoff and his associates (295, 296, 297, 383, 384). These authors found that nonprecipitating but active binding fragments with 3.5 S. sedimentation coefficients could be prepared by another method (297). The same type of rabbit antibody was treated with pepsin. The size of the molecule was reduced from 7 S. to 5 S. It would still precipitate with the antigen, showing that both antibody combining sites were still present on the molecule, but it would not fix complement (396, 397). The ability to precipitate but not to fix complement suggests that the third fragment may be involved in fixation of the antibody to the cell (306), and fixation of the complement. This relationship is schematically represented by Talmage in Figure 15. However, on treating the reduced molecule with agents capable of breaking the disulfide bonds such as cystine, 2-mercaptoethylamine, thioglycollate, and cyanide, two equal univalent 3.5 S. fragments were formed. This suggests that the biosynthesis of rabbit antibody may include linkage of these two nearly identical univalent subunits through one or more disulfide bonds (221). If only four disulfide bonds were loosened, the antibody split into two unequal fractions with the first containing 75 per cent and the second 25 per cent of the protein molecule (409). Other studies by Wiederman, Franklin and their associates (429) have shown that breaking of the disulfide bonds does not destroy the ability of human 7 S. gamma globulin antibody to react with antigen but does destroy their ability to fix complement (354). However, Reiss and Plescia (335) reacted antigen-antibody-complement and then digested the product with papain and came to the conclusion that, under these conditions, complement was not fixed to Fragment III but to Fragment I or II. Schur and Becker (354) reported that the 5 S. fragment from papain digestion does fix complement at a reduced rate. Some of these univalent fragments of the antibody could be recombined into bivalent precipitating antibodies by passing them through an 1R-120 ion exchange resin or by treatment with a bifunctional organic mercurial (296). This success suggested the possibility of artificially combining univalent fragments from two different antibodies. This was also accomplished (298), and, as expected, the synthesized antibody would not precipitate with either antigen but did give some precipitation with an appropriate mixture of the two antigens. More recent work by Stelos, Roholt and Pressman (383, 384) shows that some antibody molecules are composed of two identical fragments both of which fall in Fraction I while other molecules are composed of two identical fragments both of which fall in Fraction II. Fraction I may be split into two subfractions, and Fraction II into two or three subfractions. Mandy and his associates (260) have found that there are differences in content of basic and acid residues among univalent fragments and that these differences are consistent with their relative

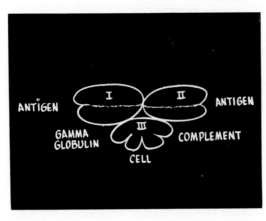

Fig. 15. Schematic presentation of the relationship of Fractions I, II, and III of antibody globulin. (Courtesy of D. W. Talmage.)

electrophoretic mobilities and strength of adherence to Cm-cellulose, indicating that 7 S. rabbit gamma globulin is heterogenous in chemical composition (167). Univalent antibody fragments derived from either papain or peptic digestion, however, have alanine as the principal terminal amino acid, with smaller amounts of aspartic acid and trace quantities of serine and theobromine (159, 160).

Edelman and Benacerraf (98) separated polypeptide chains from the antibody molecule as identifiable H and L chains. By a different procedure Fleischman, Pain, and Porter (127) derived A (H) and B (L) polypeptide chains. The first authors associated the chief antibody activity with the B (L) polypeptides, while the second found the A (H) most active. Roholt in 1963 (344) confirmed the B (L) location but suggested that antibodies might differ or the result might vary with the methods employed; see the report of Metzger and Singer (277).

Fahey and McLaughlin (116) have dissected the 6.6 γ-globulins, the $\beta_2A(\gamma_1A)$-globulins, the γ_1-macroglobulins and the Bence-Jones proteins as shown in Figure 16.

Thorbecke and Franklin (403) have found that the cross-reactions between 7 S. and 19 S. globulins in the rabbit are due to the fact that the two gamma globulins share some antigenic determinants present on protein antibody fragments I and II. Protein antibody III from 7 S. globulins show no evidence of cross reacting with 19 S. gamma globulins either in immunoelectrophoresis or Ouchterlony plates (304). The cross-reaction between the 7 S. and 19 S. components of human gamma globulin has been found to be due to common antigenic groups associated with the two fragments which contain the antibody-combining sites. A similar relationship appears to hold for the β_{2a} (γ_{1a}) normal and myeloma globulins in man (130, 130a).

These studies confirm again the conclusions of many investigators that precipitating antibodies must have two combining sites to build up an aggregate which can be seen. However,

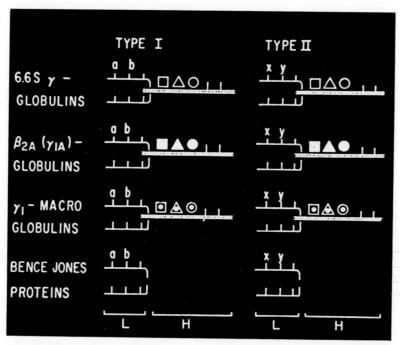

Fig. 16. Diagrammatic representation of relationships between two types of molecules (I and II) in each of the major gamma globulin groups (6.6 S γ-globulins, β_{2A}-globulins, γ_1-macroglobulins, and γ_μ-globulins (Bence Jones proteins). "L" chains are indicated to the left and "H" chains to the right of each half of the diagram. The a and b symbols indicate type I antigenic determinants and x and y indicate type II determinants. The specific 6.6 S γ-globulin ($\square$, $\triangle$, $\bigcirc$) and β_{2A}-globulin ($\blacksquare$, $\blacktriangle$, $\bullet$) and γ_1-macroglobulin ($\boxdot$, $\triangle$, $\odot$) determinants are separately represented. (From Fahey. *J. Immunol.*, 91:448, 1963.)

the failure of an antibody to precipitate when exposed to the antigen does not necessarily prove that only one binding site is available. Nisonoff and Pressman (294) showed that mild acetylation resulted in complete loss of precipitating activity, but the ability to bind homologous hapten was affected only slightly, and Pruzansky and Feinberg (330) have shown that precipitating antibodies become nonprecipitating after heating at 56° for 30 minutes although it would coprecipitate with unheated serum, sensitize guinea pigs to anaphylaxis, precipitate in agar gel, and sensitize the red blood cells of sheep for the hemagglutinin test. These results confirm the hypothesis of Marrack and Orlans (262) that an antibody with both combining sites intact may fail to precipitate.

The Carbohydrate Fraction of Gamma Globulin. Many globulins contain 2 to 3 per cent of carbohydrate in the form of a true glycopeptide which seems to be located in Fragment III and may play a role in complement fixation, binding to skin receptors, hypersensitivity response, and antigenicity of gamma globulin in heterogenous species (106, 126, 434).

The Organs which Produce Antibodies. The spleen and lymph nodes and lungs are very active in the production of antibodies, but they are not the only organs which have this capacity. Thompson and Olson (401) have shown that the normally nonvascular cornea can produce antibodies, while Koshland and Burrows (224, 225) have demonstrated the production of fecal antibodies for Asiatic cholera at local sites in the intestinal tract. In chronic syphilis of the central nervous system the antibody which is detected by the Wassermann reaction may be absent from the serum but present in abundance in the spinal fluid, suggesting local production.

The proportional participation of spleen, lymph nodes, and other tissues depends upon the size of the dose of antigen and its route of administration. The thymus and Peyer's patch tissue were not stimulated to form antibodies in detectable amounts by intravenous injections of antigen but were stimulated by the same dose if given subcutaneously or intraperitoneally (388). When the antigen was injected locally in rabbits, the prompt removal of the regional lymph nodes or spleen reduced the magnitude of the antibody response to a second local injection. After an original intravenous

stimulation, however, only splenectomy reduced the anamnestic response (378, 380, 433). Normal rats with an intact spleen gave excellent antibody responses to sheep erythrocytes or heat-killed *Klebsiella pneumoniae* when injected intravenously. The splenectomized rats responded poorly to small intravenous injection of these antigens but gave as good response as normal animals when the same dose was given intraportally or intraperitoneally. Multiple injections, even in splenectomized animals, induce excellent antibody production. These experiments are consistent with the clinical observations that the removal of the spleen in certain familial and acquired types of hemolytic anemia in man often produces dramatic improvement in the patient.

When bits of living splenic tissue, lymph nodes, Peyer's patches, or thymus are removed from immunized animals before the animals have produced antibodies and are transferred to normal animals of the same species, antibodies to the original antigen appear in the serum of the recipient animal (170, 193, 252, 378, 379). In the experiments by Stoner and Hale (388) not only did the recipient animals produce antibodies, but the specific anamnestic or recall reaction could be elicited by a subsequent injection of the original antigen.

Cytophilic Antibody. Sorkin, Boyden, and their associates (371) have studied the production of antibodies by isolated cells from the spleen of hyperimmunized rabbits. The absorption of antigen by the immune cells from the spleen was measured by the binding of I^{131} human serum albumin and the production of antibody in vitro by measuring the C^{14} amino acids incorporated in the antibody and in the antigen-antibody precipitate. Spleen cells from immunized animals bound much more antigen than cells from normal animals, but exposure of the normal cells to serum of the immunized animals conferred on them the ability to bind the antigen. The binding occurred even when all precipitin had been removed from the serum. This property of immune serum was designated by the authors as the "cytophilic" antibody (168a) (Fig. 17).

No Antibody Formation in Neonatal Animals. The antibody-producing mechanism

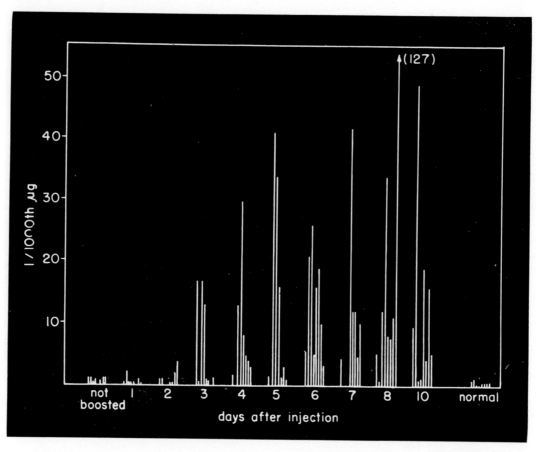

Fig. 17. Cytophilic antibody levels: in hyperimmune animals after a booster injection of antigen. (After Sorkin, Rhodes, and Boyden. *J. Immunol.*, 86:101, 1961.)

does not mature until after the birth of the animal, and few newborn animals would be expected to survive the attack of the multitude of parasites, bacteria, fungi, and viruses which exist in the external environment. Nature usually provides passively transferred antibodies from the mother animal, however, which protect the newborn for a period of weeks or months after birth. In animals where the placenta is penetrable to globulins, such as man, the antibodies are transferred directly through the placenta before birth, but in animals where the placenta is not penetrable, such as the cow and pig, the animal is born without globulins and without globulin antibodies (Fig. 18), and the antibodies must be passed on to the newborn by the ingestion of colostrum. When newborn pigs have not received antibodies from colostrum, they frequently die of otherwise harmless *E. coli* or infection by other normal inhabitants of the intestinal tract (357, 358).

Agammaglobulinemia. This disease was discovered by Bruton in 1952 (43) and there are now over 100 such cases in the literature (41, 149, 443). These patients synthesize only traces of gamma globulin (Fig. 19) and cannot synthesize detectable levels of antibodies. Isohemagglutinins are usually low or undetectable in the serum except for patients with AB antigens (148, 149, 150) and plasma cells are absent from the tissues. Patients with agammaglobulinemia do not produce antibodies when challenged with pneumococci, diphtheria toxoid, and typhoid-paratyphoid organisms. They are, as one would suspect, very susceptible to repeated infections with bacteria but usually react in a normal manner to viral infec-

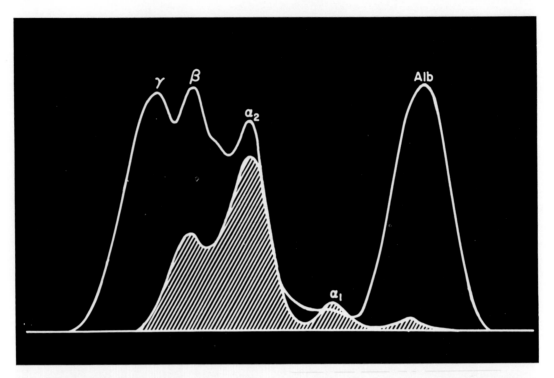

Fig. 18. Determination of serum protein by paper electrophoresis of serum from normal adult pigs and newborn piglets. The black area shows the proteins in the adult and the shaded area in the neonatal animal. (After Sterzl, Kosta, Mandel, Riha, and Holub. *Mechanisms of Antibody Formation,* Academic Press.)

tions, although a few have shown gangrenous reaction to vaccinia virus and some have had more than one attack of mumps (149). They tolerate skin grafts from other individuals for years (155, 156) but develop the delayed tuberculin type allergy in a normal manner.

The congenital form of the disease occurs predominantly in male infants. The acquired form develops in both males and females and is more prevalent in adults (443). Some infants have difficulty in synthesizing globulins for a period of months after birth, and this must be differentiated from true genetic agammaglobulinemia (Fig. 19). These unfortunate patients do produce very small amounts of gamma globulin and can presumably produce small but undetectable amounts of antibody which might be sufficient to protect them from diseases of viral origin (15).

Antibody-forming Cells. Numerous attempts have been made to locate the site of antigen deposition, although it is obvious that the cells which take up the antigen first are not necessarily the ones which manufacture the antibody globulin (70, 177, 304). Among the various methods of identifying the antigen in cells have been devised are: (1) tagging the antigen with a dye (254, 348), (2) injecting the antigen which has been labeled with an isotope by either the external or internal method (109, 377), (3) locating the isotope-containing antigen by autoradiography (143), (4) injecting fluorescein labeled serum albumin (351), or (5) following the injection of antigen by the injection of its specific antibody which has been labeled with fluorescein by the method perfected by Coons and his associates (69, 70, 71, 72). These studies revealed that the macrophages, histiocytes, Kupffer's cells of the liver, reticuloendothelial system, and plasma cells regularly contained antigen which is always in the cytoplasm and sometimes in the nuclei. Cells

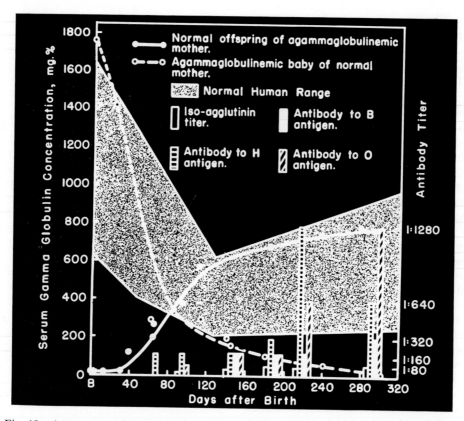

Fig. 19. Appearance of gamma globulin and antibody synthesis in the newborn period. The normal human range for the first 320 days of life is shown in the stippled areas. (After Zak and Good. *J. Clin. Invest.*, 38:579, 1959.)

of this type are found concentrated in such organs as spleen, lymph nodes, lungs, and bone marrow. Renal tubular cells, cells of the glomerular tufts, hepatic cells, and fibroblasts contained smaller amounts of antigen. Antigen was not demonstrated with certainty in lymphocytes.

Theoretically, the cells of the body which can produce normal globulin should be able to produce antibody globulin, if we ignore for the moment the possibility of globulins being formed by one type of cell and absorbed by another. Gitlin, Landing, and Whipple (148) treated human tissues with fluorescein-labeled antibodies specific for human gamma globulin, human albumin, human B-lipoprotein, B₁ metal-containing globulin, and found fluorescence in the nuclei of many types of cells.

The cells which produce antibodies are highly specialized and arise rather late in the evolutionary cycle (199, 366). The mechanism seems to be absent in invertebrates. It is present but poorly developed in some fish; antibodies are made, but they are not as specific as those of higher animals. The macrophage whose natural function is to phagocyte and digest the worn out cells of the body is an obvious candidate for the antibody producing cell. All particulate antigens, such as bacteria, viruses, and red blood cells, are phagocytized and digested by monocytes. Girard and Murray (147) found that monocytes could concentrate antibodies from the serum but could not synthesize antibodies. These results have been confirmed by Roberts (343) and Hunt and Myrvik (198). However, Fishman (124) has suggested that macrophages digest and prepare particulate antigens for adsorption by the true antibody-producing cells. Later work suggests the process is not a passive one limited to solubilizing the antigen but an active one in which RNA-antigen-fragment complexes are formed which function as a template when transferred to plasma cells (125, 260a, 319, 320, 373).

The lymphocytes were the next obvious candidate for the antibody-producing cells. Lymph nodes do contain an abundance of antibody-producing cells, and usually a stimulation of the lymph node by endotoxins or other agents also stimulates the number of antibody-producing cells. Most workers agree that the immature large or intermediate lymphocytes can produce antibodies but suspect that the mature small lymphocytes are end cells which cannot produce antibodies. Gowans (161) in 1962 demonstrated, by injecting lymphocytes with labeled DNA, RNA, or protein into incompatible donors, that certain small lymphocytes could revert to primitive antibody-producing cells.

It is well known that small lymphocytes are involved in the passive transfer of tuberculin-like allergy, and these cells, when labeled with thymidine can be seen to accumulate at the site of the tuberculin reaction. Small lymphocytes (414, 415) seem to play a role in the immunogenic rejection of skin grafts and the development of "runt disease" (96, 209, 289, 324, 412). In these reactions the lymphocytes do not need to accumulate at the site of the reaction but can effect the rejection of transplanted tissue even when the sensitized lymphocytes are enclosed in Millipore filters (191, 192). Ersley (110) observed no evidence of concentration of antibodies in the lymphocytes of rabbits actively immunized against a number of specific types of pneumococci.

Production of Antibodies by Plasma Cells. The bursa of the newly hatched chick (311, 438) and the thymus of mammals (66, 78, 202, 280, 281) seems to contain the precursors of the antibody-producing cells. If the bursa of the chick or the thymus of animals is removed surgically during the first few days of life, the animals do not develop antibodies either spontaneously or when challenged with good antigens. Miller and his associates (281) have shown that the thymus is essential for the recovery of the immune mechanism following the irradi-

ation of adult mice. If the thymus is removed before irradiation, the lymph nodes remain small, the mouse does not produce antibodies, and allogenic skin grafts are not rejected. Apparently, certain precursors of the plasma cells migrate from the thymus to the lymph nodes after recovery from the immediate effect of irradiation (281a).

Levey and his coworkers (245) have shown that neonatally thymectomized C3Hf/LW mice which had been implanted with cell-tight Millipore diffusion chambers containing isologous thymic tissue did not show depletion of lymphocytes in the peripheral blood, involution of the lymphoid organs, or any characteristic sign of the wasting syndrome. Furthermore, some humoral factor derived from the diffusion chamber restored the capacity of mice to die from the intracerebral inoculation of lymphocytic choriomeningitis virus.

The albumin of the serum is produced by cells in the liver, but liver cells cannot synthesize either normal or antibody globulins. The globulins are formed by specialized cells known as **plasma cells,** which are found scattered throughout the body but are more concentrated in the lymph nodes, spleen and lungs (7, 9). Globulins, in contrast to albumin, are not produced in intrauterine life or for some days or weeks after birth. Presumably, the premature plasma cells must migrate from the original focus in the bursa of the chicken and thymus of the mammal to the lymph nodes, spleen, lungs, and other areas. A maturing process of weeks is required even after migration before the cells become competent manufactors of globulins (157). Birth itself, whether normal, premature, or by operation (369, 370) seems to trigger the migration and the maturation of the antibody-producing cells. The introduction of bacteria into the intestinal tract of the newborn animal accelerates the production of gamma globulin and of antibodies (240, 385). When animals are raised in a sterile environment by the method introduced by Reyniers (336), the gamma globulin remains low. Some gamma globulin is produced, presumably to the dead bodies of bacteria in the sterilized food or to other naturally antigenic substances in the food. Electrophoretic studies of the serum of germ-free rats by Grabar and his associates (165) showed the presence of the same major antigenic components observed in the serum of normal rats, but the amounts were reduced. There is no disagreement about the fact that well-developed germinal centers in lymph nodes are the best morphologic evidence of immunologic competence (428).

Contact with an antigen is the stimulant to a really astonishing rapid multiplication and maturation of plasma cells (60). It can be shown by Coons' fluorescent technic (71, 426) that antigen is taken in by many types of cells either by phagocytosis, pinosis (63, 247), or some other mechanisms. In cells other than primitive plasma cells, the antigen is sequestered or destroyed without stimulating antibody formation. In contrast, the primitive plasma cell is stimulated by the ingested antigen first to rapid multiplication and subsequently to the rapid manufacture of antibody globulin (95, 319, 353). A second stimulation some weeks or months later

results in a much more rapid and abundant production of specific antibody (Fig. 20). Only a few, perhaps 2 or 3 per cent, of the cells from a lymph node are capable of being stimulated by antigen to form antibody (37, 39, 196). The effectiveness of these few cells, however, is so great that the transplantation of a few pieces of lymph node from a normal man into a patient with agammaglobulinemia conferred on the latter the ability to produce antibodies against the typhoid bacillus (263).

The cellular changes found in the primary and secondary response to antigen have been studied by White (428) and others (379, 380). If the antigen is injected into the foot pad of an animal, the regional lymph nodes on the injected side of the body receive the maximum stimulation, although all primitive plasma cells in the body receive some stimulation. There is a rapid multiplication of plasma cells in the regional lymph nodes on the injected side, but only a few of them show detectable amounts of antibody (Fig.

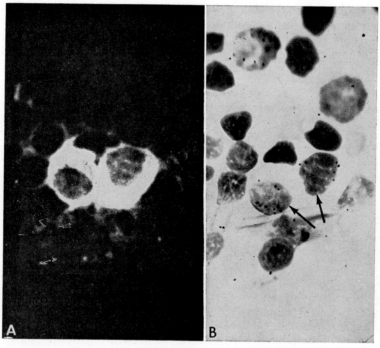

Fig. 20. Note two cells in A showing bright specific cytoplasmic fluorescence indicating antibodies to bovine gamma globulin. The same two cells are seen in B showing tritium grains in the nuclei indicating recent cell division. The mononuclear cell at the top of B also has tritium grains in the nuclei but this is not an antibody-producing cell and so is not seen in A. (After Baney, Vazquez, and Dixon. *Proc. Soc. Exper. Biol. & Med.,* 109:1, 1962.)

21A). The nodes on the contralateral side show only slight, if any, stimulation, and it is difficult to find antibody-containing cells. An injection of the same antigen into the previously uninjected foot pad caused the primary type of response described above. In contrast, a reinjection of a much smaller amount of antigen into the original foot pad caused an explosive mitotic multiplication of plasma cells (Fig. 21B), with the rapid production in a period of days of massive quantities of antibodies (Fig. 21C). Weigle (420) has studied the quantitative relationship between the dose of antigen and antibody response in primary and secondary stimulation. A much larger dose is required for the primary stimulation. Dixon (86, 88, 89) found on the day of maximum synthesis of antibody to bovine gamma globulin in the rabbit that the ratio of normal gamma globulin synthesized to that of specific antibody gamma globulin was 30:1. With the secondary response, the ratio was reduced to 8:1, while in a hyperimmune animal the ratio was 2:1, or approximately one-half of all the newly synthesized gamma globulin was specific antibody to bovine gamma globulin. Askonas and Humphrey (8) have calculated that antibody can be formed in 10 minutes but 30 minutes is required for it to emerge from the cell. Apparently antibodies are synthesized, like other proteins, on the ribosomes (440), but some time is required for their orderly release (30, 189).

Nonspecific stimulation of plasma cells can be accomplished by the injection of lipopolysaccharide (417), endotoxins (23, 222, 389, 418) and even carbon particles. Primitive plasma cells stimulated to multiplication by the nonspecific or nonantigenic agents will respond specifically when stimulated with specific antigens.

Increased amounts of DNA and RNA can be found in antibody-producing cells (102, 173, 257, 411). The antibodies are produced directly from *de novo* synthesis from amino acids and not from polypeptides (6, 166, 337, 338, 391, 436).

Schooley (353) and Nossal and Mäkelä (301) have studied the plasma cells in the process of synthesizing antibodies by administering H₃ thymidine, H₃ leucine, and H₃ cytidine. A maximum generation time of 12 to 14 hours (39, 408) was calculated from the early plasmoblast, while the apparently nondividing plasma cells in the lymph nodes had a mean life of only eight to 12 hours. Electron microscopic pictures of human antibody-producing cells reveal an abundance of rough surfaced endoplasmic

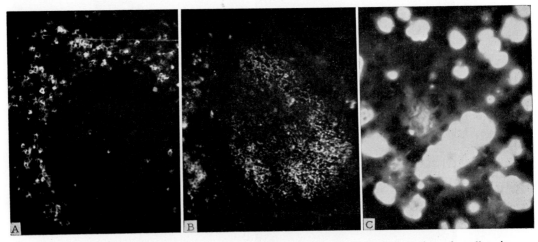

Fig. 21. A, popliteal lymph node of rabbit three weeks after a single injection of ovalbumin into the foot. Some plasma cells are present in the madella but practically none in the lyphoid nodule. B, 17 days after a second injection in the foot. The germinal center is now filled with antibody-producing cells. C, higher magnification, showing mulberry-like masses of diphtheria antitoxin (Russell bodies) in cells at the germinal center of the popliteal lymph node. (After White. *Mechanisms of Antibody Formation,* Academic Press.)

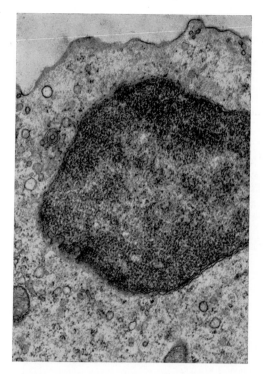

Fig. 22. This is a normal "inactive" lymphocyte. Note the complete absence of rough endoplasmic reticulum (ER) in cytoplasm. × 28,000. (Courtesy of Dorothea Zuker-Franklin.)

reticulum (Figs. 22, 23, 24) (26, 425). Pictures of this reticulum in a typical plasma cell are shown by Zucker-Franklin (444) in Figure 24 and in an "intermediate" cell in Figure 23. The nucleolus seems to be involved in RNA synthesis, while the centriole play a role in the formation of the mitotic spindle. The "intermediate" cell has much less reticulum and is less altered from the normal cell. This may be significant, since Cruchard and his associates (75) believe that the transitional cell of Fagreaus makes the 19 S. gamma globulins. This conclusion is supported by the work of Bauer and his associates (19).

Different types of gamma globulin can be synthesized by the lymph nodes, bone marrow, and spleen, but not necessarily by the same cells (11). The very imaginative studies by Ambrose and Coons (4) have shown that antigen stimulated cells in vitro will not produce antibodies in tissue cultures unless the culture medium contains a physiological amount of cortocoid hormones.

Although there is some competition among antigens for the antibody-producing cells (74), Hektoen and Boar (187), by arranging the proper size doses, injected 35 purified antigens into rabbits simultaneously and then found that the rabbits produced specific antibodies to 34 of the 35; this did not indicate, however, whether each plasma cell was making antibodies to only one or to more than one antigen.

White (427, 428) stimulated his animals with two different antigens simultaneously and then examined sections from lymph nodes to see if each plasma cell was making antibodies to only one or to both antigens. Coons' fluorescent technic was employed, with one antigen carrying a green and the other a red fluorescent dye. He found that each specific antibody-producing cell in the lymph nodes was red or green and not a mixture of the two, suggesting that each plasma cell was making antibodies to only one of the two antigens. A more direct ap-

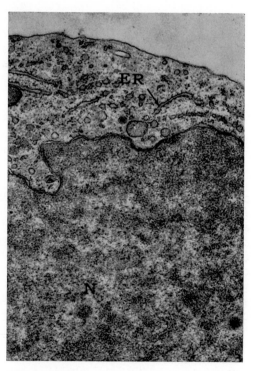

Fig. 23. This is a transitional cell from normal thoracic duct fluid. Note the development of rough ER (arrow). × 22,000. (From Zuker-Franklin. *J. Ultrastructure Research,* 9:325, 1963.)

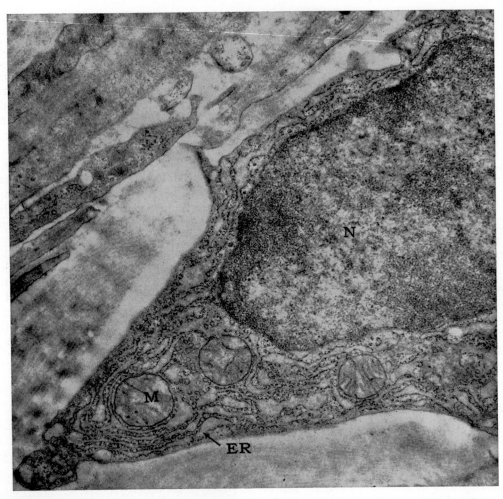

Fig. 24. This is a section of a normal plasma cell from a human lymph node. The cytoplasm is filled with ER. N = nucleus, M = mitochondria. × 21,000. (Courtesy of Dorothea Zuker-Franklin.)

proach has been made to the problem by Attardi and his associates (12) and Mäkelä and Nossal (256, 301, 302). Attardi and his coworkers used two different antigenic types of bacteriophage and injected their animals over a two-year period. Antibody formation was measured by phage plaque inhibition of single cells. In these studies 15 to 22 per cent of the active cells produced antibodies to both types of bacteriophage. Mäkelä and Nossal used a simple system in which rats were immunized with the H and O salmonella antigens and single cells in droplets were tested for immobilization, adherence and agglutination. Of 1,333 cells tested, 445 produced either anti-H or anti-O antibodies

and only four produced both kinds of antibodies. From 43 to 67 per cent of the plasma cells tested were active antibody producers. These results suggested that each active plasma cell synthesized only one type of antibody globulin, although diploid cells could synthesize two types of antibodies. This selectivity seems to begin with the phagocytosis of partulate material by monocytes, since Perkins and Leonard (320) found that monocytes from mice would ingest red cells from a wide variety of animals but after 30 minutes in the monocyte, the monocyte was altered so that only an occasional red cell from a different animal would be phagocytized. If this type of selec-

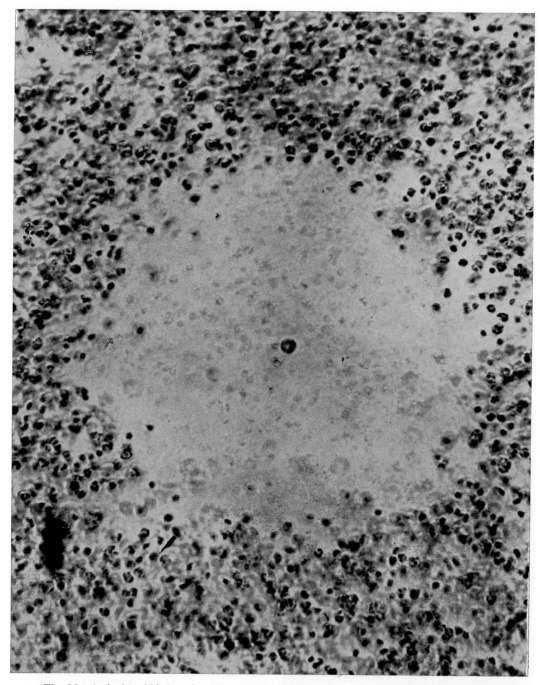

Fig. 25. A single rabbit lymph node cell, in the center of the plaque, produced an antibody specific for the red cells shown in the preparation. After an hour of incubation, during which time the antibody became fixed to the cell, hemolysis was induced by the introduction of complement. (From Jerne and Nordin. *Science,* 140:405, 1963.)

tivity should extend to the plasma cell, then an almost unlimited supply of different types of plasma cell would not be required to produce multiple antibodies to multiple antigens simultaneously. Jerne and Norden (206) have introduced a new technic by which hemolyzing antibodies produced by a single plasma cell can be measured. (Fig. 25). This should provide a method for showing whether plasma cells can or cannot make antibodies to a number of antigenically different red cells but to only one type at a time.

Plasma cells may develop into tumor cells and continue to produce large amounts of globulins, but the tumor cells are no longer capable of synthesizing antibodies (8, 10, 328).

Suppression of Antibody Formation with Analogs and Cortisone. Antibody formation may be suppressed by the injection of analogs to purine and pyrimidine (27, 94, 134, 136, 137, 355, 356, 386) or by the injection of amino acid analogs such as B-3-thienylalanine (239) or glutamic acid and phenylalanine (437). Chlor-

amphenicol also suppresses antibody formation in vitro (278). Treatment with cortisone inhibits antibody formation (111) of both the precipitating and nonprecipitating types in the primary response, but the same or larger doses prevent neither in the secondary response (31). In most of the cortisone studies, soluble antigen such as bovine serum albumin or bovine serum globulin have been used, but cortisone also suppresses antibody formation to rabies vaccine (Fig. 26).

Suppression of Antibody Formation with Excess Antigen. In 1949 Felton (120) discovered that the capsular polysaccharides of the pneumococci would immunize mice against homologous living pneumococci in doses of 0.01 to 5 μg., but doses of 50 to 500 μg. not only failed to stimulate immunity but also prevented subsequent immunization with smaller doses of the same antigen or even dead intact pneumococci. Pneumococcal polysaccharides could be detected in the tissue of the mice receiving the larger doses six to 12 months after the primary injection. Felton assumed that the antibody mechanism was overwhelmed by the excess of antigen and described the phenomenon as "immunological paralysis." The persistence of polysaccharide in the tissue which can react with specific antibody suggested to Kaplan and his associates (218) and Stark (377) that the antibodies might be produced at a normal rate and could combine with the polysaccharide but would soon be catabolized thus freeing the polysaccharide, which cannot be digested by the tissues, to recombine with more antibodies. A restudy of the problem by Gitlin, Monckeberg, and Janeway (150) and Brooke and Karhovsky (42) revealed new evidence that the immune mechanism is really suppressed by the excessive dose of polysaccharide. These investigators found that immune mice were no longer immune after receiving a larger dose of pneumococcal polysaccharide. Paralyzed mice could be protected by the transfer of spleen and lymph node cells from normal mice (291), but cells from paralyzed mice would not protect normal mice. An absence of antibody-forming cells in paralyzed mice was demonstrated with the fluorescent antibody technic by Sercarz and Coons (363). The same type of paralysis was found in newly hatched chicks by Hirata, Garvey, and Campbell when large doses of bovine serum albumin and human gamma globulin were injected (190).

Jones (207) and his associates have injected C^{14} labeled *Klebsiella* polysaccharides into rats and they recovered as much as 80 per cent of the injected material by a combination of enzy-

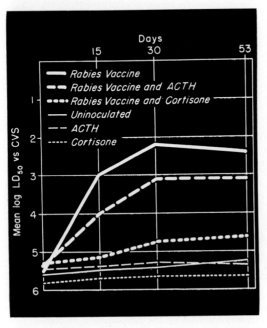

Fig. 26. Mean log LD_{50} compared with CVS titers of rabbits receiving rabies vaccine with and without simultaneous cortisone and ACTH. (After Burns, Shelton, Lukeman, and Grogan. *Pub. Health Rep.,* 75:441, 1960.)

matic and extractive procedures. They noted that the polysaccharide antigen had a greater affinity for nucleic acid in vivo than in vitro and suggested that this might play some part in the production of immunologic paralysis.

Suppression of Antibody Response with Excess Antibody. Rowley reported in 1950 that a second and third injection of sheep erythrocytes into adult rats produced a much poorer hemolysin response than did the primary injection. These observations were confirmed and extended by Taliaferro and Taliaferro (390). Rowley suspected that the presence of antibody from the primary stimulation was inhibiting the formation of antibody to subsequent injections of erythrocytes. Recently Neiders, Rowley, and Fitch (292) have confirmed his suspicion by obtaining sustained suppression of the hemolysin response in passively immunized rats. Similar results were reported by Uhr and Baumann with passively transferred antibodies (407).

Immune Tolerance of Antigen in Newborn Animals. Substances which are known to be good antigens in adult animals fail to produce antibodies when injected into newborn animals and birds one to two days after birth. Soluble antigens like those from serum are more effective in producing this type of response for a longer period than particulate antigens such as typhoid bacilli (18, 38, 93, 421). Much smaller doses are required to induce tolerance in the newborn animal than "immune paralysis" in the adult animal. This could be due in part to the poorly developed antibody-forming mechanism in the newborn animal. There is a good correlation between the size of the original dose and the duration of the tolerance period. With soluble antigen which can be catabolized in the animal body, in contrast to the pneumococcal polysaccharide which cannot be catabolized, one would expect that the tolerance would disappear some time after the last of the original antigen was destroyed and that tolerance could be prolonged by periodic reinjection of the original antigen. Richard Smith (369, 370) has maintained tolerant rabbits up to two years by injection of bovine serum albumin. If the injected antigen were living primitive red and white blood cells which could go on growing in the new host, the immune tolerance could persist for life. Immune tolerance, induced by injecting neonatal rabbits with serum proteins, can be terminated promptly by the injection of a cross reacting antigen or the same antigen if physically attenuated by heat (423).

Suppression of Antibody Formation by Exposure to X-ray. Sublethal doses of x-rays have a profound destructive effect on the cell of the lymph nodes, spleen, and bone marrow, and a corresponding depressing effect on the production of antibodies. The initial inductive phase of the primary antigen response is inhibited with a smaller dose of x-ray than that required for an equal suppression of the secondary antigenic response. This difference has been regarded as proof that there is some fundamental difference in the mechanism of the initial inductive phase of antibody formation and that seen in the second or later response to the same antigen. However, after nonspecific stimulation of lymph node cells with endotoxins or carbon particles, more x-ray is required for suppression of antibody formation. The difference in effect in the primary and secondary response seems to be qualitative rather than quantitative (318). Chase (64) suggested some years ago that the same mechanism might be operative in the suppression of antibodies in such widely different situations as (1) suppression of antibody formation with analogs, cortisone, or excess antigen, (2) the newborn animal, and (3) suppression by irradiation. In each instance the dose of antigen was excessive for the number of available antibody-producing cells, although in certain instances, such as the newborn, the irradiated, and the analog treated, only a minute amount of antigen was needed to be a great excess, since there was a deficiency of antibody forming cells. All later studies support Chase's conclusions (1, 367).

When animals are given a sublethal dose of x-ray, the antibody-forming cells of the body are suppressed. These animals cannot make antibodies for several weeks but can act as recipients of antibody forming cells from other animals. Harris and his associates (170, 171, 172, 173, 175) have studied the formation of agglutinin to the Shiga dysentery bacillus by cells which had been exposed to the bacilli or to extract of the bacilli in the normal animal and in the test tube before injection into the irradiated animal.

In animals given high doses of radiation the antibody-forming cells are completely destroyed, and the animal dies unless they are replaced. The replacement can be made with bone marrow, lymph node, or splenic cells from the same inbred strain, from the same species, or from other species of animals (67). Mice have been provided with cells from rats (65, 258, 299), and rats have been provided with hemopoietic cells from either rats or rabbits (239). Lethally irradiated isologous mice have been used by Perkins, Robinson, and Makinodon (318) as in vivo tissue cultures for the study of antibody response cell dose relation, the effect of type, dose, and route of antigen as well as the source of antibody-forming cells. If host and donor are of the same species and the same genetic constitution, there is no reaction between host and grafted tissue, and if the cells have been exposed to antigen in the original host, they will produce antibodies in the new host (144). When the transferred cells are from another genetic strain of animal or another host, such as rat cells into irradiated mice, there is excellent protection against the immediate effect of irradiation, but the late effect may be poor. The immunologically competent cells may begin to make antibodies against the mouse host tissue, giving rise to dwarfing or "runt disease" as described by Billingham (29) and by Jutila and Weiser (210) (Ch. 15, Fig. 4).

Theories of Antibody Formation. The exact mechanism of antibody formation remains a mystery, although over 60 years of speculation and experimentation has been expended upon the subject. A satisfactory theory must explain a number of important facts: (a) the extraordinary degree of specificity possessed by antibodies, (b) the very large number of specific antibodies produced by the introduction of relatively small amounts of antigen, (c) the greatly increased rate and amount of antibodies produced following even smaller amounts of antigen when the injection is for a second or third time, (d) the mechanism by which antibody-producing cells recognize the antigens of the animal's own tissues and refrain from producing antibodies to these antigens. The original theory of Buchner that the antibodies contain some constituents of the antigen is obviously incorrect because of the excess of antibody produced and because readily recognized hapten groups in synthesized antigens cannot be found in their corresponding antibodies (33).

Current theories of antibody formation can be divided into two groups: the **selective theories** and **instructive theories.** In the selective theories the foreign antigen selects and stimulates certain types of cells to produce antibody, while in the instructive theories the same foreign antigens instruct certain specific cells to produce specific antibodies. **Ehrlich's "side chain" theory** (100) was the first of the selective theories. Ehrlich

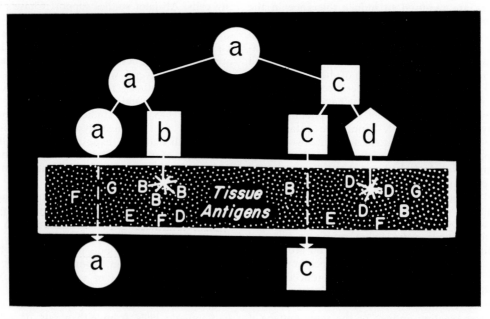

Fig. 27. Separation of "self" from "nonself" by destruction of potential antibody-producing cells directed against "self" components (tissue antigens) occurs in the vulnerable phase before birth. After birth the residual cell population is now capable of reacting to foreign antigens. (From *Physician's Bulletin,* 25:50, 1960. Eli Lilly and Co.)

believed that all of the cells of the body had specific chemical groups, which were called "side chain," for each different type of natural antigen. Foreign antigens damaged these side chains, however, so they had to be cast off and regenerated. The regeneration was carried to excess, and the excess receptors were released into the serum to circulate as antibodies. This was the dominant theory for many years but was finally discarded because of the improbability of normal cells having available the hundreds of thousands of specific receptors necessary to react with each of the known natural and synthetic antigens. The "selective" feature of Ehrlich's theory has been revived recently, however, and will be discussed later.

The **template theory** was introduced between 1930 and 1932 independently by Alexander (2), Breinl and Haurowitz (40) and Mudd (285). This was the first of the instructive theories. The antigen itself forms a template, about which the newly formed globulin molecules are folded into a mirror image of the antigen. With the discovery that the antibody globulin is synthesized directly from the amino acids, this theory has been modified and refined by Pauling (312, 317), by Haurowitz and his associates (182), and by Garvey and Campbell (142). Haurowitz visualizes the polypeptide chains of the antigen unfolding and being held in the expanded position by forces generated by nucleic acids, while the amino acid groups are duplicated in a specific mirror image pattern as determined by the specific shape and electrostatic field of the template surface (33).

The template theory explains satisfactorily most of the known phenomena of antibody formation. It cannot explain the continuation of antibody synthesis after the disappearance of antigen, however, and it is not very helpful in explaining the ability of the organisms to recognize its own antigen as "self" and refrain from producing antibodies. Recent reports by Richter and Haurowitz (337, 338) and Campbell and Garvey (57) show that protein antigens do persist much longer than anticipated. A new report suggests that the immunogenic components may exist as nucleoprotein-antigen complexes (119).

On the other hand, Buckley, Whitney, and Tanford (45) have shown that antibody globulin can be completely uncoiled but when released it recoils, in the absence of specific antigen, into its original shape with full antibody reactivity. This suggests that the order of sequence of the amino acids might be more important than the presence of the original antigen.

The **adaptive self-duplicating enzyme theory** was introduced by Burnet and Fenner in 1949 as the **"indirect template" theory.** This theory was elaborated upon but not basically altered by Burnet in 1956 (47, 48). According to this theory, the presence of the antigen in the cell results in the modification of the enzymes involved in the synthesis of normal globulin (50) in such a manner that they become independent self-duplicating units which are capable of continuing the manufacture of antibodies after the disappearance of the antigen. This theory would explain the rapid and huge production of antibodies in the anamnestic reaction and the continuing production of antibodies after the disappearance of antigens. This theory intrigued biologists but was never accepted by chemists, although it was used by Burnet to predict the existence of immunologic tolerance which was later observed in nature and reproduced under experimental conditions. Although Burnet used the theory to predict the existence of immunologic tolerance, he was not satisfied with the mechanism of action proposed and abandoned it in favor of the clonal selection theory (50, 51).

The **clonal selection theory of antibody production** is a selection theory like that proposed by Ehrlich but much more sophisticated. Jerne in 1955 (204) suggested that low levels of natural antibodies could combine with antigen and be phagocytized and hence stimulate antibody production. This basic concept was modified by Talmage in 1957 and 1959 (392, 393) who calculated that there could be as many as 5,000 different natural globulins producing cells which could react with almost any foreign antigen and then multiply rapidly as the result of stimulation by the antigen (402).

Burnet's clonal selection theory (50, 51) is somewhat more specific than that proposed by Talmage. Burnet asumes that there is a tremendous mutation rate, before birth, in certain mesenchymal cells which are to be future globulin-synthesizing cells. Those which happen by chance to produce globulin which would combine with the animal's own body protein are destroyed or at least rendered non reactive or tolerant to the body's own antigens (Fig. 27). It seems likely that this mutation process would continue after birth and perhaps on to old age. When an antigen foreign to the body is introduced, it reaches some cells which are already producing a specific antibody globulin which unites with the antigen. This union of antigen and "normal" antibody must be very stimulating to the globulin-producing cells, because they begin to multiply at an almost unbelievable rate and produce specific antibody at a comparable rate.

It is known that the animal body can produce up to 20 or more specific antibodies to different specific antigens simultaneously, but this does not mean that each adult cell is producing more than one type of antibody. The fluorescent antibody studies of Coons (72) and White (427) indicate that each antibody-producing cell is making only one type of antibody. The elegant study of Nossal (301, 302) with cells from rats simultaneously immunized against two *Salmonella* serotypes showed that only an occasional cell produced antibodies to both types, and these could be explained as diploid heterozygotes. Attardi and his coworkers (12) injected two types of bacteriophages into animals repeatedly over a period of weeks and months and found that most cells produced only one type of antibody, none produced three types, but more produced two types than in the experiment of Nossal. The clonal theory would seem to be well established if the fluorescent antibody studies showed that the antibody-producing cells were actually in clones, as one would expect from the clonal theory. In the one reported experiment of this type, White (427) used a green fluorescing indicator for one antigen and a red fluorescing indicator for the other. Each antibody-producing cell was either red or green, and they were arranged in a definite clonal pattern in the germinal center of lymph nodes. Lederberger (241) looks with

favor on the clonal theory because it proposes no novel reactions, merely the mutability of DNA and the role of DNA presumably through RNA as a code of amino acid sequence in antibody.

Rittenberg and Nelson's (340) recent review of the theories of antibody production with specific reference to the role of macrophages, nucleic acid, and antibody production suggests that the macrophages prepare antibody "inducers" which may be nucleoprotein and that these nucleoproteins serve as intracellular mediators of antibody formation. The actual production of antibody may be at the microsomal level, where the synthesis of protein occurs (260a).

REFERENCES

1. Albright, J. F., and others. Fed. Proc., 22: 266, 1963.
2. Alexander, J. Protoplasma, 14:296, 1932.
3. Allen, P. Z., and Kabat, E. J. Immunol., 82:340, 358, 1959.
4. Ambrose, C. T., and Coons, A. H. Fed. Proc., Abstract., 22:266, 1963.
5. Arnon, R., and Sela, M. Science, 132:86, 1960.
6. Askonas, B. A., Humphrey, J. H., and Porter, R. R. Biochem. J., 63:412, 1956.
7. ——— and Humphrey, J. H. Biochem. J., 68:252, 1958; 70:212, 1958.
8. ——— Mechanisms of Antibody Formation, Holub, M., and Jarošková, L., eds., New York and London, Academic Press, 1960, p. 23.
9. ——— Immunochemical Approaches to Problems in Microbiology, Heidelberger, M., Plescia, O. J., and Day, R. A., eds., New Brunswick, N.J., Rutgers University Press, 1961, p. 343.
10. ——— and Fahey, J. L. J. Exp. Med., 115:641, 1962.
11. Asofsky, R., and Thorbecke, G. J. J. Exp. Med., 114:471, 1961.
12. Attardi, G., and others. Bact. Rev., 23:213, 1959.
13. Baer, H., and Bowser, R. T. Science, 140: 1211, 1963.
14. Bardawil, W. A., and others. Am. J. Path., 34:607, 1958.
15. Baron, S., and others. J. Immunol., 88:443, 1962.
16. Bartel, A. H., and Campbell, D. H. Arch. Biochem. Biophysics, 82:232, 1959.
17. Bassett, E. W., Beiser, S. M., and Tanenbaum, S. W. Science, 133:1475, 1961.
18. Battisto, J. R., and Miller, J. Proc. Soc. Exp. Biol. & Med., 111:111, 1962.
19. Bauer, D. C., and others. J. Exper. Med., 117:889, 1963.
20. Bearn, A. G. Bull. N.Y. Acad. Med., 37: 593, 1961.
21. Beeson, P. B., and Gobel, W. F. J. Exper. Med., 70:239, 1939.

22. Bellanti, J. A., and others. Fed. Proc., 21: 30, 1962.
23. Benacerraf, B., and others. J. Exper. Med., 110:27, 1959.
24. ——— and others. J. Exper. Med., 117: 937, 951, 1963.
25. Benedict, A. A., and others. J. Immunol., 90:399, 1963.
26. Bernhart, W., and Granboulan, H. Ultrastructure of Immunologically Competent Cells, Ciba Symposium Cellular Aspects of Immunity, London, Churchill Ltd., 1960, p. 92.
27. Bieber, S., and others. Proc. Soc. Exp. Biol. & Med., 111:334, 1962.
28. Bigley, N. J., and others. J. Immunol., 90: 416, 1963.
29. Billingham, R. E. Ann. N.Y. Acad. Science, 73:782, 1958.
30. Bisset, K. A. J. Endocrinol., 6:99, 1949.
31. Blumer, and others. J. Immunol., 88:669, 1962.
32. Boivin, A., and Mesroibeanu, L. Compt. Rend. Soc. Biol., 112:76, 1933.
33. Boyd, W. C. Fundamentals of Immunology, 3rd ed., New York, Interscience, 1956.
34. ——— Introduction to Immunochemical Specificity, New York, Interscience, 1962.
35. ——— and others. J. Immunol., 89:463, 1962.
36. ——— Science, 140:1057, 1963.
37. Boyden, S. V., Dorkin, E., and Spärck, J. V. Mechanisms of Antibody Formation, Holub, M., and Jarošková, L., eds., New York and London, Academic Press, 1960, p. 237.
38. ——— and Sorkin, E. Immunol., 5:370, 1962.
39. Bradley, S. G., and Watson, D. W. J. Immunol., 90:782, 1963.
40. Breinl, F., and Haurowitz, F. Ztschr. f. Physiol. Chem., 192:45, 1930.
41. Brem, T. H., and Morton, M. E. Ann. Int. Med., 43:465, 1955.
42. Brooke, M. S., and Karhovsky, M. J. J. Immunol., 87:205, 1961.
43. Bruton, O. C., and others. Am. J. Dis. Child., 84:632, 1952.
44. Buchanan, D. J., and others. J. Immunol., 83:552, 1959.
45. Buckley, C. E. III, Whitney, P. L., and Tanford, C. Proc. Nat. Acad. Sc. U.S., 50: 827, 1963.
46. Burger, M. Bacterial Polysaccharides, Springfield, Ill., Charles C Thomas, 1950.
47. Burnet, F. B., and Fenner, B. The Production of Antibodies, New York, Macmillan Company, 1949.
48. ——— and others. Australian J. Exp. Biol. & Med. Science., 15:227, 1937.
49. ——— Enzyme, Antigen and Virus, Cambridge University Press, 1956.
50. ——— Australian J. Science, 20:67, 1957.
51. ——— The Clonal Selection Theory of Acquired Immunity, Nashville, Vanderbilt University Press, 1959.
52. Butler, V. P., and others. Proc. Nat. Acad. Sciences, 48:1597, 1962.
53. Campbell, D. H., and others. J. Am. Chem. Soc., 70:2496, 1948.
54. ——— and Bulman, N. Prog. Chem. Organic Natural Products, 9:443, 1952.
55. ——— and others. Science, 122:1079, 1955.
56. ——— and Garvey, J. S. Int. Arch. Allergy, 12:70, 1958.
57. ——— and Garvey, J. S. Laboratory Investigation, 10:1126, 1961.
58. Cann, J. R., and others. J. Immunol., 66: 137, 1951.
59. ——— and Loveless, M. H. J. Immunol., 72:270, 1954.
60. Capalbo, E. E., and others. J. Immunol., 89:1, 1962.
61. Cebra, J. J. J. Immunol., 86:190, 197, 205, 1961.
62. Chan, P. C. Y., and Deutsch, H. F. J. Immunol., 85:37, 1960.
63. Chapman-Andresen, C. Exp. Cell. Research, 12:397, 1957.
64. Chase, M. W. Ann. Rev. Microbiol., 13: 349, 1959.
65. Chin, P. H., and Silverman, M. S. J. Immunol., 85:120, 1960.
66. Claman, H. N., and Talmage, D. W. Science, 141:1194, 1963.
67. Congdon, C. C. Blood, 12:746, 1957.
68. Coons, A. H., and Kaplan, M. H. J. Exper. Med., 91:1, 1950.
69. ——— and others. J. Exper. Med., 93:173, 1951.
70. ——— Ann. Rev. Microbiol., 8:333, 1954.
71. ——— Leduc, E. H., and Connolly, J. M. J. Exp. Med., 102:49, 1955.
72. ——— J. Cellular. Comp. Physiol., 50, Suppl. 1:242, 1957.
73. Crampton, C. F., and others. J. Immunol., 71:319, 1953.
74. Cremer, N. E. J. Immunol., 90:685, 1963.
75. Cruchaud, A., and others. J. Exp. Med., 115:1141, 1962.
76. Cushing, J. E., and Campbell, D. H. Principles of Immunology, New York, McGraw-Hill Book Co., 1957.
77. Dacie, J. V. Am. J. Med., 18:810, 1955.
78. Dalmasso, A. P., and others. Proc. Soc. Exp. Biol. & Med., 111:143, 1962.
79. Datta, S. P., and Stone, W. H. J. Immunol., 90:857, 1963.
80. Davis, B. D., and others. J. Immunol., 50:1, 1945.
81. De Carvalho, S. J. Lab. Clin. Med., 56:333, 1960.
82. Deicher, H. R. G., and others. J. Exper. Med., 109:97, 1959.
83. Derick, C. L., and Swift, H. F. J. Exper. Med., 49:615, 883, 1929.
84. Deutsch, H. F., and others. J. Immunol., 56:183, 1947.
85. Dixon, F. J., and others. J. Exper. Med., 96:313, 1952.
86. ——— and others. J. Immunol., 72:179, 1954; 68:693, 1952.
87. ——— and Maurer, P. H. Riassunti d. Comunicazioni, sixth Internat. Congr. Microbiol. (abstracts). I, 461, Roma, Italia, 1953. J. Immunol., 74:189, 418, 1955.
88. ——— and others. J. Exper. Med., 103: 425, 1956.
89. ——— and Weigle, W. O. J. Exper. Med., 110:139, 1959.
90. Dodd, M. C., and others. Science, 137:688, 1962.
91. Dray, S. Science, 132:1313, 1960.

92. Dray, S., and Nisonoff, A. Proc. Soc. Exper. Biol. & Med., 113:20, 1963.
93. Dresser, D. W. Immunol., 5:378, 1962.
94. Dutton, R. W., and Pearce, J. D. Immunol., 5:414, 1962.
95. ——— and Harris, G. Nature, 197:608, 1963.
96. Dvorak, H. F., and Waksman, B. H. J. Exper. Med., 116:1, 1962.
97. Eagle, H., and Fleischman, R. J. Exper. Med., 87:369, 1948.
98. Edelman, G. M., and Benacerraf, B. Proc. Natl. Acad. Sci. U.S., 48:1035, 1962.
99. Edsall, J. T., and Anson, M. L. Advances in Protein Chem., 3:383, 1947.
100. Ehrlich, P. Gesammelte Arbeiten, Berlin, Hipschwald, 1904.
101. ——— and others. J. Immunol., 89:391, 1962.
102. ——— and others. J. Exper. Med., 90:157, 1949.
103. Eisen, H. N., and others. J. Exper. Med., 95:473, 1952.
104. ——— and Belman. J. Exper. Med., 98:533, 1953.
105. ——— and others. J. Immunol., 73:296, 1954.
106. ——— and Pearce, J. H. Ann. Rev. Microbiol., 16:101, 1962.
107. Enders, J. F. J. Clin. Investigation, 23:510, 1944.
108. Epstein, W. V., and Fudenberg, H. J. Immunol., 89:293, 1962.
109. Erickson, J. D., and others. J. Immunol., 71:30, 1953.
110. Ersley, A. J. Immunol., 67:281, 1951.
111. Fagraeus, A., and Berglund, K. J. Immunol., 87:49, 1961.
112. Fahey, J. L. Science, 131:500, 1960.
113. ——— and Morrison, E. G. J. Lab. Clin. Med., 55:912, 1960.
114. ——— and Humphrey, J. H. Immunol., 5:104, 1962.
115. ——— and Lawrence, M. E. Fed. Proc., 21:19, 1962.
116. ——— and McLaughlin, C. J. Immunol., 91:438, 448, 484, 1963.
117. Farah, F. S., and others. J. Exper. Med., 112:1195, 1960.
118. Farr, R. S., and Dixon, F. J., Jr. J. Immunol., 85:258, 1960.
119. Friedman, H. Proc. Soc. Exper. Biol. & Med., 113:1040, 1963.
120. Felton, L. D., and others. J. Immunol., 74:17, 205, 1955.
121. Ferguson, L. C. J. Am. Vet. M.A., 111:466, 1947.
122. Finkelstein, M. S., and Uhr, J. W. Fed. Proc., 22:226, 1963.
123. Finland, M., and Curnen, E. C. Science, 87:417, 1938.
124. Fishman, M. Nature, 183:1200, 1959.
125. ——— J. Exper. Med., 114:837, 1961.
126. Fleischer, S., and others. Biochem. Biophysics, 92:329, 1961.
127. Fleischman, J. B., and others. Arch. Biochem. Biophys. Supplement I., 1:174, 1962.
128. Forssman, J. Ztschr. f. Biochem., 37:78, 1911.
129. Franklin, E. C. J. Immunol., 85:138, 1960.
130. ——— and Stanworth, D. R. J. Exper. Med., 114:521, 1961.
130a. ——— J. Immunol., 91:730, 1963.
131. Freund, J. Ann. Rev. Microbiol., 1:291, 1947.
132. ——— Am. J. Clin. Path., 21:645, 1951.
133. Friedman, M., and Yeatman, J. J. Immunol., 75:97, 1956.
134. Friedman, R. M., and others. J. Exp. Med., 114:173, 1961.
135. Friou, G. J. J. Immunol., 80:476, 1958.
136. Frisch, A. W., and Davies, G. H. J. Immunol., 88:269, 1962.
137. ——— and others. J. Immunol., 89:300, 1962.
138. Fudenberg, H. H., and Kunkel, H. G. J. Exp. Med., 114:257, 1961.
139. ——— and Franklin, E. C. Ann. Int. Med., 58:171, 1963.
140. Gaines, S., and others. Proc. Soc. Exp. Biol. & Med., 104:602, 1960.
141. Gajewski, M., and others. Fed. Proc., 22:327, 1963.
142. Garvey, J. S., and Campbell, D. A. J. Immunol., 76:36, 1956.
143. Gavosto, F., and Ficq, A. Nature, 172:406, 1953.
144. Gengozian, N., and others. J. Immunol., 86:113, 1961.
145. Gilden, R. V., and Tokuda, S. Science, 140:406, 1963.
146. Gill, T. J., and Doty, P. J. Mol. Biol., 2:65, 1960.
147. Girard, K. F., and Murray, E. F. D. Can. J. Biochem. & Physiol., 32:14, 1954.
148. Gitlin, D., and others. J. Exper. Med., 97:163, 1953.
149. ——— and others. New Eng. J. Med., 260:72, 1959.
150. ——— and others. J. Immunol., 86:627, 1961.
151. Glenny, A. T., and Hopkins, B. E. J. Hyg., 21:142, 1922.
152. Goebel, W. F. Science, 91:20, 1940.
153. ——— and others. J. Biol. Chem., 148:1, 1943.
154. Gold, E. F., and Benedict, A. A. J. Immunol., 89:234, 1962.
155. Good, R. A., and Varco, R. L. J.A.M.A., 157:713, 1955.
156. ——— and others. Ann. New York Acad. Sc., 64:882, 1957.
157. ——— and others. Mechanisms of Antibody Formation, Holub, M., and Jarošková, L., eds., New York and London, Academic Press, 1960, p. 118.
158. Goodman, J. W., and Kabat, E. A. J. Immunol., 84:333, 347, 1960.
159. ——— Science, 139:1292, 1963.
160. ——— and Gross, D. J. Immunol., 90:865, 1963.
161. Gowans, J. L. Ann. New York Acad. Sci., 99:432, 1962.
162. Grabar, P. Les Globulines du Serum Sanguin. Liége, Desoer, 1957.
163. ——— Ann. Rev. Biochem., 19:453, 1950.
164. ——— Immunochemical Approaches to Problems in Microbiology, Heidelberger, M., Plescia, O. J., and Day, R., eds., New Brunswick, New Jersey, Rutgers University Press, 1961, p. 20.
165. ——— and others. J. Immunol., 88:679, 1962.

166. Green, H., and Anker, H. S. J. Gen. Physiol., 38:283, 1955.
167. Gyenes, L., and others. Fed. Proc., 22:495, 1963.
168. Hairata, A. A., and others. J. Immunol., 89:132, 1962.
168a. ——— J. Immunol., 91:625, 1963.
169. Hall, C. E. Introduction to Immunochemical Specificity, Boyd, W. C., ed., New York, Interscience, 1962, p. 6.
170. Harris, S., and others. J. Immunol., 72:148, 1954.
171. ——— and Harris, T. N. J. Immunol., 74:318, 1955.
172. ——— and others. J. Immunol., 75:112, 1955.
173. Harris, T. N., and Harris, S. J. Exper. Med., 90:167, 1949.
174. ——— and others. J. Immunol., 80:308, 1958.
175. ——— and others. J. Immunol., 88:199, 206, 1962.
176. ——— and others. Immunol., 6:168, 1963.
177. Haurowitz, F. Chap. 2 in Chemie der Antigene und der Antikörper, in Fortschritte der Allergielehre, Kallos, P., ed., Basel, S. Karger, 1939, p. 19.
178. ——— J. Immunol., 43:331, 1942.
179. ——— and others. Biochem. J., 41:304, 1947.
180. ——— Biol. Rev., 27:247, 1952.
181. ——— Ann. Rev. Microbiol., 7:389, 1953.
182. Hawes, M. D., and Coombs, R. R. A. J. Immunol., 84:586, 1960.
183. Heidelberger, M., and Kendall, F. F. J. Exper. Med., 64:161, 1936.
184. ——— and Kabat, E. A. J. Exper. Med., 67:181, 1938.
185. ——— J. Biol. Chem., 144:555, 1942.
186. ——— and others. Immunol., 5:666, 1962.
187. Hektoen, L., and others. J. Inf. Dis., 40:641, 1927.
188. Hennessy, A. V., and others. J. Immunol., 75:401, 1955.
189. Helmreich, E., and others. J. Biol. Chem., 236:464, 1961.
190. Hirata, and others. J. Immunol, 84:576, 1960.
191. Hirsch, H. M. Lancet, 79:340, 1959.
192. ——— Bact. Rev., 26:336, 1962.
193. Hochwald, G. M., and others. J. Exper. Med., 114:459, 471, 1961.
194. Holman, H. R., and Kunkel, H. G. Science, 126:162, 1957.
195. ——— and Deicher, H. R. G. J. Clin. Invest., 38:2059, 1959.
196. Holub, M., and Řiha, J. Mechanism of Antibody Formation, New York and London, Academic Press, 1960, p. 30.
197. Hooker, S. B. J. Allergy, 8:113, 1937.
198. Hunt, W. B., Jr., and Myrvik, Q. N. Bact. Proc. Abstracts, 62nd Annual Meeting, 1962, p. 74.
199. Immunologic Phenomenon in Cold-Blooded Vertebrates. Symposium. Fed. Proc., Part I, 22:1131, 1963.
200. Ishizaka, T., Campbell, D. H., and Ishizaka, K. Proc. Soc. Exp. Biol. & Med., 103:5, 1960.
201. Itoh, T., and Southam, C. M. J. Immunol., 91:469, 1963.
202. Jankovic, B. D., and others. J. Exper. Med., 116:159, 177, 187, 1962.
203. Jerne, N. K. Acta Path. Microbiol. Scandinav. Suppl., 87:1951.
204. ——— Proc. Nat. Acad. Sci. U.S., 41:849, 1955.
205. ——— and Avegno, P. J. Immunol., 76:200, 1956.
206. ——— and Nordin, A. A. Science, 140:405, 1963.
207. Jones, R. S., and others. Proc. Soc. Exp. Biol. & Med., 110:323, 1962.
208. Josephson, A., and Franklin, E. C. Fed. Proc., 20:13, 1961.
209. Journey, L. J., and Amos, D. B. Cancer Res., 22:998, 1962.
210. Jutila, J. W., and Weiser, R. S. J. Immunol., 88:621, 1962.
211. Kabat, E. A., and Mayer, M. M. Experimental Immunochemistry, 2nd ed., Springfield, Ill., Charles C Thomas, 1961.
212. ——— and others. J. Exp. Med., 91:433, 1950.
213. ——— and Berg, D. J. Immunol., 70:514, 1953.
214. ——— Blood Group Substances, New York, Academic Press, 1955.
215. ——— J. Cellular Comp. Physiol., 50:suppl. 1, 79, 1957.
216. ——— Fed. Proc., 21:694, 1962.
217. ——— and others. J. Immunol., 90:810, 1963.
218. Kaplan, M. H., and others. J. Exper. Med., 91:15, 1949.
219. ——— J. Immunol., 90:595, 1963.
220. Karush, F., and Marks, R. J. Immunol., 78:296, 1957.
221. ——— Immunochemical Approaches to Problems in Microbiology, Heidelberger, M., Plescia, O. J., and Day, R. A., eds., New Brunswick, N.J., Rutgers University Press, 1960, p. 368.
222. Kind, P., and Johnson, A. G. J. Immunol., 82:415, 1959.
223. Klein, G. C., and others. Proc. Soc. Exp. Biol. & Med., 111:298, 1962.
224. Koshland, M. E., and Burrows, W. J. Immunol., 65:93, 1950.
225. ——— J. Immunol., 70:359, 1953.
226. Kuhns, W. J. J. Immunol., 75:105, 1955.
227. ——— and Dukstein, W. J. Immunol., 79:154, 1957.
228. Kunkel, H. G., and others. Science, 140:1218, 1963.
229. Landsteiner, K. München. Med. Wchnschr., 2:1812, 1903.
230. ——— and Van der Scheer, J. J. Exper. Med., 50:407, 1929.
231. ——— and Jacobs, J. J. Exper. Med., 61:643, 1935.
232. ——— and Van der Scheer, J. J. Exper. Med., 63:325, 1936.
233. ——— and Van der Scheer, J. J. Exper. Med., 69:705, 1939.
234. ——— J. Exper. Med., 75:269, 1942.
235. ——— and Chase, M. W. Proc. Soc. Exper. Biol. & Med., 49:688, 1942.
236. ——— The Specificity of Serological Reactions, 2nd ed., Cambridge, Mass., Harvard University Press, 1945.
237. Lapresle, C., and Durieux, J. Ann. Inst. Pasteur, 92:62, 1957.

238. Lapresle, C., and others. J. Immunol., 82: 94, 1959.
239. Lavia, M. F., and others. Proc. Soc. Exp. Biol. & Med., 104:562, 1960.
240. Lecce, J. G., and Reep, B. R. J. Exper. Med., 115:491, 1962.
241. Lederberger, J. Science, 129, 1649, 1959.
242. Lee, C. L., and others. Fed. Proc., 22:326, 1963.
243. Leskowitz, S., and Kabat, E. A. J. Immunol., 75:171, 1955.
244. Levine, L., and others. Proc. Nat. Acad. Sc., 46:1038, 1960.
245. Levey, R. H., and others. Science, 142:483, 1963.
246. Levy, H. B., and Sober, H. A. Proc. Soc. Exp. Biol. & Med., 103:250, 1960.
247. Lewis, W. H. Johns Hopkins Hosp. Bull., 49:17, 1931.
248. Libby, R. L., and Madison, C. R. J. Immunol., 55:15, 1947.
249. Lo Spalluto, J., and others. J. Clin. Invest., 41:1415, 1422, 1962.
250. Loveless, M. H., and Cann, J. R. J. Immunol., 74:329, 1955.
251. McDuffie, F. C., and others. J. Immunol., 81:48, 1958.
252. McKenna, J. M., and Stevens, K. M. J. Exper. Med., 111:573, 1960.
253. ——— and others. Science, 135:370, 1962.
254. McMaster, P. D., and Kruse, H. J. Exper. Med., 94:323, 1951.
254a. Mage, R. G., and Kabat, E. A. J. Immunol., 91:633, 1963.
255. Maisel, H., and Goodman, M. Fed. Proc. Abstracts, 22:496, 1963.
256. Mäkelä, O., and Nossal, G. J. V. J. Immunol., 87:447, 457, 1961.
257. Makinodan, T., and others. J. Immunol., 72:39, 1954.
258. ——— Proc. Soc. Exp. Biol. & Med., 96: 714, 1957.
259. Malley, A., and Campbell, D. H. Fed. Proc., 21:14, 1962.
260. Mandy, W. J., and others. Science, 140: 901, 1963.
260a. Marks, E. P., and Reinecke, J. P. Science, 143:964, 1964.
261. Marrack, J. R. Antibodies to Enzymes, in The Enzymes, Myrback, K., and Sumner, J. B., eds., New York, Academic Press, 1950, Vol. I.
262. ——— and Orlans, E. S. Brit. J. Exper. Path., 35:389, 1954.
263. Martin, C. M., and others. J. Clin. Inves., 36:405, 1957.
264. Mason, J. H., and others. J. Path. & Bact., 33:783, 1930.
265. Mathies, M., and Stravitsky, A. B. Fed. Proc., 21:26, 1962.
266. Maurer, P. H. J. Exp. Med., 100:497, 515, 1954.
267. ——— Proc. Soc. Exp. Biol. & Med., 96: 394, 1957.
268. ——— J. Exp. Med., 107:125, 1958.
269. ——— and Mansmann, H. C., Jr. Proc. Soc. Exp. Biol. & Med., 99:328, 1958.
270. ——— and others. J. Immunol., 83:193, 1959.
271. ——— J. Immunol., 88:330, 1962.
272. ——— Fed. Proc. Abstracts, 220:555, 1963.
273. ——— and others. J. Immunol., 90:381, 388, 393, 493, 1963.
274. ——— Proc. Soc. Exp. Biol. & Med., 113: 553, 1963.
275. ——— J. Immunol., 72:119, 1954.
276. Meischner, P., and others. J. Immunol., 85:27, 1960.
277. Metzger, H., and Singer, S. T. Science, 142: 674, 1963.
278. Michaelides, M. C., and Coons, A. H. J. Exper. Med., 117:1035, 1053, 1063, 1075, 1963.
279. Milgrom, F., and Witebsky, E. "Autoantibodies and Autoimmune Diseases," J.A.M.A., 181:706, 1962.
280. Miller, J. F. A. P. Lancet, 2:748, 1961.
281. ——— and others. Proc. Soc. Exper. Biol. & Med., 112:785, 1963.
281a. ——— Science, 144:1544, 1964.
282. Mirick, G. S., and others. J. Exper. Med., 80:391, 1944.
283. Morgan, W. T. J., and Partridge, S. M. Biochem. J., 35:1140, 1941.
284. Morse, J. H., and Heremans, J. F. J. Lab. & Clin. Med., 59:891, 1962.
285. Mudd, S. J. Immunol., 23:423, 1932.
286. Müller-Eberhard, H. T., and Kunkel, H. G. Clin. Chem. Acta, 4:252, 1959.
287. Murakami, W. T., and others. J. Immunol., 89:116, 1962.
288. Najarin, J. S., and Feldman, J. D. J. Exper. Med., 115:1083, 1962.
289. ——— and Feldman, J. D. Ann. New York Acad. Sci., 99:470, 1962.
290. Neber, J., and Dameshek, W. Blood, 2: 371, 1947.
291. Neeper, C. A., and Seastone, C. V. J. Immunol., 91:374, 378, 1963.
292. Neiders, M. E., and others. J. Immunol., 88:718, 1962.
293. Neill, J. M., and others. J. Immunol., 74: 120, 1955.
294. Nisonoff, A., and Pressman, D. Science, 128:659, 1958.
295. ——— Biochem. & Biophysics Research Communication, 3:466, 1960.
296. ——— and others. Arch. Biochem. & Biophysics, 88:241, 1960.
297. ——— and others. Arch. Biochem. & Biophysics, 89:230, 1960.
298. ——— and Rivers, M. M. Arch. Biochem. & Biophysics, 93:460, 1961.
299. Noell, P. C., and others. Cancer Research, 16:258, 1956.
300. Northrop, J. H. J. Gen. Physiol., 25:465, 1942.
301. Nossal, G. J. V., and Mäkelä, O. J. Exper. Med., 115:209, 231, 1962.
302. ——— J. Immunol., 88:604, 1962.
303. Ogata, T., and others. J. Immunol., 83: 397, 1959.
304. Oucherlony, O. Immunochemical Approaches to Problems in Microbiology, Heidelberger, M., Plescia, O. J., and Day, R. A., eds., New Brunswick, N.J., Rutgers University Press, 1961, p. 5.
305. Oudin, J. J. Exper. Med., 112:107, 1960.
306. Ovary, Z., and Karush, F. J. Immunol., 86:146, 1961.
307. ——— and Benacerraf, B. Fed. Proc. Abstracts, 22:266, 1963.

308. Overman, J. R., and Hanan, R. Proc. Soc. Exper. Biol. & Med., 82:427, 1953.
309. ———— and Kilham, L. J. Immunol., 71:352, 1953.
310. ———— J. Immunol., 73:244, 1954.
311. Papermaster, B. W., Friedman, D. I., and Good, R. A. Proc. Soc. Exp. Biol. & Med., 110:62, 1962.
312. Pardee, A. G., and Pauling, L. J. Am. Chem. Soc., 71:143, 1949.
313. Parfentjev, I. A. U.S. Patent, 2,065,196. 1936.
314. Parks, J. J., and others. J. Immunol., 87:199, 1961.
315. Partridge, S. M., and Morgan, W. T. J. Brit. J. Exper. Path., 23:84, 1942.
316. Paul, J. R., and Bunnell, W. W. Am. J. M. Sc., 183:90, 1932.
317. Pauling, L., and others. Physiol. Rev., 23:203, 1943.
318. Perkins, E. H., and others. J. Immunol., 86:533, 1961.
319. ———— Fed. Proc. 22:No. 1313, 380, 1963.
320. ———— and Leonard, M. R. J. Immunol., 90:228, 1963.
321. Perlman, E., and Goebel, W. F. J. Exper. Med., 84:235, 1946.
322. Petermann, M. L. J. Am. Chem. Soc., 68:106, 1946.
323. Plotz, H., and Wertman, K. Proc. Soc. Exper. Biol. & Med., 59:248, 1945.
324. Porter, K. A., and Cooper, E. H. J. Exper. Med., 115:997, 1962.
325. ———— Nature, 182:670, 1958.
326. ———— Biochem. J., 73:119, 1959.
327. Poston, M. A., and Smith, D. T. Bact. Proc., 1951, p. 80,
328. Potter, M. J. Exper. Med., 115:339, 1962.
329. Pressman, D., and Sherman, B. J. Immunol., 67:15, 21, 1951.
330. Pruzansky, J. J., and Feinberg, S. M. J. Immunol., 88:256, 1962.
331. Race, R. R., and Sanger, R. Blood Groups in Man, Springfield, Ill., Charles C Thomas, 1950.
332. Raffel, S., and others. J. Exper. Med., 90:53, 1949.
333. ———— Immunity, Hypersensitivity, and Serology, 2nd ed., New York, Appleton-Century-Crofts, Inc., 1961.
334. Rapp, F. J. Immunol., 88:732, 1962.
335. Reiss, A. M., and Plescia, O. J. Science, 141:812, 1963.
336. Reyniers, J. A. New York Acad. Science, 78:47, 1959.
337. Richter, M., and Haurowitz, F. J. Immunol., 84:123, 1960.
338. ———— and Haurowitz, F. J. Immunol , 84:420, 1960.
339. Rickli, E. E., and Campbell, D. H. Fed. Proc. Abstracts, 22:No. 2356, 555, 1963.
340. Rittenberg, M. B., and Nelson, E. L. American Naturalist, 94:321, 1960.
341. Ritzmann, S. E., and others. Arch. Int. Med., 105:939, 1960.
342. Robbins, J. B., and others. Fed. Proc. Abstracts, 22:499, 1963.
343. Roberts, K. B. Brit. J. Exper. Path., 36:199, 1955.
344. Roholt, O. A. Science, 141:726, 1963.
345. Rose, N. R., and others. J. Immunol., 84:649, 1960.
346. ———— and others. J. Immunol., 88:229, 1962.
347. Royal, G. C., and others. J. Immunol., 71:22, 1953.
348. Sabin, F. R. J. Exper. Med., 70:67, 1939.
349. Sage, H., and others. Fed. Proc. Abstracts, 22:555, 1963.
350. Salk, J. E. Science, 101:122, 1945.
351. Schiller, A. A., and others. J. Gen. Physiol., 36:489, 1953.
352. Schoenheimer, R., and others. J. Biol. Chem., 144:545, 1942.
353. Schooley, J. C. J. Immunol., 86:331, 1961.
354. Schur, P. H., and Becker, E. L. Science, 141:360, 1963.
355. Schwartz, R. J. Clin. Invest., 38:1394, 1959.
356. Schwartz, R. S., and Dameshek, W. J. Immunol., 90:703, 1963.
357. Segre, D., and Kaeberle, M. L. J. Immunol., 89:782, 790, 1962.
358. ———— and others. Fed. Proc. Abstracts, 22:No. 631, 266, 1963.
359. Sela, M., and others. Science, 123:1129, 1956.
360. ———— Biochem. & Biophys. Acta, 40:382, 1960.
361. ———— and Arnon, R. Biochem. J., 75:91, 103, 1960.
362. ———— Paper contributed to a Symposium on Poly-alpha-amino acids, to be published by the Wisconsin University Press, 1962.
363. Sercarz, E. E., and Coons, A. H. J. Immunol., 90:478, 1963.
364. Sevag, M. G. Immuno-Catalysis, Springfield, Ill., Charles C Thomas, 1951.
365. Shulman, N. R., and others. J. Clin. Invest., 41:1059, 1962.
366. Sirotinin, N. N. Mechanisms of Antibody Formation, eds., Holub, M., and Jarošková, L., New York and London, Academic Press, 1960, p. 113.
367. Siskin, G. W., and others. J. Immunol., 90:929, 1963.
368. Smith, E. E. B., and others. J. Biol. Chem., 235:1876, 1960.
369. Smith, R. T. Mechanisms of Antibody Formation, Holub, M., and Jarošková, L., eds., New York and London, Academic Press, 1960, p. 313.
370. ———— Mechanisms of Antibody Formation, Holub, M., and Jarošková, L., eds., New York and London, Academic Press, 1960, p. 148.
371. Sorkin, E., and others. J. Immunol., 86:101, 1961.
372. Speer, V. C., and others. J. Immunol., 83:632, 1959.
373. Speirs, R. S., and Speirs, E. E. J. Immunol., 90:561, 1963; Scientific American, 210:58, 1954.
374. ———— Science, 140:71, 1963.
375. Springer, G. F., and others. J. Exper. Med., 113:1077, 1961.
376. Stahmann, M. A., and others. J. Immunol., 83:534, 1959.
377. Stark, O. K. J. Immunol., 74:130, 1955.
378. Stavitsky, A. B. J. Immunol., 75:214, 1955.
379. ———— J. Immunol., 79:189, 1957.
380. ———— Mechanisms of Antibody Formation, Holub, M., and Jarošková, L., eds., New York and London, Academic Press, 1960, p. 225.

381. Steinberg, A. G., and others. J. Hum. Genet., 12:44, 1960.
382. Stelos, P., and Taliaferro, W. H. J. Inf. Dis., 104:105, 1959.
383. —— and others. J. Immunol., 88:572, 1962.
384. —— and others. J. Immunol., 89:113, 1962.
385. Sterzl, J., and others. Mechanisms of Antibody Formation, Holub, M., and Jarošková, L., eds., New York and London, Academic Press, 1960, p. 130.
386. —— Nature, 185:256, 1960.
387. Stollar, D., and Levine, L. J. Immunol., 87:477, 1961.
388. Stoner, R. D., and Hale, W. M. J. Immunol., 75:203, 1955.
389. Strauch, D., and others. J. Immunol., 82:298, 1959.
389a. Sturgill, B. C., and others. Proc. Soc. Exper. Biol. & Med., 115:246, 1964.
390. Taliaferro, W. H., and Taliaferro, L. G. J. Infect. Dis., 89:143, 1951.
391. —— and Talmage, D. W. J. Infect. Dis., 97:88, 1955.
392. Talmage, D. W. Ann. Rev. Med., 8:239, 1957.
393. —— Science, 129:1643, 1959.
394. Tanaka, N., and Leduc, E. N. J. Immunol., 77:198, 1956.
395. Tanenbaum, S. W., and Beiser, S. M. Proc. Nat. Acad. Sc., 49:662, 1963.
396. Taranta, A., and Franklin, E. C. Science, 134:1981, 1961.
397. —— and Franklin, E. C. Science, 134:1981, 1962.
398. —— Fed. Proc., 22:No. 2004, 496, 1963.
399. Taylor, A. R., and others. Virology, 7:348, 1959.
400. Tempelis, C. H. Proc. Soc. Exp. Biol. & Med., 110:393, 1962.
401. Thompson, R., and Olson, H. J. Immunol., 65:633, 1950.
402. Thorbecke, G. J. Mechanisms of Antibody Formation, Holub, M., and Jarošková, L., eds., New York and London, Academic Press, 1960, p. 247.
403. —— and Franklin, E. C. J. Bact., 87:753, 1961.
404. Treffers, H. P., and Heidelberg, M. J. Exper. Med., 73:125, 1941.
405. —— and others. J. Exper. Med., 86:83, 95, 1947.
406. Tullis, J. L. J.A.M.A., 180:958, 1962.
407. Uhr, J. W., and Baumann, J. B. J. Exper. Med., 113:935, 959, 1961.
408. Urso, P., and Makinodan, T. J. Immunol., 90:897, 1963.
409. Utsumi, S., and Karush, F. Fed. Proc. Abstract, 22:496, 1963.
410. Valentine, R. C. Nature, 184:1838, 1959.
411. Vaughan, J. H., and others. J. Immunol., 84:258, 268, 1960.

412. Vredevoe, D. L., and Hildemann, W. H. Science, 141:1272, 1963.
413. Wacker, W. B., and Dodd, M. C. J. Immunol., 86:690, 1961.
414. Waksman, B. H., and others. J. Exper. Med., 114:997, 1961.
415. —— Medicine, 41:93, 1962.
416. Waldenstrom, J. Acta Med. Scandinav., 117:216, 1944.
417. Ward, P. A., and others. J. Exper. Med., 109:463, 1959.
418. —— and Johnson, A. G. J. Immunol., 82:428, 1959.
419. Webb, T., and Lapresle, C. J. Exper. Med., 114:43, 1961.
420. Weigle, W. O. Mechanisms of Antibody Formation, Holub, M., and Jarošková, L., eds., New York and London, Academic Press, 1960, p. 283.
421. —— J. Exper. Med., 114:111, 1961.
422. —— J. Immunol., 87:599, 1961.
423. —— J. Exper. Med., 16:913, 1962.
424. Weitz, B. J. Hyg., 50:275, 1952.
425. Welsh, R. A. Am. J. Path., 40:285, 1962.
426. White, R. G., Coons, A. H., and Connolly, J. M. J. Exper. Med., 102:74, 1955.
427. —— Nature, 182:1383, 1958.
428. —— Mechanisms of Antibody Formation, Holub, M., and Jarošková, L., eds., New York and London, Academic Press, 1960, p. 25.
429. Wiedermann, G., and others. Proc. Soc. Exp. Biol. & Med., 113:609, 1963.
430. Wiener, A. S. Blood Groups and Transfusions, 3rd ed., Springfield, Ill., Charles C Thomas, 1943.
431. —— J. Exper. Med., 94:213, 1951.
432. Williams, C. A., Jr., and Grabar, P. J. Immunol., 74:158, 307, 404, 1955.
433. Winebright, J., and Fitch, F. W. J. Immunol., 89:891, 900, 1962.
434. Winzler, R. J. The Plasma Proteins, 1:309, New York, Academic Press, 1960.
435. Witebsky, E., and others. J. Immunol., 75:269, 282, 291, 1955; 76:408, 1956.
436. Wolf, B., and Stavitsky, A. B. Fed. Proc., 15:623, 1956.
437. —— J. Immunol., 81:404, 1958.
438. Wolfe, H. R., and others. Fed. Proc., 21:22, 1962.
439. Wright, C. S., and others. J. Lab. & Clin. Med., 37:165, 1951.
440. Wust, C. J., and Novelli, G. D. J. Immunol., 90:734, 1963.
441. Yagi, Y., and others. J. Immunol., 89:736, 1962.
442. Yčas, M. Symposium on Information Theory in Biology, Yorkey, Y. P., ed., New York, Pergamon, 1958.
443. Zinneman, H. H., and others. J.A.M.A., 156:1399, 1954.
444. Zucker-Franklin, D. Fed. Proc., 22:380, 1963.

13

Reactions Between Antigens and Antibodies

By definition an antibody must react with its specific antigen in some measurable manner. Different names have been given to these reactions, depending upon the experimental conditions under which the tests were made. **Agglutinins** were demonstrated by Gruber and Durham (78) in 1896, **precipitins** by Kraus (126) in 1897, **bacteriolysins** and **bacteriocidins** by Pfeiffer (200) in 1894, **opsonins** by Wright (259) in 1903, and **complement-fixing antibodies** by Bordet (18, 19) in 1901. These original investigators and their successors believed that these were separate and distinct antibodies, partly because not all of the reactions could be demonstrated in a single specimen of serum but primarily because there were poor quantitative correlations between the titers obtained for the "different" antibodies. Thus a single serum might contain complement-fixing antibodies in a titer of 1:128, whereas the same serum's agglutinin titer to the same antigen might be 1:10,000.

Zinsser announced his **unitarian hypothesis,** which claimed that there was only one type of antibody responsible for the various types of reactions, in 1921 (262). The antibody combines specifically with the antigen and alters the antigen in such a manner that a variety of reactions occur depending upon the conditions under which the experiment is conducted, as shown in Table 1.

When heat-killed organisms, such as *Salmonella typhosa,* are injected into a rabbit, the animal reacts to the antigens in the bodies of the bacilli and forms specific antibodies. The serum of the animal will then agglutinate suspensions of living and dead typhoid bacilli; will alter the surface of the living organism so that phagocytosis can be accelerated; will precipitate soluble proteins prepared from the bacilli; in the presence of complement will kill and lyse living typhoid bacilli; and will fix complement either with the whole organism or with extracts of the organisms. The antibody formed following the injection of a soluble antigen is usually measured by the precipitin or complement-fixation tests, but if the original soluble antigen is coated on colloid particles, the same

Table 1. Physical Manifestations of Antigen-Antibody Reactions

PHYSICAL STATE OF ANTIGEN	ANTIBODY	ACCESSORY SUBSTANCES	EFFECT IN THE TEST TUBE	USUAL NAME GIVEN TO ANTIBODY PRODUCING THE EFFECT
Particulate Suspensions: Bacteria, RBC	Antibody	Electrolytes	Clumping of the particles	Agglutinin
Soluble: Extracts of Bacteria, Horse Serum	Antibody	Electrolytes	Precipitation	Precipitin
Particulate or Soluble	Antibody	Complement	Fixation of complement	Complement-fixing antibody
Particulate	Antibody	Leukocytes	Phagocytosis	Opsonin
Particulate with Cell Wall that is lysed easily: Certain Bacteria, RBC	Antibody	Complement	Lysis of the cell	Bacteriolysin (bacteria)
Living Bacteria	Antibody	Complement	Death of the bacteria	Bacteriocidin

219

serum will then cause a clumping or agglu-tination of the particles (34, 73). A serum which contains too few antibodies to give a precipitin test may, nevertheless, give an agglutination reaction because fewer anti-bodies are required to cause aggregation of the larger particles. Zinsser's unitarian theory recognizes the fact that living organisms con-tain many separate and distinct antigens each of which gives rise in the infected ani-mal to its own specific antibody, which un-der appropriate conditions will give all of the reactions described above (264).

The presence in the serum of a man or animal of antibodies which react with a specific organism suggests that the host is or has been infected with that agent, al-though there are exceptions to this rule, which will be discussed later. The presence of antibodies in the serum, even in great abundance, by no means assures the recov-ery of the patient, because the antibodies may have been formed to an antigen other than the one which is responsible for the virulence of the infecting organism. The serum protection or neutralization test is a more reliable method for measuring immu-nity. If the serum from a man or animal who has recovered from a bacterial or virus dis-ease protects an animal from inoculations with the same infectious agent, we can as-sume that specific protective antibodies are present even though we do not know which antibody played the major role in the pro-tection. Certain viruses which produce cyto-pathologic changes in cells in tissue cultures, including the three antigenic types of polio-myelitis virus, may be readily identified by the addition of known protective antiserum to some of the duplicate cultures (50). By varying the conditions of the experiment we can identify the specific virus or demonstrate the presence of specific neutralizing anti-bodies, provided one of the agents is known and standardized.

THE PRECIPITIN REACTION

The precipitin test is the simplest of all the antigen-antibody reactions and lends itself to quantitative study with single pure antigens and their respective antibodies. By quantitative methods the antigen or anti-

body can be measured in terms of milligrams of weight or other equally exact units to an accuracy of 5 per cent or less. This is in contrast to the qualitative methods which depend upon visual end points detected in a series of dilutions and seldom permit the reading of relative antibody contents more accurately than a twofold dilution or 100 per cent (237).

The Mechanism of the Antigen-Antibody Reaction.   The nature of the union between the antigen and its specific antibody has been under investigation for many years. The mechanism does not consist of chemical co-valent bonds or semipolar double bonds, since the process is reversible under certain conditions. The observed result is a second-ary reaction or a series of secondary reac-tions resulting in observable precipitates, agglutination, or lysis of the organisms. The **initial or primary reaction between antigen and antibody is not readily observable but is known to occur almost instantaneously after antigen and antibody are brought into contact.** The process of binding complexes of the original antigen and antibody mecha-nism is under way before the end of the first minute of exposure, as shown in Figure 1, where the purified virus of avian erythro-myeloblastic leukosis was mixed with anti-viral immune serum and the result recorded with electron micrographs.

In Figure 2 the antibody is shown with two binding sites (A) and the antigen with five binding sites (B), although we know that the actual number of the latter may approach 20. The antibody may be attached to the antigen at only one binding site, as in (C), or by both, as in (D).

The relation between the hapten-carrier protein and its antibodies is shown diagram-matically in Figure 3. The carrier protein with its diazotized atoxyl groups (C) is in-jected into a rabbit and stimulates the forma-tion of antibodies (A). If the rabbit serum is now mixed, in the proper proportions, with some of the hapten-carrier protein in a test tube, the antibodies (A) bind the react-ing groups on the carrier protein (C) until sufficiently large aggregates (D) are formed to give a visible precipitate. If, however, the rabbit serum is mixed with a solution of atoxyl (B) or the arsenic acid alone, the

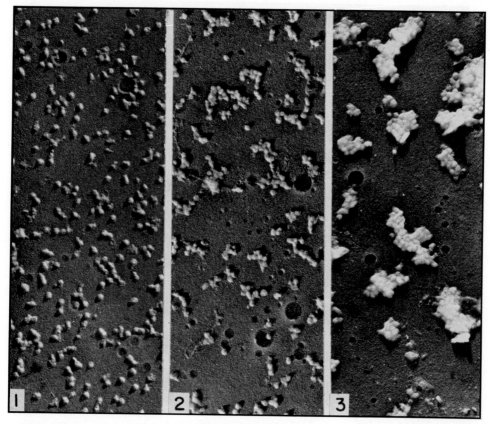

Fig. 1. Virus of avian erythromyeloblastic leukosis. Precipitation of virus with antiviral immune serum from the chicken. 1, virus in plasma; 2, aggregation of virus particles after 1 minute exposure to antiserum; 3, after 3 minutes exposure. Electron micrographs X 13,800. (After Eckert, Sharp, Beard, Green, and Beard. *J. Nat. Cancer Inst.*, 16:593, 1955.)

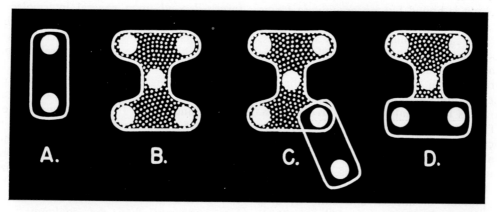

Fig. 2. Multiple binding sites for antigen and antibody. Precipitating antibodies have two binding sites: A, antigens have 2 to 30. B, an antibody may be attached to an antigen by one binding site, C, or by both, D. (After Raffel. *Immunity*, 2nd ed., Appleton-Century-Crofts.)

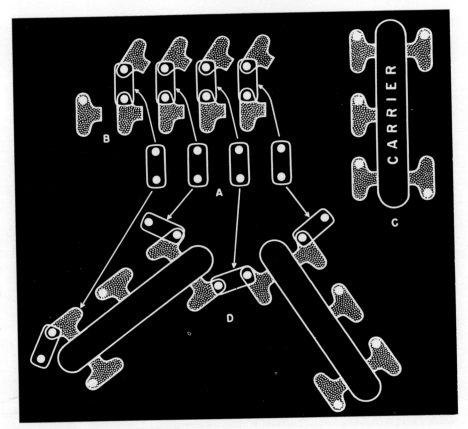

Fig. 3. Specificity of haptens. Antibodies may combine with a hapten without producing a precipitate or with a hapten-carrier and cause precipitation. A, antibodies; B, antibody-hapten combination; C, carrier protein with hapten groups, and D, antibodies linking carrier protein molecules into groups which will precipitate. (After Raffel. *Immunity,* 2nd ed., Appleton-Century-Crofts.)

antibody is bound but no precipitate forms because the hapten has only a single binding site and cannot build up visible aggregates. Proof that the antibodies are all bound is furnished by adding a solution of the hapten-carrier protein (C) and observing the absence of precipitation. This phenomenon is known as **hapten inhibition of precipitation.**

The mechanism of binding in the primary reaction may be (1) coulomb forces, (2) Van der Waals forces, or (3) hydrogen bonding. The coulomb forces depend upon the negative and positive charges present in the proteins of antigen and antibody and, according to the experiment of Singer (218), account for about one-half of the strength of the antigen-antibody bonds, with the remainder being due to Van der Waals forces and hydrogen bonding. The Van der Waals

forces depend upon general intermolecular attractions operating as instantaneous dipolar moments. These forces decrease very rapidly with distance, being inversely proportional to the seventh power of distance, but are quite strong between molecules that can bring their surfaces into close contact. Hooker and Boyd (103), Pauling and Pressman (195) and Karush (119) visualize the antibody-binding site as a cavity into which the hapten- and antigen-combining groups fit snugly. This type of structure is visualized by Boyd (25) in Figure 4 and by Pauling in Figures 5 and 6. While these forces may be less important than the coulomb forces where antigens contain positive and negative charges, they are most important with blood group substances where there are no positive or negative groups in the portions

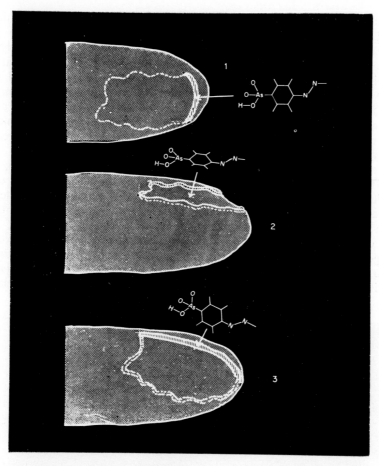

Fig. 4. Schematic drawing of the possible types of cavities (determinants) in antibody molecules. 1, invaginated; 2, shallow trough; 3, slit trench. (After Boyd. *Introduction to Immunochemical Specificity,* Interscience Publishers.)

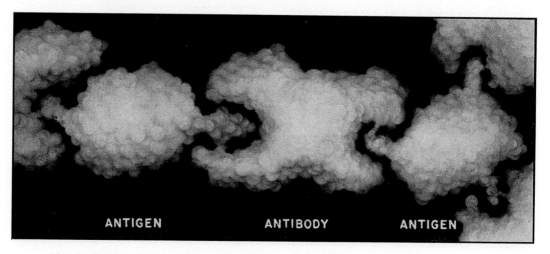

Fig. 5. Binding site of antigen and antibody. The structure of the haptenic group of an azoprotein, ovalbumin-*p*-azosuccinanilate ion. (After Pauling. *Endeavour,* 8:43, 1948.)

of the molecule responsible for antigenic specificity (119). Boyd has presented evidence that the forces between antibody and carbohydrate antigen are mainly hydrogen bonds. In his monograph *Introduction to Immunochemical Specificity* (25), he discusses these forces in some detail and presents evidence of the energy involved in the antigen-antibody reaction.

Quantitative Precipitin Tests. The Type III pneumococcal polysaccharide which has been often used in quantitative studies contains no nitrogen so that total nitrogen formed in the precipitate is derived from the antibody. In other studies crystallized egg albumin or crystallized serum albumin of known nitrogen content have been employed. In these experiments the nitrogen in the precipitate is determined by the micro-Kjeldahl method or Folin's colorimetric phenol method, but the nitrogen found is derived in part from the antibody and in part from the antigen. To arrive at the amount of antibody nitrogen contained in the precipitate, one must have determined previously the total of the nitrogen in a unit of the antigen and the total of the nitrogen in the precipitate after complete precipitation. If the original antigen nitrogen is subtracted from the precipitable nitrogen, then the difference has been added by the antibody. The results are usually reported as gamma of Ab.N., or in micrograms or milligrams of nitrogen.

The amount of precipitate formed is influenced by the purity of the antigen, the ratio of antigen to antibody, the pH of the solutions, the concentration of electrolyte, the

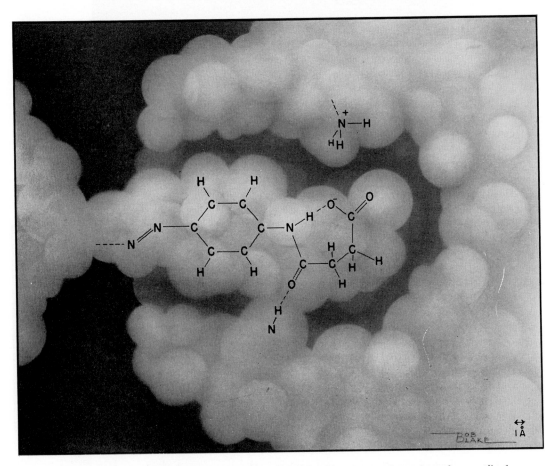

Fig. 6. Antigen and antibody. The postulated structure of a small portion of an antibody-antigen precipitate. (After Pauling. *Endeavour,* 8:43, 1948.)

dilution of the system, the time allowed for the reactions, and the temperature. The details of the methods can be found in the book *Experimental Immunochemistry* by Kabat and Mayer (117).

A majority of the quantitative studies of precipitin reactions have been made with antibodies obtained by the immunization of rabbits, but antibodies from the horse and from man have been used in certain investigations. The rabbit is an excellent producer of precipitins, in contrast to the guinea pig, while the mouse produces precipitins but has a very small volume of blood. The exact nature of the antigen-antibody in the precipitin test has been a subject of controversy for many years. Nevertheless, Heidelberger has devised a series of equations from the law of mass action which account quantita-tively for the behavior of most precipitating systems.

The chief difficulty in determining the antigen:antibody ratio is the presence of multiple binding sites on antigen and antibody so that the antigen may bind a large or small amount of antibody, depending upon the proportions in which the two components are mixed. In Figure 7, a known constant amount of antibody was added to each of the six test tubes, after which gradually increasing amounts of antigen were added to each tube. The per cent of total antibody precipitated is indicated by the heavy line drawn across the tube. In tubes 1 and 2 a small amount of antigen was added, and every binding site on the antigen was quickly covered by one of the binding sites on the antibody. In tube 1 the ratio

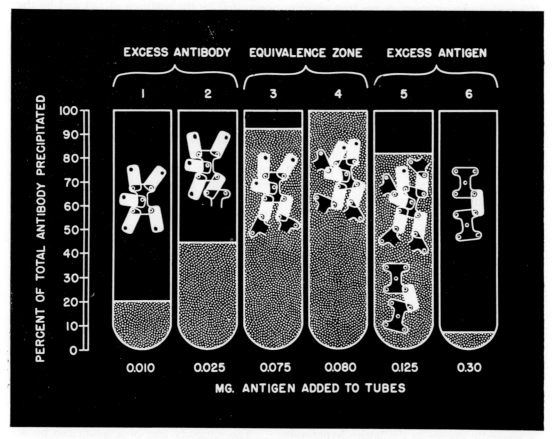

Fig. 7. Antigen-antibody reactions with excess antibody and excess antigen. The reaction occurring in each of the six test tubes is described in the text. (From Raffel. *Immunity,* 2nd ed., Appleton-Century-Crofts.)

of antibody to antigen was 5:1, and in tube 2 it was 4:1. As a result of insufficient antigen in tube 1, only 18 per cent of the total antibody was precipitated, and 45 per cent in tube 2, leaving uncombined antibodies free in the supernatant fluid. **This type of precipitate with a high ratio of antibody to antigen is found in the region of antibody excess.**

When a larger amount of antigen was added to tube 3, more of the antibodies combined with the antigen at both binding sites, giving an antibody:antigen ratio of 3:1. Although 95 per cent of the antibody was removed from the supernate, it required three times as much antigen to remove twice as much antibody as in tube 2. The addition of a little more antigen to tube 4 resulted in all of the antibody being combined with a ratio of antibody:antigen of 5:2. This type of reaction, where there is no free antigen or antibody in the supernate, is found in what is known as the **equivalence zone.**

In tube 5 there was a slight excess of antigen, and nearly all of the antibodies were bound at both reacting sites to give a ratio of antibody to antigen of 2:1; however, there were enough free binding sites to enable the antibody:antigen complexes to form aggregates which would precipitate. About 85 per cent of the antibody was precipitated, the remaining 15 per cent staying in solution because, as seen in the lower figure in tube 5, the antigen and antibody combined in such a manner that there were no free binding sites to form aggregates for precipitation. With the addition of more antigen to tube 6, only 12 per cent of the antibody was precipitated, and the ratio of antibody to antigen fell to 3:2. Most of the antibody was firmly bound to antigen, and no bridging links were available for forming precipitating aggregates. This type of reaction, with a low ratio of antibody to antigen and a decreasing amount of precipitation, is found in the **region of antigen excess.**

The combination of antibody and antigen described in the preceding paragraphs was visualized by Marrack in 1934 (144) and is generally known as the **lattice hypothesis.** Its quantitative relationships were worked out by Heidelberger (91) and his associates, and formulas were devised for expressing the various combinations of antibody:antigen ratios found in the different zones (193). Some criticism of the lattice hypothesis has been recorded (102), and other theories explaining the quantitative aspects of the antigen-antibody reaction have been proposed by Boyd (23), Haurowitz (86, 87) and Teorell (233).

When antigen and antibody are mixed in a solution in the absence of an electrolyte, no precipitate forms, but precipitation occurs immediately after the addition of a suitable amount of electrolyte. If antibody is added in the right proportions to a particulate antigen in the absence of an electrolyte, the antigen and antibody combine but do not precipitate. The particulate antigen-antibody complex can be removed from the solution by centrifugation. The absence of antigen and antibody in the supernate can be demonstrated by the addition of salt and by the addition of antigen to one tube and antibody to another. When the sedimented antigen-antibody complex is resuspended in water containing a minimal concentration of 0.005 N. sodium chloride equivalent, flocculation occurs immediately. Lecithin in horse serum and cephalin in rabbit serum (108) are also essential for flocculation and agglutination. The electrolyte and lipids are accessory, not primary, factors, since precipitation does not occur in the region of great antigen excess even in the presence of electrolyte and essential lipids.

Dissociation of Antigen-Antibody Complex. The large aggregates which form the visible precipitates will dissolve in weak acid or weak alkaline solutions, but the primary antigen-antibody complex remains intact. The addition of 15 per cent sodium chloride causes some of the antigen-antibody complexes to dissociate, leaving free antibody in solution (145, 180). When the pH of the solution containing the primary complexes is altered from 3.5 to 2.5 or 11.7 or 12.3, antibodies are freed from the antigen (123, 145, 238). The antigen-antibody reaction per se does not involve structural changes in either antigen or antibody.

The antibody titer of a serum can be determined by using a constant amount of antigen, adding twofold dilutions of the serum, and reading the last tube which gives a visible precipitate as the end point. Early investigators almost invariably used a large amount of antigen, and the most potent serums rarely gave precipitates when diluted more than 1:10 or 1:20. We know now that it was because beyond that point the antibodies continued to react with antigen to form primary complexes which were soluble in an excess of antigen that no precipitate appeared. The reverse procedure was then employed by using a constant amount of serum and diluting the antigen. Fantastically high titers were obtained, up to 1:100,000 or 1:1,000,000, but the investigators were measuring the potency and purity of the antigen, not the titer of the antibody (41, 206). This remains a useful method for the identification of an animal species from blood stains, however. Several dilutions of saline extracts of the dried blood stains are added to several series of tubes, each series containing a constant amount of serum with antibodies to blood of a different animal. Cross-reactions between blood of related species are inhibited by the excess of antigen, which allows the specific reaction to continue on to higher dilutions of antigen. By the use of this method it has been possible to recognize the animal source of dried blood stains, even after months of drying, in dilutions as high as 1:50,000.

Quantitative titrations of precipitins in an antigen-antibody system can be performed if the antigen or antibody is pure. An experiment of this type from the studies of Martin (146) is shown in Table 2. In the vertical columns the antigen was kept constant while the serum is diluted, but in the horizontal columns the serum was kept constant while the antigen is diluted. The tubes were allowed to stand until precipitates formed, after which aliquots of the supernate were tested by the ring precipitin test for the presence of excess antigen or excess antibody, as suggested by Culbertson (41). The results of these tests are shown in the lower half of the table. The heavy lines in the upper

Table 2. Titration of Rabbit Antipneumococcus Type I Antiserum with Specific Polysaccharide Antigen
(Martin)

Dilution of Serum	ANTIGEN CONCENTRATION EXPRESSED IN μG PER ML											
	256	128	64	32	16	8	4	2	1	0.5	0.25	0.125
1:25	+	+	+	+	+	+	+	+	+	+	+	−
1:50	+	+	+	+	+	+	+	+	+	+	+	−
1:100	+	+	+	+	(+)	+	+	+	+	+	+	−
1:200	−	+	+	+	+	+	+	+	+	+	+	−
1:400	−	−	+	+	+	+	+	+	+	+	+	−
1:800	−	−	−	+	+	+	+	+	+	+	+	−
1:1,600	−	−	−	−	−	+	+	+	+	+	+	−
1:3,200	−	−	−	−	−	−	−	−	+	+	+	−
1:6,400	−	−	−	−	−	−	−	−	−	−	+	−
1:12,800	−	−	−	−	−	−	−	−	−	−	−	−
				SUPERNATANT EXAMINATIONS							
1:25	A	A	−	a	a	a	a	a	a	a	a	
1:50	A	A	A	−	a	a	a	a	a	a	a	
1:100	A	A	A	A	(−)	a	a	a	a	a	a	
1:200	A	A	A	A	A	−	a	a	a	a	a	
1:400	A	A	A	A	A	A	−	a	a	a	a	
1:800	A	A	A	A	A	A	A	−	−	a	a	
1:1,600	A	A	A	A	A	A	A	A	−	−	−	
1:3,200	A	A	A	A	A	A	A	A	−	−	−	
1:6,400	A	A	A	A	A	A	A	A	A	−	−	

+ = Precipitate.
− = No precipitate
A = Excess antigen in supernatant
a = Excess antibodies in supernatant
() = Optimal ratio (fastest reacting mixture)

half of the table indicate the ratios of antigen to antibody, where there was complete precipitation with neither antigen nor antibody in the supernate. The precipitate appeared first (optimum ratio) in the tube which contained 16 µg. per ml. of antigen and a 1:100 dilution of the antiserum. The student should refer to Figure 7 for aid in interpreting this table. In the region of excess antibody in the supernate, Tubes 1 and 2 in Figure 7 and in the lower half of the table, there was no inhibition of precipitation even though the amount of antigen varied from 0.25 to 32 µg. per ml. In contrast, however, there was a progressive inhibition of precipitation by an excess of antigen, 1 µg. of antigen preventing precipitation in a 1:6,400 dilution of serum and 256 µg. of antigen preventing precipitation in a 1:200 dilution of serum. The equivalence zone is shown as Tube 4 in the figure and as the heavy lines in the upper part of the table.

The effect of the amount of antigen used on the titers obtained by the serum dilution method is obvious. Thus if a concentration of 128 µg. of antigen per ml. had been used, the titer of the serum would have been estimated as 1:200, whereas a titer of 1:6,400 was obtained when an antigen containing 0.25 µg. was employed. An arbitrary but rather low dilution of serum, 1:25 to 1:200, should be titrated against dilutions of the antigen to obtain the smallest amount of antigen which will give a visible precipitate in a specified period of time. This amount of antigen is then used in a series of tubes to which dilutions of serum are added to determine the true antibody titer of the serum, which in this case was 1:6,400. Since a 1:6,400 dilution of serum precipitated 0.25 µg. of antigen, 1 ml. of undiluted serum should be capable of precipitating 1,600 µg. or 1.6 mg. of antigen (145).

The optimal proportions method of precipitin

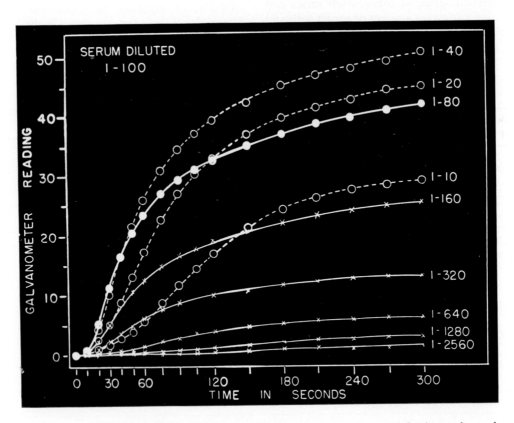

Fig. 8. Speeds of formation of precipitate. Shown by galvanometer deflections; observed with mixtures containing constant amounts of serum and varying amounts of antigen. Open circles, supernates contain excess antigen; crosses, supernates contain excess antibody; closed circles, supernates contain neither excess antigen nor excess antibody. (From Martin. *J. Lab. & Clin. Med.*, 28:870, 1943.)

titration was introduced by Dean and Webb (44) in 1926. The serum is held constant and the antigen diluted as in the horizontal columns in Table 2. The antibody titer is calculated in terms of the amount of antigen which flocculated most rapidly with the serum being tested. Marrack (144) suggests that the unit of antibody be expressed as the amount of antibody which reacts optimally with 1 μg. of antigen. In Figure 8 a titration of this type is shown, where the speed of precipitation is measured by the galvanometer deflections (146). Precipitation occurred most rapidly when there was a final serum dilution of 1:100 and an antigen dilution of 1:80 which contained 0.0125 mg. of pneumococcus Type I polysaccharide. The titer of this serum in terms of antigen would be calculated as 1,250 units per milliliter of serum since 1:100 dilution of serum reacted optimally with 0.0125 mg. or 12.5 μg. of antigen. When the serum was diluted 1:200, only half as much antigen was required to give the optimal reaction. The largest amount of precipitate was formed when the antigen was in slight excess (1:20 and 1:40), but much less was formed when there was great antigen excess (1:10). The tube which precipitated first was usually a mixture in the equivalence zone, as in this example, but systems are known in which the most rapid flocculation occurs in slight excess of antibody or slight excess of antigen. The studies of Boyd (23) and others (21) have shown that physical and chemical differences between various types of antibodies will influence the velocity of flocculation, rendering this method much less reliable than the immunochemical ones.

The **Danysz phenomenon,** which was discovered by Danysz while studying the neutralization of diphtheria toxin and antitoxin, also occurs in reactions between simple protein molecules and their antibodies. Over a wide range of antigen:antibody ratios more precipitate is obtained when antigen is added to antibody than when antiserum is added to antigen (167). This phenomenon will be discussed in more detail in the chapter on toxins and antitoxins.

The flocculation test used in the diagnosis of syphilis may be regarded as a modified precipitin test or as an agglutination test. The antigen is extracted from beef hearts and is nonspecific but, when used with the proper controls, gives valuable information about the presence of an infection with the treponema of syphilis. Similar antigens are used in the complement-fixation test for syphilis which will be discussed in more detail later in this chapter.

Immunodiffusion. As noted above, quantitative studies of antigens and antibodies have been limited to relatively pure antigens and their respective antibodies. When two or more different antigens were injected into animals, as illustrated by material such as blood serum, egg white, or bodies of bacteria, a specific antibody is produced by each antigen of the reacting animal. Precipitates were formed when the antigen was brought in contact with the antibodies, but the precipitate was composed of a mixture of the various components. The possibility of separating out a single antigen from a complex mixture of antigens and identifying a specific antibody in a mixture of antibodies is a relatively recent achievement (201).

In 1932 Petrie (198) added antisera to agar media on which he grew pneumococci, meningococci, and dysentery bacilli and found that products of the growing colonies diffused out into the agar, which contained the antibodies until the optimal zone for precipitates was reached and a ring of precipitate or halo was formed. The identification of organisms could be easily made by this reaction. Later Petrie and Steabben (199) used antitoxins made from the toxins of *Cl. perfringens, Cl. septicum,* and *Cl. novyi (oedematiens)* in the agar to identify by the halo formation the presence of these species of anaerobes. The next advance was made by Oudin (188), who modified the old test tube ring test by adding a small amount of agar to the serum to form a gel. He found that a series of rings appeared corresponding to the number of specific antigens and antibodies in the material. Other modifications made by Ouchterlony (187), Elek and Levy (49), Muñoz and Becker (161), and others (118) made possible the use of petri dishes in which the precipitates appear as a series of straight lines (256). The identification of specific antigen and antibody can be made with accuracy by the use of the double diffusion technic. In Figure 9, made for us by Dr. Crowle, antibodies to ovalbumin are distinguished from antibodies to bovine gamma globulin by lines of identity with known ovalbumin. With higher antigen and lower antiserum concentration, the optimal density of the bands was independent of time of diffusion and antigen concentration but proportional to antibody concentration (89). With the double diffusion method seven antigens have been identified in egg white (10) and twelve in *Salmonella typhosa* (223, 251). The first practical application of the double diffusion technic was the differentiation of toxin from nontoxin-producing strains of diphtheria bacilli as shown in Figure 3 in Chapter 27. The

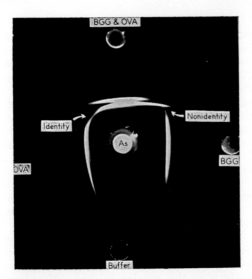

Fig. 9. Precipitin bands in a microimmunodiffusion test proved by reactions between guinea pig antiserum (As) and two antigens, chicken ovalbumin (OVA) and bovine globulin (BGG), used singly and mixed. Reactions of identity and nonidentity are identified. (Courtesy of Alfred J. Crowle.)

mathematics of the double diffusion technic have been studied by a number of investigators (3, 51, 11, 125).

In very complex mixtures of proteins and other materials a preliminary separation into fractions facilitates and makes possible the final antigenic analysis of mixed antigen. The antigen may be spread out by (1) paper-strip electrophoresis, (2) paper curtain electrophoresis, or (3) by column anion cell exchange cellulose. These technics are described in the books by I. Smith (220) and by Bloch and his associates (15). After obtaining partial purification by these methods, the fractions can now be subjected to the very elegant method of Williams and Grabar (255) (Fig. 10) known as immunoelectrophoresis. The protein solution is spread out over an agar-covered glass plate by their separate mobilities in an electric field. Then antiserum is added to a trough cut in the agar, and as it diffuses into the agar, it reacts with the dispersed antigen, forming a series of arcs (Fig. 10). With further purification a single antigen can be identified (7, 8). The details and methods of immunodiffusion are reviewed in Crowle's book (40a).

The Agglutination Reaction. Of all the serologic technics used in the diagnosis of infectious diseases, the agglutination test is the simplest to perform and has the widest range of usefulness (264). In principle, the test consists of setting up a series of tubes containing progressively increasing dilutions of serum and adding a saline suspension of living or dead bacteria to each tube. After a suitable incubation period, the tubes are examined for evidence of visible clumping, and the titer is expressed as the greatest dilution of serum which produces agglutination of the organisms.

The agglutination process can be followed microscopically by mixing a loopful of the bacteria suspension with a loopful of diluted homologous antiserum and observing the clumping of the organisms in a hanging drop preparation (Figure 11). The "spot" agglutination technic is an extremely rapid and useful method for the preliminary identification of cultures grown on solid media. A drop of diluted specific immune serum is placed on a glass slide; some of the organisms of a suspected colony are removed by touching it with a loop, and a suspension of the organisms is made directly in the drop of serum. Agglutination occurs almost immediately if the organisms contain the antigens homologous with the antibodies in the serum. The mixture dries out rapidly and although titrations of antibody content cannot be made by this technic, it is valuable as a rapid method of eliminating colonies when an individual is attempting to pick organisms of a particular antigenic type. **The agglutination reaction may be used to identify an unknown organism isolated from a patient, provided known antibody serums are available; or a known organism may be used to diagnose the type of infection in a patient by demonstrating a rising titer of agglutinins in the serum.**

Since agglutination, like precipitation, does not occur in the absence of electrolytes, most tests are performed in 0.9 per cent NaCl. Agglutination may occur spontaneously at a low pH level and is known as **acid agglutination.** By careful adjustment of the pH toward the acid side, but not enough to cause spontaneous agglutination in the control tubes, antibodies may be detected in serums which fail to agglutinate under standard conditions. Any condition which increases contact between individual organ-

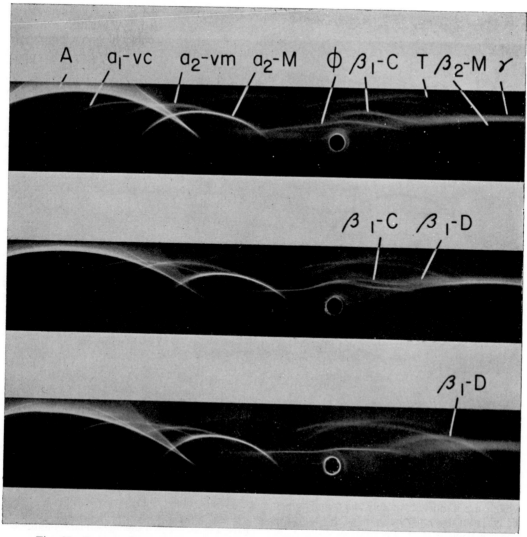

Fig. 10. Immunoelectrophoretic analyses of normal mouse plasma. At the top of the figure β_1-C appears as a single component, but various treatments effect a partial dissociation of β_1-C and β_1-D, while aging and more treatment effected a total conversion to β_1-D. (After Williams. *J. Exper. Med.*, 114:311, 1961.)

isms will increase the rate if not the titer of agglutination. The tubes are usually incubated in a water bath at temperatures ranging from 37° to 56° C., with the tubes only partially immersed in the water to induce convection currents which bring the organisms into intimate contact. Temperatures above 56° C., however, may have a deleterious effect on the antibody. Shaking and centrifugation forces a more rapid and effective contact but must be carried out under carefully controlled conditions (152).

The optimal time of incubation varies with the type of organism employed as antigen. In most laboratories the tubes are incubated for several hours and, after a preliminary reading, are stored in the icebox overnight and re-examined the following morning. The low temperature prevents growth of the organism if live antigen is used and prevents the growth of accidental contaminants while providing time for the primary complexes to build up to visible floccules (see Fig. 1).

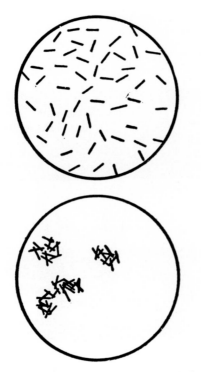

Fig. 11. Drawing of microscopic agglutination.

Quantitative agglutination methods, analogous to the quantitative precipitin methods, can be employed under certain conditions. Although the whole organism should be considered as a "bag" of antigens, the antibodies can react only with the antigen that covers the surface of the "bag." In those organisms possessing flagella, which are almost invariably different antigenically from the surface antigen of the body, there will be at least two kinds of antigen-antibody reactions proceeding simultaneously. This difficulty can be avoided by using flagella which have been removed from the organism by differential centrifugation, by using the bodies of organisms which have been freed of their flagella antigens by chemical methods, or by using a nonflagellated mutant strain. Bacteria, insoluble precipitates, and erythrocyte stromas (91, 236) have been used in quantitative immunochemical studies to derive formulas for describing the reactions. After the antigen has been freed of extraneous materials by washing, an aliquot is analyzed for its nitrogen content. The total nitrogen found in the agglutinated material minus the nitrogen content of the antigen gives the nitrogen content of the antibody (117). Fortunately, with insoluble antigens there is no inhibition of agglutination in regions of antigen excess.

The Nature of the Antigen-Antibody Reaction in Agglutination. A bacillus is tremendous in size when compared with a molecule of albumin or globulin. Adler (1) has found that a typical bacillus, *S. typhosa* 901, has 5.6×10^5 antigen receptors on its surface, in contrast to 62 potential and about 30 effective receptors on the surface of the ovalbumin molecule (183). It is obvious that fewer molecules of antibody will be required to link the larger bodies together into visible aggregates. This may be the explanation for the observed fact that a single antibody serum usually gives a higher titer when measured for agglutinins than for precipitins. Studies by Adler (1), Miles (156), and others (33, 174) have shown that the antigen receptors occur in patches and are not evenly distributed over the surface of the bacilli.

As mentioned before, the agglutination reaction is not inhibited by an excess of antigen, presumably because the antigen is fixed in the surface layer of the large organisms and cannot surround the antibody and block its combining sites. Under certain conditions agglutination is inhibited in antibody excess but appears and proceeds to a high titer as the serum is diluted. This type of reaction is seen most often with high-titer serum from patients with brucellosis and *Salmonella* infections and is known as the **prozone phenomenon** which occurs in the **proagglutinoid zone.** Some patients with chronic brucellosis have a very high prozone, and the sera of others fail to agglutinate at any dilution. These observations suggested to Zinneman, Glenchur, and Hall (260, 261) that some patients might have an incomplete or univalent antibody which could combine with the bacilli without effecting agglutination. These investigators have isolated the agglutinating antibodies and the blocking antibodies, as shown in Figure 12. Apparently the blocking antibodies have a greater affinity for the antigenic sites on the bacilli than the agglutinating antibody, since the addition of a small amount of sera containing the blocking antibody to sera containing agglutinins but having no prozone now shows a prozone. The degree of the prozone is proportional to the amount of blocking antibodies added. The blocking antibodies appear first in the gamma globulin fraction but shift after a few months to the beta globulins, where they remain (260, 261). These studies indicate that the prozone in patients with *Brucella* infections, and possibly those with *Salmonella* infections, is produced by the presence of specific blocking antibodies and not by an excess of agglutinating antibodies. This type of blocking antibody will be designated blocking antibody Type I to dis-

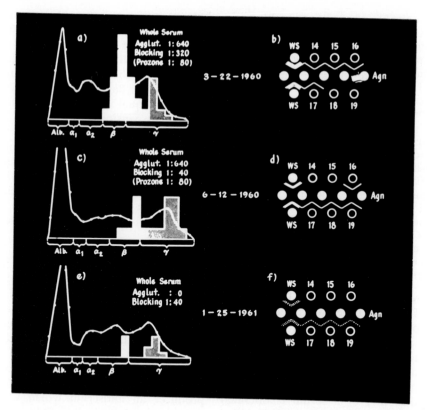

Fig. 12. The titers of agglutinating and blocking antibodies are superimposed graphically on the electrophoretic curve obtained from the protein contents of the starch-block sections. b, d, and f show the precipitin lines obtained by the method of agar-gel diffusion. (After Zinneman, Glenchur, and Hall. *New England J. Med.*, 265:872, 1961.)

tinguish it from blocking antibody Type II, which occurs in the serum of Rh negative mothers who are incubating Rh positive infants, and from blocking antibody Type III, which is found in patients with hay fever and asthma who are being treated by injections of pollens.

Blocking antibody Type I is a univalent antibody which binds the reacting sites of *Brucella* organisms so they cannot react with normal bivalent antibrucella antibodies and thus induce the prozone phenomenon. If such antibodies are present in excessive amounts, the organism may not agglutinate even in high dilutions of serum (71).

Blocking antibody Type II is an incomplete antibody found in the alpha and beta globulins (31) which will unite with Rh positive erythrocytes without producing agglutination but which binds all the reacting sites so that these erythrocytes cannot be agglutinated by a bivalent antibody which would otherwise agglutinate them.

Blocking antibody Type III occurs in the slow-moving gamma globulins. It is induced by the injection of pollens into either normal or allergic patients and has more affinity for pollen than the naturally acquired univalent antibody of the allergic patient (32, 136). It unites with the pollen in the blood or tissue fluids, thus preventing or blocking the union of pollen with the univalent antibody and thereby preventing the appearance of typical allergic symptoms.

Blocking antibodies of Types II and III will be discussed in more detail later in the chapter under the heading "Mechanism of Reaction Between Antigen and Incomplete or Univalent Antibodies."

The conglutination phenomenon is seen when normal bovine serum is used as a substitute for saline as the diluent for the antibody serum. In the presence of antibodies, complement and bovine serum bacteria or erythrocytes are found to agglutinate which would not agglutinate when saline was used as the diluent. This subject has been reviewed in detail by Marrack (144) and Coombs (39), Osler (185), and Sage (214). Wiener (254) reported that incomplete antibodies incapable of agglutinating Rh positive erythrocytes in routine tests could often cause agglutination if serial dilutions were made in normal plasma instead of saline. The active agent in the normal plasma was identified by Pedersen (196) as a high-molecular-weight dissociable complex of albumin and globulin which contains large amounts of lipid and possibly carbohydrate. This substance is apparently absorbed by antibody-coated erythrocytes, causing them to agglutinate without the necessity of a bivalent bridging antibody. Dilutions of plasma result in dissociation of the complex into albumin, gamma globulin, and lipid; hence this mechanism plays no part when the original antibody serum is diluted serially in saline. Hole and Coombs (100) report that the phenomenon seen with the Rh erythrocytes occurs in the absence of complement and is different, therefore, from the original conglutination.

Types of Agglutination H, O, and Vi. Weil and Felix (250) demonstrated in 1917 that the somatic "O," or body, antigens of the proteus bacillus were different from the "H," or flagellar, antigens and produced recognizable differences in the clumps of agglutinated organisms in the test tube.

The anti-H titer of a serum is obtained by using living organisms or organisms killed with heat or formalin. Very high titers are obtained, since relatively few antibodies are required to makes the flagella tangle themselves into large loose floccules (Fig. 13). High titers indicate infection or vaccination but are not a measure of immunity, since the flagellar antigens are not essential for the virulence of the organisms.

The anti-O titer of a serum is determined by using as the antigen organisms which have had their flagella destroyed by the addition of an equal volume of absolute alcohol. A thick suspension of the flagellated bacilli is incubated with alcohol at 37° C. for 24 to 36 hours. In the anti-O titratins many more antibodies are required to bind the bodies together into small, compact, but visible particles (Fig. 13). The titers are much lower, but there is correlation between the presence of anti-O antibody in the serum and immunity.

The Vi antigen is present only in freshly isolated strains of bacilli and is limited to *S. typhosa,* a few other *Salmonella,* and a few nonpathogenic enteric organisms. It lies superficial to the O antigen and covers the flagella in a thin molecular layer so that neither an anti-H nor anti-O antibody containing serum will agglutinate an organism having the Vi antigen. The injection into rabbits of organisms having the Vi antigen produces an antiserum which will agglutinate them in rather low but specific titers. The agglutinated clumps are small and compact. The name "Vi," an abbreviation for virulence, was given this antigen when it was believed that it was essential for virulence, but more work has revealed that the Vi anti-

Fig. 13. Macroscopic agglutination reaction. Left, coarse flocculation (H-type). Center, fine flocculation (O-type). Right, control, homogeneous suspension of bacteria in saline.

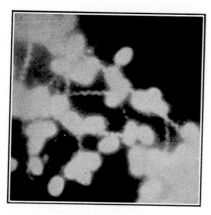

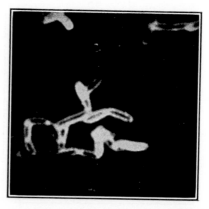

Fig. 14. H agglutination of *S. typhosa* as observed in darkfield. (From Pijper. *J. Path & Bact.*, 47:1, 1938.)

Fig. 15. Early stage of O agglutination of *S. typhosa* as observed in darkfield. (From Pijper. *J. Path. & Bact.*, 47:1, 1938.)

gen is not as important as well preserved O antigens. However, vaccines against typhoid fever are usually made from freshly isolated strains which have both the Vi and O antigens.

A dramatic visualization of the process of the Vi, O and H agglutination was obtained by Pijper (202), who used a method of darkfield cinematography in studies which employed living motile typhoid bacilli. He observed that the addition of the anti-H serum, obtained by immunization with whole flagellated organisms, first produced a reduction in motility; the flagella, which were observed easily in the dark field, became thick and rigid. As these now nonmotile organisms came in contact with each other by chance collision, they stuck together and the clumps of organisms grew. The thickened rigid flagella became entangled, and the clumps were large and loose (Fig. 14). In the macroscopic agglutination tests the large flaky clumps often are likened to snowflakes and are referred to as the "H type of agglutination" (Fig. 13, Left).

When anti-O serum (prepared by injection of an animal with alcohol-treated organisms) is added to a suspension of motile typhoid bacilli, the organisms, their motility unimpaired, literally drive themselves into each other. The collisions are much more dramatic than those observed in the H type of agglutination, the darkfield preparations showing bacilli moving at apparently tremendous speeds and diving into the rapidly

forming clumps from which they never emerge. The clumps formed by this type of agglutination are compact, since the cohesion is between the surfaces of the bacterial bodies (Figs. 15, 16). Macroscopically, O type agglutination resembles small hailstones (Fig. 13, Center) rather than snowflakes.

In Vi agglutination the flagella also are paralyzed, and the bacilli agglutinate by physical contact. A characteristic feature of this type of agglutination is that the body cells tend to stick together in parallel rows (Fig. 17).

Cross-agglutination, especially in low titers, can be expected in closely related organisms which share antigens in common, such as the *Salmonella* and *Shigella* or the

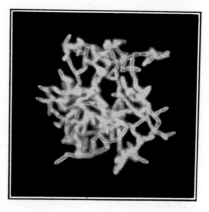

Fig. 16. Late stage of O agglutination of *S. typhosa* as observed in darkfield. (From Pijper. *J. Path. & Bact.*, 47:1, 1938.)

Fig. 17. Vi agglutination of *S. typhosa* as observed in darkfield. (From Pijper. *J. Path. & Bact.,* 47:1, 1938.)

Brucella group and *Past. tularensis;* but it often occurs in such unexpected places as between Type II pneumococci and Type B *Klebsiella pneumoniae* or between pneumococcus Type XIV and human blood group isoantigen. In practical laboratory work the cross-reacting agglutinins are diluted out as the serum is diluted and cause no real difficulty, but for quantitative work on the antigenic analysis of closely related organisms, such as the *Salmonella* and *Shigella* group, it is necessary to absorb out and eliminate the cross-reacting antibodies by the method of agglutinin absorption.

Agglutinin Absorption. Antigenic analyses usually are performed by agglutinin absorption technics which are based on the general principle that separate specific antibodies are formed in response to each different type of antigen in the bacillus. Thus a bacterium, *X,* might be composed of the hypothetical antigens *A, B, C,* and *D,* and an animal injected with such an organism would respond with the corresponding antibodies *a, b, c,* and *d.* Each of the antibodies is a separate globulin dissolved in the serum, and any one of these antibodies is capable of agglutinating the organism if the antigen corresponding to the antibody is on the surface of the bacterium and therefore is in a position to combine with the antibody.

The phenomenon of cross-agglutination can be illustrated by postulating another bacterium, *Y,* composed of antigens *A, E, F,* and *G,* so that an anti-*Y* serum would con-

tain the corresponding antibodies *a, e, f,* and *g.* Because of the common antigen *A* present in both *X* and *Y* organisms, not only would the anti-*X* serum agglutinate the suspension of the bacillus *X,* but, because of its content of *a,* some agglutination of bacillus *Y* would be expected; similarly, an anti-*Y* serum not only would agglutinate bacterium *Y* to full titer but also would agglutinate a suspension of bacillus *X.* The titer of serum against the heterologous organism would be much lower than against the homologous bacterium, since the single antibody responsible for the cross-agglutination would be diluted out very quickly.

Proof of the above explanation lies in the results obtained by agglutinin absorption experiments. By such a procedure, an antiserum can be absorbed to the point where it agglutinates only the homologous organism. The method consists of mixing heavy suspensions of the heterologous organisms with the serum to be absorbed, incubating for a sufficient time and then centrifuging the organism out of the mixture, which leaves the unabsorbed antibodies in the supernate. Thus if an anti-*X* serum containing *a, b, c,* and *d* were mixed with bacillus *Y,* composed of *A, E, F,* and *G,* the antibody *a* would be adsorbed on the surface of the bacillus *Y,* and after centrifuging, only antibodies *b, c,* and *d* would be capable of agglutinating only bacillus *X.*

Such an agglutination absorption technic is used extensively in the determination of *Salmonella* species, and the antigenic patterns have been worked out so thoroughly that the unknown organism can be identified by its reaction in various serums absorbed to detect only specific antigens.

It should be emphasized that the proper concentrations of the bacterial suspensions and the serum dilutions used in the absorbing of various serums must be determined empirically. Although it may be suspected that the various antigens in a bacterium are present in different ratios, there is no reason to believe that the separate antibodies in the corresponding serum occur in the same proportion, since some of the antigens may have a greater antibody-inciting power than others.

Although the phenomenon of cross-agglutination may be considered by some as a handicap to the clinical laboratory because of occasional confusion created by the agglutination of heterologous organisms, it is worth noting that some cross-agglutination reactions are of great benefit. For example, the Weil-Felix reaction or agglutination of *Proteus OX19* by serums of patients with the rickettsial diseases, typhus fever, and spotted fever is one of the most important tests performed by the routine diagnostic laboratory. Although more specific serologic reactions can be obtained by use of the complement-fixation test employing *Rickettsia* grown in chick embryos, the latter procedure is not as safe and useful as the direct agglutination of the nonspecific *Proteus* bacillus.

Inhibition of Agglutination by Surface Antigens. The Vi antigen is an example of this phenomenon, since it covers up both the H and O antigens and prevents agglutination in standard O and H serums. For many years bacteriologists were puzzled by the observation that *S. typhosa* freshly isolated from the blood stream failed to agglutinate, but after several transfers in meat extract broth, it agglutinated to full titer. We know now that the surface Vi antigen was lost by repeated subcultures in broth. Another example is found in *E. coli* isolated from localized infections in the internal organs of man. Some 80 per cent of these strains will not agglutinate in anti-O serum, but if the bacilli are boiled to destroy the labile surface antigen, they agglutinate in a normal manner (53, 157).

Cold Agglutinins. As early as 1903 Landsteiner (130) demonstrated the presence of low titers of agglutinins for human red blood cells in the plasma of normal individuals. These agglutinins were demonstrated only at 5° C. and lower temperatures. Following certain infections, particularly the supposed viral disease called primary atypical pneumonia, there was a great increase in the titers, and the agglutination occurred at temperatures up to 25° C. (197). The antigen used is a 1 per cent suspension of human type O, Rh negative red cells (29) which after mixing with serial dilutions of the patient's serum is incubated at 20° C. to 25° C. The majority of the patients giving positive agglutination tests with red cells also agglu-

tinate the MG streptococcus (158), although some react to one and not to the other. The antibody occurs in the gamma globulin fraction of the whole serum, is of high molecular weight, and has many physical and chemical characteristics of the blood group agglutinins (75).

Hemagglutinins. The cold agglutinins described above are often called **autohemagglutinins.** In addition to this type, the term **hemagglutinin** has been employed to describe two entirely different procedures; in one a virus or rickettsia, or their soluble products (35) cause red blood cells to agglutinate, and in the other the antigen, usually a polysaccharide, is absorbed on red cells, after which a very few specific antibodies will bring about the agglutination of the cells (230). For convenience the hemagglutinating systems will be designated Types I, II, and III.

Type I, the autohemagglutination found in primary atypical pneumonia, is characterized by the requirement of a low temperature for its reactivity.

In Type II, hemagglutination of human (or most animal) red blood cells is used to measure the quantity of virus present in a chick embryo or tissue culture. If a known quantity of virus is used, antibodies can be measured by their ability to prevent the agglutination.

The Type III hemagglutination is a mechanical trick for making more sensitive the ordinary type of agglutination (68). When polysaccharide or lipopolysaccharide from tubercle bacilli (70, 155, 219), *Past. pestis* (36), *Past. tularensis* (4), *P. aeruginosa* (65) is adsorbed to red blood cells, specific agglutination can be accomplished with serum which contained too few antibodies to agglutinate the original bacilli. The antigen may be adsorbed on colloid particles and used for agglutination (34). This colloid or hemagglutination procedure may be neutralized by incubating the antigen with the serum containing the antibody before the sensitized cells are added. For some years it was believed that this type of hemagglutination measured an incomplete or univalent antibody, but more recent work has shown quite conclusively that it is actually a method of measuring minute quantities of classical bivalent antibodies (81). Theoretically, it should be possible to diagnose a case of typhus fever by detecting specific antigens in the blood or urine days before specific antibodies appear in the blood (46). See Neter's review of hemagglutination and hemolysis (175).

Normal Agglutinins. As man and animals age, different types of antibodies can be demonstrated in their serums. Thirty years ago this was attributed to nonspecific aging because not enough specific infections could be identified to account for the number of antibodies. It is possible that there may be fortuitous binding or linking of the chains of amino acids in the globulin molecules to form functioning antibodies, but it is much more likely that subclinical infections and the ingestion of food containing antigens common to infectious organisms (58, 59) accounts for the accumulation of antibodies.

COMPLEMENT

Complement is the name given to a substance of mixed globulin composition which occurs as a constituent in the plasma of all normal animals. The investigations of Nuttal (182), Pfeiffer and Issaeff (200), and Bordet (18) showed that complement was destroyed by heating to 56° for 30 minutes or disappeared spontaneously within a time of hours if allowed to stand at room temperature. It also disappears, but more slowly, at icebox temperature.

The five components of complement are shown in Table 3, and their isolation by chemical methods may be found in the publications of Pillemer (203), Leon (131), Mayer (150), Kabat and Mayer (117), and Osler (185). More recently the method of ion exchange chromatography (221) has been employed by Becker (12) and Fahey (54) for the isolation and purification of the components of complement. Becker (10, 12,

13) suggests that C'_1 is a proteolytic enzyme similar to proteolytic enzymes with esterase activity (97, 132), such as chymotrypsin or trypsin, and concludes that the natural protein substrates for C'_1 are C'_4 and C'_2 (227).

Hegedus and Greiner (90) studied the components of the complement in the sera of man, guinea pigs, rabbits, dogs, horses, pigs, cows, rats, and sheep. The cow and horse lacked C'_2, while the sheep lacked both C'_2 and C'_4. These investigators assumed that the components of complement derived from the sera of different species would be mutually substitutive. This was later denied by some workers but has been confirmed by Bier and his associates (14) although the exchange is not always accomplished easily. Guinea pig serum is an excellent source of complement and contains about 0.25 to 0.40 milligrams of complement protein per milliliter or about 0.5 per cent of the total serum proteins. The reaction sequence of the various components of complement are shown in Table 4, as visualized by Mayer (150, 151) and Osler (185). The letter E represents erythrocytes, A antibody, and C' with the appropriate subnumbers the presently known C' components. Mayer has found that the C'_2 step results in the production of a hemolytically inactive product. Mueller-Eberhardt and his associates (160), using the immunofluorescent method, have found in the serum of patients with lupus erythematosus and amyloidosis a globulin designated β-1C, which seems to be a moiety of the third component of complement. The euglobulin of C'_1 has been resolved by Lepow (134) with the aid

Table 3. The Components of Complement
(From Raffel)

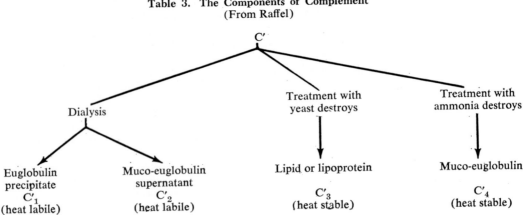

of chromatography into C'_{1q}, C'_{1r} and C'_{1s}, as shown in Table 4.

The kinetics of complement fixation and immune hemolysis has been under study by Becker (10), Mayer (150, 151), Kabat and Mayer (117), and Stroud (227). McKee and Jeter (139, 140), have found that antibodies can be produced against complement.

Complement does not combine with antigen alone; it is loosely bound by antibody alone and firmly bound by the antigen-antibody combination. In this sense the reaction can be considered analogous to the agglutination and precipitation phenomena in which the specific antigen-specific antibody complexes are affected nonspecifically by the action of electrolytes. Thus if a mixture of bacteria and complement is incubated and the bacteria are removed by centrifugation, the complement remains unchanged in the supernate. If the bacteria are mixed with specific antibody, however, the antibody cannot be found in the fluid after centrifugation. If both complement and sensitizing antibody are mixed with the bacteria, neither can be recovered after normal removal of the bacteria. Ovary and Karush (190) found that Fraction III of the antibody would not precipitate but would combine with cells, and Taranta and Franklin (232) noted that the peptin digested 5 S. antibody molecule would precipitate but could not fix complement (208). Furthermore, Pruzansky and Feinberg (205) have reported that heating rabbit antisera at 56° for 30 minutes or at 70° to 80° for 10 minutes results in the loss of ability to precipitate but leaves intact the facility to fix complement. With these obser-

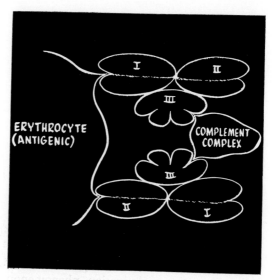

Fig. 18. Schematic drawing indicating a possible mechanism for specific hemolytic antibody to fix to the cell by their reactive groups I and II while complement is fixed between the Fraction III group. (Courtesy of David W. Talmage.)

vations in mind, Talmage suggests that the fixation of complement may be represented schematically as shown in Fig. 18.

It is the lack of specificity of complement which makes it such a valuable reagent in serologic investigations because it can enter into almost any antigen-antibody combination.

This principle is applied in the setting up of the complement-fixation test, which is based on the fact that unless complement is fixed by the particular antigen-antibody system, it remains free to enter into an entirely different antigen-antibody combination.

Table 4. Reaction Sequence in Immune Hemolysis *

1. $E + A \longrightarrow EA$

2. $EA + C'_{1q} + C'_{1r} + C_{1s} \xrightarrow{CA^{++}} EAC'_1$

3. $EAC'_1 + C'_4 \longrightarrow EAC'_{1,4}$

4. $EAC'_{1,4} + C'_2 \xrightarrow{MG^{++}} EAC'_{1,4,2}$

5. $EAC'_{1,4,2} + C'_{3a} + C'_{3b} + C'_{3c} \longrightarrow E°$

6. $E° \longrightarrow GHOST + HEMOGLOBIN$

* Originally outlined by Mayer and modified by Osler (1961) and Lepow (1963)

THE HEMOLYTIC SYSTEM

Bordet discovered the phenomenon of immune hemolysis in 1898 when he injected erythrocytes from the rabbit into guinea pigs and found that the serum of the latter had acquired the power of first agglutinating and later lysing the erythrocytes of the rabbit (18). If the serum was allowed to stand at room temperature for several days or was heated at 50° to 60° C. for 30 minutes, it would still agglutinate but would no longer lyse the rabbit red blood cells, The addition of fresh serum from a normal animal (complement) restored the hemolytic activity. Apparently fewer antibodies are required to lyse than are needed to agglutinate red cells, since the agglutination phenomenon disappears as the serum is diluted. Measurements of the velocity of hemolysis, rather than the percentage of cells hemolyzed, have shown that the antibody can be released after the cell is hemolyzed to attack a fresh cell, whereas the complement remains bound and unavailable (22). The cell walls, or stromata, are left as empty ghosts after the lytic process. In contrast to the antibody produced by injecting sheep erythrocytes into rabbits, the antibody made to sheep cells by patients with infectious mononucleosis shows a low titer by hemolysis and a high titer by agglutination. The same is true of the normally occurring human isoagglutinin.

The major hemolytic antibody function is performed by two species of molecules, a γ^2 globulin with a molecular weight of about 160,000 and the heavier γ^1 globulin weighing approximately 1,000,000. The heavier type of antibody (18 S.) is produced in greater amounts during the earlier stages of immunization with a variety of Forssman type of antigens. Stelos and Taliaferro (224) have shown that the Forssman type of antigens in sheep cells, guinea pig kidney, and human type A red blood cells are not identified serologically. Relatively pure Forssman antigen of sheep red blood cells was obtained by Rapp by washing the erythrocyte stroma thoroughly and then heating to 100° C. to destroy the isophile antigen (185). Rabbits given about 10 injections of red cells prepared in this manner and bled five to seven days after the last injection yielded a high titer of hemolysins. These antibodies were almost exclusively anti-Forssman. Repeated injections of red cells result in an increase in the γ^2 globulin, which Goodman and Masaitis (72) have found to be the antibody which can dissociate after hemolysis and hence pass from one red cell to another. Optimal sensitization with the anti-Forssman antibody requires about 1,000 molecules per erythrocyte, but the minimal number seems to be about two, provided they are on adjoining antigenic sites of a single erythrocyte (185). Only a small fraction, 0.01 to 1.6 per cent of the cell surface, need be involved in the reaction (92). The hemolytic activity and the complement-fixing activity of such a serum are not necessarily identical. Complement may be fixed by various combinations of C'_1, C'_4, and C'_2, but no lysis occurs until C'_3 is present (185).

The red blood cells of the sheep are usually injected into rabbits to produce hemolyzing antibodies, although almost any type of red cell can be used including those of man. The hemolysins are relatively stable and, if kept sterile, can be stored for years in the icebox with little change in titer. The red blood cells of the sheep are much more fragile but if collected directly in Alsever's solution (5) and stored in the icebox may be usable for one to two months. Fresh complement from a pool of guinea pigs must be standardized as soon as the serum is separated and used within a few hours. Lyophilized complement, which can be obtained from commercial sources, is stable before dilution.

The studies of Mayer and his associates (149) and Kent (120, 121) have shown that Mg^{++} and other divalent ions, such as Ca^{++}, Ni^{++}, and Co^{++}, are essential for the hemolytic action of complement and, if not present in optimal amounts, may become the limiting factor rather than the complement which is being titrated. The anticomplementary action of citrate, oxalate, or phosphate is explained by their ability to bind and remove the Mg^{++}.

Although the specific relationship and arrangements of the various reagents in the hemolytic system are not known, their functional relationships are presented in diagrammatic form in Fig. 19. The diagram shows that lysis occurs only when complement and antibody are present in the mixture. **Thus, the suspension of sensitized red cells can be considered as an indicator for the detection of the presence or absence of free complement and is used in this manner in regular complement-fixation tests.**

Titration of Complement. The unit of complement usually is defined as the smallest amount which causes complete lysis of a standardized suspension of sensitized red cells under specified conditions of time and temperature. Since lysis depends upon the mutual action of complement and hemolysin, both reagents must be standardized, but the accepted procedure is to hold constant the amount of the more stable hemolysin and to vary the amount of the guinea pig serum. The amount of complement must be predetermined by tests employing varying dilutions of complement in a known amount of hemolysin.

In the usual procedure a 2 per cent suspension of washed sheep cells is mixed thoroughly with a standardized amount of hemolysin and allowed to stand at room temperature from 10 to 30 minutes. To aliquot portions of these sensitized cells are added progressively increas-

ing dilutions of complement and the mixtures are incubated in a 37° C. water bath for 30 minutes. The greatest dilution of complement showing complete hemolysis is said to contain one unit.

Although the unit just described may be determined easily and without the necessity of special equipment, it leaves much to be desired, especially in the quantitative complement-fixation technic. The main defect lies in the difficulty of obtaining an accurate end point. Kolmer (124), for example, in his technic of complement-titration describes the unit as contained in the smallest amount of complement which produces "sparkling hemolysis" of the sensitized cells, but designates as the "full unit" the amount of complement contained in the next lowest dilution. He recommends the use of two full units in the routine serologic tests. The use of double the full unit rather than twice the ordinary unit certainly is a more conservative technic, because the slight increase of amount of complement employed in the first stage of the complement-fixation test makes less likely the obtaining of a false positive reaction but it also makes the test itself slightly less sensitive.

In recent years many laboratories have employed as a unit of complement that amount which lyses exactly 50 per cent of the sensitized

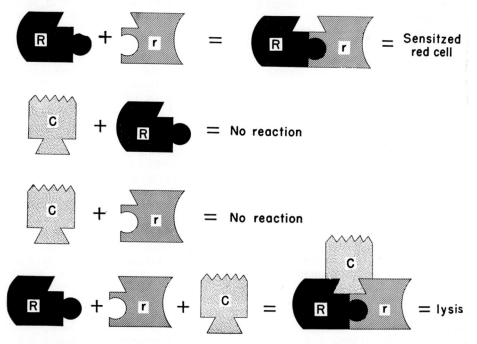

Fig. 19. Schematic representation of the hemolytic system. R, sheep red cells; r, antisheep cell antibodies or hemolysin; C, complement.

red cells (121). By means of a spectrophotometer the percentage of hemolysis produced by various quantities of complement has been determined. If the percentages of hemolysis are plotted as ordinates against the amount of complement added, as abscissas, a sigmoid curve is obtained which is flattened at both ends and rather steep in the middle. Around the point of 50 per cent hemolysis, slight changes in complement concentration cause marked changes in the percentage of red cells hemolyzed. At both ends of the curve the reverse is true. It is possible, therefore, to determine with great accuracy the amount of complement producing lysis of one half of the cells. In the actual complement-fixation test, at least three of these 50 per cent units are used.

THE COMPLEMENT-FIXATION TEST

The complement-fixation test, devised by Bordet and Gengou in 1901 (19) for the demonstration of specific antibodies, is based on the same principle as that described for the hemolytic system except bacteria or soluble antigens are used. Although technically more difficult than agglutination or precipitation, it permits greater variability in the physical state of the antigen. Viruses cloudy from contaminating tissue and fungi of irregular size in clumps may function satisfactorily as antigens.

The procedure involves two separate reactions: the first and very important step of the test is the inactivation of serum, which is necessary in order to destroy any complement which may be present in the serum. This is accomplished by heating the serum for 30 minutes at 56° C. The sensitizing antibody, however, is unchanged by this heating procedure.

After inactivation, both antigen and complement are added, the mixture is shaken and placed in the icebox or in a 37° C. water bath, depending upon the type of fixation employed. Numerous technics are employed in performing this test, and the quantities of each reagent and the time and temperature of fixation vary with the technic employed. In general, fixation in the icebox for three hours is a more sensitive test than that employing fixation for 30 minutes in the 37° C. water bath. The amount of complement usually used is two units, as determined by the end-point titration method, or three 50 per cent end-point titration units. The various reagents and their methods of attachment are represented schematically in Figure 20. **As described in the hemolytic system, complement enters into combination only with the**

antigen-antibody system and at the end of the first incubation period it is fixed only in the mixture which contained antigen and antibody (positive serum). Complement is free if antibody is absent (negative serum).

Since the fixation of complement cannot be visualized, the presence or absence of fixation is determined by testing for complement by the addition of sensitized red cells. After incubation for 30 minutes at 37° C., the tubes are examined for hemolysis. **The presence of hemolysis indicates a negative complement-fixation test, since the presence of free complement at the end of the first incubation period is evidence that antibody for the test antigen was absent from the original serum. Absence of hemolysis indicates a positive test,** since antibody must have been present to react with antigen and to bind the complement.

In this description of the complement-fixation test, the controls have been omitted purposely for simplicity and in order to emphasize that two immunologic reactions were concerned in the completed test. The description also ignores the dilution of the antiserum. In quantitative titrations, a number of serum dilutions are tested. In practice, however, numerous controls must be set up in order to be aware of the possible introduction of unavoidable technical errors. Glassware must be cleansed thoroughly and freed of minute traces of foreign substances, such as soap, which interfere with the reaction.

Controls. Since two labile substances—namely, red cells and complement—are concerned in the complement-fixation test, any extraneous factor present in any one of the other reagents will affect the results of the test.

Control of the Patient's Serum. Some serums are anticomplementary, possessing the property of inactivating complement. The cause of this anticomplementary activity is unknown, but it is found more commonly in serums which have been drawn several days before being tested. The percentage of anticomplementary serums in a usual day's run of Wassermann tests, for example, is low, but it occurs sufficiently often to necessitate the inclusion of a serum control for anticomplementary activity in every complement-fixation test. Equal quantities of inactivated serum are added to two tubes, and in the usual set-up in Wassermann racks the duplicate or control tube is placed in the front row, and the test, containing the same amount of serum, in the back row. In some types of complement-fixation tests it is specified that the control contain a quantity of serum double the amount used in the test itself. **The**

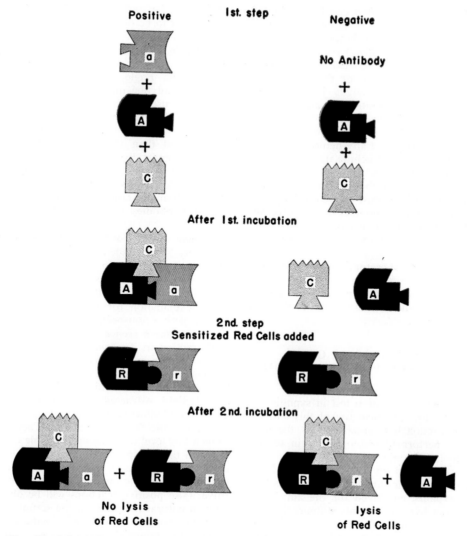

Fig. 20. Schematic representation of complement-fixation test. A, antigen; a, antibody; R, r, and C as in Figure 19.

control differs from the test only in that no antigen is added. If the serum is not anticomplementary, complete hemolysis should occur at the end of the second incubation period, regardless of whether or not antibodies were present in the original serum. If hemolysis does not occur in the control, it indicates that the serum is anticomplementary, since the absence of antigen in the mixture precluded the possibility of fixation of the complement by an immunologic mechanism. When such a reaction is obtained in the control, another sample of serum from the patient should be obtained and the test repeated, since the results of the reaction in the test mixture cannot be interpreted.

If the anticomplementary control was neglected in a Wassermann test for syphilis, the results would be tragic, because, in the absence of such a control, the anticomplementary activity would be interpreted as a positive test. The work of Heimer and his associates (93) has revealed at least three inhibitors of complement in human serum. These are (1) an unidentified factor with marked affinity for zymosan, (2) a pseudoglobulin, and (3) a euglobulin from serum of patients with rheumatoid arthritis.

The Antigen Control. The antigen is controlled for anticomplementary activity by a similar technic, and the mixtures contain no antibody. Although some antigens are anticomplementary, this effect often can be eliminated by dilution. The test dose of antigen should be no stronger than one-fourth the amount that causes any inhibition of hemolysis.

Some antigens cannot be used in the complement fixation test because of their hemolytic activity. The hemolytic activity is determined by mixing double quantities of antigen with sensitized cells and incubating at 37° C. Hemolysis under these conditions has no relation to complement activity, and any hemolysis caused by the antigen would preclude its use, since it would produce a falsely negative test even if the serum contained antibodies. The combining power of the antigen must be determined empirically by testing a number of positive serums. The other reagents usually are controlled by the preliminary titration of complement for use in a test.

In a serologic laboratory running Wassermann tests it is practical to control the whole procedure by saving known positive and known negative serums and including them in the next day's run of tests.

APPLICATIONS OF THE COMPLEMENT-FIXATION REACTION

The complement-fixation test in syphilis was not only the first practical use of this antigen-antibody reaction but remains today the most frequently performed serologic test in routine diagnostic laboratories.

Wassermann and his associates (242, 243), who developed the first complement-fixation test for **syphilis,** employed for the antigen an extract from livers of infants stillborn because of congenital syphilis. The livers are swarming with *Treponema pallidum,* and in the absence of a culture of the organism, the choice of such organs as a source of antigen was quite logical. Marie and Levaditi, however, showed that extracts or normal livers gave results equally as good as those obtained with syphilitic livers. The next step was made by Poges and Meier who found that the active agent in the antigen was an alcohol-soluble, acetone-insoluble, lecithin fraction of tissue lipoids and that beef hearts were a better source than either normal or syphilitic livers. Finally Pangborn (192) isolated a phospholipid from beef hearts named **cardiolipin,** which can be standardized by chemical methods. This purified antigen is used both in the Wassermann test and the various precipitin or flocculation tests for syphilis; however, the optimal amounts of cholesterol and lecithin for use with cardiolipin in the floc-

culation test for syphilis are different (27) from those found to be optimal for the complement-fixation test.

Precipitin or Flocculation Tests for Syphilis. These tests, known as the Kahn, Kline, Mazzini, Hinton, Eagle, and V.D.R.L. tests, are precipitin and flocculation tests which do not require the use of complement and hence can be used with serum which is anticomplementary. However, they are somewhat more difficult to read than the standard Wassermann test. The report by Rapp and his associates (207) that tissue powder derived from rat livers would remove the anticomplementary effect in human serums without affecting the specific antibodies deserves further investigation.

Biologic False Positive Tests for Syphilis. After one has excluded the false positive tests which are technical in nature, there remain certain biologic false positive tests which seem to be inherent in the system.

The explanation for a specific complement-fixation with a nonspecific antigen seems to depend upon the presence of a common phospholipid fraction in *Treponema pallidum* and the tissues of man and animals. As a result of inflammation in the tissues, an abundance of antibodies are produced which will react with the phospholipid extracted from normal tissues. Certain difficulties could be anticipated from such a specific "nonspecific" test. There seems to be a low level of antibodies capable of reacting with the phospholipid antigen in the blood of normal individuals, and if the complement-fixation or flocculation tests are made too sensitive, false positive reactions will be obtained. Certain natural inhibitors in the serum also inhibit the reactivities of these "natural" antibodies. In certain diseases, however, such as leprosy, malaria, infectious mononucleosis, and especially lupus erythematosus, the antibodies are increased, so that biologic false positive tests for syphilis are obtained. A full list of diseases giving biologic false positive tests for syphilis will be found in the chapter on syphilis.

Neurath, Volkin, Craig and associates (178) isolated a serum lipid probably identical with human serum lecithin which inhibits specifically serologic flocculation reactions of the biologic false positive type (240). However, this procedure is time-consuming and not inexpensive.

Complement Fixation with Protein Antigen from Treponema pallidum. Antibodies specific for *T. pallidum* have been found in the blood of patients with syphilis and demonstrated by precipitin tests (215), agglutination tests (83, 141, 142), immune adherence tests (171), and treponema immobilization tests (170). The treponemas are grown in the testicles of the rabbit and freed of gross tissue contamination by differential centrifugation. Living organisms are employed in all except the precipitin test, but all these procedures are much too difficult and expensive to be employed in routine laboratory work. The *Treponema pallidum* immobilization test (TPI) does not become positive as early in the disease as the standard Wassermann test, but it persists longer. Most important of all is the fact that it is negative with serums which give biologic false positive Wassermann tests.

Portnoy and Magnuson (204) have removed the lipid fractions from the treponema and obtained a protein antigen with which a specific Wassermann test can be obtained with the standard Wassermann technic. This test becomes positive as early as the Wassermann, gives fewer positives than the TPI later in the disease but, like the TPI, is negative with serums which cause biologic false positive Wassermann tests with lipoid antigens.

The isolation and purification of the protein antigen from the Reiter treponema is now employed in the complement-fixation test (RPCF) (42). The fluorescent treponemal antibody test has been used with both *T. pallidum* (43) and the Reiter treponema (122).

Use of Complement-Fixation Tests for Other Disease. In many instances this is the only test which will reveal the presence of specific antibodies. There may be difficulty in making the test depending upon the amount and physical state of the antigen, such as (1) the small amount of viral antigen available, (2) a cloudy antigen, or (3) a particulate spontaneously agglutinating antigen as seen with most fungi. The difficulty may depend upon the second stage of precipitation where visible floccules do not appear because (1) the quality of the antibody is too poor to bring about aggregation, (2) the amount of antibody is too small to produce visible floccules, or (3) the proportions of antigen-antibody are unfavorable for flocculation (74, 206). **The success of the complement-fixation reaction apparently depends upon the fact that complement enters into the antigen-antibody combination early in the stage of combination.**

Certain difficulties may also be encountered in the complement-fixation reaction because of the varied behavior of complement and hemolysin derived from different species of animals.

Indirect Complement-Fixation Test. Under certain conditions the antibodies present in the serum may combine with the antigen without fixing complement. Thus hemolysis occurs which is interpreted as an absence of antibody. Antibodies of this type have been found in chicken, turkey, and duck serums; in ornithosis or psittacosis; and in some instances of natural infection of cattle with foot and mouth disease (209). Rice (210) devised the indirect complement-fixation test for this type of antibody (216). The test is set up in duplicate with Set 1 being an ordinary direct test. Set 2 has the same initial mixture of test serum, antigen, and complement. After incubation, saline is added to the direct test and a standard antiserum of known ability to combine with the antigen and fix complement is added to the indirect test, after which both sets are incubated a second time. Finally, sensitized red cells are added to both sets, incubated, and read for hemolysis. The presence of hemolysis in the direct test may be caused by (a) the absence of antibodies in the test serum or (b) the presence of an antibody which failed to fix the complement. If there are no antibodies in the serum, the standard antiserum in the indirect test combines with the antigen and fixes complement, so that the red cells in the hemolytic system remain unhemolyzed. If, however, there are antibodies in the serum which combine with the antigen but fail to fix complement, then the standard antiserum cannot fix the complement and the red cells in the hemolytic system utilize the free complement and hemolyze.

A discovery of considerable practical importance was made by Brumfield and Pomeroy (28) in 1957 when they added unheated fresh chicken and turkey sera and found that direct complement fixation could be obtained with sera from birds with ornithosis, Newcastle disease, and infectious bronchitis (47, 209). Presumably chicken and turkey antibody cannot fix guinea pig complement because of species incompatibility, unless a heat labile factor from an avian species is present. Kabat and Mayer (117) suggest that a similar mechanism may apply to certain sera from cattle, since Marucci (147) succeeded in detecting foot and mouth disease antibody in heat inactivated cattle sera by direct complement fixation when fresh unheated vesicular fluid was used as the antigen. This suggestion has been confirmed by Boulanger and Bannister (20), who found that the addition of fresh unheated serum from calves of about six months of age made possible the direct complement fixation for foot and mouth disease of cattle.

Conglutinating Complement Absorption Test. Under conditions where the guinea pig com-

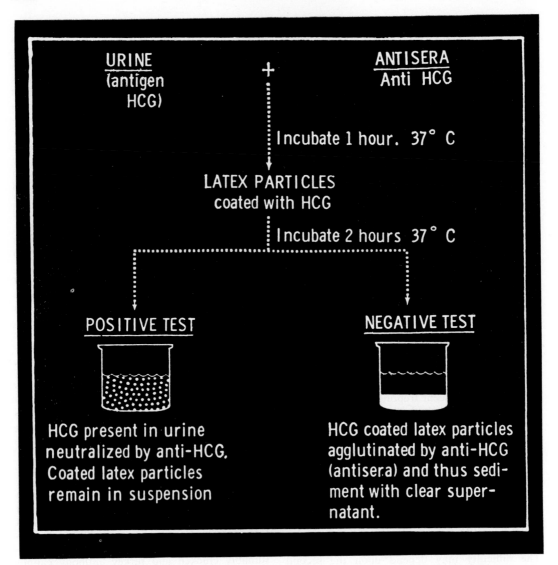

Fig. 21. Immunologic test for pregnancy. If human chorionic gonadotropic hormone is present in the urine it will combine and neutralize the added anti HCG, so that the latex particles coated with HCG will not precipitate after further incubation. If the HCG is not present, the added anti HCG precipitates the latex particles. (After Henry and Little. *J.A.M.A.,* 182:110, 1962.)

plement is not fixed by the antigen-antibody reaction, Coombs and Hole (37, 39) have employed the nonhemolytic complement of the horse. The known (or suspected) antigen is added to the suspected (or known) antibody plus the horse complement and incubated (16). The indicator system is sheep erythrocytes and inactivated bovine serum which contains normal antisheep cell antibodies and conglutinin. If complement has been absorbed by the antigen-antibody reaction in the first step, none will be available to potentiate the agglutination of the sheep cells in the final step; this is a positive test. But if the antigen or antibody is absent from the first step, complement is free to cause the agglutination of the sheep cells in the final step, and this is a negative test.

Complement Fixation with Tissue Cells. Cytoplasmic effects analogous to hemolysis have been demonstrated in tissue culture cells as a result of antigen-antibody complement reactions (129). In their experiments Easton and his associates (48) found that the cytotoxic antibody was fixed permanently to the surface antigen of the cell membrane but did no observable damage until complement was added, after which a permanent defect appeared in the cell membrane. A simple method for obtaining quantitative measurements of the cytotoxic antibody has been described by Hirata (98). The cells to be tested are counted in an electric counter, after which they are exposed to cytotoxic antibodies and complement. After a suitable period of incubation, the damaged cells are destroyed by tryptic digestion, after which the preparation is counted again with the electric counter.

Immunologic Test for Pregnancy. Several serologic tests for the determination of human chorionic gonadotropic hormone in pregnancy have been developed in recent years (138). These are a precipitin test (38), a hemagglutination inhibition test (252), inhibition of latex agglutination (95), and a complement-fixation test (26). The inhibition of latex agglutination seems to be the most practical (95) and is shown in Figure 21.

BACTERIOLYSINS AND BACTERIOCIDINS

The observations of Pfeiffer in 1894 (200) that the serum of guinea pigs which had recovered from experimental cholera contained some substance which would lyse and kill the cholera vibrio was the first step in the evaluation of our knowledge of antibodies and their activities. This led directly to the discovery of complement and indirectly to the hemolytic system and complement fixation. Bacteriolysins resemble agglutinins in exhibiting a prozone effect in the presence of excess antibodies. This was known in the older literature as the **Neisser-Wechsberg phenomenon** (168). At present the Neisser-Wechsberg phenomenon is more often considered as the inhibiting effect of excess hemolysin (sheep cell antibody) on complement acting to inhibit hemolysis of sheep cells, or, more generally, the inhibiting effect of excess antibody of any type on any hemolytic reaction.

Cholera vibrios and certain other gram-negative bacteria are lysed easily by specific antibody and complement, while others seem to be killed but not lysed. Gram-positive organisms are resistant to both bacteriocidins and bacteriolysins.

Quantitative studies on bacteriolysins have been handicapped by the absence of a suitable laboratory test. The reduction in number of organisms found in plate counts following exposure to antibody and complement might have resulted from either agglutination or lysis or a combination of both. The introduction of quantitative measurement by the turbidimetric growth assay made it possible for Muschel and Treffers (162) to show that the quantitative relations among bacteria, antibody, and complement parallel exactly those found for the lysis of erythrocytes by antibody and complement, including the enhancing activity of the Mg ion. They found that 700 to 860 molecules of antibody and 1.5×10^7 molecules of complement are necesary to kill one *S. typhosa* organism at the 50 per cent end point. The antibody covered only 0.03 to 0.7 per cent of the bacterial surface.

Complement and specific antibodies will kill *S. typhosa* regardless of whether the antibody is directed against the Vi or O antigen. The fatal effect is produced on the surface of the cell, since Adler (2) has found that *S. typhosa* on whose surface flagella antigen from *E. coli* had been adsorbed were killed after exposure to complement and specific anticolon flagella antigen. The lysis phenomenon appears to depend upon the presence of lysozyme in the serum. Amano (6) and Inoue (107) and their associates have found that the small amount of lysozyme present in the serum will not lyse organisms directly but will do so after complement and specific antibody have reacted with a surface antigen. Muschel and his associates (163) have found that lysozyme is indispensable for spheroplast formation. These investigators reported that mice immunized with as little as 0.2 μg. of a purified Vi antigen preparation react to a challenge of living virulent *S. typhosa* with a rapid conversion of the organism to protoplasts.

PHAGOCYTOSIS

Metchnikoff and his students at the Pasteur Institute (153, 154) discovered and emphasized the importance of phagocytosis in immunity. He designed the large phagocytic cells of the blood and tissues as macrophages and the small cells as microphages, with sometimes one and sometimes the other playing the major role in the ingestion and destruction of the invading organism. The large phagocytic cells of Metchnikoff are known now as **monocytes** and **clasmatocytes,** and the small ones as polymorphonuclear **leukocytes.** At the same time Ehrlich, Pfeiffer, and other German workers were studying the bactericidal effect of antibodies in the serum and regarded the phagocytic cells as scavengers which cleaned up the dead bacteria after they had been killed by the antigen-antibody reaction. As in most controversies of this type, both groups were right in what they affirmed and wrong in what they denied. Metchnikoff was right in that phagocytic cells can and do ingest a great variety of organic and inorganic material of microscopic size, including many types of nonpathogenic bacteria, without the assistance of a specific antibody (60, 159). On the other hand, many highly virulent organisms cannot be phagocytized until their surface has been altered by a specific antibody. In the body, however, a certain number of virulent encapsulated organisms are phagocytized in the absence of demonstrable antibodies, by the mechanism described by Wood (258) as **surface phagocytosis.** The phagocytic cell must trap the organism against a solid surface, such as the alveolar wall of an air sac in the lung or between two leukocytes before it can be ingested (61, 62, 244). The history of phagocytosis before 1900 was reviewed by Hirsch in 1959 (99) and the current literature by Suter (229) Robineaux and Pinet (212), and Hirsch (99a).

Opsonins and Bacteriotropins. The term **opsonin** was applied by Wright and Douglas (259) to designate a substance present in fresh normal serum which acted on bacteria in such a way that they were rendered susceptible to phagocytosis (222). The activity of this substance, later identified as complement, was destroyed by heating to 60° C. for 15 minutes. One of Wright's experiments, shown in Table 5 demonstrates that the opsonin acts on the bacteria and not on the leukocytes. Neufeld and Rimpau (176, 177) noted that serum from immune animals also possessed the ability to act on

Table 5. Phagocytosis Influenced by Heat-labile Factor in Serum

(A. E. Wright and others, 1903)

MIXTURES	AVERAGE NO. BACTERIA PER LEUKOCYTE
Washed leukocytes + staphylococci	1.2
Leukocytes + serum + staphylococci	20.0
Leukocytes + serum, then washed and staphylococci added	2.4
Staphylococci + serum, then washed and leukocytes added	18.4
Leukocytes + heated serum + staphylococci	4.2

bacteria and render them susceptible to phagocytosis, but such serums could be heated to 70° C. without destroying this effect. The name **bacteriotropin** was applied to this heat-stable antibody responsible for stimulating phagocytosis. The authors undoubtedly destroyed the complement in their antibody-containing serum but probably left some complement adherent to the washed leukocytes which they used in their experiments. On the other hand, Wright used supposedly normal human serums and a staphylococcus, but almost everyone has some specific antibodies to this organism as a result of previous contact. It has been shown by Ward and Enders (241) and others that there is a reciprocal relationship between the amount of complement and the amount of antibody in the phagocytic system. With this in mind, it seems probable that Wright was dealing with minimal amounts of antibody and maximal amounts of complement. This conclusion is supported by the observations of Jeter and his associates (114), who found that specific antibodies to human complement prevented phagocytosis of *D. pneumoniae* in the presence of specific antibody. We agree with Ward and Enders that the term "bacteriotropin" should be discarded in favor of the term "opsonin," which has priority. Ward and Enders have shown that the antibody responsible for phagocytosis is identical with that responsible for precipitation and death of bacteria. Furthermore, an excess of antigen may combine with and neutralize the opsonic effect of the specific antibody, as shown in Table 6. In this experiment the antibody was specific for Type II pneumo-

Table 6. Effect of Excess Antigen in Blocking Phagocytosis

(Ward and Enders)

DILUTION OF ANTISERUM	CONCENTRATION OF SPECIFIC CARBOHYDRATES	No. TYPE II PNEUMOCOCCI PHAGOCYTOSED BY 50 CELLS
1:32	0	414
1:32	Type I, 1:800	369
1:32	Type II, 1:800	5
1:32	Type III, 1:800	413
No serum	0	12

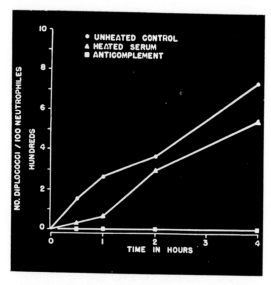

Fig. 22. Comparison of phagocytic activity of human neutrophils for *D. pneumoniae*. The top line shows the rate of phagocytosis with unheated antibody-containing serum. The second line shows the decrease in the first hour with the heated serum. The third line shows complete absence of phagocytosis when anticomplement serum was added. (After Jeter, McKee, and Mason. *J. Immunol.*, 86:386, 1961.)

cocci and was specifically neutralized by an excess of polysaccharides from Type II but not from Type I or Type III.

McKee and Jeter (139) found in 1956 that antibodies to complement prevented phagocytosis of *D. pneumoniae* in the presence of specific antibody. These studies were extended by Jeter and his associates in 1961 (114). Some of the results are shown in Figure 22. Serum heated to destroy complement showed a depression of phagocytosis for the first hour, as compared with the unheated control, after which phagocytosis increased and approached but did not overtake the control. In contrast, the tubes which had the anticomplement added showed no phagocytosis. The possibility raised by Osler (185) that the antibody produced in the rabbit was directed not against C_1 but against some unknown serum contaminant has not been answered, but the experiments do show that the antibodies reacted with something in the crude complex now known as complement to prevent phagocytosis. In a more recent study antibody prepared against mouse complement was used to investigate its effect on resistance and immunity in the intact animal. **It was found that active and passive immunity to infections in mice with *D. pneumoniae* was reduced by the injection of the anticomplement antibody,** but, as would be expected, there was no reduction in the neutralization of tetanus toxoid by specific antitoxin (140).

The effect of fragments of antibodies on phagocytosis has been studied by Shands and Suter (216a). The phagocytosis of latex particles by chicken fibroblasts in tissue culture as described by Overman (191) seems to be a mechanical process not dependent upon specific antibody and complement.

The species of microorganisms phagocytized by Hela cells in tissue cultures is controlled by the species of serum in the tissue culture medium. This eliminates specific antibody and probably complement. Shepard (217) found that serum from some horses, heat-modified chicken serum, and, especially, bovine fetal serum facilitated the phagocytosis of the various species of *Mycobacteria*.

IMMUNE-ADHERENCE PHENOMENON

This phenomenon has been studied in some detail by Nelson and Nelson (169). The investigators restricted the term to the temperature-dependent attachment of complexes containing antigen, antibody, and complement to a receptor located on the surface of primate erythrocytes and on the surface of certain nonprimate species of platelets. Direct microscopic observations revealed the attachment of the particulate antigen, or the reaction may be visualized by hemagglutination indirectly by soluble antigen in the presence of antibody and complement. The system operates with extremely small amounts of antigen and complement. Nelson (172) has reported that immune adherence of staphylococci occurs in vivo in monkeys, and Kabat and Mayer (117) suggest that this may be another possible mechanism whereby complement functions in host defense against pathogenic agent, particularly with those organisms which are not susceptible to the bacteriolytic and bactericidal action of complement.

DETECTION OF SMALL AMOUNTS OF ANTIGEN BY ANTIGEN-ANTIBODY REACTIONS

The antigen-antibody reaction system is extraordinarily sensitive as compared to chemical reactions but, as noted in the intro-

duction to this chapter, the same classical bivalent antibodies seem to vary widely in potency, depending upon the system used for their detection. In the experiment conducted by Sterzl (225) with stimulated splenic cells transferred to newborn rabbits, the primary induced phase of antibody formation was detected first by passive hemagglutination, followed by agglutination, complement fixation, and finally precipitation (Fig. 23). The amount of antibody nitrogen per milliliter of serum needed to obtain threshold reactions was 0.005 for the hemagglutination, 0.05 for agglutination, 0.1 for complement fixation, and 5.0 for precipitation.

The variations in the antibody producing ability of different antigens is equally variable, for reasons which are not understood. In general bacterial antigens and polysaccharide antigens are more effective stimulators of antibody than soluble protein antigens. In Table 7 we have rearranged the data

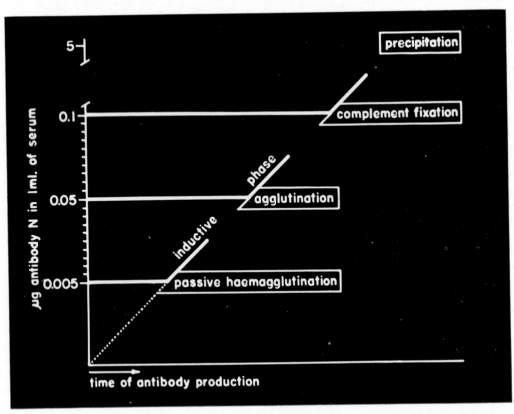

Fig. 23. As new antibodies are formed they are detected first by the passive hemagglutination method and last by the more insensitive precipitin test. (After Sterzl. *Mechanisms of Antibody Formation,* Academic Press.)

Table 7.

MATERIAL	RECIPIENT	RESPONSE	AMOUNT DETECTABLE	AUTHOR
Soluble antigen of Shigella	rabbit lymph node cells	agglutinin production	0.0001 μg.	Harris & Harris (84)
Pneumopolysaccharides—Type II	mice	protection	0.0005 μg.	Felton et al. (58)
Pneumopolysaccharides—Type I	mice	protection	0.005 μg.	Felton et al. (59)
Ovalbumin	guinea pig	cutaneous anaphylaxis	0.015 μg.	Ovary (189)
Alum precipitated diphtheria toxoid	lymph nodes of mice & rabbits	antitoxin hemagglutination	0.02 μg.	Stavitsky (226)
Hemocyanin conjugated with S-35 sulphanilic acid	rabbit liver	Specific radioactivity 5 μC/mg	ca. 0.04 μg.	Garvey & Campbell (66)
Bovine albumin coupled with S-35 sulphanilic acid	rat spleen	Specific radioactivity 5 μC/mg	ca. 0.04 μg.	Hawkins & Haurowitz (88)
Pneumopolysaccharides—Type III	mice	protection	0.05 μg.	Felton et al. (59)
Bovine albumin coupled with S-35 sulphanilic acid	guinea pigs	anaphylactic sensitization	0.1 mg.	Garvey & Campbell (67)
Bovine y-globulin in mouse liver	mice	vascular reaction of ear	0.1 μg.	McMaster & Kruse (143)
P-32 Tobacco Mosaic virus	mouse liver	Specific radioactivity 0.6 μC/mg	ca. 0.1 μg.	Erickson et al. (52)
C-14 Ovalbumin	rabbit liver	Specific radioactivity 0.03 μC/mg	ca. 0.2 μg.	Humphrey (106)

presented by Humphrey (106) to illustrate the variations in the delicacy of the various methods as determined by nature of the antigen, the animal species, and method of measuring the results. Not shown in the Table is Coons' method of fluorescent antibody detection which requires about 10 μg. of pneumococcal polysaccharide for detection. The most delicate methods for the detection of antibodies are that of Nossall (181), which measures by the agglutination of the flagella of salmonella the antibodies produced by a single plasma cell, and that of Jerne and Nordin (113), which measures the hemolysin produced by a single cell.

THE PROPERDIN SYSTEM AND IMMUNITY

Properdin was isolated from normal serum by Pillemer and his associates (203) in 1954, and its nature and significance have been matters of controversy since that time. It was associated with 19 S. gamma globulin and was isolated from normal serum by absorption with zymosan. Properdin itself has no bactericidal or virocidal properties, but when combined with complement, or a complement-like factor, and Mg^{++}, it was found to kill many gram-negative bacteria, to neutralize several viruses, and to lyse certain abnormal erythrocytes (133, 9). The investigators believed that the properdin system was a new mechanism which helped in the natural nonspecific defenses of man and animan against infection.

Human properdin was concentrated 2500-fold over the level found in normal serum by absorption to an elution from zymosan (235). Even the concentrated product was antigenically heterogeneous and was contaminated with a variety of normal human serum constituents, including phosphatase, lysozyme, and zymosan agglutinin, but the authors believed these could be distinguished from properdin itself. Primary stimulation of rabbits with the partially purified properdin induced antibodies to several normal constituents of human serum. Antibodies to properdin did not appear after primary stimulation but did appear after restimulation. Antibody to properdin reacted with properdin as a single-line agar diffusion and could be differentiated from the antibodies to 7 S. or 19 S. gamma globulins. The properdin antibody prevented the inactivation of C'_3 by zymosan, the hemolysis of PNH erythrocytes, the lysis of certain bacteria, and the inhibition of some viruses (96, 97). The authors concluded that this is a single substance with multiple biologic properties.

Although lysozyme was present in the partially purified properdin described above, Hook, Carey, and Muschel (101) could not substitute lysozyme for properdin in the in vitro lysis of PNH erythrocytes, for toxoplasmacidal activities, or for the inactivation of C'_3. Furthermore, a lysozyme-depleted serum containing complement on properdin possessed full activity. In Leon's study of the reactions between dextrans and the properdin-complement system, some evidence was produced to suggest that properdin might function as an antibody (131). The report that germ-free rats have lower titers of properdin than conventional animals (79) may be interpreted as evidence for properdin being an antibody or for its action being dependent upon the presence of some "natural" antibodies.

Nelson (173) **has suggested that properdin might be an antibody to zymosan and that the activity of the properdin system could be attributed to the combined activities of multiple "normally acquired" antibodies.** Lepow and his associates have shown that partially purified properdin does contain antibodies to zymosan, but this agglutinin was unrelated to properdin activity. Oswa and Muschel (186) have found that the major bactericidal action of normal serum was dependent upon the presence of specific antibodies and in the absence of antibodies the normal serum was lacking in bacteriocidal action even when the properdin system was present. More recently Lepow (133) has proposed a modification of the original theory in which specific antibodies are the essential element and properdin is not an antibody but the properdin system potentiates and supplements the specific antigen-antibody reaction.

Aggressions and Virulins. These terms were used in the older literature to designate substances possessed by bacteria which overcome body defense and prevent their phagocytosis by leukocytes. They have been discarded in favor of a more specific explanation for the observed phenomenon, such as (1) damage to the leukocyte by leukocidin produced by the organism and (2) neutralization of antibody by an excess of antigen (Table 6), or damage to the leukocyte by an allergic reaction between a constituent of the organism and the sensitized cell.

FIXED TISSUE ANTIBODIES

These antibodies, or presumed antibodies, are fixed to the cells of individuals or animals that show the tubercular-like type of allergy. They are never free in the serum, but can be transferred by transferring living cells from the allergic animal to the normal animal of the same species. The little that is known of this mechanism will be presented in Chapter 17.

THE MECHANISM OF REACTION BETWEEN ANTIGEN AND INCOMPLETE OR UNIVALENT ANTIBODIES

The initial reaction between antigen and antibodies is specific and almost instantaneous, but the visible reactions, such as precipitation, agglutination, complement fixation, and lysis, are more delayed reactions and depend upon both specific and environmental factors. Antibodies which bind with antigen without producing an observable reaction are called **nonprecipitating, incomplete,** or **univalent.**

Incomplete antibodies were recognized first in the serum of patients with asthma, hay fever, eczema, and similar allergic diseases and were designated **reagins** to differentiate them from classical antibodies to the extent that (1) they are free in the serum and (2) they can be passively transferred from man to man by the injection of the serum (135). But they differ from classical antibodies because (1) they do not precipitate with their specific antigens in the test tube, (2) they do not pass the placental barrier, (3) they are relatively heat-labile, being destroyed by a temperature of 60° C. in 30 to 60 minutes, and (4) they remain fixed for a period of weeks in local areas of skin after passive transfer. In contrast to the bivalent precipitating antibodies which are confined to the slow moving gamma globulins these incomplete antibodies are found primarily, if not exclusively, in the fast gamma globulin and slow beta globulin (30, 32, 78, 56, 105, 82). The incomplete, nonprecipitating antibody found in this type of allergy belongs to the 7 S. type (223, 94). This type of incomplete antibody is induced by the inhalation or ingestion of pollens or other allergins and has less affinity for its specific antigen than does the antibody induced by the subcutaneous injection of the same allergins. This behavior is the reverse of that observed with the incomplete antibody found in chronic brucellosis where the incomplete antibody has more affinity for the antigen than does the bivalent classical antibody (260, 261).

The term **reagin** used for these incomplete antibodies should be discarded because the same term has been used to describe the bivalent antibody found in the blood of patients with syphilis which gives the Wassermann reaction with the nonspecific lipoidal antigens.

A second type of incomplete antibody appears in the blood of Rh negative women who are carrying a child who has inherited from the father an Rh positive type of red blood cell. These incomplete antibodies can pass the placenta and induce hemolysis of the infant's red blood cells (254). Coombs and his associates (38) have suggested that the failure of the Rh antibodies to agglutinate the Rh-positive cells may be due solely to the location of the antigen on the cells. The univalent antibodies of the Rh type attach themselves to the Rh positive cells but cannot cause agglutination. The antibody is human globulin, and if an antihuman globulin antibody produced in a rabbit is added to the test tube, these bivalent antibodies will link the globulin coated red cells into agglutinating masses, as illustrated in Figure 4 of Chapter 14.

Marrack (144) has suggested that there may be some incomplete anti-Rh antibodies that cannot be detected by the antiglobulin method. These incomplete antibodies may be either β-2 M globulins, and the antiglobulin sera used may not contain anti-β-2 M antibodies; or they may be "incomplete" gamma globulins, lacking the determinants with which the antibodies in the antiglobulin sera react.

An incomplete or nonprecipitating antibody may result from a defective job of manufacturing. This is illustrated by the experiments of Kuhns (127), who injected purified diphtheria toxoid into normal medical students and into students with allergic diseases or a family history of allergic disease. The normal students manufactured bivalent flocculating antitoxin, but the students from allergic families made some bivalent antitoxin but varying amounts of nonflocculating antitoxin. This antibody would neutralize toxin, but in other respects it was identical with the incomplete antibodies found in typical hay-fever-type individuals.

Another type of incomplete, nonagglutinating antibody was found in the sera of patients with chronic brucellosis (261). This was a molecule of small molecular weight (4.5 to 5.6 S.) which migrated characteristically with the beta globulins. This molecule had a greater affinity for the binding sites on the brucella organisms than the classical bivalent gamma globulin antibody and hence bound all available sites, causing either a proagglutinated zone or preventing completely agglutination of the organism.

In experimental animals the type of antigen, the route of injection, and the animal species may determine whether the antibodies would be exclusively complete or incomplete. The injection of small doses of human, sheep or rabbit erythrocytes into Webster mice results in a high titer of incomplete, nonprecipitating antibodies (64). Nonprecipitating antibodies of the blocking type have been produced in rabbits by multiple injection of bovine albumin in Freund's adjuvant, while the same antigen adsorbed onto alum produced only classical bivalent antibodies after intramuscular or intravenous injection (57). Under certain conditions of immunization the horse produces nonprecipitating antibodies exclusively (115).

Incomplete antibodies may appear early or late in the process of immunization or late in the same process, but the two types do not necessarily have the same biologic characteristics. Richter and Haurowitz (211) found that nonprecipitating antibodies were present in the circulation of rabbits injected with soluble antigen for many months after the classical precipitating antibodies had disappeared. These observations were confirmed by Blumer and his associates (17), who found that the late-appearing nonprecipitating antibodies would not sensitize guinea pigs for anaphylactic shock, although the nonprecipitating antibodies reported by Kabat and Benacerraf (116) early in the immunization period would sensitize to anaphylaxis.

Physical, chemical, and enzymatic alteration

of the antibody molecule may alter its biologic activity. Corresponding degradation may or may not occur in the intact animal. Mild pepsin digestion, which reduces the 7 S. molecule to 5 S., results in an antibody which will precipitate but will not fix complement (232). Nonprecipitating fragments of antibody obtained from papain hydrolysates will not agglutinate or sensitize red blood cells but can prevent their subsequent agglutination by untreated antibodies (80).

Mild acetylation results in a complete loss of ability to precipitate but causes only a slight loss of ability to bind specific hapten (179). Heating rabbit antisera at 56° C. for 30 minutes (205) or at 70° to 80° C. for 10 minutes results in the loss of ability to precipitate but leaves intact the ability to coprecipitate with unheated sera, fix complement, and give passive cutaneous anaphylaxis, as well as passive systemic anaphylaxis (148).

Bivalent, complete antibodies may not precipitate in the regions of antibody and antigen excess, as shown in Figure 7. These pseudo-incomplete antibodies were studied by Zinsser in 1930 (263). When serial additions of egg albumin are added to serum containing antiegg albumin antibody until no more precipitate ensues, the total amount of precipitated antibody is only 78 per cent of that obtained by the addition of the optimal amount of antigen in one portion. The remaining 22 per cent of "nonprecipitable" antibody will now coprecipitate if an antigen-antibody precipitate is induced in the supernate by the addition of fresh whole antiserum and antigen. The addition of complement plus antigen, without new antibody, will precipitate the nonprecipitable antibody (24).

FATE OF ANTIGEN IN VIVO

Particulate antigen, such as bacteria and red blood cells, are readily removed from the circulation by the cells of the reticuloendothelial system, although the process can be accelerated by the presence of specific antibodies (239, 224). Certain insoluble proteins, such as hemocyanin, ferritin, egg albumin, and denatured and chemically altered serum proteins, are eliminated from the circulation, probably by phagocytosis, before antibody synthesis begins.

Soluble serum protein antigens circulate in the blood for a relatively long period of time, and their elimination can be measured by the isotopic technic introduced by Talmage and his associates in 1951 (231). The stages in the process of elimination have been defined by Weigle (249) as (1) equilibration phase, (2) exponential phase and (3) immune phase. These phases are illustrated in the central solid line in Figure 24. The equilibration phase shows a rapid drop in the circulating antigen, which is explained by the equilibration of those proteins between the intra- and extra-vascular fluid spaces. In the exponential phase the protein is eliminated at a logarithmic rate which is determined by the normal rate of catabolism of the particular host's own serum. This phase usually lasts longer in man than in rabbits, guinea pigs and mice. In patients with agammaglobulinemia and in newborn babies (see Fig. 19 in Chap. 12), who cannot synthesize specific antibodies, this phase lasts a very long time. The specific elimination resulting from antibody production is illustrated in Figure 24, where there is a sharp break in the curve on the eighth day and complete elimination of all antigen by the thirteenth day. With bovine serum albumin immune elimination takes place in the rabbit between the ninth and fifteenth day (246, 247).

When the first antibodies appear in the serum, they encounter an excess of antigen so soluble complexes are formed. For a time, as shown in Figure 24B, the amount of antigen is decreased. As the antibody production increases, the system passes through the equivalence zone, where large, precipitable aggregates are formed and these are readily eliminated by phagocytosis (194). Only after all antigen is eliminated do detectable amounts of free antibody appear in the serum (see Fig. 12 in Chap. 12). In some individual rabbits the rate of antibody production is slow, the soluble complexes build up in the serum, and the phase of rapid elimination is not evident (Fig. 24B). Under this condition the complement in the serum is not reduced, but when antibodies are produced more rapidly and large precipitable complexes occur, the complement is utilized (Fig. 24A). This observation suggests that complement is not involved in the formation of soluble complexes but is bound up and removed when precipitation occurs. Guinea pig and rabbit complement precipitates the soluble complexes in vitro better than human and pig complement (245).

The soluble complexes in the serum can be detected by virtue of the differential solubility of the albumin antigen and the globulin antibody in 50 per cent ammonium sulfate saturation (55), and they can be demonstrated by starch block electrophoresis (248). Actively or passively sensitized animals eliminate antigen at the same rate (45). The larger complexes,

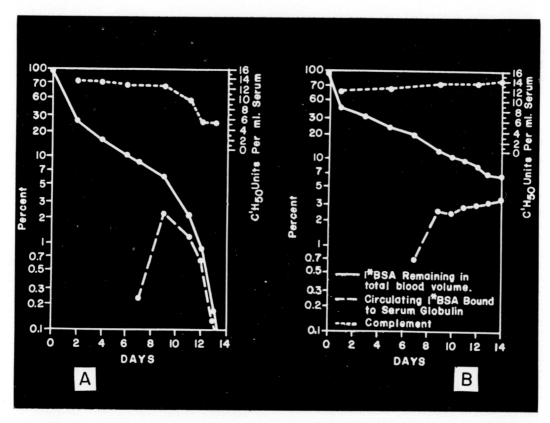

Fig. 24. The formation and elimination of antigen-antibody complexes from the circulating blood of rabbits. (After Weigle and Dixon. *Proc. Soc. Exper. Biol. & Med.,* 99:226, 1958.)

formed near equilibration, migrate with the gamma globulin, while the smaller complexes, formed in greater antigen excess, migrated with the beta globulins.

The production of any considerable amount of soluble complexes in antibody excess has been difficult to achieve, but Forster and Weigle (63) added very slowly small amounts of antigen to antibodies while mixing vigorously and achieved soluble complexes with egg albumin, bovine serum, albumin, and bovine gamma globulin. The concentration of antibodies required increased with the molecular weight of the antigens.

The studies of Najjar and his associates (164, 165, 166) indicate that antibodies which have formed complexes with antigen are modified sufficiently so they in turn become antigenic and produce new antibodies. The new antibodies-to-antibody complex may in turn stimulate still other antibodies for several generations.

Biologic Action of Antigen-Antibody Complexes. Under certain conditions reactions of

antigen and antibodies occur in the bodies of man and experimental animals without any local damage or systemic reactions. Under other conditions severe local and systemic lesions occur. Damaging results have been observed by the injection of antigen after both active and passive immunization and by the injection of preformed antigen-antibody complexes into normal rabbits. The most striking lesions in the rabbit have been glomerulonephritis and those associated with serum sickness (69, 249). Antigen-antibody complexes which were prepared in the test tube in moderate to marked antigen excess were found to be most toxic. These same types of complex produced in mice glomerulonephritis, arthritis, and endocarditis (137).

The injection of soluble antigen-antibody complexes, found in antigen excess, into the skin of normal guinea pigs results in local inflammation resembling passive cutaneous anaphylaxis (109, 110, 111). The injection of the same type of antigen-antibody complexes intravenously produces fatal anaphylaxis in guinea pigs, mice, and rabbits (249). Osler and his associates (184) have shown that a poisonous substance known as "anaphylatoxin" is released in vitro by antigen-antibody mixtures, so it is assumed that the same type of reaction occurs in vivo after the injection of the nontoxic antigen-antibody complexes.

Ishizaka and Campbell and their associates (108, 111, 112) have shown that the local skin lesions depend upon both the species and animal in which the antibody is produced and the antigen-antibody ratio in the antigen-antibody complexes. The complexes formed with antibodies made by the horse and chicken are not toxic when injected into the skin. When the complexes were composed of the reactants in the molar ratio, Ag_2Ab_2 and complexes poorer in antigen showed skin reactivity. Complexes found at the equivalence point had the highest complement-fixing activity but much poorer skin reactivity (111). Aggregates which do not fix complement do not produce cutaneous reactions. Ishizaka and Campbell (110) have shown that a molecular reaction takes place in the antibody as a result of its reaction with antigen, which is evident by increase in levorotation. The optical change indicates the presence of some factors which damage the skin, since the Ag_2Ab complex and the simple hapten (R)-anti-R complexes, which do not damage the skin, do not produce levorotation.

The ability of the soluble antigen-antibody complex to produce capillary penetrability depends upon the source of the antibody rather than the nature of the antigen (108, 109, 110).

Complexes of antigen-antibody formed in antigen excess will dissociate into free antigen and antibody when injected into the skin of normal guinea pigs, provided the antiserum used was produced in guinea pigs. Since free antibody passively sensitized the skin, cutaneous anaphylaxis resulted when the specific antigen was injected into the prepared skin site. Similar tests with complexes formed with antibody prepared from mouse and rabbit antibody showed no dissociation when injected into the skin of guinea pigs (213).

BIOLOGIC ACTIVITIES OF AGGREGATED GAMMA GLOBULIN

Normal gamma globulins from man and cow can be caused to aggregate into masses comparable in size to those caused by true antigen-antibody reactions by such nonspecific measures as exposure to heat. These nonspecifically aggregated globulins induce skin reactions in normal guinea pigs and fix complement by a method comparable to, if not identical with, the true antigen-antibody reaction (112). Later work by Sugahara and his associates (228) compared the results with aggregates made from rabbit γ-globulin. They were injected into guinea pig skin and produced positive reactions. The aggregates formed with α-globulin, and βl-globulin had no biologic activity. Ishizaka and Ishizaka (112) found that aggregated γ-globulin would also cause agglutination of erythrocytes and platelets (169). This occurred in the absence of complement, but the process was accelerated by complement. Finally, the lack of parallelism between the degree of skin reaction and the fixation of C' fixing potencies in soluble gamma globulin is not identical with the activities of true antigen antibody reactions (112).

C' REACTIVE PROTEIN

This is not a true antigen-antibody reaction, although the protein in question develops during certain febrile illnesses and is demonstrated by a precipitin test. In 1930 Tillett and Francis (234) described the existence of a protein in the sera of patients with pneumonia and other infectious diseases which could be precipitated by exposure to the C-polysaccharide from the bodies of pneumococci (76). A similar and analogous protein has, designated **Cx-reactive protein,** been found in acute phase rabbit serum (77, 128).

This protein is not present in the sera of normal man and rabbits but can be induced in rabbits by injecting typhoid vaccine (77) and in man by performing surgical operations.

Wood (257) found that the protein was bound to a lipid, and Hornung and Morris (103a) concluded that the CRP, which appears following surgery, is an α-globulin.

REFERENCES

1. Adler, F. L.   Proc. Soc. Exper. Biol. & Med., 79:590, 1952.
2. ——— J. Immunol., 70:79, 1953.
3. Aladjem, F., and others.   J. Immunol., 83:221, 1959.
4. Alexander, M. M., and others.   J. Exper. Med., 91:561, 1950.
5. Alsever, J. V., and Ainslie, R. B.   New York State J. Med., 41:126, 1941.
6. Amano, T., and others.   Biken's J., 1:13, 1958.
7. Augustin, R.   Quart. Rev. Allergy, 9:504, 1955.
8. ——— Mechanism of Antibody Formation, Hollub, M., and Jarošková, L., eds., New

York and London, Academic Press, 1960, p. 94.

9. Baltch, A. L., and others. J. Immunol., 88: 361, 1962.
10. Becker, E. L. J. Immunol., 77:469, 1956.
11. —— and Neff, J. C. J. Immunol., 83: 571, 1959.
12. —— J. Immunol., 84:299, 1960.
13. —— Immunogenic Approach to Problems in Microbiology, Heidelberger, M., Plescia, O. J., and Day, R. A., eds., New Brunswick, New Jersey, Rutgers University Press, 1960, p. 245.
14. Bier, O. G., and others. J. Exper. Med., 81: 449, 1945.
15. Bloch, R. J., Durrum, E. L., and Zweig, G. A Manual of Chromatography and Paper Electrophoresis, 2nd ed., New York, Academic Press, 1958.
16. Blomfield, A. M., and others. J. Hyg., 48: 73, 1950.
17. Blumer, H., and others. J. Immunol., 88: 669, 1962.
18. Bordet, J. Ann. Inst. Pasteur, 12:688, 1898; 13:220, 1899.
19. —— and Gengou, O. Ann. Inst. Pasteur, 15:129, 289, 1901.
20. Boulanger, P., and Bannister, G. L. J. Immunol., 85:368, 1960.
21. Bowen, H. E., and Wyman, L. J. Immunol., 71:86, 1953.
22. Bowman, W. M., and others. J. Exper. Med., 94:87, 1951.
23. Boyd, W. C. J. Exper., 74:369, 1941; 75: 407, 1942.
24. —— Fundamentals of Immunology, 3rd ed., New York, Interscience Publishers, Inc., 1956.
25. —— Introduction to Immunochemical Specificity, New York and London, Interscience Publishers, Inc., 1962, p. 118.
26. Brody, A., and Carlstrom, G. Lancet, 2:99, 1960.
27. Brown, R. J. Immunol., 52:17, 1946.
28. Brumfield, H. P., and Pomeroy, B. S. Proc. Soc. Biol. & Med., 102:278, 1959.
29. Butler, W. T. J. Immunol., 90:663, 1963.
30. Campbell, D. H., and others. J. Allergy, 21:519, 1950.
31. Cann, J. R., and others. J. Immunol., 66: 137, 1951.
32. —— and Loveless, M. H. J. Immunol., 72:270, 1954.
33. Caselitz, F. H. Ztschr. f. Immunitätsforsch. u. exper. Therap., 109:149, 1952.
34. Cavelti, P. A. J. Immunol., 57:141, 1947.
35. Chang, R. Shih-Man, and others. J. Immunol., 73:8, 1954.
36. Chen, T. H., and Meyer, K. F. J. Immunol., 72:282, 1954.
37. Coombs, R. R. A., and Hole, N. H. J. Hyg., 46:296, 1948.
38. —— and others. Brit. J. Exper. Path., 32:195, 1951.
39. —— The Serology of Conglutination and Its Relation to Disease, Philadelphia, F. A. Davis, 1962.
40. Coons, A. H. Internat. Rev. Cytol., 5:1, 1956.
40a. Crowle, A. J. Immunodiffusion, New York, Academic Press, 1961.

41. Culbertson, J. T. J. Immunol., 23, 439, 1932.
42. D'Alessandro, D., and Dardanoni, L. Am. J. Syph., Gonor. & Med., 37:137, 1953.
43. Deacon, W. E., and Hunter, E. F. Proc. Soc. Exp. Biol. & Med., 110:352, 1962.
44. Dean, H. R., and Webb, R. A. J. Path. & Bact., 29:473, 1926.
45. Dixon, F. J., and Maurer, P. H. Proc. Soc. Exp. Biol. & Med., 84:442, 1953.
46. Downs, C. M., and others. J. Immunol., 75:35, 1955.
47. Dreesman, G. Fed. Proc., 22:325, 1963.
48. Easton, J. M., and others. J. Exp. Med., 115:275, 1962.
49. Elek, S. D., and Levy, E. Brit. J. Exper. Path., 31:358, 1950.
50. Enders, J. R. Ann. Rev. Microbiol., 8:473, 1954.
51. Engelsberg, J. J. Immunol., 82:467, 1959.
52. Erickson, J. O., and others. J. Immunol., 71:30, 1953.
53. Ewing, W. H., and Kauffman, F. Pub. Health Rep., 65:1341, 1950.
54. Fahey, J. L. Science, 131:500, 1960.
55. Farr, R. S. J. Infect. Dis., 103:239, 1958.
56. Feinberg, R. J., and Flick, J. A. Proc. Soc. Exp. Biol. & Med., 96:71, 1957.
57. —— J. Immunol., 81:14, 1958.
58. Felton, L. D., and others. J. Bact., 69:519, 1955.
59. —— and others. J. Immunol., 74:205, 1955.
60. Fenn, W. O. J. Gen. Physiol., 4:373, 1922.
61. Foley, M. J., and others. J. Exper. Med., 110:603, 1959.
62. —— and Wood, W. B., Jr. J. Exper. Med., 110:617, 1959.
63. Forster, O., and Weigle, W. O. J. Immunol., 90:935, 1963.
64. Frisch, A. W., and Davies, G. H. Proc. Soc. Exp. Biol. & Med., 101:281, 1959.
65. Gaines, S., and Landy, M. J. Bact., 69:628, 1955.
66. Garvey, J. S., and Campbell, D. H. J. Immunol., 76:36, 1956.
67. —— and Campbell, D. H. J. Exper. Med., 105:361, 1957.
68. George, M., and Vaughn, J. H. J. Immunol., 88:191, 1962.
69. Germuth, F. G., Jr., and MacKinnon, G. E. Bull. Johns Hopkins Hosp., 101:13, 1957.
70. Gernez-Rieux, C. H., and Tacquet, A. Progr. Explor. Tuberc., 5:66, Basel, S. Karger, 1952.
71. Glenchur, H., Zinneman, H. H., and Hall, W. H. J. Immunol., 86: 421, 1961.
72. Goodman, H. S., and Masaltis, L. J. Immunol., 85:391, 1960.
73. Goodner, K. Science, 94:241, 1941.
74. —— and Horsfall, F. L., Jr. J. Exper. Med., 64:201, 1936.
75. Gordon, R. S., Jr. J. Immunol., 71:220, 1953.
76. Gotschlich, E., and Stetson, C. A. T. J. Exp. Med., 111:441, 1960.
77. Gottlieb, A. A. Proc. Soc. Exp. Biol. & Med., 110:568, 1962.
78. Gruber, M., and Durham, H. E. München med. Wchnschr., 43:206, 1896.
79. Gustafsson, B. E., and Laurell, A. Proc. Soc. Exp. Biol. & Med., 105:598, 1960.

80. Gyeney, L., and Sehon, A. H. Fed. Proc., 20:13, 1961.
81. ——— J. Immunol., 89:483, 1962.
82. Halpern, B. H., and Holzer, A., eds. Symposium II on Physico-Chemical Properties of Allergic Antibodies. Third International Congress of Allergy. Editions Médicales Flammarion, Paris, 1958.
83. Hardy, P. H., Jr., and Neil, E. E. J. Exper. Med., 101:367, 1955.
84. Harris, S., and Haris, T. N. J. Immunol., 80:316, 1958.
85. Harshman, S., and Najjar, V. A. Ann. N.Y. Acad. of Sciences, 1963.
86. Haurowitz, F. Chemie der Antigene und der Antikörper, in Fortschritte der Allergielehre, ed. by P. Kallos, Basel, S. Karger, 1939. Chap. 2, p. 19.
87. ——— Ann. Rev. Microbiol., 7:359, 1953.
88. Hawkins, J. D., and Haurowitz, F. Biochem. J., 72:59, 1959.
89. Hayden, A. R., and Becker, E. L. J. Immunol., 85:591, 1960.
90. Hegedus, A., and Greiner, H. Z. Immunitätsforsch., 92:1, 1938.
91. Heidelberger, M., and Treffers, H. P. J. Gen. Physiol., 25:523, 1942.
92. ——— and Mayer, M. M. Advances in Enzymol., 8:71, 1948.
93. Heimer, R., and others. J. Immunol., 89:382, 1962.
94. Heimlich, E. M., and others. J. Allergy, 31:364, 1960.
95. Henry, J. B., and Little, W. A., J.A.M.A., 182:110, 1962.
96. Hinz, C. F., Jr., and others. J. Immunol., 85:547, 1960.
97. ——— and others. J. Exp. Med., 113:177, 193, 1961.
98. Hirata, A. A. J. Immunol., 91:625, 1963.
99. Hirsch, J. G. Bacteriol. Revs., 23:48, 1959.
99a. ——— and Strauss, B. J. Immunol., 92:145, 1964.
100. Hole, N. H., and Coombs, R. R. A. J. Hyg., 45:450, 490, 497, 1947.
101. Hook, W. A., and others. J. Immunol., 84:569, 1960.
102. Hooker, S. B., and Boyd, W. C. J. Immunol., 33:337, 1937.
103. ——— and Boyd, W. C. J. Immunol., 42:419, 1941.
103a. Hornung, M., and Morris, T. M. Proc. Soc. Exper. Biol. & Med., 111:25, 1962.
104. Horsfall, F. L., Jr. J. Bact., 35:207, 1938.
105. Humphrey, J. H., and Porter, R. R. Lancet, 1:196, 1957.
106. ——— Mechanisms of Antibody Formation, Hollub, M., and Jarošková, L., eds., New York and London, Academic Press, 1960, p. 44.
107. Inoue, K., and others. Biken's J., 2:1, 1959.
108. Ishizaka, K., and others. J. Exp. Med., 109:127, 1959.
109. ——— and Campbell, D. H. J. Immunol., 83:105, 116, 1959.
110. ——— and Campbell, D. H. J. Immunol., 83:318, 1959.
111. ——— and others. J. Immunol., 86:590, 1961.
112. Ishizaka, T., and Ishizaka, K. J. Immunol., 89:709, 1962.

113. Jerne, N. K., and Nordin, A. A. Science, 140:405, 1960.
114. Jeter, W. S., and others. J. Immunol., 86:386, 1961.
115. Kabat, E. A., and others. J. Exper. Med., 81:1, 1945.
116. ——— and Benacerraf, B. J. Immunol., 62:97, 1949.
117. ——— and Mayer, M. M. Experimental Immunochemistry, 2nd ed., Springfield, Ill., Charles C Thomas, 1961.
118. Kaminski, M. J. Immunol., 75:367, 1955.
119. Karush, F. J. Am. Chem. Soc., 78:5519, 1956.
120. Kent, J. F., and others. J. Immunol., 53:37, 1946.
121. ——— and others. J. Lab. & Clin. Med., 33:747, 1948.
122. ——— and others. Proc. Soc. Exp. Biol. & Med., 109:584, 1962.
123. Kleinschmidt, W. J., and Boyer, P. D. J. Immunol., 69:247, 257, 1952.
124. Kolmer, J. A. Approved Laboratory Technic, 5th ed., New York, Appleton-Century-Crofts, Inc., 1951, pp. 816-817.
125. Korngold, L., and Van Leeuwen, G. J. Immunol., 78:172, 1957.
126. Kraus, R. Wien. Klin. Wchnschr., 10:736, 1897.
127. Kuhns, W. J. J. Immunol., 75:105, 1955.
128. Kushner, I., and Kaklan, M. H. J. Exp. Med., 114:961, 1961.
129. Lachmann, P. J., and others. J. Exp. Med., 115:63, 1962.
130. Landsteiner, K. München Med. Wchnschr., 2:1812, 1903.
131. Leon, M. A. J. Immunol., 85:190, 1960.
132. Lepow, I. H., and Ross, A. J. Exp. Med, 112:1107, 1960; J. Immunol., 92:456, 1964.
133. ——— Immunochemical Approaches to Problems in Microbiology, Heidelberger, M., Plescia, O. J., and Day, R. A., eds., New Brunswick, N.J., 1961, p. 280.
134. ——— J. Exper. Med., 117:983, 1963.
135. Loveless, M. H. J. Immunol., 41:15, 1941.
136. ——— and Cann, J. R. J. Immunol., 74:329, 1955.
137. McCluskey, R. T., and Benacerraf, B. Am. J. Path., 35:275, 1959.
138. McKean, C. M. Am. J. Obstet. Gynec., 80:596, 1960.
139. McKee, A. P., and Jeter, W. S. J. Immunol., 76:112, 1956.
140. ——— and Jeter, W. S. J. Immunol., 88:702, 1962.
141. McLeod, C. P., and Magnuson, H. J. Pub. Health Rep., 68:747, 1953.
142. ——— and Stokes, P. S. Pub. Health Rep., 70:379, 1955.
143. McMaster, P. D., and Kruse, H. J. Exper. Med., 93:323, 1951.
144. Marrack, J. R. Incomplete Antibodies in Immunochemical Approach to Problems in Microbiology, Heidelberger, M., Plescia, O. J., and Day, R. A., eds., New Brunswick, N.J., Rutgers University Press, 1961, p. 43.
145. Martin, D. S., and others. J. Gen. Physiol., 26:533, 1943.
146. ——— J. Lab. & Clin. Med., 28:870, 1477, 1943.
147. Marucci, A. A. Am. J. Vet. Res., 18:785, 1957; 19:979, 1958.

148. Maurer, P. H., and Thorpe, R. M. J. Immunol., 84:318, 1960.
149. Mayer, M. M., and others. J. Exper. Med., 84:535, 1946.
150. ——— Progress in Allergy, Kallos, ed., Basel, S. Karger, 5:215, 1958.
151. ——— Immunochemical Approach to Problems in Microbiology, Heidelberger, M., Plescia, O. J., and Day, R. A., eds., New Brunswick, N.J., Rutgers University Press, 1960, p. 268.
152. Mayer, R. L., and Dowling, N. F. J. Immunol., 51:349, 1945.
153. Metchnikoff, E. Ann. Inst. Pasteur, 3:61, 265, 1889; 5:456, 1891; 9:433, 1895.
154. ——— L'immunité dans les maladies infectueuses, 1901.
155. Middlebrook, G., and Dubos, R. J. J. Exper. Med., 88:521, 1948.
156. Miles, A. A. Brit. J. Exper. Path., 20:63, 1939.
157. ——— and Pirie, A. W. The Nature of the Bacterial Surfaces, Sprignfield, Ill., Charles C Thomas, 1949.
158. Mirick, G. S., and others. J. Exper. Med., 80:391, 1944.
159. Mudd, S., and others. J. Exper. Med., 49:779, 797, 815, 1929; 52:313, 1930.
160. Mueller-Eberhard, H. J., and Nilsson, U. J. Exper. Med., 111:217, 1960.
161. Muñoz, J., and Becker, E. L. J. Immunol., 65:47, 1950.
162. Muschel, L., and Treffers, H. P. J. Immunol., 76:1, 11, 20, 1956.
163. ——— and others. J. Immunol., 82:38, 1959.
164. Najjar, V. A., and Fisher, J. Biochem. & Biophys. Acta, 20:158, 1956.
165. ——— and others. Biochem. & Biophys. Acta, 26:114, 1957.
166. ——— and Robinson, J. P. J. Pediatrics, 55:777, 1959.
167. Neff, J. C., and Becker, E. L. J. Immunol., 73:286, 1954.
168. Neisser, M., and Wechsberg, F. München. med. Wchnschr., 48:697, 1901.
169. Nelson, D. S., and Nelson, R. A., Jr. Yale J. Biol. & Med., 31:185, 201, 1959.
170. ——— and Mayer, M. M. J. Exper. Med., 89:369, 1949.
171. ——— Science, 118:733, 1953.
172. ——— Proc. Roy. Soc. Med., 49:55, 1956.
173. Nelson, R. A., Jr. J. Exper. Med, 108:515, 1958.
174. Neter, E., and others. Proc. Soc. Exper. Biol. & Med., 79:255, 1952.
175. ——— Reviews, 20:166, 1956.
176. Neufeld, F., and Rimpau, R. Deutsche. med. Wchnschr., 30:1458, 1904.
177. ——— Zeitschr. f. Hyg. u. Infektionskr., 51:283, 1905.
178. Neurath, H., and others. Am. J. Syph., Gonor. & Ven. Dis., 31:347, 436, 1947.
179. Nisonoff, A., and Pressman, D. Science, 128:659, 1958.
180. Northrop, J. H. J. Gen. Physiol., 25:465, 1942.
181. Nossal, G. J. V. Brit. J. Exper. Path., 41:89, 1960.
182. Nuttall, G. Zeitschr. f. Hyg. u. Infektionskr., 4:351, 1888.

183. Ogata, T., and others. J. Immunol., 69:13, 1952.
184. Osler, A. G., and others. J. Exper. Med., 110:311, 1959.
185. ——— Functions of the Complement System in Advances in Immunology, New York, Academic Press, 1961, Vol. I, p. 131.
186. Oswa, E., and Muschel, L. H. J. Immunol., 84:203, 1960.
187. Ouchterlony, O. Acta path. et microbiol. Scandinav., 32:231, 1953.
188. Oudin, J. Methods in Medical Research, Chicago, The Year Book Publ., 1952, Vol. 5.
189. Ovary, Z. Progress in Allergy, Vol. 5, 1958.
190. ——— and Karush, F. J. Immunol., 86:146, 1961.
191. Overman, J. R. Proc. Soc. Exp. Biol. & Med., 107:896, 1961.
192. Pangborn, M. C. J. Biol. Chem., 143:247, 1942; 153:343, 1944.
193. Pappenheimer, A. M., Jr. Valence of Antibodies, in Pappenheimer, A. M., Jr., The Nature and Significance of the Antibody Response, New York, Columbia University Press, 1953, p. 111.
194. Patterson, R., and others. J. Immunol., 89:471, 1962.
195. Pauling, L., and Pressman, D. J. Am. Chem. Soc., 67:1003, 1945.
196. Pederson, K. O. Ultracentrifugal Studies on Serum and Serum Fractions, Uppsala, Almqvist and Wiksells Boktryck, A. B., 1945.
197. Peterson, O. L., Ham, T. H., and Finland, M. Science, 97:167, 1943.
198. Petrie, G. F. Brit. J. Exper. Path., 13:380, 1932.
199. ——— and Steabben, P. Brit. Med. J., I:377, 1943.
200. Pfeiffer, R., and Issaeff. Ztschr. f. Hyg. u. Infektionskr., 17:355, 1894.
201. Phillips, J. H., and others. J. Am. Chem. Soc., 80:2710, 1958.
202. Pijper, A. J. Path. & Bact., 47:1, 1938.
203. Pillemer, L., and others. Science, 120:279, 1954.
204. Portnoy, J., and Magnuson, H. J. J. Immunol., 75:348, 1955.
205. Pruzansky, J. J., and Feinberg, S. M. J. Immunol., 88:256, 1962.
206. Raffel, S. Immunity, 2nd ed., New York, Appleton-Century-Crofts, 1961.
207. Rapp, F., and others. Proc. Soc. Exper. Biol. & Med., 90:335, 1955.
208. Reiss, A. M., and Plescia, O. J. Fed. Proc. Abstract, 22:612, 1963.
209. Rice, C. E., and Brooksby, J. B. J. Immunol., 71:300, 1953.
210. ——— and others. Canad. J. Comp. Med., 25:151, 1961.
211. Richter, M., and Haurowitz, F. J. Immunol., 84:420, 1960.
212. Robineaux, R., and Pinet, J. Ciba Found. Symposium on Cellular Aspects of Immunity, 1960, p. 5.
213. Rosenberg, L. T., and Tachibana, D. K. J. Immunol., 89:47, 1962.
214. Sage, H. J., and others. J. Immunol., 90:347, 1963.
215. Saurino, V. R., and Delamater, E. D. Am. J. Syph., 36:353, 1952.

216. Schmidt, N. J., and Harding, H. B. J. Bact., 71:217, 223, 1956.
216a. Shands, J. W., Jr., and Suter, E. Fed. Proc., 22:2006, 1963.
217. Shepard, C. C. J. Immunol., 85:356, 361, 1960.
218. Singer, S. J. J. Cellular Comp. Physiol., 50: Supp. 1. 51, 1957.
219. Smith, D. T., and Scott, N. B. Am. Rev. Tuberc., 62:121, 1950.
220. Smith, I. Chromatographic and Electrophoretic Techniques, New York, Interscience Publishers, 1960.
221. Sober, H. A., and Peterson, F. A. Federation Proc., 17:1116, 1958.
222. Spiegelberg, H. L., and others. J. Immunol., 90:751, 1963.
223. Stanworth, D. R. Comparative Studies on the Chromatographic Fractions of γ Globulin from Allergic and Normal Sera. Abstracts, 3rd International Congress of Allergy, Excerpta Medica, Oct., 1958.
224. Stelos, P., and Taliaferro, W. H. J. Infectious Dis., 104:105, 1959.
225. Steril, J. Mechanisms of Antibody Formation, Holub, M., and Jarošková, L., eds., New York and London, Academic Press, 1960, p. 107.
226. Stravitsky, A. B. J. Infect. Dis., 94:306, 1954.
227. Stroud, R. M., and others. Fed. Proc. Abstract, 22:613, 1963.
228. Sugahara, T., and others. J. Immunol., 90:960, 1963.
229. Suter, E. Bacteriol. Revs., 20:94, 1956.
230. Taliaferro, W. H., and Jaroslow, B. Abstr. Inf. Microbiol. Congress, Stockholm, 1958.
231. Talmage, D. W., and others. J. Immunol., 67:243, 1951.
232. Taranta, A., and Franklin, E. C. Science, 134:1981, 1962.
233. Teorell, T. J. Hyg., 44:227, 237, 1946.
234. Tillett, W. S., and Francis, T. J. Exp. Med., 52:573, 895, 1930.
235. Todd, E. W., Pillemer, L., and Lepow, I. H. J. Immunol., 83:418, 428, 1959.
236. Treffers, H. P., and others. J. Exper. Med., 75:135, 1942.
237. ——— Serology and Immuno-chemistry, in Dubos, Bacterial and Mycotic Infections of Man, Philadelphia, J. B. Lippincott Co., 1952, p. 119.
238. Turner, E. W., and Boyer, P. D. J. Immunol., 69:265, 1952.

239. Uhr, J. W., and others. J. Exp. Med., 115:655, 1962.
240. Volkin, E. J. Immunol., 61:143, 1949.
241. Ward, H. K., and Enders, J. F. J. Exper. Med., 57:527, 1933.
242. Wassermann, N. A., and others. Deutsche med. Wchnschr., 32:745, 1906.
243. ——— and Schuct, A. Ztschr. f. Hyg. u. Infektionskr., 55:451, 1906.
244. Weaver, R. E., and Seastone, C. V. J. Immunol., 88:661, 1962.
245. Weigle, W. O., and Maurer, P. H. J. Immunol., 79:211, 319, 1957.
246. ——— J. Immunol., 81:204, 1958.
247. ——— and Dixon, F. J. Proc. Soc. Exp. Biol. & Med., 99:226, 1958.
248. ——— and Deichmiller, M. P. J. Immunol., 84:434, 1960.
249. ——— Advances in Immunology, Taliaferro, W. H., and Humphrey, J. H., eds., New York, Academic Press, 1961, Vol. VI, p. 283.
250. Weil, E., and Felix, A. Wien. Klin. Wchnschr., 30:1509, 1917.
251. Whiteside, R. E., and Baker, E. E. J. Immunol., 88:650, 1962.
252. Wide, L., and Gemzell, C. A. Acta Endocr., 35:261, 1960.
253. Wiener, A. S. Blood Groups and Transfusions. 3rd ed., Springfield, Ill., Charles C Thomas, 1943.
254. ——— and Gordon, E. B. J. Lab. & Clin. Med., 33:181, 1948.
255. Williams, C. A., Jr., and Grabar, P. J. Immunol., 74:158, 397, 494, 1955.
256. Wilson, M. W., and Pringle, B. H. J. Immunol., 75:460, 1955.
257. Wood, H. F., and others. J. Exper. Med., 111:601, 1960.
258. ——— and others. J. Exper. Med., 84:365, 377, 387, 1946.
259. Wright, A. E., and others. Proc. Roy. Soc. London, 72:357, 1903; 73:128, 1904.
260. Zinneman, H. H., and othres. J. Immunol., 83:206, 1959.
261. ——— and others. Chronic Renal Brucellosis, New Eng. J. Med., 265:872, 1961.
262. Zinsser, H. J. Immunol., 6:289, 1921.
263. ——— J. Immunol., 18:483, 1930.
264. ——— and others. Immunity, Principles and Application in Medicine and Public Health, New York, The Macmillan Co., 1939.

14

The Human Blood Groups and Immunohematology

In 1900 Ehrlich and Morgenroth were able to detect antigenic differences among goats by immunizing one animal with the red blood cells of another. The resulting antibodies were termed **isoantibodies,** since they reacted with the antigens (isoantigens) that distinguished individual members of the same species. During the same year Landsteiner (10) published his first account of observations on similar differences among the blood cells of human beings. This study, which was originally described as an incidental finding in conjunction with a report on a completely unrelated topic, was extended and more fully described in a subsequent publication (11).

Such was the humble beginning of the field of immunohematology. Since that time, at least 11 separate and independent systems of blood group antigens and antibodies have been identified. These have been shown to be hereditary characteristics, unalterable throughout the life of an individual and transmitted from generation to generation according to the laws of simple Mendelian inheritance.

The importance of the blood groups and a clear understanding of the antigens and antibodies involved has been clearly demonstrated in making blood transfusion a relatively safe therapeutic procedure. Contingent upon the availability of this vital form of adjunct therapy, remarkable advances in modern surgery and other fields of medicine have been made possible.

The subsequent discovery of the Rh blood group system led to the explanation of the pathogenic course of hemolytic disease of the newborn, a serious complication of pregnancy. In connection with this system of isoantigens, new varieties of human agglutinins as well as radically different methods for their detection were brought to light. These made available hitherto unknown serologic tools, whose use not only led to the eventual discovery of additional blood group systems but also provided a new perspective of the basic mechanism of the isoimmune response.

Aside from these important contributions, the blood groups, since they are easily demonstrable human characteristics, essentially unaffected by other hereditary traits, have valuable applications in the study of human genetics, anthropology, forensic pathology, and other forms of basic science.

THE ABO BLOOD GROUP SYSTEM

It was shown by Landsteiner (11) and later by von Decastello and Sturli (7) that the red blood cells of human beings could be divided into four distinct groups, based on agglutination reactions with normal human sera. These are referred to as O, A, B, and AB. Landsteiner attributed these reactions to the presence or absence of two agglutinable antigens, A and B on the surface of the cells. At the same time, he demonstrated a reciprocal relationship of the antigens on the cells to antibodies present in the plasma or serum. Thus, erythrocytes of an individual belonging to the blood group O have neither the A nor the B antigen, but the plasma contains both anti-A and anti-B isoagglutinins, whereas the group A individual having A antigen has only anti-B antibodies and so forth.

The isoagglutinins, anti-A and anti-B, occur with a precise regularity even without apparent antigenic stimulation. For this reason, they are believed by many to be naturally occurring, perhaps being formed because of genetic influence. They normally appear in the serum three to six months after birth and remain throughout life. The sera of newborn infants are devoid of all isoagglutinins of their own origin. Furthermore, they are incapable of being immunized by blood group antigens until after the so-called Immunologische Wendepunkt or time of sero-maturation, which occurs at approximately age three months. Up to that time, any isoagglutinins present in their plasma are of maternal origin, acquired through transplacental passage. While this system is based on three antigens, A, B, and O, only the isoagglutinins anti-A and anti-B are normally found in human serum. Blood-grouping sera containing these antibodies are used to identify the four groups, since they will agglutinate the cells containing the corresponding antigens according to the scheme shown in Table 1. In view of the regularity of the iso-antibodies' occurrence associated with these groups, it is considered mandatory to test for their presence with standard cells containing the appropriate antigens before the group can be established definitely.

The A, B, and O antigens are well developed even before birth. They occur not only on the red cells, but have been shown to exist in all other body cells and tissues with the exception of brain and the spinal cord in the form of lipid-like, alcohol extractable compounds. In addition, approximately 78 per cent of individuals have these antigens, corresponding to their blood groups occurring as water soluble polysaccharides in all their body secretions, with the exception of the cerebro-spinal fluid. These latter individuals are known as "secretors," while the remaining 22 per cent, with antigens only in their tissues, are termed "non-secretors." These traits are hereditary characteristics

transmitted by means of two genes *Se* and *se. Se,* the gene for secretion is dominant, while *se* is recessive.

These antigens, aside from imparting blood group specificity on human cells occur in certain lower animals, plants, and bacteria. They are extremely interesting compounds and have been extensively studied by a wide variety of immunochemical methods. Soluble group A and B specific substances are extracted and purified commercially from hog and horse gastric mucosae. These materials are useful for reducing the amount of anti-A and anti-B agglutinins in the plasma of group O blood by means of specific immunologic combinations. Inasmuch as they are fully antigenic in man, in contrast to the rabbit, in which they act as haptens, they can be employed for the purpose of increasing the titer of anti-A and anti-B antibodies in group B and A individuals for the production of extremely potent grouping sera.

The anti-A or anti-B isoantibodies, present in the plasma of the recipient of a blood transfusion, may attack and destroy the red cells of the donor blood if it belongs to a different group. This is a major incompatibility, and the massive destruction leads to the hemoglobinemia and hemoglobinuria that are characteristic of a hemolytic transfusion reaction. For this reason, it is most desirable to give only blood of the same ABO group. In extenuating circumstances, however, this may not always be possible. In such situations group O blood, which lacks the A and B antigens, can usually be given to individuals belonging to any of the four groups with relative safety, since none of them have antibodies directed against the O antigen. Thus, the person of group O has been termed the

Table 1. The ABO Blood Groups

BLOOD GROUP DESIGNATION	REACTIONS				ANTIGENS ON RED CELLS	ANTIBODIES IN SERUM
	CELLULAR		SERUM			
	ANTI-A	ANTI-B	A CELLS	B CELLS		
A	+	−	−	+	A	anti-B
B	−	+	+	−	B	anti-A
AB	+	+	−	−	A and B	none
O	−	−	+	+	none	anti-A and anti-B

"universal donor." Although the plasma of such blood contains both anti-A and anti-B antibodies, they are diluted or neutralized in the recipients' circulation during transfusion, so that they are not in sufficient quantity to hemolyze a significant number of cells in group A, B, or AB recipients. In addition, the commercially available A- and B-soluble specific substances, previously mentioned, may be added in order to reduce the titer of anti-A and anti-B agglutinins. However, so-called dangerous universal donors exist whose anti-A and anti-B antibodies (or both) are extremely potent and of a variety that is resistant to neutralization by A and B substances. Such excess antibodies may produce some destruction of the recipients' cells, or they may be sequestered and destroy donor cells from a subsequently administered transfusion of blood belonging to the same group as the recipient, if it should be other than O.

In contrast, the group O individual cannot receive blood from any ABO group other than his own, because his plasma contains both anti-A and anti-B antibodies. Donor cells of group A, B, or AB, entering the circulation of such a patient, would be sensitized immediately, with the resulting effect of lysis. By the same token, the AB individual, since he possesses neither anti-A nor anti-B antibodies, can receive blood belonging to any of the four groups and is, therefore, called a "universal recipient."

In any transfusion the consequences of antibodies in the recipient's plasma directed against antigens on the donor cells are always most severe. On the other hand, antibodies in the plasma of the donor to a recipient's erythrocytic antigens, even when in substantial quantity, have little if any harmful effects (20). This can be best understood by considering the kinetics of a blood transfusion. In the former instance, a relatively small amount of antigen in the form of 250 ml. of donor cells is introduced into a large pool of antibody contained in the recipient's total plasma volume (approximately 3,000 ml.). The large number of antibody molecules have a good opportunity to combine with the infused cells, causing very rapid and massive destruction. In the latter situation, however, a relatively small number of antibodies contained in 250 ml. of donor plasma

is exposed to the recipient's total blood volume. In this case, there are many more cells than antibodies, allowing a lesser chance of the contact necessary for sensitization. Eventually this does take place, but at a much slower rate and with minimum harmful effects.

The Subgroups of A. Von Dungern and Hirszfeld (28) in 1911, reported that the blood group A was composed of at least two separate subgroups, called A_1 and A_2. This finding was based on experiments in which a group B serum, containing anti-A antibodies, was absorbed with certain selected group A red blood cells. After absorption, the serum still reacted with some but not all group A erythrocytes. From this observation, it was concluded that there were two types of A antigen, one occurring in all group A and AB blood and another, A_1, found in approximately 80 per cent of all blood belonging to these groups. This concept also conceded the existence of two kinds of anti-A antibody; namely, an anti-A, which reacted with all group A cells, and an anti-A_1, which reacted only with group A_1 cells. Thus, by the use of unabsorbed anti-A serum and an anti-A_1 serum prepared by absorption with A_2 cells, it is possible to subdivide both group A and AB into A_1 and A_2 bloods and A_1B and A_2B bloods. This distinction, however, can only be made between the cells of adults, since the A_1 antigen does not attain its full in vitro serologic characteristics until after the first year of life.

Besides using these reagents, it is also possible to distinguish group A_1 cells by means of specific phytohemagglutinins or lectins. Many of these compounds have been isolated from the seeds of various plants. They are not antibodies but, purely by chance, have a chemical configuration complementary to certain blood group antigens and can cause specific clumping of cells. An anti-A_1 lectin of this type, prepared from the seeds of *Dolichos biflorus,* is currently available.

It is not possible to prepare an anti-A_2 serum by absorption of an anti-A serum with A_1 cells, since, in reality, the identification of the A_2 antigen depends merely upon establishing the absence of an A_1 component. However, the serum of certain A_1 and A_1B individuals may contain weak, naturally occurring antibodies that will agglutinate A_2 cells. These antibodies are not specific for A_2, since they will react with group O cells as well. It is considered that these agglutinins are directed against an antigen called H, which is a basic ground substance from which the A and B antigens are derived. This material is found in a large quantity in group O cells and in the secretions of group O secretors. It is present to a lesser extent in A_2 cells and is practically absent from A_1 cells.

The sera of approximately 2 per cent of A_2 individuals and 26 per cent of A_2B individuals contain anti-A_1 antibodies. As a rule, these, as well as anti-H, are specific cold agglutinins reacting better at lower temperatures than at 37° C. In view of their low thermal amplitude, they have little if any significance in transfusions, where the reaction takes place at body temperature. They can, however, create difficulty in blood grouping and compatibility testing and could conceivably present problems in the transfusion of surgical patients undergoing radical procedures under conditions of profound hypothermia.

Additional subgroups of the A antigen have been described to date, called A_3, A_4, and A_5. The relationship of these in terms of their reactivity with certain select antisera, as well as the theoretical amounts of A and H substances present, are depicted in Figure 1. Subgroups of the blood group B have also been found, but these are not as easily distinguishable and at present are still not completely understood.

The four major blood groups are inherited by means of four allelomorphic genes: A_1, A_2, B, and O. It is to be understood, of course, that it is possible to increase the total number of genes to include all of the A subgroups. For the sake of simplicity, however, it is best to limit the discussion to only the first two, which are of major importance. One of the four genes is transmitted to an offspring by each of the two parents. As illustrated in Table 2, they then combine to form two genotypic combinations, giving rise to the six phenotypes discernible by agglutination reactions, obtained with the three standard antisera: anti-A, anti-B, and anti-A_1. It is not possible to distinguish the phenotypes A or B resulting from the genotypes AA or BB from those resulting from the

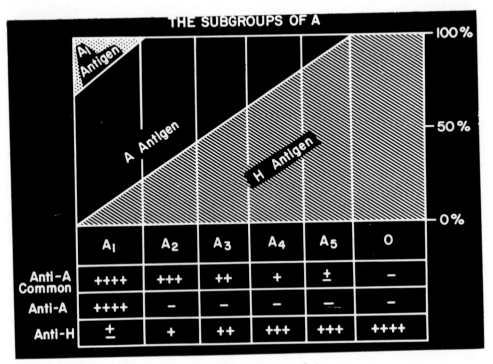

	A_1	A_2	A_3	A_4	A_5	O
Anti-A Common	++++	+++	++	+	±	−
Anti-A	++++	−	−	−	−	−
Anti-H	±	+	++	+++	+++	++++

Fig. 1. The subgroups of A.

genotypes AO or BO, except by family studies, since an anti-O capable of reacting with the product of the heterozygous O gene has not been found.

Table 2. Inheritance of the ABO Blood Groups Genes O, A₁, A₂, B

POSSIBLE GENOTYPES	PHENOTYPE (DETECTABLE ANTIGENS ON RED CELL)	FREQUENCY IN WHITE POPULATION
O/O	O	0.4359
A₁/A₁, A₁/O, A₁/A₂	A₁	0.3487
A₂/A₂, A₂/O	A₂	0.0968
B/B, B/O	B	0.0845
A₁/B	A₁B	0.0256
A₂/B	A₂B	0.0085

THE MNSs BLOOD GROUP SYSTEM

The first antigens of this system (M and N) were discovered in 1927, by Landsteiner and Levine (12). By means of two antisera, produced in rabbits, three types of individuals could be distinguished: those whose red cells reacted only with anti-M, who were called M (genotype *MM*-28 per cent); those giving agglutination only with anti-N, called N (genotype *NN*-22 per cent); and those reacting with both antisera, designated as MN (genotype *MN*-50 per cent). These antigens were shown to be inherited by means of two allelomorphic genes, *M* and *N,* which are completely independent of the other blood groups. As a rule, no naturally occurring antibodies are found in this system, with the possible exception of the sera of certain young children where weak anti-M or anti-N may occasionally be found.

In 1947, Walsh and Montgomery (29) discovered an unusual antibody by which Sanger and Race (26) identified an additional antigen of this system, which they designated S. At the same time, they postulated an allelic gene to S, which they named *s.* Anti-s was found in 1951, thus establishing the hypothesis. It has since been shown that the genes responsible for the M and N antigens, as well as those responsible for the production of S and s, are genetically linked, and a combination of any two is transmitted from generation to generation as a unit.

A few transfusion reactions and cases of hemolytic disease have been reported as a result of immunization to the antigens of this blood group system; nevertheless, they are of limited clinical importance. In view of the fact that the genotypes of this system are directly discernible with the aid of the four available antisera, however, they are of paramount importance in their forensic applications, especially in determining disputed paternity.

Several other blood group antigens notably: Hunter and Henshaw (found principally in Negroes), Miltenberger (Miᵃ), Verweyst (Vw), and Mtᵃ have been shown to be inherited along with MNSs and, therefore, to belong to this blood group system. In addition, an antibody, anti-U, has been described which reacts with all cells, except those lacking both S and s. Such cells (SᵘSᵘ) are very rare and occur exclusively in members of the Negro race.

THE P BLOOD GROUP SYSTEM

The P antigen was first described by Landsteiner and Levine in 1927 (12). Approximately 79 per cent of American Caucasians are P positive. A naturally occurring anti-P can usually be detected as a specific, cold agglutinin in a large percentage of P negative individuals.

For 28 years this system enjoyed a state of relative serenity. Then in 1955 Sanger (24) called attention to the relationship of this antigen to the Tjᵃ antigen of what was, at that time, thought to be part of a separate (Jay) blood group system. The Tjᵃ antigen is present on the red cells of practically everyone tested. Its antibody is extremely potent and hemolytic and has caused severe transfusion reactions. This relationship seems to be similar to that of A₁ and A₂ of the ABO groups, and these findings have required a modification of the terminology used in this system. The original antigen described by Landsteiner and Levine is now referred to as P₁ and its antibody as anti-P₁. Cells not reacting with this serum, but reacting with the old anti-Tjᵃ, which now becomes anti-P+P₁, are called P₂. Cells negative with both antisera are termed pp.

THE Rh BLOOD GROUP SYSTEM

The observations of Levine and Stetson (17) in 1939 and of Landsteiner and Wiener (13) in 1940 led to an advance in our knowledge of blood groups that was secondary in clinical significance only to Landsteiner's discovery of the ABO system.

Levine and Stetson described an antibody in the serum of a mother whose fetus died in utero after eight months gestation. Following delivery, the woman suffered a hemolytic reaction when she was transfused with her husband's ABO compatible blood. The authors postulated that the woman had become sensitized during pregnancy by a fetal antigen which had been inherited from its father and that the maternal antibody, reacting with the same antigen on the husband's red cells, was responsible for the transfusion reaction. In 1940, Landsteiner and Wiener found that the sera of rabbits immunized with red cells of Rhesus monkeys, and containing an anti-Rhesus red cell agglutinin (anti-Rh), would agglutinate the red cells of approximately 85 per cent of white humans.

It was then discovered that the maternal antibody described by Levine and Stetson, and antibodies in the sera of other victims of previously unexplained transfusion reactions, were identical with the anti-Rh antibody in the sera of Landsteiner and Wiener's rabbits.

In the following year, Levine and his coworkers (14, 15, 18) pointed out the great clinical importance of this anti-Rh antibody as a frequent cause of erythroblastosis fetalis, a serious acquired hemolytic anemia of the newborn. Levine not only confirmed his original hypothesis of maternal isoimmunization by fetal blood group antigens inherited from the father, but also showed that once the

mother had developed antibodies to the Rh antigen, the subsequent passage of these anti-Rh antibodies through the placenta into the fetal circulation caused the destruction of the infant's Rh positive red cells, the basic pathogenic process of the disease.

Since Levine's original observation, immune antibodies to a large number of the many known blood group antigens have been implicated as a cause of hemolytic disease of the newborn. It was shown by Witebsky (32) in 1946 that this disease could occur due to an incompatibility of the ABO blood groups between mother and child. This condition is fulfilled when the mother's blood is group O while that of the father is either group A_1, A_1B, or B. Formerly it was believed that only the group O mother was a source of potential complications, but recently it has been shown that occasionally the group A or group B mother can also have diseased children. Under any of these circumstances, the foreign antigen of the fetus can stimulate the mother to produce an immune form of anti-A or anti-B differing in serologic properties from her own naturally occurring isoagglutinins.

It is interesting to note that statistics have led certain investigators (4, 6) to believe that in heterospecific pregnancies the existence of ABO incompatibility between mother and fetus exerts a protective influence, so that the likelihood of developing Rh antibodies is from two to three times less than in homospecific pregnancies, where these incompatibilities do not exist. A possible explanation for this may be attributed to rapid removal of the immunizing red cells from the maternal circulation by naturally occurring isoantibodies in heterospecific cases. This takes place so quickly that the weaker Rh antigen might not be present long enough to exert a suitable immunizing stimulus. The

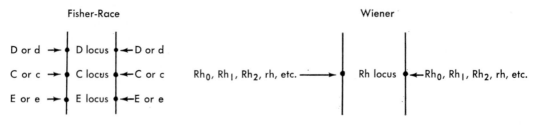

Fig. 2. Schematic representation of two theories for the inheritance of Rh.

Table 3. Standard Notations for the Rh Antigens, Anti-Rh Antibodies, and Eight Possible Genotypic Combinations

ANTIGENS		CORRESPONDING ANTIBODIES		POSSIBLE GENETIC COMBINATIONS			
Fisher-Race	Wiener	Fisher-Race	Wiener	Fisher-Race	Wiener	Often Used	Gene Frequency
D	Rh_0	Anti-D	$Anti-Rh_0$	cDe	Rh_0	R_0	0.0257
C	rh'	Anti-C	Anti-rh'	CDe	Rh_1	R_1	0.4076
E	rh''	Anti-E	Anti-rh''	cDE	Rh_2	R_2	0.1411
d	Hr_0	(Anti-d)	$(Anti-Hr_0)$	CDE	Rh_z	R_z	0.0024
c	hr'	Anti-c	Anti-hr'	cde	rh	r	0.3886
e	hr''	Anti-e	Anti-hr''	Cde	rh'	R'	0.0098
				cdE	rh''	R''	0.0119
D^u	**Rh_0**			CdE	rh_y	R_y	very rare

A or B antigens, being much more potent, however, could initiate the production of immune isoantibodies with a stimulus of relatively shorter duration.

Originally it was thought that the Rh factor was a single antigen, but subsequent discovery of anti-Rh antibodies of different specificity revealed a number of genetically related antigens now included in the Rh system. Fisher, recognizing the interrelationship of the four Rh antigens then known, postulated the existence of six antigens determined by three pairs of closely linked genes located at three adjacent loci on a pair of chromosomes. Fisher and Race (8) proposed a new nomenclature, using the symbols C, c, D, d, E, and e to designate the six antigens, and anti-C, anti-c, anti-D, etc., to designate the antibodies specific for these antigens. Both this mode of inheritance and nomenclature were different from those originally proposed by Wiener. He postulated that a series of multiple alleles existed, whereby a single gene on one locus was responsible for the ultimate production of a single antigenic grouping composed of from two to three separate antigens. These two theories are illustrated in Figure 2, and the two nomenclatures for the six standard Rh antigens and their antibodies along with the eight possible combinations in which the genes determining them can be arranged on a chromosome, are given in Table 3. The most common Rh genotypes of the English people are listed in Table 4. It should be noted that, although 85 per cent of Caucasians are Rh_0 positive, the frequency of this trait is 94 per cent among Negroes and 99 per cent among Orientals.

Numerous arguments have been presented for and against the validity of each of these theories, but as yet no definite conclusions have been reached. At the present, most experts seem to favor Wiener's theory of inheritance but prefer the simpler notation of Fisher and Race. Recently a completely new nomenclature for this blood group system was proposed by Rosenfield et al. (23), which is still in the developmental stages. While realizing that the Wiener notation may be more correct genetically, the authors feel that the student beginning this study should first learn the Fisher-Race nomenclature, which is used more universally and is perhaps more easily remembered.

Since the discovery of the five original antigens (d has not been recognized because a real example of anti-d has never been found), a number of alternative forms (allelomorphs) have been recognized—i.e., D^u, C^w, c^u, C^x, E^u, e^s, e^i, and others. In addition, compound antigens such as: f(ce) and V(ce^s) and their respective antibodies have recently been described. The latter antigen occurs almost exclusively in Negroes. If one adds to the eight arrangements listed the genotypes resulting from a substitution of these allelomorphs for the five standard antigens, a large number of different possible combinations results.

Table 4. Most Common Rh Genotypes of the English People

CDe/cde	(R_1r)	31.7%	
CDe/CDe	(R_1R_1)	16.6%	Rh_0 Positive
CDe/cDE	(R_1R_2)	11.5%	
cDE/cde	(R_2r)	10.9%	
cde/cde	(rr)	15.1%	Rh_0 Negative

Fortunately, from the practical viewpoint the complexities of the Rh blood group system can be greatly simplified. The essential fact to be borne in mind is that the $D(Rh_0)$ antigen is by far the most potent of all the Rh antigens and probably accounts for over 90 per cent of the clinical difficulties encountered with this system. For this reason, the anti-D serum is the standard Rh grouping serum; cells agglutinated by it are called Rh_0 positive and all others not agglutinated by it —therefore, not containing the D antigen— are considered Rh_0 negative.

In recent years the clinical importance of the D^u variant has been established. The red cells of individuals possessing this antigen in lieu of normal D are not agglutinated by the anti-D sera routinely employed, and special tests must be performed in order to detect its presence. Even though D^u gives a very weak or negative reaction in in vitro tests, it can stimulate production of anti-D antibodies in an Rh_0 negative individual. By far the greatest percentage of D^u individuals, however, are not capable themselves of eliciting anti-D antibodies when injected with cells containing a normal D antigen. For these reasons, the D^u variant must be tested for and those individuals who possess it classified as Rh_0 positive. The only person considered as Rh_0 negative, therefore, is one who has been shown to be lacking both the D antigen and its D^u variant.

While D is the most potent of the Rh antigens, immunization of the Rh_0 negative individual (cde/cde) by both the C and D, or D and E antigens is of frequent occurrence. Likewise, immunization of the C__ __/ C— — individual by the c antigen or of the __ __E/__ __E individual by the e antigen provoking anti-c or anti-e respectively, can occur occasionally.

Unlike the ABO blood group system, there are no regularly occurring natural isoagglutinins to any of the Rh antigens. All of the antibodies are the result of immunization. Each of these cases results from the inoculation of red cells containing the offending antigen into an individual lacking on his own erythrocytes that antigen or combination of antigens provoking the antibodies. This inoculation of red cells can occur from a fetus through defects in the placenta, as in the case of isoimmunization of pregnancy by intramuscular injection of blood or through blood transfusion. In view of the complications resulting from prior immunization to the Rh antigens in pregnancy and transfusion, it becomes imperative to guard against this eventuality by using only Rh_0 negative blood for the transfusion of Rh_0 negative individuals.

With the number of anti-Rh sera of different specificity available, and the various technics by which they may be employed, it is possible, by grouping tests, to predict with a fairly high degree of accuracy the most probable Rh genotype of an individual. Besides being of value in medicolegal testing, this has allowed a prediction of the outcome of future pregnancies in women already immunized by the $D(Rh_0)$ antigen. Information as to whether such a man is homozygous or heterozygous with respect to the D antigen is of considerable importance, since, as is shown in Figure 3, all the children of a homozygous father will be Rh_0 positive and, therefore, affected, while, theoretically at least, half the children of a heterozygous man will be Rh_0 negative and consequently normal.

The zygosity of the D gene can not be determined serologically, since antisera to the product of its supposed allelic gene (d) are nonexistent. Based on statistics gathered from data in large-family studies, regarding the gene frequencies and most probable combinations of the six Rh antigens, it is possible to make a fairly accurate presumption of the status of D, depending on the zygosity of C and E which can be readily demonstrated. When an Rh_0 positive individual is homozygous for either C or E, then D is most likely homozygous. If, on the other hand, he is heterozygous for either C or E, then D is also heterozygous. Finally, Rh_0 positive individuals who possess both C and E, regardless of whether they are hetero- or homozygous, are usually homozygous for D.

The Anti-Rh Antibodies. During the course of examining maternal sera for Rh antibodies in order to test the hypothesis concerning the pathogenesis of hemolytic

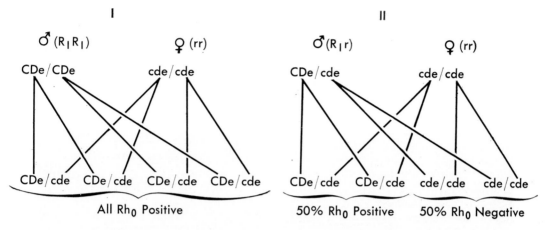

Fig. 3. Rh genotypes of possible offspring of Rh$_o$ negative mother and (I) homozygous fathers and (II) heterozygous fathers.

disease of the newborn, numerous investigators found that antibodies were demonstrable in only 30 to 50 per cent of all clinically proven cases. This apparent discordance, with the explanation of Levine, was resolved when Race in Great Britain (22) and Wiener in the United States (30) simultaneously discovered that an antibody of an entirely new serologic variety was involved in the majority of cases. They found that it united specifically with its antigen in vitro and in vivo but was not capable of producing visible agglutination in vitro. Previously, in searching for antibodies according to the classical procedure, which utilized physiologic salt solution as a diluent and test cell suspending medium, no antibody could be detected by direct agglutination. If, by contrast, normal adult human serum, bovine albumin, or almost any colloidal or proteinaceous material was used as a milieu for the reaction, then visible agglutination would occur, and the antibody could be demonstrated directly. The serum-active variety of Rh antibody became known as an "incomplete" antibody, in contrast to the saline-active or "complete" antibody.

At first, it was thought that this new type of agglutinin was "univalent"—i.e., possessed but a single site for combining with antigen and therefore could not form the antigen-antibody bridges, between adjacent cells required for the latticework that is observed as clumping or agglutination. It was later shown, however, that if the antigenic receptor sites on the cell were altered by treatment with proteolytic enzymes such as papain, ficin, trypsin, or bromelin, direct agglutination would be achieved in saline diluents, even with incomplete antibodies. Recent physicochemical studies on purefied antibodies indicate that the complete agglutinins are large molecules composed of 19 S. gamma globulin, while the incomplete varieties are smaller 7 S. gamma globulins. It is entirely possible, therefore, that the incomplete antibody is too short to form a firm bond between antigens on adjacent red cells, without some alteration of the physical conditions. This can be accomplished either by the use of colloids or through further exposure of antigens that may be located in deep fissures by enzymatic degradation of the surrounding cell wall. Some of these concepts are diagramed schematically in Figure 4.

The Coombs Antihuman Globulin Test. Another extremely important method for demonstrating incomplete antibodies was devised by Coombs, Mourant, and Race (5). An antiserum against the species specific human serum proteins was made by immunization of rabbits. These anti-human-serum antibodies could then be made to react with their specific antigens, which in this case were the anti-Rh antibodies (constituents of human serum) attached to the Rh antigens of the red cells. This second antigen-antibody reaction was capable of producing visible agglutination of the antibody-coated cells (Figure 3).

The discovery of this sensitive test proved of considerable clinical importance. It demonstrates the in vivo antibody sensitization of erythrocytes, such as that which occurs in infants with erythroblastosis and in certain forms of adult acquired hemolytic anemia. It is performed by first thoroughly washing the red cells with copious volumes of saline to remove all traces of unbound globulin from the cells. The anti-human-globulin

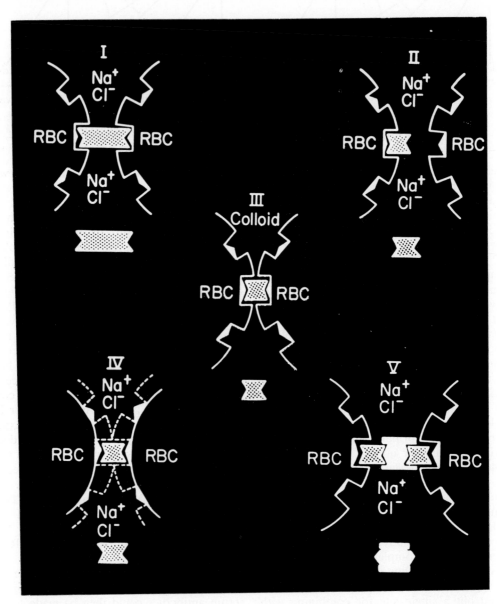

Fig. 4. In saline solution, adjacent red cells are held apart by electrostatic forces. The complete antibody is of sufficient length to bridge this distance (I). The incomplete antibody is too short (II). Colloids alter these charges, allowing the cells to come closer together, resulting in bridging (III). Enzymatic degradation in effect permits the antigenic sites to approximate each other more closely (IV). The antiglobulin antibody acts as a bridge (V).

serum is then added to the cells and, if sensitized by an attached antibody (a human globulin), agglutination will take place.

When this test is performed for the purpose of detecting antibodies that have combined with their red cell antigens in vivo, it is known as the "direct antiglobulin test." It is also possible to employ the same procedure to determine the antigens present on a cell by using specific incomplete antibodies, or to identify unknown, incomplete antibodies in the serum of an immunized individual with test cells of known antigenic composition. In these cases the cells to be tested are first incubated in vitro with the antisera, to permit sensitization; the Coombs test is then performed as before. Agglutination indicates that the cell contains the antigen or that the unknown serum contains the antibodies, depending upon what information is desired. Whenever this reaction involves in vitro sensitization of the erythrocytes, the test is known as the "indirect antiglobulin test."

The routine use of this serologic tool eventually uncovered the existence of still another type of incomplete antibody, which, though capable of sensitizing cells containing the specific antigens, would fail to agglutinate the cells regardless of the suspending media. Immune isoantibodies of this variety are most frequently found associated with blood group systems to be described later.

Since the original description of the Coombs test in 1945, the specificity of the reaction has been studied extensively. It has been demonstrated that antibodies such as incomplete anti-D of the Rh system react preferentially with a Coombs serum prepared against human gamma globulin (anti-gamma Coombs). Certain other incomplete antibodies belonging to other blood group systems, however, can be demonstrated by this method only when a Coombs serum directed against the non-gamma globulin portion of human serum (anti-non-gamma Coombs) is employed. It is believed that in the latter reaction the rabbit antibody is reacting with human complement, bound by the original antigen-antibody reaction, rather than with the antibody molecule itself. When carrying out tests with such antibodies, therefore, it becomes imperative to add fresh, normal human serum as a source of complement.

It was felt by many investigators that the antiglobulin technic was the most sensitive method for the detection of incomplete antibodies, and therefore its utilization would insure the detectibility of all antibodies of this type. Our knowledge, concerning the serologic reactivity of the various forms of blood group antibodies, has reached the stage where it is quite evident that this procedure is no longer the panacea of immunohematologic investigation. Examples of incomplete antibodies have been found, such as immune anti-A, that react very poorly, if at all, in the Coombs test. These same agglutinins, however, give good reactions when colloidal diluents are used.

A test, useful for the detection of the sensitization of infant's erythrocytes with antibodies demonstrable only in colloidal diluents, is the "adult serum, serum+albumin slide sensitization test" of Witebsky (31). In this test, the serum of the infant is removed and the packed cells mixed on a slide with undiluted, normal, adult human serum. This procedure brings about clumping of the cells if they are coated with incomplete anti-D, while unsensitized cells remain in a homogeneous suspension. An extension of the original test involves the use of a mixture of equal parts of adult human serum and 30 per cent bovine albumin, which proved to be far superior to the serum alone in cases where the offending antibody is anti-D. In ABO sensitization, however, serum was found better. In view of the good reactions obtained in this test with antibodies that react poorly by the Coombs technic, it is an important diagnostic tool.

THE LUTHERAN BLOOD GROUP SYSTEM

Approximately 8 per cent of white Americans are Lu^a positive. Anti-Lu^a appears occasionally in Lu^a negative individuals following multiple transfusions but usually disappears rapidly thereafter and may be responsible for certain mild transfusion reactions. Thus far, several examples of the antithetical antibody, anti-Lu[b], have been found.

THE KELL BLOOD GROUP SYSTEM

This blood group system, discovered in 1946, is defined by two antigens K (Kell) and k (Cellano), both of which have an ability to provoke their respective antibodies in transfused patients and pregnant women lacking the responsible antigens. This is particularly true of K, which occurs in about 9 per cent of all individuals, 91 per cent being Kell negative. Only 1 in 500 people lack the k antigen; consequently, it is of minor importance, except in the rare instance when it might be necessary to find k negative blood (genotype *KK*) with which to transfuse a patient immune to this antigen.

These antigens are exceptionally good antigens, second in strength only to D of the Rh system. As a result, immunization to K due to transfusion and pregnancy is being recognized with increasing frequency. The antibodies produced are usually incomplete, of the type demonstrable only by means of the antiglobulin reaction. In addition, anti-K is one of the few examples of a complement-binding blood group antibody, capable of causing rapid intravascular hemolysis. Naturally occurring antibodies are not usually found.

Two additional antigens belonging to this system have been described (1, 2). One of these, of low incidence, is called "Penney" (Kp[a]) and the other of high incidence designated "Rautenberg" (Kp[b]). The genetics of this system are not yet completely understood, since some individuals have been reported whose red cells give no reaction with any of the four antisera available and therefore appear to be devoid of all known antigens in the Kell system (3).

Another antibody, anti-Js[a], was found in the serum of a multi-transfused patient by Giblett in 1958 (9). She was able to show that it identified a new antigen, "Sutter" (Js[a]), which until very recently seemed to be independent of the other known blood group systems. Thus far several additional examples of this antibody as well as an anti-Js[b], which detected the allelic antigen Js[b], have been found. There is recent evidence that perhaps some association exists between these antigens and the Kell blood group system, since those individuals whose cells give no reaction with Kell antisera are also Js(a−b−) (27). The antigen Js[a] is present on the cells of approximately 20 per cent of Negroes, but is apparently absent from the blood of Caucasians. It may prove to be of value in the study of anthropology.

THE LEWIS BLOOD GROUP SYSTEM

The Lewis antigens, Le[a] and Le[b], are unique among all of the others conferring blood group specificity, since they are not part of the red cell structure. Instead, they are soluble antigens, found in body fluids, which adhere to the erythrocyte surface and thereby render the cells agglutinable by the specific antisera anti-Le[a] or anti-Le[b]. By means of these reagents three phenotypes are discernible: Le(a+b−), Le(a+b+), Le(a−b−). The last is found in greatest frequency among Negroes.

At first, it was believed that the genes responsible for the production of these antigens were linked to the secretor genes, since Le(a+) individuals were usually found to be non-secretors of A, B, and H, while secretors of these substances were usually Le(a−). This hypothesis has since been disproved, and the current explanation of the observed relationship involves the phenomenon of gene interaction rather than gene linkage. This can be best understood by imagining a limited amount of precursor material, from which soluble A, B, H, or Lewis substances can be formed. In a secretor A, B, or H are made first, leaving very little for the formation of Lewis, even though the individual has inherited the appropriate gene from one of his parents. Consequently, no Le[a] antigen is present in this serum, to become attached to the cells, and they give a negative reaction with anti-Le[a]. If, on the other hand, the person is a non-secretor who has inherited a Lewis gene, sufficient precursor substance is available to make soluble Lewis substances that can render the cells Le(a+).

The antibodies of this system are likewise

unique. They are frequently found as naturally occurring antibodies, especially in the sera of Le(a−b−) individuals. In addition, they can also be produced as a result of immunization, and have been proven to be the cause of hemolytic transfusion reactions. In vitro the antibodies may behave as specific, complete, cold agglutinins, when tested at 4° C. At 37° C. they behave as incomplete antibodies, best demonstrated with an anti-non-gamma Coombs reagent. In the presence of complement, they can produce specific lysis of red cells containing the appropriate antigen.

THE DUFFY BLOOD GROUP SYSTEM

The antigens of this blood group system are designated by the symbols Fy^a and Fy^b. Anti-Fy^a reacts with about 65 per cent of all bloods. Sanger, Race, and Jack (25) noted that approximately 82 per cent of Negro bloods gave negative reactions with both anti-Fy^a and anti-Fy^b, and they proposed a third allelomorph, Fy, suggesting that perhaps someday a new antibody might be found, with which Fy might be identified as Fy^c.

Only one or two examples of anti-Fy^b have been found; however, immunization by Fy^a through transfusion or pregnancy is not exceptionally rare, and like anti-K, anti-Fy^a is being detected more frequently. These antibodies can be responsible for serious and fatal transfusion reactions as well as hemolytic disease of the newborn. As a rule, naturally occurring antibodies are not found in this system, all of which arise from antigenic stimulation, which results in the production of incomplete agglutinins, detectable only by the antiglobulin method.

THE KIDD BLOOD GROUP SYSTEM

This system is identified by the antigens Jk^a and Jk^b. Approximately 75 per cent of individuals are Jk^a positive, and 25 per cent Jk^a negative. Only a very few examples of Kidd antibodies have been encountered, but it is known that they are capable of producing transfusion reactions and hemolytic dis-

ease of the newborn. Like anti-K and anti-Fy^a, the anti-Jk^a antibodies may be detected only by the antiglobulin technic, and even then with difficulty, unless an anti-non-gamma Coombs serum is used and a source of complement is provided.

Like the Duffy system, the genetics of the Kidd blood groups have been complicated by the recent finding of several individuals of non-Caucasian ancestry whose red cells give no reaction with either anti-Jk^a or anti-Jk^b and therefore appear as Jk(a−b−) phenotype (21).

THE DIEGO BLOOD GROUP SYSTEM

The Diego antigen was discovered by Levine, Koch, McGee, and Hill in 1954 (16). Thus far two additional examples of anti-Di^a have been found, all associated with hemolytic disease of the newborn. Although virtually absent from Caucasians, it is found in a fairly high frequency in North and South American Indians and Asiatic Mongoloids. Numerous investigators have studied the incidence of this antigen in widely diversified populations, and it has been shown to be a potent genetic marker of certain ethnic groups. It is therefore of great importance in anthropologic investigations.

SEX-LINKED BLOOD GROUPS

The discovery of the antigen Xg^a by Mann, Cahan, Gelb, Fisher, Hamper, Tippett, Sanger, and Race in 1962 (19), was the first instance in which a gene responsible for the production of a characteristic blood group antigen was located on a sex chromosome. This finding was made when it was noticed that a new antibody reacted more frequently with the red cells of females who have two X chromosomes than with those of males with but a single X chromosome. The presence of this readily identifiable characteristic offers a unique opportunity for the study and mapping of other human traits whose genes reside on this chromosome. Undoubtedly it will prove to be an extremely important aid to our better understanding of human genetics, inherited diseases, and other sex-linked characteristics.

OTHER BLOOD GROUPS

In addition to the discovery of the blood group systems already mentioned and summarized in Table 5, considerable data have been accumulated on a large number of unrelated blood group antigens and antibodies. Some of these of relatively low incidence, such as Jobbins, Becker, Romunde, and Swann, are confined to specific individuals or

Table 5. Approximate White and Negro Blood Types in the United States

These figures are adapted from studies at the Knickerbocker Foundation, Inc., New York, and the Lister Institute, London, 1955

SYMBOL	GENOTYPES	APPROXIMATE PER CENT			REACTIONS WITH ANTISERA				
		AVERAGE	WHITE	NEGRO					

ABO Blood Group System

SYMBOL	GENOTYPES	AVERAGE	WHITE	NEGRO	A	A_1	B		
O	OO	44	43	51	0	0	0		
A_1	A_1A_1, A_1A_2, A_1O	42	34	21	+	+	0		
A_2	A_2A_2, A_2A_3, A_2O		10	6	+	0	0		
B	BB, BB_w, BO	10	9	17	0	0	+		
A_1B	A_1B	3	3	1	+	+	+		
A_2B	A_2B, A_xB	1	1	3	+	0	+		

MNSs Blood Group System

SYMBOL	GENOTYPES	AVERAGE	WHITE	NEGRO	M	N	S	s	U
	MS MS	4	6	1	+	0	+	0	+
	MS MSᵘ				+	0	+	0	+
	MS Ms	11	14	7	+	0	+	+	+
	Ms Ms	12	8	15	+	0	0	+	+
	Ms MSᵘ				+	0	0	+	+
	MSᵘ MSᵘ		0	very rare	+	0	0	0	0
	NS NS	1	1	1	0	+	+	0	+
	NS NSᵘ				0	+	+	0	+
	NS Ns	5	6	3	0	+	+	+	+
	Ns Ns	18	15	21	0	+	0	+	+
	Ns NSᵘ				0	+	0	+	+
	NSᵘ NSᵘ		0	very rare	0	+	0	0	0
	MS NS	3	4	1	+	+	+	0	+
	MS NSᵘ				+	+	+	0	+
	MSᵘ NS				+	+	+	0	+
	MS Ns	20	24	16	+	+	+	+	+
	Ms NS				+	+	+	+	+
	Ms Ns	29	22	35	+	+	0	+	+
	Ms NSᵘ				+	+	0	+	+
	MSᵘ Ns				+	+	0	+	+
	MSᵘ NSᵘ		0	very rare	+	+	0	0	0

P Blood Group System

SYMBOL	GENOTYPES	AVERAGE	WHITE	NEGRO	P_1	$P+P_1$			
P_1	P_1P_1	80	79	94	+	+			
	P_1P_2				+	+			
	P_1p				+	+			
P_2	P_2P_2	14	21	6	0	+			
	P_2p				0	+			
p	pp		rare	rare	0	0			

Symbol	Genotypes	Approximate Per Cent			Reactions with Antisera				
		Average	White	Negro					

Rh Blood Group System

Symbol	Genotypes	Average	White	Negro	C	D	E	c	e
R_1R_0	CDe/cDe	29	34	24	+	+	o	+	+
R_1r	CDe/cde				+	+	o	+	+
R_1R_1	CDe/CDe	10	17	3	+	+	o	o	+
rr	cde/cde	14	15	6	o	o	o	+	+
R_2R_0	cDE/dDe	12	12	12	o	+	+	+	+
R_2r	cDE/cde				o	+	+	+	+
R_1R_2	CDe/cDE	8	13	2	+	+	+	+	+
R_0R_0	cDe/cDe	10	2	49	o	+	o	+	+
R_0r	cDe/cde				o	+	o	+	+
R_2R_2	cDE/cDE	2	2	2	o	+	+	+	o
r'r	Cde/cde	1	1	1	+	o	o	+	+
r"r	cdE/cde	1	1	1	o	o	+	+	**+**
The rest	—	0.5	0.5	0.5			—		
V	—	3	0.5	27			V +		

Lutheran Blood Group System

Symbol	Genotypes	Average	White	Negro	Lu^a	Lu^b
Lu^a	Lu (a + b −)	6	8	4	+	o
	Lu (a + b +)				+	+
Lu^b	Lu (a − b +)	94	92	96	o	+
	Lu (a − b −)	very rare			o	o

Kell Blood Group System

Symbol	Genotypes	Average	White	Negro	K	k
K+	KK	.2	.2	.2	+	o
	Kk	6	9	2	+	+
K−	kk	94	91	98	o	+

Lewis Blood Group System

Symbol	Genotypes	Average	White	Negro	Le^a	Le^b
Le^a	Le (a + b −)	22	22	22	+	o
Le^b	Le (a − b +)	70	72	55	o	+
	Le (a − b −)	8	6	22	o	o

Duffy Blood Group System

Symbol	Genotypes	Average	White	Negro	Fy^a	Fy^b
Fy^a	Fy (a + b −)	13	17	9	+	o
	Fy (a + b +)	25	49	2	+	+
Fy^b	Fy (a − b +)	28	34	22	o	+
	Fy (a − b −)		0	68	o	o

Kidd Blood Group System

Symbol	Genotypes	Average	White	Negro	Jk^a	Jk^b
Jk^a	Jk (a + b −)	41	25	57	+	o
	Jk (a + b +)	42	50	34	+	+
Jk^b	Jk (a − b +)	17	25	9	o	+

families, and have been termed "private blood groups." Others, of high frequency, such as Vel and Gerbich, are present in the vast majority of the population with minor exceptions and are called "public blood groups." Through the years, as investigations have progressed, it has been possible to incorporate a fair number of these into the well-established systems; many of them, however, still remain.

It should be pointed out, that the individuality of human blood does not cease with the red cells. Recent discoveries have shown that even human gamma globulin has individual specificity. In this regard, the Gm and Inv groups of human serum have thus far been defined. Furthermore, a thorough study of the antigens of leukocytes and platelets has shown that, even though these cells share some erythrocytic antigens, they have, in addition, complete systems of antigens unique to their own type of cell.

If one were to calculate the total number of genotype combinations possible from the presently known isoantigens of human blood, an astronomic figure would most certainly result. In 1954 Race and Sanger predicted that the day predicted by Landsteiner when blood would be as individual as fingerprints was foreseeable by ordinary people. This prediction must now be modified, since it is apparent that that day is already here.

REFERENCES

1. Allen, F. H., and Lewis, S. J. Vox Sanguinis, 2:81, 1957.
2. ——— Lewis, S. J., and Fudenberg, H. Vox Sanguinis, 3:1, 1958.
3. Chown, B., Lewis, M., and Kaita, H. Nature, London, 180:711, 1957.
4. Clarke, C. A., Finn, R., McConnell, R. B., and Sheppard, P. M. Internat. Arch. Allergy, 13:5, 1958.
5. Coombs, R. R. A., Mourant, A. E., and Race, R. R. Brit. J. Exper. Path., 26:255, 1945.
6. Davidsohn, I., Stern, K., and Mackeviciute, M. Proc. VI Cong. Internat. Soc. Blood Transfusion, 1956.
7. Decastello, A. von, and Sturli, A. München. med. Wchnschr., 1:1090, 1902.
8. Fisher, R. A. Cited by Race, R. R., in Nature, London, 153:771, 1944.
9. Giblett, E. R. Nature, London, 181:1221, 1958.
10. Landsteiner, K. Zentralbl. f. Bakt., 27:257, 1900.
11. ——— Wien. klin. Wchnschr., 14:1132, 1901.
12. ——— and Levine, P. Proc. Soc. Exper. Biol. & Med., 24:941, 1927.
13. ——— and Wiener, A. S. Proc. Soc. Exper. Biol. & Med., 43:223, 1940.
14. Levine, P., Burnham, L., Katzin, E. M., and Vogel, P. Am. J. Obst. & Gynec., 42:925, 1941.
15. ——— Katzin, E. M., and Burnham, L. J.A.M.A., 116:825, 1941.
16. ——— Koch, E. A., McGee, R. T., and Hill, G. H. Am. J. Clin. Path., 24:292, 1954.
17. Levine, P., and Stetson, R. E. J.A.M.A., 113:126, 1939.
18. ——— Vogel, P., Katzin, E. M., and Burnham, L. Science, 94:371, 1941.
19. Mann, J. D., Cahan, A., Gelb, A. G., Fisher, N., Hamper, J., Tippett, P., Sanger, R., and Race, R. R. Lancet, i:8, 1962.
20. Mohn, J. F., Lambert, R. M., Bowman, H. S., and Brason, F. W. Brit. J. Haematol., 7:112, 1961.
21. Pinkerton, F. J., Mermod, L. E., Liles, B. A., Jack, J. A., and Noades, J. Vox Sanguinis, 4:155, 1959.
22. Race, R. R. Nature, London, 153:771, 1944.
23. Rosenfield, R. E., Allen, F. H., Swisher, S. N., and Kochwa, S. Transfusion, 2:287, 1962.
24. Sanger, R. Nature, London, 176:1163, 1955.
25. ——— Race, R. R., and Jack, J. Brit. J. Haematol., 1:370, 1955.
26. ——— Race, R. R., Walsh, R. J., and Montgovery, C. Heredity, 2:131, 1948.
27. Stroup, M. Personal Communication, 1963.
28. von Dungern, E., and Hirszfeld, L. Zeitsch. f. Immun., 8:526, 1911.
29. Walsh, R. J., and Montgomery, C. Nature, London, 160:504, 1947.
30. Wiener, A. S. Proc. Soc. Exper. Biol. N.Y., 56:173, 1944.
31. Witebsky, E., Rubin, M. I., Engasser, L., and Blum, L. J. Lab. and Clin. Med., 32:1339, 1947.
32. ——— Blood, 3: (Supp. 2) 66, 1948.

15

Tissue Transplantation Immunity

Tissue transplantation has aroused interest since early times. John Hunter transplanted a variety of skin appendages in man and lower animals and started a short-lived vogue for transplanting teeth. Skin has been used to cover burns with good initial results, corneal transplantation is a very adequate method for correcting corneal opacity, and bone, aorta, and cartilage have been used extensively for many years.

The transplantation of a dog's head was a sensation in the earlier part of this century, and tumor transplantation has been practiced intensively as a means of obtaining increased yields of tumor and also in an attempt to learn more of the possibilities of stimulating immunity to cancer. Recently transplantation of kidneys in man and in dogs has received much attention, and there are widespread hopes that organ transplantation will become a practicable means of correcting congenital abnormalities and a wide variety of chronic diseases.

Blood transfusion is a special case of tissue transplantation. Fortunately, many of the antigens on the red cell are weak, and a fierce reaction can be avoided by giving blood which is compatible for the ABO factors and for the antigen D of the Rh system. **Tissue antigens are much more numerous, and more of them are able to elicit strong immunity, so that matching for compatibility is only one of the problems to be solved; control of the immune system and the ability to suppress specific reactions are also essential.**

Thus the study of tissue antigens which proceeded in a rather leisurely fashion until a few years ago is now being very intensively pursued. From these studies have already come many observations of funda-mental theoretical importance. Interest has overlapped into the areas of allergy, bacteriology, and preventive medicine, and the development of information concerning the leukocyte antigens will aid studies of genetic linkage by providing a large series of readily available markers.

Immunity to foreign tissues does not differ fundamentally from immunity to any other foreign antigen; the reactions are modified because of the large mass of antigen and often because of the close antigenic similarity between graft and host, but the organism has only a limited number of reactions to rely upon. Some of these are specific immunologic reactions of antibody and immune lymphoid cells; the others are largely nonspecific enzymatic processes for the disposal of the foreign tissue after it has been altered by the primary reaction.

The study of immunity to tissues can be divided into three major divisions; only one of these, transplantation immunity, will be dealt with in this chapter. The other two branches, auto immunity and immunity to tumors, are to some extent special cases. The antigens primarily involved in these responses may be different, often less is known of the reaction, and—especially with respect to the study of tumor immunity—intensive research has been devoted to a detailed study of the differences between normal and malignant tissues. Because all three branches are closely related, however, some reference will be made to each of these types of reaction, but the student is referred to specialized reviews or monographs for more detailed information.

Development of Immunity. Before birth the embryo is insulated from the environment by the defenses of the mother. It has

277

a very poorly developed lymphoid system and the antibodies it possesses are those which have crossed the placenta. After birth, a variety of antibodies, mostly of the gamma-2 or 7 S. variety, passes with the milk to supplement the existing level. Repeated exposure to extraneous antigens soon stimulates the lymphoid system to proliferate and to assume the well-organized adult form. Delayed hypersensitivity reactions can be elicited, and antibodies can be made as fresh stimuli are encountered even at a very early age, although active immunity usually becomes apparent only after weaning. If the animal remains protected from bacterial infection—as, for instance, in a germ-free environment — the immunologic system remains poorly developed (84). When an animal raised under germ-free conditions is returned to an ordinary "healthy" animal room, exposure to the normal bacterial flora of the animal colony may cause death, or, if the animal survives, the lymphoid and reticuloendothelial systems mature rapidly.

While exposure to antigen is a necessary stimulus to the proper development of the lymphoid system, its maturation and development also appear to require the presence of the thymus gland. If the thymus of mice (61) or the bursa of Fabricius (22) and the thymus (89) of chickens are removed or destroyed, the lymphoid system remains rudimentary. The immune response to a wide variety of antigens is poor (see 26) and transplants of skin even from another species may survive indefinitely (61). Thymectomized animals do not grow properly, and many die in a few weeks. They will recover if given thymus or spleen fragments from another animal.

The full story of the actions of the thymus has not yet been worked out. Cells from the thymus migrate to other lymphoid centers, and ablation of the thymus during neonatal life may prevent the proper development of germinal centers. Since transplants of spleen will restore immunologic activity to a thymectomized mouse, the implication is that the cells which have migrated from the thymus to the spleen must be self-replicating. A humoral component is also implicated (59), since extracts of thymus will stimulate lymphoid development (53). The critical period of thymic activity is very early after birth. Within a few days thymectomy is less effective, and mice thymectomized after a month show little more than a slight loss in antibody titer as compared to sham-operated controls. The thymus has other effects; for example, thymectomy may have a dramatic effect in myasthenia gravis, a disease in which antibodies to muscle components are often found (60), and will prevent the occurrence of lymphatic leukemias of thymic origin in mice (51).

With increasing independence, the growing animal is faced with repeated exposure to a wide variety of microorganisms and to many foreign substances in its diet and in its environment, such as dust, pollen, and various animal and plant products. Each new stimulus acts to trigger off a new specific immunity, many of which are long-lasting, especially when, as usually happens, they are reinforced by repeated exposure to the same antigen.

Because of its exposure to bacterial and other environmental antigens, the animal builds up immunity to a wide spectrum of antigens. Some of the antigens encountered are similar to those found as an integral part of many mammalian tissues and cells (49, 74). It is possible that antibodies to blood group substances are formed as a result of exposure to bacteria and plant cells which coincidentally share either A or B antigens. Similarly, certain bacterial antigens are similar to other types of tissue antigens.

The usual reaction to a foreign substance, whether from a bacterium or house dust or any other extraneous antigenic material, is to develop immunity to the foreign antigen. If, as we believe, a number of important bacterial antigens are also found in the tissue of the animal or person infected, an immune response would also affect the tissues of the body itself. In this respect, the defense could be more devastating than the disease and a generalized auto immune reaction could develop. It has been essential during development to build in some blocking device to prevent the organism from making an immune reaction against its own normal cells and secretions.

Ehrlich observed that the serum of an animal would rarely react against his own tissues and coined the expression "horror autotoxicus" to express the idea that auto-reactions were forbidden. Exceptions became recognized with increasing frequency, however, and it is now known that although auto-antibodies can rarely be detected in the serum of a normal individual, they are by no means uncommon in some pathologic states, especially in diseases of the thyroid. The borderline area between nonreactivity and active immunization is quite small. Serum removed from a guinea pig and reinjected immediately does not immunize. If the same serum is treated with alkali, the denatured proteins are recognized as being different and antibodies are formed (56). Drugs such as Sedormid, nonantigenic in themselves, will selectively couple with platelets. The complex acts as an antigen, the antibody formed reacts immediately with the drug-treated platelets and destroys them, and a severe thrombocytopenic purpura may follow (1). Similar slight modifications are believed to be responsible for a variety of autoimmune diseases, but the agents coupling with the red cell or tissue have not been identified.

Older theories of immunologic reactivity could not explain the horror autotoxicus except by suggesting that if a tissue antigen was present, it was geneticaly impossible for the animal to develop immunity—i.e., that the capacity to form antibody and to make antigen were mutually exclusive. Too many exceptions are known for this to be tenable. Burnet and Fenner suggested that antibody formation was a fixed property of certain primitive lymphoid cells and that each specific type of cell could make only one type of antibody (19). The immunologic cells of the developing embryo were extremely vulnerable to the action of antigen and were destroyed on first exposure to their specific antigen. Because of this holocaust in prenatal life, no reactive cells were later available to respond to the same antigen, and it was thus impossible for the animal to respond to its own tissues, and auto-immunity to the majority of the tissues of the body became impossible. These authors believed that in later life exposure to an antigen stimulated the appropriate cell to divide and to continue dividing until enough antibody to neutralize the antigen was produced.

A second view is that there is so much antigen accumulating at the sites of antibody production that the available antibody-producing cells cannot deal with the overload and become choked by the excess, thus producing a state of immunologic paralysis. This is most apt to occur in the embryo or new-born, where the amount of lymphoid tissue is minimal. Paralysis of this type can even be produced in adults if large amounts of antigen are given (32). In this situation, unlike that envisioned by Burnet and Fenner, it can be proved that the cells capable of forming antibody have not been killed by the gross excess of antigen, since the period of paralysis is followed by a period of normal antibody production (80). The antibody-forming cells remain fully saturated with antigen released by the normal turnover of cells of most tissues.

Failure to react against antigens found in the body before or at the time of birth extends to all antigens on the surface of cells bathed in lymph or tissue fluid in which macrophages and histiocytes, which can migrate to lymph nodes, are found. Failure to react also follows exposure to a variety of antigens which are not normally found in the body if exposure to these is given early and in adequate amounts, and if the antigenic differences are not too great. This exclusion does not apply to many intracellular antigens or to substances such as thyroglobulin, lens protein, or myelin which are secreted into vesicles with no venous or lymphatic drainage, which are only formed later in life, or where any turnover of cells is dealt with by phagocytic cells which do not migrate (i.e., in the brain or testis).

Tolerance. The inability of an immature animal to recognize a tissue from another animal as foreign is known as immunologic tolerance. It was observed by Owen (68) that dizygotic twin cattle sharing a common placenta could have two dissimilar types of circulating red cells. This phenomenon is known as **chimerism.** Red cell precursors from the dissimilar twin could colonize and persist without inducing an immune reaction. Medawar and his colleagues (9) later showed that a similar state of chimerism could be deliberately induced by the injection of a suspension of spleen, liver, and kidney cells into unborn or newborn animals. Dunsford et al. (30) found a chimeric state occurring in man, and other examples have since been reported in which two distinct types of red cell are found in the same individual, the second population coming from a dizygotic twin.

The ease with which tolerance can be induced at any given age depends upon the species. Tolerance in rabbits or mice is best induced before or at birth (16). In some strains of rats it can readily be induced up to 10 days of age (94), while others appear to be more mature at birth and tolerance can only be induced within a day or two of birth. While it was first thought that the ability to become tolerant was restricted to very young animals, Brent and Gowland (17) found that the induction of tolerance was dose dependent. An amount of antigen which would produce complete tolerance at birth will produce only partial tolerance after a few days. Tolerance could be produced in mice up to a week of age if the amount of antigen was proportionately increased. Howard et al. (45) found that the correlation between the amount of antigen required and the weight of lymphoid tissue was closer than the correlation with age. The spleen grows very rapidly in the mouse during the first three or four days after birth; the amount of antigen needed to induce tolerance increases proportionately. Thus the ease with which tolerance can be induced in the newborn is a reflection of the minute amount of lymphoid tissue present in the neonatal animal rather than any special property of the neonatal immunologic system; yet there **are** qualitative changes in the immune response at certain ages, such as the antibody response of adult mice (64). The resistance to incompatible transplanted tumors is much greater in two-month-old mice than in weanlings; this resistance also weakens in old animals.

The immunologically immature animal is, then, tolerant to those antigens to which it is exposed during fetal life or shortly after birth. It is not tolerant to antigens which it meets in moderate amounts in later life. More direct evidence that tolerance to the tissues of the animal's own body was acquired and not innate was provided by Triplett (85), who removed one complete section of the hypophysis of an immature tree frog tadpole, grew the explant in the dermis of another animal, and later reimplanted the same fragment into the original animal, now immunologically competent. The transplant, although of the animal's own tissue, was promptly rejected. Control animals in which only half the gland was removed did not react against the autograft. Tolerance appears to be specific for normal healthy tissues, and it has been suggested by Boyden (13) that damaged or aged cells present new antigens, either through denaturation or by increased permeability, and are thus recognized as "foreign" and then removed. This concept is in complete conflict with generally accepted theories, and, while there is little direct evidence to support it, the suggestion is provocative and auto-antibodies have frequently been found where there was no known auto-immune disease.

Although the term "tolerance" was at first restricted to situations in which live cells capable of division were injected, Cinader (24) soon showed that tolerance could follow the injection of albumin, and his observations have been repeatedly extended and confirmed. It has been shown that tolerance can be produced to red blood cells, and it is now agreed that tolerance can be produced and maintained by a wide variety of antigens, provided that excess antigen is maintained (63). If the antigen is not self-replicating, tolerance wanes as the antigen is metabolized or excreted.

It is possible to produce a tolerance-like state in the adult by destroying much of the lymphoid system. X-irradiation (88) and immuno-depressants such as the folic acid or purine antagonists have been found to be effective (87). To produce tolerance in the adult, the lymphoid system is first depressed and then an excess of antigen is given. It is not easy to induce tolerance to cells from a different species, or even to cells of another member of the same species, if the antigenic diversity between them is great.

The tolerant state can be broken by injecting normal or, preferably, immune lymphoid cells into a tolerant host, thus adding a population of cells not clogged with excess antigen (12). More interestingly

Weigle (91) has found that injecting an antigen modified by the addition of two extra chemical groups will provoke an immune response not only to the modified antigen but also to antigen originally used to promote tolerance. If only one of the additional groups is introduced, tolerance is unaffected and no antibody is formed to the slightly altered protein. There is a built-in stability and some blurring of specificity.

Tolerance is of considerable importance both practically and theoretically. Practically because it offers the greatest possibility for transplantation in humans without producing an immunologic cripple; theoretically because it can be used to explore the initiation of immunity.

Transplantation Immunity. When a fragment of tissue or a whole organ is transferred to a new host, it will settle down and begin to grow as if it were about to become a permanent part of its new host, if the new blood supply is adequate. After a few days a series of dramatic changes is observed. Grossly the graft may become swollen, with obvious inflammation of the surrounding tissue, hemorrhage within the graft and in the graft bed, and, finally, shrinkage and death of the graft.

Microscopically the changes vary somewhat with different species and with different kinds of tissue. The best-documented examples are skin graft rejections in rabbit, mouse, or man. Medawar's classic description (57) should be referred to for a detailed account, but essentially the first change is a progressive infiltration with small round cells that resemble lymphocytes. These cells penetrate the substance of the graft in very large numbers and surround the individual cells of the transplant. Small mononuclear cells are also found in large numbers in the graft bed. The small vessels supplying the graft become dilated, there is edema of the surrounding tissues, and thrombosis of the vessels leads to "ischemic necrosis" of the surviving cells. Finally, there is extensive fibrosis and the graft tissue is absorbed or sloughed off.

Variations in pattern are seen with different tissues, with different sites, and with different degrees of incompatibility. If graft and host are genetically very similar, the graft may continue in an uneasy state of survival for months, and an accumulation of macrophages and plasma cells may predominate over the small lymphocytoid cells. If the graft is of tumor cells, the most reactive host cell may be the macrophage, and phagocytosis of the tumor cell may be the most obvious means of graft destruction (Fig. 1, 2).

Rejection of a graft is accompanied by the appearance of antibodies in the serum (Fig. 3). These antibodies, which may be of several different types, are specifically directed against the graft. Some of them are cytotoxic in the presence of complement and, under certain special conditions, can transfer immunity both to skin grafts and to tumors (3). The titers tend to remain low after a single application of tissue.

A second graft, placed on the same or on a different site is more rapidly rejected. Second grafts become transiently vascularized and die after only a few days. There is cellular infiltration, but this is more marked in the graft bed than in the substance of the graft; there is a greater preponderance of plasma cells and macrophages, and plasma cells are numerous in the regional lymph node. The antibody response is also markedly higher. This is the second set reaction. For a very limited time after rejection of a first graft, a second graft will never heal in, capillaries do not develop, the graft survives only by diffusion, and appears chalky white; there is no cellular infiltration, and the whole graft can easily be pulled off and gradually turns brown and falls off. This is the "white graft reaction."

When a skin graft is applied to an incompatible recipient, antigen is carried to the regional lymph node. The passage of antigen is quite rapid: a graft excised 24 hours after being transplanted will already have sensitized the recipient. If the passage of antigen is blocked, immunity does not develop. Tiny fragments of tissue placed subcutaneously do not immunize unless they come into contact with a blood vessel (58). Ablation of the lymph nodes and of the lymphatics delays the onset of graft rejection, while various kinds of barrier can be placed between the graft and the draining lymphatics to prevent immunization. Woodruff (93) found

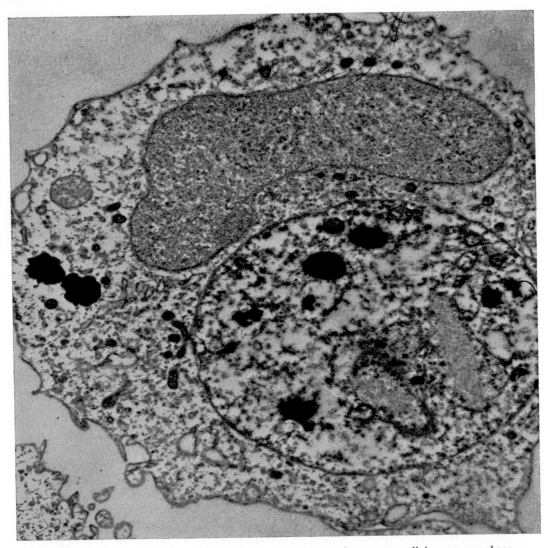

Fig. 1. Phagocytosis and early digestion of a mouse ascites tumor cell by a macrophage. X 15,900. (Courtesy of Dr. Leon Journey.)

no immunity developing if a piece of cell-impermeable membrane was placed underneath a skin graft. In our laboratory we have found that tumor cells grown inside a chamber made of this type of membrane do not immunize the host unless they can escape through the pores. Billingham and Silvers (11) found that the unique ability of the Syrian hamster to carry transplants in its cheek pouch was due to the existence of a subcutaneous sheet of mucoidal material which prevented the passage of antigen. Generally, if antigen does escape to reach

the neighboring lymphatics, the host rapidly becomes immune and may be able to destroy the graft despite the presence of the barrier. Direct passage to the lymph node via the lymphatics appears to be more effective than passage through the bloodstream, and in some special situations, such as the anterior chamber of the eye or within the substance of the brain, no immune reaction develops against the graft even when a good vascular supply is secured.

Normally antigen reaches the node shortly after the graft is applied, and a few days

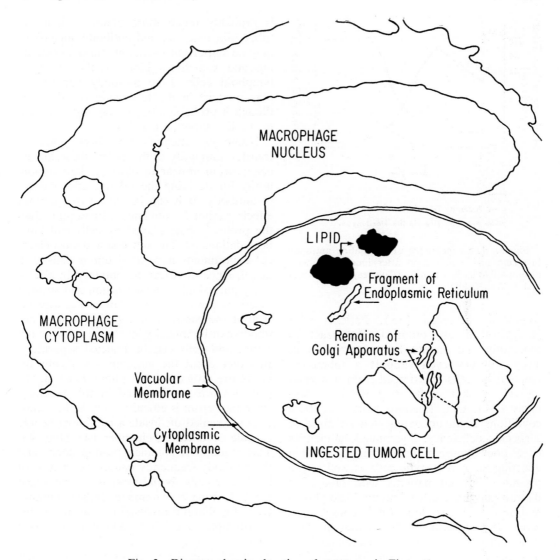

Fig. 2. Diagram showing location of structures in Figure 1.

later an immune reaction can be observed. This reaction appears to be largely directed by two prime agents, antibodies and cells. The antibody may give the specificity to the reaction and the cells accomplish much of the actual work of graft destruction. It has been thought that two kinds of antibody may be involved in graft destruction; one is tightly adherent to cells, the other is found free in the serum.

Other serum factors,—complement and a range of factors affecting capillary permeability—may also be involved. Graft rejec-

tion is delayed or may not occur when the recipient is unable to produce antibodies and also when it is unable to respond to a suitable test stimulus, such as tuberculin, to produce a delayed cellular type of hypersensitivity reaction. An example of the first condition is agammaglobulinemia, and of the second, Hodgkin's disease. Patients with agammaglobulinemia have low or undetectable antibody levels, form a poor response to bacterial invasion and do not respond normally to a skin graft; rejection is sometimes delayed for months, or a graft may be

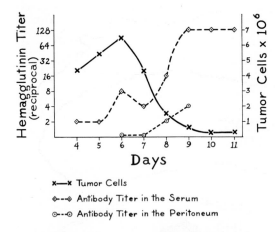

x——x Tumor Cells
◇--◇ Antibody Titer in the Serum
◎--◎ Antibody Titer in the Peritoneum

Fig. 3. The appearance of circulating antibody in serum and ascites fluid after inoculation with incompatible ascites tumor. (Courtesy of B. Amos and J. Wakefield.)

completely accepted (35). Patients with Hodgkin's disease often do not react to tuberculin and cannot be sensitized to it. They will not even support a tuberculin reaction by cells transferred from a normal individual; skin grafts may persist indefinitely (34). Unfortunately, neither of these conditions is an uncomplicated example of a specific deficiency. Agammaglobulinemics have poor lymph node organization often affecting the lymphocytic cells as well as the plasma cells and patients with Hodgkin's disease may have other immunologic abnormalities, such as low total complement levels. It is generally believed that the lack of a homograft reaction in agammaglobulinemics reflects the importance of antibodies, however, and that the sluggish reaction in Hodgkin's disease reflects on the importance of a cellular reaction.

Interest has centered around these two factors, although complement and other auxiliary factors, such as proteolytic and hydrolytic enzymes working to complete the destruction of the cell damaged by the primary agents, and permeability factors altering the blood supply to the graft are recognized (3).

Graft rejection has been thought to resemble the tuberculin reaction since lymphocytes invade the reaction site of both, and both reactions can be transferred with lymphocytes but not with serum. Graft rejection

is probably much more complex than the tuberculin reaction, and antibody appears to play an important part, sometimes augmenting and sometimes blocking the effect of lymphoid cells. Free antibody appears to play no part in the tuberculin reaction, although it probably does in the host response to the live tubercle bacillus.

Numerous attempts have been made to transfer immunity with serum. Experiments using serum appear to offer the best opportunity for deciding the relative effectiveness of antibody. If it can be shown that certain effects cannot be obtained with serum, then the probable part played by cells will have been delineated. The simplest and most clear-cut experiments have used tumor cells as a target, since these can be obtained in a relatively pure single cell suspension and stromal reactions can be largely ignored. For demonstrating the passive transfer of immunity, antibody can be mixed with tumor cells, or the serum and cells can be injected separately. In either event the antibody specifically inhibits the growth of the tumor (38). Lymphocytes are not involved in this reaction, since the serum is effective even if the tumor cells are sealed off inside a cell-impermeable capsule or diffusion chamber (4) (Fig. 4). This reaction is complement-dependent and the antibody frequently causes direct lysis of the tumor cells. While most is known about the 7 S. type of gamma globulins, another type of globulin is involved in some reactions.

Attempts to produce skin graft rejection have been successful but with considerably more difficulty. Immune serum from another species is effective, but iso immune serum (i.e., produced within a species) appears to be reactive only if it is injected into the graft site or if the permeability of the local blood vessels is increased as by painting with bromobenzene or xylene. Under these conditions destruction of tumor or of skin has been reported in rats (23) and in mice (83).

Immunity can also be transferred with lymph node cells. Just as with serum, the effect is best demonstrated with tumor cells mixed directly with the immune lymphoid cells. The immunity is at first centered around the regional lymph node. Lymph nodes from channels draining the graft bed of a primarily immunized host are potent, while those from other areas of the body are not. Para-doxically, although all the nodes from a hy-perimmune animal may be active, the specific activity appears to decrease with hyperim-munization. Lymph node cells from a hyper-immune animal are no better and may be less effective than cells from an animal once stimulated. Very few immune cells are needed to produce an effect if they are mixed di-rectly with the target (92). If the two are injected separately, the requirement for lymphoid cells is greatly increased, and in-stead of a fraction of one lymph node, pooled cells from the draining lymph nodes from as many as four animals may be needed (62).

Two major differences have been recorded between the effect of lymph node cells and that of serum antibody. Lymph node cells have a greater range of reactivity and will also destroy an established solid graft. Whereas antibodies are very effective against lymphoid tumors and very high concentra-tions may be necessary for destruction of sarcoma or normal tissue cells, lymph node cells can destroy most types of grafted tissue, apparently with equal ease.

Attempts to follow transferred lymph node cells to the reaction site in their new host have been disappointing. The great majority go directly to the spleen or lymph nodes of the recipient and remain there. The few that are found in the reaction site appear to have arrived there by chance. To investigate this McClusky and his colleagues (55) took groups of three guinea pigs. One group was immunized to picryl bovine gamma globulin and was given tritiated thymidine; the second was immunized to para chlorobenzoyl chlo-ride and was not labeled; the third was in-jected with lymphoid cells from each of the others and then challenged with each anti-gen. In most experiments only about 2 per cent of the cells at the reaction site were labeled, and there was no difference in the proportion of labeled to unlabeled cells be-tween the two sites. In another series of ex-periments the unimmunized host animal was labeled prior to injection. Most of the cells at the reaction site were now labeled, and it was possible to show not only that most of the cells in this type of reaction were of host origin, but also that most of them had un-

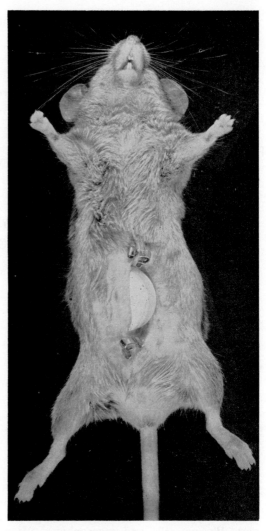

Fig. 4. Implantation of a diffusion chamber in a mouse. The chamber, a disc of plastic closed with porous membrane, is filled with cells and placed in the peritoneal cavity.

dergone cell division within 18 hours of their appearance at the site.

The manner in which a lymph node cell works and even the effective cell type within the node are not known. The majority of the numerous host cells which invade a graft probably have no direct effect on the graft. It might be supposed that they release dif-fusible substances which pass to the graft site, but there is no evidence for this unless the substance is one of a special class of cell-bound antibodies quite recently observed (13, 21). In other experiments the lymphoid

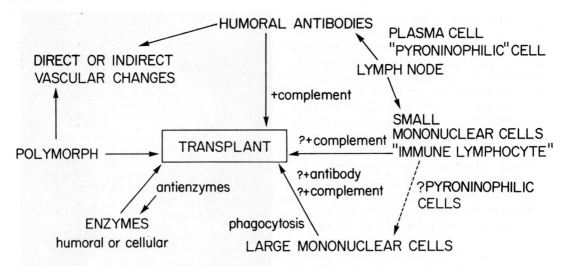

Fig. 5. Schematic representation of many of the known factors which react upon a graft.

cells appear to play a direct part in the reaction and to be killed as a result of it. When target cells and fragments from an immune node were grown in the same diffusion chamber, the target remained unaffected, despite the presence of immune cells until the two types of cell came into contact. If the tumor was on one wall of the chamber and the lymph node cells on the other, or if both were on the same membrane but had not yet grown into contact, no reaction was seen. When the two cell types met, the great majority of cells in the chamber, lymphocyte or target, died following the contact (2).

Other types of host cells can also play a part. Plasma cells and macrophages often congregate at a graft site, especially in second grafts or where the process of rejection is rather indolent (44). Plasma cells probably act as a local source of antibody. Macrophages remove any dead cells but can themselves transfer immunity to a normal animal. They appear to have two completely different activities. In the presence of antibody they are actively phagocytic for tumor cells. Transferred to a nonimmune host, they confer immunity even when washed free of antibody and even though they are believed to be unable to make antibody (67).

Many of the features of the homograft reaction are probably attributable to the effects of antibody carried on the surface of lymphocytes, either immune lymphocytes or

normal cells, especially those which have recently undergone division (Fig. 5). However, antibody can also block the effect of these cells. This will be considered below with some of the other anomalous reactions.

Unusual Forms of Graft Rejection. One of the most interesting effects is obtained when a graft reacts against its host. This occurs when the graft itself consists of lymphoid cells or lymphoid precursors. In its most extreme form the lymph node or spleen graft kills the host. The possibility of the graft reacting against its host was raised by Simonsen (77) and by Dempster (29). Numerous studies have been made by these and other investigators and a comprehensive review published by Simonsen (78). The observation that a homogenate of a mixture of tissues injected into a newborn animal in an attempt to induce tolerance would sometimes kill the animal was described by Billingham and his colleagues (8). In certain strains, the young become very sick with rapid loss of weight, loss of hair, exzema, and diarrhea, and finally die. This phenomenon is known as "runt disease." A careful account of the pathologic changes in this disease in the young rat has been published (10). The disease is caused by the activity of lymphoid cells alone or present in the tissue homogenate (Fig. 6).

Only certain strain combinations are affected; in others it seems probable that the

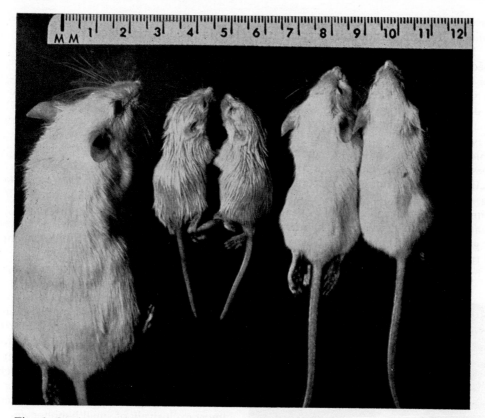

Fig. 6. Mother and litter of runted and normal offspring. Note the characteristic "oily" coats of the two animals in which runting was induced with homologous immune cells. (After Jutila and Weiser. *J. Immunol.*, 88:621, 1962.)

reaction is not sufficiently intense to damage or kill the host, or that since the immunologic system in some strains is better developed at birth, the newborn animal is already able to react against the transferred spleen and destroy it before the grafted cells have become firmly established. Schlesinger and Goitein (75) found that runt disease could be readily induced in Swiss mice when there were many animals in the same litter. If there were three or fewer in the litter, the individual mice were much larger, appeared to be more mature and did not become runted after treatment with foreign spleen cells.

A phenomenon comparable to runt disease but found in adult animals is referred to as the "graft-versus-host reaction." Most easily elicited when spleen is injected, it is also manifested when bone marrow is transferred. Graft-versus-host reactions occur when the immunologic competence of the recipient is decreased, as by lethal irradiation. Lethal irradiation with replacement bone marrow therapy has been considered as a possible treatment for leukemia. When tested in mice, the marrow cells usually protect against the immediate effects of up to 800 roentgens of whole body X-irradiation. In suitable groups 95 or 100 per cent survival at 30 days compared to no survival in controls receiving only irradiation is reported (46). If the marrow has been taken from a different strain of mice, the animals begin to die after 30 days and at death are found to have no lymphoid tissue remaining. If spleen from the same donor is mixed with bone marrow or given alone, death usually occurs within 10 days. At first there is hyperplastic replacement of the spleen and lymph nodes, but a very rapid exhaustion of the lymphoid cells supervenes and the animal dies in a manner similar to the final stages of runt disease in baby mice, diarrhea being a very prominent feature. Antibodies against the host have not been convincingly demonstrated, and the cause of death may be another manifestation of the type of destruction seen when host cells react with their target in a diffusion chamber (90) or in the intact animal (15). A similar syndrome is seen, however, in baby mice treated with corticosteroids. Thymic involution in these animals suggests that runting may result from destruction of the thymus by steroids (76) (Fig. 7).

Simonsen and his colleagues (79) injected parental cells into newborn F₁ hybrid mice. The graft cell could react against the parent, and runt disease should always follow, since the hybrid, having all the antigens of the parent, should not be able to react against the injected parental cells even if its immunologic maturation was relatively advanced. Some anomalous survivals were obtained, suggesting that certain antigens could be recessive and therefore present in the homozygous parent but not in the hybrid. Similar suggestions have been put forward by several other workers. While this is a topic of tremendous interest, it is very complex and not finally resolved. There is a strong possibility that some transplantation antigens are recessive, but the particular antigens involved have not been defined.

Gowans (41) has exploited graft versus host reactions to show that mature lymphocytes are not the end cells they were once supposed to be and that they are capable of differentiation into a biologically different type of cell. Gowans injected thoracic duct lymphocytes into incompatible animals. The thoracic duct cells were of two kinds: large lymphocytes, formerly thought to be less mature and capable of possible transformation, and small lymphocytes, generally supposed to be fully differentiated. Populations rich in large lymphocytes or composed almost exclusively of small lymphocytes were labeled and injected. Three distinct labels attached to DNA, RNA, or protein were used to avoid possible errors in interpretation arising from phagocytosis of the injected cells by host cells. The large lymphocytes migrated to the gut and were lost. The small lymphocytes settled down, mainly in the spleen, and rapidly differentiated into a large, rather primitive-looking cell with a pyroninophilic cytoplasm.

Turk and Stone have emphasized the importance of a similar cell in the early stages of immunization to various haptens capable of eliciting delayed hypersensitivity (86). Large pyroninophilic cells appear on the third day after painting with the sensitizing agent, reach a maximum on the fourth day, and then decline rapidly. These cells appear to differentiate into lymphocytes. Delayed hypersensitivity appears to be related to the appearance of the pyroninophilic cells.

When lymphoid cells are injected into a susceptible newborn mouse, they proliferate rapidly, causing splenic enlargement. Simonsen (78) has used the increase in spleen

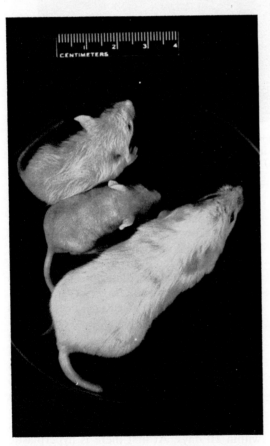

Fig. 7. Runt-like disease in mice induced by injection of hydrocortisone on day after birth. One normal animal (bottom) and two treated litter mates. (From Schlesinger and Mark. *Science,* 143:965, 1964.)

weight as a measure of the degree of reactivity and finds a close correlation between antigenic diversity and the degree of hypertrophy of the spleen. Mitosis and transformation also seem to follow exposure of peripheral lymphocytes or cells from spleen or lymph node from an immune subject to contact with a wide variety of specific antigens (31), as well as to certain nonspecific agents such as phytohemagglutinin (66).

Enhancement. A phenomenon in which antibody has an opposite effect to its more familiar lytic and suppressive role has been described under the title of "immunological enhancement" (47).

Typically it is exhibited by mouse sarcomas such as SA 1, a sarcoma indigenous to the A strain. SA 1 does not kill C57BL mice unless they are pretreated. The pretreatment may be passive, using rabbit or mouse antibody, or active, using a modified form of tumor for immunization. Passive enhancement is simply transferred by injecting serum from rabbits or C57BL mice which have been immunized against the live tumor. Like passively transferred immunity, it is of relatively short duration, lasting for up to a month after rabbit serum and for only a few days with mouse antibody. Active enhancement is best demonstrated by injecting C57BL mice with freeze-dried (lyophilized) SA 1 and then by challenging them with live tumor. The injection of lyophilized tumor induced a rather weak but long lasting "immunity," hemagglutinins can be detected for a year after immunization, and enhancement appears to persist as long as antibody is present.

It is not known whether enhancement is a common natural occurrence; for example, it has been thought that enhancing antibodies may be responsible for such conditions as the sudden flare up in the rate of human cancer growth after incomplete removal. The effects of enhancement are not limited to sarcoma; it can be demonstrated with other types of tumor and with skin (65). The amount of antigen injected and the route of administration are both critical.

The case of sarcoma 1 has been mentioned. This is a tumor which is extremely resistant to the lytic effects of antibody. Using a benz-pyrine induced ascites tumor called BP8 Gorer and Kaliss (39) were able to demonstrate an interesting relationship between enhancement and immunity. Large doses of antibody would completely inhibit growth of the tumor, while smaller doses would enhance it. The progress of the tumor was followed histologically in normally resistant animals. In both enhanced and untreated animals there was an initial host-cellular response. In the untreated animals the cellular reaction, predominantly histiocytic, continued and the tumor was destroyed. In the animals treated with small amounts of serum the host-cellular response was suddenly arrested, and bizarre giant cells were seen at the edge of the tumor. There was then an abrupt outgrowth of tumor cells with no effective cellular response from the host, which later died with massive growth of tumor.

Batchelor and Silverman (7) have also shown interference by antibody with the function of immune cells. Immunity to BP8 can be readily transferred with lymph node cells; growth of the tumor is rapidly suppressed. Minute doses of antiserum alone had little or no effect on the growth of the tumor during the period of observation. When antiserum and immune cells were administered to the same animal, the effect of the lymph node cells was negated and the tumor grew as well as it did in the controls.

In a possibly analogous situation, Linder (54) found that animals given an ovarian graft could support a subsequent skin graft. Ovary, although subjected to the same type of immune reaction as other classes of graft, will survive in more heterozygous mice than will skin from the same donor. If the skin was put on first, both skin and ovary were promptly rejected. If the ovary was allowed to remain for about 30 days, Linder found accelerated rejection of skin, showing that the animal had become immunized, but if the ovary was in place for 90 days or longer, enhanced survival of a subsequent skin graft was reported.

Peer (71), working with humans, reported that skin grafts from child to mother would occasionally persist for very long periods. Breyere and Barrett (18) made a similar observation in mice: that females crossed with males of a different strain would accept grafts from the second strain, whereas control females would not. The mechanism involved in these two cases is possibly similar but is not known. It has been shown, however, that multiparous women often have antibodies which can be demonstrated as leukoagglutinins (69, 73). The antigens are present in the husband and in some of the children. It is possible that these are enhancing antibodies.

The mechanism responsible for immunologic enhancement has been the topic of much speculation. Kaliss and his colleagues (48) believe that two types of antibody may be formed as a result of immunization—one an enhancing antibody, the other inhibitory —and that the outcome of treatment depends upon the concentration of inhibiting antibody; in high doses it overcomes the enhancing activity. The antigenic specificity appears to be the same for both types of antibody. Snell and his colleagues believe that the antibody exerts its effect by neutralizing the antigens on the transplanted cell (82). Thus the existence of a weak and ineffective level of immunity blocks the stimulation of an effective response. Gorer (37) believed that only one type of antibody was involved and that at low concentrations it had a direct stimulatory effect on tumor growth. Among the more provocative observations are those of Boyse (15a) using lymphoma, and Batchelor and Silverman (7) with carcinoma that enhancement can be produced with as little as 0.0005 ml. of whole serum, probably representing only about 0.5 μg. of antibody protein.

Genetic Basis for Transplantation. The success or failure of a graft to take is determined by the extent to which the antigens of the graft differ from those of the host. There are considerable differences between the number of antigens present on various tissues: thus skin, white cells, and spleen appear to have most of the known transplantation antigens, while fibrous tissue and cartilage are poorly antigenic; kidney, lung, and other organs are intermediate. Some of the antigens are present on red cells, but others are not. The occurrence of transplantation antigens on the red cells appears to be quite fortuitous. In some species, such as mouse and rat, the strongest antigens are on the red cell as well as on the tissues; in rabbit they almost certainly are not. The situation in man is uncertain, the ABO antigens have been believed to be transplantation antigens by many investigators, but this has been denied by as many more.

The antigens are structural and probably represent many different chemical classes. They are antigenic simply because some of the groupings exposed to the surface differ from corresponding structures found in the new host. They represent the final product of the action of a gene and may be several metabolic steps removed from the gene itself. The presence of an antigenic group on a tissue will depend upon the functioning of other metabolic steps, themselves gene controlled, necessary for the production of the final product. Genes which are active in pancreas may be dormant in testis; thus pancreas will have antigens absent from testis and vice versa, although the gene complement of the two cells is identical.

For any given tissue the metabolic processes activated at a comparable stage in development are similar for all members of a species, so the transplantation antigens of that tissue will also have a characteristic pattern. The appearance of the antigen will be dependent upon specific metabolic processes of the cell; the form which the antigen takes will be determined by which allelic form of the gene is present in the nucleus. This is not necessarily true of tumors, since genes which would normally be suppressed or inactive may become activated following the chromosomal changes so characteristic of tumors. Genes which might normally be active only in early development, or only in another type of tissue could be activated in the unbalanced neoplasm, or perhaps even more extremely in the unbalanced tissue culture cell.

To investigate the properties of a transplantation antigen, it is necessary to know something of its tissue distribution, of its linkage to other measurable characteristics, and of the number of allelic forms it may take. The problem has been relatively simple in the mouse, where inbred strains are available and where the principal antigen is found on the red cell. It is complicated in man because there are apparently many strong antigens, families are small and not inbred, and there is no known coincidence of transplantation antigens with red cell blood group factors.

In the mouse Gorer (36) found that tumor rejection was associated with the appearance of antibodies which would agglutinate the red cells of the tumor animal. The gene responsible (H-2) was found to be closely linked to the gene responsible for producing a short tail (fused) (40), so it was possible to follow the transplantation or histocompatibility gene in crosses set up with fused. Hybrids were set up between a stock containing fused and one carrying the histocompatibility gene being investigated. These hybrids were then crossed with other mice carrying neither fused nor the allele in question. The offspring consisted of two classes. Those with fused tails did not have the antigen, while animals with normal tails produced the antigen, could grow the tumor, and their cells were agglutinated by antitumor sera (Table 1).

Table 1. The Influence of H-2 on Tumor Transplantation

From Gorer, Lyman, and Snell

	Tumor Present	Tumor Absent	Total
H-2a Present	28	3	31
H-2a Absent	1	37	38
Total	29	40	69

Linkage between H-2 and Fused

	Antigen Present	Antigen Absent	Total
Fused	0	37	37
Normal	37	5	42
Total	37	42	79

Linkage to fused is now seldom used, since reference antibodies are so widely available, but similar crosses are still set up to follow the segregation of a given allele and to see if an unknown antigen is part of the H-2 system.

Snell has devised a system, laborious to set up but brilliantly simple to use once the matings have been done, for deriving two lines of mice which are identical except that one line carries a fragment of chromosome controlling a single transplantation factor

from a completely unrelated strain (81). For all practical purposes the strains differ only by the products of a single gene. Grafting between the two sublines gives valuable information regarding the strength of the immune response to the antigen in question without confusion from reactions to any other antigens. It would be possible to set up similar lines to study biochemical mutants such as low beta glucuronidase. Such a system is adaptable to any mutant characteristic, being most easily applied to visible mutations, as of coat color (43).

Snell's system depends upon the availability of a suitable marker or selective agent. Snell has relied upon the antigenic individuality of tumors. Some tumors carry a lot of one particular antigen, another tumor in the same strain will have a similar preponderance of a second antigen, and so on. Two mice, one carrying the tumor, the other carrying the gene to be introduced into the tumor-bearing stock, are crossed, and the resultant F_1 is allowed to breed among itself. All the mice are inoculated with tumor; those possessing the antigen found on the tumor, die. Those mice homozygous for the allele being introduced can reject the tumor and live. One of the survivors is crossed back to a mouse of the original tumor line, and the process is repeated. With each back-mating, fresh genetic material is added from the tumor-bearing line with a corresponding loss of genes from the second strain (81).

By this means strains coisogenic for a number of transplantation genes have been produced, making it possible to investigate the effects of four antigens. H-1, H-3, and H-4 are relatively weak. H-2, as mentioned above, is much stronger, but from a comparison of the speed of rejection of tumor between two coisogenic lines differing at other loci, it is apparent that there is considerable summation of effect from weaker factors.

The mouse H-2 system has been compared to the human Rh system because it appears to consist of a system of closely linked genes. Just as in the Fisher-Race CDE nomenclature, the individual H-2 antigens are also designated by letters. H-2a, one of the more completely studied strains has antigens ACDEFHKMRYA′B′C′. Evidently H-2 is much more complicated than Rh. Of the hundreds of possible combinations 18 phenotypes are known, and a large number of individual antigens carried by them have been recorded (2). H-2 is determined by a segment of chromosome rather than by a single locus; each of the series of genes within the region controls the configuration of part of the final molecule. Unlike Rh, crossing over has often been observed between the individual recons. The nature of the determinant groups of the antigen itself are not known. They were once thought to be carbohydrate, rather like the ABO antigens, but this has been disproved. The antigen has not been completely purified, but a concentrated product has been isolated in several laboratories. The most highly purified product has a high specific activity and is capable of inhibiting hemagglutination at the level of 2 μg. per ml. (28). In this form it is a lipoprotein, 30 per cent lipid and very little carbohydrate; further purification is needed before a more detailed analysis is possible.

Other antigens are less well defined. Two, designated H-5 and H-6, have been detected serologically as hemagglutinogens; other factors are known, but no detailed description has been published. Each of those so far described has a characteristic tissue distribution. H-2 is found in large amount on epithelium and reticulo-endothelial tissues, in very small amounts in kidney and muscle, and is virtually absent from brain and testis (6). H-5 is abundant on red cell stroma and in kidney and testis, and H-6 is richest on red cells, testis, spleen, gut, and brain (5). Fragmentary evidence of other antigens shows that each appears to have a completely unrelated distribution pattern. If an antigen is absent from a tissue, it can have no part in rejection of a graft of that tissue; for practical purposes, it is therefore important to determine the antigenic constitution of each tissue.

The antigens of each individual system, H-1, H-2, etc., are determined by genes which segregate independently of each other. To obtain an estimate of the number of antigens present on one strain but absent from another, the two strains are hybridized and then a test tissue, usually skin or tumor, is transplanted to the hybrids. Skin usually gives the more complete answer; tumor tends to highlight the strongest antigens, since tumors can frequently grow through weak immune reactions.

A mouse of strain A is crossed to strain B. The F_1 hybrid, AB has all the dominant antigens of both parents and will accept a graft from either. The F_1 is then mated among itself (F_2) or else crossed to one of the parent lines (back-cross). Grafts from the other parent are placed on the progeny. Only those offspring which have all the major antigens of the donor parent will accept the graft. All the other animals will lack one or more factors, will become immunized, and will reject the graft. A scheme for two independently segregating antigens is shown in Table 2. Only one fourth of the animals in a backcross or nine sixteenths of an F_2 will accept the graft. As the number of antigens increases, the number of successful transplants decreases. For a backcross the proportion of successes is $(\frac{1}{2})^n$, for the $F_2 (\frac{3}{4})^n$, so that for systems where more than seven antigens are segregating the chance of success is remote. An estimate of 15 antigens is commonly given for the mouse.

Similar experiments cannot be performed in man, but the number of antigens is known to be large. Of 71 grafts from different donors placed on one recipient, none survived for more than five and one-half weeks, and an estimate of at least 20 antigens has been suggested (54a). In a recent study on normal subjects, Rapaport and his colleagues (71a) found only 1 test graft out of a series of 71 persisted for 21 days. Most of the grafts were rejected between 7 and 10 days. Chance compatibility is evidently a rare event. The number of antigens again appears to be large.

Antigenic Typing in Man. Genetic information can be accumulated only slowly from grafting experiments, and grafting cannot be carried out on a very large scale. Consequently, another method of identifying antigens has been sought. It has been shown that white cells carry many of the antigens present on skin. Recipients immunized with white cells or white cell extracts show accelerated rejection of skin grafts from the same and frequently from unrelated donors (33, 52).

Antileukocyte antibodies are found in about 10 per cent of patients receiving blood

Table 2.

SEGREGATION OF
HISTOCOMPATIBILITY GENES
I GENE
Tumor or skin from line I will grow in any mouse with antigen A.

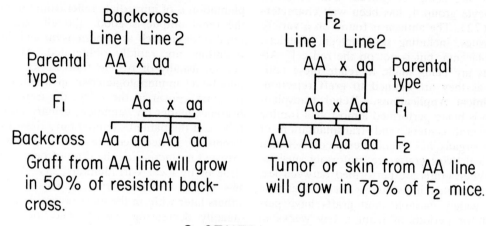

Backcross

Line I   Line 2

Parental type   AA x aa

F_1 Aa x aa

Backcross   Aa aa Aa aa

Graft from AA line will grow in 50% of resistant back-cross.

F_2

Line I   Line 2

AA x aa   Parental type

Aa x Aa F_1

AA Aa Aa aa F_2

Tumor or skin from AA line will grow in 75% of F_2 mice.

2 GENES
Tumor or skin from line I will grow only in mice having both A. and B.

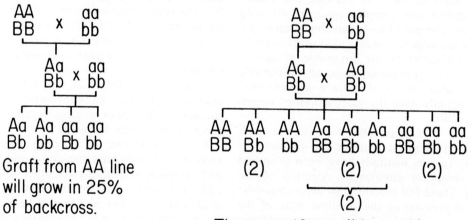

AA   aa
BB x bb

Aa   aa
Bb x bb

Aa Aa aa aa
Bb bb Bb bb

Graft from AA line will grow in 25% of backcross.

AA   aa
BB x bb

Aa   Aa
Bb x Bb

AA AA AA Aa Aa Aa aa aa aa
BB Bb bb BB Bb bb BB Bb bb
(2)   (2)   (2)
              (2)

There are 16 possible combinations of the gametes resulting in 9 different genotypes. Graft will grow in 9/16 or 56.3% of F_2 mice.

transfusions (27). Frequently these antibodies give rise to mild transfusion reactions. Antileukocyte antibodies are also found in some 25 per cent of women who have had more than 4 children (69, 70). In this case the passage of white cells from the fetus across the placenta is the probable stimulus. Genetic studies have been performed with some of the antisera, and various white cell groups are being recognized. One of these, leukocyte group 4, has been well characterized (72). The antigen is found on a variety of tissues, including skin, spleen, platelets, and placenta, but is not on the red cell. Attempts are being made to relate these antigens as they are defined to graft rejection.

Clinical Applications. Renal transplantation is being performed almost as a routine in several centers, and transplantation of other organs has been attempted. Between identical twins grafts are uniformly successful. When grafts are performed between less closely related individuals, the results have been widely variable, and grafts have persisted for periods of from a few weeks to several years. Renal grafting, although technically more difficult, appears to be more successful than skin homografting, partly because of the intensive efforts made to insure graft survival, but also because the kidney is probably less complex antigenically than is skin. The old observation that uremic patients are slow to reject a skin graft is probably unrelated to the favorable results of kidney transplantation, since all measurable biochemical effects of uremia are corrected very rapidly once the grafted kidney begins to function.

Since it is impossible to obtain a graft from an identical twin in the majority of cases, various methods have been proposed to prevent or circumvent rejection of the graft. These fall broadly into two categories: (1) depression of the immune state of the patient to a level at which he can no longer respond effectively to even a strong antigen and (2) genetic matching.

Immunologic depression has been extensively used. Massive whole body x-irradiation has been effective (50), but the patient is made very sick, and extraordinary care is needed to prevent death from bacterial infection. Local irradiation is being used ex-

tensively especially in Europe (42). The use of drugs to depress the immune response is being widely used, especially in the numerous experiments on dogs (20). Various purine and pyrimidine antagonists are used alone or with corticosteroids to further depress the lymphocytes. Thymectomy and splenectomy to remove some of the lymphoid tissue are also being performed.

The usual clinical course after renal transplantation is of immediate relief from uremia; the renal output is good, and all signs of renal disease, such as hypertension and fluid retention, are rapidly obliterated. After a period, usually of two to four weeks, there may be an immunologic crisis in which lymphocytes appear in the urine, the transplant becomes tender on palpation, urinary output falls, and the patient's temperature rises. Frequently the attempted rejection is promptly arrested by increasing the dose of depressant drug or by local x-irradiation (25). After a few weeks a second crisis may occur, and others later with, in the most favorable cases, steadily decreasing severity and increasing time intervals. Unfortunately, a number of patients do not respond to therapy and reject the transplant, and others die as a result of therapy. Most of the suppressive measures used are empirical, and there is no question that the results improve when the appropriate treatment schedules are known.

However, treatment which necessitates a stay of as long as a year in hospital, maintenance on drugs, and such mutilating or hazardous procedures as are now needed does not constitute an ideal approach. The successes with other organs appear to fall short of those with kidney.

From the genetic studies with lower animals, it is known that the closer the donor and recipient resemble each other antigenically, the weaker will be the reaction to the graft and the easier it becomes to suppress the response. For such weak factors as antigen linked to the Y chromosome in the mouse, a mere increase in size of the graft may be enough to prevent rejection. For many combinations where there is no H-2 incompatibility, it is possible to obtain tolerance with relatively low amounts of x-irradiation, followed by the administration of marrow, but the most effective treatment appears to be through the establishment of tolerance through a course of immunodepressant drug, such as amethopterin, followed by the administration of donor antigen. The antigen may be from various sources, bone marrow or platelets appear to be promising.

Transplantation as a therapeutic measure is still in the early experimental stage. Information yet to be obtained concerning leucocyte and tissue groups is likely to be of tremendous value in human genetics. A wealth of new genetic markers will become available, and the ultimate clinical applications are immeasurable.

REFERENCES

1. Ackroyd, J. F.   Clin. Sci., 13:409, 1954.
2. Amos, B.   Prog. Med. Genetics, 3:106, 1964.
3. ———— Prog. Allergy, 6:468, Karger, Basel/New York, 1962.
4. ———— and Wakefield, J. D.   J. Nat. Cancer Inst., 22:1077, 1959.
5. ———— Zumpft, M., and Armstrong, P. Transplantation, 1:270, 1963.
6. Basch, R. S., and Stetson, C. A.   Ann. N.Y. Acad. Sci., 97:83, 1962.
7. Batchelor, J. R., and Silverman, M. S.   Ciba Foundation Symposium on Transplantation, London, Churchill, 1962, p. 216.
8. Billingham, R. E., and Brent, L.   Phil. Trans. Roy. Soc. London, B242:439, 1959.
9. ————Brent, L., and Medawar, P. B.   Nature, London, 172:602, 1953.
10. ———— Defendi, V., Silvers, W. K., and Steinmuller, D.   J. Nat. Cancer Inst., 28:365, 1962.
11. ———— and Silvers, W. K.   Ciba Foundation Symposium on Transplantation, London, Churchill, 1962, p. 90.
12. ———— Silvers, W. K., and Wilson, D. B.   J. Exp. Med., 118:397, 1963.
13. Boyden, S. V.   Cell-bound Antibodies, Philadelphia, Wistar Institute Press, 1963, p. 7.
14. ———— and Sorkin, E.   Immunology, 3:272, 1960.
15. Boyse, E. A.   Immunology, 2:170, 1959.
15a. ———— Old, L. J., and Stocker, E.   Nature, 194:1142, 1962.
16. Brent, L.   Prog. Allergy, 5:271, Karger, Basel/New York, 1958.
17. ———— and Gowland, G.   Conceptual Advances in Immunology and Oncology, New York, Hoeber, 1963, p. 355.
18. Breyere, E. J., and Barrett, M. K.   J. Nat. Cancer Inst., 25:1405, 1960.
19. Burnet, F. M., and Fenner, F.   The Production of Antibodies, 2nd ed., Melbourne, Macmillan, 1949.
20. Calne, R. Y., Alexander, G. P. J., and Murray, J. E.   Ann. N.Y. Acad. Sci., 99:743, 1962.
21. Cell-bound Antibodies: Conference of the National Academy of Sciences, Philadelphia, Wistar Institute Press, 1963.
22. Chang, T. S., Glick, B., and Winter, A. P.   Poultry Sci., 34:1187, 1955.
23. Chutna, B.   Transplantation Bull., 28:23, 1961.
24. Cinader, B., and Dubert, J. M.   Brit. J. Exper. Path., 36:515, 1955.
25. Human Kidney Transplant Conf., Transplantation, 2:147, 1964.
26. Conference on the Thymus, Univ. Minn., 1964, in press.
27. Dausset, J.   Acta Haemat., 20:156, 1958.
28. Davies, D. A. L.   Ciba Foundation Symposium on Transplantation, London, Churchill, 1962, p. 45.
29. Dempster, W. J.   Brit. J. Surg., 40:447, 1953.
30. Dunsford, I., Bowley, C. C., Hutchison, A. M., Thompson, J. S., Sanger, R., and Race, R. R.   Brit. M. J., 2:81, 1953.
31. Elves, M. W., and others.   Lancet, 1:1292, 1963.
32. Felton, L. D.   J. Immunol., 61:107, 1949.
33. Friedman, E. A., Retan, J. W., Marshall, D. C., Henry, L., and Merrill, J. P.   J. Clin. Invest., 40:2162, 1961.
34. Good, R. A., Kelly, W. D., and Gabrielson, A. E.   Mechanism of Cell and Tissue Damage Produced by Immune Reactions, 2nd Intern. Symp. on Immunopathology, Basel/Stuttgart, Benno Schwabe, 1962, p. 353.
35. ———— Varco, R. L., Aust, J. B., and Zak, S. J.   Ann. N.Y. Acad. Sci., 64:882, 1957.
36. Gorer, P. A.   J. Path. and Bact., 47:231, 1938.
37. ———— Ann. N.Y. Acad. Sci., 73:707, 1958.
38. ———— and Amos, D. B.   Cancer Res., 16:338, 1956.
39. ———— and Kaliss, N.   Cancer Res., 19:824, 1959.
40. ———— Lyman, S., and Snell, G. D.   Proc. Roy. Soc., B135:499, 1948.
41. Gowans, J. L.   Ann. N.Y. Acad. Sci., 99:432, 1962.
42. Hamburger, J., Vaysse, J., Crosnier, J., Auvert, J., Lelanne, C. M., and Dormont, J.   Rev. Franç. Etudes Clin. et Biol., 7:20, 1962.
43. Hauschka, T. S., and Holdridge, B. A.   Ann. N.Y. Acad. Sci., 101:12, 1962.
44. Hildemann, W. H., and Walford, R. L.   Ann. N.Y. Acad. Sci., 87:56, 1960.
45. Howard, J. G., Michie, D., and Woodruff, M. F. A.   Ciba Foundation Symposium on Transplantation, London, Churchill, 1962, p. 138.
46. Ilbery, P. L. T., Koller, P. C., and Loutit, J. F.   J. Nat. Cancer Inst., 20:1051, 1958.
47. Kaliss, N.   Ann. N.Y. Acad. Sci., 101:64, 1962.
48. ———— Dagg, M. C., and Stimpfling, J. H.   Transplantation, 1:535, 1963.
49. Kaplan, N. S.   J. Immunol., 90:595, 1963.
50. Kuss, R., Legrain, M., Mathe, G., Nedey, R., and Camey, M.   Post-grad. Med. J., 38:528, 1962.
51. Law, L. W., and Miller, J. H.   J. Nat. Cancer Inst., 11:425, 1950.
52. Lawrence, H. S., Rapaport, F. T., Converse, J. M., and Tillett, W. S.   J. Clin. Invest., 39:185, 1960.
53. Levey, R. H., Trainin, N., and Law, L. W.   J. Nat. Cancer Inst., 31:199, 1963.
54. Linder, O. E. A.   Ann. N.Y. Acad. Sci., 99:680, 1962.

54a. Longmire, W. P., Jr., Stone, H. B., Daniel, A. S., and Goon, C. D. Plast. & Reconstr. Surg., 2:419, 1947.

55. McClusky, R. T., Benacerraf, B., and McClusky, J. W. J. Immunol., 90:466, 1963.

56. ——— Miller, F., and Benacerraf, B. J. Exper. Med., 115:253, 1962.

57. Medawar, P. B. J. Anat., London, 78:176, 1944.

58. Merwin, R. M., and Hill, E. L. J. Nat. Cancer Inst., 14:819, 1954.

59. Metcalf, D. Canadian Cancer Conf., 3:351, Academic Press, New York, 1959.

60. Milgrom, F., and Witebsky, E. J. Amer. Med. Assn., 181:706, 1962.

61. Miller, J. F. A. P. Ciba Foundation Symposium on Transplantation, London, Churchill, 1962, p. 384.

62. Mitchison, N. A. Proc. Roy. Soc., B142:72, 1954.

63. ——— Biological Problems of Grafting, Springfield, Ill., Thomas, 1959, p. 239.

64. Moulton, M., and Storer, J. B. Transplantation Bull., 30:150, 1962.

65. Nelson, D. S. Brit. J. Exper. Path., 43:2, 1962.

66. Nowell, P. C. Exp. Cell Res., 19:267, 1960.

67. Old, L. J., Boyse, E. A., Bennett, B., and Lilly, F. Cell-bound Antibodies, Philadelphia, Wistar Institute Press, 1963, p. 89.

68. Owen, R. D. Science, 102:400, 1945.

69. Payne, R. Blood, 19:411, 1962.

70. ——— and Hackel, E. Amer. J. Human Genetics, 13:306, 1961.

71. Peer, L. Ann. N.Y. Acad. Sci., 73:584, 1958.

71a. Rapaport, F. T., Lawrence, H. S., Thomas, L., Converse, J. M., Tillett, W. S., and Mulholland, J. H. J. Clin. Invest., 41:2166, 1962.

72. Rood, J. J., van, and Leeuwen, A. van. J. Clin. Invest, 42:1382, 1963.

73. ——— Leeuwen, A. van, and Eernisse, J. G. Vox Sang., 4:427, 1959.

74. Rowley, D., and Jenkin, C. R. Nature, 193:151, 1962.

75. Schlesinger, M., and Goitein, R. Transplantation, 1:481, 1963.

76. ——— and Mark, R. Science, 143:965, 1964.

77. Simonsen, M. Acta. Path. Microbiol. Scand., 32:36, 1953.

78. ——— Prog. Allergy, 6:349, Karger, Basel/New York, 1962.

79. ——— Engelbreth-Holm, J., Jensen, E., and Poulson, H. Ann. N.Y. Acad. Sci., 73:834, 1958.

80. Siskind, G. W., Paterson, P. Y., and Thomas, L. J. Immunol., 90:929, 1963.

81. Snell, G. D. J. Nat. Cancer Inst., 21:843, 1958.

82. ——— Winn, H. J., Stimpfling, J. H., and Parker, S. J. J. Exp. Med., 112:293, 1960.

83. Stetson, C. A., and Jensen, E. Ann. N.Y. Acad. Sci., 87:249, 1960.

84. Thorbecke, G. J. Ann. N.Y. Acad. Sci., 78:237, 1959.

85. Triplett, E. L. J. Immunol., 89:505, 1962.

86. Turk, J. L., and Stone, S. H. Cell-bound Antibodies, Philadelphia, Wistar Institute Press, 1963, p. 51.

87. Uphoff, D. E. Transplantation Bull., 28:12, 1961.

88. van Bekkum, D. W. Mechanisms of Immunological Tolerance, Publishing House of the Czechoslovak Acad. Sci., Prague, 1962, p. 385.

89. Warner, N. Conference on the Thymus, in press, 1964.

90. Weaver, J. M., Algire, G. H., and Prehn, R. T. J. Nat. Cancer Inst., 15:1737, 1955.

91. Weigle, W. O. J. Exper. Med., 116:913, 1962.

92. Winn, H. J. J. Immunol., 86:228, 1961.

93. Woodruff, M. A. A. Ann. N.Y. Acad. Sci., 64:1014, 1957.

94. ——— and Simpson, L. O. Brit. J. Exp. Path., 36:494, 1955.

16

Toxins and Antitoxins

Most toxins are antigens, and all antitoxins are antibodies, but they are sufficiently different in their mode of action and methods of titration from bacterial antigens and antibodies to justify presentation in a separate chapter. Ancient peoples, and many primitive tribes today, recognized the presence of powerful poisons in plants such as **ricin** from the castor oil bean (48), **abrin** from Indian licorice seed, and the **venoms** of certain snakes, spiders, and scorpions. They practiced a type of immunization with sublethal doses of these poisons. The first scientific approach of this type was made in 1887 by Sewall (212), who showed that gradually increasing sublethal doses of rattlesnake venom would protect pigeons from multiple lethal doses of the poison. Sewall's studies stimulated Calmette's (39) famous investigations of snake venoms and antivenoms and led logically to the production of diphtheria antitoxin.

More recent studies on the **snake venoms** (37, 78, 119, 133, 173) have shown that they may be classified into neurotoxic, hemolytic, hemorrhagic types, and that a particular venom might have two or three or all of these toxic properties in varying proportions (173). Except for the coral snake, which is related to the cobra, all the other poisonous snakes of North America are pit vipers and induce the hemorrhagic and hemolytic syndromes. Rattlesnake (crotalidae) venom convents fibrinogen to fibrin and the circulating blood loses its ability to clot (133).

Coral snakes are not aggressive and cause only 1 to 2 per cent of the bites by poisonous snakes in this country. There is very little local reaction at the site of the bite and often a delay of about two hours before the severe and frequently fatal symptoms appear. There is no antitoxin available for the venom of the North American coral snake. Antivenom for the South American coral snake is manufactured by the Institute Butantan, São Paulo, Brazil, but this product is not licensed for use in the United States (191).

Keegan and his associates (111), however, have found that this antivenom protects mice from multiple fatal doses of venom from the North American coral snake.

The venomous scorpions of the world have been studied and their venoms and antivenoms compared. There is enough common toxin to suggest the possibility of developing a polyvalent scorpion antitoxin for general use (82).

Poisoning by the bites of spiders is as frequent or more frequent than that of snakes or scorpions (59a). Methocarbamol has been found to be the best drug for relaxing the muscle spasm which is so characteristic of the toxic effect of spider bites (99).

Certain bacteria produce toxins of almost unbelievable potency. Van Heyningen (250) has calculated that one molecule of diphtheria toxin is 4,000 times more lethal than one molecule of aconitine; tetanus toxin is 2,000,000 times as lethal, and botulinus type A toxin and the neurogenic toxin of *Shigella dysenteriae* (252) are even more potent.

Bacterial toxins are usually classified as **exotoxins** or **endotoxins. The exotoxins, by definition, are those excreted into the medium** in which the organism is growing, and the **endotoxins are those liberated only after disintegration of the organism.** In addition there are certain other products of bacteria, enzymatic in nature, such as streptokinase, coagulase, and the hyaluronidases, which are not inherently toxic, but which do aid the organism in its invasion of the body. These will be discussed at the end of the chapter. The recent literature on toxins and anti-

Table 1. Criteria for Differentiation of Exotoxins from Endotoxins

Exotoxins	Endotoxins
1. Are found characteristically in the fluid medium in which the bacteria are cultured. Although the toxins are probably formed within the cell, they are excreted rapidly, maximum concentrations usually being found in cultures five to seven days old.	1. Are closely bound to the bacterial cell, the toxic products being liberated in the animal body only after the destruction of the cell by mechanical disruption or autolysis of old organisms.
2. Are highly toxic, small laboratory animals usually succumbing to injections of 0.001 ml. or less.	2. Are weakly toxic, fatal doses for small laboratory animals ranging from 0.5 to 1.0 ml. or more.
3. Produce toxic effects which are highly specific for certain tissues such as heart muscle, nerves and adrenals. Such effects often are sufficiently characteristic to identify the toxin.	3. Produce nonspecific toxic effects such as local lesions at the sites of injection and generalized nonspecific reactions such as fever.
4. Are relatively unstable, rapidly losing their toxicity upon exposure to temperatures of 60° C. or above and deteriorating rapidly upon storage at room temperature or exposure to ultraviolet light.	4. Are relatively stabile, retaining their toxic effects after heating to 60° C. and remaining unchanged upon storage or exposure to ultraviolet light.
5. Are highly antigenic, stimulating the production of large amounts of neutralizing antitoxins when injected into animals.	5. Are weakly antigenic, specific neutralizing antitoxins not being formed to an appreciable extent in immunized animals.
6. Are converted into toxoids by treatment with formalin. Such toxoids retain their antigenic power but lose their toxicity.	6. Are not converted into toxoids by treatment with formalin.

toxins has been reviewed by Van Heyningen (252) and Oakley (154).

The criteria commonly employed in the differentiation of exotoxins from endotoxins are listed in Table 1 with the full knowledge that many toxic products of bacterial metabolism will not fit comfortably into either classification. An example of this difficulty in classification is the **enterotoxin** of *Staphylococcus aureus,* which resembles an exotoxin in that it is excreted into the medium but has the rapid action, heat resistance, and poor antigenicity of an endotoxin.

ENDOTOXINS

The endotoxins of the gram-negative bacilli of the intestinal tract, such as the *Salmonella* and *Shigella,* will be discussed first, since in this instance the specific species antigen and the endotoxin are one and the same protein-polysaccharide-lipid complex. The specific antigenicity of the complex is determined by the carbohydrate which is not toxic. The protein fraction has little antigenicity but possesses a remarkable capacity for combining with and making antigenic

the carbohydrates isolated from other gram-negative species and from gum arabic, agar, and human group-A polysaccharides (146). These complex antigens have been studied in detail by Boivin and his associates (30) and others (91, 92, 126, 150, 152, 184, 185, 186, 261, 262, 263) and are frequently referred to in the literature as "Boivin antigens."

Chemically endotoxins are extremely complex. The carbohydrate is in the form of a large polysaccharide complex (184), and the lipid fraction is a mixture of at least 16 different components (152). Westphal (263) believes that the toxicity depends upon the lipid A portion of the endotoxin complex, but Rabi and his coworkers could prepare lipid A type fractions which were nontoxic. Their most toxic fraction contained large molecular polysaccharides. The work of Noll and Braude (151) tends to favor the idea that the toxicity is the result of certain physiochemical properties characteristic of the entire molecule rather than the autonomous property of one of its components. The toxicity may be related to the size of the particles. This has been demonstrated for the chemical toxicity of the cell wall of Group A streptococci by Robertson, Schwab, and Cromartie (197). Support but not proof of the concept that particle size determines the toxicity of endotoxin preparation has been published by both Robertson and his associates (196) and Rabi and his coworkers (186).

The toxicity of the endotoxin portion of the lipo-polysaccharide protein complex prevents large-scale immunization with multiple strains of gram-negative enteric bacteria. Progress in eliminating the toxicity while retaining the specific antigenicity has been reported by Noll and Braude (151) and by Luderitz, Westphal, and their associates (130). Noll and Braude destroyed the toxicity by reductive treatment with $LiAlH_4$, which eliminated the ether-bound fatty acid. Westphal and his associates made an artificial nontoxic antigen by linking the terminal sugar of an *E. coli* antigen to serum albumin. The antibodies reacted specifically to the artificial antigen and also to the original pathogenic *E. coli* and to the related *Salmonella* strains.

Endotoxins of the Boivin antigen type are found in the smooth strains of *Salmonella, Shigella, Brucella, Neisseria, Vibrio comma, Escherichia, Pseudomonas aeruginosa, Serratia,* and other members of the family *Enterobacteriaceae*. Endotoxins derived from these species of organisms all give the same type of symptoms when injected into animals, although each gives rise to its own specific antibacterial antibodies. **The symptoms are characterized by pyrexia, shock, diarrhea, prostration, hyperglycemia followed by hypoglycemia, congestion, edema, and hemorrhages into the abdominal viscera and lungs.** The inability of man and animals to produce antitoxins to these endotoxins has always been a mystery but might be explained by the assumption that the carbohydrate hapten-like moiety is a good antigen and the toxic moiety a poor antigen. Some such mechanism might also explain the phenomenon of more rapid death in a highly immune animal than in a normal animal following the injection of moderately large numbers of organisms, as observed by Pfeiffer. In this instance, the bacteriolysins would lyse the organisms rapidly, thus free-

ing a fatal dose of endotoxin. Some examples of bacterial, rickettsial (155), and viral (3) endotoxins are given in the following paragraph.

Heat-labile toxins have been extracted from the bodies of *Bord. pertussis* (13) and *Brucella* (251). These toxins are antigenic and can be converted into toxoids. Another potent toxin has been extracted by Dubos from *H. influenzae* type B (61), which causes hemorrhagic lesions in rabbits. A toxin has been extracted from *Pasteurella pestis* which has an activity for mice of 1,300 L.D.$_{50}$ per mg. This toxin is a protein with a molecular weight of 74,000 (5, 12) and when injected into animals induces the formation of antitoxin which will neutralize the toxin. There is general agreement (127) that death in plague is caused by processes initiated by the action of the plague toxin, although the antitoxin, without the help of antibacterial antibodies, will not protect experimental animals (107). Its mode of action seems to be very specific, since it inhibits the exogenous respiration of mitochondria obtained from the heart of the toxin-sensitized rat and mouse and not from the toxin resistant rabbit (156). The plague toxin is often referred to in literature as an "endotoxin" but it has the high toxicity (6, 224), good antigenicity, and specific effect of an exotoxin.

There is evidence that a toxin is produced as *B. anthracis* grows in the tissues (219). Both patients with anthrax and experimentally infected animals show obvious signs of intoxication. In 1947, Watson, Cromartie, and their associates (256) succeeded in extracting a substance from the lesions of anthrax which would produce edema when injected into the skin of rabbits. Later a toxic factor was found in the blood of moribund animals, and finally the toxin was obtained in synthetic culture media by both English (90, 118) and American investigators (240).

The toxic effect was found to be dependent upon two fractions, neither of which was toxic when injected alone. One was the nontoxic protective antigen isolated and purified by Strange and Thorne in 1958 (230), and the other was a factor which was adsorbed on fritted-glass filters which allowed passage to the protective antigen. A third factor was described by Stanley and Smith in 1961 (225) and by Beall, Taylor, and Thorne in 1962 (16). This factor, also absorbed on fritted-glass filters, would produce cutaneous edema in the guinea pig but would not kill the animal, while the original filter factor, when purified, killed but would not produce cutaneous edema. Since the two factors are active only when given with the nontoxic protective antigen, we would conclude that this toxin has three dissociating fractions.

Animals infected with *B. anthracis* or injected with crude toxins develop a severe alkaline phosphatasemia, but this is not specific for anthrax since the same increase follows the injection of filtrates from cultures of *B. cereus* and *B. thuringiensis* (216).

Bacillus cereus, when grown in the synthetic medium developed for *B. anthracis,* also produces two nontoxic fractions which become toxic when combined. *B. cereus* produces even more phospholipase than *B. anthracis,* but the phospholipase is independent of the toxicity (144).

The toxins of the rickettsias, which cause typhus fever and scrub typhus are heat-labile and bound to the organism. Large doses may kill rabbits in 30 to 45 minutes and rats and mice in one to two hours (49). Rabbits dying in 30 to 45 minutes have hemoglobinemia, hyperkalemia associated with electrocardiographic changes, and hypotension. With smaller doses the intravascular hemolysis and hyperkalemia are less marked, and the animals may live 24 hours. Rats and mice do not have hemoglobinemia or hyperkalemia but do show hemoconcentration (168, 266).

Some strains of poliomyelitis virus produce a toxin which kills tissue culture cells. This effect is quite distinct from the regular cytopathogenic effect and cannot be neutralized by specific antipolio antibodies (3). Not enough is known about this toxin to classify it as an endotoxin or an exotoxin. The virus of mumps (253) and influenza viruses produce a toxin which is neutralized by an antiserum.

The C-polysaccharide of the cell walls of group A streptococci behave in some respects like an endotoxin (196). A rather large fragment of the cell wall with complex structure is necessary for toxicity. The toxicity can be neutralized with a specific antiserum or it may be destroyed by treatment with the enzyme glucosaminidase, which destroys the serologic reacting site of the C-polysaccharide (206). The endotoxins of group A streptococci have been studied by Cremer and Watson (51). They were found to induce tolerance which was nonspecific from type to type, resembling the cross-reactions observed among the gram-negative intestinal bacteria but much less potent than the intestinal organisms.

Biologic Effects of Classical Endotoxins. These toxins form a part of the cell wall of the intact organism and when freed are found to be composed of a lipo-protein-carbohydrate complex, which is presumably synthesized by the cytoplasmic mambrane. Dasinger and Suter (52) produced spheroplasts from *S. paratyphi* with penicillin and found that the endotoxin potency was reduced by $1 - 5$ to $1 + 9$ as compared with the same culture with an intact cell wall. There is serologic evidence that some cell wall constituents remain in spheroplasts (258) or the cytoplasmic membranes of true L-form mutants may continue to make some endotoxin.

Crude toxins of this type seem to have about the same potency regardless of the species or inherent virulence of the strain from which they were derived. A great variety of biologic effects are produced, such as (1) fever, (2) altered response to adrenalin, (3) vasomotor shock, (4) hemorrhagic necrosis in malignant tumors, (5) abortion of pregnant animals, (6) skin necrosis with endotoxins, (7) the local and generalized Schwartzman reaction, and (8) the nonspecific protective effect of endotoxins.

The Pyrogenic Activity of Endotoxins. The mechanism of fever production following the injection of endotoxin has been reviewed by Bennet and Beeson (18, 19) Bennet and Cluff (20), Wood (268) and Thomas (239). Man, cat, horse, and rabbit have the same threshold to pyrogenic stimulation by endotoxin (113). However, larger doses are much more pyrogenic and toxic to man than to the rabbit (Fig. 1). Dogs and chimpanzees are less susceptible than the other species studied. During the past 20 years there has been an enormous increase in the use of intravenous injections of whole blood and fluids. Frequently the patients developed, within 30 to 120 minutes after such an injection, a sharp chill followed by high fever which lasted for several hours. It was finally learned that the reactions were caused by endotoxins derived from saprophytic bacteria which were contaminating the distilled water or which were growing in improperly cleansed rubber tubing. Since endotoxins are heat-stable, no amount of boiling or autoclaving prevented the reactions.

This pyrogenic material is very potent. Favorite and Morgan (72a) induced marked febrile reactions in man with 0.1 μg. of a purified toxin from *S. typhosa*. In 1955 Landy and Johnson (124) isolated a lipopolysaccharide from *S. typhosa* 0 901 which was even more toxic (0.002 μg. producing

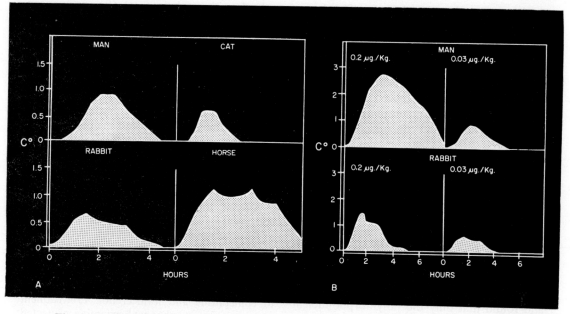

Fig. 1. A, the febrile responses of four species to 0.03 μg of endotoxin per kilogram of body weight. B, comparison of the febrile responses of man and rabbit to different dose levels of endotoxin. (From Keene, Silberman, and Landy. *J. Clin. Invest.*, 40:295, 1961.)

fever in rabbits, and 0.01 to 0.04 μg., in man). This toxic lipopolysaccharide retained a high degree of antigenicity as shown by the rabbit experiment in which a single intravenous injection of 0.001 μg. induced a significant agglutination titer to *S. typhosa* O 901.

When daily injections of pyrogens are given rabbits, they have less and less fever and finally cease to react. After a rest period of several weeks their reactivity returns. **This altered reactivity is called tolerance, not immunity, since there is no evidence that antigen-antibody reaction is involved.** The tolerance seems to depend either upon an increased activity of the reticuloendothelial system with a more rapid disposal of foreign materials (18) or upon an interference with a reaction between the endotoxin and a cellular or plasma factor (8, 129). Both polymorphonuclear leukocytes and monocytes have the ability to detoxify antitoxins (205). The inactivation of endotoxins by blood plasma was found by Keene and his associates (114) to have the characteristics of an enzyme-catalyzed reaction. The products of enzymatic degradation of

endotoxin by plasma were nonpyrogenic. Primarily this tolerance is nonspecific, so that tolerance induced by one endotoxin from a *Shigella* organism gives increased resistance to endotoxins derived from *Salmonella,* etc. However, in some instances there is a specific tolerance to the endotoxin used for inducing tolerance, so the tolerance is of a higher order and persists longer (1, 98, 141, 142). Griesman, Woodward, and their associates (86) have shown that naturally acquired specific tolerance to endotoxin develops early in convalescence in man experimentally infected with either *S. typhosa* or *Past. tularensis.* However, the experimental disease was aborted by treatment within 14 to 20 days. In the naturally occurring disease, with a febrile course of six to eight weeks, fever from endotoxins could be followed by fever from allergy to the endotoxin (see Chapter 17), and this part of the reaction would respond to corticoid hormone therapy.

Passive transfer of tolerance can be shown for the endotoxin used to induce tolerance (20), but it is not very striking. This is consistent with the inability of endotoxin to produce a good anti-endotoxin. The lesser degree of tolerance to a heterologous endotoxin might be explained by a nonspecific stimulation of the reticuloendothelial system of the recipient (75), which destroys the original endotoxin and prevents the formation of endogenous pyrogens. Granulocytes have some effect, but macrophages are more effective in destroying the toxicity of endotoxin (10, 205). There are substances in the serum, perhaps derived from cells, which will destroy endotoxins. These are located in Cohn's Fractions IV_1 and III_0 (202, 274).

Evidence is accumulating for the belief that there are two stages in this pyrogenic reaction or that there are both an exogenous and endogenous pyrogen. Bennet and Beeson (19) examined separately the pyrogenic effect of all the tissues and organs of rabbits and found that only the polymorphonuclear leukocytes were pyrogenic. This endogenous pyrogen was heat-labile, and the rabbits did not develop tolerance to it after repeated injections. The investigations of Grant and Whalen (85a) and of Atkins and Wood (8) suggest that the endotoxin acts on the white blood cells or some other tissue element to produce the labile fast-acting pyrogen (44). More recent studies by Rafer, Collins, and Wood (187) and others (73, 80) have shown that the pyrogenic endogenous toxin is indeed derived from polymorphonuclear leukocytes (96, 117). The pyrogenic component is a nondialiazable protein with less than 1 per cent carbohydrate, which is different from (1) pyrogenic endotoxin, (2) Menkin's "pyrexin," and (3) the pyrogenic polysaccharide of Landy and Shear (125). The production of endogenous pyrogens is blocked by sulfhydryl-reactive enzyme inhibitions (109).

Neutropenic animals produce less endogenous pyrogens (80), as would be expected. The production of endogenous pyrogens from granulocytes is not limited to exogenous endotoxin. Theoretically any substance or mechanism which results in a rapid destruction of granulocytes might produce endogenous pyrogen and fever. This has been observed (1) in metal fume fever (170) when the granulocytes are destroyed rapidly, (2) in tuberculin shock in tuberculin-sensitive animals (89), and (3) in

animals with staphylococcal (9), pneumococcal, and streptococcal infections (116). Endogenous but not exogenous pyrogens can be absorbed from the serum by betonite (172).

It has been known for many years that pus was pyrogenic, whether induced by an injection of turpentine or by the infection with organisms which do not contain endotoxins. Surgeons have known for generations that collections of pus in the body induced and maintained fever even when the pus was "sterile," and that the fever promptly disappeared after adequate drainage. The studies mentioned above suggest that the white blood cells in the pus could have been the source of the pyrogen.

Altered Response to Adrenalin. Gourzis and his associates (85) believe that the damage to tissue exposed to endotoxins is not due to a direct toxic effect but is secondary to an increased responsiveness to adrenergic stimuli. When rabbits were pretreated with endotoxin from *E. coli,* they gave exaggerated responses to epinephrine and levarterenol. Pretreatment with reserpine or phenoxybenzamine protected the rabbits from the lethal effect of endotoxins. This heightened response to epinephrine is the basis of Thomas's method of assaying the potency of endotoxins by skin tests in rabbits with epinephrine. Thomas could detect amounts of endotoxin as low as 1 μg. (238), and his observations have been confirmed by Buccino and his associates (36).

Evidence is accumulating which suggests that at least one of the physiologic defects in shock is the increased viscosity of the plasma. This defect can be corrected promptly by removing 1,000 ml. of blood and replacing this amount with 1,000 ml. of low-molecular-weight dextran. The initial infusion is followed by the infusion of another 2,000 ml. over the next two days (215).

Vasomotor Shock and Death from Endotoxins. Death from shock following septicemia with various gram-negative organisms from the intestinal tract is being encountered with increasing frequency in general hospitals (220, 221). These deaths can be attributed to the action of endotoxins from the organism, although the exact mechanism involved is not understood. Weismann and Thomas (259) have found that the lysosomal enzymes of the rabbits' liver are released rapidly after an intravenous injection of a shock-producing dose of endotoxin. An adequate dose of cortisone can prevent the shock, presumably by protecting the lysosomes. Rubenstein and his associates (201) have utilized the indirect immunofluorescent method to localize the endotoxin in the vascular system. After the toxin has been injected intravenously, they found a patchy distribution throughout the peripheral vascular system as well as in the leukocytes and in the cells of the reticuloendothelial system, suggesting that the endotoxin may be acting directly on the vessels to produce the peripheral vascular collapse of lethal endotoxemia.

A variety of unrelated conditions apparently increases the susceptibility of experimental animals to fatal shock following the injection of standard doses of endotoxins. The infection of mice with *Brucella* organisms (2) and with the vaccine against tuberculosis known as BCG (234) lowers the resistance of the animal to fatal shock after injection of endotoxins. The elevation of the metabolic rate by thyroxin (84) or triiodothyronine (140) increases the susceptibility to shock. Blockade of the reticuloendothelial system with throtrast (50), the intravenous injection of zymosan (17), or small preliminary doses of endotoxins (50) also increases the susceptibility to endotoxins. Even more unusual is the finding that changing the normal bacterial flora of the intestines may increase or decrease the susceptibility to endotoxins (207, 208). Most surprising of all was the finding of Halberg and his associates (87) that doses of endotoxins which were not fatal during the middle of the night were fatal to similar mice when given in daylight hours. A search for a common factor in this variety of predisposing causes of fatal shock from endotoxins led Spink (220, 221) and Gourzis et al. (85) to the conclusion that the endotoxins are most damaging when they are superimposed upon an already existing vasoconstriction regardless of how the latter was produced. The endotoxins first increase the susceptibility of the animal to adrenalin (85) and increase the vasoconstriction, after which there is vasodilatation, venous pooling of the blood, anoxemia, and irreversible shock.

The blood of dogs dying of shock from experimentally produced hemorrhage was found to kill when injected into normal animals by Fine, Ravin, and their associates (192, 210). The authors attributed the lethal effect of this blood to endotoxins absorbed from the intestinal tract during the last few hours of life. Pretreatment of the experimental dogs with antibiotics to eliminate bacteria from the intestinal tract reduced the death from shock. These results were confirmed by Blattenberg and his associates (29). Nagler and his coworkers (148) confirmed Fine and Ravin's observations about the toxicity of the blood of dogs dying of shock but could not find evidence that this toxicity was from endotoxins from the intestinal tract.

Pretreatment with reserpine or phenoxybenzamine will protect animals against the fatal effect of endotoxins. After shock is established, treatment with corticoid hormones, in large doses, is often helpful. Spink (220, 221) has obtained good results with large doses of hydrocortisone, given intravenously, and the pressor drug metaraminol (222) and even better results with angiotensin II combined with synthetic *d*-aldosterone (222, 223). Spink and Su (223) have found that unsaturated fatty acids protect mice from death from exotoxins and snake venom but have no protective effect on endotoxins. Shubin and Weil (215) have confirmed Spink's observations on the necessity of giving a vasopressor agent as well as large doses of corticoid hormones in combating severe shock from bacterial endotoxins.

Hemorrhagic Necrosis in Malignant Tumors. This phenomenon was discovered empirically in man and later studied in animals (7, 275). The endotoxin-induced necrosis begins with a slowing of the circulation in the tumor, but not in other parts of the body, and this is followed by venous stasis, engorgement, and hemorrhage. Unfortunately, the reduction in the size and painfulness of tumors is temporary.

Endotoxin Induced Abortion of Pregnant Animals. Moderately sized doses of endotoxin may produce hemorrhage in the placenta of pregnant animals, which results in abortion without any obvious damage to the tissues of the fetus or to the maternal tissues. Zahl and Bjerknes (275) noted the resemblance of the reaction to that noted in tumors. Later studies by Takeda and Tsuchiya (235) attributed the hemorrhage to a Shwartzman type of reaction. The investigations of Reder and Thomas (195) have shown that drugs which inhibit the Shwartzman reaction do not prevent abortions. This seems to be a specific effect of endotoxin analogous to if not identical with the hemorrhages found in tumors after the injection of endotoxins.

Skin Tests with Endotoxins. It has been known for many years that endotoxins would produce reactions when injected into the skin of the rabbit, but the results were variable and this procedure was not recommended as a method of assaying the potency of endotoxins. However, Larson and his associates (126) have found that endotoxin from a number of different enteric bacteria could be assayed successfully if the intradermal injections were given on the lateral surface of the thorax and abdomen but not when given on the ventral surface. The minimal skin test dose was about one-thousandth of the lethal dose for mice.

It seems probable that tuberculin-type delayed sensitivity would develop to the protein part of the lipo-polysaccharide-protein complex. This would complicate the skin test and perhaps increase the morbidity following parenteral injections. Uhr (248) has reported that newborn guinea pigs are highly susceptible to the lethal effect of endotoxin but do not show the delayed type of skin reaction to endotoxin. Schaedler and Dubos (207) found that germ-free animals, after vaccination with certain strains of *Enterobacteriaceae*, became more susceptible to the lethal effect of endotoxins. The increasing severity of the local reaction to repeated doses of *Salmonella* vaccine in man may be this type of allergy, since there is no reason for the reaction to the endotoxin as such to increase in this manner.

Endotoxins and the Shwartzman Phenomenon. Endotoxins from the gram-negative bacilli provide the material for the Shwartzman reaction. The purified lipo-polysaccharide used by Landy and Johnson (124) was effective in doses of 1 μg. or less as either the preparatory or provocative dose in the localized Shwartzman reaction. Somewhat larger doses, 5 to 20 μg., produced the characteristic lesions of the generalized Shwartzman reaction.

The **Shwartzman phenomenon is** a manifestation of a nonspecific toxin and is **not an antigen-antibody reaction.** It will be discussed in more detail, however, in the chapter on allergy, because it must be differentiated from the Arthus and tuberculin types of reaction, which are antigenically specific.

Protective Effect of Endotoxins. Endotoxins, in doses far below the lethal level, have a nonspecific stimulating effect on the maturation of plasma cells. Animals prepared in this manner give a more prompt and a higher antibody titer than control animals which have not received endotoxins (46). Endotoxins from meningococci (47) and typhoid bacilli (124) have an adjuvant effect of antibody production when given in doses sufficient to prepare rabbits for the generalized Shwartzman reaction. Examples of both increased and decreased effect on resistance have been reviewed by Hook and Wagner (98, 254).

EXOTOXINS OF MAJOR CLINICAL IMPORTANCE

The exotoxins produced by *C. diphtheriae, Cl. tetani, Cl. botulinum,* and *Clostridia* which produce gas gangrene are of major

importance and require treatment with specific antitoxins (218).

The exotoxins in general are specific in their reactions, affecting a specific substrate and producing characteristic symptoms. Some are known to be enzymes, such as the alpha toxin of *Cl. perfringens,* which is a lecithinase and the kappa toxin, which is a collagenase. The toxin produced by *Pseudomonas tabaci* which causes "wild fire" disease in tobacco is an antimetabolite of methionine (269). Streptolysin-O has a hemolytic effect resembling that of saponin (101), and the botulinus type A toxin acts on the motor nerve endings to interfere with the release but not the synthesis of acetylcholine (250).

DIPHTHERIA TOXIN AND ANTITOXIN

All the biologic products used by the physician in the prophylaxis and therapy of diphtheria are dependent, in final analysis, upon the production in the laboratory of a potent diphtheria toxin. The first diphtheria toxins produced were the sterile filtrates of broth cultures which contained, in addition to the toxin, many impurities of unknown composition.

A great improvement in diphtheria toxin production resulted from the extensive studies of Mueller and his associates on the nutritional requirements of *C. diphtheriae.* Mueller (147) succeeded in cultivating diphtheria bacilli in a medium which contained no substance having a molecular weight greater than that of the amino acids. Since 1937 the Massachusetts antitoxin and vaccine laboratory has employed only chemically defined media in the preparation of toxin for conversion into the toxoid used so widely in clinical medicine (161).

Pappenheimer and his associates (166) have studied the kinetics of the toxin production. They found that the toxin was indeed synthesized in the bacterial cells from amino acids and excreted by the cells into the medium. To produce toxin, however, the medium must be deficient in iron and the organisms must be infected with a temperate phage.

To produce a good toxin in a synthetic medium, the amounts of the various constituents must be controlled with extreme care, since toxin production may be inhibited by some substances which are present in minute amounts as impurities. For example, Pappenheimer and Johnson (158) found that 0.5 mg. of iron per liter of culture medium inhibited the formation of toxin, and that the greatest yield of toxin was obtained when the medium contained only 0.04 mg. of iron per liter. Pappenheimer (162) reported later that a greater toxin yield occurred when the iron concentration was 100 μg. per liter. Diphtheria toxin has been isolated in a highly purified form by a number of investigators (4, 32, 65, 128, 158) and in 1953 was obtained in crystalline form by Pope and Stevens (179). It is a relatively stable protein at neutral pH with a molecular weight of 72,000 and assayed 3,200 Lf per milligram N. The purified antitoxin has 211,000 units per gram (179).

Pope and Stevens (180) identified 24 antigens in crude culture filtrate of C. diphtheriae, but most of these were unrelated to the crystalline toxin protein complex. The crystalline toxin could be separated by chemical methods into four different fractions with much less toxicity. This does not prove that the components exist as separate entities under normal conditions (181). Digestion of purified toxin revealed three distinct antigenic sites, only one of which was associated with toxicity (77, 193).

Nature of Toxin and Mechanism of Action. The addition of iron to the culture media of C. diphtheriae stimulates the production of larger amounts of a cytochrome B-like enzyme. Every four atoms of iron in excess of the optimal concentration inhibit the synthesis of one molecule of toxin and four molecules of a porphyrin pigment which accumulates simultaneously. The diphtheria toxin is believed to be the protein fraction of the organism's cytochrome B, which accumulates together with the porphyrin when there is insufficient iron to combine the four molecules. Indirect evidence obtained from studies in the silkworm (164) support this hypothesis. According to the theory diphtheria intoxication in man would result from a metabolic competition with the protein fraction of the cytochrome B. This would explain the delay in the development of diph-

theria intoxication in animals, since the animals' supply of cytochrome B must first be exhausted before symptoms of interference in its synthesis become manifest.

Clinical infection with the *gravis* type of C. diphtheriae is characterized by an excessive amount of local edema, and local edema can be seen in the skin of guinea pigs infected with the *gravis* type organism. Branham has isolated a heavy component (40-60 S.) from crude toxin which is responsible for the edematous reaction (34).

The effect of diphtheria toxin on the heart has been restudied by Wittels and Bressler (266a). There was no evidence that the toxin had interfered with the synthesis of cytochrome b or with the formation of ATP. The fatty degeneration of the heart was apparently caused by 1, a marked depression in the rate of oxidation of long-chain fatty acids; 2, a markedly decreased concentration of carnitine; and 3, an excessive accumulation of triglycerides.

DIPHTHERIA ANTITOXIN

Diphtheria Antitoxin. Commercial diphtheria antitoxin is usually produced in horses, although a limited amount is made in cows for the benefit of individuals who have become hypersensitive to horse serum. Subcutaneous injections of diphtheria toxoid are employed, but toxin may be used if the first dose is preceded by an injection of antitoxin. The antitoxin can be concentrated by the method developed by Parfentjev (167), which consists of a digestion of the plasma with a pepsin solution of pH 4.0 to 4.5 followed by a precipitation of the antitoxin with ammonium sulfate. The pepsin splits the molecule in a plane at right angles to the long axis (171), yielding an active antitoxic fraction which is resistant to heat and an inactive fraction which is denatured rapidly by heat (178).

Since diphtheria toxin is relatively unstable, losing its toxicity on simple storage, it was necessary to establish a more constant reference point for the titration of both the toxin and the antitoxin. Ehrlich succeeded in preserving an antitoxin indefinitely by drying the serum in vacuo and preserving it at low temperatures in the presence of anhydrous phosphoric acid. Portions of this dehydrated antitoxin were sent to institutions in several countries, where they are preserved.

The official standard unit of antitoxin is that amount of antitoxin which is contained in 1/6000 of a gram of a certain dried unconcentrated horse serum antitoxin which has been maintained since 1905 at the National Institutes of Health at Bethesda, Maryland. This National Institutes of Health unit, or American unit, is the same as the International unit of diphtheria antitoxin. In terms of protective units, **the standard unit of antitoxin contained sufficient antitoxin to neutralize 100 M.L.D.'s of the particular toxin which Ehrlich had prepared and had employed in the titration of his standard antitoxin.**

Diphtheria antitoxin, like many other biologic products, is produced and distributed by commercial companies which are licensed by the government. Minimum requirements for factors such as potency and methods to be used in the testing of the products are defined explicitly by the National Institutes of Health.

Units of Diphtheria Toxin. A series of units for standardizing diphtheria toxin have been described. These are (1) the minimum lethal dose for a guinea pig (M.L.D.), (2) the L_0 dose, (3) the L_+ dose, (4) the L_r dose, and (5) the L_f dose (Fig. 2).

The minimal lethal dose, as defined by Ehrlich, is the smallest amount of toxin which will kill a guinea pig weighing 250 g. within four days after subcutaneous injection. Diphtheria toxin standardized by this method is used in the **Schick test** to ascertain the susceptibility of an individual to the disease diphtheria. The toxin is diluted so that 0.1 ml. contains 1/50 M.L.D., and this amount is injected intracutaneously.

Ehrlich introduced both the L_0 unit and the L_+ unit. **The L_0 unit is the greatest amount of toxin which, when mixed with one unit of antitoxin and injected subcutaneously into a guinea pig weighing 250 g. will produce no toxic reaction.** This unit requires

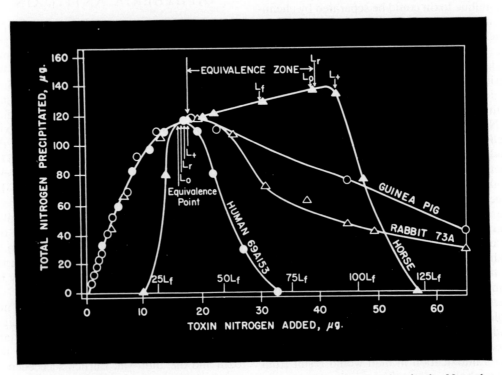

Fig. 2. Diphtheria toxin-antitoxin reaction in the serums of man and animals. Note the sharp equivalence zone in human serum and the broad equivalence zone in horse serum. (From Cohn and Pappenheimer. *J. Immunol.,* 63:291, 1949.)

an experienced investigator to determine if the guinea pig is normal or slightly injured by excess toxin. To eliminate this difficulty Ehrlich introduced a unit with death of the animal as an end point. **The L_+ unit is the smallest amount of toxin which, when mixed with one unit of antitoxin injected subcutaneously into a guinea pig weighing 250 g. will cause death in the animal within four days.** Theoretically, 101 M.L.D.'s of toxin should kill the animal, since 100 M.L.D's should serve to neutralize the unit of antitoxin and the remaining M.L.D. should kill the guinea pig. In practice Ehrlich found that much more than 101 M.L.D. was required to kill the guinea pig. The amount varied with different samples of toxin and rapidly increased as the toxin aged. He discovered that there was a spontaneous conversion of toxin into "toxoid." The latter had lost its toxicity but retained its ability to bind antitoxin.

Römer (199) observed in 1909 that an erythematous swelling followed the intracutaneous injection of small amounts of diphtheria toxin and that the reaction could be neutralized by antitoxin. Usually the minimal reacting dose was 1/250 to 1/500 of a M.L.D. **The L_r is the smallest amount of toxin which after mixing with one unit of antitoxin will produce a minimal skin lesion when injected intracutaneously into a guinea pig.** In practice fractional units of toxin and antitoxin are employed in the range of 1/20 to 1/500 units and the rabbit has been substituted for the guinea pig. This method has the advantage of conserving animals and of permitting multiple tests to be performed simultaneously on the same animal.

A test tube method for titrating toxin and antitoxin was introduced by Ramon (189) in 1922. The titration depends upon the observation of the first tube to flocculate in a series of tubes containing **constant amounts of toxin and varying amounts of antitoxins. The flocculating, or L_f, unit of diphtheria toxin is defined as that amount of toxin which flocculates most rapidly with one unit of antitoxin in a series of mixtures containing constant amounts of toxin and varying amounts of antitoxin.** The L_f value must be calculated from the several dilutions (15, 33, 58). The L_f unit is less reliable than the

units which are derived from experiments on animals but has two unique advantages. It is inexpensive and rapid and can be used to titrate toxoid which cannot be titrated by the methods requiring animals. As the toxin deteriorates, with age or after treatment with formalin the M.L.D. and L_0, L_r, and L_+ values decrease to zero while the L_f remains constant.

Farrell, Reid, and Kormendy (72) have introduced a delicate method of measuring small amounts of antitoxin in undiluted serum of the horse and man and in the whole blood of infants. Diphtheria toxin destroys monkey kidney cells in tissue cultures but the cells can be protected by antitoxin. This method will measure 0.001 units per ml., but the smallest amount shown in Figure 3 is 0.156 units per ml.

Danysz Phenomenon. In 1902 Danysz observed that if diphtheria toxin was added to antitoxin in two separate fractions and a sufficient time interval allowed between the addition of the first fraction and the second, the resulting mixture was more toxic than if the same total quantity of toxin had been added at one time. This phenomenon, also known as the **Danysz effect,** was interpreted by its discoverer as an indication that toxin

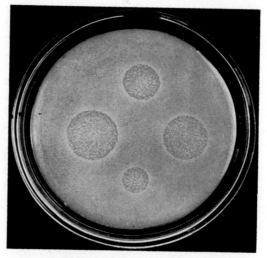

Fig. 3. Zones of inhibition of the destructive action of diphtheria toxin by specific antitoxin—10, 2.5, 0.625, and 0.156 units per milliliter; in monkey kidney cells in tissue culture. (From Farrell, Reid, and Kormendy. *J. Immunol.,* 90:201, 1963.)

combines with antitoxin in multiple proportions.

The Danysz effect can be visualized by referring to Figure 7 in Chapter 13 where it can be seen that the addition of one half of the optimal amount of toxin would result in a situation where there is excess antitoxin and under these conditions each molecule of toxin binds the maximal amount of antitoxin. When the second half of the toxin is added later, there is insufficient antitoxin free to neutralize it, so the mixture is toxic. After a period of time, however, readjustment occurs in the system and the mixture becomes nontoxic.

Pappenheimer and Robinson (159) showed that throughout the flocculation zone there was a direct proportionality between the L_f units of toxin added to a constant amount of antitoxin and the total amount of nitrogen contained in the precipitated floccules. In this rather wide equivalence zone, the supernates were free of both toxin and antitoxin, and the increase in precipitated nitrogen could be accounted for quantitatively by the amount of nitrogen in the added toxin. **This experiment proves beyond all doubt that diphtheria toxin and antitoxin combine in multiple proportions.** There is no precipitation in the region of antitoxin excess. This phenomenon of solubility in mixtures containing excess antibody, formerly thought to be characteristic of the toxin-antitoxin reaction, may be dependent upon other factors, such as the type of animal furnishing the antibody (160) or the method employed in the active immunization of the animal (246).

The following equations, taken from Pappenheimer's review (161), present the modern concept of the toxin-antitoxin reaction which is visualized as taking place in steps: (a) a rapid combination of toxin and an antitoxin and (b) a slower aggregation of the molecules.

RAPID   SLOW

$$T \quad + A \rightleftarrows TA \rightleftarrows (TA)_w \quad \text{(soluble)}$$
$$TA \quad + A \rightleftarrows TA_2 \rightleftarrows (TA_2)_x \quad \text{(insoluble)}$$
$$TA_2 + A \rightleftarrows TA_3 \rightleftarrows (TA_3)_y \quad \text{(insoluble)}$$
$$TA_3 + A \rightleftarrows TA_4 \rightleftarrows (TA_4)_z \quad \text{(soluble in presence of excess A)}$$

where T represents toxin; A represents antitoxin; w, x, y, and z represent the average number of molecules in the various aggregates.

It should be emphasized that there can be formed all kinds of intermediate complexes with formulas such as T_2A_3 and T_2A_5.

The broad equivalence zone with antitoxin made by the horse is a biologic accident (45). Human antitoxin shows a sharp equivalence zone, with the L_f, L_0 and L_+ being practically equivalent (Fig. 2). The equivalence zone is not quite so sharp with antitoxin from the rabbit, guinea pig, and monkey in the region of excess toxin, but following absorption with p-proteins they fail to precipitate when the amount of toxin added exceeds about twice that required for maximal precipitation. The results correspond to those predicted by the theory of Heidelberger and Kendall (95). Human and rabbit antitoxins are associated with the γ_2-globulin fraction of serum rather than the γ_1-globulin fraction as is the case in the horse.

Cohn and Pappenheimer calculated from their data that man synthesized 50,000 molecules of antitoxin for each molecule of toxoid injected.

The administration of ACTH or cortisone does not inhibit or reduce the amount of antitoxin produced by man (93).

Another major contribution to our knowledge of the nature of antitoxin was made by Kuhns, Laurence, and Pappenheimer in 1951. These investigators found that some individuals having allergic conditions or belonging to families with allergic diseases, would produce univalent antitoxin in remarkably high titers after the injection of toxoid prepared from purified diphtheria toxin. This antitoxin neutralized toxin but would not flocculate and in all other respects behaved like the univalent (atopic reagin) antibody usually found in individuals with hay fever-asthma-urticaria syndromes (see Chapter 17).

Further studies by this group of investigators (121) have revealed that a number of antibodies are produced as a result of infection with the diphtheria bacillus. These are (1) the classical bivalent flocculating antitoxin, (2) nonprecipitating (univalent) antitoxin which occurs in gamma 1 fraction of the serum, (3) a nonprecipitating type of antitoxin which migrates like the precipitin type in the gamma 2 fraction (121), (4) antibacterial antibodies to the protein of the bacillus which are of no practical value, (5) allergy to the proteins of the bacillus, and (6) allergy to the toxin as a protein (38, 163). Allergy of the latter type has been transferred passively to normal individuals by the white blood cells of man (165).

The biologic products of practical use to the investigator and physician are (1) standardized diphtheria toxin for use in the Schick test, (2) standard antitoxin for (a) prophylaxis and (b) therapy, and (3) plain fluid toxoid and alum precipitated toxoid for active immunization.

TETANUS TOXIN AND ANTITOXIN

The exotoxin of *Clostridium tetani,* called "tetanospasmin," is a much more toxic material than is diphtheria toxin. For example, the National Institutes of Health require that the parent tetanus toxin used for the manufacture of tetanus toxoid shall have an M.L.D. for guinea pigs no greater than 0.0001 ml., or 10,000 M.L.D. per ml. of toxic broth, whereas diphtheria toxin is acceptable when it contains only 400 M.L.D.'s of toxin per ml. Eaton (65), using a modification of the concentration procedure which he had employed in the isolation of diphtheria toxin, obtained preparations in which the M.L.D. for 500 g. guinea pigs contained from 0.000009 to 0.000018 mg. of nitrogen; or from 55,000 to 110,000 guinea pig M.L.D.'s per mg. of nitrogen. More recently Pillemer (175), utilizing alcohol extraction methods in the purification of tetanus toxin, obtained preparations which, when tested for their lethal effects on mice, gave the fantastic figure of 75,000,000 M.L.D.'s per mg. of nitrogen.

Tetanus toxin, like diphtheria toxin, is produced by culturing the organisms in a broth medium followed by filtration of the culture to remove the bacterial bodies. Broth cultures of tetanus bacilli, of course, must be incubated under anaerobic conditions.

Considerable improvement in the production of a potent tetanus toxin has resulted from experiments concerned with the com-position of the media used for toxin production. The classic medium, a veal-infusion-Witte's peptone-glucose substrate, produced a satisfactory toxin which contained about 100,000 M.L.D.'s per mg., but toxoids prepared from this toxin often caused anaphylactic reactions when injected into humans. Taylor (236) substituted hog's stomach autolysate for the peptone and succeeded in obtaining excellent toxin yields. Toxoids prepared from these toxins were used extensively to immunize humans and at the time of Taylor's publication no case of anaphylaxis had been reported. Mueller and Miller (147), by combining Taylor's hog stomach autolysate with beef heart and glucose and increasing the iron content of the medium, obtained toxins at least five times as potent as those obtained on Taylor's medium.

The crystalline toxin is unstable and spontaneously converts to highly antigenic toxoid on standing at $0°$ C. Pillemer has suggested that the molecules condense through their toxic groups (176). Tetanus toxin is a selective neurotoxin acting upon the nerve cells of the cerebrospinal axis, although it will also paralyze the cholinergic motor fibers to the iris of the eye. The toxin is believed to act on the synthesis and liberation of acetylcholine (250). The toxin reaches the nerves of the spinal axis through lymph spaces in the nerve trunk and not through the axis cylinders or the blood stream (270, 271, 272).

Units of Tetanus Toxin and Antitoxin. Although there is an increasing tendency to use white inbred Swiss mice as test animals for the measurement of tetanus toxin, the official M.L.D. is the **smallest amount of toxin which causes death within four days in guinea pigs weighing 350 g.**

The most important unit of toxin for the standardization of tetanus antitoxins is the T. D., or test dose, corresponding in principle to the L_+ dose of diphtheria toxin but differing in the actual amount of the substance used. The **test dose** of toxin is distributed by the National Institutes of Health and is defined as **that amount of toxin which when combined with 0.1 unit of standard antitoxin will result in the death of a 350 g. guinea pig in approximately four days with symptoms of tetanus.**

The official standard unit of antitoxin

which has been used continuously since 1907 is the amount of antitoxin contained in 0.00015 g. of a dried unconcentrated horse serum antitoxin. This unit, known as the **National Institutes of Health unit** or **American unit,** is double that of the **International unit,** 3,000 International units being equivalent to 1,500 American units.

The Flocculation Test. Until recently considerable difficulty has been encountered in the development of an accurate flocculation test which could be substituted for the more expensive animal titration method in the preliminary estimation of the strength of a toxin, toxoid, or antitoxin. Ramon and Descombey in 1926 (190) described the flocculation reaction but observed that flocculation also occurred in zones which did not correspond to the point at which the toxin and antitoxin neutralized each other. That these zones were due to additional antigens in the toxin was shown by Moloney and Hennessy (145)who detected two antigens distinct from the toxin which were capable of flocculating with antitoxin. One of these antigens was heat-labile (H. L. antigen); the other was heat-stabile (H. S. antigen). These two separate antigens could be purified and in turn could be used to precipitate from the antitoxin those antibodies responsible for their specific flocculation. After removal of these antibodies, only specific antitoxin was left in the serum, and subsequent tests showed optimal flocculation to occur only at the true neutralization point. Mueller and Miller (147) reported no difficulty in determining a single clear-cut flocculation zone when they used the highly potent toxin produced in their beef heart-hog's stomach autolysate medium. Pillemer (175), however, noted an occasional false flocculating zone, which he was able to eliminate by using the method of Moloney and Hennessy.

Bolyn and Moskowitz (31) have recovered tetanus antitoxin from toxin-antitoxin precipitates which had 1,470 units per mg. nitrogen by the flocculation test and 1,330 units per mg. of nitrogen by animal protection tests.

Minimum Requirements of Tetanus Biologics. Tetanus antitoxin is subject to the same minimum requirements as diphtheria antitoxin in regard to safety, sterility, po-

tency, and dating. Identical technics also are employed in the determination of potency except that 350-g. guinea pigs are used. The official test dose of toxin, distributed by the National Institutes of Health, is used as in the diphtheria antitoxin titrations, the T.D. being substituted for the L_+ dose of toxin.

The minimum requirements for **tetanus toxoids** are the same as for diphtheria toxoid except that the parent toxin is required to have a T. D. of 0.01 ml. or less, or an M.L.D. for the guinea pig no greater than 0.0001. Antigenicity tests also are identical except that the guinea pigs actively immunized with plain toxoid can receive an immunizing dose as large as one-third of the volume of toxoid recommended for the total human immunizing dose. Bioassays of tetanus toxoid in mice, guinea pigs, and man have been described by Ipsen (104).

The extensive use of tetanus toxoid during and after World War II has revealed that immunization is effective for a much longer period than originally anticipated. Rueg-segger (203) has reported that one course of tetanus toxoid gives protection from tetanus for four to five years and that a booster dose of tetanus toxoid causes a rapid rise in antitoxin even when the original immunization was 15 to 20 years in the past. In experimental animals given booster doses of tetanus toxoid, prolongation of life begins as early as three hours after the injection, although a measurable increase in tetanus antitoxin in the blood requires about three days (105).

Combined Toxoids. At the present time combined tetanus and diphtheria toxoids are used almost exclusively by pediatricians in the routine immunization of children. Such mixtures are acceptable to the National Institutes of Health, provided that each of the toxoids meets the minimum requirements.

BOTULINUS TOXIN AND ANTITOXIN

Five antigenically different types of botulinus toxins are known (272). Types A, B, and E (60, 83) cause disease in man, type C in birds and type D in animals. A and B are both proteins which have been obtained in crystalline form. Type A, crystallized by Lamanna and his associates (183), had a molecular weight of 900,000, but Type A, crystallized by Kegeles and associates (115), had a molecular weight of 1,130,000. Both forms, however, contained nearly 40 million mouse L.D.$_{50}$ per mg. (183). Type B, purified by Lamanna and Glassman (123), had a molecular weight of 60,000 and was somewhat less toxic for mice. The botulinus toxins are unusual in that they are readily absorbed by mouth and are not broken down to smaller units in the intestinal tract (94).

Botulinus toxin, in contrast to tetanus toxin, has no primary effect on the brain or spinal cord (56) **but acts on the motor nerve endings to interfere with the release but not the synthesis of acetylcholine** (252). Polyvalent antitoxin which will neutralize the toxins of both types A and B toxins have been prepared for use in man, but it is difficult to make the diagnosis and obtain the antitoxin in time to save the patient's life. Toxoids have been prepared from Types A, B, and E (83, 194). Those prepared from Type A and B have remained antigenic for three years when stored at 4° C. (273). Purified toxins of A, B, C, and D, have been converted into toxoids and absorbed on aluminum phosphate and tested in animals and man. Antitoxin was found to all five toxins but in somewhat smaller amounts than to any one toxoid given alone (74).

GAS GANGRENE TOXINS AND ANTITOXINS

The *Clostridium* present in the clinical disease known as gas gangrene produce a variety of different kinds of exotoxins (132, 136, 218). The champion is *Cl. perfringens,* which produces 10 separate exotoxins, and the runner-up is *Cl. novyi (Cl. oedematiens),* which produces six exotoxins (135).

Lecithinase. The most important of these toxins for man is the *alpha* toxin of *Cl. perfringens* (200), which has been identified as the enzyme lecithinase C. (134). Its corresponding antitoxin is the significant antibody required for recovery (70). Four *Clostridium* produce a single biochemical type of lecithinase: these are the alpha toxin of *Cl. perfringens,* the beta and gamma toxins of *Cl. novyi (Cl. oedematiens),* and the lecithinase of *Cl. bifermentans* (143). Except for a dis-

tant relationship between the lecithinases of *Cl. perfringens* and *Cl. bifermentans,* each is immunologically distinct and induces its own specific antitoxin (135).

Collagenase. A second important exotoxin of *Cl. perfringens* is the kappa toxin, a proteolytic enzyme which has been identified as a collagenase (26). At least three proteolytic enzymes are elaborated by *Cl. histolyticum* (138) and the most important one is a collagenase (250). The proteinases of *Cl. perfringens, Cl. histolyticum, Cl. chauvoei,* and *Cl. septicum* are not inhibited by normal serum, while those elaborated by *Cl. botulinum, Cl. tetani, Cl. novyi (Cl. oedematiens),* and *Cl. sporogenes* are inhibited. This may account for the lack of invasiveness seen in the latter group of *Clostridium.*

Hemolysins. The lecithinases described above are hemolytic, as are the delta and theta toxins of *Cl. perfringens.* The primary lethal toxin of *Cl. septicum* is hemolytic (23).

Necrotizing Toxins. The lecithinase and the beta, epsilon, and iota toxins of *Cl. perfringens* necrotize tissue. *Cl. novyi (Cl. oedematiens)* (153) and *Cl. histolyticum* (138) also produce a powerful necrotizing toxin.

Antitoxins. Antitoxins have been prepared against the toxins of many of the exotoxin-producing organisms, and toxoids for active immunization also have been made. Except for the staphylococcal and streptococcal antitoxins, all of the methods of titration are similar to those described for the diphtheria and tetanus antitoxins and are based on the use of reference antitoxins provided by the National Institutes of Health.

Gas gangrene antitoxin is polyvalent, containing antitoxins against two or more of the toxins produced by the anaerobic organisms associated with gas gangrene—namely, *Clostridium perfringens, Cl. histolyticum, Cl. septicum, Cl. novyi (Cl. oedematiens),* and *Cl. bifermentans.* For titration mice are used, and, except for *Cl. novyi (Cl. oedematiens),* the injections of the toxin-antitoxin mixtures are made intravenously. The time period of observation is three days, during which time at least one third of the mice injected with the control toxin-antitoxin mixture should die. Toxoids have been prepared against *Cl. perfringens* and *Cl. novyi* (*Cl. oedematiens*) and have been shown to immunize animals, protecting them against subsequent injections with lethal doses of either the toxins or the organisms. Satisfactory antitoxin titers also have been obtained by immunization of humans (247).

A new hyperbaric method of treatment is emerging which may be more effective than therapy with antitoxins, antibiotics or a combination of both. This is oxygen treatment administered in a closed chamber where pure oxygen can be given at two to three atmospheric pressure. In Holland, where this method of therapy originated, experimentally infected animals and some patients have been cured (35).

EXOTOXINS OF MINOR CLINICAL IMPORTANCE

These toxins are of minor importance because they are not very toxic or because they are produced in small amounts in the body. Included in this group are the erythrogenic toxins of scarlet fever, streptolysin-O, and other oxygen-labile hemolysins; streptolysin-S; alpha, beta, gamma, and delta (67) toxins of staphylococci; the leukocidins; staphylococcal enterotoxin; and the exotoxin of *Sh. dysenteriae*. The exotoxin of the dysentery bacillus, when isolated in the laboratory, was found to be as lethal as botulinus toxin (251), but, fortunately, under natural conditions of infection only minute amounts of toxin are produced. The exotoxin of the staphylococci is usually of minor importance in staphylococcal infections but sometimes in children and occasionally in adults may be responsible for the toxemia and death of the patient (108).

The erythrogenic toxin which causes the red skin in scarlet fever is the best known of these minor toxins. Only a small number of strains of group A are capable of synthesizing this toxin. It has a very selective action on the skin, since 1 mg. of precipitable protein diluted 100,000,000 times may give a red reaction in the skin of man while large amounts of unmodified toxin may be injected subcutaneously, for purposes of immunization, without producing symptoms (227).

There are three antigenic types of erythrogenic toxin, known as A, B, and C. Type A occurs with the greatest frequency and is known to be a heat-coaguable protein with a molecular weight of above 27,000 (100, 120, 226). Type B has been studied by Stock and Lynn (228). This also is a protein which is not precipitable by protamine. Toxin B, unlike Toxin A, was destroyed by trypsin. Toxin C was isolated and identified by Watson (257).

The scarlet fever antitoxin neutralizes the erythrogenic toxins and blanches the skin but has no effect on the multiplication of the organisms in the body.

Streptolysin-O is elaborated by most members of Group A streptococci, by "human" group C and large colony forms of group G. Streptolysin-O and other oxygen-labile lytic toxins, such as the theta toxin of *Cl. perfringens*, the tetanolysin of *Cl. tetani*, hemolysin of *Cl. histolyticum* (101), and the pneumolysin of *D. pneumoniae*, are active only in the reduced state and are reversibly inactivated by mild oxidizing agents. They have a saponin-like effect on red blood cells and, like saponin, are inhibited by cholesterol in the test tube but not by cholesterol present in the serum (25). Any one of the four hemolysins are inactivated by the specific antitoxins to any of the others, although they are not identical in structure (244, 245).

The streptolysin-O is a protein containing neither carbohydrates nor fat (169) and has a cardiotoxic action on the frog's heart. A single sublethal dose does not stop the heart, but if the heart is washed with Ringer's solution and then infused with the same size dose, it stops beating in systole. Bernheimer (24, 25) isolated the inhibiting substance from normal hearts and found it to be cholesterol or a cholesterol-like substance. This material also inhibited the lethal effect of the toxin in mice. Furthermore, when mice were injected with sublethal doses of toxin, they became refractory to a lethal dose for a period between six and 40 hours after the primary injection. Apparently the sublethal dose caused the heart to mobilize an increased amount of the available inhibitor for a limited period of time. The same phenomenon was observed with saponin, and animals resistant to saponin were resistant to streptolysin and vice versa. This resistance differs from the classical immunity which is induced by either active or passive immunization.

Halbert and his associates (88) have suggested that streptolysin-O may be bound by specific antibodies only to be released later by the disintegration of the antibodies, after which there is progressive damage to the heart producing rheumatic heart disease.

Streptolysin-S is produced, along with streptolysin-O, by most strains of group A streptococci, although some strains produce only the O and others only the S. Since the streptolysin-O is oxygen-labile, the hemolysis seen around the colonies on the surface of blood agar plates is caused exclusively by streptolysin S. Weld in 1934 (260) extracted this oxygen-stable hemolysin from living hemolytic streptococci by shaking them in normal serum. Since then it has been the subject of intensive investigation by Todd (244, 245) and by Bernheimer and his associates (24, 25). Streptolysin-S is a very toxic substance which, when injected into animals, produces intravascular hemolysis of the red cells and parenchymatous degeneration of the internal organs (14). The chemical nature of this poison is not known, but the reaction which releases the material in the streptococcal-serum mixture must be enzymatic, since it is inhibited by classical enzyme poisons. This toxin is not an antigen in the usually accepted sense and does not produce an antibody response in the body (102). The "antibody" which is present in the serum of normal man and animals appears to be a labile phospholipoprotein complex which may decrease rather than increase in the presence of infection with a streptolysin-S-producing strain of streptococcus (102, 229).

Our knowledge of the exotoxins of *Staphylococcus aureus* is fairly recent and still incomplete. The work of Blair and Carr (27) suggests that the toxin production like that of *C. diphtheriae* may depend, at least in some instances, upon a lysogenic state. Most toxin-producing strains are lysogenic, and some non-toxin-producing strains have become toxin producers after being infected with phages isolated from toxin-producing strains.

The **toxins produced by** *Staphylococcus aureus* **are labeled alpha, beta,** and **delta toxins** (79). The alpha toxin is probably the most important and lyses the red cells of the rabbit, ox, and sheep in this order of sensitivity. Both oxygen and CO_2 are essential for a good yield of toxin, and both are found in the edematous fluid surrounding an area of local infection. The toxin behaves as a protein (267). Besides being hemolytic, it necrotizes the skin when injected locally (dermonecrotic) and may kill the animal, suggesting that cells other than red cells in the body are susceptible to its effects. Kumar, Lindorfer, and their associates (122) have isolated pure alpha hemolysin from *S. aureus* by continuous flow paper electrophoretic methods and found that the hemolysins, dermonecrotic effect, Neisser-Wechsberg leukocidin, and the lethal effect were all from one toxin (Fig. 4).

In contrast to the alpha toxin, the beta toxin lyses only sheep and ox red cells. It does not necrotize the skin but causes an erythematous flush and is lethal for rabbits but not mice. This toxin is responsible for the "hot-cold" type of hemolysis. When micrococci which produce beta but not alpha toxin are planted on blood agar plates made with sheep cells and then incubated at 37° C., a zone of darkening appears but no real hemolysis occurs. When the plate is removed from the incubator and cooled to room temperature, the cells in the darkened zone hemolyze and the area becomes transparent. If the plate is now returned to the incubator, the clear zone persists but becomes surrounded by a second darkened zone.

The delta toxin is produced by strains which produce alpha and beta toxins but not by strains which lack this ability or by those which are coagulase negative. The hemolytic zone has a sharp edge but occurs only in an atmosphere of CO_2 or on plates buffered at pH 6. These toxins have been reviewed by Van Heyningen (250) and by Marks (139).

Leukocidins are produced by several organisms. The streptococcal leukocidin seems to be identical with streptolysin-O. One staphylococcal leukocidin is identical with the alpha toxin which is usually assayed by the methylene blue method of Neisser-Wechsberg (149). This one does not affect human leukocytes. The second leukocidin, discovered by Panton and Valentine (182, 249), develops early during incubation and destroys human as well as rabbit leukocytes by a somewhat different method from alpha toxin. This leukocidin has been identified as the delta toxin (8, 103, 106, 122). A third leukocidin, which is the second leukocidin which effects human leukocytes has been studied by Gladstone and Van Heyningen (81). These and other metabolic products of staphylococci were reviewed by Blair in 1962 (28).

Proteinase. Group A streptococci synthesize an extracellular enzyme which resembles papain in certain respects. The organisms produce a precursor which is then changed by autocatalysis into proteinase. Elliott (68) obtained both the proteinase and the precursor in crystalline form. Kellner and Robertson (112) found that this enzyme produced myocardial necrosis when injected into rabbits.

Enterotoxins. Enterotoxins are produced by many coagulase-positive strains of *S. aureus* which also produce hemolysins. It is a distinct

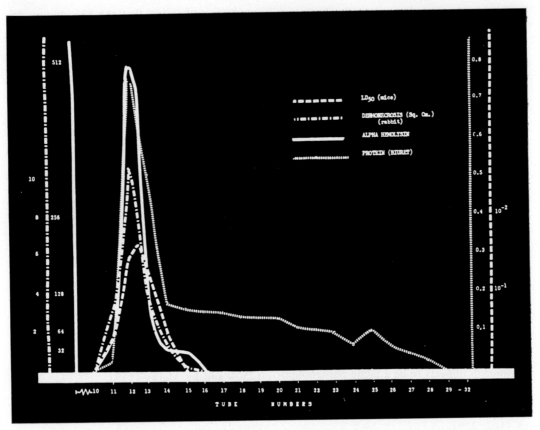

Fig. 4. Electrophoretic migration of alpha hemolytic, dermonecrotic, lethal activities, and protein of a purified alpha toxin. (From Kumba and Lindorfer. *J. Exper. Med.*, 115:1095, 1962.)

toxin, protein in nature (21, 22) but poorly antigenic (233). However, three antigenic types have been differentiated (40, 41, 232, 237). The toxin may resist boiling for 30 minutes and is not neutralized by antitoxins made to the other toxin of staphylococcus.

Monkeys and men are the only naturally susceptible animals, although assay of toxin content can be made with cats (237). Sugiyama and his associates (231) have found that an intravenous injection of thorotrast 18 hours before intragastric challenge with enterotoxin makes young Rhesus monkeys very susceptible to the emetic effect of the enterotoxin. The symptoms of nausea and vomiting appear a few hours after the ingestion of the toxin or food containing the toxin but usually disappear after 24 hours. The disease is rarely if ever fatal.

The exotoxin of *Shigella dysenteriae* is produced by both the S and R forms of the organism. It is a simple protein which produces neurologic symptoms in mice, rabbits, and man

(62). The purified toxin is about 10,000,000 times as potent as the O antigen, equalling the toxicity of tetanus and botulinus toxins. Fortunately the cultures of *Sh. dysenteriae* are much less toxic than those of *Clostridium* because a far smaller amount of toxin is produced per cell (251). This toxin can be converted into a toxoid by treatment with formalin in contrast to the endotoxin or O antigen which is not altered by formalin.

FOOD POISONING

Food poisoning may be divided into two types: (1) the toxic type and (2) the infectious type (54). The toxic type of food poisoning is caused by toxins which exist preformed in the food before ingestion. The incubation period of this type is very short, three to four hours, as might be expected. Most toxins are protein in nature and are readily destroyed by the proteolytic enzymes of the intestinal tract, but the exotoxin of *Cl. botulinum* and the enterotoxin of *Staphylococcus aureus* are resistant to their action. The mortality is high from botulinus poisoning, because this toxin acts directly on the motor nerve endings, causing paralysis. Treatment with polyvalent botulinus antitoxin may be effective if given soon after the onset of symptoms. Fortunately, this toxin is readily destroyed by heating and if all home-canned and pickled foods were boiled before being served, this type of poisoning would disappear.

The enterotoxin of *S. aureus* probably causes more cases of food poisoning at the present time than all the other types combined. The nausea, vomiting, and diarrhea are distressing but almost never fatal; recovery is usually complete in 24 to 36 hours. Unfortunately, this toxin is relatively heat-resistant, and temperatures which destroy the cocci have no effect on the toxin. The mode of action of this toxin is unknown, and there is no specific therapy (55).

The chimpanzee is 10 times as susceptible to staphylococcal enterotoxin as *Macaca mulatta* and almost as susceptible as man (265). Bergdoll, Surgilla, and Dack (21) have found that most strains producing enterotoxins are serologically identical. A second antigenic type has been reported by Casman (40, 41).

Another nonspecific type of food poisoning has been recognized with greater frequency in the past 10 years. When foods are heavily infected with such organisms as *E. coli, P. vulgaris, P. morgani, S. faecalis,* and *B. cereus,* they may produce the toxic type of food poisoning. The nature of the poisons is unknown, but they may be cleavage products of food or enzymes which have a special affinity for some constituent of the human intestinal tract. The studies of Deibel and Silliker (59) indicate that enterococci are not a cause of food poisoning.

The infectious type of food poisoning is usually caused by certain members of the **Salmonella** or rarely the **Shigella** group of organisms. The incubation period is eight to 24 hours, and the toxins are produced as the organisms grow in the intestinal tract. The symptoms are not caused either by the bodies of the whole organism or by the isolated O antigens, since feeding these products to human volunteers is innocuous. There is some mortality with this type of food poisoning, and patients who do not recover within 24 to 48 hours should be treated with an effective antibiotic, such as chloramphenicol or tetrachlorocycline.

Food poisoning with heat resistant strains of *Cl. perfringens* has been reported by Hobbs and his associates (97). These strains do not produce enough of the recognized exotoxins to explain the symptoms so the presence of an "endotoxin" has been assumed.

NONTOXIC BACTERIAL METABOLITES OF AID TO THE INVADING ORGANISM

It is probable that a number of apparently nontoxic substances synthesized by the invading organism do in effect interfere with the metabolism of the host and render the host more susceptible to infection. An example of this interference with host metabolism is the nontoxic "toxin" of *Pseudomonas tabaci* which has been shown to be an analog of methionine (269). Our knowledge of most of these substances is fragmentary and incomplete, and only a few of the better understood ones, such as hyaluronidase, streptokinase, streptococcal deoxyribonuclease, and coagulase, will be discussed briefly.

Hyaluronidase. Hyaluronic acid is an essential constituent of the intracellular ground substance of many tissues. It is also produced as a capsule by certain strains of Group A hemolytic streptococci (71, 174, 198, 204, 211). Many organisms produce the enzyme hyaluronidase (69), which by hydrolyzing the intracellular ground substance facilitates spread of the infection (57, 63, 76).

Streptokinase. A number of gram-positive organisms, including the streptococci, staphylococci, and the gas gangrene organisms, produce substances which cause the lysis of fibrin clots. This lytic agent was described by Tillett and Garner in 1933 (241) as fibrolysin. The investigations of Christensen (42, 43) have shown that the streptococcal product was not the actual lytic subject but a kinase which acted upon a normal constituent of the blood, plasminogen, to form the active proteolytic enzyme plasmin (213, 214). Pillemer and his associates (177) have found that this same plasmin inactivates complement and its components in the test tube.

The studies of Madison (137) and Dack and others (53) suggest that most of the highly virulent strains of streptococci produce streptokinase. These kinases display a marked specificity: hemolytic streptococci from cows produce a streptokinase which specifically liquefies fibrin clots from cow serum; streptococci from dogs act on fibrin of the dog; and human strains liquefy only human fibrin. Purified streptokinase may be injected into the pleura in cases of hemothorax in order to liquefy the clot so that the exudate can be aspirated through a needle (242, 243).

Streptococcal Deoxyribonuclease. This agent, which originally was called streptodornase, resembles pancreatic deoxyribonuclease (DNAase) and, like it, depolymerizes deoxyribonucleoprotein and deoxyribonucleic acid by splitting the complex molecules successively into simpler polynucleotides. Magnesium ions are required for the reaction (131, 213). Most streptococci in groups A and B produce this enzyme, although the latter do not synthesize streptokinase. Wannamaker (255) identified three serologically distinct types of deoxyribonuclease in 1958, followed by a fourth in 1962. These have been designated as A, B, C and D types. Type B is found most frequently.

A large part of the sediment found in pleural and pericardial exudates is deoxyribonucleoprotein, which the enzyme can attack and liquefy (243). Purified preparations of streptokinase and streptococcal deoxyribonuclease are nontoxic but are antigenic, giving rise to the appearance of specific antibodies in the blood of patients infected with group A streptococci and in patients treated with the purified enzymes (243). This statement about the lack of toxicity of streptokinase may have to be revised in the light of the report of Christensen (43) that the intravenous injection of the enzyme into rabbits may cause lesions of the heart similar to those produced by the streptococcal proteolytic enzyme (112). Relatively pure preparations of both enzymes are now available commercially.

Coagulase. Some strains of staphylococci, colon bacilli, and *B. subtilis* produce a metabolic product which coagulates citrated or oxalated blood plasma from man and rabbits. The pathogenic strains of *Staphylococcus aureus* and also of the *albus* variety regularly produce coagulase, while the nonpathogenic strains do not (219). Those strains which produce food poisoning by means of an enterotoxin also are usually coagulase positive (71). Coagu-

lase is relatively heat-stabile, gives reactions suggesting that it is protein in nature, and acts on some normal constituent in the serum to produce clotting (110). There are two antigenic types of coagulase; some strains produce type I, some type II, and others produce both of these types (188). Among the 800 strains of *Staphylococcus aureus* studied by Schwabacher and others (209), 654 were coagulase positive, and of these 91.1 per cent produced an hemolysin and 93.6 per cent hyaluronidase.

The exact nature and chemical structure of coagulase is unknown. It has been suggested (250) that it is a prothrombin-like substance which, with a normal factor present in plasma, forms a thrombin-like substance which in turn reacts with fibrinogen to form fibrin (64). Most coagulase positive strains of staphylococci also produce hyaluronidase (209), give a rapid phosphatase test (264), and possess a lipase (76). Coagulase is antigenic, as shown by the presence of specific antibodies in the blood of patients who have recovered from staphylococcal infection and by injecting the coagulase into rabbits (64, 188).

The importance of coagulase in infection is under investigation. It has been assumed that the production of a fibrin network about a focus of cocci would interfere with phagocytosis, and it has been shown that coagulase will neutralize the antibacterial activity of normal human serum against *S. aureus* (66). Smith and Dubos (217) have reported that coagulase positive *S. aureus* would produce progressive abscess formation in the kidneys of mice, while coagulase negative strains would not. This late effect of coagulase may be more important than the initial one which inhibits phagocytosis.

REFERENCES

1. Abernathy, R. S. J. Immunol., 78:387, 1957.
2. ——— and others. J. Immunol., 81:271, 1958.
3. Ackermann, W. W., and others. J. Immunol., 81:1, 1958.
4. Agner, K. J. Exper. Med., 92:337, 1950.
5. Ajl, S. J., and others. J. Bact., 70:158, 1955.
6. ——— and others. J. Immunol., 80:435, 1958.
7. Algire, G. H., and others. J. Nat. Cancer Inst., 8:53, 1947.
8. Atkins, E., and Wood, W. B., Jr. J. Exper. Med., 102:499, 1955.
9. ——— and Freedman, L. R. J. Clin. Invest., 39:969, 1960.
10. ——— Physiol. Rev., 40:580, 1960.
11. Baggi, C. F., and Prodi, G. Proc. Soc. Exper. Biol. & Med., 86:461, 1954.

12. Baker, E. E., and others. Proc. Soc. Exper. Biol. & Med., 64:139, 1947.
13. Banerjea, A., and Munoz, J. J. Bact., 84:269, 1962.
14. Barnard, W. G., and Todd, E. W. J. Path. & Bact., 51:43, 1940.
15. Bayne-Jones, S. J. Immunol., 9:481, 1924.
16. Beall, F., and others. J. Bact., 83:1274, 1962.
17. Benacerraf, B., and others. Proc. Soc. Exper. Biol. & Med., 100:796, 1959.
18. Bennett, I. L., and Beeson, P. B. Medicine, 29:365, 1950.
19. ——— and Beeson, P. B. J. Exper. Med., 98:477, 1953.
20. ——— and Cluff, L. E. Pharm. Rev., 9:427, 1957.
21. Bergdoll, L. M., and others. J. Immunol., 83:334, 1959.
22. ——— and others. Arch. Biochem. & Biophys., 33:259, 1951.
23. Bernheimer, A. W. J. Exper. Med., 80:309, 1944.
24. ——— Bact. Rev., 12:195, 1948.
25. ——— Streptococcal Infections, New York, Columbia University Press, 1954, p. 19.
26. Bidwell, and Van Heyningen, W. E. Biochem. J., 42:140, 1948.
27. Blair, J. E., and Carr, M. J. Bact., 82:984, 1961.
28. ——— Bact. Rev., 26:375, 1962.
29. Blattenberg, B., and others. Proc. Soc. Exper. Biol. & Med., 107:620, 1961.
30. Boivin, A., and others. Compt. rend. Soc. de biol., 113:490, 1933; 114:302, 307, 1933.
31. Bolyn, A. E., and Moskowitz, M. J. Immunol., 75:441, 450, 1955.
32. Bowen, H. E. J. Immunol., 68:429, 1952.
33. ——— and Wyman, L. J. Immunol., 70:235, 1953.
34. Branham, S. E., and others. J. Immunol., 82:397, 1959.
35. Brummelkamp, W. H., and others. Surgery, 49:299, 1961.
36. Buccino, R., and others. Proc. Soc. Exper. Biol. & Med., 110:724, 1962.
37. Buckley, E. E., and Poges, N., eds. Venoms, American Association for the Advancement of Science, Washington, D.C., Publication 44, 1956.
38. Bunch, C. P., and others. J. Immunol., 39:427, 1940.
39. Calmette, Z. Ann. Inst. Pasteur, 9:225, 1895.
40. Casman, E. P. J. Bact., 79:849, 1960.
41. ——— and others. J. Bact., 85:715, 1963.
42. Christensen, L. R. J. Gen. Physiol., 28:363, 1945.
43. ——— Streptococcal Infections, New York, Columbia University Press, 1954, p. 39.
44. Cluff, L. E., and Bennett, I. L., Jr. Bull. Johns Hopkins Hosp., 101:281, 1957.
45. Cohn, M., and Pappenheimer, A. M., Jr. J. Immunol., 63:291, 1949.
46. ——— and Morse, S. I. J. Exper. Med., 111:689, 1960.
47. Condie, R. M., and others. Proc. Soc. Exper. Biol. & Med., 90:355, 1955.
48. Coulson, E. J., and others. J. Allergy, 21:34, 1950.
49. Cox, H. R. Ann. Rev. Microbiol., 7:197, 1953.
50. Cremer, N., and Watson, D. W. Proc. Soc. Exper. Biol. & Med., 95:510, 1957.
51. ——— and Watson, D. W. J. Exper. Med., 112:1037, 1960.
52. Dasinger, B. L., and Suter, E. Proc. Soc. Exper. Biol. & Med., 111:399, 1962.
53. Dack, G. M., and others. Proc. Soc. Exper. Biol. & Med., 32:1431, 1934.
54. ——— Ann. Rev. Microbiol., 7:327, 1953.
55. ——— Food Poisoning, Chicago, University of Chicago Press, 1956.
56. Davies, J. R., and others. J. Physiol., 120:618, 1953.
57. Davison, M. M., and others. J. Bact., 58:717, 1949.
58. Dean, H. R., and Webb, R. A. J. Path. & Bact., 29:473, 1926.
59. Deibel, R. H., and Silliker, J. H. J. Bact., 85:827, 1963.
59a. Dillaha, C. J., and others. J.A.M.A., 188:33, 1964.
60. Dolman, C. E., and others. Can. J. Pub. Health, 41:215, 1950.
61. Dubos, R. J. J. Bact., 43:77, 1942.
62. ——— and Geiger, J. W. J. Exper. Med., 84:143, 1946.
63. Duran-Reynals, F. Bact. Rev., 6:197, 1942.
64. Duthie, E. S., and Lorenz, L. L. J. Gen. Microbiol., 6:95, 1952.
65. Eaton, M. D. J. Bact., 31:347, 367, 1936.
66. Ekstedt, R. D., and Nungester, W. J. Proc. Soc. Exper. Biol. & Med., 89:90, 1955.
67. Elek, S. D., and Levy, E. J. Path. & Bact., 62:541, 1950.
68. Elliott, S. D. Streptococcal Infections, New York, Columbia University Press, 1954, p. 56.
69. Emmart, E. W., and Cole, R. M. J. Immunol., 70:596, 1955.
70. Evans, D. G. Brit. J. Exper. Path., 28:24, 1947.
71. Evans, J. B., and Niven, C. F., Jr. J. Bact., 59:545, 1950.
72. Farrell, L. N., and others. J. Immunol., 90:201, 1963.
72a. Favorite, G. O., and Morgan, H. R. J. Clin. Invest., 21:589, 1942.
73. Fessler, J. H., and others. J. Exper. Med., 113:1127, 1961.
74. Fiock, M. A., and others. J. Immunol., 90:697, 1963.
75. Freedman, H. H. J. Exper. Med., 112:619, 1960.
76. Frion, G. J., and Wenner, H. A. J. Infect. Dis., 80:185, 1947.
77. Fulthorpe, A. J. J. Immunol., 5:30, 1962.
78. Gaertner, C., and others. J. Immunol., 88:526, 1962.
79. Gillespie, W. A., and Adler, V. G. J. Path. & Bact., 64:187, 1952.
80. Gillman, S. M., and others. J. Exper. Med., 114:729, 1961.
81. Gladstone, G. P., and Van Heyningen, W. E. Brit. J. Exper. Path., 38:123, 1957.
82. Glenn, W. G., and others. Science, 135:434, 1962.
83. Gordon, M., and others. J. Bact., 74:533, 1957.
84. Gordon, P., and Lipton, M. A. Proc. Soc. Exper. Biol. & Med., 105:162, 1960.
85. Gourzis, J. T., and others. J. Exper. Med., 114:593, 1961.

85a. Grant, R., and Whalen, W. J. Am. J. Physiol., 173:47, 1953.
86. Greisman, S. E., and others. J. Clin. Invest., 42:1064, 1963.
87. Halberg, F., and others. Proc. Soc. Exper. Biol. & Med., 103:142, 1960.
88. Halbert, S. P., and others. J. Exper. Med., 113:571, 1961.
89. Hall, C. H., Jr., and Atkins, E. J. Exper. Med., 109:339, 1959.
90. Harris-Smith, P. W., and others. J. Gen. Microbiol., 19:91, 1958.
91. Haskins, W. T., and others. J. Exper. Med., 114:665, 1961.
92. ———— and others. Proc. Soc. Exper. Biol. & Med., 112:113, 1963.
93. Havens, W. P., Jr., and others. J. Immunol., 68:389, 1952.
94. Heckly, R. J., and others. J. Exper. Med., 111:745, 1960.
95. Heidelberger, M., and Kendall, F. E. J. Exper. Med., 61:573, 1935.
96. Heron, J. C., and others. J. Exper. Med., 113:1115, 1961.
97. Hobbs, B. C., and others. J. Hyg., 51:75, 1953.
98. Hook, E. W., and Wagner, R. R. J. Immunol., 83:302, 1959.
99. Horen, W. P. J.A.M.A., 185:839, 1963.
100. Hottle, G. A., and Pappenheimer, A. M., Jr. J. Exper. Med., 74:545, 1941.
101. Howard, J. G. Brit. J. Exper. Path., 34:564, 1953.
102. Humphrey, J. H. Brit. J. Exper. Path., 30:345, 365, 1949.
103. Hunt, G. A., and Moses, A. J. Science, 128:1574, 1958.
104. Ipsen, J., Jr. J. Immunol., 70:426, 1953.
105. ———— J. Immunol., 86:50, 1961.
106. Jackson, A. W., and Little, R. M. Can. J. Microbiol., 3:101, 1957.
107. Jawetz, E., and Meyer, K. J. Immunol., 49:1, 1944.
108. Joyner, A. L., and Smith, D. T. Surg., Gynec. and Obst., 63:1, 1936.
109. Kaiser, H. K., and Wood, W. B., Jr. J. Exper. Med., 115:27, 37, 1962.
110. Kaplan, M. H., and Spink, W. W. Blood, 3:573, 1948.
111. Keegan, H. L., and others. Pub. Health. Rep., 76:540, 1961.
112. Kellner, A., and Robertson, T. J. Exper. Med., 99:495, 1954.
113. Keene, W. R., and others. J. Clin. Invest., 40:295, 1961.
114. ———— and others. J. Clin. Invest., 40:302, 1961.
115. Kegeles, G. J. Am. Chem. Soc., 68:1670, 1946.
116. King, M. K., and Wood, W. B., Jr. J. Exper. Med., 107:305, 1958.
117. ———— J. Exper. Med., 112:809, 1960.
118. Klein, F., and others. Science, 138:1331, 1962.
119. Kochwa, S., and others. J. Immunol., 82:107, 1959.
120. Krejci, L. E., and others. J. Biol. Chem., 142:785, 1942.
121. Kuhns, W. J. J. Immunol., 75:105, 1955.
122. Kumar, S., and Lindorfer, R. K. J. Exper. Med., 115:1095, 1107, 1962.

123. Lamanna, C., and Glassman, H. N. J. Bact., 54:575, 1947.
124. Landy, M., and Johnson, A. G. Proc. Soc. Exper. Biol. & Med., 90:57, 1955.
125. ———— and Shear, M. J. J. Exper. Med., 106:77, 1957.
126. Larson, C. L., and others. J. Exper. Med., 111:1, 1960.
127. Lawton, W. D., and others. J. Immunol., 84:475, 1960.
128. Lepow, I. H., and Pillemer, L. J. Immunol., 69:1, 1952.
129. Lequire, V. S. J. Infect. Dis., 88:194, 1951.
130. Luderitz, O., Westphal, O., and others. Nature, 188:556, 1960.
131. McCarty, M. J. Exper. Med., 88:181, 1948; 90:543, 1949.
132. McClung, L. S. Ann. Rev. Microbiol., 10:173, 1956.
133. McCreary, T., and Werzel, H. J.A.M.A., 170:268, 1959.
134. MacFarlane, M. G. Biochem. J., 47:267, 1950.
135. ———— Mechanisms of Microbial Pathogenicity, Cambridge University Press, 1955, p. 57.
136. MacLennan, J. D. Bact. Rev., 26:177, 1962.
137. Madison, R. R. Proc. Soc. Exper. Biol. & Med., 31:1018, 1934.
138. Mandl, I., and others. J. Clin. Investigation, 32:1323, 1953.
139. Marks, J. J. Path. & Bact., 62:597, 1950; 64:175, 1952.
140. Melby, J. C., and Spink, W. W. Proc. Soc. Exper. Biol. & Med., 101:546, 1959.
141. Mergenhagen, S. E., and Jensen, S. B. Proc. Soc. Exper. Biol. & Med., 110:139, 1962.
142. Michael, J. G., and others. Nature, 191:296, 1961.
143. Miles, E. M., and Miles, A. A. J. Gen. Microbiol., 4:22, 1950.
144. Molnar, D. M. J. Bact., 84:147, 1962.
145. Moloney, P. J., and Hennessy, J. N. J. Immunol., 48:345, 1944.
146. Morgan, W. T. J., and Partridge, S. H. Biochem. J., 34:169, 1940; 35:1140, 1941.
147. Mueller, J. H., and Miller, P. A. J. Immunol., 50:377, 1945.
148. Nagler, A. L., and others. J. Exper. Med., 114:195, 205, 1961.
149. Neisser, M., and Wecheberg, F. Ztschr. f. Hyg. Infektionskr., 36:299, 1901.
150. Neter, E., and Ribi, E. Proc. Soc. Exper. Biol. & Med., 112:269, 1963.
151. Noll, H., and Braude, A. E. J. Clin. Invest., 40:1935, 1961.
152. Nowotny, A. J. Am. Chem. Soc., 83:501, 1961.
153. Oakley, C. L., and others. J. Gen. Microbiol., 1:91, 1947.
154. ———— Ann. Rev. Microbiol., 8:411, 1954.
155. Owen, C. R., and Larson, C. L. J. Exper. Med., 103:753, 1956.
156. Packer, L., and others. J. Bact., 78:658, 1959.
157. Pappenheimer, A. M., Jr., and Johnson, S. J. Brit. J. Exper. Path., 17:335, 1936.
158. ———— J. Biol. Chem., 120:543, 1937.
159. ———— and Robinson, E. S. J. Immunol., 32:291, 1937.
160. ———— J. Exper. Med., 71:263, 1940.

161. —— J. Bact., 43:273, 1942.
162. —— J. Biol. Chem., 167:251, 1947.
163. —— and Lawrence, H. S. Am. J. Hyg., 47:233, 1948.
164. —— and Williams, C. M. J. Gen. Physiol., 35:727, 1952.
165. —— J. Immunol., 75:259, 1955.
166. —— and others. J. Gen. Microbiol., 28:531, 1962.
167. Parfentjev, I. A. U.S. Patent 2,065,196; 1936.
168. Paterson, P. Y., and others. J. Immunol., 72:12, 1954.
169. Pentz, E. I., and Shigemora, Y. J. Bact., 69:210, 1955.
170. Pernis, B., and others. Proc. 30th Int. Cong. on Occupational Health, 1960, p. 770.
171. Petermann, M. L., and Pappenheimer, A. M., Jr. J. Phys. Chem., 45:1, 1941.
172. Petersdorf, R. G., and others. Proc. Soc. Exper. Biol. & Med., 106:234, 1961.
173. Piananida, M., and Muic, N. J. Immunol., 73:115, 1955.
174. Pike, R. M. J. Infect. Dis., 83:12, 19, 1948.
175. Pillemer, L. J. Immunol., 53:237, 1946.
176. —— and others. J. Exper. Med., 88:205, 1948.
177. —— and others. J. Exper. Med., 97:573, 1953.
178. Pope, C. G. Brit. J. Exper. Path., 20:132, 201, 213, 1939.
179. —— and Stevens, M. F. Brit. J. Exper. Path., 34:56, 241, 1953.
180. —— and Stevens, M. F. Brit. J. Exper. Path., 39:139, 150, 490, 1958.
181. —— and Stevens, M. F. Brit. J. Exper. Path., 40:410, 1959.
182. Proom, H. J. Path. & Bact., 44:425, 1937.
183. Putnam, F. W., and others. J. Biol. Chem., 165:735, 1946; 176:401, 1948.
184. Rabi, E., and others. Bact. Rev., 25:427, 1961; J. Bact., 87:391, 1964.
185. —— and others. J. Exper. Med., 114:647, 1961.
186. —— and others. J. Bact., 84:803, 1962.
187. Rafer, G. W., and others. J. Exper. Med., 14:831, 1960.
188. Rammelkamp, C. H., Jr., and others. J. Exper. Med., 91:295, 1950.
189. Ramon, G. Compt. rend. Soc. de biol., 86:661, 1922.
190. —— and Descombey, P. Compt. rend. Soc. de biol., 95:434, 1926.
191. Ramsey, G. F., and Klickstein, G. D. J.A.M.A., 182:949, 1962.
192. Ravin, H. A., and others. Proc. Soc. Exper. Biol. & Med., 97:436, 1958.
193. Raynaud, M., and Relyveld, E. H. Ann. Inst. Pasteur, 97:636, 1959.
194. Reames, H. R., and others. J. Immunol., 55:309, 1947.
195. Reder, R. F., and Thomas, L. J. Immunol., 84:189, 1960.
196. Robertson, B. S., and others. J. Exper. Med., 112:751, 1960.
197. —— and Cromartie, W. J. J. Bact., 84:882, 1960.
198. Rogers, H. J. Biochem. J., 42:633, 1948.
199. Römer, P. H. Ztschr. f. Immunitätsforsch. u. exper. Therap., 3:208, 1909.
200. Roth, F. B., and Pillemer, L. J. Immunol., 70:533, 1953.
201. Rubenstein, H. S., and others. Proc. Soc. Exper. Biol. & Med., 111:458, 1962.
202. Rudbach, J. A., and Johnson, A. G. Proc. Soc. Exper. Biol. & Med., 111:631, 1962.
203. Ruegsegger, J. M. Arch. Int. Med., 106:410, 1960.
204. Russell, B. E., and Sherwood, N. P. J. Infect. Dis., 84:81, 1949.
205. Rutenburg, S. H., and others. J. Exper. Med., 112:801, 1157, 1960.
206. Schab, J. H. J. Exper. Med., 116:17, 1962.
207. Schaedler, R. W., and Dubos, R. J. J. Exper. Med., 113:559, 1961.
208. —— and Dubos, R. J. J. Exper. Med., 115:1149, 1161, 1962.
209. Schwabacher, H., and others. Brit. J. Exper. Path., 26:124, 1945.
210. Schweinburg, F. B., and Fine, J. J. Exper. Med., 112:793, 1960.
211. Seastone, C. V. J. Exper. Med., 77:21, 1943.
212. Sewall, H. J. Physiol., 8:203, 1887.
213. Sherry, S., and Goeller, J. P. J. Clin. Investigation, 29:1588, 1950.
214. —— J. Clin. Invest., 33:1054, 1954.
215. Shubin, H., and Weil, M. H. J.A.M.A., 185:850, 1963.
216. Slein, M. W., and Logan, G. F., Jr. J. Bact., 83:359, 1962.
217. Smith, J. M., and Dubos, R. J. J. Exper. Med., 103:87, 1956.
218. Smith, L. D. S. Introduction to the Pathogenic Anaerobes, Chicago, University of Chicago Press, 1955.
219. Smith, W., and Hale, J. H. Brit. J. Exper. Path., 25:101, 1944.
220. Spink, W. W. Ann. Int. Med., 53:1, 1960.
221. —— Arch. Int. Med., 106:433, 1960.
222. —— and Vick, J. Proc. Soc. Exper. Biol. & Med., 109:521, 1962.
223. —— and Su, C. K. Proc. Soc. Exper. Biol. & Med., 112:463, 1963.
224. Spivack, M. L., and Karler, A. J. Immunol., 80:441, 1958.
225. Stanley, J. L., and Smith, H. J. Gen. Microbiol., 26:49, 1961.
226. Stock, A. H. J. Biol. Chem., 142:777, 1942.
227. —— and Verney, E. J. Immunol., 69:373, 1952.
228. —— and Lynn, R. J. J. Immunol., 86:561, 1961.
229. Stollerman, G. H., and others. J. Clin. Investigation, 29:1636, 1950.
230. Strange, R. E., and Thorne, C. B. J. Bact., 76:192, 1958.
231. Sugiyama, H., and others. J. Bact., 80:265, 1963.
232. —— and others. Proc. Soc. Exper. Biol. & Med., 113:468, 1963.
233. Surgalla, M. J., and others. J. Immunol., 69:357, 1952.
234. Suter, E. J. Immunol., 89:377, 1962.
235. Takeda, Y., and Tsuchiya, L. Jap. J. Exper. Med., 23:9, 105, 1953.
236. Taylor, E. M. J. Immunol., 50:385, 1945.
237. Thatcher, F. S., and Robinson, J. J. Applied Bact., 25:378, 1962.
238. Thomas, L. J. Exper. Med., 104:865, 1956.
239. —— Arch. Int. Med., 101:452, 1958.

240. Thorne, C. B., and others. J. Bact., 79:450, 1960.
241. Tillett, W. S., and Garner, R. L. J. Exper. Med., 58:485, 1933.
242. ——— and Sherry, S. J. Clin. Investigation, 28:173, 1949.
243. ——— Harvey Lecture Series 1949-1950, Springfield, Ill., Charles C Thomas, 1951, p. 149.
244. Todd, E. W. J. Hyg., 39:1, 1939.
245. ——— Brit. J. Exper. Path., 22:172, 1941.
246. Treffers, H. P. Ann. Rev. Microbiol., 1: 263, 1947.
247. Tytell, A. A., and others. J. Immunol., 55: 233, 1947.
248. Uhr, J. W. J. Exper. Med., 115:685, 1962.
249. Valentine, F. C. O., and others. Lancet, 1:526, 1936.
250. Van Heyningen, W. E. Bacterial Toxins, Springfield, Ill., Charles C Thomas, 1950.
251. ——— and Gladstone, G. P. Brit. J. Exper. Path., 34:202, 1953.
252. ——— Mechanisms of Microbial Pathogenicity, Cambridge University Press, 1955.
253. Wacker, W. B., and others. J. Immunol., 89:525, 1962.
254. Wagner, R. R., and others. J. Immunol., 83:87, 1959.
255. Wannamaker, L. W. J. Exper. Med., 107: 797, 1958.
256. Watson, D. W., and others. J. Int. Dis., 80: 121, 1947.
257. ——— J. Exper. Med., 111:255, 1960.
258. Weinberger, H. J., and others. J. Bact., 59: 765, 1950.
259. Weissmann, G., and Thomas, L. J. Exper. Med., 116:4133, 1962.
260. Weld, J. T. J. Exper. Med., 59:83, 1934.
261. Westphal, O. Pyrogens. Tr. 2nd Conf. Pallisaccharides in Biol., Josiah Macy, Jr. Foundation, Madison, N.J., Madison Printing Co., 1957.
262. ——— and others. Pharm. Acta Helv., 33: 401, 1958.
263. ——— Ann. Inst. Pasteur, 98:789, 1960.
264. White, M. L., and Pickett, M. J. Am. J. Clin. Path., 23:1181, 1953.
265. Wilson, B. J. J. Bact., 78:240, 1959.
266. Wisseman, C. L., Jr., and others. J. Immunol., 86:613, 1961.
266a. Wittels, B., and Bressler, R. J. Clin. Invest., 43:630, 1964.
267. Wittler, R. G., and Pillemer, L. J. Biol. Chem., 174:23, 1948.
268. Wood, W. B., Jr. New Eng. J. Med., 258: 1023, 1958.
269. Woolley, D. W., and others. J. Biol. Chem., 198:807, 1952.
270. Wright, E. A. J. Immunol., 71:41, 1953.
271. Wright, G. P. Proc. Roy. Soc. Med., 46: No. 5, p. 319 (section on path.), p. 19, 1953.
272. ——— Mechanisms of Microbial Pathogenicity, Cambridge University Press, 1955, p. 78.
273. Wright, G. G., and others. J. Immunol., 84:384, 1960.
274. Yoshioka, M., and Johnson, A. G. J. Immunol., 89:326, 1962.
275. Zahl, P. A., and Bjerknes, C. Proc. Soc. Exper. Biol. & Med., 56:153, 1944.

17

Allergy

The introduction of modern chemotherapy has reduced materially the severity of many common infections. Concomitant with this change, there has been a relative increase in allergic diseases and an actual increase of sensitivity to the chemotherapeutic agents and antibiotics (53, 117, 191).

In this chapter the term "allergy" is used in its original sense—that is, an "altered capacity to react" to a subsequent exposure to a particular substance (403, 404). In many instances an exaggerated reaction occurs which has been designated as hypersensitivity and used incorrectly as a synonym for allergy. **Allergy is** more **comprehensive and includes hyposensitization** and **anergic reactions** as well as the **hypersensitive ones.**

Many of our common diseases or syndromes are allergic in type. These may be of spontaneous origin, as illustrated by asthma, hay fever, or eczema, or induced by therapy, as in the case of serum sickness and drug sensitivity. **In some diseases, such as tuberculosis, the allergic element is a dominant factor in producing symptoms, and in many other infections the allergic state plays an important role in prognosis and treatment.**

The dramatic, immediate therapeutic response of some but not all of these allergic conditions to treatment with ACTH and the corticoid hormones necessitates a restudy and revaluation of the allergic states.

Some of the better known allergic syndromes are listed in Table 1. They may be classified roughly into those conditions which give (a) immediate skin reactions (that is, within 20 to 30 minutes after the intracutaneous injections or cutaneous application of the proper allergen) and (b) those where the skin reaction is delayed for 24 to 48 hours. Antibodies are usually present in the serum of patients, and animals who give the immediate type of skin test and can be transferred passively from man to man or from one animal to another by the injection of serum. The antibodies present in the diseases characterized by the delayed skin test cannot be transferred passively with serum.

Four more or less distinct clinical types of allergic reactions can be recognized. Temporarily these have been designated as **precipitin allergies, atopic allergies, allergy of infection,** and **drug allergies.** Mixed forms of allergy do occur, and the separation into types is not as clear cut as indicated by the table, but the exceptions will be noted as the subject is developed.

The precipitin allergies, in which precipitins are usually present in the patient's serum, are artificially induced syndromes in man and animals. The antigen is usually serum or some other soluble protein but may be an antigenic polysaccharide (16) or a synthetic antigen (211). These classic antibodies are characterized by (a) giving an observable precipitate in the test tube, (b) being relatively thermostabile, (c) passing the placental barrier, and (d) being passively transferred with the serum to other animals.

HYPERSENSITIVITY IN ANIMALS

The phenomenon of allergy was discovered accidentally in animals during the course of experiments designed for other purposes. Since experiments on man must necessarily be limited to the mild and harmless reactions, animal experimentation was essential for the acquisition of knowledge concerning the prevention of the severe and

321

Table 1. Allergic Diseases Classified by Type of Skin Reaction

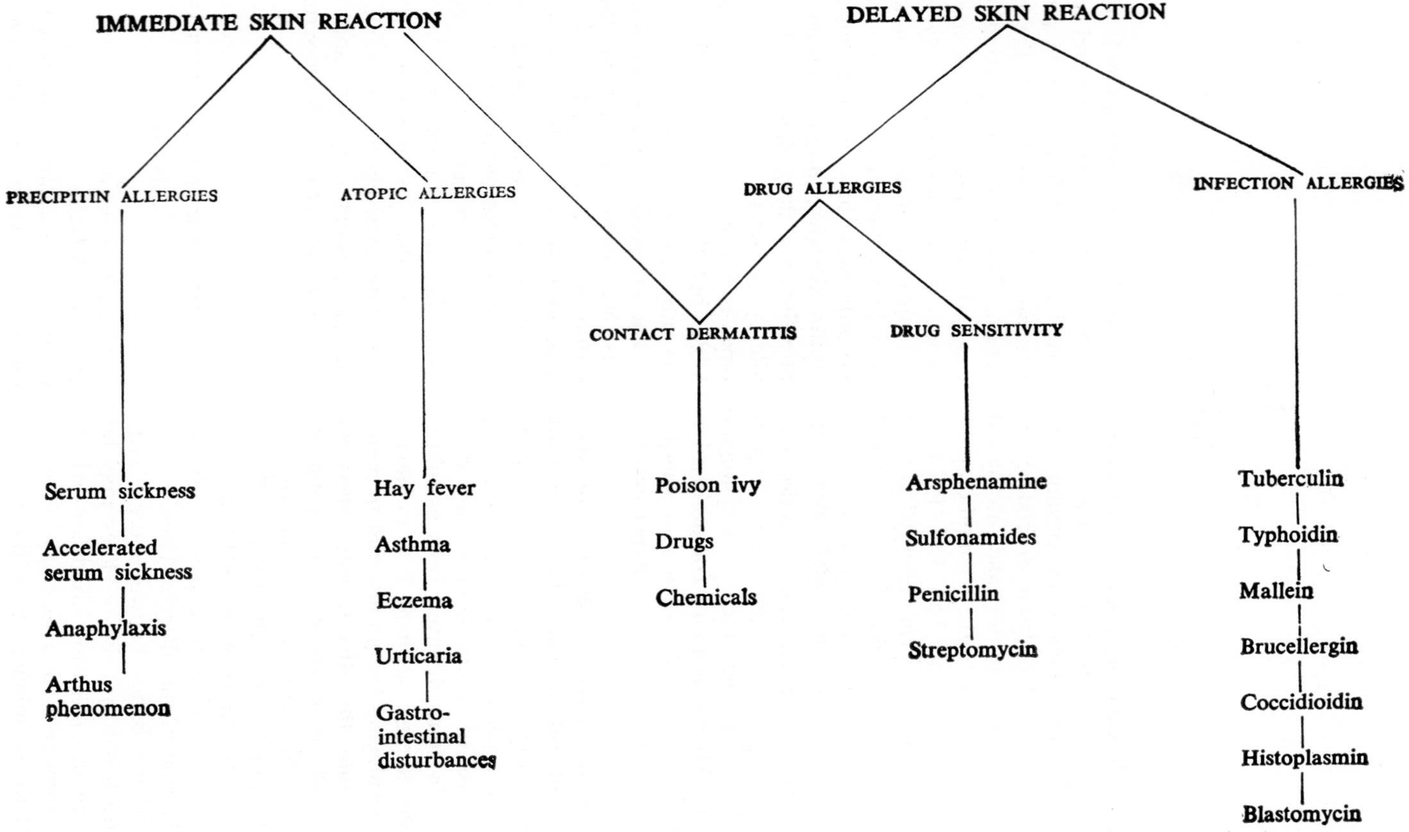

IMMEDIATE SKIN REACTION

PRECIPITIN ALLERGIES

- Serum sickness
- Accelerated serum sickness
- Anaphylaxis
- Arthus phenomenon

ATOPIC ALLERGIES

- Hay fever
- Asthma
- Eczema
- Urticaria
- Gastrointestinal disturbances

DELAYED SKIN REACTION

DRUG ALLERGIES

CONTACT DERMATITIS

- Poison ivy
- Drugs
- Chemicals

DRUG SENSITIVITY

- Arsphenamine
- Sulfonamides
- Penicillin
- Streptomycin

INFECTION ALLERGIES

- Tuberculin
- Typhoidin
- Mallein
- Brucellergin
- Coccidioidin
- Histoplasmin
- Blastomycin

often fatal reactions which developed in man during diagnostic and therapeutic procedures.

A systematic study of the phenomenon was initiated following the incidental and accidental discovery by a number of investigators that solutions of proteins which were harmless on primary injection often caused severe symptoms and even death in laboratory animals when reinjected some days or weeks after the primary inoculation. Magendie had observed as early as 1837 the sudden death of dogs after repeated injection of egg albumin; and Flexner reported that a second dose of dog serum killed rabbits. Portier and Richet (298) experimented with extracts of the tentacles of sea anemones. Arthus (10) injected horse serum into rabbits and Theobald Smith reported to Ehrlich in 1904 the characteristic and usually fatal effect of injecting guinea pigs with normal horse serum after they had been given mixtures of diphtheria toxin and antitoxin. The materials used by Richet and his associates had a primary toxicity for dogs and it was against this primary toxic effect that they were trying to "immunize" the dogs. To their surprise, however, the animals became much more susceptible and even died from smaller doses. **Richet coined the term anaphylaxis, the antithesis of prophylaxis, for this phenomenon.**

Typical attacks of anaphylaxis have been induced in guinea pigs, rabbits, dogs (355), mice (55), monkeys (100), horses (414), calves, horses (75), and pigeons (208). The rat may be made susceptible to anaphylaxis if injected with antigen after the removal of the suprarenal gland (100, 295). Susceptibility to anaphylaxis is induced in rats and mice (233) by injecting the antigen together with pertussis vaccine (195, 246, 263, 285). Rats injected with horse serum and pertussis vaccine develop anaphylaxis to horse serum if both the thymus and spleen are removed but not if either is retained (78).

The fact that passive sensitization can be blocked by prior introduction into the body of normal serum globulins suggests that the normal globulins compete for a specific site of attachment for the antibody globulins (149, 151). **The reaction pattern is some-**

what different in the various species, but all reactions are of the immediate type.

Anaphylaxis in the Guinea Pig. The anaphylactic state is readily established in the guinea pig by a single subcutaneous injection of 0.0001 ml. to 0.1 ml. of horse serum or 0.1 to 1 mg. of crystalline ovalbumin. The shock is induced by injecting intravenously 10 to 21 days later a somewhat larger amount of the original antigen, such as 0.05 ml. to 0.5 ml. of horse serum in 30 to 60 seconds. Shock may also be induced by injecting still larger amounts intraperitoneally, but the reaction is more irregular and is often milder. **Within a minute after the intravenous injection of the antigen the animal becomes restless: its hair bristles, and it usually scratches its nose and sneezes and often discharges feces and urine. The pig may give a few spasmodic jumps before respiratory difficulty becomes severe. The animal is entirely preoccupied with breathing: the pig may recover slowly in the next 10 minutes or may die in convulsions in the next two or five minutes —literally gasping for breath. The heart continues to beat for several minutes after breathing has stopped, and if the animal is autopsied immediately, the lungs are found to be distended with air.**

Quantitative studies by Coulson and his associates (83) and others show that maximum degrees of sensitivity are developed in 21 days with small doses and that the incubation period is more prolonged with larger doses.

The guinea pig has an abundance of smooth muscle about the bronchi, and the contraction of these muscles under the stimulation of the antigen-antibody reaction explains the respiratory difficulty (16). Dale (92) showed that spasm could be produced by perfusion of the antigen through the extirpated lungs of sensitized guinea pigs. Schultz found that strips of intestinal tissue from a sensitized guinea pig would contract with the antigen in vitro, and Dale (91) improved the technic by using the horn of the virgin guinea pig uterus. The Schultz-Dale technic necessitates the removing of the uterine horns of a sensitized virgin guinea pig, attaching one end of the horn to a clamp, and tying the other end to a lever which records the contractions on a moving smoked drum. The uterine strips are suspended in Locke's or Ringer's solution, to which the test substances are added at will. This method is extraordinarily sensitive. Dale and Hartley (93) found that a uterine horn of a guinea pig sensitized to horse serum contracted when 1 ml. of a 1:10,000,000 dilution of horse serum was added to a bath which contained 150 ml. of solution. The reaction is very specific and delicate enough to differentiate between egg albumin from hen or duck egg. Furthermore, after a uterine strip had contracted as a result of stimulation by a specific antigen and relaxed to its original length, it would not respond to a second immediate contact with the antigen, indicating that it had been desensitized. That the muscle itself was not damaged was proved by the typical contraction produced upon the addition of histamine to the bath. Studies with this method also demonstrated that the antibodies were fixed to the tissue cells. The uterine muscle could be washed free of all blood or serum by perfusion either in the animal body or after removal, and yet typical contractions would result when the specific antigen was added to the bath. Also, the uterus could be removed from the body of a normal guinea pig and sensitized passively by a perfusion with antiserum. But with most strains of guinea pigs a delay of four to five hours is necessary before a response of the uterus to the addition of antigen could be obtained, re-emphasizing the point that **the antibody must be attached to the cell before the reaction can be elicited.**

Anaphylaxis in the Rabbit. The rabbit is more difficult to sensitize than the guinea pig, usually requiring several doses of antigen, and even then many animals do not exhibit the fatal syndrome. **After an intravenous injection of the specific antigen, the rabbit may develop arrhythmic respiration followed by panting. The ears become hyperemic, then blanch; the animal becomes weak, falls on its side, gives a few convulsive movements, and dies suddenly with the eyes in exophthalmus and the head retracted. Frequently, however, the reaction is quite mild, without convulsions or death. Autopsy may show extreme dilatation of the right side of the heart, with engorgement of the inferior vena cava, portal vein, and liver.** Coca showed in 1919 that the heart failure resulted from the constriction of the relatively large amounts of smooth muscle which occur about the pulmonary arterioles. McKinnon and his associates (256) suggested that the cause of death in the rabbit was not constriction of the pulmonary arterioles but rather obstruction from multiple pulmonary emboli. However, a restudy of the problem by Weigle (412), in 1961, confirmed the original views of Coca.

Other changes, such as decrease in coagulability of the blood and reduction in the number of leukocytes and platelets in the blood, have been described by Dragstedt and his associates (105) and Rocha e Silva (332).

In contrast to the guinea pig, the rabbit develops a high titer of precipitins and is shocked most readily when the titer is highest; furthermore, no waiting period is necessary for the attachment of antibodies to cells in order to produce anaphylaxis in passively sensitized rabbits. These observations suggest that in the rabbit the reaction of antigen and antibody in the blood stream and on the cellular elements of the blood may be more significant than the reaction on the fixed tissue cells.

As in the case of the guinea pig, a shocking reaction temporarily desensitizes the rabbit, and partial anaphylactic desensitization can be accomplished by a few subcutaneous injections of a small amount of antigen in the course of three to four hours. This procedure is often necessary when rabbits are being immunized by a series of alternate courses of injections and resting periods.

Anaphylaxis in the Dog. A series of injections of native proteins is usually required to sensitize dogs. **A few minutes after the intravenous injection of the specific antigen, the dog becomes restless, salivates, vomits, and develops a diarrhea, which may be bloody. The blood pressure and body temperature fall, the respiration becomes slow and labored, muscle tone is lost, and the animal dies in collapse.** In some instances the dog recovers rapidly from the initial phase of the shock, only to relapse and die several hours later. The blood is altered by a loss of coagulability, decrease in neutrophils, decrease in serum **complement, and accumulation of white cells in the lungs** (355). The liver is the chief shock organ (247) and is found to be enormously distended and congested with blood in the animals which die promptly. Those which die after several hours show congestion of the gastrointestinal tract as well as the liver. In moderately sensitized dogs Manwaring has shown that anaphylaxis could be prevented by operative exclusion of the liver; in highly sensitized dogs, however, shock will occur even after extirpation of the liver. Dulaney and her associates (107) have shown that passive anaphylaxis can be produced in the dog.

Anaphylaxis in the Rat and Mouse. It is difficult if not impossible to induce enough antibodies in rats and mice to precipitate an anaphylactic reaction unless strenuous methods are employed, such as repeated doses of antigen with adjuvants (264), removal of the suprarenal gland (99, 100), or injection of the animals with pertussis vaccine (78, 192). This last procedure produces a very profound change in the metabolism of the animals, which makes them form more antibodies in a shorter period of time, but also renders them excessively sensitive to death from endotoxins, x-rays, cold, and other forms of shock. Mice become extremely sensitive to histamine and serotonin (388) and become very susceptible to fatal anaphylactic shock when the shock is induced by active or passive immunization (195, 263). However, the mouse does not become more sensitive to passive cutaneous anaphylaxis than to the Schultz-Dale reaction. The shock organ of the rat seems to be the small intestine (251).

An adequate explanation is not available for the derangement of the metabolism of these animals by adrenalectomy or pertussis vaccination (111, 193). Halpern and his associates (150) showed that a combination of epinephrine and cortisone completely restores the histamine resistance of adrenectomized mice, but the effect of this combination on pertussin-treated mice has not been reported. Some strains of mice are more resistant and others more susceptible to anaphylaxis (337), and some strains become progressively more susceptible to endotoxin but not to histamine and pertussin vaccine (1). Fishel and his associates (122) found that the pertussin-treated mice detect histamine and serotonin at the same rate as normal mice and that the protection induced by acetylcholine against serotonin is an epinephrine-mediated response (120). The authors suggest that sites of localized hyper-reactivity of the pertussin-treated animals are the target cells of histamine and serotonin and that the basic defect is a functional intolerance between two types of adrenergic effector systems.

Passive Anaphylaxis. The appearance of antibodies in the serum about the time the animal became susceptible to anaphylaxis suggested that the actual cause of the reaction was an antigen-antibody reaction in the intact animal. Serum from an actively sensitized guinea pig confers passive sensitivity to anaphylaxis to a normal guinea pig. The serum need not be from the same species, and it is a standard procedure to passively sensitize guinea pigs with antibodies made by the rabbit. This was a particularly fortunate combination, since the rabbit makes precipitating antibodies more readily than the guinea pig, while the guinea pig is definitely more susceptible to fatal anaphylaxis than the rabbit. The guinea pig cannot be passively sensitized with antibodies from the fowl, cow, and horse and cannot be sensitized with antibodies from the pigeon. Bramwell (48) suggested that these antibodies, for some unknown reason, cannot attach themselves to the muscle cell of the new host.

In the guinea pig a period of time is usually required for the newly introduced antibodies to become attached to the cells of the new host. This period may be as short as three to six hours (24), or maximum fixation may not be complete for several days. The usual time allowed is 24 hours. The isolated guinea pig uterus, chopped guinea pig lung (15), and segments of the ileum can be passively sensitized. In these instances also a period of time is required for the antibody to become fixed to the cells, and the electrical charge of the new protein molecule plays an important role in the antibody fixation (38). As an exception, however, a few strains of guinea pig can react almost immediately after the passive transfer of antibodies. Brown (52) noted this when the passively transferred control serum was followed by the antigen, and Zinsser and Enders (427) when the antigen was followed by the antibody containing serum. The immediate type of susceptibility to anaphylaxis is characteristic of passive anaphylaxis in the rabbit. In this instance, the primary shock tissue seems to be the platelets of the rabbit (332). Our observations up to this point have been limited to the classical precipitation antibody. Other studies have shown that anaphylaxis can be produced by the passive transfer of serum which contains "early" but not "late" nonprecipitating antibodies (41). The precipitating antibodies travel with the gamma globulin, while the early nonprecipitating antibodies move with alpha globulin (206). Kabat and Bernacerraf (178) have found that guinea pigs could be passively sensitized to anaphylactic shock with approximately the same quantity of nonprecipitating as precipitating antibodies. Kuhns and Pappenheimer (206) demonstrated that the nonprecipitating "reagin" type of antitoxin produced by atopic individuals in response to injection of toxoid would sensitize guinea pigs passively to anaphylaxis. In this instance the amount required to induce fatal anaphylaxis was equivalent to about 0.023 mg. of antibody nitrogen. The symptoms of anaphylaxis caused by nonprecipitating antibodies appear identical with those due to classical precipitating antibodies.

Passive Reversed Anaphylaxis. This is a more complicated procedure in which the antigen is injected into a normal animal and allowed time to fix to the cells of the body, after which the corresponding specific antibody serum is injected (177, 427, 430). A different type of reversed anaphylaxis is produced when a Forssman antibody, such as an antisheep erythrocyte serum produced in the Forssman negative rabbit, is injected into a guinea pig which has the heterophile antigen in its tissues (194).

Haptens and Anaphylaxis. Animals have been sensitized with artificially conjugated antigens having relatively small but chemically known radicals which determine specificity. Fatal shock could be produced with either the antigen used for the sensitization or with another protein containing the same chemical group. The chemical radical **hapten** alone will not form a precipitate with the antibody in a test tube but in some way will combine with the antibody, thus preventing precipitation when the complete antigen is added later. These haptens on injection into a sensitized animal will not produce anaphylaxis but will prevent the animal from reacting to a subsequent injection of the complete antigen. Some more complex haptens which are not antigenic will form a precipitate with antibody, however, and may produce anaphylaxis directly without the necessity of the protein carrier (16, 389). Examples of these are polysaccharides of *Pneumococcus* and *Klebsiella* as well as certain conjugated proteins with two determining groups.

Anaphylaxis with Antigen-Antibody Complexes. Both Germuth and McKinnon (138) and Weigle and Maurer (411) reported the production of anaphylaxis in normal guinea pigs by the injection of antigen-antibody complexes formed in moderate antigen excess (412). Antigen-antibody complexes formed in great antigen excess were less reactive, and those formed in the equivalence zone would not produce anaphylaxis. The latter complexes are known to be much larger than those formed in antigen excess and tend to precipitate, after which they are phagocytized and destroyed (74, 363). Complexes formed in antigen excess are soluble and continue to circulate for a long time. Antigen-antibody complexes are not an efficient method for producing anaphylaxis, since approximately 50 times as many antibodies are required as by the ordinary passive serum method. This suggests that there is a progressive disassociation of antigens and antibodies (280), after which the antibody becomes fixed to the reactive smooth muscle cells and then the free antigen reacts with the antibody-cell complex (410).

Quantitative Studies of Anaphylaxis. Studies of this type have been reported by Kabat and his associates (179, 182). The passive type of anaphylaxis must be employed, since it is necessary that the nitrogen content of both serum antibody and antigen be known. When small quantities of antibody are used, the shocking dose of antigen must be in the region of antigen excess as determined by the test tube precipitin test. With large amounts of antibodies,

however, shock would occur even in the region of antibody excess (182). Kabat and Landow (180) found that 0.03 mg. of rabbit antibody nitrogen would sensitize a guinea pig sufficiently for a fatal anaphylactic reaction, while the isolated guinea pig uterus needed only 0.01 µg. of antibody nitrogen to induce a specific reaction. The Schultz-Dale guinea pig uterus reaction is a more sensitive measure of antibodies than the precipitin test in the equivalence zone, the complement-fixation reaction, or anaphylaxis in the intact animal. Passive cutaneous anaphylaxis in the mouse has a degree of sensitivity comparable to that of the guinea pig uterus (37).

Protracted Anaphylaxis. Death from anaphylactic shock may occur within a few minutes after an intravenous injection of the specific antigen used to immunize the guinea pig. A little more time is required for the onset of symptoms and fever. Animals may die if the antigen is given intraperitoneally, but if death does not occur immediately, the animal makes a complete recovery after a day or so and is resistant to shock from the same antigen. Subcutaneous injection of the specific antigen rarely causes acute anaphylactic death. Haptens also can produce "hyposensitization," which is attributed to a temporary saturation of the antibody sites and not a neutralization of antibody or exhaustion of the tissue. A syndrome designated "chronic anaphylaxis" was described by Dean and his associates in 1936 (97). This syndrome was induced by the intravenous injection into guinea pigs of large amounts of antibodies preformed in the rabbit, after which a large dose of specific antigen was injected intravenously. These observations were confirmed and extended by Germuth and McKinnon in 1957 (138) and Stone in 1959 (373). The same syndrome could be produced in actively sensitized guinea pigs if large amounts of antibodies had been induced by injecting the antigen with an adjuvant (373) and a large dose of antigen was injected subcutaneously. This syndrome is characterized by pruritus, dyspnea, erection of the papillae of the skin, hypothermia, shock and death after one to 30 hours. The most striking feature at necropsy was stasis and/or hemorrhage of the stomach and intestinal wall. Intraperitoneal injections of antihistamines eliminated the respiratory symptoms but not death from collapse. Stone suggests that the prolongation of the shock syndrome is caused not only by slow absorption of antigen from a subcutaneous injection site, but also by the formation of soluble antigen-antibody complexes when small quantities of antigen came in contact with large quantities of antibodies circulating in the blood. The same mechanism would operate regardless of whether the excess antibodies were actively or passively acquired.

Stone (373) noted that the elimination of the acute respiratory phase of anaphylaxis, presumably due to histamine, brings the guinea pig closer to other animals in their general reactions.

The Mechanism of Anaphylaxis. The reactions of antigen and cell-fixed antibody produces soluble products which initiate the varying syndromes in different animals. By 1927 Lewis and Harmer (226) were convinced that histamine or a histamine-like substance (H) was released from the cells and induced the essential characteristics of anaphylaxis. Later studies, which have been summarized by Code (75), Dragstedt (104), and Dale (91) make a very convincing case for histamine-like substances as the chief reacting agent. In a study of bronchospasm in the isolated lung of sensitized guinea pigs by Liacopoulos and coworkers (228) 1,000 to 100,000 molecules of histamine were released to the perfusion outflow for each molecule of specific antigen sequestered in the lung. This suggests that the release of histamine is an enzymatic process.

Both precipitating and nonprecipitating antibodies are capable of inducing anaphylaxis, but the nonprecipitating antibodies must be those which appear early in immunization (178) but not by nonprecipitating antibodies which appear late in immunization (41), although the late nonprecipitating antibodies have the same electrophoretic mobility and sedimentation (327). The nonprecipitating antibodies could be measured by the bis-diazotized benzidine (BDB) technic as modified by Gordon (145). To explain the necessity for the injection of an excess of antigen to produce anaphylaxis, Pruzansky, Feinberg and Harris (300) assert that the excess is necessary to develop an adequate rate of diffusion of the antigen into the shock organs.

Complement does not seem to be necessary for the release of histamine in anaphylaxis (188), but it may be required for some of the other reactions which are induced by the union of antigen and antibody. Osler and his associates (273) showed that the old "anaphylatoxin" required the presence of serum containing complement as well as antigen and antibody. The anaphylatoxins, developed in the test tube, when injected intravenously into guinea pigs, produce a rapid type of death which resembles anaphylaxis. Oda and Puck (267) found that C′ was required for the destruction of cells by antigen and antibody. The evidence

for and against complement in anaphylaxis has been reviewed by Christian and Thurer (70).

Histamine, when injected into guinea pigs in the proper dose, does duplicate the respiratory syndrome of anaphylaxis but not that found in the rat or mouse. Antihistamines will prevent the respiratory syndrome of anaphylaxis induced in antigen-antibody reactions in the guinea pig but not in the rat or mouse (140). In contrast epinephrine and norepinephrine do protect mice. Katz (187) noted that the addition of specific antigen to the whole blood from a sensitized rabbit caused a shift of histamine from cells to plasma. The later work of Humphrey and Jacques (163) and Barbaro (18) showed that the major part of the histamine released in the blood of rabbits by antigen-antibody reaction came from the platelets. Although plasma is necessary for this reaction to occur in vitro, the thermolabile components of complement are not needed, and there is some doubt about the function of the thermostabile components (18). The same antigen-antibody reaction which releases histamine may also release histaminase (77, 231). This enzyme appears in the blood of the guinea pig in 30 seconds (233) and of the rat in six to 13 minutes after the injection of the antigen (234).

A derivative of the amino acid tryptophane, 5-hydroxytryptamine, seems to play a predominant rate in the anaphylaxis found in rats and mice. The name **serotonin** was given to this compound because it is found normally in the serum and gives tone to blood vessels. Serotonin kills mice with symptoms which resemble anaphylaxis, just as histamine does the guinea pig. The mouse uterus has been found to be 1,000 times as sensitive to serotonin as to histamine. Serotonin is released from the mast cells of the body and from the enterochromaffin cells of the intestines, along with histamine and heparin (44, 405). Reserpine protects mice from anaphylactic shock, but the action is not a direct one (140). Although the histamine plays a large role in anaphylaxis in some species of animals and serotonin a comparable rate in others, there is evidence that a number of additional reactive products are produced by the antigen-antibody reaction in the living body.

Boyd (47) refers to Wentz's theory which proposes that different tissues release different biologic active substances during anaphylaxis, depending upon the chemical nature of the tissue. For example, histamine may be isolated from most cells, from platelets, and from the lungs while choline is being released from the heart and adrenalin from the adrenal glands.

To this list must be added serotonin and heparin from mast cells.

Rocha e Silva (331) suggested in 1941 that the antigen-antibody reaction activated and released a proteolytic enzyme within cells, and this enzyme released histamine. Burdon and his associates (56) and others (398, 431) have restudied the effect of anaphylaxis on proteolytic enzymes. Burdon found that an abnormal activation of fibrinolytic enzymes in the clotted blood is a characteristic feature of severe or fatal anaphylactic shock of guinea pigs but concluded that fibrinolytic activity is probably the result rather than the cause of anaphylaxis.

The slow reacting substances of Kellaway and Trethewie, also known as "bradykinin" are not well understood but could be very important. One of these substances, known as SRS-A, has been isolated by the addition of antigen to allergic human lungs in vitro. The characteristics of SRS-A were reviewed by Brocklehurst in 1962 (49). It contracts smooth muscle and also contracts the duodenum of the rabbit and the ileum of the guinea pig. Its action is much slower than that of histamine and acetylcholine. It is not destroyed by boiling briefly or by the action of chymotrypsin. It has no effect on the horn of the rat's uterus but stimulates the contraction of the bronchi in man. It may be derived from mast cells. While it does not have the typical properties of a lipid, it may form complexes with the cell membranes of smooth muscle fibers to alter the ion flux across the membrane.

The new antihistaminics were synthesized for the purpose of neutralizing directly and chemically the histamine liberated by the anaphylactic type of reaction (45). They prevent the immediate skin test induced by histamine and in fact neutralize all the known specific effects of histamine except the stimulation of the secretion of hydrochloric acid in the stomach (76, 254). The antihistamines prevent anaphylaxis in the guinea pig but not in mice. In the guinea pig both active and passive anaphylaxis are prevented but not the type of anaphylaxis caused by the Forssman antibody (5) or the nephritis in rabbits produced with antikidney serum (419). They also reduce but do not abolish completely the vascular and myocardial lesions produced in rabbits by chronic anaphylaxis. In contrast to the antihistamines, ACTH failed to protect guinea pigs against histamine intoxication or anaphylactic shock (99, 133, 210).

The accumulation of small, subreacting doses of the specific antigen or a mild to moderate reaction produces a state of refractoriness to fatal anaphylaxis for a period of several days. The mechanism of this temporary hyposensitization is not understood. This refractory state can be induced by a mild shock with an unrelated antigen-antibody combination (301) and by the injection of normal human gamma globulin into guinea pigs sensitized to other antigens (70).

Passive Cutaneous Anaphylaxis. "Hives" and "wheals" were observed in some patients with serum sickness which followed the injection of horse serum. This led to the injection of normal horse serum, in a 1:10 dilution, into the layers of the skin as a test for antibodies fixed to the tissue which might give the patients anaphylaxis, if horse serum was injected a second time. A positive reaction begins within three to five minutes and reaches a maximum in 20 to 40 minutes and disappears completely in one to three hours. The reaction depends upon a dilation of the capillaries and vessels, which leak out clear fluid into the tissues to produce the wheal. The cells are not injured and soon recover as the extravasated fluid is drained away in the lymphatics. The reaction is characterized by a central white, irregular area of edema surrounded by a larger area of reticulated erythema. This type of skin reaction can be duplicated by the intracutaneous injection of a minute amount of histamine as described by Lewis (226). **This is a direct skin test for the immediate type of allergy when the antigen is injected into the skin to test for the presence of antibodies in the tissues.** Transient skin reactions of the wheal or hive type were produced in normal animals by Opie in 1924 (271) and Chase in 1947 by the injection of a mixture of antigen and antibody into the layers of the skin (65). The injection of either the antigen or antibody separately had no effect.

The production of passive anaphylaxis or reversed passive anaphylaxis in normal previously unsensitized animals had been practiced for many years. However, a minimum of 0.03 mg. of antibody nitrogen (181) is required to passively sensitize the guinea pig for fatal anaphylaxis.

In 1952 Ovary (276) described a passive cutaneous reaction in which a small amount of antibody-containing serum was injected locally into the layers of the skin. Then, after three to six hours, the antigen is mixed with an intense dye such as Evans' blue and injected intravenously. When the circulating antigen reaches the skin site of the previously injected specific antibodies, a reaction occurs which results in a dilation of the capillaries. The blue dye leaks through the capillaries and makes a readily visible blue spot. This test is much more sensitive than passive anaphylaxis in the intact animal, since 0.03 mg. of antibody nitrogen is required for fatal anaphylaxis while the passive cutaneous test will detect 0.003 μg. in rabbit and guinea pig sera (223, 276, 278). Antibody nitrogen down to 0.1 mg. has been detected in human serum. Rabbit antibody was found by passive skin reaction in the mouse at the level of 0.4 to 0.8 μg. and in the rat the level of 0.5 to 1.0 μg. (278). However, Muñoz and Anacker (262) found that the mice are almost as sensitive as the guinea pig when antibodies from other mice are used rather than antibodies from the rabbit, but 15 times more mouse antibody is required to sensitize rats' skin than mouse skin. This species difference may account for the poor showing of human antibody in guinea pig skin noted above.

Reversed passive cutaneous anaphylaxis can be induced if the antibody is injected intravenously and followed 24 to 48 hours later by injection of the antigen intracutaneously. In this type of experiment blue dye is injected intravenously before the intracutaneous injection of the antigen. Ovary (277) found that the same amount of antibody (0.03 mg.) nitrogen was required to sensitize a 250-gm. guinea pig for fatal anaphylaxis as for the reversed passive cutaneous anaphylaxis. Maximal reaction of the RPCA was obtained if 48 hours was allowed for tissue fixation of the antibodies.

This delicate method of measuring antibodies has been used by Chase (63) and by Rosenberg (335, 336) to measure antibodies produced by passively transferred white blood cells and has been found by Bier and his associates (37) to be as sensitive as the more laborious Schultz-Dale test. The type of antibody involved in the PCA is the classical 7 S. type; the 19 S. antibody of mouse and rabbit do not give PCA (126, 257, 282).

Anderson (3) found that antibodies digested to 5 S. with pepsin would still provoke the reverse passive cutaneous anaphylaxis, although not as effectively as the native antibody, but would not fix complement. Splitting the 5 S. precipitating antibody into the nonprecipitating 3.5 S. fragment almost eliminated the capacity to provoke reversed passive cutaneous anaphylaxis.

Benacerraf and his associates (29) showed that the 7 S. gamma globulin antibody of the guinea pig could be separated by electrophoretic mobility in a 7 S_1. and/or 7 S_2. fraction. These globulins possessed common as well as different antigenic determinants. The 7 S_1. could mediate (1) passive systemic anaphylaxis or (2)

passive cutaneous anaphylaxis but would not fix complement. The 7 S_2. did fix complement, hemolyzed red cells in the presence of complement, and produced the hemorrhagic lesion of the Arthus reaction but did not sensitize for the passive systemic or cutaneous anaphylaxis. 7 S_1. will produce edema but not hemorrhage in the Arthus reaction. However, both produce cutaneous anaphylaxis in the rat. Less antibody is needed to produce the reaction if the antigen is a small molecule such as pollen, wasp, or bee toxin (223).

Ovary named this passive cutaneous reaction, passive cutaneous anaphylaxis (PCA). However, certain significant differences between passive anaphylaxis and the passive cutaneous anaphylaxis should be emphasized. (1) The injection of mice with pertussis vaccine increases the susceptibility of mice to both active and passive anaphylaxis but does not increase their susceptibility to either direct or reversed passive cutaneous anaphylaxis (262). (2) Complement is essential for the PCA (272), but has not proven necessary for anaphylaxis (18). Antihistamines prevent the cutaneous reaction of the PCA and the pulmonary reaction in systemic anaphylaxis, but not reactions in other organs, although these may lead to death (373). Horse, cow, and goat antibodies (276, 278) which fail to fix complement and to sensitize guinea pigs for anaphylactic shock also fail for passive cutaneous anaphylaxis (305). Horse antipneumococcal antibodies will fix complement, however, and will give PCA reactions in the skin of rats (272). Simple haptens will not produce systemic anaphylaxis or passive cutaneous anaphylaxis, but they can combine in vitro with antibody and temporarily reduce or prevent shock from exposure to the complete antigen (281).

Antigen-antibody complexes, made in antigen excess, produce typical passive cutaneous anaphylaxis reactions (335, 336, 412).

PCA can be induced in the guinea pig with serum from patients suffering from lupus if purified DNA (158) is used as the antigen. The mechanism of action of the PCA depends upon local antigen-antibody-cell-complement interactivity.

Ishizaka and Campbell (165) have found that a molecular change occurs in the antibody when the antigen and antibody react, and this results in an alteration of the molecule which causes optical rotation to the left. The altered antibody, or some produce of the reaction, causes the capillaries to become more permeable to intravascular fluid. Antigen-antibody mixtures which do not cause optical rotation of antibody also fail to cause dilation of the capillaries.

Ovary and Karush (280) have prepared purified rabbit antihapten antibody and split the antibody with papain into three fractions described by Porter. Fraction I and II contain only one binding site and cannot precipitate. These fractions can bind the reacting sites on the antigen and prevent the PCA, but they cannot sensitize the local cells or give either PCA or RPCA because they lack a binding site for tissue cells and for complement (see Fig. 15 in Chapter 12 and Fig. 12 in Chapter 18). But Fraction III, which has no binding sites for antigen, does have binding sites for tissue cells and for complement. This fraction can give good reversed passive cutaneous reactions.

Van den Berg, Oort and Rijssel (402) have studied the location of fluorescent antigen in passive cutaneous anaphylaxis and in reversed Arthus reaction. As shown in Fig. 1B, most of the antigen passing through the walls of the blood vessels is taken up by the granulocytes with only small amounts found in the vessels' walls or free in the tissue. No serious damage to the capillaries or vessels occurs when the antigen reacts with the antibodies, and the skin is restored to normal as soon as the excess local edema has subsided.

The studies of Oort and Turk (270) with I^{131} labeled human serum albumin and purified tuberculin protein show rapid disappearance of antigen from the site of the intradermal injection in both normal and sensitized animals but somewhat less rapid in the sensitized. Thorne, Eiring and Smith (386) have made similar observations (Fig. 2).

Anaphylactoid Reactions. A syndrome resembling anaphylaxis in animals can be produced by the intravenous injection of substances such as bacteriologic peptones, typhoid vaccine, bile, agar, gum acacia, starch, and arsphena-

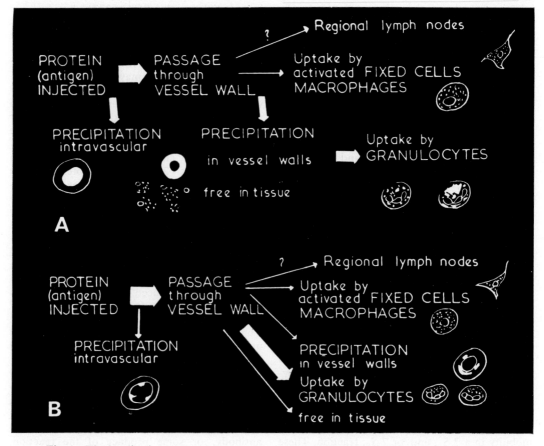

Fig. 1. The localization of fluorescent antigen in reversed Arthus reaction (A) and in passive cutaneous anaphylaxis (B). (From Van den Berg, Oort, and van Ritssel. *Immunology*, 5:389, 1962.)

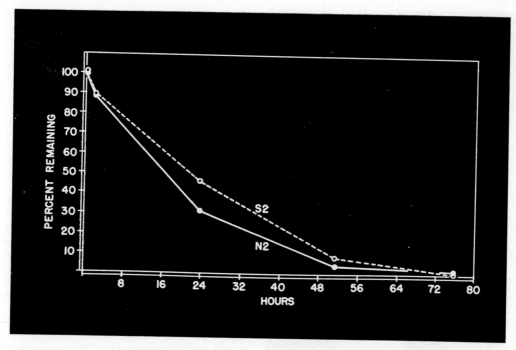

Fig. 2. Serum albumin labeled with I[131] was injected into the skin of a rabbit S2 which had been sensitized to serum albumin. The percentage of activity remaining at the site of injection was recorded over the next 75 hours. The rate of disappearance in a normal rabbit N2 is shown as a control.

mine. Even serum from a normal animal becomes "toxic" after being incubated with such substances as kaolin, barium sulfate, starch, or agar. Whole blood may give anaphylactoid reactions if withdrawn and reinjected in the "pre-clot stage." Hanzlick and Karsner (154) concluded that death was in most instances due to circulatory rather than to respiratory failure and was caused by the occlusion of small vessels with white cells and fibrin. The fatal type of shock produced in dogs with Witte's peptone, however, can be prevented by pyribenzamine and presumably other antihistamines (95).

The Arthus Reaction. The original allergic reaction in the rabbit reported by Arthus was a local rather than a systemic manifestation. As Arthus gave, at appropriate intervals, injection after injection of horse serum beneath the skin of rabbits, progressively more severe reactions occurred at the site of each succeeding injection. The early reactions were (a) transient local edema, followed later by (b) hyperemia and hemorrhage and finally by (c) induration, necrosis, and sloughing. The intensity of the reaction varies directly with the level of the precipitins in the blood (104, 278, 358).

Although 24 hours or more are required for the development of the necrotic lesions, which have more than a superficial resemblance to a necrotic tuberculin reaction, the initial damage is vascular and occurs very quickly after the introduction of the antigen (319, 321). Later authors demonstrated that nonvascularized, but sensitized tissues of the rabbit, such as the cornea, were less affected by contact with the antigen. But Parks and his associates (288, 289) have found guinea pigs and rabbits more often will give diffuse precipitation in the cornea if the antibody level is very high in the serum and a small amount of antigen remains in the cornea. An instance of severe Arthus reaction is shown in Figure 3. Precipitating antibodies were very high in the serum and tissues of the rabbit. Antigen injected into the skin produces a ratio of antigen excess at the local site. Under these conditions soluble complexes are formed which drain away rapidly, as shown in S2 of Figure 2. In the normal unsensitized rabbit (N2) the antigen disappears even more rapidly (Fig. 2).

The Arthus reaction has been produced in rats and mice by sensitizing with an antigen and adjuvant followed by an intralabial injection of the antigen (131). There are certain

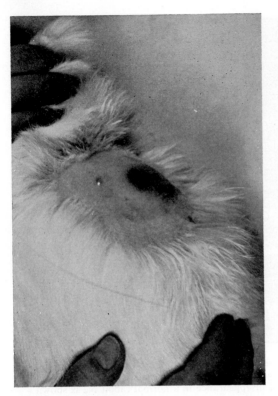

Fig. 3. A moderately severe Arthus reaction in the skin of a rabbit sensitized to serum albumin. (Courtesy of Dr. Gil Eiring.)

fundamental differences between the Arthus type reaction and both systemic anaphylaxis and passive cutaneous anaphylaxis, although all three depend upon antigen-antibody reaction of the classical type. (1) The presence of the precipitin type antibody is necessary for the Arthus reaction while anaphylaxis can be induced by either the precipitable or nonprecipitable type of antibody (23, 24, 204). (2) The Arthus reaction is dependent upon union with the tissues of circulating precipitins and the specific antibody (124) (Fig. 1A). (3) No preliminary period is required for the antibody to become fixed to the cell; the reaction can be elicited immediately after the intravenous injection of antibody by the local injection of antigen. (4) Although the cellular reaction begins immediately, the physical manifestations are progressive up to 24 or 48 hours, with hemorrhage and ischemic necrosis of the tissues, in contrast to the capillary dilation of passive cutaneous anaphylaxis and the contraction of smooth muscle in systemic anaphylaxis. (5) The amount of antibody required to sensitize the same size guinea pig to fatal anaphylaxis (24) is 2,500

times as much as is required to passively sensitize a strip of guinea pig smooth muscle to anaphylactic contraction (24). (6) Horse, rat, and bird antisera, which contain precipitins, but will not fix complement, can produce severe Arthus reaction (29) but not PCA (277, 278).

Koutras and Schilling (202) studied the rate of absorption of I^{131} bovine albumin serum obtained from the local site of an Arthus reaction, as compared with the absorption of the same antigen from a normal unsensitized guinea pig. The rate of disappearance of the labeled serum albumin was slower, although even in the sensitized animal 30 to 50 per cent of the serum left the site of injection in one to two hours. These findings were confirmed in part by the study of Thorne, Eiring, and Smith (386) in our laboratory with rabbits sensitized to human serum albumin. The rapid disappearance of the injected antigen could be due to the formation of soluble antigen-antibody complexes at the local site of antigen excess.

A somewhat different explanation for the local toxic effect in the Arthus reaction is suggested by the experiment of Ishizaka, Ishizaka and Sugahara (166), who found that aggregated human and rabbit gamma globulin, obtained by coupling with bis-diazotized benzidine, induced Arthus-like reaction when injected into the skin of normal guinea pigs. Neither aggregated bovine or chicken gamma globulin showed this activity and horse gamma globulin aggregates were much inferior to that prepared from the gamma globulin of man and rabbits.

Hyposensitization, to protect from the Arthus reaction, is somewhat more difficult to achieve than in the systemic anaphylactic reaction, probably because of the greater amount of antibodies involved in the Arthus reaction. However, multiple small, subcutaneous doses of antigen given at 15 minute intervals may accomplish hyposensitization. Hyposensitization has been reported to occur at times after massive amounts of antigen given subcutaneously as a single dose. In this instance we might assume that the excess antigen made soluble complexes with the circulating antibodies and that soluble complexes do not initiate the Arthus type reaction. In other instances the hyposensitization may occur from nonspecific shock or shock from an unrelated antigen and antibody system (372).

Neither cortisone nor ACTH will prevent or modify the Arthus reaction in animals passively sensitized. They do not prevent the reaction in actively sensitized rabbits if given after the development of precipitins (123), but cortisone and, to a much less degree, ACTH, if given through the period of immunization, markedly reduce the amount of precipitins formed and thus reduce the severity of the Arthus reaction (139). ACTH also reduces the number of vascular lesions in chronic serum sickness in rabbits (323). The depressant effect on antibody production of corticosteroids in rabbits is rather unique, and in other animals, including man, the depressant effect on antibody production may be minimal or absent. Hanon and Overman (153) studied the effect of cortisone on antibody production in rabbits simultaneously immunized to two different types of antigens, one soluble, bovine albumin, and one particulate, sheep red cells. Cortisone markedly depressed antibody formation to albumin but failed to effect antibody to the particulate sheep cell antigen (153).

The success of ACTH and cortisone in partially inhibiting the active Arthus reaction may be explained by their known ability to inhibit the formation of antibodies to blood serum proteins (100, 153).

Acute Serum Sickness in Animals. Acute serum sickness, in contrast to anaphylaxis, can be produced in the rabbit if large amounts of horse serum are given in a single primary injection. Fleisher and Jones (127) found that 5 to 10 ml. of horse serum per kilogram of rabbit was necessary and that the rabbits developed fever, erythema, and edema of the ears after five to six days. Under these conditions antibodies to horse serum were found while there was still a relatively large amount of antigen circulating in the blood, and the reaction proceeded until all the horse serum was eliminated. After a period of rest a new attack of serum sickness could be induced at an accelerated rate, two to three days, if again a large dose of horse serum was given sufficiently slow to prevent death from anaphylaxis.

Horses are said to develop hives as a part of the serum sickness syndrome (137). In general animals do not develop sickness as often or in as florid a manner as man.

Chronic Serum Sickness. This syndrome appears in the literature and was in the previous editions of this book as **chronic anaphylaxis.** As mentioned before, all of these allergic manifestations depend upon the reaction of antigens with their specific classical antibodies, but the mode of action, the time sequence, and the ultimate result are so different that each should be kept separate in the student's thinking. **Classical anaphylaxis** is an acute process which kills the animal in a few minutes or renders it temporarily nonreactive. In no instance do the symp-toms recur unless more antigen is injected at a later date when the antibodies are again ready to react. **Protracted anaphylaxis** is essentially the same process spread out over a period of hours, but not exceeding 24, caused by the slow absorption of large amounts of antigen from a subcutaneous deposit. If death does not occur, recovery is complete, and there are no recurrences unless new specific antigen is injected into the animal. **Serum sickness requires an incubation period** of days while the animal makes specific antibodies against the specific antigen which is circulating in the blood stream. The reaction spreads out over a period of days because it requires this amount of time to synthesize enough antibodies to eliminate all of the antigen. After recovery the animal is well unless more specific antibody is injected. Since antibodies are present now in or on the cells, and perhaps circulating blood, one may see on reinjecting the specific antigen an (a) immediate active cutaneous reaction, (b) a localized Arthus reaction or (c) a fatal, systemic anaphylactic reaction, depending upon the dose of antigen, route of injection, or presence or absence of precipitin in the blood. If the animal does not die of shock, it may have a second attack of serum sickness which will develop after a much shorter time than that required for the initial attack of serum sickness. **The syndrome previously referred to as "chronic anaphylaxis" is truly chronic serum sickness induced by very large doses of antigen.**

Longcope (235) gave repeated injections of antigen to sensitized dogs, cats, rabbits, and guinea pigs and found varying types of chronic lesions developing in the heart, blood vessels, kidneys, and other organs. Similar results were obtained by Hawn and Janeway (155) with single large doses of horse serum. They used both beef gamma globulin and albumin as well as whole serum. Antibodies to the globulin appeared in one week, and the lesions were confined chiefly to the kidneys and nonarterial structures in the heart, while the lesions due to albumin were maximal at two weeks and affected chiefly the arteries. Rich (320) and his associates have injected into the rabbit doses of horse serum in amounts as large as 10 ml. per kilogram. Sometimes only one injection was introduced, and at other times injections of smaller amounts were given one to seven days before the animals were sacrificed. Many of the lesions found in these animals resembled those known to occur in patients who have had sensitivity reactions to foreign serum, sulfonamides, or iodides. Others were similar to, if not identical with, the lesions seen in periarteritis nodosa. Many of these lesions resembled local anaphylactic reactions of the Arthus type.

Glomerulonephritis has been produced in rabbits with bacterial antigens. A more complicated type of nephritis results from the injection of organ-specific antibodies. Rabbit kidney tissue will induce antibodies when injected into the duck, and this antiserum damages the kidney when reinjected into the rabbit. Lesions of the lungs can also be produced by organ-specific antibodies (168).

The antibodies formed early during the primary antibody response have less avidity for the antigen than those produced later in the disease. These later, more avid antibodies may explain in part the severity and more prolonged course of experimental serum sickness in the rabbit (115). Dixon and his associates (103) produced chronic glomerulonephritis by injecting rabbit with BSA daily in varying doses over a period of several months. Gemuth and McKinnon (138) found that antigen-antibody complexes formed in moderate antibody excess, when injected into the rabbit in large doses, produced anaphylaxis which was sometimes fatal; if not fatal, it was followed by the symptoms and lesions of serum sickness.

The Shwartzman Phenomenon. This phenomenon was mentioned in the chapter on toxins and antitoxins because it can be induced by endotoxins. It will be discussed in more detail here because it must be differentiated from the Arthus phenomenon, which it resembles in time of appearance, manner of development, and ultimate appearance. This peculiar type of local tissue reactivity was described by Shwartzman (356) in 1928, who observed that if a single injection of a culture filtrate of *S. typhosa* was made into the skin of a rabbit and the same material then was injected intravenously 24 hours later, a severe hemorrhagic and necrotic lesion developed at the site of the original skin injection. The reaction was surely nonspecific in that the filtrate used for the preparatory skin injection showed the same reaction following the intravenous injection of the filtrate from another organism. For example, a skin site prepared with a meningococcus filtrate would react after the intravenous injection of not only the meningococcus filtrate but also typhoid bacillus and colon bacillus filtrates. This lack of specificity excludes the possibility that the

lesion is the result of an antigen-antibody combination, but also the time interval between the preparatory and the eliciting injection is too short to account for the reaction on the basis of antibody formation, especially when the extent and severity of the lesion are taken into consideration.

The localized Shwartzman reaction, like the classical Arthus reaction, is most easily produced in the rabbit. Shwartzman did succeed in producing the reaction in the golden Syrian hamster. Occasionally a successful experiment is reported for guinea pigs and goats, snakes, and mice (8) but Johnstone and his associates (173) failed to produce this type of lesion in monkeys, dogs, guinea pigs, small swine, and goats. The hemorrhagic lesions of the placenta of pregnant mice can be produced by the same endotoxins which produce the localized Shwartzman in the rabbit (328). Localized Shwartzman reactions have been produced in the oral mucosa of rats by endotoxin from oral *Veillonella* (330) and a localized lesion in the rabbit's colon by a single, not a double, dose of endotoxin given in the superior mesenteric artery (62).

The classical generalized Shwartzman reaction requires two doses. In this instance both the preparatory and the shocking dose are given intravenously. A precipitous drop in the leukocytes and platelets (35, 73, 370) is essential for the reaction, and it does not occur if these have been previously depleted by treatment with x-ray, nitrogen mustard, or benzene (7, 303). The characteristic lesion is found in the kidney where there is glomerular damage and cortical necroses, but lesions are found sometimes in the myocardium (40, 46, 84). The acute hemorrhagic pancreatic necrosis produced in rabbits and goats by Thal and Brackney (381) is really a localized Shwartzman, since the preparatory dose was injected directly into the pancreatic duct although the shocking dose was given intravenously.

The characteristic hemorrhagic necrotic lesions can be prevented by previous treatment with heparin (73, 143), dicumarol (308, 364), and tronexam (8). Although the anticoagulants prevent the thrombosis which is essential for the evolution of the lesions, heparin does not prevent the leukopenic, pyrexis, or lethal effects of the endo-toxin (143). ACTH and cortisone will reduce (248, 361) if not abolish the reaction if given between the preparatory and the shock-ing dose. Prolonged treatment with cortisone or the intravenous injection of thorotrast, trypan blue, or colloid carbon do substitute for the preparatory dose, however, so that rabbits developed the typical lesions after a single injection of endotoxin (360, 384).

The systemic Shwartzman reaction is characterized by the intravascular precipita-tion of an eosinophilic, periodic acid Schiff (PAS) positive material. This is most fre-quently deposited in the blood vessels of the kidney, liver, spleen, or lungs. The gross bilateral renal cortical necrosis results from obstruction to the blood flow to the glo-meruli (34). The generalized lesion resem-bling those of the Shwartzman, which were produced in pregnant rats by McKay and Wong (255) by feeding diet low in to-copherol and high in oxidized cod liver oil, may or may not be related to the true generalized Shwartzman phenomenon.

The role of the reticuloendothelial system in the Shwartzman reaction was reviewed by Lewis Thomas in 1957 (382). The reticulo-endothelial system which clears the damage from the first intravenous injection is not able to do the same job for the second in-jection (219). Proteolytic enzymes appar-ently play a role in the production of the lesions. Trypsin potentiates the local reac-tion (4), while trypsin inhibitors given at the time of the provocative dose inhibits partially or completely the local reaction and the renal lesion of the generalized reac-tion (71).

There is no proof that man is susceptible to the Shwartzman reaction, although there is suggestive evidence that some of the hem-orrhagic lesions of meningococcemia may be of this type (40). The mechanism for the development of the provocative and shock-ing materials during infection in man are being investigated. Kerby (189) has found acid mucopolysaccharide in human leuko-cytes not unlike the polymers which Thomas and his associates (385) used as the pre-paratory factor in the generalized Shwartz-man reaction in rabbits. Although ordinary filtrates of group A streptococci contain

neither the provocative nor the shocking fac-tor, Schwab, Watson, and Cromartie (344) found that a substance could be extracted from streptococcal lesions in the skin of rab-bits which would function as the preparatory factor and the shocking reaction could be caused by reduced filtrates of group A strep-tococci which contained streptolysin-O.

The Arthus and Shwartzman reactions depend upon very different immunologic principles, although the local hemorrhagic lesions appear identical on inspection and even in microscopic sections. Stetson's (367) work offers an adequate explanation for this paradox. He studied the two phenomena separately and finally produced both simul-taneously in different skin areas of the same rabbits. In the Shwartzman reaction the preparatory injection of a suitable endotoxin damages the local vascular bed during the following 24 hours. The intravenous injec-tion of the same or of another suitable endo-toxin causes an immediate neutropenia and thrombopenia, with the development of leukocyte-platelet thrombi in the small veins of the prepared area with subsequent hem-orrhages. To obtain the Arthus reaction, one must have an animal with a reasonably high precipitin titer in its blood. Only the local injection is necessary, but this must be made with the specific antigen to which the precipitins were formed. In this instance the specific antigen produced both the local vas-cular damage and also, escaping from the site of the injection, the systemic neutro-penia and thrombopenia. The only differ-ence noted by Stetson (368) was the time of appearance for the local reaction, which was well developed within one hour with the Shwartzman but required three to four hours for the Arthus to reach a similar degree of intensity.

HYPERSENSITIVITY IN MAN

Serum sickness, accelerated serum sick-ness, anaphylaxis, and the Arthus phenom-enon all occur in man after the injection of therapeutic serums. In contrast to the ob-servation in animals, serum sickness is very common, while anaphylaxis and the Arthus phenomenon are rarely encountered.

Serum sickness in man. The use of antitoxin for the treatment of diphtheria necessitates the parenteral injection of relatively large amounts of normal as well as immune globulins from the horse. Some of the patients showed no untoward reactions, but others developed a characteristic syndrome which is now known as serum sickness. The first thorough study of this condition was published by Von Pirquet and Schick (403, 404) in 1905. The extensive investigation of Ehrlich's pupil, Otto, in Germany, of Rosenau and Anderson, and Wells (417) in this country laid the foundation for our knowledge of anaphylaxis and serum sickness.

Serum sickness is essentially an artificially induced disease with a definite incubation period, characteristic symptoms, and certain specific serologic and allergic reactions (403, 404). The average incubation period is six to 10 days following the initial injection of horse serum into a normal individual. After specific antibodies have been produced, they react with the residue of the horse serum which is still circulating in the blood and may give rise to mild, moderate, or severe symptoms. These symptoms may include fever, neutropenia, adenitis, erythematous, or urticarial skin eruptions, edema at the site of the original injection and of the eyelids, face, and ankles, and, in very severe cases, arthralgia or hematuria. With crude horse serum there may be one or more recurrences of the eruption, since antibody formation to the various serum proteins may be established at different rates. The symptoms last from three hours to two weeks (67, 200).

When the symptoms subside, a re-examination of the patient's blood serum reveals the absence of horse serum and the presence of specific precipitins (236), and in many instances heterophile agglutinins for sheep cells (293). **If 0.1 ml. of 1:10 dilution of normal horse serum is injected intracutaneously an immediate reaction occurs within the next 20 to 30 minutes characterized by an urticarial wheal surrounded by a red area.** The entire reaction disappears within another 30 to 60 minutes except in instances of marked hypersensitivity where edema and redness may be present for six to 12 hours.

If a drop of 1:10 horse serum is placed on the conjunctivae of the eye, the conjunctival mucosae become fiery red and edematous in 20 to 30 minutes. This reaction can then be abolished by a drop of adrenalin.

The precipitins persist in the serum for some weeks or months and then disappear, but, while present, this type of sensitivity passes the placenta, and can be passively transferred to adults by either the direct or indirect method (185). Although the circulating precipitins disappear fairly soon, a more permanent change has occurred in the cells of the body so that the skin and ophthalmic tests may persist for the remainder of the patient's life. **In general, the larger the dose of serum, the greater the percentage of patients who develop serum sickness and the more severe the disease,** but variableness among individuals is as great as that seen in natural infectious disease. Many individuals produce antibodies at such a rate that the excess horse serum is slowly destroyed without an explosive reaction and completely without symptoms. This type of response is the ideal one and corresponds to a "subclinical infection." The proof of this occurrence is obtained by examining the serum of such a patient several weeks after the horse serum was injected and finding the presence of precipitins and the absence of horse serum. Such patients usually develop positive skin and ophthalmic tests, which may persist as long as those which follow severe cases of serum sickness. A few individuals lack the ability to produce specific antibodies to the injected horse serum; consequently, no precipitins are found and the horse serum continues to circulate for months (236). These patients, of course, have no symptoms, and, while this is a desirable way for the body to handle an inert, harmless foreign protein such as horse serum, similar failure to react to a living virus or bacterium would result in the unlimited multiplication of the living antigen and the death of the patient. **This type of reaction may be referred to as a hyposensitive or anergic reaction.** It is probable that in some diseases, such as histoplasmosis, with a very high rate of infection and a very low rate for clinical disease, progressive infections occur only in individuals who have a defect in their immunologic mechanisms. There are all gradations in the ability to form antibodies, from those who fail completely to those who make them slowly and with difficulty or those who make antibodies swiftly and in great excess. As we shall see later, the latter type of reaction may also be undesirable.

Accelerated Serum Sickness. No immediate reaction occurs when horse serum is injected a second time if a sufficient period has elapsed for the elimination of antibodies from the serum and the cells. The cells have been altered by the original contact with horse serum, however, so the anamnestic or recall phenomenon results in a more rapid production of antibodies and a shortening of the incubation period to one to three days. Accelerated serum sickness occurs also in patients with circulating or fixed antibodies, even though they have been hyposensitized to prevent anaphylaxis.

Commercial "purified" diphtheria antitoxin contains both alpha and gamma globulins, and precipitins are formed to both, but the alpha type seems to be detected more readily by the tanned red cell hemagglutinin technic (334). Using the same technic, Arbesman and his associates (6, 7) found that some individuals who developed serum sickness had antibodies in their serum before the injection of horse serum. They suggested that these patients may have been sensitized by horse dandruff, which is known to contain small amounts of horse serum albumin. The same group of workers (6, 7) studied an atopic patient who was given bovine tetanus antitoxin after an injury. He was already sensitive to horse serum, from a previous injection of this material, and had by the hemagglutination method a preexisting titer to horse serum of 1,000-2,000 but none to bovine serum. He developed serum sickness to the bovine antitoxin with precipitins to the alpha globulin and a hemagglutination titer of 100,000. A transitory "atopic reagin" skin-sensitizing antibody also appeared in the serum. When an individual with the ability to produce the atopic type of antibodies is given foreign serum, three distinct types of antibodies may appear: (1) classical precipitating antibodies, which can produce arthritis in the patient and passively transfer sensitivity for the Arthus reaction, the PCA, or anaphylaxis to guinea pigs; (2) a nonprecipitating antibody, which can transfer anaphylaxis but not the PCA or Arthus to guinea pigs; and (3) antibodies which cause urticaria and edema in the patient and passively transfer, by means of the Prausnitz-Kustner reaction, this capacity to the skin of a normal individual (305). Reisman and his associates (317) found good correlation with the tanned hemagglutinin test and complement fixation, precipitation, and passive cutaneous anaphylaxis. The antigen stimulation is so severe that plasma cells appear in the circulating blood. This has not been observed in any other disease state (52). Patients with severe serum sickness may have temperatures up to 104° to 106° F. and be prostrate for days, but they almost never die, in contrast to the brief but frequent fatal reaction to anaphylaxis. **A syndrome with all of the characteristics of serum sickness develops to penicillin.** This must be interpreted as the primary antigenic response to penicillin even though the patient has been treated with penicillin several times before without reactions.

Anaphylaxis in Man. If horse serum is injected into an individual who has been recently sensitized, and who has circulating antibodies or antibodies fixed to cells, a local edematous reaction occurs at the site of the injection, and there may be a generalized reaction. Intravenous injection may produce a severe and occasionally fatal anaphylactic shock, which may appear immediately, within a few minutes, or may be delayed for four to 12 hours. Urticaria and edema are present, and the picture in man may resemble that of any type of experimental animal or any combination of animals. Most of the **fatal reactions, however, have occurred in individuals who were known to have asthma and who had hypertrophied bronchial musculature induced by previous attacks of asthma.** In these instances the death was due to respiratory failure, and the syndrome duplicated that regularly seen in anaphylaxis in guinea pigs. **The prompt administration of epinephrine, intravenously or subcutaneously, will usually abort an attack of anaphylaxis.** Anaphylactic reactions to serum can be kept to a minimum if, whenever possible, the serum is given in the lower arm or leg so that a tourniquet can be applied to stop the absorption of the serum while the epinephrine is being administered. **A bottle of epinephrine and a sterile syringe should always be available when serum of any kind is being injected into man.**

With the increasing use of toxoid immunization against diphtheria and tetanus, the need for serum therapy has decreased, with a corresponding decrease of serum sickness and anaphylaxis from serum. **But with the increasing use of penicillin, both the serum sickness-like syndrome and anaphylaxis to penicillin are increasing.** By 1954 Welch and his associates (416) reported that 100 to 200 instances of anaphylaxis to penicillin were occurring annually in the United States.

Arthus Phenomenon in Man. Man seems to be intermediate between the rabbit and the guinea pig in his ability to produce precipitins, and a good titer of precipitins is essential for the production of the Arthus phenomenon. Red edematous areas are not at all unusual following subcutaneous or intramuscular injection of horse serum in patients who have had a previous injection of serum some days or weeks before. In rare instances extensive necrotic lesions develop (200, 312). We have observed one such instance in a child who was given a large dose of scarlet fever antitoxin into the tissues of the buttock without untoward reaction. The patient was apparently well after a few days, but one week later fever recurred and a red erythematous rash appeared over the body. This was almost certainly a manifestation of serum sickness but was interpreted by the local physician as a recurrence of scarlet fever. A second and larger dose of scarlet fever antitoxin resulted in a severe necrotic reaction which sloughed out a large area of the buttock at the site of the injection.

Hyposensitization. When a patient has once received a parenteral injection of horse serum, even though the amount was only the fraction of a milliliter which is contained in the mixture of toxin-antitoxin formerly used for immunization against diphtheria, one should suspect a permanently altered reaction or allergy to horse serum and always perform the skin and ophthalmic tests

before injecting more horse serum. Incidentally, the test for skin sensitivity should be performed with a 1:10 dilution of normal horse serum and not the refined therapeutic serums which are to be injected. In our experience the refined serums may give either false negative or false positive skin tests, but usually the latter. Even when the sensitivity tests are positive, the therapeutic serums can still be given without danger of inducing anaphylaxis if the patient is properly "hyposensitized." This term refers to an empirical method of injecting minute but gradually increasing amounts of horse serum or therapeutic serums until by an adjustment of an essentially unknown type, the patient can tolerate the full dose without reaction. Depending upon the size of the skin reaction, the initial dose should be 0.1 ml. of a 1:10, 1:100, or 1:1000 dilution of the serum administered subcutaneously. Subsequent doses are doubled—e.g., 0.1 ml., 0.2 ml., 0.4 ml., and 0.8 ml.—and administered every 15 minutes. The next stronger dilution is administered in like manner until 1 ml. of undiluted serum has been taken without reaction. The remainder of the therapeutic dose can then be given. **It is advisable to administer the hyposensitizing doses and the first therapeutic dose into an arm or leg, so that a tourniquet can be applied if the patient shows signs of anaphylactic reaction.** In all instances adrenalin 1:1000 should always be available in a syringe on the bedside table, so that it can be administered promptly to counteract the symptoms of anaphylaxis. Serum should be administered with the greatest caution, and then only if absolutely necessary, to patients with a history of asthma. Sometimes these patients have severe anaphylactic or anaphylactoid reactions even after a course of hyposensitization. After a nonfatal anaphylactic reaction, the patient is usually hyposensitized temporarily, and more serum can be given during the next 12 to 24 hours without untoward reactions. But we have seen a few asthmatic patients where a second anaphylactic shock followed a second dose of therapeutic pneumococcal serum within 24 hours, so adrenalin should always be available in the room when serum is being administered.

Treatment. Procaine hydrochloride, 1 g. in 500 ml. of physiologic saline, has been administered to relieve the itching and edema of serum sickness (366), and also in a similar type of generalized reaction in cases of penicillin sensitivity (106). The antihistaminic drugs have been used with fair success to control the symptoms of serum sickness (116). Corticoid hormones are of little value, since they do not interfere with the reaction of already synthesized antibodies (112, 125, 245, 260). Occasionally a fulminating type of serum sickness appears which is characterized by rapidly developing necrotic skin lesions. This type of reaction might be called a generalized Arthus reaction, or it might have the features of the delayed tuberculin type reaction superimposed on the usual serum sickness type of reaction. The prompt administration of ACTH or other corticoid hormones may save the lives of these patients.

Allergy to Wasp and Bee Stings. Disorders of the human respiratory tract are known to be caused by the inhalation of scales, hairs, wings, and body fragments or other body emanations of flying insects. Percutaneous instillations of salivary secretions from the bites of insects such as mosquitoes, gnats, and flies also cause allergic reactions in some instances (350). The allergy caused by the inhaled material probably belongs with the atopic allergies, which will be discussed in the next section, but the reactions to the stings of wasps, bees, and other stinging insects are related to serum sickness in man and will be discussed here.

It has been calculated that many more deaths occur each year in the United States from stinging insects than from the bite of venomous snakes. Benton and his associates (33) have collected large amounts of venom from honey bees by giving electric shocks which cause the discharge of venom without killing the bees.

The sting of a wasp or bee is painful to everyone and is accompanied by local swelling and reaction, partly due to the tissue reaction to formic acid, but we are referring here to something much more dangerous. This is a hypersensitive reaction to proteinaceous materials in the bee or wasp venom which renders the individual so susceptible that he or she may die with the symptoms of anaphylaxis from the sting of a single wasp or bee. The studies of Loveless and her associates (241, 242, 243) form the basis for the brief description of this syndrome in man and its prevention.

The allergic reactions to wasp and bee stings are related immunologically to the serum disease syndrome. The initial stings do not produce a violent reaction, and in many instances severe stings are tolerated before true allergic reaction occurs. As in serum disease, hives, edema, malaise, adenopathy, and hyperpyrexia occur after a period of incubation. In other patients, the immunologic changes occur below the threshold of clinical symptoms as in serum sickness, and suddenly the patient has an anaphylactic reaction when there is a new sting.

The allergic patient will give an immediate skin reaction in high dilutions of venom. This reaction alone does not differentiate between that to classical precipitating antibodies or the atopic type of antibodies, but, as noted above, both types may occur in patients after serum sickness.

Since the skin reaction is the immediate type, hyposensitization can be effected by multiple injections every 15 to 30 minutes. Loveless (60) thinks that the blocking type of antibodies develops after venom therapy or recent stingings. Patients who have been treated with multiple injections in a single day or with repository venom may experience stings without untoward reactions (241, 242). But such individuals should be cautioned to avoid locations where they might receive stings. In the event of a critical reaction in the field, they can use sublingual HCl or intramuscular epinephrine HCl (1:2000 0.5 ml. "ampins" of Moore, Kirk Laboratories, Inc., Worcester, Mass.).

THE ATOPIC ALLERGIC DISEASES

Hay fever, asthma, eczema, urticaria, and some types of gastrointestinal disturbances belong to the group of atopic allergic diseases (307). The term "atopy" (not in place, or a strange disease) was applied to this group of clinical syndromes by Coca. Diseases of this type show a familial distribution, although it is a susceptibility to sensitization and not sensitization itself which is inherited; furthermore, they must be considered as one unit when tracing inheritance, since a grandfather with hay fever can have one son who develops asthma and a grandson who has urticaria (82, 397).

Ratner and Silberman (313) have calculated that over 10 per cent of a random population will have allergies of this type. Heredity is of considerable importance since 22.4 per cent of allergic patients had one allergic parent, 43 per cent had an allergic parent or grandparent and, if brothers and sisters were included, 54.4 per cent had a positive family history of allergy. If both parents were allergic, 55 per cent of the children developed the disease. Inheritance, however, is only one of the determining factors, since Bowen (46) found that among 59 pairs of monozygotic twins allergies requiring medical treatment were present in one twin in 52 instances and both twins in only seven instances. With sufficient intensive exposure almost everyone can develop some degree of allergy. Wiener (418) has suggested that atopic allergy may be transmitted by means of a single pair of allelomorphic genes, Hx or h in which H determines nonallergy and h allergy. Three genotypes would be possible: HH would be the pure normal, hh, pure allergy where symptoms begin before puberty, and Hh, which appear normal but transmitted the trait or developed allergy after puberty. Support for the genetic control of atopic allergy is found in the studies of Patterson, Page, and Good (292), who found no evidence of respiratory allergy in 23 congenital sex-linked (male) agammaglobulinemic patients. Four children had eczema which was thought to be atopic but may have been delayed-type allergy. Attempts at production of allergy in agammaglobulinemic patients with extracts of the round worm Ascaris, which usually produces immediate sensitivity in normal individuals (96), failed to give this type but did sensitize them to the delayed type of allergy.

There are thousands of substances which can sensitize these unfortunate individuals but the more common allergens are (a) grass and tree pollens, (b) dander, feathers and hairs, (c) eggs (371), milk and chocolate, (d) house dust, bacteria (378, 379), and fungi. Rimnington (329) has reported that nearly 50 per cent of asthmatics react to house dust, and house dusts from different countries cross-react in patients. Dusts from unused lofts and empty buildings do not react, however, which relates the active material to man and his environment. It is suggested that this factor might be carbohydrates from cotton and kapock, but bacteria and fungi should be considered also.

Prausnitz-Kuestner Test. The presence of antibodies in the serum of these patients was discovered by Prausnitz and Kuestner (299) in 1921. Since Kuestner was sensitive to fish, he injected a very small amount of his serum in the normal skin of Prausnitz, and after an incubation period of 24 hours an extract of fish was injected into the same area and into a normal control area. An immediate wheal and erythema reaction occurred at the prepared site after 20 to 30 minutes but not in the control area. The antibodies remain fixed at the site of the injection, but the antigen may be injected into some remote tissue, or the blood stream, or may be ingested or inhaled, and still the wheal and flare occurs at the prepared site in the skin. **This method of demonstrating the presence of antibodies in the serum of atopic patients is known by the name of its discoverers, the Prausnitz-Kuestner (PK) reaction.**

The specific circulating antibodies (a) will not precipitate the specific antigen in the test tube, (b) are relatively heat-labile, being destroyed by a temperature of 60° C. in 30 to 60 minutes, (c) do not pass the placental barrier, (d) remain fixed in local areas of skin after passive transfer for a period of weeks, and (e) **do not passively sensitize guinea pigs to anaphylaxis of PCA. The professional allergist refers to the antigens which stimulate this type of antibodies in susceptible individuals as allergins or atopins.** The antibodies are sometimes called **reagins** to distinguish them from classical precipitating antibodies. Unfortunately, the term "reagin" has been applied also to the antibody which is responsible for the Wassermann reaction in the serum of syphilitics.

Van Arsdel and Sells (401) have found

that human leukocytes as well as cells of the skin and mucosa are saturated with skin-sensitizing antibodies. This can be shown by the release of histamine when the leukocytes are incubated in a test tube with the specific antigen. Furthermore, skin-sensitizing antibodies from the serum of patients with allergy to ragweed could be passively transferred to leukocytes of normal individuals so that histamine would be released when they were incubated with the ragweed pollen.

The Prausnitz-Kuestner reaction was employed by Layton and his associates (216) to detect atopic antibodies among 107 individuals who were working in a castor bean processing plant (217). Many of these individuals had allergic diseases presumably from the castor bean. It seemed undesirable to use human subjects for the passive transfer because of danger of serum hepatitis and possible later damage suits, so the authors transferred the serum to the skin of the Philippine crab-eating monkey, *Macaca irus*. The reactions were intensified by the injection of Evan's blue along with the antigen.

Perlman's (296) investigations have shown that commercial skin-testing antigen must be standardized by biologic testing in man, since chemical tests were not satisfactory.

Kuhns and Pappenheimer (206) found that individuals having the atopic type of allergy, or belonging to families which carried this trait, could react to diphtheria toxoid with the production of a univalent type of antitoxin which would neutralize diphtheria toxin but would not flocculate with toxin. This antibody could be passively transferred and meet all the other criteria of an atopic antibody. In this series of experiments some individuals produced only the univalent, passively transferable antibody. Others produced only the classic type of precipitable antibody, while the remainder made varying amounts of both kinds of antibodies. The minimum amount of this atopic antibody required to passively sensitize the skin of a normal individual was found to be 0.03 μg. of antitoxin regain nitrogen per ml. (206).

The production of more than one type of antibody by man has been observed in cases of serum sickness in atopic individuals where three different types may be observed: (1) classical precipitating antibodies, which will sensitize guinea pigs to anaphylaxis; (2) nonprecipitating antibodies, which will sensitize guinea pigs to anaphylaxis; and (3) atopic antibodies (185) which will sensitize human skin to the Prausnitz-Kuestner reaction but will not sensitize guinea pigs to anaphylaxis. Palczuk and Flick (284) found three men who failed to produce measurable precipitins to subcutaneous injection of specific pneumococcal polysaccharide but did develop typical skin-sensitizing atopic type antibodies.

Atopic individuals are also somewhat more susceptible to sensitization by penicillin (415). They may develop symptoms resembling serum sickness and produce both precipitating antibodies and atopic skin-sensitizing antibodies. Subsequent exposure to penicillin after sensitization is effected may result in anaphylaxis which can be fatal.

The skin-sensitizing antibody migrates electrophoretically with the γ_1 globulin. Kuhns (203) found that the ability of the atopic type antitoxin to passively sensitize the human skin depended upon the atopic antitoxin, which seemed to be the γ_1 fraction but must be protected by some β or α_2 globulins.

Loveless in 1941 (239) transferred blood from the allergic individual into a normal subject and found that the antibodies disappeared from the circulation within a few hours and became fixed to the skin, conjunctivae, mucosa, and probably other organisms. For a time the normal individual reacted like a sensitized atopic subject. The injection of the specific pollen produced a local skin reaction, and exposure of the eyes and mucosa of the nose induced hay fever, while inhalation of the pollen caused asthma. Similar studies by Sherman in 1957 (354) showed that the atopic antibodies remained fixed to the skin of the normal individual for many weeks. Wright and Hopkins (423) produced the reversed skin reaction in man by injecting the specific antigen into the skin and then injecting the serum from an atopic subject intravenously. As expected, an urticarial wheal appeared at the site where the antigen had been injected.

Rackerman (304) reported the data on 50 fatal cases of asthma. The pathologic findings in the younger individuals were identical with those of fatal anaphylaxis to classical type of precipitating antibodies. Although clinical asthma is associated with edema of the bronchial mucosa, there must be actual contraction of the bronchial muscles. This idea is supported by the studies of Schild (343), who suspended tracheal rings, removal by lobectomy, in a bath of physiologic salts, and observed the contraction of the rings when the appropriate pollen was added. Rackerman (304) found a somewhat different picture in the older asthmatics, where there was usually bacterial infection, and probably allergy of the delayed bacterial type, as well as the atopic allergy. In these patients the mucous excretion was excessive and sometimes caused death by mechanically plugging the medium and smaller bronchi.

The atopic antibodies coprecipitate with precipitin antibodies, as does the nonprecipitating antibody which can produce anaphylaxis in guinea pigs. A somewhat more specific method of isolation has been proposed by Pruzansky and Patterson (301), who incubated specific I^{131} labeled antigen with the serum of an atopic individual and then, after these reactions had formed their loose binding, added rabbit anti-human globulin, which bound the human globulin atopic antibody and caused a precipitate.

The atopic or "reagin" antibody occurs in the β_2 and β_2 M-globulins (14, 121, 424, 425), and their reactivity can be destroyed by proteolytic digestion (11). In contrast, the blocking antibody, induced by the parenteral injection of pollens, resembles the classical precipitating antibody and is confined to the γ_2 globulin fraction of the serum (424, 425).

A simple method for measuring atopic antibodies in human sera would be very useful. For a time it was believed that a hemagglutination test utilizing red blood cells to which pollen had been attached by the tanned red cell method (6) or the bis-diazotizing benzidine technic of Gordon and his associates (145) would supply such a method. Unfortunately, later work by Agustin and Hayward (13) showed that the hemagglutinin antibodies were in a different fraction of the serum from the skin-sensitizing antibody. Matthews and Spears (251) determined that the hemagglutinin antibodies could be absorbed out of the serum without reducing the skin sensitivity antibodies. Perelmutter, Freedman, and Sehon (294) confirmed the work of Matthews and Spears but were unable to remove the skin-sensitizing antibodies by still more intensive absorption with erythrocyte-WSR conjugates.

The skin-sensitizing human antibodies have been conjugated to fluorescent dyes and the site of localization determined. The most marked reactions were in macrophages and in pericapillary cells, with much less reaction in epithelial cells and endothelial cells of small blood vessels (310, 311). Rappaport (311) also found that the specific atopic antibody was located in epithelial cells of the skin surface and several glands and hair follicles, and also

in macrophage and perivascular cells. These latter two types were involved in the specific cutaneous reactions. We agree with the conclusion of Raffel (305) that the atopic antibodies are synthesized by cells related to but not identical with the cells which produce the classical precipitating antibodies.

Direct Skin Tests. Direct skin tests are usually employed as a part of the study of allergic patients. The allergens are either scratched into the skin or are injected intracutaneously. Positive reactions are obvious in 15 to 30 minutes and are characterized by primary erythema, spreading flare, and central whealing which resembles what Sir Thomas Lewis calls the "triple response." The same type of immediate reaction is given by patients sensitized to horse serum and may be induced in normal individuals by the injection of a 0.1 ml. of 1:1,000 dilution of histamine.

Skin tests are not without danger, however, and one or more deaths have resulted from intracutaneous skin tests, without prior scratch tests, with each of the following allergens (351): (1) mustard, (2) cotton seed, (3) flax seed, (4) ginger, (5) buckwheat, (6) mushroom, (7) seafood, and (8) nut meat (351). **A syringe filled with adrenalin and a tourniquet should always be available on the table when skin tests are being performed.**

The incidence of the immediate wheal and flare skin test in allergic and nonallergic individuals was investigated and reviewed by Curran and Goldman in 1961 (90). The literature indicated that the per cent of reactors in nonallergic subjects could be as low as 5 per cent or as high as 50 per cent. The authors found 9 per cent of nonallergic persons reacting even when both scratch and intracutaneous tests were used. They read as positive reactions which were 10 mm. in diameter or greater and ignored smaller reactions, and they obtained a careful history of allergy in the family. It is known that as many as 50 per cent of nonallergic individuals from allergic families will give positive skin tests (90), which might be explained if they inherited the Hh combination of genes, and also that almost all atopic individuals gave positive skin tests to allergin to which they had no clinical sensitivity, suggesting sensitivity at a level below clinical expression.

Purification of Pollen Extracts. The crude pollen extracts which are used routinely in allergy clinics are very complex. For example, Augustin (14) found the pollen extracts from Timothy and Cocksfoot grass contained at least 15 components which were antigenic to rabbits. Augustin and her associates in England, Goldfarb and Callaghan (59) in Chicago, and Sehon and Richter (218, 347) in Montreal, Canada, have concentrated on the isolation and purification of the active antigen in pollen. A combination of procedures has been used as shown in Figure 4. These were (a) ultrafiltration, (b) isoelectric precipitation, (c) salt fractionation, (d) fractionation on DEAE-cellulose and gel diffusion. Most of the fractions proved to be very stable proteins of low molecular weight with electrophoretic mobility spectrums wider than that of serum proteins (12, 13). Sehon and Richter's (347) fraction was 50 times as potent as the original water-soluble ragweed fraction, with a skin test dose of 10^{-4} μg. Goldfarb and Callaghan's (59) fraction of ragweed gave positive skin tests of a concentration corresponding to 2×10^{-6} to 2×10^{-7} μg. N per milliliter, while the purified antigen obtained by Augustin and Hayward produced local skin lesions in doses of 10^{-7} to 10^{-8} of purified pollen proteins.

Atopic Allergies in Animals. Spontaneous atopic allergies occur in dogs, cows, and some other animals (421). Patterson and Sparks (291) reported a study of spontaneous asthma in the dog. The allergic dog gave the typical wheal and flare skin reaction to pollen, and the antibodies had the char-

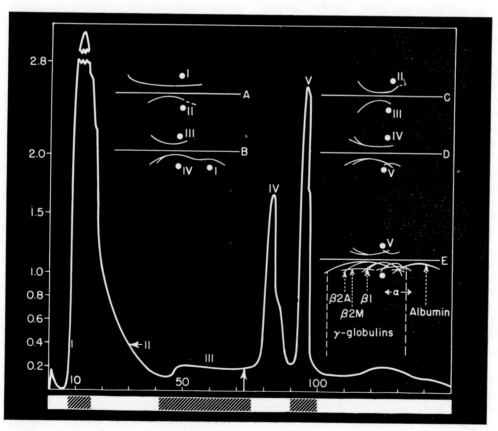

Fig. 4. Fractionation of post-treatment pollen reaginic serum. (From Augustin. *Mechanism of Antibody Formation*, Academic Press.)

acteristics of atopic antibodies. The injection of serum from the allergic dog passively sensitized normal dogs to skin reactions to pollen and bronchial asthma if challenged by the respiratory route. The intravenous and intestinal injection of pollen in the passively sensitized dogs resulted in shock of the anaphylactic type, and necropsy showed marked changes in the liver and intestines.

Asthma can be produced in guinea pigs by forcing the animal to inhale large amounts of pollen. Burkey (57) induced the atopic type of sensitivity to ragweed and other pollens by injecting guinea pigs with the pollen and staphylococcus toxoid. Sherman (353) succeeded, with the help of an adjuvant, in producing nonprecipitating antibodies in the serum of rabbits which could be passively transferred to man.

The Shock Organs in Atopic Allergy. It has always been a mystery why one patient will have hay fever, another asthma, and a third urticaria after exposure to the same allergen. It has been suggested that the initial exposure may have sensitized a local area and that antibodies are produced in larger amounts in that area. Benecerraf and his associates (28) have found that classical precipitating antibodies, and we assume nonprecipitating antibodies also, can accumulate at areas of mild inflammation. Perhaps some such mechanism may explain asthma, hay fever, and urticaria, as well as fixed drug eruptions which recur at exactly the same sites in the skin each time the drug is ingested.

The white blood cells themselves may act as a shock organ. Rabbits injected with ovalbumin or bovine gamma globulin could produce nonprecipitating antibodies which passively sensitized the skin of guinea pigs or man but would not induce passive anaphylaxis in guinea pigs. This antibody specifically lysed white blood cells (406). The passive transfer experiments of Redd and Vaughn (314) suggest that eosinophilia which is so characteristic of allergic states results from antigen-antibody reactions within the body and is not dependent upon active antibody production. These observations might explain the marked fluctuation in the eosinophil count which occur so often

in allergic patients and in patients infected with parasitic worms (269).

Nonantibody Allergy. In some instances an edematous reaction may be the result of physical allergy, such as photosensitivity, allergy to cold, or dermographia where there is a transitory increase in histamine, but in other patients it seems to be truly psychogenic (146).

Treatment. The basic method of treatment of this group of diseases is avoidance of the allergens or, if this is not possible, hyposensitization. The subcutaneous injection of minute (1:100,000) but gradually increasing amounts of the offending antigen results in the production of thermostabile antibody which can mask and block out the heat-labile antibody, thus preventing the reaction between the allergen and its atopic antibody. The new antibody is heat-stabile, does not remain long at the site of injection in the skin, passes the placenta, and in general behaves like a classic precipitin, except that it does not form an observable precipitate with its antigen and does not fix complement or confer either the PCA or the RPCA reaction on the skin of the guinea pig (126). Loveless (240) produced blocking antibodies in man by the injection of pollen and then transferred serum into a hay fever victim, who was protected for a period of time from hay fever, even though exposed to the specific pollen.

The daily injection of pollens and other allergens over many months each year is time-consuming and boring to the physician, and an expensive nuisance to the patient. In 1940 Loveless discovered that both normal subjects and atopic individuals would produce blocking antibodies following the subacute injection of pollen extract (238). In 1947 she (240, 243) introduced the concept of repository antigen and found that 20, 50, and even 100 times the usual hyposensitization dose could be used if it was incorporated in Freund's adjuvant without the dead *Mycobacterium*. Under this condition the antigen was fed slowly into the patient's circulation without danger of shock. In general this method has been successful (85), but certain complications can arise. A new type of atopic antibody can be produced in the patient if the mixture of antigen in the adjuvant contains some to which the patient was not already sensitized, and the injection of pollen in the adjuvant mixture may induce a delayed type of allergy in nonallergic patients, although it does not to the atopic individual (20, 81).

Epinephrine is the drug of choice for the treatment of acute reactions in atopic individuals as well as the drug of choice for anaphylaxis. It is known as the physiologic antagonist of histamine. Ephedrine is longer lasting but less potent than epinephrine. The antihistaminic drugs will prevent the Prausnitz-Kustner type wheal in the skin and the relative mild cases of urticaria and hay fever but have little or no effect in classical asthma of either the intrinsic or extrinsic types. In contrast, the corticoid hormones have no effect on the passively transferred skin test but are very effective in asthma (43, 61, 309, 345). The modern methods employed in the treatment of clinical allergins may be found in the review by Spain (363), Segaloff (346) and Burrage (58).

DELAYED HYPERSENSITIVITY

In the delayed type of hypersensitivity there is no observable reaction at the site of injection for a period of 6 to 12 hours. After this time a faint redness appears which becomes progressively more severe. The reddened area becomes indurated and hard from the invasion of lymphoid and mononuclear cells. The reaction reaches a peak in 24 to 72 hours but usually persists for three or four more days. In very severe reactions the central area becomes edematous and then necrotic, with all of the cells in the central area being destroyed, not primarily those cells of the blood vessels. Hemorrhage and thrombosis are conspicuously absent, in contrast to their frequent occurrences in the antibody specific Arthus reaction and the nonspecific local Shwartzman. Although the appearance of the three types of reactions may seem identical, at 48 hours the time of onset of symptoms serves to differentiate the Arthus and Shwartzman from the delayed reaction. The former begins in 30 to 60 minutes, in contrast to the

3 to 6 hours required for the delayed type. Furthermore, the Shwartzman is not a specific antigen-antibody reaction; the Arthus is a specific antigen-antibody reaction and can be passively transferred with serum but not with blood cells, while **the delayed type of allergy is antigenically specific and can be transferred with white blood cells but not with serum.**

The delayed type of allergy is found most often with certain specific types of infection and is often called "the allergy of infection," but it does occur in the local type of allergy caused by contact with chemicals and drugs and with certain systemic drug reactions, which vary from aspirin to penicillin.

The Allergy of Infection. The delayed allergy of infection was discovered by Koch early in his study of experimental tuberculosis in guinea pigs and rabbits and is often referred to as the **tuberculin type allergy.** It was this type of allergy which explains the peculiar second type of response of tubercle bacilli known as the **Koch phenomenon.**

Koch noted that the injection of virulent tubercle bacilli subcutaneously into a normal guinea pig resulted, after 10 to 15 days, in the slow development of a nodule at the site of injection, which, after a period of several weeks, softened and developed into a chronic ulcer. If the same size dose of virulent bacilli was injected, under similar conditions, into a guinea pig which had been infected at least a week previously, the local reaction developed within 24 to 48 hours, the ulceration was shallow and healing occurred in 10 to 14 days. Although the local lesion healed, the sensitized animals eventually died of the disease, as did the controls. Koch believed that the sloughing reaction was a desirable one, since bacilli were eliminated and the new lesion healed more rapidly; consequently, he sought for an extract from dead tubercle bacilli which would give the local reaction. The first successful extract made by Koch is now called old tuberculin, or O.T. The active principle of tuberculin as shown by Seibert (348) is a tuberculoprotein which has many of the characteristics of a hapten, since it can hyposensitize but cannot sensitize or immunize (393). Von Pirquet recognized the tuberculin reaction as a type of allergy about 1903 and introduced his scratch-test-tuberculin method in 1907 to detect healthy as well as ill individuals who harbor tubercle bacilli in their bodies. Tuberculin is now usually introduced into the body by the intracutaneous method of Mantoux (see Chapter 29).

Animals infected with tubercle bacilli at times develop small amounts of classic antibodies which can be measured as agglutinins, opsonins, precipitins, and complement-fixing antibodies (130). In most instances in experimental animals and in man the concentration of antibodies is so low that they cannot be measured by ordinary methods. **The characteristic "antibody" of tuberculous infection behaves quite differently from both the classic antibody and those found in atopic allergy. They cannot be transferred from animal to animal (429) or man to man by either direct transfer of serum or by the Prausnitz-Kustner reaction.** They are obviously firmly attached to the fixed and wandering white cells of the body, as shown by the persistence of sensitivity in tissue cultures, which was demonstrated first by Rich and Lewis (324) in 1928 and confirmed by other investigators (94). In sharp contrast to these results, tissue cultures made from tissues of rabbits sensitized to the Arthus type of reaction and from tissues of guinea pigs susceptible to anaphylactic shock show absolutely no reaction when exposed to the homologous antigen. Finally, **Chase (63) succeeded in transferring passively tuberculin sensitivity from guinea pigs by introducing intraperitoneally or intravenously a large number of white blood cells. The passive transfer of tuberculin sensitivity by means of white blood cells has been confirmed for the guinea pig (89, 196, 257) and for man (212).** The experiment of Cummings and Hudgins (88) is particularly significant, since the white blood cells from guinea pigs whose tuberculin test had been reduced or suppressed by hormone therapy transferred sensitivity to normal guinea pigs.

The general reactions which follow the subcutaneous or intravenous injection of tuberculin are also slow in developing, requiring 6 to 24 hours to kill sensitized guinea pigs. Autopsies on such animals, if the injection was given subcutaneously, show a local reaction of hemorrhage and necrosis and a local reaction about each individual tuberculous lesion in the animal body.

Spontaneous sensitization of the delayed type occurs regularly in tuberculosis, brucellosis (156), typhoid fever, glanders (176, 426), streptococcal infections (98, 428), pneumococcal infections (175, 387), chancroid, echinococcus infections, tertiary stage of syphilis (325), vaccinia (162), mumps (113), lymphogranuloma venereum (128), influenza, measles, herpes simplex (333), toxoplasmosis, coccidioidomycosis, histoplasmosis, and blastomycosis (199).

Most of the antigens which give rise to delayed hypersensitivity are protein; pure polysaccharides, such as the pneumococcal capsular polysaccharide, usually induce specific classical antibodies but not delayed hypersensitivity. The delayed hypersensitivity to polysaccharides in fungus diseases, as reported by Edwards and associates (110), may have contained polypeptides. The active antigen of the tests seems to be a peptide containing polysaccharide. The blood group substances A and B contain polysaccharides and peptides, and Jankovic and Waksmann (169) have found that injections in guinea pigs, using dead tubercle bacilli in the adjuvant, result in specific humoral antibodies oriented to the carbohydrate structure and the delayed hypersensitivity to the polypeptide "back bone" structure of the molecule. Indeed, Ben-Efraim and his associates (31) induced in guinea pigs a prolonged state of delayed hypersensitivity, not associated with detectable circulating antibodies, by injecting a multichain copolypeptide p(Tyr-Glu)-p Ala—pLys. However, cross-reactions of the delayed type were observed with chemically related polypeptides.

The Mechanism of the Delayed Type of Reaction. There are no shock organs for the delayed type of hypersensitivity. The epithelial cells of the entire body can react, as can the cornea, conjunctivae, and those internal organs and tissues which have been tested, such as testes, kidney, and meninges. Apparently everyone is conditioned genetically to develop this type of sensitivity if properly stimulated. This is true of even the agammaglobulinemic patients who cannot synthesize classical antibodies and atopic antibodies (142). The only apparent exception is some patients with sarcoidosis or Hodgkin's disease (209, 409). It is assumed that this is an acquired defect. Both types of patients make classical antibodies readily but cannot develop the delayed type of hypersensitivity. This capacity can be passively transmitted with white blood cells to the sarcoid patient (167) but not to those with Hodgkin's disease (2, 188).

The primitive cells which are capable of producing some type of sessite antibody which remains fixed to the white cells is apparently derived from the thymus of the mammal, since the removal of that gland shortly after birth prevents the development of both classical antibodies and the delayed type sensitivity (258). There is some evidence that the antibody-producing cells are concentrated in the bursa of the chick (422), and the delayed type of hypersensitivity cell in the thymus of the chick, but this difference may be quantitative rather than qualitative (72).

Except for the failure to isolate the hypothetical "antibodies" from the cells, the development of the tissue change which makes possible the delayed type of reaction parallels those already described for the classical precipitating antibodies. They are (1) exposure to foreign antigen, (2) incubation period, (3) intensification of reaction following repeated exposures, (4) natural decline in reactivity with elapse of time, (5) hyposensitization by injection of small doses, (6) anamnestic reaction on restimulation, and (7) production of tolerance to the delayed type of sensitivity by feeding the antigen by mouth (64) or by injection of fresh protein antigen at a critical period in the process of developing the allergy (86, 87). In the last instance the delayed type of hypersensitivity was blocked but not the humoral antibodies and the immediate type of hypersensitivity.

Zinsser in 1921 (427) differentiated the delayed type of reaction found in tuberculosis, glanders, and typhoid fever from the Arthus type of reaction by passive transfer of serum, which transferred the Arthus but not the delayed reaction. The delayed type of reaction occurs in practically a pure uncomplicated state in experimental and clinical tuberculosis. The classical type of antibodies is either completely absent or at most present in insignificant amounts. The problem becomes much more complex in experimental pneumococcal pneumonia in the rabbit, where both types of allergy can coexist at a maximum level. The studies of Tillett and Francis (387) and Julianelle (175) show that the intravenous injection of dead, type-specific pneumococci into rabbits produces classical antibodies directed toward capsular polysaccharides but no delayed reaction at all. The actively immunized animal gave immediate wheal reactions when the pure capsular polysaccharide was injected into the skin, but no reaction to nucleoprotein from the bodies of the pneumococci. The antibodies in the serum could be passively transferred to normal animals to give (a) passive immunity, (b) precipitins in the blood, and (c) immediate skin reactions to the specific polysaccharides. In contrast to these results, the injection of dead, type-specific pneumococci cutaneously or subcutaneously resulted in the development of delayed reactions to the whole body of the pneumococci and to the isolated nucleoprotein but no reaction to the capsular polysaccharide. Reinoculation each week up to four to six weeks increased the degree of local reaction until large necrotic lesions were being produced. These animals had no antibodies to the specific capsular polysaccharide but a low titer of agglutinins to all pneumococci, regardless of specific type. The antibodies which were produced were presumably directed to the common protein of the pneumococcus species. These animals were immune to reasonable doses of pneumococci—not only to the specific type injected, but also to other types. However, this immunity could not be passively transferred to normal rabbits with serum. To prove that there was no defect in the immune mechanism of these animals, the authors reinjected some of the rabbits intravenously with the dead specific pneumococci and produced a high titer of immunity with antibodies to the capsular polysaccharide. The animals now gave an immediate reaction to the pneumococcal polysaccharide and a delayed reaction to the nucleoprotein simultaneously. Rich and Brown (322) produced a high degree of immunity and a high degree of allergy to the specific type of pneumococci and transferred the immunity to normal rabbits with serum but left the allergy behind. In the studies by Chase and his associates (66) the delayed type of hypersensitivity could be transferred to another animal by white cells only, while the precipitating antibody could be transferred by serum only.

These experiments not only separated sharply classical antibody immunity from delayed hypersensitivity but indicated some facts about the mechanism involved. Obviously, something happened to the pneumococci injected into the skin and to the cells in the skin and regional lymph nodes which did not happen when the pneumococci were injected intravenously. Raffel (305) has suggested that the skin may have acted as an adjuvant and referred to skin-sensitizing chemicals, such as pycrylchloride and dinitrophenol, which give rise to delayed hypersensitivity when painted on the skin but to classical antibodies when linked to a protein and injected intravenously.

The complexity of the mechanism of the delayed hypersensitivity is illustrated by the studies of Lewis and Seibert in 1931 (225). They grew tubercle bacilli in synthetic media and isolated their constituents. The protein would elicit the typical delayed tuberculin reaction in tuberculous guinea pigs, but all attempts to produce delayed hypersensitivity by injecting this protein into rabbits and guinea pigs failed. In this instance the opposite of the expected results were obtained, since the animal developed classical precipitating antibodies and could be shocked by anaphylactic reaction and the antibodies could be passively transferred with serum. The sensitization could be pushed to the limit, which would give the Arthus phenomenon, but no delayed type of sensitivity could be produced with pure protein. If however, as shown by Raffel and others, a wax-like lipid (307) or a lipopolysaccharide which is an ester of a long-chain fatty acid (mycolic acid) plus a polysaccharide is injected with the tuberculoprotein, typical delayed tuberculin sensitivity develops, which can be elicited by the pure tuberculoprotein but not by the waxes and lipopolysaccharide. Dienes (101, 102) had already induced typical tuberculin allergy to such simple proteins as egg white and serum albumin by producing tuberculous granuloma in guinea pigs with dead tubercle bacilli and then injecting the simple proteins into the granulomas. These animals developed such a high degree of allergy that very small doses of serum or egg white killed the guinea pigs, with the slow type of shock characteristic of tuberculin shock. These revolutionary findings of Dienes were confirmed by Hanks (152) under the watchful eye of Hans Zinsser. The mechanism was restudied in even greater detail by Raffel and Forney (305, 306).

The adjuvant effect of the wax or lipopolysaccharide from the tubercle bacilli not only potentiated the development of the delayed type reaction to bland proteins but also increased greatly the ability of the animal to produce antibodies. For example, guinea pigs, which usually are poor precipitin producers to bland proteins, could develop with these adjuvants plus antigen a high precipitin titer and give the Arthus type reaction.

The principle of intensifying the local reaction and holding the antigen in contact with the damaged cells is the essential element in the very successful use of Freund's adjuvants. Bland antigens, or even homologous tissue, like normal brain, when injected with heat-killed tubercle bacilli and water in oil emulsions such as Falba, induced the delayed type of sensitivity and when the brain was used as the antigen antibodies develop which produce local necrotic lesions in various parts of that organ (129).

It was assumed from the time of Koch that the tuberculin sensitivity was an essentially protective mechanism, until this concept was challenged by Rich (319, 320, 326). The weight of evidence is slowly swinging in favor of Rich's views, although we do not yet know how to produce even relative immunity in man or animals without at the same time inducing the undesirable allergy.

Hyposensitization with tuberculin and tuberculin-like substances can be accomplished in man and animals, but the process is slow and laborious. The initial dose of a diluted tuberculin should be 0.1 ml. given subcutaneously, and subsequent doses should not be increased by increments greater than 0.1 ml. or given more often than every 48 hours. The initial dilution of the antigen should be estimated from the size of the skin reaction (351, 359).

Recurrent boils of the skin and styes of the eyelids as well as certain types of chronic infections of the lungs have been treated empirically by physicians with autogenous vaccines made from the patient's own cultures in belief that the excessive delayed type of allergy, which could be demonstrated by skin tests, was interfering with the specific humoral immunity. The experiments of Johnston, Cluff, and Goshi (172) have shown that rabbits after a series of infection would develop boils with smaller doses of the organism than normal animals. Julianelle and Weigard (176) reported that two different types of skin tests might be found if the patient were having recurrent boils. The polysaccharide isolated from the organism gave an immediate 20- to 30-minute reaction, while the injection of protein isolated from the same organisms gave a delayed tuberculin-like reaction. When an autogenous vaccine is made from the heat-killed but intact cocci, both types of reaction may be observed in succession, with the first disappearing completely before the second appears.

The delayed type of hypersensitivity responds in a specific manner to the administration of corticoid hormones and not at all to antihistamines. The corticoid hormones reduce somewhat the nonspecific inflammation of endotoxin reactions, but the effects are not nearly so dramatic as that on the symptoms produced by the delayed type of hypersensitivity. However, the administration of corticoid hormones can increase the severity of a tuberculous process or activate an apparently healed lesion. Fortunately, the simultaneous administration of adequate amounts of specific chemotherapeutic drugs will prevent the detrimental effect of the hormones.

Transferring Delayed Hypersensitivity with White Blood Cells. Transferring delayed hypersensitivity by means of white blood cells from lymph nodes or from the peritoneum have been mentioned above. The cells involved were primarily lymphoid in type and were not leukocytes. The transfers had to be made within the species—that is, from guinea pig to guinea pig, or from rabbit to rabbit. The skin of the recipient became allergic almost immediately, but the allergy lasted only a few weeks, as might be expected of passive transfer. Metaxas and Metaxas-Buehler (257) showed that when multiple tuberculin tests were performed simultaneously, the reactions were much smaller than when only one was performed, suggesting that the preformed cells were involved in the reaction.

The relatively rapid disappearance of the passively transferred sensitivity of the delayed type is attributed to the inability of the homologous cell to survive in the host. This concept is supported by the work of Bauer and Stone (19, 374), who used an inbred strain of guinea pigs and found that the passively transferred sensitivity persisted at a high level for three to four weeks. Chase (68) used two other highly inbred strains of guinea pigs and found that the tuberculin allergy persisted after passive transfer with white blood cells for more than one and one-half years. Najarian and Feldman (265) used guinea pigs with a very high degree of allergy and tagged the rapidly dividing lymphoid cells with thymidine. The labeled cells were then injected into normal guinea pigs and a tuberculin test performed. The positive tuberculin skin test in the recipients was found to contain many of the tagged cells, while nonspecific inflammation and specific inflammation of delayed allergy to a different antigen did not show the accumulation of this type of cell. Turk (392) did not find any accumulation of tagged cells at the site of the new tuberculin reaction, but he may have waited too long to test for their presence. In 1963 Feldman and Najarian (119) studied in guinea pigs the dynamics and quantitative aspects of the passively transferred hypersensitivity to tuberculin. They found that less than 1 per cent of the injected H3-thymidine-labeled lymphoid cells could be detected at the site of the tuberculin reaction in

the skin. But only an occasional labeled cell appeared at the site of a nonspecific area of inflammation. The best evidence for the specificity of the reaction is shown by the observation that there were 10 times as many labeled cells at the site of the reaction at 24 hours than at six hours. Two concurrent reactions occur: (1) accumulation of sensitized and labeled cells in response to specific antigen and (2) infiltration of mononuclear cells, from the host, as a result of the inflammation. The latter are obviously more numerous.

More evidence for the specificity of the lymphoid cell in this reaction is supplied by the studies of Waksman and his associates (408), who produced in the rabbit an antilymphocytic serum to guinea pig's lymphoid cells. When this serum was injected into guinea pigs who had received serum and cells by passive transfer, it was found that the delayed type of skin reaction was suppressed, but not the passive cutaneous anaphylaxis or the reversed Arthus reaction.

There is one report of the transfer of delayed hypersensitivity in man by means of lymphoid cells (249), and in this instance both classical antibodies and delayed hypersensitivity were transferred. All of the other studies in man have been performed with cells from the circulating blood, which were predominantly leukocytes.

Man develops a higher degree of delayed hypersensitivity to a smaller stimulus than any other animal, not excepting the guinea pig. Certainly, the number of white blood cells which would hardly sensitize a guinea pig readily sensitize a man. Leukocytes have been used to passively sensitize man to tuberculin (213), streptococcal, viral (214, 215, 311), fungal (310), and chemical reactants (63, 340). A unique feature of this type of delayed hypersensitivity in man which is transferred with leukocytes from the blood, is that it persisted for many months and up to two years (190, 215).

The Transfer Factor in Delayed Hypersensitivity. Even more unusual than the persistence of the passively transferred delayed hypersensitivity in man is the fact that the transfer can be effected with leukocytes which have been disrupted by freezing and thawing, by sonic vibration, or by digestion with ribonuclease or deoxyribonuclease. Lawrence (214) has named the unknown substance which gives this result the "transfer factor." There seem to be two stages in the development of delayed hypersensitivity which follow the passive transfer of leukocytes from man to man. Sensitivity occurs immediately after transfer, as in animals, but this sensitivity is slight in degree and soon decreases. After two or three weeks, however, an even more marked degree of allergy appears, and this type persists for months and even up to a few years. In the transfer experiment with tuberculosis, streptococcal, and viral infections, it might be assumed that the recipients of the passive cells already had a degree of allergy which was at an undetectable level and that this had been boosted to a good level by the introduction of new antigen as a skin test. This mechanism could have been in operation in the experiment where tuberculin was inoculated with leukocytes and supernate. These objections cannot be raised against the studies of Rappaport and his associates (310), however, for they transferred delayed hypersensitivity to coccidioidin to students in New York who had never been west of the Mississippi River and who could not have had a previous infection with *Coccidioides immitis.* In this experiment the leukocytes were treated with DNase and the passively transferred hypersensitization persisted for at least 18 months. Klein and Patnode (197) found that tuberculin testing in man resulted in an increase in the serum alpha-1 globulin during a vigorous tuberculin reaction and suggested that the "tuberculin antibody" might be present in this globulin. The same suggestion was made by Cole and Favor in 1955 (80) and Jeter, Laurence, and Seebohm in 1957 (171); but at the time this chapter goes to press, a definite experiment has not been published to show whether the extra alpha-1 globulin is the "fixed tissue antibody" or merely an associated by-product of the formation of the fixed tissue antibody.

Endotoxin Shock Compared to Tuberculin Shock. Stetson (368, 369) has called attention to the truly remarkable resemblance of endotoxin shock in rabbits and tuberculin shock in the same animals. Both endotoxin and tuberculin produce a delayed type of skin reaction, and death from the intravenous injection of either is a slow one, varying from 12 to 24 hours. Hemorrhages in the intestines and in serous cavities are a feature of each. Furthermore, sensitization with tubercle bacilli increases greatly the susceptibility to death from endotoxins, and, finally, normal rabbits may be killed by an intravenous dose of some commercially prepared tuberculins. Tolerance can be acquired to each, and corticoid hormones reduce the severity of the reaction to each. If death could have been consistently produced in normal unsensitized rabbits, the evidence would have been complete to prove that the

delayed type of hypersensitization was only another form of reaction to endotoxin. Subsequent studies have shown that some lots of commercial tuberculin from a few manufacturers did contain endotoxins as contaminants. Although the resemblance of endotoxin shock and tuberculin shock is even greater than the resemblance of the local Arthus reactions to the local Shwartzman reaction, the two can be differentiated. Endogenous pyrogens are released from leukocytes by both endotoxin and tuberculin, but this is not a specific reaction, since the same release is found in other bacterial infections and in "fume fever" from the inhalation of chemicals. Moses and Atkins (261) have shown that tolerance develops more quickly to tuberculin and without increasing the tolerance to endotoxins. The tolerance to tuberculin does not depend upon blockade of the reticuloendothelial system with thorotrast. Corticoid hormones reduce somewhat the systemic effect of endotoxins but produce marked total suppression of the tuberculin allergy. The two phenomena have been separated by Gruenwald and his associates (148).

Thomas (383) reported that cortisone reduced materially the local cutaneous reaction to intracutaneous injection of endotoxin. There is evidence that animals acquire the delayed type of hypersensitivity from harboring gramnegative bacteria in their intestinal tract (221, 223). Therefore we cannot decide whether the cortisone effect in the skin lesion was a nonspecific effect on the inflammation from the endotoxin as an endotoxin or an inflammation from a specific delayed type of hypersensitivity to the endotoxin or a combination of both.

The experiment of Sells and Braude (349) gives a very clear-cut differentiation between the skin reaction in man to endotoxin and to tuberculin. The authors adsorbed (1) tuberculin and (2) *E. coli* endotoxin onto human red blood cells. The cells were then injected intracutaneously into the skin of man. All subjects reacted to the endotoxin, but only the subjects who were known to be sensitive to tuberculin reacted to the tuberculin. The reaction to the endotoxin was induced by the third hour and was characterized by polymorphonuclear cells, and the reaction to tuberculin did not start until after the fifth hour and the cellular increase was largely monocytic. The new work of Trakatellis, Stinespring, and Axelrod (390, 391) **presents convincing evidence of the fundamental difference between shock from endotoxins and tuberculin.** These investigators sensitized guinea pigs with BCG and then fed a diet deficient in pyridoxine to some normal and some tuberculin-sensitized guinea pigs. Under these conditions the sensitized guinea pigs on the pyridoxine-deficient diet failed to react to local or systemic tuberculin but reacted in a normal manner to shock from endotoxins. The pyridoxine deficient animals also reacted, in other experiments, with anaphylaxis to soluble antigens.

Delayed Allergy to Endotoxins and Exotoxins. Brucella are known to have an endotoxin (1) and a nucleoprotein which has no toxic effect on uninfected animals. Heilman and his associates (156) have found the brucellergin in a 1:10 dilution is not toxic to splenic cell cultures from normal guinea pigs but cytopathic for cell cultures made from animals who have been infected with brucella for one month. Gruenwald's experiments, mentioned above, showed that the endotoxic part of pertussis vaccine could be separated from the delayed hypersensitivity part and the allergy giving delayed skin reactions could be passively transferred to normal rats by white cells but not by serum.

Physicians who engage in repeated immunizations of groups of students against typhoid bacilli see a sequence of increasing reactions in some students each time the vaccine is repeated. Usually there is little or no redness and swelling in the arm after the initial injection, since the amount of endotoxin in the regular immunizing dose is very small. Some students never react severely to repeated vaccinations, but others give larger and larger local reactions, which in a few instances are accompanied by a systemic reaction with chills and fever. Since the amount of endotoxin is the same in all doses, we must assume that a delayed type of hypersensitivity has developed to the endotoxin itself or to some associated material. In Spink's (365) discussion of shock in man he points out that in man and in animals shock from endotoxin is less frequent and less severe in the young than in the old and concludes that "acquired hypersensitivity to endotoxin plays a significant role in the genesis of shock." The experience of the senior author supports the conclusion drawn by Spink. Furthermore, in most patients with typhoid fever the administration of corticoid hormones eliminated all or practically all of the toxic symptoms.

There is good evidence that delayed type of allergy can develop to the diphtheria toxin molecule. Tht studies of Bunch and his associates (54) in our laboratory showed that there were two different antigens in the standard Schick test material which would produce delayed hypersensitivity skin tests in some medical students. The first was a heat-stable factor, presumably a protein of the organism, which was easily detected because it gave the same size skin reaction in the heated control for the Schick test as in the Schick test itself. The second factor seemed to be the toxin itself but not the same molecular groups which mediated the toxicity, since the toxin would produce strong delayed hypersensitive cutaneous reaction even when the student's serum contained from 0.5 to 2.0 units of antitoxin. Sensitivity of this type gave false positive Schick tests which could not be detected by the controls. When the toxin was destroyed by heat or when the toxic molecule was covered by an excess of diphtheria antitoxin, there was no reaction in the control test. The action of formalin on the toxic molecule, which destroys its toxicity but leaves its antigenicity, evidently also left its ability to react with the delayed hypersensitive cutaneous reaction even when the blood contained an abundance of antitoxin. The studies of Edsell and his associates (109) with a highly purified toxin and toxoid confirmed the results obtained in our laboratory.

The delayed type of hypersensitivity to tetanus toxoid occurs with less frequency but has been observed in some instances. In these patients the hypersensitivity followed the first intramuscular injection of the tetanus toxoid. There was no reaction until about six days after the injection which showed that the allergy did not pre-exist. Skin tests with tetanus toxoid were of the severe delayed type. In one physician patient an abundance of tetanus antitoxin was found in blood serum removed at the time of the positive skin test.

Allergic Encephalitis. This particular type of reaction, which is often fatal, occasionally follows the injection of rabies vaccine which is prepared from the spinal cord of rabbits. The injection of cord or brain tissue in the rabies vaccine suggested that antibodies of some type which could then attack the patient's brain proteins were produced. With the use of adjuvants the syndrome has been produced in mice (268), rat, monkey, and guinea pig (229, 230). Although the nature of the antibodies is obscure, the development of the disease can be prevented by the administration of cortisone to the monkey during the period of vaccination (183).

Stone found that severe and lethal allergic encephalitis could be transferred by lymphoid cells in histocompatible guinea pigs, but this could not be done with randomly bred intact rats unless the rat's spleen had been removed (290). The peculiar type of arthritis induced in rats by the injection of killed tubercle bacilli in oil by Waksman and his associates (407) could be passively transferred to other rats. The delayed allergy in homograph rejection in rabbits could be transferred to normal rabbits with lymphoid cells, but treating the sensitized cell with ribonuclease prevented the passive transfer (170).

THE JONES-MOTE TYPE
OF DELAYED
HYPERSENSITIVITY

This early type of reaction was described by Jones and Mote in 1934 (174), who injected repeated doses of rabbit serum into the skin of man. Independently and simultaneously the same type of reaction was reported by Simon and Rackerman (357), who injected guinea pigs' serum into the skin of man. The reaction begins three to six days after the initial cutaneous dose with a small flat area of redness which persists for 18 to 24 hours. The cellular response is predominantly mononuclear cells. The Jones-Mote reactions are mild and never produce necrosis of the skin. After a series of daily reactions, there is an abrupt transition from the delayed to the acute wheal and flare of the direct cutaneous anaphylaxis. Coincidently with this change in the type of the skin reactions, clasical precipitating antibodies appear in the serum for the first time.

We are following the example of Raffel (305) and Crowle (87) in separating the Jones-Mote type of delayed hypersensitivity from the tuberculin type. **It is probable that this type of reaction is the first detectable stage in the development of classical precipitating antibodies.**

Perhaps the Jones-Mote type of delayed hypersensitivity should have been called the Dienes type, because he described it in detail between 1930 and 1932 (101, 102, 184). He knew it was a mild transient reaction which was usually followed by the immediate type of reaction and classical precipitating antibodies. But he also described the typical delayed tuberculin type of reaction, which was severe, often necrotic, and persisted for months or years with or without classical antibody formation to the same soluble protein. He was the first to suggest that the delayed reaction was an intermediate stage

in the development of classical antibody. **Dienes clearly distinguished the Jones-Mote type of delayed hypersensitivity from the tuberculin type on the basis of method of production as well as severity.** The Jones-Mote is induced by the injection of soluble protein without any tubercle bacilli, while the tuberculin type allergy can be induced to the same protein if injected into a granuloma formed by dead tubercle bacilli but not by granuloma to beryllium (338).

The Jones-Mote type of delayed hypersensitivity can be fitted neatly into a pattern for the development of classical precipitating antibodies if one makes a few unproven assumptions. The antibody must be an early one, perhaps even earlier than the known early 19 S. antibodies. It may resemble 19 S. antibodies in some respects but differ in others. It must (1) fail to elicit anaphylaxis, (2) fail to sensitize PCA, (3) have a broad cross-reaction but (4) poor avidity for antigen and (5), like 19 S. antibodies, inhibit to some degree the action of 7 S. antibodies. With some exceptions, these are the characteristics of 19 S. antibody as reviewed by Kunkle in 1961 (207). The 19 S. antibodies of the primary reaction are readily replaced by classical 7 S. type antibodies with a second stimulation. Mathies and Stravitsky (252) produced only 19 S. antibodies by a primary injection of a small dose of T_2 bacteriophage. But a second dose produced 7 S. antibodies. However, our hypothetical antibody must differ from the known 19 S. antibody by having a high affinity for tissue cells. One example of a nonprecipitating antibody which has a high affinity for tissue cells is known. This is the atopic nonprecipitating antibody involved in the Prausnitz-Kuestner skin reaction. These antibodies are present in the serum and in the epithelial cells of the skin. But when transferred into normal individuals by Loveless (240) and Sherman (354), they promptly left the blood and became fixed to the cells of the skin and remained there for a period of many weeks. Ovary and Karush (281) have described another antibody, or rather a fragment of an antibody, which has some of the necessary properties to fit into the hypothetical scheme outlined above. These authors isolated the nonprecipitating fragment which Porter (380) calls the fragment III of classical precipitating antibodies and found that it had a strong affinity for tissue cells but no binding sites for antigens. It would not produce a PCA reaction but would induce a reversed PCA. If antibodies with high tissue affinity like this fragment had an imperfect binding site for antigen, the nature of fixation might be such as to produce the delayed type of hypersensitivity. The studies of Salvin and Smith (339, 340), Bernacerraf and Levine (25), Leskowitz (222), and Gell and Silverstein (135) indicated that the antibody involved in this type of delayed hypersensitivity is usually directed toward a protein or to the protein carrier of a hapten, and the area of reaction with the antigen is considerably broader and less specific than that of classical antibodies with a hapten or a hapten-like binding site in the natural protein. These findings do not contradict the type of antibody required to fit the theory proposed above.

The Jones-Mote reaction has been transferred from animal to animal and from man to man by the injection of leukocytes but not by transfer of serum (32). This phenomenon has been considered by some investigators as positive proof of the identity of the Jones-Mote reaction and the tuberculin type of delayed hypersensitivity. There is, however, an initial stage in the development of classical precipitin type of antibodies when the antibodies are being produced in the cells, and as yet there are no free antibodies in the serum. In instances where the Jones-Mote type of sensitivity has been transferred with cells as soon as antibodies appear in the serum the immediate type of skin reaction appears and the delayed reaction disappears.

X-irradiation, which suppresses the formation of classical antibodies, does not prevent the development of the Jones-Mote type of reaction (339, 342, 396). This is not inconsistent with the classical antibody theory, since it is known that irradiated animals lose their plasma cells and apparently make 19 S. and possibly other undetectable antibodies during the period of recovery (see the discussion of radiation effect in Chapter 12).

There are certain other important differences in the Jones-Mote "delayed reactivity" and the tuberculin type of delayed reactivity. For example, hyposensitization is easily accomplished by an injection of a small amount of antigen, in contrast to hyposensitization of the tuberculin type, which is very difficult to accomplish (394, 395).

Raffel and Newel (306) found that a sufficiently small dose of protein (79) could produce the Jones-Mote type of reaction for three weeks without ever developing into the classical immediate type of reaction. The same authors noted that the injection of antigen-antibody complexes, made in antibody excess, gave no immediate reaction but a delayed one which was followed by the immediate reaction after the appearance of classical precipitating antibodies. Crowle's experiments (86, 87) are equally convincing in disassociating the immediate and delayed reactions in mice.

Chase (69) has described another difference in the tuberculin-like delayed hypersensitivity of the Jones-Mote type. As the dose of antigen was increased, the area of redness became larger and larger without any increase of induration in the center. In contrast, increasing doses of tuberculin cause some increase in the centrifugal area of redness but a more marked increase in the central area of induration. We have confirmed these observations of Chase (Fig. 5). In reading the current literature, it is essential for one to determine from the methods used whether the author has produced the Jones-Mote type of delayed hypersensitivity or the more severe tuberculin type of hypersensitivity. For example, the delayed hypersensitivity induced in rabbits by the intracutaneous injection of pneumococci (175) was a true tuberculin type of sensitivity. It occurred in the absence of antibodies in the serum, and repeated injections failed to change the reaction into an immediate one or to induce antibodies in the serum. The repeated skin tests failed to hyposensitize but increased the severity of the skin reactions up to the sixth weekly injection.

The severe necrotic reactions induced by Dienes (102) by injecting serum albumin into a tuberculous granuloma were the tuberculin type. The delayed hypersensitivity induced by Gordon (144) when he injected homologous guinea pig serum in a complete Freund's adjuvant with dead tubercle bacilli was the delayed tuberculin type. The pigs could not be hyposensitized by a larger dose of normal guinea pig serum which would hyposensitize to anaphylactic producing antibodies. Since the serum was from another guinea pig, there were no classical antibodies produced. Similar results were obtained by Maurer (253), who treated human serum with ethylene oxide and then injected it into man. No classical antibodies were produced after one and one-half years of immunization. The skin reaction of the delayed type appeared and persisted and could be passively transferred in man by white cells from the blood. The last two series of experiments laid a solid foundation for the accidental sensitization of man to his own proteins with the development of severe tuberculin type hypersensitivity and some types of autoimmune diseases.

George and Vaughn (136) succeeded in producing both the Jones-Mote reaction and the delayed tuberculin reaction separately and then

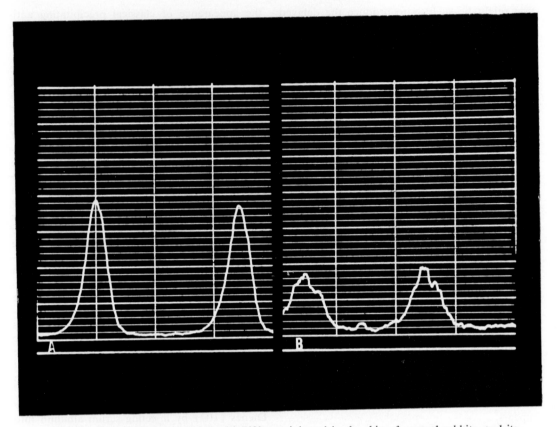

Fig. 5. Human albumin labeled with I[131] was injected in the skin of normal rabbits, and its spread or disappearance was followed graphically. The area of spread after four minutes is shown in A and after 24 hours in B. (Courtesy of Thorne, Eiring, and Smith.)

both together in guinea pigs and were able to distinguish the two in each instance. The authors sensitized guinea pigs by injecting living BCG tubercle bacilli. Three months later half of the guinea pigs were immunized with egg albumin by subcutaneous and intravenous injection. The protein antigen was not injected into areas of previous tuberculous granulomas. Skin tests with egg albumin and tuberculin produced immediate hypersensitivity to egg albumin and typical delayed hypersensitivity to tuberculin. Mononuclear cells from the peritoneum of the infected pigs were transferred to a special type of tissue culture and tested separately with egg albumin and tuberculin. The tuberculin inhibited migration while the egg albumin did not. When, however, other guinea pigs were immunized with egg albumin in Freund's adjuvant, which contains dead tubercle bacilli, both immediate and delayed reactions were given by egg albumin, and this material now inhibited the migration of sensitized monocytes in tissue cultures.

The most convincing evidence of all has been presented by Benacerraf and his associates (26), who synthesized a polypeptide antigen from three or four amino acids and found that this structure gave specific classical antibodies. But when this synthetic polypeptide was diazotized to a hapten and injected in Freund's adjuvant the classical antibodies were formed to the hapten and delayed tuberculin-like sensitivity to the carrier polypeptide (Fig. 6). For the first time in immunologic history the exact chemical structure was known for both the small hapten and the large carrier. The authors suggest that it would be possible to label the hapten and carrier polypeptide with different isotopes and follow their respective pattern in body cells and in the formation of antibodies (26, 221).

In contrast to the examples given above, the 1962 studies of Kuhns (205) with diphtheria toxoid immunization were typical Jones-Mote type of delayed hypersensitivity. The reactions occurred after a series of injections and before

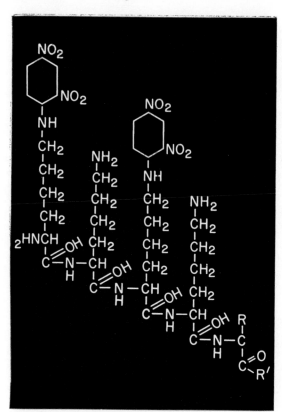

Fig. 6. DNP polylysine showing the polylysine chain where the L-lysine amino acids are united by peptide linkages, and where two dinitrophenyl groups are conjugated to the free epsilon amino groups of lysine side chains. (Courtesy of Dr. Baruj Benacerraf.)

Karush and Eisen Theory of Delayed Hypersensitivity. This theory proposed to explain all types of allergic reactions, whether classical or immediate, Jones-Mote type, delayed or tuberculin type (186). The only unique element in the theory is the assumption that the first antibodies produced will have an extremely high affinity for the antigen. This concept of great affinity for antigen is contrary to the previous belief that the early antibodies have a poor affinity for antigen (see Chapter 12). The theory presented in the preceding pages assumes that the early antibodies have a low affinity for antigen, and this is offered as the explanation for the delay in collecting enough antigen to produce an observable delayed reaction.

ALLERGY TO DRUGS

Allergy to drugs may manifest itself as a systemic reaction which stimulates serum sickness, anaphylaxis, arthralgia, scarlatiniform or morbilliform rashes, asthma, urticaria, exfoliative dermatitis, and granulomatous reaction to iodide and bromide, or it may be localized to the point of contact between the drug and the skin as in contact dermatitis. The so-called fixed eruption reaction to phenolphthalein and some other drugs (375, 376) seems to be an exception, since in this instance the drug is taken by mouth and the eruption appears repeatedly at a local site on the skin.

Drug hypersensitivity must be differentiated from drug intolerance. The latter term designates an exaggerated response on the part of the body to the usual physiologic action of the drug. Although there is great variety in the types of systemic response to drug sensitivity, they are the responses of allergy and **bear no relation to the normal pharmacologic effect of the drug.**

The drugs most commonly found responsible for drug hypersensitivity reactions are opiates, salicylates, barbiturates, iodides, bromides, arsenicals, sulfonamides, and the antibiotics. The sulfonamides and antibiotics are now the most frequent cause of drug sensitivity, not because they are more prone to induce this type of reaction but because they are in almost constant use by a large part of the population (374). Man may produce several types of antibodies to in-

the development of immediate wheal reactions and the appearance of antitoxins in the serum. These results are in contrast to the spontaneous development of a persistent tuberculin type of hypersensitivity to diphtheria toxin and toxoid when the original experience of the subject was a spontaneous infection with *C. diphtheriae* (318). The sequence of development of allergic reactions to flea bites in the guinea pig (32) suggests that these are of the Jones-Mote type. These were (1) induction of sensitivity, (2) predominantly delayed skin reactivity, (3) delayed and immediate responses, (4) predominantly immediate responses, and (5) nonreactivity. The introduction of minute amounts of antigen by the flea bites would be a good way of inducing the delayed type of reactivity, but the repeated bites could boost the reaction to stages of the immediate type. Finally, the disappearance of reaction suggests an easily hyposensitized type of allergy.

sulin (9, 424, 425). With aspirin and para-aminosalicylic acid the antibodies seem to be directed mainly against the salicylate and not the acetyl group (413).

The rate at which man is becoming allergic to drugs is appalling. Best (36) reported that 42 drugs were recognized for the first time in the year 1962 as a cause of blood dyscrasia.

Skin rashes follow the use of penicillin in 6 per cent of children, 11 per cent of physicians, and 24 per cent of adults who frequently consult physicians. Brown (50, 51) estimates that sensitivity in the general population is increasing at the rate of about 1 per cent each year. The more severe types of reaction are somewhat less frequent but more dangerous (297). Welch and his associates (416) collected the literature in 1954 and found that at least 100 to 200 instances of anaphylaxis occur annually, many of which are fatal. Penicillin and other antibiotics apparently combine with serum protein to form a complete antigen which produces antibodies in the patient (297).

Reactions from sensitivity to penicillin and to a lesser degree other antibiotics have become one of our most common diseases. In 1945 there was one type of penicillin which was produced in limited quantity, but by 1956 there were 17 different antibiotics available, with 121 commercial preparations. Over 2,500,000 lbs. of antibiotics were produced that year, with penicillin being about 25 per cent of the total. Many more kinds of penicillin are available now.

Sensitivity to penicillin continues to increase year by year as more people are exposed and re-exposed (420). The Venereal Disease Board and the Public Health Service (53) found that reactions to penicillin had increased from 5.95 per 1,000 treated in 1954 to 9.73 per 1,000 treated in 1959, or at a rate of increase of 63 per cent. Attempts to develop methods of detecting sensitivity to penicillin before the drug is injected are meeting with some success. Ley and his associates (227) have found that human erythrocytes from all groups would adsorb penicillin of G, O, and K types and were agglutinated when subsequently exposed to sera of patients who were known to have had a reaction to penicillin. There was com-plete cross-reaction to the different types of penicillin (114). Penicillin T was coupled to human red blood cells by the bis-diazotized-benzidine reaction, after which they would agglutinate with antibodies in sera of patients who had reacted to penicillin. Here, again, cross-reactions between various penicillins were found, but not nearly all patients who have had a clinical reaction with penicillin showed positive agglutination (400).

Skin tests to determine hypersensitivity to penicillin may be dangerous. Feinberg (118) recommended that the scratch test be performed with a solution of crystallized penicillin which contained 50 units per milliliter. If this test is negative, 0.02 ml. of a solution which contains only 1,000 units per milliliter should be injected intracutaneously. Kern (191) recommended the scratch test and eye test made with a solution which contained 10,000 units per milliliter, and if they are both negative, 0.02 ml. of the same solution should be injected cutaneously. Several synthetic fragments of the penicillin molecule have been used for skin tests. These seem to be safe and more effective as detectors of sensitivity. Levine and Ovary (224) used penicilloyl-HγG. Parker and his associates (286, 287) used penicilloyl-polylysine in testing over 3,600 patients.

Patients with allergic tendencies are more likely to develop allergy to penicillin. Depot penicillin in rheumatic fever prophylaxis gives increased numbers of reaction. Topical application to inflamed skin and mucosa induced more sensitivity than parenteral injection, and parenteral injection induced more sensitivities than oral penicillin. Antihistamines given in the same syringe with penicillin will not prevent reaction.

If hypersensitivity is suspected from the history or from a skin test and penicillin must be given, then the patient should be pre-treated with corticoid hormones. The penicillin should be given in a lower arm or leg so that a tourniquet can be applied if a reaction begins. Epinephrine in a dose of 0.5 ml. of a 1:1000 dilution should be given, of which 0.2 ml. can be injected at the site of the penicillin injection. In severe reactions 0.2 ml. can be given intravenously if blood is drawn into the syringe to dilute the epinephrine. The 0.5 ml. dose of epinephrine should be repeated every three or four minutes until the patient is out of shock. Antihistamines can be given by mouth. Diphenhydramine hydrochloride (Benadryl) 50 mg. and chlorpheniramine maleate (Chlor-trimeton) 10 mg. may be administered intramuscularly or intravenously. Aminophylline intravenously may be helpful in the presence of asthma. Artificial respiration followed by oxygen therapy may be necessary if the patient is in severe shock when seen. Corticoids do not work rapidly enough in severe shock and penicillinase is of no value. In severe serum sickness syndromes, however, and in protracted shock, corticoid hormone or penicillinase may be very effective (22, 259). Penicillinase should be used with caution, because anaphylactic shock has been reported after therapy with this enzyme (315). No therapeutic agent is without its risks. Patients have died following oral penicillin and fatal cases of anaphylaxis have followed the use of throat lozenges containing penicillin (161). Chronic recurrent asthma has followed repeated doses of aspirin (132) and from eating an orange (30) and serum anaphylaxis from an injection of chymotrypsin (352).

The so-called inert ingredients in pills and capsules are a frequently overlooked source of drug sensitivity (309). These drugs are small molecules and cannot by themselves induce antibody formation, but they apparently become attached, under certain conditions, to proteins of the body and then function in a manner similar to Landsteiner's "conjugated proteins." The introduction of drugs and antibiotics into areas of inflammation, such as wounds of the skin or inflamed mucous membranes of the throat, results in sensitivity more frequently than when the same drugs are taken by mouth or injected into a noninflamed area.

The antibodies formed under these conditions are variable, sometimes being fixed to the cell and transferable only with cells and at other times free in the serum and easily transferred passively by the Prausnitz-Kustner method.

The classic example of contact dermatitis is that afforded by contact with poison ivy (134). The leaves of the primrose, oil from ragweed, and many chemicals used in the manufacture of furniture and textiles or leather will also produce typical contact dermatitis. Certain drugs produce contact dermatitis when applied locally but give systemic reactions when sensitivity is induced by the systemic route, as illustrated by sensitivity to intravenous injections of procaine.

An effective orally administered poison ivy extract is now on the market (198), but even this can cause trouble either from overdosing or from development of increased hypersensitivity (377).

Chase (64) sensitized the skin of guinea pigs by local applications of 2-4 dinitrochlorbenzene and similar chemical substances. Under certain conditions three types of antibodies developed: (1) classic antibodies, which gave direct or passively transferred anaphylaxis; (2) atopic reagins transferable by the Prausnitz-Kustner technic; and (3) antibodies of the delayed type of clinical sensitivity, which are transferable by white blood cells. Chase prevented the development of skin sensitivity by feeding 2-4 dinitrochlorbenzene by mouth to guinea pigs. This effect may be similar to that of introducing an excess of pneumococcal carbohydrate into the tissue, since the animals can be passively sensitized by the transfer of cells from other sensitized guinea pigs.

The usual method of testing for contact dermatitis is to fasten a piece of the suspected leaf, fabric, or a few crystals of a chemical to a piece of adhesive tape and apply it to the skin for 24 hours. Methods of using the patch test and its dangers have been reviewed by Grolnick (147). The Urbach-Gottlieb (399) studies indicate that antibodies may at times be passively transferred from man to man by transferring the fluid from a recently raised blister to the skin of a normal individual. Apparently contact dermatitis due to poison ivy is not affected by cortisone (17), which was expected since Crepa and Cooke (84) demonstrated passive transfer sensitivity to poison ivy from guinea pig to guinea pig with serum. Najarian and Feldman (266) transfused thymidine-labeled cells in cases of contact dermatitis and found that the labeled lymphocytic cells concentrated at the site of the reaction.

In man the immediate type of skin reaction has been seen in some instances of sensitivity to salvarsan, formaldehyde, phthalic anhydride, sulfathiazole, and sulfadiazine.

The response to therapy is as varied in drug sensitivity as the clinical types of diseases and kinds of antibodies. Some cases of systemic sensitivity respond fairly well to the antihistamines (116, 164), while severe necrotic types of penicillin reactions are usually fatal unless treated with corticoid hormones.

Other Allergic Reactions. The immediate and dramatic response of rheumatic fever and rheumatoid arthritis to ACTH and cortisone supports the previous impression that these diseases were essentially allergic in nature, as though there were some body substance which had been modified and made antigenic by metabolic products of *Streptococcus.*

The results have been encouraging but less dramatic in other so-called collagen diseases, such as periarteritis nodosa, lupus erythematosus, dermatomyositis, and scleroderma. Very encouraging results have been obtained in pemphigus vulgaris and in Loeffler's syndrome but not in typical eosinophilia (160). A group of chronic eye afflictions, such as iritis, iridocyclitis, uveitis, scleritis, and vernal conjunctivitis with local eosinophilia, have responded satisfactorily to cortisone (59).

A pattern of reaction is slowly evolving which suggests that allergic reactions mediated by classic antibodies such as precipitins are not affected by cortisone and ACTH (160). But those mediated by the atopic reagins and the fixed tissue antibodies of the tuberculin type are blocked by an effect on the tissues and not by the neutralization of either antigen or antibody (39). However, when large amounts of these hormones are given, particularly cortisone, there may be interference with the production of antibodies (36, 106, 283), and other factors involved in resistance, so that severe bacterial infections may develop in animals and man.

REFERENCES

1. Abernathy, R. S., and Spink, W. W. J. Immunol., 77:418, 1956.
2. Aisenberg, A. C. J. Clin. Invest., 41:1964, 1962.
3. Anderson, J. M. Science, 140:193, 1963.
4. Antopol, W., and Chryssanthou, C. Proc. Soc. Exper. Biol. & Med., 103:725, 1960.
5. Arbesman, C. E., and others. J. Allergy, 21:25, 1950.
6. ——— and others. J. Allergy, 31:257, 1960.
7. ——— and others. J. Allergy, 31:317, 333, 342, 1960.
8. Arndt, W. F., and Schneider, H. A. J. Exper. Med., 112:167, 1960.
9. Arquilla, E. R., and Finn, J. J. Exper. Med., 118:55, 1963.
10. Arthus, M. Arch. internat. de physiol., 7:471, 1908-09.
11. Augustin, R. Immunol., 2:148, 230, 1959.
12. ——— Mechanism of Antibody Formation, New York, Academic Press, 1960.
13. ——— and Hayward, B. J. Immunol., 3:45, 1960.
14. ——— and Hayward, B. J. Immunol., 5:424, 1962.
15. Austen, K. F., and Brocklehurst, W. E. J. Exper. Med., 114:29, 1961.
16. Avery, O. T., and Tillett, W. S. J. Exper. Med., 49:251, 1929.
17. Baldridge, G. D., and Kligman, A. M. J. Invest. Dermat., 17:257, 1951.
18. Barbaro, J. F. J. Immunol., 86:369, 377, 1961.
19. Bauer, J. A., Jr., and Stone, S. H. J. Immunol., 86:177, 1961.
20. Becker, R. J., and others. J. Allergy, 32:229, 1961.
21. ——— Proc. Soc. Exper. Biol. & Med., 69:247, 1948.
22. ——— Ann. Int. Med., 1228, 1958.
23. Benacerraf, B. J. Immunol., 64:1, 1950.
24. ——— and Kabat, E. A. J. Immunol., 62:517, 1949.
25. ——— and Levine, B. B. J. Exper. Med., 115:1023, 1962.
26. ——— J. Exper. Med., 118:945, 1963.
27. ——— Nature, 200:544, 1963.
28. ——— and others. J. Immunol., 73:318, 1955.
29. ——— and others. J. Exper. Med., 117:937, 951, 965, 1963.
30. Bendersky, G., and Lupas, J. A. J.A.M.A., 173:255, 1960.
31. Ben-Efraim, S., and others. Science, 139:1222, 1963.
32. Benjamin, E., and others. Proc. Soc. Exper. Biol. & Med., 108:700, 1961.
33. Benton, A. W., and others. Science, 142:228, 1963.
34. Berken, A., and Wolman, M. J. Immunol., 89:490, 1962.
35. Berthrong, M., and Cluff, L. E. J. Exper. Med., 98:331, 1953.
36. Best, W. R. J.A.M.A., 185:286, 1963.
37. Bier, O. G., and others. Proc. Soc. Exper. Biol. & Med., 106:29, 1961.
38. Binaghi, R., and others. J. Immunol., 87:269, 1961.
39. Bjørneboe, M., Fischel, E. E., and Stoerk, H. C. J. Exper. Med., 93:37, 1951.
40. Black-Schaffer, B., and others. Arch. Path., 43:28, 1947.
41. Blumer, H., and others. J. Immunol., 88:669, 1962.
42. Blunt, J. W., Jr., and others. Proc. Soc. Exper. Biol. & Med., 73:678, 1950.
43. Bordley, T. E., and others. Bull. Johns Hopkins Hosp., 85:396, 1949.

44. Boretus, L. O. Acta Physiol. Scand., 48: 431, 1960.
45. Bovet, D. Ann. New York Acad. Sc., 50: 1089, 1950.
46. Bowen, R. J. Allergy, 24:236, 1953.
47. Boyd, W. C. Fundamentals of Immunology, New York, Interscience Publishers, 1956.
48. Bramwell, F. W. R., and others. Antibodies and Embryos, London, Athlone Press, 1951.
49. Brocklehurst, W. E. Prog. in Allergy, 6: 539, 1962.
50. Brown, E. A. Drug Allergy, Quart. Rev. Allg. and Applied Immunol., 7:51, 1953.
51. ——— J.A.M.A., 157:814, 1955.
52. Brown, R. Proc. Soc. Exper. Biol. & Med., 31:700, 1934.
53. Brown, W. J., and others. Pub. Health Reports, 76:189, 1961.
54. Bunch, C. P., and others. J. Immunol., 39: 427, 1940.
55. Burdon, K. L. J. Pediat., 48:372, 1956.
56. Burdon, K. L., and others. J. Allergy, 32: 55, 63, 1961.
57. Burkey, E. L. Am. J. Ophthal., 19:782, 841, 1936.
58. Burrage, W. S., and others. Ann. Int. Med., 43:1001, 1955.
59. Callaghan, O. H., and Goldfarb, A. R. J. Immunol., 89:612, 1962.
60. Cann, J. R., and Loveless, M. H. J. Allergy, 28:379, 1957.
61. Carryer, H. M., and others. J. Allergy, 21: 282, 1950.
62. Chamovitz, R., and others. Proc. Soc. Exper. Biol. & Med., 109:527, 1962.
63. Chase, M. W. Proc. Soc. Exper. Biol. & Med., 59:134, 1945.
64. ——— Proc. Soc. Exper. Biol. & Med., 61: 257, 1946.
65. ——— J. Exper. Med., 86:489, 1947.
66. ——— The Allergic State in Bacterial and Mycotic Infections of Man, 3rd ed., Philadelphia, Lippincott, 1958.
67. ——— Models for Hypersensitivity Studies in Cellular and Humoral Aspects of the Hypersensitive State, New York, Hoeber-Harper, 1959, p. 751.
68. ——— Fed. Proc., abstract, 22:617, 1963.
69. ——— Personal communication, 1962.
70. Christain, C. L., and Thorer, R. J. J. Immunol., 88:93, 1962.
71. Chryssanthou, C., and Antopol, W. Proc. Soc. Exper. Biol. & Med., 108:587, 1961.
72. Claman, H. N., and Talmage, D. W. Science, 141:1194, 1963.
73. Cluff, L. E., and Berthrong, M. Bull. Johns Hopkins Hosp., 92:353, 1953.
74. Cochrane, C. G., and others. J. Exper. Med., 110:481, 1959.
75. Code, C. F., and Hester, H. R. Am. J. Physiol., 127:71, 1939.
76. ——— and others. Ann. New York Acad. Sc., 50:1177, 1950.
77. ——— and others. J. Physiol., 156:207, 1961.
78. Cody, T. R., and Code, C. F. Fed. Proc., 22:379, 1963.
79. Coe, J. E., and others. Fed. Proc., 22:267, 1963.
80. Cole, L-R., and Favor, C. B. J. Exper. Med., 101:391, 1955.
81. Connell, J. T., and Sherman, W. B. J. Immunol., 91:197, 1963.
82. Cooke, R. A., and others. Allergy in Theory and Practice, Philadelphia, W. B. Saunders and Co., 1947.
83. Coulson, E. J., and others. J. Immunol., 61:1, 11, 1949.
84. Crepa, S. B., and Cooke, R. A. J. Allergy, 19:353, 1948.
85. Criep, L. H., and others. Internat. Arch. of Allergy & Applied Immunol., 20:1, 1962.
86. Crowle, A. J. Proc. Soc. Exper. Biol. & Med., 110:447, 1962.
87. ——— Delayed Hypersensitivity in Health and Disease, Springfield, Ill., Charles C Thomas, 1962.
88. Cummings, M. M., and Hudgins, P. C. J. Immunol., 69:331, 1952.
89. ——— and others. Pub. Health Rep., 62: 994, 1947.
90. Curran, W. S., and Goldman, G. Ann. Int. Med., 55:777, 1961.
91. Dale, H. H. Brit. Med. J., 32:281, 1948.
92. ——— J. Pharmacol. & Exper. Therap., 4: 167, 1912-13.
93. ——— and Hartley, P. Biochem. J., 10: 408, 1916.
94. David, J. R., and others. Fed. Proc., abstract, 22:618, 1963.
95. Davis, J. C., Jr., and Haterius, H. O. Proc. Soc. Exper. Biol & Med., 70:275, 1949.
96. Davidson, A. G., and others. J. Allergy, 18: 359, 1947.
97. Dean, H. R., and others. J. Hyg., 36:570, 1936.
98. Derick, C. L., and Swift, H. F. J. Exper. Med., 49:615, 883, 1929.
99. Dews, P. B,. and Code, C. F. Proc. Soc. Exper. Biol. & Med., 77:141, 1951.
100. ——— and Code, C. F. J. Immunol., 70: 199, 1953.
101. Dienes, L. J. Immunol., 20:221, 1931.
102. ——— Arch. Pathol., 21:357, 1936.
103. Dixon, F., and others. Fed. Proc., 19:205, 1960.
104. Dragstedt, C. A. Physiol. Rev., 21:563, 1941.
105. ——— and Feinberg, S. M. Allergy in Practice, 2nd ed., Chicago, The Year Book Publishers, Inc., 1946.
106. Dressler, S., and Dwork, R. E. J.A.M.A., 133:849, 1947.
107. Dulaney, A. D., and others. Proc. Soc. Exper. Biol. & Med., 87:146, 1954.
108. Editorial. J.A.M.A., 166:927, 1958.
109. Edsall, G., and others. Am. J. Hyg., 53: 283, 1951.
110. Edwards, P. Q., and others. Am. Rev. Resp. Dis., 83:528, 1961.
111. Einbinder, J. M., and others. J. Immunol., 88:78, 1962.
112. Eisen, H. N., and others. Proc. Soc. Exper. Biol. & Med., 65:39, 1947.
113. Enders, J. F., and others. J. Exper. Med., 81:119, 1945.
114. Epp, M. Science, 130:1472, 1959.
115. Farr, R. S. J. Infect. Dis., 103:239, 1958.
116. Feinberg, S. M. Ann. New York Acad. Sc., 50:1186, 1950.
117. ——— J.A.M.A., 178:815, 1961.
118. ——— and others. J. Allergy, 33:285, 1962.

119. Feldman, J. D., and Najarian, J. S. J. Immunol., 91:306, 1963.
120. Fink, M. A. Proc. Soc. Exper. Biol. & Med., 92:673, 1956.
121. Fireman, P., and others. J. Exper. Med., 117:603, 1963.
122. Fishel, C. W., and others. J. Immunol., 89:8, 1962.
123. Fischel, E. E. Bull. New York Acad. Med., 26:255, 1950.
124. ——— and Kabat, E. A. J. Immunol., 55: 337, 1947.
125. ——— and others. Proc. Soc. Exper. Biol. & Med., 77:111, 1951.
126. Fisher, J. P., and Cooke, R. A. J. Allergy, 28:150, 1957.
127. Fleisher, M. S., and Jones, L. J. Exper. Med., 54:597, 1931.
128. Frei, W. Klin Wchnschr., 4:2148, 1925.
129. Freund, J. Ann. Rev. Microbiol., 1:291, 1947.
130. ——— and others. J. Exper. Med., 64: 573, 1936.
131. ——— and Stone, S. H. J. Immunol., 76: 138, 1956.
132. Friedlander, S., and Feinberg, S. M. Ann. Int. Med., 26:734, 1947.
133. ——— and Friedlander, A. S. J. Allergy, 21:803, 1950.
134. Gaillard, G. E. J. Allergy, 21:55, 1950.
135. Gell, P. G. H., and Silverstein, A. M. J. Exper. Med., 115:1037, 1053, 1962.
136. George, M., and Vaughn, J. H. Proc. Soc. Exper. Biol. & Med., 111:514, 1962.
137. Gerlach, W. Virchows Arch. Path. Anat., 247:294, 1923.
138. Germuth, F. G., and McKinnon, G. F. Bull. Johns Hopkins Hosp., 101:13, 1957.
139. ——— and others. J. Exper. Med., 94: 139, 1951.
140. Gershon, M. D., and Ross, L. L. J. Exper. Med., 115:367, 1962.
141. Good, R. A. Host-Parasite Relationship in Living Cells, Springfield, Ill., Charles C Thomas Co., 1957.
142. ——— and others. J. Clin. Invest., 36:894, 1957.
143. ——— and Thomas, L. J. Exper. Med., 97:871, 1953.
144. Gordon, J. Immunol., 5:153, 1962.
145. ——— and others. J. Exper. Med., 108: 37, 1958.
146. Graham, D. T., and Wolf, S. J.A.M.A., 143:1396, 1950.
147. Grolnick, M. Ann. Allergy, 7:368, 1949.
148. Gruenwald, R., and others. Proc. Soc. Exper. Biol. & Med., 108:109, 1961.
149. Halpern, B. N. J. Immunol., 88:683, 1962.
150. ——— and others. Brit. J. Pharmacol., 7: 287, 1952.
151. ——— and others. Immunol., 2:351, 1959.
152. Hanks, J. H. J. Immunol., 28:105, 1935.
153. Hanon, R., and Overman, J. R. Proc. Soc. Exper. Biol. & Med., 84:420, 1953.
154. Hanzlick, P. J., and Karsner, H. T. J. Pharmacol. & Exper. Therap., 14:229, 379, 425, 1920.
155. Hawn, C. V. Z., and Janeway, C. A. J. Exper. Med., 85:571, 1947.
156. Heilman, D. H., and others. J. Immunol., 85:258, 1960.
157. Heimlich, E. M., and others. J. Allergy, 31:364, 1960.
158. Helmuth, R. G., and others. J. Immunol., 84:106, 1960.
159. Henderson, J. W., and Hollenhorst, R. W. Proc. Staff Meet. Mayo Clinic, 25:459, 1950.
160. Herbert, P., and others. J. Allergy, 21:12, 1950.
161. Hesch, D. J. J.A.M.A., 172:13, 1960.
162. Hooker, S. B. J. Infect. Dis., 45:255, 1929.
163. Humphrey, J. H., and Jacques, R. J. Physiol., 128:9, 1955.
164. Irwin, J. W., and others. New England J. Med., 245:246, 1951.
165. Ishizaka, K., and Campbell, D. H. J. Immunol., 83:318, 1959.
166. ——— and others. J. Immunol., 86:220, 1961.
167. Israel, H. L., and others. Am. Rev. Tuberc., 62:408, 1950.
168. Jahiel, J., and Jahiel, R. J. Allergy, 21:102, 1950.
169. Jankovic, B. D., and others. J. Exper. Med., 116:159, 1962.
170. ——— and Dvorak, H. F. J. Immunol., 89:571, 1962.
171. Jeter, W. S., and others. J. Bact., 74:680, 1957.
172. Johnston, T. E., and others. J. Exper. Med., 113:235, 249, 259, 1961.
173. Johnstone, D. E., and others. Proc. Soc. Exper. Biol. & Med., 99:15, 1958.
174. Jones, T. D., and Mote, J. R. New England J. Med., 210:120, 1934.
175. Julianelle, L. A. J. Exper. Med., 51:441, 449, 463, 1930.
176. ——— and Wieghard, G. W. J. Exper. Med., 62:11, 23, 31, 1935.
177. Kabat, E. A. Am. J. Med., 3:535, 1947.
178. ——— and Benacerraf, B. J. Immunol., 62:97, 1949.
179. ——— and Boldt, M. H. J. Immunol., 48: 181, 1944.
180. ——— and Landow, H. J. Immunol., 44: 69, 1942.
181. ——— and Mayer, M. M. Experimental Immunochemistry, Springfield, Ill., Charles C Thomas, 2nd ed., 1961.
182. ——— and others. J. Immunol., 56:377, 1947.
183. ——— and others. J. Immunol., 68:265, 1952.
184. Kaplan, M. H., and Dienes, L. Mechanisms of Hypersensitivity, Boston, Little, Brown and Co., 1959.
185. Karelitz, S., and Glonig, A. J. Immunol., 47:121, 1943.
186. Karush, F., and Eisen, H. N. Science, 136: 1032, 1962.
187. Katz, G. Science, 91:221, 1940.
188. Kelley, W. D., and others. Ann. New York Acad. Sci., 87:187, 1960.
189. Kerby, G. J. Clin. Invest., 34:1738, 1955.
190. Kern, M., and Eisen, H. N. J. Exper. Med., 110:207, 1959.
191. Kern, R. A. J.A.M.A., 179:19, 1962.
192. Kind, L. S. J. Immunol., 74:387, 1955.
193. ——— J. Immunol., 82:32, 1959.
194. ——— and Donch, J. Proc. Soc. Exper. Biol. & Med., 111:241, 1962.
195. ——— and Roffler, S. K. J. Immunol., 86: 324, 1961.

196. Kirchheimer, W. F., and Weiser, R. S. Proc. Soc. Exper. Biol., & Med., 66:166, 1947.
197. Klein, G. C., and Patnode, R. A. Proc. Soc. Exper. Biol. & Med., 113:627, 1963.
198. Kligman, A. M. Arch. Dermat., 77:149, 1958.
199. Knight, R. A., and Marcus, S. Am. Rev. Tuberc., 77:983, 1958.
200. Kojis, F. G. Am. J. Dis. Child., 64:93, 313, 1942.
201. Kopeloff, L. M., and Kopeloff, N. J. Immunol., 36:83, 101, 1939.
202. Koutras, G. A., and Schilling, R. F. Proc. Soc. Exper. Biol. & Med., 108:48, 1961.
203. Kuhns, W. J. J. Immunol., 89:652, 1962.
204. ———— J. Exper. Med., 97:903, 1953.
205. ———— Proc. Soc. Exper. Biol. & Med., 111:282, 1962.
206. ———— and Pappenheimer, A. M., Jr. J. Exper. Med., 95:363, 375, 1952.
207. Kunkel, H. G., and others. Immunochemical Approach to Problems in Microbiology, New Jersey, Rutgers Univ. Press, 1961.
208. Kyes, P., and Strauser, E. R. J. Immunol., 12:419, 1926.
209. Lamb, D., and others. J. Immunol., 89:555, 1962.
210. Landau, S. W., and others. Bull. Johns Hopkins Hosp., 88:395, 1951.
211. Landsteiner, K. The Specificity of Serological Reactions, 2nd ed., Cambridge, Mass., Harvard University Press, 1946.
212. Lawrence, H. S. Proc. Soc. Exper. Biol. & Med., 71:516, 1949.
213. ———— J. Clin. Invest., 34:219, 1955.
214. ———— Cellular and Humoral Aspects of the Hypersensitive State, New York, Hoeber, 1959.
215. ———— Ann. New York Acad. Sc., 87:223, 1960.
216. Layton, L. L., and others. Proc. Soc. Exper. Biol. & Med., 108:623, 1961.
217. ———— and others. Proc. Soc. Exper. Biol. & Med., 112:945, 1963.
218. Lea, D. J., and Sehon, A. H. Internat. Arch. Allergy & Applied Immunol., 20:203, 1962.
219. Lee, L. J. Exper. Med., 115:1065, 1962.
220. ———— and Stetson, C. A. J. Exper. Med., 111:761, 1960.
221. Leskowitz, S. J. Exper. Med., 117:909, 1963.
222. ———— J. Immunol., 89:434, 1962.
223. ———— and Ovary, Z. Immunol., 5:1, 1962.
224. Levine, B. B., and Ovary, Z. J. Exper. Med., 114:875, 1961.
225. Lewis, J. H., and Seibert, F. B. J. Immunol., 20:201, 1931.
226. ———— and Harmer, I. M. Heart, 14:19, 1927.
227. Ley, A. B., and others. Science, 127:1118, 1958.
228. Liacopoulos, P., and others. J. Immunol., 91:348, 1963.
229. Lipton, M. M., and Freund, J. J. Immunol., 70:326, 1953.
230. ———— and Freund, J. J. Immunol., 71:98, 1953.
231. Logan, G. B. Proc. Soc. Exper. Biol. & Med., 104:532, 1960.
232. ———— Proc. Soc. Exper. Biol. & Med., 107:466, 1961.
233. ———— Proc. Soc. Exper. Biol. & Med., 111:171, 1962.
234. Long, D. A. J. Hyg., 57:227, 1959.
235. Longcope, W. T. J. Exper. Med., 18:678, 1913.
236. ———— and Mackenzie, G. M. Proc. Soc. Exper. Biol. & Med., 17:133, 1920.
237. ———— and Rackemann, F. M. J. Exper. Med., 27:341, 1918.
238. Loveless, M. H. J. Immunol., 38:25, 1940.
239. ———— J. Immunol., 41:15, 1941.
240. ———— J. Am. Med. Women's Assoc., 12:383, 1957.
241. ———— J. Immunol., 89:204, 1962.
242. ———— Fed. Proc., 21:271, 1962.
243. ———— J. Immunol., 79:68, 1957.
244. ———— and Facker, W. R. Ann. Allergy, 14:347, 1956.
245. Malkiel, S. J. Immunol., 66:379, 1951.
246. ———— and Hargis, B. J. Proc. Soc. Exper. Biol. & Med., 80:122, 1952.
247. Manwaring, W. H. Zeitschr. f. Immunol., 8:1, 1911.
248. Marcus, W., and Donaldson, D. M. J. Immunol., 69:101, 1952.
249. Martin, C. M., and others. J. Clin. Invest., 36:405, 1957.
250. Martin, D. S., and Smith, D. T. Am. Rev. Tuberc., 39:488, 1939.
251. Mathews, K. P., and Spear, H. J. J. Immunol., 87:274, 1961.
252. Mathies, M., and Stravitsky, A. B. Fed. Proc., 21:26, 1962.
253. Maurer, P. H. J. Exper. Med., 113:1029, 1961.
254. Mayer, R. L. Ann. New York Acad. Sc., 50:1127, 1950.
255. McKay, D. G., and Wong, T. C. J. Exper. Med., 115:1117, 1127, 1137, 1962.
256. McKinnon, G. E., and others. Johns Hopkins Hosp. Bull., 101:258, 1957.
257. Metaxas, M. N., and Metaxas-Buehler, M. J. Immunol., 75:333, 1955.
258. Miller, J. F. Lancet, 2:748, 1961.
259. Minno, A. M., and Davis, G. M. J.A.M.A., 165:222, 1957.
260. Mirick, G. S. Bull. Johns Hopkins Hosp., 88:332, 1951.
261. Moses, J. M., and Atkins, E. J. Exper. Med., 114:939, 1961.
262. Muñoz, J., and Anacker, R. L. J. Immunol., 83:640, 1959.
263. ———— and Maung, M. Proc. Soc. Exper. Biol. & Med., 106:70, 1961.
264. ———— and others. J. Immunol., 80:77, 1958.
265. Najarian, J. S., and Feldman, J. D. J. Exper. Med., 114:779, 1961.
266. ———— and Feldman, J. D. J. Exper. Med., 117:775, 1963.
267. Oda, M., and Puck, T. T. J. Exper. Med., 113:599, 1961.
268. Olitsky, P. K., and others. Proc. Soc. Exper. Biol. & Med., 75:276, 1950.
269. Oliver-Gonzalez, J. Ann. Rev. Microbiol., 8:353, 1954.
270. Oort, J., and Turk, J. L. Immunol., 6:148, 1963.
271. Opie, E. L. J. Immunol., 9:231, 1924.

272. Osler, A. G., and others. J. Exper. Med., 106:811, 1957.
273. ———— and others. J. Exper. Med., 110:311, 1959.
274. ———— and Knipp, E. A. J. Immunol., 78:19, 1957.
275. ———— and Knipp, E. A. J. Immunol., 78:30, 1957.
276. Ovary, Z. Abstracts of First Internat. Congress of Allergy, Zurich, 1951, New York, S. Karger, 1952.
277. ———— J. Immunol., 81:355, 1958.
278. ———— Prog. Allergy, 5:459, 1958.
279. ———— and Bier, O. G. J. Immunol., 71:6, 1953.
280. ———— and Karush, F. J. Immunol., 84:409, 1960.
281. ———— and Karush, F. J. Immunol., 86:146, 1961.
282. ———— and others. J. Exper. Med., 112:953, 1960.
283. Overman, J. R., and Hanon, R. Proc. Soc. Exper. Biol. & Med., 82:427, 1953.
284. Palczuk, N. C., and Flick, J. A. J. Immunol., 83:339, 1959.
285. Parfentjev, I. A. Proc. Soc. Exper. Biol. & Med., 89:297, 1955.
286. Parker, C. W., and others. J. Exper. Med., 115:821, 1962.
287. ———— and others. J. Exper. Med., 116:803, 821, 1962.
288. Parks, J. J., and others. J. Immunol., 87:199, 1961.
289. ———— and others. J. Immunol., 89:323, 1962.
290. Paterson, P. Y., and Didakow, N. C. Proc. Soc. Exp. Biol. & Med., 108:768, 1961.
291. Patterson, R., and Sparks, D. B. J. Immunol., 88:262, 1962.
292. Patterson, R. D. A., and others. J. Allergy, 33:406, 1962; J. Immunol., 90:35, 1963.
293. Paul, J. R., and Bunnell, W. W. Am. J. M. Sc., 183:90, 1932.
294. Perelmutter, L., and others. J. Immunol., 89:623, 1962.
295. Perla, D., and Marmorston, J. Natural Resistance and Clinical Medicine, Boston, Little, Brown & Co., 1941.
296. Perlman, F. J. Allergy, 30:24, 1959.
297. Peters, G. A., and others. Proc. Staff Meet. Mayo Clinic, 30:634, 1955.
298. Portier, P., and Richet, C. Compt. rend. Soc. de biol., 54:170, 1902.
299. Prausnitz, C., and Kuestner, H. Centralbl. f. Bakt., 86:160, 1921.
300. ———— and others. J. Immunol., 84:292, 1960.
301. ———— and others. J. Immunol., 82:497, 1959.
302. ———— and others. J. Allergy, 33:381, 1962.
303. Race, G. J., and Reed., D. W. South. M. J., 46:207, 1953.
304. Rackemann, F. M. J. Allergy, 15, 249, 1944.
305. Raffel, S. Immunity, 2nd ed., New York, Appleton-Century-Crofts, Inc., 1961.
306. ———— and Newel, J. M. J. Exper. Med., 108:823, 1958.
307. ———— and others. J. Exper. Med., 90:53, 1949.
308. Rall, D. P., and others. Proc. Soc. Exper. Biol. & Med., 88:241, 1955.
309. Randolph, T. G. Ann. Allergy, 8:519, 1950.
310. Rapaport, B. Z., and others. J. Immunol., 84:358, 368, 1960.
311. ———— J. Exper. Med., 112:55, 725, 1960.
312. Ratner, B. Allergy, Anaphylaxis, and Immuno-therapy, Basic Principles and Practice, Baltimore, Williams and Wilkins, Co., 1943.
113. ———— and Silberman, D. E. Ann. Allergy, 10:1, 1952.
314. Redd, L., and Vaughn, J. H. Proc. Soc. Exper. Biol. & Med., 90:317, 1955.
315. Reisch, M. J.A.M.A., 169:394, 1959.
316. Reisman, R. E., and others. J.A.M.A., 176:1004, 1961.
317. ———— and others. J. Allergy, 32:531, 1961.
318. Relyveld, E. H., and others. C. R. Acad. Sc. (Paris), 252:620-1, 1961.
319. Rich, A. R. The Pathogenesis of Tuberculosis, 2nd ed., Springfield, Ill., Charles C Thomas Co., 1950.
320. ———— Harvey Lecture, 42:106, 1947.
321. ———— Physiol. Rev., 21:70, 1941.
322. ———— and Brown, J. H. Proc. Soc. Exper. Biol. & Med., 27:695, 1929-30.
323. ———— and Griffith, P. C. Bull. Johns Hopkins Hosp., 86:131, 1950.
324. ———— and Lewis, M. R. Bull. Johns Hopkins Hosp., 50:115, 1932.
325. ———— and others. Bull. Johns Hopkins Hosp., 52:179, 1933.
326. ———— and others. Bull. Johns Hopkins Hosp., 87:549, 1950.
327. Richter, M., and others. Canad. J. Biochem. & Physiol., 40:105, 1962.
328. Rieder, R. F., and Thomas, L. J. Immunol., 84:89, 1960.
329. Rimington, C. Treatment of Asthma, Baltimore, Williams & Wilkins, 1951.
330. Rizzo, A. A., and Mergenhagen, S. E. Proc. Soc. Exper. Biol. & Med., 104:579, 1960.
331. Rocha e Silva, M. J. Immunol., 40:399, 1941.
332. ———— Ann. New York Acad. Sc., 50:1045, 1950.
333. Rose, H. M., and Molloy, E. Fed. Proc., 6:432, 1947.
334. Rose, N. R., and others. J. Allergy, 33:250, 1962.
335. Rosenberg, L. T. J. Immunol., 81:136, 1958.
336. ———— and others. Proc. Soc. Exper. Biol. & Med., 98:451, 1958.
337. Rothberg. R., and Talmage, D. W. J. Immunol., 86:302, 1961.
338. Salvaggio, J. E., and others. Fed. Proc., 22:267, 1963.
339. Salvin, S. B., and Smith, R. F. J. Exper. Med., 109:325, 1959.
340. ———— and Smith, R. F. J. Exper. Med., 111:465, 1960.
341. ———— and Smith, R. F. J. Exper. Med., 114:185, 1961.
342. ———— and others. J. Exper. Med., 115:707, 1962.
343. Schild, H. O. Histamine, Boston, Little, Brown & Co., 1956.
344. Schwab, J. H., and others. Proc. Soc. Exper. Biol. & Med., 82:754, 1953.

345. Segal, M. S., and Herschfus, J. A. Ann. Allergy, 8:786, 1950.
346. Segaloff, A. Ann. Allergy, 12:565, 1954.
347. Sehon, A. H., and Richter, M. J. Immunol., 82:190, 1959.
348. Seibert, F. B. Chem. Rev., 34:107, 1944.
349. Sell, S., and Braude, A. I. J. Immunol., 87: 119, 1961.
350. Shaffer, J. H. J.A.M.A., 177:473, 1961.
351. Sheldon, J. M., and others. J.A.MA, 151: 785, 1953.
352. Sherline, D. M., and Blackwell, W. J. J.A.M.A., 181:1079, 1962.
353. Sherman, W. B. Experimental Production of Skin Sensitizing Antibodies, New York, Columbia University Press, 1953, p. 126.
354. ——— J. Allergy, 28:62, 1957.
355. Sherwood, N. P., and others. J. Immunol., 59:279, 1948.
356. Shwartzman, G. J. Exper. Med., 48:247, 1928.
357. Simon, F. A., and Rackemann, F. M. J. Allergy, 5:439, 1936.
358. Siqueira, M., and Bier, O. G. Proc. Soc. Exper. Biol. & Med., 107:779, 1961.
359. Smith, D. T., and Martin, D. S. North Carolina M. J., 8:160, 1947.
360. Smith, R. T., and others. Proc. Soc. Exper. Biol. & Med., 82:712, 1953.
361. Soffer, L. J., and others. Science, 111:303, 1950.
362. Sorkin, E., and Boyden, S. V. J. Immunol., 82:332, 1959.
363. Spain, W. C. Ann. Int. Med., 38:188, 1953.
364. Spanoudis, S., and others. J. Immunol., 75: 167, 1955.
365. Spink, W. W. Ann. Int. Med., 57:538, 1962.
366. State, D., and Wangensteen, O. H. J.A.M.A., 130:990, 1946.
367. Stetson, C. A., Jr. J. Exper. Med., 94:347, 1951.
368. ——— J. Exper. Med., 101:421, 1955.
369. ——— Cellular and Humoral Aspects of Hypersensitive States, New York, Harper, 1959.
370. ——— and Good, R. A. J. Exper. Med., 93:49, 1951.
371. Stevens, K. M., and others. Proc. Soc. Exper. Biol. & Med., 113:188. 1963.
372. Stone, S. H. Proc. Soc. Exp. Biol. & Med., 98:269, 1958.
373. ——— J. Immunol., 82:138, 1959.
374. ——— Science, 134:619, 1961.
375. Sulzberger, M. B. J. Allergy, 21:85, 1950.
376. ——— and others. J. Allergy, 18:92, 1947.
377. Swarts, W. B., and Rourke, T. A. J.A.M.A., 170:1409, 1959.
378. Swineford, O., Jr. J. Allergy, 25:260, 1954.
379. ——— J. Allergy, 26:157, 1955.
380. Taranta, A., and Franklin, E. E. Science, 134:1981, 1962.
381. Thal, A., and Brackney, E. J.A.M.A., 155: 569, 1954.
382. Thomas, L. The Physiopathology of the Reticulo-endothelial System, Blackwell, Oxford Press, p. 226, 1957.
383. ——— Arch. Int. Med., 110:782, 1962.
384. ——— and Good, R. A. J. Exper. Med., 96:605, 1952.
385. ——— and others. J. Exper. Med., 102: 249, 263, 1955.
386. Thorne, N. A., and others. Unpublished studies.
387. Tillett, W. S., and Francis, T., Jr. J. Exper. Med., 54:587, 1931.
388. Tokuda, S., and Weiser, R. S. J. Immunol., 86:292, 1961.
389. Tomesik, J. Proc. Soc. Exper. Biol. & Med., 24:812, 1927.
390. Trakatellis, A. C., and others. J. Immunol., 91:39, 46, 1963.
391. ——— and others. J. Immunol., 91:89, 1963.
392. Turk, J. L. Immunol., 5:478, 1962.
393. Turkey, J. W., and others. Am. Rev. Tuberc., 62:77, 1950.
394. Uhr, J. W., and Baumann, J. B. J. Exper. Med., 113:935, 1961.
395. ——— and Pappenheimer, A. M., Jr. J. Exper. Med., 108:891, 1958.
396. ——— and Scharff, M. J. Exper. Med., 112:65, 1960.
397. Unger, L. Bronchial Asthma, Springfield, Ill., Charles C Thomas Co., 1945.
398. Ungar, G., and others. J. Exper. Med., 113:359, 1961.
399. Urbach, E., and Gottlieb, P. M. Allergy, 2nd ed., New York, Grune & Stratton, 1946.
400. Van Arsdel, P. P., Jr., and others. J.A.M.A., 185:584, 1963.
401. ——— and Sells, C. J. Science, 141:1190, 1963.
402. Van den Berg, C., and others. Immunol., 5:389, 1962.
403. Von Pirquet, C. Serum Sickness, Baltimore, Williams & Wilkins Co., 1951.
404. ——— and Schick, B. Die Serumkrankheit, Leipzig und Wien, Deuticke, 1905.
405. Waalkes, T. P., and others. J. Exper. Biol. & Med., 95:479, 1957.
406. Waksman, B. H. J. Immunol., 70:331, 1953.
407. ——— and others. J. Immunol., 85:403, 1960.
408. ——— and others. J. Exper. Med., 114: 997, 1961.
409. Warwick, W. J., and others. Fed. Proc., 20:18, 1961.
410. Weigle, W. O. Advances in Immunology, Vol. 1, New York, Academic Press, 1961.
411. ——— and Maurer, P. H. J. Immunol., 79:211, 223, 1957.
412. ——— and others. J. Immunol., 85:469, 1960.
413. Weiner, L. W., and others. J. Immunol., 90: 788, 1963.
414. Weiser, R. S., and others. J. Infect. Dis., 68:97, 1941.
415. Welch, H., and others. Antibiotic Med. & Clin. Therapy, 4:800, 1957.
416. ——— and others. Antibiotics & Chemotherap., 4:607, 1954.
417. Wells, H. G. Chemical Aspects of Immunity, New York, Chemical Catalogue Co., 1929.
418. Wiener, A. S., and others. Ann. Eugenics, 7:141, 1936.
419. Winternitz, W. W., and Hackel, D. B. Proc. Soc. Exper. Biol. & Med., 78:294, 1951.
420. Winton, S. S., and Nora, E. D. Am. J. Med., 18:66, 1955.
421. Wittich, F. W. Animal Allergy in Treatment of Asthma, Baltimore, Williams & Wilkins, 1951.

422. Wolfe, H. R., and others. Fed. Proc., 21: 22, 1962.
423. Wright, G. P., and Hopkins, S. J.   J. Path. Bact., 53:243, 1941.
424. Yagi, Y., and others.   J. Immunol., 91:83, 1963.
425. ——— and others.   J. Immunol., 90:760, 1963.
426. Zinsser, H.   J. Exper. Med., 34:495, 1921.
427. ——— and Enders, J. F.   J. Immunol., 30: 327, 1936.

428. ——— and Grinnell, F. B.   J. Immunol., 10:725, 1925.
429. ——— and Mueller, J. H.   J. Exper. Med., 41:159, 1925.
430. ——— and others.   Immunity, Principles and Applications in Medicine and Public Health, New York, The Macmillan Co., 1939.
431. Zweifach, B. W., and others.   J. Exper. Med., 113:437, 1961.

18

Infection-Resistance and Epidemiology

Less than 300 of the tens of thousands of known microorganisms have acquired the ability to produce disease in man and animals. Parasitism is an abnormal condition and implies that the organism either had originally or had acquired by mutation some peculiar biochemical qualities which distinguish it from its normal harmless relatives. The importance of these unique qualities has been emphasized in Dubos' monograph on *Biochemical Determinants of Microbial Diseases* (74). In only a few instances has the biochemical mechanism of infection been determined with any reasonable degree of accuracy. Furthermore, all normal animals, including man, have a certain degree of resistance even to the organisms which are classified as pathogenic, so only a small but varying proportion of the population which is infected actually develops clinical symptoms or pathologic lesions. The solution to the many unsolved problems of infection and resistance will require the cooperation of the biochemist, immunologist, pathologist, physiologist, sociologist, and physician.

A microorganism is classified as a pathogen if it has the ability to incite disease in susceptible animals. In this definition qualifying terms such as "dosage of organisms," "route of infection," and "resistance of the animal body" have been omitted deliberately, because such factors are concerned more properly with the problems associated with virulence. Such a subdivision into pathogenic, nonpathogenic, and the various intermediate varieties of microorganisms is very convenient. Streptococci and diphtheria bacilli, for example, must be classified as pathogens, although many strains of each organism are too feeble to cause infection unless the resistance of the host is extremely low or

tremendous numbers of bacteria are introduced. On the other hand, some of the various species of bacteria found in different parts of the body are nonpathogenic under all circumstances and, if they are cultured from lesions, can be recognized as harmless immediately. There are organisms which have an intermediate position in such a classification. The colon bacillus, for example, is a constant inhabitant of the normal bowel but can cause cystitis, pyelitis, abscess formation, and septicemia.

Virulence is the term used to designate the disease-inciting powers of a particular microorganism and especially a specific strain. Virulence is measured by the number of organisms required to kill members of a particular animal species under standardized conditions in a definite period of time. The confusing effect of the naturally occurring variations in resistance, even among closely inbred strains of animals, can be minimized by employing as an end point the dose of organisms which kills 50 per cent of the animals. **The end point is known as the L.D.$_{50}$** (18). For very exacting work the slope of the increasing death rate with increasing numbers of organisms should be plotted as well as the L.D.$_{50}$ (90). From such data, dose response equations for the invading organisms can be calculated (237, 308).

Some microbiologists include under the term "virulence" all the properties of a microorganism which enable it to **infect, invade, and kill** the host, while others prefer to separate **communicability** and **invasiveness from** killing power or **virulence. Communicability** may be defined as the ability of the organism to spread under natural conditions from animal to animal, man to man, or animal to man. **Invasiveness** describes the rapid spread of the organism throughout the tissues of the host, while **virulence** is reserved for the property of causing death in an infected animal. These characteristics of microorganisms are important, regardless of whether they are considered as separate and distinct attributes of the microorganism or included under the general term "virulence." For example, pneumococci when injected into mice in very small numbers invade the tissues rapidly and cause death in a short period of time. The pneumococcus can be described as highly virulent for mice under these experimental conditions. But under natural conditions the pneumococcus lacks communicability, and does not spread naturally from mouse to mouse; consequently, **pneumococcal pneumonia is not a spontaneous disease of mice.** Both the human and bovine types of tubercle bacilli will kill rabbits when injected in proper doses. Both spread rapidly through the tissues of the animal, so both have equal invasiveness (184). But larger doses of human tubercle bacilli than bovine bacilli are required to kill rabbits, so the bovine strain is more virulent for this animal. Furthermore, experimental bovine tuberculosis will spread naturally from rabbit to rabbit while the human type does not, so **the human type lacks communicability for the rabbit but has a higher communicability than the bovine type for man.**

Variations in these factors should be kept in mind when studying epidemic diseases in man. An organism may retain its high communicability but lose much of its invasiveness, virulence, or both. Coburn (62) has emphasized the importance of variations in communicability among strains of group A hemolytic streptococci.

Invasiveness as it applies to the blood stream of man is described in the clinical literature as **bacteremia, septicemia,** or **pyemia.** These terms are often used loosely and inaccurately. The term **bacteremia,** the broadest and most conservative, means that organisms are in the blood as demonstrated by a positive blood culture. They are not necessarily pathogenic and may be transient invaders from the tonsils or intestinal flora (251). The term **septicemia** implies that the

organisms found in the blood are producing symptoms in the patient which the physician describes as toxic or "septic." **Pyemia** indicates that the organisms in the blood are producing symptoms but also are initiating localized abscesses in the tissues of the host.

The communicability, invasiveness, and killing power of an organism may be profoundly altered by the **portal of entry into the body.** In this instance the alteration is brought about by the defensive mechanisms of the body and not by a change in the properties of the organism. *Salmonella typhosa,* which normally invades the body through the intestinal mucosa after being taken in with food or water, rarely, if ever, invades the body through a scratch on the skin. In contrast, certain group A hemolytic streptococci which readily invade through a scratch on the skin, producing septicemia and death, may be swallowed with impunity. *Pasteurella tularensis,* when introduced into the body through a scratch on the skin of the finger or hand, is usually localized to the lymph nodes of the arms and axillae, rarely invades the blood, and has a mortality of about 5 per cent. But the same organism, if introduced into the tissues by the bite of a deer fly or tick, readily invades the blood, producing a septicemia which has a mortality of about 90 per cent. *Pasteurella pestis* in the clinical form of the disease known as pneumonic plague or "black death" threatened the existence of the human race in the Middle Ages (359). In this instance communicability from man to man by means of droplet infection was extremely effective, invasiveness rapid and certain, and death almost 100 per cent. On the other hand, the form of the disease known as bubonic plague depends for its communicability upon an adequate supply of infected fleas from infected rats, so the incidence of infection is much lower. Furthermore, when introduced into the body by the bite of the flea the invasiveness is slowed and sometimes stopped by the lymph nodes until active immunity can develop. This form of the disease has a mortality of only 70 to 90 per cent. The influence of the defenses of the body on the invasiveness of the organism will be discussed in more detail later in the chapter.

INFECTION

Every pathogenic organism has its own unique biologic and biochemical qualities which make possible invasion and multiplication in the body of the host (139, 208); those which are successful parasites must also succeed in leaving the body, before death or recovery, to find a new host.

Botulinus. *Clostridium botulinum* is an obvious exception to the general pattern of infection, since this organism produces its exotoxin in food materials which are then eaten by the victim. The toxin is unique in resisting inactivation by the digestive enzymes. After absorption it seeks out and acts specifically upon the cholinergic nerve endings in the peripheral somatic and autonomic nerve fibers. Botulism should be defined as an intoxication rather than an infection.

Tetanus. *Clostridium tetani* produces its exotoxin within the body of the host, but, because of its feeble powers, the spores must either be introduced, along with dirt, chemicals, or bacteria capable of initiating an area of inflammation or be introduced into an area already devitalized by mechanical or thermal injury. The area of infection is usually insignificant in size and gives minimal symptoms, yet the organism remains localized and synthesizes enough toxin to kill the patient. The toxin travels in the lymph surrounding the peripheral nerve fibers until it reaches and acts specifically on the nerve cells in the cerebrospinal axis (352).

Diphtheria. *Corynebacterium diphtheriae* has its natural habitat in the upper respiratory tract of man. It may pass from man to man without initiating disease, or the disease may be subclinical and unrecognizable and yet effectively immunize the individual. Nontoxin-producing strains are frequently present in the nasopharynx of healthy individuals. Most, if not all, toxin producing strains have had their metabolism disorganized by infection with a temperate bacteriophage (17, 97, 108). They metabolize normally in the presence of an adequate supply of iron, but in the region of about 100 μg per liter of medium an exotoxin is produced.

Gas Gangrene. The clostridia of the gas gangrene group of organisms, primarily *Cl. perfringens*, *Cl. novyi*, and *Cl. septicum*, resemble *Cl. tetani* by having their spore forms in the soil. These are usually introduced into the body by means of a wound which damages and devitalizes the tissues. A great variety of exotoxins are produced (see Chapter 16), some of the more important being enzymes such as **lecithinase** and **collagenase** which attack their corresponding substrates in the body thus providing an ever increasing area suitable for the growth and metabolism of the organisms (196).

Pneumococcal Pneumonia. *Diplococcus pneumoniae* is the best example of an organism whose virulence depends upon the presence of a nontoxic capsule. The nasopharynx of man is the normal habitat of this coccus, and it is constantly passing from man to man without producing disease. The nucleoproteins of the bodies of the cocci are the same for all types, but there are over 75 specific antigenic polysaccharides which form the capsules. The capsular polysaccharides are defensive weapons which protect the organism from phagocytosis (86, 288). Furthermore, the capsular material slowly dissolves in the body fluids, circulates in the blood, and neutralizes specific antibodies as they are formed. Mice and men, but not rabbits (79, 116, 197), can be readily immunized by the injection of minute doses of the specific capsular polysaccharide; however, larger doses not only fail to immunize but produce a refractory state described by Felton as "immunogenic paralysis." A slow accumulation of pneumococcal polysaccharides in the tissues of man occurs with age and could account in part for the increasing susceptibility of the very old to pneumococcal pneumonia (87).

The development of pneumococcal pneumonia in man, even with a highly virulent pneumococcus, is a complex process involving a number of known and unknown factors, such as a chilling of the body or infection with the viruses of the common cold. During this preliminary period the pneumococci multiply rapidly and probably are protected from the action of lysozyme (290) and endogenous antibodies by the excessive production of mucus (226, 227). Masses of organisms covered with mucus are then aspirated into one or more lobes of the lungs and initiate a fulminating infection which consolidates the lobes in 24 to 48 hours. The only known toxic substance synthesized by the pneumococcus is an oxygen-labile hemolysin which is not produced in sufficient amount to hemolyze the red cells of the patient but may have some cardiotoxic effect.

The profound prostration of the patient and eventual death from peripheral circulation collapse may be the result of an **allergic reaction** to the nucleoproteins of the pneumococcus. An experimental basis for this hypothesis was laid by the work of Zinsser and Grinnell in 1927 (357) and clinical confirmation supplied by the observations of Finland and others in 1950 (89). Patients with the classical symptoms of pneumonia were treated with ACTH. The symptoms disappeared like magic in 24 to 48 hours, and the patients thought they were well even though the lungs were still consolidated; viable organisms remained in the sputum, and in one instance pneumococci continued to circulate in the blood. Complete recovery occurred without the use of antiserum, sulfonamides, or antibiotics.

Streptococcal Diseases. *Streptococcus pyogenes* is a gram-positive coccus with a capsule which functions as a defensive weapon, a number of exotoxins which function as offensive weapons, and a number of nontoxic metabolic products which assist the organism in its invasion of the body. The characteristic skin rash of scarlet fever is satisfactorily explained by the erythrogenic exotoxin synthesized by certain strains of group A hemolytic streptococci, but the mechanism by which most of the other infections are achieved, including rheumatic fever, remains obscure.

These cocci are primary pathogens of man and are passed from individual to individual through the air and by physical contact. The M protein, which determines the type specificity, occupies a superficial position on the capsule and this antigen alone, or in cooperation with hyaluronic acid in the capsule, protects the streptococci from phagocytosis (214). Streptolysins, which are also leukocidins, proteinase, hyaluronidase, and streptokinase all aid the organism in its invasion. After infection has been established, the reaction between the cocci and the tissues of the host produces another substance described by Schwab and Watson (279) as a **tissue thromboplastin** which increases the virulence of the organism. This substance may be identical with the **necrosin** previously described by Menkin (206).

A variety of antigenic materials are introduced into the body of the host when the cocci invade and the host responds by making specific antibodies to each. At least five different antibodies have been detected in the serums of patients convalescing from scarlet fever and seven in patients with rheumatic fever (112). The significance or usefulness of these antibodies remains unknown. In the rheumatic fever complication of streptococcal infections, far from being immune, the individual remains susceptible to repeated attacks with each new exposure to streptococci. A bacterial type of allergy is suspected in rheumatic fever either to some

product of the streptococcus or to some tissue component changed by streptococcal toxin to an antigen for the patient.

Typhoid Fever. *Salmonella typhosa* produces a type of infection in which the **somatic antigen which is essential for virulence is an endotoxin**.

This organism is taken into the body through the intestinal tract in food or water but may be killed by the acid gastric juice and its enzymes. After passing the barrier, the Vi surface antigen affords some protection against lysozyme, phagocytosis, and antibodies specific for the O antigen. The bacilli invade tissue cells and multiply in their cytoplasm, after which they invade the blood stream and often maintain a bacteremia for two to three weeks.

The patient becomes profoundly intoxicated from the somatic antigen liberated from the bacilli. The host responds by producing both anti-Vi antibodies and antisomatic antibodies which, with the aid of complement, lyse the organisms. Since these antibodies, however, cannot neutralize the liberated endotoxin the patient remains intoxicated and may even become worse as a result of the operation of this mechanism of immunity. If the patient survives for four to eight weeks, recovery ensues and a relatively permanent immunity is established.

It has been assumed that the intracellular habitat of *S. typhosa* gives it protection against both specific antibodies and from antibiotics which are effective in eliminating the organism from the extracellular spaces. It has been assumed, also, that L forms of *S. typhosa* develop in the cytoplasm of cells, and this form of the organism is known to be resistant to antibiotics. However, the studies of Showacre, Smadel, and their associates (286) with tissue cultures have shown that both extra- and intracellular organisms stopped dividing simultaneously when streptomycin, chloramphenicol, penicillin, in large doses, and synnemantin were added to the cultures. Penicillin and synnemantin induced spheroplasts in extracellular bacilli but not in those located within healthy cells. Intracellular spheroplasts did form in dying cells and in cells damaged by saponin; and healthy cells could phagocytize spheroplasts formed extracellularly. The persistence of *S. typhosa* in the tissues for a period of weeks, even after specific antibodies have been formed and antibiotics have been administered, apparently depends upon the very small number of nondividing or stationary phase organisms which are located within cells (286). The stationary phase or dormant bacilli are not killed by the antibiotics, and these cells are protected from the circulating antibodies by the tissue cell wall (192). Nevertheless, they are eliminated in time if antibodies continue to circulate and an antibiotic treatment is continued. Recovery apparently results from the development of an acquired ability of the tissue cells themselves to destroy the invading bacilli. This type of immunity depends upon stimulating the cells by living bacilli (210). Monocytes from immunized animals will destroy the bacilli without the addition of serum antibodies and can transfer immunity after being transferred to other animals of the same species (270). Under some conditions the plasma itself may aid in the destruction of bacteria by a nonspecific mechanism. Jenkins and Benacerraf (150) observed that plasma from mice infected with BCG tubercle bacilli and stimulated with endotoxin would assist in some unknown manner the destruction of phagocytized *Salmonella* which would grow in the macrophages from normal mice.

The series of experiments by Gaines and his associates (100) have shown that chimpanzees can be effectively immunized with either acetone-killed or heat-killed organisms if preserved with phenol. However, purified O antigen did not protect, although some protection was afforded by purified Vi antigen.

The disease can be shortened by treatment with chloramphenicol and other antibiotics, but not suddenly and dramatically, because of the continuing intoxication by the liberated endotoxins. Allergy to the somatic protein antigen may develop during the course of the disease, and this adds to the total intoxication of the patient. The allergic part of the syndrome can be controlled by the use of cortisone (294, 347).

Cholera. *Vibrio comma,* which causes cholera, resembles the *Salmonella* and *Shigella* organisms in having a somatic antigen, which is an endotoxin. This vibrio, which is a primary pathogen of man, neither invades the blood stream nor invades deeply into the intestinal tissues. The chief offensive weapons of this organism seem to be (1) a mucinase, discovered by Burnet and Stone (43), which causes a shredding of the intestinal mucosa and (2) a phospholipid substance, found by Burrows and his associates (45), which increases the permeability of the intestinal membranes to water and electrolytes. Profound dehydration usually kills the patient but adequate replacement of water and electrolytes will reduce the mortality from the usual 50 to 70 per cent to 5 per cent (250).

Antibodies called "copraantibodies" (46) are manufactured by cells in the intestinal tract and appear in the feces several days before the classical antisomatic antibodies are found in the serum. Specific antibodies to the mucinase are produced and a protective substance, which may not be an antibody, appears in the serum and neutralizes the toxic phospholipid. The body as a whole is not properly stimulated to produce lasting immunity. Vaccines give some immunity but must be repeated at least every six months.

Plague. *Pasteurella pestis* is primarily a disease of certain types of rodents, particularly rats and squirrels. Man is a terminal host for the bubonic form of the disease but becomes a transmitting host in the pneumonic type. Virulent strains have a well-developed protein capsule or envelope and, beneath that, a molecular layer of polysaccharides (47). The body of the bacillus contains a toxin (58) which kills by producing necrosis of cells and hemorrhages into the tissues. Antibodies are produced against the polysaccharides, but they are not protective. The avirulent strains have the same amount of toxin in the bodies of the organisms as the virulent ones, however; the lack of virulence depends upon the inability of the organism to survive and multiply in the body of the host.

The protein envelope acts as a defensive weapon preventing phagocytosis and allowing the organism to multiply until enough toxic protein has accumulated to kill the host. Specific antienvelope antibodies are produced by the infected animal, which permits phagocytosis and destruction of the organism. If they are not formed soon enough, or in large enough amounts, however, the animal dies from the accumulated endotoxin. If treatment with antibiotics is delayed, the animal or patient dies from the accumulated toxin, even though the organisms are all killed (189).

There are four known independent virulence factors for *Past. pestis*: (1) protein envelope antigen, (2) a somatic antigen which is a toxin, (3) Vw antigens which occur in organisms which do not have envelope antigens (50), and (4) pesticins I and II (36). A virulent strain can be recognized by its (a) purine independence, (b) pigmented colony on agar medium containing hemin, (c) protein envelope antigen, and (d) Vw antigens. In addition to these properties virulent strains require Ca^{++} for aerobic growth at 37° C. (124). The recent investigations of Brubaker and Surgalla (36) showed the Vw− avirulent strains are always C^{++} independent, but a Vw+ which was Ca^{++} independent but avirulent was found.

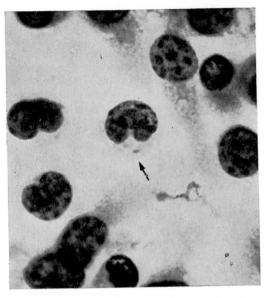

Fig. 1. Monocyte culture infected with *Past. pestis.* A small organism is shown in the centrally located monocyte two hours after infection. (From Cavanaugh and Randall. *J. Immunol.,* 83:348, 1959.)

Bacot and Martin in 1914 (14) found that polymorphonuclear leukocytes from their own blood readily phagocytized and killed phage bacilli from the stomachs of heavily infected fleas, but these leukocytes would not phagocytize bacilli removed from the spleens of rats which had just died of plague. The bacilli from the fleas' stomachs had no capsules, while those from the rats' spleens had well developed capsules. These authors also observed that leukocytes from susceptible animals could readily phagocytize and kill nonencapsulated bacilli up to three to five hours, after which a change occurred and a nonencapsulated but phagocytic resistant form (R) appeared in the tissues of the infected animal.

The production of plague by organisms which should have been avirulent remained a mystery until the studies of Cavanaugh and Randall appeared in 1959 (56). Burrows and Bacon (48, 49) showed that virulent or potentially virulent plague bacilli do occur in three types: (a) phagocytosis-sensitive S type, (b) phagocytosis-resistant R type, and (c) M type, which is rich in Factor I and highly resistant to phagocytosis. Cavanaugh and Randall (56) found that phagocytosis-sensitive S type and virulent *Past. pestis* are phagocytized and killed by polymorphonuclear leukocytes of normal mice and guinea pigs while they multiply in the mono-

cytes of the same animals (Figs. 1, 2). On release from the damaged monocytes the bacilli are found to be encapsulated and are highly resistant to phagocytosis by either neutrophils or monocytes.

The toxin in plague is a protein with a molecular weight of about 74,000 (1). This toxin is a much better antigen than the endotoxins of the gram-negative bacilli but not nearly as good an antigen as the typical exotoxins (329). Antitoxin has been demonstrated in the blood of animals and man after recovery. Ajl and his associates (2) have purified this toxin by continuous paper ionophoresis until only one band was found in gel diffusion studies and the product had an intravenous L.D.$_{50}$ for the mouse of 0.2 μg. Spivack and Karler (304a) used continuous electrochromatography to obtain a product which gave only one band of precipitate and had an L.D.$_{50}$ by intravenous injection of the mouse which ranged from 0.1 to 0.3 μg. With such purified products Packer and his associates (231) found that the plague toxin inhibited the respiration of mitochondria from the toxin-susceptible mouse and rat but not the mitochondria from the toxin-resistant rabbit. Antitoxin produced in rabbits by the injection of purified toxin (329) prevents the death of experimentally infected animals but has not been employed in the treatment of man.

Tularemia. *Pasteurella tularensis* is primarily a disease of wild rodents, particularly rabbits. Man is infected by the introduction of the

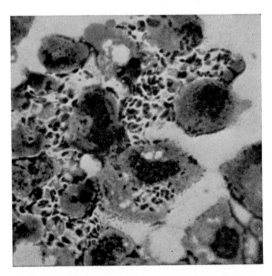

Fig. 2. Encapsulated S-type *Past. pestis* with the cytoplasm of monocytes after 48 hours of incubation. (From Cavanaugh and Randall. *J. Immunol.,* 83:348, 1959.)

organism into a cut or scratch or by the bite of an insect which has fed on an infected animal. The organism has no visible capsule but does have a specific antigenic polysaccharide which can be employed in the hemagglutinin test. The protein of the organism is toxic, and allergy develops to this protein fraction during the course of the disease.

Flemming and Foshay (92) reported that virulent strains of *Past. tularensis* possessed citrulline uridase while an avirulent strain lacked this enzyme. More recent studies have shown that citrulline uridase negative mutants from a virulent strain may retain the full virulence (200). Weinstein and his associates (332) have found that the rate of pyruvic oxidation was directly related to the virulence of the strain, whereas the endogenous respiration rate was inversely correlated with virulence.

A restudy of the mechanism of immunity in man by Carlisle and Saslaw (54) has emphasized again the lack of correlation between agglutinins, precipitins, hemagglutinins, and properidin levels and the level of clinical immunity. This was shown in a group of human volunteers who were vaccinated with Foshay's phenolized (killed) vaccine or viable attenuated vaccine and then challenged with *Past. tularensis* aerosol.

McCrumb (190) reported in 1957 that patients with clinical tularemia treated within 36 hours of onset with chloramphenicol often relapsed when the drug was withdrawn while those treated with streptomycin did not relapse. These observations were confirmed in a larger series of laboratory acquired tularemia by Vosti and his associates (325). The latter workers also found that four to six antigen-antibody lines appear in the sera of the convalescent patient. The presence of line D seemed to be correlated with immunity. If this line did not appear, the patients were subject to spontaneous relapse or, if no relapse occurred, were theoretically subject to reinfection.

In the animal studies by Allen (4) the white cells of the spleen and peritoneum of immunized mice could passively transfer immunity to other mice, but this could not be accomplished with serum from the immunized animal.

Animals can be immunized with living attenuated organisms and even dead organisms. Agglutinins and other classical antibodies are present in the blood of the convalescent and immunized animals, but there is a reason to question the effectiveness of these antibodies, because patients with very high antibody titers succumb to the disease. In 1954 Larson and his associates (170) prepared a soluble antigen which effectively immunized mice without stimulating the formation of classical antibodies.

Anthrax. Anthrax is primarily a disease of herbivorous animals but is transferred to man in a sporadic manner. Originally it was believed to be the simplest of all infections, since the enormous number of organisms in the blood were assumed to kill by blocking the circulation to certain vital organs. Intensive work with this organism since the beginning of World War II by the investigators at Fort Detrick (69, 330, 351), and by Gladstone and his associates in England (105) has revealed that the mechanism of infection is extraordinarily complex and not the same for all species of susceptible animals.

In certain respects the anthrax bacillus resembles the pneumococcus, since it has a capsule which functions as a defensive weapon. But here the similarity ends and the differences begin to appear. The capsule is not a polysaccharide but a polypeptide composed of 100 d (−) glutamic units. The capsular substance does not act by neutralizing antibodies but by neutralizing a natural bactericidal property of the tissues which has been identified as a polypeptide with a high lysine content (330). The capsular material acts as an aggressin and facilitates the invasion of the host. In naturally immune species, such as the rat, dog, and swine, the spores germinate, capsules are synthesized, and multiplication occurs for about 12 hours. About this time the tissue polypeptides are mobilized, the capsules disappear, and the organisms degenerate, with phagocytosis playing an insignificant role (Figs. 3, 4). The same sequence of events occurs in a naturally susceptible species which has been artificially immunized.

The capsular polypeptide, like the pneumococcal polysaccharide, stimulates the production of specific antibodies. These anticapsular antibodies are protective for the mouse and will protect normal mice by passive transfer, but they afford no protection whatsoever for guinea pigs, rabbits, and sheep.

Although neither the capsular polypeptide nor somatic proteins are toxic, a toxin is produced by the growth of the organism in the tissues of a susceptible animal. Cromartie and his associates (69) extracted this toxin from the edematous fluid of an infected animal and showed that it produced edema, fragmentation of collagen, hemorrhage, and cellular infiltration when injected into a normal animal. Furthermore, this edema fluid induces a solid active immunity in guinea pigs, rabbits, and sheep. A race began to see who could induce a culture

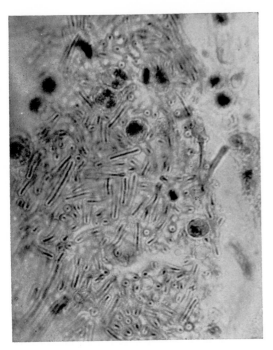

Fig. 3. Photomicrograph of encapsulated *B. anthracis* organisms in the skin of a nonimmunized rabbit 12 hours after injection of spores. Note the almost complete absence of white blood cells. (Giemsa stain. × 1,600.) (From Cromartie, Watson, Bloom, and Heckly. *J. Infect. Dis.*, 80:14, 1947.)

since it is composed of at least three components with distinct biologic activity. Two of the components which are absorbed from crude toxin by fritted glass filters are unrelated to the protective antigen. But one factor, when combined with the protective antigen, kills rats and mice but does not produce cutaneous edema in the guinea pig. The second component, along with the protective antigen, produces cutaneous edema in the guinea pig but is not lethal for rats and mice. The separation of these three components was accomplished independently and simultaneously by two groups of workers, Beal and his associates (19) at Fort Detrick and Stanley and Smith (307) in England.

Another characteristic of the intoxication caused by anthrax infections, and by the injection of crude toxins, is the immediate development of a marked alkaline phosphatemia. This was assumed to be the result of lecithinase, which is a known product of anthrax and related organisms. However, careful fractionation of anthrax toxin by Slein and Logan (293) and of *B. cereus* toxin by Molnar (212) has

of the anthrax bacillus to synthesize the "immunizing antigen" in the test tube. The first lap was won in 1946 by Gladstone (105), who found that an immunizing filtrate factor was produced in a complete medium containing serum. The job was continued by Wright and his associates (351), who have obtained a heat-labile filtrate factor from organisms growing in a synthetic medium. An alum precipitate of the active material produced solid active immunity when injected in rabbits, guinea pigs, and monkeys. Fifty-five human volunteers have received injections of this material but their immunity has not been challenged (351).

The alum precipitation factor has had extensive tests in cattle (149). This immunizing agent is completely harmless as compared to a few deaths from SH-15 spore vaccine (163), and Carbazoo-R nonencapsulated spore vaccine. Protection from the immunizing agent was excellent at one month, but 48 per cent of the cows died of anthrax when infected after three and one-half months (149).

The anthrax toxin is extremely complex,

Fig. 4. Photomicrograph of *B. anthracis* organisms in the skin of a rat 12 hours after the injection of a sublethal dose of spores. Note the presence of necrotic leukocytes and the absence of capsules. (Giemsa stain. × 1,600.) (From Cromartie, Bloom, and Watson. *J. Infect. Dis.*, 80:1, 1947.)

shown that the phosphatemia is not the result of lecithinase but of some unknown factor which withdraws phosphate from the bones.

An understanding of the actual immunizing agent in anthrax has been materially advanced by the studies of Klein and his associates (163), who devised an index of immunity for the guinea pig with which they could measure more accurately the effect of various immunizing agents. With this method they found that the injection of an attenuated but living vaccine increased the immunity by 10 to 15 times. The protective antigen alone increased the immunization 100-fold while a combination of protective antigen and living attenuated vaccine increased the immunity by a factor of 100,000,000.

Tuberculosis. *Mycobacterium tuberculosis* is an important cause of death in this country and almost certainly the chief cause of death in the world at the present time. It is somewhat ironic that 75 years of study by bacteriologists has not revealed the mechanism by which the bacillus invades the body. These organisms possess neither endotoxins nor exotoxins and fail to produce detectable toxin substances while growing in the tissues (248). The nearest approach to toxin is the water-soluble "cord-factor" which accumulates at the bacterial surface of virulent strains when these are grown in aqueous media. This substance, which can be removed with organic solvents without killing the bacilli, appears to be an ester, with a molecular weight of about 1,500, which yields a mycolic acid with alkaline hydrolysis (27). Doses in the range of 1 to 10 μg. per mouse seem to accelerate the disease and increase the death rate.

Virulent bacilli have no resistance to phagocytosis and grow readily in the cytoplasm of living monocytes for many days without any apparent injury to the cell. Eventually, however, these bacillus-packed monocytes do die, but it is not known if death results from the slow accumulation of some type of toxin, from an allergic reaction to tuberculoprotein, or from interference with some vital metabolic process of the monocyte. Cells from allergic animals grown in tissue cultures are readily killed by doses of tuberculin which are harmless to the cells of normal animals (252).

Some type of relative immunity does develop after a period of weeks, as shown by the rather sudden disappearance of many but not all of the bacilli from the tissues. Although antibodies of the classical type can be produced in animals with living bacilli, with whole dead bacilli, and with several antigenic fractions of the bacilli, there is no evidence that these antibodies have a protective action (246, 247, 248). In contrast to these negative experiments, the monocytes from partially immune animals have acquired the ability to destroy tubercle bacilli, in the absence of serum, from the same animal. This was demonstrated by Lurie (181), who injected monocytes and bacilli into the eyes of rabbits, and by Suter in tissue cultures (311).

Tubercle bacilli are destroyed in areas of caseation without the cooperation of cells of any type (256). Their growth would certainly be slowed by the low oxygen supply in such areas, but actual destruction may depend upon the bacterial effect of basic peptides with high arginine content (75, 76), activated spermine (125, 126), tissue lipids, or other tissue metabolites.

The most dramatic event which follows the introduction of tubercle bacilli into animals or man is the development of allergy to tuberculoprotein. Raffel (248) has shown that the allergy to tuberculoprotein is mediated by the presence of a phospholipid fraction of the bacillus. After the allergic state is established, the injection of a minute amount of tuberculin into a sensitized animal or man produces the symptoms of a severe infection or intoxication, although much larger amounts of tuberculin can be injected into normal animals or man without producing any detectable symptoms. **The constitutional symptoms of tuberculosis are caused primarily if not exclusively by this allergy to tuberculin.** Many other symptoms and signs of disease are the indirect results of the necrotizing effect of the tuberculin reaction in the body, such as pleural and pericardial effusion, cavity formation in the lungs, and pulmonary hemorrhages. It is tragic that these violent reactions play no useful role in the destruction of tubercle bacilli (248, 256).

The symptoms caused by the reaction to the endogenously produced tuberculin in man and animals can be suppressed almost completely by the administration of corticoid hormones, but the progress of the disease is accelerated unless effective chemotherapeutic or antibiotic agents are administered simultaneously (213, 327).

Coccidioidomycosis. *Coccidioides immitis* is a fungus which grows in the soil of certain limited geographic areas of the world. Man and animals are usually infected by breathing dust containing the arthrospores of the organism. Neither exotoxins nor endotoxins have been demonstrated, and nothing is known of the mechanism by which the organism establishes itself in the body.

At least two types of antibodies are produced by the host; the first is measured as a precipitin

and the second by the complement-fixation reaction. There seems to be a correlation between
the presence of the precipitins and immunity but
not between the complement-fixation titer and
immunity (296). The complement-fixing antibodies are apparently made to antigens of the
organism which have nothing to do with the
virulence of the organism, but they are a measure of the extent of the infection and usually
are highest in titer the day before death. They
are, however, of great prognostic significance,
since the titers drop with improvement and disappear after recovery. Complement-fixing antibodies behave in an analogous manner in histoplasmosis and blastomycosis. A tuberculin-
like allergy develops in all three of these fungus
infections.

Typhus Fever. Typhus fever is acquired by
man from the bite of an infected human body
louse or the bite of an infected rat flea. *Rickettsia prowazekii* and *Rickettsia typhi* are obligate
intracellular parasites. Partial starvation, certain vitamin deficiencies, or other conditions
which interfere with the optimal nutrition of the
cells of the body increase the susceptibility of
the host to infection with rickettsias (91, 241).

An endotoxin is produced by these rickettsias
when growing in the embryonated chicken egg.
This endotoxin will kill animals but is neutralized by antiserum from convalescent patients
and animals (119).

The organism synthesizes a glutaminase
(153), but it is doubtful if this aids infection.
The humoral immunity to typhus is solid and
usually lasts for the life of the individual. In
rare instances a mild form of the disease recurs
in the patient many years after the first infection and under conditions where a new infection would be impossible. This recurrent type
of disease is known as Brill's disease or Brill-
Zinsser disease. Zinsser (358) suggested in 1934
that both the solid immunity and the occasional
recurrence resulted from the persistence of the
organism in the body. His theory has been confirmed by the isolation of rickettsias from patients with Brill-Zinsser disease (217).

Influenza. The virus of influenza is extraordinarily mutable, with new antigenic types appearing every few years. Furthermore, the duration of effective immunity is less than one
year. This combination of new types and brief
immunity results in an almost continuous circulation of the infection in the general population but with epidemic peaks every two to
three years. Fortunately, the disease has had a
relatively low mortality since 1918.

This virus is a little over 100 mμ. in diameter and contains a soluble antigen, called the

S antigen, which is about 10 mμ. The S antigen, probably a protein, is found in all types
of influenza virus, and stimulates the formation
of antibodies which can be measured with the
complement-fixation method but has no protective effect. A second fraction of the virus
is an enzyme-like material which causes agglutination of chicken and human red blood
cells. This factor is antigenic and stimulates
antibodies which inhibit the hemagglutination
reaction. The third antigen is associated with
the viral body and stimulates the formation of
antibodies which will neutralize the virus in
vitro, fix complement, and protect animals in
passive transfer experiment. The bodies of the
virus contain a toxin which kills animals, if
given in sufficiently large doses, even when the
virus has been inactivated with heat or chemicals.

Burnet (44) visualizes the mechanism of the
infection as occurring in a series of steps. The
active enzymatic groups are on the surface of
the virus, and these must neutralize the inhibiting effect of the mucopolysaccharides of the
saliva and bronchial mucus (6) before the
virus can attach itself to specific receptors on
the surface of the cells. After adsorption the
virus enters the cell and presumably multiplies
in the one-step pattern characteristic of the
bacteriophages. Thus a new crop of virus particles bursts from the cells every five to six
hours for the type A virus and every nine to
ten hours for the type B virus (35). The symptoms increase in severity as more and more
cells are infected and larger and larger amounts
of toxin-containing viruses become available
until enough specific antibodies are produced
to stop the spread of the virus from cell to cell.

The epidemiologic and serologic studies of
Hennessy, Davenport, and Frances (71, 120)
have demonstrated some unexpected aspects of
humoral immunity to influenza viruses. The
first type of virus to infect a particular individual leaves a lasting impression on the immune
mechanism even though the measurable antibodies and effective immunity disappear. Infection with a second or third type of virus
stimulates its own specific antibodies but produces an even greater quantity of antibodies to
the type which caused the original infection.

Poliomyelitis. The virus of poliomyelitis is
quite small, having a diameter of only 27 mμ.,
but, like all viruses, is complex biochemically.
There are three distinct antigenic types, with
little, if any, cross-immunity between them, although treatment with formalin uncovers a
common ancestral antigen which gives cross-
reactions with the complement-fixation test

(25). The only suggestion of toxin production is the ability of chick adapted strains to kill the embryo (51). The polio virus is composed of RNA and a protein but without lipids and carbohydrates except for that occurring in the nucleic acid. The RNA can infect cells in tissue culture, which can in turn synthesize the new RNA surrounded by its specific protein (3, 66).

Poliomyelitis is almost as contagious as measles and infects an entire family or other closed group even more rapidly than measles (136, 137). The virus multiplies in the nasopharynx and small intestine and then invades the blood stream. Paralysis may occur when the virus reaches the central nervous system either by way of the blood or by passing along the nerve trunks. A large percentage of those infected remain intestinal carriers for some months and thus provide a human reservoir of infection. Fortunately, from 90 to 95 per cent of the infections are subclinical (137) but, unfortunately, nonimmune adults are more prone to develop paralytic disease than children.

Subclinical, abortive, and clinical cases all establish a relative permanent immunity. This is not a tissue cell immunity, since Enders and his associates (82) have shown that a wide variety of human cells from presumably immune adults when grown in tissue culture support a luxuriant growth of the virus. Protective antibodies seem to be present in equal amounts in both beta and gamma globulins (230). The degree of immunity in monkeys and men is not always parallel to the amount of protective antibodies present in the serum. This suggests that minute or even undetectable amounts of antibodies may protect it or may implicate another nonhumoral type of immunity, as suggested by Bachtold and his associates (12). The nonhumoral type of immunity might indeed be the new substance called "interferon" by Isaacs and his associates (145, 146).

Theiler's Encephalomyelitis Virus. This virus of rodents illustrates the dependence of viruses on cellular metabolism. Rafelson, Pearson, and their associates (244, 245) found that lysine and histidine inhibited the multiplication of the virus. The virus in turn inhibited the incorporation of glucose into the building-up of those two amino acids in the cell.

Viruses to Vaccines. Very slight but genetically controlled changes in the metabolism of a virus may determine whether it will act as a killer or an immunizing vaccine (165). The virulent yellow fever virus grows well in the visceral organs of monkeys but not in brain tissue. Theiler (318) adapted the yellow fever virus to brain tissue, after which it grew better in the brain than in visceral organs. The neurotropic virus, when injected parenterally, could infect but could not produce a progressive disease. Its antigenicity was unaltered, as shown by the immunity which developed in the vaccinated animals (319). Other examples of the changes which occur when "viruses" are changed into "vaccines" have been discussed by Habel (110) and Lwoff (185).

RESISTANCE

It is customary to divide immunity into two main classes: natural or innate immunity and acquired immunity. Acquired immunity is subdivided into natural and artificial, active and passive, as shown in Table 1.

Natural or Innate Immunity. The term "innate immunity" is used to indicate resistant mechanisms which are not acquired during the lifetime of an individual and, therefore, are concerned with species, race, and genetically controlled biochemical and biologic reactions in the living body. Although our knowledge of the mechanism of this basic immunity is fragmentary, the importance cannot be overemphasized (9, 321). Not only is this the explanation for resistance to the nonpathogenic microorganisms, but it forms the foundation for acquired immunity to the pathogenic organisms (182). Vaccines, antibodies, and antibiotics may fail to produce the expected cures when something has gone wrong with the basic mechanism of defense.

A large part of the available information about the various means of defense has been obtained by experiments in animals in which one or another of these mechanisms has been deliberately altered. Nature not infrequently performs such experiments in man, which we fail to interpret because of our limited knowledge.

Mechanical Barriers against Infection. The intact skin and mucous membranes of the body afford effective protection against nonpathogenic organisms and considerable protection against pathogens. Certain bactericidal and fungicidal fatty acids in the sebaceous secretions of the skin afford additional protection. The natural flow of tears, saliva, and urine remove bacteria mechanically, but these secretions also contain bactericidal substances such as lysozyme. Nasal secretions, saliva, and sputum from normal individuals contain mucopolysaccharides capable of inhibiting the agglutinations of human red blood cells by the influenza virus (6) and presumably afford considerable nonspecific protection against this virus.

The thin film of mucus which covers the surface epithelium of the respiratory tract, from the nares to the terminal bronchioles, traps bacteria, fungi, and viruses, after which they are swept by the cilia from the upper respiratory tract into the esophagus and from the lower respiratory tract up to the mouth, where they are swallowed. In most instances the gastric juices complete the destruction of the trapped organism. The cough reflex is a supplemental mechanism designed to dislodge larger accumulations of mucus and foreign material from the bronchi (226, 227).

Temperature. Temperature is an important factor in the survival and multiplication of microorganisms in the body and may explain some instances of species immunity to known pathogens. Pasteur made the first observation of this type when he showed that hens, which are normally immune to anthrax, could be infected if their temperature is lowered to the mammalian range. Tubercle bacilli, pathogenic for mammalian species, will not infect cold-blooded animals, while tubercle bacilli from frogs, snakes, fish, etc., fail to infect the warm-blooded mammals. *Mycobacterium ulcerans* isolated by MacCallum of Australia has a restrictive pathogenicity apparently imposed by temperature (194). This organism grows readily at room temperature but will not grow at 37° C. It produces ulcers limited to the skin and subcutaneous tissue of man and when injected into mice multiplies only in the tips of the ears and tail.

Bisset (24) isolated a gram-negative bacillus from the tissues of healthy fish. The organism was alive but did not multiply when the fish were kept at 10° C. When the temperature of the water was raised to 20° C., the bacilli began to multiply, causing a reaction on the part of the host, and in some instances antibodies were produced which killed the organisms. The lizard (83, 84) and the frog (167), as well as the fish, can synthesize antibodies when the temperature is in the range of 25° to 35° C.

Temperature-dependent pneumococcal infections have been studied in some detail. Pasteur (234) recorded in 1881 that the pneumococci which he had isolated from human saliva would kill rabbits but not domestic fowl. These findings were confirmed in some detail by Strouse (309) in 1909, who found that the pigeon's resistance to pneumococci depended upon the bird's temperature at 41.5° C. Bull and McKee (41, 42) reported in 1921 that fowl serum would passively protect mice and guinea pigs against virulent pneumococci and that the protection was type specific. Kelley (157) found that swine serum resembled chicken serum in its ability to destroy pneumococci by passive transfer. A restudy of fowl serum by

Table 1. Classification of Immunity

(After Prof. Andrés Soriano)

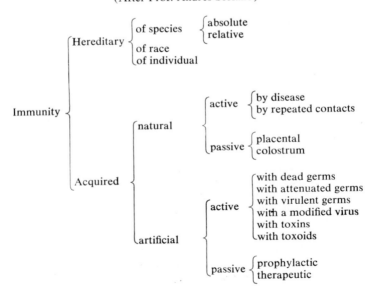

Andrews and McKinnon in 1961 (7) showed that there was a bactericidal effect of the serum which was independent of temperature. The serum from chicken protected mice at the normal lower temperature of this mammal. The serum was not lytic in vitro for pneumococci, but pneumococci, when injected into the skin of chickens, changed from gram-positive to gram-negative in a two- to three-hour period and disappeared in 24 hours without any evidence of agglutination or phagocytosis. This protective factor was not present when the chicks were hatched, since three-hour-old chicks died when infected with pneumococci. About 50 per cent of the maximal protective power of the serum of the adult bird was present four to five days after birth or long before evidence of humoral antibody protection was detectable. The protective substance was concentrated in the beta globulin fraction of the serum.

The temperature dependence of type III pneumococci in the rabbit is well known. In 1936 Enders, Shaffer, and their associates (81) and Rich and McKee (253) reported simultaneously that type III pneumococci which could not grow in culture at 41° C. would not kill rabbits who normally had this or a higher temperature. Muschenheim and his coworkers (220) did the reverse experiment in 1943, which produced fatal infections in rabbits with type III pneumococci by reducing the temperature of the rabbit either mechanically in a cold room or by dosing with barbiturates.

The lesions of leprosy in man may be to some degree temperature-dependent (21), since the destructive lesions occur on the cooler parts of the body, such as the skin, nose and buccal mucosa, pharynx, and larynx, but not in the lungs, liver, spleen, or gastrointestinal tract. Lesions are frequent in the testes but almost unknown in the ovary. Sheppard (285) in 1960 succeeded in infecting the foot pad of mice with leprosy bacilli from man and found the generation time was 0.9 months.

Gonococci are readily killed at a temperature of 40° to 41° C., and gonococcal arthritis was treated routinely with "fever therapy" before the introduction of sulfonamides and antibiotics. The virulence of viruses may be temperature-dependent. A mutant may be selected which is either more or less virulent for the original host. In 1925 Armstrong (8) selected vaccine virus particles which were resistant to 37.5° C. and passed them repeatedly in the testicles of rabbits. This new strain became much more virulent for rabbits and would produce fatal viral pneumonia, although the original strain would not infect the lungs of rabbits. The living polio vaccines now in use were derived by selecting mutant strains which would grow at 39° C. but not at 40° or 41° C.

Fever is basically a protective but complex mechanism which depresses the invading organism but also stimulates antibody production, phagocytosis, and possibly other systems in the host.

The oxygen tension in the tissue may be too high or too low for the multiplication of certain pathogens. The exotoxin-producing clostridia cannot survive in normal well-oxygenated tissues. Dogs normally carry certain of these organisms in their intestinal tract, from whence they gain access to the blood from time to time but do not produce infection unless an area of low oxygen concentration is produced by trauma or some other means. Such a mild procedure as maintaining a tourniquet on one limb for a number of hours may result in the development of gas gangrene in that limb (10).

In contrast to these obligate anaerobes, the tubercle bacillus is an obligate aerobe which grows best in the well-oxygenated lungs and poorest in the liver and other internal organs. Animals experimentally infected with tubercle bacilli and kept in an atmosphere with a low oxygen content showed less progression of the disease than the controls (255).

Essential Metabolites. The presence or absence of or an imbalance in certain essential metabolites may determine the pathogenicity of a particular organism. The importance of the presence or absence of a particular essential metabolite has been demonstrated for certain infections in plants and in experimental animals. Lewis (176) and Dubos (75) have emphasized the necessity of a proper balance between the biochemical factors to prevent disease (348).

Woolley's (350) studies on the "toxin" of *Pseudomonas tabaci,* which causes necrotic spots on the leaf of tobacco plants, reveal some of the complexities of biochemical reactions in disease. The organism synthesizes a new amino acid, tabotoxinine, which acts as an analog of methionine, thus **depriving the living cells of methionine and inducing a deficiency necrosis rather than a toxic necrosis.**

A study of experimental malaria in rats and monkeys revealed that a deficiency of p-aminobenzoic acid prevented the development of the parasite. The diet employed was milk, which apparently supplied enough PABA for the animal but not enough for the parasite. When PABA was added to the milk, malaria developed in the animals. The well-known relative immunity of infants to malaria can now be explained as a deficiency of an essential metabolite for the parasite in the infant's diet of milk (114). Certain mutants of *Salmonella typhosa* and *Klebsiella pneumoniae* requiring purines or PABA for growth in the tissues will not produce disease in mice unless proper amounts of these metabolites are injected into the animal (13, 101). The mutants mentioned above were obtained from laboratory strains of organisms, but Formal and his associates (94) have isolated from the stools of a human carrier a spontaneously occurring mutant of *S. typhosa* which requires xanthine for virulence. A back mutation in the laboratory to xanthine independence restored the virulence of the strain. These observations suggest that mutations which increase virulence as well as those which reduce it may be occurring spontaneously in nature from time to time.

The survival time for mice infected with *S. typhimurium* is shortened by treating the animals with substances which poison the Kreb's cycle or by creating an imbalance of metabolites by daily injections of citrate or succinate (22, 23). Organisms apparently dead after treatment with heat, chlorine H_2O_2, or ethyl alcohol can be restored to viability by incubation with various metabolites of the tricarboxylic acid cycle (118).

Tissue Metabolites with Bactericidal Properties. These substances play an ill defined but important role in protecting the body against invasion by microorganisms (226, 292).

A number of investigators, between 1885 and 1900, demonstrated the existence of antimicrobial substances in blood, leukocytes, and lymphatic tissues. Subsequent works have shown that these fell into several large classes. These were: I, opsonins or complement; II, normal antibodies; and III, tissue metabolites with bactericidal properties. The role of complement has been discussed in Chapter 13, and normal antibodies will be discussed later.

Lysozyme was discovered by Flemming in 1922 and is present in many tissues and body fluids. It acts on both gram-positive and gram-negative organisms (23, 225). This enzyme hydrolyzes the acetylamino polysaccharide constituent of bacterial membranes (74) and kills the cell (Fig. 5 C). Lysozyme is present in high concentration in granulocytes and is released in an active form by minor injury to the cells (122, 160, 161, 162). Its activity is inhibited by mucin, polysaccharide acids from encapsulated organisms, heparin, and the Vi antigen of *S. typhosa* (29, 290). Under certain conditions lysozyme is inactivated by heparin and citrate and potentiated by calcium (73). Lysozyme is

most effective for a wide variety of organisms when acting in cooperation with minimal subeffective doses of natural antibodies (328).

Nucleins, Histones, and Protamines. These bactericidal substances, which have been known since the end of the last century, have been reviewed by Skarnes and Watson (292). The basic nature of the histones and protamines is well established. The histones possess large amounts of the two basic amino acids, lysine and arginine (68), whereas the protamines contain large concentrations of arginine and are usually low in lysine (166). The importance of histones in the destruction of bacteria in the animal body has been studied in detail by Spitznagel (304), who used differential staining technics.

Basic Peptides of Tissues. Early in World War II investigators at Camp Dietrick were directed to the tissue components present in the rat but not in the rabbit, which would determine the fate of virulent anthrax organisms when injected into tissues (Fig. 4). Bloom and his associates (28) extracted a nondialyzable substance from the thymus, pancreas, and caecum of various species which would kill virulent anthrax bacilli. The antibacterial thymus peptide contained little arginine but 29 per cent lysine. It was active against *B. anthracis*, *B. subtilis*, *S. aureus*, *S. hemolyticus*, *E. coli*, and certain viruses (330). A synthetic polylysine was four times as active as the naturally occurring one, suggesting that the lysine was the essential reactant. Dubos and Hirsch (75, 125, 126, 127) isolated a second basic peptide which was active against the tubercle bacillus. This substance was low in lysine and high in arginine. This material called **spermine** occurs in many tissues of man and animals and can kill tubercle bacilli in the test tube after activation by spermadine oxidase (125). Proof of the effectiveness of spermine in the animal body is lacking, but it is interesting that the guinea pig kidney, which contains spermine oxidase, is much more resistant to infection with the tubercle bacillus than the rabbit kidney, which lacks this enzyme (75).

Several investigators (292) have suggested that three basic peptides combine with nucleoproteins and other negatively charged surface constituents of bacteria and viruses, thus disrupting important cell functions. The union is believed to occur through electrostatic bonding. The neutralizing effect of nucleic acid and long-chain polysaccharides offers indirect evidence that the basic molecular substances produce their deleterious effect in man by reactions with the nucleoproteins of the cells.

Beta-Lysin, Myrvik-Weiser Factor and Leukins. A heat-stable bactericidal factor was recognized in serum as early as 1887 but the name beta-lysine was given it by Pettersson in 1936 (238). This factor withstood dialysis and extraction with fat solvents and required a temperature of 64° to 75° C. for 30 minutes for inactivation. In contrast to alexin and complement, its action was directed primarily against gram-positive organisms.

The Myrvik-Weiser factor is easily separated from lysozyme, as shown in Figure 5 B and C (221, 222, 223) and by lysozyme reactivation, although both may be inactivated by heparin and citrate and activated by calcium (73). Later work by Myrvik and his associates (224) revealed that two nondialiazible components were needed as cofactors. The component I is present normally in high titers in rabbit serum and in low titers in human serum but increases in human serum in "acute phase" reactions. Component II is present in moderate amounts in normal human serum and is not increased by "acute phase" reactions. Component I from the rabbit will form a complete bactericidal system with Component II from the rabbit. This

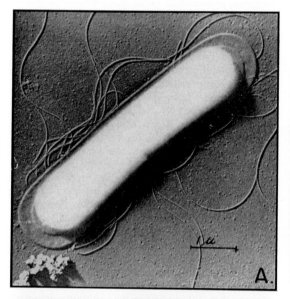

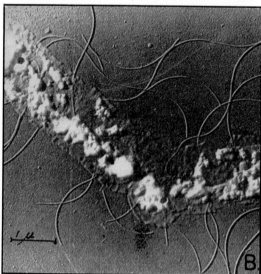

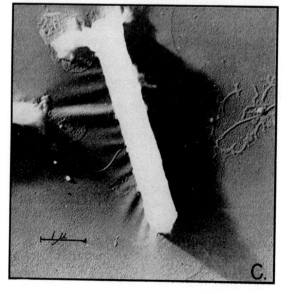

Fig. 5. Electron micrographs of *B. subtilis*. A, normal organism with flagella. B, lysis with natural antibacterial substance. Shows flagella originating from bulbous structure in cell wall. C, lysis of cell wall with lysozyme. (From Myrvik and Weiser. *J. Immunol.*, 74:9, 1955.)

bactericidal system is not transferred from the mother to the fetus (109). Skarnes and Watson (292) suggest that the factor is related or identical to the serum beta lysin of Pettersson. The beta lysin was believed erroneously to have been derived from leukocytes but the source is still undetermined.

Leukins. Hankin (111) in 1891 obtained an anthracidal substance from the lymph nodes of the dog and cat which he called a beta globulin. Schneider (278) in 1909 isolated the active material from leukocytes and contributed the name "leukins." Some confusion occurred later because leukocytes contain at least two bactericidal factors, one being leukins and the other phagocytins (292). Skarnes and Watson (291) isolated a leukin from rabbit polymorphonuclear leukocytes which they assumed came from the nucleus. It was very heat-stabile at acid or neutral pH, surviving 100° C. for two hours, and proved to be active in concentration of 2 to 5 μg. per milliliter in vitro. This leukin contained a large amount of the basic amino acid arginine. Large acidic polymers blocked the activity. Leukin and leukin-like substances have been obtained from the leukocytes of man, rabbit, dog, guinea pig, and rat. Bloom and his associates (30) have reported an inhibiting effect of extract from the mononuclear cell of the rat upon tubercle bacilli.

Phagocytin. Simultaneously in 1894, Buchner in Germany and Denys and Havet in France extracted from leukocytes bactericidal substances which killed gram-negative organisms such as cholera vibrios and typhoid bacilli. Their results were confirmed by Hiss in 1908 (132) and Zinsser in 1910 (356). The series of studies by Hirst (127, 128, 129, 130) and Cohn and Hirsch (65) have characterized this substance, which Hirst named "phagocytin." It kills gram-negative bacteria preferentially but is also active against group A streptococci and staphylococci (130). Phagocytin lacked properdin actively and was only slightly inactivated after two hours at 65° C. at an acid pH. It was not dependent upon divalent ions for its action and had optimal bactericidal effect on the acid side of neutrality. The granules of PMN's contain 70 to 80 per cent of the cellular phagocytin (65).

Lacterin. Lacterin synthesized by the cow and excreted in the milk has a high bactericidal effect on group A hemolytic streptococci (11, 340), but this is as yet no evidence that lacterin is effective after absorption into the body.

Heme compounds are bactericidal for certain gram-positive cocci and bacilli, and Dubos (75) has suggested that they may act as anti-metabolites for certain porphyrins essential for metabolism.

Lipids, organic acids, and CO$_2$, which accumulate in areas of inflammation, may be bactericidal for certain organisms while favoring the growth of others (75).

Colicins, Pyocins, Megacins, and Pesticins. This interesting group of bactericidal substances have been reviewed by Fredericko (96) and Brubaker and Surgalla (37, 38).

Colicins are produced by individual strains of *E. coli* and *Salmonella* and *Shigella*. Nearly 20 different colicins are known, and they are designated in alphabetic order (269). They are antigenic protein-like substances whose biosynthesis is associated with the death of the organisms. They act on related species or on certain specific strains of the same species. The action of these bactericidins is conditioned by the presence of specific receptors.

Pyocin is produced by certain strains of *Pseudomonas aeruginosa*. The O-containing strains of *Salmonella* and *Shigella* are resistant to pyocin but the R mutants are very susceptible. Pyocin is quite different from the more general bactericidal substance known for 50 years as pyocyanin.

Megacin is produced by many strains of *B. megaterium*. It is believed that megacinogeny (148) is due to a highly defective lysogeny which results in a new protein synthesis of a lethal character.

Pesticins are produced by most strains of *Past. pestis* and inhibit the growth of *Past. pseudotuberculosis* and strains of *Past. pestis* which are not pesticin producers (37, 38). It appears that colicinogenic determinants or episomic elements are infective particles which replicate independently within the cytoplasm of bacterial cells and remain integrated units attached to the chromosome (37, 38). Fredericq observed the transfer of colicinogeny in the F$^+$ × F$^-$ system by bacterial conjugation. When F$^+$col$^+$ is the donor, the colicinogeny is transferred to F$^-$col$^-$ recipient (96). He concluded that colicinogeny is not governed by chromosome genes but by cytoplasmic determinants.

INTERFERON

In 1937 Findlay and MacCallum found that monkeys infected with Riff Valley fever virus were protected from the fatal effects of yellow fever virus. This was not an instance of protection by antibodies, because antibodies against Riff Valley fever virus have no effect on the yellow fever virus. This phenomenon was called "virus interference" and was found to be very common when tested in chick embryos and in tissue cultures. In 1943 Werner and Gertrude Henle found that viruses could be killed by gentle heat and by ultraviolet light and still retain their ability to interfere with the growth of other viruses. The third and most important step was made by Isaacs and Lindenmann (144) in 1957, who found that tissue cells infected with influenza virus contained a substance which would inhibit the multiplication of many other types of viruses (Fig. 6). This material was isolated and named "interferon." The active agent is a protein with a molecular weight of 63,000. It is not antigenic when injected into animals unrelated to the one which furnished the cells in which the original virus was grown to make the interferon. The interferon is somewhat more potent when used in the same species, but interferon made from monkey kidney cells is effective when tested on human tissue cells. Isaacs (146) suggests that the function of interferon in normal cells is to help control the synthesis of nucleic acid, and perhaps the control is exercised by regulating the supply of ATP.

Normal cells treated with interferon produced lactic acid more rapidly and in larger amounts than did untreated cells, and at the same time they took up more oxygen. Isaacs (146) suggests that interferon acts by uncoupling oxidation from phosphorylation, giving a reduced supply of ATP. Since it is known that viruses cannot multiply inside a cell unless plentifully supplied with ATP, it would be most desirable to introduce a situation where the cell could make enough ATP for its own needs but not enough to fuel viral synthesis.

Experimental influenza in mice and vaccinal lesions in the skin of rabbits have been cured by treatment with interferon. At the present time the cost of production prevents extensive laboratory or clinical investigations.

THE PROPERDIN SYSTEM

The bactericidal system was reported by Pillemer and his associates in 1954 (168, 173, 239, 240). A globulin with a molecular weight about eight times that of gamma globulin was described as the essential factor. But it was inactive until supplemented by complement and magnesium ions. The possibility that the properdin effect was nothing more than the action of "natural antibodies" was considered but discarded. The weight of evidence, however, has

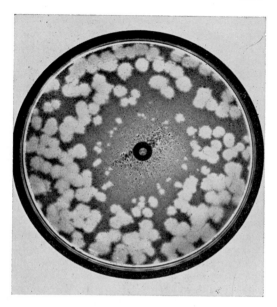

Fig. 6. Inhibition of viruses by interferon in tissue cultures. The clear areas about the periphery of the petri dish show areas of chick cells destroyed by an encephalitis virus. Interferon placed in the tiny cup in the center diffused outward and protected the surrounding cells. (From Isaacs. *Scientific American,* 204:51, 1961.)

swung in favor of the idea that this bactericidal effect of properdin is indeed the effect of natural antibodies in combination with complement, magnesium ions, and possibly lysozyme. This concept is discussed in Chapter 13.

NATURAL ANTIBODIES

The bactericidal activity of serum against gram-negative bacilli was demonstrated by Nuttal in 1888 and Bochner in 1889. Some of this effect was almost certainly determined by the presence of tissue metabolites, as described by Skarnes and Watson (292), but some was mediated by true antibodies. The latter were present in small amounts but reacted with such a variety of bacteria, and usually with increasing numbers as the animal aged, that they were assumed to be the result of a maturing process in the animals and not induced by a specific antigen (339). Heat-stable bactericidal activities which are nonspecific for species and do not require complement may or may not be "natural antibodies." Those which are heat-labile, specific for certain species, and not restored by the addition of fresh guinea pig serum are true antibodies (207, 326).

Natural antibodies can be defined as specific

antibodies for definite species of bacteria, which require the presence of complement for lyses. A lack of specificity was assumed at one time because of the great number of organisms which were lysed by a single serum, but we know now that all animals are indeed stimulated by a great variety of antigens in their food and from bacteria growing in their intestinal tract. This belief is supported by the observation that germ-free animals have fewer kinds of normal antibodies than comparable animals reared on conventional diets and by the curative effect of commercial human gamma globulin in various types of infections which have resisted therapy with antibiotics alone. The specificity of the antibodies can of course be demonstrated in differential absorption studies.

Recent investigations have affirmed the specificity of the antibodies and shown that the quantity which is sufficient to restore bactericidal activity to absorbed serum is exceedingly small (218). Measured by their bactericidal activity, the natural antibodies in the serum of normal guinea pigs, rabbits, and men are directed against the O and R but not Vi antigens (219). In the delicate testing system described by Wardlaw (328) both complement and lysozyme were required.

Normal serum from various mammals is frequently bactericidal for gram-negative bacteria in the absence of demonstrative agglutinins, although antibodies may be detectable by the hemagglutination technic.

Landy, Michael, and Whitby (169) have called attention to certain errors in the methods for assaying these minimal level antibodies and devised a more accurate one. The bactericidal effect of a specific serum is frequently titrated by progressive dilution to determine the smallest quantity of serum which effects a specific reduction in the bactericidal inoculum. In such tests all the necessary components in the serum are diluted simultaneously. Thus the procedure actively measures the particular component which happens to be limiting. Landy and his associates employ a serum containing complement but free of antibodies to the test organisms. The gradual addition of known increments of normal mammalian serum will restore the bactericidal activity to the extent that factor is present in the test serum. This method is much more sensitive than specific precipitation, agglutination, or complement fixation and comparably to that known as "passive hemagglutination," which uses tanned erythrocytes coated with protein antigens, or the tests based on the reaction of lytic antibody and complement.

SPECIFIC ANTIBODY PRODUCTION

The antibody-producing mechanism is another gift of nature which forms a part of the natural endowment of immunity. A large part of Chapter 12 is devoted to the nature and production of specific antibodies. In many instances the survival of the host depends upon the ability of the body to produce antibodies against the antigens of bacteria and viruses which are essential for the virulence of the organism. Not all antibodies are protective; indeed, the "antibodies" responsible for the allergic diseases are harmful. The importance of the antibody-producing mechanism is best illustrated by the variety and severity of infections which develop in the newly discovered syndromes of congenital (40) and acquired agammaglobulinemia (34, 265, 355), where the unfortunate individuals lack the ability to produce certain types of antibodies.

PSEUDO-NATURAL ANTIBODIES

Many investigators have reported the production of antibodies to encapsulated strains of *Bacillus anthracis*. It was assumed that the *d*-glutamyl-polypeptide of the capsule acted as a hapten. A reinvestigation of this problem by Leonard and Thorne (174) leaves open the original question concerning the antigenicity of glutamyl-polypeptide but establishes firmly the fact that some sera from normal animals and rabbit sera from animals immunized with *Sh. flexneri, Past. pestis, Past. tularensis, S. typhosa,* and *B. anthracis* contain nonspecific proteins which precipitated with glutamyl-polypeptide in such a manner that they were readily measured as precipitins in test tubes, as precipitin titers in agar gel, and even as complement-fixing antibodies. Serum lysozyme also reacted with activated polypeptides. The reactions were strongest in aqueous solution and decreased with the increase in concentration of NaCl. Most of the serum proteins which reacted in this manner could be removed by adsorption with benonite.

ADEQUATE PROTEINS AND VITAMINS

Adequate proteins and vitamins are essential for maximum natural defense against bacteria, and deficiencies of proteins and vitamins may reduce the normal resistance to infections with bacteria and rickettsias, but there is some experimental evidence that these same deficiencies may increase the resistance to viral infections. The body cell which serves as host to the virus must be healthy and vigorous (95, 306) to support the multiplication of virus. Protein deficiency may reduce the number and efficiency of the phagocytes (53). A deficiency in vitamins A and C, even when relatively mild but prolonged, seems to increase man's susceptibility to tuberculosis (103, 186, 187). Thiamin deficiency increases the susceptibility of rats to rat leprosy (15) and mice to pneumonia (349). Pantothenic acid deficiency decreases the natural resistance of rats to murine typhus (91) and to bacterial infection (280, 360). Riboflavin deficiency increases the susceptibility of mice to spontaneous salmonella infections (164) and rats to murine typhus (241). Niacin and tryptophan deficiency in dogs results in a fatal infection called "black tongue." In man this deficiency is followed by severe fusospirochetal infection of the mouth and vagina (298). Folic acid deficiency renders monkeys extremely susceptible to infection with group C streptococci (272). Para-aminobenzoic acid, in excessive amounts, increases the resistance of man and animals to rickettsial infections (266, 354), while sulfonamides makes them more susceptible. Vitamin C deficiency in tuberculous guinea pigs resulted in ulceration of the intestinal tract (187). The ulcers did not occur in the control tuberculous animals which received the same diet supplemented by vitamin C, even though the latter died of progressive tuberculosis (187). Dramatic improvement occurred in patients with intestinal tuberculosis who received vitamins A, C, and D (186).

The effect of a deficiency of thiamin, pyrodoxine, and pantothenic acid on the resistance of rats to infection has been investigated by Furness and Axelrod (99), and the effect of riboflavin deficiency by Wertman and Sypherd (337). The results of niacin, tryptophase, pyridoxine, vitamins B 12, folic acid and riboflavin deficiency have been studied by Wertman and his associates (335, 336). With thiamin deficiency in the rat there was a reduction in the total number of peripheral leukocytes, a reduction in granulocytes at the site of infection, and a reduction in complement. There was an apparent reduction in the ability of the phagocyte to ingest *D. pneumoniae.* The reduced resistance seemed to depend upon the reduced cellular migration and the reduced complement activity. An adequate supply of protein for young mice determines their resistance to *Myco. bovis, Myco. fortuitum, Staph. aureus* and *Klebsiella pneumoniae* (77). Dia-

The Effect of a Natural (N) and a Synthetic (S) Diet on Survivorship Following Infection in Nine Different Genetic Circumstances

Pathogen genotype		Host genotype		
		Inbred, selected, resistant	Random-bred (outbred) nonselected	Inbred, selected, susceptible
Uniformly virulent		N-Died / S-Died	N-Died / S-Died	N-Died / S-Died
Mixed virulent and avirulent		N-Survived / S-Survived	N-Survived ↑ Dietary effect / S ↓ Died	N-Died / S-Died
Uniformly avirulent		N-Survived / S-Survived	N-Survived / S-Survived	N-Survived / S-Survived

Fig. 7. The effect of natural and synthetic diet on the survivorship of mice infected with Salmonella under nine different conditions. (From Schneider. In *Biological Foundations of Health Education,* Columbia University Press.)

betes also reduces the number and efficiency of the phagocytes.

The effect of fecal flora of special colonies of rats have been studied by Schaedler and Dubos (274). These animals were more susceptible to infection with *Staphylococcus aureus* and *Klebsiella pneumoniae* but more resistant to death from endotoxins. Another apparent contraindication resulting from alteration in diet has been reported by Schneider and his coworkers (275, 276). A synthetic diet which reduced the susceptibility of mice to acute disseminated encephalomyelitis at the same time made male but not female mice highly susceptible to a fatal infection with a strain of *Pasteurella* which was harmless for animals on an adequate diet. Some unknown factor in raw cabbage, which is not vitamin C, increases the resistance of guinea pigs infected intraperitoneally with *S. typhiminum* (228).

The effect of diets and vitamins and resistance to certain bacterial infections is obvious, but the mechanism is obscure and may be extraordinarily complex (277). For exact work it would be desirable to follow the procedure outlined by Schneider in Figure 7, where the genetic status of both the experimental animal and the infecting organism were known as well as the specific deficiency in diet. Working with a resistant factor found in some samples of wheat, and egg white, Schneider shows the effect of nine variables. When a strain of high virulence was employed, all animals died, regardless of the diet, while all survived when the strain was avirulent. When a deliberate and exact mixed culture of virulent and avirulent organisms was used for the infection, the inbred selective resistant animals survived, while the inbred selective susceptible animals all died, regardless of diet. But random outbred selective animals lived if the diet was natural but died when the diet was synthetic. This is a significant result if it can be applied to man, since he is random bred and is frequently infected with organisms of mixed degree of virulence. Under these conditions, life or death may be determined by some small factor in the diet.

GENETICALLY CONDITIONED NATURAL RESISTANCE

This type of resistance is ultimately the most important factor in innate immunity (88, 142, 331, 333). The increased immunity may manifest itself as resistance to a toxin, resistance to invasions, or in an increased ability to produce antitoxin or bacterial antibodies. Actually all of the mechanisms of natural immunity discussed above are under genetic control (106, 143).

HORMONE BALANCE

A balance of hormones is essential for maximum tissue resistance, but, like many other factors in immunity, its effects become obvious only when missing. The acne infections of the skin which are so distressing during puberty and some of the fungus infections of the hair in young children disappear spontaneously when a natural balance of the sex hormones is achieved. During sexual maturity the vaginal epithelium is very resistant to infection, but it is much more susceptible during infancy and after menopause. The administration of estrogen increases the epithelial cell layer, restores glycogen, increases acidity, and usually eliminates the complicating infections (175, 317). Lurie's (180) genetically susceptible strain of rabbits responded to injections of chorionic gonadotropin by becoming even more susceptible to the human tubercle bacillus, while their resistance was increased almost to that of the normal animal by the administration of estrogen (183). The administration of the thyroid hormone induces an even greater degree of re-

sistance (184). The opposite effects have been reported with thyroid products in mice infected with staphylococci (299) and *Candida albicans* (216), and rats infected with streptococci (249). Kass (155) has suggested that the contradiction may be more apparent than real. Melby and his associates (205) have shown that triodothyronine increases the susceptibility of animals to endotoxins. Tubercle bacilli have neither endotoxins nor exotoxins, and the animals would not have had to combat a toxin effect while in a state of hyperthyroidism which seemed to inhibit the growth of tubercle bacilli. The presence of toxic substances in the staphylococci and streptococci could have contributed to the death of the animals in these experiments. Diabetes in man is known to increase the susceptibility to pyogenic cocci, tubercle bacilli, and phycomycetes (*Mucor, Rhizopus,* etc.). The change from an apparently harmless saprophyte to a highly virulent mycotic infection is most dramatic. Although the mechanism for reducing the resistance of the patient is not known, recovery is rapid if the diabetes can be brought under control before the irreparable damage has been done to the blood vessels. Elder and Baker (80) found that this state of susceptibility could be induced in rabbits by producing acute diabetes with alloxan.

Large doses of either cortisone or ACTH lower the natural resistance of experimental animals to a great variety of bacterial, viral, and mycotic infections (177, 179, 287, 314). There is some evidence that ACTH produces less damage to the innate resistance of animals than cortisone (213, 327). Whether this difference is due to varying responses of different animal species to ACTH stimulation or to the production by the adrenal gland, under ACTH stimulation of another hormone which has an anti-infective influence, remains unsettled. Ghione (104) of Italy has reported encouraging results with 4-chlorotestosterone, which is an anabolic steroid comparable to testosterone. This steroid hastens the healing of some infections and neutralizes the proinfective action of cortisone.

Cortisone does not interfere with the union of antigens and antibodies and toxins and antitoxins. Cortisone does not interfere with the neutralizing effect of diphtheria antitoxin when it is given four days before the toxin, but it does interfere when active tetanus is present and antitoxins, with or without cortisone, are indicated. The studies of Chang and Weinstein (57) show that the administration of cortisone under these conditions is not only without benefit but, in fact, sharply decreases the effectiveness of the antitoxin. Bowen and his associates (31) found that 5 mg. cortisone reduced the survival time of nonimmunized mice to *S. typhiminum* from 100 per cent to 0 per cent but had no effect on the survival of actively immunized mice. Payne and his associates (236) reported that both active and passive immunization protected cortisone-treated mice from doses of *Past. pestis* which were fatal for nonimmunized mice.

Cortisone has a dual effect in infection. When the adrenals have been removed or destroyed by infection, small doses of cortisone are protective, but large doses increase the risks of infection. This phenomenon is illustrated in the classical experiment by Kass and Finland (154), who studied the effect of graduated doses of cortisone in adrenalectomized mice, giving various doses of virulent pneumococci. Doses of 5 μg. to 100 μg. increased the resistance of the mice, while 200 μg. was not as effective as 25 μg. and 500 μg. was less effective than 5μg. An even more complex situation seems to be operating in experimental tuberculosis in guinea pigs treated with cortisone and streptomycin. These studies were done in our laboratory (213, 327). Infected animals, sensitized and partially immunized by a prior injection of living attenuated tubercle bacilli (R1), died with massive caseation of the lungs when treated with either ACTH or cortisone. If streptomycin was given simultaneously, the animal did as well or better than controls treated with streptomycin alone. But when the experiments were repeated with animals not previously sensitized, the streptomycin failed to neutralize completely the bad effects of cortisone and ACTH. This result suggests that both some immunity from previous exposure to the organism and streptomycin was needed to afford maximum protection from the harmful effects of ACTH and cortisone.

Patients with damage of the suprarenal gland resulting in the development of Addison's disease and animals whose adrenals have been removed have an increased susceptibility to many types of infections. Small doses of adrenal corticoid hormones, as replacement therapy, may restore the resistance of the patient or animal to normal (123). Even with intact adrenal glands there may be some relative deficiency of cortisone in severe infections, and small doses of hormone may increase the survival rate (140, 258). This type of therapy is being used more and more in man, but in all instances it is advisable to give simultaneously an antibiotic known to be effective against the particular invading organism.

DESTRUCTION OR INDIFFERENCE TO FOREIGN MATERIALS

This type of reaction may be a manifestation, if not the cause, of some types of natural immunity. The lecithinase synthesized by *Cl. perfringens* is a highly fatal exotoxin for most animal species, including man, but lecithinase produced by *B. cereus* is practically harmless because it is neutralized by a component of normal serum (60). The lecithinase of *Cl. bifermentans* also has a low toxicity, but the cause for this is unknown (208). Although the rough avirulent strains of *Sh. dysenteriae* produce as much and as potent a neurotoxin as the smooth virulent strains, this toxin is of no practical importance because the rough strains are unable to invade the tissues (324), and the toxin itself, in contrast to that of diphtheria toxin, has no local destructive, aggressive effect (5). The toad and the frog are immune to diphtheria and tetanus toxin apparently because their tissues do not react with the toxins. The tissues of the rat absorb diphtheria toxin slowly and inefficiently, which may explain why the minimal lethal dose is 1,000 times greater than that of the guinea pig (63).

Somewhat different manifestations occur when the foreign agent is a harmless protein. Longcope and Mackenzie in 1920 (178) noted that a few individuals injected with large amounts of horse serum containing type-specific antipneumococcal antibodies did not make precipitins and did not develop serum sickness. This is the type of reaction one would expect from an individual with hypogammaglobulinemia, but this defect was not considered because it was not known in 1920.

The senior author has seen a few nurses and physicians who never developed a positive tuberculin reaction although they were repeatedly exposed to patients with tuberculosis. A few also reported that BCG vaccine had failed to produce a positive allergic reaction to tuberculin. Their immunity to tuberculin seemed to be good, since they did not develop clinical infections although repeatedly exposed.

If a virus is introduced into the tissues before or shortly after birth, it may be "recognized" as a normal constituent of the tissues and allowed to survive without the host forming antibodies against this living foreign agent. Experiments in which the virus of lymphocytic choriomeningitis was injected into mice in vitro a few hours before birth have been performed by Traub (322, 323) and by Hotchin and Weigard (138). The virus persisted in a high titer, there was no antibody formation or illness, and the animals grew to maturity and passed the infection on to their offspring. Traub (323) concluded that the infections of the offspring of virus carriers occurred during gestation. Not only could they pass the virus on to their embryo, but they could pass the virus through their milk to suckling mice which acquired immunologic tolerance to the LCM virus. If the virus is injected a few days after birth, there is an active response which determines three different types of results: (1) complete suppression of the virus with immunity to reinfection, (2) death from infection, and (3) tolerance and "immunological paralysis" and the persistence of the virus. This third result becomes rarer as the animal increases in age and is extremely rare in adult mice.

The attenuated hog cholera virus vaccine is usually propagated in young nonimmune pigs of about three months of age. Viremia develops, followed by a clearing of the blood as the pig develops immunity. A somewhat different type of reaction occurs when the virus vaccine is injected into pigs of only six weeks of age. The viremia reaches a very high level and persists without antibody production. Some virus particles mutate in the body to a fully virulent strain which has cytopathogenicity for tissue cultures, a property not present in the ancestral strain. Under natural conditions the fully virulent virus could be transmitted from the mother to piglets in vitro, who then become carriers to perpetuate the disease (16).

Manire and Galasso (199) maintained a

Fig. 8. Random migration pattern of polymorphonuclear leukocytes in the presence of a fragment of muscle which has been subjected to the action of pepsin for four hours. (From Harris. *J. Path. & Bact.,* 66:135, 1953.)

balanced growth of meningopneumonitis virus in Hela cell cultures for almost a year, with excellent yield of fully virulent virus and more than 100 successful transfers of the cells. This is an interference phenomenon, or an instance of tolerance at the cellular level, but it does remind us that viruses can persist in man and animals for years without apparent harm to the host.

THE PHAGOCYTIC SYSTEM

The introduction of sanitary engineering, universal immunization for some diseases, and the specific antibiotics has reduced dramatically the infections which are "caught" from patient to patient. At the present time there are increasing numbers of infections caused by staphylococci, enterococci, and gram-negative bacilli, which seem to depend upon subtle changes in the equilibrium between host and parasite (156). **Phagocytosis is the first line of defense against these endogenous infections and where it is successful the animal and man are not even aware of the successful operation in eliminating a few invading organisms which, if left to multiply, could have overwhelmed the defenses and caused serious or even fatal disease** (204).

Phagocytosis is certainly the most primitive type of defense against disease-producing germs (26, 158). Free-living amoebae can phagocytize and digest or egest harmful bacteria.

The phagocytic system of the body shares with the humoral antibody system, the chief burden of protecting the host from infections.

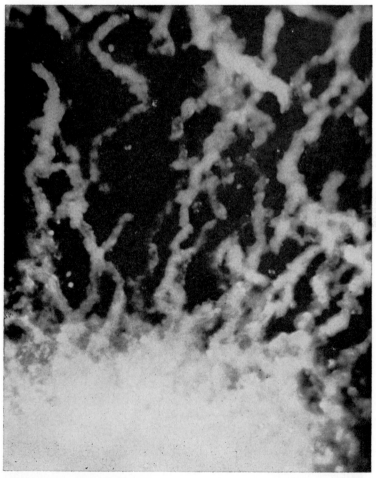

Fig. 9. Effect of a clump of *Staphylococcus epidermidis* (*Staphylococcus albus*) on the migration pattern of polymorphonuclear leukocytes. The leukocytes are moving directly to the mass of organisms. (From Harris. *J. Path. & Bact.*, 66:135, 1953.)

Metchnikoff was the first investigator to appreciate the importance of this system of phagocytic or "eating cells" and introduced the name **microphages** for the polymorphonuclear leukocytes of the blood, and **macrophages** for the clasmatocytes and histiocytes of the tissue (128).

When bacteria or other noxious substances are introduced into the body, the first visible response is a slowing of the capillary circulation, after which polymorphonuclear leukocytes seem to stick to the walls of the vessels. These subsequently migrate through the capillaries and invade the intracellular spaces. The chemical and hormonal substances responsible for this behavior are not known (113). Lymphocytes are not seen sticking to the wall of the capillaries, but in some experiments performed by the senior author and Leroy Gardner in 1925, lymphocytes migrated from capillaries into the free peritoneal fluid before the peak of the polymorphonuclear leukocyte cells. The monocytes arrived later, accumulated, multiplied, and phagocytized, and digested the injured red cells, lymphocytes, and PMN's. If the inflammatory process persists for many days, they become the predominant cell type.

Some organisms are supposed to repel the leukocytes, and others to attract them, while still others neither repel nor attract. Those which repel were said to exert negative chemotaxis (172) while those which attracted have positive chemotaxis. Harris (113) questions the frequency and importance of negative chemotaxis, but the importance of positive chemotaxis is illustrated by Figures 8 and 9, where the

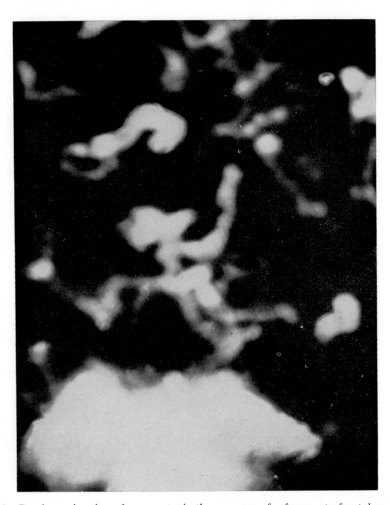

Fig. 10. Random migration of monocytes in the presence of a fragment of autolyzed muscle. (From Harris. *Brit. J. Exper. Path.,* 34:276, 1953.)

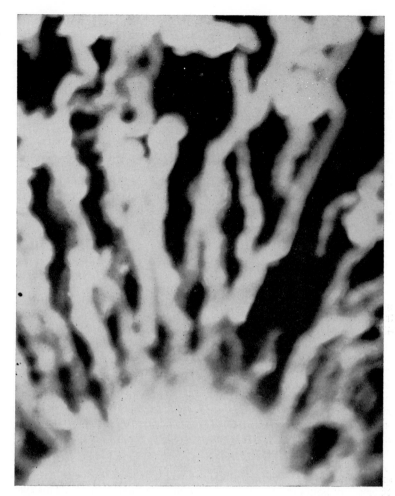

Fig. 11. Direct migration of monocytes toward a mass of *Myco. tuberculosis.* (From Harris. *Brit. J. Exper. Path.,* 34:276, 1953.)

migration of leukocytes was photographed by a dark-field technic, which leaves their trail plainly visible on the film. In Figure 8 the polymorphonuclear leukocytes migrate in a random fashion in the proximity of a fragment of muscle which has been subjected to the action of pepsin for four hours. In contrast to this result, Figure 9 shows polymorphonuclear leukocytes migrating directly toward a clump of *Staphylococcus albus.* In Figure 10, monocytes migrate in a random fashion in the presence of a fragment of autolyzed muscle, while in Figure 11 they migrate directly toward a clump of *Mycobacterium tuberculosis.* There is some evidence that polysaccharide substances from the surface layers of the organism are responsible for positive chemotaxis (312). Bacteria may attract leukocytes but resist phagocytosis, as

shown with encapsulated pneumococci. In this instance the leukocytes are not injured, but with *B. anthracis* leukocytes seemed to be attached and then killed (Fig. 4). The mechanism of specific antibody conditioned phagocytosis is obviously very complex, since it necessitates a union between the antibody and organism (32). Talmage suggests that antibody fragment I or II or both bind the organism while fragment III attaches itself to the surface of the cell while a process of invagination will bring the organism into the cell (Fig. 12).

The mechanism by which cells destroy ingested microorganisms is not known (268). The cytoplasm of both microphages and macrophages becomes more acid after phagocytosis, and the increased acidity may be deleterious to the organism. A trypsin-like enzyme active

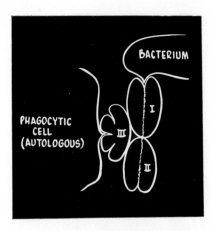

Fig. 12. Diagrammatic relationship between the three antibody fragments, the organisms, and the cell wall just before phagocytosis. (Courtesy of Dr. David W. Talmage.)

at about neutrality is present in microphages, and a pepsin-like enzyme active in weak acid is found in macrophages (334). Wilson (341) has studied the fate of hemolytic streptococci in human leukocytes. They are always enclosed in vacuoles within a few moments after ingestion. Sometimes the ingested organism was egested and might or might not continue to multiply, depending upon how long it remained in the vacuole. The fluid in such a cytoplasmic vacuole has remarkable digestive ability. It will readily destroy the rod-shaped melanin granules from the retina of the eye, although these granules resist for many hours the most drastic chemical treatment in vitro (297).

Leukocytes from human blood show a very high anaerobic glycolysis and over 20 times more glucose carbon is metabolized to lactate than converted to CO_2. Phagocytosis, which occurs under either aerobic or anaerobic conditions, requires work by the cells, and increased oxygen uptake during phagocytosis under aerobic conditions has been demonstrated with such inert material as insoluble starch, polystyrine, *Myco. tuberculosis, B. subtilis, Staphylococcus aureus, D. pneumoniae,* and *Sarcina lutea.* It has been demonstrated with three types of phagocytic cells: (1) polymorphonuclear leukocytes, (2) monocytes, and (3) mouse ascitic tumor cells (273). With phagocytosis under anaerobic conditions there is a significant increase in glycolysis, glucose utilization, and lactate production.

The granules in the polymorphonuclear leukocytes play a significant role in the intracellular destruction of bacteria which have been phagocytized. The granules are really "little bags of enzyme" which contain lysozyme, phagocytin, and other active agents. These granules were isolated intact from the destroyed PMN cell by Cohn and Hirsch (65). In the process of phagocytosis, bacteria are really enclosed by an invagination of the original cell wall. There is no obvious fluid separating the organism from the cell wall membranes, although this often develops after a few hours. Almost immediately after phagocytosis, granules accumulate at the border of the newly phagocytized organism and rupture into the microscopic space between the wall of the vacuole and the organism and liberate their enzymes. This process was observed by Robineaux and Frédéric in France (257), who utilized a phase-contrast microscope, and by Hirsch (131) in this country, who made moving pictures to show the process (Fig. 13). Spitznagel and Chi (303, 304) have observed the deposition of a basic protein on phagocytized bacteria.

Nonpathogenic microorganism and virulent strains of pathogenic organisms are usually phagocytized and destroyed by the microphages or macrophages. Virulent organisms may be protected from phagocytosis by the presence of a capsule or envelope antigen. The surface antigen which protects from phagocytosis is *d*-glutamyl-polypeptide for *B. anthracis,* polysaccharide for pneumococci, and M protein for group A streptococci. Staphylococci in culture usually lack a capsule, although it was known that the high virulent (Smith) strain which has a capsule was less readily phagocytized than nonencapsulated strains. This surface antigen or capsule which prevents phagocytosis contained

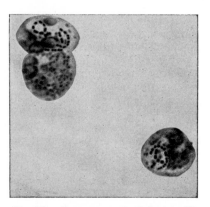

Fig. 13. The disappearance of the specific granules of polymorphonuclear leukocytes in the presence of phagocytosis cocci. (Redrawn from color photograph. From Hirsch and Cohn. *J. Exper. Med.,* 112:1005, 1960.)

carbohydrates and amino acids and would actively immunize mice (215). A few more encapsulated strains have been discovered. However, Rogers and Melly (262, 263, 264) have found that almost all adult sera contain opsonins for the encapsulated Smith strain. Furthermore, some recently isolated strains which do not resist phagocytosis nevertheless produce opsonins for the virulent Smith strain when injected into rabbits. The findings suggested to Rogers (263) that *Staphylococcus aureus* may resemble virulent *B. anthracis,* which has no capsule on ordinary media but develops a capsule when injected into a susceptible animal.

Wood and his associates (300, 344, 345) have shown that considerable numbers of virulent encapsulated organisms can be phagocytized when leukocytes trap them against a solid surface such as the wall of an alveolus in the lung, a net of fibrin, or even between two cells. **This "surface phagocytosis," which operates in the absence of specific antibodies, is difficult to evaluate as a basic mechanism of defense.** Perhaps the mechanism can eliminate minimal numbers of virulent organisms and prevent infection. Certainly it is important where the organisms have been injured but not killed by sulfonamides and antibiotics (70).

Another specific factor which accelerates phagocytosis was discovered in dog leukocytes by Pollack and Victor (243) in 1955. This soluble substance was present in the leukocytes of the dog, which is resistant to brucella, but not in the leukocytes of the susceptible guinea pig. It accelerated the phagocytosis of brucella organisms by human, guinea pig, and dog leukocytes.

Other cells of the body can phagocytize microorganisms, particularly the monocytes of the blood and the endothelial cells of the liver, spleen, lymph nodes, and bone marrow. **The pathologist Aschoff visualized the tissue macrophages as a functional system which he named the reticulo-endothelial system.** The efficiency of this system in removing microorganisms from the blood has been demonstrated in experimental animals by Bull (41) and Hopkins and Parker (135), and in a series of studies by Martin and Kerby (159, 201, 202, 203) and others (261). The phagocytes continue removing organisms from the blood even when the disease is progressing to fatal termination. Martin and Kerby have confirmed Hopkins and Parker's original observation that bacteremia does not persist unless new organisms are being introduced as rapidly as the old ones are removed. If the reticuloendothelial system is saturated or "blockaded" by the injection of thorotrast, the removal mechanism is impaired and animals become less resistant to infection (203). The encapsulated organism *Klebsiella pneumoniae* is removed by this mechanism in the absence of a specific antibody in the serum, but the rate of removal increased from 43 to 85 per cent in animals immunized prior to infection.

Man is unaware of the frequency with which nonpathogenic and potentially pathogenic bacteria from the tonsils and intestinal tract invade the blood stream but are removed by this clearing mechanism. In one series of patients undergoing tonsillectomies, blood cultures made immediately after operation revealed bacteria in the blood in 28 per cent (251).

Highly pathogenic as well as nonpathogenic organisms are removed from the blood by this mechanism, but the pathogenic ones colonize in the tissues and later reinvade the blood stream unless they have been destroyed in the tissues by some other natural or acquired mechanism of immunity (72, 129, 141, 261, 353).

The studies of Brunner and his associates (39) suggest that viruses, like bacteria, are cleared from the blood stream by the reticuloendothelial system. This mechanism could be blockaded with thorotrast or accelerated with specific antiserum. However, the recent studies of Jenkins and Rowley (151) have shown that both bacteria and colloid particles, and presumably viruses, must be coated with a serum factor before they can be phagocytized. This suggests that the apparent blockade of the reticuloendothelial system by colloid may be nothing more than a depletion by the colloid particles of the serum factor needed for phagocytosis.

Human hela cells in tissue culture do not normally phagocytize bacteria but can be induced to do so by the addition of sera from horse, guinea pig, chicken, sheep, or cow. The results are relatively specific, since the phagocytosis of certain organisms is induced by the serum of some but not other animals (102, 284). There may be a cellular basis for passive as well as active immunity. The original work of Lurie (180) indicated that the basis for immunity in tuberculosis was the "trained" monocyte. This has been confirmed for brucellosis by Holland and Pickett (133), and for tuberculosis by Sever (281), and for typhoid infection in the mouse by Saito and his associates (270). The more recent studies of Fong and his colleagues (93) show that allergy to tuberculin is transferred by lymphocytes while cellular resistance cannot be transferred with lymphocytes or PMN's but could be transferred in series by histocytes and monocytes. Miya and Marcus and their associates (211) have demonstrated in in vitro studies that trained leukocytes from immunized animals and mice are more active in digesting phagocytized organisms, even in the absence of antibody-containing serum, than leukocytes from normal animals.

The importance of the phagocytic cells in natural resistance against microorganisms of low or questionable virulence (338) can be appreciated only under conditions where they are drastically reduced. Alcohol, to the point of stupefaction; benzol poisoning; silica (67); and agranulocytosis, whether from toxins or allergic reactions to drugs, result in malignant infections with a high death rate. Antibiotic therapy has materially reduced the mortality by holding the infections in check until the bone marrow has regenerated. Even the presence of specific antibodies may not protect the animal if the phagocytic cells are destroyed, as shown by the experiments of Rich and McKee (254) in which rabbits previously immune to pneumococci were found to die readily from the same pneumococcus strain when challenged after the white cells had been reduced by benzol poisoning.

Many virulent microorganisms are readily phagocytized, after which they come to live and multiply within the cytoplasm of the cell. Meningococci and gonococci are found in large numbers in polymorphonuclear leukocytes. Leprosy and tubercle bacilli are found characteristically in monocytes. Viruses and rickettsias must find a residence in either the cytoplasm or nucleus of living cells in order to survive. Certain protozoa, such as *Leishmania donovani,* and fungi, such as *Histoplasma capsulatum,* live and multiply in macrophages (353). The chronicity of brucellosis and many other diseases where the parasites have an intracellular habitat probably depends upon the difficulty with which antibiotics penetrate the cells (282). The student should consult the review of phagocytosis by Suter (283, 312) and the symposium on nonspecific resistance to infection (313).

NONSPECIFIC STIMULATION AND SPECIFIC IMMUNITY

Stimulating experimental animals with the nonvirulent BCG strain of tubercle bacilli (150, 310, 311), stimulating doses of x-ray (20, 209), and small doses of endotoxin (64, 134, 150, 271) can increase the resistance of animals to a variety of microorganisms. The nonspecific stimulation of specific resistance apparently depends upon the observation that the precursors of antibody-producing plasma cells are caused to multiply by the stimulation. Then when specific antigens are introduced, they are ready and available to produce antibodies earlier and in greater amounts than other animals which have received the same antigen without the previous nonspecific stimulation (see Chapter 12).

Endotoxins from gram-negative bacteria may induce specific resistance to the species from which they were derived but also temporary nonspecific resistance to other organisms (see the discussion of endotoxins in Chapter 16). A specific example of endotoxin-stimulated resistance is presented by Sprinz and his associates (305), who found that guinea pigs reared in a germ-free environment died of ulcerative enteritis in 48 hours after an oral dose of *Sh. flexneri,* but controls could be protected by feeding *E. coli,* which were harmless, some weeks prior to the dose of *Sh. flexneri.* In this instance profound tissue changes occurred in the intestinal mucosa as a result of the introduction of *E. coli.* Another more complex example was studied by Pirsch and Mika (242). In these experiments guinea pigs which had been infected with *Brucella suis* were refractory to the lethal effect of a subsequent infection with *Coxiella burnetti,* but the nonspecific resistance was easily abolished by treating the animals with cortisone. Nonspecific decrease of resistance has also been encountered. A deficiency of potassium seems to promote infection of the kidney (346) and urea itself in the urinary tract seems to reduce phagocytosis to *E. coli* and *Proteus* species and thus increase infection (59, 60).

ACQUIRED IMMUNITY

Acquired immunity is specific and usually is subdivided into two main groups, active and passive. **Active immunity refers to the specific immunity built up by an individual in response to the introduction of microorganisms or toxins.** Such immunity can be obtained either in a natural manner —**naturally acquired active immunity**—or as the result of deliberate immunization with a vaccine or toxoid **artificially acquired active immunity.** The highest degree of specific, naturally acquired active immunity is found in individuals who have had a disease such as measles or typhoid fever and have recovered. Other individuals may build up specific resistance to certain diseases following infections which are so mild as to go unrecognized clinically. Still others may acquire an active immunity by repeated exposures to very small quantities of virulent organisms. This type of immunity is developed rather slowly but is long-lasting.

Artificially acquired active immunity is produced by the injection of materials with the express purpose of stimulating the body cells to make their own antibodies. In some instances bacteria are used, as in typhoid and pertussis vaccine; in other instances modified viruses such as vaccinia are inoculated and immunity to toxins can be produced by injections of toxoids (32). Living attenuated bacteria are rarely used because of the danger of producing infection, but excellent results of vaccination against tuberculosis with BCG (Bacille Calmette-Guérin), a living organism, are being obtained in certain areas where the incidence of infection and the fatality rate are disproportionately high. This type of immunity, like naturally active immunity, is built up slowly but is relatively long lasting. The processes used to render vaccines harmless, such as killing by heat, chemical methods, or ultraviolet light radiation, cannot avoid entirely the introduction of minor changes in antigenic structure which makes them somewhat less effective immunizing agents than the original living organisms (78, 191, 289).

Passive immunity refers to the protection afforded by the introduction into one individual of antibodies contained in the serum of another individual or animal who has been actively immunized. In such instances the body cells of the animal or person receiving the protection are not stimulated to form new antibodies. This type of immunity can occur under natural conditions—**naturally acquired passive immunity**—and is exemplified by the resistance to some common infection of newborn infants who have received some of their mothers' antibodies through the placental membrane. **Artificially acquired passive immunity** refers to the type of protection given when the serum of an immune person or animal is injected into the body of the patient. This type of immunity has its greatest utility in the treatment of certain infections, because the protective antibodies can be supplied immediately and in

quantity. The resulting immunity, however, is of short duration and if the individual is treated before his own cells are stimulated to antibody formation, he will soon become fully as susceptible as if he had never been infected.

The role of active and passive immunity, both naturally and artificially acquired, will be discussed in more detail in the chapters dealing with specific infections.

EPIDEMIOLOGY

The epidemiologist studies the health of the entire community as a unit and expresses his results in statistical terms (295, 316, 343). His crude data are derived from the clinical diagnoses reported by practicing physicians and from the information given on the death certificates. Reliable diagnoses depend to a large extent upon the accuracy of the laboratory work, and no amount of skillful manipulation of figures can compensate for incomplete laboratory studies or careless reporting by the practicing physician.

The terms **contagious** and **infectious disease** have become so blurred by usage that both should be discarded in favor of **communicable disease.** Some diseases, such as measles, scarlet fever, and diphtheria, have short incubation periods and are readily recognized as communicable diseases, while others, such as tuberculosis and leprosy, have incubation periods of months or years. Some diseases may be classified as communicable although they are transmitted from person to person with difficulty and rarely become epidemic. Other diseases, such as measles, mumps, smallpox, and chicken pox, are readily transmitted and regularly produce epidemics in the community if there is a sufficiently large number of nonimmune individuals.

A disease which spreads rapidly and attacks a number of individuals within a few days or weeks is said to be **epidemic** (*epi,* upon, and *demos,* people). Inherent in this definition is the concept of time, numbers, and place. A large number of cases (1,000) may occur in a populous city over a period of months and not be called epidemic, while 50 cases in 10 days in a village of 1,000 population would certainly be defined as an epidemic. A disease which is present more or less constantly in a certain geographic area or which is limited to certain classes of individuals is defined as **endemic** (*en,* in, and *demos,* people). Thus cholera is endemic in India and plague in Tibet, but from time to time these infections spread to other infected areas and produce epidemics. If the new epidemic sweeps over the world, as did cholera in 1883, and influenza in 1918, the disease is called **pandemic** (*pan,* all, and *demos* people). The last great pandemic was that of Asian influenza in 1957-1958. Figure 14 shows the origin in China and the path both East and West over the entire world. When a few isolated cases occur from time to time in a given area, they are spoken of as **sporadic.**

The incidence of a certain disease is expressed as the rate or number of cases in a unit of population of a given area in a definite unit of time. This population unit may be 1,000, 10,000, or 100,000. Thus we express the prevalence of tuberculosis in the city of Newark, N.J., for the year 1915 as

250 cases per 100,000 population and note that the rate was reduced to 130 per 100,000 by the year 1949. Data expressing the incidence of diseases are called **morbidity statistics.** The infections which result in death are recorded in the mortality statistics which should indicate the percentage of the infected patients who die and what the ratio of death is to the population unit in a certain geographic area in a definite time unit. Thus the mortality from tuberculosis in Newark, N.J., declined from 190 per 100,000 for the year 1915 to 50 in 1949, although the death rate per clinical case remained at approximately 50 per cent. The **morbidity statistics** deal with all cases which can be recognized clinically, regardless of the outcome. In a particular geographic unit, if there were 500 cases of typhoid fever, of which 50 died, the mortality statistics would include only the 50 fatal cases while the morbidity statistics would report the total 500. In general, the mortality rates are more accurate than the morbidity rate because the diagnosis is more exact and the re-

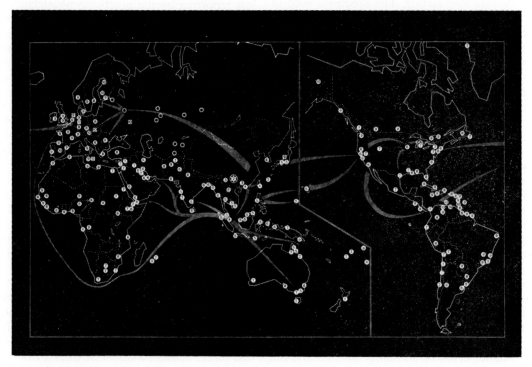

Fig. 14. The paths followed by waves of infection during the Aisan influenza epidemic from February, 1957, to January, 1958. * Probable origin in South Central China. O—First cases from May to August. O—First wave. Second wave. The number indicates the month in which the first cases were observed. (From Le Courrier. UNESCO, May, 1958.)

porting more conscientious. **A constant ratio between the number of deaths and the number of clinical cases does not exist.** For example, at different times in different areas in this country, the ratio of mortality to morbidity has varied from 1:3 to 1:1,000 for smallpox; 1:20 to 1:800 for measles; and 1:5 to 1:24 for typhoid fever.

The incubation period is the interval of time between the introduction of the infectious agent and the development of the first clinical symptoms. This may be as brief as two to three hours for bacterial food poisoning, as short as 56 hours for streptococcal sore throat, or as long as 100 days for the virus of serum hepatitis (235).

The infectious period is that period in the host-parasite relationship when the infectious agent is leaving the original host. This may occur predominantly (a) during the incubation period before the appearance of symptoms, (b) early in the disease, (c) during the height of the disease, (d) during convalescence, or (e) from a chronic carrier. **The most difficult type to evaluate and control is the subclinical infection where transmission may occur either during the incubation period, as in poliomyelitis, or in the postinfectious period when the individual has become immune but remains a healthy carrier, as in pneumococcal and meningococcal infections. Chronic carriers constitute the chief reservoir of infection for the large group of organisms which invade the intestinal tract.**

MECHANISM OF TRANSMISSION

The mechanism of transmission determines in part whether the resulting diseases will be sporadic or epidemic. Disease may be acquired (a) by direct contact; (b) through the respiratory tract; (c) through the intestinal tract; (d) directly from animals, or by way of their secretions such as milk, urine, or feces; and (e) indirectly from animals through insect vectors.

Most of the common sporadic infections with staphylococci, streptococci, and anaerobic bacilli, anthrax, and glanders are caused by direct traumatic contact with contaminated material. Epidemics do not occur except in unusual conditions where occupa-

tional groups are involved, as when workers in a tannery are exposed to hides heavily infested with anthrax spores. The venereal diseases—syphilis, gonorrhea, chancroid, and lymphogranuloma venereum—are transmitted by direct physical bodily contact. Such infections may be sporadic, or they may become universal.

Infections acquired by way of the respiratory tract include the major uncontrollable epidemic diseases afflicting mankind. The common cold, viral influenza, measles, mumps, chickenpox, smallpox, poliomyelitis, tuberculosis, scarlet fever, and diphtheria are characteristically epidemic in nature. The bacterial and viral pneumonias, Q fever, and meningococcal meningitis are sporadic but may become epidemic under conditions of overcrowding.

Infections acquired through the intestinal tract are characteristically epidemic, and, although they were formerly numerous as the respiratory diseases, they are now largely controlled by sanitary measures, such as sewage disposal, pasteurization of milk, purification of water, and protection of food from direct or indirect fecal contamination. These diseases include typhoid fever, cholera, dysentery, and the salmonellas. Man is the natural host and, with the exception of certain salmonellas, the only host for these organisms. **Human carriers are now the chief source of infection with the intestinal organisms which pass to the new host through a series of intermediate steps** such as (a) fingers or utensils—mouth; (b) fingers—food—mouth; (c) formites—fingers—food—mouth; (d) flies—food—mouth; and (e) fingers—flies—food—mouth. The intestinal infections are much easier to control than are the respiratory diseases, as shown by the experiences in our army cantonments in 1917 where intestinal infections were $\frac{1}{45}$ of the expected rate for the same age group in the home communities but the respiratory infections were vastly increased in spite of well-planned and skillful efforts to prevent them.

Diseases which are caused by direct contact with animals, such as anthrax, glanders, rabies, ratbite fever, ornithosis and tularemia, are usually sporadic, although brucellosis transmitted by the milk of goats and cows, may occur in true epidemic form. Leptospirosis is transmitted to man by the contamination of food and water with leptospira excreted in the urine of rats and dogs.

Many of the important epidemic diseases are transmitted by insects. These must be subdivided according to the original host and the type of insect vector. The host may be man, animal, or insects. Man is the primary host for the organisms producing (a) yellow fever, (b) malaria, (c) dengue fever, (d) sand fly fever, (e) African sleeping sickness, (f) relapsing fever, and (g) epidemic typhus. Mosquitoes transmit (a), (b), and (c); biting flies, (d) and (e); lice and ticks, (f); and lice (g). A patient with one of these diseases should be protected from biting insects while a direct attack is being made on the insect vector. Animals are the primary reservoir for (a) endemic typhus, b) plague, (c) tularemia, (d) Rocky Mountain spotted fever, (e) Colorado tick fever, (f) St. Louis en-

cephalitis, (g) equine encephalomyelitis, (h) rickettsialpox, and (i) scrub typhus. Rat fleas transmit (a) and (b); ticks, (c), (d), and (e); mosquitoes, (f) and (g); and mites, (h) and (i). Control measures may be directed both against the reservoir animal and the insect vector. Since the rickettsia causing Rocky Mountain spotted fever and the virus of Colorado tick fever are transmitted transovarially, the insect becomes a permanent reservoir of infection.

A THEORY OF EPIDEMICS

A pure uncomplicated epidemic is rarely observed except under unusual circumstances such as the introduction of a single case of a highly infectious disease such as measles into an isolated island community (Fig. 15). Under these conditions, measles is no longer a relatively benign disease limited to child-

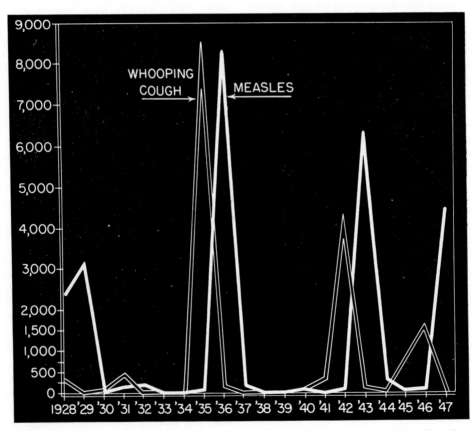

Fig. 15. Epidemics of whooping cough and measles in Iceland. (From data from Sigurdsson. *Am. J. Hyg.,* 51:109, 1950.)

hood but attacks individuals of all ages, as exemplified by the epidemics on Fiji and Sandwich Islands, during which a mortality of 20 to 25 per cent was produced. Both the number and severity of the cases increase rapidly, reach a plateau, and then slowly decline. At first the contact rate increases as more and more cases occur, but the effective contact rate soon slows and begins to decline as the susceptible individuals are replaced by convalescent cases who are immune. The disease disappears while there are still a considerable number of susceptible individuals in the community, as shown by their contracting the disease when it is introduced a second time at a later date. The laws of chance operate more and more effectively as the number of immune individuals increases, and the epidemic finally "burns itself out" before all of the susceptible individuals have been infected. In a large civilized community there are cases of measles present at all times as well as relatively large numbers of both immune and susceptible people. Endemic and epidemic periods tend to alternate in an undulating manner as the proportion of immune to susceptible individuals varies. The peaks of the epidemics usually occur in the winter and spring months, when other factors, such as crowding, increase the contact rate.

Evans (85) has questioned the evidence that the excessively high mortality from measles in the Fiji Island epidemic was exclusively or even primarily a lack of genetic resistance, since subsequent epidemics did not show a much higher mortality than in European countries. Sanitary conditions and associated secondary infections could have been the determining factor in the heightened mortality. The senior author observed an epidemic of measles in an army camp in World War I where secondary infection with hemolytic streptococci resulted in a very high death rate.

Beginning with Sir William Horner in 1906 and Soper in 1929 (302), an attempt was made to formulate a mathematical equation which would both explain and predict the behavior of epidemics. This work has been continued by Frost, Reed, and Hedrick (115), McKendrick (193), and Wilson and Burke (342). Since susceptibility to measles is practically 100 per cent and there is no known variation in the virulence of the virus, the dynamics of the reaction depend solely on the flow of the virus through a population containing a varying proportion of immune and susceptible individuals. With such a formula, if one knows (a) the number of current cases, (b) the number of susceptible individuals, (c) the number of the total population, and (d) assumes an arbitrary value for the "contact risks" in one period of time of 14 days, the number of new cases arising in the subsequent time units of 14 days can be calculated.

The problem of epidemics becomes even more complex when the disease under investigation produces a relative rather than an absolute immunity, so that the size of the inoculum, the virulence of the organism, and the genetically conditioned constitution of the individual influences both the morbidity and mortality of the disease. Stallybrass states that the case fatality of pneumonia is highest at the time of its prevalence and that this is true of a number of other diseases. Moreover, his studies of the fatality of diphtheria and scarlet fever in Liverpool from 1900 to 1915, computed by a method adapted from that used for corrected death rates, show that the effect of age on fatality was eliminated and that there was a definite indication of the variations in virulence of the invading organisms. His tables on the relation of density of population to case fatality in scarlet fever and enteric fever would also indicate a dependence of case fatality upon more rapid transmission.

There are probably many outbreaks in which case fatality does not parallel the morbidity rate. Professor E. B. Wilson has applied mathematical analysis to a hypothetical epidemic in which an assumption of fluctuating virulence was made as follows: In a closed population an individual introduces an infection the activity of which, measured by case fatality rates, diminishes, in each source of infection, progressively in the course of four days. Each case, in other words, passes a strain which has a case fatality of 0.8 for two days, 0.4 for the third day, and 0.2 for the fourth day. The daily contact rate is held constant at 0.0002. Calculations of the morbidity and fatality rates on this basis resulted in curves which showed a parallelism comparable to that actually observed in many epidemics (321).

MacDonald (195) has constructed epidemiologic models for the study of vector-borne disease which is quite different from the airborne diseases.

In addition to the factors influencing epidemics which we have discussed, there are a great many other variables, some of them of considerable importance, depending upon the complexities of life. Variations in the habits of personal hygiene, housing, public sanitation, and climates naturally exert important effects upon the spread of disease (235) but cannot be discussed with any degree of completeness in a short chapter (90). To some extent these matters are dealt with in the sections devoted to individual diseases.

Experimental Epidemiology. Topley has advanced the theory that civilized man should be considered as an "infected herd," since, for reasons we cannot explain now, the "herd" reacts differently under different conditions, although the individuals composing the herds are comparable. It is obvious that the latter factor cannot be evaluated or controlled except in experimentally induced epidemics in animals (321). Controlled epidemics have been produced in mice with several types of viruses and bacteria by Amoss, Traub (322), Theiler (318), Webster (331), Greenwood and others (107), Topley (321), and Clark and others (61).

If an epidemic is induced in a colony of 100 or more mice by a natural method with *Salmonella typhimurium,* there are always survivors, a part of which are still infected, at least as asymptomatic carriers, since a new epidemic results when 100 normal mice are added to the colony. In the second epidemic wave there is a higher death rate among the new animals than among the survivors of the first epidemic. But some mice which escaped the first epidemic die in the second, and if the procedure is constantly repeated, almost all of the original mice will die in succeeding epidemics. A persisting epidemic can be induced if a small increment of normal mice is added at frequent intervals. In general, the larger the increments of normal mice added the more prolonged and severe are the epidemic waves. On the other hand,

Topley found that the separation of a large infected group into smaller units resulted in a lower total death rate than if the entire group were left together. **Both Topley and Webster have shown that the characteristics of the individual epidemics depend largely upon the virulence of the original infecting organism.** Some differences in strains were observed: for example, one strain had a high killing power but little ability to persist in the tissues of the survivors, while another produced a few deaths but showed a greater tendency to persist and spread. Little if any difference was detected in strains isolated from early or late fatal cases or from carriers which had survived, suggesting that the waxing and waning epidemics are not due to the fluctuation in the virulence of the organisms. In one instance, however, Topley and Greenwood observed in their *S. typhimurium* experiments that the virulence of the strains isolated between the twenty-eighth and sixtieth day of the epidemic were five times greater than that of the original culture. **There is clinical evidence, particularly from army camps, that mutations in the virulence of viral and bacterial strains do occur as well as mutations which result in resistance to the sulfonamides and antibiotics** (188).

INFECTION AND DISEASE

"Infection" and "disease" are not synonymous terms. In many instances the infecting organism is destroyed by the body defenses before sufficient toxins or other metabolic products have been synthesized to produce symptoms. These inapparent or subclinical infections may induce temporary or permanent immunity or no immunity at all, depending upon the specific immunizing ability of the organisms. On the other hand, intrinsically harmless but antigenic substances may induce severe disease and even death as a result of antigen-antibody reaction or allergic reaction.

Antigen-Antibody Reactions. In the preceding section on infections emphasis was placed on the particular antigen of the organism which determined its ability to survive and multiply in the body. While it is recognized that all of the antigens of an organism are capable of stimulating antibodies

(171), those stimulating antibodies which do not afford protection to the animal were temporarily ignored. When discussing infection and disease, however, they cannot be ignored, because the major part of the symptoms in some diseases result from antigen-antibody reactions between these essentially harmless antigens and their antibodies.

Serum sickness may be regarded as an example of this type of disease. Figure 16 illustrates a type of syndrome which was produced regularly in this laboratory by Dr. R. E. Conover. Graded doses of horse serum were injected daily into rabbits in an attempt to stimulate the multiplication of a microorganism. Fever, dyspnea, anorexia, and loss of weight appeared about the time precipitins to horse serum were detected in the serum. In some instances the animals died as a result of their reactions, while in other instances the animals finally cease to react, presumably from overloading the antibody-producing mechanism with an excess of horse serum. In a second series of experiments

carried out by Dr. Stuart Bondurant, an attempt was made to prevent the daily rise in temperature which followed the injection of horse serum by pretreatment with antihistamines, such as pyribenzamine, or with continuous intravenous injections of ACTH. Neither type of treatment prevented the daily spike in the temperature, indicating that the febrile rise was not mediated by a histamine-like reaction or by a delayed bacterial allergy reaction. The marked neutropenia which accompanies antigen-antibody reactions of this type in the rabbit does suggest that the fever may have resulted from an endogenous pyogen released by the disintegration of leukocytes (see Chapter 16).

The violent and frequently fatal anaphylactic reactions to horse serum or penicillin and the nonfatal necrotizing reactions of the Arthus type are other examples of disease resulting from antibody reactions to inherently harmless antigens.

Allergic Reactions.   The hay fever-asthma syndromes illustrate another type of clinical

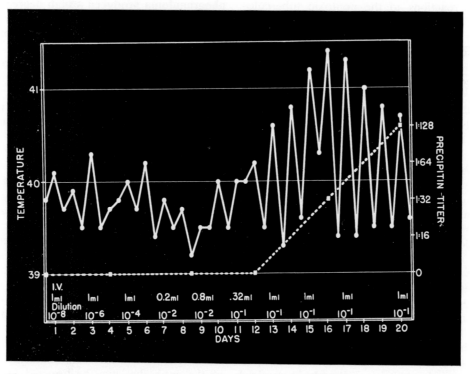

Fig. 16.   Fever associated with antigen-antibody reactions. Graded doses of horse serum were injected daily into rabbits to simulate the multiplication of an organism. Fever appears between the twelfth and fourteenth days, about the time precipitins are first detected in the blood.

disease in which harmless material, such as pollens, induce severe symptoms mediated by nonprecipitating antibodies.

The somatic immunizing antigen of *S. typhosa* functions as an endotoxin but can sensitize the body to give it reactions of the tuberculin type, thus increasing the severity of the disease. The individual who has been immunized by a subclinical infection with *C. diphtheriae* and has diphtheria antitoxin in his serum may have developed a sensitivity to the toxin as a protein and will give a severe local reaction to the toxin in the Schick test. In many other instances of bacterial, viral, and mycotic diseases, allergies of the delayed or tuberculin type play a minor or even a major role in pathogenesis. **The tuberculin or bacterial type of allergy may increase the susceptibility of the animal to infection by interfering with the ineffectiveness of specific antibodies even when these have been transferred passively** (233).

It was noted in the chapter on allergy that the major symptoms of tuberculosis are largely, if not exclusively, the results of allergic reactions to the nontoxic tuberculoprotein. The violent symptoms of classical lobar pneumonia, mentioned in the early part of this chapter, are primarily allergic. Here the reaction seems to be to the nontoxic nucleoprotein of the pneumococci. But allergy seems to develop to the endotoxins themselves in the later stages of typhoid fever and brucellosis (55, 117).

It has been known for the past 50 years that certain patients with recurrent boils which have resisted all other forms of therapy may recover in a period of days after subcutaneous injection of the proper doses of an autogenous vaccine. The more scientific-minded physicians doubted the causal relationship between the injection of the vaccine and the cessation of boils because the recovery was more rapid than would be expected from an immunizing vaccine and because no proper foundation had been laid in experimental animals for this type of therapy. The first objection is easily answered: **the vaccine does not act as an immunizing agent but as a hyposensitizing material and perhaps as a booster in an already immunized individual.** The second objection has been answered by the work of Johnson, Cluff, and Gosh (152), who succeeded in hypersensitizing rabbits to staphylococci by a series of subcutaneous injections so ultimately 1/100 as many staphylococci were needed to produce a boil as were needed originally in the same rabbit. It is the personal opinion of the senior author that certain other chronic staphylococcal infections of the eye, sinuses, bronchi, and lungs are mediated by excessive hypersensitization and are curable by hyposensitization.

Immunity in Viral, Fungal and Parasitic Infections. **The best-known type of immunity in viral infections is the passively transferred classical antibody type. This is the basis for serum protection of animals, embryonated eggs, and tissue cultures** (98). Children with congenital agammaglobulinemia are apparently an exception, since they recover from viral disease with as good permanent immunity as normal children. Perhaps only minute amounts of antibody are needed, or perhaps cellular immunity is sufficient for protection. **Some viruses, such as vaccinia, herpes simplex, mumps, and lymphogranuloma produced a high degree of allergy. The newly discovered interferon** (144, 145) **may be the most important mechanism for immunity to viruses.**

Classical immunity plays a subordinate role in fungal diseases. Cellular and tissue immunity, as in tuberculosis, seemed to be the major factor. Allergy of either the atopic or tuberculin type is frequently present in fungus infections.

All known types of immunity operate in parasitic infections. The blood and tissue eosinophilia is probably the result of antigen and antibody reactions, and allergy plays an important role in some infections and in diagnosis. Skin tests are available for toxoplasmosis, trichinosis, and echinococcus infections. In addition to these classical manifestations of the reaction to parasites, some more obscure reactions also occur. A strong protective reaction occurs in 12 hours after feeding eggs of *Hymenolepis nana* to mice (121). Somewhat later in the course of infection immunity may develop to the larvae, which prevents them from maturing (52), or the antibodies may be directed to an essential excretion of the parasite and not to its body antigen. Taliaferro (315) has found an antibody in rats which had been infected with *Trypanosoma lewisi* which prevented the multiplication of the parasites but had no other observable effect. The antibody was given the name of **ablastin.**

Oliver-Gonzales (229) has described a simple practical method of diagnoses by exposing lyophilized *S. mansoni* eggs to serum from infected patients and observing the development of a circumoval precipitate after 12 hours of incubation.

Reactions between Species of Microorganisms and Species of Animals. In considering the whole problem of infectious disease, it should be kept in mind constantly that the infectious agent is a living organism which must, for its survival, adapt itself continuously to changes in environment brought about by the resistant mechanisms of the host. The immune reactions of the animal body also must be considered as changing continuously in response to the emergencies created by the presence in its tissues of living organisms which are also struggling for survival.

The ecologic concept of disease has been emphasized by Theobald Smith (301) and by Zinsser. Nature is not concerned with the fate of the individual organisms which may perish by the billions or the individual animals or men who may die by the thousands, but is concerned with the survival of the microorganisms as a species and the animal as a species. In a state of ideal parasitism, the organism lives in or on the host without producing injury, and in turn the host does not mobilize its defenses to destroy the organism. From this point of view the microorganism which kills its host rapidly is a bungling amateur (301).

In general, epidemic diseases tend to become milder either by a reduction in the invasiveness or virulence of the microorganism or by the selective survival of hosts with increased genetically controlled natural resistance. In some instances a disease may become milder as a result of herd immunization without a loss of virulence of the organisms or the breeding of a resistant host. With a decline in herd immunization the disease reappears in a fully virulent form. Changes of this type have been observed with scarlet fever and diphtheria (198), and we have

seen another example in the increase in the frequency and severity of poliomyelitis which preceded the vaccine era.

The Control of Infectious Diseases. The physician shares with the epidemiologist the responsibility of knowing (a) the source of the infection, (b) the route of invasion, (c) the location of the infection in the body, (d) the pathway of exit from the body, and (e) the method of survival in nature between episodes of active infection. The physician must know these facts about each particular infection in order to protect the individuals in immediate contact with the patient. The epidemiologist and sanitary engineer are not concerned with the diagnosis and treatment of the individual patient, but with the life cycle of the disease producing agent, and they therefore direct their activities toward general measures which affect the entire community, such as mass vaccinations and the elimination of mosquitoes and lice as well as the control of the purity of water and milk supplies. A thorough knowledge of immunology is essential for the practicing physician. Some organisms produce their damage with exotoxins which can be neutralized by specific antitoxins; others poison the body with endotoxins for which there are no effective antitoxins; while still others induce such a high degree of sensitivity in the patient's tissues that severe symptoms and even death may result from originally harmless metabolic products. There is a marked variation in the reactions of different individuals to the same infection. Some produce effective antibodies readily, while others cannot. **A combination of genetic, nutritional, environmental, and possibly psychic factors in the patient react with such variables as the location of the organism in the body, their numbers, and virulence to produce mild, severe or fatal infections.**

REFERENCES

1. Ajl, S. J., and others. J. Bact., 70:158, 1955.
2. ——— and others. J. Immunol., 80:435, 1958.
3. Alexander, H. E., and others. Virology, 5: 172, 1958.
4. Allen, W. P. J. Exper. Med., 115:411, 1962.
5. Amies, C. R. J. Path. & Bact., 67:25, 1954.

6. Andrews, C. H., and others. Brit. J. Exper. Path., 35:264, 1954.
7. Andrews, E. C., Jr., and McKinnon, G. E. Am. J. Path., 39:579, 1961.
8. Armstrong, C. Pub. Health Reports, 44: 1183, 2635, 1929.
9. Arvidson, M., and others. Acta path. et microbiol. Scandinav., 27:263, 1950.
10. Aub, J. C., and others. War Med., 5:71, 1944.
11. Auclair, J. E. J. Dairy Research, 21:323, 1954.
12. Bachtold, J. G., and others. J. Immunol., 75:475, 1955.
13. Bacon, G. A., and others. Brit. J. Exper. Path., 31:703, 714, 1950.
14. Bacot, A. W., and Martin, C. J. J. Hyg. (Camb. Plague Supplement), 3:423, 1914.
15. Badger, L. F., and others. Pub. Health Rep., 55:1027, 1940.
16. Baker, J. A., and Sheffy, B. E. Proc. Soc. Exper. Biol. & Med., 105:675, 679, 1960.
17. Barksdale, W. L., and Pappenheimer, A. M., Jr. J. Bact., 67:220, 1954.
18. Batson, H. C. J. Immunol., 66:737, 1951.
19. Beall, F. A., and others. J. Bact., 83:1274, 1962.
20. Benacerraf, B. Bact. Rev., 24:35, 1960.
21. Bennett, I. L., Jr., and Nicastri, A. Bact. Rev., 24:16, 1960.
22. Berry, L. J., and Mitchell, R. B. J. Infect. Dis., 93:75, 1953.
23. ———— and others. J. Infect. Dis., 94:144, 1954.
24. Bisset, K. A. J. Path. & Bact., 58:251, 1946.
25. Black, F. L., and Melnick, J. L. Proc. Soc. Exper. Biol. & Med., 89:353, 1955.
26. Bliznakov, E. G. Proc. Soc. Exper. Biol. & Med., 112:367, 1963.
27. Bloch, H., and Noll, H. Brit. J. Exper. Path., 36:8, 1955.
28. Bloom, W. L., and others. J. Inf. Dis., 80: 41, 1947; 83:116, 1948.
29. ———— and Prigmore, J. R. J. Bact., 64: 855, 1952.
30. ———— and others. J. Inf. Dis., 92:70, 1953.
31. Bowen, S. T., and others. Proc. Soc. Exper. Biol. & Med., 94:482, 1957.
32. Boyd, J. S. K. Lancet, 1:113, 1946.
33. Boyden, S. J. Exper. Med., 115:453, 1962.
34. Brem, T. H., and Morton, M. E. Ann. Int. Med., 43:465, 1955.
35. Briody, B. A. Bact. Rev., 14:65, 1950.
36. Brubaker, R. R., and Surgalla, M. J. J. Bact., 82:940, 1961.
37. ———— and Surgalla, M. J. J. Bact., 84: 615, 1962.
38. ———— and Surgalla, M. J. J. Bact., 84: 539, 1962.
39. Brunner, K. T., and others. J. Immunol., 85:99, 1960.
40. Bruton, O. C., and others. Am. J. Dis. Child., 84:632, 1952.
41. Bull, C. G. J. Exper. Med., 24:7, 1916.
42. ———— and McKee, C. R. Am. J. Hyg., 1:284, 1921.
43. Burnet, F. M., and Stone, J. D. Australian J. Exper. Biol. & M. Sc., 25:219, 1947.
44. ———— Bull. Johns Hopkins Hosp., 88:157, 1951.
45. Burrows, W., and others. Proc. Soc. Exper. Biol. & Med., 57:306, 308, 311, 1944.
46. ———— and others. J. Infect. Dis., 81:261, 1947.
47. Burrows, T. W., and Bacon, G. A. Brit. J. Exper. Path., 35:134, 1954.
48. ———— and Bacon, G. A. Brit. J. Exper. Path., 37:286, 481, 1956.
49. ———— and Bacon, G. A. Brit. J. Exper. Path., 39:278, 1958.
50. ———— Ann. N.Y. Acad. Science, 88:1125, 1960.
51. Cabasso, V. J., and others. Proc. Soc. Exper. Biol. & Med., 85:167, 1954.
52. Campbell, D. H. J. Immunol., 35:465, 1938.
53. Cannon, P. R. J.A.M.A., 128:360, 1945.
54. Carlisle, H. N., and Saslaw, S. Proc. Soc. Exper. Biol. & Med., 110:603, 1962.
55. Carpenter, C. M., and others. J. Exper. Med., 115:613, 1962.
56. Cavanaugh, D. C., and Randall, R. J. Immunol., 83:348, 1959.
57. Chang, Te Wen, and Weinstein, L. Proc. Soc. Exper. Biol. & Med., 94:431, 1957.
58. Chen, T. H., and Meyer, K. F. J. Immunol., 72:282, 1954.
59. Chernew, I., and Braude, A. I. J. Clin. Invest., 41:1945, 1962.
60. Chu, H. P. J. Gen. Microbiol., 3:255, 1949.
61. Clark, P. F., and others. Bact. Rev., 13:99, 1949.
62. Coburn, A. F., and others. Brit. J. Exper. Path., 35:279, 1954.
63. Coca, A. F. J. Immunol., 6:387, 1921.
64. Cohn, Z. A., and Morse, S. I. J. Exper. Med., 111:667, 689, 1960.
65. ———— and Hirsch, J. G. J. Exper. Med., 112:983, 1005, 1015, 1960.
66. Colter, J. S., and others. Virology, 4:522, 1952.
67. Comolli, R., and Perin, A. Proc. Soc. Exper. Biol. & Med., 113:289, 1963.
68. Crampton, C. F., and others. J. Biol. Chem., 215:787, 1955.
69. Cromartie, W. J., and others. J. Infect. Dis., 80:1, 14, 28, 121, 1947.
70. Darnell, J. E., Jr., and others. J. Clin. Invest., 34:1237, 1955.
71. Davenport, F. M., and others. Fed. Proc., 14:460, 1955.
72. Derby, B. M., and Rogers, D. E. J. Exper. Med., 113:1053, 1961.
73. Donaldson, D. M., and Marcus, S. J. Immunol., 81:292, 1958.
74. Dubos, R. J. The Bacterial Cell, Cambridge, Mass., Harvard University Press, 1945.
75. ———— Biochemical Determinants of Microbial Diseases, Cambridge, Mass., Harvard University Press, 1954.
76. ———— and Hirsch, J. G. J. Exper. Med., 99:55, 1954.
77. ———— and Schaedler, R. W. J. Exper. Med., 110:935, 1959.
78. Edsall, G. Pub. Health Rep., 76:811, 1961.
79. Ekwurzel, G. M., and others. Pub. Health Rep., 53:1877, 1938.
80. Elder, T. D., and Baker, R. D. Arch. Path., 61:159, 1956.
81. Enders, J. F., Shaffer, M. F., and others. J. Exper. Med., 64:7, 281, 307, 425, 1936.
82. ———— J. Immunol., 73:62, 1954.

83. Evans, E. E., and Cowles, R. B. Proc. Soc. Exper. Biol. & Med., 101:482, 1959.
84. ———— Proc. Soc. Exper. Biol. & Med., 112:531, 1963.
85. Evans, C. A. Bact. Rev., 24:341, 1960.
86. Felton, L. D., and Bailey, G. H. J. Infect. Dis., 38:131, 1926.
87. ———— and others. J. Immunol., 76:69, 1956.
88. Fink, M. A., and Quinn, V. A. J. Immunol., 70:61, 1953.
89. Finland, M., and others. Am. J. Med., 8:21, 1950.
90. Finney, D. J. Statistical Method in Biological Assay, London, L. Griffin, 1952.
91. Fitzpatrick, F. K. Am. J. Pub. Health, 38:676, 1948.
92. Fleming, D. E., and Foshay, L. J. Bact., 70:345, 1955.
93. Fong, J., and others. J. Exper. Med., 115:475, 1962.
94. Formal, S. B., and others. J. Bact., 68:117, 1954.
95. Foster, C., and others. J. Exper. Med., 79:221, 1944.
96. Fredericq, P. Colicins. Ann. Rev. Microbiol., 11:7, 1957.
97. Freeman, V. J. J. Bact., 61:675, 1951.
98. Friedman, R. M., and Baron, S. J. Immunol., 87:379, 1961.
99. Furness, G., and Axelrod, A. E. J. Immunol., 83:133, 627, 1959.
100. Gaines, S., and others. J. Exper. Med., 114:327, 1961.
101. Garber, E. D., and others. Proc. Nat. Acad. Sc., 38:693, 1952.
102. Gerber, D. F., and Watkins, H. M. S. J. Bact., 82:815, 1961.
103. Getz, H. R., and others. Am. Rev. Tuberc., 64:381, 1951.
104. Ghione, M. Proc. Soc. Exper. Biol. & Med., 97:773, 1958.
105. Gladstone, G. P. Brit. J. Exper. Path., 27:394, 1946.
106. Gowen, J. W. Bact. Review, 24:192, 1960.
107. Greenwood, M., and others. Experimental Epidemiology, Medical Research Council, London, Special Reports Series, 209, 1936.
108. Groman, N. B. J. Bact., 69:9, 1955.
109. Gusdon, J. P. J. Immunol., 88:494, 1962.
110. Habel, K. Mechanism of Active Induced Immunity with Attenuated Living Vaccines in Dynamics of Virus and Rickettsiae Infections, New York, Blakiston, 1954.
111. Hankin, E. H. Proc. Roy. Soc. (London), 48:93, 1891.
112. Harris, T. N. Proc. Soc. Exper. Biol. & Med., 90:33, 1955.
113. Harris, H. Bact. Rev., 24:3, 1960.
114. Hawking, F. Brit. M. J., 1:425, 1954.
115. Hedrich, A. W. Am. J. Hyg., 17:613, 1933.
116. Heidelberger, M., and others. J. Exper. Med., 85:227, 1947.
117. Heilman, D. H., and others. J. Immunol., 85:258, 1960.
118. Heinmets, F., and others. J. Bact., 67:5, 1954.
119. Henderson, R. G., and Topping, N. H. National Institutes of Health Bull., Washington, D.C., No. 183, U.S. Government Printing Office, 1945, p. 41.
120. Hennessy, A. V., and others. J. Immunol., 75:401, 1955.
121. Heyneman, D. J. Immunol., 88:217, 1962.
122. Hiatt, R. B., and others. J. Clin. Invest., 31:721, 1952.
123. Higgenbotham, R. D., and Dougherty, T. F. Proc. Soc. Exper. Biol. & Med., 90:253, 1953.
124. Higuchi, K., and Smith, J. L. J. Bact., 81:605, 1961.
125. Hirsch, J. G. J. Exper. Med., 97:327, 345, 1953.
126. ———— J. Exper. Med., 99:79, 1954.
127. ———— J. Exper. Med., 103:589, 1956.
128. ———— Bact. Rev., 23:48, 1959.
129. ———— Bact. Rev., 24:133, 1960.
130. ———— J. Exper. Med., 111:323, 1960.
131. ———— J. Exper. Med., 116:827, 1962.
132. Hiss, P. H. J. Med. Research, 19:323, 1908.
133. Holland, J. J., and Pickett, M. J. J. Exper. Med., 108:343, 1958.
134. Hook, E. W., and Wagner, R. R. J. Immunol., 83:302, 1959.
135. Hopkins, J. G., and Parker, J. T. J. Exper. Med., 27:1, 1918.
136. Horstmann, D. M. J.A.M.A., 142, 236, 1950.
137. ———— Ann. Int. Med., 43:526, 1955.
138. Hotchin, J., and Weigand, H. J. Immunol., 86:392, 401, 1961.
139. Howie, J. W., and O'Hea, A. J. Mechanisms of Microbial Pathogenicity, Cambridge, England, Cambridge University Press, 1955.
140. Ilavsky, J., and Foley, E. J. Proc. Soc. Exper. Biol. & Med., 84:211, 1953.
141. Inglot, A., and Davenport, F. M. J. Immunol., 88:551, 1962.
142. Ipsen, J., Jr. J. Immunol., 72:243, 1954.
143. ———— J. Immunol., 83:448, 1959.
144. Isaacs, A., and Lindenmann, J. Proc. Roy. Soc., 1473:258, 1957.
145. ———— Scientific American, 204:51, 1961.
146. ———— Proc. Roy. Soc. Med., 55:725, 1962.
147. Isabel, W. L., and others. J. Immunol., 90:804, 1963.
148. Ivanovics, G. Bact. Review, 26:108, 1962.
149. Jackson, F. C., and others. Am. J. Vet. Res., 18:771, 1957.
150. Jenkins, C., and Benacerraf, B. J. Exper. Med., 112:403, 419, 1960.
151. ———— and Rowley, D. J. Exper. Med., 114:363, 1961.
152. Johnson, T. E., and others. J. Exper. Med., 113:235, 249, 259, 1961.
153. Karp, A. J. Bact., 67:450, 1954.
154. Kass, E. H., and Finland, M. Advances in Internal Med., 9:45, 1958.
155. ———— Bact. Review, 24:177, 1960.
156. ———— Ann. Int. Med., 56:46, 1962.
157. Kelley, W. H. J. Exper. Med., 55:877, 1932.
158. Kent, R. J. Embryol. & Exper. Morph., 9:128, 1961.
159. Kerby, G. P., and Bennett, I. L. Proc. Soc. Exper. Biol. & Med., 78:48, 1951.
160. ———— Proc. Soc. Exper. Biol. & Med., 81:129, 381, 1952.
161. ———— and Eadie, G. S. Proc. Soc. Exper. Biol. & Med., 83:111, 1953.
162. ———— J. Immunol., 67:450, 1954.

163. Klein, F., and others. J. Immunol., 88:15, 1962.
164. Kligler, I. J., and others. Proc. Soc. Exper. Biol. & Med., 57:132, 1944.
165. Koprowski, H., and others. J.A.M.A., 160·954, 1956.
166. Kossel, A. The Protamines and Histones, London, Longmans, Green and Co., 1928.
167. Krueger, R. G., and Twedt, R. M. J. Immunol., 90:952, 1963.
168. Landy, M., and Pillemer, L. J. Exper. Med., 103:823, 1956.
169. ———— and others. J. Bact., 83:631, 1962.
170. Larson, C. L., and others. J. Immunol., 73:221, 1954.
171. Lawton, W. D., and others. J. Immunol., 84:475, 1960.
172. Leclainche, E., and Vallée, H. Ann. Inst. Pasteur, 14:202, 1900.
173. Leon, M. A. J. Exper. Med., 103:285, 1956.
174. Leonard, C. G., and Thorne, C. B. J. Immunol., 87:175, 1961.
175. Lewis, R. M., and Adler, E. L. J.A.M.A., 106:2054, 1936.
176. ———— Am. Naturalist, 87:273, 1953.
177. Le Maistre, C., and Tompsett, R. J. Exper. Med., 95:393, 1952.
178. Longcope, W. T., and MacKenzie, G. M. Proc. Soc. Exper. Biol. & Med., 17:133, 1920.
179. Louria, D. B., and others. J. Clin. Invest., 39:1435, 1960.
180. Lurie, M. B., and Zappasodi, P. Arch. Path., 34:151, 1942.
181. ———— J. Exper. Med., 75:247, 1942.
182. ———— Am. J. Med., 9:591, 1950.
183. ———— Ann. New York Acad. Sc., 52:1074, 1950.
184. ———— Am. Rev. Tuberc., 61:765, 1950; 67:265, 1953; 73:434, 1956.
185. Lwoff, A. Bact. Rev., 23:109, 1959.
186. McConkey, M. Am. Rev. Tuberc., 21:627, 1930.
187. ———— and Smith, D. T. J. Exper. Med., 58:503, 1933.
188. McCoy, E. Ann. Rev. Microbiol., 8:257, 1954.
189. McCrumb, F. B., Jr., and others. J. Infect. Dis., 96:38, 1955.
190. ———— Trans. Assoc. Amer. Phys., 70:74, 1957.
191. ———— Ann. Int. Med., 52:1161, 1960.
192. McCune, R., and others. J. Immunol., 85:447, 1960.
193. McKendrick, A. G. Edinburgh M. J., 47:117, 1940.
194. MacCallum, P., and others. J. Path. & Bact. 60:93, 1949.
195. MacDonald, G. Pub. Health Rep., 76:753, 1961.
196. Macfarlane, M. C. Mechanisms of Microbial Pathogenicity, Cambridge, England, Cambridge University Press, 1955, p. 57.
197. MacLeod, C. M., and others. J. Exper. Med., 82:445, 1945.
198. Magill, T. P. J. Immunol., 74:1, 1955.
199. Manire, G. P., and Galasso, C. J. J. Immunol., 83:529, 1959.
200. Marchette, N. J., and Nicholes, P. S. J. Bact., 82:26, 1961.
201. Martin, S. P., and Kerby, G. P. J. Exper. Med., 92:45, 1950.
202. ———— and Kerby, G. P. Proc. Soc. Exper. Biol. & Med., 81:73, 1952.
203. ———— and others. J. Immunol., 68:293, 1952.
204. Melly, M. A., and others. J. Exper. Med., 112:1121, 1960.
205. Melby, J. C., and others. Clin. Research Proc., 6:280, 1958.
206. Menkin, V. Proc. Soc. Exper. Biol. & Med., 75:350, 1950.
207. Michael, J. G., and others. J. Exper. Med., 115:131, 1962.
208. Miles, A. A. Mechanisms of Microbial Pathogenicity, Cambridge, England, Cambridge University Press, 1955, p. 1.
209. Miller, C. P., and others. Proc. Soc. Exper. Biol. & Med., 108:183, 1961.
210. Mitsuhashi, S., and others. J. Bact., 81:863, 1961.
211. Miya, F., and Marcus, S. J. Immunol., 86:526, 652, 1961.
212. Molnar, D. M. J. Bact., 84:147, 1962.
213. Morgan, T. E., and others. J. Bact., 67:257, 1954.
214. Morris, M., and Seastone, C. V. J. Bact., 69:195, 1955.
215. Morse, S. I. J. Exper. Med., 115:295, 1962.
216. Murphy, W. H., and others. Proc. Soc. Exper. Biol. & Med., 99:213, 1958.
217. Murray, E. S., and others. J.A.M.A., 142:1059, 1950.
218. Muschel, L. H., and Treffers, H. P. J. Immunol., 76:1, 1956.
219. ———— and others. Proc. Soc. Exper. Biol. & Med., 97:376, 1958.
220. Muschenheim, C., and others. J. Inf. Dis., 72:187, 1943.
221. Myrvik, Q. N., and Weiser, R. S. J. Immunol., 74:9, 1955.
222. ———— Ann. N.Y. Acad. Sci., 66:391, 1956.
223. ———— and others. J. Immunol., 81:118, 123, 1958.
224. ———— and Leake, E. S. J. Immunol., 84:247, 1960.
225. Noller, E. C., and Hartsell, S. E. J. Bact., 81:482, 1961.
226. Nungester, W. J. Bact. Rev., 15:105, 1951.
227. ———— Ann. Rev. Microbiol., 8:363, 1954.
228. O'Dell, B. L., and others. Proc. Soc. Exper. Biol. & Med., 108:512, 1961.
229. Oliver-Gonzales. J. Exper. Parasit., 13:12, 1963.
230. Opton, E. M., and others. J. Immunol., 75:178, 1955.
231. Packer, L., and others. J. Bact., 78:658, 1959.
232. Pappenheimer, A. M., Jr. Mechanisms of Microbial Pathogenicity, Cambridge, England, Cambridge University Press, 1955, p. 40.
233. Parfantjev, I. A. Proc. Soc. Exper. Biol. & Med., 90:373, 1955.
234. Pasteur, L. Bull. Acad. Méd., Paris, S 2, 10:94, 1881.
235. Paul, J. R., and others. J. Immunol., 66:695, 1951.
236. Payne, F. E., and others. J. Inf. Dis., 96:168, 1955.
237. Peto, S. Biometrics, 9:321, 1953.
238. Pettersson, A. Z. Immunitätsforsch., 88:210, 1936.

239. Pillemer, L., and others. Science, 120:279, 1954.
240. ———— and others. J. Exper. Med., 103:1, 1956.
241. Pinkerton, H., and Bessey, O. A. Science, 89:368, 1939.
242. Pirsch, J. B., and Mika, L. A. J. Bact., 77:185, 1959.
243. Pollack, A. D., and Victor, J. Proc. Soc. Exper. Biol. & Med., 89:561, 1955.
244. Rafelson, M. E., Jr., and others. Arch. Biochem., 29:69, 1950.
245. ———— and others. J. Biol. Chem., 193:205, 1951.
246. Raffel, S. J. Infect. Dis., 82:267, 1948.
247. ———— Experientia, 6:410, 1950.
248. ———— Immunity, Hypersensitivity, Serology, 2nd ed., New York, Appleton-Century-Crofts, Inc., 1961.
249. Reichlin, S., and Glaser, R. J. J. Exper. Med., 107:219, 1958.
250. Reimann, H. A., and others. Am. J. Trop. Med., 26:631, 1946.
251. Rhodes, P. S. J.A.M.A., 157:877, 1955.
252. Rich, A. R., and Lewis, M. R. Bull. Johns Hopkins Hosp, 50:115, 1932.
253. ———— and McKee, C. M. Bull. Johns Hopkins Hosp., 59:171, 1936.
254. ———— and McKee, C. M. Bull. Johns Hopkins Hosp., 64:434, 1939.
255. ———— and Follis, R. H., Jr. Bull. Johns Hopkins Hosp., 71:345, 1942.
256. ———— The Pathogenesis of Tuberculosis, 2nd ed., Springfield, Ill., Charles C Thomas Co., 1951.
257. Robineaux, J., and Frédéric, J. Comp. rend. Soc. biol., 149:486, 1955.
258. Robinson, H. J., and others. Proc. Soc. Exper. Biol. & Med., 84:312, 1953.
259. Rogers, D. E. J. Exper. Med., 103:713, 1956.
260. Rodriguez-Molina, R., and Oliver-Gonzales, J. J.A.M.A., 182:131, 1962.
261. Rogers, D. E. Bact. Rev., 24:50, 1960.
262. ———— and Melly, M. A. J. Exper. Med., 111:533, 1960.
263. ———— and Melly, M. A. Yale J. Biol. & Med., 34:360, 1962.
264. ———— J.A.M.A., 181:38, 1962.
265. Rohn, R. J., and others. Am. J. M. Sc., 229:406, 1955.
266. Ross, S., and others. Pediat., 2:163, 1948.
267. Rous, P. J. Exper. Med., 41:379, 1925.
268. Rowley, D. J. Exper. Med., 111:137, 1960.
269. Rude, E., and Goebel, W. F. J. Exper. Med., 116:73, 1962.
270. Saito, K. J. Bact., 84:500, 1962.
271. Sanford, J. P., and others. J. Exper. Med., 115:383, 1962.
272. Saslaw, S., and others. J. Exper. Med., 84:263, 1946.
273. Sbarra, A. J., and Karnovksy, M. L. J. Biochem., 234:1355, 1959.
274. Schaedler, R. W., and Dubos, R. J. J. Exper. Med., 115:1149, 1161, 1962.
275. Schneider, H. A. Ann. N.Y. Acad. Med., 66:25, 334, 1956.
276. ———— J. Exper. Med., 105:319, 1957.
277. ———— Bact. Reviews, 24:186, 1960.
278. Schneider, R. Arch Hyg., 70:40, 1909.
279. Schwab, J. H., and Watson, D. W. J. Infect. Dis., 95:267, 1954.
280. Seronde, J., Jr. Proc. Soc. Exper. Biol. & Med., 85:521, 1954.
281. Sever, J. L. Proc. Soc. Exper. Biol. & Med., 103:326, 1960.
282. Shaffer, J. M., and others. J. Exper. Med., 97:77, 1953.
283. Shands, J. W., Jr., and Suter, E. Fed. Proc., 22:2006, 1963.
284. Shepard, C. C. J. Bact., 77:701, 1959.
285. ———— J. Exper. Med., 112:445, 1960.
286. Showacre, J. L., and others. J. Immunol., 87:153, 1961.
287. Shwartzman, G. Effects of ACTH and Cortisone Upon Infection and Resistance, New York, Columbia University Press, 1953.
288. Sia, R. H. P., and Zia, S. H. Proc. Soc. Exper. Biol. & Med., 29:791, 1932.
289. Simon, H. J. Attenuated Infection, Philadelphia, J. B. Lippincott and Co., 1960.
290. Skarnes, R. C., and Watson, D. W. J. Bact., 70:110, 1955.
291. ———— and Watson, D. W. J. Exper. Med., 104:829, 1936.
292. ———— and Watson, D. W. Bact. Review, 21:273, 1957.
293. Slein, M. W., and Logan, G. F., Jr. J. Bact., 83:359, 1962.
294. Smadel, J. E., and others. Ann. Int. Med., 34:1, 1951.
295. Smillie, W. G., and Kilbourne, E. D. Preventive Medicine and Public Health, 3rd ed., New York, Macmillan Co., 1963.
296. Smith, C. E., and others. J.A.M.A., 160:546, 1956.
297. Smith, D. T. Bull. Johns Hopkins Hosp., 32:1, 1921.
298. ———— and Smith, S. G. Tr. Am. Clin. & Climatol. A., 49:226, 1933.
299. Smith, J. M., and Dubos, R. J. J. Exper. Med., 103:119, 1956.
300. Smith, M. R., and others. J. Immunol., 90:914, 1963.
301. Smith, T. Parasitism and Disease, Princeton, N.J., Princeton University Press, 1934.
302. Soper, H. E. J. Roy. Stat. Soc., 92:34, 1929.
303. Spitznagel, J. K. J. Exper. Med., 114:1063, 1079, 1961.
304. ———— and Chi, H. Y. Am. J. Path., 43:679, 1963.
304a. Spivack, M. L., and Karler, A. J. Immunol., 80:441, 1958.
305. Sprinz, H., and others. Am. J. Path., 39:681, 1961.
306. Sprunt, D. H. J. Exper. Med., 75:297, 1942.
307. Stanley, J. L., and Smith, H. J. Gen. Microbiol., 26:29, 1961.
308. Stearman, R. L. Bact. Rev., 19:160, 1955.
309. Strouse, S. J. Exper. Med., 11:743, 1909.
310. Sulitzeanu, D., and others. Immunol., 5:116, 1962.
311. Suter, E. J. Exper. Med., 97:235, 1953.
312. ———— Bact. Rev., 20:94, 1956.
313. Symposium on Non-Specific Resistance to Infection, Bact. Rev., 24:1, 1960.
314. Syverton, J. T., and others. Proc. Soc. Exper. Biol. & Med., 80:123, 1952.
315. Taliaferro, W. H. Bact. Review, 12:1, 1948.
316. Taylor, I., and Knowelden, J. Principles of Epidemiology, Boston, Little, Brown and Co., 1957.
317. Te Linde, R. W. J.A.M.A., 110:1633, 1938.

318. Theiler, M. Medicine, 20:443, 1941.
319. —— "The Virus," in Yellow Fever, New York, McGraw-Hill, 1951, p. 125.
320. Thompson, R., and Shibuya, M. J. Bact., 51:671, 1946.
321. Topley, W. W. C., and Wilson, E. B. Principles of Bacteriology and Immunology, 3rd ed., Baltimore, Williams and Wilkins Co., 1946.
322. Traub, E. J. Exper. Med., 69:801, 1939.
323. —— Zentralbl. Bakt. I., (Orig.), 177:453, 472, 1960.
324. Van Heyningen, W. E., and Gladstone, G. P. Brit. J. Exper. Path., 34:202, 1953.
325. Vosti, K. L., and others. J. Clin. Invest., 41:1436, 1962.
326. Waisbren, B. A., and Brown, I. 88:249, 1962.
327. Wanzer, S. H. J. Bact., 67:264, 1954.
328. Wardlaw, A. C. J. Exper. Med., 115:1231, 1962.
329. Warren, J., and others. J. Bact., 70:170, 1955.
330. Watson, D. W., and Bloom, W. L. Proc. Soc. Exper. Biol. & Med., 81:29, 1952.
331. Webster, L. T. Medicine, 11:321, 1932; 25:77, 1946.
332. Weinstein, I., and others. 83:1010, 1962.
333. Weir, J. A., and others. Science, 117:328, 1953.
334. Weiss, C., and Czarnetsky, E. J. Arch. Path., 20:233, 1935.
335. Wertman, K., and others. J. Immunol., 72:196, 1954.
336. —— and Groh, M. J. Immunol., 82:241, 1959.
337. —— and Sypherd, P. S. J. Immunol., 85:511, 1960.
338. —— and Henry, J. J. Immunol., 89:314, 1962.
339. Whitby, J. L., and others. Bact. Rev., 25:437, 1961.
340. Wilson, A. T., and Rosenblum, H. J. Exper. Med., 95:25, 1952.
341. —— J. Exper. Med., 98:305, 1953.
342. Wilson, E. B., and Burke, M. H. Proc. Nat. Acad. Sc., 28:361, 1942; 29:43, 1943.
343. Winslow, C. E. A. The Concept of Epidemic Disease, Princeton, N.J., Princeton University Press, 1944.
344. Wood, W. B., Jr., and others. J. Exper. Med., 84:387, 1946.
345. —— Bact. Rev., 24:41, 1960.
346. Woods, J. W., and others. J. Clin. Invest., 40:599, 1961.
347. Woodward, T. E., and others. Ann. Int. Med., 34:10, 1951.
348. Woodward, J. M., and others. J. Bact., 67:58, 1954.
349. Wooley, J. G., and Sebrell, W. H. J. Bact., 44:148, 1942.
350. Woolley, D. W., and others. J. Biol. Chem., 198:807, 1952.
351. Wright, G. G., and others. J. Immunol., 72:263, 1954; 73:387, 1954.
352. Wright, G. P. Mechanisms of Microbial Pathogenicity, Cambridge, England, Cambridge University Press, 1955, p. 78.
353. Wu, W. G., and Marcus, S. J. Immunol., 91:313, 1963.
354. Yeomans, A., and others. J.A.M.A., 126:349, 1944.
355. Zinneman, H. H., and others. J.A.M.A., 156:1390, 1954.
356. Zinsser, H. J. Med. Res., 22:391, 1910.
357. —— and Grinnell, F. B. J. Bact., 14:301, 1927.
358. —— Am. J. Hyg., 20:513, 1934.
359. —— Rats, Lice and History, Boston, Little, Brown and Co., 1935.
360. Zucker, T. F., and Zucker, L. M. Proc. Soc. Exper. Biol. & Med., 85:517, 1954.

PATHOGENIC BACTERIA

19

The Pneumococcus and Pneumonia

Family: *Lactobacteriaceae* Orla-Jensen. Tribe: *Streptococceae* Trevisan. Genus: *Diplococcus* Weichselbaum. Species: *Diplococcus pneumoniae* Weichselbaum.

Pneumococci, streptococci, and staphylococci are known collectively by physicians as the pyogenic or "pus-producing" cocci. Before the introduction of antibiotics, they, along with the tubercle bacilli, were the most frequent cause of death from infections in this country (Fig. 1). Although all three groups of pyogenic cocci contain numerous specific antigenic types and subspecies, the pneumococci are the least complex and will be presented first.

Lancet-shaped diplococci, now recognized as pneumococci, were found independently in human saliva by Sternberg (66) and by Pasteur (56) in 1881. Although both investigators produced septicemia in rabbits with this organism, they did not associate the diplococci with pneumonia, probably because they had not envisioned that healthy individuals could be carriers of virulent cocci. The discovery that these diplococci caused lobar pneumonia was made independently and simultaneously by A. Fränkel (24) and Weichselbaum (75), who published the results of their studies in 1886.

Morphology and Staining. The pneumococci are rather large, lancet-shaped cocci which usually occur in pairs and are surrounded by definite **capsules.** In smears the cocci also may be found singly, in short chains, and occasionally in long chains; and in the latter condition the capsule appears to enclose the entire chain with or without indentations opposite the points of division.

Type III pneumococci are characteristically spherical in shape both in exudates from the body and in culture. Long chains may be induced consistently by cultivation in a medium

deficient in magnesium (57). Swollen and irregular involution forms are found regularly in cultures from 24 to 48 hours old.

The pneumococcus is **nonsporogenous** and **nonmotile** and possesses no flagella. **The organism stains readily** with the usual aniline dyes and is **gram-positive** when fresh actively growing cultures are examined, but numerous gram-negative forms may be found in old cultures. **Capsules** are produced by virulent strains (Fig. 2).

Pneumococci are **bile soluble.** Rapid autolysis in bile or 10 per cent desoxycholate within 5 to 10 minutes is the most reliable test for the differentiation of pneumococci from other coccal forms. If glucose is present in the broth in which the pneumococci are grown, the increased acidity causes a precipitation and gelling after addition of the deoxycholate solution unless the culture has been readjusted to pH 7.4.

Cultural Characteristics. For best growth, the media used for the cultivation of this organism should have a pH of 7.6 to 7.8. Although the organisms will grow in a slightly acid medium, any marked acidity will result in prompt death of the culture.

Pneumococci require a large number of amino acids and vitamins for growth, but they have been cultured successfully in a chemically defined medium (1, 30). They are **aerobic** but **facultatively anaerobic.** Growth is rarely observed at temperatures below 25° C. or above 41° C., the optimal temperature being about 37.5° C. Glucose and glycerine increase the rate of multiplication, but the increased acid production resulting from the enhanced growth soon kills the culture unless the acid is neutralized by the addition of 1 per cent powdered calcium carbonate to the medium.

On **meat infusion blood-agar plates** the pneumococci develop, after 24 to 48 hours' incubation, small round, somewhat flattened, trans-

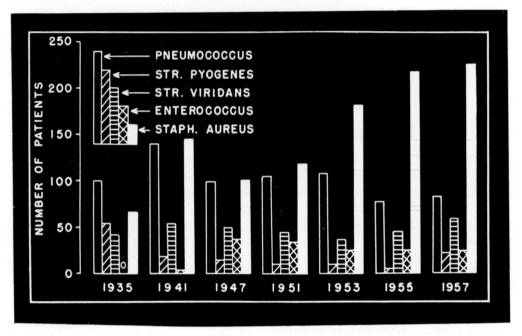

Fig. 1. Bacteremia occurrence of gram-positive cocci in blood cultures before antibiotics in 1935 and after antibiotics in 1941-1957. Note the reduction in pneumococci and *Streptococcus pyogenes* and the increase in enterococci and *Staphylococcus aureus*. (From Finland, Jones, and Barnes. *J.A.M.A.*, 170:2188, 1959.)

parent colonies. In suitable nutrient **broth** growth is rapid, and within 24 hours there is a faint, uniform clouding of the fluid. In **poured blood-plates** after 48 hours' incubation, pneumococci produce in the depth of the medium small round compact colonies surrounded by a zone of greenish discoloration which is identical in appearance with that formed by colonies of α-hemolytic streptococci.

The addition of 1 per cent glucose and 5 per cent defibrinated rabbit's blood to meat infusion broth adjusted to pH 7.8 results in a very rapid growth of organisms. This mixture, known as **Avery's medium** or **Avery's artificial mouse,** facilitates early isolation and identification of pneumococci since direct typing by the **Quellung** method may be done on cultures 12 to 18 hours after inoculation.

Inulin is fermented by most but not all strains of pneumococci; a positive test is therefore confirmation, but a negative test does not exclude the possibility that the organism is a pneumococcus. Pneumococci, in contrast to other cocci, are inhibited by quinidine. Colonies suspected of being pneumococci are streaked over the surface of a blood agar plate, and paper disks are applied after streaking. If the organism in question is a pneumococcus, there will be a clear zone free of organisms about each disk.

The **intraperitoneal inoculation** of a **white mouse** is not only the most rapid and most reliable method of obtaining pure cultures of pneumococci from contaminated materials, but it is also an accurate means of determining the pathogenicity of the strain. Type XIV, however, is avirulent for the mouse (45), and Type III A 66 almost avirulent for the rabbit.

Resistance. Pneumococci survive in dried sputum for several months if protected from direct sunlight. They die in a few days after growth on ordinary media but may be kept alive and virulent for months or years by the method of freezing and drying introduced by Flosdorf and Mudd (21). The organism is killed readily by heat at 52° C. for 10 minutes, in one hour by direct sunlight, and in one and one-half hours after exposure to diffuse sunlight. Pneumococci are much more readily destroyed by phenol, bichloride of mercury, potassium permanganate, and other antiseptics than are the micrococci and streptococci and are particularly susceptible to soaps, bile, sodium oleate, dyes, and certain derivatives of quinine.

Pneumococci were not inhibited by the original sulfanilamide but were inhibited by the

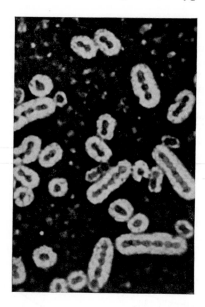

Fig. 2. Pneumococcus from spinal fluid. Preparation stained by P. Bruce White method to show capsules. × 1,800. (Courtesy of Dr. Josephine Bittner and Dr. C. F. Robinow.)

later sulfonamides, such as sulfadiazine, although resistance to the drugs often appeared in a period of days. Pneumococci are extremely sensitive to penicillin, which not only inhibits the growth, but actually kills the organisms. Up to the present time resistant strains to penicillin have not appeared, and penicillin remains the drug of choice (54, 64).

Variability. The encapsulated form of pneumococci has been called the smooth (S) phase, and the nonencapsulated the rough (R) phase, and these terms are found consistently in the older literature. Shinn (62) discovered a variant form in old pneumococcal cultures which, on agar, grew as a wrinkled colony and showed a filamentous mycelium-like growth typical of the R forms of other species. Another extremely rough strain has been studied in some detail by Taylor, who labeled her organism E R (4, 43, 44, 70).

Transformation of Specific Types. The protein bodies of all pneumococci seem to be identified in chemical and antigenic structure. The specificity of the various types, as well as the virulence, depends upon the complex polysaccharide capsule.

The first evidence that one type of pneumococcus could be converted into another specific capsular type was presented by Griffith in 1923. To accomplish this, Griffith injected into mice a mixture of the living R form of one type of pneumococcus and heat-killed suspension of virulent pneumococci of another type. Dawson and Sia (12) brought about this sort of transformation in vitro by growing R forms of one type of pneumococcus in a medium containing homologous anti-R serum and whole heat-killed S organisms of another type. Alloway, carrying these experiments further, transformed R pneumococci of any type into S forms of different types by cultivating them in broth containing filtered solutions of alcoholic precipitates of extracts of the S forms. In this medium R pneumococci, irrespective of their type derivation, developed and thereafter retained all the type-specific characteristics of the S pneumococci from which the extract was prepared. The R forms of pneumococci appear to be potentially capable of producing capsular polysaccharides at any time. In the recent comprehensive studies by Avery, MacLeod, and McCarty (7), an extract of Type III pneumococcus in a dilution of 1:600,000,000 converted a nonencapsulated culture, derived from a Type II pneumococcus, into a typical Type III organism (Fig. 3). Later work by McCarty and Avery showed that the biologically active converter was associated with the deoxyribonucleic acid fraction and was probably gene-

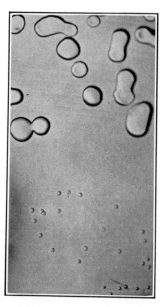

Fig. 3. Conversion of Type II to Type III pneumococcus. Small colonies are S forms of Type II which were changed to large colonies which are M forms of Type III. (From Avery, MacLeod, and McCarty. *J. Exper. Med.*, 79:137, 1944.)

like in nature. Deoxyribonucleic acid extracts from R type of organism cannot effect this transformation. Taylor (69, 70), however, has shown that the S form contains a substance which will transform her ER into typical R forms, which then can be transformed into S by the capsular transforming principle. The S forms contain both transforming principles, but only one is active in a single transformation. Other gene-like materials in the transforming extracts determine the type of M protein and the amount of capsular material (3, 5, 32). Later work by Hall and Gale (27) has shown that the genetic marker of streptomycin resistance was transferred between pneumococcal strains in vivo. Reciprocal capsular transformations have been studied by Ravin (57); and, finally, Ottolenghi and Hotchkiss (55) have concluded that the transforming activity of early-growth-phase cultures of pneumococci provide a natural mechanism of genetic recombination for this species.

Antigenic Structure. In 1910 Neufeld and Händel discovered that the pneumococci could be divided into specific groups by immunologic methods. Their work was soon confirmed by Cole, and Dochez and Gillespie (14), who differentiated Types I, II, III, and a heterologous group IV. Subsequently, Cooper and her associates (11) separated group IV into some 30-odd types. At present there is a total of 77 recognized types (39).

The nucleoproteins of the various pneumococcus types are apparently closely related if not identical with those of the streptococci. Antibodies to these antigens, however, have no protective value.

The pneumococci resemble the β-hemolytic streptococci in having a **group specific somatic carbohydrate** (71) which is found in all pneumococci but not in streptococci. MacLeod and Avery (41) found this C carbohydrate to be highly antigenic but unrelated either to the capsular polysaccharides or to normal constituents of human and animal serums. The heterophile antigen of the pneumococcus also contains some of the C carbohydrate (25).

Animals immunized with the whole bodies of unencapsulated organisms or with extracts of encapsulated pneumococci containing nucleoprotein, C carbohydrate, and M proteins but no capsular material develop antibodies but have little if any increased resistance to infection against virulent encapsulated organisms. **The essential antigen in the pneumococcus is the capsular polysaccharide, which determines both its virulence and its specific type.** Virulent strains are rapidly displaced by mutant aviru-

lent strains in a period of 36 to 48 hours when grown in brain heart infusion broth, since there seems to be better adaption for growth in an artificial medium (10). Fresh blood favors the survival of the virulent types, and mouse inoculation immediately eliminates all avirulent forms. The pneumococci can be typed by the agglutination of the intact organism, by the precipitation of the specific capsular polysaccharides, or by swelling of the capsule when the organisms are mixed with the proper type-specific rabbit antiserum. This latter phenomenon, which was described first by Neufeld in 1902 and redescribed in 1931, is known as the Neufeld or **Quellung** reaction (51). Although this phenomenon is referred to as a "swelling of the capsule," in reality no swelling occurs. The antibody changes the optical properties so that the capsule can be seen. The presence of polysaccharide in urine and spinal fluid can be detected by a precipitation reaction with known antiserums (43).

CHEMICAL STRUCTURE OF THE CAPSULE. Avery and his coworkers at the Rockefeller Hospital studied the antigenic structure of the pneumococci for over 30 years and have contributed a large part of our definitive knowledge of these organisms. An enormous amount of research, on both the chemical and physiologic phases, was devoted to the study of the pneumococcus capsule after it was learned that both the type specificity and the virulence were dependent upon the presence of this substance. Dubos (15) has described the capsular materials as being essentially or exclusively polysaccharides of high molecular weights which often are acidic in nature and frequently possess acetyl and amino groups. The great asymmetry of their molecules accounts for the viscosity of their solutions and for their anisotropy of flow. From Heidelberger's (28) reviews of the subject it is apparent that the chief polysaccharide of each type of pneumococcus is chemically distinct. Heidelberger, Rebers, and their associates (29) have studied the minor chemical differences in the capsules of Types II, V, and VI, and their results indicate the same cross-precipitation between Type II and Types V and VI. Although 77 capsular types are known, Austrian (4, 5) has found that 50 per cent of clinical pneumococcal disease is caused by Types I to VIII. **When injected in minute amounts, the capsular polysaccharides are antigenic for mice (16, 48) and man and have been used successfully to produce immunity in man against pneumococcal pneumonia (16).** Larger doses may induce **immunogenic paralysis** and render the animal more susceptible to infection (13, 17, 65). This phenomenon is discussed in some detail in Chapter 12.

COMMON ANTIGENS. Similar, if not identical, polysaccharides are widely distributed in nature and induce antibodies which give cross-reactions with certain of the specific types of pneumococci. Felton and his associates (18) extracted hemicelluloses from 50 different plants which stimulated cross-reacting antibodies to one or several types of pneumococci. Among these plants were collards, tomatoes, pumpkins, and squash. Man might acquire immunity from these sources. Some pneumococci give cross-reaction with type B *H. influenzae,* and others with type A and C (46). The fungus *Sporotrichum schenckii* has antigens which cross-react with five different types of pneumococci (50). The specific Type II polysaccharide of the pneumococcus occurs also in yeast and in type B *Klebsiella pneumoniae. Salmonella kirke, Bacillus anthracis,* and probably other bacteria contain cross-reacting polysaccharides. The cross-reactions between pneumococcus Type XIV and the group A antigen of human blood formerly gave difficulty in the serum therapy of that type of pneumonia (8, 34).

ENZYMATIC HYDROLYSIS. Although the capsular material is essential for virulence, it is not necessary for the life and growth of the pneumococcus. The capsules can be destroyed by **enzymatic hydrolysis** without affecting the viability of the culture. The first observation of this kind was by Avery and Dubos in 1931 (6, 7). Other bacteriolytic enzymes active against pneumococcus polysaccharides have been found by Dubos (15) in immune serums, in leukocytes, and in animal tissues.

Bacterial Metabolites. Pneumococci produce a hemolysin which gives the characteristic green zone about colonies growing on blood agar plates. A **pneumolysin** appears in cultures, which is related physiologically and antigenically to the O-hemolysin of β-hemolytic streptococci (72). A **proteose-like** material can be extracted from the bodies of the pneumococci which causes purpura in mice (36). Some strains produce small amounts of a thermolabile **leukocidin** (53), and others a hyaluronidase (33). None of these metabolites are particularly toxic, and relatively enormous amounts of autolysates of pneumococci or endotoxins are required to kill guinea pigs and rabbits. The **capsular polysaccharides** are nontoxic but are of great importance in determining the pathogenicity of the pneumococcus. The capsule of living pneumococci protects the organism from phagocytosis, and the capsular material from the dead pneumococci, known

as the soluble specific substance or S.S.S., is so soluble that it diffuses through the tissues where it meets and combines with the antibodies as they are formed by the patient. This antibody-neutralizing effect of the polysaccharide explains the nature of the "virulin" which Rosenow (60) extracted from cultures of pneumococci and from the lungs of patients dead from pneumococcal pneumonia.

The **C reactive** protein is not a metabolite of the pneumococcus or a specific antibody to the **somatic group carbohydrate** but is an abnormal protein that appears in the serum of patients with pneumonia and other diseases and has the peculiar property of precipitating the C carbohydrate of pneumococci (41). In 1947 McCarty (40) isolated this **C reactive protein** in crystalline form from human pleural and abdominal fluid. Later Wood and McCarty (77) immunized rabbits with this human protein and used the antiserums to measure quantitatively the C reactive protein in the serums of patients with rheumatic fever and other diseases (31, 38).

SKIN TESTS WITH POLYSACCHARIDES. Tillett and Francis (71) injected specific purified polysaccharides intradermally into patients with pneumonia and observed the reactions which varied with the immunologic status of the patient. The dose was 0.1 ml. of a physiologic saline solution containing 0.01 mg. of the specific polysaccharide (22, 23). In the early days of the disease when there was an excess of specific polysaccharide in the blood and tissues, the test was negative. But after a spontaneous crisis or after adequate serum therapy, when there was an excess of specific antibodies in the blood and tissues, the intradermal injection of the polysaccharide was followed in 20 to 30 minutes by the appearance of a wheal with pseudopodia surrounded by an area of erythema.

Phagocytosis. Phagocytosis is the essential mechanism for the destruction of pneumococci in the body. Polymorphonuclear leukocytes and monocytes readily ingest and destroy nonencapsulated organisms. Animals which have not been previously exposed to pneumococci cannot phagocytize the encapsulated organism unless specific antibodies are supplied. Serums from most so-called normal individuals have the ability to phagocytize and destroy moderate numbers of pneumococci. These antibodies are more probably specific antibodies induced by previous subclinical infections with the pneumococcus. This latter view is supported by the work of Ward (73), and Ward and Enders (74), who have shown that the specific polysaccharides completely inhibit the normal homologous opsonins as well as the opsonins acquired by active and passive immunization.

The assumption that leukocytes cannot phagocytize encapsulated pneumococci without the assistance of specific opsonins recently has been questioned by Barry Wood (78). He pointed out that all the laboratory studies on phagocytosis have been carried out in containers with smooth surfaces, as found in test tubes and flasks. When rough surfaces were employed, such as filter paper or lungs of rats after fixation with formaldehyde, encapsulated pneumococci were phagocytized in the absence of specific opsonins. This observation affords an explanation for the phagocytosis and elimination of pneumococci from the lungs of animals treated with sulfonamides at a time when there are no free opsonins present.

Allergy. The role of allergy in pneumococcal infections has been neglected (35), although it was emphasized by Zinsser and Grinnell (79) as early as 1927. The specific proteins are common to all types of pneumococci; therefore, a sensitivity to the protein bodies may be present in a patient as a result of previous subclinical infection with pneumococci before the development of a pneumococcal pneumonia. The sudden explosive onset of pneumonia in the adult with chills, fevers, bloody sputum, and rapid consolidation of the lungs suggests an allergic reaction in contrast to the slower, more gradual development of bronchial or lobular pneumonia which is usually seen in children.

The importance of the allergic factor is strongly supported by the observations of Finland and his associates (20) who eliminated practically all of the toxic symptoms of patients with lobar pneumonia by the administration of ACTH although the virulent organisms remained in the sputum and in some cases in the blood for several days after the institution of therapy. Antibodies to the specific type of pneumococcus appeared in the serum at the expected time and all the patients recovered without receiving either specific serum, sulfonamides or antibiotics.

Spontaneous Disease in Animals. Pneumococci occasionally have been isolated from the upper respiratory tract of apparently healthy guinea pigs, rabbits, horses, calves, dogs, and monkeys (19, 61). Epidemics of pneumococcal pneumonia have been reported in monkeys (76), guinea pigs (51), and rats (47). There is no evidence that man contracts pneumococcal infections from animals.

Experimental Pneumococcal Infections. White mice and rabbits are very susceptible to experimental infections with the pneumococcus; but guinea pigs, dogs, rats, and cats are more resistant and birds are practically immune (2). Subcutaneous inoculations of virulent pneumococci into mice and rabbits usually result in an edematous exudation at the point of inoculation, which leads to septicemia and death within 24 to 72 hours. Intravenous inoculation usually is followed by death more rapidly than that following subcutaneous injection. Intraperitoneal inoculation of mice and rabbits results in the formation of a rapidly spreading peritonitis. In almost all of these infections, death is preceded by septicemia and the microorganisms can be recovered from the heart's blood.

A definite pathologic process called **dermal pneumonia** has been produced by injecting virulent pneumococci into the skin of rabbits (26). Dermal pneumonia may end by crisis, lysis, or fatal septicemia and has been most helpful in the study of a number of pathologic and immunologic problems.

The lobar type of pneumonia has been produced in **mice** by alcohol intoxication of animals whose resistance had been modified by partial immunization; in **rats** by intratracheal inoculation of virulent pneumococci suspended in mucin (78); in **dogs** by suspending the pneumococci in a solution of starch (75). Blake and Cecil (9), however, induced typical lobar pneumonia in **monkeys** without modifying the resistance of the animals or protecting the organism with mucin or starch.

Clinical Types of Infection in Man. Pneumococcal pneumonia, particularly the lobar type, is the most characteristic of pneumococcal infections. In addition to pneumonia, pneumococci can produce **sinus infection, otitis media, osteomyelitis, arthritis, peritonitis, corneal ulceration** and **meningitis.** The common complication of pneumococcal pneumonia are **septicemia, empyema, endocarditis, pericarditis, meningitis** and **arthritis.** Secondary pneumococcal pneumonias follow viral infections such as measles and influenza less frequently than streptococcal ones but more frequently than staphylococcal infections.

Recurrent Pneumonia. True recurrences, after months or years, are observed more frequently in pneumonia than in any other acute infectious disease (68). Recurrences are particularly common in patients with congenital or acquired agammaglobulinemia.

Blood Cultures in Pneumonia. During the course of pneumonia, pneumococcus septicemia is common. Fränkel in 1902 stated that he believed in most, if not all, cases of pneumonia the organisms are present in the blood stream at some stage of the disease.

Mortality. The death rate in pneumonia depends upon the race, sex, age, and general condition of the patient, the type of infecting pneumococcus, the degree of involvement of the lung, the presence or absence of septicemia, the occurrence of complications, the promptness of specific therapy, and many other factors. General experience has indicated that the average case mortality varies from 20 to 30 per cent in untreated patients. The highest death rates occur in infections with Types I, II, and III, ranging from about 35 to 50 per cent. When patients with pneumococcal pneumonia are not diagnosed and treated with antibiotics, the mortality remains as high as before. With prompt antibiotic therapy the death rate has been reduced to 5 per cent (58), and the failure is primarily in elderly people and in those with debilitating diseases. The poorest results in primary pneumococcal infections are found in patients with pneumococcal meningitis, especially in those with pneumococcal otitis media and meningitis. Before antibiotics the mortality was 99 per cent; with antibiotics it ranges from a low of 7 per cent to a high of 72 per cent (54). It is lowest in children and increases progressively after the age of 40 years (64).

Transmission. Considering that 25 to 50 per cent of the population carry virulent pneumococci in their nasopharynges (19), one alternately wonders why pneumococcal attack rates are not infinitely higher and why anyone ever gets clinical pneumonia. Pneumococci disappear from the nasopharynx of the convalescent case in two or three weeks unless he has a focus in a nasal sinus. Straken, Hill, and Lovell (67) have shown that even the asymptomatic carriers constantly are losing old types and acquiring new types of pneumococci. Smillie and Jewett (63) and Finland (19) have traced the asymptomatic epidemic spread of a specific type of pneumococcus through a family group and observed the sporadic development of clinical cases of pneumonia.

It is obvious that a number of conditions must be fulfilled before obtaining a single case of clinical pneumonia, such as a susceptible individual, the presence of a virulent pneumococcus and, most important of all, additional immunologic, environmental, or accidental factors which precipitate the infection. Among the additional factors may be listed virus infections, overcrowding, dusty industries, poor nutrition, excessive fatigue, chilling, and alcoholism. Among the immunologic factors, one might speculate on failure to produce antibodies and a hypersensitivity to pneumococcus proteins which facilitates the development of pneumonia, although the importance of these factors has not been established. The accidental factor may be merely the mechanical one of aspirating mucus-coated pneumococci from the upper air passages in such a manner that they become lodged in the smaller bronchioles for a few hours.

True **epidemics of pneumonia** have occurred in families, in army camps during World War I, in the mining industries in South Africa and among workers constructing the Panama Canal. For a discussion of the general features of these epidemics, Finland's (19) review should be consulted.

Treatment. A prompt diagnosis is essential in obtaining the best results with either antibiotic or sulfonamide therapy. Fortunately, it is not necessary to type the pneumococcus before starting treatment, since all types are equally susceptible to these therapeutic agents. The greatest hazard in the treatment of pneumonia in the present era is not the elimination of the pneumococcus but the development of a secondary and often fatal infection with staphylococci which are resistant to penicillin and other antibiotics.

Pneumococci are very susceptible to penicillin and to the broad-spectrum antibiotics. In ordinary pneumococcal pneumonia, even with septicemia, doses of 500,000 to 1,000,-000 units of penicillin daily effect a prompt cure. In contrast, truly heroic doses are required in pneumococcal meningitis to effect a transfer of the antibiotic through the blood-brain barrier of the meninges. We quote the doses suggested by Spink (64) for treating the disease. Penicillin should be given intravenously in a dose of one million units per hour until definite improvement occurs. This should be followed by intramuscular penicillin every six hours in doses of four to five million units and continued for two to three weeks. Sulfadiazine is given orally as long as penicillin is administered. Intrathecal administration of penicillin is not recommended. Large doses of penicillin given intrathecally will produce hemorrhagic reactions in the brain, and the modern physician seems incapable, psychologically, of giving very small harmless but effective doses of 1,000 to 5,000 units daily.

Prevention. It will rarely be necessary for health officers working in civilized communities to be called upon to prevent epidemics of primary pneumonia. They will develop under conditions as those prevailing in military camps and badly managed industrial communities, schools, or labor camps where laborers are forced to sleep in ill-ventilated barracks.

Active Immunization. During World War II MacLeod, Hodges, and Heidelberger (42) injected one-half of the soldiers in an Army Air Force technical school with a single dose containing 0.03 to 0.06 mg. of polysaccharides from Types I, II, V, and VII pneumococci. These types, together with Types IV and XII, were the predominant types present in that camp during the previous winter. For control purposes, Types IV and XII were not included in the mixture. There was a reduction in pneumonia from all types after vaccination but most sharply in those types included in the polysaccharide vaccine. Evidence of immunity appeared in two weeks, reached a maximum in six weeks, and lasted for at least six months. Felton (17) and others have emphasized the importance of minute doses, since larger doses persist in the tissues (37) for months and prevent the elaboration of specific antibodies. The soldiers just mentioned gave an apparently adequate primary response but failed to respond with increased antibody production when given a booster dose. We should know more about the optimal dose (49), the speed of antibody formation (52), and the size and intervals for booster doses.

Prophylactic vaccination with the specific polysaccharides may offer the most direct and effective method of preventing epidemics of pneumonia under conditions where general health and sanitary measures have not proved effective or where a situation of extreme emergency exists.

REFERENCES

1. Adams, M. H., and Roe, A. S.   J. Bact., 49: 401, 1945.
2. Andrews, E. C., and McKinnon, G. E.   Am. J. Path., 39:779, 1961.
3. Austrian, R., and MacLeod, C. M.   J. Exper. Med., 89:439, 451, 1949.
4. ———   Bact. Rev., 16:31, 1952.
5. ———   Am. J. Med. Sci., 238:133, 1959.
6. Avery, O. T., and Dubos, R. J.   J. Exper. Med., 54:51, 73, 1931.
7. ———   and others.   J. Exper. Med., 79:137, 1944.
8. Beeson, P. B., and Goebel, W. F.   J. Exper. Med., 70:239, 1939.
9. Blake, F. G., and Cecil, R. L.   J. Exper. Med., 31:499, 1920.
10. Carta, G., and Firshein, W.   J. Bact., 84:473, 1962.
11. Cooper, G., and others.   J. Exper. Med., 55: 531, 1932.
12. Dawson, M. H., and Sia, H. P.   J. Exper. Med., 54:681, 1931.
13. Dixon, F. J., and others.   J. Immunol., 74: 189, 1955.
14. Dochez, A. R., and Gillespie, L. J.   J.A.M.A., 61:727, 1913.
15. Dubos, R. J.   The Bacterial Cell, Cambridge, Mass., Harvard University Press, 1946.
16. Felton, L. D., and others.   J. Infect. Dis., 56:101, 1935.
17. ———   and others.   J. Bact., 69:519, 1955.
18. ———   and others.   J. Immunol., 74:17, 205, 1955.
19. Finland, M.   Medicine, 21:307, 1942.
20. ———   and others.   Am. J. Med., 8:21, 1950.
21. Flosdorf, E. W., and Mudd, S.   J. Immunol., 29:389, 1935.
22. Francis, T.   J. Exper. Med., 57:617, 1933.
23. Francis, T., Jr., and Tillett, W. S.   J. Exper. Med., 52:573, 1930.
24. Fränkel, A.   Ztschr. f. klin. Med., 10:426, 1886.
25. Goebel, W. F., and Adams, M. H.   J. Exper. Med., 77:435, 1943.
26. Goodner, K.   J. Exper. Med., 48:1, 1928: 54:847, 1931.
27. Hall, R. H., and Gale, G. O.   Proc. Soc. Exper. Biol. & Med., 101:487, 1959.
28. Heidelberger, M., and Dilapi, M. M.   J. Immunol., 61:153, 1949.
29. ———   and Rebers, P. A.   J. Bact., 80:145, 1960; 82:920, 1961.
30. Hoeprich, P. D.   J. Bact., 74:587, 1957.
31. Hokama, Y., and others.   J. Immunol., 85: 72, 1960.
32. Hotchkiss, R. D.   Genetic Chemistry of Pneumococcal Transformation, Harvey Lect., 1954.
33. Humphrey, J. H.   J. Path. & Bact., 56:273, 1944.

34. Ivanovics, G. Ztschr. f. Immunitätsforsch. u. exper. Therap., 97:402, 1940; 98:373, 1940.
35. Julianelle, L. A. J. Exper. Med., 51:625, 633, 643, 1930.
36. ———— and Reimann, H. A. J. Exper. Med., 43:87, 1926; 45:609, 1927.
37. Kaplan, M. H., and others. J. Exper. Med., 91:15, 1950.
38. Libretti, A., and others. J. Bact., 79:306, 1957.
39. Lund, E. Acta path. et microbiol. Scandinav., 27:720, 1950.
40. McCarty, M. J. Exper. Med., 85:491, 1947.
41. MacLeod, C. M., and Avery, O. T. J. Exper. Med., 73:191, 1941.
42. ———— and others. J. Exper. Med., 82:445, 1945.
43. ———— and Krauss, M. R. J. Exper. Med., 86:439, 1947.
44. ———— and Krauss, M. R. J. Exper. Med., 91:767, 1953.
45. ———— and McCarty, M. J. Clin. Invest., 21:647, 1942.
46. MacPherson, C. F. C., and others. J. Bact., 57:443, 1949.
47. Mirick, G. S., and others. Am. J. Hyg., 52:48, 1950.
48. Morgan, P., and others. Proc. Soc. Exper. Biol. & Med., 80:512, 1952.
49. Murray, F. J., and others. J. Immunol., 64:421, 1950.
50. Neill, J. M., and others. J. Immunol., 74:120, 1955.
51. Neufeld, F., and Etinger-Tulczynska, R. Ztschr. f. Hyg. u. Infektionskr., 112:492, 1931; 114:324, 1932.
52. Nunes, D. S. Canad. J. Research, 28 (Sect. E):298, 1950.
53. Olmstead, M., and Oram, F. J. Immunol., 26:283, 1934.
54. Olsson, R. A., and others. Ann. Int. Med., 55:545, 1961.
55. Ottolenghi, E., and Hotchkiss, R. D. Science, 132:1257, 1960.
56. Pasteur, L. Bull. Acad. nat. méd., 10:76, 1881.
57. Ravin, A. W. J. Bact., 77:296, 1959.
58. Reimann, H. A. Ann. Int. Med., 56:144, 1962.
59. Rochford, E. J., and Mandle, R. J. J. Bact., 66:554, 1953.
60. Rosenow, E. C. J. Infect. Dis., 4:285, 1907; 11:480, 1912.
61. Seegal, B. C., and others. Proc. Soc. Exper. Biol. & Med., 34:812, 1936.
62. Shinn, L. E. J. Bact., 33:18, 1937.
63. Smillie, W. G., and Jewett, O. F. Am. J. Hyg., 32:79, 1940.
64. Spink, W. W., and Su, C. K. J.A.M.A., 173:1545, 1960.
65. Stark, O. K. J. Immunol., 74:126, 1955.
66. Sternberg, G. M. Nat. Bd. Health Bull., 1881.
67. Straken, E., and others. Rep. on Pub. Health & Med. Subjects, No. 90, Ministry of Health, His Majesty's Stationery Office, London, 1939.
68. Strauss, E., and Finland, M. Ann. Int. Med., 16:17, 1941.
69. Taylor, H. E. The Nature of the Bacterial Surface, Oxford, Blackwell Scientific Publications, 1949.
70. ———— J. Exper. Med., 89:399, 1949.
71. Tillett, W. S., and Francis, T. J. Exper. Med., 52:561, 1930.
72. Todd, E. W. J. Path. & Bact., 39:299, 1934.
73. Ward, H. K. J. Exper. Med., 51:685, 1930.
74. Ward, H. H., and Enders, J. F. J. Exper. Med., 57:527, 1933.
75. Weichselbaum, A. Med. Jahrb., Wien, 1:483, 1886.
76. Wisner, B. Compt. rend. Soc. de biol., 98:458, 1928.
77. Wood, H. F., and McCarty, M. J. Lab. & Clin. Med., 30:616, 1951.
78. Wood, W. B., and Irons, E. N. J. Exper. Med., 84:365, 377, 387, 1946.
79. Zinsser, H., and Grinnell, F. B. J. Bact., 14:301, 1927.

20

The Streptococci

Family: *Lactobacteriaceae* Orla-Jensen. Tribe: *Streptococceae* Trevisan. Genus: *Streptococcus* Rosenbach. Type Species: *Streptococcus pyogenes* Rosenbach.

Man is one of the most susceptible of all animals to streptococcal infections, and no organ or tissue of the body is completely immune. Streptococci cause epidemic diseases, such as scarlet fever, erysipelas and epidemic sore throat; important infections, such as puerperal fever and probably rheumatic fever; and innumerable varieties of local lesions. Pasteur (76) saw chains of streptococci in patients with puerperal sepsis, and Koch (43) saw them in pus from wound infections, but pure cultures were obtained first by Fehleisen in 1883 and by Rosenbach (83) in 1884. The latter adopted the term "streptococcus," previously introduced by the surgeon Billroth, and named the organism *Streptococcus pyogenes*.

Studies of the nucleoproteins of streptococci by both the precipitin and complement-fixing reaction show that all streptococci have common nucleoproteins which are closely related to those of the pneumococci and shared in part by the staphylococci (49). Other antigenic relations to pneumococci (61) are known, and the English bacteriologists prefer to classify the pneumococcus as a species of *Streptococcus*. However, we agree with Bergey's classification, which recognizes *Diplococcus pneumoniae* as a separate genus because of its type specific polysaccharide capsule. The corresponding surface antigen which gives virulence to *Streptococcus pyogenes* is the M protein.

In the 1957 edition of Bergey's Manual there are 19 recognized species, all of which are aerobic but facultatively anaerobic to microaerophylic. There are 13 strictly anaerobic species, but 1 becomes aerotolerant with repeated transfers (68). The aerobic streptococci are subdivided into the **Pyogenes Group,** with 8 species; the **Viridans Group,** with 7 species; the **Enterococcus Group,** with 2 species; and the **Lactic Group,** with 2 species.

In this chapter we shall discuss the pathogenic group as a whole. In the following chapter we shall consider in some detail the relation of streptococci to scarlet fever, erysipelas, suppurative and septicemic conditions, and several other important diseases of man.

Morphology and Staining. The individual streptococcus is a spherical microorganism measuring from 0.5μ to 1μ in diameter. In the characteristic chains, however, adjacent cocci are elongated in the axis of the chain. The pathogenic streptococci, when grown upon favorable fluid and certain solid media, often produce long chains made up of eight or more individuals (Fig. 1). Cole (13) and Hahn (32) have shown by direct and indirect fluorescent staining that streptococci grow new cell walls by localized growth at the point of contact between two cells (Fig. 1) and not over the entire circumference of the cell, as logic would suggest. It is not difficult to visualize the formation of long chains, since it can be assumed that the cocci remain attached after division; but the mechanism of chain-splitting is more complex, since it appears to depend upon at least one and probably two or more enzymes (13). The "long-chain-reaction" as a test for detection of type-specific antibody to streptococci of group A was introduced by Stollerman and Ekstedt in 1957 and developed in more detail in later publications (96). Streptococci grown in homologous type antiserum form chains of an average length exceeding that found when the same organisms are grown simultaneously in normal serum and in heter-

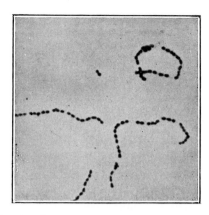

Fig. 1. *Streptococcus pyogenes.* Gram stain. × 1,200.

ologous type serum. The test appears to depend upon the presence both of M protein in the streptococci and of free antibody specific to that type of M protein in the serum. The results correlate with direct bacteriocidal tests in detecting type specific antibody in human sera.

Streptococci from human infections are **gram-positive,** although certain varieties isolated from human feces and animal tissues are gram-negative. The cocci are gram-positive in young cultures but variable or even gram-negative in cultures several days old. They are **nonsporogenous** and, except for a few saprophytic strains, **nonmotile.** Virulent strains produce a capsule which contains both hyaluronic acid (85) and M type-specific protein.

Cultural Characteristics. Only a limited number of strains will grow in a chemically defined medium (8, 75, 90), and even here the medium must be supplemented with 15 amino acids, all the B-complex vitamins, purines, pyrimidines, and the peptide-like "streptogins" (90, 94, 103). The addition of reducing substances, such as cystein or thioglycollate, is necessary to initiate growth. Many extracellular enzymes and toxins are not produced even in such complex synthetic media, and investigators have had to compromise by using the dialyzable components of complex meat infusion-peptone media. Streptococci grow best at a pH of 7.4 to 7.6. With most species growth is optimal at 37° C. and sharply reduced at 40° C. Hemolytic streptococci metabolize glucose with the formation of lactic acid, which limits growth, but massive growth can be obtained in the presence of excess glucose if the lactic acid is neutralized continuously.

The pyogenic streptococci grow readily on all the richer artificial media. For primary iso-lation the media should contain whole blood, blood serum, or transudates such as ascitic or pleural fluids. The addition of glucose in 0.5 per cent concentration increases the rate of growth of the organism but causes a change in the ability of the organism to lyse red blood cells.

On **blood-agar plates** at 37° C. small, grayish and delicate opalescent colonies are visible usually within 18 to 24 hours. They are round with smooth or very slightly corrugated edges, and on the surface of the medium they resemble small droplets of fluid. Depending upon the phase of dissociation, the colonies may vary from the slimy or mucoid type to the finely granular or even dry form. In poured blood-agar plates **hemolysis** of the red cells in the medium surrounding the colony is characteristic of certain streptococci. The hemolytic effect is usually less intense in streaked blood-agar plates (Figs. 2, 3).

Brown (11) based his classification on the hemolytic properties as produced on blood-agar as follows: (a) the α type, which produced a greenish discoloration and partial hemolysis of the red cells surrounding the colony, although an outer clear zone may develop on preservation of the cultures in the icebox; (b) the β type, which produced a clear zone of hemolysis about the colony with no intact corpuscles and no further extension of the area on refrigeration; and (c) the γ type, which exerted no effect upon the red blood cells in the medium. To obtain clearly differentiated types of hemolysis, horse or rabbit's blood should be used, and the medium should be glucose-free. The type of hemolysis surrounding the colonies in blood-agar plates is the

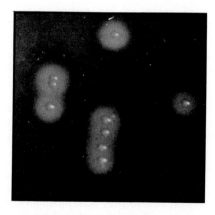

Fig. 2. Hemolytic streptococcus. Yeast blood agar. 3 ×. Notes β type hemolysis. (From Li, Koibong. *J. Bact.,* 69:326, 1955.)

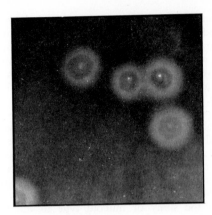

Fig. 3. Hemolytic streptococcus. Note central elevation and flattened colony. Yeast blood agar. 3 ×. (From Li, Koibong. *J. Bact.,* 69:326, 1955.)

easiest method of classifying the aerobic streptococci into large groups; those producing the α type of hemolysis are known collectively as the *viridans* group; those producing the β type are referred to usually as the *hemolyticus* group; and those which have no effect on the blood cells are classified as the *Streptococcus anhemolyticus* group. Further differentiation into subgroups can be accomplished only by special and detailed antigenic studies and observations of various cultural characteristics.

Resistance. In sputum, exudates, and animal excreta, streptococci may remain alive for several weeks. On ordinary culture media, at room temperature, the organisms usually die within 10 days to two weeks. They will remain alive for several weeks in tubes of defibrinated rabbit's blood kept in the ice chest and even longer when temperatures of 1° to 2° C. are maintained. Streptococci may be kept alive, with virulence unchanged, for months or years, if lyophilized by the method described by Flosdorf and Mudd (24).

Some varieties of streptococci die after 10 minutes' exposure to temperatures of 55° C., and practically all species are killed in 30 to 60 minutes at 60° C. The pasteurization temperature of 62° C. (143.6° F.) for 30 minutes destroys all pathogenic streptococci in milk. Streptococci are killed within 15 minutes by tincture of iodine; phenol 1:200; cresol 1:175; bichloride of mercury 1:200 to 1:500; mercurochrome 2 per cent; and hexylresorcinol 1:1,000. The triphenyl-methane dyes are less effective on streptococci than on staphylococci. Practically all varieties of pathogenic streptococci are susceptible to the bacteriostatic effects of the sulfonamides, except *S. faecalis*

and other members of the enterococcus group. Resistance to the effects of the drug, however, is acquired readily when inadequate doses are administered, and these resistant strains may induce epidemics. Penicillin is very effective in relatively small doses against the beta-hemolytic streptococci belonging to Lancefield's group A but is somewhat less efficacious against organisms belonging to groups B, C, E, F, and G. Many individual strains require very large doses and the enterococci are resistant. Anaerobic hemolytic streptococci may be 250 times as resistant to penicillin as the aerobic streptococci (1). Fortunately, in the animal resistance to penicillin is acquired slowly, if at all, so that prolonged and repeated treatment with penicillin is practical.

Streptococci in general are susceptible to aureomycin, chloramphenicol, and terramycin. Streptomycin is very variable in activity: some strains are inhibited by as little as 1 μg. and others require as much as 120 μg. per milliliter of culture fluid. Bacitracin seems to be effective against anaerobic and microaerophilic strains which are resistant to penicillin and other antibiotics (65, 67, 68). Resistance to streptomycin is acquired rapidly and to a high level of the drug. Resistance to chlortetracycline (2), chloramphenicol and oxytetracycline develops to about the same degree and facility as to penicillin.

Variability. Dawson, Hobby, and Olmstead (18) described three types of colonies of group A streptococci which they designated as **mucoid, matt,** and **glossy** (Fig. 4). In this instance the matt type is rough but virulent, while the glossy is smooth but avirulent. Large hyaluronic acid capsules give the mucoid colonies their characteristic appearance (85). In general, the mucoid and matt colonies contain large amounts of M protein and are virulent, while the glossy colonies contain little or no M protein and are avirulent. Variants have been described, however, in which the matt type was avirulent and the glossy type virulent (97). Another variant has been described which had the colony shape of the glossy type but was mucoid and virulent (58) (Fig. 4). L forms of bacterial colonies have been isolated from both alpha- and beta-hemolytic streptococci.

Antigenic Structure. The antigenic structure of the streptococci is extremely complex, in contrast to the simplicity of the pneumococci. The streptococci were divided into groups by Rebecca Lancefield in 1933 (50) on the basis of specific carbohydrates which could be extracted from the cell walls. Nearly all of

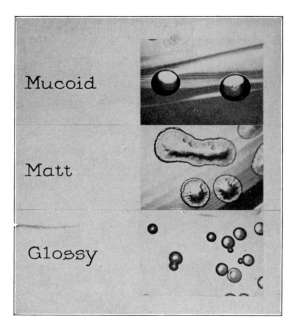

Fig. 4. Colony forms of group A streptococci. (From Lancefield. *Harvey Lect.*, 36:251, 1940-41.)

the hemolytic streptococci pathogenic for man were found to fall in group A, although a few strains pathogenic for man occur in groups C, D, E, F, G, and M (80).

The specific carbohydrate forms a large part of the cell wall and later studies, reviewed by Krause and McCarty (47) and Slade and Slamp (91), have shown that the streptococcal antigen, both group and type, may be composed of a polymer made up of a single sugar, or several sugars with side chains composed of sugars and amino sugars. An amino sugar may be the terminal unit on the side chain. Variables such as the length and composition of the side chain, type of linkage between components, optical rotation of the sugars, and presence of alpha and beta forms are very likely essential for the specificity of this antigen; so there are 17 group antigens as well as 26 cell-wall antigens in group D (23).

Group B streptococci have a polysaccharide capsular antigen analogous to that of the pneumococcus. Transformation of resistance to streptomycin has been achieved among serologic groups F, H, and O by Perry and Slade (78).

The serological groups tested in Table 1 contain most of the known strains of hemolytic streptococci, although new ones are encountered from time to time which do not fall into any of the known groups. Although the group carbohydrate is on the surface of the cell wall of the streptococci, it is not a capsule and plays no part in the virulence of the organism. Griffith (30, 31) determined the specific types of streptococci in group A by the agglutination method. The protein on the surface of the streptococci which stimulates the formation of agglutinins is called the T protein. Some T antigens are restricted to a single type of streptococci, but others are shared by several different types, which makes this method of classification impractical.

The specific type of streptococci in group A are now classified by means of the M protein, which is a surface protein. This method of classification was worked out by Lancefield and her associates (51, 52). Each type has a single specific type of M protein, with the single exception of type 14, where some strains have one M protein and some a different M protein but never both at once (102).

In group A streptococci the M protein corresponds to the capsular polysaccharide of the pneumococcus, since this is not only specific for the type but is essential for the virulence of the organism. Here immunity to the M protein is equivalent to immunity to that strain of streptococcus, and clinical recurrences are rare with the same type of streptococcus (20, 52).

In many strains hyaluronic acid forms a capsule enclosing the surface M antigen. The

Table 1. Antigenic Classification of Streptococci

GROUP	SPECIES	HABITAT
A	S. pyogenes	man
B	S. agalactiae	mastitis in cows
C	S. equi	horses
	S. zooepidemicus	animals
	S. equisimilis	man and animals
	S. dysagalactiae	man and animals
D	S. faecalis	milk, man, and animals
	S. durans	milk, man, and animals
	S. zymogenes	man
	S. liquefaciens	man and animals
E	1 type	milk and swine
F	4 types	man
G	S. anginosus	man and dog
H	S. sanguis	man
K	1 type	man
L		man, dog, and pig
M		dog and man
N *	S. lactis	milk
	S. cremoris	cream
O		man
Viridans group	See Tables 2, 3, 4	man
Microaerophilic streptococci	(Meleney 1931, 1935)	man
Anaerobic streptococci	13 species	man

* Not hemolytic but has group carbohydrate. Groups A to E described by Lancefield, 1933; Groups F and G by Lancefield and Hare, 1935; H and K by Hare, 1935; L and M by Fry; and Group N assigned by Shattock and Mattick, 1943; and Group O by Boissard and Wormald (9).

ability to resist phagocytes seems to depend upon the combined effect of the M protein and the hyaluronic acid capsule (25). The presence or absence of the hyaluronic acid does not seem to influence the intraperitoneal infection of mice, but when mice are challenged by the aerosol method, both M protein and hyaluronic acid are necessary for infection (3, 17). Not all the factors necessary for virulence have been delineated. Only a few human strains have a high degree of virulence for mice, but strains with low initial virulence increase the virulence with mouse passage and **change the colony morphology from smooth to matt** (56). White mouse passage increases streptolysin-S production without increasing virulence (93).

Another complication in the evaluation of hyaluronic acid in the virulence of streptococci is the unusual biologic phenomenon of strains of streptococci which produce hyaluronic acid but also produce hyaluronidase. The destructive effect of hyaluronidase can be prevented in the test tube by the addition of the hyaluronidase inhibitor, alginic acid sulfate, to the medium (100).

The mechanism of action of the M protein has not been determined. Kantor and Cole (41, 42) have found that M protein or a factor which cannot be separated from M protein precipitates fibrinogen from plasma of man and acts in a manner analogous to the coagulase of a virulent staphylococcus.

The M protein is manufactured in the protoplast and spherocyte and then transferred to the superficial layer of the cell wall (26, 27, 29). The M protein derived by the original method of extraction was somewhat toxic and

Table 2. Some Selected Characteristics Showing the Interrelationships of the Enterococci

(Sherman, 1938)

	S. faecalis	S. liquefaciens	S. zymogenes	S. durans
Hemolysis in Blood Agar	—	—	+	+
Gelatin Liquefied	—	+	±	—
Strong Reducing Action	+ *	+ *	+ *	—
Glycerol Fermented	±	+	+	—
Mannitol Fermented	+	+	+	—
Sorbitol Fermented	+	+	+	—
Sucrose Fermented	±	+ *	+ *	— *

* Occasional variation from type reaction; extremely rare exceptions not noted.

was not a good antigen, so high titer antibodies were difficult to prepare. Barkulis and Jones and their associates (4, 5) have isolated the cell wall containing the M protein and used it for the immunizing agent. By this method Kantor and Cole (41) have obtained good antibody titer. Hayashi and Walsh (37) have immunized rabbits with cell walls from three types simultaneously, suggesting the possibility of a polyvalent vaccine at least for the dominant types of group A streptococci.

Moody and his associates (71, 72) have found that a **specific fluorescein-labeled antibody** could be used to identify groups A, B, C, D, F, and G streptococci and 37 of the 47 type specific group A strains. Sera were not prepared from the other types. The throat swabs were cultured in 2 ml. Todd Hewitt broth and incubated for two to four hours, after which slides were made and stained with the fluorescent antibody technic. In the first 573 specimens studied, 536, or 93.4 per cent, were identified as group A strains, 10 as B, three as C, two as D, three as F, and seven as G (77).

Group A streptococci are much more sensitive to the antibiotic bacitracin. Planting on media containing bacitracin therefore serves as a nonserologic method for tentatively separating group A from other groups of streptococci (64).

Groups A, B, C, E, F, G, H, K, L, M, and O produce hemolysins and were originally designated as hemolytic streptococci. Group D organisms containing both hemolytic and nonhemolytic types are frequently called "enterococci" in the French and American literature (80, 87, 88, 89).

The *Streptococcus lactis* type from milk and cream, (Table 3) Group N, are not hemolytic but do have a group specific carbohydrate (86).

Table 3. Some Selected Characteristics of S. faecalis and S. lactis

(Sherman, 1938)

	S. faecalis	S. lactis
Lancefield Group D	+	—
Growth at 45° C.	+	—
Growth in 6.5% NaCl	+	—
Growth at pH 9.6	+	—
Sorbitol Fermented	±	—
Glycerol Fermented	+	—
Mannitol Fermented	+	±

The alpha hemolytic streptococci of the viridans type have no common carbohydrate but for convenience have been included in Table 4 as have the microaerophilic and anaerobic streptococci. Horsfall (38) found six serologic types of *S. salivarius* with capsular polysaccharides analogous to pneumococci. A new member of the viridans group designated *Streptococcus* MG (70) occurs with great regularity in the saliva or sputum of patients with primary atypical pneumonia, and antibodies to this organism are frequently found in the serums. Although the MG agglutination, like the cold agglutination of RBC, is useful in diagnosis, it is known now that a pleuropneumonia-like organism is the cause of primary atypical pneumonia. Schwab (84) has found an intercellular streptolysin in group A strains which seems to differ from the extracellular streptolysin-S. The streptolysin-S isolated from *S. zymogenes*, group D, by Irwin and Seely (40) is different from the streptolysin-S isolated by Todd (1934). The human strains of group M have been restudied by Rifkind and Cole (81) and *S. faecalis* by Deibel (19).

The antigenic complexity of the group A streptococci is emphasized by the tests of Halbert and Auerbach (33), who studied sera from patients with clinical and subclinical

Table 4. The Viridans Streptococci: Additional Characteristics
(Sherman, 1937)

	S. salivarius	S. equinus	S. bovis	Varieties of S. bovis	S. thermophilus	S. mitis
Growth in 2% NaCl	+	+	+	+	−	+
Starch Hydrolyzed	−	±	+	−	−	−
Sodium Hippurate Hydrolized	−	−	−	−	−	−
Esculin Split	±	+	+	+	−	−
Gelatin Liquefied	−	−	−	−	−	−
Milk Curdled	±	−	±	±	+	+
Final pH in Glucose Broth	5.4-4.0	4.5-4.0	4.5-4.0	4.5-4.0	4.5-4.0	5.8-4.2
Acid Produced from						
Arabinose	−	−	±	−	−	−
Maltose	+	+	+	+	−	+
Sucrose	+	±	+	+	+	+
Lactose	+	−	+	+	+	+
Trehalose	±	±	±	±	−	±
Raffinose	±	±	+	+	±	−
Inulin	±	±	−	−	−	−
Glycerol	−	−	−	−	−	−
Mannitol	−	−	±	±	−	−
Sorbitol	−	−	±	−	−	−
Salicin	±	±	+	+	−	±

streptococcal infections and found 12 antibodies by electrophoresis and at least 15 by agar gell diffusion. Crawford (15) investigated the complement fixation test with an L-form antigen from type 18 *S. pyogenes* and showed a high degree of qualitative and quantitative correlation with the antistreptolysin-O titers of naval recruits.

Bacteriophage. Bacteriophages which lyse types 1, 6, 12, 25, and human C hemolytic streptococci have been studied by Krause and McCarty (44, 45, 46). Some strains were made lysogenic.

Bacterial Metabolites. The injection of washed, heat-killed, intact streptococci into experimental animals produces surprisingly little reaction, suggesting that the somatic antigens have little toxicity and that the endotoxins are not very potent. As they grow on suitable media, however, they liberate a variety of specific toxic and non-toxic substances. Table 5 lists these extracellular metabolites. Patients with rheumatic fever usually have antibodies against both streptolysin-O and deoxyribonuclease, but in the series studied by Olitsky and his associates (74) 12 per cent were positive to the antideoxyribonuclease test and negative to the ASO test. Wannamaker added a fourth antigenic type of deoxyribonuclease in 1962 (98, 99). Hyde and Watson (39) found that not all group A streptococci produce DPNases, but they are all antigenically related, regardless of the type or group from which the enzymes were derived.

Table 5. Bacterial Metabolites

Extracellular Metabolites	Antibodies
Erythrogenic toxin	Antitoxin
Streptolysin-O	Antistreptolysin-O
Streptolysin-S	None
Alpha hemolysin	
Diphosphopyridine nucleotidase	Antibody
Streptokinase	Antistreptokinase
Deoxyribonuclease A	Seriologically
Deoxyribonuclease B	distinct enzyme
Deoxyribonuclease C	which attacks
Deoxyribonuclease D	the same substrate
Ribonuclease	
Hyaluronic acid	None
Hyaluronidase	Antihyaluronidase
Proteinase	Antiproteinase
Amylase	?

The nature of these metabolites has been discussed in Chapter 16.

Alpha Hemolysis. The green zone observed around the colonies of alpha-hemolytic streptococci was formerly attributed to the direct action of hydrogen peroxide, but later work suggests the presence of an oxidation-reduction system in which one component is intracellular. Other organisms such as pneumococci, micrococci, and *E. coli* also produce green discoloration of blood media by the same mechanism (95).

Allergy. Lawrence (54) found that 45 per cent of 472 adult patients, without evidence of streptococcal infections, gave positive skin tests of the delayed type to intact streptococcal cells or certain isolated fractions of the cells. Sensitivity of the delayed type was transferred to a group of originally negative reactors by the injection of viable leukocytes from streptococcus-positive human donors. These observations provide a solid basis for suspecting that allergy to streptococci or their products may play an important role in rheumatic fever and certain types of nephritis.

The toxic cellular reaction reported by Cromartie, Schwab, and Crawford (16) following three hours after the intradermal infection of C. polysaccharide from the cell wall is probably a true toxic, and not an allergic, reaction.

Spontaneous Disease in Lower Animals. A variety of focal and epizootic diseases in animals are caused by streptococci.

One of the most important is mastitis in cattle caused by S. agalactiae of group B (59). This organism is not pathogenic for man. Occasionally group A streptococci may cause mastitis in cattle and induce epidemic sore throat in man if the milk is not pasteurized before consumption. S. dysgalactiae and S. uberis, group C, are less common causes of mastitis but may induce abortions, metritis, arthritis, wound infections, septicemia and erysipelas. S. equi, group C, causes "strangles" in horses, mules and donkeys. This disease may be epizootic but can be prevented by active immunization with a properly prepared vaccine, or bacterin (7). Occasionally the urethra of stallions is infected with a streptococcus which causes secondary infections in the genitalia of mares and prevents fertilization. Group C streptococci cause arthritis in lambs and avian streptococcosis, septicemia, peritonitis and salpingitis in chickens. Prophylactic vaccination is said to be effective in avian streptococcosis (55). Group D streptococcus, which may be hemolytic or nonhemolytic, causes "foul brood" in bees, and infects both man and animals.

Guinea pigs not infrequently have epizootic lymphadenitis (10) caused by group C streptococci, and organisms from the same group induce epizootic pneumonia in rabbits. Dogs carry nonpathogenic group M streptococci but are infected by strains belonging to group G and L (53). Cats may develop fatal and communicable septicemia (6), and mice are occasionally infected (48). Moore (73) described a type of septicemia in chickens caused by anaerobic streptococci.

Experimental Infections in Laboratory Animals. Artificially produced infections of lower animals have for a long time been used as a measure of the **pathogenicity and virulence** of streptococci. Different races of pyogenic streptococci show considerable variations in virulence, and there are few organisms pathogenic for animals and man which show comparable fluctuations in virulence.

The character or severity of the lesion in man gives little evidence as to the virulence of the organism for animals. Prolonged cultivation upon artificial media usually results in the reduction of the virulence of a streptococcus by dissociation. The passage of a streptococcus through rabbits or mice will usually, though not always, enhance its virulence for susceptible animals in general.

Among the domestic animals, those most susceptible to experimental streptococcus infection are white mice and rabbits. Inoculation of rabbits at the base of the ear with virulent streptococci may result in the formation of a lesion indistinguishable histologically from erysipelas in man (63). Guinea pigs and rats are less easily infected, and the larger domestic animals—cattle, horses, goats, cats, and dogs—are relatively refractory to most of the strains of human origin.

Clinical Types of Infection in Man. The streptococci are ubiquitous and undoubtedly cause a greater variety of clinical types of disease than any other microorganism (98). They can produce disease in every organ and tissue of the body in a pattern analogous to that of the staphylococci. In addition to these general infections, streptococci cause specific diseases, such as scarlet fever, erysipelas, epidemic sore throat, and subacute bacterial endocarditis. The streptococci are important in rheumatic fever and rheumatoid arthritis, but the exact mechanism by which they produce these diseases in man has not been established. The specific streptococcal diseases will be discussed in Chapter 21.

Infections of the skin with the various types of hemolytic streptococci cause **carbuncles, streptococcal impetigo, cellulitis, lymphangitis, and erysipelas.** Streptococcal impetigo is indistinguishable clinically from staphylococcal impetigo, and each small epidemic is usually caused by only one type of organism (92), although the older streptococcal lesions may become secondarily infected with staphylococci. There is an unexplained specificity of the streptococci which cause impetigo, since they do not progress to cellulitis, lymphadenitis, or erysipelas.

In other instances, following a scratch or abrasion of the skin, the hemolytic streptococcus produces a small, red, soggy, edematous and rather insignificant looking lesion which may be the beginning of a rapidly fatal **septicemia.** Surgeons and pathologists in particular are endangered by infections of this type, since they are exposed frequently to strains of streptococci of already proven virulence. Before the introduction of sulfonamides and penicillin, the danger of streptococcal infections of **surgical wounds** was a constant source of anxiety to the surgeon and to members of the patient's family.

Streptococci frequently infect the mucous membranes of the upper respiratory tract, causing **sinusitis, tonsillitis, pharyngitis, laryngitis, otitis media,** and **mastoiditis.** Extensions from the middle ear or from the mastoid cells often result in **meningitis** and **brain abscess.** Invasion from the pharynx to the deeper structures may lead to the development of **peritonsillar abscesses, Ludwig's angina,** or **mediastinitis.**

Primary **streptococcus pneumonia,** usually of the bronchial or lobular type, is not infrequent. The streptococci often invade the pleura from the lungs and initiate **empyema** or metastasize to the brain and initiate either meningitis or abscess or both. Under conditions of crowding which occur in army camps or refugee stations, the carrier rate for hemolytic streptococci may become as high as 70 to 89 per cent, and **epidemics** of streptococcus pneumonia may develop (22).

Streptococci, both aerobic and anaerobic varieties (65), are the chief cause of **puerperal sepsis** and will be discussed in more detail in Chapter 21.

Hemolytic streptococci are pre-eminently **secondary invaders** superimposed upon other bacterial and particularly viral diseases. A secondary streptococcal infection in diphtheria materially increases the severity of the disease. Death in cases of smallpox frequently is the direct result of first a local, and finally a blood stream infection with streptococci. Most of the deaths reported in epidemics of **measles** and **influenza** are caused by secondary infections with hemolytic streptococci (62).

Transmission. It has been known for many years that 8 to 10 per cent of apparently normal individuals carry hemolytic streptococci in their throats (21). Under conditions of crowding, especially in the winter months when virus colds are prevalent, the percentage of carriers may be increased to 75 per cent (22).

Epidemiologic investigations during World War II in the army camps in the United States have shown conclusively that ordinary throat carriers expel only a few streptococci into the air and may be hospitalized on the general medical wards.

The **nasal carrier** is the dangerous carrier (34, 35, 57). The nasal carrier not only dispenses hundreds of thousands of streptococci into the air, but infects his hands, clothing, and other inanimate objects.

Coburn (12) and Schwentker and others have emphasized the importance of another characteristic of streptococci—namely, the ability to become established in a new host under natural conditions. This property of **communicability** depends partly upon the production of certain metabolic products and toxins and partly upon other unknown factors. It is a common observation that many strains with high invasiveness and toxigenicity very rarely spread from patient to patient, while many strains which produce relatively mild disease symptoms are spread rapidly from patient to patient (60).

Cornfeld and his associates (14) studied the carrier rate in 1,000 school children in Philadelphia during one entire school year. The monthly rate ranged from a low of 7 per cent to a high of 28.8 per cent. In other series collected from the literature, the carrier rate in school children ranged from 40 to 60 per cent. In each series, however, there were many strains which could not be typed, and their clinical and epidemiologic significance could not be evaluated.

Treatment. Most strains of β hemolytic streptococci are inhibited readily in the body by both sulfonamides and penicillin. Inadequate and intermittent doses of sulfonamides should be avoided to prevent the development of strains which are resistant to the drug. Resistant strains of certain specific types of streptococci were isolated from some of the men in army camps where sulfadiazine in doses of 1 g. per day were administered to the entire personnel. Fortunately, resistance to penicillin occurs rarely.

The treatment of scarlet fever, erysipelas, puerperal sepsis, subacute bacterial endocarditis, focal infection, rheumatic fever, rheumatoid arthritis, microaerophilic, and anaerobic streptococcal infections will be discussed in Chapter 21.

Prevention. The dangerous nasal carriers of hemolytic streptococci should be strictly isolated. The problem of eliminating disease-producing streptococci from the air of operating rooms has been solved by Hart (36) by the use of ultraviolet light. Wells (101) has utilized ultraviolet light for the elimination of organisms from schoolrooms, and Robertson (82) has had partial success in disinfecting the air in hospital wards by the use of triethylene-glycol vapor.

It has been assumed for many years that active vaccination was impractical because of the great number of specific types. But a surprising number of the latent streptococci infections are caused by a few well-known types. For example, about 20 per cent of all the typable strains isolated in Cleveland, Ohio, Washington, D.C., and Chicago were type 12. Minute doses of cell wall vaccines from types 12 and 5 have produced anamnestic rises in antibody titers. Experiments are under way with cell wall vaccines by Potter, Stollerman, Siegel and their associates (79).

REFERENCES

1. Abraham, E. P., and others. Lancet, 2:177, 1941.
2. Alemeier, W. A., and Culbertson, W. R. J.A.M.A., 145:449, 1951.
3. Bailly, M. D. J. Immunol., 64:245, 1950.
4. Barkulis, S. S., and Jones, M. F. J. Bact., 74:207, 1957.
5. ——— J. Bact., 76:109, 1958.
6. Bayne-Jones, S. J. Infect. Dis., 31:474, 1922.
7. Bazeley, P. L. Australian Vet. J., 16:243, 1940; 18:141, 1942.
8. Bernheimer, A. W., and Pappenheimer, A. M., Jr. J. Bact., 43:481, 495, 1942.
9. Boissard, J. M., and Wormald, P. J. J. Path. & Bact., 62:37, 1950.
10. Boxmeyer, C. J. J. Infect. Dis., 4:657, 1907.
11. Brown, J. H. Monographs Rockefeller Inst. M. Research, No. 9, New York, 1919.
12. Coburn, A. F. U.S. Nav. M. Bull., 42:325, 1944.
13. Cole, R. N., and Hahn, J. J. Science, 135:722, 1962.
14. Cornfeld, D., and others. Ann. Int. Med., 49:1305, 1958.
15. Crawford, Y. E. J. Immunol., 89:698, 1962.
16. Cromartie, W. J., Schwab, J. H., and Craddock, J. G. Am. J. Path., 37:79, 1960.
17. Custod, J. T., and others. Proc. Soc. Exp. Biol. & Med., 103:751, 1960.
18. Dawson, M. H., and others. J. Infect. Dis., 62:138, 1938.
19. Deibel, R. H., and others. J. Bact., 86:1275, 1963.
20. Denny, F. W., Jr., and others. J. Clin. Invest., 36:1092, 1957.
21. Dingle, J. H., and others. New England J. Med., 236:157, 1947.
22. ——— Streptococcal Infections, New York, Columbia University Press, 1954, p. 20.
23. Elliott, S. D. J. Exp. Med., 111:621, 1960.
24. Flosdorf, E. W., and Mudd, S. J. Immunol., 29:389, 1935.
25. Foley, M. J., and others. J. Exp. Med., 110:603, 617, 1959.
26. Fox, E. N. J. Bact., 85:536, 1963.
27. Freimer, E. H., and others. J. Exp. Med., 110:853, 1959.
28. Fry, R. M. Lancet, 1:199, 1938.
29. Gooder, H., and Maxted, W. R. Symposia Soc. Gen. Microbiol., 11:151, 1961.
30. Griffith, F. J. Hyg., 26:363, 1927.
31. ——— J. Hyg., 34:542, 1934; 35:23, 1935.
32. Hahn, J. J., and Cole, R. M. J. Bact., 83:85, 1962.
33. Halbert, S. P., and Auerbach, T. J. Exp. Med., 113:131, 1961.
34. Hamburger, M., and Green, M. J. J. Infect. Dis., 77:68, 1945; 79:33, 1946.
35. Hare, R. J. Path. & Bact., 41:499, 1935.
36. Hart, D. J.A.M.A., 117:1610, 1941.
37. Hayashi, J. A., and Walsh, G. J. Bact., 82:736, 1961.
38. Horsfall, F. L., Jr. J. Exp. Med., 93:229, 1951.
39. Hyde, R. M., and Watson, D. W. Proc. Soc. Exp. Biol. & Med., 112:825, 1963.
40. Irwin, J., and Seeley, H. W., Jr. J. Bact., 76:29, 1958.
41. Kantor, F. S., and Cole, R. M. Proc. Soc. Exp. Biol. & Med., 102:146, 1959.
42. ——— J. Exper. Med., 112:77, 1960.
43. Koch, R. Untersuchungen über die Aetiologie der Wundinfektionskrankheiten, Berlin, 1878.
44. Krause, R. M., and McCarty, M. Bacteriol. Proc., p. 80, 1956.
45. ——— J. Exper. Med., 114:127, 1961.
46. ——— J. Exper. Med., 115:49, 1962.
47. ——— J. Exper. Med., 116:131, 1962.
48. Kutschera, F. Centralbl. f. Bakt., I. Abt., 46:671, 1908.
49. Lancefield, R. C. Proc. Soc. Exper. Biol. & Med., 22:109, 1924.
50. ——— J. Exper. Med., 42:377, 397, 1925; 47:91, 469, 481, 843, 857, 1928; 57:571, 1933; 59:441, 1934; 67:25, 1938.
51. ——— Harvey Lect., 36:251, 1940-41.
52. ——— J. Immunol., 89:307, 1962.

53. Laughton, N. J. Path. & Bact., 40:471, 1948.
54. Lawrence, H. S. J. Immunol., 68:159, 1952.
55. Lee, C. D. Diseases of Poultry, Ames, Iowa, Iowa State College Press, 1943, p. 346.
56. Leedom, J. M., and Barkulis, S. S. J. Bact., 78:687, 1959.
57. Lemon, H. M. New England J. Med., 237:988, 1947.
58. Li, Koibong. J. Bact., 69:326, 1955.
59. Little, R. B., and Plastridge, W. N. Bovine Mastitis, A Symposium, New York, McGraw-Hill Book Co., 1946.
60. Loosli, C. G., and others. J. Lab. & Clin. Med., 36:342, 1950.
61. Lund, E. Acta path. et microbiol. Scandinav., 27:110, 1950.
62. MacCallum, W. G., and others. J.A.M.A., 70:1146, 1918.
63. Marbaix. La Cellule, 1892.
64. Maxted, W. R. J. Clin. Path., 6:224, 1953.
65. Meleney, F. L. Ann. Surg., 91:287, 1930; 94:961, 1931; 101:997, 1935; 110:1067, 1939.
66. ———— Surg., Gynec. & Obst., 56:847, 1933.
67. ———— Treatise on Surgical Infections, New York, Oxford University Press, 1948.
68. ———— and others. Ann. Surg., 131:129, 1950.
69. Mergenhagen, S. E., and Scherp, H. W. J. Bact., 74:749, 1957.
70. Mirick, G. S., and others. J. Exper. Med., 80:391, 1944.
71. Moody, M. D., and others. J. Bact., 75:553, 1958.
72. ———— J. Bact., 85:553, 1958.
73. Moore, V. A. Pathology of Infectious Diseases in Animals, New York, 1916.
74. Olitsky, I., and others. J. Bact., 84:1011, 1962.
75. Pappenheimer, A. M., Jr., and Hottie, G. B. Proc. Soc. Exper. Biol. & Med., 44:645, 1940.
76. Pasteur, L. Bull. Acad. nat. méd., 8:260, 271, 1879.
77. Peeples, W. J., and others. Pub. Health Rep., 76:651, 1961.
78. Perry, C., and Slade, H. D. J. Bact., 85:636, 1953.

79. Potter, E. V., and others. J. Clin. Invest., 41:301, 1962.
80. Rantz, L. A., and Kirby, W. M. M. Arch. Int. Med., 71:516, 1943.
81. Rifkind, D., and Cole, R. M. J. Bact., 84:163, 1962.
82. Robertson, O. H. Am. Rev. Tuberc., 55:109, 1947.
83. Rosenbach, A. J. F. Mikroorganismen bei den Wundinfektionskrankheiten des Menschen, Wiesbaden, 1884.
84. Schwab, J. H. J. Bact., 79:448, 1960.
85. Seastone, C. V. J. Exper. Med., 70:347, 1939.
86. Shattock, P. M. F., and Mattick, A. T. R. J. Hyg., 43:173, 1943.
87. Sherman, J. M. Bact. Rev., 1:3, 1937.
88. ———— J. Bact., 35:81, 1938.
89. ———— and others. J. Bact., 45:249, 1943.
90. Slade, H. D. Streptococcal Infections, New York, Columbia University Press, 1954, p. 65.
91. ———— and Slamp, W. C. J. Bact., 84:345, 1962.
92. Smith, D. T., and Burky, E. L. Bull. Johns Hopkins Hosp., 35:78, 1924.
93. Snyder, I. S., and Hamilton, T. R. Proc. Soc. Exp. Biol. & Med., 106:836, 1961.
94. Sprince, H., and Woolley, D. W. J. Exper. Med., 80:213, 1944.
95. Stinebring, W. R., and Morton, H. E. J. Bact., 62:395, 1951.
96. Stollerman, G. H., and Ekstedt, R. J. Exper. Med., 106:345, 1957; 112:671, 687, 1960.
97. Swift, H. F. Bacterial and Mycotic Infections of Man, Philadelphia, Lippincott, 1952, p. 265.
98. Wannamaker, L. W. Streptococcal Infections, New York, Columbia University Press, 1954, p. 157.
99. ———— J. Exper. Med., 107:797, 1958.
100. Warren, G. H., and Gray, J. Proc. Soc. Exper. Biol. & Med., 102:125, 1959.
101. Wells, W. F., and others. Am. J. Hyg., 35:97, 1942.
102. Wiley, G. G., and Wilson, A. T. J. Exper. Med., 113:451, 1962.
103. Woolley, D. W., and Hutchings, B. L. J. Bact., 39:287, 1940.

21

Streptococcal Diseases

Scarlet Fever, Erysipelas, Epidemic Sore Throat, Puerperal Sepsis, Subacute Bacterial Endocarditis, Acute Nephritis, Rheumatic Fever, Rheumatoid Arthritis, Microaerophilic and Anaerobic Streptococcal Infections

SCARLET FEVER

Sydenham in 1675 gave the first detailed and accurate description of the infection we now call scarlet fever. He contributed the name "febris scarlatina" and differentiated the disease from measles and rubella.

The discovery of the erythrogenic toxin by Dick and Dick (1924, 1925) (14) and Dochez and Sherman (15) explained most of the puzzling features of the disease to everyone's satisfaction. The potency of scarlatinal toxin is determined by intradermal injection into the skin of susceptible human subjects. The unit is the skin test dose (STD) which has been defined by the Dicks. The **Dick test** is performed by injecting intradermally into the skin of the forearm one STD of toxin contained in 0.1 ml. of volume. A positive **Dick test** indicates that the individual is **susceptible to the disease.** On the other hand, a positive **Schultz-Charlton** reaction (60), performed by the injection of antitoxin into a reddened area of skin indicates the **presence of scarlet fever.**

The erythrogenic toxin explains many of the various clinical features of the disease. Scarlet fever rarely occurs in infants under six months of age or in adults over 50 years of age. If a group of children is exposed to a patient with scarlet fever, some will not be infected, some will develop scarlet fever, and others may develop no more than an acute pharyngitis and yet transmit scarlet fever to other susceptible children. Children may revert from a positive Dick reaction to a negative state without having any evidence of clinical disease. To produce the clinical syndrome of scarlet fever, the streptococcus must have the ability to elaborate erythrogenic toxin and this power is independent of other factors which are of importance in determining the virulence of the organism; therefore, the streptococci involved in a particular epidemic may produce either very mild or very severe infections. The severity of the secondary suppurative lesions in the sinuses, ears, mastoid processes, and glands also would depend in part upon the inherent virulence of the strain. The two most serious complications of scarlet fever, **acute hemorrhagic glomerular nephritis** and **acute rheumatic fever,** will be discussed later in this chapter.

Additional work has shown that there are yet a number of unsolved problems concerning the nature of the erythrogenic toxin. Hooker and Follensby (29) have shown that there are two erythrogenic toxins, A and B. Both are produced by the Dochez N.Y. 5 strain but other strains may have either one or the other (15).

Stock and Lynn (65) have purified type B and find it, like type A, a pure protein. Watson's investigations (75) have revealed that a number of group A strains produce erythrogenic toxins in vivo in contrast to group B and C which did not produce them. The A toxin was produced by types 28, 12, 17, and 10 (N.Y. 5); B toxin was found in 19 and 10 (N.Y. 5); a new toxin designated C was obtained from type 18.

Treatment. Both sulfonamides and penicillin are very effective. Penicillin eliminates the toxicity and fever of scarlet fever, reduces the number of complications, and shortens the carrier period. Chlortetracycline, chloramphenicol, and oxytetracycline are also effective in the treatment of scarlet fever, but no more so than penicillin.

Prevention. The control of scarlet fever has been attempted by quarantine, pasteurization of milk, active immunization, passive immunization, and sulfonamide prophylaxis.

QUARANTINE. Quarantine or isolation periods for scarlet fever vary from four to six weeks in different states. The disease is transmitted by streptococci contained in materials from the nose and throat and pus from localized infections of the ears and sinuses and not by means of desquamating skin. It would seem more logical to quarantine the patient not for an arbitrary time period fixed by law but rather until the streptococci have been eliminated from the local lesions and particularly the nose and throat.

PASTEURIZATION OF MILK. Davis and Rosenow (13) and others have recorded large outbreaks of scarlet fever in Chicago and elsewhere traceable to milk. The infection may be from the udder of the cow which has become infected with a group A streptococcus, or the milk may have been contaminated by human carriers in the process of milking and bottling. In either instance, pasteurization is indicated as a prophylactic measure.

ACTIVE IMMUNIZATION. The Dicks have proved, and many others have confirmed their findings, that injections of the scarlatinal streptococcus toxin into human beings causes the Dick test to become negative. Upon this basis, accepting the negative Dick test as an evidence of resistance, procedures have been established for the active immunization of children and adults against scarlet fever (14).

SULFONAMIDE PROPHYLAXIS. Sulfadiazine in doses of 1 g. daily has effectively prevented the development of new cases of scarlet fever in army camps, but such prophylactic measures should be supervised carefully and in civilian practice should be used with caution in order to prevent the development of strains of scarlet fever-producing streptococci which are resistant to

chemotherapy. Oral penicillin should be even better than sulfonamide as a prophylactic agent and will not induce the appearance of penicillin resistant strains.

RHEUMATIC FEVER

Cheadle (7) in 1889 suggested that polyarthritis, Sydenham's chorea, and heart disease were all a part of the same clinical syndrome. One of the chief manifestations of rheumatic fever is damage to the heart and the resulting syndrome is known as **rheumatic heart disease.**

Rheumatic fever is rare in children under three years of age and after middle life. Taranta's (69) studies of twin siblings suggests that genetic susceptibility is not likely.

Hemolytic streptococci are known to be associated constantly with the onset and with recurrences of the disease, but not necessarily with the active phase of the infection (Fig. 1). The clinical evidence is almost conclusive that rheumatic fever follows an infection by streptococci, but many different types of group A streptococci are involved and no one metabolite can be incriminated, such as the erythrogenic toxin in scarlet fever. Antibodies to all of the antigenic metabolites appear in the serum of patients with rheumatic fever.

Although there is a very good correlation between the height of the antistreptolysin titer and the occurrence of rheumatic fever (55), Halbert and his associates (20, 21) have shown the streptolysin-O, when injected intravenously into rabbits, causes focal cardiac lesions; and they have suggested that the toxin may be the cause of the cardiac lesions in man. The frequency and severity of rheumatic fever is most evident in the lower economic groups (10), but this may be due to such diverse factors as crowded living conditions, poor food, more virulent strains of streptococci (48, 66), and recent migration from a rural area (64).

A study of the epidemiology of rheumatic fever in the armed forces during World War II by Rammelkamp and his associates (52) showed that about 3 per cent of the airmen admitted to the hospital with exudative ton-

sillitis and pharyngitis from group A streptococci developed rheumatic fever within 35
days from the initial streptococcal infection.
Both Stollerman (66) and Nicholas and
Steel (47), however, have found a much
lower rate (0.3 per cent) of rheumatic fever
in school children who were exposed to less
epidemic strains of streptococci which were
flowing through the school population. It is
significant that 3.2 times as many group A
streptococci were isolated from children with
tonsils as from children without tonsils.
There is general agreement that the carrier
rate decreases as the children grow older,
suggesting specific acquired immunity (59).
Nicholas and Steele (47), Saslaw and Jablon (59), and Mozziconacci (45) have observed that some children are always free of
hemolytic streptococci, and others are intermittent carriers, while a few are constant
carriers.

Recent studies from England (2) and
from the United States (4, 64) have shown
that the total amount of rheumatic fever—
and particularly the severe forms, including
chorea—have progressively declined since
the beginning of the century. The more recent, but not the earlier, decline can be
attributed to the widespread use of penicillin.

Murphy and Swift (46) have produced
myocardial lesions with damage to collagen
tissue by the periodic injection in sequence
of a number of types of streptococci into
rabbits over a period of two and one-half
years. It is apparently essential that the types
be different, since specific immunity to a
single type renders reinfection with that type
difficult if not impossible (68).

A prolonged incubation period is essential
for the production of rheumatic fever (Fig.
1). In one army camp where there were

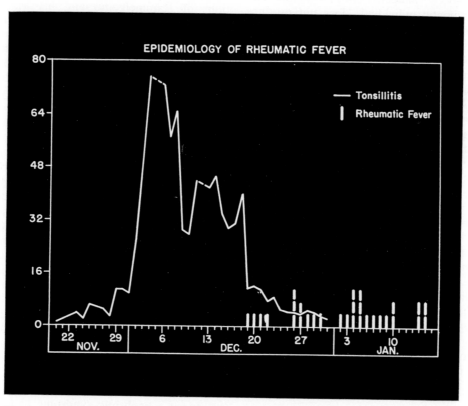

Fig. 1. Epidemiology of rheumatic fever. During a severe milk-borne epidemic of hemolytic
streptococcal infections in Denmark in 1926, 30 cases of rheumatic fever appeared late in the
epidemic. The scale on the left indicates the daily number of cases of tonsillitis. (From Madsen
and Kalbak. *Acta path. et microbiol. scandinav.*, 17:305, 1940.)

high incidences of streptococcal pharyngitis, scarlet fever, and rheumatic fever, sulfadiazine was given to the entire personnel. There were no new cases of the pharyngitis or scarlet fever after one week, but new cases of rheumatic fever occurred for three weeks and then ceased (8, 9, 52). This lag period in the elimination of rheumatic fever suggests that the streptococcus sets in motion in certain susceptible individuals some complex immunologic response which is the definite cause of the disease (37).

This problem has not been solved. Florio and his associates (19) found that neither white blood cells nor fibroblasts from human skin or heart of either normal individuals or patients with rheumatic fever were damaged by exposure to streptococci or streptococcal products. This suggests that the alteration is not an allergy of the tuberculous type. Other studies have shown that the injection of streptococcal antigens into rheumatic and nonrheumatic individuals does not produce the symptoms of rheumatic fever (16). In contrast to these negative results, Kaplan and Meyeserian (30) have shown that there is a cross between certain group A streptococcus antigens and human heart tissue. This suggests the possibility that the streptococci might under certain specific conditions induce the formation of autoantibodies to the patient's own heart antigens.

Treatment. Prolonged rest in bed, for weeks or months, is essential for the healing of the myocardial lesions. Salicylates reduce fever and improve the general symptoms.

Prevention. The prevention of streptococcal infections prevents rheumatic fever. Prompt and vigorous treatment of streptococcal infections with sulfonamides and penicillin reduces but does not entirely prevent the disease. The administration of cortisone in small doses during the acute phase of infection does not prevent the development of rheumatic fever. Penicillin does not influence the course of rheumatic fever but when given as a prophylactic prevents streptococcal infections, and thereby subsequent recurrences of the disease (9, 44, 49, 66). Group A streptococci rapidly develop resistance to sulfonamides and tetracycline (33) but not to penicillin and erythromycin. Carriers of

beta-hemolytic streptococci of group A can be protected from an attack of rheumatic fever for a period of six weeks by a dose of 1,200,000 units of penicillin (44).

ACUTE HEMORRHAGIC GLOMERULONEPHRITIS

Acute nephritis occurs as a complication of scarlet fever in 0.03 to 18 per cent of patients. It occurs also as a complication of acute rheumatic fever, but in a completely irregular and unpredictable percentage. It appears most frequently after rather mild pharyngeal infections, which are not followed by either scarlet fever or acute rheumatic fever. The irregular manner in which the disease follows streptococcal infections led Reed (57) and Rammelkamp and Weaver (53) to the conclusion that a particular type of group A hemolytic streptococcus was the etiologic agent (54). The investigations of Rammelkamp and his associates (53, 54) and others (57) have confirmed this theory. **Most cases of acute hemorrhagic glomerulonephritis follow infection with type 12; but some follow type 1, 4, 18, 25, or 49** (3). Wannamaker and Pierce (72, 73) reported a family outbreak of acute nephritis associated with type 49 streptococcus.

Some patients die in the acute phase of the disease, but those that recover have type specific antibodies in their serum which are present for a period of years. Recurrences are rarely seen, even though the patient may carry the specific type of streptococcus in his nasopharynx for 14 weeks to 10 months or longer. No one knows the mechanism involved in this hemorrhagic reaction in the kidney. A somewhat similar type of hemorrhagic nephritis occurs occasionally in serum sickness presumably as a result of an antigen-antibody reaction.

Chronic glomerulonephritis rarely if ever develops subsequent to acute hemorrhagic glomerulonephritis. Chronic nephritis is a recurrent disease with some characteristics which suggest an allergic reaction of the tuberculin type (36, 76). Sharp (61) has produced a **nephrotic syndrome** in mice by injecting group A streptococci of types 3, 14, and 19.

ERYSIPELAS

In the Middle Ages both erysipelas and acute ergot poisoning were called Saint Anthony's fire. Fehleisen (17) in 1883 isolated a hemolytic streptococcus from the lesions and reproduced the disease in man by intradermal inoculation of the organisms from cultures.

After an incubation period of three to seven days a small, bright red spot appears at the site of the inoculation and the patient develops symptoms suddenly, often with a chill, followed by nausea, vomiting and prostration. The bright red, swollen, edematous skin often is covered with small or large vesicles. The spreading edges of the lesions are demarcated sharply from the surrounding normal skin, and the progress of the inflammatory area can be charted hour by hour.

The streptococci which cause erysipelas belong to several specific types of group A. The potent erythrogenic toxins produced by these erysipelas strains can be neutralized by both erysipelas antitoxin and the scarlet fever antitoxin.

The disease is contagious from person to person but does not produce explosive epidemics analogous to scarlet fever. In contrast to scarlet fever, one attack of erysipelas may predispose the individual to additional attacks.

Recurrent Erysipelas. There are two clinical types of recurrent erysipelas. The first type occurs early, often within a few weeks after the original infection. The same skin area is involved, and streptococci are present in the skin, but the symptoms are usually milder than those of the primary attack. The second type of recurrence occurs months and years later, with an explosive onset of fever and redness of the area involved in the original attack. Streptococci usually cannot be recovered from the inflamed skin. It is thought that the recurring attacks are due to the hypersensitiveness of the patient to streptococcus proteins as a result of the original infection. Skin sensitivity in the area of the original disease is greater than that in other areas of the body (1). The injection of culture filtrates or streptallergen may precipitate an artificial erysipelas over the area of the original infection.

Amoss (1) has shown that patients subject to recurrent erysipelas of the face may harbor hemolytic streptococci in the sinuses. Those showing recurrences in the legs often have fungus infections about the toes which favor the local growth of streptococci and, consequently, production of the antigen in these sites causes allergic reactions in the leg. Repeated attacks of erysipelas of the leg result gradually in the production of **elephantiasis** from damage to the lymphatic system.

Treatment. Sulfonamides and penicillin are effective in the primary and early recurrences. Recurrent attacks of the late type do not respond so dramatically, and such patients should be treated for sensitivity to streptallergens and desensitized. Desensitization rarely is permanent and should be repeated from time to time. Careful foot hygiene should be exercised to prevent attacks of "athlete's foot" which open the way for the streptococcal infection.

Prevention. The prevention is the same as for other types of streptococcal infection.

EPIDEMIC SORE THROAT FROM CONTAMINATED MILK

Epidemics of sore throat traceable to milk have been observed in England since 1875. The onset is usually accompanied by sudden chilliness, with muscular soreness, headache, and nausea. The cases are similar to the milder forms of influenza. The first observed epidemic in this country occurred in Boston in 1911 and was studied by Winslow. There were 48 fatal cases. Since that time a number of similar epidemics have been described, the most extensive being that which took place in Chicago in 1911, studied by Capps and Miller, and by Davis and Rosenow (13). There were 10,000 cases, hardly any of which came from the west side of the city. Of 622 cases investigated, 87 per cent or 537 used milk from a certain dairy, and 79 per cent of the fatal cases used the same milk. There was a coincident epidemic of sore throats among the employees of the dairy, where bovine mastitis was found in

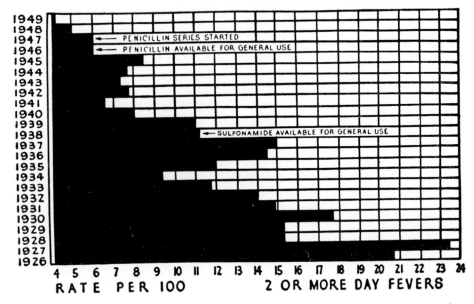

Fig. 2. Puerperal morbidity. Reduction in puerperal morbidity following the introduction of sulfonamide and penicillin. (From Keettel and Plass. *J.A.M.A.*, 142:324, 1950.)

the cows. Almost 5 per cent of the cows of this dairy had mastitis, and streptococci were isolated from the milk of a cow and from the throat of a girl on the same farm.

Almost any of the group A hemolytic streptococci may be responsible for an epidemic of this type and occasionally group C streptococci of animal origin are implicated. The organisms may be introduced into the milk from a mastitis in the cow or from the nasopharynx of a human carrier.

PUERPERAL SEPSIS

Before the work of Semmelweis was accepted, women died by the tens of thousands from streptococcal puerperal infections carried, for the most part, on the hands and in the nasopharynx of the attending physician.

The most dangerous and rapidly fatal form of puerperal fever is caused by various types of group A and human C hemolytic streptococci. The studies of Harris and Brown (23) and Colebrook (11) have shown that anaerobic streptococci which are normal inhabitants of the vagina also less frequently cause the disease. *Staphylococcus aureus*, the *Clostridium* group of anaerobes including the tetanus bacillus, the colon

bacillus, and other organisms occasionally cause puerperal fever.

Treatment. Infections with the hemolytic streptococci respond readily to treatment with the sulfonamides and penicillin (31). The anaerobic streptococcus infections are quite resistant to these bactericidal agents, but the progress of recovery often is aided by very large doses of penicillin supplemented by bacitracin and other antibiotics (40).

Prevention. Every effort should be made to protect the prospective mother from contact with individuals carrying hemolytic streptococci. Scrupulously aseptic technics in predelivery examinations and in delivery rooms are now routine, and adequate protection from droplet infections should be the objective. Prophylactic treatment with penicillin has materially reduced morbidity (Fig. 2).

SUBACUTE BACTERIAL ENDOCARDITIS

Although acute endocarditis may be caused by *Staphylococcus aureus*, *Streptococcus pyogenes*, *Diplococcus pneumoniae*, *Neisseria gonorrhoeae*, *Brucella*, and occasionally other organisms, most instances of endocarditis are of the subacute variety and are caused by the *viridans* or *enterococcus* group (group D) types of streptococci. In a few instances *Haemophilus parainfluenzae,* microaerophilic and anaerobic streptococci, *Erysipelothrix erysipeloides, Candida krusei,* and *Histoplasma capsulatum* have been isolated from the blood or from the heart valves at necropsy (50).

The presence of a congenital heart lesion or an active or healed rheumatic valvular lesion predisposes to the development of endocarditis.

Treatment. There was a recovery rate of less than 1 per cent in cases of subacute bacterial endocarditis before the introduction of penicillin. Most strains of the viridans group of streptococci are moderately susceptible to penicillin.

Penicillin-susceptible strains usually respond readily to one million units daily given for six to eight weeks. Resistant strains may require 10 to 20 million units and supplementary treatment with streptomycin and the newer antibiotics. Resistance does develop to the newer antibiotics more rapidly than to penicillin but less rapidly than to streptomycin (24). By early diagnosis and adequate treatment a recovery rate of over 90 per cent can be expected (18, 22, 32, 70).

Prevention. Patients with congenital heart lesions or old rheumatic carditis should be given prophylactic penicillin therapy before the extraction of teeth or undergoing operations upon the upper respiratory tract.

RHEUMATOID ARTHRITIS

Rheumatoid arthritis is a chronic disease with systemic manifestations involving especially the synovial linings of the joints. Many investigators believe rheumatoid arthritis to be an infectious disease (56), but others insist that it is metabolic in origin. Hemolytic streptococci frequently are found in the nasopharynges of patients with rheumatoid arthritis, but the association is not nearly as definite as in rheumatic fever.

In 1948 Rose and his associates (58) detected the presence of an antibody in the serums of patients with rheumatoid arthritis. The test system was somewhat complex, requiring the sensitization of sheep red cells with nonagglutinating quantities of rabbit antisheep cell serum. Some factor in the serums of patients with rheumatoid arthritis would cause an agglutination of the sensitized cells. Heller and his coworkers (26) treated sheep red cells with tannic acid and then coated them with pooled human gamma globulin (Cohn fraction II). These treated cells are agglutinated when exposed to the serum of patients with rheumatoid arthritis. Their results have been confirmed in two large series of clinical cases (6, 63).

The rheumatoid factor is a macrogamma globulin with a molecular weight around 1,000,000 and an ultracentrifugal sedimentation rate of 19 S. (42). Heimer, Federico, and Freyberg (25) isolated this factor and Kunkel, Franklin, and Müller-Eberhardt (34) suggested that the macromolecule might be an antibody to the normal 7 S. gamma globulin in the serum. This opinion has been supported by other investigators (42, 43, 71).

There is evidence that the rheumatoid factor is the result of the disease rather than the cause. This idea is supported by the study of Craig, Kirby, and Persons (12), who found that C-reactive protein was present in 81 per cent of the patients with acute rheumatic fever and in 91 per cent of these with positive hemagglutination tests. There is no doubt that there are profound alterations in the tissues, since Levine, Franklin and Thorbeck (35) have reported that lymph nodes from normal individuals synthesize 7 S. globulin while lymph nodes from patients with rheumatoid arthritis synthesize 19 S. globulin.

The rheumatoid factor can be measured by hemagglutination or by the flocculation of latex particles and particles of betonite which have been coated with factor II human globulin (5). Svartz's (67) success in inducing pigs to form the rheumatic factor by infecting them with group B *Streptococcus agalactiae* has not yet been confirmed.

Treatment. The dramatic response of patients with acute rheumatoid arthritis following administration of corticoid hormones (27, 28, 74) is suggestive evidence that an antigen-antibody reaction analogous to but differing from that in rheumatic fever is involved in this disease. The evidence is not nearly as conclusive that streptococci cause the initial sensitization. Relapses occur almost uniformly when the hormones are withdrawn, suggesting either that the initial inciting agent remains for a long time in the body of the patient or that the initial alteration to the agent requires months or years for a reversal to normal.

MICROAEROPHILIC AND ANAEROBIC STREPTOCOCCAL INFECTIONS

Microaerophilic streptococci associated with a chronic, burrowing type of gangrene of the subcutaneous tissues have been studied by Meleney (38, 39). They are associated at times with micrococci and colon bacilli but often occur alone. They are found to be anaerobic on primary isolation but adjust themselves to aerobic conditions after a few transfers.

The strictly anaerobic streptococci have been studied by a number of investigators. These organisms are apparently normal inhabitants of the vagina and frequently cause puerperal fever. Anaerobic streptococci have been isolated from empyema. They also are a part of the fusospirochetal symbiosis which causes the most common form of pulmonary abscess and gangrene (51, 62).

Meleney found that the local lesions (40) caused by microaerophilic streptococci respond slowly to treatment with zinc peroxide or zinc peroxide supplemented by sulfonamides. Both microaerophilic and anaerobic streptococci are rather resistant to penicillin but somewhat more susceptible to the newer antibiotics, particularly bacitracin and chloramphenicol (41). The use of two or more antibiotics simultaneously may give better results than one alone. These two groups of streptococci deserve more study.

REFERENCES

1. Amoss, H. L. Ann. Int. Med., 5:500, 1931.
2. Begg, T. B., and others. Brit. Med. J., 11:223, 1962.
3. Bernstein, S. H., and Stillerman, M. Ann. Int. Med., 52:1026, 1960.
4. Bland, E. F. New England J. Med., 262:597, 1960.
5. Block, K. J., and Bunim, J. J. J.A.M.A., 169:307, 1959.
6. Bunim, J. J., and others. J. Chronic Diseases, 1:168, 1955.
7. Cheadle, W. B. The Various Manifestations of the Rheumatic State, London, Smith, Elder and Co., 1889.
8. Coburn, A. F. The Factor of Infection in the Rheumatic State, Baltimore, Williams & Wilkins Co., 1931.
9. ———— J.A.M.A., 126:88, 1944.
10. ———— Ann. Int. Med., 47:402, 1957.
11. Colebrook, L., and others. Lancet, 2:30, 1942.
12. Craig, H. W., and others. J. Lab. & Clin. Med., 49:635, 1957.
13. Davis, D. J., and Rosenow, E. C. J.A.M.A., 58:773, 1912.
14. Dick, G. F., and Dick, G. H. J.A.M.A., 81:1166, 1923; 82:265, 301, 544, 1246, 1924; 83:84, 1924; 84:803, 1477, 1925; 93:1784, 1929; 98:1436, 1932.
15. Dochez, A. R., and Sherman, L. J.A.M.A., 82:544, 1924.
16. Editorial II. J.A.M.A., 181:250, 1962.
17. Fehleisen. Die Aetiologie des Erysipelas, Berlin, 1883.
18. Finland, M. J.A.M.A., 166:364, 1958.
19. Florio, L., and others. J. Immunol., 80:12, 26, 1958.
20. Halbert, S. P., and Auerbach, T. J. Exper. Med., 113:131, 1961.
21. Halbert, S. P., and others. J. Exper. Med., 113:759, 1013, 1961.
22. Hamburger, M., and others. J.A.M.A., 175:554, 1961.
23. Harris, J. W., and Brown, J. H. Bull. Johns Hopkins Hosp., 44:1, 1929.
24. Harvey, J. C., and others. J. Clin. Invest., 28:987, 1949.
25. Heimer, R., and others. Proc. Soc. Exper. Biol. & Med., 99:381, 1958.
26. Heller, G., and others. J. Immunol., 72:66, 1954; 74:340, 1955.
27. Hench, P. S., and others. Proc. Staff Meet., Mayo Clin., 24:167, 181, 1949.
28. ———— and others. J.A.M.A., 144:1327, 1950.
29. Hooker, S. B., and Follensby, E. M. J. Immunol., 27:177, 1934.
30. Kaplan, M. H., and Meyeserian, M. Lancet, I:760, 1962.
31. Keettel, W. C., and Plass, E. D. J.A.M.A., 142:324, 1950.
32. Kerr, A.. Jr. Subacute Bacterial Endocarditis, Springfield, Ill., Charles C Thomas, 1955.
33. Kuharic, H. A., and others. J.A.M.A., 174:1779, 1960.
34. Kunkel, H. G., Franklin, E. C., and Müller-Eberhardt, H. J. J. Clin. Investigation, 38:424, 1959.
35. Levene, H. I., and others. J. Immunol., 86:440, 1961.
36. Longcope, W. T., and others. J. Clin. Invest., 5:7, 1927; 4:449, 1927.
37. McCarty, M. Rheumatic Fever, A Symposium, Minneapolis, University of Minnesota Press, 1952.
38. Meleney, F. L. Surg., Gynec. & Obst., 56:847, 1933.

39. ——— Ann. Surg., 94:961, 1931; 101:997, 1935; 110:1067, 1939.
40. ——— Treatise on Surgical Infections, New York, Oxford University Press, 1948, p. 80.
41. ——— and others. Ann. Surg., 131:129, 1950.
42. Mellors, R. C., and others. J. Exper. Med., 113:475, 1962.
43. Mikkelsen, W. M., and others. Ann. Int. Med., 52:1051, 1960.
44. Morris, A. J., and Rammelkamp, C. H., Jr. J.A.M.A., 165:664, 1957.
45. Mozziconacci, P., and others. Acta Paediat., 50:33, 1961.
46. Murphy, G. E., and Swift, H. F. J. Exper. Med., 89:687, 1949; 91:485, 1950.
47. Nicholas, W. C., and Steele, C. P. J.A.M.A., 181:197, 1962.
48. Paul, J. R. Am. J. Med., 2:66, 1947.
49. Phibbs, B., and others. J.A.M.A., 166:1113, 1958.
50. Porterfield, J. C. J. Gen. Microbiol., 4:92, 1950.
51. Proske, H. O., and Sayers, R. R. Pub. Health Rep., 49:839, 1934.
52. Rammelkamp, C. H., Jr., and others. Rheumatic Fever, A Symposium, Minneapolis, University of Minnesota Press, 1952.
53. ——— and Weaver, R. S. J. Clin. Invest., 32:345, 1953.
54. ——— Streptococcal Infections, New York, Columbia University Press, 1954, p. 197.
55. Rantz, L. A., and others. Am. J. Med., 5:3, 1948.
56. Rawls, W. B., and Chapman, G. H. J. Lab. & Clin. Med., 21:49, 1935.
57. Reed, R. W. Canad. M. A. J., 68:448, 1953.
58. Rose, H. M., and others. Proc. Soc. Exper. Biol. & Med., 68:1, 1948.
59. Saslaw, M. S., and Jablon, J. M. Circulation, 21:679, 1960.
60. Schultz, W., and Charlton, W. Ztschr. f. Kinderh., 17:328, 1918.
61. Sharp, J. T. Proc. Soc. Exper. Biol. & Med., 104:428, 1960.
62. Smith, D. T. Am. Rev. Tuberc., 16:584, 1927.
63. Smyth, C. J. Ann. Int. Med., 53:1, 1960.
64. Stamler, J. Am. J. Cardiol., 10:319, 1962.
65. Stock, A. H., and Lynn, R. J. Immunol., 86:561, 1961.
66. Stollerman, G. H. J.A.M.A., 177:823, 1961.
67. Svartz, N. J.A.M.A., 177:50, 1961.
68. Swift, H. F. Ann. Int. Med., 30:715, 1949.
69. Taranta, A., and others. Second Pan American Congress on Rheumatic Disease, Washington, D.C., June 3, 1959.
70. Tomsett, R., and Pizette, M. Arch. Int. Med., 109:146, 1962.
71. Vaughn, J. H., and Butler, V. P., Jr. Ann. Int. Med., 56:1, 1962.
72. Wannamaker, L. W., and Pierce, H. C. Lancet, 81:561, 1962.
73. ——— Fed. Proceed., 21:231, 1962.
74. Ward, L. E. J.A.M.A., 170:1318, 1959.
75. Watson, D. W. J. Exper. Med., 111:255, 1960.
76. Zinsser, H. Bull. New York Acad. Med., 4:351, 1928.

22

The Micrococci

Family: *Micrococcaceae* Pribram. Genera: *Staphylococcus, Micrococcus, Gaffkya, Sarcina, Methanococcus,* and *Peptococcus*

Micrococci were identified in pus by Pasteur in 1889 and by Ogston in 1881. Although Becker was the first to grow the organism in pure culture, the classic work of Rosenbach in 1884 laid the foundation for our present knowledge of this group.

In the seventh edition of Bergey's Manual the family *Micrococcaceae* is divided into six genera. The strictly aerobic strains which may oxidize, but which cannot ferment, glucose are designated as *Micrococcus* (Figs. 1 and 2); aerobic, but facultative anaerobic strains, which ferment glucose anaerobically with the production of acid, are designated as *Staphylococcus;* cells occurring in tetrads and packets of eights, as *Gaffkya;* white, yellow, orange, and red chromogens occurring in packets, as *Sarcina;* obligate anaerobes occurring in chains, pairs, but never in packets, which produce methane, as *Methanococcus;* and the same types which do not form methane, as *Peptococcus.*

Elek (64) has proposed a different classification. Coagulase-positive strains which produce acid from glucose would be called *Staphylococcus aureus;* coagulase-negative strains which produce acid and acetone from glucose would be called *Staphylococcus saprophiticus;* coagulase-negative cells, arranged in tetrads and packets, which produce acid but not acetone from glucose would be *Staphylococcus lactis* (N. Sp.); coagulase-negative cocci producing pink colonies on agar and acid, but not acetone, from glucose would be *Staphylococcus roseus;* and coagulase-negative cocci which do not produce acid and acetone from glucose would be *Staphylococcus afermentans* (type strain, *Micrococcus lysodeikicus* Flemming).

Cowan (47) proposes three genera: I, *Staphylococcus;* II, *Micrococcus;* and III, *Sarcina,* with one species of *Staphylococcus* for the coagulase-positive and one for the coagulase-negative strains. The *Micrococci* should be divided into those which alter glucose and other sugars, those which do not, and those which form pink colonies. The anaerobic species should be included in the *Sarcina,* since the original isolates on which the species was founded was a strict anaerobe. At least some order is evolving in this group.

The strains of *S. epidermidis* and strains of *Micrococcus* have been studied by Jones and her associates (103). They concluded that the catalase-positive but coagulase-negative coccus which is pathogenic for pigs and mice should be classified as a *Staphylococcus,* but not as a member of *S. aureus* or *S. epidermidis. S. aureus* strains are all catalase-positive (131). A somewhat different classification has been presented by Baird-Parker (7) based on physiologic and biochemical reactions (13).

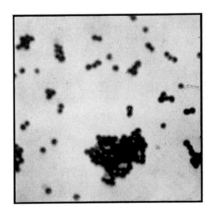

Fig. 1. *Staphylococcus aureus.* Gram stain. × 2,000.

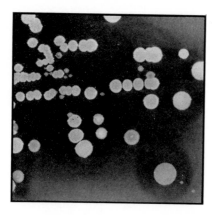

Fig. 2. Colonies of *S. aureus*. Note zone of hemolysis.

STAPHYLOCOCCUS AUREUS AND STAPHYLOCOCCAL DISEASES

Genus: *Staphylococcus* Rosenbach. Species: *Staphylococcus aureus* Rosenbach

Staphylococcal infection is primarily a disease of man. Every tissue and every organ is susceptible to invasion by these cocci, and the resulting disease is characterized by inflammation, necrosis, and abscess formation. The infections vary from mild furuncles on the skin to the almost uniformly fatal pyemias. Except for staphylococcal impetigo the disease is sporadic, not epidemic. When penicillin was first employed in the therapy of these infections, only a few strains were found with natural spontaneous resistance, and there was every reason to believe that staphylococcal infections of all types had been brought under control. The versatility of the cocci was underestimated, however, since the number of strains isolated from hospitalized patients and personnel (71) which are resistant to penicillin has increased to over 75 per cent in less than 15 years. Each new antibiotic, in turn, has been hailed as the answer to penicillin resistance, and each in turn has given rise to resistant strains necessitating a battery of laboratory tests to discover an effective antibiotic for the specific patient.

Before the days of antibiotics more serious infections were produced by pneumococci than by staphylococci (Fig. 1 in Chapter 19). The availability of the antibiotics has reduced the importance of the former and at the same time produced a change in the ecologic cosmos which is resulting in the **selection of highly virulent penicillinase producing strains** which are gradually replacing the virulent or less virulent strains which cannot synthesize penicillinase. Both penicillinase- and nonpenicillinase-producing strains rapidly acquire resistance to other antibiotics, but that is of little advantage to the nonpenicillin-synthesizing strains, since they will be eliminated by penicillin treatment.

Highly virulent strains of staphylococci existed before the discovery of penicillin. In 1928, at Bundaberg, Australia, a vial of toxin-antitoxin, used for immunization of children against diphtheria, became infected and was subsequently used for the injection of 21 children 12 of whom died within two days of symptoms resembling an intoxication (106). The strain isolated from abscesses, which formed in the surviving children, was found to produce very potent exotoxins when grown in semisolid agar under increased CO_2 (35). This highly virulent strain has been preserved, and when tested for phage type by Roundtree (159, 160) in 1959 was found to be a penicillin-susceptible strain of phage type 52/52A/80/81. This strain has become the highly virulent hospital strain throughout the world. It was already present in this country by 1927. A collection of 194 phage-typed strains, isolated between 1927 and 1947, revealed the fact that 22 per cent were type 80/81 when tested by Blair and Carr (21, 22) in 1960. One of these penicillinase-producing 80/81 strains was isolated at the very beginning of the penicillin era by Blair (20) under conditions which precluded a previous exposure to penicillin.

The 80/81 and a few other strains are known as hospital epidemic strains (12, 72, 150, 153, 166). The strains colonize in the nose and on the skin of hospital employees and are taken home by patients who spread it into the community. The spread is accelerated by the promiscuous use of penicillin for minor infections; this eliminates the penicillin-susceptible strains carried by individuals and permits the recolonization by resistant strains (17). If the present trend continues, we may expect that a few highly virulent, penicillin-resistant phage types will drive out of the population all of the penicillin susceptible strains.

Morphology and Staining. *Staphylococcus aureus* is a typical sphere, although one side may be somewhat flattened when the cells are grouped in the irregular grape-like clusters which gave to the organism its generic name (Fig. 1). The average diameter of the sphere is 0.8 μ, but individual organisms or entire strains occasionally vary between the extreme limits of 0.4 and 1.2 μ. In smears from pus the cocci are seen singly, in pairs, in clusters, and even in short chains. The irregular clusters are found characteristically in smears from cultures grown on solid media. In broth cultures short chains and diplococcal forms occur so frequently that it often is impossible to distinguish between staphylococci and streptococci by their morphology alone.

Staphylococci are **nonmotile,** although they may exhibit marked Brownian motion when examined in a hanging drop. They are **nonsporogenous** and **gram-positive,** but a few gram-negative forms may occur in the center of clusters, in organisms phagocytized by cells, and in old dying cultures.

No definitive statement can be made in respect to the presence or function of a capsule. An ovious capsule on a few specific strains was reported by Lyons (118) in 1937 and Price and Kneeland (148) in 1956. A large capsular structure, induced by growing a specific strain of *S. aureus* in high concentration of lactose and mannitol, was designated a "pseudocapsule" by Sall, Mudd, and Tauber (162). Sall's (163) studies in 1962 indicated that the "pseudocapsule" is coagulase which is produced in excess in this medium.

The original Smith strain of *Staphylococcus* resisted phagocytosis by rabbit leukocytes and was virulent for mice (45). The parent strain could be dissociated into a diffuse colony with high virulence and a compact colony which was not virulent (73, 96) (Fig. 3). Both these virulent and nonvirulent colonies produced the same amount of soluble coagulase and beta hemolysin, so the difference seemed to depend upon a surface antigen (110). This surface antigen or capsular material (129), by agar gel diffusion, seemed to contain at least four antigens (196). The reports of Fisher from Australia (75) and Stamp from England (177) suggest that this surface antigen induces

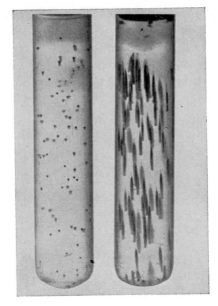

Fig. 3. Appearance of Smith compact strain (left) and diffuse strain (right) in plasma salt agar. (From Koenig. *Yale J. Biol. & Med.,* 34:549, 1962.)

antibactericidal, and not antitoxic, immunity in experimental animals.

The Smith strain (157) and four new strains isolated by Tompsett (183) share two striking peculiarities for virulent strains of *Staphylococcus:* they are negative to the slide coagulase test and are not typable by phage (157). These findings suggest a superficial surface antigen which might block both the coagulase reaction and the attachment of phage.

Although the virulent Smith type diffuse strain is rarely isolated, Rogers (157) has suggested that all virulent staphylococcal strains may rapidly acquire a surface antigen and capsule when inoculated into a living animal, as is known to be the case with virulent strains of *Pasteurella pestis* and *Bacillus anthracis.* This theory is supported by the observations of Rogers that virtually all normal human serums have detectable opsonizing antibody against the Smith diffuse variant; and some recently isolated strains from human infection, which did not resist phagocytosis by leukocytes, did stimulate the production of heat-stable antibody and could opsonize the Smith strain (158). If the existence of such a surface antigen or capsule could be established, then the pathogenic staphylococci would be analogous to pathogenic pneumococci and streptococci where a surface antigen is essential for full virulence. This concept is supported by the observations of Wiley (197) that the size of the capsule is related directly to virulence for embryonated eggs. However, the capsular material which is initiated by cultivation in bicarbonate media is not related antigenically to either the free or bound coagulase (65).

Cultural Characteristics. Laboratory strains of staphylococci grow equally well on meat extract or meat infusion media at a temperature of 37° C. The optimal temperature for growth lies at or about 35° C., although growth occurs readily at temperatures as low as 15° C. and as high as 40° C.

The most characteristic and luxuriant growth occurs under **aerobic** conditions, but staphylococci are **facultatively anaerobic** and will grow in an atmosphere of hydrogen. The optimal reaction of the medium is pH 7.4.

On **nutrient agar plates** the colonies are usually round, 1 to 2 mm. in diameter, convex, opaque, glistening, with an entire edge and are soft or butter-like in consistency (Fig. 2). Typical growth is **golden-yellow,** but this color may vary in shade and intensity.

On **blood-agar plates** the colonies are usually larger, and certain varieties are surrounded by zones of **hemolysis.** Primary cultures should be planted by streaking or pouring petri dishes of blood-agar medium. Young colonies in the depth of the medium develop no pigment and, because they often are surrounded by a zone of hemolysis and are extremely small, may be confused with colonies of beta hemolytic streptococci.

Staphylococci can be grown in a synthetic medium if both thiamine and nicotinic acid are included; however, uracil is necessary for anaerobic growth (23).

Pathogenic strains usually oxidize mannitol, and all strains oxidize simple sugars without gas. Litmus, methylene blue, and rosaniline are **decolorized,** and nitrates are reduced to **nitrites,** but **indol** is **not formed** in peptone water.

The growing importance of *Staphylococcus* in hospital infections, in food poisoning, and in mixed infections with gram-negative bacilli in man has forced our attention on a more selective medium for the differentiation of these organisms from others in pus with a mixed flora (2), from foods of all kinds (6), and from the dust from the air, floors, and furniture in hospitals (2). Chapman's (42) alkaline brom-thymol-blue agar containing potassium tellurite, for the isolation of staphylococci from the feces was followed by Mait-

land and Martyn's (121) salt agar, with salt as the inhibitor and mannitol as a differential sugar. Ludham's tellurite medium (Fig. 4A) was modified by Innes (97) by reducing the content of Lemco and halving the concentration of tellurite and by the addition of egg-yolk and 1 per cent sodium chloride (TEA) (Fig. 4B). Baird-Parker (6) added glycine-pyruvate to give egg-tellurite-glycine-pyruvate agar (ETGPA), certain species of *Proteus* give colonies which are indistinguishable from those of staphylococci on both TEA and ETGPA, but *Proteus* is always prevented from swarming, and the *Proteus* colonies are easily differentiated by gram stain or subculture. Colonies of staphylococci should be subcultured, since the coagulase test may be false negative if slide coagulase tests are preformed on colonies from these media. There are other new media, including egg-yolk azide agar (94), polymixin agar (69), and fibrinogen-tellurite-glycine agar (52). To these should be added the blood-mannitol-fluorescein amide of Kimler (107), where fluorescein under ultraviolet light identifies *S. aureus* colonies which have oxidized mannitol.

Pigment Production. Very young colonies of *Staphylococcus aureus* are always colorless, but as growth takes place, a pigment is elaborated which is soluble in alcohol, ether, chloroform, and benzol and has been classified as a **lipochrome.** The pigment remains in the colony and does not diffuse into the media, but its solubility in tissue exudates gives pus and sputum a faint, golden yellow color which should suggest the possibility of this type of infection. The staphylococci originally were separated into species on the basis of pigment production. Thus the golden staphylococcus was named *Staphylococcus aureus,* the white *S. albus,* and the lemon-colored *S. citreus.* Pigment does not develop in cultures grown under anaerobic conditions and often is not abundant in and on blood-agar plates incubated at 37° C. Transferring colonies to plain agar or Löffler's medium and incubating at room temperature result in maximum production of pigment.

Virulence and the ability to produce coagulase is associated with, but does not depend upon, the color of the colony. Only a few of the very yellow *S. aureus* isolates fail to produce coagulase, while only a few of the *S. albus* colonies do produce coagulase.

Resistance. Staphylococci are among the most resistant of all the nonsporulating bacteria. On agar slants cultures remain alive at room temperature or in the icebox for months.

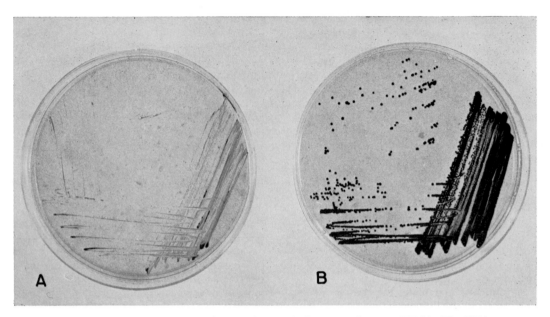

Fig. 4. Selective growth of staphylococci on tellurite egg-yolk agar (TEA). The TEA was made by adding egg yolks and sodium chloride to Ludham's medium. A, growth on Ludham's medium. B, growth on TEA. (From Alder, Gillespie, and Waller. *J. Applied Bact.,* 25:436, 1962.)

When dried on threads, paper, or cloth or in pus, they are viable for six to 14 weeks. *Staphylococcus aureus* is killed in 15 minutes by 2 per cent phenol, in 10 minutes by 1 per cent bichloride of mercury, in three minutes by 3 per cent hydrogen peroxide, and in one minute by tincture of iodine. Alcohol in 50 to 70 per cent solution requires 60 minutes to kill micrococci.

A strain of *Staphylococcus aureus,* which is killed in 10 minutes but not in five by phenol diluted 1:90, is used by the U.S. Food and Drug Administration as a standard test organism for evaluating other antiseptics. Abraham and others (1) employed a standard strain of this organism to establish the unit of penicillin. Susceptible staphylococci usually are killed by 0.1 to 1 unit of penicillin and 1 to 120 μg. of streptomycin per milliliter.

It was mentioned in the introduction that penicillinase-producing strains were in existence before the antibiotic penicillin was discovered. As a rule, penicillin-susceptible strains do not develop penicillinase or resistance when exposed to the drug either in the test tube or by treatment. Geronimus and Cohen (78) observed the increase in penicillinase production by a factor of 19 to 29 after exposure in the test tube. Hamburger and his associates (87)

isolated a strain of *Staphylococcus,* phage type 6/7/47/54/75/971, which was inhibited by 31.2 μg of penicillin before treatment, but strains isolated after one week of treatment, with many millions of units of penicillin each day, required from 1,500 to 2,000 μg. per milliliter. This highly resistant strain subsequently reverted in experimental lesions produced in dogs to a susceptible level of 0.05 μg. per milliliter. These observations suggest that some strains of staphylococci have the genetic mechanism for the induction of penicillinase production, while other strains lack this ability. This concept is supported by the experiment in which resistance to streptomycin and to novobiocin have been transferred by lysogenic phage (55, 128). Both streptomycin resistance and free coagulase production has been transduced by specific phage types (111). Patte and Baldwin (147) employed phage 80 to transfer resistance to chlorotetracycline and novobiocin and also the ability to synthesize penicillinase. Blair and Carr (22) have induced penicillinase synthesis with a phage and have conferred toxin production upon certain nontoxigenic strains by lysogenization with a phage derived from a toxigenic strain. Strains susceptible to typing by phage groups II and III but resistant to typing by phage group I or phage 81 were not transduced.

The synthesis of 6-aminopenicillanic acid was followed very quickly by the appearance of several semisynthetic penicillin homologs (171). The best-known are **methicillin, oxacillin,** and **ancillin** (90, 161), but new ones seem to appear each month. All of the new penicillins are much more expensive and somewhat less efficient against penicillin-susceptible strains than old penicillin G; hence they should be reserved for serious infections with penicillin-resistant staphylococci. Methicillin must be given parenterally, while oxacillin can be administered either parenterally or orally (77). These penicillins induce resistance to staphylococci in the test tube, and the organisms retain their high virulence (11, 190). The mechanism of resistance is unknown but is somewhat different from the elaboration of a penicillinase.

Resistance and even dependence (75) occur with great rapidity to streptomycin, dihydrostreptomycin, and erythromycin (153). Strains resistant to chlorotetracycline are usually also resistant to oxytetracycline and vice versa. Cross-resistance also occurs between erythromycin and carbomycin. Resistance is building up to neomycin, bacitracin, and, to a lesser degree, chloramphenicol (74). Ristocetin, kanamycin, and vancomycin are effective with penicillin-resistant organisms but are rather toxic (187). Resistance to kanamycin has appeared in a single phage type, type 54, however, and more may be expected (86).

Another, but less important, type of resistance to penicillin ocurs in association with the appearance of G type (93) and L form colonies (176).

Variability. The golden yellow staphylococci may give rise to white or translucent, colorless colonies with or without a corresponding change in colony formation and virulence. This phenomenon has been studied by a number of investigators. In general the variants follow the patterns observed in the study of other organisms and one may obtain the mucoid yellow, smooth yellow, rough yellow, mucoid white, smooth white (156), and the G type of Hadley (93).

Antigenic Structure. Rantz and his associates (152) discovered an antigen which was common to all the gram-positive cocci and to a number of gram-positive bacilli (116, 143). The Rantz Antigen has been extracted by treatment with lysosome from certain strains of staphylococci and used to sensitize erythrocytes which in turn could be used as an antigen to detect hemagglutinins in serum (84). Neter and his associates (136) found that this hemagglutinin reaction was inhibited by human and animal serum and that the serum factor was heat-stabile at 75° C.

Staphylococcus aureus contains both antigenic proteins and antigenic carbohydrates. Julianelle and Wieghard (105) isolated one type of carbohydrate, A, from pathogenic strains and a second, B, from strains that were not pathogenic. When rabbits were inoculated with whole cocci from representative strains of group A and group B, specific precipitins of high titer were produced. The pure polysaccharides were not pathogenic for rabbits and mice and not antigenic for the rabbit when separated from the carbohydrate-protein complex. Group A carbohydrate gave the immediate (20 to 30 minutes) "wheal and erythema" type of reaction when injected intradermally in patients with staphylococcal infections.

Julianelle and Wieghard (105) also isolated a complex protein from staphylococci which produced precipitins when injected into rabbits. The purified protein was not toxic for rabbits or mice, but when injected intradermally in patients with staphylococcal infections, it induced a slowly developing, 24 to 48 hours, type of reaction known as the protein or tuberculin type of sensitivity. If patients having staphylococcal infections are tested with either autogenous vaccines or commercial toxoids, the delayed type of skin reaction is usually obtained. An occasional patient shows only the immediate wheal type of reaction, while others give first the immediate and later the delayed reaction.

Agar gel diffusion studies have shown that *S. aureus* contains at least seven antigens of which at least two are in the cell wall (16, 205), and cell-wall antigens would be involved in grouping staphylococci by agglutination. When grown in the presence of acridine acid fluorochrome, coagulase-positive *S. aureus* exhibits changes in the number and shape of the precipitin bands, which suggests the loss of the virulence factors of coagulase and hemolysins (174).

Cowan (46) found by slide agglutination three serologic types among the coagulase-positive, virulent strains of staphylococci. Thompson and Khorazo (182) have identified three serologic types among the saprophytic strains. By 1948 13 subtypes were recognized (91), but these were not generally used (174). Anderson and Heilesen (4) applied modern methods of antigenic analysis to staphylococci and found three kinds of antigens: I, heat-stabile; II, heat-labile and trypsin-stabile; and III, heat-labile and trypsin-labile. This work founded the basis for Oeding's (140) serologic analysis and typing, which by 1954 was capable of typing 94.6 per cent of strains isolated in hospitals (131). Cowan's serologic groups I, II, and III correspond approximately to phage groups I, II, and III, and those, in turn, seem to have antigenically distinct coagulase antigens (146). Fluorescent antibody reagents for identifying the antigenic factors have been prepared by Cohen and Oeding (44).

Phage Typing. Phages have been isolated from natural sources, such as sewage, which will lyse most coagulase-positive staphylococci, and often a number of saprophytic coagulase-negative strains as well, but these are of no value for specific typing. Fisk found that most strains of *S. aureus* were lysogenic; that is to say, they carry phages to which they themselves are immune but which will lyse some other members of the same species. Fisk developed a primitive method of typing by cross culture, in which a spot of inoculum of some staphylococcus strain was superimposed upon a lawn of a second strain, and the appearance of plaques of lysis indicated that one of the pair carried a phage virulent for the other (146). The current phage typing method is a direct descendant of the scheme proposed by Wilson and Atkinson (202) in 1945. Each specific phage was propagated on a specific susceptible strain of staphylococcus until it developed a high titer, and then the virus was separated by filtration and added in the proper dilution to one spot on a test plate. Usually about 25 phages are used, since this is a practical number to add to a single plate culture. The details of specific typing can be found in the publication of Williams and Rippon (198), Blair and Carr (22), Jackson, Dowling, and Lepper (100), Parker (146), Anderson and Williams (5), and Wentworth (193).

The phage groups, as defined by Parker, are shown in Table 1. Phage 81 lyses many strains which otherwise have patterns in group I, but it also forms part of some group III pathogens. Strains lysed only by 42D are placed in group IV. Phage 81 and 187 cannot be assigned to any one group. The 42D are encountered frequently in milk but occasionally in man, and their association with food poisoning suggests that this is primarily an animal staphylococcus (146). The production of enterotoxin is confined primarily to phage group III and IV. In phage group I the 52, 52A, 80, 81 complex of strains predominate in hospital infections. In phage II strains which react only with phage 71 appear to be specifically associated with vesicular skin lesions, such as staphylococcal impetigo, and pemphigus of the newborn (145).

The study of phage typing is not complete, since many strains which cannot be typed by this method have been isolated. As late as 1961 Willmark and Finland (189) added one new phage to the 80/81 complex, one to the other group I phages, three to group III, and one to the miscellaneous group. With the six new phages it was possible for the author to type 73 per cent of the 158 strains which had not been typable with the conventional set of phages.

Bacterial Metabolites. Bernheimer and Schwartz (16) studied the metabolites of four well-known coagulase-positive, virulent strains of *S. aureus,* and three coagulase-negative, saprophytic strains of *S. epidermidis.* **The coagulase-positive staphylococci showed 15 different products,** or about twice as many as the coagulase-negative strains. Using commercial antitoxin prepared against the Wood strain, staphylococci isolated from lesions in man produced, on the average, six to seven lines of precipitate, while coagulase-negative strains formed none. The number of lines is directly related to virulence for the mouse. **The materials of the diffusable product were different from the best known staphylococcal enzymes and toxins.**

The known metabolites can be classified as follows: I, nontoxic metabolites; II, exotoxins; and II, enterotoxins.

Table 1. The Lytic Groups of Staphylococcus Typing Phages which are Included in the Internationally Agreed Set of Basic Typing Phages
(From Parker)

LYTIC GROUP	PHAGES IN GROUP							
I	29	52	52A	79	80			
II	3A	3B	3C	55	71			
III	6	7	42E	47	53	54	75	77	83A
IV	42D							
Not allotted		81	187					

NONTOXIC METABOLITES. These are shown in Table 2, with an indication of their antigenicity.

Table 2. Nontoxic Metabolites

1. Surface antigen	Protective antibodies
2. Coagulase (3 antigen types)	Anticoagulase
3. Hyaluronidase	Antihyaluronidase
4. Fibrinolysin	Antifibrinolysin
5. Gelatinase	?
6. Protease (2 antigen types)	Antiprotease
7. Lipase	Antilipase
8. Egg-yolk factor (Tributyrinase)	Anti-egg-yolk factor
9. Phosphatase	?

The **surface antigen** has been discussed already under the section on the capsule of the organism. Our knowledge of this antigen is fragmentary. The observations of Rogers (157) suggest but do not prove that there is only one antigenic type of surface antigen. The compact colony type of the Smith organism is coagulase-positive, produces alpha hemolysis, and is typable with phage, but has low virulence for mice; while the diffuse colony type has high virulence for mice, but is coagulase-negative, and does not type by phage, suggesting the presence of the surface antigen which prevents the attachment of the phage and which prevents the coagulase reaction (157), and also prevents phagocytosis (129).

The Coagulase. The ability of virulent strains of staphylococci to coagulate plasma was noted by Leo Loeb in 1903, but worked out in detail by Much in 1908 (132) (Fig. 5). This coagulase has been purified by Blobel and his associates (24) and others by paper and starch electrophoresis. Staphylocoagulase is certainly an antigenic protein, but in the form in which it occurs in the organism, it will not clot fibrinogen. The actual coagulative principle, coagulase-thrombin, is an enzyme which is activated by the action of coagulase and its plasma factor (CRF). Coagulase alone has no esterase activity, but after incubation with the plasma factor, Drummond and Tager (57) found that coagulase-CRF exhibits two enzymatic activities, proteolytic and esterolytic, in addition to clotting. The same three activities are shown by other proteins which have coagulating properties, such as thrombin, trypsin, and certain snake venoms (57, 58). The older literature denies the similarity of "coagulase-thrombin" and thrombin because the former was supposed not to be inhibited by heparin (64). The more detailed study by

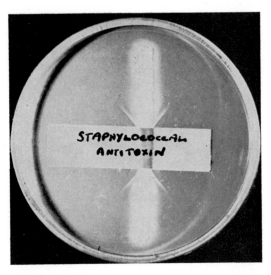

Fig. 5. Plasma agar plate showing staphylo-coagulase effect which is inhibited by commercial antitoxin. (From Elek and Levy. *J. Path. & Bact.*, 62:548, 1950.)

Sanders (164) in 1962 with 30 strains of staphylococci shows that heparin does prolong clotting time. Finally, the work by Drummond and Tager (59) in 1963 has shown that the products of fibrinogen clotting by coagulase-CRF and by thrombin are similar.

The existence of three antigenic types of coagulase was established by Rammelkamp and his associates (151) in 1950. These findings were confirmed by Duthie and Lorenz (63) in 1952 and extended to show that a fourth type was present in bovine strains. Some human strains produce more than one antigenic type of coagulase, and most sera from normal individuals has anticoagulase to one of the human types but not to the bovine type of coagulase (194).

There is a fairly good, but not absolute, correlation between Cowan's three serologic types of staphylococci, the three major phage groups, and the three antigen types of coagulase (10, 25, 127).

The exact contribution of coagulase to the pathogenicity of staphylococci has not been determined. It is known, however, from the work of Yotis and Ekstedt (206) that a component in normal human serum which prevents the multiplication of coagulase-negative strains of staphylococci can be neutralized by the addition of purified coagulase. This suggests that coagulase may protect, at least temporarily, the staphylococci which are invading the tissues.

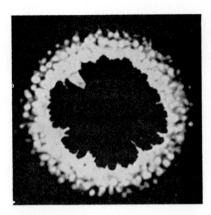

Fig. 6. Mueller phenomenon around a single colony of staphylococcus incubated for 10 days on an agar plate containing hemoglobin and rabbit serum. (From Quie and Wannamaker. *J. Bact.,* 82:770, 1961.)

Hyaluronidase. Coagulase-negative strains of staphylococci do not produce hyaluronidase, but the enzyme is produced by 93.6 per cent of coagulase-positive strains (165). Duran-Reynals (61) concluded from his studies that the invasive properties corresponded to the amount of "spreading factor" (hyaluronidase) present in the filtrate.

Strain SaB_2 of *S. aureus* synthesizes hyaluronidase in a defined medium only in the presence of tyrosine and tryptophan, even though these amino acids are not required for optimal growth. Glycine is necessary for growth; glycyl-1-tyrosine and glycyl-1-tryptophan enhances both growth and hyaluronidase production (123).

There is evidence that staphylococci produce at least one other mucin-splitting enzyme which is active against vaginal mucin and is capable of destroying the Francis inhibitor (14).

There is only one antigenic type of hyaluronidase, and this produces a specific type of neutralizing antibody. Hyaluronidase from the rabbit's testicle is different antigenically from that made by the staphylococci (15). Anti-hyaluronidase serum gives no protection against the toxins produced by staphylococci (28).

The spreading effect of hyaluronidase is rapidly neutralized by the products of inflammation, so the only effect of this metabolite would be very early in the initial stages of invasion (64).

FIBRINOLYSIS OR STAPHYLOKINASE. About 81 per cent of the coagulase-positive strains of staphylococci from man produce staphyloki-nase, but it is produced by 30 per cent of the coagulase-negative strains and 38 per cent of the coagulase-positive strains isolated from animals (64). Lack (114) found that the mechanism of staphylococcus fibrinolysin was similar to that of streptococcus fibrinolysin, and that the agent acted as an activator of plasma and serum enzyme precursor to yield the lytic agent.

Neter (135) and others have shown that fibrinolysin is antigenic. It is difficult to visualize the effect of fibrinolysin in activating infections. In instances of blood clots in veins which are infected with staphylococci, however, the lytic effect of this agent might release infected fragments of the clot to travel through the blood and produce metastatic lesions in distant organs or tissues.

Mueller's Phenomenon was readily explained by Quie and Wannamaker (149) as a manifestation of staphylokinase (Figs. 6 and 7). This phenomenon was described by Mueller (133) in 1927 and was characterized by the appearance of multiple, small satellite areas of clearing around colonies of staphylococci incubated for several days on human blood agar. Most strains of *S. aureus* produce this effect, but other organisms do not. Mueller suspected that the plaques were produced by a living agent, like a phage, but all attempts to identify the agent failed. The appearance of the satellite areas is shown in Figure 6 from the studies of Quie and Wannamaker (149), who **identified the active agent as staphylokinase,** and reproduced the phenomenon in a bacterial-cell-free system (Fig. 7). The key to the spotty distribution of the areas of particu-

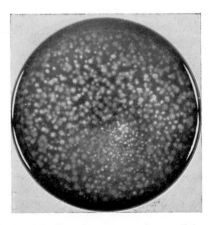

Fig. 7. Mueller phenomenon in a cell-free system. This is the appearance of the phenomenon after 48 hours of incubation. (From Quie and Wannamaker. *J. Bact.,* 82:770, 1961.)

late proteolysis was found by Alkjaersig (3) to depend upon the activation of plasminogens intrinsic within clots. In Mueller's phenomenon multiple aggregations of plasminogen occur in certain areas of the blood agar plates, and the staphylokinase activated the proteolytic enzyme plasmin in these areas (149).

Gelatinase is produced by 47 per cent of staphylococci from human lesions and 98 per cent of those from animal lesions, but also from 60 per cent of the coagulase-negative, saprophytic staphylococci. Gelatinase production bears no relation to coagulase production, hemolysis, or virulence (64, 185). The antigenicity of gelatinase has not been demonstrated.

An enzyme distinct from gelatinase is responsible for the softening of inspissated serum. Indeed, Elek and Levy (64) have identified two apparently distinct proteases, one of which was and the other was not inhibited by antitoxins made to the Wood 46 strain. The second one may be antigenic, but this particular one was not being produced by the Wood 46 strain.

These proteolytic enzymes may explain the rapid necrosis of tissues, including bone, which is characteristic of staphylococcal infections.

Lipase. Over 99.5 per cent of coagulase-positive strains of staphylococci from man are lipolytic, and 75 per cent of the strains from animals are lipolytic, while 30 per cent of coagulase-negative, saprophytic strains also produce the enzyme (64). Lipase is antigenic, and commercial antitoxins contain appreciable amounts of antibody. There is no evidence that lipase plays a specific role in the pathogenicity of staphylococci.

Other lipase-like enzymes are produced by staphylococci. The first of these was identified by Gillespie and Alder (79), when they observed that certain coagulase-positive staphylococci produced a dense opacity which microscopically consisted of amorphous material and fatty droplets when grown for three days in glucose-yolk broth. Only a few animal strains produced the effect, but a high percentage of strains from man did so. Commercial antitoxins neutralize this effect, but normal human or rabbit serum does not (64). Drummond and Tager (56, 57, 58) separated the egg-yolk factor, probably tributyrinase, from phosphatase and staphycoagulase by cellulose column zone electrophoresis. Blobel and his associates (26) also isolated the egg-yolk factor by high voltage electrophoresis in a vertical cellulose column and found that it was antigenic. A strong tributyrinase reaction was given by the isolated egg-yolk factor. Shah and Wilson (167) have found that the egg-yolk factor is a lipase with a requirement for a fatty acid acceptor.

Weld (192) observed the development of macroscopically visual lipid plaques on the surface of human blood agar plates when they were inoculated with certain strains of coagulase-positive S. aureus. The plaque consisted primarily of **octadecenoic acid.** Staphylococcal antitoxin prevents the appearance of the plaque, suggesting that a specific lipase releases this acid from the lipids in human plasma (192).

Phosphatase. Barber and Kuper (9) reported an excellent correlation between acid phosphatase activity and pathogenicity as well as phosphatase activity and coagulase production (27). Pan and Blumenthal (143) used quantitative methods of assay and found, on the average, that coagulase-negative strains produced 4.0 units of acid phosphatase and coagulase-positive strains 19.6 units. Phage group I produced more acid phosphatase than strains from other groups, and in group I those having an 80 in the phage type averaged 25.3 units while those without an 80 averaged 18.3 units. A few coagulase-negative strains of staphylococci produced more acid phosphatase than some coagulase-positive strains, however, so testing for acid phosphatase is not only more difficult but a less specific indicator of virulence than the coagulase test.

Inniss and Sanclemente (98) did not get a clear-cut separation of coagulase and phosphatase, but this was accomplished by Zoli and Sanclemente (207) in 1963. Drummond and Tager (57, 58) succeeded in separating the two by cellulose column zone electrophoresis in 1962.

Exotoxins. The exotoxins produced by virulent strains of S. aureus are shown in Table 3. It should be noted that the enterotoxin which causes food poisoning has not been included. This toxin, which resists boiling and in other ways does not correspond to either typical exotoxins or endotoxins, will be discussed later in this chapter.

Practically all of the virulent strains of staphylococci are carrying temperate phages. It is known that the production of diphtheria toxin is a direct result of disordered metabolism depending upon the presence of a temperate phage. By analogy, this raises the question of whether the toxin produced by staphylococci is also the direct result of temperate phage. A partial answer has been provided by Blair and Carr (22), who in 1961 showed that the

Table 3. Exotoxins

Hemolysin (Rabbit, sheep, cow, and goat RBC)	Hemolysin (Sheep, ox, and goat RBC)	Hemolysin (Human, monkey, horse, rat, mouse, and guinea pig RBC)	Leukolysin (Man and other WBC, except sheep)
Lethal Effect	Toxic for rabbits and kittens	None	
Dermonecrotic	Erythema	Erythema	
Neisser-Wechsberg Leukocidin (Rabbit WBC only)	———	Panton-Valentine Leukocydin (Human and rabbit WBC)	

capacity to produce toxin was conferred upon certain nontoxogenic strains by lysogenization with a phage derived from a toxogenic strain.

Alpha Hemolysin. This is the most common hemolysin produced by virulent human strains of streptococci, but, curiously enough, it hemolyzes the red cell of the rabbit, sheep, cow, and goat, but not those of man. This toxin also destroys the white blood cells of rabbits, but not those of man. This effect is known in the literature as the **Neisser-Wechsberg-Leukocidin.** This alpha toxin kills white leukocytes of rabbits by stopping the respiration and plays a definite role in the production of experimental abscesses in animals (106, 115, 184). However, the dermonecrotic effect on the skin and the lethal effect is common for man and animals. For over 30 years opinion has been divided between those who thought that each of these effects came from a separate toxin and those who believed that each effect was a different manifestation of the same toxin. Conclusive proof was presented in 1962 by Madoff and Weinstein (120), by Kumar and Lindorfer (112), and by Goshi and others (85) (Fig. 8) that since one single toxin produced all the effects described above, one antitoxin would neutralize all of the separate effects. Elek and Levy (64) found that 96 per cent of the coagulase-positive human pathogens produced alpha hemolysin, 74 per cent of the coagulase-positive animal strains produced alpha hemolysin, and 87 per cent of the coagulase-positive skin strains produced alpha hemolysin, but no hemolysin was produced by coagulase-negative skin strains. Brown (30) concluded that coagulase production determined the pathogenicity of a strain, that alpha hemolysin production was more directly related to the virulence—the more alpha hemolysin, the more virulent the strain. Dineen (54) found the same relationship with penicillinase —the more penicillinase produced, the more virulent the strain. Neither of these conclu-

sions are supported by the older literature collected by Elek (64).

Beta Hemolysin. Glenny and Stevens in 1935 (82) demonstrated a second serologically distinct hemolysin. Sheep, ox, and goat red blood cells were hemolyzed by the toxin, while those of the rabbit and most other animals were not. The results in man are variable but generally negative (64). This toxin produces strong reactions but no necrosis when injected into the skin. It has no effect on white blood cells but has some general toxic effect on rabbits and kittens. Man is stimulated by this toxin, however, since about one-third of adults have demonstrable beta antilysin in their

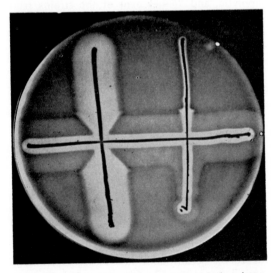

Fig. 8. Sheep blood agar plate showing interactions between hemolysins. The horizontal streak is a beta-delta strain. The vertical streak on the left is a pure alpha and on the right a delta strain. The inhibition of the alpha effect in the zone of the beta action and the potentation of the delta action are visible. (From Elek and Levy. *J. Path. & Bact.,* 68:31, 1954.)

serum. Beta hemolysin is present in 88 per cent of coagulase-positive strains of *S. aureus* from animals, present in only 11 per cent of human strains and 9 per cent of coagulase-positive skin strains, and absent in coagulase-negative skin strains.

The most dramatic characteristic of beta hemolysin is the hot-cold type effect on sheep red cells. After incubation at 37° C. a zone of discoloration appears about the colonies, which is replaced by complete hemolysis when the plate is kept overnight in the refrigerator. Similar concentric rings of hemolysis are produced. Beta hemolysin can be converted into toxoid (32).

Delta Hemolysin. Williams and Harper discovered a third type of hemolysin in 1947, which was not neutralized by either alpha or beta antitoxin. This hemolysin produced a narrow but well-defined zone of laking around the colonies when exposed to human, rabbit, sheep, horse, rat, mouse, and guinea pig. The association of delta lysin with human pathogenicity is at least as high as that of alpha lysin, and it does not occur in coagulase-negative staphylococci (64).

The Panton-Valentine leukocidin may be the same as the delta toxin and is equally effective against leukocytes of man and rabbit, but poorly active against mouse leukocytes, and inactive against guinea pig white cells. It destroys the granules of the white cell of man and rabbit but does not lyse the cells (96). It is heat-labile and is neutralized by antigens present in some commercial antitoxins but not by cholesterol. Gladstone and Van Heyningen (81) refer to another factor, which they call leukolysin and which acts on all cell species except the sheep; it is heat-stabile and is neutralized by cholesterol but not by commercial antitoxin. This leukolysin attacks the nucleus of the cell and may cause rupture without affecting the granules. This factor is produced by some coagulase-negative staphylococci.

The Distribution of Hemolysin in Pathogenic and Nonpathogenic Staphylococci. Elek (64) suggests that there are only three antigenic different hemolysins in coagulase-positive strains, but an epsilon hemolysin occurs in 95 per cent of coagulase-negative skin strains, and 5 per cent have no hemolysins.

In the discussion presented above we have assumed, for simplicity, that each coagulase-positive staphylococcus produced only a single hemolysin. Actually this is not always true. Elek and Levy have found that the most common pattern among human strains is the alpha-delta, while animal strains most often show the complete alpha-beta-delta pattern. The coagulase-negative strains are identified by a lack of hemolysins or the presence of an unneutralizable hemolysin. All seven possible combinations of alpha, beta, and epsilon are shown in Table 4, and the reactions between the toxin in Figure 8. It can be seen that the several hemolysins may either enhance or suppress the effect of the others.

Although the staphylococcal hemolysins are not related antigenically to streptolysin, they are related to some of the hemolysins produced by some species of *Clostridium* (40).

Enterotoxin. At least three emetic toxins are produced by certain strains of staphylococci. They are distinctive proteins which are nonhemolytic, nondermonecrotic, nonparalytic, and, unlike lysins, resistant to both the heat of boiling for 30 minutes and to the proteolytic action of pepsin and trypsin (181). They are rather weak antigenically, but can be detected by precipitation reactions, hemagglutination (181), gel diffusion, and colony-halo reactions (Fig. 9) (179). It is important for the student to remember that these endotoxin-producing strains usually, but not always, produce a full complement of the standard toxic and nontoxic metabolites discussed in the preceding pages.

Thatcher and Robinson (181) noted no strict relation between phage type and the ability to produce enterotoxin, but other investigators have found that the group III strains are more frequent producers of the

Table 4.   The Frequency of the Various Hemolysin Combinations
(After Elek and Levy)

		No. of Strains	PERCENTAGE OCCURRENCE OF HEMOLYSIN COMBINATIONS								
			α	β	δ	αβ	αδ	αβδ	βδ	ε	Nil
I.	Human pathogens	200	3	0	4	0	82	11	0	0	0
II.	Animal pathogens	59	0	7	0	5	10	59	17	0	2
III.	Coagulase-positive skin strains	23	4	0	9	0	74	9	0	0	4
	Coagulase-negative skin strains	77	0	0	0	0	0	0	0	95	5

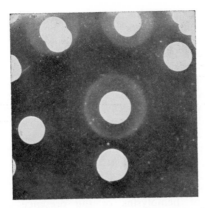

Fig. 9. Halo of enterotoxin-antitoxin precipitate surrounding the colony in the center of the photograph. (From Sugiyama, Bergdoll, and Dack. *J. Bact.,* 80:265, 1960.)

toxin, especially of 42D from group IV, which is a bovine strain.

An unofficial classification of the three enterotoxins was proposed at the 1962 meeting of the American Society of Microbiology. Type A is represented by Caseman's 196E (37) and Thatcher and Robinson's ML5 (181); type B is Caseman's 243 (37, 38), Thatcher and Robinson's L16 (181), and Sugiyama, Bergdoll, and Dack's S6 (180); type C is represented by 137 from phage pattern 42D. Thatcher and Robinson's (181) rare "Tadmore" is also from a phage type 42D and may be a C or possibly a D. Type A (196E) is the cause of common food poisoning, while 243 is associated with enteritis. Many strains isolated from cases of enteritis produce both 196E and 243 (37) (Fig. 10).

Man is the best test animal for enterotoxin assay, followed by the monkey (201) and the cat. The chimpanzee is believed to be a little more resistant than man, but the *Macaca mulatta* is 10 times as resistant as the chimpanzee, although more susceptible than the cat. However, Sugiyama and his associates (180) have found that an intravenous injection of thorotrast 18 hours before intragastric challenge with enterotoxins A and B makes the Rhesus monkey very susceptible to the emetic action of the enterotoxin. Monkeys can be dosed by mouth and have not shown the complete effect of hemolysins, although this is not true of cats, which must be tested by the intraperitoneal route. With adequate controls, however, Thatcher and Robinson (181) have obtained excellent assays with cats. Denny and Bohrer (53) also obtained excellent results with the cat if the toxin was prepared by (1) digestion with pepsin, (2) ultrafiltration, and (3) heating.

Hodge (92) analyzed 75 outbreaks of food poisoning in 1960. Of these 71 per cent were associated with coagulase-positive strains, 60 per cent with *S. aureus* strains, and 37 per cent were hemolytic. The incubation period was from one to four hours in 79.2 per cent of the cases, five to eight hours in 14.3 per cent, and more than eight hours in only 6.5 per cent. Cooked, high-protein food, leftovers, and food mixtures accounted for 67 per cent of the outbreaks. The staphylococci grew and produced the toxin when the cooked food was kept unrefrigerated, warmed, or both for four hours or more (92). Custard-filled puffs and eclairs, potato salad, chicken salad, egg salad, and sandwiches are particularly dangerous. Two large epidemics occurred in 1959, from infected ham. In the first epidemic 1,000 individuals were ill, and the organism was identified as phage type 6/47/53. In the second 216 persons were ill and a phage type 7 was recovered (83).

The incubation period is short, two to six hours, and the onset of symptoms is sudden and violent, with nausea, vomiting, diarrhea, and sometimes sudden collapse, suggesting the onset of cholera. Death rarely, if ever, occurs, and recovery is usually complete in 24 to 48 hours. This is the most common type of food poisoning in this country, exceeding the combined cases of salmonella (Chapter 34) and clostridia poisoning (Chapter 47).

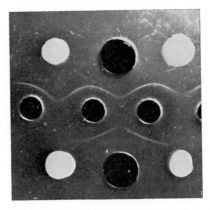

Fig. 10. Identity of immune precipitate band developed by colonies of a staphylococcus strain with that produced by highly purified S6 enterotoxin. Left to right, top row: S6 colony, purified S6 enterotoxin, 291 strain; middle row: purified S6 antiserum-Wells; bottom row: 196E colony, purified S6 endotoxin, and 269 colony. (From Sugiyama, Bergdoll, and Dack. *J. Bact.,* 80:265, 1960.)

Spontaneous Disease in Animals. The renewed interest in staphylococcus infections, in general, has resulted in the uncovering of a surprising amount of infection and a high carrier rate of coagulase-positive as well as coagulase-negative strains of staphylococci in the nose of domestic animals. Dogs and cats are frequent carriers and often carry human strains including the epidemic, hospital phage type 80/81 (127, 141, 154). The udder of cows is frequently infected (168), and over half of the *S. aureus* strains isolated from milk were typable with 42D type phage. However, both cows and dairymen may be infected with the 80/81 phage type (188). Pagano and his associates (141) have shown that senior veterinary students are much more prone to staphylococcal infestations and even infections with human strains apparently acquired by contact with animals and not by direct contact with a hospital or human patient.

In general, the animal strains are phage-specific and not typable by phage selected for human strains. Parker (146) suggests that specific sets of typing phage be developed for cows, dogs, cats, sheep, and horses.

Experimental Disease in Laboratory Animals. Rabbits are relatively susceptible to pathogenic strains of staphylococci; mice may be infected, but the guinea pig is relatively resistant. Spontaneous infections with staphylococci occur in some colonies of rabbits.

The results of animal experiments vary somewhat with the age and general resistance of the rabbit, the route of inoculation, and the method of preparing the cultures as well as the specific invasiveness of a particular strain. Rabbits less than four months old are not susceptible to either the dermonecrotic or lethal toxins (33). Subcutaneous or intramuscular inoculations usually result in a localized abscess which ruptures, drains, and heals. Intraperitoneal inoculations generally are fatal. Burky (33) inoculated rabbits intravenously with 10-day-old broth cultures from 75 strains. The organisms which produced exotoxins killed the rabbits in two days without abscess formation. Strains which produced no demonstrable toxin killed the rabbits in one to 30 days, with abscess formation in the internal organs. A third group composed of nontoxogenic and noninvasive strains produced no deleterious effect on the rabbits. Burky also has shown that rabbits given intravenous injections of toxin develop not only specific antibodies but also a state of **hypersensitivity** to the broth in which the toxin was produced. The presence of the toxins in the broth seems to modify the tissue response to the

other antigens. When an extract of the crystalline lens of the eye was added to the culture broth, rabbits injected with the lens broth toxin became very **allergic** to lens protein (34). Rabbits injected with toxin combined with an extract of low ragweed, produced precipitins for the ragweed, and developed anaphylactic-like symptoms when dusted with low ragweed pollen.

Wiley (195) has developed a virulence test in chick embryo which shows increased virulence in strains which have capsules. Johanovsky (101) has transferred delayed hypersensitivity to staphylococci by white lymphoid cells and noted a concomitant increased susceptibility to infection with staphylococci. This result was supported by those of Johnston, Cliff, and Goshen (102), who produced active hypersensitivity in rabbits by repeated injections of staphylococci into the skin and found that fewer and fewer organisms were required to produce a furuncle as hypersensitivity of the skin increased.

Clinical Types of Infection in Man. Man is more susceptible than laboratory animals to staphylococcal infections. Garre (76) rubbed a pure culture into the unbroken skin of his forearm and produced a series of carbuncles which left 17 scars.

The clinical forms of the disease in man depend upon the size of the dose, the route of invasion, the presence or absence of antibodies from previous infections, the presence or absence of a state of hypersensitivity, as well as the variations just described in the antigens and toxins of the invading staphylococcus.

The most common type of infections in man are pimples, boils, and carbuncles, paronychia infections, cystitis, and pyelitis. Nearly 90 per cent of staphylococci isolated from the skin infection known as impetigo were susceptible to phage type 71 (80, 145). This is suggestive, but not definitive, evidence that the phage type can be correlated with a specific type of clinical disease (199, 200).

The most dangerous types of staphylococcal infections are septicemia, endocarditis (170), meningitis (122), brain abscess, puerperal sepsis, orbital and cavernous sinus thromboses, osteomyelitis, and pneumonia. Empyema, pulmonary abscess, and bronchiectasis may follow pulmonary infections.

Occasionally epidemics of staphylococcal vaginitis have occurred in children and have been confused with gonococcal vaginitis. General metabolic diseases, especially diabetes, render the individual abnormally susceptible to infections with the staphylococcus. Secondary staphylococcal infections were a minor cause of death in the pandemic influenza of 1917-1918 but became the chief cause of death in the mild influenza epidemic of 1939-1940 (70).

Before the introduction of antibiotics the mortality from staphylococcal septicemia was over 80 per cent, which is comparable to the mortality of bubonic plague. Following the introduction of penicillin, the mortality fell to 28 per cent beteen 1942 and 1944 but has risen to over 50 per cent (176) since the appearance of staphylococci resistant to penicillin and other antibiotics. The mortality from staphylococcal pneumonia in children is increasing (29), and postoperative wound infections are becoming more common and more severe (95). Patients treated for pneumococcal pneumonia with oxytetracycline (99) and certain other antibiotics may have the pneumococci eliminated only to die of secondary infections with antibiotic resistant staphylococci.

The most disturbing situation is the appearance of **staphylococcal enteritis** or **pseudomembranal enteritis** (50, 51, 66, 99, 117, 175). The oral administration of antibiotics eliminates many of the normal bacteria from the intestinal tract (Chapter 10), and if an antibiotic resistant strain of staphylococcus is already present or becomes implanted, this disease develops with great rapidity and has a high mortality.

No adequate explanation has been offered by cultural or antigenic studies for the particular type of staphylococcal infection of the skin known as impetigo contagiosa. The lesion is not a pimple or boil but a small vesicle or bulla filled with fluid. Epidemics of impetigo occur frequently in school children (172), and bullous impetigo has been reproduced in human volunteers with cultures of *Staphylococcus aureus* isolated from patients (138).

Transmission. The rate at which penicillin-resistant staphylococci are colonized in the nose of hospital attendants is truly appalling (29, 191, 200). Vogelsang and Bøe (186) reported in 1962 that 75 per cent of the staff and 50 per cent of the patients in their hospital were carrying a penicillin-resistant staphylococcus. The danger inherent in this situation is explained in the 1960 report of a surgeon who was carrying three phage types simultaneously in his nose (134). A series of patients operated on by his team developed wound infections containing the 80/81 type, which was one of the types he was carrying. Even more dramatic was the 1963 publication of Walter and his associates (191) who reported that a laboratory technician, fully masked and gowned, waiting in the corner of the operating room during an operation and never coming within six feet of the operating table, nevertheless infected two patients with this specific phage-type staphylococcus.

The 80/81 resistant strain readily acquires resistance to tetracycline, streptomycin, and erythromycin (49, 68, 125, 166) and produces fatal epidemics in infants.

These resistant organisms are carried home by the patient and then are spread about the family (113, 137, 142) and community and may infect the family dogs and cats, which will in turn carry them to veterinary hospitals and increase the carrier rate of the senior veterinary student (141).

From birth until death man lives in an atmosphere periodically saturated with potential or actually pathogenic staphylococci. Bryce and Burnet (31) have demonstrated the passive transfer of antihemolysins from the mother to the fetus. Within a few weeks after birth there was a rapid fall of the antihemolysin titers, followed by a gradual return of active antihemolysins during childhood. Kobak and Pilot (109) studied a group of mothers who reacted to the dermonecrotic toxin while their newborn infants did not; yet at the end of the first year of life, 65 per cent of the children gave positive skin tests.

Biologic Products. No effective antibactericidal serums have ever been developed. Antitoxins neutralized the toxins but had no effect on the organisms (8, 104), while the antibiotics inhibit or kill the organisms but cannot neutralize the exotoxins. The production of commercial antitoxin was discontinued after the discovery of penicillin, but it is obvious that it should be reintroduced to control the toxemia while an effective antibiotic is being sought in the laboratory.

Stock vaccines, killed by formaldehyde or by heat at 60° C. for one hour, are available commercially, and autogenous vaccines can be prepared readily in any routine laboratory. Staphylococcus toxoid, prepared commercially by treating the toxic filtrates with formaldehyde, is in common use.

Treatment. Empirical therapy is hazardous in areas where penicillin and other antibiotics have been used promiscuously for colds, boils, and other minor ailments. Cultures should be isolated from each patient and tested in the laboratory for susceptibility to penicillin and other antibiotics, and the most effective should be employed.

Gram stains should always be made on all pus, tissue, and exudate which reaches the laboratory to establish the presence of gram-positive organisms in the original material. Positive cultures alone may be from a contaminant, even a penicillin resistant contaminant (203).

In critically ill patients empirical therapy may have to be started after the culture is plated but before they have grown. If penicillin-resistant staphylococci are suspected, the new penicillinase-resistant penicillin, such as methicillin or oxacillin, can be given (77, 90, 171). It should be realized, however, that the new penicillinase-resistant penicillins are much more expensive and not as effective as penicillin G, so the older type penicillin should be used if the laboratory reports a penicillin-susceptible strain. Ristocetin, kanamycin, and vancomycin are definitely more toxic than penicillin, but they have cured many patients who were resistant to penicillin (67, 187, 204). Staphylococci are slow to develop resistance to chloramphenicol (129). Although chloramphenicol occasionally induces agranulocytosis, the risk is justified when the staphylococcus is resistant to other antibiotics.

The senior author has employed autogenous vaccines for more than 30 years in the treatment of recurrent furunculosis and certain other types of chronic staphylococcal infections, including those of the lung. Experimental evidence from studies of rab-

bits indicates the hypersensitivity induced by either active infection (102) or passive transfer results in the animal's becoming more susceptible to staphylococcal infection. In 1960, McCoy and Kennedy (119) reported excellent results in 44, improvement in 11, and failure in only five cases observed in patients treated with autogenous vaccines. Autogenous vaccine seems to be as effective in the treatment of staphylococci which are resistant to most or all known antibiotics as it is in that of those strains which are susceptible.

The presence of the hypersensitive state should be suspected not only when the patient has recurrent boils, but in all subacute and chronic infections, regardless of their location in the body. The presence of hypersensitivity can be demonstrated by intradermal skin tests with vaccines or toxoids, and desensitization induced by gradually increasing subcutaneous doses of the specific antigen. Occasionally antibiotic therapy is ineffective until partial desensitization has been accomplished (173).

Prevention. Direct spread by physical contact can be prevented by cleanliness of the skin and the protection of all cuts and abrasions from contaminations. Airborne infections in the operating room have been adequately controlled by the use of a special type of ultraviolet light (89). The major method of spread, by droplet infection from the nasopharynx, awaits the general solution of all airborne infectious agents.

A new and highly original but logical approach has been suggested for the elimination of penicillin-resistant staphylococci from the nose and throat of the multitudinous carriers of penicillin-resistant staphylococcus in hospitals and other closed ecological groups.

It has been a common observation that many asymptomatic nasal carriers of penicillin-sensitive staphylococci resist the spontaneous implantation of penicillin-resistant strains until the original resistant strains have been eliminated by treatment with penicillin. After treatment with penicillin, resistant strains readily colonize in the nose (17). This phenomenon suggested to Shinefield and his associates (169) that the process might be reversed by selecting a strain of penicillin-susceptible staphylococci which would be a better colonizer than the penicillin-resistant strains. Strain 502A, a coagulase-positive organism with high colonizing ability and low virulence, was discovered and tested in clinical trials in New York, Ohio, Louisiana, and Georgia. The colonization of human infants in nurseries by the introduction of small doses of 502A into the nose and on the umbilical cord prevented the subsequent colonization with virulent penicillin-resistant strains. This 502A strain spread spontaneously to other human contacts. Identification by serologic and phage technics made it possible to distinguish 502A from other staphylococci and to show that the strain had not induced disease (60).

STAPHYLOCOCCUS EPIDERMIDIS
(Winslow and Winslow)

This organism was described by Welch as the cause of minor skin infections, especially stitch abscesses. The colonies are white, and most of all the cultures previously called *S. albus* are really *S. epidermidis*. It is coagulase-negative and ferments glucose but not mannitol under anaerobic conditions (108).

MICROCOCCUS (Cohn)

These organisms occur in irregular masses, but not in packets; most are gram-positive, but some are variable and may be mistaken for gram-negative. A few species are motile, most make white colonies, but some form orange, yellow, or red pigment. They are saprophytic, facultative parasitic, but never pathogenic. Bergey's Manual recognizes 16 species.

GAFFKYA TETRAGENA

Genus: *Gaffkya* Trevisan. Type Species: *Gaffkya tetragena* (Gaffky) Trevisan

There are two recognized species of *Gaffkya*, one of which inhabits man, while the other produces a disease in lobsters (*G. homari*). In 1881 Gaffky isolated a micrococcus which occurred characteristically in groups of four, or tetrads. Observed in smear preparations or from pus, the tetrads are slightly larger in size than the ordinary staphylococcus, flattened along their adjacent surfaces, and surrounded by thick halo-like **capsules** (Fig. 11). Preparations from cultures rarely have demonstrable cap-

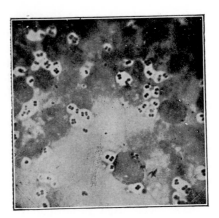

Fig. 11. *Gaffkya tetragena.*

sules. The micrococcus is gram-positive and usually shows metachromatic staining.

Cultivation. *Gaffkya tetragena* grows readily on the usual laboratory media, forming white or yellow colonies.

Variability. Dissociation occurs regularly in old cultures of some strains, with white colonies giving rise to yellow, pink, brown, or translucent colonies. Reimann (155) isolated from a single strain five different types which were characterized by immunologic specificity and different pigments in their respective M, S, and R phases.

Pathogenicity. *G. tetragena* is not pathogenic for laboratory animals.

Although Reimann (155) isolated this organism from the blood, spinal fluid, and joint fluid of a nonfatal infection and collected from the literature 170 instances of infection in man, he is of the opinion that its pathogenicity for man is fortuitous, depending upon the low resistance of the patient rather than the virulence of the micrococcus. *G. tetragena* has been responsible for 13 cases of bacterial endocarditis (88). This organism is susceptible to penicillin and other antibiotics (124).

SARCINA (Goodsir)

Division occurs, under favorable conditions, in three perpendicular planes, producing regular packets. They are gram-positive, but some strains are easily decolorized; and an occasional strain is motile. Ten species are recognized in Bergey's Manual. The aerobic species produce yellow, orange, and red pigments. The anaerobic species are not pigmented. Most species are saprophytic, but a few may be facultative parasitic.

METHANOCOCCUS
(Kluyver and Van Niel)

These cocci occur singly and in masses and are gram-variable. They are anaerobic, produce methane, and are saprophytic. Two species are recognized.

PEPTOCOCCUS
(Kluyver and Van Niel)

These anaerobic cocci may appear singly or in pairs, tetrads, or masses. Methane is not produced, but they ferment a number of organic compounds. Eleven species are recognized, and all but one are from man.

REFERENCES

1. Abraham, E. P., and others. Lancet, 2:177, 1941.
2. Alder, B. G., and others. J. Applied Bact., 25:436, 1962.
3. Alkjaersig, H., and others. J. Clin. Invest., 38:1086, 1959.
4. Andersen, E. K., and Heilesen, B. Dermato. & Venereol., acta., Stockholm, 31:679, 1951.
5. Anderson, E. S., and Williams, R. E. O. J. Clin. Path., 9:94, 1956.
6. Baird-Parker, A. C. J. Applied Bact., 25:441, 1962.
7. ———— J. Gen. Microbiol., 30:409, 1963.
8. Baker, L. D., and Shands, A. R. J.A.M.A., 113:2119, 1939.
9. Barber, M., and Kuper, S. W. A. J. Path. & Bact., 63:65, 1951.
10. ———— and Wildy, P. J. Gen. Microbiol., 18:92, 1958.
11. ———— J. Clin. Path., 14:385, 1961.
12. Bauer, A. W., Perry, D. M., and Kirby, W. M. M. J.A.M.A., 173:475, 1960.
13. Bayne-Jones, S., and Zinninger, P. Bull. Johns Hopkins Hosp., 32:299, 1921.
14. Bergamini, L. Z. Bakt., Abt. I., Oric., 165:122, 1956.
15. Bergqvist, S. Acta path. et microbiol. scandinav., acta, Suppl. 91, 1951, p. 186.
16. Bernheimer, A. W., and Schwartz, L. L. Proc. Soc. Exper. Biol. & Med., 106:776, 1961.
17. Berntsen, C. A., and McDermott, W. New Eng. J. Med., 262:637, 1960.
18. Blair, J. E. Bacterial and Mycotic Infection of Man, Dubos, R. J., ed., Philadelphia, J. B. Lippincott Co., 1958, p. 310.
19. ———— and Carr, M. J. Infect. Dis., 93:1, 1953.
20. ———— Personal communication.
21. ———— and Carr, M. Science, 132:1247, 1960.
22. ———— and Carr, M. J. Bact., 82:984, 1961.
23. ———— Bact. Rev., 26:375, 1962.
24. Blobel, H., and others. J. Bact., 79:807, 1960.
25. ———— and Berman, D. T. J. Immunol., 85:244, 1960.
26. ———— and others. J. Immunol., 87:285, 1961.
27. Blumenthal, H. J., and Pan, Y. L. Proc. Soc. Exper. Biol. & Med., 113:322, 1963.
28. Bøe, J. Acta path. et microbiol. scandinav., 21:587, 1944.
29. Browne, A. F., and others. J.A.M.A., 170:1274, 1959.
30. Brown, J. J. J. Path. & Bact., 79:257, 1960.
31. Bryce, L. M., and Burnet, F. M. J. Path. & Bact., 35:183, 1932.
32. ———— and Rountree, P. M. J. Path. & Bact., 43:173, 1936.
33. Burky, E. L. J. Immunol., 24:93, 115, 127, 1933; 25:419, 1933.
34. ———— J. Ophthalmol., 19:782, 841, 1936.
35. Burnet, F. M. J. Path. & Bact., 32:717, 1929, 33:1, 1930; 34:471, 1931.
36. Carter, C. H. J. Bact., 77:670, 1959.
37. Caseman, E. P. J. Bact., 79:849, 1960.
38. ———— and others. J. Bact., 85:715, 1963.
39. ———— and Bennett, R. W. J. Bact., 86:18, 1963.
40. Celarek, J., and Fejgin, B. C. R. Soc. Biol. (Paris), 122:133, 137, 1936.
41. ———— and Fejgin, B. C. R. Soc. Biol. (Paris), 126:137, 1937.
42. Chapman, G. H. J. Bact., 47:211, 1944.
43. Chapman, J. A., and others. Proc. Roy. Soc., 158:498, 1963.
44. Cohen, J. O., and Oeding, P. J. Bact., 84:735, 1962.
45. Cohn, Z. A., and Morse, S. I. J. Exper. Med., 110:419, 1959.
46. Cowan, S. T. J. Path. & Bact., 48:169, 1939.
47. ———— J. Applied Bact., 25:324, 1962.
48. Dack, G. M. Food Poisoning, 3rd ed., Chicago, The Univ. of Chicago Press, 1956.
49. Dauer, C. C. Publ. Health Rep., 76:159, 1961.
50. Dearing, W. H., and Heilman, F. R. Proc. Staff Meet. Mayo Clinic, 28:121, 1953.
51. ———— and Needham, G. M. J.A.M.A., 124:1597, 1960.
52. Deneke, A., and Blobel, H. J. Bact., 83:533, 1962.
53. Denny, C. B., and Bohrer, C. W. J. Bact., 86:347, 1963.
54. Dineen, P. J. Immunol., 86:496, 1961.
55. Dowell, C. E., and Rosenblum, E. D. J. Bact., 84:1071, 1962.
56. Drummond, M. C., and Tager, M. J. Bact., 78:407, 413, 1959.
57. ———— and Tager, M. J. Bact., 83:432, 1962.
58. ———— and Tager, M. J. Bact., 83:975, 1962.
59. ———— and Tager, M. J. Bact., 85:628, 1963.
60. Dubos, R. J.A.M.A., 184:1038, 1963.
61. Duran-Reynals, F. J. Exper. Med., 58:161, 1933; 61:617, 1935.
62. ———— J. Exper. Med., 58:161, 1933.
63. Duthie, E. S., and Lorenz, L. L. J. Gen. Microbiol., 6:95, 1952.
64. Elek, S. D. Staphylococcus pyogenes, Edinburgh and London, E. A. S. Livingstone, Ltd., 1959.
65. Fahlberg, W. J. Bact. Proc., 1963, p. 77.
66. Fairlie, C. W., and Kendall, R. E. J.A.M.A., 153:90, 1953.

67. Fekety, F. R., and others. Ann. Int. Med., 57:2.4, 1962.
68. Felton, H. M., and others. South. Med. J., 52:387, 1959.
69. Finegold, S. M., and Sweeny, E. E. J. Bact., 81:636, 1961.
70. Finland, M., and others. Arch. Int. Med., 70:183, 1942.
71. ———— J.A.M.A., 158:188, 1955.
72. ———— and others. J.A.M.A., 170:2188, 1959.
73. Finkelstein, R. A., and Sulkin, S. E. J. Bact., 75:339, 1958.
74. Fisher, M. W. Arch. Int. Med., 105:413, 1960.
75. Fisher, S. Australian J. Exper. Biol. & Med. Sci., 38:479, 1960.
76. Garre. Fortschr. d. med., 3:165, 1885.
77. Geraci, J. E., and others. Proc. Staff Meet. Mayo Clinic, 37:137, 1962.
78. Geronimus, L. H., and Cohen, S. J. Bact., 76:117, 1958.
79. Gillespie, W. A., and Alder, V. G. J. Path. & Bact., 66:187, 1952.
80. ———— Brit. Med. J., I:1044, 1957.
81. Gladstone, G. P., and Van Heyningen, W. E. Brit. J. Exper. Path., 38:123, 1957.
82. Glenny, A. T., and Stevens, M. F. J. Path. & Bact., 40:201, 1935.
83. Googins, J. A., and others. Pub. Health Rep., 76:945, 1961.
84. Gornzynski, E. A., and others. J. Bact., 80:207, 1960.
85. Goshi, K., and others. Bull. Johns Hopkins Hosp., 112:15, 31, 1963.
86. Griffith, L. J., and others. J. Bact., 81:157, 1961.
87. Hamburger, M. Arch. Int. Med., 105:668, 1960.
88. Hansen, J. E., and others. Ann. Int. Med., 40:1207, 1954.
89. Hart, D. J.A.M.A., 117:1610, 1941.
90. Hewitt, W. L. J.A.M.A., 185:264, 1963.
91. Hobbs, B. C. J. Hyg. Camb., 46:222, 1948.
92. Hodge, B. E. Pub. Health Rep., 75:355, 1960.
93. Hoffstadt, R., and Youmans, G. P. J. Infect. Dis., 51:216, 1932.
94. Hopton, J. J. Appl. Bact., 24:121, 1961.
95. Howe, G. W. New England J. Med., 251:411, 1954.
96. Hunt, G. A., and Moses, A. J. Science, 128:1574, 1958.
97. Innes, A. G. J. Appl. Bact., 23:108, 1960.
98. Inniss, W. E., and Sanclemente, C. L. J. Bact., 83:941, 1962.
99. Jackson, G. G., and others. Ann. Int. Med., 35:1175, 1951.
100. ———— and others. J. Lab. & Clin. Med., 44:14, 29, 1954.
101. Johanovsky, J. Nature, 182:1454, 1958.
102. Johnson, J. E., and others. J. Exper. Med., 113:235, 249, 259, 1961.
103. Jones, D., and others. J. Bact., 85:62, 1963.
104. Joyner, A. L., and Smith, D. T. Surg., Gynec. & Obst., 63:1, 1936.
105. Julianelle, L. A., and Wieghard, C. W. J. Exper. Med., 62:11, 23, 31, 1935.
106. Kellaway, and others. J. Path. & Bact., 33:889, 1930.

107. Kimler, A. J. Bact., 82:106, 1961.
108. Kjellander, J. O., and others. Proc. Soc. Exper. Biol. & Med., 113:1023, 1963.
109. Kobak, A. J., and Pilot, I. Proc. Soc. Exper. Biol. & Med., 28:584, 1931.
110. Koenig, M. G. Yale J. Biol. & Med., 34:537, 1962.
111. Korman, R. Z., and Berman, D. T. J. Bact., 84:228, 1962.
112. Kumar, S., and Lindorfer, R. K. J. Exper. Med., 115:1095, 1107, 1962.
113. Kundsin, R. B., and others. J.A.M.A., 185:159, 1963.
114. Lack, C. H. Nature, 161:559, 1948.
115. Lam, G. T., and others. J. Bact., 86:87, 1963.
116. Lenhart, N. A., and others. J. Immunol., 91:771, 1963.
117. Lundsgaard - Hansen, P., and others. J.A.M.A., 173:1008, 1960.
118. Lyons, C. Brit. J. Exper. Path., 18:411, 1937.
119. McCoy, K. L., and Kennedy, E. R. J.A.M.A., 174:35, 1960.
120. Madoff, M. A., and Weinstein, C. J. Bact., 83:914, 1962.
121. Maitland, H. B., and Martyn, G. J. Path. & Bact., 60:553, 1948.
122. Meade, R. H., III. J.A.M.A., 185:1023, 1963.
123. Mergenhagen, S. E. Proc. Soc. Exper. Biol. & Med., 97:703, 1958.
124. Mock, F. S., and Wynne, E. S. J. Infect. Dis., 87:10, 1950.
125. Moorman, R. S., Jr., and Sell, S. H. 54:137, 1961.
126. Morrison, R. B. J. Appl. Bact., 25:432, 1962.
127. Morrison, S. M., and Kennedy, K. K. Pub. Health Rep., 76:673, 1961.
128. Morse, M. L., and La Belle, J. W. J. Bact., 83:775, 1962.
129. Morse, S. I. J. Exper. Med., 115:295, 1962.
130. ———— J. Exper. Med., 116:229, 1962.
131. Mossel, D. A. A. J. Bact., 84:1140, 1962.
132. Much, H. Biochem. Z., 14:143, 1908.
133. Muller, L. Compt. rend. Soc. Biol., 96:189, 1927; 97:900, 1927.
134. Nahmias, A. J., and others. J.A.M.A., 174:1269, 1960.
135. Neter, E. J. Bact., 34:243, 1937.
136. ———— and others. J. Immunol., 88:411, 1962.
137. Novack, A., and Feldman, H. A. Arch. Int. Med., 110, 726, 1962.
138. O'Brien, J. P. J. Invest. Dermat., 15:95, 1950.
139. Oeding, P., and Vogelsang, T. M. Acta Path. Microbiol. Scandinavia, 34:47, 1954.
140. ———— Bact. Rev., 24:374, 1960.
141. Pagano, J. S., and others. Science, 131:927, 1960.
142. Page, M. I., and others. J.A.M.A., 183:1063, 1963.
143. Pan, Y., and Blumenthal, H. J. J. Bact., 82:124, 1961.
144. Parker, M. T., and others. J. Hyg., 53:458, 1955.
145. ———— and Williams, R. E. O. Acta Paediat. Stockholm, 50:101, 1961.
146. ———— J. Appl. Bact., 25:389, 1962.

147. Patte, P. A., and Baldwin, J. H. J. Bact., 82:875, 1961.
148. Price, K. M., and Kneeland, Y., Jr. J. Bact., 71:229, 1956.
149. Quie, P. G., and Wannamaker, L. W. J. Bact., 82:770, 1961.
150. Quinn, E. L., and Kass, E. H. Biology of Pyelonephritis, Henry Ford Hospital International Symposium, Boston, Little, Brown & Co., 1959, p. 46.
151. Rammelkamp, C. H., Jr., and others. J. Exper. Med., 91:295, 1950.
152. Rantz, L. A., and others. J. Infect. Dis., 98:211, 1956.
153. Rantz, L. R., and Rantz, H. H. Arch. Int. Med., 110:739, 1962.
154. Ravenholt, R. T., and others. Pub. Health Rep., 76:879, 1961.
155. Reimann, H. A. J. Clin. Invest., 14:311, 807, 1935. J. Bact., 31:385, 407, 1936; 33:499, 513, 1937.
156. ——— Proc. Soc. Exper. Biol. & Med., 96:411, 1957.
157. Rogers, D. E. J.A.M.A., 181:38, 1962.
158. ——— and Melly, M. A. Yale J. Biol. & Med., 34:560, 1962.
159. Roundtree, P. M. J. Gen. Microbiol., 20:620, 1959.
160. ——— Personal communication.
161. Sabath, L. D., and Finland, M. Proc. Soc. Exper. Biol. & Med., 111:547, 1962.
162. Sall, T., and others. J. Exper. Med., 113:693, 1961.
163. ——— J. Bact., 83:1238, 1962.
164. Sanders, E. Proc. Soc. Exper. Biol. & Med., 109:185, 1962.
165. Schwabacher, H., and others. Brit. J. Exper. Path., 26:124, 1945.
166. Shaffer, T. E. Ann. Int. Med., 50:614, 1959.
167. Shah, D. B., and Wilson, T. B. J. Bact., 85:516, 1963.
168. Sharpe, M. E., and others. J. Appl. Bact., 25:403, 1962.
169. Shinefield, H. R., and others. Am. J. Dis. Child., 105:646, 1963.
170. Shubin, H., and others. J.A.M.A., 167:1218, 1958.
171. Simon, H. J., and Ranz, L. A. Ann. Int. Med., 57:335, 1962.
172. Smith, D. T., and Burky, E. L. Bull. Johns Hopkins Hosp., 35:78, 1924.
173. ——— and Martin, D. S. North Carolina Med. J., 8:160, 1947.
174. Sonea, S., and others. J. Bact., 84:1056, 1962.
175. Speare, G. S. Am. J. Surg., 88:523, 1954.
176. Spink, W. W. Arch. Int. Med., 94:167, 1954.
177. Stamp, L. Brit. J. Exper. Med., 42:30, 1961.
178. Steel, K. J. J. Appl. Bact., 25:445, 1962.
179. Sugiyama, H., and others. J. Bact., 80:265, 1960.
180. ——— and others. Proc. Soc. Exper. Biol. & Med., 113:468, 1963.
181. Thatcher, F. S., and Robinson, J. J. Appl. Bact., 25:378, 1962.
182. Thompson, R., and Khorazo, D. J. Bact., 34:69, 1937.
183. Tompsett, R. Antimicrob. Agents & Chemother., p. 100, 1962.
184. Trauber, J. H., and others. J. Bact., 86:51, 1963.
185. Vogelsang, T. M., and others. Acta Path. Microbiol. Scandinavia, 54:218, 1962.
186. ——— and Bøe, J. Acta Path. Microbiol. Scandinavia, 54:225, 1962.
187. Waisbren, B. A., and others. Arch. Int. Med., 106:179, 1960.
188. Wallace, G. D., and others. Pub. Health Bull., 75:457, 1960.
189. Wallmark, G., and Finland, M. Proc. Soc. Exper. Biol. & Med., 106:73, 1961.
190. ——— Arch. Int. Med., 110:787, 1962.
191. Walter, C. W., and others. J.A.M.A., 186:908, 1963.
192. Weld, J. T., and others. Proc. Soc. Exper. Biol. & Med., 112:448, 1963.
193. Wentworth, B. B. Bact. Rev., 27:253, 1963.
194. White, B. B., and others. J. Comp. Path., 72:19, 1962.
195. Wiley, B. B. Canad. J. Microbiol., 7:933, 1961.
196. ——— and Wonnacott, J. C. J. Bact., 83:1169, 1962.
197. ——— Bact. Proc., 1963, p. 76.
198. Williams, R. E. O., and Rippon, J. E. J. Hyg., 50:320, 1952.
199. ——— and Jevons, M. P. Zbl. Bakt., 181:349, 1961.
200. ——— Bact. Rev., 27:56, 1963.
201. Wilson, B. J. J. Bact., 78:240, 1959.
202. Wilson, G. S., and Atkinson, J. O. Lancet, 1:647, 1945.
203. Wise, R. I. Ann. Int. Med., 55:344, 1961.
204. Woodley, D. W., and Hall, W. H. Ann. Int. Med., 55:235, 1961.
205. Yoshida, A., and Heden, C. G. J. Immunol., 88:389, 1962.
206. Yotis, W. W., and Ekstedt, R. D. J. Bact., 78:567, 1959; 80:719, 1960; 83:137, 1962.
207. Zolli, Z., Jr., and San Clemente, C. L. J. Bact., 86:527, 1963.

23

The Neisseria Group of Organisms and
Epidemic Cerebrospinal Meningitis

The gram-negative cocci associated with man, with the exception of *N. gonorrhoeae,* are inhabitants of the mouth and upper respiratory tract. *N. meningitidis* causes endemic and epidemic meningitis; *N. catarrhalis,* and *N. flavescens* are isolated occasionally from the spinal fluid in cases of mild chronic meningitis, while other members of the group are nonpathogenic. The morphologic similarity between members of the group and the presence of common proteins and somatic carbohydrates suggest that all gram-negative cocci originated from a common ancestor.

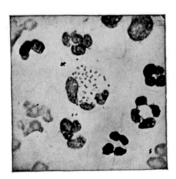

Fig. 1. Meningococci in spinal fluid.

In the 1957 edition of Bergey's Manual, only two genera are recognized in the family of *Neisseriaceae* Prévot. The first genus is the *Neisseria* Trevisan, which is aerobic but facultatively anaerobic, and the second, *Veillonella* Prévot, which is anaerobic (58).

The organisms occur characteristically in pairs with the long axes of the oval cells parallel to the line of division, and there is a definite flattening of the adjoining sides of the organisms making up a pair. In pure cultures, however, only a minority of the organisms will have this characteristic morphologic arrangement (Figs. 1, 2).

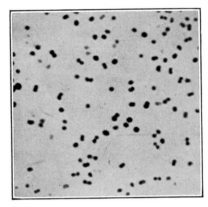

Fig. 2. Meningococci. Organisms from a 24-hour culture. × 2,000.

There are some irregularities in the way the organisms take the stain. Metachromatic granules are present frequently, and gram-positive forms occur, especially in the center of a clump. Much more care is required in the decolorization procedure than is necessary in the staining of other gram-negative organisms. Indeed, very young organisms may be gram-positive, and this may be associated with their susceptibility to penicillin (43).

Classification of this group of organisms has been made on the basis of carbohydrate oxidations, as shown in Table 1. To obtain oxidation with *N. meningitidis* and *N. gonorrhoeae,* rabbit or human serum should be added to the medium and a heavy inoculum used.

The production of acid by the bacterium

Table 1. Oxidation Reactions of Neisseria

ORGANISM	GLUCOSE	MALTOSE	FRUCTOSE	SUCROSE
N. gonorrhoeae	+	0	0	0
N. meningitidis	+	+	0	0
N. catarrhalis	0	0	0	0
N. sicca	+	+	+	+
N. haemolysans	+	+	+	+
N. flavescens	0	0	0	0
N. caviae	0	0	0	0
N. subflava	+	+	0	0
N. flava	+	+	+	0
N. perflava	+	+	+	+

can be determined by incorporating a suitable indicator into a semisolid medium.

NEISSERIA MENINGITIDIS

Family: *Neisseriaceae* Prévot. Genus: *Neisseria* Trevisan. Species: *Neisseria meningitidis* (Albrecht and Ghon) Holland.

Weichselbaum (60) isolated *N. meningitidis* from six cases of epidemic meningitis in 1887. *Neisseria meningitidis* is of great importance in medicine because of its tendency to cause dramatic and explosive **epidemics** of **cerebrospinal meningitis.** Meningococcic meningitis occurs sporadically during the interepidemic periods, but the annual morbidity rates remain rather constant and, in general, are not far different from those of meningitis caused by pneumococci, streptococci, *Haemophilus influenzae,* and tubercle bacilli. Before the introduction of sulfonamides, the case fatality rate from sporadic and epidemic infections was extremely variable, being as high as 90 per cent in some instances and as low as 20 per cent in others. The over-all case fatality rate averaged about 70 per cent.

During an epidemic purpuric spots on the skin occur in more than 50 per cent of the cases of meningococcic meningitis but are seen less commonly in interepidemic infections.

Man is the only natural host for *N. meningitidis.* The organisms live in the nasopharynges of apparently normal individuals and are passed from man to man, as are pneumococci.

Morphology and Staining. Smears from the spinal fluid of infected patients show the characteristic intracellular diplococci (Fig. 1), usually in pairs but sometimes as tetrads or even larger aggregations. In the early stages of the disease many of the organisms are found extracellularly. *N. meningitidis* is **nonmotile** and **nonsporogenous.**

The organism stains readily with aniline dyes and usually shows the presence of metachromatic granules when stained with Löffler's methylene blue or Neisser's stain. It is **gram-negative** but often retains the blue dye when thick smears of spinal fluid are inadequately decolorized.

Cultural Characteristics. *N. meningitidis* is a **strict aerobe,** which grows best in a rich medium (7, 45, 50), at pH 7.4 to 7.6 and at 37° C. It can be cultivated in synthetic media (22, 26, 48).

After 24-hour incubation on a suitable medium, smooth, moist, elevated, bluish gray colonies appear. They are somewhat larger than colonies of pneumococci and less opaque than those of micrococci and have no effect on the blood cells in the medium. Autolysis occurs even during development of the colonies, which explains the appearance of swollen and poorly stained cocci in smears. The growth is augmented by incubating the culture in an atmosphere of 10 per cent carbon dioxide (44, 56). Meningococcus colonies give the **characteristic oxidase** test upon the application of a solution of tetramethyl-*p*-phenylenediamine, but the reaction does not differentiate meningococci from gonococci and other members of the *Neisseria* group.

Resistance. Meningococci are very delicate organisms and are killed in 24 hours by drying or exposure to sunlight. Heating to 50° C. or exposures to high dilutions of the usual antiseptics quickly destroys the organisms. Subcultures die after three to four days' incubation on blood agar and must be transferred frequently. During World War II, Levine and Thomas (33) devised a growth, shipment, and maintenance medium which preserved the viability of the organism for five to eight weeks.

Lyophilization shortly after isolation is the best method of preserving the organisms in their smooth, virulent phase.

Meningococci are very susceptible to both **sulfonamides** and **penicillin.** Chlortetracycline and the other new antibiotics also destroy these cocci (18).

Variability. Freshly isolated organisms of group A and group C are **encapsulated** and have the typical colony form just described. The organisms of group B usually are **nonencapsulated,** and the colonies are smaller, rougher, and may develop a yellowish tint. Colonies of virulent organisms readily develop papillae on the surface and subcultures from these papillae develop as avirulent dissociated organisms.

Miller and Bohnhoff (42) have isolated two types of variants by growing meningococci on media containing 0.07 g. per ml. of streptomycin. One variant could be cultivated on the usual streptomycin-free medium, and these subcultures proved to be virulent and resistant to streptomycin. The second type of variant, however, could not be subcultured on streptomycin-free media. It was proved later that **streptomycin had become an essential growth factor** for these organisms. This variant was incapable of infecting guinea pigs unless the animals were receiving large doses of streptomycin, in which case the organisms produced a fatal infection.

Antigenic Structure. Meningococci and gonococci are known to share eight heat-stabile antigens (61). The meningococci also contain a somatic polysaccharide which is common to all *Neisseria,* pneumococci, and some strains of *Klebsiella* (28, 51).

The early attempts to classify meningococci on an antigenic basis have been reviewed by Gordon (25, 46, 47). A new classification appears in the seventh edition of Bergey's Manual, in which the groups are designated A, B, C, and D (11) (Table 2).

Group specificity is determined by a specific capsular polysaccharide in groups A and C (10, 12) and by a polysaccharide-polypeptide complex in group B (38). Specific types within the groups do occur, but these tend to cross-agglutinate with each other and even the gonococcus is frequently agglutinated by serums from organisms in group B (11). Alexander and Redman (1, 2) have transformed an R-avirulent group C into a virulent group A by a deoxyribonucleic acid extract of a group A organism. Catlin's studies (14, 15) show the genes produced in the interior of the cell accumulate in a "pool" in the slime layer. This seems to be the mechanism for genetic recombination in the genera, since genetic changes in *N. intracellularis* have been elicited by deoxyribonucleate preparations obtained from *N. sicca* (15). The specific hapten of the group C capsule was found by Watson and Scherp (59) to be sialic acid polymers containing hexosamine units. The capsular material is antigenic but not toxic (39).

Typing can be done by the standard test tube method, the centrifugation technic (37), precipitin test, capsular swelling in the presence of specific antiserum, or the addition of the homologous antiserum to the agar medium before pouring plates and observation of the development of a halo about the specific colonies (49). Of the more than 1,500 strains, isolated from clinical cases of meningitis during World War II, which were typed in one central laboratory, 91.6 per cent were group A, 1.6 per cent were group B, 5.6 per cent group C, and only 0.2 per cent could not be classified (50). Since World War II the epidemic group

Table 2. Relationship Among the Various Classifications of Meningococci
(Branham, 1953)

DOPTER AND PAURON, 1914	GORDON AND MURRAY, 1914	GRIFFITH AND SCOTT, 1916	NICOLLE, DEBAINS AND JOUAN, 1918	COMMON USE SINCE 1940	RECOMMENDED BY COMMITTEE 1950
Meningococcus	I III	I	A	I	A
Parameningococcus	II IV	II	B	II IV	B D
			C	II alpha	C
			D *		

* Relation of this D to other groups is unknown.

A organisms have been sharply reduced and the endemic groups B and C have become prevalent (47).

Bacterial Metabolites. Potent endotoxins are found in the bodies of dead meningococci. The active endotoxin of meningococci of group C is a lipopolysaccharide with about 20 per cent lipid, less than 1 per cent protein, and less than 1 per cent nucleic acid (39). Sialic acid forms an integral part of the lipo-protein polysaccharide complex. The purified lipid was not toxic.

SHWARTZMAN PHENOMENON. In 1929 Shwartzman (53) demonstrated a necropurpurogenic factor in meningococci. The meningococci filtrates contained less of the preparatory than of the provocative agents. Black-Schaffer, Hiebert, and Kerby (6) in 1947 made a comparative study of eight strains of *N. meningitidis* isolated from patients with the characteristic purpuric skin lesions and 10 strains from patients who had no demonstrable skin lesions. Although the Shwartzman materials were produced by all strains, regardless of origin, in general, the more potent filtrates were from cultures derived from patients with purpuric spots. The usual variation in susceptibility of different rabbits to the injection of identical quantities of the same filtrates was noted. There was no correlation between the antigenic type of the meningococcus and its ability to produce purpura in rabbits. The experimental evidence justified their conservative conclusion that meningococcic purpura is most apt to occur through the fortuitous infection with a purpurogenic strain of an individual with marked susceptibility to the Shwartzman materials.

A small proportion of the patients with purpuric meningococcemia develop hemorrhages and necrosis of the adrenal glands, resulting in collapse and death with characteristic symptoms known as the Waterhouse-Friderichsen syndrome (63). Adrenal damage was found in two rabbits in the series studied by Black-Schaffer and others (6).

The clinical syndrome known as the Waterhouse-Friderichsen syndrome can occur in the absence of gross hemorrhage in the adrenal glands (5). The same syndrome can be produced by septicemia with *Mimea polymorpha* (55).

Experimental Disease in Laboratory Animals. The introduction of a few virulent meningococci into the yolk sac of 10-day-old chick embryos results in a fatal infection. Septicemia and hemorrhagic lesions can be produced in 12-day-old chicks (13), but adults are immune. Meningitis has been produced in monkeys (57) and in rabbits (9) by intrathecal injection of freshly isolated cultures.

Some strains of meningococci possess virulence and kill mice after the intraperitoneal injection of 100,000 organisms but other strains require such large doses that it often is difficult to determine whether or not the animals die from the infection or from intoxication with endotoxin. If, however, the meningococci are suspended in **mucin** and injected intraperitoneally, as few as two to 10 organisms of a highly virulent strain produce fatal infections of mice (41). Strains of meningococci can be kept at their maximum virulence by repeated passages in mice. The use of mucin in the inoculum has proven very satisfactory in that an experimental disease can be produced in mice, which permits study and evaluation of the therapeutic effects of sulfonamides, penicillin, and streptomycin.

Clinical Types of Disease in Man. Man is infected by way of the nasopharynx. In progressive infections the organisms gain entrance into the lymph channels which, by draining into the blood, initiate a bacteremia which results in the formation of metastatic lesions in the lungs, joints, ears, eyes, skin, and particularly the **meninges.** A direct extension from the nasopharynx to the meninges by way of the nerve fibers or the perineural lymphatics occurs rarely if at all.

Invasion of the blood stream is followed very quickly by clinical manifestations of chills, fever, malaise, myalgia, severe headaches, and meningitis (16, 54). Purpuric spots occur in a small percentage of sporadic cases, but during epidemics a majority of patients show these lesions; hence, the name **spotted fever.** The purpuric spots result from a thrombosis of capillaries or subterminal vessels in the skin, followed by the extravasation of red blood cells to produce small, bright red spots which in 12 to 24 hours become dark red, purple, and finally blue-black. Meningococci have been demonstrated in smears and can be cultured from the early red stage of the purpuric lesions. Blood cultures always should be made before patients are given sulfonamides or penicillin.

In some instances the clinical picture of infection is that of **chronic meningococcemia.** The organisms apparently invade the blood periodically, producing a small number of large spots over a period of weeks or even months. Such patients may recover, develop the characteristic syndrome of meningococcic meningitis, or form lesions on the heart valves producing bacterial endocarditis. Meningococcic **bacterial endocarditis** can be caused by both group A and B meningococci (21).

Prompt removal and examination of a specimen of spinal fluid before the administration of sulfonamides or penicillin is essential for an early and accurate diagnosis of meningococcic meningitis. When typical gram-negative cocci are found in sufficient numbers in smears from the spinal fluid, group A and group C organisms can be typed directly by the Quellung reaction by use of immune rabbit serums. Group B organisms do not give this reaction. If no organisms are seen on direct smear, the intraperitoneal inoculation of mice with spinal fluid and mucin may give in 12 hours enough organisms for typing.

Relapses of meningococcal meningitis are frequent, and occasionally patients may have two or more recurrences within a period of two years (61).

Agglutinins appear in the patient's blood in titers of 1:80 and 1:360 after 5 to 15 days (37) and persist for three to four months. Complement-fixing antibodies appear during convalescence (11), but none of the antibodies appears sufficiently early to be of aid in diagnosis.

Treatment. All the sulfonamide preparations are effective against the meningococci, but **sufadiazine,** because of its low toxicity, **is used most frequently at the present time.** These chemotherapeutic agents readily penetrate the meninges to give a spinal fluid concentration of 50 to 60 per cent of that found in the blood. Those properties of the sulfonamides which enable them to pass through the intact meninges are probably effective also in obtaining deeper penetration into the plastic exudates on the meninges.

Penicillin is as effective as the sulfonamides in eliminating organisms from the blood stream. The antibiotics filter through the meninges with difficulty, although some early cases have been cured with parenteral penicillin alone. In critically ill patients there is a theoretical advantage in using both sulfonamides and penicillin because meningococci develop resistance to penicillin much less readily than they do to the sulfonamides. The case fatality rate has been reduced to about 5 per cent (34, 17, 27, 29).

There is no specific skin test available for determining susceptibility, immunity, or allergy.

Transmission. The epidemiologic pattern for meningococcus meningitis is very complex. In interepidemic periods the sporadic cases occur chiefly in children, being analogous in this respect to *H. influenzae* infections. In one series of 3,557 cases, 27 per cent were in children less than five years of age and 45 per cent were less than 15 (4). In the epidemics which occur every 10 to 11 years, the most severe infections occur in adults, especially among soldiers. When once started, however, the disease spreads quickly to the civilian population. The attack rate among those exposed is very low, almost as low as that for poliomyelitis. Single cases in families are the rule rather than the exception, but multiple cases in a family of children have been reported (52) and the prophylactic administration of sulfadiazine to the exposed members has been suggested. Doctors, nurses and attendants on wards for patients with meningitis contract the disease only occasionally, but they regularly have a much higher carrier incidence (36.7 per cent) than the average of the population (4 per cent). Although over 38 per cent of the convalescent patients may remain carriers for variable periods, it is difficult to trace the development of new cases to a patient, a convalescent, or even a known carrier (35).

The types of meningococci harbored in the nasopharynx vary somewhat in the interepidemic and epidemic periods. In an interepidemic period, Laybourn (32) found group B meningococci to be the most frequent type found in carriers and in patients with meningitis.

As a result of studies made during World War I, it was assumed that epidemics developed in army camps as a result of crowding large numbers of nonimmune recruits into barracks, which promoted a rapid increase in carrier rate and a rapid transfer of organisms from individual to individual (24). The studies during World War II, which were reviewed by Aycock and Mueller (3) in 1950, do not support this simple explanation for epidemic meningitis.

Prevention. Isolation of carriers as a means of preventing epidemic meningitis is not practical because of their great number. The decentralization of masses of individuals would probably prove successful if it could be effected.

Two or three days of prophylactic treatment with relatively small doses (1 to 2 g.) of sulfadiazine administered to the entire personnel has been shown to eliminate the organisms from the nasopharynges of the carriers and to have stopped an epidemic (30, 31, 50). Prolonged periods of mass treatment should be avoided to prevent the development of sulfonamide resistant strains. As this chapter was being revised a rumor reached us that a highly virulent and totally sulfonamide resistant strain of *N. meningiditis* had appeared in San Diego, California (40).

OTHER GRAM-NEGATIVE MICROCOCCI

Neisseria catarrhalis. This organism is a diplococcus described first by R. Pfeiffer (23), who found it in the sputum of patients suffering from catarrhal inflammations of the upper respiratory tract (23).

Culturally *N. catarrhalis* grows more readily than the meningococcus upon ordinary culture media. The colonies of *N. catarrhalis* are coarsely granular and distinctly white, in contradistinction to the finely granular, grayish meningococcus colonies. *N. catarrhalis* will develop at temperatures below 20° C., while the meningococcus will not grow at temperatures below 25° C. No acid is produced from any of the carbohydrates.

Neisseria sicca. This organism, described by von Lingelsheim (57), is a gram-negative diplococcus often found in the normal pharynx, which can be recognized by its dry, crenated colonies on simple media. According to Elser and Huntoon (20), it sediments spontaneously in salt solution, and this, together with the fact that the colonies are formed in a way almost

impossible to break up, makes it easy to distinguish from the meningococcus. This organism produces acid in glucose, fructose, maltose, and sucrose.

Neisseria haemolysans. *N. haemolysans* was named by Thjøtta and Bøe in 1938. Colonies are delicate and grow slowly but are characterized by a large zone of beta hemolysis by the second or third day. Acid is produced from glucose, fructose, maltose, and sucrose.

Neisseria flavescens. During an epidemic of meningitis in Chicago, Branham (8) isolated *N. flavescens* from the spinal fluid of a number of patients. The organisms grew poorly on glucose agar but very well on blood agar and semisolid agar. A golden yellow pigment was produced in the colonies. The various strains were homologous but did not agglutinate in antimeningococcal serum. *N. flavescens* lacks the ability to oxidize the usual carbohydrates.

Neisseria caviae. This organism was isolated from the pharyngeal region of the guinea pig by Pelczar in 1953 (19). Colonies are a light caramel to dark brown color. Some strains are weakly hemolytic against rabbit's blood. No acid formed from carbohydrates.

Neisseria subflava. This is the yellow colony type from Elser and Huntoon's chromogenic group III (20). The colonies are yellowish-gray and adhere to the medium. Sugar reactions, like *N. meningitidis,* produce acid from glucose and maltose. Differentiated by color and growth at 22° C.

Neisseria flava. This is from Elser and Huntoon's chromogenic group II (20) and is more definitely yellow than *N. subflava.* Acid is produced from glucose, fructose, and maltose. This organism has produced endocarditis (36).

Neisseria perflava. This bright yellow *Neisseria* is from Elser and Huntoon's chromogenic group I (20). The yellow pigment can stain the sputum yellow, as does the pigment from *S. aureus. N. perflava* produces acid from glucose, fructose maltose, and sucrose.

VEILLONELLA

These are the anaerobic strains of the Family *Neisseriaceae* which include Genus II. *Veillonella* Prévot 1933. The type species are *Veillonella parvula* (Veillon and Zuber) Prévot. Six species are recognized in the seventh edition of Bergey's Manual. They may be associated with disease as opportunists and secondary invaders but rarely, if ever, as primary invaders in healthy tissues. The species are differentiated by colony morphology and chemical reactions (31, 51a).

REFERENCES

1. Alexander, H. E., and Redman, W.   Am. J. Dis. Child., 84:737, 1952.
2. ――― and Redman, W.   J. Exper. Med., 97:797, 1953.
3. Aycock, W. L., and Mueller, J. H.   Bact. Rev., 14:115, 1950.
4. Beeson, P. B., and Westerman, E.   Brit. M. J., 1:497, 1943.
5. Berkson, D. M., and others.   J.A.M.A., 170:1387, 1959.
6. Black-Schaffer, B., and others.   Arch. Path., 43:28, 1947.
7. Boor, A. K.   Proc. Soc. Exper. Biol. & Med., 50:22, 1942.
8. Branham, S. E.   Pub. Health Rep., 45:1131, 1930.
9. ――― and Lillie, R. D.   Pub. Health Rep., 47:2137, 1932.
10. ――― and Carlin, S. A.   Proc. Soc. Exper. Biol. & Med., 49:141, 1942.
11. ――― Bact. Rev., 17:175, 1953.
12. ――― and Wormald, M. F.   J. Bact., 66:487, 1953.
13. Buddingh, G. J., and Polk, A. D.   J. Exper. Med., 70:485, 499, 1939.
14. Catlin, B. W.   J. Bact., 79:579, 1960.
15. ――― Science, 131:608, 1960.
16. Daniels, W. B.   Arch. Int. Med., 81:145, 1948.
17. Dingle, J. H., and Finland, M.   War Med., 2:1, 1942.
18. Dowling, H. F., and others.   J.A.M.A., 139:755, 1949.
19. Ellinghausen, H. C., Jr., and Pelczar, M. J., Jr.   J. Bact., 70:448, 1955.
20. Elser, W. J., and Huntoon, F. M.   J. Med. Research, 20:369, 1909.
21. Firestone, G. M.   Am. J. M. Sc., 211:556, 1946.
22. Frantz, I. D.   J. Bact., 43:757, 1942.
23. Ghon, A., and Pfeiffer, H.   Ztschr. f. klin. Med., 44:262, 1902.
24. Glover, J. A.   J. Hyg., 17:367, 1918.
25. Gordon, M. H.   J. Hyg., 17:290, 1918.
26. Grossowicz, N.   J. Bact., 50:109, 1945.
27. Hine, T. G. M.   Medical Research Council, Spec. Rep., Series 3, No. 3, 99.
28. Kabat, E. A., and others.   J. Exper. Med., 80:299, 1944.
29. Kinsman, J. M., and D'Alonzo, C. A.   Ann. Int. Med., 24:606, 1946.
30. Kuhns, D. M., and others.   J.A.M.A., 123:335, 1943.
31. Langford, G. C., Jr., and others.   J. Bact., 59:349, 1950.
32. Laybourn, R. L.   South. M. J., 24:678, 1931.
33. Levine, M., and Thomas, A. R.   J. Bact., 53:33, 1947.
34. Lohrey, R. C., and Toomey, J. A.   J. Pediat., 28:86, 1946.
35. Mathers, G., and Herrold, R. D.   J. Infect. Dis., 22:523, 1918.
36. Matlage, W. T., and others.   Ann. Int. Med., 33:1494, 1950.
37. Mayer, R. L., and Dowling, H. F.   J. Immunol., 51:349, 1945.
38. Menzel, A. E. O., and Rake, G.   J. Exper. Med., 75:437, 1942.
39. Mergenhagen, S. E., and others.   J. Immunol., 90:312, 1946.
40. Millar, J. W.   J.A.M.A., 186:139, 1963.
41. Miller, C. P.   Proc. Soc. Exper. Biol. & Med., 32:1138, 1935.
42. ――― and Bohnhoff, M.   J.A.M.A., 130:485, 1946.
43. Mitchell, P., and Moyle, J.   Nature, London, 166:218, 1950.
44. Morton, H. E.   J. Bact., 50:589, 1945.
45. Mueller, J. H., and Hinton, J.   Proc. Soc. Exper. Biol. & Med., 48:330, 1941.
46. Murray, E. G. D.   Medical Research Council, Spec. Rep. No. 124, 1929.
47. ――― and Branham, S. E.   Atti Del VI Congresso Internazionale Di Microbiologia, Roma, 1953, Vol. I, Sez. 1, p. 7.
48. Nemes, J. L., and others.   J. Infect. Dis., 88:156, 1951.
49. Petrie, G. F.   Brit. J. Exper. Path., 13:380, 1932.
50. Phair, J. J., and Schoenbach, E. B.   Am. J. Hyg., 40:318, 1944.
51. Rake, G., and Scherp, H. W.   J. Exper. Med., 58:341, 361, 1933.
51a. Rogosa, M.   J. Bact., 87:162, 1964.
52. Rotondo, C. C., and Handleman, N. I.   J. Pediat., 27:576, 1945.
53. Shwartzman, G.   Proc. Soc. Exper. Biol. & Med., 26:207, 1929.
54. Thomas, H. M., Jr.   J.A.M.A., 123:264, 1943.
55. Townsend, F. M., and others.   U.S. Armed Forces M. J., 5:673, 1954.
56. Tuttle, D. M., and Scherp, H. W.   J. Bact., 64:171, 1952.
57. von Lingelsheim, W.   Klin. Jahrb., 15:373, 1906.
58. Warner, G. S., and others.   J. Infect. Dis., 90:97, 1952.
59. Watson, R. G., and Scherp, H. W.   J. Immunol., 81:331, 337, 1958.
60. Weichselbaum, A.   Fortschr. d. Med., 5:573, 620, 1887.
61. Weinstein, L., and Stanley, E. D.   New England J. Med., 234:364, 1946.
62. Wilson, J. F.   J. Path. & Bact., 72:111, 1956.
63. Wright, D. O., and Reppert, L. B.   Arch. Int. Med., 77:143, 1946.

24

Neisseria gonorrhoeae and Gonococcal Infections

Family: *Neisseriaceae* Prévot. Genus: *Neisseria* Trevisan. Species: *Neisseria gonorrhoeae* Trevisan

The name **gonorrhea** was introduced by Galen about 130 A.D., although it is obvious from surviving records that the disease was recognized by the ancient Chinese and Hebrews. Neisser in 1879 described diplococci, which he found consistently in the purulent secretions of acute cases of urethritis and vaginitis and in smears made from the acute conjunctivitis of the newborn. *Neisseria gonorrhoeae* (50) was cultivated by Leistikow in 1882 (34) and by Bumm in 1885. The latter maintained pure cultures of the organism by serial transfers on coagulated human blood serum and established its etiologic significance by reproducing the disease in human volunteers (10).

Both gonorrhea and syphilis declined precipitously after the introduction of penicillin, but this dramatic success led to complacency and a reduction in appropriations for the control of venereal disease. This has resulted in a rapid increase in the venereal disease rate in the past five years, especially in teen-age adolescents (58). It has been estimated by the officials in the Public Health Service that 1.5 million new cases of gonorrhea occur each year in the United States, although only about one sixth of these are reported to Public Health authorities (58).

Although the characteristic disease produced by *N. gonorrhoeae* is gonorrhea, occasionally the gonococcus and other species of *Neisseria* have been isolated from stomatitis and from meningitis (8, 31, 64).

Morphology and Staining. In smears from urethral discharges the gonococcus is seen as an oval or spherical coccus, 0.8 μ by 0.6 μ. The organisms, found frequently in pairs with the adjacent sides flattened, usually are intracellular (Fig. 1). In smears there is often irregularity in the distribution in the phagocytic cells, many polymorphonuclear leukocytes containing no organisms while a few cells may contain as many as 20 to 50 or even more cocci per cell. A few extracellular forms are always present in acute gonorrhea, but in chronic cases the intracellular position is the exception rather than the rule. In smears from pure cultures,

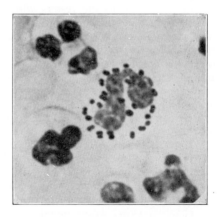

Fig. 1. Gonococci from urethra showing cocci within a leukocyte. (Courtesy of J. Kurung.)

about 25 per cent of the organisms are in the typical diplococcal form, the others occurring as single cocci, tetrads, or clusters of eight or more. The gonococcus is **nonsporogenous, nonmotile** and does not have a capsule except in its mucoid variant phase (2).

N. gonorrhoeae stains readily with aniline dyes. Good results are obtained with methylene blue alone or eosin followed by methylene blue. Excellent preparations also may be made with polychrome stains such as Pappenheim-Saathoff methyl green-pyronine. The gonococcus is **gram-negative.** The presence of gram-negative intracellular diplococci in smears of pus from the male urethra is presumptive evidence of gonorrhea. In exudates from the vagina or from the eye, however, the morphologic picture is less reliable, since other gram-negative cocci are present frequently in these regions. In staphylococcal infections of the conjunctivae, dead organisms may fail to retain the blue dye and by taking the counterstain they may appear in the smears in the form of gram-negative intracellular cocci; hence, considerable emphasis must be placed on the shape of the cocci as well as on their staining reactions.

In medicolegal cases the diagnosis of gonorrhea may be questioned if it is based only on the examination of stained smears. Unless the organisms have been isolated and identified, it is a wiser procedure for the laboratory to report only the finding of gram-negative intracellular diplococci resembling gonococci.

The diagnosis of gonorrhea in men by the fluorescent antibody technic, introduced by Deacon and his coworkers in 1959 (19) proved so successful that it was applied to the study of females in 1960 (20). The results on dried smears were superior to the results with conventional staining, and the combination of dried staining and staining after incubating the collecting swab for 16 to 20 hours proved even more reliable than culture (20).

Cultural Characteristics. The gonococcus is a delicate aerobic but facultative anaerobic organism which usually requires an atmosphere of 2 to 10 per cent CO_2 (44) and an optimal temperature of 35° to 36° C. and a pH of 7.2 to 7.6. Growth ceases below 30° and above 38.5°. This organism has been grown in a chemically defined medium (6, 29, 47). Agar contains inhibiting substances which can be neutralized by the addition of starch, gastric mucin, charcoal (47), whole blood (38), the insoluble fraction of whole yeast autolysate (11, 29, 43, 44, 45). The addition of crystal violet and the growth-promoting substance from yeast to the standard chocolate agar facilitates growth. Gerhardt and Heden (28) found that gonococcus grew luxuriantly in water which had been added as an overlay to solid medium. Such growth was remarkably free of contaminating chemical substances from the solid medium.

On **chocolate agar,** after 48 hours' incubation, round, convex, smooth, grayish white colonies 0.5 to 1 mm. in diameter appear. On further incubation, the colonies may increase in size

and develop a roughened surface with crenated edges. The colonies are soft and somewhat slimy when touched with a platinum loop.

Colonies of gonococci, meningococci, and other bacteria synthesizing **indophenol oxidase** turn a bright purple when a plate is flooded or sprayed with a 1 per cent solution of tetramethyl-*p*-phenylenediamine. The excess dye should be removed quickly by tilting or inverting the plate. The organisms are not killed by this short exposure and may be subcultured during the next 30 minutes. The oxidase reaction may be prevented by acid formed from the oxidation of glucose but becomes positive with the addition of a neutralizing reagent (9).

Cultural methods yield twice as many positives as the direct smear technic (63, 67, 71). When specimens cannot be cultured for several hours, they should be collected on small, tightly wrapped cotton swabs, and prevented from drying by immersing in a little broth (45) or preferably a mixture of starch, gentian-violet and broth (52). **Glucose** is oxidized with the formation of acid without gas; catalase is produced.

Resistance. Gonococci succumb to drying within one or two hours. Moist heat kills them at 55° C. in less than five minutes and at 42° C. in five to 15 hours (11). They are very susceptible to the usual antiseptics, especially to $AgNO_3$, which, in a 1:4,000 dilution, destroys gonococci in two minutes. Cultures maintained at room temperature die in one to two days and after four to six days at 37° C.

Contrary to the opinions expressed in the previous edition of this text, they can be preserved by lyophilization. Cultures which have been preserved by this method were found to be viable after 21 years by Miller and Simons (41) and after 24 years by Morton (46).

Gonococci are very susceptible also to **sulfonamides** and **penicillin.** Resistant strains, however, developed rapidly as each new sulfonamide, in succession, was introduced in treatment (28). Penicillin on a weight for weight basis is from 10 to 25 times as effective as the other available antibiotics (14).

Variability. Atkin described two types of colonies in 1925 (3). Type I predominated in recently isolated cultures but were gradually replaced in stock cultures by type II which were smaller, opaque and yellowish white. The dwarf type colony was isolated by Raven in 1934 (53) and Morton and Shoemaker in 1945 (44). The latter investigators succeeded in dissociating the dwarf colony and recovering the large normal sized one (44). Other colonial changes have been described by Miller and Bohnhoff (39). Mahoney and his associates (36) could not correlate colonial type and pathogenicity by injecting the organisms into human volunteers.

Antigenic Structure. Wilson (72) reviewed the antigenic structure of *N. gonorrhoeae* and *N. meningitidis* and found that at least eight heat-stable antigens were shared by each species. Fresh isolated gonococcus cultures were frequently inagglutinable unless heated at 100° C. for 30 minutes. Subsequent fluorescent antibody studies by Deacon and his associates (19) have demonstrated the presence of a species specific antigen which possesses characteristics similar to the Vi antigen of *S. typhosa* and the K antigen of the *Escherichia* group. Cross-reactions with *N. meningitidis* and *N. catarrhalis* were removed by absorbing the fluorescent antibody with serogroups A and ACF antigens. It is possible that this surface antigen gives virulence to the gonococcus. The presence of a virulent antigen in the gonococcus is suggested by the studies of Van Slyke and others (68) who produced experimental gonorrhea in human volunteers by the direct transfer of small amounts of urethral discharge containing only a few gonococci, whereas very large doses of organisms from freshly isolated cultures were required to reproduce the disease. Complement fixation, as might be expected, does not give a sharp differentiation between gonococcal infection and infection with other *Neisseria* (37).

Bacterial Metabolites. In addition to catalase and the indophenol oxidase, which is responsible for the "oxidase reaction," Tauber and Russell (61) have demonstrated the presence of diphosphopyridine nucleotide oxidase, alcohol dehydrogenase, and diphosphopyridine nucleotide-linked lactic dehydrogenase. All *Neisseria* contain a cyanide-sensitive, aerobic cysteine oxidase and a cysteine desulfhydrase.

Endotoxins. The bodies of gonococci contain an endotoxin which kills laboratory animals when injected in large amounts. This endotoxin is similar to the endotoxin of the meningococcus. No exotoxin has been demonstrated.

Experimental Disease in Laboratory Animals. Although laboratory animals can be killed with large doses of living or dead gonococci, death is obviously due to the endotoxin. Monkeys and even anthropoid apes cannot be infected.

Boor and Miller (7) found a single strain of gonococci which would produce a fatal infection in mice when injected intraperitoneally along with mucin, and Miller and others (40)

produced local infections in the anterior chambers of the eyes of young albino rabbits.

Clinical Types of Infection in Man. The incubation period for gonococcal urethritis in controlled human experiments was three to five days, with extremes of one to 31 days (68).

The majority of gonococcal infections occur in the male and female genital tracts, but, because of the prevalence of gonorrhea, extragenital infections are of fairly frequent occurrence even though the percentage of such infections is small. **Cystitis, proctitis, stomatitis, and conjunctivitis** are local infections. The organisms also invade the blood stream giving rise to **septicemia, arthritis, osteomyelitis, endocarditis, and meningitis.**

Gonococcal ophthalmia is the most frequent serious complication produced by *N. gonorrhoeae*. The eyes may be infected by organisms which the individual is carrying himself or from organisms carried by others. Ophthalmia of the newborn may be due to other organisms, but it is almost always caused by the gonococcus. It is acquired by the child, in the course of delivery, from the secretions of the mother, and, if not attended to, may lead to blindness.

Fortunately, the method introduced by **Credé** has, to a very large extent, done away with this accident. Credé, many years ago, introduced the method of instilling a 2 per cent silver nitrate solution into the conjunctival sacs of every child at birth. It is extremely important that this should be done properly, that the entire conjunctival sac be bathed in the fluid. **The method is so important that it is regarded as a matter of very serious and inexcusable omission if, under any circumstances, in dealing with any class of the population, the physician managing a childbirth fails to carry out this measure as soon as feasible after birth.**

There are some studies which suggest that penicillin applied locally may be as effective as silver nitrate (1) and one study in which local silver nitrate supplemented by 50,000 units of penicillin intramuscularly was definitely superior to silver nitrate alone in preventing ophthalmia (71).

Vulvovaginitis in children was considered a major hazard in children's wards in hospitals, in boarding schools, and orphanages before the report of Cohn and his associates in 1940 (13) that vulvovaginitis is relatively rare in the absence of sexual contact and that true epidemics probably do not occur.

Transmission. The data acquired from various surveys show, according to Vonderlehr and Usilton (69), that the incidence is highest in cities from 50,000 to 500,000 population, and lowest in metropolitan and rural areas. (35)

The male rarely becomes asymptomatic. Carriers of *N. gonorrhoeae* (35) are usually readily demonstrated when there are symptoms, either by smears or by culture and by the new fluorescent antibody technic of Deacon (18, 19, 20). The story is quite different in the female. Garson and Barton (27) found that only from 50 to 75 per cent of symptomatic females had positive smears or cultures, although the percentage that could be diagnosed by the direct and delayed antibody test of Deacon (20) was slightly larger. Even more important than the problem of transmission was the finding of Harris and his associates (30) that 20.6 per cent of females admitted to jail, without sign of symptoms of gonorrhea, nevertheless harbored *N. gonorrhoeae* when examined by the delayed fluorescent antibody method. Even this high figure of 20.6 per cent does not represent the true rate of infection, since a re-examination of 74 of the subjects yielded additional positive tests. These discouraging results caused Garson and Barton, as late as 1960, to conclude that the most sensitive, if not the most practical, indicator of gonococcus in the female is the anterior urethra of a susceptible male (27).

Gonococci remain viable for a short time on inapparently soiled wearing apparel, bed clothing, towels, and hands. Physicians, nurses, and attendants constantly must be alert to the danger of infection from these sources.

Treatment. In 1937 Dees and Colston (23) reported the successful use of sulfanilamide in the treatment of gonorrhea. In the first series of reports there was a rapid and complete cure in more than 90 per cent of the patients. Later reports, however, showed the percentage of cures was dropping to 80, 70, and finally to 50 per cent. Such a disappointing result was caused by the rapid appearance of sulfonamide-resistant strains which succeeded in perpetuating the disease. Each new sulfonamide was highly successful when first introduced, but its effectiveness was lost as resistant strains appeared. Penicillin was then discovered and found to be effective against sulfonamide-resistant strains.

Resistance to penicillin treatment has been reported from time to time—for example, the report of Epstein from Korea in 1959 (25). Patients may, indeed, become resistant to penicillin therapy when adhesions or strictures prevent the arrival of the drug at the seat of the infection, but the *N. gonorrhoeae* when isolated are still susceptible to penicillin. Organisms resistant to penicillin in the test tube and diagnosed as *N. gonorrhoeae* have invariably proven, on further study, to be mistakes in diagnosis. Most if not all of these fall into the group of pseudogonococcal forms found in the genus *Herellea* (16), *Mimeae* (26), and *B. anitratum* and B5W (16).

In denying the existence of penicillin resistance in *N. gonorrhoeae* up to the present time, we are referring to resistance comparable to that encountered daily with *S. aureus,* where the resistance to penicillin is effective in any conceivable dose.

Another more subtle but not yet alarming change in resistance to penicillin has been occurring over the past 10 years in both the United States (62, 63) and in Germany (54). Cultures isolated in 1955 were inhibited by 0.005 to 0.2 units of penicillin G per milliliter, with only 20 per cent requiring 0.1 to 0.2 units. But in 1961 32 per cent of the cultures required 0.2 to 0.6 units per ml., and the upper limit is now 0.7 units. This change has not been sufficient to interfere with the successful treatment of gonorrhea with the usual doses of penicillin now employed. In rare instances, an associated infection with a penicillinase-producing organism, such as a *Streptococcus* (55, 56), or a colon bacillus (4) may destroy the effectiveness of the penicillin (15).

N. gonorrhoeae is so susceptible to antibiotics one can cure most patients with a single dose. Tiedemann and his associates (65) evaluated the relative efficiency and cost of 11 different antibiotics in 1962. The most expensive ($1.04), but most effective, was 3 grams of oral phosphate potentiated tetracycline (500 mg. every four hours); it had a low relapse rate of 3.4 to 3.6 per cent. The least expensive ($0.74) was 1,200,000 units of benzathine penicillin G, which did, however, have a relapse rate of 7 per cent. The other drugs were more expensive and had a high relapse rate.

The very intractable vulvovaginitis of children responds well to penicillin treatment (49), and prompt cures have been obtained in cases which resisted the combined treatment with sulfonamides and theelin (33). Extragenital forms of gonococcal infection including arthritis (52) usually respond satisfactorily to penicillin therapy and other antibiotics (12).

Prevention. Man is the only known host for *N. gonorrhoeae,* and the organism may survive for years in the genitalia of the female without any symptoms, suggesting its presence. As stated in the previous edition of this text, "One of the most important factors that has prevented earlier progress in the prevention of venereal disease has been public ignorance." Venereal diseases essentially are social problems and cannot be solved by medical means alone.

Eagle and his associates (24) have shown that one 250,000 unit tablet of penicillin taken by mouth shortly after exposure will prevent the development of gonorrhea but not necessarily nonspecific urethritis.

PSEUDOGONORRHEA

Strains of *"N. gonorrhoeae"* reported as highly resistant to penicillin when studied in a central laboratory have all been instances of infection with organisms belonging to the genus *Herellea,* which is gram-negative and frequently occurs in a diplococcal form (Figs. 2, 3) resembling *Neisseria;* and if isolated from the genitalia are naturally assumed to be *N. gonorrhoeae* (17). DeBord described the *Mimeae* and distinguished three genera: *Mimea, Herellea,* and *Colloides* (21, 22). These organisms in contrast to *N. gonorrhoeae* rapidly became strongly resistant to penicillin. Svihes and his associates (59) studied 36 cases of urethritis in U.S. soldiers stationed in Naples, Italy, and found that one-third were caused by *N. gonorrhoeae* and two-thirds were caused by *Mimeae*

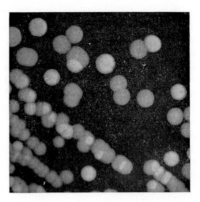

Fig. 2. *Bacterium anitratum.* Note the opaque mucoid colonies and the flatter grayish nonmucoid colonies. × 4. (From Ferguson and Roberts. *J. Bact.,* 59:171, 1950.)

and all 18 penicillin resistant cases were caused by *Mimeae.*

Infections with these organisms are not limited to the urethra. Townsend and his co-workers (66) isolated the organism from the blood and reported two cases which died with symptoms characteristic of the Waterhouse-Friderichsen syndrome usually caused by *N. meningitidis.* Olafsson and his co-workers (51) found cases of meningitis caused by *Mimea polymorpha.* In the studies by Murray and Truant (48) and in the excellent review by Daly, Postic, and Kass (16) in 1962, the newly described organisms are related to some old ones in the literature. It seems that the *Diplococcus mucosus,* isolated by Von Lingelsheim in 1906-1908 (70), was shown by Seelinger in 1953 (57) to be identical with *B. anitratum* which was iso-

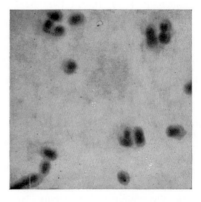

Fig. 3. Crystal violet capsule stain of *Bacterium anitratum.* Preparation of Kleineberger-Nobel. (From Ferguson and Roberts. *J. Bact.,* 59:171, 1950.)

lated and named by Schaub and Hauber in 1948 (56). Daly, Postic, and Kass (16) concluded that *Diplococcus mucosus, B. anitratum,* B5W, *Moraxella lwoffi* var. *glucidolytica, M. glucidolytica, Actineobacter anitrinum,* and *Neisseria winogradski* are all identical with *Herellea vaginicola* (42).

Seven capsular types have been recognized, but there are certainly more, since only 75 per cent of the strains studied fell into the seven types (16). Type I seems to be most common and really acquires resistance to penicillin, streptomycin, and tetracycline.

NONSPECIFIC URETHRITIS

When *N. gonorrhoeae* cannot be isolated from a case of urethritis after repeated attempts at culture on suitable media, the case is diagnosed as nonspecific urethritis (5). Gram-positive cocci of various kinds and pleuropneumonia-like organisms have been isolated from some of these patients, but their etiologic significance has not been established.

Nonspecific urethritis of all types has reached a rate in some areas of 23.9 cases per 1,000 men per annum. Cases usually recover following intense therapy with sulfadiazine and penicillin, urethral irrigations, and sounding (4).

The discovery of Taplin and his associates (60) that *Mimeae-Herellea* organisms can be isolated from the skin of normal males affords a good explanation for the frequency of this infection.

REFERENCES

1. Allen, J. H., and Barrere, L. E. J.A.M.A., 141:522, 1949.
2. Almaden, P. J. J. Infect. Dis., 62:36, 1938.
3. Atkin, E. E. Brit. J. Exper. Path., 6:235, 1925.
4. Baier, G. F. Bull. U.S. Army M. Dept., 9:679, 1949.
5. Benford, T. T., and Holmes, E. M. Urol. & Cutan. Rev., 50:133, 1946.
6. Boor, A. K. Proc. Soc. Exper. Biol. & Med., 50:22, 1942.
7. ———— and Miller, C. P. J. Infect. Dis., 75:47, 1944.
8. Branham, S. E., and others. J.A.M.A., 110:1804, 1938.
9. Bucca, M. A., and others. J. Ven. Dis. Inform., 28:40, 1947.
10. Bumm, E. von. Beiträge zur Kenntniss des Gonococcus, Wiesbaden, 1885.
11. Carpenter, C. M. The Gonococcus, in Diagnostic Procedures and Reagents, New York, Am. Pub. Health Assn., p. 982, 1945.
12. Chen, C. H., and others. J.A.M.A., 143:742, 1950.
13. Cohn, A., and others. J. Ven. Dis. Inform., 21:208, 1940.
14. ———— and others. Am. J. Syph., Gonor. & Ven. Dis., 33:86, 1949.
15. Collins, H. S., and others. Am. J. Syph., Gonor. & Ven. Dis., 33:263, 1949.
16. Daly, A. K., and others. Arch. Int. Med., 110:580, 1962.
17. Deacon, W. E. J. Bact., 49:511, 1945.
18. ———— and others. Proc. Soc. Exper. Biol. & Med., 101:2, 1959.
19. ———— and others. Proc. Soc. Exper. Biol. & Med., 101:322, 1959.
20. ———— and others. Pub. Health Rep., 75:125, 1960.
21. De Bord, G. G. J. Bact., 38:119, 1939.
22. ———— J. Lab. & Clin. Med., 28:710, 1943.
23. Dees, J. E., and Colston, J. A. C. J.A.M.A., 108:1855, 1937.
24. Eagle, H., and others. J.A.M.A., 140:940, 1949.
25. Epstein, E. J.A.M.A., 169:1055, 1959.
26. Gangarosa, E. J., and Cary, S. G. J.A.M.A., 173:1808, 1960.
27. Garson, W., and Barton, G. D. Pub. Health Rep., 75:119, 1960.
28. Gerhardt, P., and Heden, C. G. Proc. Soc. Exper. Biol. & Med., 105:49, 1960.
29. Gould, R. G., and others. J. Bact., 47:287, 1944.
30. Harris, A., and others. Pub. Health Rep., 76:93, 1961.
31. Johnston, J. Am. J. Syph., Gonor. & Ven. Dis., 35:79, 1951.
32. Landy, M., and Gerstung, R. B. J. Immunol., 51:269, 1945.
33. Lee, H. F., and Sussman, W. J. Pediat., 28:590, 1946.
34. Leistikow. Berl. klin. Wchnschr., 19:500, 1882.
35. Lentz. J. W., and others. Pub. Health Rep., 77:653, 1962.
36. Mahoney, J. F., and others. Am. J. Syph., Gonor. & Ven. Dis., 30:1, 1946.
37. ———— and others. Am. J. Syph., Gonor. & Ven. Dis., 26:38, 1942.
38. McLeod, J. W., and others. J. Path. & Bact., 39:221, 1934.
39. Miller, C. P., and Bohnhoff, M. J. Bact., 54:8, 1947.
40. ———— and others. Proc. Soc. Exper. Biol. & Med., 60:354, 1945.
41. Miller, R. E., and Simons, L. A. J. Bact., 84:1111, 1962.
42. Mitchel, P. D., and Burrell, R. G. Bact. Proc., 1963, p. 64.
43. Morton, H. E. J. Bact., 50:589, 1945.
44. ———— and Shoemaker, J. J. Bact., 50:585, 1945.
45. ———— and Leberman, P. R. U.S. Naval M. Bull., 43:409, 1944.
46. ———— Personal Communication, 1963.
47. Mueller, J. H., and Hinton, J. Proc. Soc. Exper. Biol. & Med., 48:330, 1941.
48. Murray, R. G. E., and Truant, J. P. J. Bact., 67:13, 1954.
49. Naegele, C. F. Arch. Pediat., 62:516, 1945.
50. Neisser. A. Centralbl. f. d. med. Wissensch., 17:497, 1879.
51. Olafsson, M., and others. N. Eng. J. Med., 258:465, 1958.
52. Peizer, L. R., and Klein, S. Pub. Health Rep., 64:599, 1949.
53. Raven, C. J. Infect. Dis., 55:328, 1934.

54. Rockl., H. München. Med. Wchnschr., 101: 708, 1959.
55. Sabath, L., and Finland, M. J. Bact., 85:314, 1963.
56. Schaub, I. G., and Hauber, F. D. J. Bact., 56:379, 1948.
57. Seeliger, H. Zbl. Bakt. (Pt. 1), 159:173, 1953.
58. Simpson, W. G., and Brown, W. T. J.A.M.A., 182:63, 1962.
59. Svihus, R. H. J.A.M.A., 177:121, 1961.
60. Taplin, D., and others. J.A.M.A., 186:952, 1963.
61. Tauber, H., and Russell, H. Proc. Soc. Exper. Biol. & Med., 110:440, 1962.
62. Thayer, J. D., and others. Bull. World Health Org., 24:327, 1961.
63. ———— and others. Pub. Health Rep., 79:49, 1964.
64. Thomas, R. B., and Bayne-Jones, S. Report of Committee for Survey of Research on the Gonococcus and Gonococcal Infections, Am. J. Syph., Gonor. & Ven. Dis., 20, Supplement, 1936.
65. Tiedemann, J. H., and others. Pub. Health Rep., 77:485, 1962.
66. Townsend, F. M., and others. U.S. Armed Forces Med. J., 5:673, 1954.
67. Usher, G. S., and Stein, R. J. Ven. Dis., Inform., 26:77, 1945.
68. Van Slyke, C. J., and others. Am. J. Syph., Gonor., & Ven. Dis., 30:1, 1946.
69. Vonderlehr, R. A., and Usilton, L. J. J.A.M.A., 109:1425, 1937.
70. Von Lingelsheim, W. Z. Hyg., 59:457, 1908.
71. Watts, S. G., and Gleich, M. M. J.A.M.A., 143:635, 1950.
72. Wilson, J. F. J. Path. & Bact., 72:111, 1956.

25

Haemophilus influenzae and Other Organisms of the Hemophilic Group

Family: *Brucellaceae* fam. nov. Genus: *Haemophilus* Winslow and others. Species: *Haemophilus influenzae* (Lehmann and Neumann) Winslow and others

The genus *Haemophilus* contains the true hemophilic or hemoglobinophilic bacteria as well as organisms for which hemoglobin is stimulative but not essential for growth (37). Whole blood contains two factors which are essential for growth of *H. influenzae:* a heat-stabile **X** factor, now known to be **hemin;** and a heat-labile **V** factor, now known to be **phosphopyridine nucleotide.**

The recognized species of *Haemophilus* are shown in Table 1. The genital strain, from cases of vaginitis, named by Dukes and Gardner (19) *H. vaginales,* was not included in the seventh edition of Bergey's Manual.

HAEMOPHILUS INFLUENZAE

The organism now known as *Haemophilus influenzae* was isolated by Pfeiffer (48) in 1892 from patients suffering from epidemic influenza and, until 1918, was believed to be the cause of this pandemic infection. However, *H. influenzae* shares with streptococci, pneumococci, and staphylococci the very important role of causing secondary pulmonary infections during epidemics of true influenza caused by the influenza virus. It is unfortunate that the name "influenza" was given to this organism, since *H. in-*

Table 1. Growth Requirements of Haemophilus

SPECIES	V FACTOR (PHOSPHOPYRIDINE NUCLEOTIDE)	X FACTOR (HEMIN)	HEMOLYSIS	HABITAT
H. influenzae	+	+	−	man
H. aegyptius	+	+	−	man
H. suis	+	+	−	swine
H. haemolyticus	+	+	+	man
H. gallinarium	+	+	−	fowl
H. parainfluenzae	+	−	−	man
H. parahaemolyticus	+	−	+	man
H. aphrophilus	−	+	−	man
H. influenzae-murium	−	+	−	mice
H. ovis	−	+	−	sheep
H. putcrium	?	?	−	ferret
H. ducreyi	−	+	+	man (genital)
H. haemoblobinophilus	−	+	−	dogs (genital)
H. citreus	?	?	±	cattle (genital)
H. piscium	−	−	+	trout

(requires diphosphothiamine)

470

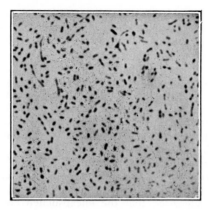

Fig. 1. *Haemophilus influenzae*. Smear from a culture of organism from meningitis; growth on chocolate agar, 24 hours.

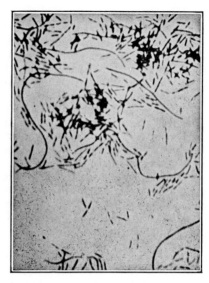

Fig. 2. *Haemophilus influenzae*. Forms from R type of colony.

fluenzae (Pfeiffer's bacillus) is not the primary cause in influenza, but this does not minimize its importance as an independent disease-producing agent.

Man is the only known natural host for *H. influenzae*. Dissociated avirulent strains can be isolated from the pharynges of almost all normal individuals and virulent encapsulated strains are found in chronic infections of the nasal sinuses and in the pharynges following viral colds. The organisms presumably are spread throughout the population in the same manner as the pneumococci are distributed. Fothergill and Wright (23) have shown that most adults have bactericidal antibodies for *H. influenzae* in their blood.

Morphology and Staining. *Haemophilus influenzae* is a very small rod, 0.5 μ in length and 0.2 to 0.3 μ in width. These small regular forms occur in abundance in smooth colonies (Fig. 1) and in most exudates. In rough colonies and exudates from healing lesions, the organisms are very pleomorphic; coccoid forms, rods, and even long filaments are found in profusion (Fig. 2). In broth cultures and in the spinal fluid, dissociation occurs so constantly that the finding of pleomorphic forms is the rule rather than the exception.

Capsules are produced in exudates and in cultures during the first six hours of growth on suitable media. The organism is **nonmotile** and **nonsporogenous.** With most aniline dyes it stains faintly, but good staining requires a five-minute exposure to Löffler's methylene blue or a five- to ten-minute treatment with 10 per cent aqueous fuchsin. *H. influenzae* is **gram-nega-**

tive, and a suggestion of polar staining is observed occasionally in the coccobacillary forms.

Cultural Characteristics. *H. influenzae* is a delicate organism with poorly developed enzyme systems (25). It is **aerobic** and grows best when incubated at 37° C. at pH 7.8. It grows poorly on blood agar but reasonably well if 5 to 10 per cent defibrinated rabbits' blood is added to hot media (80° to 90° C.) to make **chocolate agar.** Wolin (63) has described a synthetic medium which gave good but not maximal growth for *H. influenzae* type b strains. Arginine and one nucleotide were essential for growth. Incorporating polyvinyl alcohol neutralizes the toxic effect of some other ingredients.

The colonies on chocolate agar after 18 to

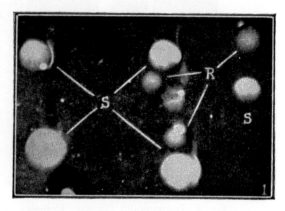

Fig. 3. Colonies of *H. influenzae,* S and R types. (From Pittman. *J. Exper. Med.,* 53:471, 1931.)

24 hours are 0.5 to 0.8 mm. colorless, transparent droplets not unlike small spots of moisture. The colonies are larger and more characteristic (Fig. 3) on the richer media of Levinthal (39) and Fildes (22). They are also larger when growing near colonies of staphylococci or other organisms which synthesize an extra supply of the **V** factor which diffuses into the medium. This phenomenon of **satellite** growth has been studied by a number of workers and can be used to differentiate species requiring **X** and **V** from those requiring only **V**, since microorganisms producing catalase stimulate the growth of species requiring both factors while catalase-negative organisms stimulate growth in those requiring **V** but not **X** (38, 50). In semisolid agar (Fig. 4) the large fluffy colonies of virulent organisms (C) are contrasted with small granular avirulent colonies (B).

All strains of *H. influenzae* reduce **nitrates** to **nitrites**. The encapsulated organisms produce **indol,** but many of the nonencapsulated strains lose this property. **Lactose** is **not oxidized.** Some of the avirulent or dissociated strains oxidize other carbohydrates in an irregular manner. *H. influenzae* is **bile-soluble** (42).

Resistance. *H. influenzae* is killed by an exposure to a temperature of 50° to 55° C. for 30 minutes. Desiccation quickly causes death, and all strains are very susceptible to the common antiseptics.

Cultures are maintained with difficulty, but organisms can be kept alive and virulent by frequent transfers on chocolate agar or by storage in the ice chest if suspended in tubes of whole, defibrinated rabbits' blood. They are preserved best by lypholization.

Hirsch and Finland (27) studied the effect of 21 antibiotics on *H. influenzae* in the test tube. **Sulfadiazine** is a reasonably effective inhibiting agent in vitro. Penicillin was effective in vitro but not in vivo. Sulfadiazine should be supplemented by **streptomycin** or **chloramphenicol.**

Variability. The studies of Pittman (50) and others (14) have shown a specific relationship between colony type and virulence. Pittman suggested that the encapsulated colonies be designated as **S** and the nonencapsulated ones **R.** The **S** colonies on Levinthal's agar are relatively large, sometimes attaining diameters of 3 mm. The colonies are oval with an entire edge, slightly mucoid in appearance, and somewhat opaque. When viewed by oblique light, they are definitely iridescent (Fig. 3). The **R** form is somewhat smaller; the surface is smooth but may be slightly domed in the center, and the edge is entire. These colonies have lost the characteristic iridescence of the **S** phase. Pittman (50) has reverted the smooth, nonvirulent, nonencapsulated form into the virulent **S** phase by cultivation in media containing anti-**R** serum and by animal passage. Alexander and Leidy (4) have transformed one encapsulated type into other types by a procedure analogous to that described for the pneumococcus.

Leidy, Hahn, and Alexander (38) have pre-

Fig. 4. Haemophilus colonies. Colonies in 0.15 per cent agar medium. A, *H. aegyptius* No. 145a, 36 hours old. B, *H. influenzae,* nontype-specific, No. 697, 24 hours old. C, *H. influenzae,* type 6, No. 38, 24 hours old. (From Pittman and Davis. *J. Bact.,* 59:413, 1950.)

pared DNAs containing the streptomycin-resistance factor from two different strains of *H. influenzae*, three strains of *H. aegyptius,* and one of *H. parainfluenzae*. Streptomycin resistance was transferred readily from *H. influenzae* to *H. aegyptius* and vice versa but less readily to *H. parainfluenzae*.

Antigenic Structure. *H. influenzae* shares many common antigens with *H. aegyptius,* but each have some specific antigens when tested by the agar gel method (46). Strains of *H. influenzae* have been classified into types a, b, c, d, e, and f by carbohydrate precipitation and by Quellung reactions (1, 2, 3, 50). Although most encapsulated strains are pathogenic, Page and his associates (47) have found some strains on which capsules could not be demonstrated by staining or by the fluorescent method. These findings suggest these same strains develop capsules in the body but not in the test tube or that there are more than six antigenic types.

Most meningeal infections with *H. influenzae* have been reported to have been caused by type b although an occasional case has resulted from infections by types a and f (3, 41).

Agglutination reactions are specific for type a through f, but the nonencapsulated strains are completely heterologous. The complement-fixation technic shows that there is a common antigen in the various strains, however, even in the absence of cross agglutination (60).

Bacterial Metabolites. *H. influenzae* produces a specific capsular polysaccharide which is not toxic but which accumulates in the blood and spinal fluid of the infected patient and thus neutralizes the newly formed specific antibodies produced by the patient in response to the infection. The amount of catalase produced is regulated by the amount of hemin in the medium (7). Hemagglutinins are produced in small quantities (28).

ENDOTOXINS. Dubos (17) isolated a toxin from an **R** derivative of type b which killed rabbits in a dose of 0.1 mg. After immunization with the toxin rabbits survived 50 **MLD.**

Experimental Disease in Laboratory Animals. Most strains isolated from cases of meningitis are pathogenic for mice. Fothergill and others (24) have established a standard method for producing a fatal infection in these animals by introducing the organisms intraperitoneally along with mucin. Blake and Cecil (8) produced pneumonia in monkeys by inoculating the mucous membranes of the upper respiratory tract with strains of *H. influenzae* known to be virulent for mice. Dochez and others

(15) have studied *H. influenzae* infections in chimpanzees. They observed that during infections with the virus of the common cold, non-type-specific and relatively innocuous strains of *H. influenzae*, carried habitually in the respiratory tracts of these animals, may be replaced by type-specific, mucoid, potentially pathogenic strains.

Bacilli resembling *H. influenzae* have been isolated from cats by Rivers and Bayne-Jones (55). Other laboratory animals are resistant to *H. influenzae* infections, although they may be killed by relatively large doses of the endotoxins.

Clinical Infections in Man. Meningitis due to *H. influenzae* occurs most frequently in children. The disease rarely begins before the age of two months and is seen only occasionally in adolescence and adults. The majority (85 per cent) of cases in influenzal meningitis occurs between the ages of two months and three years (24). Meningitis in adults forms 1 to 3 per cent of the total cases (16, 29, 43). All usually occur in patients with chronic infections of the sinuses, middle ear, or mastoid cells or in patients with agammaglobulinemia and other debilitating conditions.

Primary influenza bacillus pneumonia is usually insidious in onset and interstitial in character and gives rise to severe cyanosis and prostration (20, 32, 45).

Secondary influenza bacillus pneumonia, following infection by the influenza virus, is a severe disease with a relatively high mortality in untreated cases. The association of *H. influenzae* with viral infections already has been discussed in the section on pneumonia in the chapters dealing with staphylococci and streptococci.

Influenza bacillus infections of the respiratory passages in children from two months to three years of age cause marked edema and result in the development of an **obstructive syndrome** which frequently causes death in less than 24 hours. The organisms often can be typed directly by means of the Quellung reaction from the mucus removed from the pharynx. Streptococci and staphylococci also cause this obstructive syndrome in infants.

Subacute bacterial endocarditis may be produced by *H. influenzae* or *H. parainfluenzae* and occasionally by *H. parahaemolyticus* (52).

Transmission.   Since nonencapsulated, nonvirulent strains of *H. influenzae* can be isolated from the nasopharynges of many normal individuals, the possibility cannot be excluded that such strains can acquire capsules and attain virulence following virus infections such as the common cold or true influenza. Normal individuals occasionally harbor virulent organisms, and it can be assumed that these virulent strains are passing constantly from man to man. Since there is only one type b which is a consistent cause of disease, the immunity resulting from clinical or subclinical infections should be a more effective protection than would be expected after an infection with a single type of pneumococcus. These two factors may explain the relative infrequency of influenza bacillus infections in adults, except during epidemics of true viral influenza in which the resistance of the patients to many bacterial infections is lowered.

The immunity of the general population to *H. influenzae* infections has been investigated by Fothergill and Wright (23). They found that whole defibrinated blood of most adults possessed marked bactericidal power for virulent strains of *H. influenzae*. The blood of newborn infants also possessed considerable bactericidal activity, which disappeared six weeks after birth. That this represented passive transference of antibodies from the mother was proved by testing the cord blood for its bactericidal power. After three years of age, an increasing number of children showed bactericidal substances in their blood, suggesting the gradual acquisition of active immunity from subclinical infections.

Biologic Products.   Commercial antibacterial serums for type-specific strains were eliminated from the market with the introduction of sulfonamides and antibiotics. Their return would be most helpful in certain specific patients.

Treatment.   Mild cases of *H. influenzae* meningitis may be cured with adequate doses of sulfadiazine, but the treatment must be continued for two weeks to allow adequate time for antibody production. Tetracycline, chlortetracycline, and streptomycin are effective but not as uniformly successful as **chloramphenicol** (42). The combination of sulfadiazine and chloramphenicol is the treatment of choice.

Young children with respiratory infections and the obstructive syndrome frequently require immediate tracheotomy and prompt treatment with sulfadiazine and chloramphenicol.

HAEMOPHILUS AEGYPTIUS AND CONTAGIOUS CONJUNCTIVITIS

This small gram-negative bacillus was found in smears from infected eyes in Egypt by Koch (35) in 1883, and in 1887 the organism was isolated in pure culture by Weeks of New York (61, 62). This bacillus requires the X and V factors for growth (22) and for maintenance of culture it must be transferred even more frequently than *H. influenzae*. Before 1950 there was no sound cultural, metabolic or antigenic evidence for separating these strains from other nonencapsulated *H. influenzae*. There was, however, epidemiologic data, presented in a previous edition of this book, which suggested that these strains from contagious conjunctivitis were in some subtle way different from ordinary *H. influenzae*.

The painstaking studies of Pittman and Davis (51) have shown conclusively that the conjunctivitis strains are indeed a different species, which is now named *Haemophilus aegyptius* (Fig. 5). In semisolid agar the colonies are somewhat intermediate in size and consistency (Fig. 4A) between nonencapsulated (Fig. 4B) and the encapsulated (Fig. 4C) strains of *H. influenzae*. *H. aegyptius* is soluble in sodium desoxycholate, reduces nitrates to nitrites, but does not produce indol. Some acid is formed from glucose and galactose, levulose is variable, and xylose is not fermented. Human red cells are agglutinated. The cross-agglutination pattern suggests that the *H. aegyptius* strains are all related directly or indirectly through three or possibly four components. This organism has very little virulence for mice even when given in mucin and fails to kill 12-day-old chick embryos but is highly virulent for eight-day-old embryos. It will produce conjunctivitis in human volunteers (9, 10) but not in laboratory animals.

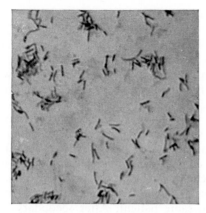

Fig. 5. *Haemophilus aegyptius.* Film, prepared with Giemsa's stain, of 5-hour-old agar culture of *Haemophilus aegyptius* strain No. 180a. × 1,000. (From Pittman and Davis. *J. Bact.,* 59:413, 1950.)

Sulfonamides have been found effective in the treatment of contagious conjunctivitis caused by this organism (44). Presumably streptomycin, chlortetracycline, chloramphenicol, and oxytetracycline would be as good as or better than sulfonamides in therapy.

HAEMOPHILUS SUIS AND INFLUENZA IN SWINE

Swine influenza was recognized as a clinical entity in 1918. Shope in 1931 demonstrated that the disease was produced by a combined attack of a virus and a bacillus (58). The virus was shown to be an influenzal virus, antigenically related to but not identical with the viruses causing human influenza. In interepidemic periods the virus survives in lung worms which appear to live in a symbiotic relationship in the lungs of swine. Under adverse climatic conditions both the virus and *H. suis* begin to multiply and an epidemic develops. This small **gram-negative** bacillus is quite similar to *H. influenzae* in that it requires the X and V factors for isolation but *H. suis* differs in that it is incapable of oxidizing carbohydrates and producing indol.

The infection in hogs resembles clinical influenza in man with a very high morbidity and relatively low mortality. To produce the infection both the virus and bacterium had to be inoculated intranasally. Pure cultures of the bacillus alone failed to cause infection when introduced into the nasal passages of swine, and no immunity to the combination of virus and organism could be demonstrated by challenge doses. The virus alone produced an exceedingly mild, febrile, disease which gave immunity against both spontaneous and experimental infections (58).

HAEMOPHILUS DUCREYI

Family: *Brucellaceae* fam. nov. Genus: *Haemophilus* Winslow et al. Species: *Haemophilus ducreyi* (Neveu-Lemaire) Bergey and others.

Haemophilus ducreyi is the cause of the soft chancre or chancroid infection of the genitalia. Approximately 10 per cent of venereal infections are caused by this organism. Ducrey (18) in 1889 demonstrated the presence of small bacilli in the purulent discharges from the lesions and successfully transferred the infection to the forearm of the patient by direct inoculation. The organism was isolated in pure culture by Besançon, Griffon, and Le Sourd (6) in 1890. *H. ducreyi* is an obligate parasite of man and usually is transmitted by direct contact. Occasionally it is transmitted indirectly during surgical manipulations by means of dressings, towels, or instruments.

Morphology and Staining. The Ducrey bacillus is extremely small, measuring 1.1 to 1.5 μ in length and 0.5 to 0.6 μ in width. In smears from the lesions the organisms appear singly and in small clusters and occasionally line up in parallel rows suggesting a school of fish. Both extra- and intracellular forms are found. The organism is **nonsporogenous** and **nonmotile.** When stained with Löffler's methylene blue, darker staining polar bodies often are apparent. By Gram's method the organism is **gram-negative.**

Cultural Characteristics. *Haemophilus ducreyi* requires the X and not the V factor for growth; thus it can be cultivated only on a very rich medium. Material from the floor of the ulcers should be streaked on a meat infusion medium which contains 3 per cent agar and at least 20 to 33 per cent defibrinated rabbit's blood. Such cultures should be incubated at 35° to 37° C. under decreased oxygen tension (11, 56). After 24 hours' incubation, the organisms appear as small, low, convex, grayish-white, smooth, glistening colonies with entire edges. After two to three days' incubation, the colonies are 1.5 to 2 mm. in diameter and may show a crateriform depression. Pus, aspirated from an unopened bubo, usually yields a pure culture; but, unfortunately, growth is obtained less frequently from buboes than from the primary ulcerating lesions (26).

The organism grows well in **broth** if 20 per cent defibrinated rabbit's blood is added. The best medium for preserving cultures is made from 0.25 per cent meat infusion agar, 1 per cent starch, and 20 per cent defibrinated rabbits' blood. After a preliminary incubation of five days, the cultures remain alive at either incubator or room temperature for 30 days, but such cultures may lose virulence after repeated transfers. Dienst (13) has found that lyophilized cultures remain virulent after storage at room temperature for 18 months.

Resistance. *H. ducreyi* is a delicate organism, being killed by a temperature of 55° C. in one hour. It is destroyed readily by drying and by the usual antiseptics.

Penicillin is ineffective, **sulfonamides** inhibit the growth, while **streptomycin, chlortetracycline,** and probably the other newer antibiotics kill the organism.

Antigenic Structure. Complement-fixation and precipitin tests suggest that all strains of *H. ducreyi* are identical (59). The organism contains an antigen which rapidly and effectively sensitizes the tissues of many patients. Vaccines made from cultures give positive skin tests when injected intradermally. These skin reactions appear after 24 to 48 hours and persist for four to five days. The hypersensitivity is apparently permanent in some but not in all patients. Reymann and others (53) found that 30 per cent of 473 Negro patients had positive skin tests, although none of them had had a recent chancroid infection. The fact that neither a positive nor a negative skin test is conclusive limits the use of the skin reaction in diagnosis.

Experimental Disease in Laboratory Animals. Most laboratory animals are resistant to infection with *H. ducreyi*. Monkeys have been infected, and Feiner and Mortara (21) in 1945 succeeded in inoculating New Zealand white rabbits with cultures by the intradermal and multipressure technics. The local necrotic lesions produced by this method resembled the chancroid lesions in man (30). A primary inoculation did not protect the rabbits from reinfection by the same method, but an allergic skin sensitivity which developed to the vaccine persisted for at least three months (31).

Anderson and Snow (5) cultivated *H. ducreyi* on the chorio-allantoic membrane of the chick embryo.

Clinical Disease in Man. After a 4- to 10-day incubation period following exposure, a small pustule appears on or about the genital organs. The pustule is surrounded by an area of redness and induration which rapidly becomes a necrotic ulcer with irregular, undermined edges. It differs clinically from the syphilitic chancre by the presence of a striking redness and edema about the lesion and the absence of induration. These characteristics are recognized by the name **soft chancre** which is sometimes applied to the lesion. Often several lesions are present in the same patient. After secondary infections have occurred, a clinical diagnosis is difficult. Cultures, biopsies, and even a direct inoculation of some of the pus into the forearm of the patient may be necessary to establish the diagnosis. The inoculation lesions have the same general characteristics as the original ones (26). Smears are positive in 43 to 65 per cent of the cases and cultures in 60 to 90 per cent (26).

The infection frequently results in lymphatic swelling in the groin, commonly spoken of as "buboes," which may develop later into abscesses.

The clinical disease has been reproduced by inoculation cultures into human volunteers. Chloramphenicol ointment applied locally was effective in prophylaxis and treatment (12).

Transmission. Chancroid occurs throughout the world and is particularly prevalent in the Negroes of the southern United States. It was a problem in both World War I and World War II. Satulsky (57) reported the occurrence of 1,555 cases in one theater of operation. The method of transmission already has been discussed.

Biologic Products. A commercial vaccine is available for intradermal skin tests and has been used for desensitization in some chronic chancroid infections.

Treatment. Treatment with oral sulfadiazine resulted in a reduction in the average period of hospitalization from 24.9 days observed in World War I to 11.2 days in World War II (57).

Both streptomycin (59) and chlortetracycline (64) are effective in cases which do not respond to sulfadiazine.

HAEMOPHILUS HAEMOGLOBINOPHILUS
(*H. canis*)

This small gram-negative bacillus was isolated from the inflamed prepuces of dogs by Friedberger in 1903 and has been isolated from the preputial secretions of normal dogs by Rivers (54), Kirchenbauer (34), and others. The organism apparently is parasitic but not pathogenic for the dog. The X factor must be supplied in the medium, but the bacillus can synthesize the V factor. It oxidizes glucose, sucrose, and mannitol, produces indol, and reduces nitrates.

Khairat (33) isolated a hemophilic bacillus resembling *H. haemoglobinophilus* from a case of human endocarditis.

HAEMOPHILUS PARAINFLUENZAE AND CLINICAL INFECTIONS

This small **gram-negative** bacillus requires the V but not the X factor and has been used for the microbiologic assay of the codehydrogenases (36) in blood and tissues. Herbst and Snell (25) have shown that *H. parainfluenzae* requires putrescine, a number of amino acids, purine bases, and nearly all the vitamins for growth. Growth is inhibited by adenine and guanine, but this effect can be neutralized by hypoxanthine or other purines. *H. parainfluenzae* is nonhemolytic. Strains previously described as hemolytic probably were *H. parahaemolyticus* (52). Both of these species can produce subacute bacterial endocarditis.

REFERENCES

1. Alexander, H. E. Proc. Soc. Exper. Biol. & Med., 40:313, 1939.
2. ———— and Heidelberger, M. J. Exper. Med., 71:1, 1940.
3. ———— and others. J. Immunol., 54:207, 1946.
4. ———— and Leidy, G. Proc. Soc. Exper. Biol. & Med., 73:485, 1950.
5. Anderson, K., and Snow, J. S. Am. J. Path., 16:269, 1940.
6. Besançon, F., and others. Presse méd., 2: 385, 1900.
7. Biberstein, E. L., and Gills, M. J. Bact., 81: 380, 1961.
8. Blake, F. G., and Cecil, R. L. J. Exper. Med., 32:691, 719, 1920.
9. Davis, D. J., and Pittman, M. Am. J. Ophth., Series 3, 32: Part II, 1949, p. 111.
10. ———— and others. J. Bact., 59:427, 1950.
11. Deacon, W. E. J. Invest. Dermat., 26:399, 1956.
12. ———— Antibiotic Med., 2:143, 1956.
13. Dienst, R. B. Am. J. Syph., Gonor. & Ven. Dis., 32:289, 1948.
14. Dingle, J. H., and Seidman, L. R. Proc. Soc. Exper. Biol. & Med., 46:34, 1932.
15. Dochez, A. R., and others. Proc. Soc. Exper. Biol. & Med., 30:314, 1932.
16. Dolphin, A., and Popham, R. D. Lancet, 2: 472, 1951.
17. Dubos, R. J. J. Bact., 43:77, 1942.
18. Ducrey, A. Monatschr. f. prakt. Dermat., 9:387, 1889.
19. Dukes, G. D., and Gardner, H. L. J. Bact., 81:277, 1961.
20. Edlund, G., and others. Acta Otolaryng., Stockholm, 52:316, 1960.
21. Feiner, R. R., and Mortara, F. Am. J. Syph., Gonor. & Ven. Dis., 29:71, 1945.
22. Fildes, P. Brit. J. Exper. Path., 1:129, 1920; 2:16, 1921; 3:210, 1922; 4:265, 1923; 5:69, 1924.
23. Fothergill, L. D., and Wright, J. J. Immunol., 24:273, 1933.
24. ———— New England J. Med., 216:587, 1937.
25. Herbst, E. J., and Snell, E. E. J. Bact., 58: 379, 1949.
26. Heyman, A., and others. J.A.M.A., 129:935, 1945.
27. Hirsch, H. A., and Finland, M. Am. J. Med. Sci., 239:33, 1960.
28. Ivler, D., and others. Proc. Soc. Exper. Biol. & Med., 114:232, 1963.
29. Jervey, L. P. Arch. Int. Med., 111:376, 1963.
30. Kaplan, W., and others. J. Invest. Dermat., 26:407, 1956.
31. ———— J. Invest. Dermat., 26:415, 1956.
32. Keith, T. A., and Schreiner, A. W. Ann. Int. Med., 56:27, 1962.
33. Khairat, O. J. Path. & Bact., 50:497, 1940.
34. Kirchenbauer, H. Ztschr. f. Infektionskr., 45: 273, 1934.
35. Koch, R. Wien. med. Wchnschr., 33:1548, 1883.
36. Kohn, H. I., and Bernheim, F. W. J. Clin. Invest., 18:585, 1939.
37. Kristensen, M. Haemoglobinophilic Bacteria, Copenhagen, 1922.
38. Leidy, G., and others. Proc. Soc. Exp. Biol. & Med., 102:86, 1959.
39. Levinthal, W. Ztschr. f. Hyg. u. Infektionskr., 86:1, 1918.
40. Lwoff, A., and Lwoff, M. Proc. Roy. Soc., London, s.B., 122:352, 360, 1937.
41. MacPherson, C. F. C. Canad. J. Research, Sect. E., 26:197, 1948.
42. McCrumb, F. R., Jr., and others. J.A.M.A., 145:469, 1951.
43. Merselis, J. G., Jr., and others. Arch. Int. Med., 110:837, 1962.
44. Miterstein, B., and Stern, H. J. Lancet, 1: 649, 1945.
45. Norman, P. S., and others. J.A.M.A., 179: 833, 1962.
46. Olitzki, A. L., and Sulitzeanu, A. J. Bact., 77:264, 1959.
47. Page, R. H., and others. Am. J. Dis. Child., 101:155, 1961.
48. Pfeiffer, R. Ztschr. f. Infektionskr., 13:357, 1893.
49. Pickett, M. J., and Stewart, R. M. Am. J. Clin. Path., 23:713, 1953.

50. Pittman, M.   J. Exper. Med., 53:471, 1931.
51. ———— and Davis, D. J.   J. Bact., 59:413, 1950.
52. ———— J. Bact., 65:750, 1953.
53. Reymann, F.   Acta path. et microbiol. Scandinav., 27:344, 1950.
54. Rivers, T. M.   Am. J. Dis. Child., 24:102, 1922.
55. ———— and Bayne-Jones, S.   J. Exper. Med., 37:131, 1923.
56. Sanderson, E. S., and Greenblatt, R. B.   South M. J., 30:147, 1937.
57. Satulsky, E. M.   J.A.M.A., 127:259, 1945.

58. Shope, R. E.   J. Exper. Med., 54:349, 373, 1931; 62:561, 1935; 64:47, 791, 1936.
59. Taggart, S. R., and others.   Am. J. Syph., Gonor. & Ven. Dis., 33:180, 1949.
60. Tunevall, G.   Acta path. et microbiol. Scandinav., 32:193, 258, 1952.
61. Weeks, J. E.   Arch. Ophth. (Old Series), 15:441, 1886.
62. ———— M. Rec., 31:571, 1887.
63. Wolin, H. L.   J. Bact., 85:253, 1963.
64. Zheutlin, H. E. C., and Robinson, R. C. V.   Am. J. Syph., Gonor. & Ven. Dis., 34:71, 1950.

26

Bordetella pertussis (Whooping Cough) and Related Organisms

BORDETELLA PERTUSSIS

Family: *Brucellaceae* fam. nov. Genus: *Bordetella* Moreno-López. Species: *Bordetella pertussis* (Holland) Moreno-López

The causative agents of whooping cough (pertussis, parapertussis, and bronchiseptica) differ from the true hemophilic bacteria in that they do not require the X and V factors for growth. Accordingly, these organisms have been removed from the genus *Haemophilus* and have been placed in a new genus, *Bordetella,* named for Bordet.

The importance of whooping cough as a cause of death in childhood is illustrated by the relative mortalities from whooping cough, measles, diphtheria, poliomyelitis, and scarlet fever shown in Figure 1.

In 1900 Bordet and Gengou observed small, ovoid bacilli in stained smears of sputum from a child suffering from pertussis. Jochmann and Krause named the organism *Bacillus pertussis* and in 1906 Bordet and Gengou (5) succeeded in culturing it. The exhaustive studies of Madsen (30), Kristensen (28), and others of the State Serum Institute in Copenhagen and the later investigations in this country leave no doubt that *Bordetella pertussis* is the primary etiologic agent of whooping cough.

Madsen's studies indicated that the infection is spread by children in the early catarrhal stage of the disease, by patients with atypical or undiagnosed infections, and by early convalescents. The cough-plate method, introduced by Chievitz and Meyer (10) in 1916, has shown not only that 75 to 90 per cent of children expel *Bord. pertussis* into the air during the catarrhal stage of the infection, but also that many of the patients continue to spread the organisms until the end of the fourth week of the disease (29, 58). Few, if any, normal individuals carry *Bord. pertussis* in their nasopharynges.

Morphology and Staining. *Bord. pertussis* is a small, ovoid rod 0.3 to 0.5 μ in width and 1.0 to 1.5 μ in length. In stained sections smaller forms, 0.2 to 0.3 μ, are found in masses between the cilia of the bronchial epithelium. In smears from nasopharyngeal secretions or sputum the organisms usually occur singly but occasionally in clumps or clusters. They are very similar morphologically to the coccobacillary form of *H. influenzae* (Fig. 2).

The organisms are **nonmotile** and **nonsporogenous** but may have a **capsule** in exudates and, when first isolated, on suitable media.

The bacilli can be stained by a five to 10-minute exposure to alkaline methylene blue, dilute carbolfuchsin, or carbonated toluidine blue. *Bord. pertussis* is **gram-negative.**

Cultural Characteristics. The medium of choice for the isolation of *Bord. pertussis* is the original glycerine-potato-blood agar of Bordet and Gengou. Material may be collected from the nasopharynx by swabbing with a specially prepared curved wire swab, or the patient may cough directly on a Bordet-Gengou plate (5, 52).

The use of penicillin to inhibit the growth of contaminating organisms facilitates the isolation of *Bord. pertussis*. Bradford and others (6) deposited a drop of penicillin containing about 1,000 units on the plate and passed the contaminated nasopharyngeal swab several times through the penicillin before streaking the plate. A more adequate distribution of the

479

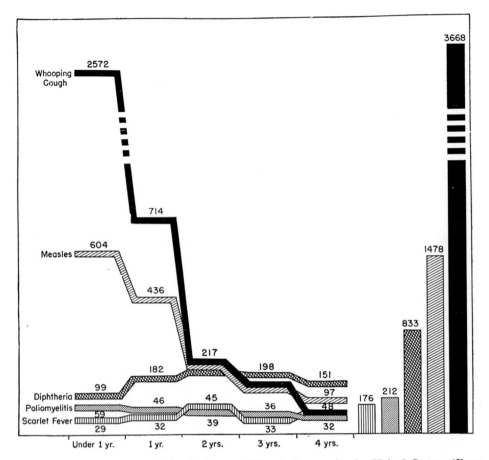

Fig. 1. Relative number of deaths from childhood diseases in the United States. (From Squibb Memoranda, 1945.)

material is effected by additional streaking with a flexible platinum loop. On these plates colonies barely visible to the naked eye appear after 24 hours, and they slowly increase to their maximum size after 48 to 72 hours' incubation. The colonies are smooth, glistening and somewhat dome-shaped, and the edges are entire. They are more opaque than the colonies of *H. influenzae* and have a grayish color suggesting a bisected pearl. A characteristic "fuzzy" zone of **hemolysis** develops about the colony.

In **broth** containing the X and V factors, growth is uniformly turbid; a viscid sediment may develop in cultures of organisms which have dissociated.

After isolation a series of subcultures on media containing decreasing amounts of blood results in the ability to grow on blood-free media, thus demonstrating that the organism can eventually become independent of the X and V growth factors. Such strains, however,

completely lose their virulence during the process.

Bord. pertussis is **aerobic.** It grows at 37° C. but will multiply slowly at lower temperatures. It produces **some acid from glucose and lactose but does not oxidize other carbohydrates, reduce nitrates, or produce indol.** Litmus milk and media-containing blood are rendered alkaline.

Resistance. *Bord. pertussis* is killed readily by drying, by the usual antiseptics, and by heating for 30 minutes at 55° C. The organism is resistant to the action of **sulfonamides** and **penicillin** but is susceptible to **tetracycline, chlortetracycline,** and **chloramphenicol** (21).

Variability. The history of the attempts to produce an effective vaccine against pertussis not only affords an excellent example of the importance of dissociation phenomena, but also emphasizes the necessity of maintaining a constant check on the antigenic structure of organisms employed for the production of vaccines. For many years in Denmark excellent protection was obtained by immunization with pertussis vaccines, while similar attempts in this country resulted uniformly in failure. Subsequent investigations have shown that the discrepancy in results lay in the fact that the Danish laboratories maintained their cultures in the virulent phase by subculturing the organisms on glycerine-blood-potato media. The Americans, on the other hand, prepared their vaccines from cultures grown on plain agar, a medium in which only avirulent dissociated organisms could thrive. In 1931 Leslie and Gardner (29) showed that there was a four phase dissociation, described as types I, II, III, and IV. In general, the colonies in phases III and IV were larger and rougher and had dense, elevated centers. Long threads resembling mycelia were seen at times in smears from the rough colonies. More important changes accompanying the S → R transformation were associated with changes in antigenic structure. Animals immunized with phase IV vaccines showed no resistance to challenge doses of *Bord. pertussis* in phase I. Gray (20) has found that significant differences in virulence can occur in organisms remaining in phase I.

Antigenic Structure. Freshly isolated cultures of *Bord. pertussis* are encapsulated and antigenically homologous, all strains being agglutinable by an antiserum prepared against any virulent strain. As the organism dissociates through phases I to IV, there is a gradual loss of virulence, accompanied by marked changes in the antigenic structure.

Eldering, Eveland, and Kendrick (14) have identified by agglutination and agglutinin adsorption 14 major antigens in *Bord. pertussis, Bord. parapertussis* and *Bord. bronchiseptica.* Antigen 1 is found in all pertussis strains, but 2, 3, 4, 5, and 7 vary from strain to strain. *Bord. parapertussis* contains antigens 7, 8, 9, 10, and 14; and *Bord. bronchiseptica,* 7, 8, 9, 10, 11, and 12. An antiserum against antigen 1 agglutinates in low titer all strains of *Bord. pertussis* and also shows fluorescent antibody staining. This result suggests the possibility that antigen 1 might be the factor associated with virulence.

Virulent strains of *Bordetella pertussis* have a surface antigen which is a **hemagglutinin** for the red cells of man, mouse, and other species (26, 48). The hemagglutinin produces specific antibodies in animals (31) and occasionally in man (72), but the antibodies afford no protection against the disease (31, 46, 66, 72).

A nontoxic surface agglutinogen has been

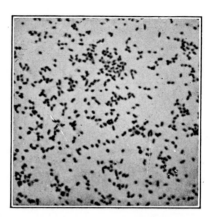

Fig. 2. *Bordetella pertussis.* Organisms from a 48-hour culture on Bordet-Gengou medium.

isolated by Smolens and Mudd (60) and by Onoue and his coworkers (42). The agglutinogen isolated by the latter was a protein antigen of low molecular weight (10,000) which adsorbed specific agglutinins and gave delayed tuberculin-like allergic reactions when injected into the skin of immune rabbits. Rabbits (60) and children (58) showed agglutination, complement fixation, and positive skin test after immunization. But all the studies have shown that this agglutination is not identical with the immunizing agent (55, 59).

Munoz, Rabi, and Larson (34) located the protecting antigen and the histamine sensitizing factor in the cell wall in 1959. In 1963 Barta (4) obtained large quantities of a mouse-protecting antigen from whole bacilli by extracting it with sodium deoxycholase. This soluble fraction was nontoxic, although the soluble fraction extract from the same type of cells, prepared by the ultrasonic method, was highly toxic.

Although agglutinins and complement-fixing antibodies (44) are formed by the patient with pertussis, they do not appear early in the disease or in sufficiently high concentrations to be of practical value in the diagnosis of whooping cough. In contrast, antibodies which protect mice appear as early as the second week of the disease (72).

Parfentjev (43) found that the injection of pertussis vaccine into mice produced an extraordinary sensitivity to histamine and was followed by susceptibility to both active and passive anaphylaxis (1, 27). This phenomenon has not been observed in the rabbit and guinea pig and may not occur in man (64).

Bacterial Metabolites. In the intermediate, rather avirulent phases of *Bord. pertussis* quantities of mucinous materials are produced which accumulate on the cilia of the trachea. It is thought that the "matting together" of these cilia is an important factor contributing to the violent coughing and the characteristic inspiratory "whoop" in pertussis.

Sutherland and Wilkinson (65) found that *Bord. pertussis, Bord. parapertussis,* and *Bord. bronchiseptica* all produce a unique copper-containing protein. This occurs in *Bord. bronchiseptica* to the level of 0.1 per cent of the bacterial dry weight.

TOXINS. Both heat-stabile (19) and heat-labile (34) toxins have been identified. Munoz and his associates located the heat-labile toxin in the protoplasm.

The action of the toxin on the lungs of rabbits has been investigated by Sprunt and Martin (62). The lethal effect of pertussis toxin in mice could be prevented by antitoxin but not by antibacterial serum (56, 70). Conversely, when mice were infected intranasally with *Bord. pertussis,* antibacterial serum was effective therapeutically, but the antitoxin did not prevent infection (2, 16). A highly potent toxin was isolated by Onoue and his associates (42) in 1963.

Experimental Disease in Laboratory Animals. Rich and others (54) produced a paroxysmal cough and lymphocytosis in chimpanzees with pure cultures of *Bord. pertussis.* Sprunt, Martin, and McDearman (61) observed the development of lymphocytosis and interstitial mononuclear pneumonia following the intratracheal injections of virulent phase I organisms. The inoculation of chick embryos results in a proliferation of the organisms in and on the mucosa of the ciliated epithelium of the trachea, bronchi, and esophagus. Very large doses of *Bord. pertussis* are required to produce death in rabbits and guinea pigs, but mice can be infected by intranasal instillations after anesthetization. Probably the most accurate virulence test is that employing the intracerebral inoculation technic introduced by Kendrick (23) and others (48, 49). Virulent phase I organisms multiply inside HeLa and monkey kidney cells and maintain their virulence (8).

Clinical Infections in Man. *Bord. pertussis* grows in and on the mucous membranes of the respiratory tract. After an incubation period of 7 to 14 days, the **catarrhal** stage begins with coryza, sneezing, and a mild cough. Phase I organisms are present in abundance at this time, and the

formation of immune bodies may have some effect in forcing the organisms into the less virulent phases II and III, phases which laboratory work has suggested to be more important in toxin production.

The catarrhal syndrome lasts about 10 to 14 days and is followed by the **spasmodic** stage, which is characterized by a violent, repetitive type of cough which forces the air out of the lungs and is followed by a sudden, forceful, inspiratory "crow" or "whoop." The spasmodic stage lasts about two weeks. Localized areas of necrosis occur in the bronchial epithelium, and patches of edema and interstitial pneumonia may appear in the lungs. The thick, ropy, mucinous bronchial secretions are expelled with great difficulty, which probably accounts for the severity of the cough. Toomey and Takacs (67) have isolated avirulent organisms from this stage of the disease which, in culture, produce large quantities of mucinous material. By this time the patient also has developed a state of **hypersensitivity** to the proteins of *Bord. pertussis.*

The **convalescent** stage usually lasts for about two weeks, but it may be much longer. At any time after the onset of the catarrhal stage, the patient may develop a severe type of pneumonia from either *Bord. pertussis* or other organisms present in the respiratory tract. Chronic infections of the lungs, such as chronic bronchitis, bronchiectasis, organizing pneumania, and bronchial asthma, may follow an attack of pertussis but these complications are the result of secondary infections.

Transmission. As mentioned previously, there probably are no carriers of *Bord. pertussis.* Certainly most patients have a history of intimate contact with an individual in the catarrhal stage of the disease. The communicability rate (85 per cent) is almost as high as that for measles and varicella.

Pertussis is sporadic in all the densely populated areas of the world, and epidemics occur every two to five years or whenever a sufficient number of susceptible individuals accumulate. Cases occur throughout the year, but the northern states have the highest incidence in January and February, and the peak is reached in the southern states in May.

The mortality rate is higher in Negroes than in members of the Caucasian race and is higher in girls than in boys (Vaughan). The most important single factor in mortality is age; the younger the child, the more severe the disease (Fig. 1). One attack of pertussis usually protects the individual for life. Immune bodies appear in the blood during convalescence but disappear slowly after some months. In some individuals, the allergic wheal type of skin test persists for months or years. A positive skin test following an intradermal injection of the agglutinogen results in the reappearance of agglutinins in the blood (60). Measurable amounts of opsonin are present in the blood of more than 50 per cent of pregnant women (24), and transplacental transmission of immune bodies probably is an important factor in protecting the infant during the first two months of life.

Treatment. Chloramphenicol is the antibiotic of choice, but both **chlortetracycline** and **tetracycline** have been used with success. The mechanical and allergic factors in whooping cough suggest the cautious use of antihistamines (47) or adrenocortical hormones in critically ill patients.

Prevention. Active immunization of all children with a mixture of diphtheria toxoid, tetanus toxoid, and pertussis vaccine should be effected about the third month of life. Children of this age or younger do not produce antibodies as readily as children nine months old, but the need for early protection is imperative and booster doses can be given at nine to 12 months. The hyperimmunization of pregnant women to increase the amount of antibodies passively transferred to the infant was suggested by Kendrick and others (24) but is opposed by Peterson and Christie (45) because young children with high titers of passively transferred antibodies are difficult if not impossible to immunize actively. Improvements in the immunizing effect of pertussis vaccines (49) should make possible a reduction in the number of organisms in the vaccine and a decrease in the local reactions (49, 71).

Pertussis vaccine is not entirely harmless; 38 severe convulsive reactions with two deaths have occurred in 10,000 immunizations (68). The vaccine should not be given to children who are ill, who react with fever to the first dose, or who have a familial history of convulsions. See Pittman's review of pertussis and pertussis vaccine control (50).

The triple vaccine without the addition of the polio virus remains stable for at least 18 months, but when polio was added, the loss in potency of the pertussis factor was 6 per cent per month, necessitating the addition of larger amounts of the pertussis vaccine and use at an earlier date (51).

BORDETELLA PARAPERTUSSIS

This organism was isolated from clinical cases of whooping cough by Eldering and Kendrick (12). It is a **gram-negative, nonmotile** bacillus resembling *Bord. pertussis* but developing a larger colony and producing a brown pigment on media containing blood. It does not require the X and V factors for growth but produces catalase. It has somatic antigens which give cross-reactions with *Bord. pertussis* and *Bord. bronchiseptica*, and antitoxins prepared from *Bord. pertussis* neutralize equally well the toxins of *Bord. pertussis, Bord. parapertussis,* and *Bord. bronchiseptica* (15, 63). Experimental pulmonary lesions have been produced in mice by Bradford and others (6).

BORDETELLA BRONCHISEPTICA

Bordetella bronchiseptica (synonyms: *Bacillus bronchisepticus* and *Brucella bronchiseptica*) was isolated in 1911 by Ferry (17) in the United States, and by M'Gowan (32) in Edinburgh from dogs suffering from distemper. The organism is a secondary invader in distemper but is a common cause of sporadic and epidemic infections in rabbits and guinea pigs. Mice are not susceptible. It is a strict **aerobe** and does not require the X and V factors for growth. It is isolated easily on blood agar plates and will grow on meat infusion agar without the addition of blood. The organism will not grow on simple synthetic media but requires niacin (69).

The colonies are small, round, and convex with a smooth glistening surface. The organism is **gram-negative** and **nonsporogenous** but, in contrast to the other members of the *Bordetella* group, **is motile**. Some strains are hemolytic. Catalase is produced, nitrates often are reduced, but **none of the carbohydrates are oxidized** by this organism. Urea is split with great rapidity (69).

Rauch and Pickett (53) isolated 38 phage types from 48 strains of *Bord. bronchiseptica.* Cross-reactions were found with strains of *Bord. parapertussis* but not with *Bord. pertussis.*

Antigens common to *Bord. pertussis, Bord. parapertussis,* and *Brucella abortus* have been found (12, 18, 43). An antitoxin prepared against the formalized exotoxin of *Bord. pertussis* neutralizes the toxin of *Bord. pertussis, Bord. parapertussis,* and *Bord. bronchiseptica* (16). More recent cross-immunity studies by Kendrick (25) suggest that *Bord. bronchiseptica* is more closely related to *Bord. pertussis* and to *Bord. parapertussis* than the latter are to each other (13, 25). This organism occasionally produces a whooping cough syndrome in children (7).

MORAXELLA LACUNATA

Family: *Brucellaceae* fam. nov. Genus: *Moraxella* Lwoff. Species: *Moraxella lacunata* (Eyre) Lwoff

In 1896 Morax (33) described a diplobacillus, which he associated etiologically with a type of chronic conjunctivitis to which he applied the name *conjonctivité subaiguë.* Soon after this, a similar microorganism was found in cases corresponding to those of Morax by Axenfeld (3). The condition which these microorganisms produce is a catarrhal conjunctivitis which usually attacks both eyes. The inflammation is especially noticeable in the angles of the eye, most severe at or about the caruncle. There is rarely much swelling

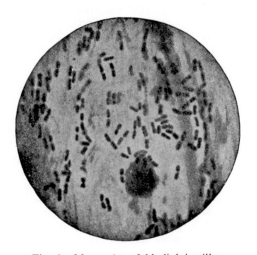

Fig. 3. Morax-Axenfeld diplobacillus.

of the conjunctiva and hardly ever ulceration. The condition runs a subacute or chronic course. Its diagnosis is easily made by smear preparations of the pus which is formed with especial abundance during the night.

Morphology and Staining. In smear preparations from the pus, the microorganisms appear as short, thick bacilli, usually in the form of two placed end to end, but not infrequently singly or in short chains. Their ends are distinctly rounded and their centers slightly bulging, giving the bacillus an ovoid form. They are usually about 2 μ in length (Fig. 3).

They are easily stained by the usual aniline dyes and are **gram-negative.**

Cultural Characteristics. The Morax-Axenfeld bacillus can be cultivated only upon alkaline media containing blood or blood serum. Some strains are hemolytic and some nonhemolytic (38).

Antigenic Structure. Oag (38) has investigated the antigenic structure of *M. lacunata.*

It grows poorly, or not at all, at room temperature.

Upon **Löffler's blood serum** colonies appear after 24 to 36 hours as small indentations which indicate a liquefaction of the medium. Axenfeld states that eventually the entire medium may become liquefied. Upon serum agar delicate grayish drop-like colonies are formed which are not unlike those of the gonococcus.

In recent years nonliquefying strains have been isolated more frequently than liquefying ones. The morphologic studies by Murray and Truant (36) and Henriksen (22) suggest that this organism is closely related to the organism called *Mimeae,* found by De Bord in chronic urethritis, and *Bacterium anitratum,* found in the intestinal tract, but is not closely related to the *Haemophilus* or *Bordetella* genera.

Lwoff in 1939 suggested the creation of the new genus *Moraxella,* to include Morax's bacillus as *Moraxella lacunata.* This was done in the seventh edition of Bergey's Manual. But in the meantime the work of Hendriksen (22), Murray and Truant (36), and Daly, Postic, and Kass (11) has shown that organisms called *Mimeae, Bacterium anitratum,* and *Moraxella lwoffi* are all closely related if not identical with the *Moraxella* and should logically be included in that genus.

Pathogenicity. Attempts to produce lesions in the lower animals with this bacillus have been universally unsuccessful. In humans, however, subacute conjunctivitis has been produced by inoculation. The nonliquefying type has been isolated from the sputum in cases of bronchial infections by Henriksen (22).

NOGUCHIA GRANULOSIS

Family: *Brucellaceae* fam. nov. Genus: *Noguchia* Olitsky and others. Species: *Noguchia granulosis* (Noguchi) Olitsky and others.

Noguchia granulosis was isolated by Noguchi in 1928 from clinical cases of trachoma in American Indians from the region around Albuquerque, New Mexico. It is a small **nonsporogenous, encapsulated, motile, flagellated, gram-negative, pleomorphic** bacillus. The organism is 0.25 to 0.3 μ in width and 0.8 to 1.2 μ in length and possesses a single polar flagellum (37).

N. granulosis is **aerobic** but **facultatively anaerobic.** Maximum growth occurs at a temperature of 15° to 30° C. at a pH of 7.8 in the semisolid medium employed for the cultivation of the *Leptospira*. Pure cultures of the organisms produce a granular conjunctivitis in monkeys and apes (39).

Closely related organisms, *Noguchia simiae* and *Noguchia cuniculi,* have been isolated from spontaneous conjunctival folliculosis of monkeys and rabbits (40).

These organisms can produce a follicular conjunctivitis in man and animals, but most investigators believe that this conjunctivitis is not trachoma, since the modern work indicates that trachoma is caused by a virus.

This organism was isolated again in 1955 from a case of chronic ulcerative blepharitis, and the patient recovered following treatment with chlortetracycline and a vaccine (9).

REFERENCES

1. Abernathy, R. S., and Spink, W. W. Fed. Proc., 15:580, 1956.
2. Anderson, G., and North, E. A. Australian J. Exper. Biol. & M. Sc., 21:1, 1943.
3. Axenfeld, T. Zentralbl. f. Bakt., I Abt., 21:1, 1897.
4. Barta, G. J. Immunol., 90:72, 1963.
5. Bordet, J., and Gengou, O. Ann. Inst. Pasteur, 20:731, 1906; 21:720, 1907.
6. Bradford, W. L., and others. Am. J. Pub. Health, 36:468, 1946.
7. Brown, J. H. Bull. Johns Hopkins Hosp., 38:147, 1926.
8. Crawford, J. G., and Fishel, C. W. J. Bact., 77:465, 1959.
9. Clapper, W. E., and Parker, J. T. J. Bact., 70:126, 1955.
10. Chievitz, I., and Meyer, A. H. Ann. Inst. Pasteur, 30:503, 1916.
11. Daly, A. K., and others. Arch. Int. Med., 110:580, 1962.
12. Eldering, G., and Kendrick, P. J. Bact., 35:561, 1938.
13. ——— and others. Bacteriol. Proc., p. 98, 1956.
14. ——— J. Bact., 83:745, 1962.
15. Evans, D. G. J. Path. & Bact., 51:49, 1940.
16. ——— J. Path. & Bact., 56:49, 1944.
17. Ferry, N. S. J. Infect. Dis., 8:399, 1911.
18. Flosdorf, E. W., and others. J. Bact., 41:457, 1941.
19. ——— and Kimble, A. C. J. Immunol., 39:475, 1940.
20. Gray, D. F. J. Immunol., 61:35, 1949.
21. Gray, J. D. Lancet, 1:150, 1950.
22. Henriksen, S. E. Acta path. et microbiol. Scandinav., 29:258, 1951.
23. Kendrick, P. L. Am. J. Hyg., 38:193, 1943.
24. ——— and others. Am. J. Dis. Child., 70:25, 1945.
25. ——— and others. J. Bact., 66:166, 1953.
26. Keogh, E. V., and North, E. A. Australian J. Exper. Biol. & M. Sc., 26:315, 1948.
27. Kind, L. S. J. Immunol., 70:411, 1953.
28. Kristensen, B. J.A.M.A., 101:204, 1933.
29. Leslie, P. H., and Gardner, A. D. J. Hyg., 31:423, 1931.
30. Madsen, T. Boston M. & S. J., 192:50, 1942.
31. Masry, F. L. G. J. Gen. Microbiol., 7:201, 1952.
32. M'Gowan, J. P. J. Path. & Bact., 15:372, 1911.
33. Morax, V. Ann. Inst. Pasteur, 10:337, 1896.
34. Munoz, J. Bact. Reviews, 27:325, 1963.
35. Murray, R. Am. J. Pub. Health, 40:686, 1950.
36. Murray, R. G. E., and Truant, J. P. J. Bact., 67:13, 1954.
37. Noguchi, H. J. Exper. Med., 48: Suppl. 2, p. 1-53, 1928.
38. Oag, R. K. J. Path. & Bact., 54:128, 1942.
39. Olitsky, P. K. Tr. Am. Acad. Ophth., 225, 1930.
40. ——— and others. J. Exper. Med., 30:375, 1934.
41. Onoue, K., and others. J. Bact., 82:648, 1961.
42. ——— and others. J. Bact., 86:648, 1963.
43. Parfentjev, I. A., and others. J. Bact., 53:597, 603, 613, 1947.
44. ——— and Viron, M. E. J. Immunol., 60:167, 1948.
45. Peterson, J. C., and Christie, A. Am. J. Dis. Child., 81:483, 501, 518, 1951.
46. Pillemer, L. Proc. Soc. Exper. Biol. & Med., 75:704, 1950.
47. Pittman, M. Proc. Soc. Exper. Biol. & Med., 77:70, 1951.
48. ——— J. Immunol., 69:201, 1952.
49. ——— J. Pediat., 45:57, 1954.
50. ——— J. Washington Acad. Sc., 46:234, 1956.
51. ——— J.A.M.A., 181:25, 1962.
52. Powell, H. M., and others. Pub. Health Rep., 66:346, 1951.
53. Rauch, H., and Pickett, M. J. Can. J. Microbiol., 7:126, 1961.
54. Rich, A. R., and others. Bull. Johns Hopkins Hosp., 58:286, 1936.
55. Robbins, K. C., and Pillemer, L. J. Immunol., 65:393, 1950.
56. Roberts, M. E., and Ospeck, A. G. J. Infect. Dis., 74:22, 1944.
57. Sant'Agnese, P. A. di. Am. J. Pub. Health, 40:674, 1950.

58. Sauer, L. W., and Tucker, W. H.   Am. J. Pub. Health, 40:681, 1950.

59. Schuchardt, L. F., and others.   J. Immunol., 91:107, 1963.

60. Smolens, J.   J. Immunol., 47:155, 1943.

61. Sprunt, D. H., and McDearman, S.   J. Exper. Med., 67:309, 1938.

62. ——— and Martin, D. S.   Am. J. Path., 19: 255, 1943.

63. Strean, L. P., and Grant, G. A.   Canad. M. A. J., 43:528, 1940.

64. Stronk, M. G., and Pittman, M.   J. Infect. Dis., 96:152, 1955.

65. Sutherland, I. W., and Wilkinson, J. F.   J. Gen. Microbiol., 30:105, 1963.

66. Thiele, E. H.   J. Immunol., 65:627, 1950.

67. Toomey, J. A., and Takacs, W. S.   J. Infect. Dis., 60:41, 1937.

68. ——— J.A.M.A., 139:448, 1949.

69. Ulrich, J. A., and Needham, G. M.   J. Bact., 65:210, 1953.

70. Verwey, W. F., and Thiele, E. H.   J. Immunol., 61:27, 1949.

71. Volk, V. K., and others.   Am. J. Pub. Health, 43:821, 1953.

72. Winter, J. L.   Proc. Soc. Exper. Biol. & Med., 83:866, 1953.

27

Corynebacterium diphtheriae and Diphtheria

Family: *Corynebacteriaceae* Lehmann and Neumann. Genus: *Corynebacterium* Lehmann and Neumann. Species: *Corynebacterium diphtheriae* (Flugge) Lehmann and Neumann

The observations of Bretonneau of Tours, published in 1826, established diphtheria as a clinical entity. The organism, described by Klebs (42) in 1883 in smears from pseudomembranes in the throats of patients with diphtheria, was isolated in pure culture the following year by Löffler (45). *C. diphtheriae* frequently is referred to as the Klebs-Löffler or the K. L. bacillus. At first Löffler was a little doubtful about the relationship of his organism to the disease diphtheria, since it was found occasionally in the throats of normal individuals and was not always present in pseudomembranes. He also was unable to explain to his own satisfaction some of the systemic manifestations of the infection which are known to be due to the action of the diphtheria toxin. The discovery of diphtheria exotoxin by Roux and Yersin (75) in 1888 eliminated all doubts as to the etiologic relationship of *Corynebacterium diphtheriae* to the disease diphtheria.

Man is the only natural host of *Corynebacterium diphtheriae*. The organism is harbored in the nasopharynx, and the infection may be acquired by contact with a patient ill of the disease, a convalescent, or a healthy carrier.

This large family contains both pathogenic and saprophilic species (14) which are usually gram-positive and have a characteristic pleomorphic morphology with Y and V forms and are often in parallel packets resembling carefully aligned logs. The animal species are nonmotile, except for *Listeria*, but some of the plant species are motile. Some species are aerobic, other microaerophilic and others anaerobic.

C. diphtheriae is a major disease in man, and *C. enzymicum*, which has been isolated from man, is pathogenic when inoculated into rabbits, guinea pigs, and mice. *C. striatum* has been isolated from the nose and throat of man and from the udders of cows with mastitis. *C. pseudotuberculosis* causes caseous lymphadenitis and ulcerative lymphadenitis in horses, cows, and other warm-blooded animals. *C. pyogenes* produces abscesses in cattle, swine, and sometimes in man (46). *C. murisepticum* produces spontaneous septicemia in mice, and *C. renale* causes urinary tract infections in cattle, sheep, horses, and dogs; while *C. kutscheri* was isolated from caseous lung lesions in mice. *C. phocae* produces an erysipelaslike lesion in seals. *C. equi* seems to be a primary pathogen of horses but also infects cattle, swine, and buffalos.

C. xerosis and *C. pseudodiphtheriticum* are saprophytes from the normal naso-pharynx, eye, and skin of man. *C. acnes* is found in acne lesions of the skin of man but may not be the cause of the disease (76). *C. parvum*, isolated from the urogenital organs of human females are not necessarily pathogenic (43).

The second genus, *Listeria*, and the third, *Erysipelothrix*, are diseases of animals which are readily transferable to man. The fourth genus, *Microbacterium*, is saprophilic in dairy products, and the fifth genus, *Cellulomonas*, and the sixth genus, *Arthrobacter*, are saprophytes from the soil.

Morphology and Staining. A tentative identification of *C. diphtheriae* frequently is made in the clinical laboratory solely on the morphologic characteristics of the organisms grown on Löffler's medium.

The bacilli usually appear as slender, straight, or slightly curved rods which vary from 1.2 μ to 6.4 μ in length and from 0.3

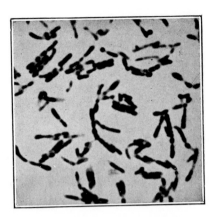

Fig. 1. *Corynebacterium diphtheriae.* Gram stain. × 2,000.

μ to 1.1 μ in width. They are rarely of uniform thickness throughout their length, and frequently show club-shaped thickenings at one or both ends. Occasionally they are widest in the center and taper towards both ends (Fig. 1).

In addition to clubbed, granular, barred, wedge-shaped, and solid staining forms, *C. diphtheriae* may produce "V," "L," and "Y" shapes, occasionally appearing as streptococcal-like chains or round forms resembling cocci (85). These bizarre structures are explainable by the studies of Bisset (7) and Hewitt (38) who found that *C. diphtheriae* is usually a multicellular organism with some of the granules being nuclei and some of the bands septums between cells. Nuclear structures and volutin granules, often called Babes-Ernst bodies (25), are apparently more numerous in organisms grown on Löffler's medium and most numerous if 8 per cent glycerine is added to this medium. They can be stained by Löffler's alkaline methylene blue, toluidine blue or by special stains such as those of **Neisser, Ljubinsky,** or **Albert** (53).

C. diphtheriae is **nonmotile, nonsporogenous,** and has no capsules. It is **gram-positive** and smears stained by Gram's method always should be examined because some other bacilli, especially certain strains of *Pseudomonas aeruginosa* (*B. pyocyaneus*), show well-stained granules and may be mistaken for *C. diphtheriae* unless the observer notes that the former organism has a thicker body and is **gram-negative.**

Cultural Characteristics. *C. diphtheriae* grows readily on meat infusion agar, pH 7.2 to 7.8, over a temperature range of 15° C. to 40° C. with an optimum between 34° C. and 37° C. (Fig. 2). It is **aerobic** and grows very poorly under anaerobic conditions.

Mueller (21, 54, 56) grew Parks No. 8 toxin-producing strain in a synthetic medium containing amino acids and small quantities of nicotinic acid, beta alanine or pantothenic acid, and pimelic acid. Later biotin was substituted for the pimelic acid (22). Recently isolated strains also require oleic acid (17).

At least three types of acid-labile compounds which are essential for the maximum production of toxin are present in pancreatic digest of casein (55, 56).

On Löffler's medium, minute, grayish-white, glistening colonies appear after 12 to 24 hours' incubation at 37° C. Mueller and Miller (56) suggest that this medium is more of a starvation than a good medium for the growth of bacilli, which probably accounts for the development of the bizarre but easily recognizable forms.

Tellurite Media. The addition of tellurite salts to the medium reduces the number of contaminants and gives to the colonies a characteristic gray or black color, which aids in the differentiation of *C. diphtheriae* into the *mitis, gravis,* and *intermedius* types (56, 70). The tellurite medium described by Mueller and Miller (40, 56, 86) is probably the best of the modifications and is available commercially (44). Saprophilic species such as *C. xerosis* and *C. pseudodiphtheriticum* as well as the unnamed diphtheroids grow well on media containing tellurite and produce colonies which resemble the *mitis* type but are not so dark and have a grayish-white periphery. Nitrates are reduced to nitrites, but indol is

Fig. 2. Colonies of *C. diphtheriae* on blood agar.

not formed. All strains produce acid from glucose and fructose; some strains oxidize other sugars and glycerol.

The *gravis* type of *C. diphtheriae* produces dark gray colonies on tellurite medium; oxidizes dextrin, starch, and glycogen; and is not hemolytic.

The *mitis* type of *C. diphtheriae* produces convex, black, and shiny colonies on tellurite medium; does not oxidize starch or glycogen; is variable with dextrin; but is hemolytic.

The *intermedius* type of *C. diphtheriae* produces small, flat, umbolate colonies with a black center and crenated periphery on the tellurite medium. It is variable with dextrin, does not oxidize starch or glycogen, and is not hemolytic.

Pearse (69) has shown that tetrazolium salts have a higher redox potential than potassium tellurite, and Monis and Rebalk (50) have applied this observation to a new method of detecting colonies of *C. diphtheriae*, since both tellurium and tetrazolium salts have some effect on the growth of *C. diphtheriae*. The colonies are grown on trypticase soy agar which contains 5 per cent human blood, for 18 to 24 hours. The colonies are then flooded with nitro blue tetrazolium (NO_2BT) in a concentration of 5 mg. per milliliter of distilled water.

Resistance. *C. diphtheriae* has been cultured from dried bits of the pseudomembrane after 14 weeks. The organism is more resistant to the action of light, desiccation, and freezing than are most nonspore-bearing bacilli. The bacilli are killed by boiling for one minute or if kept at a temperature of 58° C. for 10 minutes. The organisms are destroyed by the usual antiseptics. Gentian violet is only moderately bactericidal but is very effective in inhibiting the growth of *C. diphtheriae*.

C. diphtheriae is moderately resistant to sulfonamides but quite susceptible to penicillin.

Variability. Although the evidence is not entirely conclusive, we prefer to follow the suggestion of Morton (51, 52) and Oeding (58) and designate the *mitis* as the **S** form, *gravis* as the **SR** form, and *intermedius* as the **sR**. True **R** forms were induced in the laboratory by both Morton and Oeding; and dwarf **D** and gonidial **G** forms by Morton (51). A rare mucoid **M** form was described by Hobby (39).

Antigenic Structure. Five agglutinating types have been found in the *gravis* strains, five in the *mitis* strains, and two in the *intermedius* strains. The same types appear in the nontoxin-producing strains, and since there is no correlation with either colony type or toxin production, classification by agglutinating type is of no practical value.

Bacteriophage. Bacteriophage which lyse cultures of diphtheria bacilli have been reported by several investigators (8, 58). Freeman (28, 29, 30) was the first to recognize the relationship between the lysogenic type of phage infection and toxic production. Freeman treated populations of known nontoxigenic cultures with a phage isolated from a toxigenic culture. Most of the bacterial cells were lysed, but the survivors were found to produce toxin. They were resistant to the original phage but were lysogenic. Freeman's observations were promptly confirmed by other investigators (5, 34, 38, 67). Frobisher and Groman (33) and others have established the fact that the conversion of a **nontoxigenic to a toxigenic bacillus** is the direct consequence of the lysogenic state and not a transformation, transduction, or selection of a toxigenic mutant.

The concentration of iron in the medium does not affect the growth of the bacilli or phage production (36), but the presence of the temperate phage in the lysogenic bacillus apparently disturbs the metabolic functions of the cell in such a manner that the toxin is produced when the supply of iron is minimal.

Bacterial Metabolites. Endotoxins of low toxicity occur in the bodies of diphtheria bacilli which will induce peripheral neuritis and paralysis after intracerebral injection in mice (32). The most significant metabolic product is the classical exotoxin. The production and standardization of diphtheria toxin are discussed in Chapter 16, page 307, and the mechanism of infection with *C. diphtheriae* in Chapter 18, p. 367.

Multiple components are associated with the exotoxin (71); three were found by Poulik (72) by continuous electrophoresis, and as many as seven in some toxins by Relyveld and his associates (73). A more recent study by Branham and co-workers (12) revealed that the toxin from the *gravis* strains contains a heavy component (40 to 60 S.) which was not present in toxin from *mitis* or *intermedius* strains. This component seems to be responsible for the local edema seen in the skin of guinea pigs injected with *gravis* toxin and in the tissues of the patients infected with the *gravis* strain of *C. diphtheriae*. Anderson and Cowles (3) found that lysogenic toxin-producing strains would lose both their phage and their ability to produce toxin after successive passages of the virulent culture in broth containing phage antibodies made by injecting phage into rabbits. Animals which survive experimental infection with toxigenic strains of *C. diphtheriae* have antiphage antibodies in their serum and this mechanism is suggested as the explanation for the appearance of nontoxin producing strains of *C. diphtheriae* during convalescence of patients with clinical diphtheria.

Groman and his associates (35) have shown that an inhibitor for phage B and related phage was produced when the host strain C_4 was treated with dilute oleic acid. The inhibitor was identified as the phage-receptor substance. Barksdale and his associates (4) have restudied the mechanism of toxin production. Certain corynebacterial phages harbor the gene which governs toxin production (tox+). Toxin production is in two stages: the first is associated with virus growth which is dependent upon bacterial cell growth and can be inhibited by certain antibiotics, and the second is a postlysis event characterized by linear increase in toxin, which may be blocked by the addition of iron. Pappenheimer and his associates (65) have shown that the toxin is synthesized *de novo* from amino acids and agree with Barksdale that the toxin is produced and excreted only by lysogenic strains of *C. diphtheriae*. Allen and Cluff (1) have found that fluorescent antitoxin will not identify toxin-producing strains of *C. diphtheriae*, presumably because the toxin is not a surface component.

Cortisone does not protect guinea pigs from the effect of diphtheria toxin, nor does it interfere with the neutralizing effect of antitoxin (74). Neither cortisone nor ACTH prevents the production of diphtheria antitoxin in man following the injection of diphtheria toxoid (37).

Experimental Disease in Laboratory Animals. Guinea pigs, cats, dogs, and pigeons are quite susceptible to subcutaneous injections of exotoxin and living cultures of *C. diphtheriae*. Rabbits are slightly more resistant, and rats and mice are relatively refractory to experimental infection. Symptoms of paralysis frequently occur in dogs and pigeons. Young chicks are five times as resistant to toxin as guinea pigs but can be used successfully as a substitute for guinea pigs in titrating toxin (11, 15, 31).

Buddingh and Henigst (15) have succeeded in producing classical pseudomembranous lesions on the surface of the chorioallantois of 11- to 15-day old chick embryos by inoculating subcultures of recently isolated strains after washing the bacilli free of preformed toxin.

VIRULENCE TESTS. As shown in the section on exotoxin, the guinea pig is indispensable in the standardization of both toxin and antitoxin.

This animal is equally valuable in determining the virulence of a particular strain of *C. diphtheriae,* and for establishing the identity of a strain of *C. diphtheriae* if the colony characteristics and the morphology are atypical.

C. diphtheriae growing on Löffler's medium are emulsified in 3 to 5 ml. of broth and then 0.1 to 0.2 ml. of the emulsion is injected intracutaneously on the shaved side of each of two guinea pigs. One guinea pig should receive a protective dose of 500 units of diphtheria antitoxin intraperitoneally **12 to 24 hours before the injection,** and nontoxigenic strains are used as controls. The other guinea pig is given 30 to 50 units of antitoxin intraperitoneally **three to four hours after** the injection which will prevent premature death without interfering with the specificity of the skin test. The animal receiving the large dose of antitoxin should show no reaction at the site of the injection while the one with the small dose should show an inflamed area at 24 hours which progresses to necrosis by the forty-eighth to seventy-second hour. Some slow toxin producers are negative on the plates but positive in the guinea pig test. If staphylococci, streptococci, or other microorganisms present in the mixed growth from a throat culture are sufficiently virulent, lesions will appear in both animals. The results should not be regarded as negative, but as inconclusive, and the test should be repeated after isolating in pure culture the organism suspected of being *C. diphtheriae*. By this method as many as six different cultures can be tested simultaneously on two guinea pigs. A number of investigators have found this method rapid and reliable (6) and in general more satisfactory than the original method where an emulsion from one culture is injected subcutaneously and the unprotected guinea pig dies in three to five days.

PLATE METHOD FOR DETECTING EXOTOXIN. In 1948 Elek (24) in England and Ouchterlony (60) in Sweden introduced a plate method for determining the production of exotoxin by strains of *C. diphtheriae*. Serum medium is poured into plates and before it hardens a strip of paper, which has been saturated with antitoxin, is gently pressed below the surface of the agar. The suspected organisms are streaked across the plate perpendicular to the strip of antitoxin saturated paper. If toxin is produced, it diffuses into the medium, and at the region of optimal proportions a thin line of precipitate forms (Fig. 3). Freeman (28), and King and others (13, 41) have found this method reasonably accurate when the brand of antitoxin is selected carefully. Potassium tellurite (0.0045 per cent) is added to plates of the type shown

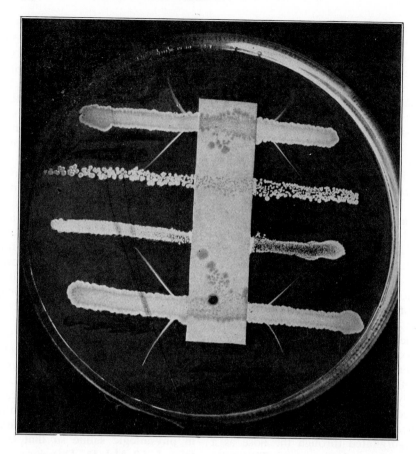

Fig. 3. In vitro virulence test. A strip of paper impregnated with antitoxin is pressed into soft warm medium. After the agar is hard, suspected cultures are streaked across the plate. If toxin is produced a straight line precipitate is formed in the medium. (From King, Frobisher, and Parsons. Courtesy of U.S. Public Health Service, C.D.C., Atlanta, Georgia.)

in Figure 3 to reduce the amount of contamination (79).

Plate Method for Detecting Small Amounts of Antitoxin in Serum. Farrell, Reid, and Kormendy (26) have introduced a delicate method of measuring small amounts of antitoxin in undiluted serum of horse and man and in the whole blood of infants. Diphtheria toxin destroys tissue culture cells, but the cells can be protected by antitoxin. Monkey kidney cells were grown in Petri dishes and then covered with a thin layer of agar to protect the cells against immediate contact with diphtheria toxin which is then added in a second thin layer. The Petri dishes are chilled to below 10° C., which arrests the adsorption of the toxin and provides time for the application of paper disks which have been saturated with known amounts of antitoxin and unknown amounts of serum and whole blood. The plates are then incubated, and

it was found that the cells disappeared except in circular areas where they were protected by the antitoxin. This method will measure 0.001 μ per milliliter, but the smallest amount shown in Figure 3 of Chapter 16 was 0.156 μ per milliliter.

Clinical Types of Infection in Man. A **local lesion** occurs in man and the diphtheria bacilli growing in the site synthesize **exotoxin** which is absorbed by the body, resulting in **systemic intoxication.** The bacilli grow rapidly on the mucous membranes and produce a grayish colored **pseudomembrane** which is usually found over the **tonsils, pharynx,** and **larynx** or in the **nose.** Occasionally the infection is confined to the **trachea** or extends to the **middle ear** or **conjunctivae.** In rare instances the infection occurs on the tongue skin, wounds, cervix, vagina, stomach, umbilicus of the newborn, or the penis after circumcision. The pseudomembranes, especially those of the larynx and trachea, are dangerous to young children because they can produce a complete obstruction of air passages by mechanical blockage.

The classic picture is not always present. Diphtheria may occur without the development of a pseudomembrane, or a pseudomembrane indistinguishable from that caused by *C. diphtheriae* may be produced by streptococci or the fusospirochetal symbionts of **Vincent's angina.** Smears should be made and stained both by Gram's method to show streptococci and by gentian violet to demonstrate the fusiform bacilli and spirochetes of Vincent's angina. Simultaneous infections with streptococci and *C. diphtheriae* or with Vincent's organisms and *C. diphtheriae* occur sufficiently often to necessitate the making of both smears and cultures on every patient with a throat infection.

Both peripheral and cranial nerves are quite sensitive to the toxin which becomes permanently fixed in the cells and cannot be displaced by antitoxin (87, 88, 89).

The voice acquires a nasal tone, and fluids may be regurgitated through the nose as a result of paralysis of the palate. The pulse becomes rapid from the effect of the toxin on the heart, and the patient may die from peripheral vasomotor collapse before damage to the heart can be demonstrated. Diminished power of accommodation of the eyes, exaggerated reflexes followed by diminished knee jerks, and tenderness over the nerve trunks may develop. Paralysis of various muscle groups such as the muscles of deglutition, respiration and the extremities may occur at any time between the third and the tenth week of the disease. The effect of the toxin on the heart usually is not apparent before the ninth day of the disease, but sudden death may occur from heart failure at any time during the next six to 10 weeks.

Although any one of the three types may produce either endemic or epidemic diphtheria, the *gravis* type is more often associated with severe epidemics in which there is a high mortality (47, 48). This may be due to the greater resistance of the *gravis* type to phagocytosis (2, 59) and to the fact that it can produce toxin in the presence of higher concentrations of iron (55).

Transmission. Diphtheria is the ideal disease for the study of the principles of public health and preventive medicine. Methods are available for the isolation of the organism from patients and from healthy carriers. The susceptibility of an individual or of an entire community can be determined by the Schick test. The degree of immunity can be estimated by the Schick test or measured by titration of antitoxin present in the blood. Active immunization can be made available to an entire population by toxoid injections, and their effectiveness can be determined by Schick testing without waiting for exposure of the individuals to challenge doses of bacilli under natural conditions. Finally, commercial antitoxin can be supplied for passive immunization either for prophylactic or therapeutic purposes.

Schick Reaction. In 1913 Schick (77) introduced the practice of injecting minute amounts of diphtheria toxin into the skin as a method of determining susceptibility to the toxin which, for all practical purposes, signifies susceptibility to diphtheria. **The Schick test dose is diphtheria toxin, diluted in physiologic saline so that 0.1 ml. contains 1/50 M.L.D.** This dose of 0.1 ml. is injected intracutaneously, usually in the skin of the forearm. A positive reaction is characterized by redness and induration, which appears after 24 to 36 hours and persists for four days or longer. If the individual's blood has 1/500 to 1/250 or more of a unit of antitoxin per milliliter, the injected toxin is neutralized and no reaction occurs. A negative reaction indicates that sufficient antitoxin is present to protect the individual against infection with diphtheria bacilli, although he may be carrying virulent bacilli in his nose or throat. **A control test always should be performed on the opposite arm using a portion of the diluted toxin which has been heated to 60° C. for 15 minutes.** The heating destroys the toxic properties but does not harm the substances from the diphtheria bacilli or the medium in which the organisms have been grown which cause reactions in some individuals. A reaction to these nontoxic materials usually reaches its maximum size 24 hours after injection and disappears by the fourth or fifth day. If the allergic reaction to the control material parallels that to the test toxin in size of the reaction and duration, the test is recorded as a **negative Schick.** If, however, the reaction to the unheated toxin is at least 50 per cent larger and persists longer than the control test, the individual is both **susceptible to the toxin** and **allergic** to the contaminating substances; such a reaction is interpreted as a combined reaction or a **positive Schick.**

Uhr and his associates (82) found that the intradermal infection of guinea pigs with toxigenic strains of *C. diphtheriae* induces marked delayed hypersensitivity to toxin, while infection with nontoxigenic strains merely produced slight susceptibility to proteins common to both toxigenic and nontoxigenic strains. The injection of toxoid results in the development of classical antitoxic antibodies but not the delayed type of hypersensitivity of the tuberculin type which is discussed in the chapter on allergy.

False Positive Schick Reactions. False positive Schick reactions are extremely rare in young children but become progressively more frequent with age and are evident in 5 to 20 per cent of young adults. These individuals usually give a strongly positive reaction to the unheated Schick material and no reaction or a transient pseudoreaction to the heated control. About 90 per cent of such reactors will be found on titration to have an abundance of antitoxin in their blood (16, 49, 62, 63). Bunch and others (16) noted that these immune individuals who gave completely negative reactions to the heated control were also negative to a control prepared by overneutralizing toxin with antitoxin and concluded that the false positive test resulted from an **allergic reaction to the toxin as a protein.**

The various types of skin reactions to the Schick test were studied by Neill and Fleming (57) in 1929 and subsequently by Pappenheimer and his associates (62, 63, 64) between 1948 and 1955. The latter investigators used toxoids prepared from highly purified toxin and found that most reactions are to the toxoid molecule itself. Moloney and Fraser (49) introduced the practice of substituting a 1:20 dilution of standard fluid toxoid for the heated control and did not

attempt to immunize the individual who gave a positive toxoid or **Moloney test.** We prefer the heated control supplemented by a Moloney test with a 1:100 dilution of fluid toxoid either at the time of the original test or after the positive and false positive reactors have been separated from the negative individuals.

Immunity. Thirty years ago most mothers in urban areas had been immunized by having clinical or subclinical diphtheria and passively transferred through the placenta enough antitoxin to protect the infant for three months or longer (66). After the loss of the passively transferred antibodies, the children became susceptible and diphtheria was characteristically a disease of childhood. The immunization of infants and preschool children with diphtheria toxoid has materially reduced the incidence of diphtheria in children (Fig. 4) but has also reduced the chances of reinforcing the immunity by subclinical infections. As a result of the change, more and more adults have positive Schick tests, the disease is becoming more prevalent in adults (78), and a much lower percentage of newborns are immune during the first months of life.

The number of cases of death from diphtheria declined steadily until 1958, when there were 923 cases and 67 deaths. Since then there has been no further decline. About 80 per cent of the cases occur in the southeastern and southwestern states (19). This localization is illustrated by the epidemic in Macon, Georgia, in 1959 (19) and the 1960 epidemic in migrant farm workers in Plainview, Texas (Fig. 5). The rapid spread of the disease over many states illustrates the low level of immunity in adults in this country at the present time.

The Carrier. Patients convalescing from diphtheria usually get rid of their bacilli spontaneously within two to four weeks, although a small percentage of them become chronic carriers. As a rule, healthy individuals exposed to cases acquire the bacilli but usually do not harbor them for more than a few days or weeks, but some persons seem unable to eliminate them. When a carrier is discovered, a **virulence test** should be performed immediately to remove from isolation those individuals with avirulent organisms

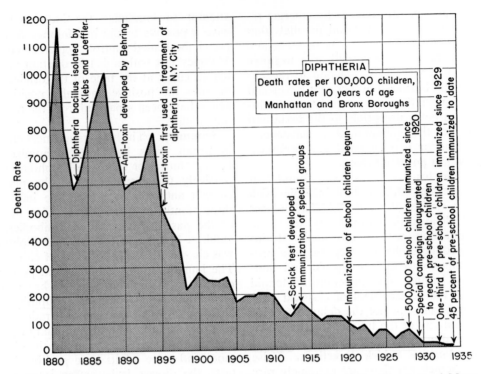

Fig. 4. Diphtheria mortality in New York City from 1880 to 1935. (Courtesy of Metropolitan Life Insurance Co.)

who are of no danger to the community. The carriers of virulent organisms are a definite menace and exceedingly difficult to free of their bacilli. Almost every known type of serum, vaccine, and antiseptic has been tried without success, even penicillin aerosol (68). The best results have been obtained by correcting pathologic conditions in the nose and throat by removing infected tonsils, adenoids, and correcting deviated septums or draining sinuses. Exposure to sunshine and improvement in diet are excellent supplementary measures.

Biologic Products. Excellent biologic products are available for the study of all phases of the diphtheria problem.

The toxin itself is used in the Schick test to determine susceptibility to the disease. Fluid toxoid, alum precipitated toxoid, protamine toxoid, and purified toxoid are available for active immunization. The mixture containing diphtheria toxoid, tetanus toxoid, and pertussis antigen is theoretically ideal for actively immunizing young infants (27).

Quadruple immunizing antigens to diph-

theria, tetanus, pertussis, and poliomyelitis are available (9). The response with diphtheria antitoxin and poliomyelitis antibodies is greater than with diphtheria and polio antigen given alone. The response to tetanus and pertussis is about the same. However, the pertussis vaccine is not as stable in the quadruple mixture and in the triple mixture (12). The booster effect of a new dose of diphtheria toxoid even after seven to 13 years is excellent (83, 84).

Refined and concentrated antitoxin is available for prophylactic passive immunization of the exposed individual and for active treatment of the patient with diphtheria.

Treatment. Diphtheria antitoxin in adequate amounts is the only specific and effective treatment for diphtheria. Two biologic facts should be kept constantly in mind: first, the speed with which the toxin becomes fixed in the tissues of the nervous system, and, second, the slowness of absorption of antitoxin injected into the subcutaneous tissues.

Although diphtheria toxin does not com-

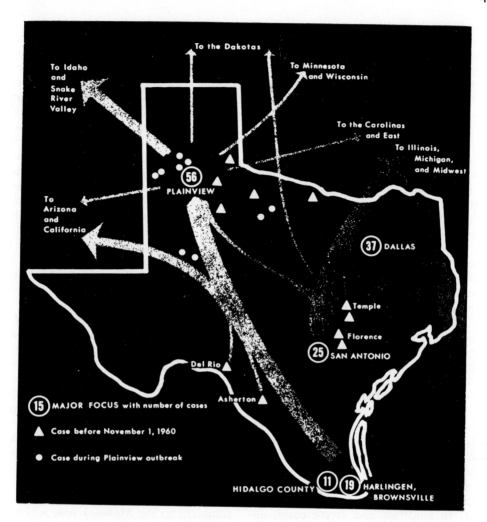

Fig. 5. The major patterns of movement of Latin American agricultural workers following an epidemic of diphtheria in Plainview, Texas, in 1960. (From Doege, Levy, and Heath. *Pub. Health Rep.*, 78:151, 1963.)

bine as rapidly with nerve tissue as does tetanus toxin, neither can it be displaced by antitoxin when once fixed. It is known that a maximum concentration of antitoxin in the blood is not reached until approximately 73 hours following subcutaneous injection. Absorption is much more rapid following intramuscular injection, and intravenous administration makes the antitoxin available immediately (89).

Cultures from all cases suspected of being diphtheria should be planted promptly on Löffler's and tellurite media. Antitoxin should be given immediately to all children and adults who show definite symptoms,

without waiting for a report on the culture.

Before being given antitoxin, the patient should be tested for hypersensitivity to horse serum to prevent the development of anaphylaxis. Normal horse serum usually is diluted 1:10 in physiologic saline and one drop instilled into the conjunctiva of one eye for the **ophthalmic test** and 0.1 ml. injected intradermally for the **skin test.** If the patient is hypersensitive to horse serum, the conjunctiva will become reddened in 15 to 30 minutes. In the skin test a wheal with pseudopodia, surrounded by an area of erythema, appears at the site of the injection. In most instances the skin reaction disappears spontaneously in about 30 minutes, and the eye can be restored to normal with a drop of adrenalin. If positive tests for hypersensitivity are obtained, the patient should be desensitized by the method described in Chapter 17. The antitoxin itself cannot be substituted for normal horse serum in the cutaneous and ophthalmic tests because of the presence of split protein products in the newer refined serums, which may give false positive reactions. The antitoxin can be used, however, in the desensitization process.

Children known to have asthma, eczema, or other allergic conditions should be tested and treated with the greatest caution because most of the known deaths from anaphylactic shock have occurred in patients of this type. A syringe filled with adrenalin should be available at the bedside from the beginning of the skin testing until several hours after the last injection is given.

The dose of antitoxin depends upon such factors as the duration of the disease and the severity of the symptoms. A dose of 5,000 units on the first day of the disease is more effective than 100,000 units on the fourth or fifth day. Mild cases in children respond satisfactorily to 3,000 to 5,000 units; moderately severe cases, 5,000 to 10,000 units; and severe infections, 10,000 to 20,000 units of antitoxin. For adults 5,000 to 10,000 units are sufficient for mild cases, but 20,000 or more should be given to the severely ill patient. In moderate and severe cases, approximately 50 per cent of the total dose should be given intravenously.

Although **penicillin** will kill *C. diphtheriae,* it has no effect on the exotoxin and cannot be substituted for antitoxin, although penicillin as a supplementary treatment suppresses secondary invaders, shortens the period of illness, and reduces the number of convalescent carriers (8, 18).

Prevention.   Children recently exposed to diphtheria can be protected for one to two weeks by the injection of 1,000 to 3,000 units of antitoxin. This passive immunity is of short duration and is lost upon disappearance of the horse serum globulins from the tissues. The child is then as susceptible to diphtheria as he was before receiving the antitoxin.

Active immunization is the key to the prevention of diphtheria. The immunization should start in infancy. Children from six to eight months of age develop antitoxin more readily than younger infants, but a review of the data (Fig. 1 in Chapter 26) and the discussion of the prevention of pertussis in Chapter 26 convinces us that, between the second and third months of life, infants should be actively immunized with the mixture composed of diphtheria toxoid, tetanus toxoid, and pertussis antigen. If the injections are repeated at the age of one year satisfactory immunity probably will be established for at least the first five years of life. Two doses of alum precipitated toxoid at three-week intervals give as good or better immunity than three doses of the fluid toxoid (80).

Young children rarely exhibit either local or general reactions to immunization, but as they grow older, more and more of them begin to develop local or even systemic reactions as a result of acquired sensitivity to the proteins of the diphtheria bacillus, the proteins of the medium, or of the toxin itself. From the age of 15, approximately 50 per cent of individuals will give reactions to either fluid or alum precipitated toxoids. Bunch, Morrow, Timmons, and Smith (16) succeeded in immunizing several groups of nurses and medical students with fluid toxoid without the development of any unfavorable reactions. The Schick positive students were subjected to the **Moloney test,** which is the intracutaneous injection of 0.1 ml. of a 1:100 dilution of fluid toxoid. Those students who gave no reaction or a reaction less than 10 mm. without induration tolerated 1 ml. doses of fluid toxoid without either local or general reactions. The injection of 1 ml. doses of fluid toxoid, or smaller doses of alum precipitated toxoid, gave severe local and general symptoms in individuals with positive Moloney tests. Severe local and general reactions do occur in some individuals even when preparations of highly purified toxoids are used (23, 63).

Although the investigation of Brandon and Fraser (10) showed that 90 per cent of the Moloney reactors are already immune, it seemed desirable to obtain negative Schick reactions in all individuals if these could be accomplished safely. By repeating the Moloney test each week for three weeks, the Schick positive, Moloney positive reactors could be changed to Schick negative. The individuals immunized by this method had excellent titers of antitoxin two months after the last injection (16).

CORYNEBACTERIUM PSEUDODIPHTHERITICUM (PSEUDODIPHTHERIA BACILLUS)

Von Hoffmann-Wellenhoff in 1888 and Löffler, at almost the same time, described bacilli, which they had cultivated from the throats of normal persons and in several instances from those of diphtheritic persons, which were in many respects similar to true *C. diphtheriae,* but differed from this chiefly in being nonpathogenic for guinea pigs. Bacilli of the same type can be isolated from the vagina (43).

Morphology and Staining. *C. pseudodiphtheriticum* is shorter and thicker than *C. diphtheriae.* It is usually straight and slightly clubbed at one end, rarely at both. When stained with Löffler's methylene blue, it occasionally shows unstained transverse bands; unlike *C. diphtheriae,* however, these bands hardly ever exceed one or two in number. In many cultures the single transverse band gives the bacillus a diplococcoid appearance.

Stained by Neisser's or Roux's method, no polar bodies can be demonstrated. It forms no spores, is nonmotile, and has no flagella.

Cultural Characteristics. On the usual culture media *C. pseudodiphtheriticum* grows more luxuriantly than *C. diphtheriae,* developing even in first isolations from the human body upon the simple meat-extract media. In agar plates its colonies are larger, less transparent, and whiter than are those of true diphtheria bacilli. *C. pseudodiphtheriticum* gives a nonglucose oxidizing colony on Mueller's tellurite medium as modified by Lev and others (44). *C. pseudodiphtheriticum* forms acid upon none of the sugars used, while *C. diphtheriae* acidifies and coagulates media containing monosaccharides and several of the more complex sugars, as given in the table in the following section dealing with *C. xerosis.*

Final differentiation can be made on the basis of animal pathogenicity, *C. pseudodiphtheriticum* is entirely innocuous to the ordinary laboratory animals.

CORYNEBACTERIUM XEROSIS

In 1884 Kuschbert and Neisser described a bacillus isolated from the eye of patients suffering from a form of chronic conjunctivitis known as xerosis. This bacillus which, morphologically, is almost identical with *C. diphtheriae,* was believed to be the etiologic factor of the disease. The frequency with which it has been isolated from normal eyes precludes this etiologic relationship, and it may be safely regarded as a harmless saprophyte which may indeed be more abundant in the slightly inflamed than in the normal conjunctiva but which has no causative relation to xerophthalmia.

Morphology. *C. xerosis* closely resembles *C. diphtheriae.* It is occasionally shorter than *C. diphtheriae,* but on the whole no absolute morphologic differentiation between the two is possible. It forms no spores and is nonmotile. Polar bodies may occasionally be seen.

Cultural Characteristics. On **Löffler's blood serum,** on **agar, glycerin agar,** and in **broth,** its growth is very similar to that of *C. diphtheriae,* but more delicate throughout. It cannot easily be cultivated upon the simple meat-extract media, nor will it grow on gelatin at room temperature. Its colonies on glycerin or glucose agar are microscopically identical with those of *C. diphtheriae.*

Differentiation. *C. xerosis* differs from *C. diphtheriae* in its acid production in sugar media. These relations were first worked out by Knapp for various sugars and the alcohol mannite and have been extensively confirmed by others.

Differentiation may be made by the use of two sugars—sucrose and glucose. *C. diphtheriae* forms acid from glucose, not from sucrose; *C. xerosis* oxidizes sucrose and glucose; *C. pseudodiphtheriticum* does not form acid from either.

C. xerosis is nonpathogenic for animals and forms no toxin.

THE DIPHTHEROID BACILLI

In addition to the bacteria just mentioned, there is a large group of microorganisms spoken of as the **diphtheroid bacilli,** largely because of their morphologic resemblance to the diphtheria bacillus. The organisms of this group are morphologically similar to the diphtheria bacillus, gram-positive, nonmotile, often show metachromatic granules, and have no spores. It is not, at the present writing, possible to formulate a classification of these organisms.

It is impossible at present to do more than indicate that the "diphtheroid bacilli" are a large heterogeneous group, held together by morphologic and superficial cultural similarity and largely consisting of saprophytes and probably harmless commensals on the human and animal body.

REFERENCES

1. Allen, J. C., and Cluff, L. E.　Proc. Soc. Exper. Biol. & Med., 112:194, 1963.
2. Amies, C. R.　J. Path. & Bact., 67:25, 1954.
3. Anderson, P. S., Jr., and Cowles, P. B.　J. Bact., 76:272, 1958.
4. Barksdale, L., and others.　J. Bact., 81:527, 1961.
5. Barksdale, W. L., and Pappenheimer, A. M., Jr.　J. Bact., 67:220, 1954.
6. Bayne-Jones, S.　Newer Knowledge of Bacteriology and Immunology, Chicago, University of Chicago Press, 1928, Chapter 56, p. 759.
7. Bisset, K. A.　The Cytology and Life History of Bacteria, Edinburgh, Livingstone, 1950.
8. Bixby, E. W.　Am. J. M. Sc., 215:509, 1948.
9. Bordt, D. E., and others.　J.A.M.A., 174:1166, 1960.
10. Brandon, K. F., and Fraser, D. T.　J. Immunol., 31:387, 1936.
11. Branham, S. E., and Wormald, M. F.　J. Immunol., 72:478, 1954.
12. ——— and others.　J. Immunol., 82:397, 1959.
13. Bretz, G. B., and Frobisher, M.　C.D.C. Bull., No. 5, 10:11, 1951.
14. Brooks, R. F., and Hucker, G. J.　J. Bact., 48:295, 1944.
15. Buddingh, G. J., and Henigst, W.　Am. J. Path., 37:477, 1960.
16. Bunch, C. P., and others.　J. Immunol., 39:427, 1940.
17. Cohen, S., and others.　J. Bact., 41:581, 1941.
18. Crawford, J. D.　New England J. Med., 239:220, 1948.
19. Doege, T. C., and Walker, R. J., Jr.　South. Med. J., 55:144, 1962.
20. ——— and others.　Pub. Health Rep., 78:151, 1963.
21. Drew, R. M., and Mueller, J. H.　J. Bact., 62:549, 1951.
22. Du Vigneaud, V., and others.　Science, 96:186, 1942.
23. Edsall, G., and others.　Am. J. Hyg., 53:283, 1951.
24. Elek, S.　Brit. M. J., 1:493, 1948.
25. Ernst, J.　Ztschr. f. Hyg. u. Infektionskr., 4:25, 1888.
26. Farrell, L. N., and others.　J. Immunol., 90:201, 1963.
27. Fleming, D. S., and others.　Canad. M. A. J., 59:101, 1948.
28. Freeman, V. J.　Pub. Health Rep., 65:875, 1950.
29. ——— J. Bact., 61:675, 1951.
30. ——— and Morse, I. V.　J. Bact., 63:407, 1952.
31. Frobisher, M., Jr., and others.　Am. J. Hyg., 35:381, 1942.
32. ——— and others.　Am. J. Pub. Health, 37:543, 1947.
33. ——— and Gorman, N. B.　Science, 117:297, 1953.
34. ——— J. Bact., 66:184, 1953; 69:9, 1955.
35. Groman, N. B.　J. Bact., 81:387, 394, 1961.
36. Hatano, M.　J. Bact., 71:121, 1956.
37. Havens, W. P., Jr., and others.　J. Immunol., 68:389, 1952.
38. Hewitt, L. F.　J. Gen. Microbiol., 5:287, 1951; 11:272, 1954.
39. Hobby, G. L.　J. Infect. Dis., 57:186, 1935.
40. Johnstone, K. I., and McLeod, J. W.　Pub. Health Rep., 64:1181, 1949.
41. King, E. O., and others.　Am. J. Pub. Health, 40:704, 1950.
42. Klebs, E.　Verhandl. d. Kong. f. inn. Med., II Abt., 139, 1883.
43. Laughton, N.　J. Hyg., 48:346, 1950.
44. Lev, M., and others.　Am. J. Clin. Path., 17:44, 1947.
45. Löffler, F.　Mitt. a. d. Klin. Gsndhtsamte., Berlin, 2:421, 1884.
46. MacLean, P. D., and others.　J. Infect. Dis., 79:69, 1946.
47. McLeod, J. W.　Bact. Rev., 7:1, 1943.
48. ——— J. Path. & Bact., 62:137, 1950.
49. Moloney, P. J., and Fraser, C. J.　Am. J. Pub. Health, 17:1027, 1927.
50. Monis, B., and Reback, J. F.　Proc. Soc. Exper. Biol. & Med., 111:81, 1962.
51. Morton, H. E.　Bact. Rev., 4:177, 1940.
52. ——— J. Bact., 40:755, 1940.
53. ——— and Francisco, A.　Stain Technol., 17:27, 1942.
54. Mueller, J. H.　Bact. Rev., 4:97, 1940.
55. ——— J. Immunol., 42:353, 1941.
56. ——— and Miller, P. A.　J. Bact., 51:743, 1946; 69:634, 1955.
57. Neill, J. M., and Fleming, W. L.　J. Infect. Dis., 44:224, 308, 1929.
58. Oeding, P.　Acta path. et microbiol. Scandinav., 27:16, 427, 907, 1950.
59. Orr-Ewing, J.　J. Path. & Bact., 58:167, 1946.
60. Ouchterlony, O.　Lancet, 1:346, 1949.
61. Pappenheimer, A. M., Jr., and Hendee, E. D.　J. Biol. Chem., 171:701, 1947.
62. ——— and Lawrence, H. S.　Am. J. Hyg., 47:233, 241, 1948.
63. ——— and others.　Am. J. Hyg., 52:353, 1950.
64. ——— J. Immunol., 75:259, 1955.
65. ——— and others.　J. Gen. Microbiol., 28:531, 1962.
66. Park and Zingher.　J.A.M.A., 5:2216, 1915; 6:431, 1916.
67. Parsons, E. L.　Proc. Soc. Exper. Biol. & Med., 90:91, 1955.
68. Paull, R., and others.　Ann. Int. Med., 24:413, 1946.
69. Pearse, E. A. G.　Histochemistry, Theoretical and Applied, 2nd ed., Boston, Little, Brown & Co., 1960, p. 539.
70. Perry, C. A., and Petran, E.　J. Lab. & Clin. Med., 25:71, 1939.
71. Pope, C. G., and others.　Brit. J. Exper. Path., 32:246, 1951.
72. Poulik, M. D.　Nature, 177:982, 1956.
73. Relyveld, E. H., and others.　Ann. Inst. Pasteur, 90:688, 1956.

74. Rosenbaum, P. R., and Obrinsky, W. Proc. Soc. Exper. Biol. & Med., 83:502, 1953.

75. Roux, E., and Yersin, A. Ann. Inst. Pasteur, 2:629, 1888; 3:273, 1889; 4:385, 1890.

76. Sabouraud, R. Ann. Inst. Pasteur, 11:134, 1897.

77. Schick, B. München. Med. Wchnschr., 60: 2608, 1913.

78. Thelander, H. E. Am. J. Dis. Child., 59:342, 1940.

79. Tinsdale, G. F. W. J. Path. & Bact., 59:461, 1947.

80. Top, F. H. Am. J. Pub. Health, 37:549, 1947.

81. Toshach, S. Canad. J. Pub. Health, 41:332, 1950.

82. Uhr, J. W., and others. J. Exper. Med., 105:1, 1957.

83. Volk, V. K., and others. Pub. Health Rep., 77:185, 1962.

84. ——— and others. Pub. Health Rep., 78: 161, 1963.

85. Wesbrook, F. F., and others. Tr. A. Am. Physicians, 15:198, 1900.

86. Whitney, O. R., and Damon, S. R. Pub. Health Rep., 64:457, 1949.

87. Zinsser, H. Nelson's Loose-Leaf Medicine, New York, Thomas Nelson and Sons, 9:205.

88. ——— J. Med. Research, 17:277, 1907.

89. ——— and others. Immunity, Principles and Applications in Medicine and Public Health, New York, The Macmillan Company, 1939, p. 504.

28

The Mycobacteriaceae

This family of organisms is included in the order of *Actinomycetales* (Buchanan) in the seventh edition of Bergey's Manual. The *Mycobacteriaceae* are related to the *Corynebacteriaceae* by some common antigens in the cell wall (7) and to the *Actinomycetaceae* by their tendency to produce branching under unusual conditions of cultivation. Since the most striking characteristic of the *Mycobacteriaceae* is their resistance to decolorization with acid alcohol, they are frequently called the **acid-fast bacteria.** These organisms are ubiquitous in nature and saprophytic forms are readily grown from soil and water. The pathogenic members of the family cause some of the most important of human infections, including leprosy and tuberculosis. Most species of birds, mammals, and cold-blooded animals are susceptible to their own specific pathogenic species, although there is considerable cross-infection between animals and man.

A number of classified and some as yet unclassified species of *Mycobacterium* from the soil are being recognized as the cause of disease in man at such an accelerated rate that a new chapter has been added to present our present but incomplete knowledge of this group of mycobacteria.

MYCOBACTERIUM LEPRAE
(Hansen)

Family: *Mycobacteriaceae* Chester. Genus: *Mycobacterium* Lehmann and Neumann. Species: *Mycobacterium leprae* (Hansen) Lehmann and Neumann

Myco. leprae of man and *Myco. leprae murium* of rats are the cause of human and rat leprosy. These two antigenically independent species have both achieved a status of complete parasitism and cannot be grown on artificial media. *Myco. leprae murium* has finally been cultured in tissue culture and grown from the fibroblast of normal rats (22, 48, 49). *Myco. leprae* of man was successfully propagated in the foot pad of mice by Shepard in 1960 (55, 56). The generation time for *Myco. leprae murium* was found to be from 10 to 13 days (22), and that for *Myco. leprae,* 20 to 30 days (56). These are now the champion slow growers of the microbiologic world and have displaced the former champions *Myco. tuberculosis* and *Treponema pallidum,* which have a generation time of 20 to 24 hours. The incubation period, as must be expected, is correspondingly prolonged. Under ideal conditions in the foot pad of mice, it may be as long as five to 10 months, and in man it is always a period of years and may be as long as 10 to 12 years.

It is difficult for residents of the temperate zone to appreciate the importance of leprosy in the tropical and subtropical countries of the world. A report by Guinto (24) in 1960 showed that there were more than 2 million registered cases of leprosy in 2 billion people in these endemic areas (Fig. 1). Translated into units, this gives one registered case for each 1,000 inhabitants, and the actual rate is obviously much greater, since many cases are not registered. The same study showed that less than 10 per cent of the registered lepers were in sanatoriums under treatment.

Leprosy is an ancient disease. It was known in India as an old disease when mentioned in the Vedas of 1400 B.C. (17). Not all the skin lesions called "leprosy" in the Old Testament of the Bible were leprosy, but almost certainly some of them were.

The lepra cell, which is a modified monocyte, was recognized by Danielssen in 1840

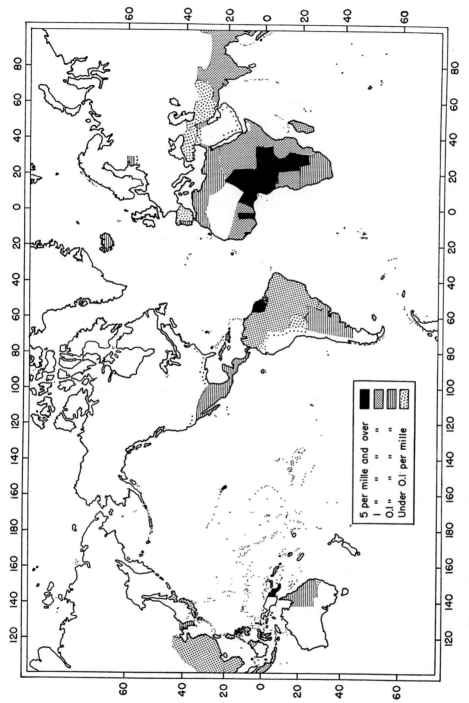

Fig. 1. Geographic distribution of leprosy. (From Rogers and Muir. *Leprosy*, John Wright & Sons, Ltd.)

5 per mille and over
1 " " " "
0.1 " " " "
Under 0.1 per mille

(8, 9) and his son-in-law, Hansen (27, 28), discovered the bacilli in the lepra cell in 1874; Neisser (43) confirmed the observation of Hansen. Lendrum (38) has proposed the name **Hansen's Disease** for the old term "leprosy."

Morphology and Staining. When stained by the Ziehl-Neelsen method, the leprosy bacilli are found predominantly in modified mononuclear or epithelioid structures called lepra cells. Large numbers of bacilli are packed in the cells in an arrangement which suggests packets of cigars. The individual rods vary in length from 1 to 7 μ and in width from 0.2 to 1.4 μ. The rods usually are straight or slightly curved and when stained may appear solid red or show granules and beads which are slightly larger than the average diameter of the cell. *Myco. leprae* is **acid-fast, gram-positive,** and **nonsporogenous.**

A study of thin sections of *Myco. leprae* in lepromatous nodules shows that this organism's structure resembles that of *Myco. tuberculosis* with a three-layered cell wall and a complex intracytoplasmic membrane system which connects with the plasma membrane (32). Surrounding the individual bacilli was another structure of low density which could have been a product of the cell or a product of the host.

Cultivation. All well-controlled attempts to cultivate *Myco. leprae* have met with failure, including the attempt to grow the organism in cultures of various types of human cells (26, 55). The chromogenic and nonchromogenic strains of *Mycobacterium* isolated from tissue of leprous patients are almost certainly saprophilic contaminants.

Antigenic Structure. Patients with leprosy may give positive skin tests with lepromin prepared from leprous nodules but react equally well to PPD or to tuberculin made from the acid-fast saprophyte, *Myco. phlei.* In complement-fixation tests using as the antigen cultured strains of leprosy bacilli, *Myco. tuberculosis* and *Myco. phlei,* the same percentage of positive reacions was obtained with all antigens. One interesting relationship was observed: the more active cases gave the highest percentage of positive complement fixation, while the less active cases had the highest percentage of positive skin tests.

Rees and his associates (48, 50, 51) have separated leprosy bacilli from the tissues of lepromatous nodules by differential centrifugations and then immunized rabbits with the bacilli. Subsequently the antiserum was used in the agar gel diffusion method and most of the antibody was directed toward the specific antigens of the bacilli, with only a little cross-reaction with the human tissue. The latter could be removed by adsorption. In two patients lepromatous antigens were demonstrated in the serum. The serum of the other patients with lepromatous leprosy gave a very faint line with bacillary antigen but very heavy lines when antigens from human tubercle bacilli were used. This confirmed the presence of cross-reaction antibodies which gave the complement-fixing reaction to human and *phlei* antigens. With the huge supply of antigen in the lepromatous patient, one may assume that practically all of the specific antibody was bound to antigen in the form of a soluble antigen-antibody complex which would not be detected by the agar gel diffusion method where the cross-reaction antibody would be free to react with the antigen from the human tubercle bacillus. Erythrocytes sensitized with tuberculin are agglutinated to a much higher titer by serums from patients with acute leprosy than by patients with tuberculosis (39). The hemagglutinin titers decreased as the patient improved with treatment. These results by Levine (39) were very encouraging, but later studies in India (54) and in the Philippines (52) indicated that the method was probably too sensitive, since it was positive in patients who had asystemic tuberculosis but presumably not leprosy and also in patients with positive lepromin tests but no clinical evidence of leprosy.

Active cases of leprosy have a high percentage of positive Wassermann and Kahn reactions, but Neurath and others (44) who studied these reactions showed that they belonged to the biologically false positive group.

Bacterial Metabolites. Dharmenda (11, 12) has analyzed leprae bacilli obtained from nodules of patients with lepromatous leprosy by the chemical methods developed by Anderson (1) for the study of human tubercle bacilli from cultures, and found proteins, polysaccharides, phosphatide, and wax. The protein was antigenic and gave a 24- to 48-hour tuberculin-like reaction in patients with leprosy.

Lepromin Test. This test was introduced by Mitsuda (42) with the hope that it would be as specific in leprosy as the tuberculin test is in tuberculosis. Lepromin is made by grinding lepromatous nodules into a paste which is then diluted with physiological saline to 20 ml. for each gram of tissue. The supernate, after filtration, is sterilized by autoclaving at 120° C. for 15 minutes and preserved by the addition of 0.5 per cent of phenol. Good preparations contain many more leprae bacilli than tissue fragments. The test dose is 0.1 ml. of lepromin injected intracutaneously as in the tuberculin test. Two types of reactions occur: the early reactions resemble the tuberculin reactions and appear in 24 to 48 hours, and the late reactions begin between the seventh and tenth day as a small papule which gradually increases in size by the twenty-fifth to the thirtieth day. In the more severe reactions the center of the nodule becomes necrotic and sloughs out (29, 58). The late lepromin reactions are caused by the intact leprosy bacilli in the lepromin, and if they are removed by filtration (45) or broken up by supersonic vibration (35) or by chemical treatment (12), the tuberculin-like reaction is intensified and the late lepromin reactions reduced or eliminated.

The negative lepromin reaction in the acute lepromatous stage of the disease can be explained by assuming that the patient is in the preallergic stage analogous to the preallergic stage in tuberculosis, in which the bacilli multiply in mononuclear cells before the tuberculin reaction becomes positive.

Positive lepromin tests can be elicited in patients with tuberculosis in areas of the world where there is no leprosy (19, 20, 58), and positive lepromin tests can be induced in normal, healthy children by vaccination with BCG, which is an attenuated bovine tubercle bacillus. Fernandez (20) vaccinated 123 children with BCG in 1943. The children were negative to both tuberculin and lepromin before vaccination, but one month later the tuberculin test was positive in 99 per cent and the lepromin test in 92 per cent. More recent studies in endemic areas of leprosy (23, 25, 52) suggest that many young children give the delayed lepromin reaction although they have had no known contact with either human tuberculosis or clinical leprosy. This led some investigators to the belief that the late reaction might be an active immunization by the bacilli injected in the lepromin test. A more likely explanation has been presented by Guinto, Mabalay, and Doull in 1962 (13, 25). These investigators could elicit a delayed lepromin-like test by injecting the whole dead bacilli of human, avian or Battey types of *Mycobacterium*. Furthermore, children giving negative tuberculin tests to 0.0001 mg. (5TU), of human PPD's have positive tests to the same amount of PPD from avian and Battey tubercle bacilli and gave typical lepromin reactions to lepromin. This suggests that both avian and Battey bacilli could sensitize to the late lepromin reaction. PPD prepared from certain strains of scotochrome tubercle bacilli (see Chapter 30) may give twice as many positive reactions in medical students as the avian and Battey strains; therefore it is likely that all the usual mycobacterial infections will cross-react with the bacillary suspensions used by Guinto and his associates (25).

Experimental Disease in Animals. Shephard (56) succeeded in 1960 in infecting the foot pads of mice with strains of human leprosy bacilli, and these infections have been passed from mouse to mouse for 10 passages without alteration in morphology or virulence. However, all attempts to cultivate human leprosy bacilli in tissue cultures of human cells have failed (55).

Myco. leprae murium can be transferred directly from rat to rat but not, as yet, to other animals; but in contrast to the human leprosy bacilli, it can be propagated in tissue cultures of fibroblasts from normal rats (22, 47, 49).

Experimental Disease in Man. Man is highly resistant to experimental infection. Danielssen and Boeck (8) inoculated a number of medical students and nurses but obtained negative results. McKinley and Soule (41) reported that of 145 recorded attempts to infect man, only one was successful: the Hawaiian criminal whom Arning inoculated in 1886. The result of this experiment has been questioned because the victim had been exposed to leprosy before he was inoculated. Balanced against these negative results are a few accidental experiments in which nurses and physicians have become infected during operations on leprous patients (46). Lagoudaky (36) deliberately inoculated himself with blood from a leprous patient and developed cutaneous lesions in less than two months after the first injection. The most convincing experiment occurred during World War II when two American marines were tattooed in June, 1943, in Melbourne, Australia, and early in 1946 they both developed leprosy which began in the areas which had been tattooed (46).

Clinical Types of Infection in Man. The clinical classification of leprosy by Pardo-Castello and Tiant (44) is shown in Table 1. The new classification adopted by the Fifth International Congress for leprosy in 1948 recognizes only three classes of leprosy, **lepromatous, tuberculoid,** and **intermediate** (5). The prognosis is poor in the lepromatous type of leprosy, where the lepromin test is negative and bacilli are found in great abundance in the lesions. The outlook is best in the tuberculoid type, where the lepromin test is positive and bacilli are few or absent

Table 1. The Correlation of the Pathology, Immunology, and Bacteriology of Leprosy
(Pardo-Castello and Tiant)

PATHOLOGY			IMMUNOLOGY LEPROMIN TEST	BACTERIOLOGY
Leprosy of the Skin	Lepromatous		Negative	Numerous bacilli
	Tuberculoid	Miliary	Positive	Rare bacilli
		Sarcoidal	Positive	Rare bacilli
		Lazarine	Positive	Abundant bacilli in necrotic areas; rare in tissues
	Nonspecific	Erythematous	Pos. or Neg. 50%	Few bacilli
		Pigmented	Pos. or Neg. 50%	Few bacilli
		Achromic	Pos. or Neg. 50%	Few bacilli
Leprosy of the Nerves	Lepromatous		Negative	Numerous bacilli
	Tuberculoid	Miliary	Positive	Rare bacilli
		Colliquative	Positive	Rare bacilli
	Nonspecific		Pos. or Neg. 50%	Few bacilli
Leprosy of Other Tissues and Organs	Lepromatous		Negative	Numerous bacilli
	Tuberculoid	Miliary	Positive	Rare bacilli
		Sarcoidal	Positive	Rare bacilli
	Nonspecific ?		?	?

In the intermediate type, which includes the old lazarine form, the lepromin test is positive, and bacilli are numerous in necrotic areas but rare elsewhere. The symptoms are severe, but the ultimate prognosis may be good. Such a reaction would be expected if a lepromatous case should develop sensitivity to lepromin accompanied by a relative degree of immunity.

Transmission. A thorough study of the transmission of leprosy in the United States was published by Badger (2) in 1959. The disease is endemic in some parts of the states of Louisiana, Texas, and Florida. Cases originated in these states both as family contacts and as casual nonfamily contacts. The more intimate and prolonged the contact, the more likely that clinical disease will be transmitted. Children are more susceptible than adults and males more susceptible than females. The incidence of infection in the white population of Louisiana has been 1.9 per 1,000 for whites and 0.7 per 1,000 for Negroes. The incidence of clinical disease in family contact over a period of years was found to be 5.1 per cent. This is greater than for poliomyelitis (1.2 per cent) and about like that of diphtheria, but the entire risk in the more acute diseases occurred in a period of days in contrast to a period of years for leprosy (2).

The clinical evidence for the transmission of leprosy is quite conclusive. There are many examples of Europeans developing leprosy after a single contact with South Sea Island prostitutes (53). It must be emphasized, however, that man actually is very resistant to the development of leprosy even when exposed over a period of years. Father Damien and possibly one or two others are the only known instances of physicians, nurses, and attendants in leprosariums contracting the disease (31). Hopkins has collected convincing evidence in support of this theory of hereditary susceptibility, but even this slight predisposition to infection can be overcome by improved economic and social conditions. Leprosy among several Norwegian families that migrated to Minnesota has not been transmitted to the grandchildren.

The incubation period is difficult to determine. It seems to vary from a minimum of a few months to a maximum of 30 years, with an average of two to seven years. Black (3) refers to a 15-year-old girl in whom he demonstrated leprosy bacilli in smears from an apparently normal ear lobe two years before the patient developed cutaneous and neural leprosy of the forearms and legs. In India 25 of 254 contacts had leprosy bacilli in their skin, and four of these subsequently developed clinical leprosy (21).

The characteristics of the onset of the older classic epidemics of leprosy can only

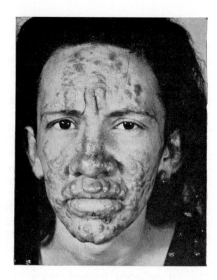

Fig. 2. Leprosy before treatment. (From Johansen and others. *Pub. Health Rep.*, 65:204, 1950.)

be surmised because of the paucity of authentic records. However, they have been observed in detail in this century in some of the Pacific Islands. For example, in 1912 a leprous woman came to Nauru from the Gilbert Islands; by 1920 four of her neighbors had leprosy, and by 1925 30 per cent of the native Nauruian population showed signs of the disease (4). This phenomenal increase to an annual attack rate of 300 per 100,000 was probably greatly facilitated by the extremely inadequate diet of the natives (6).

Treatment. Therapy with certain of the sulfone drugs has changed the popular reaction of the masses toward leprosy. Although the new drugs are bacteriostatic rather than bactericidal and have to be given for years (57), at least they offer hope so families will bring in their children for treatment before they are in the last stages of the disease.

The relative values of the different sulfones have been reviewed by Doull (15, 16, 17). The most widely used drug at the present time is p, p'-sulfonyldianiline (DDS). Enough drug to treat a patient for a whole year may be purchased for about $1.00.

Modifications of the original drug, such as glucosulfone sodium (promin), sulfoxone sodium (diazone, diamidin), or solapsone (sulphetrone), have somewhat less toxicity but are much more expensive (14, 15, 16, 17). Streptomycin and dihydrostreptomycin may improve some patients who do not respond to sulfones. Diphenyl thiourea has shown some promise (15).

The treatment of experimentally induced leprosy in the foot pad of mice by Shephard and Chang (56) suggests that DDS, isonicotinic acid hydrazide, and para-aminosalicitic acid all suppressed the growth of the leprae bacilli in the local lesions. Cortisone has been injected locally into painful nerves with some temporary relief, and it has been used both as a local injection and as an ointment in some inflammatory lesions of the eye. The corticoid hormones have a temporary beneficial effect in leprae reactions of erythema nodosum (12, 14). Theoretically, hyposensitization with the common antigen present in human tuberculin would produce more lasting improvement. Erickson and associates (18, 33, 34) have reported that 3.6 per cent of the patients have the disease arrested after two years of treatment and 73 per cent after nine years of treatment (Figs. 2, 3). The steroid "fucidin" (ZN6), which is so effective against *Staphylococcus,* was also effective against a strain of the human tubercle bacillus, but it is has not been tried on patients with leprosy (30).

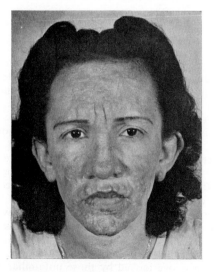

Fig. 3. Leprosy after 12 months' treatment with Promacetin. (From Johansen and others. *Pub. Health Rep.*, 65:204, 1950.)

Prevention. McCoy's (40) observations, extending over the past 30 years, suggest that it is not necessary to isolate in an institution a leper who develops his symptoms in a temperate region when the disease is not endemic. In endemic areas rigid isolation of all acute lepromatous and nonspecific types of cases is necessary.

Children, in particular, are very susceptible to leprosy and should be removed from contact with infected parents. Adult males and females should be segregated in leprosariums and procreation discouraged. In tropical countries where segregation is difficult or impossible sterilization of the male by section of the vas deferens has proved effective (60).

The use of BCG as an immunizing agent was mentioned in a previous edition of this text because it induced positive lepromin tests in school children and because there was one theory that the universal tuberculinization of Western Europe improved the resistance of the population to leprosy, if not to tuberculosis, and helped in the elimination of leprosy. Recently it was shown that BCG would immunize rats against experimental infection with *Myco. leprae murium.* Many children have been given BCG in South America to help protect them against tuberculosis and/or leprosy, but many years will be required to evaluate the results.

RAT LEPROSY

This disease, caused by *Myco. leprae murium,* was discovered among rats in Odessa by Stefansky in 1903. Since then it has been found in many parts of the world (10, 40, 59). Rat leprosy occurs spontaneously among house rats and is characterized by subcutaneous indurations, swelling of lymph nodes, emaciation, and sometimes ulceration and loss of hair. The disease is chronic, and rats often live for six months to one year after becoming infected. The characteristic lesion is a thickened area under the skin of the abdomen or flank which resembles adipose tissue except that it is less shiny and more nodular and gray than fat. The resemblance to fat is so close, however, that it often is overlooked by those unfamiliar with the condition. Acid-fast bacilli resembling *Myco. leprae* are found in large numbers in the mononuclear cells of the subcutaneous tissues and in the lymph nodes and nodules in the liver and lungs.

Rats can be infected by direct inoculation of infected tissues, but the disease probably is transmitted naturally from rat to rat by fleas (40, 59).

Although the disease is not exactly like leprosy, the resemblance is sufficiently great to suggest that rats are a potential source of human leprosy. The distribution of the disease in various parts of the world, however, does not correspond with the distribution of human leprosy, and the rat cannot be infected with tissues from cases of human leprosy.

Garbutt and his associates (22) and Reese and his coworkers (49, 50) have cultured the rat leprosy bacilli in cultures of rat fibroblasts. They have collected the specific antigens elaborated by the bacilli in culture and studied them with the gel diffusion method, using antisera produced by rats infected with the organisms and antiserums induced in rabbits by injecting bacilli freed from experimental lesions in rats. There seemed to be one or more specific antigen characteristic of *Myco. leprae murium* with very little cross-reaction with *Myco. tuberculosis* of man (51).

REFERENCES

1. Anderson, R. J., and others. J. Biol. Chem., 94:653, 1932; 97:617, 1932; 113:637, 1936; 114:431, 1936; 121:669, 1937.
2. Badger, L. F. Epidemiology in Leprosy in Theory and Practice, ed. Cochrane, R. G. Bristol, John Wright & Sons, Ltd., 1959.
3. Black, S. H. Chapter on the Pathology of Leprosy, in the Mycobacterial Diseases, Lancaster, Pa., The Science Press, 1938.
4. Bray, G. W. Proc. Roy. Med. (Trop. Med.), 23:1370, 1930.
5. Canizares, O. Arch. Dermat. & Syphy., 59:584, 1949.
6. Chaudhury, A. K. R. Indian M. J., 40:211, 1946.
7. Cummins, C. S. Internat. Rev. Cytol., 5:25, 1956.
8. Danielssen, D. C., and Boeck, W. Om Spedalskhed Christiania, 1847.
9. ——— and Boeck, W. Traité de la Spedalskhed ou Elephantiasis des Grecs, Paris, J. B. Baillière, 1848.
10. Dean, G. Zentralbl. f. Bakt., 34:222, 1903.
11. Dharmendra. Indian J. M. Research, 30:1, 1942; 31:125, 129, 1943.
12. ——— Leprosy in India, 25:123, 1953.
13. Doull, J. A. Vet. Admin. Tech. Bull. T. B., 10-98; March 15, 1954.
14. ——— and Wolcott, R. R. New England J. Med., 254:20, 1956.
15. ——— J.A.M.A., 173:363, 1960.
16. ——— and others. Internat. J. Leprosy, 29:291, 1961.

17. Doull, J. A. Tice's Practice of Medicine, IV:57, 1962.
18. Erickson, P. T. Ann. New York Acad. Sc., 54:115, 1951.
19. Fernandez, J. M. M. Rev. argent. dermatosif., 23:425, 1939.
20. —— Rev. argent.-norteam. cien. méd., 1: 592, 1943.
21. Figureredo, N., and Disai, S. D. Indian J. M. Sc., 3:253, 1949.
22. Garbutt, E. W., and others. J. Gen. Microbiol., 27:259, 1962.
23. Guinto, R. S., and Wade, H. W. Internat. J. Leprosy, 26:328, 1958.
24. —— Leprosy Briefs, 12:21, 26, 1960.
25. —— and others. Internat. J. Leprosy, 30: 152, 1962; 31:81, 1963.
26. Hanks, J. H. Internat. J. Leprosy, 15:21, 31, 48, 1947; 18, 33, 1950.
27. Hansen, G. A. Norsk mag. f. Loegevidensk., 3R., 4:1, 1874.
28. —— Virchow's Arch., 79:32, 1880. References quoted from the article on Leprosy by E. Muir in A System of Bacteriology in Relation to Medicine, London, 5:345-382, 1930.
29. Harrell, G. T., and Horne, S. F. Am. J. Trop. Med., 25:523, 1945.
30. Hilson, G. R. Lancet, 1:931, 1962.
31. Hopkins, R. Chapter on Heredity in Leprosy, in the Mycobacterial Diseases, Lancaster, Pa., The Science Press, 1938.
32. Imaeda, T., and Convit, J. J. Bact., 83:43, 1962.
33. Johansen, F. A., and Erickson, P. T. J.A.M.A., 144:985, 1950.
34. —— and others. Pub. Health Rep., 65: 195, 1950.
35. Kitano, H., and Inoue, T. Internat. J. Leprosy, 9:29, 1941.
36. Lagoudaky, S. J. Trop. Med. & Hyg., 39:81, 1936; 40:77, 1937.
37. Latapi, F., and Chevez Zamora, A. Internat. J. Leprosy, 16:421, 1948.
38. Lendrum, F. C. Am. J. Trop. Med. & Hyg., 1:999, 1952.
39. Levine, M. Proc. Soc. Exper. Biol. & Med., 76:171, 1951.
40. McCoy, G. W. Pub. Health Rep., 23:981, 1912; 63:1522, 1948.
41. McKinley, F. B., and Soule, M. H. J.A.M.A., 98:361, 1932.
42. Mitsuda, K. Internat. J. Leprosy, 4:491, 1936.
43. Neisser, A. Breslauer ärztl. Ztschr., 20:1879.
44. Neurath, H., and others. Am. J. Syph., Gonor. & Ven. Dis., 31:436, 1947.
45. Pardo-Castello, V., and Tiant, F. R. J.A.M.A., 121:1264, 1943.
46. Porritt, R. J., and Olsen, R. E. Am. J. Path., 23:805, 1947.
47. Rees, R. J. W. Brit. J. Exper. Path., 4B:19, 1962.
48. —— International Conference on Mycobacterial and Fungal Antigens, Am. Rev. Resp. Dis., 1964.
49. —— and Tee, R. O. Brit. J. Exper. Path., 43:480, 1962.
50. —— and Waters, F. F. R. Pathogenesis of Leprosy, CIBA Foundation Study Group, London, J. A. Churchill, 1963.
51. —— International Conference on Mycobacterial and Fungal Antigens, Am. Rev. Resp. Dis., 1964.
52. Rheins, M. S., and others. Internat. J. Leprosy, 25:104, 1957.
53. Rogers, L., and Muir, E. Leprosy, Bristol, England, John Wright & Sons, Ltd., 1946.
54. Roy, A. N., and Banerjee, G. Ann. Biochem. & Exper. Med., 17:111, 1957.
55. Shepard, C. C. J. Exper. Med., 112:445, 1960.
56. —— and Chang, Y. T. Proc. Soc. Exper. Biol. & Med., 109:636, 1962.
57. Urrets Zavalia, A. Rev. brasil. de leprol., 17:5, 1949.
58. Weeks, K. D., and Smith. D. T. Am. J. Trop. Med., 25:519, 1945.
59. Wherry, W. B. J. Infect. Dis., 5:507, 1908; 46:263, 1930.
60. Wilson, R. M. Internat. J. Leprosy, 3:201, 1935.

29

Mycobacterium tuberculosis and Tuberculosis

Family: *Mycobacteriaceae* Chester. Genus: *Mycobacterium* Lehmann and Neumann. Species: *Mycobacterium tuberculosis* (Zopf) Lehmann and Neumann

Tuberculosis is no longer the most common cause of death in countries with a high standard of living but remains the number-one killer in the world as a whole. In the United States the death rate reached a low of 5.4 per 100,000 in 1961 and now ranks as twelfth among the causes of death. The precipitous decline in the death rate can be attributed primarily to the effect of new chemotherapeutic agents. The rate of decline has slowed, however, for there are still more than 10,000 deaths each year in this country and over 50,000 new cases. There are about 2 million individuals with active and inactive disease and over 30 million who have a positive reaction to tuberculin as a result of a previous subclinical infection with tubercle bacilli. It has been estimated that 2 million new cases will arise from the 30 million infected, and that there will remain over 7 million infected in the year 2000 even if no new infections occur (178).

The reduction in the number of new cases of clinical tuberculosis is very slight when compared with the reduction in the number of deaths (Fig. 1), which should force our attention on the medical, economic, and social importance of the living patients. The nature of the disease necessitates a prolonged period of treatment for which the economic cost is staggering. An estimate of the cost for the diagnosis and treatment of tuberculosis in the year 1952 in the United States was $350,000,000 exclusive of the construction cost of hospitals and the training of personnel, or about $15,000 for each patient (128).

The occurrence of obvious tuberculosis in the bones of some of the Egyptian mummies suggests that tuberculosis is an ancient disease (259). Characteristically it is a disease of civilizations where masses of people are herded together under suboptimal sanitary conditions. With improvement in the standard of living, the disease has decreased even in the absence of any specific measures directed toward its prevention (52).

Fracastorius (1484-1553) arrived at some remarkably accurate conclusions regarding the infectious nature of tuberculosis and its method of transmission, but it was not until 1865 that Villemin (252) transmitted the disease from man to rabbits. Baumgarten may have seen the bacillus in infected tissues in 1878 but credit for the discovery of the cause of tuberculosis necessarily goes to Robert Koch (110), who isolated the tubercle bacillus in 1882. Koch (a) found the bacillus associated constantly with the clinical disease, (b) isolated it in pure culture, (c) reproduced the disease in guinea pigs and rabbits with the culture, and (d) recovered the bacillus in pure culture from the experimentally infected animals. These rigid requirements must be fulfilled before a particular microorganism can be accepted as the cause of a specific infectious disease and are known now, in honor of Koch, as **Koch's postulates** (216).

Morphology and Staining. Tubercle bacilli are slender, straight or slightly curved rods with rounded ends. They vary in width from 0.2 to 0.5 μ and in length from 1 to 4 μ. True branching is seen occasionally in old cultures and sometimes in smears from caseous lymph nodes. Branching forms may be produced at will under certain specific cultural conditions (34, 250, 270).

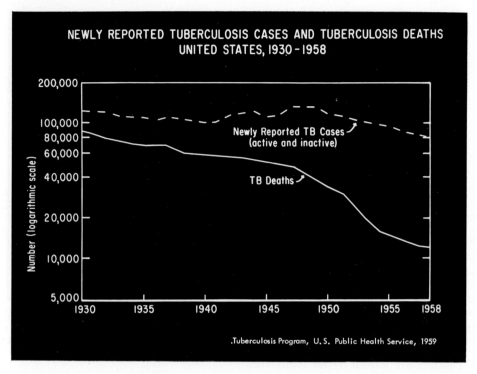

Fig. 1. Decline in death rate without corresponding decrease in new cases.

The bacilli are **acid-fast, nonmotile,** and **nonsporogenous,** and have **no capsules** (Fig. 2). The electron micrograph of thin sections by Kioke and Takeya (111) of *Mycobacterium avium* shows that the rather thick wall is composed of three layers enclosing a plasma membrane which is also three layers in thickness. The relative thickness of the cell wall as shown by conventional methods can be seen in Figure 2. Another interesting structure observed by Takeya and his associates (239) in cell wall "ghosts" was a "paired fibrous structure" which appeared to cover the entire cell envelope. These macromolecular structures, which measured approximately 5-8 μ in width, have not been in other bacteria and may contain, as part of their structure, some of the lipids characteristic of the mycobacteria (266). Kioke's sections also revealed membranous intracytoplasmic structures originally believed to correspond to the mitochondria of the cells of higher organisms (268), which seems to be continuous with the lamellae of the cytoplasmic membrane. The arrangement of the unit membrane resembles a cross-section of an onion. This arrangement, which increases the functioning cytoplasmic membrane, may intensify the metabolic activity of the organism.

Thacore and Willet (241) have produced spheroplasts from tubercle bacilli by cultivation in the presence of lysozyme and a high osmotic concentration of sucrose (Fig. 3). These spherical bodies rupture in the absence of a stabilizing agent. Some of the granules stained by the

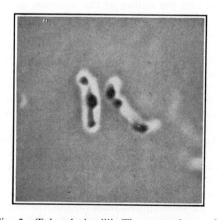

Fig. 2. Tubercle bacilli. The protoplasm of the bacillus has been stained by the Ziehl-Neelsen method and the unstained cell wall outlined by the addition of nigrosin. × 3,600. (From Yegian and Vanderlinde. *J. Bact.*, 54:777, 1947.)

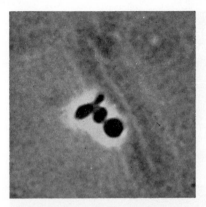

Fig. 3.   Spheroplast formation by lysozyme treatment. (From Thacore and Willett. *Proc. Soc. Exper. Biol. & Med.*, 114:43, 1963.)

Feulgen technic are probably nuclei, while other granules have the staining reaction of mitochondria (268). The dark bodies seen in electron micrographs (Fig. 4) are interpreted by Knaysi as nuclei and the colorless bodies as vacuoles.

Tubercle bacilli from either cultures or secretions usually are stained by the Ziehl-Neelsen method. The carbolfuchsin is allowed to act for 12 to 24 hours, or the process can be speeded up by steaming the preparation for five to 10 minutes. The excess stain is washed off

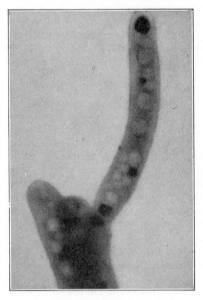

Fig. 4.   Electron micrograph of *Myco. tuberculosis* var. *avian.* The dark bodies are nuclei and the clear ovals vacuoles. (From Knaysi, Hillier, and Fabricant. *J. Bact.*, 60:423, 1950.)

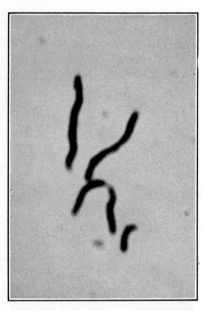

Fig. 5.   Tubercle bacilli stained uniformly by the Ziehl-Neelsen method. × 3,600. (From Yegian and Kurung. *Am. Rev. Tuberc.*, 56:36, 1947.)

with water, and the slide is decolorized by washing for a few seconds with 95 per cent alcohol containing 5 per cent HCl. After counterstaining for one minute with methylene blue, the bacilli are seen as brilliant red rods against a deep sky-blue background (Fig. 5). The bacilli can be stained without heating if the surface altering agent tergitol is added to the carbolfuchsin.

The peculiar staining reaction of acid-fast bacilli and the nature of the inclusion granules (Figs. 6 and 7) have been studied in detail by Yegian and his associates (271, 272, 274, 275). The older conception that acid-fastness depends upon the presence of a waxy sheath about the cell is no longer tenable.

The **gram-positiveness** of tubercle bacilli is independent of the mordant effect of iodine and appears to depend upon the same factors which are responsible for the acid-fastness.

Much's Granules. In many specimens of pus from cold abscesses, granulomatous lesions of lymph nodes, and serous exudates, and in some samples of sputum, acid-fast organisms cannot be found, even though such materials produce tuberculosis when inoculated into animals. By staining such specimens with a modified Gram stain, Much (155) demonstrated the presence of gram-positive granules in short chains or irregular clumps. Much believed that these structures were nonacid-fast tubercle

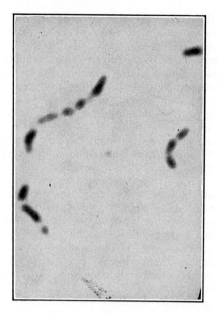

Fig. 6. Granular forms of tubercle bacilli stained by the Ziehl-Neelsen method. × 3,600. (From Yegian and Kurung. *Am. Rev. Tuberc.*, 56:36, 1947.)

bacilli and, although his observations have been confirmed many times, there is a difference of opinion concerning the significance of these forms. Kahn (97) and Yegian and Porter (184, 274) have shown that trauma will convert young acid-fast organisms into nonacid-fast forms. However, Kahn's studies also revealed that certain nonacid-fast forms were not due to trauma and were viable on subculture (97, 98, 99). Kahn's observations have been confirmed by Brieger and his associates (21, 22) who found nonacid-fast granules in cells of experimentally infected animals which would not grow on artificial media but would grow into typical acid-fast bacilli in tissue culture. There is no convincing evidence for the existence of a filterable stage in the life cycle of the tubercle bacilli (100).

Cultural Characteristics. The saprophytic acid-fast bacilli grow readily on ordinary media at room temperature. Tubercle bacilli will not grow on the usual type of media but do **grow slowly** in inspissated serum, coagulated egg, or potato medium after two to three weeks' incubation at 37° C. Youmans (276) found that the generation time of tubercle bacilli on the Proskauer-Beck basal synthetic medium was 20.5 to 24 hours but could be shortened to 13.2 to 15.7 hours by adding beef serum or proantithrombin to the basal medium. The

addition of 5 per cent glycerin inhibits the growth of the vole bacillus (260, 261, 262), has little or no effect on the bovine bacillus, but accelerates appreciably the growth of the human and avian strains. Tubercle bacilli will grow over a pH range of 6.0 to 7.6. The optimal pH for the maintenance of virulence is pH 6.8; cultures of human and bovine organisms grown at pH 6 rapidly become attenuated (218). **The optimal temperature for the isolation of avian strains is 40° C., human and bovine strains 37° C., and bacilli from cold blooded animals 25° C.** (6). After a number of generations in the laboratory, however, temperature requirements of the organisms are less exacting.

Tubercle bacilli are **obligate aerobes** and will not grow in the absence of oxygen. Even a moderate reduction in the oxygen tension results in an appreciable decrease in the metabolism of the bacilli (104).

Avian bacilli develop smooth, creamy, soft colorless colonies on solid media after seven to 10 days' incubation. In broth the organisms grow diffusely throughout the culture fluid, making a smooth homogenous suspension with a minimum of sediment.

Human and bovine strains grow slowly on **inspissated serum** or **coagulated egg medium,** producing, after 10 to 20 days, small, dry,

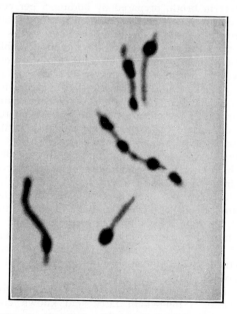

Fig. 7. Beading of tubercle bacilli artificially produced. Ziehl-Neelsen stain. × 3,600. (From Yegian and Kurung. *Am. Rev. Tuberc.*, 56:36, 1947.)

Fig. 8. Culture of *Myco. tuberculosis* in flask of glycerin bouillon.

scaly colonies with corrugated surfaces. The bovine strains grow more slowly and less luxuriantly than bacilli of human origin. On **glycerin broth,** prepared by adding 5 per cent glycerin to beef or veal infusion peptone broth, growth of the human and bovine strains is confined to the surface of the medium. A thin, gray, almost transparent veil-like film grows over the surface of the broth. This film gradually thickens into a white or slightly yellowish, wrinkled membrane which covers the entire surface of the culture fluid (Fig. 8). Tubercle bacilli adapt themselves with difficulty to this floating type of existence and it is best to culture them first on an egg or glycerin egg slant which contains an abundance of water of condensation or one to which 1 or 2 ml. of glycerin broth has been added. When a veil-like film extends out over the fluid in the bottom of the tube, pieces of this membrane may be removed and carefully floated on the surface of the glycerin bouillon. Transplanted pieces which sink to the bottom of the flask fail to develop.

Dubos and Davis (50) found that a derivative of a long-chain fatty acid known commercially as Tween 80 alters the surface conditions of the organism in broth media so that tubercle bacilli multiply much more rapidly, giving a smooth homogeneous type of growth throughout the culture medium. On hydrolysis free oleic acid, which is toxic for the organism, is liberated but this effect may be neutralized by adding small amounts of bovine albumin to the medium. Since homogeneous suspensions of organisms grown on other types of media are prepared with great difficulty, the advantages of Dubos' medium are obvious (56, 67).

After primary isolation, tubercle bacilli grow readily on **synthetic media** containing glycerol, asparagin, citrate, and inorganic salts (124, 125, 126). Amigen, ammonium malate, or a combination of amino acids may be substituted for asparagin but give no better growth. While growing on synthetic media, the tubercle bacillus synthesizes all of the known B-complex vitamins (183). The addition of vitamins to the synthetic media does not increase appreciably either the rate or quantity of growth.

For primary isolation, the media introduced by Lowenstein and by Petragnani have replaced those of Dorset, Petroff, and Corper.

When contaminating organisms are present the material should be treated with sodium hydroxide or sulfuric acid and concentrated by centrifugation before culturing even on selective media. Since some of the bacilli are destroyed by the acid or alkali treatment, we usually culture uncontaminated materials, such as spinal fluid, pleural fluid, or tissue biopsies on Sula's synthetic medium (230), which contains 10 per cent ascitic fluid, or Tarshis' medium, which contains blood and penicillin. Molecular membrane filters have been used to concentrate the bacilli from the spinal fluid and to provide isolated colonies for the study of the neutral red reaction and cording.

Both **glucose** and **glycerin** are utilized by tubercle bacilli but no characteristic fermentations of diagnostic value have been discovered (235). Theobald Smith found that human bacilli grown on a glycerin medium produced first an alkaline reaction which gradually shifted to the acid side as growth continued. In contrast, an alkaline pH was retained by the bovine strains. Reactions of individual strains, however, are too irregular for titration curves to be of much value in the differentiation of human from bovine strains (260).

The latest methods of cultivation and identification of human tubercle bacilli and other classified and unclassified mycobacteria can be found in the *Handbook of Tuberculosis Laboratory, Methods of the Veterans Administration and the Armed Forces,"* Veterans Administration, Washington, D.C., 1962.

Resistance. Tubercle bacilli may remain viable in culture media for two to eight months. Organisms from cultures are killed in two hours when exposed to direct sunlight but bacilli contained in sputum require an exposure of 20 to 30 hours. When protected from direct sunlight, they live in putrefying sputum for weeks and in dried sputum for as long as six to eight months. Droplets of dried sputum adhering to dust particles in the air may be infectious for 8 to 10 days (208). Tubercle bacilli are resistant to the usual chemical disinfectants. A 5 per cent solution of phenol requires 24 hours to disinfect sputum; hypochlorites are not at all effective.

Fortunately, tubercle bacilli possess no greater resistance to moist heat than other bacteria. Pasteurization temperatures are, therefore, efficacious in eliminating them from milk and milk products.

Streptomycin (256), **isonicotinic acid hydrazide** (INH) (236), and **pyrazinamide** are remarkably effective in eliminating tubercle bacilli from experimentally infected animals and from patients with acute forms of tuberculosis, but resistant organisms appear in the sputum after a few months of treatment (73, 149, 273). Pyrazinamide may damage the liver, but streptomycin and INH are relatively harmless in therapeutic doses. **Para-aminosalicyclic acid** (PAS) (55, 113, 227) is not as effective as the other drugs but has the unique ability to delay the emergence of resistance to the more effective drugs when given concomitantly with them (17, 87, 246, 277). There is some evidence that PAS reduces the rate of elimination of INH from the body (150). Tubercle bacilli resistant to streptomycin, PAS, and pyrazinamide are virulent for man and animals. Most tubercle bacilli which develop resistance to INH have lost most or all of their ability to synthesize **catalase.** These catalase deficient strains have lost most, if not all, of their ability to produce progressive disease in animals (107, 149) and can be used as a substitute for BCG in the immunization of animals (88).

Pigmentation. Most saprophysic acid-fast bacteria produce chromogenic colonies. The color may be yellow, pink, orange, or brick-red. In general, tubercle bacilli isolated from cold-blooded animals develop as colorless colonies. Bovine strains usually are colorless, but some strains develop a pink color when grown on glycerin egg media or a green coloring on Sauton's medium (112), and many avian strains develop pink colonies on glycerin egg media. When grown on an ox serum medium, the human bacillus frequently shows yellow or

Fig. 9. Rough colonies of H37R$_v$. (Grown by William Steenken; photographed by Joseph Kurung.)

orange-yellow colonies. The varieties of color found among the unclassified species of *Mycobacterium* by Timpe and Runyon (243) will be discussed in Chapter 30.

Odor. All cultures of true tubercle bacilli have a rather pleasant aromatic fruity odor, but this is not true of the saprophytic acid-fast bacilli.

Variability. Tubercle bacilli were dissociated by Petroff in the Trudeau Laboratory in 1927. In the early reports from the laboratory, the standard smooth (S) and rough (R) terms were transposed in an effort to associate the symbol S with virulence even though the colonies were actually rough (179, 180). The standard nomenclature employed since 1936 uses S to designate a smooth colony and R to designate a rough one (163). With few exceptions the virulent organisms produce R colonies (Fig. 9), but there also are R colonies which are avirulent (Fig. 10). Smooth colonies have been obtained from avian strains of intermediate virulence (179, 223), and S strains from human and bovine bacilli of high virulence (218). Usually, however, tubercle bacilli show only the R form. S forms have not been isolated from cultures of H37 and BCG (223). In 1935 Steenken suggested a new terminology in which the standard S and R designations are retained but sub letters are added; for example, R$_v$ = rough virulent; R$_a$ = rough avirulent; R$_{in}$ = rough intermediate; S$_{ch}$

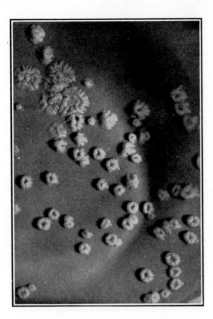

Fig. 10. Rough colonies of H37R$_a$. Note the larger, flatter, intermediate colonies. (Grown by William Steenken; photographed by Joseph Kurung.)

= smooth chromogenic; S$_{cha}$ = smooth, chromogenic avirulent. This classification has been used in the reports from the Trudeau Laboratory since 1935 and now is accepted as standard.

Tubercle bacilli are very versatile in producing a variety of colony forms as a result of very slight changes in environment (224). A dissociate must be subcultured for months or even years before it can be considered as a stabilized variant (225).

The confusing effect of egg oil on colony form was discovered by Steenken in 1940. When tubercle bacilli are grown on media containing egg, the egg oil will convert artificially and mechanically both R$_v$ and R$_a$ colonies into S forms. When subcultured on egg-free media the colonies revert to their standard forms.

The relatively avirulent R$_1$, which has been used for over 50 years to produce hypersensitivity and relative immunity in animals, dissociates into a standard form, R$_{1v}$, which will produce a progressive disease in guinea pigs which have experimental silicosis and a second form, R$_{1a}$, which will not infect either normal or silicotic guinea pigs (226, 228). The BCG attenuated strain of Calmette and Guerin which is used in immunizing man against tuberculosis is even less virulent than R$_1$, but it also shows dissociates morphologically re-sembling those of R$_1$, with BCG$_a$ being almost completely avirulent.

Antigenic Structure. By agglutination, agglutinin absorption, and complement-fixation, the acid-fast bacteria may be separated into **mammalian, avian, cold-blooded,** and **saprophytic types** (81, 267). The avian bacilli have specific antigens by which they can be separated into subtypes (83, 202) and also have an antigen in common with both human and bovine organisms (267). The surface of the tubercle bacillus is composed of a polysaccharide (145) or a lipoprotein polysaccharide which stimulates the production of agglutinins and precipitins when injected into animals (64, 156).

Parlett and Youmans (173, 174, 175) have investigated the antigens of mycobacteria by the Ouchterlony diffusion precipitation technic. Selbert and her associates (206) have isolated a series of tubercle polysaccharides and tubercle proteins which produced antibodies when injected into rabbits. However, animals with high antibody titers had no increased immunity to tuberculosis.

The observation that tuberculopolysaccharide and, to a less extent, tuberculoprotein A and B specifically interfered in vitro and in vivo with antigen-antibody reactions may explain why patients seriously ill with tuberculosis usually fail to show any evidence of antibody formation which can be measured by agglutination, precipitation, or complement fixation. Seibert's observations support those of Gerstl and his associates (76), who found that the whole serum from patients with severe cases of tuberculosis had no demonstrable complement-fixing antibodies but a specific fraction of the same sera had a high titer of complement-fixing antibodies. The behavior of man in respect to the complement-fixation reaction is in sharp contrast to the rabbit, which shows a progressive increase in titer as the disease progresses (65).

Middlebrook (146, 147, 148) has extracted from tubercle bacilli one or more antigens which are capable of sensitizing either sheep or human erythrocytes in such a manner that they agglutinate with the sera of patients having tuberculosis and the sera of individuals with tuberculosis infection in the absence of clinical disease. These antigens are present in old tuberculin (75, 210). If the erythrocytes are treated with tannic acid by the method of Boyden they absorb more and different types of antigens (20). Park (172) found that red blood cells could be fixed with alcohol and formalin, sensitized with tuberculin, and then stored in the frozen lypholized state for at least two months. Takahashi's (237, 238) studies suggest that the sera of patients may contain antipolysaccharide, antiprotein, and antiphosphatid antibodies. The first are detected by the original Middlebrook test, the second by the tanned red cells of Boyden, and the third by the phosphatidekaolin-agglutination test of Takahani (238). Parlett's (173, 175) agar diffusion test reveals even more antibodies. Allerhand and Zitrin (2) could concentrate the antibodies from the sera of patients with acute tuberculosis by continuous flow paper electrophoresis.

Dead tubercle bacilli produce a low grade immunity of brief duration. Living but attenuated strains, such as BCG and R_{1v}, induce a much better immunity which lasts for months or even a few years (198, 199). It is obvious that the immunizing antigen contributes only a minute fraction of the whole bacillus, and a much better vaccine might be obtained by isolating and concentrating the immunizing antigen. Some progress has been made along these lines by two groups of investigators. Weiss and Dubos (261) found that a methanol extract of the whole bacillus induced immunity in mice comparable to that of the whole bacillus, and Youmans and his associates (278) found that a fraction of tubercle bacilli identical with or contained in the mitochondrial fraction induced immunity in mice. More recent studies with mice by Crowle (33) showed that only Anderson's wax B and PMKO were capable of eliciting statistically significant immunity. In contrast, the work of D. W. Smith and Robertson (215) in guinea pigs shows that PMKO, wax D, and the toxic cord factor were not effective immunizers while definite immunity was established by living BCG vaccine and defatted dead vaccine.

All attempts to transfer immunity from one animal to another of the same species have failed (186, 188, 189), and there are many reasons for believing that immunity is not mediated by the classical types of humoral antibodies. In contrast to these negative findings, Lurie (129, 130) demonstrated that monocytes from immunized rabbits retained their ability to destroy tubercle bacilli when transferred to the anterior chamber of the eyes of normal rabbits. Suter (231) cultivated monocytes from immune animals in tissue cultures and confirmed Lurie's observations.

Later Allison, Zappasodi, and Lurie (4) found that monocytes from genetically selected resistant rabbits had a higher acid phosphatase than ordinary rabbits, and this was increased in both the normal and the genetically resistant animals by immunization with BCG (232). A limited amount of immunity was transferred from immunized to normal mice and guinea pigs by living cells teased from lymph nodes and spleen by Suter (233). The more detailed work of Fong, Chin, and Elberg (60) revealed that PMNs did not transfer resistance or hypersensitivity; lymphocytes transfer hypersensitivity but not resistance; while histocytes transfer immunity which was still detectable after a second transfer to a normal animal.

Hypersensitivity to tuberculoprotein can be transferred from animal to animal and from tuberculin-sensitive individuals to previously tuberculin-negative ones by the injection of white blood cells. This phenomenon was discovered by Chase (27, 116) and confirmed by a number of other investigators (35, 118, 119, 144, 222). Cortisone can suppress completely the tuberculin skin test without interfering with the passive transfer of hypersensitivity to a normal animal (36). Disrupted cells retain the ability to transfer hypersensitivity (37, 119). The specific alteration required for passive transfer develops with surprising speed, since Tomcsanyi and his associates (244) found that white cells from the peritoneum of guinea pigs, 24 hours after infection, could effect the transfer. The sensitivity transferred by white cells of ordinary stock guinea pigs persists for only a few weeks in contrast, to that in man, which Lawrence (120) found persisted for months and years. Lawrence also found that disrupted human cells could transfer the tuberculin sensitivity and named the unknown substance the **transfer factor.** Bauer and Stone (14) suspected that the white cells did not persist in heterologous stock guinea pigs and showed that they persisted for several weeks in isologous guinea pigs. Chase (28) succeeded in transferring hypersensitivity in inbred guinea pigs which persisted for 550 days. Fong and his associates (60) showed that the hypersensitivity seemed to be transferred specifically by lymphocytes, and Najarian and Feldman (161) reported a specific accumulation of thimidine-labeled lymphoid cells at the site of the tuberculin reaction in the guinea pigs which were passively sensitized. These findings have not been confirmed by all investigators (102). White blood cells of experimentally infected guinea pigs and patients with clinical tuberculosis share with the cells of the skin sensitivity to tuberculin.

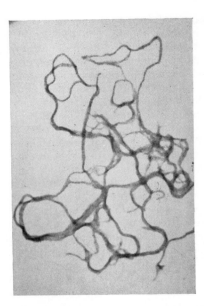

Fig. 11. Cord growth of virulent H37R$_v$. (From Yegian and Kurung. *Am. Rev. Tuberc.*, 65:181, 1952.)

Johnson and Scherago (94) have shown that sensitized cells are inhibited in their migration in vitro by PPD. This sensitivity decreases or may disappear after specific chemotherapy, while the degree of skin sensitivity remains unchanged.

Factors Influencing Virulence. It has not been possible to identify a particular structure, antigen, or toxin which could explain the virulence of tubercle bacilli. Middlebrook, Dubos, and Pierce (146) in 1947 noted that virulent strains of human and bovine bacilli grew in strands or cords (Fig. 11), while avirulent dissociates of the same strains showed no particular arrangement of the organism (Fig. 12). Strains of low virulence, such as BCG, occupy an intermediate position in this ability to produce the cord-like growth. In an aqueous medium the cord factor, which is insoluble in water, accumulates at the bacterial surface and can be removed with organic solvents without killing the bacteria. Bloch and Noll (19, 162) have isolated the cord factor and determined its molecular weight and chemical structure. Cording, however, has been observed in saprophytic strains and is certainly not the sole factor in determining virulence (234). Most virulent strains are capable of binding the dye neutral red in the form of its red salt in alkaline aqueous media, while most avirulent strains lack that ability (51, 79). The migration of polymorphonuclear leukocytes is inhibited by virulent strains (3, 17, 18) but not by

avirulent strains or strains avirulent for a particular species of animal (138).

Bacteriophage. Strains of bacteriophage have been isolated from soil (67, 86) and from stools of patients with clinical tuberculosis (135) which are active against human, bovine, avian, and certain unclassified *Mycobacterium* (26, 198).

Bacterial Metabolites. The acid-fast bacilli produce neither exotoxins nor endotoxins. The "cord factor" described by Bloch (18) and Noll (162) has some toxicity for mice when given in very large doses. This factor is found primarily in the wax C fraction and appears to inhibit various dehydrogenase systems in the animal (18).

The violent toxic systems induced in spontaneously infected humans and in experimentally infected animals by the injection of minute amounts of tuberculin are manifestations of allergy to tuberculoprotein and not endotoxin reactions. This has been discussed in detail in the Chapter on Allergy.

Lipoidal substances constitute from 25 to 40 per cent of the dry weight of tubercle bacilli and include both saturated and unsaturated fatty acids. Several types of tuberculoproteins (203, 204, 205) are produced by the organism, and polysaccharides are present which give precipitin reactions with immune serum in dilutions up to 1:1,000,000. Both polysaccharides and proteins can induce spe-

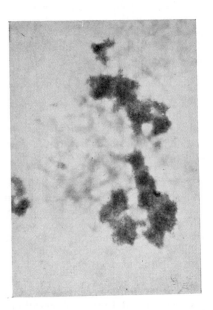

Fig. 12. Absence of cord growth with avirulent H37R$_a$. (From Yegian and Kurung. *Am. Rev. Tuberc.*, 65:181, 1952.)

cific classical antibodies in susceptible animals, but these antibodies afford no protection against infection. Neither polysaccharides nor proteins will stimulate the delayed tuberculin type of allergy in animals unless they are combined with wax D (189), which is a lipopolysaccharide. These findings explain the observations of Dienes and Schoenheit (44) that animals develop a tuberculin-like allergy to simple proteins, such as egg albumin and serum albumin, when these proteins are injected into a tuberculous lesion. The wax D also explains the great adjuvant effect of dead tubercle bacilli when they are incorporated in water or oil emulsions, as described by Freund and McDermott (66). Simple proteins added to this adjuvant result in a very great production of classical antibodies and also tuberculin-like allergies to the simple proteins.

Willett's 1963 review (266) describes the fractionation of the lipids of the tubercle bacillus. Waxes A and phosphatides are ethanol-ether-soluble but acetone-insoluble. Waxes B, C, and D are chloroform-soluble from the fraction which is insoluble in ethanol-ether (63).

Both the immunizing and the sensitizing factors seem to reside in the cell wall. Larson, Rabi, and their associates (117) found that rabbits injected intracutaneously with purified cell walls developed delayed types of allergies to tuberculin cell wall and protoplasm, but protoplasm alone could not induce hypersensitivity.

Both the human H_{37} and the bovine Ravenel strains synthesize all the known B-complex vitamins, including biotin and folic acid (183). Very large amounts of nicotinic acid were synthesized by the human type tubercle bacilli, and only small amounts by the bovine organism. Later investigations by other workers showed that the human type was the only *Mycobacterium* which could synthesize excessive amounts of nicotinic acid, and this forms the basis for Konno's niacin test for the human tubercle bacillus (114). Runyon's modification of Konno's test is preferred in this country to the original test (108, 201).

Catalase is produced by both virulent and saprophytic strains of mycobacteria, but the ability to synthesize catalase seems to be one of the factors necessary for virulence, since there is a reasonably good correlation between the loss of ability to synthesize catalase and the loss of virulence in strains which have become resistant to INH (149).

The Phenomenon of Koch. Koch (109) found, in his early experiments, that a primary inoculation of tubercle bacilli into the groin of a guinea pig resulted, after 10 to 14 days, in the gradual development of a local swelling that became necrotic and produced an open ulcer which persisted until the death of the animal. At necropsy there was swelling and caseation of the lymph nodes, massive disease in the spleen, liver, and lungs, and less extensive infection of other organs. The injection of the same number of tubercle bacilli into a tuberculous animal produced quite a different sequence of events. After 24 to 48 hours a local inflammation appeared at the site of the inoculation, followed by the development of a shallow ulcer which healed promptly without the development of caseation of the adjacent lymph nodes. Although these animals eventually died of tuberculosis, the evidence of local healing indicated the presence of at least some degree of resistance. This accelerated reaction in the infected and sensitized animal is known as the **phenomenon of Koch.** Aronson and McGettigan (8) have produced the Koch phenomenon in man by injecting tuberculin-sensitive individuals with BCG vaccine. The injection of concentrated filtrates of broth cultures or extracts of tubercle bacilli into a local area of the skin of animals infected with tubercle bacilli produces inflammation or necrosis comparable to that produced by the intact living or dead bacilli. These products of the tubercle bacillus are referred to as tuberculins.

Tuberculin. Between 1891 and 1901 Koch prepared a series of tuberculins, and subsequently more than 50 kinds of tuberculin were investigated (13) of which only two have survived the test of time. These are Koch's original preparation known as Old Tuberculin (OT) and Seibert's purified protein derivative (PPD).

To prepare Old Tuberculin tubercle bacilli are grown in slightly alkaline 5 per cent glycerine-peptone bouillon for six to eight weeks. At the end of this time, the entire culture is boiled for one hour to kill the bacilli, and the organisms are filtered off and discarded. The filtrate is evaporated at 80° C. in a water bath until reduced to one tenth of the original volume of the medium. In addition to the metabolic products of the tubercle bacilli, tuberculin contains glycerin, peptones, and mineral salts included in the original medium. To prevent false positive reactions due to these materials, a control must be prepared. The **control** for OT is made by evaporating some of the uninoculated medium to one tenth of its volume. Both the OT and the control contain 50 per cent glycerin, which probably is sufficient to preserve them indefinitely if stored in dark brown bottles in the refrigerator, although 0.5 per cent phenol usually is added as an additional precaution. The tuberculin is stable in its concentrated form but becomes unstable when diluted with physiologic saline.

The test dose of OT is calculated on the obviously erroneous assumption that 1 ml. contains 1,000 mg. of tuberculin. The active proteins, however, constitute only a minute fraction of the OT. The series of dilutions in common use is shown in Tables 1 and 2. The control is diluted in the same manner as the tuberculin.

The purified protein derivative of tuberculin contains a mixture of tuberculoproteins having molecular weights of 2,000 to 9,000, in contrast to the native antigenic tuberculoprotein studied by Seibert, which had a molecular weight of 32,000 (126).

PPD is a dry powder which is "dry diluted" with lactose and made into tablets in the proper proportions so solutions can be made which will contain 0.00002, 0.0001, or 0.005 mg. in the injection dose of 0.1 ml. Some errors may occur in making the "dry" dilutions of 0.00002 and 0.0001 mg.; hence it is more accurate and more economical to use a tablet of the 0.005 mg. diluted in buffered saline to make the 0.0001 and 0.00002 mg. strengths.

PPD is stable indefinitely in the dry form. When dissolved in physiological saline, which contains a buffer and phenol, some of the active tuberculin adheres to the wall of the glass container. This reduces only slightly the strength of the solution. Freshly prepared vials may be kept for as long as nine months in the refrigerator without appreciable loss of potency (53). But vials which have been used frequently become contaminated with saprophitic bacteria which utilized the tuberculoprotein for growth.

The more dilute solution or first test dose, 0.00002 mg., is equivalent to 0.01 mg. of a potent OT. The intermediate dose, 0.0001 mg., is equivalent to 0.05 mg. of OT, while the second dose of PPD, 0.005 mg., is roughly equivalent to 1.0 mg. of OT. It should be noted that the 0.005 mg. dose of PPD is 50 times the intermediate dose of 0.0001 mg., rather than 20 times, as is the case with the OT. Empirical testing of patients with tuberculosis and individuals with positive tuberculin tests has shown that this increased amount of PPD is necessary to give equivalent reactions to the 1.0 mg. dose of a potent OT.

False positive tuberculin reactions will not develop in individuals who are skin tested over periods of months or years with 0.0001 and 0.005 mg. of PPD (11, 248), provided that the individual has never been infected with either a tubercle bacillus or one of the other classified or unclassified mycobacteria (106). However, individuals who give small reactions or even zero reactions to the 0.0001 mg. dose but who are positive to the 0.005 mg. dose often get a booster effect from the 0.0001 mg. dose; this reaction is not evident in 2 to 4 days but appears after 1 week, reaches its maximum at 1 month, and persists for 6 to 12 months (58). In addition to the "booster" effect noted above, another type of reaction appears after repeated injections of tuberculin in the same area of the skin. This reaction is characterized by the appearance of a red area three to four hours after the intracutaneous injection of tuberculin, which increases for six to 12 hours, reaching a maximum at 24 hours, but disappears before 48 hours. This phenomenon has been studied in some detail by Duboczy and his associates (48, 49). This is the type of reaction seen in man following the injection of small doses of egg albumin or serum albumin and described as the Jones-Mote type of allergy. When large doses of protein are used, the delayed type of allergy is followed by the classical immediate type of skin test characteristic of classical antibody formations. Seibert has produced classical antibody by injecting rabbits with purified tuberculoproteins. The senior author has produced similar, if not identical reactions, by repeated skin tests in guinea pigs with 1:10 dilutions of OT and with second strength PPD. The OT was found to be much more effective in giving this type of reaction than the PPD.

If the patient really had a true positive reaction before the series of tests began, one would expect the three-to-four hour reaction to be followed by a larger true reaction as a result of the "booster" effect of tuberculin described by Ferebee and Mount (58). This result was noted by Duboczy (49), who also produced an occasional reduction in specific allergy as a result of repeated testing which seems to overwhelm the reaction mechanism. It is apparent that repeated skin testing over a period of weeks or months should not be performed in the same area of the skin.

Tuberculin Tests. Koch originally injected his tuberculin subcutaneously, and positive results were estimated from the severity of the constitutional symptoms and the degree of febrile reaction. The temperature after six to 12 hours often exceeded 104° F. (40° C.). This method is useful in veterinary practice but should not be used on patients because the generalized tuberculin reaction may reactivate a smoldering tuberculous infection. To avoid this danger, von Pirquet (254) introduced the scratch test. Two drops of undiluted tuberculin were deposited on the skin, after which the superficial layers of the skin were scratched with a needle and the tuberculin allowed to dry. Degrees of sensitivity could not be measured by this method. **Mantoux** (136, 137) introduced the **intracutaneous skin test** in 1908, which made quantitative measurements possible. By this method 0.1 ml. of any one of a number of dilutions of OT or PPD can be injected into the superficial layers of the skin and the degree of induration measured in millimeters 48 to 72 hours later. Indurations measuring less than 5 mm. are read as doubtful or negative. Reactions of 1 to 3 cm. are frequently seen in highly allergic patients, and a vesicle often forms in the center of the inflamed area. Actual ulceration of the skin may occur beneath the vesicle but it is extremely rare for a febrile or constitutional reaction to follow the most severe cutaneous reaction. Most false negative tests result from injecting the tuberculin into the deeper layers of the skin, where it drains away from the local area through the lymphatics. Patients critically ill with tuberculosis or other diseases, and especially patients with tuberculous effusion of the pleura, pericardium, meninges, or peritoneum may fail to react to tuberculin or react only to the strong doses, such as 1 mg. of OT or second strength PPD (0.005). The physiologic conditions governing the degree of the tuberculin reaction have been reviewed by Pepys (176).

In cattle 0.1 ml. of OT is injected either into the skin of the caudal fold of the tail or into the lower palpebra (103). For monkeys and primates a comparable dose of OT or PPD is injected into the subcutaneous tissues of the margin of the upper eyelid. Positive reactions show swelling and redness of the eyelid in 16 hours, and this lasts for 72 hours.

The patch test was introduced by Vollmer in 1937 (253). Old tuberculin made four times as strong as Koch's OT was dried on adhesive tape, after which the tape was attached to the skin of the arm or back. A control, made of concentrated medium, was included. The patch test was left on for 48 hours, and the reading made 48 hours after the patch had been removed (240). The results were very good in young preschool children but yielded progressively more false negatives in older children and adults. This patch test is not recommended

for school surveys or for diagnostic testing of patients.

The several **multiple puncture** methods are modifications of Von Pirquet's scratch test procedure. The first was the Heaf test popularized in England, the second the Sterneedle test, and finally the Tine test. In the Heaf test a special tuberculin of intermediate concentration is spread on a small area of the skin, and then the tuberculin is introduced into the superficial layer of the skin by small needle points, which are activated by a spring gun. The advantage of this method over the Von Pirquet is the uniformity in the number and depth of the punctures, while the disadvantages are the cost of the Heaf gun and the possibility of transferring serum hepatitis. The Sterneedle test avoids the danger of hepatitis by using detachable metal heads with needles which can be sterilized in bulk so that a sterile one is used for each subject; its disadvantages are the original cost of the gun and the cost of the individual needle-holding head. The Tine tests are individually prepared and are presterilized units which are used once and discarded; the concentrated tuberculin is dried on the Tine points before sterilization (12), no expensive gun is required, and the possibility of transferring serum hepatitis is eliminated. These methods are slightly less accurate than the Mantoux intracutaneous test and are not recommended as ideal for either school surveys or diagnostic studies. The Tine test may be the practical answer for the busy physician in office or clinic practice, however, provided doubtful reactions are rechecked by the Mantoux test (12).

Maha (134) found excellent correlation between the Tine test and the Mantoux test in 676 college students. Incidentally, only 8 per cent of the American students were positive, while 62 per cent of the foreign students had positive reactions, showing the greater frequency of primary tuberculosis infections in the foreign students.

Doses of Tuberculin. The doses of tuberculin employed in a particular study are sometimes recorded as 0.1 ml. of a specific dilution, or as milligrams of OT or PPD, or in tuberculin units (TU). Comparable doses of OT, PPD, and TU are given in Tables 1 and 2. OT from different laboratories varies much more in potency than PPD (205). Both PPD and OT contain a mixture of tuberculoproteins which vary in their ability to elicit reactions (205).

Children under six months of age who had not been exposed to tuberculosis gave negative

Table 1. Dilutions of Tuberculin

Amount of OT	Amount of Saline (ml.)	Resulting Dilution	Dose Injected (ml.)	Tuberculin Injected (mg.)
1 ml.	9	1:10	0.1	10
1 ml. of 1:10	9	1:100	0.1	1
1 ml. of 1:100	9	1:1,000	0.1	0.1
1 ml. of 1:1000	9	1:10,000	0.1	0.01
1 ml. of 1:10,000	9	1:100,000	0.1	0.001

Table 2. Comparable Doses of OT and PPD

Dilution of OT	Tuberculin Injected (mg.) *	PPD Injected (mg.) †	Tuberculin Units (TU)	Strength
1:100,000	0.001		0.1	
1:10,000	0.01	.000002	1.0	First
1:2,000	0.05	.0001	5.0	Intermediate
1:1,000	0.1		10.0	
1:100	1.0	.005	100.0	Second

    * Based on 1 ml. of concentrated OT = 1,000 mg.
    † Based on milligrams of Protein.

reactions to 0.005 mg. of PPD (69), and adult bush Negroes in Dutch Guiana failed to react to the same dose (99). However, when Furcolow and his associates (69) gave 2 to 10 times as concentrated PPD to the young children, false positive reactions were obtained. BCG vaccination is usually administered only to individuals who have a negative reaction to 100 TU. After vaccination with the BCG used in this country, some individuals react to 5 or 10 TU but many do not react to less than 100 or 250 TU. Nevertheless, the reaction to the strong dose of tuberculin must be regarded as specific, since the subjects failed to react to the same large dose before vaccination. The degree of allergy, following BCG vaccination, does not necessarily indicate the degree of immunity (194).

Some individuals, particularly Negroes and patients having skin, eye, or glandular infections, have a remarkable sensitivity to tuberculin. They may give positive reactions to 0.01 TU and often give large reactions with necrotic centers when injected with 1 TU. Patients suspected of having tuberculosis of the eye or skin should be given an initial dose of 0.01 TU and the dose increased, if negative, as indicated in the table. Other patients, even those with extensive disease, will not be harmed by an initial dose of 10 TU. In the surveys of school children in Minnesota the initial dose was 0.1 mg. of OT followed by 1 mg. for those giving negative reactions to the first dose (157, 158, 159).

It has been assumed from the time of the introduction of the Mantoux test that this test was much superior to all scratching and puncturing procedures because the needle delivered an exact amount of tuberculin to the sensitized cells in the skin and practically all of the active principle in the tuberculin remained at the site of the injection. It was known, of course, that a slightly deeper injection would result in a rapid disappearance of the tuberculin and a false-negative test. Only since the introduction of iodinated isotopic PPD have we learned about the rapid disappearance of tuberculin from the site of injection. Oort and Turk (165) have found that approximately 50 per cent of the intracutaneous Mantoux dose disappeared in one hour, 75 per cent in five hours, and 96 per cent in 24 hours. The amount of tuberculin remaining in the skin of the sensitized guinea pig, between 24 and 48 hours, was twice that remaining in the skin of a normal guinea pig. This sounds impressive until one recalls that this is in the neighborhood of only 2 to 4 per cent of the amount originally injected. The facility with which the major part of the dose injected disappears through the lymphatics gives a good physiologic basis for the varied result of a standard dose of tuberculin when the capillaries are artificial or naturally constricted or dilated, as emphasized by Pepy (176). Preliminary observations with I^{131} PPD in normal and sensitive guinea pigs carried out by Thorne, Eiring, and Smith in our laboratory several years ago confirm the result of the more detailed study by Oort and Turk (165). There are clinical observations to show that some tuberculin does remain fixed to the cells in the skin for weeks and months when (1) a subreacting dose is given to a sensitized individual and (2) a large dose is given to a person who has not yet developed the allergy characteristic of tuberculosis. It is known that individuals receiving corticoid hormones may not react to tuberculin but will react several weeks later at that site when the corticoid has been discontinued. The persistence of tuberculin at the site of injections may explain some of the observations made by Duboczy (49).

Duplicate Mantoux tests performed with the same tuberculin on the two arms, or on two places on the same arm, by the same operator can show varying results. The studies of Guld (82) demonstrate excellent agreement when the degree of allergy was high, but when the degree of allergy to the 5 TU dose is in the range of 5 to 9 mm. the disagreement between the two tests can be as great as 16.2 per cent. In view of this one observation, a single negative test to 5 TU of tuberculin by the Mantoux method should not be taken as proof of the absence of sensitivity to some type of *Mycobacterium,* and the 5 TU test should be repeated in duplicate or the 100 TU should be given. The unclassified strains of mycobacteria described in the next chapter usually give less severe allergic reactions than the human bacilli, and duplicate tests are recommended with the new PPDs prepared for each of these unclassified mycobacteria.

Many carefully controlled studies on man and animals were carried out by Palmer and his associates (166, 167, 169) to prove that a specific reaction of 8, 10, 12, or 15 mm. of 5 TU would prove the individuals had been infected with the human tubercle bacillus and not with one of the unclassified types. Certainly a large majority of these stronger reactions were caused by the human bacillus, but there were always a certain number of individuals who had large cross-reactions from other classified or unclassified mycobacteria which could not be separated on the basis of size from reactions to human bacilli.

In practical clinical work with patients, a conclusive negative tuberculin test may be of more value than a positive test, since a positive merely proves previous infection and not that the patient's present symptoms are from active tubercular disease. On the other hand, there is both clinical and experimental work showing that **patients in good physical condition who give negative tuberculin tests to 1-100 OT, or 0.005 mg. of PPD (100 TU) have not been infected and are not now suffering from infection with either human or other classified** or unclassified *Mycobacterium* **organisms** (23). Something less than 1 per cent will be found as exceptions to this rule.

The Prognostic Significance of a Strong Reaction to the 100 TU Dose of PPDs. In the study by Palmer, Jablon and Edwards (169) it was found that 8.6 per cent of 68,754 Navy recruits tested with 5 TU or PPDs had reactions of 10 mm. or more. The annual incidence of active tuberculosis appearing in this group during the next year was five times as great as that in the recruits who failed to react or had less than 9 mm. reaction to 5 TU. Although the rate was 157 per 100,000 per year in the strong reactions, the actual number of cases was only 37, while 72 cases developed in those considered to be nonreactors because there were more recruits in this group. In the following four years the incidence of disease **decreased in the originally strong reactors and increased in those originally negative.** In the British study the 15 mm. reaction to 3 TU had an incidence of clinical tuberculosis of 367 per 100,000 the first year of testing, compared to an incidence of 77 in those having 5-14 mm. reactions to 3 TU but positive to 100 TU. The rate decreased in the strong reactions each year and was practically the same in both groups after seven and a half to 10 years (23). Individuals with the strong reactions may have had microscopic tissue activity without clinical symptoms and were more subject to the development of clinical activity, but in time they became more resistant.

THE CLINICAL AND EPIDEMIOLOGICAL SIGNIFICANCE OF A POSITIVE REACTION TO THE 100 TU

It has been known for many years that patients acutely ill with tuberculosis, or other diseases, may fail to give a positive tuberculin reaction to 1 TU or 5 TU and occasionally even to 100 TU. It was assumed that this resulted from some type of hyposensitization, some exhaustion reaction, or a physiologic inability of the skin to react. This phenomenon is not infrequently seen in patients with miliary tuberculosis and generalized primary infections. Formerly these patients practically always succumbed to these diseases, but now, with the help of the new chemotherapeutic drugs, most of them recover; and when they do recover, they react normally to a 1 TU and a 5 TU dose of tuberculin. When an individual in good health fails to react to 5 TU but reacts to 100 TU of either OT or PPD, it was assumed that his initial infection had been handled so effectively that he was gradually losing his allergy and consequently his ability to react to tuberculin. The evidence for the alteration of the tuberculin reaction in the absence of reinfection has been presented by Rich (194), Dahlstrom (38), and Long (125) and in the more recent review by Smith, Johnston, Cain, and Schumacher (214).

This comfortable explanation for the origin of the 100 TU reactions was challenged by Dr. Caroll Palmer (167) and his associates in 1950. Palmer believed that the 100 TU reactors had never been infected with the human tubercle bacillus at all but with some other organism, presumably a *Mycobacterium* species from the soil. He came to this conclusion from a study of the beginning and evolution of tuberculosis in 26,000 student nurses in 76 training schools during the years 1943-1949 (167). On admission to the school of nursing, a geographic and a contact history was obtained from each student, and all were tested with 5 TU (0.0001 mg.) of PPD. Those negative to this dose were retested with 100 TU (0.005 mg.) of PPD. Students from Texas and Oklahoma reacted positively to 5 TU at a rate of 25 percentage, but in all other areas the rate of reaction did not exceed 15 per cent. The result of the 100 TU dose was quite different: the median percentage in the ten southeastern states was about 64, in contrast to 28 for the remainder of the states. Calcified lesions were present in a fairly high percentage of the 5 TU reactions, but not often in those positive only to the 100 TU dose. Furthermore, the 5 TU reactions frequently gave a history of previous contact with patients who had clinical tuberculosis, while those reacting only to 100 TU did not give a significant history of contact (54). The tuberculin studies by Pollock, Sutherland, and D'Arcy Hart (182) of 7,646 Royal Air Force recruits in England carefully confirmed Palmer's findings of a relationship between the severity of the reaction and contact with a case of tuberculosis, but this was interpreted as evidence of recent or severe infection and not as evidence of infection limited to the human bacillus. In general, there was almost universal disagreement here and in Europe with Dr. Palmer's theory, and he was challenged to produce this *Mycobacterium* from the soil which was giving the 100 TU reactions. This challenge was successfully met when Edwards, Edwards, and Palmer (53) presented the evidence of "Battey" infec-

tions in 46,190 naval recruits. The Navy recruits were given simultaneous tests with 5 TU of PPD^{-S} and 5 TU of PPD^{-B}. The positive reactions to the PPD made from the Battey bacillus was between 25 and 26 per cent, and almost exactly the same percentage of reactions to the Battey PPD was found in medical students in Illinois by Youmans (277) and in North Carolina by Smith and his associates (214). Male university students in Maryland had about the same rate of reactions, but female students were much lower. The Duke students who were simultaneously tested with human, avian, and Battey PPD showed almost as many positive reactions to the avian and the Battey tuberculin. The relation between the avian and Battey sensitivity will be discussed in Chapter 30, but the fact remains that sensitivity to avian or Battey tuberculin excels that to the human type PPD in this country and in England (41, 192, 193).

Apparently all of these infections with avian or Battey *Mycobacterium* can be detected by the strong doses of tuberculin such as 1-100 OT or second strength PPD (96), because of the cross-reacting antigen in species of mycobacteria and their tuberculins. Palmer's theory that many, but not all, of the reactions to 100 TU were reactions to some other type of *Mycobacterium* not the human *Mycobacterium tuberculosis,* was proven. There is ample evidence, however, that a minority of reactions to 100 TU or PPDs are due to infections with the human bacillus which have been brought under control and the sensitivity attenuated (214).

Before Palmer's first theory had been proven, he proposed the elimination of testing with 100 TU doses since the reaction would be "nonspecific" and the result confusing rather than helpful. The 5 TU dose of human PPD did indeed detect 99.6 per cent of culture-proven cases of clinical tuberculosis in one sanatorium where all the patients were tested simultaneously rather than on admission (69). In the same sanatorium 12 years later with older patients (84), however, 5 per cent were missed by this dose. When Lester and Atwell tested the patients on admission, 8.7 per cent were missed by the 5 TU dose. At the Durham Veterans Administration Hospital 6.1 per cent were missed by the 5 TU dose (95), while 10 per cent were missed in the St. Albans Naval Hospital (121), 17.6 per cent at the Mayo Clinic (123), and 31 per cent at the Duke Hospital (95).

The evidence seems to be conclusive that the 5 TU dose will not detect all the clinical cases

of tuberculosis caused by the human tubercle bacillus. **Many of those missed by the 5 TU dose, but not all, could be detected by the 100 TU dose.** Four important facts can be learned as a result of the 100 TU dose in individuals who are known to be negative to the 5 TU dose of PPD^{-S}. **(1) Those negative to the 100 TU dose, provided they are not clinically ill, may be assumed to be free of infection and disease from both classified and unclassified mycobacteria. (2) Individuals negative to 5 TU PPD^{-S} but positive to 100 TU of OT, PPD^{-S} and PPD^{-B} may be infected with another classified or unclassified mycobacteria, which may be detected by retesting, in duplicate, with 5 TU doses of PPD made from the other mycobacteria (214). (3) Individuals positive to 100 TU have an immunity to reinfection tuberculosis about as great as individuals who have been vaccinated with BCG and much greater than those giving 15 mm. or more of reaction to 3 TU and 5 TU (23, 168); therefore, they can be assigned to the care of patients with tuberculosis without being given BCG. This relative immunity must have resulted in many instances from a subclinical infection with one or another of the unclassified mycobacteria.** The evidence for the immunity of this group was furnished by the 10-year BCG study of the British Research Group (23) and later by Palmer's (68) restudy of the student nurses who were negative to 5 TU PPD^{-S} but positive to 100 TU of PPD^{-S}. Individuals who are negative to both 5 TU and 100 TU can be assumed to have escaped infection with both human and other classified or unclassified mycobacteria. They are easily infected on exposure to patients with tuberculosis and should be given BCG if their occupation or place of residence will expose them to individuals with active tuberculosis.

Experimental Disease in Laboratory Animals. Monkeys and anthropoid apes are very susceptible to experimental infections with the human and bovine strains of tubercle bacilli but comparatively resistant to the avian type.

The primates acquire tuberculosis spontaneously from casual contact with man.

The **guinea pig,** the **mouse,** and the **rabbit** are the most useful animals for laboratory studies. Only a few bacilli are required to infect guinea pigs, and, since they are equally susceptible to the human and bovine strains, guinea pig inoculation is an ideal diagnostic method for the detection of small numbers of organisms in contaminated material. **Contaminated material** should be treated by one of the **concentration** methods before planting cultures or inoculating guinea pigs. Two guinea pigs usually are inoculated simultaneously in the subcutaneous tissues of the groin. An induraton at the site of inoculation, accompanied by palpable lymph nodes, frequently is observed after four to six weeks. After six weeks the animals should be injected intracutaneously with 0.1 ml. of a 5 per cent solution of OT. Infected animals develop an intense local reaction, which proceeds to the development of an open ulcer, while the uninfected animals show only a transient erythema. The positive tuberculin reactors should be killed and the bacilli demonstrated by smears and cultures of the lesions or by the reinoculation of additional guinea pigs. The negative reactors should be held for another six weeks and then retested with tuberculin. Some colonies of guinea pigs are infected spontaneously with *Pasteurella pseudotuberculosis* which produces caseation in the lymph nodes and lesions in the spleen and liver. The possibility of this infection is one of the reasons for insisting upon a positive tuberculin test or the demonstration of typical acid-fast organisms in the lesions before reporting a guinea pig inoculation as positive for tuberculosis.

As shown in Table 3, animal inoculation is one method of determining the various types of tubercle bacilli.

The rabbit usually is employed for the differentiation of human and bovine strains. Two animals are injected by the intravenous route, one receiving 1 mg. and the other 0.01 mg. Bacilli are removed from the surface growth

Table 3. Pathogenicity of Tubercle Bacilli for Laboratory Animals

ANIMAL	HUMAN TYPE	BOVINE TYPE	AVIAN TYPE	MURINE TYPE	JOHNE'S BACILLUS
Guinea Pig	++++	++++	0	+	0
Rabbit	++	++++	+++	+	0
Calf	+	++++	++	——	++
Fowl	0	0	++++	——	——
Vole	+	++++	+	+++	——

of a broth culture, blotted with sterile filter paper, weighed, and then suspended in 2 to 3 ml. of physiologic saline for injection. Both rabbits die after six to eight weeks if the culture is of the bovine type. If the organism is a human type bacillus, the animal receiving the smaller dose survives. Occasional strains of intermediate virulence are encountered which cannot be differentiated by this method (217).

In the relatively resistant rat, allergy does not develop and the infected monocytes become packed with bacilli without the development of any evidence of reaction between the bacilli and the host cells. Small doses of avian tubercle bacilli produce chronic disease in rabbits, but large doses induce a fulminating fatal infection known as the **Yersin type** of tuberculosis. The dog is more resistant than the mouse but less resistant than the rat (61).

Variation in Virulence. It has been known for years that the human and bovine types of tubercle bacilli, in contrast to the avian, have a remarkable degree of stability both in colony morphology and in virulence. The human strain $H_{37}R_v$ and the bovine strain Ravenel, when kept on suitable media, have maintained a constant degree of virulence for over 50 years. Freshly isolated strains from the United States and Europe have a comparable high degree of virulence. Therefore, the studies of Mitchinson, Bhatia and their associates (16, 151), which showed that the human tubercle bacilli of low virulence for guinea pigs were producing severe and fatal disease in malnourished patients in southern India, came as a surprise. The reverse of this was seen when prisoners of war with far advanced pulmonary tuberculosis were released from concentration camps and given good food. Many of these former prisoners made a rapid recovery from tuberculosis without benefit of specific chemotherapeutic drugs.

Clinical Types of Infection in Man. Man is very susceptible to **tuberculous infection** but remarkably resistant to **tuberculous disease.** In certain epidemics in school children initiated by an open case of tuberculosis in a teacher or fellow student as many as 50 to 70 per cent of the students became infected as measured by the tuberculin reaction although only a few developed clinical disease during the period of observation (89, 90).

Tubercle bacilli gain entrance to the body by inhalation, ingestion, or directly through the skin (80). Inhalation is the most frequent method of infection, and invasion through the skin the most unusual. The local manifestations of a primary infection vary somewhat with the route of invasion. With inhalation the primary lesion develops in the lungs and the tracheobronchial lymph nodes are infected most extensively. With ingestion the primary lesion may be in the mouth or tonsils with an enlargement of the lymph nodes of the neck, producing a condition called **cervical adenitis** or **scrofula** (78). If the organisms penetrate the intestinal mucosa, the primary lesion occurs in the wall of the intestine and is accompanied by **mesenteric adenitis** with or without **peritonitis.** When entrance is by way of the skin, there develops an ulceration at the point of invasion accompanied by an extensive involvement of the regional lymph nodes.

Tubercle bacilli multiply unchecked when first introduced. The infecting organisms may be held temporarily and mechanically in the regional lymph nodes but in a period of days they reach the thoracic ducts and the general circulation, so that eventually all parts of the body are infected by a generalized dissemination before the conditions of **hypersensitivity** and **relative resistance** can be developed. The tuberculin test becomes positive between the fourth and the twelfth week after infection, and after its appearance the bacilli spread slowly, if at all, through the lymphatics.

Most of the bacilli scattered throughout the body during the early part of the primary infection do not find locations suitable for development and disappear but some remain in microscopic foci and may give rise one to 10 years later to infections of the **bones, joints, lungs,** and other organs. Of particular importance are those which reach the brain: some develop into tuberculomas which become encapsulated and heal or calcify, while others rupture into the meninges and initiate a tuberculous **meningitis** followed by a blood stream invasion called **miliary tuberculosis.** Miliary tuberculosis also may result from the rupture of a caseous lymph node into a vein or into one of the large lymph vessels without the development of an associated meningitis.

In countries with a high standard of living and a good tuberculosis control program the incidence of tuberculous infection in children has decreased rapidly during the past

40 years (74). In Minnesota, for example, 47.3 per cent of the school children had positive tuberculin tests in 1926, but the incidence was reduced to 3.9 per cent by 1954 (158, 159). In many instances primary infections have been postponed to adult life and often present very difficult diagnostic problems (209).

REINFECTION TUBERCULOSIS. This is almost exclusively a disease of the lungs. Most pathologists believe that reinfection develops from the extension of infection to the lungs from a caseous focus resulting from a primary infection in the lymphatic system (157, 181). Our experimental studies (211, 212) and clinical experience are in accord with this view. However, many clinicians and some pathologists believe that most reinfection tuberculosis in adults is from an exogenous source (142). The evidence for this point of view is summarized in a series of excellent reports by Medlar (139, 140, 141). Since the patient already is hypersensitive to tuberculin when the reinfection takes place, severe symptoms occur and **chronic pulmonary tuberculosis** develops. The pulmonary form of the disease is the chief cause of morbidity and mortality. The age of the patient at the time of the initial infection (280) seems to determine the rapidity with which clinical disease appears (Fig. 13).

CONGENITAL TUBERCULOSIS. This form of the disease occurs but is quite unusual. Most cases of childhood tuberculosis, even in infants of only a few weeks of age, are **acquired in the home.**

SILICOTUBERCULOSIS. The inhalation of inorganic dust containing free silica injuries the lungs and predisposes the individual to the development of pulmonary tuberculosis. The mortality rate from tuberculosis of workmen exposed to silica dust may be as high as 190 per 100,000 as compared with 65 for the unexposed workers (47). In certain mines the mortality is much higher (70, 71, 72). Gardner produced experimental

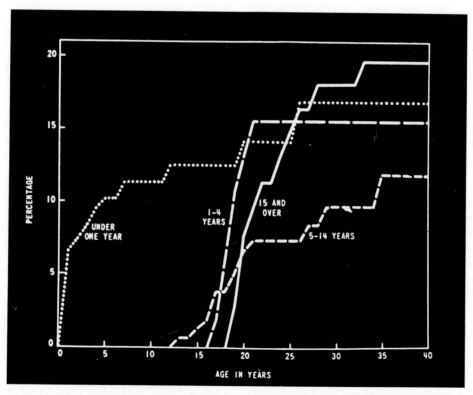

Fig. 13. Influence of age at time of infection on age when disease develops. (From Zeidberg, Dillon, and Gass. *Am. Rev. Tuberc.,* 70:1009, 1954.)

silicosis in guinea pigs and studied the influence of an associated infection with tubercle bacilli. The presence of silica lowered the resistance of the tissues so much that even the relatively avirulent R₁ strain regularly produced progressive fatal infection in the silicotic guinea pigs (70, 72). Vorwald found that BCG also produces a fatal disease in silicotic guinea pigs suggesting that this vaccine should not be given to individuals who are going to be exposed to silica dust (255).

Dust from organic materials and inorganic dusts other than those containing silica do not predispose the individual to the development of tuberculosis.

SARCOIDOSIS. This clinical syndrome is characterized by involvement of skin, glands, bones, lungs, and other internal organs and is difficult to differentiate from some forms of tuberculosis. The etiologic agent is unknown, but the pathologic reaction is characterized by a granulomatous reaction, with foreign body giant cells and noncaseating tubercles. The tuberculin test is nearly always negative, and most patients fail to develop allergy to tuberculin after vaccination with BCG (92, 219). Tuberculin-negative sarcoid patients, however, can be passively sensitized by the injection of white blood cells from patients with positive tuberculin tests (249). When suspensions of sarcoid tissue are injected intracutaneously into sarcoid patients, about 90 per cent develop a lesion at the site of inoculation, while normal individuals and patients with other diseases give reactions in only 7 per cent (40). This test is known as the **Kveims reaction.**

Transmission. For practical purposes man may be regarded as the sole carrier of tuberculosis in the United States at the present time. Tuberculosis has been eliminated almost completely from herds of cattle as a result of tuberculin testings on a large scale followed by the slaughter of all positive reactors. Any residual foci of infection can be controlled completely by universal pasteurization of milk and milk products.

Some individuals develop chronic pulmonary tuberculosis with cavity formation in the lungs and tubercle bacilli in the sputum without obvious symptoms of the disease. These **carriers** of tubercle bacilli spread the infection throughout the community as they go about their usual occupations. For the detection of carriers, it is essential that sputum be examined with care, regardless of the patient's clinical diagnosis and apparent lack of pulmonary symptoms.

With the rapid reduction in the number of tuberculin reactions in the adult population and the increase in primary infections in adults, the time is approaching when a tuberculin test will become a part of the routine study of all patients analogous to the white blood cell count, Wassermann test, and the urine analysis (211).

In 1917 Theobald Smith (216) described the factors regulating the virulence of the human type tubercle bacillus. If a strain suddenly acquires increased virulence and the host dies before the bacilli can be transmitted to another individual, the organisms are buried with their victim. On the other hand, if the virulence falls below a certain critical level, open pulmonary lesions are not produced and the organisms are not transmitted. From the standpoint of the tubercle bacillus, the weak point in its cycle of transmission of tuberculosis lies in the very large number of individuals who must be infected in order to produce a single chronic case with a cavity in the lung to serve as a disseminator of the disease. The detection and isolation of the carrier will break the chain of transmission.

The inborn native resistance of the patient probably has more to do with determining the course of tuberculosis than any other factor, including modern treatment. The medical profession believed for centuries that tuberculosis was inherited in certain families, that some races were highly susceptible and others were highly resistant to the disease. These "superstitions" were discarded by the modern physician after Koch discovered the tubercle bacillus. However, the basic importance of the constitution of the patient has been proved by genetic studies. Strains of guinea pigs have been obtained by selective breeding which were (a) more susceptible and (b) less susceptible than the parent stock (269). Even more convincing evidence has been produced by Lurie's (130, 131, 132) selective genetic strains of rabbits. Comparative studies of **monozygotic** and **dizygotic twins** have shown that in a very large percentage of cases, the monozygotic twins react in an identical manner to a tuberculous infection (101, 251). Of particular importance was the extreme variation in the monozygotic twin units, some pairs being found very resistant while others were very susceptible to progressive disease.

Puffer's (185, 186) study of tuberculous and nontuberculous families in Tennessee presents convincing evidence that some families are more susceptible to tuberculosis than others and that these susceptible families are being reduced gradually in number because of their inability to reproduce themselves. This automatic selective mechanism probably has been in operation in Europe and among peoples of European descent for centuries, which accounts in part for the steady decline in the death rate from tuberculosis. The members of the Jewish race have no increased resistance to **tuberculous infection** but have a definite resistance to **tuberculous disease** (190). In contrast, first and second generations of Irish and Italian emigrants were quite susceptible to tuber-

culous disease. The astonishing susceptibility of the North American Indian and the Eskimo is well known. In this country the Negro (30) and the Mexican Indian have a definitely higher mortality rate than the Caucasians (Fig. 14).

The difference between the white race and the Negro is shown best by the studies of Roth (200) in which he compared the attack rate of white and Negro soldiers in the U.S. Army between 1922 and 1936. The food, clothing, housing, medical care, and other environmental factors were identical. The morbidity rate was 210 per 100,000 for the white soldiers and 256 for Negro soldiers, but the mortality rate was 24 per 100,000 for the whites and 99 for the Negroes. The death rate of the Negro was approximately four times as great as that of the white. Furthermore, the disease is more rapidly fatal in the Negro, the average duration of a fatal infection in the Negro being one-fourth that in the white. The reduction in the duration of the disease compensates for the greater mortality, so that the Negro population is exposed to about the same

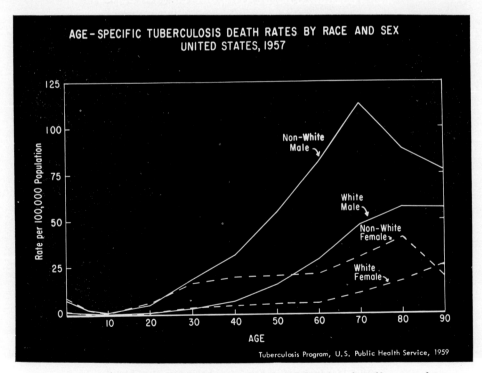

Fig. 14. Increase in death rate in males after 30 and females after 60 years of age.

number of days of potential infection per case as is the white.

In most instances of excessively high mortality, such as that existing among the Indian, Eskimo, Negro, Mexican, Filipino, and Puerto Rican, there is a combination of racial susceptibility and poor environment. The environmental factor is much more important, not only in a quantitative sense but also because it can be corrected in a single generation, while the genetic factor requires centuries.

Changing Epidemiologic Pattern. Forty years ago the death rate from tuberculosis was excessively high in infants, adolescents, and young adults and relatively low in late middle age and in old age (45, 46). With the improvement in the standard of living and the adoption of the control measures recommended by the National Tuberculosis Association, a large proportion of the open carriers of tubercle bacilli have been dis-

covered, isolated in sanatoriums, and treated. This has resulted in a sharp reduction and death in infancy, adolescence, and the early years of adult life (68). Forty years ago the death rate for females was always higher than that of males in all age groups and all races. This is no longer true. The highest death rates are now in nonwhite and white males after the age of 30 and in nonwhite and white females after the age of 60 (Fig. 14). This is considerable variation in the new case rate by states. The number of newly reported cases of tuberculosis each year has not declined proportionally to the decrease in deaths (Fig. 1) and the influence of puberty on the activation of clinical disease is still apparent (Fig. 15).

Small Epidemics of Tuberculosis. Large epidemics of tuberculosis were precipitated when tubercle bacilli were introduced, for the first time, in groups of races who had never been exposed to the infection. This

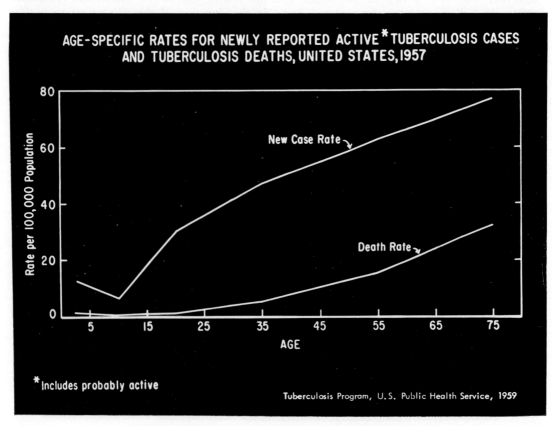

Fig. 15. Increase in new cases beginning at puberty.

has been observed in the North American Indian, in Central African states, and in the South Sea Islands. Indeed, the Alaskan Indians and Eskimos are only now emerging from a major epidemic which has persisted on a high level for about 100 years.

The great success in protecting infants, school children, and young adults from infection with tubercle bacilli has resulted in concentrating large numbers of highly susceptible individuals. Small epidemics usually arise from infections caused by a single individual. There were two epidemics in ships traced to one active case on each ship (164). One school teacher in Denmark infected 70 of 105 tuberculin negative students. After infection, 41 of the 105 developed primary infections, demonstrated by x-ray and by the isolation of tubercle bacilli from gastric lavage. Fifteen of the students developed post-primary (reinfection) progressive type of tuberculosis over the next 12 years. A summary of the epidemic, which was reported by Hyge (91), is shown in Figure 16. A severe school epidemic which developed in the Whitesboro School District in New York State was traced to one bus driver. Among 228 children who rode this bus for less than 40 days, 66, or 28.9 per cent, reacted to tuberculin; and 42, or 18.4 per cent, developed active pulmonary infections. In a group of 30 who rode the bus for more than 40 days, 56.7 per cent developed positive tuberculin tests and 30 per cent active pulmonary tuberculosis. This epidemic was reported by Rodgers (197) in 1962. Many of these children will develop progressive reinfection tuberculosis over the next 12 years. This epidemic is shown in Figure 17.

Many other smaller epidemics have appeared in recent years in American schools, including one unpublished epidemic from Stark County, Ohio, where 44 of 44 students were infected by one school teacher who skipped his annual x-ray examination. This teacher had laryngeal as well as pulmonary tuberculosis and was a dangerous carrier. A Veteran's Hospital patient studied by Riley and his associates (195) contaminated the air in his room so thoroughly that it infected 15 guinea pigs in three days in the room to which the air was evacuated. This patient also had tubercular laryngitis, and Riley calculated that he was more infectious than the average child with measles.

These localized epidemics are possible because of the very low incidence of tuberculin-positive reactions in school children and in Navy recruits. The Navy recruits for some years have had about 6 per cent positive tuberculin reactions and most school

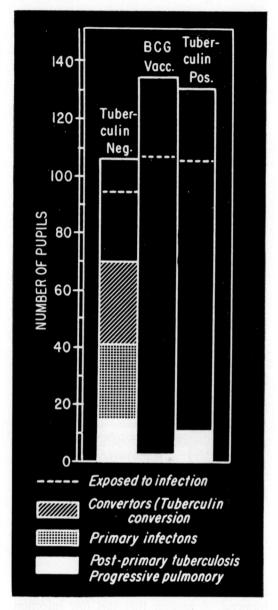

Fig. 16. A 12 year follow-up on children infected by one teacher. (From Hyge. *Danish Med. Bull.*, 4:13, 1957.)

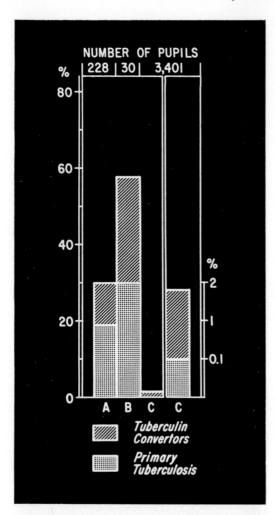

NUMBER OF PUPILS

Fig. 17. Epidemic in New York School caused by one bus driver. (From Rodgers. *Pub. Health Rep.,* 77:401, 1962.)

in 20 years, prior to enlistment, or an annual average conversion rate of 0.3 per cent per year. In the sister ships which had no clinical cases of the disease, however, the Navy recruits increased their tuberculin reaction from 6 per cent to 12 per cent in an average time of three years, or a rate of 2 per cent per year (164). Among 50,669 employed at the Veterans Hospital in 1962, 1,347, or 2.81 per cent, did convert from negative to positive (247). In these groups the conversion for a 20-year period for the Navy would be 40 per cent and that for the Veterans' employees over 50 per cent.

Treatment. Success in the treatment of tuberculosis depends primarily upon measures which conserve and support the patient's innate and acquired resistance to the disease. Rest, both mental and physical, good food, fresh air, and pleasant surroundings, preferably in a sanatorium, give the patient the best possible chance for recovery. Tuberculous patients have a high requirement for ascorbic acid (vitamin C) and possibly also for vitamins A and D. Supplementing the diet with these vitamins is often advantageous (133).

The precipitous decline in the death rate since 1945 (Fig. 1) is attributable primarily to the combination of new drugs and improved thoracic surgery (85, 127, 246). The discovery that the administration of two drugs simultaneously postponed for months or years the emergence of drug-resistant strains has been an important factor in this success (246). The death rate from progressive primary tuberculosis in children, principally miliary tuberculosis and tuberculous meningitis, has been reduced from 21.5 per cent in 1946 to 1.5 per cent in 1954 (59, 122). Occasionally the bacilli are eliminated completely by INH or PAS therapy, and the children become tuberculin-negative to 100 TU (196). In other instances the tuberculin reaction becomes weaker for a few weeks after INH is started and then becomes much stronger as the patient's nutrition improves (84).

Cortisone, metacortin, and corticotrophin reduce or even abolish the tuberculin reaction and at the same time alleviate the symptoms of tuberculosis. Unfortunately, the ultimate effect is to disseminate the disease

children are below this figure. It is a mistake, however, to assume that this low infection rate will persist during the remainder of the individual's life. After leaving school, there is a greater contact with carriers of tubercle bacilli and the rate of tuberculin conversion accelerates. Specific data for the rate of increase is available from only three sources in this country. The first is the county-wide surveys in Minnesota; the second, the conversion rates on Navy ships in the Atlantic Ocean; and the third, the employee of the Veterans Administration Hospital. The Navy recruits developed 6 per cent positive tests in animals (132, 152, 207, 221, 258) and in man. Fortunately, the harmful effect of the hormones can be neutralized by the simultaneous administration of antituberculous drugs (93, 152, 207, 358).

Under our present concepts of the pathogenesis of tuberculosis the patient need not have symptoms of illness to justify the diagnosis of active disease which requires the use of the new drugs. Any individual with a positive tuberculin test and a pulmonary lesion which appears in the x-ray as a soft infiltration certainly should be treated without waiting for the developed symptoms. Furthermore, Comstock (31, 32) reported on the relapse rate of untreated patients who had scarred lesions in the lungs by x-ray and who had been classified as inactive was up to 10 per cent in white and 30 per cent in Negro patients over a period of five years. Such a relapse rate justifies the treatment of these patients.

There is general agreement that a child of three years or less who has a positive tuberculin test is a potentially active case and should be treated for one year with INH alone. There is less agreement about treating older individuals. The study of the disease rate in 611 children with positive tuberculin tests at an average age of three years who were followed to an average age of 32 years revealed that almost 10 per cent developed clinical tuberculosis and 3.6 per cent died. Most of the deaths occurred before the discovery of the new chemotherapeutic agents (160). Those who are known recent converters from a negative to a positive skin test are usually treated with INH alone for one year. Other adults who do not know when they contacted their tuberculosis are usually x-rayed every three months for 18 months or treated with INH for one year or both.

There is some confusion in the literature as to whether the administration of INH under these circumstances should be regarded as treatment or prophylaxis. Those with detectible lesions and those with a recent conversion should certainly be called treatment.

The development of resistance by the tubercle bacilli to the new tuberculosis drugs was observed shortly after their introduction. This has remained a major problem in the treatment of the individual patients. It was anticipated that resistant tubercle bacilli would escape from the patient and begin to spread in the population in the same manner as sulfonamide-resistant gonococci or penicillin-resistant staphylococci. Organisms resistant to INH and to a less degree to streptomycin have appeared in considerable number in new patients in countries where self-medication with these drugs was permitted (10, 242). Nearly 10 years elapsed in this country before an appreciable number of resistant organisms began to appear in new untreated cases of tuberculosis. A dangerous rise in resistant organisms is appearing in the slums of the big cities where the patients are irregular in their use of the prescribed drugs (29, 77). It is evident that the resistant strains will eventually spread over the entire country and destroy the usefulness of the effective drugs unless these patients who are harboring them are detected and rigorously isolated until they are cured or are dead.

Prevention. Theoretically tuberculosis could be prevented and eventually eradicated if every active case was diagnosed, isolated, and treated. The application of these procedures is the cause of the declining incidence and death from tuberculosis in Western countries. The new drugs have speeded up the process but did not initiate it, nor can they alone eliminate tuberculosis.

Tuberculin testing of school children has become a refined technic for finding isolated spreaders of tubercle bacilli in the community. In the California schools (15) 109,151 children in nine areas were tested once and 70,000 were retested a second year. The over-all reaction rate was 0.96 per cent in the sixth year of age and 4.6 per cent at 14 years. The over-all figures are misleading, since the white Caucasian students had only 2.1 per cent positive, while the Negro rate was 5.3, and the Latin American 11.1. The degree of reaction was important, since no clinical cases were found in the contacts of children whose skin test was less than 9 mm. of induration to 5 TU PPD. The number and severity of the reactions were related to the amount of tuberculosis in the students' environment. There were both conversions and reversions in the tuberculin tests. The conversion rate was highest in areas with patients and the reversion rate highest in areas without patients (15). The conversion rate was 20 per cent in children who had small supposed negative reactions in the first year. This was probably another instance of the booster effect of the tuberculin test in individuals who have any degree of allergy to any of the classified or unclassified mycobacteria.

Two secondary methods of preventing tuberculosis have been advocated. **In the first, called isoniazid prophylaxis,** the drug is given in one daily dose of 300 mg. of INH to individuals who have positive tuberculin tests but no detectable lesion or to those who have been in close contact with a known active case regardless of whether their tuberculin is positive or negative. The results reported in the study by the Public Health Service in 1,463 household contacts was about 80 per cent (58), as compared to the 1,351 controls who received a placebo for one year. There was no obvious difference between the treated and the whole group during this year which followed the cessation of prophylaxis (154). The disadvantages of the isoniazid prophylaxis are (1) the duration of administration, (2) the expensive supervision of the subjects, and (3) its uselessness if the infecting organism is resistant to INH (143).

The second accessory method of prevention is active vaccination of tuberculin negative individuals with BCG.

After years of investigation Calmette and Guérin (24, 25) obtained a bovine strain of tubercle bacillus with a low and relatively fixed degree of virulence. This organism known as the Bacillus of Calmette and Guérin or BCG has been used to vaccinate some 10,000,000 individuals (229). This vaccine is harmless when properly prepared and administered but gives relative rather than absolute immunity.

The vaccine should be administered only to those individuals who have a negative tuberculin reaction to 0.005 mg. of PPD or 1 mg. of OT. If a positive reaction to the larger dose of tuberculin does not develop by the end of the third month, the procedure can be repeated. Positive tuberculin reac-

tions usually are obtained in 92 to 100 per cent of the individuals receiving the vaccine, and the state of hypersensitivity persists for three to four years or longer. The accidental vaccination of a tuberculin-positive individual results in the rapid development, at the site of inoculation, of a superficial ulceration which persists for a few weeks but does not injure the patient.

The vaccine may be administered by the **intracutaneous** method of Wallgren (7, 257), or the **transcutaneous** or multiple puncture method of Rosenthal (198, 199).

Four large-scale vaccination trials have been completed in the past 10 years. They were the 20-year study of BCG and placebos in the North American Indian by Aronson and his associates (9). The 19-year study of infants in the slums of Chicago by Rosenthal and his coworkers (199), the five-year study of school children in Puerto Rico and Georgia by the U.S. Public Health Service (170, 171), and the 10-year study of British school children in England (23). BCG afforded about 80 per cent protection in the Aronson, Rosenthal, and British study, but only 36 per cent in Puerto Rico and apparently no protection in the Georgia students.

The British children have been subjected to the most elaborate and meticulous follow-up studies and revealed an 83 per cent protection after five years and a 79 per cent protection after 9 to 10 years following a single BCG vaccination. In many ways the British study has been the most conclusive study of all. They alone of all the investigators kept the original positive reaction to 3 TU and to 100 TU separate but studied simultaneously with the BCG vaccinated and the controls. The breakdown rate in these asymptomatic x-ray negative children was four times as great as in the BCG vaccinated group (Table 4).

The only obvious difference in the four studies was the method of selecting the subject for vaccination. In the Aronson, Rosenthal, and British study only those individuals who were negative to 100 TU (1-100 OT or second strength PPD) were selected for study and control, but in the U.S. Public Health study individuals who were negative and gave 5 mm. or less reaction to 5 TU (0.0001 mg.

Table 4.   BCG and Controls in British Study

IMMUNOLOGY STATUS	No. CHILDREN	No. STARTING IN 3 MONTHS	ANNUAL INCIDENCE PER 100,000
A. Negative not vaccinated	13,200	64	194
B. Negative not vaccinated	6,400	33	206
Total	19,600	97	198
A. Negative BCG vaccinated	14,100	13	37
B. Negative BCG vaccinated	6,400	5	31
Total	20,500	18	35
A. Positive to 3 TU	15,800	69	175
B. Positive to 3 TU	8,600	37	172
Total	24,400	106	174
A. Positive to 100 TU	6,500	12	74
B. Positive to 100 TU	3,500	6	69
Total	10,000	18	72
Total of 3 TU + 100 TU	34,400	124	144

From *British Medical Journal*, 1:413, 1956.

PPD) were included in the study and control group. This method of selection introduced a minimum of 31.4 per cent of "immunes" in the Puerto Rico group and a minimum of 52.7 "immunes" in the Georgia group. In fairness to these excellent investigators of the U.S. Public Health Service, one should realize that it was not known at the time of the actual vaccinations that these low-grade tuberculin reactions would be about as immune as those who had already been vaccinated with BCG. The British study revealed that those children negative to 3 TU but positive to 100 TU behaved like "immunes," and Palmer's subsequent restudy of the student nurses showed the same phenomenon (168). Presumably most of this immunity was induced by previous subclinical infection with various types of unclassified mycobacteria. Experimental infection of guinea pigs with these strains of mycobacteria gave definite evidence of protection, although not as good in the guinea pig as BCG (62, 105, 171, 265, 279).

The advantage of BCG prophylaxis over isoniazid prophylaxis depends upon the following: (1) the ease and rapidity of the procedure (two tuberculin skin tests and one inoculation with BCG is all that is required), (2) no supervisory cost, and (3) theoretically BCG should protect as efficiently against tubercle bacilli resistant to INH, streptomycin, etc., as to susceptible organisms.

BCG vaccination can be recommended for special groups in which the morbidity rates are high and the factors favoring rapid transmission of the organisms temporarily uncontrollable (1, 42). Such groups include the Indians, the inhabitants of certain slum areas in the large cities, Naval recruits and other military personnel who are confined to crowded quarters and who are exposed to uncontrolled infection, and, lastly, nurses, medical students, and hospital attendants whose professional duties necessitate almost constant exposure to infection (1, 42, 245).

The control of tuberculosis is a very complex problem involving both the isolation of carriers in sanatoriums and the general improvement of economic conditions. The prevention of tuberculosis depends upon the isolation and elimination of the carrier (43). Since leprosy was eliminated from most European countries during the fifteenth and sixteenth centuries by prompt detection and rigid isolation of all lepers, **it is not too optimistic to visualize that tuberculosis can be eliminated from the United States by more intensive and prolonged application of the methods now being applied to the control of the disease** (220).

Global eradication of tuberculosis was suggested by Perkins in 1959 (177) and Soper in 1962 (220). The Arden House Conference outlined a plan for the elimination of tuberculosis from the United States (5).

REFERENCES

1. Abruzzi, W. A., Jr., and Hummel, R. J. New England J. Med., 248:722, 1953.
2. Allerhand, J., and Zitrin, C. M. J. Immunol., 89:252, 1962.
3. Allgower, M., and Bloch, H. Am. Rev. Tuberc., 59:562, 1949.
4. Allison, M. J., and others. Am. Rev. Resp. Dis., 84:364, 1961.
5. Arden House Conference on Tuberculosis. Am. Rev. Resp. Dis., 81:482, 1960.
6. Aronson, J. D. Am. Rev. Tuberc., 30:727, 1934.
7. —— and Palmer, C. E. Pub. Health Rep., 61:801, 1946.
8. —— and McGettigan, M. J. Immunol., 66:715, 1951.
9. —— and others. Arch. Infect. Med., 101:881, 1958.
10. Augier, J. Rev. Tuberc. (Paris), 25:590, 1961.
11. Badger, T. L., and Spink, W. W. New England J. Med., 217:423, 1937.
12. —— and others. Am. Rev. Resp. Dis., 87:338, 1963.
13. Baldwin, E. R., and others. Tuberculosis, Philadelphia, Lea & Febiger, 1927.
14. Bauer, J. A., and Stone, S. H. J. Immunol., 86:177, 1961.
15. Baum, H. L., and others. Am. Rev. Resp. Dis., 87:877, 1963.
16. Bhatia, A. L., and others. Tubercle, 42:317, 1961.
17. Bloch, H., and others. Am. Rev. Tuberc., 59:554, 1949.
18. —— Ann. N.Y. Acad. Sci., 85 (5):1075, 1960.
19. —— and Noll, H. Brit. J. Exper. Path., 36:8, 1955.
20. Boyden, S. V., and Sorkin, F. J. Immunol., 75:15, 22, 1955.
21. Brieger, E. M., and others. J. Hyg., 49:189, 1951.
22. —— and Glauert, A. M. Tubercle, 35:80, 1954.
23. British Medical Research Council. Brit. Med. J., 1:973, 1963.
24. Calmette, A. Ann. Inst. Pasteur, 22:593, 1924; 26:889, 1928.
25. —— J.A.M.A., 96:58, 1931.
26. Cater, J. C., and Redmond, W. B. Am. Rev. Resp. Dis., 87:726, 1963.
27. Chase, M. W. Proc. Soc. Exper. Biol. & Med., 59:134, 1945.
28. —— Fed. Proc. (abs.), 22:617, 1963.
29. Chavis, A. D., and others. Am. Rev. Resp. Dis., 84:647, 1961.
30. Comstock, G. W. Am. Rev. Tuberc., 73:157, 1956.
31. —— and Porter, M. E. Pub. Health Rept., 74:621, 1959.
32. —— Pub. Health Rept., 77:461, 1962.
33. Crowle, A. J. Proc. Soc. Exper. Biol. & Med., 109:969, 1962.
34. Csillag, A. J. Gen. Microbiol., 30:21, 1963.
35. Cummings, M. M., and others. Pub. Health Rept., 62:994, 1947.
36. —— and Hudgins, P. C. J. Immunol., 69:331, 1952.
37. —— and others. Am. Rev. Tuberc., 73:246, 1956.

38. Dahlstrom, A. W. Am. Rev. Tuberc., 42:471, 1940.
39. Daines, L. L., and Austin, H. Am. Rev. Tuberc., 27:600, 1933; 30:209, 1934.
40. Danbolt, N. Acta dermat.-venereol., 31:184, 1951.
41. D'Arcy Hart, P., and others. Tubercle, 43:268, 1962.
42. Dickie, H. A. Ann. Int. Med., 33:941, 1950.
43. Diehl, H. S., and others. J.A.M.A., 138:8, 1948.
44. Dienes, L., and Schoenheit, E. W. Am. Rev. Tuberc., 92:105, 1929.
45. Drolet, G. J. Chapter on Epidemiology of Tuberculosis, in Clinical Tuberculosis, Philadelphia, F. A. Davis Co., 1947.
46. —— and Lowell, A. M. Dis. Chest, 42:364, 1962.
47. Drury, W. H. Pub. Health Rept., 36:159, 1921.
48. Duboczy, B. O. Am. Rev. Resp. Dis., 87:615, 1963.
49. Duboczy, E. O., and Brown, B. T. Am. Rev. Resp. Dis., 84:69, 1961.
50. Dubos, R. J., and Davis, B. D. J. Exper. Med., 83:409, 1946.
51. —— and Middlebrook, G. Am. Rev. Tuberc., 58:698, 1948.
52. —— Biochemical Determinants of Microbial Diseases, Cambridge, Mass., Harvard University Press, 1954.
53. Edwards, L. B., and others. Tubercle, 44:153, 1963.
54. Edwards, P. Q., and Edwards, L. B. Am. Rev. Resp. Dis., 81:1, 1960.
55. Feldman, W. H., and others. Proc. Staff Meet. Mayo Clin., 22:473, 1947.
56. Fenner, F., and Leach, R. H. Am. Rev. Tuberc., 68:321, 1953.
57. —— Am. Rev. Tuberc., 73:650, 1956.
58. Ferebee, S. H., and Mount, F. W. Am. Rev. Resp. Dis., 87:614, 1963.
59. Fitzsimons, J. M. Tubercle, 44:87, 1963.
60. Fong, J., and others. J. Exper. Med., 115:475, 1962.
61. Francis, J. Am. Rev. Tuberc., 73:748, 1956.
62. Freerksen, E. Dtsch. Med. Wchr., 84:35, 1533, 1959; 84:36, 1617, 1959.
63. Fregnan, G. B., and Smith, D. W. J. Bact., 83:819, 1963.
64. Freund, J. Am. Rev. Tuberc., 12:124, 1925.
65. —— and others. J. Exper. Med., 64:573, 1936.
66. —— and McDermott, K. Proc. Soc. Exper. Biol. & Med., 49:548, 1942.
67. Froman, S., and others. Am. J. Pub. Health, 44:1326, 1954.
68. Frost, W. H. Am. J. Hyg., 30:Sect. A. 91, 1939.
69. Furcolow, M. L., and others. Pub. Health Rept., 56:1082, 1941.
70. Gardner, L. U. J. Indust. Hyg. & Toxicol., 14:18, 1932.
71. —— Am. J. Pub. Health, 23:1240, 1933.
72. —— Am. Rev. Tuberc., 53:511, 1946.
73. Garrod, L. P. Am. Rev. Tuberc., 62:582, 1950.
74. Gedde-Dahl, T. Am. J. Hyg., 56:139, 1952.
75. Gernez-Rieux, Ch., and Tacquet, A. Ann. Inst. Pasteur de Lille, 4:2, 1954.
76. Gerstl, B., and others. Am. Rev. Tuberc., 72:345, 1955.

77. Gerszten, E., and others. J.A.M.A., 185:6, 1963.
78. Gillam, P. M. S., and Knowles, J. P. Tubercle, 44:112, 1963.
79. Goldman, E. C., and Goldman, D. S. Am. Rev. Tuberc., 73:674, 1956.
80. Grady, E. D. Am. Rev. Tuberc., 63:526, 1951.
81. Griffith, A. S. Tubercle, 6:417, 1925.
82. Guld, J. Acta Tuberc. Scand., 28:222, 1953.
83. Harpoth, H. Ztschr. f. Tuberk., 79:140, 1938.
84. Hewell, B., and Suyemoto, D. Am. Rev. Tuberc., 69:733, 1954.
85. Hinshaw, H. C. Am. J. Med., 9:654, 1950.
86. Hnatko, S. I. Canad. J. Microbiol., 2:39, 1956.
87. Hobby, G., and others. Am. Rev. Tuberc., 60:808, 1949.
88. Hobby, G. L., and others. Am. Rev. Tuberc., 70:527, 1954.
89. Horton, R., and others. J.A.M.A., 149:331, 1952.
90. Hyge, T. V. Acta Tuberc. Scandinav., 21:1, 1947.
91. ——— Danish Med. Bull., 4:13, 1957.
92. Israel, H. L., and others. Am. Rev. Tuberc., 62:408, 1950.
93. Johnson, J. R. Am. Rev. Tuberc., 72:825, 1955.
94. Johnson, R. W., and Scherago, M. Am. Rev. Resp. Dis., 87:739, 1963.
95. Johnston, W. W., and others. Am. Rev. Resp. Dis., 81:189, 1960.
96. ——— and Smith, D. T. Fed. Proc., 22:206, 1963.
97. Kahn, M. C. Am. Rev. Tuberc., 20:150, 1929.
98. ——— and Schwarzkopf, H. J. Bact., 25:157, 1933.
99. ——— Am. J. Hyg., 24:456, 1936.
100. ——— and Nonidez, J. F. Am. Rev. Tuberc., 34:361, 1936.
101. Kallmann, F. J., and Reisner, D. Am. Rev. Tuberc., 47:549, 1943.
102. Kay, K., and Rieke, W. O. Science, 139:487, 1963.
103. Kelser, R. A. Manual of Veterinary Bacteriology, Baltimore, Williams and Wilkins Co., 1933, p. 308.
104. Kempner, W. Am. Rev. Tuberc., 40:157, 1939.
105. Klugh, G. A., and Pratt, P. C. Am. Rev. Resp. Dis., 85:78, 1962.
106. Knight, R. A., and others. Am. Rev. Resp. Dis., 87:615, 1963.
107. Knox, R., and others. Am. Rev. Tuberc., 73:726, 1956.
108. Koch, M. L., and others. Am. Rev. Resp. Dis., 84:750, 1961.
109. Koch, R. Deutsche med. Wchnschr., 1891, 1901.
110. ——— Berl. klin. Wchnschr., 19:221, 1882.
111. Koike, M., and Takeya, K. J. Biophys. Biochem. & Cytol., 9:597, 1961.
112. Kolle, W. Deutsche med. Wchnschr., 58:304, 1932.
113. Kolmer, J. A. Am. Rev. Tuberc., 64:102, 1951.
114. Konno, K. Science, 124:985, 1956.
115. Krasnow, I., and others. Am. Rev. Tuberc., 71:361, 1955.

116. Landsteiner, K., and Chase, M. W. Proc. Soc. Exper. Biol. & Med., 49:688, 1942.
117. Larson, C. L., and others. Am. Rev. Resp. Dis., 83:184, 1961.
118. Lawrence, H. S. Proc. Soc. Exper. Biol. & Med., 71:516, 1949.
119. ——— J. Clin. Investigation, 33:951, 1954.
120. ——— Ann. Rev. Med., 11:207, 1960.
121. Ledwith, J. W., and Gray, J. A. C. Am. Rev. Resp. Dis., 84:268, 1961.
121a. Lester, C. F., and Atwell, R. J. Am. Rev. Tuberc., 78:399, 1958.
122. Lincoln, E. M. Am. Rev. Tuberc., 69:682, 1954.
123. Lindberg, E. F., and others. Proc. Staff Mayo Clinic, 38:148, 1963.
124. Long, E. R. J. Infect. Dis., 37:368, 1925.
125. ——— Am. Rev. Tuberc., 9:215, 1925; 13:393, 1926; 22:467, 1930; 40:607, 1939.
126. ——— and Seibert, F. B. Am. Rev. Tuberc., 35:281, 1937.
127. ——— and Ferebee, S. H. Pub. Health Rept., 65:1421, 1950.
128. ——— Ann. Int. Med., 37:1095, 1952.
129. Lurie, M. B. Am. Rev. Tuberc. (Supplement), 44:1, 1941.
130. ——— J. Exper. Med., 75:247, 1942.
131. ——— and others. J. Immunol., 68:369, 1952.
132. ——— and others. Science, 113:234, 1951.
133. McConkey, M. Am. Rev. Tuberc., 43:425, 1941.
134. Maha, G. E. J.A.M.A., 182:304, 1962.
135. Mankiewicz, E., and van Walbeer, M. Arch. Enviro. Health, 5:122, 1962.
136. Mantoux, C. Compt. rend. Acad. d. sc., 147:355, 1908.
137. ——— Compt. rend. Soc. de biol., 67:356, 1909.
138. Martin, S. P., and others. J. Exper. Med., 91:381, 1950.
139. Medlar, E. M. Am. Rev. Tuberc., 55:517, 1947.
140. ——— J.A.M.A., 141:593, 1949.
141. ——— Am. J. Med., 9:611, 1950.
142. ——— Am. Rev. Tuberc., 71:part II, 1, 1955.
143. Menon, N. K. Tubercle. 44:34, 1963.
144. Metaxas, M. N., and Metaxas-Buehler, M. J. Immunol., 75:333, 1955.
145. Meynell, G. G. J. Path. & Bact., 67:137, 1954.
146. Middlebrook, G., and others. J. Exper. Med., 86:175, 1947.
147. ——— and Dubos, R. J. J. Exper. Med., 88:521, 1948.
148. ——— J. Clin. Investigation, 29:1480, 1950.
149. ——— Am. Rev. Tuberc., 69:471, 1954.
150. ——— Abstr. Ann. Meet. Nat. Tuberc. A., p. 63, 1956.
151. Mitchinson, D. A., and others. Tubercle, 41:1, 1960.
152. Morgan, T. E., and others. J. Bact., 67:257, 1954.
153. Morgante, O., and Murray, E. G. D. Canad. J. Microbiol., 1:331, 1955.
154. Mount, F. W., and Ferebee, S. H. Am. Rev. Resp. Dis., 85:490, 821, 1962.
155. Much, H. Berl. Klin. Wchnschr., 45:691, 1908.
156. Mudd, S., and Mudd, E. B. H. J. Exper. Med., 46:167, 1927.

157. Myers, J. A.   J.A.M.A., 146:1492, 1951.
158. ——— and others.   J.A.M.A., 158:1, 1955.
159. ——— and others.   J.A.M.A., 159:185, 1955.
160. ——— and others.   Am. Rev. Resp. Dis., 87:354, 1963.
161. Najarian, J. S., and Feldman, J. D.   J. Exper. Med., 114:779, 1961.
162. Noll, H., and others.   Biochem. & Biophys. Acta, 20:299, 1956.
163. Oatway, W. H., and Steenken, W., Jr.   J. Infect. Dis., 59:306, 1936.
164. Ochs, C. W.   J.A.M.A., 179:247, 1962.
165. Oort, J., and Turk, J. L.   J. Immunol., 6:148, 1963.
166. Palmer, C. E.   Am. Rev. Tuberc., 68:678, 1953.
167. ——— and others.   Pub. Health Rept., 65: Part 2, 1111, 1950.
168. ——— Bull. Union Internat. Contre Tuberc., 27:106, 1957.
169. ——— and others.   Am. Rev. Tuberc., 76:517, 1957.
170. ——— and others.   Am. Rev. Tuberc. & Resp. Dis., 77:877, 1958.
171. ——— and Hopwood, L.   Proc. XVI Internat. Tuberculosis Conf., Toronto, Canada, Sept. 13-14, 1961, p. 398.
172. Park, H. K.   Proc. Soc. Exper. Biol. & Med., 109:156, 1962.
173. Parlett, R., and Youmans, G. P.   Am. Rev. Tuberc., 73:637, 1956.
174. Parlett, R. C.   Am. Rev. Resp. Dis., 84:580, 1961.
175. ——— Ann. N.Y. Acad. Med., 98:637, 1962.
176. Pepys, J.   Am. Rev. Tuberc., 71:49, 1955.
177. Perkins, J. E.   Am. Rev. Resp. Dis., 80:138, 1959.
178. ——— Ann. N.Y. Acad. Sci., 106:5, 1963.
179. Petroff, S. A., and Steenken, W., Jr.   J. Exper. Med., 51:831, 1930.
180. ——— and others.   Am. Rev. Tuberc., 19:9, 1929.
181. Pinner, M.   Pulmonary Tuberculosis in the Adult, Springfield, Ill., Charles C Thomas Co., 1945.
182. Pollock, T. M., and others.   Tubercle, 40:336, 1959.
183. Pope, H., and Smith, D. T.   Am. Rev. Tuberc., 54:559, 1946.
184. Porter, K. R., and Yegian, D.   J. Bact., 50:563, 1945.
185. Puffer, R. R.   Familial Susceptibility to Tuberculosis, Cambridge, Mass., Harvard University Press, 1944.
186. ——— and others.   Am. Rev. Tuberc., 65:111, 1952.
187. Raffel, S.   J. Infect. Dis., 82:267, 1948.
188. ——— Experientia, 6:410, 1950.
189. ——— Immunity, Hypersensitivity, Serology, New York, Appleton-Century-Crofts, Inc., 2nd ed., 1961.
190. Rakower, J.   Am. Rev. Tuberc., 67:85, 1953.
191. Redmond, W. B., and Cater, J. C.   Am. Rev. Resp. Dis., 82:781, 1960.
192. Research Committee of British Tuberculosis Association, Tubercle, 44:1, 1963.
193. ——— Tubercle, 44:119, 1963.
194. Rich, A. R.   The Pathogenesis of Tuberculosis, Springfield, Ill., Charles C Thomas Co., 1951.

195. Riley, R. L., and others.   Am. Rev. Resp. Dis., 85:511, 1962.
196. Robinson, A., and others.   New England J. Med., 252:983, 1955.
197. Rogers, E. F. H.   Pub. Health Rept., 77:401, 1962.
198. Rosenthal, S. R.   J.A.M.A., 157:801, 1955.
199. ——— and others.   Am. Rev. Resp. Dis., 84:690, 1961.
200. Roth, R. B.   Am. Rev. Tuberc., 38:197, 1938.
201. Runyon, E. H.   Am. Rev. Tuberc., 79:663, 1959.
202. Schaefer, W.   Ann. Inst. Pasteur, 58:388, 1937.
203. Seibert, F. B.   Chem. Rev., 34:107, 1944.
204. ——— Schweiz. Ztschr. Tuberk. Separatum, Fasc., 3:1, 1950.
205. ——— and Dufour, E. H.   Am. Rev. Tuberc., 69:585, 1954.
206. ——— and others.   Am. Rev. Tuberc., 73:547, 1956.
207. Shane, S. J., and Riley, C.   New England J. Med., 249:829, 1953.
208. Smith, C. R.   Am. Rev. Tuberc., 45:334, 1942.
209. Smith, D. T.   New England J. Med., 241:198, 1949.
210. ——— and Scott, N. B.   Am. Rev. Tuberc., 62:121, 1950.
211. ——— Am. Rev. Tuberc., 67:707, 1953.
212. ——— and others.   Am. Rev. Tuberc., 70:547, 557, 570, 1954.
213. ——— and Johnston, W. W.   Am. Rev. Resp. Dis. In press.
214. ——— and others.   Am. Rev. Resp. Dis., 83:213, 1961.
215. Smith, D. W., and Robertson, J. A.   Am. Rev. Resp. Dis., 85:398, 1962.
216. Smith, Theobald.   J.A.M.A., 68:669, 1917.
217. ——— J. Exper. Med., 3:451, 1898; 6:1, 1901.
218. Smithburn, K. C.   J. Exper. Med., 63:95, 1936.
219. Sones, M., and Israel, H. L.   Ann. Int. Med., 40:260, 1954.
220. Soper, F. L.   Am. J. Pub. Health, 52:734, 1962.
221. Spain, D. M., and Molomut, N.   Am. Rev. Tuberc., 62:337, 1950.
222. Stavitsky, A. B.   Proc. Soc. Exper. Biol. & Med., 67:225, 1948.
223. Steenken, W., Jr.   Proc. Soc. Exper. Biol. & Med., 33:253, 1935-36.
224. ——— Am. Rev. Tuberc., 42:422, 1940.
225. ——— and Gardner, L. U.   Yale J. Biol. & Med., 15:393, 1942-43.
226. ——— Am. Rev. Tuberc., 54:51, 1946.
227. ——— and Wolinsky, E.   Am. J. Med., 9:633, 1950.
228. ——— and others.   Am. Rev. Resp. Dis., 87:615, 1963.
229. Strom, L.   Sem. Hop. Paris, 25:1414, 1956.
230. Sula, L.   Pub. Health Rept., 63:867, 1948.
231. Suter, E.   J. Exper. Med., 97:235, 1953.
232. ——— and Hullinger, L.   Ann. N.Y. Acad. Sci., 88:1237, 1960.
233. ——— Am. Rev. Resp. Dis., 83:535, 1961.
234. Suter, W. E., and Dubos, R. J.   J. Exper. Med., 93:559, 1951.
235. Sweeney, E. E., and Jann, G. J.   J. Bact., 84:459, 1962.

236. Symposium. Am. Rev. Tuberc., 65:357, 365, 376, 392, 402, 429, 1952.
237. Takahashi, Y., and others. J. Exper. Med., 113:1141, 1961.
238. ——— Am. Rev. Resp. Dis., 85:708, 1962.
239. Takeya, K., and others. J. Biophys. Biochem. Cytol., 9:496, 1961.
240. Taylor, G. Am. Rev. Tuberc., 40:236, 1939.
241. Thacore, H., and Willett, H. P. Proc. Soc. Exper. Biol. & Med., 114:43, 1963.
242. Thomas, H. E. Tubercle, 42:1, 1961.
243. Timpe, A., and Runyon, E. H. J. Lab. & Clin. Med., 44:202, 1954.
244. Tomcsanyi, A., and others. Am. Rev. Resp. Dis., 85:72, 1962.
245. Tuberculosis Control Advisory Committee to the Public Health Service, Pub. Health Rept., 77:680, 1962.
246. Tucker, W. B., and Livings, D. G. Am. Rev. Tuberc., 72:756, 1955.
247. ——— Report to the Board of Directors of the National Tuberculosis Association, May 1963.
248. Tukey, J. W., and others. Am. Rev. Tuberc., 62:77, 1950.
249. Urbach, F., and others. New England J. Med., 247:794, 1952.
250. Vera, H. D., and Rettger, L. F. J. Bact., 39:659, 1940.
251. Verschuer, O. von. Proc. Roy. Soc. London, s.B., 128:62, 1939-40.
252. Villemin, J. A. Compt. rend. Acad. d. sc., 61:1012, 1865.
253. Vollmer, H., and Goldberger, E. W. Am. J. Dis. Child., 54:1019, 1937; 58:527, 1939.
254. von Pirquet, C. Wien. klin. Wchnschr., 20:1123, 1907.
255. Vorwald, A. S., and others. Am. Rev. Tuberc., 69:766, 1954.
256. Waksman, S. A. J.A.M.A., 135:478, 1947.
257. Wallgren, A. Yale J. Biol. & Med., 15:411, 1942-43.
258. Wanzer, S. H., and others. J. Bact., 67:264, 1954.
259. Webb, G. B. Tuberculosis, New York, Paul B. Hoeber, Inc., 1936.
260. Weinzirl, J., and Dingle, J. H. J. Bact., 23:281, 1932.
261. Weiss, D. W., and Dubos, R. J. J. Exper. Med., 103:73, 1956.
262. Wells, A. Q., and others. Am. Rev. Tuberc., 72:53, 1955.
263. ——— J. Gen. Microbiol., 9:149, 1953.
264. ——— and others. Am. Rev. Tuberc., 72:53, 1955.
265. Wenkle, W. C., and others. Am. Rev. Tuberc., 57:385, 1948.
266. Willett, H. P. Ann. N.Y. Acad. Sci., 106:16, 1963.
267. Wilson, G. S. J. Path. & Bact., 28:69, 1925.
268. Winterscheid, L. C., and Mudd, S. Am. Rev. Tuberc., 67:59, 1953.
269. Wright, S., and Lewis, P. A. Am. Naturalist, 55:20, 1921.
270. Xalbarder, C. El Origen Del Bacilo De Koch, Pub. del Institute Antituberculoso, Barcelona, 1954.
271. Yegian, D., and Baisden, L. J. Bact., 44:667, 1942.
272. ——— and Kurung, J. Am. Rev. Tuberc., 56:36, 1947.
273. ——— and others. J. Bact., 58:257, 1949.
274. ——— and Porter, K. R. J. Bact., 48:83, 1944.
275. ——— and Vanderlinde, R. J. Am. Rev. Tuberc., 61:483, 1950.
276. Youmans, A. S., and Youmans, G. P. J. Bact., 60:561, 569, 1950.
277. Youmans, G. P., and others. Lancet, 67:403, 1947.
278. ——— and others. J. Bact., 70:557, 1955.
279. ——— and others. Am. Rev. Resp. Dis., 83:903, 1961.
280. Zeidberg, L. D., and others. Am. Rev. Tuberc., 70:1009, 1954.

30

Classified and Unclassified Mycobacteria

It has been known for many years that *Mycobacterium bovis* frequently, and *Mycobacterium avium* occasionally, produced disease in man which was indistinguishable clinically from that caused by *Mycobacterium tuberculosis*. In recent years there has been a dramatic decrease in infections caused by the bovine species but an increase or an increased recognition of disease caused by the avian organism. During the past 10 years it has become evident that a newly recognized group of mycobacteria, temporarily designated as unclassified mycobacteria, produce disease in man much more frequently than the well-known bovine or avian organisms. These mycobacteria are unique in that they have no regular animal host but seem to come from the soil; consequently, they are endemic in type and vary in frequency, type by type, depending upon locale, soil, and other climatic and environmental factors. There is no evidence at the present time that they can be transmitted directly from man to man, but organisms of these types can and do produce severe and even fatal disease in man. As late as 1956 (111) a series of cases was reported from the Mayo Clinic where the clinical and pathological evidence for pathogenicity was conclusive. There was obviously more than one type involved and the organisms were easily differentiated from all known pathogenic mycobacteria, but the new ones could not be characterized or named.

The pioneer work of Runyon (84, 85, 86) finally brought some order into this chaotic group of organisms. He collected from this and other countries hundreds of strains where there was good evidence of association with disease. Careful morphological, cultural, metabolic and animal studies enabled him to classify most of the cultures into four main groups designated as groups I, II, III, and IV. Each of these groups will be discussed in more detail later. Confirmation of the diagnostic value of Runyon's Groups has been published from every country where his methods have been applied including the U.S.S.R. By 1945, 150 strains had been collected and studied, but they were considered variants of true tubercle bacilli (86). Approximately 5 per cent of the patients entering the Mayo Clinic with disease caused by acid-fast organisms were found to have one or another of the unclassified types of mycobacteria (72).

MYCOBACTERIUM BOVIS

Mycobacterium bovis (Bergey and others 1934) was differentiated from *Myco. tuberculosis* by Theobald Smith in 1896. The rods often are shorter and plumper than the human tubercle bacillus, and primary isolation is somewhat more difficult. Since growth is not stimulated by glycerin, the colonies are rather small compared to the human species on glycerol agar. When grown on Lowenstein and Petragnani media, the colonies are about the same size. The optimum pH is between 6.0 and 6.5. **The Nician test is negative with the bovine bacillus** (53a, 54).

Myco. bovis produces spontaneous tuberculosis infections in ox, man, monkey, goat, sheep, pig, cat, parrot, and cockatoo. Experimentally it is highly pathogenic for rabbits and guinea pigs; slightly pathogenic for dogs, horses, rats, and mice; but not pathogenic for fowls. Fifty years ago most dairy herds were heavily infected with bovine bacillus, and in the absence of pasteurization the raw milk produced disease in man, particularly extrapulmonary lesions, such as those of glands and bone, and joint disease in children. Although somewhat less virulent for man than the human species, progressive fatal pulmonary disease did occur.

However, tuberculin testing of cows with the slaughter of the positive reactors, has reduced the incidence of infection in cows to less than 3 per cent in this country. Bovine infections of man have been eliminated where pasteurized milk is consumed. There is still a minimal amount of spread from cows to swine.

MYCOBACTERIUM PARATUBERCULOSIS

Mycobacterium paratuberculosis, Bergey and others, 1923.

This disease of cattle and sheep was described by Johne and Frothingham (47) in 1895. It was transmitted to normal calves by Bang (5) in 1906. The infection is confined to the mucosa and submucosa of the ileum, cecum, and upper colon. The lesions are proliferative and granulomatous and contain enormous numbers of acid-fast bacilli both inside and outside the large monocytic cells. The lesions do not caseate or ulcerate. The disease causes diarrhea and prevents the proper adsorption of food. The incubation period is long and the progress of the disease slow but invariably fatal.

All attempts at cultivation of the bacillus failed until Twort (1910-1911) incorporated heat-killed tubercle bacilli or timothy bacilli in the egg-glycine medium (106). Antihemorrhagic vitamin K-like compounds can be substituted for extract of acid-fast organisms (117). *Mycobacterium paratuberculosis* is a small acid-fast rod, 1 to 2 μ long and 0.5 μ wide. It is nonsporogenous and nonmotile and grows best under aerobic conditions at 37.5° C. The isolated organism in pure culture reproduces the disease in cows. Goats, man, guinea pigs, rats, and mice are not susceptible.

Since *Mycobacterium paratuberculosis* shares some antigens with *Myco. avium,* avian tuberculin can be used as a skin test in cows suspected of having Johne's disease. A positive test would necessitate the slaughter of the cow, however, with the differentiated diagnosis being made at necropsy. A tuberculin has been made from cultures of *Myco. paratuberculosis* which reacts in infected cows but also can react in cows infected with *Myco. avium.* The degree of allergy is not very high in Johne's disease which is consistent with the lack of caseation in the lesions. The skin test becomes negative in the terminal stages of the disease, while the complement-fixation test appears early in the process and is usually present to death. Sigurdsson (93) has isolated a specific antigen from the tissue and has some evidence that sheep can

be immunized by the injection of heat-killed organisms suspended in mineral oil. Streptomycin has been used with some success in therapy of the disease in cattle (58).

SKIN ULCERS IN COWS

Between 1930 and 1934, Daines and his associates (19) studied a peculiar type of ulceration of the skin in cows. The lesion contained acid-fast organisms which were easily cultivated but could not be classified with any of the known species of mycobacteria. They were not pathogenic for laboratory animals, and their pathogenicity for cows was limited to ulcerations of the skin. But they did sensitize the cows to human and bovine tuberculin, which required the slaughter of the cows. No internal lesions could be found at necropsy. It seems likely that these organisms belong to the general group of unclassified mycobacteria which are now being classified.

MYCOBACTERIUM AVIUM

Mycobacterium avium Chester, 1901

This organism was isolated from birds by Strauss and Gamaleia in 1891. The acid-fast rods are short and resemble the bovine species more closely than the human (68). Avian bacilli grow on the usual media employed for the isolation of the human tubercle bacillus at the same rate or a little faster than the human species. The optimal pH is 6.8 to 7.3, and the optimal temperature is 40° C., although they will grow from 30° C. to 44° C. Smith and Steenken (98) found these avian strains grow more luxuriantly in the thioglycollate medium than other species of mycobacteria. In contrast to human and bovine bacilli, the colonies are smooth and dome-shaped, and the organisms make a homogenous suspension in physiologic saline. This makes possible the serologic classification of the avian strain which is not possible with human and bovine strains because of their spontaneous clumping in saline. In two patients with human infections with the avian bacillus, Karlson (52) not only isolated a typical avian culture which was virulent for chickens but demonstrated a high titer of agglutinin in the patient's serum. The organism isolated from the patient was agglutinated also by sera from spontaneously infected hens. As early as 1937, Schaefer (90) identified two serotypes of pathogenic avian bacilli. A more recent re-study of avian strains by Schaefer and Reggiardo

(91) have confirmed the two serotypes and added a third, composed of strains of avian bacilli which have been isolated from disease in swine. Most avian strains, in contrast to human and bovine strains, rapidly lose virulence on artificial media, but Schaefer has found that these avian strains can still be classified in one or another of the three serotypes even after their virulence has disappeared.

Avian bacilli are strongly catalase-positive but niacin-negative (54). Stock strains of virulent avian bacilli were dissociated by Petroff and Steenken (80) and Winn and Petroff (115) in 1933. They found four colonial types: smooth, flat-smooth, rough, and deep yellow-smooth. The white-domed, smooth colony had the greatest degree of virulence for animals and was the colony type which is usually isolated from man and animals. The flat-smooth had less virulence, and the rough or yellow-smooth were almost avirulent. It should be emphasized that virulence is not genetically linked with color, however, since a highly virulent yellow avian strain was isolated by Karlson and his associates (53) from a trumpeter swan, and these cultures retained the yellow color for 10 years after they lost their initial virulence for chickens and rabbits. When studied by Schaefer (91) in 1963, it agglutinated in avian serotype serum.

The infected fowl excretes large numbers of virulent avian bacilli in her feces and they have remarkable survival ability in the soil. Feldman (28) has collected the evidence for this in his monograph. The natural autolytic rotting process, which occurs when an infected chicken is buried, does not destroy the virulent avian bacilli. They are known to have survived, in a virulent form, for more than four years in the soil of an abandoned chicken yard. One investigator believes that they can actually multiply in the soil under favorable conditions (28).

Dormer and his associates (21) reported an epidemic of avian infection, with 60 per cent of the herd reacting to tuberculin, apparently caused by birds' contaminating a pile of sawdust which was used as bedding for calves. The sawdust was eliminated and the entire herd given isoniazid therapy for two and a half years. After these drugs were removed, 70 calves were born and all remained negative to tuberculin.

One may assume that avian bacilli could be transmitted to the respiratory tract of man and animals in a manner analogous to that known for *Histoplasma capsulatum.*

Avian bacilli produce spontaneous disease in domestic fowls and other birds and can spread from these sources to cows, swine, and man.

Feldman (29) has found that avian infection is a more serious problem than bovine infections in cows at the present time, citing the infection of a herd of cows with avian bacilli after grazing in a pasture on which chicken manure had been used as a fertilizer.

Avian infection is usually asymptomatic in cows and sheep but produces a specific allergy which is more reactive to tuberculin made from Johne's bacillus and the avian bacillus than to tuberculin made from the human and bovine bacilli. Karlson's (51) studies have shown that tuberculosis is now 180 times as frequent in swine as in cows; most of the infections occur with the avian bacillus, some with bovine, and a few with other types of mycobacteria. In 1955, 3 to 5 per cent of the swine slaughtered in the Middle West and 1.5 per cent of those slaughtered in the southeastern states had tuberculosis (51). Swine may have an asymptomatic infection, but caseous lesions in the lymph nodes are the most common form of clinical disease, and this is occasionally fatal. Scammon, Froman, and their associates (89) had no difficulty in isolating avian strains from caseous lymph nodes, and the bacilli were virulent for chickens when first isolated but rapidly lost virulence on reculture. Specific bacteriophages were found which would lyse the swine avian strains but not the chicken avian strain. Later studies by Froman and Scammon (34) revealed that the avian strains were not susceptible to lysis unless the avian cultures had been incubated at 42° C. instead of the usual 37° C. With this change in technic some similar phage types were found among avian strains isolated from fowl and swine and certain Battey strains isolated from man. Schaefer and Reggiardo (91) have found two serologic types of avian strains and a third type in avian strains isolated from swine.

Avian infection in man, formerly believed to be extremely rare, is now being reported with increasing frequency (94). It is probable that a good many of the organisms diagnosed as the Battey type of Runyon's type III nonphotochromogen are really avian bacilli. Gentry (35) of the North Carolina State Sanatorium at McCain, North Carolina, has 25 strains isolated from patients with clinical pulmonary disease which were pathogenic for rabbits when first isolated and which grew poorly at 37° C. but reasonably well at 42° C. The temperature differential in growth and pathogenicity for rabbits suggests that these isolates were virulent avian bacilli, although no inoculation of fowls was done. Some of these strains have been sent to Schaefer for serotyping, and a few were found to agglutinate in avian type antiserum.

A very carefully standardized avian PPD is made by Weybridge Laboratories, New Haw, Surrey, England, and their PPD has been used in skin testing surveys in England, the United States, South Africa, and elsewhere. A group of 146 medical students at the Duke University School of Medicine were tested with 5 TU of Seibert's human PPD (PPD^{-S}), avian PPD (PPD^{-A}), and PPD made from the "Boone" strain of the Battey type (PPD^{-B}). Only 7.5 per cent reacted with 6 mm. or more to the PPD^{-S}, with 1.4 per cent reacting to PPD^{-S} alone, while 20.1 per cent reacted to PPD^{-A} and 26.7 per cent to PPD^{-B}. Among this group 13.1 per cent reacted to PPD^{-A} but not to PPD^{-B}, while 19.2 per cent reacted to PPD^{-B} but not to PPD^{-S}. Reactions to the avian PPD are more frequent than to the human in most parts of England (42). Hart (42) found 4.3 per cent reacted only to human PPD, while 12.2 per cent reacted only to avian PPD. In Suffolk, England (100), the ratio in one group was 5.9 to 7.6, and in a second group 4.4 to 8.3. In certain parts of India 15 to 36 per cent reacted to avian, in contrast to 0.4 to 1.3 per cent which reacted to human PPD (83). Edwards and her associates (24), Engbaek and Magnusson (27), and Johnston and Smith (48, 49) have sensitized guinea pigs with avian, Battey, and other types of classified and unclassified mycobacteria and then tested for cross-reaction to purified PPD from the same types. The avian and Battey gave definite cross-reactions with all other types of mycobacteria, but the greatest cross-reactions were between the avian and Battey strains. This makes it impossible to determine whether the numerous reactors to avian PPD have been infected with an avian or a Battey strain or whether the Battey is truly an attenuated avian bacillus, as has been suggested by some investigators.

MYCOBACTERIUM ULCERANS

Mycobacterium ulcerans MacCallum, 1950

This new pathogenic species for man was isolated by MacCallum and his associates (67) in Australia in 1948. The acid-fast rods are 0.2 by 1.5 to 3 μ in culture but somewhat larger from tissues, where they are frequently beaded. Primary colonies after nine weeks are 2 to 3 mm. in diameter, round, smooth, low convex, opaque, and white to pale cream color. Subcultures appear in two to three weeks. On Petra-

gnani's medium primary growth after four weeks, colonies were minute, transparent, and dome-shaped; in older cultures they became convex to flat, with irregular outline and round surface with a lemon to mustard yellow color. This species will not grow at all at 41° C. **Growth is optimal between 30° C. and 33° C. but very limited at 25° C. and 37° C.** *Myco. ulcerans* was found to be antigenically distinct from other known mycobacteria by both complement-fixation and skin test (30).

Myco. ulcerans causes skin ulcers in man which are characterized by indolent extensions from areas of inconspicuous induration to involve large new areas. *Myco. ulcerans* has been isolated from the sputum of one patient who was found to have specific antibodies in his blood for his own and for stock culture of *Myco. ulcerans* (79). Rats and mice can be infected with cultures, but guinea pigs, rabbits, fowls, and lizards are resistant. As one might expect from the low-temperature requirement of *Myco. ulcerans,* the organisms cannot multiply in the internal organs of mice and rats. Following intravenous injections ulcerations appear on the scrotum, feet, tail, ears, and nose. Intracerebral inoculations also result in lesions of the tail, feet, nose, and ears, but not in the brain.

Myco. ulcerans must be differentiated from *Myco. balnei,* isolated and named by Linell and Norden (64) since this species also grows best at 33° C.; it will grow slowly at 37° C., however. Both species produce ulcerations when minimal numbers of organisms are inoculated into the foot pad of mice, but lesions appear in one week when *Myco. balnei* is used and not for four months after the injection of *Myco. ulcerans* (31). The inoculation of chick embryos incubated at 33° C. resulted in rapid multiplication of *Myco. balnei* but not *Myco. ulcerans,* while neither grew when the eggs were incubated at 37° C. Presumably antibiotics used for the treatment of *Myco. tuberculosis* would be effective in the treatment of *Myco. ulcerans* infections.

MYCOBACTERIUM MARINUM

Mycobacterium marinum Aronson, 1926 (*Mycobacterium balnei* Linell and Norden, 1954)

This organism was isolated from tuberculous lesions found in salt water fish by Aronson in 1926 (1, 2). The bacilli may be short, thick, and uniform-staining when occurring in clumps in the tissue, although long, thin beaded and barred rods could be seen scattered about in tissue. The organism grows on agar slants in 5 to 7 days, giving soft, white, glistening, elevated colonies which gradually became lemon-yellow and later orange-yellow in color (38). Growth occurs in glycerol agar medium in 14 to 18 days with colonies which have irregular edges but the same color changes. The growth is more luxuriant on Dorset's or Petroff's egg media. *Myco. marinum* apparently mutated to a rough type colony in Aronson's laboratory. The strain sent to the Type Culture Collection was a smooth colony and has kept the original characteristic but strains sent to other private collectors were often the rough type.

The optimum temperature of growth is between 18° C. and 20° C. It will not grow at 45° C. and is killed by 60° C. for one hour (38). When first isolated, the organism would infect salt-water fish, goldfish, frogs, mice, and pigeons, but not rabbits or guinea pigs. Although isolated originally from salt-water fish, *Myco. marinum* can produce spontaneous disease in goldfish and can be isolated from the slime and the glass walls of some aquaria (66). It was somewhat surprising that this low-temperature-dependent mycobacterial species should have been pathogenic for mice, but this behavior was not investigated at that time.

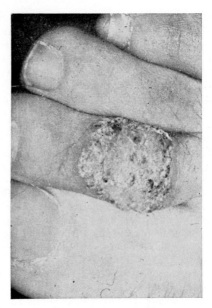

Fig. 2. Verrucous lesion of the toe suggesting tuberculosis verrucosa cutis. (Photograph by James A. Philpott, Jr. Courtesy of Norma Johannis, Colorado State Department of Health.)

MYCOBACTERIUM BALNEI

Mycobacterium balnei Linell and Norden, 1954

In 1949-1950, Linell and Norden studied an epidemic of skin infections in 80 patients in the town of Orebro, Sweden (64). The lesions were most often located on the outside of the elbows (Fig. 1), although they could occur on other parts of the body (Fig. 2). The infection began as a small papule which grew to the size of a bean and then began to ulcerate and discharge pus which contained acid-fast organisms. The lesion healed spontaneously, but sometimes not until two years had elapsed. Subsequent to the studies of Linell and Norden epidemics of the same type were found in Seattle and in Colorado (74).

Since the ulcerations were limited to the skin and subcutaneous tissue, Linell and Norden suspected the presence of a *Mycobacterium* with low temperature dependence like that of *Myco. ulcerans* and incubated all of the cultures at 31° C. The organisms grew poorly or not at all at 37° C. The authors not only isolated the particular organism from the lesions of the patients but from the water of the swimming pool and finally proved their pathogenicity for man by inoculating themselves and reproducing the disease.

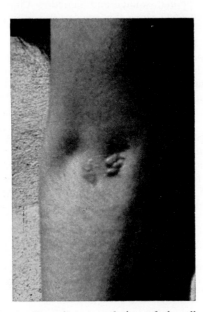

Fig. 1. Granulomatous lesion of the elbow of six months duration showing granulations and some satellite lesions. (Photograph by Mary S. Romer. Courtesy of Norma Johannis, Colorado State Department of Health.)

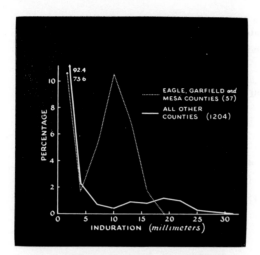

Fig. 3. Increased incidence of reactions to 5 TU of PPD−^{s} in three counties in Colorado attributed to cross-reactions from *Myco. marinum* (*balnei*). (From Palmer and Edwards. *Bull. Internat. Union against Tuberc.*, 32:373, 1961.)

When grown on Lowenstein-Jensen medium at 31° C., the organism produces soft grayish-white colonies with slightly yellow streaks, but after being taken out of the incubator and exposed to daylight at room temperature, they showed an intense orange-yellow to orange and finally a red color (64). One strain dissociated into smooth and rough colonies without an immediate loss of virulence in the rough type. Schaefer and Reggiardo (91) studied 25 strains by the agglutination method and found only one serotype.

Mice were most susceptible to the artificial infections with local lesions appearing in the scrotum, tail, paws, and lungs after intraperitoneal infections. Syrian golden hamsters were about as susceptible as mice. Scrotal lesions appear in some rabbits after intraperitoneal inoculation. Guinea pigs, chickens, rats and tortoises could not be infected. Clark and Shepard (14) have shown that both *Myco. marinum* and *Myco. balnei* have a wide and identical range of pathogenicity for poikilothermic species of animals. The differentiation of *Myco. ulcerans* and *Myco. balnei* by inoculations of minute doses into the foot pad of mice has already been presented in the section on *Myco. ulcerans*.

Recently a restudy of strains of *Myco. marinum* and *Myco. balnei* by Ruth Gordon has shown that the two organisms are identical in every respect. Hence *Myco. balnei* has, with regrets, been reduced to synonymy with *Myco. marinum* (40).

We do not know how frequently subclinical infections with these organisms occur in this and other countries, but it must have been rather extensive in the Colorado area because Palmer and Edwards (76) detected a very high incidence of unexplained low grade reactions to human PPD in Navy recruits from some counties in Colorado (Fig. 3) which was not evident in the Navy recruits from other states (Fig. 4). As mentioned above, Colorado was the site of the largest epidemic of this infection recognized in this country up to the present time. However, there are fairly strong cross-reactions from PPD made from human, bovine, BCG, and balnei *Mycobacterium* (Table 1). Linell and Norden (64) tested 16 individuals, who had been infected only with balnei, with 10 TU of human, avian, and balnei PPD and found strong cross-reactions with both human and avian.

Green, from the Weybridge Laboratories in England, devised a new method for measuring in sensitized guinea pigs the degree of cross-reactions between PPD's made from various species of mycobacteria (41). This method detects very small differences in cross-reactions, since increasing amounts of the tuberculin giving the weaker cross-reactions are injected until the size of the cross-reaction equals that of the homologous reaction. Green and Patterson (64) applied this method to PPD's made from

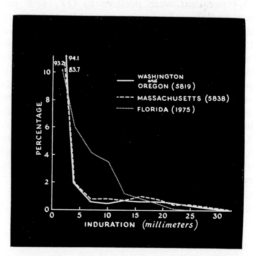

Fig. 4. Increased incidence of cross-reactions to 5 TU PPD−^{s} in Navy recruits from Florida attributed to cross-reactions to Battey type infection. (From Palmer and Edwards. *Bull. Internat. Union against Tuberc.*, 32:373, 1961.)

Table 1. Chart of Specificity Factors, from Green 1951, with Data on *M. balnei*, Green & Paterson

(From Linell and Norden)

TYPE OF SENSITIZATION	TYPE OF PPD						
	HUMAN	BOVINE	BCG	AVIAN	JOHNE	PHLEI	BALNEI
Human	1	½	2	20	30	150	13
Bovine	1	1	2	40	30	150	
BCG	1	½	1	20	30	150	
Avian	20	40	40	1	3	100	
Johne	10	10	10	3	1	50	
Phlei	150	150	150	100	50	1	
Balnei	23						1

human and balnei organisms on guinea pigs sensitized to either human or balnei. Thirteen weight units of the balnei PPD gave the same size reaction in guinea pigs sensitized with human bacilli as one unit of the human PPD. In the reverse experiment, 23 weight units of human PPD was required to give the same size reaction as one unit of balnei PPD when the guinea pig was sensitized with the balnei bacillus (Table 1). This shows the balnei infection can be detected more readily by a small dose of human tuberculin, as a cross-reaction, than an infection with human bacillus by the balnei PPD. These experimental results explain the cross-reactions reported by Aronson in his last study in 1959 (3), where he showed in an industrial school for boys with 1,322 subjects that 55.4 per cent were positive to OT, 47.9 per cent to Battey, 56.6 per cent to *Myco. kansasii*, and 77.8 per cent to balnei at a dose level of 1 TU to 10 TU. The high percentage of reactions to balnei suggests that there could have been a local source of balnei infection, but this possibility was not investigated. The cross-reactions show more specificity in the 55 tuberculin-negative subjects who were vaccinated with BCG and then retested two months later by Aronson for Linell and Norden (64). Aronson found that 96.4 per cent gave positive reactions to 0.1 mg. of OT and 72.4 per cent to 0.0001 mg. of PPD from balnei.

MYCOBACTERIUM FORTUITUM

Mycobacterium fortuitum Cruz, 1938

This organism was isolated from abscesses in man by Cruz (17) in 1938. Later studies by Gordon and Smith (39) and Wells and his associates (114) showed that a series of cultures isolated from lymph glands in cows by

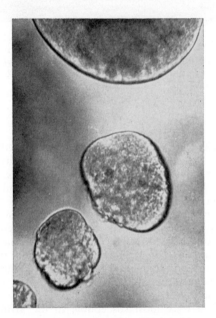

Fig. 5. Colonies of strain 444 of *Myco. fortuitum* on Bennett's agar at six days. × 680. (From Gordon and Mihm. *J. Gen. Microbiol.*, 21:736, 1959.)

Minett (73) in 1932, but not named, were identical with *Myco. fortuitum* Cruz (17). These cows, during life, gave stronger reactions to avian PPD than to bovine PPD. *Myco. fortuitum* has been isolated from cold-blooded animals and from the soil. One of the two soil isolates sent to Wells by Ruth Gordon killed mice, while the other did not (114).

Myco. fortuitum, after 72 hours cultivation on glycerol agar, appear as acid-fast rods 1 to 3 μ long, although some coccoid forms and some long-beaded and occasionally swollen nonacid-fast bacilli are seen. In pus long and

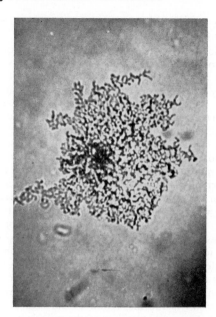

Fig. 6. Colony of strain 1025 of *Myco. fortuitum* on soil-extract agar at 10 days. × 780. (From Gordon and Mihm. *J. Gen. Microbiol.*, 21:736, 1959.)

intravenous inoculation, characterized by abscesses and granulomatous formations in the internal organs (56). Rabbits and guinea pigs could not be infected, but rabbits were sensitized to tuberculin made from *Myco. fortuitum*.

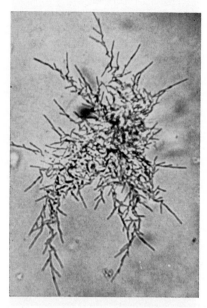

Fig. 7. Colony of strain 964 of *Myco. fortuitum* on soil-extract agar at 12 days. × 780. (From Gordon and Mihm. *J. Gen. Microbiol.*, 21:736, 1959.)

filamentous forms appear, and sometimes there is definite branching. On glycerol agar after two to three days at 28° C. the growth is soft and butyrous, waxy and nodular (Figs. 5, 6, 7, 8). When grown on MacConkey's agar, a change occurs in the indicator. *Myco. fortuitum* does not utilize oxalate or mucate (40).

This is the most rapid growing of all the pathogenic species of mycobacteria and must be distinguished from the other saprophilic rapid growing species (Fig. 9). *Myco. fortuitum* has an enzyme which releases free phenolphthalein which can then be detected by treatment with alkali (109). The red color appears in one to 30 minutes after the addition of the alkali. All 68 strains tested by Wayne (108) were positive by this test. The named saprophytes can also be separated by the arylsulphatase test, but some of the unclassified rapid growers also give a positive test (55).

Froman (34) has a bacteriophage specific for *Myco. fortuitum* and Redmond has two specific phages for the species. Fregman, Smith, and Randall (33) isolated a specific glycolipid, designated mycoside F, from strains of *Myco. fortuitum*.

The best growth occurs between 28° C. and 35° C., but it will grow at 40° C. but does not survive at 60° C. for four hours. *Myco. fortuitum* is highly pathogenic for mice, following

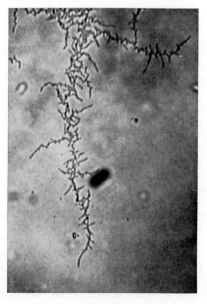

Fig. 8. Portion of colony of strain 1026 of *Myco. fortuitum* on soil-extract agar at 10 days. × 780.

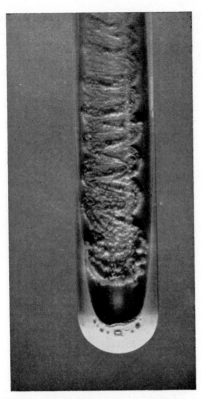

Fig. 9. Culture of *Myco. fortuitum*. Note the rough type of growth which is easily mistaken for the human *Myco. tuberculosis*. This is the strain used for the production of PPD^{-F}.

from other mycobacteria when guinea pigs were infected with *Myco. fortuitum* (Fig. 10).

Most of the original isolations of the fortuitum organisms were from abscesses in cows and local abscesses in man or from the soil. It was many years before the organism was isolated from the sputum of man. McMillen and Kushiner (65) in Chicago were the first to recover the organism with any frequency from the sputum. By 1957 they had diagnosed 17 cases of *Myco. fortuitum* infections. **There is little doubt that many strains of *Myco. fortuitum* have been incorrectly diagnosed as *Myco. tuberculosis* when the cultures are not inspected for three to four weeks after they have been plated.** At that time *Myco. fortuitum* presents a colorless, somewhat rough-looking, growth which is usually identical to that seen with the human tubercle bacillus (Fig. 9). In older cultures a very faint color may be seen which is also seen with human bacilli. The secret of isolating *Myco. fortuitum* is the inspection of cultures at four to 14 days and selection of the colorless, rapid growers for specific study. The occasional *Myco. fortuitum* which requires three to four weeks for growth will be found to be rapid growers on subculture. Other characteristics are rapid

There was some cross-reaction with avian and bovine but not with human tuberculin. The studies made by Edwards and her associates (26) with PPD's made from human and other classified and unclassified mycobacteria showed that the fortuitum organism gave a specific reaction to the PPD^{-F} with very slight cross-reactions with human, avian, Battey, and photochromes. In Edwards' study of 3,415 Navy recruits only 7.7 per cent gave skin reactions of more than 2 mm. to 5 TU of PPD^{-F} with an average of 4.8 μ (Table 2). This was the lowest reaction to any of the specific PPD's but probably represents true primary infections, since the cross-reactions to fortuitum are so slight (26, 49).

In a study of 82 medical students by Smith and Johnston (95) with PPD^{-F} supplied by Dr. Lydia Edwards of the U.S. Public Health Service, 14.6 per cent gave positive reactions of 5 mm. or more of induration. The study of Smith and Johnston (95) in this laboratory showed very little cross-reaction with PPD's

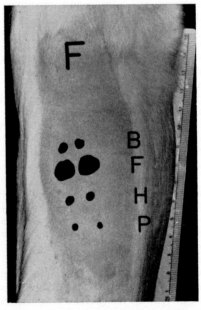

Fig. 10. Tuberculin reactions in a guinea pig sensitized with 4 mg. of *Myco. fortuitum*. Note the larger size of the reaction to PPD^{-F}. The double tests serve to detect mechanical errors in the test. (From Smith and Johnston. *Am. Rev. Resp. Dis.* In press.)

Table 2. Frequency and Mean Size of Reactions Among Navy Recruits to 0.0001 mg. of PPD
Antigens Prepared from Various Strains of Mycobacteria

(From Edwards. Ann. N.Y. Acad. Sci., 106:36, 1963)

PPD ANTIGEN	PREPARED FROM	NUMBER TESTED	REACTIONS OF 2 MM. OR MORE PERCENTAGE	MEAN SIZE (MM.)
PPD-S	M. tuberculosis	212,462	8.6	10.3
PPD-F	M. fortuitum	3,415	7.7	4.8
PPD-240	Unclassified; group 3	3,729	12.0	5.8
PPD-Y	M. kansasii	13,913	13.1	6.2
PPD-63	Unclassified; group 3	9,473	17.5	7.0
PPD-sm	M. smegmatis	14,239	18.3	5.7
PPD-ph	M. phlei	15,229	23.1	6.4
PPD-216	Unclassified; group 2	10,060	28.4	9.0
PPD-A	M. avium	10,769	30.5	6.7
PPD-B	Unclassified; (Battey type)	212,462	35.1	7.7
PPD-269	Unclassified; group 3	8,402	39.0	7.2
PPD-G	Unclassified; group 2	29,540	48.7	10.3

growth on ordinary media at 37° C. and at room temperature, surface growth on broth, and uniform resistance to PAS and streptomycin. Usually they are susceptible to INH and tetracycline (56). Wherever this specific procedure of inspecting the cultures at 7 to 14 days is being employed, *Myco. fortuitum* strains are being isolated. We found our first one only a few months ago by this procedure. *Myco. fortuitum* is being recognized by Corpe and his associates (15) at the Battey State Hospital in Georgia, where the first Battey type organisms were isolated. Magnusson (70) studied three strains of fortuitum isolated from patients in Denmark. The State Laboratories of Florida have looked for unusual classified and unclassified mycobacteria with the greatest interest in the past five years. Among 407 cultures of unclassified mycobacteria isolated in one year, 8 per cent were identified as *Myco. fortuitum* (43).

THE VOLE BACILLUS

Mycobacterium microti Reed *nom. nov.*

This organism was isolated by Wells (112, 113) from the field mouse or vole in 1937. These acid-fast organisms are somewhat longer and thinner than other mammalian species in culture. Irregular S-shaped, hook-shaped, semicircular, and circular forms have been seen in tissue of infected voles. Growth is slow on all types of media, often requiring as long as four to five weeks for the appearance of minute colonies. Primary growth does not occur on media containing glycerol, and growth is not enhanced by the presence of glycerol in subculture. The growth is definitely slower than that of the human and bovine species.

This organism is the cause of general tuberculosis in voles. Local but not systemic infections are induced in guinea pigs, rabbits, and calves. The vole bacillus was used as a vaccine in man, along with BCG, in the British study of the effectiveness of BCG. The percentage of protection after seven and a half to 10 years was practically the same as from BCG (10).

MYCOBACTERIA FROM REPTILES AND FISH

Mycobacterium thamnopheos Aronson, 1929

This species was isolated from a bush snake by Aronson (1). It was found to be pathogenic for snakes, frogs, lizards, and fish, but not for guinea pigs, rabbits, and fowls. This organism has not been isolated from man.

Mycobacterium platypoecilus,
Baker and Hagan, 1942

This species was isolated from a tropical platy fish. Optimal temperature is 25° C., and growth does not occur at 37° C. The colonies are white when grown in the dark but develop a deep orange color when grown in the light (4).

In 1958 Parisot (78) reviewed the literature of *Mycobacterium* which produced tuberculosis in fish and called attention to the prevalence of infection in salmon with two species described in the literature but not included in Bergey's Manual.

SAPROPHYTIC MYCOBACTERIA

Mycobacterium phlei,
Lehmann and Neumann, 1899

This organism is a rapid-growing saprophilic species which was described by Moeller in 1898 as timothy grass bacillus and raised to species rank by Lehmann and Neumann in 1899. Growth appears in two to four days on glycerol agar. This may be soft, smooth, butyrous, deep-yellow to orange, waxy and coarsely wrinkled, suggesting the presence of both smooth and rough type colonies. Growth occurs from 28° C to 52° C. but survives 60° C for four hours. The organism is distributed widely in soil, dust, and on plants. It is not pathogenic for fish, frogs, chickens, and mammals, including man.

Edwards (26) found PPD prepared from *Myco. phlei* gave an average reaction of 6.4 mm. in 23.1 per cent of 15,229 Navy recruits. However, these may have been cross-reactions from other mycobacterial infections.

Mycobacterium smegmatis Trevisan, 1889

This organism was isolated by Trevisan in 1889 from human smegma and called the smegmas bacillus (59, 60). Growth on glycerol agar appears after two to three days which is white, rough, and finely wrinkled, and by 14 days is waxy and cream-yellow to orange. Smooth forms appear as well as the rough. It grows best between 28° C. and 45° C. and does not survive 60° C. for four hours. It is almost constantly present in smegma and is also distributed widely in soil, dust, and water. The presence of *Myco. smegmatis* in voided specimens of urine may suggest an erroneous diagnosis of tuberculosis of the kidneys.

Edwards (26) found that PPD made from *Myco. smegmatis* gave an average reaction of 5.7 mm. in 18.3 per cent of 14,229 Navy recruits. These may have been cross-reactions from infections with other mycobacterial species.

THE UNCLASSIFIED MYCOBACTERIA

Mycobacteria found in pure culture at necropsy, biopsy, and in unopened abscesses under circumstances which indicate that they were the cause of the disease have been known for over 50 years. These organisms did not produce disease when injected into guinea pigs, rabbits, or chickens and could not be differentiated by the then available cultural and metabolic tests from saprophilic species from soil and water. Their existence before the introduction of the modern chemotherapeutic agents eliminates them as mutants resulting from therapy (16, 44, 57, 81, 84, 85, 86, 104, 118, 121).

The first real progress in the classification of the unclassified mycobacteria came in 1954 when Timpe and Runyon (105) reported their studies of several hundred isolates from 120 patients with pulmonary disease. They divided the strains into four major groups, designated I, II, III, and IV. Subsequently Runyon (85) and his associates have studied thousands of strains which have been isolated in this and other countries. The following description of the four main groups was supplied to me by Dr. Ernest Runyon for publication in this text:

GROUP I. **Photochromogens,** commonly associated with tuberculosis-like disease.

PIGMENTATION. Little or none if grown in dark; bright yellow to orange or brick red if grown in continuous light. Young, actively growing, nonpigmented colonies will become yellow in the dark incubator six to 12 hours after exposure, 45 cm. from a 30-watt lamp for one hour. Mature colonies exposed to light produce little or no color.

GROWTH RATE. About as for tubercle bacilli or slightly more rapid at 37° C.; at 20 to 25° C. growth from small inocula is visible in three to four weeks. *Myco. balnei,* Norden, also photochromogenic, is easily distinguished by its failure to grow at 37° C. on Lowenstein-Jensen medium. *Myco. balnei* is not known to occur in sputum but has been isolated from skin lesions. Other photochromogens are known but are not problems because they do not occur in bronchial discharge and are rapid growers.

COLONIES. Usually smooth with some tendency to roughness; more readily dispersed than tubercle bacilli. Occasional strains are completely rough. On cornmeal glycerol agar colonies are somewhat rough, some strains showing serpentine cords. Growth in Proskauer and Beck liquid medium occurs as a flaky or granular sediment with the eventual formation of a pellicle.

CELLS. Average size larger than tubercle bacilli, often quite long, banded and beaded, strongly acid-fast. *Myco. kansasii* may be suspected as soon as the first sputum smear is found to show these unusually large bacilli.

PATHOGENICITY FOR ANIMALS. (a) In guinea pigs 5 mg. dry weight of bacteria inoculated subcutaneously does not cause progressive disease. Most animals become at least weakly tuberculin positive. One mg. inoculated intracardially often results in death within four to five weeks. (b) In mice 0.001 mg. inoculated intravenously or 3 mg. intraperitoneally usually causes disease. This is indicated by failure to gain weight, formation of lesions in lungs, liver, spleen or kidneys, and at times death. Heat-killed inocula fail to produce this response.

Group II. The yellow-orange-red **Scotochromogens.** These organisms are being recovered with surprising frequency from adenitis in children, but are rare as independent agents of pulmonary disease in man. Usually considered to be saprophytes unless occurring under exceptional circumstances.

SYNONYMS. "Orange bacilli," Buhler and Pollak. Similar or identical bacteria have been given species names by various authors as *Myco. marianum, Myco. scrofulaceum,* Prissick and Masson, *Myco. paraffinicum,* Davis et al., *Myco. aquae,* Galli-Valerio.

PIGMENTATION. Yellow or orange from the beginning of growth in the dark; more reddish if grown continuously in light. Sedimented growth in Proskauer and Beck liquid medium is yellow.

GROWTH RATE. At 37° C. about as for tubercle bacilli or a little more rapid. Growth occurs, but more slowly, at 20 to 25° C.; usually fails to grow at 45° C. from minimum inocula.

COLONIES. Almost always smooth, rarely rough. Often of stringy or gummy consistency. Colony types on cornmeal glycerol agar similar to those of group III. Growth in Proskauer and Beck is in the form of a heavy yellow sediment.

CELLS. Variable in size, strongly acid-fast, rarely exhibit cord formation.

PATHOGENICITY FOR ANIMALS. None. Only rarely are lesions produced and then only with very large inocula.

Group II scotochromogens often occur as single colonies in specimens from patients known to have true tuberculosis or as laboratory contaminants.

Group III. "Battey" bacilli, **Nonphotochromogens.** Causes pulmonary disease in man; similar or identical strains have been reported from humans without evidence of disease. The acid-fast bacilli described as *Nocardia intracellularis,* Cuttino and McCabe, appear to be identical.

PIGMENTATION. Usually weak or none; if present, usually slowly developing and not as described for groups I and II. Sedimented growth in Proskauer and Beck liquid medium usually white or more tan than yellow.

GROWTH RATE. As described for groups I and II. Growth from minimum inocula at 45° C. may indicate avian strains.

COLONIES ON EGG MEDIUM. Small, smooth, circular; easily dispersed in water. On cornmeal glycerol agar young colonies are usually asteroid, some strains showing a proportion of darker, rough colonies with loose serpentine cords. Growth in Proskauer and Beck occurs as a fine, whitish easily dispersible sediment.

CELLS. Highly pleomorphic but often very short. Non acid-fast cells often seen, at times in *Nocardia*-like filaments.

PATHOGENICITY FOR ANIMALS. Not uniform, some strains being as pathogenic as group I strains. Other strains lack evidence of pathogenicity for laboratory animals. Guinea pigs usually become tuberculin positive.

Group IV. The Rapid Growers. Most of these encountered in clinical material will be *Myco. fortuitum* but occasionally other species such as the well-known saprophytes *Myco. phlei* or *Myco. smegmatis* may be found. The inability of *Myco. fortuitum* to grow at 45° C. helps to distinguish this species from *Myco. phlei* and *Myco. smegmatis.* Other strains may be found which do not conform to species descriptions in Bergey's Manual. Strains not identified as species are conveniently referred to as group IV strains. Besides rapid growth, strains of this group are characterized by very marked drug resistance and avirulence for mice. *Myco. fortuitum* from human lesions may form kidney lesions in mice.

With continuing study of the organisms in

each of the four groups by more investigators, it has become evident that at least two species can be removed from the designations. These are *Myco. fortuitum* Cruz, 1938, from Group IV; and *Myco. kansasii* Hauduroy, 1955, from Group I. *Myco. fortuitum* was known before but not recognized as an important cause of pulmonary disease in man. The newly named species *Myco. kansasii* (102) discovered by Buhler and Pollak (12) in 1953 was known as the "yellow bacillus." With the emphasis by Runyon on the change in color when exposed to light, it became relatively easy to differentiate this organism from the human tubercle bacillus when in its white phase, and from chromogenic saprophytes when in the yellow phase. It was soon recognized that this organism was regularly associated with clinical disease and that it was worldwide in distribution although much more frequent in some geographic areas than in others (6a, 50, 105).

THE PHOTOCHROMES

Mycobacterium kansasii Hauduroy, 1955. Kansa-si. L. (from American Indian) Kansasius; L. gen. noun kansasii of kansas. Common name, Photochromogen; "yellow bacillus" of Buhler and Pollack

Rods, usually longer and broader than tubercle bacilli, characteristically show alternate stained and unstained bands, especially in young liquid cultures containing oleic acid and polyoxyethylene sorbitan mono-oleate, and usually arranged in curving strands, nonmotile, and acid-fast. This bacillus contains a mycoside A (33, 96, 97) formerly called Ga, in the alcohol-ether extracted lipids. This specific mycoside is a glycolipid containing 2-0-methyl fucose, 2-9-methyl rhamnose, and 2:4-di-0-methyl rhamnose. The lipid moiety contains mycocerosic acid and an unidentified aromatic alcohol (97).

Glycerol Egg Slants. After two weeks of incubation in the dark, colonies appear which are raised, with irregular surface and margins, and are ivory or off-white in color. If grown in lighted incubators, the colonies are lemon-yellow but becoming orange or even red-orange with age. Colonies are usually but not always more smooth and moist than *Myco. tuberculosis* but drier than *Myco. avium.*

Oleic Acid-Albumin Agar. The colonies are smooth and flat, with some wrinkling. The colonies are light at the periphery and dark toward the center and show a definite central spot. The margins are regular or slightly undulated.

Glycerol Agar. Colonies are similar but somewhat larger.

Broth Without Glycerol. Growth is poor and occurs at the bottom of the medium.

Broth With Glycerol. Growth begins as a granular sediment but later forms a pellicle.

Corn Meal Agar With 3 Per Cent Glycerol. The colonies are small and must be studied with the low power of the microscope (100X). They are thin, roughly circular, with margins more or less indented, or shallowly lobed strands can be seen which are usually rather loose, but may be tight and occasionally absent. When strands are absent, the texture is nearly homogenous with the margin entire. Thickening and pigmentation occur primarily at the center of the colony. Knobs may be present in the central area and growth ("rhizoids") may penetrate the agar.

Growth occurs at room temperature in three weeks and in one to two weeks at 31° C. to 37° C. There is no growth at 45° C.

Biochemical Reactions. Niacin negative; catalase strongly positive; peroxidase negative; arylsulphatase positive.

Distinctive Characteristics. Definite yellow pigmentation within 24 hours after 1-hour exposure of actively growing culture to bright light. Characteristic long, broad, banded cells are present in young cultures from liquid media. Growth is very slow at room temperature. *Myco. kansasii* is less susceptible to drugs such as streptomycin, para-aminosalicylic acid, and isoniazid than *Myco. tuberculosis.* The prompt growth and primary isolation at 37° C. differentiates it from *Myco. marinum* (*Myco. balnei*) which is photochromogenic. *Myco. marinum* colonies grow more rapidly and are smoother.

Dissociation. Mankiewicz (71) has reported the isolation of photochromogenic colonies which dissociate into photochromogenic and nonphotochromogenic variants on subculture. The photochromogenic types continue to give off nonphotochromogenic variants. If this phenomenon occurs in the patient, some patients could give nonphotochromogenic isolates which would be difficult to diagnose. One would assume, however, that the biochemical reactions and the pathogenicity for mice and hamsters would remain the same.

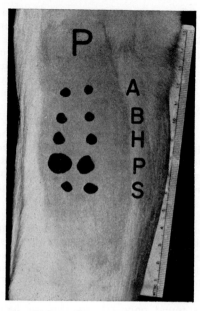

Fig. 11. Tuberculin reaction in a guinea pig sensitized with 4 mg. of *Myco. kansasii*. Note the specific reaction to PPD−Y (P) and the small but uniform cross-reaction with PPD−A, PPD−S (H), and PPD−SCOT (S). The double test serves to detect mechanical errors. (From Johnston and Smith. *Proc. Soc. Exper. Biol. & Med.* In press.)

Pathogenicity. *Myco. kansasii* produces pulmonary and extrapulmonary disease in man which practically is indistinguishable from that produced by *Myco. tuberculosis*. Progressive disease can be produced in hamsters when large doses (10^6 and 10^7) of viable organisms are injected intravenously or intraperitoneally into hamster. It is not pathogenic for guinea pigs, rabbits, or fowls, but large doses of organisms (4 mg. moist weight) injected into guinea pigs produced a high degree of specific sensitivity to PPD prepared from *Myco. kansasii* type strains (Fig. 11). A double infection with *Myco. tuberculosis* and *Myco. kansasii* results in a marked reinforcement of both the human and photochrome but not the battey and fortuitum (Fig. 12).

Gernez-Rieux and Tacquet (36) found that silica dust increased the pathogenicity of *Myco. kansasii* for guinea pig lungs. In contrast, Wayne (108) has found that strains of *Myco. kansasii* which have been single and occasional isolates from individuals without obvious clinical disease have a low degree of pathogenicity for the guinea pig's skin. They can be differ-

entiated from the more virulent strains, which have been isolated from patients with clinical disease, by a reduction in catalase activity. This is an interesting but not surprising finding, since we have noted in the section on *Myco. fortuitum* that one of the two soil isolates of this organism was found to be pathogenic for mice while the other one was not.

Antigenic Structure. Schaefer and Reggiardo (91) did agglutination-adsorption studies on 30 typical strains of *Myco. kansasii* and found only one serologic type. However, Nassau and his associates have found that *Myco. kansasii* shares common antigens with human and other mycobacteria but has at least one antigen which is not present in *Myco. tuberculosis* (75). *Myco. kansasii* organisms absorbed the agglutinin from the sera of rabbits immunized to either the human and the *Myco. kansasii* organisms, while human tubercle absorbed agglutinins specific for the human but left intact the agglutinin to *Myco. kansasii*.

Guinea pigs sensitized to 4 mg of *Myco. kansasii* by a method which gives a high degree of sensitivity to 5 TU of PPD show a low but rather uniform cross-reaction to PPD−S, PPD−A, PPD−B, and PPD−SCOT (Fig. 11), and a larger specific reaction to its own PPD (49). Guinea pigs sensitized to human R_1 by the same method give a large reaction to human R_1 and the least cross-reaction to PPD from *Myco. kansasii* (Fig. 13). However, a super infection of either one or the other results in a marked increase in the cross-reacting PPD (Fig. 12). We have already reported that students giving 20 to 50 mm. reactions to 5 TU PPD−S give almost as large a cross-reaction to PPD−Y, and much smaller reaction to PPD−A, PPD−B, and PPD−SCOT. The same phenomenon has been seen in some patients with culture proven *Myco. tuberculosis*. Edwards and Palmer (22) tested 103 patients with culture proven *Myco. kansasii* from the Suburban Cook County Hospital, Hinsdale, Illinois, with 5 TU of PPD from the respective organism. The patient infected with the human strain showed overlapping degrees of reaction but with a statistically significant increase in the human antigen. But there was complete overlapping, with no statistical difference in those infected with *Myco. kansasii*. The results of our guinea pig study would suggest that the patient with cultures of *Myco. kansasii* who had reactions of the same size to both human PPD and kansasii PPD had had a subclinical infection with the human bacillus as well as a clinical infection with *Myco. kansasii*. Our

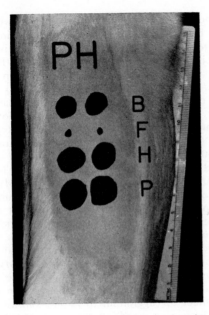

Fig. 12. Tuberculin reactions in a guinea pig sensitized with 4 mg. *Myco. kansasii* and resensitized with 4 mg. of *Myco. tuberculosis* (R_1). Note the reinforcement of the reaction to PPD^{-Y} (P) and PPD^{-S} (H) but not to PPD^{-F}. (From Johnston and Smith. *Proc. Soc. Exper. Biol. & Med.* In press.)

a sputum positive member remains in the family for months or years (61). However, the infection is much more prevalent in some geographic areas than in others. In the Suburban Cook County Hospital Sanatorium, Hinsdale Illinois, during a period of less than four years, 1,360 patients were admitted with cultures positive for mycobacteria. 975 (71.1 per cent) were *Myco. tuberculosis* and 385 (28.3 per cent) were unclassified (6, 8). Among the unclassified, 18.4 per cent were *Myco. kansasii,* of which 13.7 were pure infections and 4.7 per cent mixed infections (45). This organism is frequently isolated in the Houston-Dallas area of Texas. Jenkins (45) had diagnosed 68 patients by 1959 and Chapman (13) had studied a large series. The percentage of isolation is much lower in the Middle West and in the Southeast. Lewis and his associates (62) found patients with unclassified mycobacteria in Florida. Gerszen and coworkers (37) reported 4 per cent from Virginia; Wolinsky (116) found only 1.2 per cent of 849 new patients in Cleveland, Ohio. Gentry (35) at the North Carolina State Sanatorium at Mc-Cain, North Carolina, found only three pa-

results with experimentally infected guinea pigs were confirmed by the studies of Chapman and his associates in Texas, who found that most of the children in his area who reacted to tuberculin of any kind reacted most often to the *Myco. kansasii* PPD and not to human PPD or the reverse; but a small number gave very large reactions to both, suggesting a double infection. This is in contrast to the results found in Georgia (22) where 145 patients infected with the human bacillus and 28 with the "Battey" bacillus were tested with 5 TU of PPD^{-S} and PPD^{-B}. Although there was some overlapping in the 5 to 10 mm. range, the separation was excellent in the 10 to 20 mm. range. However in the 20 to 25 mm. range the sizes were identical, which suggests that these reactors may have had a double infection with both the human and Battey organisms. Lewis and his associates (63) confirmed the results of Edwards and Palmer by separating the human infected and Battey infected patient by using 5 TU of PPD^{-S} and PPD^{-B}.

Source of Infection. There is no evidence that this organism spreads directly from man to man or that children become infected when

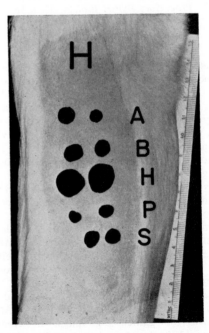

Fig. 13. Tuberculin reactions in a guinea pig sensitized with 4 mg. of the human R_1 culture. Note the large reaction to the homologous PPD and cross-reaction with avian, Battey, scotochrome, and photochrome. (From Johnston and Smith. *Proc. Soc. Exper. Biol. & Med.* In press.)

tients with *Myco. kansasii* in a ten year period and all of these came from one part of one of the 100 counties in the state. During the same period of time, over 100 patients were found to have other types of unclassified mycobacteria.

Chapman and Bernard (13) failed in many attempts to isolate *Myco. kansasii* from (a) soil, (b) tap water, (c) stagnant water, or (d) utensils used in the hospital but did isolate what appeared to be *Myco. kansasii* from the raw milk of two dealers in the area of their patients. On inquiry they learned that 33 of the patients had consumed milk from one or the other of these dealers.

Clinical Disease. Primary infections must be more frequent than reinfections with *Myco. kansasii* but are less frequently detected. Lymph node enlargement, especially in the neck may be the most frequent clinical form of the disease. In Black and Chapman's (7) series in Texas among 28 children with cervical adenitis, six were caused by *Myco. tuberculosis,* eight by *Myco. kansasii,* two by scotochromogens, and two by nonphotochromogens (Battey type). A few children have hilar lymph node disease without adenitis (45). In Jenkins' (45) series of 68 patients from Houston, Texas, the disease was most frequent in white males, Negro males, Negro females, Latin American males, and Latin American females in this order. The onset is most often insidious but may be abrupt with pleural pain, fever, and hemorrhages. The later symptoms occur in 23 per cent of Jenkins' patients. Cavities were present in 65 per cent of the 68 patients. Symptomatology of reinfection pulmonary disease is indistinguishable from that shown by infection with *Myco. tuberculosis.*

Treatment. *Myco. kansasii* is usually less susceptible to streptomycin, PAS, and INH than *Myco. tuberculosis,* but some individual strains may be susceptible to streptomycin and isoniazid. Some strains resistant to the major drugs may be susceptible to cycloserine, viomycin, amithiazone, and promizone (99). Jenkins (45) suggests surgical intervention should be considered as soon as it becomes evident that the drugs are not effective in eliminating the organism from the sputum.

THE SCOTOCHROMES

These are the yellow and orange growers in a dark incubator which become more reddish when grown in the light. They are almost as slow to grow as true human tubercle bacilli. The colonies are smooth and soft but become dome-shaped as growth continues. **Catalase activity is hyperactive, but niacin is not produced and cords are not formed (54). The scotochromes are not pathogenic for laboratory animals.**

These slow-growing scotochromes frequently appear as single colonies in cultures of the sputum of patients who almost certainly do not have a mycobacterial disease. Hence, they were suspected of being contaminants from the air either of the sputum before it reached the laboratory or of the sputum or media in the laboratory. The frequency with which they appear in the gastric washings was much greater than in sputum, and this was a puzzle until it was learned that they could be grown from unsterilized tap water used in the gastric lavage (37). For many years their pathogenicity for man was questioned, although they were occasionally isolated from spinal fluid in clinical cases of meningitis, from lobes removed by lobectomy, and from internal organs, especially the lungs, at necropsy.

Evidence for primary pathogenicity for at least some strains of scotochrome mycobacteria has come from two different sources. They are frequently found as the sole etiologic agent in cervical adenitis in young children. This was reported by Prissick and Masson (82) from Canada in 1956. The author suggested the name *Myco. scrofulaceum* for strains isolated from this source. The scotochromes are now being isolated from cervical lymph nodes in various parts of the world. In this country they have been studied most intensively by Davis and Comstock (20) in Georgia, Wayne in California (110), Schaefer and Reggiardo (91) in Colorado, and Wolinsky (116) in Cleveland, Ohio. The second source of evidence was from skin tests with standardized PPD made from scotochromes isolated from cervical lymph nodes. With the PPD−G made from the Gause strain, Edwards (26) found a reaction rate of 48.7 per cent among 29,540 Navy recruits. A second PPD from another cervical lymph node isolate, known as Bridge No. 236, was tested on medical students by Youmans in Illinois and Smith and Johnston in North Carolina. Youmans (121) found 47.5 per cent gave 5 mm. or more reaction to

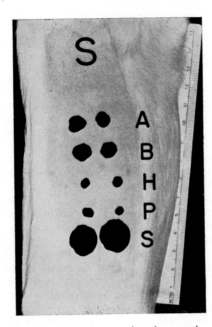

Fig. 14. Tuberculin reaction in a guinea pig sensitized with 4 mg. of a scotochrome culture. The homologous PPD is largest but there are good cross-reactions with avian and Battey, but poor cross-reactions with human and photochrome. (From Smith and Johnston. *Am. Rev. Resp. Dis.* In press.)

5 TU of the Bridge strain, and Smith and Johnston (95) found 51.8 per cent gave 5 mm. or more to the same dose. However, the reaction rate in first-year nursing students was only 22.5 per cent, or less than one-half as many as in the medical students. Edwards (26) has some evidence that not all scotochrome isolates have the same or the same amount of tuberculoprotein antigens. A third PPD was prepared from strain 216 and tested on 10,769 Navy recruits, with positive reactions appearing in only 28.4 per cent, in contrast to 48.7 per cent in the 29,540 who were injected with the PPD made from the Gause strain (26).

Guinea pigs must be constantly exposed to saprophilic species of scotochromes and should give positive skin reactions if scotochrome mycobacteria could invade and grow in guinea pig tissue. No direct testing of normal stock guinea pigs has been done because of the very limited supply of the scotochrome PPD, but several hundred guinea pigs sensitized with other mycobacteria, such as avian, human, photochrome and Battey, have been tested with a battery of PPD's, including the Bridge scotochrome PPD. Under these condi-

tions all of the observed reactions to the scotochrome were of the cross-reaction type, with no instance of as large a reaction as previously observed when the scotochrome was used to sensitize the pigs. These observations suggest that certain strains of scotochromes have a high degree of invasiveness but a low degree of pathogenicity for man while they have neither for the guinea pigs.

Classification of Scotochromes. Wayne (108, 110) collected 59 strains of scotochrome mycobacteria and subjected them to seven different biochemical tests. The author concluded that 28 strains were like the cervical lymph node isolates and 31 were quite different in their ability to hydrolyze Tween 80. The first group of 28 was designated as group I and the remaining 31 as group II. Seventeen of the twenty-eight in group I were suspected by clinicians as the etiologic agent of disease, while only 5 of 31 in group II were thought to have clinical significance. Since 26 of the 31 in group II were single isolations from sputum or gastric washings, they could be saprophytes.

Schaefer (91) performed agglutination studies on hundreds of strains of unclassified mycobacteria isolated from man and animals in many different countries. Most of these were isolated from lymph nodes in children, but the remainder were from pulmonary infections; all were isolated under conditions which suggested primary pathogenicity. Among the 90 isolates from human lymph nodes, 83.5 per cent were identified as scotochromes, 5.5 per cent as avian, and 11 per cent remained unclassified. The avian serotype was usually the "Battey" variety of group III nonphotochromes and was not pathogenic for chickens. Among the 83.5 per cent classified as group II scotochromogens, 40 were identified as serotype *M. scrofulaceum*, 28 as serotype Lunning, and 15.5 as serotype Gause. The Bridge 236, used in skin testing of students and guinea pigs by Smith and Johnston (95) was a *M. scrofulaceum* serotype, while the good reactions in Navy recruits were produced by the Gause strain and the poor one, designated as 216, was not typed. Serotyping combined with the biochemical tests of Wayne (108, 110) may provide a practical procedure for separating the pathogenic from the saprophytic species of scotochromes.

Guinea pigs sensitized to scotochrome, Bridge 236, gave appreciable cross-reactions with avian and Battey but very little cross-reaction with human or photochrome (Fig. 14). Guinea pigs sensitized to human tubercle

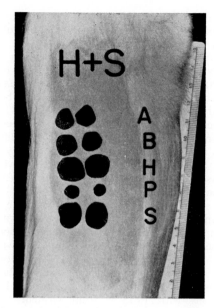

Fig. 15. Tuberculin reaction in a guinea pig sensitized with 4 mg. of human R_1, followed two months later by 4 mg. of scotochrome. The homologous reaction to human and scotochrome are quite large; this is also true of the avian and Battey which have had the effect of a double cross-reaction. However, the reaction to photochrome has not been increased by the double infection with human or scotochrome. (From Smith and Johnston. *Am. Rev. Resp. Dis.* In press).

tomycin. The minor drugs to be tested should include kanamycin.

THE NONPHOTOCHROMOGENS

(Battey Type). This group of nonphotochromogens is the most complex and the least well delineated of all the unclassified mycobacteria. Unquestionably strains of this type have been isolated from patients with pulmonary disease for the past 75 years but since they were soft in consistency, would grow slowly at room temperature, and were not pathogenic for guinea pigs, they were discarded as contaminants. Our current knowledge of this group began at the Battey State Hospital for Tuberculosis at Rome, Georgia, in 1950. The unusual alertness of the clinical and laboratory staff revealed that about 1 per cent of all hospital admissions from 1950 to 1955 had a peculiar type of *Mycobacterium* in their sputum. Some were mixed infections with typical human tuberculosis, but 65 patients showed the newly recognized organism only and consistently in repeated cultures (16). The experience of Cuttino and McCabe (18) illustrates the ease with which this organism can be misdiagnosed. A year before the first reported case from the Battey Hospital, these authors isolated a peculiar *Mycobacterium* from a biopsy during life and from the internal organs at necropsy which was growing luxuriantly in the cytoplasm of mammalian cells without producing necrosis. The organism was strongly acid-fast, grew readily on all kinds of ordinary laboratory media, and was not pathogenic for mice, guinea pigs, rabbits, or fowl. Because it showed profuse branching, when observed in hanging drop slides, it was named *Nocardia intercelluraris nov. sp.* by the authors. It was known that *Myco. tuberculosis* of man would branch when observed in hanging drops (107) and extensive branching had been found in experimental avian tuberculosis in chickens by Winn and Petroff (115) as early as 1933. Later studies in HeLa cell tissue cultures showed that branching in the cells is quite characteristic of both Battey bacilli and virulent avian tubercle bacilli (11, 92) (Figs. 16 and 17). Shepard (92) found that the *Nocardia intercellularis* grew and branched in the same manner as avian and Battey strains. Mycologists, without exception, have classified *N. intercellularis* as a *Mycobacterium,* and Bojail and Cerbon (8, 9) and others agree that it belongs to the Battey type of group III nonphotochromogens. Magnusson (69, 70) prepared sensitin from *N. intercellu-*

bacilli (R_1) gave large homologous reactions, with very small cross-reactions to photochromes, more to scotochromes, and most to avian and Battey (Fig. 13). A double infection with human and scotochrome, regardless of which was the primary infection, resulted in small reactions to photochrome but equally large reaction to human, scotochrome, avian, and Battey (Fig. 15).

Diagnosis. It must be borne in mind that the vast majority of scotochromes isolated are saprophytes. When isolated from a lymph node, spinal fluid, blood, or surgically excised pulmonary tissue, in the absence of other pathogenic organisms, however, the pathogenicity of the strain may be assumed for purposes of therapy. Isolates from sputum and gastric washings must be viewed with skepticism unless every precaution to eliminate contamination had been taken, and the same organisms appear in considerable numbers in a series of cultures.

Treatment. Most strains of scotochromes are highly resistant to PAS, some are susceptible to INH and somewhat more to strep-

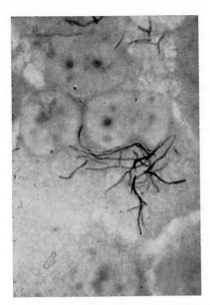

Fig. 16. Avian strain from swine after fifth day of growth in HeLa cells. Note branching. × 1,200. (From Brosbe, Sugihara, and Smith. *J. Bact.*, 84: 1282, 1962.)

laris and from Battey strains and found the allergic reactions were identical.

The original description of group III non-photochromogenic organisms, as recorded above, states that its pathogenicity is variable. Some isolates kill mice but not guinea pigs. The general biologic and chemical characteristics, except for virulence for mice, rabbits, and chickens, are the same for typical avian strains and avirulent strains. Both kinds of organisms are niacin-negative, with poor to negative cord formation and positive catalase production. Most virulent avian strains grow better at 45° C. than 37° C., while most Battey strains grow better at 37° C. than 45° C. Stock strains of avirulent avian which were once virulent, may adapt to good growth at 37° C., however, and are then indistinguishable by the usual tests from avirulent Battey strains. However, it should be kept in mind that Battey strains, completely avirulent for laboratory animals, are regularly isolated from animal lymph nodes and from biopsies and necropsies in man in pure culture as the sole explanation for the disease. If a group III nonphotochromogenic organism is isolated from a patient, it should be subjected to virulence tests with mice, rabbits, chickens, and guinea pigs. If the guinea pig escapes infection but the other animals succumb, then this is a virulent avian bacillus and not a Battey bacillus. However, even

guinea pigs will be killed with large doses (2 to 4 mg. of moist weight) of a highly virulent strain of the avian bacillus (28).

Certain slight differences between avian and Battey strains, other than virulence, have been reported by investigators who for one reason or another are reluctant to accept the basic identity of avian and Battey strains. These differences are (1) slightly less strong reaction to homologous PPD (24, 25, 27); (2) differences in the metabolism of tehalose and xylose (103); (3) avian bacilli do not have arylsulphatase activity while Battey bacilli do (55).

The standard PPD−B, which has been used so extensively in this country and in India and Europe, was prepared from a single strain isolated from a patient named Boone at the Battey Hospital in Georgia. Edwards (24) and everyone else (95) have found that animals sensitized with some Battey strains give almost, but not quite, as large reactions with PPD−A from virulent avian organisms as from the animal avirulent Boone strain. In contrast, five other strains studied by Edwards (25, 26) which seemed to be identical with the avian-Battey strain culturally, produced a type of sensitivity which was poorly delineated by either PPD−A or PPD−B. In Edwards' (25) 1961 studies seven strains of Battey including the Boone strain produced a type of sensitivity which gave iden-

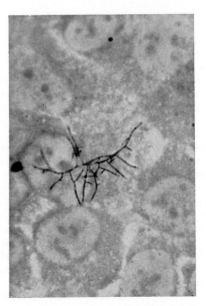

Fig. 17. Battey strain from human pulmonary disease after three days growth in HeLa cells. Note branching. × 1,200. (From Brosbe, Sugihara, and Smith. *J. Bact.*, 84:1282, 1962.)

tical degrees of cross-reaction with PPD^{-S}, PPD^{-Y}, PPD^{-G}, PPD^{-A}, PPD^{-B}, and PPD^{-F}. In contrast, four other culturally identical strains showed a different pattern of cross-reactions. Runyon (87) has confirmed and extended Edwards' (23) studies and found that certain other group III nonphotochrome organisms reacted in cross-reactions like the type species, Battey-Boone, while others were obviously different. Among those producing sensitivity reactions like the Boone strain were two strains isolated from saliva and bronchial secretions of normal individuals by Edwards and Palmer (23) in 1959. In addition to these, one of thirteen soil and water strains and all of the Battey strains from dogs in Japan and swine in Australia reacted with the avian-Battey-Boone complex. These results suggest that there are at least two, and possibly more, antigenically different types of nonphotochromogens which are culturally identical with the Battey-Boone. Edwards' (26) study of tuberculin sensitivity in Navy recruits supports this view (Table 2). She tested 212,462 Navy recruits with 5 TU of the PPD^{-B} made from the Boone strain and found 35 per cent gave 2 mm. or more a reaction with an average size of 7.7 mm. A group of 10,769 were tested with PPD^{-A} from a virulent avian strain, and 30.5 per cent gave an average reaction of 6.7 mm. However, PPD made from two other strains of nonphotochromogens gave only 12 per cent and 17.5 per cent reactions. Lewis and his associates in Florida (63) have separated their group III nonphotochromogen types into III-A and III-B. The III-A organisms are white, buff, and pale yellow while the III-B are pale orange. The latter are also called "yellow Batteys." Some of the III-A group are pathogenic for mice and could be true avian strains. The III-B yellow strains are not pathogenic for mice. This suggests that both white strains III-A, which are not pathogenic for mice and other animals, and the III-B yellow strains may be the same antigenic type and may be pathogenic for man. The subculture which we have of the original Battey-Boone strain is a pale orange, especially on Lowenstein medium, and is not pathogenic in very large doses for mice and rabbits. This strain has the same shade of orange-yellow, as shown by the pigmented virulent avian strain received from Karlson (53).

The agglutination studies of Schaefer (91) with adsorbed serum show an even more complex antigenic mosaic. Some of the nonphotochromogenic strains isolated from disease in man are really virulent avian bacilli. Schaefer

(91) studied 16 of these and found that eight were avian type I and 8 were avian type II. Among 16 strains of nonphotochromogens isolated from lymph nodes in children, one was avian serotype I, 4 were avian serotype II, 7 were "Battey"-Davis, 3 were "Battey-Watson," and 1 was "Battey"-Boone. The distribution of serotypes was somewhat different among the 25 strains isolated from patients with pulmonary disease. In this group, 5 were avian I, 3 were avian II, 2 were "Battey"-Davis, 6 were "Battey-Watson," 4 were "Battey"-Boone, and 5 were "Battey"-Yandle.

YELLOW BATTEYS AND BATTEY-LIKE SCOTO-CHROMES. There is a considerable amount of confusion in the literature concerning the use of the terms "photochrome," "scotochrome," and "nonphotochrome" for organisms which have other characteristics which clearly indicate their proper classification. For example, the yellow avian (53) isolates from the swan developed a yellow color when incubated in a dark incubator and could therefore be called "scotochrome." The nonpigmented mutants of a typical photochrome species, studied by Mankiewicz (71) would be called "nonphotochrome." On the other hand, in Schaefer's (91) study of serotypes with adsorbed sera among these agglutinating specifically with the "Davis" type of Battey, 10 were nonphotochromes but 2 were pigmented and called "scotochromes." In serotype "Watson"-Battey, 7 were nonphotochromogens and in the "scrofulaceum" type, 40 were scotochromogens, but 4 were nonphotochromogens of the Battey type. Certainly a sero-specific type agglutination should take precedence over such a labile characteristic as color in the classification of the unclassified mycobacteria. In the guinea pig studies by Johnston and Smith (48, 49) in this laboratory, animals sensitized with the Battey-Boone strain of *Mycobacterium* gave large reactions to the homologous PPD^{-B} and almost equally large reactions to PPD^{-A}, less extensive cross-reactions with scotochromes and progressively less with human, photochrome, and fortuitum (Fig. 18). Double infections with Battey-Boone and human showed equally large reactions with avian, Battey, human, and scotochrome, but much smaller reactions with photochromes and fortuitum (Fig. 19).

Source of Infection. The soil has always been considered a likely source of endemic infections with the unclassified mycobacteria. In 1959 Edwards and Palmer (23) made a very original attempt to isolate Battey-type organisms from the bronchial secretions and

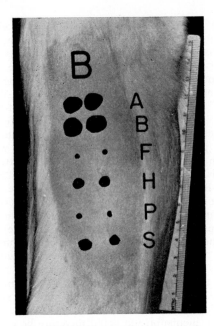

Fig. 18. Tuberculin reaction in a guinea pig sensitized to 4 mg. of Battey-Boone nonphotochromogen. Note the large reaction to PPD−B and equally large reaction to PPD−A, less to scotochrome, and still less to human, photochrome, and fortuitum. (From Smith and Johnston. *Am. Rev. Resp. Dis.* In press.)

saliva of healthy individuals in Georgia, where it was known that there was a high incidence of Battey-type skin sensitivity. Secretions were collected from 122 individuals who were known to be clinically well and free of pulmonary disease by x-ray. Suspicious colonies were isolated from 30 individuals. Fourteen were classified as *Actinomycetaceae* and 16 as *Mycobacterium*. Ruth Gordon studied the mycotic strains and Ernest Runyon the mycobacteria (23). The results are shown in Table 3. Subsequent study of the skin sensitizing antigens from the seven nonphotochromogens of the Battey type showed that two were typical Battey-Boone types while the others were not (87). The presence of pathogenic species of *N. madurae*, *N. asteroides*, *Myco. fortuitum*, and Battey-Boone type nonphotochromogens in the small series emphasizes the hazard of breathing dust-ladened air.

Clinical Disease. Skin tests suggest the infection with the Battey-Boone type of *Mycobacterium* must be more frequent than infection with the *Myco. tuberculosis* but less frequent than with the pathogenic scotochromogen. The Battey-type organisms are less frequently found as a cause of adenitis

but more frequently present in pulmonary disease. Among the 116 patients studied by Lewis and associates (63) in Florida the disease occurs most frequently in white males over 40 years of age. The symptoms and on x-ray findings were indistinguishable from patients with *Myco. tuberculosis* infections. Fifty-two per cent of the cases were far advanced, and 78 per cent showed cavities by x-ray.

Treatment. Most Battey-type strains were resistant to isoniazid, paraminobenzoic acid, and streptomycin, but some were susceptible. In general the nonpigmented strains were more resistant than the pigmented strains. Both types showed more susceptibility to cycloserine, viomycin, kanamycin, and streptovaricin than to the better-known antibiotics.

Surgical treatment should be used when possible because of the poor results with drugs, but the increased age of the patient and complications limit its use. The chances of an arrest of the disease is much less than of patients infected with *Myco. tuberculosis.*

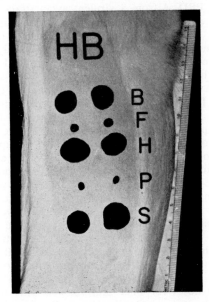

Fig. 19. Tuberculin reaction in a guinea pig sensitized with 4 mg. of Battey-Boone and resensitized two months later with 4 mg. of human R_1. Note the large homologous reactions to PPD−B and PPD−S and the large cross-reaction of PPD−SCOT with small cross-reaction to PPD−Y and PPD−F. (From Smith and Johnston. *Am. Rev. Resp. Dis.* In press.)

Table 3. Organisms Isolated from Bronchial Secretions and Saliva

(From Edwards and Palmer)

ACTINOMYCETACEAE		MYCOBACTERIUM	
Nocardia madurae	10	Battey type	7
Streptomyces rimosis	2	Scotochrome	4
Streptomyces sulfurels	1	Myco. fortuitum	3
Nocardia asteroides	1	Other Group IV	2
	14		16

THE RAPID GROWERS OF GROUP IV

Rapid growers of group IV are isolated very frequently from soil and water and occasionally from sputum. One rapid grower, the non-pigmented *Myco. fortuitum*, is pathogenic for man and animals; this species has been described in some detail earlier in this chapter. There is no evidence that the saprophilic rapid growers will produce disease. However, PPD made from *Myco. smegmatis* or from *Myco. phlei* did give reactions in Navy recruits. Eighteen per cent of 14,239 recruits reacted to 5 TU PPD made from smegmatis and 23 per cent of 15,229 recruits reacted to 5 TU PPD made from *Myco. phlei* (26). We do not know at the present time whether reactions resulted from subclinical infection or whether they represent cross-reactions. We suspect the latter is true since all mycobacteria seem to share some common antigens.

MULTIPLE INFECTIONS WITH MYCOBACTERIAL SPECIES

It is a mathematical certainty that some patients and perhaps more normal individuals will have primary infections with two or more mycobacteria. In the past, when practically every young adult had been infected with a human tubercle bacillus, these infections with other and less virulent forms of mycobacteria had little effect on the size of the tubercle reaction, which would be greatest to the more virulent human bacillus. However, such infections, if they came before infection with *Myco. tuberculosis*, might have had an immunizing effect against clinical disease with *Myco. tuberculosis*. Experimental work has shown that *Myco. kansasii* gives in animals almost as good immunity as BCG. Avian and Battey strains give significant immunity, while scotochromes give less,

but definitely measurable, immunity (32, 77, 120).

The largest known series of tuberculin testing with PPD's prepared from known and unknown species of *Mycobacterium* were performed by Lydia Edwards and her associates on Navy recruits. As seen in Table 2, all reactions of 2 mm. or more were recorded. The percentage of reactions in these 20-year-old boys was 8.6 for PPD^{-S}, made from the human strain *Myco. tuberculosis*. The smallest per cent 7.7 was to PPD^{-F}, made from *Myco. fortuitum*. PPD^{-Y} from *Myco. kansasii* ranked third, with a reaction rate of 13.1 per cent. Fourth in rank was PPD^{-A} from *Myco. avium* with a reaction rate of 30.5 per cent. This was followed by fifth-place PPD^{-B} made from the Battey-Boone group III organism, which produced reactions in 35.1 per cent. The sixth and highest (48.7 per cent) reaction was given by PPD^{-G} made from the Gause strain of scotochrome group II.

When 6 mm. was considered the minimal positive degree of reaction, the Navy recruits gave 25.3 per cent positive reaction to PPD^{-B}. Some of the same PPD^{-B} was supplied to Youmans, Smith, and Sartwell for testing in students. Youmans' (119) medical students had a reaction rate of 27 per cent. Smith's (94) medical students had a reaction rate of 26.7 to PPD^{-B} and 20.1 to PPD^{-A}, while Sartwell's (88) male college students in Maryland had a reaction rate to PPD^{-B} of 26 per cent, but the female students in his series gave a much lower percent of reaction. This slight variation from 26 to 27 in college and medical students could hardly have been coincidental. The lower figure of 25.3 per cent in Navy recruits can be explained on the basis of their younger age.

Jensen and his associates (46) performed

Table 4. Reactions of Medical Students and Student Nurses to 5 TU of PPDs

(From Smith and Johnston)

NUMBER	HUMAN %	BATTEY %	PHOTO-CHROME %	SCOTO-CHROME %	FORTUITUM %	NOCARDIA %
Medical 164	14.6	24.3	14.0	51.8	—	0
Nurses 80	6.2	17.5	7.5	22.5	—	0
Medical 82	12.2	—	—	—	14.6	—

studies with PPD^{-S}, PPD^{-A}, and PPD^{-B} and then attempted passive transfer of sensitivity with white-blood cells. Individuals sensitive to all three usually transferred sensitivity to all three. Those reacting only to avian or Battey or both usually transferred sensitivity to both, but not cross-sensitivity to human.

The agreement on the degree of reaction to PPD from strains of scotochrome mycobacteria is equally striking. Edwards and her associates (26) tested 29,540 Navy recruits with PPD^{-G} made from a scotochrome isolated from a lymph node from a child by the name of Gause and found that 48.7 per cent gave reactions of 2 mm. or more. A second tuberculin (PPD-236) was prepared from a strain of scotochrome isolated from a cervical lymph node of a child by the name of Bridge and supplied to Youmans in Chicago, Illinois, and Smith and Johnston in Durham, North Carolina. Youmans' medical students gave positive reactions of 5 mm. or greater in 47.5 per cent (121), while Smith and Johnston's medical students were positive in

51.8 per cent. However, freshmen nursing students were positive to the same PPD at a rate of only 22.5 per cent (95) (Table 4).

It is obvious that some medical students have had only a single infection, all the other reactions being definitely cross-reactions. In these instances the reaction to the homologous type of tuberculin is obviously the largest. The experiments with guinea pigs suggest that a double infection will give two large reactions, one to each of the infecting organisms, but, in addition, a third or fourth may be almost equally large as a result of a "double" cross-reaction (95). All the experimental guinea pigs have large reactions to PPD from both human and avian bacilli, when the second strength (0.005 mg.) dose is employed. This suggests that all mycobacterial infections could be detected as "cross-reactions" with this strong dose of tuberculin. Consequently, a negative reaction to the second strength dose or to a double second strength (0.01 mg.) eliminates the possibility of any type of mycobacterial infection, provided the patient is

Table 5. Slight Degrees of Allergy to 5 TU Detected by Second-Strength PPDs

NUMBER	HUMAN 5 TU	PHOTO-CHROME 5 TU	BATTEY 5 TU	SCOTO-CHROME 5 TU	HUMAN PPD-2ND	HUMAN OT 1-100	AVIAN PPD-2ND
26	0	0	0	0	0	0	0
27	0	0	0	0	14	15	24
36	0	0	0	+	20	19	32
4	0	0	0	+	0	0	0
9	0	0	0	+	9	9	9
3	0	0	+	+	3	3	3
3	0	0	+	0	3	3	3
108	0	3	15	52	49	49	71

All photochrome and Battey reactions were detected by human and avian.
8 scotochrome reactions missed by second strength avian.
24 of 27 negative to all 5 TU doses were detected by avian second strength.

not in an anergic state of reaction (Table 5).

At the present time we are using the following procedure of skin testing. The patient is tested with 5 TU (0.0001 mg.) of PPD's or a 1-2000 (0.05 ml.) of OT. If the reaction is less than 5 mm. of induration, the patient is retested with second strength PPD^{-S} (0.005 mg.), second strength PPD^{-A}, and 1-100 OT. If the reactions are negative, there is no detectable mycobacterial sensitivity of any type. If the reaction is positive, there has been a mycobacterial infection but we do not know which one. We then retest with all available PPD at the 5 TU level but using two tests for each PPD to eliminate technical false negatives. On retesting the largest reaction may now be Battey, photochrome, scotochrome, or fortuitum, which should alert the laboratory to watch for this particular species. If the patient has had two or more mycobacterial infections, it may not be possible to conclude which is the more important.

REFERENCES

1. Aronson, J. D. J. Inf. Dis., 39:315, 1926; 44:215, 1929.
2. ———— J. Inf. Dis., 44:215, 1929.
3. ———— Am. Rev. Tuberc. & Pul. Dis., 79:731, 1959.
4. Baker, T. A., and Hagan, W. A. J. Inf. Dis., 70:248, 1942.
5. Bang, B. Berl. Herarztl. Wchnschr., 1906, p. 759.
6. Beaven, P. W., and Bayne-Jones, S. J. Inf. Dis., 49:399, 1931.
6a. Bjerkedal, T. Acta tuberc. et pneum. scandinav., 43:275, 1963.
7. Black, B. G., and Chapman, J. S. Am. Rev. Resp. Dis., (abs.), 1963.
8. Bojalil, L. J., and Cerbon, J. Am. Rev. Resp. Dis., 81:382, 1960.
9. ———— and others. J. Gen. Microbiol., 28:333, 1962.
10. British Research Council. Brit. Med. J., 1:973, 1963.
11. Brosbe, E. A., and others. J. Bact., 84:1282, 1962.
12. Buhler, V. B., and Pollak, A. Am. J. Clin. Path., 23:363, 1953.
13. Chapman, J. S., and Bernard, J. S. Am. Rev. Resp. Dis., (abs.), 1963.
14. Clark, H. F., and Shepard, C. C. J. Bact., 86:1057, 1963.
15. Corpe, R. F., and Stergus, I. J.A.M.A., 177:262, 1961.
16. Crow, H. E., and others. Am. Rev. Tuberc. & Pul. Dis., 75:199, 1957.
17. Cruz, J. C. Acta med. Rio de Janeiro, 1:297, 1938.
18. Cuttino, J. T., and McCabe, A. M. Am. J. Path., 25:1, 1949.
19. Daines, L. L., and Austin, H. Am. Rev. Tuberc., 27:600, 1933; 30:209, 1934.
20. Davis, S. D., and Comstock, G. W. J. Ped., 58:771, 1961.
21. Dormer, B. A. South African M. J., 35:429, 1961.
22. Edwards, L. B., and Palmer, C. E. Am. J. Hyg., 68:213, 1958.
23. ———— and Palmer, C. E. Am. Rev. Resp. Dis., 80:747, 1959.
24. ———— and others. Am. J. Hyg., 71:218, 1960.
25. ———— and others. Proc. XVI Internat. Tuberc. Conf., Toronto, Canada, Sept. 10-14, 1961.
26. ———— Ann. N.Y. Acad. Sci., 106:32, 1963.
27. Engbaek, H. C., and Magnusson, M. Acta Tuberc. Scandinav., 40:1, 1961.
28. Feldman, W. H. Avian Tuberculosis Infections, Baltimore, Williams & Wilkins Co., 1938.
29. ———— Am. Rev. Resp. Dis., 81:666, 1960.
30. Fenner, F., and Leach, R. H. Austral. J. Exper. Biol. & Med., Sci., 30:1, 11, 1952.
31. ———— Am. Rev. Tuberc., 73:650, 1956.
32. Freerksen, F. Deutsche Med. Wochen., 84:1533, 1959.
33. Fregman, G. B., and others. J. Bact., 82:517, 1961.
34. Froman, S., and Scammon, L. Am. Rev. Resp. Dis., (in press).
35. Gentry, W. H. Personal communication.
36. Gernez-Rieux, Ch., and Tacquet, A. Bull. Internat. Union against Tuberc., 29:330, 1959.
37. Gerszen, E., and others. Am. Rev. Resp. Dis., (abs.), 1963.
38. Gordon, R. E. J. Bact., 34:617, 1937.
39. ———— and Smith, M. M. J. Bact., 69:502, 1955.
40. ———— and Mihm, J. M. J. Gen. Microbiol., 21:736, 1959.
41. Green, H. H. Vet. J., 102:267, 1946.
42. Hart, D. A., and others. Tubercle, 43:268, 1962.
43. Hartwig, E. C., and others. Am. Rev. Resp. Dis., 85:84, 1962.
44. Hauduroy, P. Derniers Aspects du Monde des Mycobactéries, Paris, France, Massan and Cit., 1955.
45. Jenkins, D. E. Bull. Internat. Union Against Tuberc., 29:295, 1959.
46. Jensen, K., and others. Am. Rev. Resp. Dis., 85:373, 1962.
47. Johne, H. A., and Frothingham, L. Deutsche Ztschr. Thiermed., 21:438, (1895).
48. Johnston, W. W., and Smith, D. T. Fed. Proc., (abs.), 1963.
49. ———— and Smith, D. T. Proc. Soc. Exper. Biol. & Med., 1964.
50. Kagramanoy, A. I. Bull. Internat. Union Against Tuberc., 29:354, 1959.
51. Karlson, A. G. Diseases of Swine, ed. H. W. Dunne, Ames, Iowa State Univ. Press, 1958, Chap. 25.
52. ———— Minnesota Med., 42:1399, 1959.
53. ———— and others. Am. J. Vet. Res., 23:575, 1962.
53a. ———— and others. Proc. Staff Meet. Mayo Clin., 39:410, 1964.
54. Koch, M. L., and others. Am. Rev. Resp. Dis., 84:750, 1961.

55. Kubica, G. P., and Beam, E. R. Am. Rev. Resp. Dis., 83:733, 1961.
56. Kushner, D. S., and others. Am. Rev. Tuberc. & Pul. Dis., 76:108, 1957.
57. Laporte, R. Ann. Institut Pasteur, 65:282, 1940.
58. Larsen, A. B., and others. Am. J. Vet. Res., 11:374, 1950.
59. Lehmann, K. B., and Neumann, R. Bakt. Diag., 2 Aufl., 2:403, 1899.
60. ——— and Neumann, R. Bakt. Diag., 2 Aufl., 2:411, 1899.
61. Lester, W., Jr., and others. Trans. 17th Conf. on Chemotherapy of Tuberculosis, Memphis, Tenn., Feb. 3-6, 1958, p. 289.
62. Lewis, A. G., Jr., and others. Am. Rev. Resp. Dis., 80:188, 1959.
63. ——— Ann. Int. Med., 53:273, 1960.
64. Linell, F., and Norden, A. Acta Tuberc. Scandinav., Supp. 33, 1954.
65. McMillen, S., and Kushner, D. S. Am. Rev. Tuberc. & Pul. Dis., 76:103, 1957.
66. ——— Personal Communication.
67. MacCallum, P., and others. J. Path. & Bact., 60:931, 1948.
68. Mafucci, A. Ztschr. Hyg. u Infektionskr., 11:449, 1892.
69. Magnusson, M., and others. Acta Tuberc. Scandinav., 40:85, 1961.
70. ——— Am. Rev. Resp. Dis., 86:395, 1962.
71. Mankiewicz, E. Can. J. Microbiol., 4:565, 1958.
72. Merckx, J. J., and others. Proc. Staff Meet. Mayo Clinic., 38:271, 1963.
73. Minett, F. C. J. Comp. Path. & Therap., 45:317, 1932.
74. Mollohan, C. S., and Romer, M. S. Am. J. Pub. Health, 51:883, 1961.
75. Nassau, E., and others. Tubercle, 39:103, 1958.
76. Palmer, C. E., and Edwards, L. B. Proc. XVI Internat. Tuberc. Conf., Bull. Internat. Union Against Tuberc., 32:373, 1961.
77. ——— and Hopwood, L. Bull. Internat. Union Against Tuberc., 32:398, 1962.
78. Parisot, T. J. Bact. Rev., 22:240, 1958.
79. Parlett, R. C., and others. Am. Rev. Tuberc., 77:462, 1958.
80. Petroff, S. A., and Steenken, W. J. J. Exper. Med., 51:831, 1930.
81. Pinner, M. Am. Rev. Tuberc., 32:424, 1953.
82. Prissick, F. H., and Masson, A. M. Can. Med. Assoc. J., 75:798, 1956.
83. Research Committee of Brit. Tuberc. Assoc. Tubercle, 44:119, 1963.
84. Runyon, E. H., and others. Am. Rev. Tuberc., 79:663, 1959.
85. ——— Bull. Internat. Union Against Tuberc., 29:69, 1959.
86. ——— Med. Clinics of North America., 43:273, 1959.
87. ——— Am. Rev. Resp. Dis., (in press).
88. Sartwell, P. E., and Dyke, L. M. Am. J. Hyg., 71:204, 1960.
89. Scammon, L. A., and others. Am. Rev. Resp. Dis., 87:97, 1963.
90. Schaefer, W. B. Ann. Institut Pasteur, 58:388, 1937.
91. ——— and Reggiardo, Z. Am. Rev. Resp. Dis. In press.
92. Shepard, C. C. Am. Rev. Tuberc. & Resp. Dis., 77:968, 1958.
93. Sigurdsson, B., and Tryggvottir, A. G. J. Bact., 59:541, 1950.
94. Smith, D. T., and others. Am. Rev. Resp. Dis., 83:213, 1961.
95. ——— and Johnston, W. W. Am. Rev. Resp. Dis. In press.
96. Smith, D. W., and others. J. Bact., 79:217, 1960.
97. ——— and others. Nature, 186:887, 1960.
98. Smith, M. M., and Steenken, W. Am. Rev. Resp. Dis., 84:447, 1961.
99. Steenken, W., and others. Am. Rev. Tuberc. & Pul. Dis., 78:454, 1958.
100. Stewart, C. J., and others. Brit. Med. J., I:7, 1961; Tubercle, 44:456, 1963.
101. Strauss and Gamele'ia. Arch. Med. exp. et Path., 1891.
102. Subcommittee on Mycobacteria. J. Bact., 83:931, 1962.
103. Sweeney, E. E., and Jann, G. J. Proc. Soc. Exper. Biol. & Med., 108:671, 1961.
104. Symposium on World Wide Distribution of Atypical Acid-fast Bacilli. Bull. Internat. Union Against Tuberc., 29:295, 1959.
105. Timpe, A., and Runyon, E. H. J. Lab. Clin. Med., 44:202, 1954.
106. Twort, F. W. Proc. Soc., London, S.B., 83:158, 1910-11.
107. Vera, H. D., and Rettger, L. F. J. Bact., 39:659, 1940.
108. Wayne, L. G. Am. Rev. Resp. Dis., 86:651, 1962.
109. ——— Am. J. Clin. Path., 36:185, 1961.
110. ——— Twenty-second Research Conf. in Pul. Dis. of the Vet. Adm. and Armed Forces, 1963, p. 226.
111. Weed, L. A., and others. Proc. Staff Meet. Mayo Clinic., 31:238, 246, 259, 1956.
112. Wells, A. G. Lancet, 1:1221, 1937.
113. ——— Brit. J. Exper. Path., 19:324, 1938.
114. Wells, A. Q., and others. Am. Rev. Tuberc., 72:53, 1955.
115. Winn, W. A., and Petroff, S. A. J. Exper. Med., 57:239, 1933.
116. Wolinsky, E. Anonymous Mycobacteria in Human Disease, ed. T. S. Chapman, Springfield, Ill., Charles C Thomas, 1960, p. 45.
117. Wooley, D., and McCarter, J. R. Proc. Soc. Exper. Biol. & Med., 45:360, 1940.
118. Youmans, G. P. Bull. Internat. Union Against Tuberc., 28:128, 1958.
119. ——— and Youmans, A. S. Am. Rev. Resp. Dis., 82:114, 1960.
120. ——— and others. Am. Rev. Resp. Dis., 83:903, 1961.
121. ——— Ann. Rev. Microbiol., 17:473, 1963.

31

Actinobacillus mallei and Glanders: Melioidosis and Actinobacillosis

ACTINOBACILLUS MALLEI AND GLANDERS

Family: *Brucellaceae* fam. nov. Genus: *Actinobacillus* Brumpt. Species: *Actinobacillus mallei* (Zopf) Thompson

Glanders is an infectious disease of horses but is transmitted occasionally to other domestic animals and to man. The microorganism causing the disease, though seen and described by several earlier authors, was obtained in pure culture and accurately described by Löffler and Schutz (19) in 1882. The potential importance of this organism is illustrated by the laboratory infections which occurred during World War II (16).

Morphology and Staining. The glanders bacillus, *Actinobacillus mallei,* is a rather small rod with rounded ends which varies from 3 to 4 μ in length and from 0.5 to 0.75 μ in width. Characteristically there are variations in size between individual organisms in a single pure culture; the rods usually are straight, but they may be slightly curved. The bacilli are **nonmotile** and nonflagellated; no spores are formed. The grouping of the bacilli in smears is not characteristic. They usually appear as single bacilli lying irregularly parallel, or frequently in chains of two or more (Fig. 1). In old cultures short, vacuolated, and almost coccoid involution forms appear. The vacuolated forms have been studied in electron-micrographs (23).

The glanders bacillus stains rather easily with the usual aniline dyes. When stained with methylene blue, in particular, there are marked irregularities, with faintly stained or entirely unstained portions. This diagnostically helpful characteristic probably represents an inherent irregularity in the normal protoplasmic composition of the bacillus, not unlike that of *C. diphtheriae*. The bacillus is **gram-negative** and is not acid-fast.

Cultural Characteristics. *A. mallei* is **aerobic;** it has an optimal temperature of 37.5° C. and fails to grow at temperatures below 22° C. or above 43° C. The glanders bacillus is cultivated easily on all of the common meat-infusion media and aparently is indifferent to moderate variations in reaction as it grows equally well upon neutral, slightly acid, or slightly alkaline substrates. The organism grows better when glycerin or small quantities of glucose are added to the medium.

Upon **agar** the colonies are not distinctive. After 24 hours at 37.5° C., they appear as yellowish white spots, transparent at first, but later they become more opaque. The colonies are round, with an even border, and appear finely granular when examined under higher magnification. As the cultures grow older, they tend to become more yellow. On **gelatin** at room temperature growth is slow, grayish white, and never abundant. The gelatin is not liquefied.

In **broth** the organism at first produces a diffuse clouding, but later a heavy, tough, slimy sediment is formed. At the same time the surface also is covered with a slimy pellicle, and the whole culture gradually becomes dark brown in color.

None of the carbohydrates is oxidized. In **milk** coagulation takes place slowly; litmus milk is acidified.

The growth upon **potato** presents certain features which are of pathognomonic value. On potato, provided it is not too acid, growth is abundant and covers the surface within 48 hours with a yellowish, transparent, slimy layer

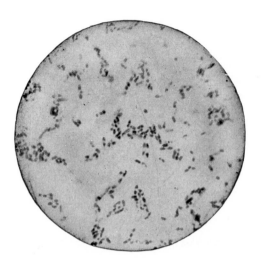

Fig. 1. Glanders bacillus. From potato culture. (Courtesy of Dr. Zettnow.)

which gradually becomes darker until it is a deep reddish brown color. A similar growth occurs in the case of *P. aeruginosa* which can be distinguished, however, by other means.

Resistance. Desiccation kills *A. mallei* in a short time, but the organisms will survive for 70 days in the water of a watering trough. When sealed in tubes and placed in a cool, dark place, the bacilli remain viable for months or even years. The organism is killed by sunlight in 24 hours and by temperatures of 60° C. for two hours, or 75° C. for one hour. One per cent carbolic acid destroys it in 30 minutes and 0.1 per cent bichloride of mercury causes death in 15 minutes. The **sulfonamides,** especially sulfadiazine, inhibit growth of the organism in both experimental animals and patients (16).

Antigenic Structure. The injection of whole organisms initiates antibody production and induces a state of **allergy** to mallein in the tissues of the animal. The serums of normal horses may agglutinate the bacilli in dilutions as high as 1:200 or even 1:400. Normal human serums sometimes agglutinate *A. mallei* in dilutions as high as 1:320 but such serums do not fix complement (16). The complement-fixation reaction, although less sensitive, is a more specific test for the presence of infection. Howe and Miller consider a positive complement-fixation in a serum diluted 1:20 to be diagnostic of the disease. McNeil and Olmstead of the New York City Department of Health prepare the antigen for complement-fixation by growing *A. mallei* on potato agar containing 1.6 per cent glycerin. From this stock culture, transplants are made upon a neutral meat-free-veal-peptone agar. After incubation for 24 hours the organisms are washed off with distilled water and killed by heating at 80° C. for four hours. After filtration through a Berkefeld filter, the antigen is again heated at 80° C. for one hour to insure sterility.

Bacterial Metabolites. *A. mallei* does not produce an exotoxin, but a weak endotoxin has been extracted from the bodies of the organisms. In comparable dosages, this endotoxin is only slightly toxic for normal animals but is capable of causing death within 12 to 24 hours after injection into infected animals. This material withstands a temperature of 120° C. and can be stored for a long time without suffering an appreciable loss in strength. This reactive material, **mallein,** is protein in nature and is analogous in its action to that of tuberculin in tuberculosis.

At the Washington Bureau of Animal Industry mallein is prepared by growing the bacilli in glycerin bouillon for five months at 37.5° C. This is then boiled for one hour and allowed to stand in a cool place for one week. The supernatant fluid is then decanted and filtered through clay filters by means of a vacuum pump. The filtrate is evaporated to one-third its original volume in a water bath, and the evaporated volume resupplied by a 1 per cent carbolic acid solution containing about 10 per cent of glycerin.

Disease in Animals. Glanders in the horse, mule, or ass may be either acute or chronic in nature.

The acute form has a violent onset with fever and prostration. After two or three days, a nasal discharge appears which is serous at first but later becomes seropurulent. The nasal mucosa becomes ulcerated, and this is often accompanied by a swelling of the regional lymph nodes which tend to become necrotic and form draining sinuses. The infection finally reaches the lungs, with death occurring within four to six weeks after the onset of the disease. In the chronic form of the disease the onset is more gradual, with fewer systemic symptoms. General lymph node enlargement is the usual finding, and there is a tendency for those in the neck to ulcerate. A thickening of the superficial lymph vessels produces the clinical syndrome of **farcy,** as it usually is designated by veterinary surgeons. This type of lymphatic involvement is not diagnostic, however, and can occur in fungus infections such as sporotrichosis or cryptococcosis. Death occurs after a period of weeks or months in a small percentage of infected animals. Complete recovery is rare, many animals continuing to have chronic open ulcers in the skin or nasal mucosa. Such animals constitute the natural reservoir of the disease.

Rabbits, guinea pigs, and hamsters are susceptible to experimental infections. As few as five to 30 organisms from a virulent strain can produce a fatal infection in hamsters (16, 24). Cattle, hogs, rats, and birds are immune. Spontaneous infections occur occasionally in cats, dogs, and menagerie animals.

STRAUSS TEST. When the organisms cannot be isolated by direct inoculation of blood agar or the more favorable potato medium, some of the pus from the ulcers or ground up pieces of tissues should be inoculated intraperitoneally into male guinea pigs. If the bacilli are present, swelling and redness in the testes develop after two or three days. Cultures then can be made from the testicular pus, spleen, or peritoneal exudates of the inoculated animals (35).

THE MALLEIN TEST. The mallein test for the diagnosis of glanders in horses should be performed by a qualified veterinary surgeon. The dose, usually 0.25 ml. of undiluted mallein, is injected subcutaneously under the skin of the breast or neck. Both local and systemic symptoms are produced. The local lesion appears as a swelling a few hours after injection; it quickly evolves into a firm, hot, diffuse indurated area which may reach a diameter of 20 to 30 cm. The swelling is intensely tender during the first 24 hours and lasts for three to nine days. General systemic effects become evident within six to eight hours after the subcutaneous injection, the infected horse developing a temperature of 104° to 106° F. (40° C. +) and showing marked symptoms of general intoxication. The temperature usually begins to fall after 10 to 16 hours, reaching the normal level in two to three days. The temperature of the horse should be taken three times during the day preceding the test and every two hours for at least 18 hours after the injection. Focal reactions may be observed in nodular lesions located in other parts of the body. In normal animals the local reactions are much smaller and more transient; the temperature rise also is insignificant. Horses with chronic bronchitis, periostitis, and few other conditions may give false positive or questionably positive reactions with mallein. It usually is considered wise, however, to slaughter all animals which give positive or even questionable mallein tests.

THE OPHTHALMIC TEST. In this test a tablet containing mallein is introduced into the conjunctival sac of the horse. In infected animals marked redness and swelling of the eye occurs 24 hours after instillation. Systemic reactions following this type of test are minimal.

Clinical Types of Infection in Man. Like the horse, man may develop either the acute or the chronic form of glanders, but the acute form is much more common in humans, whereas the majority of the infections in horses are of the chronic type.

The infection usually begins in the skin at the point of a scratch or abrasion but may start as an ulceration of the mucosa as in the horse (15, 22). Laboratory infections occasionally occur from inhaling droplets of moisture containing the bacilli (16). Direct infection through the skin from contact with cultures may result.

The clinical type of the disease varies with the portal of entry. Infection by way of the skin results in the development of a nodule at the site of infection which is surrounded by an area of lymphangitis and swelling. A generalized papular eruption may occur which may become pustular and resemble the lesions of variola. This form of the disease is usually fatal within 8 to 10 days.

An infection of the nasal mucous membranes may produce a clinical picture of lymphatic involvement which resembles the chronic form of the disease which is seen in the horse. This form of the disease in man is more frequently fatal than it is in the horse.

Laboratory infection resulting from inhalation begins as a pneumonitis which resembles certain viral infections of the lung (16). Multiple, focal, necrotizing lesions develop as the disease progresses (31). Granulomatous lesions are found at necropsy in patients who die of glanders (Fig. 2). Nodules may be distributed generally throughout the body, and A. mallei often is obtained in pure culture from the center of such lesions.

DIAGNOSIS. Blood cultures usually are negative except in the terminal stages of the disease. There is a persistent neutropenia with a relative lymphocytosis. Agglutinin titers of 1:40 or 1:80 are found during the first week of the disease, and the titers rapidly increase to the diagnostically signifi-

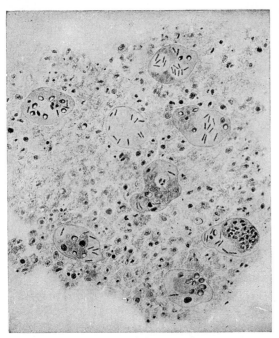

Fig. 2. Glanders bacillus in tissue. (Courtesy of Dr. James Ewing.)

cant levels of 1:640 or 1:1,280 during the second week (14, 16). The **complement-fixation test** is negative during the first week and sometimes during the second, but becomes positive usually during the third week of the disease. Both agglutinins and complement-fixing antibodies may persist for a year in the serums of patients who recover. The **mallein skin test** is performed by injecting intradermally 0.1 ml. of a 1:10,000 dilution of commercial mallein. The test becomes positive in a majority of the patients during the third or fourth week of the disease and remains positive for years. A positive test resembles a tuberculin reaction and is read after a 24- or 48-hour interval. Normal individuals either have no reaction at the site of the injection or develop a red area which fades almost completely within 48 hours (16).

Transmission. Glanders was formerly a relatively common disease among farmers, stablemen, veterinarians, and others who came into intimate contact with horses. In 1919 von Brunn reviewed 403 cases of glanders in man. Following the introduction of the mallein test and the systematic slaugh-

ter of all animals giving positive reactions, the disease has become rare in most parts of the world except in some of the Balkan countries. A case in man was reported by Herold and Erickson in 1938 (15) and another by McGilvray in 1944 (22). Howe and Miller (16) have emphasized the danger of laboratory infections and report six examples.

Treatment. Howe and Miller (16) have obtained excellent results by intensive and persistent treatment with sulfadiazine.

Prevention. An effective immune state in horses does not follow recovery from natural infection. All attempts to induce active immunity in animals with vaccines have been unsuccessful; therefore, vaccines presumably would not be effective as immunizing agents for man. The slaughter of solepeds (horse, mule, ass) that carry the infection is the obvious method of eliminating the disease.

PSEUDOMONAS PSEUDOMALLEI AND MELIOIDOSIS

Family: *Pseudomonadaceae* Winslow and others. Genus: *Pseudomonas* Migula. Species: *Pseudomonas pseudomallei* (Whitmore) Haynes comb. nov.

A disease resembling glanders in man was first described by Whitmore and Krishnaswami (39, 40) in Rangoon in 1912. The chief features of the disease are septicemia, pyemia, and the formation of characteristic granulomatous nodules in nearly all parts of the body. The infection has occurred not only in man but also in epizootic form among guinea pigs and rabbits in certain laboratories. As the disease occurs also in wild rats, it is supposed that these animals are the natural reservoir of the infection from which man is infected by the bite of the rat flea *Xenopsylla cheopis*, or the *Aëdes aegypti* mosquito (4). The patient's serum may agglutinate the organisms in a dilution of 1:2,560 (13), and since the *Ps. pseudomallei* strains are serologically homogenous (7), one could use a known culture to test for agglutinins in suspected cases. Erythrocytes from man, horse, and other animals

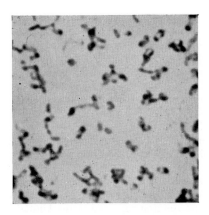

Fig. 3. *Pseudomonas pseudomallei.* (From Gunter and Fisher. *Ann. Int. Med.,* 28:1157, 1948.)

can be sensitized to mallein, after which they will agglutinate in the serums of experimentally infected animals (5). Cases of the disease have been reported chiefly from Malaysia, Indochina, and Ceylon. In 1921 Stanton and Fletcher named the disease **melioidosis** because the ancient Greeks applied the term "melis" to a variety of conditions resembling glanders (32, 33, 34).

When Whitmore studied the organism isolated by him from lesions of this disease, he recognized that it was related to the glanders bacillus and, therefore, named the organism *Bacillus pseudo-mallei.* Other names given to the organism are *Bacillus whitmori, Pfeifferella whitmori, Malleomyces pseudomallei,* and finally in the seventh edition of Bergey's Manual of Determinative Bacteriology it is listed as *Pseudomonas pseudomallei.*

The organism as described by Whitmore and Stanton and Fletcher is 1 to 2 μ long, and 0.5 μ broad (Fig. 3). Longer and broader forms are found in broth cultures. The organism is **motile, does not form spores,** and is **gram-negative.** Moody (26) found that individual bacilli could be identified on a slide even in the presence of large numbers of other types of organisms after treating the slide with a fluorescence-labeled antibody.

This bacterium is aerobic, grows well on the usual culture media, and has an optimal temperature for growth of 37° C. The colonies, which are at first whitish and opaque, become yellow or brown and wrinkled (Fig. 4). Some difficulty may be encountered in differentiating *Ps. pseudomallei* from nonpig-

mented *Pseudomonas* (38). Mucoid and rough variants have been described, and on primary isolation a variety of colonies may appear, varying from smooth to rough and from white to yellow and orange (30). Virulence was not restricted to one colonial type. The cultures are said to have an earthy, moldy odor. Gelatin is liquefied, but indole is not produced. The organism forms **acid without gas in glucose** and acid with coagulation in milk. *Ps. pseudomallei* differs chiefly from *A. mallei* in its **motility** and ability to liquefy gelatin. The organism has been grown in a simple chemically defined medium (18) and has been found to produce both a heat-labile and a heat-stabile toxin (29).

There is a close antigenic relationship between *Ps. pseudomallei* and one of the serologic groups of the glanders bacillus (32, 33, 34). A bacteriophage has been found which lysed 11 of 18 strains of *Ps. pseudomallei,* one of four strains of *A. mallei,* and three of six coliform strains (41).

Dannenburg and Scott (10) produced disease in mice and hamsters by both subcutaneous and inhalation inoculation. Nigg and Johnston (27) infected rabbits, guinea pigs, and monkeys to obtain sera for the study of the complement-fixation method. Practically 100 per cent of the animals developed complement-fixing antibodies in 10 to 12 days after inoculation.

The recognized cases of melioidosis are usually rapidly fatal, but more reports of chronic infections involving lungs and glands (12, 13), bone, joints and legs (20) are appearing in the literature. American soldiers were infected during World War II in Burma (6),

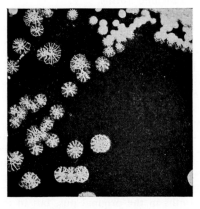

Fig. 4. Highly wrinkled colony growth of *Ps. pseudomallei.* (From Gunter and Fisher. *Ann. Int. Med.,* 28:1157, 1948.)

Guam (25), and the Philippine Islands (13). The first known case originating in the western hemisphere was reported by McDowell and Varney in 1947 (21). This infection is being recognized with increasing frequency (3, 11, 42).

Nigg (27) used her complement-fixation method to study sera from natives of Thailand and found evidence of subclinical infection in 8.3 per cent of 337 sera. A group of 138 sera from the United States had no positive reactors.

Penicillin (6) is ineffective in patients and the other antibiotics seem to be palliative only (6, 8, 12).

ACTINOBACILLOSIS

Family: *Brucellaceae* fam. nov. Genus: *Actinobacillus* Brumpt. Species: *Actinobacillus mallei* Zopf, 1885, Thompson, 1933

Actinobacillus lignieresii was isolated in Argentina in 1902 by Lignières and Spitz. The organisms were cultured from cows with the clinical syndrome of actinomycosis. Later work has shown that the *Actinobacillus* is responsible for 50 to 60 per cent of the infections of cattle usually designated as "actinomycosis" (36, 37).

The bacillus is a **nonsporogenous, nonencapsulated, nonmotile, gram-negative** rod about 0.4 μ in width and 1 to 15 μ in length. The organism is pleomorphic and at times coccobacillary forms predominate. Bipolar staining is observed frequently. In the tissues the bacilli occur in clusters in the center of granules which resemble the "sulfur granules" of actinomycosis but are **gram-negative** and **do not show branching forms.**

The organism is **aerobic** but **facultatively anaerobic,** although incubation in an atmosphere containing 10 per cent CO_2 is said to favor primary isolation. The optimal temperature for growth is 37° C. Most primary cultures have been obtained by pouring plates of serum and ascitic fluid agar with ground-up pieces of infected tissue or by seeding shake tubes of serum agar (9).

After 24 to 48 hours' incubation, small, 1.5 mm., circular, translucent, bluish gray colonies with entire edges appear which, upon further incubation, reach a size of 4 mm. If kept in a sealed container, the organisms may survive for months in the original pus, but in cultures they die unless transferred every three or four days. The bacillus is killed in 10 minutes by a temperature of 62° C.

There is general agreement that *Actinobacillus lignieresii* is related both antigenically and culturally to *Actinobacillus mallei* and *Pseudomonas pseudomallei* (32, 37).

The spontaneous disease in cattle apparently is spread by direct contact. Guinea pigs and mice can be infected by intraperitoneal inoculation. The injection of large doses of the organism intraperitoneally into a male guinea pig produces a swelling of the testicles resembling the Strauss reaction in glanders (page 565).

Ravant and Pinoy in 1911 reported the first incidence of the disease in man. The second case, and the first reported in the United States, was found by Thompson and Willius in 1932 (36). A fatal human infection with *Actinobacillus lignieresii* characterized by an acute, suppurative bronchopneumonia was reported by Beaver and Thompson (2). A review of the literature with a report of the necropsy findings in a case of *Actinobacillus* endocarditis was published by Custis and his associates (9) in 1944.

Potassium iodide is quite effective in the treatment of the spontaneous disease in cattle and has been used with some success in the more chronic forms of the disease in man (36). The acute form of the disease in man should be treated with sulfonamides and penicillin or, possibly, streptomycin.

Actinobacillus actinoides was isolated from a chronic pulmonary infection in calves by Theobald Smith in 1918.

Actinobacillus actinomycetemcomitans has been isolated from confirmed cases of actinomycosis in man by Klinger (17) and Bayne-Jones (1). Culture strains are not pathogenic for animals, and the role of the organism in the disease actinomycosis still is obscure.

REFERENCES

1. Bayne-Jones, S. J. Bact., 10:569, 1925.
2. Beaver, D. C., and Thompson, L. Am. J. Path., 9:603, 1933.
3. Beaver, P. R., and others. Am. J. Clin. Path., 24:1231, 1954.
4. Blanc, G., and Baltazard, M. Compt. rend. Acad. d. sc., 213:541, 670, 1941.
5. Boyden, S. V. Proc. Soc. Exper. Biol. & Med., 73:289, 1950.
6. Cox, C. D., and Arbogast, J. L. Am. J. Clin. Path., 15:567, 1945.
7. Cravitz, L., and Miller, W. R. J. Infect. Dis., 86:46, 1950.
8. Cruickshank, J. C. Brit. M. J., 2:410, 1949.
9. Custis, D. L., and others. Arch. Path., 38:332, 1944.
10. Dannenberg, A. M., and Scott, E. M. J. Immunol., 84:233, 1960.

11. Garry, M. W., and Koch, M. L. J. Lab. & Clin. Med., 38:374, 1951.
12. Green, R., and Mankikar, D. S. Brit. M. J., 1:308, 1949.
13. Gunter, L. B., and Fisher, M. W. Ann. Int. Med., 28:1157, 1948.
14. Harries, E. J., and others. Lancet, 1:363, 1948.
15. Herold, A. A., and Erickson, C. G. South. M. J., 31:1022, 1938.
16. Howe, C., and Miller, W. R. Ann. Int. Med., 26:93, 1947.
17. Klinger, R. Centralbl. f. Bakt., I Abt., Orig., 62:191, 1912.
18. Levine, H. B., and others. J. Bact., 67:350, 1954.
19. Löffler, F., and Schutz. Deutsche med. Wchschr., 8:707, 1882.
20. Mayer, J. H. J. Bone & Joint Surg., 27:479, 1945.
21. McDowell, F., and Varney, P. L. J.A.M.A., 134:361, 1947.
22. McGilvray, C. D. J. Am. Vet. M. A., 104:255, 1944.
23. Miller, W. R., and others. J. Bact., 55:115, 1948.
24. ———— and others. J. Bact., 55:127, 1948.
25. Mirick, G. S., and others. J.A.M.A., 130:1063, 1946.
26. Moody, M. D., and others. Bacteriol. Proc., p. 81, 1956.
27. Nigg, C. J. Immunol., 91:18, 1963.
28. ———— and Johnston, M. A. J. Bact., 82:159, 1961.
29. ———— and others. Proc. Soc. Exper. Biol. & Med., 89:17, 1955.
30. ———— and others. J. Bact., 71:530, 1956.
31. Robins, G. D. Studies from Royal Victoria Hosp., Montreal, Vol. 2, No. 1, 1906.
32. Stanton, A. T., and Fletcher, W. Tr. 4th Congr. Far East. A. Trop. Med., 2:196, 1921.
33. ———— J. Hyg., 23:347, 1925.
34. ———— Lancet, 1:10, 1925.
35. Strauss, I. Arch. de méd. expér., 1:460, 1889.
36. Thompson, L., and Willius, F. A. J.A.M.A., 99:298, 1932.
37. ———— J. Bact., 26:221, 1933.
38. Wetmore, P. W., and Gochenoor, W. S. J. Bact., 72:79, 1956.
39. Whitmore, A. J. Hyg., 13:1, 1913.
40. ———— and Krishnaswami, C. S. Indian M. Gaz., 47:262, 1912.
41. Wolochow, H., and Green, L. B. Bacteriol. Proc., p. 60, 1956.
42. Ziskind, J., and others. Am. J. Clin. Path., 24:1241, 1954.

32

The Enterobacteriaceae

Billions of aerobic, gram-negative, non-sporulating bacilli are found in the excreta of man and animals. They also are present in large numbers in soil and water and on grains, grasses, and decaying vegetable material.

The principal division and groups of *Enterobacteriaceae* are shown in Table 1 as

Table 1. Simple Classification of
Enterobacteriaceae

TRIBES	GENERA
Escherichieae	*Escherichia* (*Esch. coli,* including Alkalescens-dispar)
	Klebsiella (including *Hafnia* and *Aerabocter* A, B, and C)
Salmonelleae	*Salmonella* (including *Arizona* and *Citrobacter*)
	Shigella
Serratieae	*Serratia*
Proteae	*Proteus* (including *Provincia* A and B)
Edwinieae	*Edwinia*

defined by Edwards and Ewing in the second edition of their *Identification of Enterobacteriaceae* (8). This classification is presented graphically in somewhat more detail in Figure 1. It can be seen that the species designated as *Escherichia freundii* in the seventh edition of Bergey's Manual has been combined with the Bethesda-Ballerup strains from *E. intermedium* (Paracolons) (6) and given the name *Citrobacter freundii* (Braak). The Arizona subgroup of *Salmonella* is designated a new genus of *Salmonella* with the type species *Arizona arizonae* (26). The Tribe III Klebsielleae Trevisan has been redefined so that the genus *Klebsiella Trevisan* is limited to **nonmotile strains** with certain

biochemical and serologic characteristics (24, 25, 29, 37). The motile strains, formerly designated as *Klebsiella,* have been transferred to Genus II *Aerobactero-Beijerinch* and to *Aerobacter B,* or *Aerobacter aerogenesi* (21). *Aerobacter A,* shown in Figure 1, is the old species known as *Aerobacter cloacae* (21). *Aerobacter C* includes those strains formerly called *Aerobacter lignefaciens* by Grimes and Hennerty; this is a psychophilic group whose biochemical activity is greater at 25° C. than at 37° C. The hafnia group from the Paracolons is made into a subspecies *hafniae* in *Aerobacter aerogenesi* (Moeller, Ewing, *comb. nov.*) (45, 46).

The seventh edition of Bergey's Manual recognizes five species of *Serratia* in Tribe III *Serratieae*. Edwards and Ewing (8) would reduce the Tribe *Serratieae* to Genus III (B1210) (Breed and Breed), with one species, *Serratia marcescens* (B1210), and with one subspecies, *kiliensis* (B1210).

Species of *Serratia* are being found as the cause of clinical disease with increasing frequency, and the laboratory is discovering that many of the strains do not have the typical pigment of *Serratia*.

In Tribe IV *Proteae* (Costellani and Chalmers) a new genus *Providencia* (8) has been created to contain two major subgroups dependent upon certain biochemical reactions. These are designated as *Providencia A* and *Providencia B* (Fig. 1) and appear in the Ewing review of *Providencia alcalifaciens* (De Salles, Gomez, Ewing *comb. nov.*) and *Providencia stuartii* (Buttiaux et. al., and Ewing *comb nov.*).

The family *Enterobacteriaceae* is divided into tribes, genera, and species by a study of biochemical reactions. The species are then subdivided by serological methods or

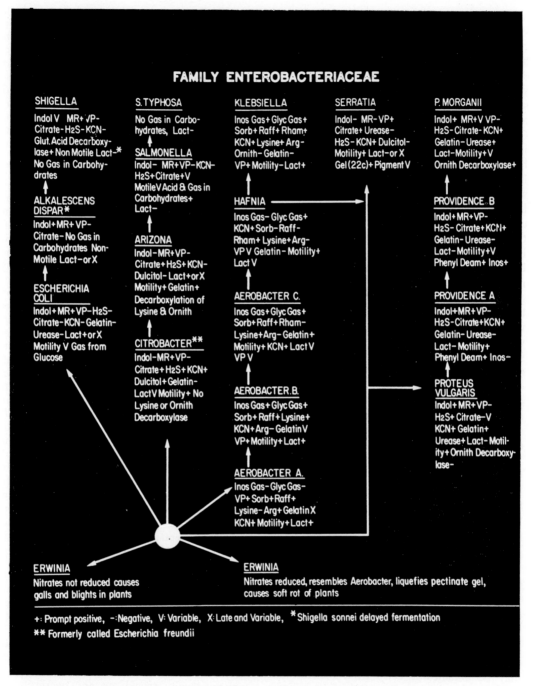

Fig. 1. Principal groups of *Enterobacteriaceae*. The arrows indicate possible, but not proved, lines of evolution. Organisms formerly designated as paracolons have been redistributed as subgroups of the well-defined *Enterobacteriaceae*.

bacteriophage typing for epidemiologic investigations. The original hypothetical ancestor of the family *Enterobacteriaceae* must have had a full complement of enzymes to enable its descendants to produce such a variety of biochemical reactions. It also possessed the potentiality of synthesizing an amazing number of different antigenic types. Changes by dissociation are constant findings (5, 29) and changes by transformation have been described (16). Loss mutation is a common occurrence; a freshly isolated strain may have lost its motility or have lost the ability to perform one of a variety of biochemical reactions characteristic of that species. **Such strains should be classified in the species to which the majority of its biochemical reactions correspond.** The phenomenon of transduction, induced by a lysogenic bacteriophage, was discovered among the *Salmonella* (25, 31, 50). Certain phages, when freshly isolated from sewage, attack various members of the *Enterobacteriaceae* family in an indiscriminate manner, which might explain some aspects of haphazard distribution of common antigens between certain strains of *E. coli* and *Shigella* (12) and between *E. freundii* and *Salmonella* (9).

Salmonella typhosa is the only member of the *Salmonella* group which possesses the Vi surface antigen. This antigen may account in part for the greater pathogenicity of *S. typhosa,* and yet it is shared with the relatively avirulent Ballerup strains of the Bethesda-Ballerup group and by certain completely avirulent strains of *E. coli* (30).

Selecting Specimens for Planting. For most enteric bacteria an ordinary stool is satisfactory for planting on special media, but this is not true of the *Shigella.* These organisms occur concentrated in bits of epithelium or in blood-stained mucus and pus on the surface of the stool. Furthermore, they die rather quickly if not cultured on appropriate media. Specimens may be obtained directly from the intestine through a proctoscope, by rectal swabs, or from a freshly passed and still warm stool. Selective material of this type can be added to preservative solutions.

Preserving Specimens. Three methods are available for preserving specimens for shipping or holding, but none of these is as effective as direct plating. Coleman (7) recommends the use of buffered glycerol-saline solutions, which should contain sufficient phenol red to give the solutions a distinctly red color. An acid reaction often kills the dysentery bacilli. Banxgang and Eliot (4) devised a buffered saline solution which contains sodium citrate and sodium desoxycholate. Approximately 1 g. of feces should be added to 8 to 10 ml. of either of these solutions and thoroughly emulsified. As a last resort, small particles of feces may be dried on blotting paper or filter paper and stored at room temperature in the dark (3).

Enrichment Media. Enrichment media are designed to suppress the normal flora of the stool and favor the multiplication of pathogens and are most useful when the latter are present in very small numbers, as often occurs late in the disease and among carriers. Two types of enrichment media are in common use. The **tetrathionate broth** of Moeller, as modified by Kauffmann (23) by the addition of brilliant green and bile, is probably best for the isolation of the *Salmonella,* particularly when subsequent plating is on brilliant green-phenol red agar. The addition of 8 to 16 mg. of sodium sulfadiazine per 100 ml. of this medium inhibits overgrowth by *Pseudomonas* (20) and the multiplication of the *Proteus* organisms. The latter may be suppressed in commercial tetrathionate broth by the addition of 0.125 mg. of sodium sulfathiazole (19). Typhoid bacilli and *Shigella* are usually inhibited by tetrathionate broth particularly if used with brilliant green. The second type of enrichment medium is the **selenite broth** of Leifson (33), which is recommended for the isolation of typhoid bacilli and *Shigella.* The addition of cystine to selenite broth improves its efficiency when growing *Salmonella* from powdered eggs (36). Antibiotics should not be added except under very exceptional conditions.

Approximately 1 g. of fresh feces, or 2 to 3 ml. of feces in preservative media are added to 8 to 10 ml. of the enrichment media and incubated for 16 to 18 hours before streaking plates. When possible, both types of enrichment media should be employed.

Differential, Inhibiting, and Selective Media. When feces are planted directly on plain agar media, the predominant colon and *Proteus* organisms usually crowd out and overgrow the pathogens. Endo's agar, Conradi-Drigalski medium, and eosin-methylene blue agar not only inhibit gram-positive bacteria but contain indicators whch distinguish bacteria that ferment lactose rapidly from those which do not attack this sugar. MacConkey's agar and the deoxycholate agar of Leifson inhibit gram-positive organisms and slow to some extent the growth of *E. coli* without inhibiting the *Salmonella* and *Shigella*.

The more complex plating media—such as the deoxycholate citrate agar of Leifson (32), the Salmonella-Shigella (S.S.) agar, the bismuth sulfite agar of Wilson and Blair (49), and the brilliant green-phenol red agar of Kristensen (28)—are not only differential but highly selective. They are available in dehydrated form from commercial sources. These media stop the swarming of *Proteus* strains, inhibit almost completely the coliform bacilli, and also inhibit some of the more delicate *Shigella* and *Salmonella*. A much heavier inoculation of feces can be made on the strongly inhibitory media than on those which are less inhibitory to *E. coli*. At least two plates should be inoculated with each specimen; one should be slightly inhibitory, and one strongly inhibitory, selected on the basis of the pathogen suspected. In many laboratories bismuth sulfite agar and S.S. agar are used for typhoid patients and suspected carriers; S.S. agar and eosin-methylene blue for *Shigella;* deoxycholate agar and brilliant green agar for *Salmonella;* and eosin-methylene blue and blood agar for the pathogenic serotypes of *E. coli*. The strongly inhibitory media should be used when plating feces from the enrichment media (1, 47).

Isolation of Colonies. The streaked plates are examined after 18 to 24 hours incubation at 37°C., for the presence of potential pathogens. Little difficulty is encountered if the original material contains a reasonable number of pathogens, but not infrequently there are only one to five potential pathogens in the entire plate and these colonies are not always typical. Walters and his associates (48) have suggested the use of microscopic examination of colonies with oblique transmitted illumination which reveals differences in both texture and color between various pathogens and between pathogens and *E. coli*. The two most common sources of error are the picking of colorless colonies which are mixed with a partially inhibited colony of *E. coli* or the picking of a colorless colony which has only recently escaped the inhibiting effect of the medium and has not produced sufficient acid from lactose to develop a color.

The colorless colonies are potential pathogens, but a number of nonpathogenic species also fail to ferment lactose and also produce colorless colonies. The most commonly encountered are *Proteus, E. freundii, Pseudomonas,* and the *Alcaligenes,* and the slow lactose fermenters formerly called paracolon bacilli. For this reason several colonies should be picked and carried through the diagnostic schema shown in Figure 2.

The colony should be picked with a slightly curved needle, after which the needle should be plunged into the center of the solid agar in the bottom of the tube and rubbed lightly over the slanting agar, as it is withdrawn. The triple sugar iron agar is Kligler's old iron agar to which 1 per cent sucrose has been added. The TSI agar tubes are incubated overnight, and those which have an acid reaction throughout are discarded. Organisms which do not ferment lactose and sucrose promptly are transferred to urea medium and the schema continued.

The organisms are identified generically by a combination of biochemical reactions (Table 2) and typing with polyvalent antiserums. Organisms which appear to be *Shigella* by biochemical reaction but fail to agglutinate in polyvalent O *Shigella* antiserum may have sufficient surface thermolabile antigens to prevent O agglutination. Such organisms should be suspended in plain physiologic saline and heated for 30 minutes at 100° C., cooled, and retested. Conversely, organisms agglutinating in polyvalent *Shigella* antiserums must be tested for their biochemical reactions to establish them as members of the genus *Shigella*.

The **methyl red** test is actually the determination of acidity in a dextrose broth culture after two to four days incubation. *E. coli* produces and maintains a high acidity which gives a red color when the indicator is added. *A. cloacae* does not produce enough acid from glucose to give a red color. Consequently, *E. coli* is said to be methyl red+ and *A. cloacae,* methyl red−. **The Voges-Proskauer reaction** is an indirect test for the synthesis of acetylmethylcarbinol while an organism is growing for two to four days in glucose broth. When alkali is added to the culture, the acetylmethylcarbinol is oxidized to diacetyl, which combines with an unknown constituent of peptone to form the colored compound. *E. coli* is VP−, while *A. cloacae* is VP+. The citrate test depends upon the ability of certain enteric organisms to utilize sodium citrate as the sole source of carbon in a synthetic medium. *E. coli* is citrate−, while *A. cloacae* is citrate+ (45, 46). These three tests, along with the test for indol production, are standard procedures in the study of enteric bacilli. Parr (38, 39) introduced the mnemonic imvic or IMViC, which serves to fix the reactions in order. Thus, *E. coli* is (+ + − −) while *A. cloacae* is (− − + +). There are 16 possible combinations of the IMViC test of which all have been found (40).

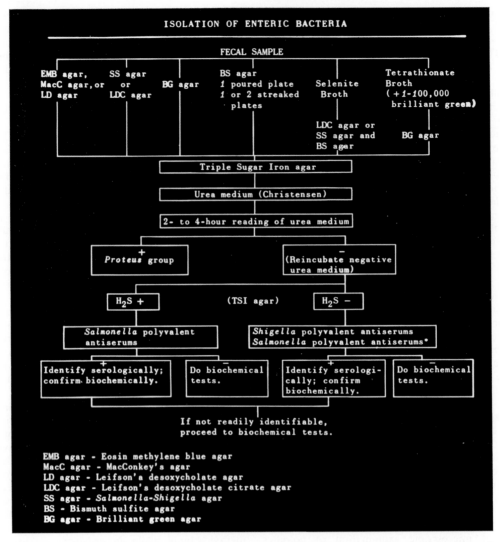

Fig. 2. Scheme for isolation and identification of enteric bacteria. (From Edwards and Ewing. *Identification of Enterobacteriaceae,* U.S.P.H.S., C.D.C. Atlanta, Ga., Burgess Publishing Co.)

Isolation of Enteric Bacteria from Blood and Body Fluids. *S. typhosa* invades the blood in the first week of the disease and may be present for two or three weeks. For its isolation, blood from the patient is added to rich laboratory media of the type used for routine blood cultures in febrile diseases of unknown etiology. A higher yield of positive cultures is obtained if bile is added to the medium. Both broth flasks of medium and poured agar plates are employed. **Blood and other body fluids are not planted on the strongly inhibitory media employed for the isolation of enteric bacteria from feces.** However, a few exceptions should be

noted: (1) when searching for typhoid bacilli in a suspected urinary carrier, the centrifugalized sediment should be planted on bismuth sulfite agar and eosin-methylene blue plates, and (2) pus from peritoneal infections, abdominal abscesses, and sputum should be plated on eosin-methylene blue media as well as standard rich media. The *Shigella* practically never invade the blood, but certain of the *Salmonella* do invade the blood and occasionally strains of *E. coli, Proteus, Klebsiella,* and *Aerobacter* are isolated. Enteric organisms other than *Salmonella* or *Shigella* have not infrequently been isolated from the respiratory tract since the

Table 2. Biochemical Reactions of Principal Groups of Enteric Bacteria
(Typical Reactions of Majority of Types)
(Edwards and Ewing, 1955)

	Shigella	Salmonella	Arizona	E. coli	E. freundii	Providence	Proteus	Klebsiella	Aerobacter cloacae
Gas from Glucose	−	+	+	+	+	+	v	+	+
Mannitol	v	+	+	+	+	−	v	+	+
Adonitol	−	−	−	−	−	+	v	+	v
Dulcitol	v	+	−	v	v	−	−	v	v
Inositol	−	v	−	−	−	−	−	+	v
Lactose	−*	−	+ or ×	+	+	−	−	+	+ or ×
Salicin	−	−	−	v	v	−	v	+	+ or ×
Sucrose	−*	−	−	v	v	×	v	+	+
Indol	v	−	−	+	−	+	v	−	v
Methyl Red	+	+	+	+	+	+	+	−	−
Voges Proskauer	−	−	−	−	−	−	v	+	+
Simmons' Citrate	−	+	+	−	+	+	v	+	+
Urea	−	−	−	−	− or ×	+	+	×	−
KCN	−	−	−	−	+	+	+	+	+
H₂S (TSI agar)	−	+	+	−	+	−	v	−	−
Gelatin	−	−	+	−	−	−	v	−	+
Nitrate	+	+	+	+	+	+	+	+	+
Motility	−	+	+	+	+	+	v	−	+

+ = promptly positive
× = delayed positive
− = negative
v = some cultures positive, some cultures negative
* = *Shigella sonnei* produces delayed fermentation of lactose and sometimes of sucrose

introduction of penicillin and other antibiotics in therapy. Also, *Candida albicans* and other yeast-like organisms are often found in almost pure cultures in the stool of patients who develop diarrhea from overtreatment with broad spectrum antibiotics. Blood agar plates should be employed when diarrhea from penicillin-resistant staphylococci is suspected (42).

The study of Finland (17, 18), McCabe and Jackson (34) and others (35, 43, 44, 26, 27) have shown the species of *Enterobacteriaceae* or *Pseudomonadaceae* now produce severe and often fatal infections five times as frequently as they did 20 years ago. Furthermore, 72 per cent of the infections (34) are acquired while the patient is in the hospital. These hospital infections equal or even exceed in frequency the better publicized hospital infections with *Staphylococcus aureus* (Fig. 3). Previous or concurrent antibiotic therapy seems to increase the prevalence of hospital infection with the gram-negative organisms (17, 18, 22).

Most bacterial infections follow a slow, step-wise progression of symptoms, whereas patients with bacteremia from gram-negative organisms progress from relative good health to prostration in a very few hours (18). The speed and severity of the onset is equalled only by the severest cases of meningococcemia. The classical symptoms of chills, fever, vomiting, diarrhea, and shock are very suggestive of shock from endotoxins. Indeed, similar symptoms have been produced in man and animals by the injection of endotoxin derived from gram-negative bacteria of this type. Steroid therapy, without a covering with the proper antibiotic, seems to increase the chance of bacteremia. The use of steroids after the development of shock may harm the patient if antibiotics specific for the particular organisms are not available. Spink (44) has emphasized the importance in treating and controlling the shock as well as the infection (43). Shubin and Weil (41) have found that the best

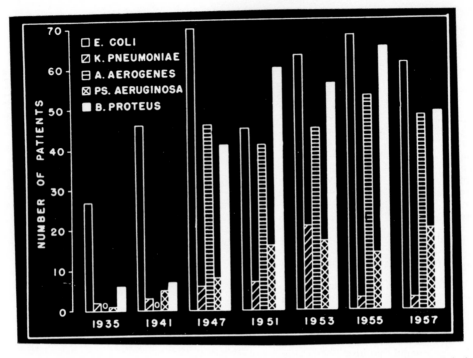

Fig. 3. Bacteremia occurrence of gram-negative bacilli in blood cultures before antibiotics in 1935 and after antibiotics in 1941. Note increase in all types after introduction of antibiotics. (From Finland, Jones, and Barnes. *J.A.M.A.,* 170:2188, 1959.)

results are obtained when both a vasopressor and large doses of corticoids are administered simultaneously.

ERWINIA

Erwineae was recognized as a Tribe of *Escherichieae* in the seventh edition of Bergey's Manual. Although Edwards and Ewing do not consider them members of the *Enterobacteriaceae,* they recognize two kinds of *Erwinia:* the nitrate-negative strains, which produce galls and blight in plants, and the pectobacterium group, which produce soil rot in plants. They liquefy sodium pectinate medium, whereas enterobacteria do not.

AEROMONAS

The *Aeromonas* are not properly members of the enteric bacteria but may be isolated from human feces and hence must be identified. The literature and classification of these organisms has been reviewed by Ewing, Hugh, and Johnson (14, 15). The original culture was isolated by Ernst (11) in 1890 from a bacteremic disease subsequently called "red-leg" of frogs. A

second large group of strains were studied by Ferguson and Henderson in 1947 and labeled C27. Some of these strains had O antigen which was identical with *Sh. sonnei* form I. Bader (2) in 1954 found other strains which were related antigenically to *Sh. sonnei* but noted that not all of them were related. He suggested the name *Ps. shigelloides.*

Ewing and his associates believe that the type species should be *Aeromonas hydrophila.* Stanier (44a) suggested two additional species to be called *A. submoniada* and *A. shigelloides* (15).

REFERENCES

1. Armstrong, E. C. Mo. Bul. Min. Health (Gr. Brit.), 13:70, 1954.
2. Bader, R. E. Ziet. f. Hyg., 140:450, 1954.
3. Bailey, W. R., and Bynoe, E. T. Canad. J. Pub. Health, 44:137, 1953.
4. Banxgang, E. N., and Eliot, C. P. Am. J. Hyg., Sec. B, 31:16, 1940.
5. Bruner, D. W. J. Bact., 64:138, 1954.
6. Carlquist, P. R. J. Bact., 71:339, 1956.
7. Coleman, M. B. Diagnostic Procedures and Reagents, New York, Am. Pub. Health Assoc., 1945, p. 247.
8. Edwards, P. R., and Ewing, W. H. Identity of Enterobacteriaceae, Minneapolis, Burgess Publishing Co., 1961.

9. Edwards, P. R., and others. J. Bact., 68: 756, 1954.
10. ——— and Fife, M. A. J. Bact., 70:382, 1955.
11. Ernst, P. Beitr. path. Anat., 8:203, 1890.
12. Ewing, W. H. J. Bact., 66:333, 1953.
13. ——— and Edwards, P. R. Internat. Bull. of Bact. Nomen. and Tax., 10:1, 1960.
14. ——— and Johnson, J. G. Internat. Bull. of Bact. Nomen. and Tax., 10:223, 1960.
15. ——— and others. Studies on the Aeromonas Group, U.S. Dept. of Health, Ed., and Welfare, Communicable Dis. Center, Atlanta, Ga., 1961.
16. Felsenfeld, O. Proc. Soc. Exper. Biol. & Med., 87:73, 1954.
17. Finland, M. New England J. Med., 263:207, 1960.
18. ——— and others. J.A.M.A., 170:2188, 1959.
19. Galton, M. M., and others. J. Infect. Dis., 91:1, 1952.
20. ——— and others. J. Infect. Dis., 95:232, 1954.
21. Hormaeche, E., and Edwards, P. R. Internat. Bull. of Bact. Nomen. and Tax., 10:71, 1960.
22. Kass, E. H., and Finland, M. Am. Rev. Med., 8:1, 1957.
23. Kauffmann, F. Zentralbl. f. Bakt., 119:148, 1930.
24. ——— Estratto de Rivista dell'Instituto Siero. Italiano, 28:485, 1953.
25. ——— Acta path. et microbiol. Scandinav., 33:409, 1953.
26. ——— Internat. Bull. of Bact. Nomen. and Tax., 9:1, 1959.
27. Koch, M. L. Antibiot. Med., 2:113, 1956.
28. Kristensen, M., and others. Brit. J. Exper. Path., 6:291, 1925.
29. Kröger, E. Zeits. Für Naturforschung, 8: 134, 1953.
30. Landy, M., and others. J. Immunol., 73:23, 1956.
31. Lederberg, J., and Edwards, P. R. J. Immunol., 71:232, 1953.
32. Leifson, E. J. Path. & Bact., 40:581, 1935.
33. ——— Am. J. Hyg., 24:423, 1936.
34. McCabe, W. R., and Jackson, G. C. Arch. Inter. Med., 110:847, 856, 1962.
35. McHenry, M. C., and others. Ann. Inter. Med., 56:207, 1962.
36. North, W. R., and Bartram, M. T. Appl. Microbiol., 1:130, 1953.
37. Ørskov, I. Acta path. et microbiol. Scandinav., 34:145, 1954.
38. Parr, L. W. Am. J. Pub. Health, 26:39, 1936.
39. ——— Bact. Rev., 3:1, 1939.
40. Sanborn, J. R. J. Bact., 48:211, 1944.
41. Shubin, H., and Weil, M. H. J.A.M.A., 185: 850, 1963.
42. Speare, G. S. Am. J. Surg., 88:523, 1954.
43. Spink, W. W., and Vick, J. Proc. Soc. Exper. Biol. & Med., 109:54, 1962.
44. ——— Arch. Int. Med., 106:433, 1960.
44a. Stanier, R. Y. J. Bact., 46:213, 1943.
45. Stuart, C. A., and others. J. Bact., 45:101, 1943.
46. ——— and others. J. Bact., 52:431, 1946.
47. Thomas, M. E. M. Brit. Med. J., 2:394, 1954.
48. Walters, E. W., and others. J. Bact., 67:247, 1955.
49. Wilson, W. J., and Blair, E. M. McV. J. Hyg,. 31:138, 1931.
50. Zinder, N. D., and Lederberg, J. J. Bact., 64:679, 1952.

33

Salmonella typhosa and Typhoid Fever

Family: *Enterobacteriaceae* Rahn. Genus: *Salmonella* Lignières. Species: *Salmonella typhosa* (Zopf) White

The control of typhoid fever is perhaps the greatest triumph of organized preventive medicine. As late as 1900 the annual death rate from typhoid fever in the United States was over 30 per 100,000 but by the year 1944 it had decreased to 0.4 per 100,000, a reduction of 99 per cent.

Not a single death from typhoid fever was reported for the year 1945 from 56 of America's largest cities. The problem, however, is not entirely solved, since in the same year death rates from 4.8 to 5.4 per 100,000 were reported from South Central states (69). There still are sufficient carriers in the population to cause explosive epidemics if our society becomes disorganized or our public health departments immobilized, as happened in Central Europe at the end of World War II.

In 1856 Budd (12) concluded, from astute clinical observations, that typhoid fever was an infectious disease that was transmitted from patient to patient. The typhoid bacillus was seen first by Eberth (21) in 1880 in the spleen and mesenteric gland of a patient dead of typhoid and was isolated by Gaffky (29) in 1884. Typhoid fever cannot be reproduced in animals, but numerous laboratory infections with pure cultures have served to establish the pathogenicity of this organism for man.

The typhoid bacillus is a highly specialized member of the genus *Salmonella*; man is the sole host. The "carrier," particularly the unrecognized one, serves as the primary source of new infections which will continue to occur until the last carrier has lived out his allotted time.

Antigenic studies have supplied convincing evidence that the typhoid bacillus belongs in the genus *Salmonella*, but **it is important for the student to remember that *S. typhosa* does not produce gas in carbohydrate media, thus furnishing a simple and practical method of differentiating it from the more common members of the group.** The exceptions are *S. gallinarum* and an occasional mutant from other types which have lost the ability to produce gas.

Morphology and Staining. *S. typhosa* is a short plump rod, 0.5 to 0.8 μ in width and from 1 to 3.5 μ in length (Figs. 1 and 2). Longer forms are seen in old cultures and in R phase colonies. The organism is actively **motile** (Fig. 3), **nonsporogenous,** and **nonencapsulated** except in the rare M phase of dissociation. The organisms stain readily with the usual aniline dyes and are **gram-negative.** An attempt to demonstrate *S. typhosa* directly in smears of feces with fluorescent antibodies was not successful because of the general cross-reactions

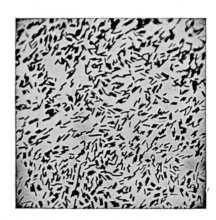

Fig. 1. *Salmonella typhosa*. From 24-hour culture on agar, showing regularity of forms.

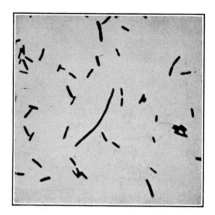

Fig. 2. *Salmonella typhosa.* Motile smooth type from 12-hour culture on infusion agar, showing variations in form. × 1,200.

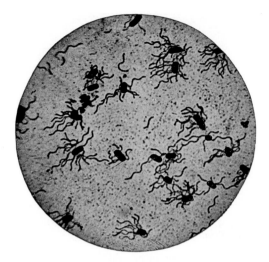

Fig. 3. *Salmonella typhosa.* Showing flagella. (From Fraenkel and Pfeiffer.)

between members of the *Enterobacteriaceae* (75).

Cultural Characteristics. *Salmonella typhosa* is **aerobic** but **facultatively anaerobic.** The bacillus grows readily on the usual laboratory media over a pH range of 6 to 8 at temperatures between 15° to 41° C., with an optimum of 37.5° C. The organisms will grow on simple synthetic media containing glucose and ammonium salts, although some strains require the addition of tryptophan. The typhoid bacillus can be isolated directly from the blood on ordinary meat infusion agar or meat infusion broth, but bile facilitates its growth and often is added to the infusion media.

The colonies after 24 hours incubation are smaller, more delicate, and more transparent than contemporary colonies of colon bacilli. On bismuth sulfite medium their appearance is jet black in contrast to the colorless colonies of *E. coli.*

S. typhosa produces **acid without gas from glucose, maltose, mannitol, dextrin** and **trehalose. Lactose** and **sucrose are not fermented.** Some strains ferment **xylose** rapidly; others slowly or not at all. The production of H$_2$S is variable; **indol is not produced,** and **gelatin is not liquefied** (1).

Resistance. *S. typhosa* remains alive in cultures for months or even years if moisture is supplied. In carefully sealed agar tubes, Hiss (37) found the organisms alive after 13 years. The bacilli remain viable in ground water for two to three weeks but may persist in fecal material in privy vaults for one to two months. Their survival in ice and snow for at least three months (58) may account for some of the waterborne epidemics (10) in the winter and spring.

The typhoid organisms are killed within five minutes by 1:500 dilution of bichloride of mercury or 5 per cent carbolic acid. They are destroyed readily in milk by pasteurization temperatures and in water by the routine methods of chlorination. Sulfonamides, penicillin, and streptomycin are not effective in therapeutically attainable doses, but **chlortetracycline** and especially **chloramphenicol** are effective (61, 65, 87, 88).

Variability. The classic S − R type of dissociation was described by Arkwright (4). Since variations of the O and H antigens occur independently, the following types may be found: smooth, motile; smooth, nonmotile; rough, motile; and rough, nonmotile. Pathogenicity depends in part (8) upon the O antigen which is present in the smooth colonies. Organisms from rough colonies, therefore, whether motile or nonmotile, are avirulent (Fig. 4). The S colonies are of medium size, round, with a uniform surface and a flattened hemispherical shape. The R colonies are larger, flatter, with rough surfaces and irregular edges.

The M phase of dissociation can be produced in S cultures by growing the organism on agar slants at 37° C., subculturing on beef agar plates containing 1 per cent glucose, and incubating at 16° for four days (53).

S. typhosa and certain other *Salmonella* will hybridize with certain strains of *E. coli* (15). Furthermore, an episomic element, Fo *lac* +, has been identified in a wild strain of *S. typhosa.* This Fo *lac* + is similar, if not identical, to the *lac* genes of *E. coli* K-12 (24).

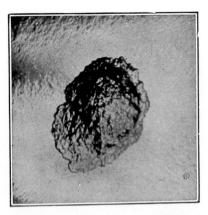

Fig. 4. Rough colony of *Salmonella typhosa* on agar. (From Grinnell.)

Antigenic Structure. At least 12 antigens have been identified in *S. typhosa* (71), and oligosaccharides will inhibit hemagglutination of erythrocytes modified with antigenic extractions of *Salmonella* (76). One of these antigens is shared with *Sh. flexnerii* (6).

The antigenic formula for *Salmonella typhosa* is IX, XII, (Vi-d), which places it in group D of the *Salmonella*. Since both the O and H antigens are shared by other species of *Salmonella*, an adequate explanation is provided for cross-agglutinations between *S. typhosa* and certain of the other paratyphoid organisms.

As in the other *Salmonella*, the virulence of the organism is determined by the presence of the O (46) and not the H antigen (23, 71).

THE VI ANTIGEN. It has been known for many years that freshly isolated cultures of typhoid bacilli, particularly those isolated from the blood, are not agglutinated by specific anti-O serum. It also was known that the bacilli became agglutinable in anti-O serum after a series of transfers on artificial media or after boiling the culture (23). An explanation of this phenomenon was furnished in the work of Felix and Pitt (25) and by Kauffmann (41), who designated the strain with the complete Vi antigen "V," those without it "W," and intermediate strains "VW." On continuous transfer, each group gave rise to the other; this is known

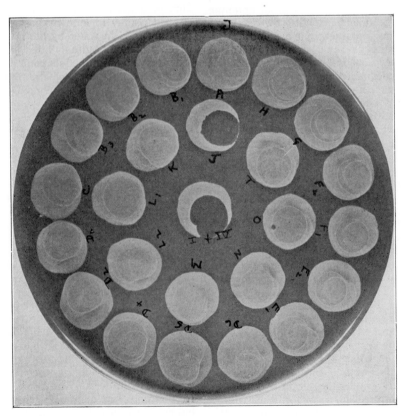

Fig. 5. Bacteriophage typing of *S. typhosa*. (From P. R. Edwards. U.S.P.H.S., C.D.C., Atlanta, Georgia.)

as the "V-W variation." In active and passive mouse protection tests only the Vi-containing vaccine and a Vi antigen effected protection against the V challenge, but when a W form challenge was employed, it was not possible to distinguish between VW immunization (80). Apparently, both O and Vi antigen are needed for maximal virulence (78, 80).

The same antigenic type of Vi antigen has been found in *Salmonella* paratyphi C (5, 7, 42) and in certain nonpathologic strains of *E. coli* (38, 42, 45) and the nonpathologic strains of "Ballerup" (43, 84, 85) which are now included in the new genus *Citrobacter* (23). Gaines and his associates (30) have reported the B ALB/c mice produced complete Vi antibodies against Vi antigen, while the "Cinnamon" strain produced only incomplete antibodies. However, the incomplete antibodies alone effected complete protection against infection.

A DNA fraction of Vi will transform smooth (O) but not rough (R) colonies from W to V type (26).

TYPING WITH BACTERIOPHAGE. Although only one type of Vi antigen can be detected by agglutination, precipitation, and protection experiments, subtle differences in this antigen can be recognized by specific bacteriophages (17), as shown in Figure 5. By utilizing various strains of bacteriophage, 98.6 per cent of the 592 V cultures of Craigie and Yen were differentiated in types A, B_1, B_2, C, D_1, D_2, E, F, G, H (18, 19), and standard typing phages are distributed by the Central Enteric Reference Laboratory of the Public Health Laboratory Service of England and Wales.

The Vi antigen is essential for the reaction of the specific bacteriophages. This subject has been reviewed by Anderson and Williams (3). The number of bacteriophage types has continued to multiply until the letters of the alphabet were exhausted and numbers were assigned, which now run from 25 to 35 inclusive (23).

SEROLOGIC DIAGNOSIS. Gruber and Durham (34) demonstrated the presence of specific agglutinins in the blood of rabbits infected with typhoid bacilli. The first practical application of the new science of immunology to clinical medicine was the introduction of a technic by Grünbaum (35) and Widal (86), for quantitative measurement of agglutinins in the serums of patients with typhoid fever. The testing of serum from a patient suspected of having typhoid fever against a known culture of *S. typhosa* is still referred to as the **Widal test** in the laboratory and the clinic. Both O and H type antigens usually are used, as well as the rela-

tively new Vi antigen. Pijper's darkfield cinematographic studies illustrate beautifully the essential difference between the O, H and Vi types of agglutination (Ch. 13, Figs. 14, 16, and 17).

The results of positive agglutination tests may be interpreted as follows:

1. For O agglutinins the significant titers are those above 1:50, since a few normal individuals have titers as high as 1:50.
2. For H agglutinins titers of 1:80 or above appear to have some diagnostic significance.
3. For Vi agglutinins the titers are always low but specific. A positive Vi agglutination is diagnostic if it is known that the patient is not a chronic carrier of typhoid bacilli.

BACTERIAL METABOLITES. *Salmonella typhosa* produces no **exotoxin.** The **endotoxin** has been identified as a specific, liquid-carbohydrate-protein complex (46). The polysaccharide fraction alone is not toxic but will neutralize the specific immune bodies produced by the whole organism (44, 47, 53).

Morgan (53) found that the endotoxin of the typhoid bacillus, when injected intracutaneously, produced edema, erythema, and necrosis. When injected intravenously into rabbits, the vascular epithelium was damaged, resulting in petechial hemorrhages, congestion, localized thrombosis and finally necrosis in the various internal organs, particularly in the liver and bone marrow. The changes were not unlike those found in patients who had died of typhoid fever. The studies reported by Greisman, Woodward and their associates (33) showed that human volunteers infected with cultures of *S. typhosa* are very susceptible to the endotoxin and excessively sensitive to the pharmacologic effect of adrenalin.

Experimental Disease in Laboratory Animals. Typical typhoid fever was produced in chimpanzees in 1911 by Metchinkoff and Besredka (51) and more recently by Edsal (22) and Gaines (31, 32) and their coworkers. The animal could be protected with either O or Vi antigens. Large doses of living or dead typhoid bacilli produce death in rabbits, guinea pigs, and mice in 24 to 48 hours from a toxemia which has no resemblance to typhoid fever in man (48, 49).

Clinical Types of Infection in Man. Typhoid fever is a generalized septicemic infection with a frequent, if not constant, bacteremia during the first two weeks of the disease. At the beginning of the infection, the gastrointestinal symptoms are minimal or absent, and the patient may be constipated, although later in the disease when the Peyer's patches of the small intestine become ulcerated, the abdominal symptoms are severe.

The **incubation period** is usually 14 days, with extremes of 3 to 21 days. During this period, which lasts from the time the organisms first gain entrance into the body until symptoms develop, the patient feels entirely well. The mechanism of infection has been described in Chapter 18, page 368.

The initial symptom of a chill or a chilly sensation occurs in only 10 per cent of the cases. The usual onset is insidious, with headache, malaise, anorexia, and congestion of the mucous membranes, especially of the upper respiratory tract (72).

A **bacteremia** probably occurs in the first week of the disease, but it cannot always be demonstrated. In the series of 1,138 cases collected by Coleman and Buxton (16) the blood cultures were positive in 89 per cent of the cases during the first week of the disease, 73 per cent in the second, 60 per cent in the third, 38 per cent in the fourth, and 26 per cent after the fourth week.

Agglutinins begin to appear in the blood serum about the end of the first or the beginning of the second week of the disease, with low titers of 1:20 to 1:40. By the end of the second or third week they have reached levels of diagnostic significance, with anti-O titers of 1:500 and anti-H titers of 1:1000 or higher. The antibody content of the serum begins to decline after six months and in one to two years usually has disappeared completely. The convalescent patient is hypersensitive to the proteins of the typhoid bacillus and reacts positively to the intracutaneous injection of typhoidin. The skin reaction is of the delayed type and is analogous to the tuberculin reaction.

Although the circulating bacilli presumably are filtered out of the blood in the liver and excreted in the bile, it is almost impossible to obtain a **positive stool culture** before the end of the first week of the disease. Hiss' studies (37) show that 10 per cent of stool cultures are positive by the tenth day of the disease, 50 per cent by the twentieth,

and 80 per cent between the twenty-fifth day and the beginning of convalescence. A preliminary incubation of the fecal specimen in the sodium tetrathionate enrichment medium should increase considerably the percentages of positive stool cultures from patients in all stages of the disease.

Rose spots are small petechial hemorrhages which appear in the skin over the anterior surface of the chest and abdomen between the tenth and fifteenth day of the disease. These spots are not unlike those seen in typhus fever, which accounts in part for the confusion between typhus and typhoid fevers that existed for many years. The rose spots appear about the time the serum agglutinins have reached a high titer and bacilli are still present in the circulating blood and may represent intracapillary or intralymphatic agglutinations. Typhoid bacilli have been grown from the excised rose spots by Neufeld (55) and Fraenkel (28).

Urine cultures are positive in about 25 per cent of the cases of typhoid fever. **Cystitis** and **pyelonephritis** are not infrequent, and about 0.1 per cent of patients become constant or intermittent **urinary carriers** of virulent typhoid bacilli.

The most frequent and serious complications of typhoid fever are **hemorrhages** from eroded blood vessels in the intestinal ulcers or **peritonitis** following the rupture of an ulcer. Less frequent complications are **osteomyelitis, metastatic abscesses** in the brain and other organs or tissues, and **meningitis** (9). The gallbladder frequently remains infected for weeks, months, or years, and this may predispose to the development of gallstones in later life. The case fatality rate is approximately 10 per cent.

THE TYPHOID CARRIER. **The carrier is the key link in the chain of events which perpetuates typhoid fever.** The convalescent patient continues to excrete typhoid bacilli in the feces and urine for three weeks to three months after apparent recovery. Patients who excrete the organisms from the third to the twelfth months are called **temporary carriers,** while those who persist for longer than one year are called **chronic carriers.** Some chronic carriers who shed bacilli at irregular intervals are called **intermittent carriers,** and they present a real and very difficult problem to the epidemiologist who is investigating sporadic cases in a local area or institution.

The carrier problem has been studied intensively by Ames and Robins (2). In a series of 3,130 recovered cases of typhoid fever in New York State exclusive of New York City, chronic carriers were found in 2.1 per cent of the males and 3.8 per cent of the females or in an average of 2.9 per cent of the total group. Only 0.3 per cent of the individuals under 20 years of age became carriers, while 10.1 per cent of those in the 50 to 59 age group developed this chronic state. There was a striking difference in sex evident in the older group, only 3.5 per cent of the males but 16.4 per cent of the females becoming chronic carriers. The carrier state may develop in patients who give no history of typhoid fever, and very mild or subclinical cases of typhoid fever probably are of frequent occurrence, particularly in vaccinated individuals (14).

Moore (50) of England (1952) devised a new method of locating a carrier by culturing sewage. Gauze strips were suspended in flowing sewage for 24 hours and then cultured for *S. typhosa*. Each tract of the sewer line was tested separately until a single house or apartment house was localized. Individual toilets and finally individual stools were cultured. Shearer and his associates (63) applied this method in an epidemic of typhoid in a California town and located the carrier.

Transmission. Typhoid fever can be transmitted by the contamination of water, milk, or food by a convalescent or chronic carrier. The bacilli may be carried mechanically from feces to food by flies. The disease also is transmitted by the contamination of bodies of water used for the cultivation of shell fish, and by fruits and vegetables which are consumed in a raw state.

Most of the major epidemics of typhoid fever in the past have been caused by contaminated water or milk. The development of modern sanitary methods, with the proper disposal of sewage, chlorination of water, and pasteurization of milk, has almost eliminated these sources as factors which spread typhoid fever.

The chronic carrier remains the chief problem in the elimination of typhoid fever from the human race. The active case of typhoid fever is, of course, a hazard to the attendants and other members of the family, but the danger is known and can be controlled by rigid isolation technics and active immunization of the attendants.

Chronic carriers among middle-aged women are five times as prevalent as among a similar age group of men, and, unfortunately, many of these women are cooks or food handlers. The most famous carrier was the cook, **Typhoid Mary,** who worked for eight families in the course of 10 years and apparently was responsible for seven epidemics of typhoid fever involving over 200 individuals (68). According to Sufrin's (73) restudy of the career of Typhoid Mary, she infected not 200, but 1,300.

A native waiter, J.S., in South Africa, has been responsible for five localized epidemics of typhoid fever since 1941 (20).

Typing by bacteriophage has facilitated materially the tracing of infections to the proper carriers, at the same time absolving from blame the innocent carriers in the same community. Epidemics continue to occur, although there are relatively few carriers in the populations (14, 54, 82).

Biologic Products. A typhoid vaccine is available commercially for active immunization. In 1896 Pfeiffer and Kolle (57) in Germany and Wright in England began the immunization of individuals by the subcutaneous injection of heat-killed cultures of typhoid bacilli. Wright's work (89) was much more extensive than that of the German investigators, and our modern methods descend directly from his investigations. The present vaccine is prepared from the Army strain #58 or from a strain which is antigenically equivalent. The bacilli are killed with formalin and preserved with 0.5 per cent phenol. *S. paratyphi A* and *S. paratyphi B* are usually included with *S. typhosa* to make a combined vaccine known as T.A.B. Each milliliter of the combined vaccine contains 1,000 million *S. typhosa* organisms and 500 million each of *S. paratyphi A* and *S. paratyphi B*. The formalin-killed vaccine. which preserves a part at least of the Vi antigen, is definitely superior to the old heat-killed vaccine (70) and the British alcoholized vaccines are even better (52).

Treatment. Sulfonamides and penicillin are ineffective, but both **chlortetracycline** and **chloramphenicol** shorten the course of the disease (59). The results obtained with chloramphenicol seem somewhat better than those obtained with chlortetracycline (59, 87, 88). However, strains resistent to chloramphenicol are beginning to appear (83).

Corticoid hormones have little effect on the endotoxin (45) but produce a striking improvement in the symptoms of patients with typhoid fever without influencing the bacteremia (87). The combination of cortisone and chloramphenicol has proven very effective (65).

It has been suggested that patients who relapse a second time following chloramphenicol therapy should be treated with typhoid vaccine (27).

The **cure** of the **chronic carrier of typhoid** is most difficult. All attempts with vaccines and chemotherapeutic agents have resulted in failure. The surgical removal of the infected gallbladder results in a cure if there is no associated infection of the biliary ducts. Urinary carriers can be cured by removing a damaged kidney, provided it can be demonstrated that the other kidney is normal (11). Unfortunately, chlortetracycline and chloramphenicol have failed to cure carriers.

The studies of Smadel (66, 67) and his associates suggest that the bacilli persist in the cells of the human host where they are protected from both specific antibodies and from antibiotics (39). Jersild and his co-workers (40) have cleared up a number of carriers by giving large doses of penicillin over a period of weeks. However, Tynes and Utz (81) found that bacilli inside gallstones could not be sterilized with antibodies and could subsequently escape and infect the bile.

Prevention. The prevention of typhoid fever depends upon control of the food and water supply, detection and isolation of chronic carriers, and active immunization.

The discovery of the Vi antigen and the Vi antibodies have been of great assistance in the detection of chronic carriers among food handlers. In the series of carrier studies by Schubert, Edwards, and Ramsey (60) 66.9 per cent were detected by the ordinary test with Vi agglutination, while 91.6 per cent were detected by the Vi hemagglutination test where sheep cells were sensitized with Vi antigen from the Ballerup strain.

Prophylactic immunization resulted in almost complete elimination of fatalities from typhoid fever among our armed forces in both World Wars I and II, although the exposure in some areas must have been almost constant. This story is reported in detail in the review by Siler (64) and Callender and Luippold (13).

Prophylactic immunization does not give absolute protection against typhoid fever (74), and recovery from an attack of the disease does not protect against a massive infection. There are many examples of laboratory workers who developed mild, severe, or fatal typhoid fever following accidental ingestion of cultures (36, 62). Usually the disease is milder and the mortality about half of that of the unvaccinated in the vaccinated. Repeated attacks of typhoid fever have been reported occasionally (27).

The **methods** employed for **prophylactic vaccination** have received a vast amount of study. The classic procedure of giving three subcutaneous injections of the bacilli at weekly intervals usually is employed. The initial dose is 0.5 ml. of the standard T.A.B. vaccine, followed by two doses of 1 ml. each. Luippold and his associates (48) reinvestigated the immunizing effect of these doses in 1947 and found that three doses of 0.5 ml. gave fewer severe reactions and some lower titers of agglutinins, but definitely higher levels of mouse protective antibodies in the serum.

Many individuals gradually become **hypersensitive** to the protein in the typhoid vaccine and give local and general reactions which become more and more severe as each series of vaccinations is repeated year by year. In 1931 Tuft (77) introduced the intracutaneous method of immunization, employing 0.1 ml. of the standard vaccine. A good titer of agglutinins was found in the serum, and the systemic reactions were eliminated almost completely. Perry (56), working in our laboratory, repeated Tuft's work and measured both the O and H agglutinins over a period of one year and confirmed Tuft's observations (77).

The single 0.1 ml. intracutaneous, or

booster dose, has been accepted as an effective and painless method of **reimmunization.** Later work by Luippold (48) indicates that the intracutaneous injection of either 0.1 or 0.2 ml. doses is less effective in primary immunization than the standard subcutaneous procedure, at least in producing an adequate level of mouse protective antibodies in the serum. The difference in amounts of protective antibodies, however, was not great, and the intracutaneous method was recommended for the elderly patient and for allergic individuals.

It has been our practice to use the standard subcutaneous method for primary immunization and the intracutaneous method for reimmunization. If, however, the initial subcutaneous dose of 0.5 ml. causes a local or systemic reaction, we interpret this to mean that the subject has had previous contact with the typhoid protein and is **allergic;** consequently, we do not hesitate to complete the immunization with two 0.1 ml. doses administered intracutaneously.

With the rapid reduction in the number of cases of typhoid fever, there is a corresponding reduction in the number of carriers. Ames and Robins (2) have calculated that the 2,490 carriers in New York State will be reduced to 193 by the year 1980.

REFERENCES

1. Almon, L. Bact. Rev., 7:43, 1943.
2. Ames, W. R., and Robins, M. Am. J. Pub. Health, 33:221, 1943.
3. Anderson, E. S., and Williams, R. E. O. J. Clin. Path., 9:94, 1956.
4. Arkwright, J. A. J. Path. & Bact., 24:36, 1921; 30:345, 1927.
5. Baker, E. E., and others. J. Immunol., 83:680, 687, 1959.
6. ———— and others. Fed. Proc., 22:206, 1963.
7. ———— and Whiteside, R. E. Proc. Soc. Exper. Biol. & Med., 105:328, 1960.
8. Batson, H. C., and others. J. Exper. Med., 91:231, 1950.
9. Bayne-Jones, S. Am. J. M. Sc., 154:55, 1917.
10. Beard, P. J. Am. J. Pub. Health, 30:1077, 1940.
11. Bondy, P. K., and Barnwell, C. H. J. Urol., 57:642, 1947.
12. Budd, W. Lancet, 2:4, 1856.
13. Callender, G. R., and Luippold, G. F. J.A.M.A., 123:319, 1943.
14. Caraway, C. T., and Bruce, J. M. Pub. Health Rep., 76:427, 1961.
15. Churcher, C. S. Science, 130:566, 1959.
16. Coleman, W., and Buxton, B. H. Am. J. M. Sc., 133:896, 1907.
17. Craigie, J., and Brandon, K. F. J. Path. & Bact., 43:233, 249, 1936.
18. ———— and Yen, C. H. Canad. Pub. Health J., 29:448, 484, 1938.
19. ———— Canad. Pub. Health J., 33:41, 1942.
20. Crocker, C. G. J. Hyg., 45:118, 1947.
21. Eberth, C. Arch. f. path. Anat., 81:58, 1880; 83, 486, 1881.
22. Edsall, G., and others. J. Exper. Med., 112:143, 1960.
23. Edwards, P. R., and Ewing, W. H. Identification of Enterobacteriaceae, 2nd ed., Minneapolis, Burgess Publishing Co., 1962.
24. Falkow, S., and Baron, L. S. J. Bact., 84:581, 1962.
25. Felix, A., and Pitt, R. M. Lancet, 2:186, 1934; J. Path. & Bact., 38:409, 1934.
26. Felsenfeld, O. Proc. Soc. Exper. Biol. & Med., 87:73, 1954.
27. Frank, W. P., and others. J.A.M.A., 147:1137, 1951.
28. Fraenkel, E. Ztschr. f. Hyg., 34:482, 1909.
29. Gaffky, G. Mitt. a. d. Kaiserl. Gsndhtsamte., 2:372, 1884.
30. Gaines, S., and others. Proc. Soc. Exper. Biol. & Med., 104:602, 1960.
31. ———— and others. J. Immunol., 86:543, 1961.
32. ———— and others. J. Exper. Med., 114:327, 1961.
33. Greisman, S. E., and others. J. Clin. Invest., 42:1064, 1963.
34. Gruber, M., and Durham, H. E. München. med. Wchnschr., 43:206, 1896.
35. Grünbaum, A. S. Lancet, 2:806, 1896.
36. Haedicke, T. A. J. Infect. Dis., 80:113, 1947.
37. Hiss, P. H. M. News, 78:728, 1901.
38. Jarvis, F. G., and others. J. Bact., 80:673, 677, 1960.
39. Jenkins, C., and Benacerraf, B. J. Exper. Med., 112:403, 419, 1960.
40. Jersild, T., and others. Antibiotic Med. & Clin. Ther., 6:292, 1959.
41. Kauffmann, F. Ztschr. f. Hyg. u. Infektionskr., 116:617, 1935.
42. ———— Die Bakteriologik der Salmonella Gruppe, Einar Munksgaard, Copenhagen, 1941.
43. ———— and Moeller, E. J. Hyg., 40:548, 1940.
44. Landy, M., and Lamb, E. Proc. Soc. Exper. Biol. & Med., 82:593, 1953.
45. ———— and others. J. Immunol., 73:23, 1954.
46. ———— and Johnson, A. G. Proc. Soc. Exper. Biol. & Med., 90:57, 1955.
47. ———— and Pillemer, L. J. Exper. Med., 103:823, 1956.
48. Luippold, G. F. Am. J. Pub. Health, 35:153, 1945.
49. ———— and others. Am. J. Hyg., 45:355, 1947.
50. Moore, B., and others. J. Hyg., 50:137, 1952.
51. Metchnikoff, E., and Besredka, A. Ann. Inst. Pasteur, 25:193, 1911.
52. Miller, W. S., and others. Am. J. Trop. Med., 31:535, 1951.
53. Morgan, W. T. J., and Partridge, S. M. Brit. J. Exper. Path., 23:151, 1942.
54. Neill, W. A., and others. New Eng. J. Med., 259:667, 1958.

55. Neufeld, F.   Ztschr. f. Hyg. u. Infektionskr., 30:498, 1899.
56. Perry, R. M.   Am. J. Hyg., 26:388, 1937.
57. Pfeiffer, R., and Kolle, W.   Ztschr. f. Hyg. u. Infektionskr., 21:203, 1896.
58. Prudden, T. M.   M. Rec., 31:341, 369, 1887.
59. Scarzella, M., and others.   South. M. J., 42:983, 1949.
60. Schubert, J. H., and others.   J. Bact., 77:648, 1959.
61. Scovel, F. G.   J.A.M.A., 148:1138, 1952.
62. Schäfer, V. W.   Arch. f. Hyg. u. Bakt., 132:15, 1950.
63. Shearer, L. A., and others.   J.A.M.A., 169:1051, 1959.
64. Siler, J. F.   Immunization to Typhoid Fever, Baltimore, Johns Hopkins Press, 1941.
65. Smadel, J. E., and others.   Ann. Int. Med., 34:1, 1951.
66. ——— J. Immunol., 84:1, 1960.
67. ——— J. Immunol., 87:153, 162, 1961.
68. Soper, G. A.   Mil. Surgeon, 45:1, 1919.
69. Special Article, J.A.M.A., 131:817, 1946.
70. Spitznagel, J. K., and Trainer, R. Y.   J. Immunol., 62:229, 1949.
71. Staub, A. M., and others.   Ann. Inst. Pasteur, 96:303, 1959.
72. Stuart, B. M., and Pullen, R. L.   Arch. Int. Med., 78:629, 1946.
73. Sufrin, M.   Pageant, 154, Oct., 1961.
74. Syverton, J. T., and others.   J.A.M.A., 131:507, 1946.
75. Thomason, B. M., and others.   J. Bact., 77:478, 1959.
76. Truszczynski, M., and Baker, E. E.   J. Immunol., 89:154, 1962.
77. Tuft, L.   J. Lab. & Clin. Med., 16:552, 1931.
78. Tully, J. G., and Currie, T. A.   J. Bact., 84:747, 1962.
79. ——— and others.   J. Inf. Dis., 113:131, 1963.
80. ——— and Gaines, S.   J. Bact., 81:924, 1961.
81. Tynes, B. S., and Utz, J. P.   Ann. Int. Med., 57:871, 1962.
82. Wagenhals, C. O., and Tannenberg, J.   J.A.M.A., 173:355, 1960.
83. Weiner, L. M., and Swanson, R. E.   J. Bact., 79:863, 1960.
84. Whitesides, R. E., and Baker, E. E.   J. Immunol., 84:221, 1960.
85. ——— and Baker, E. E.   J. Immunol., 86:538, 1961.
86. Widal, F.   Bull. Soc. méd. Hôp. de Paris, 13, 1896.
87. Woodward, T. E., and others.   Ann. Int. Med., 60:144, 1964.
88. ——— and others.   J. Clin. Investigation, 29:87, 1950.
89. Wright, A. E.   Brit. M. J., 2:1153, 1903.

34

Salmonella and Salmonellosis

The *Salmonella* produce disease in reptiles, birds, mammals, and man. The clinical symptoms vary from a mild enteritis to a rapidly fatal septicemia. *S. typhosa* is a parasite of man and has been discussed in the previous chapter. Certain strains of *S. paratyphi A, S. paratyphi B,* and *S. paratyphi C* are primary pathogens for man, while other strains are found predominantly in animals. *S. dublin* is found primarily in horses, *S. abortusovis* in sheep, *S. choleraesuis* in hogs, and *S. pullorum* and *S. gallinarum* in fowls. *S. typhimurium,* originally isolated from mice and called "mouse typhoid," is distributed widely throughout the animal kingdom. It can be carried by either man or animal and is statistically the most frequent cause of *Salmonella* food poisoning in man. Man may acquire infection directly from chicks (1) or from commercial egg powder (23, 41) and then transmit the infection to other individuals.

Seligmann and his associates (21, 45) found many healthy human carriers of *Salmonella* among food handlers, nurses and attendants in hospitals, and there is no doubt that man is exposed intermittently to *Salmonella* organisms from both human and animal sources.

In 1885 Salmon and Smith (39) isolated the first member of this group of organisms, *S. choleraesuis,* from cases of hog cholera. It is known now that hog cholera is caused by a virus, and that the bacillus was present as a secondary invader. In 1888 persons in Germany developed food poisoning from eating contaminated meat, and Gärtner (22) cultured *S. enteritidis* from the spleen of a patient who died during this epidemic. In 1892 Löffler (30) isolated *S. typhimurium* from a typhoid-like disease in mice. A further advance in the knowledge of these organisms was the differentiation of *S. paratyphi A* and *S. paratyphi B* by Schottmüller (43) in 1900. Kauffmann (25, 27) and Edwards and Ewing (12, 18) have collaborated with the other members of the international subcommittee in producing the 1961 edition of **Kauffmann-White schema** for the antigenic classification of the *Salmonella* (13).

More than 600 specific antigenic types of *Salmonella* have been given specific names, and new ones are being added each month. One may question the logic of giving specific names to antigenic types of *Salmonella* when the antigenic types of pneumococci and streptococci are designated by numbers; nevertheless, some specific identification is essential to enable the epidemiologist to trace an epidemic to its source.

Morphology and Staining. The *Salmonella* as a group are identical in morphology and staining reactions with *S. typhosa*, except for *S. pullorum* and *S. gallinarum*, which are nonmotile. An occasional mutant strain is encountered which has lost its motility without losing its pathogenicity. The flagella antigens are not essential for virulence but are important in antigenic classification. Organisms resembling *Salmonella,* but apparently nonmotile, should be inoculated into one arm of a U-tube containing a semisolid agar medium. If the organism is motile, growth will appear in the uninoculated arm of the tube.

Cultural Characteristics. The growth requirement and colony formation of the *Salmonella* as a group correspond to that of *S. typhosa* which has been described in the previous chapter (31).

Biochemical Reactions. In general, the biochemical reactions of the *Salmonella* are identical, but in a few instances they are different and are useful as a supplement to antigenic analysis (Table 1). *S. typhosa* and *S. gallinarum*

Table 1. Biochemical Reactions of Salmonella
(Edwards and Ewing, 1955)

	ARABINOSE	TREHALOSE	DULCITOL	XYLOSE	H$_2$S	STERN'S GLYCEROL-FUCHSIN BROTH	SIMMONS' CITRATE	JORDAN'S TARTRATE	GAS PRODUCTION
S. paratyphi A	+	+	+ 1-3	−	−	−	−	−	+
S. paratyphi B	+	+	+	+	+	v	−	v	+
S. paratyphi C	(+)	+ 1-3	+	+	+	−	+	+	+
S. choleraesuis	−	−	×	+	−	−	+	+	+
S. choleraesuis var. kunzendorf	−	−	×	+	+	−	+	+	+
S. decatur	+	+	+	+	+	++	+	+	+
S. typhisuis	+	+ 1-2	+ 2-6	+	−	−	−	−	+
S. typhi	v	+	×	v	(+)	−	−	+	−
S. sendai	+	+	×	+ 4-5	−	−	−	−	+
S. miami	−	+	−	+	+	++	+	+	+
S. pullorum	+	+	−	+	+	−	−	−	(+)
S. gallinarum	+	+	+ 1-3	+	+	−	−	+ 1-3	−

++ = positive, lilac in one day.
 + = prompt positive. Figures beside + indicate day of incubation on which reaction may become positive.
(+) = usually positive, negative strains occur.
 v = variable.
 × = late or irregularly positive.

do not produce gas in carbohydrates. *S. paratyphi A* does not ferment xylose and certain strains of *S. typhosa, S. anatum,* and *S. newington* either fail to attack this carbohydrate or ferment it very slowly. *S. paratyphi A* and the "human" type of *S. paratyphi B* do not ferment d-tartrate. *S. typhisuis* can be recognized by its sparse growth on artificial media.

S. sendai and *S. miami* have the same antigenic formula (1, 9, 12:a-1, 5) but differ in biochemical reaction as shown in Table 1. *S. miami* grows much more vigorously on artificial media, grows in Bitter's glucose broth, Stern's glycerol-fuchsin broth, utilizes citrate, and produces H$_2$S, while *S. sendai* does not. *S. miami* is found in this country and usually produces an acute gastroenteritis in man, while *S. sendai* is found in the Orient and causes a typical enteric fever resembling typhoid.

Although *S. gallinarum* and *S. pullorum* cannot be distinguished by serologic tests, Trabulsi and Edwards (50) are convinced that they are distinct biochemical types. In addition to the differences shown in Table 1, all of the *S. pullorum* cultures produce rapid de-carboxylation of ornithine, whereas none of the *S. gallinarum* cultures are positive in seven days. All of the *S. gallinarum* produce acidity and

a marked precipitate in Hinshaw's medium, but the *S. pullorum* cultures do not.

Resistance. *Salmonella* in milk and milk products are destroyed by pasteurization, and contaminated water can be made safe by boiling or chlorination. The organisms are moderately susceptible to the usual antiseptics but somewhat more resistant than colon bacilli to the action of certain dyes and other substances. The differential inhibiting properties of these substances are utilized by their incorporation into the various isolation media.

Sulfonamides and penicillin are ineffective in therapeutically attainable levels, but the newer antibiotics, **chloramphenicol** (9), **chlortetracycline** (54), and **oxytetracycline** (42) seem more promising.

Variability. The *Salmonella* exhibit the usual **S** to **R** type of dissociation. With the change to the R type the colony becomes rough, and fails to agglutinate in anti-O serum, and loses its pathogenicity, although the organisms usually remain motile. With the development of the R form colony, a polysaccharide characteristic of most, if not all, *Salmonella* is exposed. This R polysaccharide disappears on further dissociation, which is characterized by the appearance of P forms (56). The R forms may agglutinate spontaneously in physiologic saline and are readily agglutinated by 1:500 trypaflavine or acriflavine (36). Dwarf colonies have been reported which are capable of producing disease. Some, at least, require preformed cystine and cannot convert inorganic sulfur to cystine (46).

Most strains of *Salmonella* carry at least one strain of prophage. Specific antigen can be transferred from one strain of *Salmonella* to another (28), thus originating a new serologic type. Crosses also occur between *Salmonella* and *E. coli* (2, 57). Zinder (58) has described a bacteriophage which grows on recipient (F⁻) and not on donor (Hfr, F⁺ or F′) *Salmonella.*

Edwards and Ewing (16) have described the use of bacteriophage for identifying strains of *S. paratyphi-B* and *S. typhimurium.*

Antigenic Structure. Members of the *Salmonella* group are classified into species by analysis of their antigenic structures. Since most *Salmonella* are motile, both the O and the flagellar H antigens are available for differentiation. When rabbits are injected intravenously with formalin-killed flagellated organisms, specific antibodies are formed to each of the various O and H antigens.

The flagellar antigens either are more effective in stimulating antibodies or are detected more easily, since the serums produced by the injection of flagellated organisms often have H titers of 1:20,000 to 1:50,000 and O titers of only 1:1,000 to 1:2,000.

The *Salmonella* are divided into large groups on the basis of their major somatic antigens, and these groups are subdivided into species according to the antigenic patterns of their flagella. Pure O and H serums of various types, therefore, are necessary for the identification of the numerous *Salmonella* species.

In the preparation of pure O antigens, the *Salmonella* which contain the proper antigens are cultivated on an agar medium to which 0.1 per cent phenol has been added, since phenol completely but temporarily suppresses the development of the flagellar antigens. The O antigen also may be prepared by treating the growth of an 18- to 24-hour agar slant culture with 1 to 2 ml. of absolute alcohol, heating at 60° C. for one hour, centrifuging and resuspending the sediment in 0.5 to 1 ml. of physiologic saline. Most *Salmonella* contain two or more specific somatic antigens, which are designated by the Roman numerals I to XLV.

Antigenic analysis of flagellar antigens is a more complex procedure. Some *Salmonella* have only one set of flagellar antigens; hence, these species are called **monophasic.** Most *Salmonella*, however, have two sets of flagellar antigens and therefore are said to be **diphasic.** In the diphasic organisms, one set, or **phase 1,** of the flagellar antigens is more or less specific for the particular *Salmonella;* the other set, or **phase 2,** is much less specific and frequently is duplicated in other species of *Salmonella* and even in other organisms of the enteric group.

The two sets of flagellar antigens do not exist as mixtures in the same organism, so that if a diphasic culture is plated and spot agglutinations are performed with organisms from isolated colonies, about half of the colonies will show agglutination in specific phase 1 antiserum and the other half in specific phase 2 antiserum. If specific phase colonies of either type are subcultured, a reversion to a mixture of phase 1 and phase 2 occurs in one or two generations. More stable phase 1 or phase 2 cultures to be used in the production of specific antiserums can be obtained by inoculating a diphasic culture into one arm of a U-tube containing semisolid agar and antiserum of either specific phase and subculturing the organism in the other phase from the uninoculated arm of the tube.

The flagellar antigen of phase 1 was labeled with small letters a, b, c, until their number exceeded the capacity of the alphabet, and they had to be designated as z subnumerals, such as z_2, z_{20}. The phase 2 antigens first were designated by the numerals 1, 2, 3, but it soon was discovered that many phase 2 organisms also had the antigens e, n, especially in association with the x, or one of the z subnumeral series. A few *Salmonella* have been found in which the phase 2 organisms contain neither the 1, 2, 3 nor the e, n . . . series, but antigens characteristic of phase 1 organisms. Edwards and his associates have described four reversible phases in cultures of *S. mikawashima* (16) and also the appearance of a new simplex type antigen by the loss of some flagellar antigen (10, 16).

The immune chemistry of the O-antigen of the entire group of *Enterobacteriaceae* has been reviewed by Kauffmann (26).

The Vi antigen found in *S. paratyphi C* is superficial to the O antigen and must be destroyed by suspending the organism in physiologic saline and placing the tubes in a boiling water bath for 10 to 20 minutes. The culture then can be studied with anti-O serums to detect its O antigens.

It is possible to identify 98 to 99 per cent of the *Salmonella* isolated in this country by the simplified method described by Edwards and Ewing (12). This requires the use of six O serums for the groups A to E, respectively; a

Vi antiserum, and six H serums. The polyvalent O antiserums are used in the slide agglutination test to establish the presence of *Salmonella* O antigens. The serologic test must be supplemented by biochemical tests, since O antigens characteristic of certain *Salmonella* are duplicated in some *Shigella* and the slow lactose-fermenting paracolon. Cultures which have been identified as *Salmonella* by biochemical tests but cannot be typed by the simplified method should be sent to a Salmonella typing center. The active centers are the State Serum Institute, Copenhagen, Denmark; The Institute of Hygiene, Montevideo, Uruguay; and the Communicable Disease Center, Chamblee, Georgia.

Serologic Diagnosis. Specific immune bodies are formed by the patient as a result of *Salmonella* infections, and the diagnosis of typhoid fever and the typhoid-like fevers frequently is made by the agglutination of known organisms with the patient's serum. In cases of acute enteritis and food poisoning, however, the patient usually is well before antibodies appear in the serum (53).

Bacterial Metabolites. The organisms of the *Salmonella* group contain potent endotoxins (32), but **exotoxins** are **not produced.** Filtrates of old cultures, when injected intravenously into rabbits, produce profound prostration and a hyperglycemia, followed by hypoglycemia and death within 24 to 36 hours. The intestinal mucosa of the animals is found to be swollen, hemorrhagic, and occasionally necrotic, suggesting that the toxin is excreted through the mucosa. Repeated injections of sublethal doses of endotoxins result in the development of a state of resistance to these "pyrogens" which is not correlated with specific antibodies. Neva and Morgan (33) have reported a similar phenomenon in patients recovering from *Salmonella* and *Shigella* infections.

Spontaneous Disease in Animals. Acute and chronic enteritis, as well as typhoidal and septicemic diseases, are produced in many animals by the various species of *Salmonella. S. typhimurium* and *S. enteritidis* give rise to epidemics in colonies of wild and domestic mice and rats, and many of the surviving animals become chronic carriers. Similar but usually less explosive epidemics occur in guinea pigs.

Infectious abortion of mares is caused by *S. abortivoequina,* and *S. abortusovis* has been isolated from sheep. Calves are particularly susceptible to infection with *S. dublin. S. typhisuis* seems to be specific for swine, and, although *S. choleraesuis* is not the cause of hog cholera, it can produce a serious disease in swine without the assistance of the virus.

Birds frequently are infected with the *Salmonella. S. gallinarum* causes fowl typhoid, and *S. pullorum* produces white diarrhea in chicks. *S. typhimurium* causes epidemic disease in canaries, *S. anatis* and *S. newington* in ducklings, *S. oranienburg* in baby quail and chickens, and *S. senftenberg* in turkey poults.

Experimental Disease in Animals. Apparently all organisms of the *Salmonella* group possess endotoxins which are capable of producing the typical endotoxic type of death in rabbits when large numbers of living or dead organisms are injected intravenously. Some of the *Salmonella* are more toxic than others, but only a few of the many species have been studied in detail. *S. choleraesuis* produces septicemia with metastatic abscesses when small numbers of living organisms are injected intravenously into the rabbit.

S. typhimurium has been used to produce experimental epidemics in colonies of mice. The introduction of a single healthy carrier soon initiates a typical epidemic disease with a high morbidity and mortality rate. The epidemic reaches a peak and then slowly declines, leaving a residue of healthy immune animals, animals with chronic enteritis, and some apparently healthy carriers (49, 51, 56).

Clinical Types of Infection in Man. The food poisoning syndrome is the most common clinical manifestation of *Salmonella* infection (20, 24). The onset of symptoms may be sudden and violent, as in cholera. In the older literature this type of acute infection was called "cholera nostras." With the exception of *S. typhosa,* all of the *Salmonella* can cause food poisoning, although infections with *S. typhimurium, S. paratyphi B, S. choleraesuis,* and *S. enteritidis* are most common. Sufficient endotoxin to cause symptoms is produced within six to 12 hours, by the rapid growth of the organism in the intestinal tract. Recovery usually is complete within two to four days (7, 11).

Salmonella food poisoning must be differentiated from that caused by the enterotoxins of staphylococci and the exotoxins of *C. botulinum.* The latter toxins are performed in the ingested food.

A second clinical type of salmonellosis is an enteritis which develops somewhat more slowly but persists for a longer period.

Patients with this type of infection have fever, superficial ulcerations of the intestinal tract with mucus and pus in the stools, and symptoms simulating those of dysentery. This type of infection is prevalent in young children and old, debilitated adults; a majority of the deaths from salmonellosis occurs in these two groups of patients.

The most severe infections caused by the *Salmonella* are those of the **typhoidal** and **septicemic** types. The patient may have a febrile disease without gastrointestinal symptoms, which lasts for weeks and which cannot be differentiated clinically from typhoid fever. The septicemic type is more dangerous, producing daily chills and a spiked temperature curve. The mortality rate may be as high as 25 per cent with this type of infection. The typhoidal type is produced most often by *S. paratyphi A*, *S. paratyphi B*, *S. paratyphi C*, *S. sendai*, and *S. typhimurium*.

S. choleraesuis is recovered most often from the septicemic type of *Salmonella* infection. In the septicemic stage focal lesions may develop in various parts of the body, producing **osteomyelitis, endocarditis, pneumonia** and **pulmonary abscess,** and **meningitis.**

It should be emphasized that all three clinical types of salmonellosis can be caused by any one of the Salmonella and in rare instances the patient progresses from the food poisoning phase on to the enteritic and eventually to the typhoidal or septicemic types of the disease.

All three types, but especially the enteritis, were present in the last major epidemic which swept through New York, New Jersey, Pennsylvania, and 21 other states in 1963. The etiologic agent was *S. derby* which was traced to eggs (40).

Transmission. It is very difficult to eradicate salmonellosis because the *Salmonella* organisms are distributed so widely in nature. Drinking water or the water of lakes, rivers and swimming pools may be contaminated by animals or man. Meats, poultry, and eggs may be infected before they reach the kitchen. In recent years, spray-dried eggs (23, 41) have become an important source of salmonellosis, particularly because of their frequent use in the preparation of salad dressings and desserts without sufficient heating to destroy the organisms.

Rats and mice, which often carry *Salmonella* in their feces and urine, are dangerous sources of infection, contaminating food both before and after it has been prepared for the table. *Salmonella* can be carried by the rat flea (17) and possibly by the cockroach (34, 52).

Perhaps the most common source of salmonellosis is the human carrier who contaminates the food during its preparation or after it is cooked. Oily salad dressings, cake fillings, and pastries are well adapted for the transmission of the organisms from the carrier to the victim.

Biologic Products. There are no effective antibacterial serums for therapeutic use. Typhoid vaccine, however, usually contains killed *S. paratyphi A* and *S. paratyphi B* in addition to *S. typhosa*.

Treatment. The treatment is physiologic. If nature has not eliminated completely the infected food, a brisk saline purge is indicated. When the patient is an infant or an elderly individual, it is most important that the fluid and electrolyte balances be restored.

Sulfonamide and penicillin therapy is ineffective. Streptomycin apparently reduces the number of organisms in the intestinal tract temporarily but has no effect on the septicemic and typhoidal forms of the disease. Preliminary reports suggest that **chloramphenicol** (9, 54) and **oxytetracycline** (42) may be curative even in the septicemic types of infection.

Prior to 1948 all cultures of *Salmonella* were susceptible to the tetracyclines. Since then, however, the widespread use of tetracyclines as therapeutic agents and as additives to livestock feed has resulted in a rapid increase in resistant isolates (38). Resistance to chloramphenicol occurs with less frequency. Man is being infected with antibiotic resistant strains of *Salmonella* either from animals or from man (35). Patients infected with chloramphenicol resistant strains have been treated with some success with the new antibiotic penicillin N. (Cephalosporin N), although this drug has a moderate degree of toxicity (35).

Prevention. Contaminated milk and drinking water originally constituted the chief causes of epidemic intestinal infections, but these sources have been eliminated almost completely by modern sanitary engineering.

All meats, poultry, and eggs, including dried eggs, should be considered as potential sources of infection. Before being served as food, they should be heated to temperatures high enough to kill the *Salmonella*.

The detection and elimination of carriers among food handlers is one of the major activities of all well organized public health units.

Vaccination with all 340 types of *Salmonella* for the production of an active immunity is not practical. Active immunization with a small number of species, however, will not be impossible, and perhaps the newer antigenic analysis will lead to the provision of polyvalent vaccines which will offer protection against most, but not all, *Salmonella* infections.

OTHER ENTERIC ORGANISMS CAUSING ENTERITIS

Arizona Group. The **Arizona group** of *Enterobacteriaceae* resembles the *Salmonella* in general biochemical reactivity, although many of them ferment lactose (14). They were found first in snakes and lizards (5), where they may produce fatal disease. However, similar cultures have been found in the feces of 44.8 per cent of 310 apparently normal snakes (29). These bacteria continue to appear in fowls, mammals, and man, in all of which they may produce either severe or fatal infection (12).

Arizona types which ferment lactose rapidly may be found in food poisoning (13). Some antigenic types spread readily to mammals and man, while others do not. Edwards (15) has reported the appearance of type 10:1,25 in a large breeding flock in North Carolina. Eggs from this source were shipped to hatcheries in Indiana and Georgia, and the chicks were distributed throughout the Southeastern states. Soon the same type appeared in chicks and spread to dogs, cats and man.

As of 1961, 330 groups and 241 serotypes had been identified (12). These organisms liquefy gelatin slowly and do not ferment dulcitol. They are the only enteric bacteria which regularly produce lysine decarboxylase rapidly and form large amounts of hydrogen sulfide. Edwards and Fife (13) have suggested that the fecal specimens be incubated on bismuth sulfide agar plates and black colonies be transferred to lysine-iron agar.

Citrobacter (*Escherichia freundii*) **Group.** These organisms more closely resemble the *Salmonella* and the Arizona group than *E. coli*. Typical cultures ferment lactose but not adonital or insitol. Dulcitol is usually fermented, and the KCN reaction is positive. Included in the group are the cultures which ferment lactose slowly or not at all; these were formerly classified *Paracolobacterium intermedium*, as proposed by Bordman, Stuart and Wheeler (4, 19), or as the *Bethesda-Ballerup* group (47, 48). In a study of 506 cultures, West and Edwards (55) established 320 groups and 167 serologic types which contained 75 distinct combinations of H-antigens.

Some members of this group are believed capable of producing enteric infections (3), but the role of the majority has not yet been determined.

REFERENCES

1. Anderson, A. S., and others. J.A.M.A., 158: 1153, 1955.
2. Barksdale, C. Bact. Review, 23:202, 1959.
3. Barnes, L. A., and Cherry, W. B. Am. J. Pub. Health, 36:481, 1946.
4. Brown, G. W. Med. J. Australia, 2:658, 1952.
5. Caldwell, M. E., and Ryerson, D. L. J. Infact. Dis., 65:242, 1939.
6. Carlquist, P. R. J. Bact., 71:339, 1956.
7. Dack, G. M. J.A.M.A., 172:929, 1960.
8. Deacon, W. E. Proc. Soc. Exper. Biol. & Med., 81:165, 1952.
9. Doran, J. H. Ann. Int. Med., 37:714, 1952.
10. Douglas, G. W., and Edwards, P. R. J. Gen. Microbiol., 29:367, 1962.
11. Edwards, P. R. Ann. N.Y. Acad. Science, 70:598, 1958.
12. ———— and Ewing, W. H. Identification of Enterobacteriaceae, Minneapolis, Burgess Publishing Co., 1961.
13. ———— and Fife, M. A. Appl. Microbiol., 9:478, 1961.
14. ———— and others. Bact. Rev., 23:155, 1959.
15. ———— and others. Canad. J. Microbiol., 2: 281, 1956.
16. ———— and others. J. Bact., 84:95, 99, 1962.
17. Eskey, C. R., and others. Pub. Health Rep., 64:933, 1949.
18. Ewing, W. H., and others. J. Infect. Dis., 94:134, 1954.
19. Eveland, W. C., and Faber, J. E., Jr. J. Infect. Dis., 93:226, 1953.
20. Feig, M. Am. J. Pub. Health, 40:1372, 1950.
21. Felsen, J., and others. J.A.M.A., 143:1135, 1950.

22. Gärtner. Korresp. Bl. ärztl. ver Thüringen, 17:233, 573, 1888.
23. Gibbons, N. E., and Moore, R. L. Canad. J. Research, 22:48, 1944.
24. Griswold, D. M. Am. J. Pub. Health, 40: 1398, 1950.
25. Kauffmann, F. The Diagnosis of Salmonella Types, Springfield, Ill., Charles C Thomas, 1950.
26. ——— and others. Zent. für Bak. Parasit. Infek. & Hyg., l. orig., 182:57, 1961.
27. ———Enterobacteriaceae, 2nd ed., Copenhagen, Elinar Munksgaard, 1954.
28. Lederberg, J., and Edwards, P. R. J. Immunol., 71:232, 1953.
29. Le Minor, L., and others. Ann. Inst. Past., 95:326, 1958.
30. Löffler, F. Zentralbl. f. Bakt., 11:129, 1892.
31. Millet, M., and others. Ann. Inst. Pasteur, 72:44, 1946.
32. Morgan, H. R., and Beckwith, T. D. J. Bact., 37:389, 1939.
33. Neva, F. A., and Morgan, H. R. J. Lab. & Clin. Med., 35:911, 1950.
34. Olson, T., and Rueger, M. E. Pub. Health Rep., 65:531, 1950.
35. Parker, R. H., and others. Arch. Int. Med., 111:799, 1963.
36. Pampana, E. J. J. Hyg., 33:402, 1933.
37. Perch, B. Acta path. et microbiol. Scandinav., 27:565, 1950.
38. Ramsey, C. R., and Edwards, P. R. Applied Microbiol., 9:389, 1961.
39. Salmon, D. E., and Smith, T. U.S. Bur. an Ind., 2nd Ann. Rep., p. 184, 1885.
40. Sanders, E., and others. J.A.M.A., 186:984, 1963.
41. Schneider, M. D. Bull. U.S. Army M. Dept., 4:477, 1945.
42. Scott, R. B., and Wooding, C. H. Tr. Pediatrics, 7:349, 1951.
43. Schottmüller, H. Ztschr. f. Hyg. u. Infektionskr., 36:368, 1901.
44. Schuetze, H. J. Hyg., 20:330, 1921.
45. Seligmann, E., and others. J. Immunol., 54: 69, 1946.
46. Stokes, J. L., and Bayne, H. G. J. Bact., 76: 136, 1958.
47. Stuart, C. A., and others. J. Bact., 45:101, 1943.
48. ——— and others. J. Bact., 52:431, 1946.
49. Topley, W. W. C., and others. J. Path. & Bact., 24:523, 1931.
50. Trabulsi, L. R., and Edwards, P. R. Cornell Veterinarian, 52:563, 1962.
51. Webster, L. T. J. Exper. Med., 52:901, 909, 931, 1930.
52. Wedberg, S. E., and others. J. Bact., 58:573, 1949.
53. Weil, A. J., and Saphra, I. J. Immunol., 74: 485, 1955.
54. Weiner, H. A., and Liebler, J. B. J.A.M.A., 145:802, 1951.
55. West, M. G., and Edwards, P. R. U.S. Pub. Health Ser. Monograph, 22:1954.
56. White, P. B. J. Path. & Bact., 35:77, 1932.
57. Zinder, N. C. Science, 131:924, 1960.
58. ——— Science, 133:2069, 1961.

35

Shigella and Shigellosis

Family: *Enterobacteriaceae* Rahn. Genus: *Shigella* Castellani and Chalmers. Type
species: *Shigella dysenteriae* (Shiga) Castellani and Chalmers

The genus *Shigella* contains fewer species than the genus *Salmonella* and is antigenically less complex.

Clinical dysentery may be caused by *Shigella, Salmonella, Entamoeba histolytica, Proteus morganii,* and virus. Organisms of the *Shigella* group are the most frequent cause of dysentery and, since the decline in typhoid fever, have assumed a position of greater relative importance as a cause of enteric infection in the United States. In 1955, 38,000 cases of shigellosis were reported in this country, as compared with 6,000 cases of typhoid and 3,500 of amebic dysentery. Since many cases are unrecognized or unreported, the figures just cited must represent only a small fraction of the number actually occurring (69). It is probable that true dysentery-producing bacilli were isolated in 1888 by Chantemesse and Widal (8) in France and in 1891 by Grigoriew (40) in Russia, but these investigators failed to establish their etiologic relationship (64).

The first member of the *Shigella* group of organisms was isolated in Japan by Shiga (56) in 1898. Shiga had failed to transmit the infection to animals or to isolate the etiologic agent. Shiga, following a suggestion of Kitasato, approached the problem by searching, in the stools of patients with dysentery, for a microorganism which would be agglutinated by the serums of patients convalescing from the disease. His labors were rewarded when he isolated the same type of organism from 34 cases and showed that all of the strains were agglutinated uniformly by convalescent serum. Control studies showed that

the bacillus was absent from the dejecta of normal individuals and of patients suffering from other diseases, and that serums from these people would not agglutinate his dysentery bacillus.

Kruse (45) isolated Shiga's bacillus, *Shigella dysenteriae,* from cases of dysentery in Germany, and Flexner (27) cultured a mannitol-fermenting dysentery bacillus from patients in the Philippines suffering from epidemic dysentery (26).

Shigella flexneri has been cultured from monkeys in captivity (47), and both *Sh. dysenteriae* and *Sh. flexneri* have been isolated from dogs (12, 28, 29). **With these rare exceptions, the organisms of the *Shigella* group are found exclusively in man and are transmitted by active cases and by both convalescent and healthy carriers.**

Morphology and Staining. Bacilli of the genus *Shigella* are short rods, 0.5 to 0.7 μ in width and 2 to 3 μ in length. They are **nonencapsulated, nonsporogenous,** and **nonmotile.** The bacilli stain with the usual aniline dyes and are **gram-negative.**

Cultural Characteristics. All members of the *Shigella* **group are aerobic** but **facultatively anaerobic.** They grow readily on the usual laboratory media at pH 6.4 to 7.8 over a temperature range of 10° C. to 40° C. with an optimum at 37° C. *Sh. dysenteriae* and *Sh. flexneri* will not grow at a temperature of 45° C., while *Sh. sonnei* grows readily at this temperature (59).

These organisms are more delicate than the *Salmonella* and are inhibited partially or completely by bismuth sulfite medium and brilliant green medium. Eosin methylene blue is least inhibitory but allows growth of *E. coli*. Sodium desoxycholate citrate, S.S. agar, and acid-fuchsin methylene blue agar (42) are intermediate in their inhibiting effect.

Sh. flexneri and *Sh. sonnei* will grow in a simple chemically defined medium containing L-aspartic acid, glucose, mineral salts, thiamin hydrochloride, and niacin. This medium does not support the growth of *Sh. dysenteriae* or *Sh. boydii* (15).

The proper collection and selection of the specimens to be planted is more important than the type of medium employed. Bits of pus or blood-tinged mucus from a freshly passed stool or fresh material collected with a proctoscope, sigmoidoscope, or rectal swab should be employed.

After 24 hours incubation, *Shigella* colonies reach a diameter of about 2 mm. The colonies are circular, convex, and colorless but moderately translucent, with smooth surfaces and entire edges. They appear whitish and more opaque when viewed against a dark background but never as opaque as typical colonies of *E. coli*. Small, tangled, hair-like projections sometimes are seen at one or more points on the periphery of the colony. Occasionally on primary isolation, and frequently on subcultures, a second type of colony appears, which is larger, more translucent, and has a ground-glass surface and an undulate or crenated edge. Such a change in colony form may be accompanied by an alteration in antigenic structure. Walters and his associates (67) have reported that the microscopic examination of colonies, after oblique transmitted illumination, reveals color and textural differences which help to differentiate S and R *Shigella* and also differentiate *Shigella* colonies from those of *E. coli* and other enteric organisms.

Colorless colonies which appear on S.S. agar or E.M.B. plates may be *Shigella*. If a number of colonies are present on the original plates, a tentative diagnosis of shigellosis can be made by direct slide agglutination with a polyvalent *Shigella* antiserum (18, 25). In all instances, however, the diagnosis should be confirmed by additional biochemical tests and by specific-type agglutination (19).

The following biochemical reactions characterize the *Shigella* group: **All ferment glucose; some ferment mannitol; and, with few exceptions, none produce gas from carbohydrates. They do not ferment salicin or adonitol; do not grow in Simmons' citrate agar; and do not form acetylmethylcarbinol, hydrolyze urea, or liquefy gelatin.** Lactose is fermented by *Shigella sonnei* but only after prolonged in-

cubation. They may be separated into groups by their biochemical reactions as shown in Tables 1, 2, and 3.

Resistance. *Shigella* may remain viable in tap water for as long as six months, in sea water for two to five months, and in ice for two months (24). It is well known that fresh milk supports the growth of the organism. Both soiled and inapparently soiled clothing may harbor living organisms for many days. The dysentery organisms resist 0.5 per cent phenol for five hours but are killed by 1 per cent phenol in 16 to 30 minutes. They are destroyed readily by pasteurization temperatures; therefore, pasteurization of milk and milk products and the boiling or chlorination of water are the most effective methods of preventing the spread of the organisms.

Chloramphenicol, oxytetracycline, and chlortetracycline are all equally effective in treatment (36, 54). Sulfonamides and streptomycin are useful, but resistant strains develop rapidly during treatment.

Variability. Arkwright (2) in 1921 dissociated *Sh. dysenteriae* into S and R colonies (2). The S colonies were smooth, round, domed, and gave homogeneous suspensions when emulsified in physiologic saline. The R colonies were larger, flatter, with rough surfaces, irregular edges and the organisms tended to agglutinate spontaneously in physiologic saline. The individual organisms in the R colonies were longer and sometimes even filamentous. Alterations in antigenic structure accompanied the changes in colony form.

Sh. flexneri shows the typical S—R dissociation and, in addition, an antigenic alteration in the S type colonies which is not reflected by a change in colony form. This phenomenon was discovered by Boyd in 1938 (4, 5) and confirmed by Weil and his associates in 1946 (73). Boyd's type A variant predominates in freshly isolated cultures; type B in old cultures. The A variant contains the specific antigen for the particular type of *Sh. flexneri*, while the B variant contains antigens common to other members of the *Sh. flexneri* group. This type of dissociation has been called phase 1 and phase 2. The use of the term "phase" is unfortunate, since the variation is quite different from the phase variation observed with the *Salmonella* in that the change always is from the specific variant A to the nonspecific B and never in the reverse direction (73).

Both specific and nonspecific variants of the S type colony of *Sh. sonnei* have been described by Wheeler and Mickle (75). True R colonies also occur in old cultures. In this instance the

Table 1. The Genus Shigella

(Edwards and Ewing, 1961)

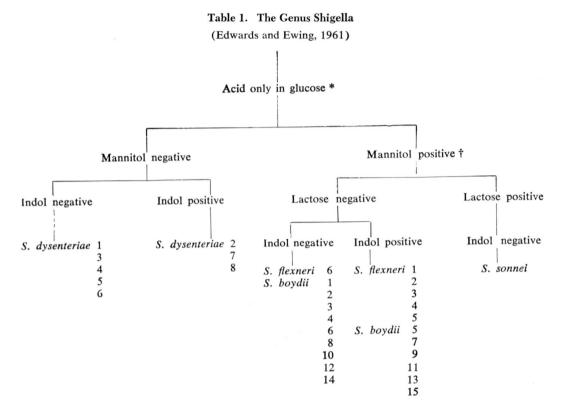

* Exceptions: *Sh. flexneri* 6 varieties may be aerogenic (Newcastle and Manchester).

† Certain cultures of *Sh. flexneri* 4, *Sh. flexneri* 6, and *boydii* 6 may not produce acid from mannitol (27, 59).

specific variant I is easily separated from the nonspecific variant II by differences in colony form. Another type of dissociation occurs in cultures of *Sh. sonnei.* This species of *Shigella,* which is characteristically slow in fermenting lactose, produces colonies with papillae or daughter colonies which ferment lactose promptly.

Dwarf D and G-like colonies have been reported for certain strains of *Sh. dysenteriae* and *Sh. sonnei.* The mucoid (M) phase of dissociation has been described but has received little study.

Antigenic Structure. The *Shigella* are less complex antigenically than the *Salmonella* and usually contain only one, or at most two, major somatic antigens. The minor antigens are nonspecific and occur in varying amounts in different species of *Shigella.* Ewing's (22) studies have shown rather extensive cross-reactions (30) between minor O antigens among the *Shigella;* and the O antigens of 10 *Shigella* serotypes were identical with the O antigens of certain strains of *E. coli* and coli

intermediates (7). This necessitates the use of biochemical as well as serologic methods for the identification of *Shigella,* since the poly-saccharide of the lipo-carbohydrate protein complex is itself antigenic when injected into mice and men (38, 39, 61). It is probable that the polysaccharide determines the specificity of the complex, as it does in the pneumococcus (38, 39). There is some doubt whether the "minor antigens" are true chemical entities or

Table 2. Biochemical Varieties of Shigella
flexneri 6

(Edwards and Ewing, 1951)

BIOTYPES	GLUCOSE	MANNITOL	DULCITOL
Boyd 88	A	A	—
Boyd 88	A	A	(A)
Manchester	AG	AG	(AG)
—	AG	AG	—
Newcastle	AG	—	(AG)
—	A	—	—
—	A	—	(A)

Table 3. Biochemical Reactions of Shigella Cultures *
(Edwards and Ewing, 1955)

SEROTYPES		GLUCOSE	MANNITOL	SUCROSE	MALTOSE	DULCITOL	RHAMNOSE	ARABINOSE	XYLOSE	SORBITOL	INDOL
S. dysenteriae	1	A	O	O	O, (A)	O	O	O	O	O	—
	2	A	O	O	v	O	A, O	O, A	O	O, (A)	+
	3	A	O	O	O, (A)	O	O	A, O	O	(A), O	—
	4	A	O	O	O, (A)	O	O	O, (A)	O	O, (A)	—
	5	A	O	O	O	(A)	O	A	O	A, (A), O	—
	6	A	O	O	O	O	O	A	O	O, (A)	—
	7	A	O	O	(A)	O	(A)	A	O	O	+
	8	A	O	O	A	O	A, O	A	A, (A)	O, (A)	+
S. flexneri	1	A	A	O	(A), O	O	O, (A)	(A), O	O	O	+(−)
	2	A	A	O	v	O	O, (A)	A, O	O	O, A	+(−)
	3	A	A	O	v	O	v	v	O	A, (A), O	+(−)
	4	A	A	O	(A), O	O	(A), O	v	O	v	+(−)
	4	A	O	O	(A), O	O	O, (A)	(A), O	A, (A), O	A, (A), O	—
	5	A	A	O	(A), O	O	O, (A)	v	O	O, A	+
	6	A	v	O	v	v	O, (A)	O, (A)	O	A, (A), O	—
	6	AG	v	O	v	v	O, (A)	O, (A)	O	O	—
S. boydii	1	A	A	O	(A), O	O	O	A	A, O	A	—
	2	A	A	O	A, (A)	O	O	A	O, A	O, (A)	—
	3	A	A	O	O	A, (A)	O	A	A	A	—
	4	A	A	O	v	O, A	O	A	O	O	—
	5	A	A	O	O	O	O	(A)	(A)	A	+
	6	A	A	O	O	(A)	O	A	(A)	A	—
	7	A	A	O	(A)	O	O	A	A	A, O	∓
	8	A	A	O	(A)	O	O	A	(A)	A, (A)	—
	9	A	A	O	(A)	O	(A)	p, A	O	A	+
	10	A	A	O	(A)	(A)	O	A	(A)	A	—
	11	A	A	O	(A)	O	A	A	A	O, (A)	+
S. sonnei		A	A	(A), O	A	O	A	A	O	O	∼

* A and AG, acid or acid and gas within 24 hours. v, reaction variable. (A), fermentation delayed 48 hours or longer. A, O, acid usually produced, occasional strain negative. O, A, usually negative but an occasional strain may produce acid. +(−), usually positive, sometimes negative. O, no reaction 30 days.

Shigella cultures do not produce blackening in TSI agar. They do not grow on Simmons' citrate agar, do not produce acetylmethylcarbinol, and do not hydrolyze urea. They are non-motile and do not produce acid from salicin, adonitol or inositol. Of the described *Shigellae*, only *Shigella sonnei* cultures produce acid from lactose and in this instance fermentation is delayed 48 or more hours. Occasional cultures of *S. dysenteriae* 2 may ferment sucrose after several days incubation. Some cultures of *S. flexneri* serotypes may ferment sucrose after being cultivated on artificial mediums for a time; freshly isolated strains do not. *S. flexneri* 6 cultures may be aerogenic and may or may not utilize mannitol. Delayed fermentation of dulcitol occurs with about 60 per cent of cultures of this type. Occasional cultures of this serotype may produce acid from rhamnose or xylose. *S. boydii* 6 cultures may require more than 24 hours to produce acid from mannitol and some may not utilize it at all.

merely the result of cross-reactions produced by chemical similarity among the various lipocarbohydrate protein complexes (55).

The serologic types of *Shigella* are shown in Table 4.

Polyvalent antiserums can be produced for each of the four groups of *Shigella* shown in Table 4. Both form I and form II of *Sh. sonnei* should be used for the preparation of the Group D antiserum. Ewing (17) advises the preparation of two additional polyvalent antiserums: one with A-D 03 and 04 (*Sh. dispar* II and I) and the other from A-D O group 1 (*Sh. alkalescens*). The organisms used to produce the Alkalescens-Dispar antiserums should be heated at 100° C. for two and a half hours to destroy labile antigens which may cause cross-agglutination with the coliform cultures which contain related antigens (44).

Sh. sonnei ferments neither xylose nor sorbitol and produces no indol. It appears to be antigenically homogeneous. *Sh. sonnei* exhibits two types of colonies which are antigenically and morphologically quite different. The S type, which is small, smooth, and shiny, probably is the true S form. The S type II form is larger, slightly umbonate, finely granular, and translucent at the edges. Both forms may be isolated from the stools of patients with the Sonne type infection, but on prolonged cultivation, the type II colonies usually become predominant. The type II form is suppressed on the standard Salmonella-Shigella agar and desoxycholate citrate medium, both of which favor the growth of type I. Serums for diagnostic agglutination should contain agglutinins for both variants of the S type of *Sh. sonnei* (75). The true R dissociate occurs in old cultures and is much larger, flatter, and more granular than the S type II colony. There are apparently some antigens common to both R and S type II, but the R variant is entirely different from the S type I (75).

The investigations of Smolens and his associates (57) show that the specific somatic antigens of the *Shigella* group are surface antigens. In the S type colony the loss of this surface antigen is accompanied by a loss of pathogenicity and specificity. Other antigenic variations have been reported by Okabe (50) and Ewing and Johnson (20).

A few strains of *Shigella* have been found to possess an additional antigen external to the O antigen which interferes with agglutination in specific anti-O serums until it has been removed by boiling.

Weil and Binder (72) have succeeded in transforming three types of *Sh. flexneri* by a method analogous to that used for the transformation of types of pneumococci.

SEROLOGIC DIAGNOSIS. The diagnosis of shigellosis by the detection of specific agglutinins in the blood of the patient is not as satisfactory as the serodiagnosis of typhoid and paratyphoid infections. Agglutinins are produced late in the disease and in much lower titers than in salmonellosis. A series of tests which shows rising titers as the patient improves, however, may be accepted as diagnostic.

Antibodies appear in the feces of patients infected with *Sh. flexneri* and *Sh. sonnei* even before they appear in the serums. These copraantibodies differ somewhat in their specificity, suggesting they are formed in different parts of the body (3).

Bacteriophage. Most strains of *Sh. sonnei* are typed by the same type of bacteriophage (63). Typing *Shigella* by phages does not look promising at the present time (71).

Bacterial Metabolites. All strains of *Shigella* possess potent endotoxins which are carbohydrate-lipid-protein complexes (3, 61) that function as the somatic antigen. The somatic antigen isolated from *Sh. sonnei* has good immunizing ability and lower toxicity than the antigens from the other types of *Shigella* (43). *Sh. flexneri* 2a synthesizes a **mucinolytic enzyme** (31) which is antigenic.

Sh. dysenteriae produces, in addition to the endotoxin, a rather powerful **exotoxin.** The R forms are as good toxin producers as the S forms but lack the ability to establish themselves in the body of the patient (66). This exotoxin has been studied in some detail by Olitsky and Kligler (51), Dubos and Geiger (13), and Van Heyningen and Gladstone (66). Effective toxoids are difficult to produce, since heat, ultraviolet light and formalin destroy a large proportion of the immunizing ability of the toxin (6).

Some strains of *E. coli* (41) and even certain strains of *Sh. boydii* (23) produce antibiotic-like substances which kill strains of *Sh. flexneri.*

Experimental Disease in Laboratory Animals. Captive monkeys may carry *Shigella,* and monkeys on a diet deficient in folic acid often develop clinical dysentery. The monkey is the only animal in which a disease resembling clinical dysentery can be induced with cultures of the organism. Large doses are required, and not all of the animals become infected (9). In this respect, the monkey resembles man in possessing a conditioned susceptibility to dysentery bacilli. Watkins (68) found definite

Table 4. Shigella Nomenclature

(Edwards and Ewing, 1955)

Shigella Commission 1953	Ewing 1949		Kauffmann and Ferguson 1947	Boyd 1940 1946	Weil, Black and Farsetta 1944	English (Older)	Other
SUBGROUP A							
S. dysenteriae							
1	I						*Bacterium shigae*
2	II						*S. ambigua, S. schmitzii, B. ambiguus*
3	III						Q771, type 8524-, *S. arabinotarda* A-
4	IV						Q1167, *S. arabinotarda* B-
5	V						Q1030
6	VI						Q454
7	VII						Q902
8							Serotype 599-52
	Type	Abbreviated Formula					
SUBGROUP B							
S. flexneri							
1a	I	I:4	1b	I	I	V	Flexner
1b	I	I:4,6	1a		I, III	VZ	
2a	II	II:4	2a	II	II	W	Strong, Hiss-Russell
2b	II	II:7,8,9	2b		II, VII	WX	
3	III	III:6,7	3	III	III	Z	
4a	IV	IV:4	4a	IV	IV		Lentz Y2
4b	IV	IV:6	4b	IV	III, IV		
							S. saigonensis, S. rio
5	V		5	V	V(V, VII)		
6	VI		6	VI	VI		*S. newcastle*
X	X	—:7,8,9			VII	X	
Y	Y	—:4			VIII	Y	Hiss-Russell
SUBGROUP C							
S. boydii							
1	I			I	IX		
2	II			II	X		
3	III			III	XI		
4	IV				XIV		
5	V				XIII		
6	VI				XII		
7	VII						Lavington, type T, *S. etousae*
8							Serotype 112
9							Serotype 1296/7
10							Serotype 430
11							Serotype 34
SUBGROUP D							
S. sonnei	*S. sonnei*		*S. sonnei*				Sonne-Duval, Sonne III, *S. ceylonensis* A

differences in the efficiency of different strains in their ability to infect monkeys and tissue culture cells in monolayers (37).

Guinea pigs are normally resistant to infection, and this resistance is due in part to the competitive effect of the natural flora of the bowel, since germ-free guinea pigs (33, 34) and guinea pigs under treatment with broad spectrum antibiotics are readily infected (35). Formal and his associates (33) have found that the combination of starvation or the injection of carbon tetrachloride plus the administration of opium makes the guinea pig susceptible to oral infection. The pathologic changes in the intestines of the animal infected by this method have been studied by Le Brec and Formal (46). Rats and dogs are very resistant, but mice can be infected by suspending the organisms in mucin and injecting them intraperitoneally.

Clinical Types of Infection in Man. Experimental dysentery was produced in human volunteers by Shaughnessy and his associates (55). Strains of *Sh. flexneri* types I, II, III, Boyd 88, and *Sh. schmitzii* were given in huge doses but only 63 to 82 per cent of the subjects developed the clinical disease. In the successful experiments, abdominal symptoms and fever began after 12 hours, followed by a severe diarrhea in 18 to 24 hours.

The symptoms in man are extremely variable even when it can be established that the epidemic is caused by one species of *Shigella* of a single type. Some patients have mild abdominal discomfort with only a few loose stools, while others have nausea, vomiting, and severe prostration. The diarrhea which begins as a thin watery discharge soon loses its fecal character and stools finally are composed of nothing but pus, mucous threads and blood. In this stage there are agonizing colicky pains and constant tenesmus.

Sh. dysenteriae infections, probably because of the associated **"exotoxin,"** have a mortality of about 20 per cent. The death rate is much lower in the other types of shigellosis, particularly in infections caused by *Sh. sonnei.* The mortality rate is always higher in young children than in adults (10, 11). Indeed, dysentery is one of the major causes of death among children in commu-

nities where sanitation facilities are inadequate.

The dysentery bacilli appear in moderate numbers in the stools but occur in profusion in the ulcers of the intestinal tract. Sometimes they reach the lymph nodes of the mesentery, but rarely, if ever, do they invade the blood stream. Therefore **it is useless to attempt to establish the diagnosis by culturing the blood. The diagnosis is made by isolating the organism from the stools or by a series of agglutination tests, which shows gradually rising titers as the patient recovers.** The dogmatic statement regarding blood culture is retained from the previous edition although Winter and his associates (76) have found in the literature reports proving bacteremia in 26 patients infected with *Sh. flexneri,* 12 with *Sh. dysenteriae,* 3 with *Sh. sonnei,* and 3 with alkalescens-dispar strains.

In the epidemic reported by Robertson (53) in 1963, 66 of 84 girls in a boarding school were infected and there was a high incidence of involvement of the central nervous system and of skin rashes suggesting a concurrent infection with one of the Coxsackie viruses, although viruses were looked for without success.

Transmission. Dysentery often is merely a nuisance in well-organized civilian life, but since the dawn of history it has been a factor of major importance in military operations. Since the mortality is low but the disability great, entire battalions may have only a few squads of men capable of raising and firing their rifles.

In Zinsser's entertaining and instructive book *Rats, Lice and History* (77), the statement is made that typhus, plague, cholera, typhoid, and dysentery have decided more battles than have all the great generals in history; that epidemics are blamed for defeats and the generals credited with the victories, while, in truth, the credit should be reversed.

Man is the sole source of the dysentery organisms. In Watt and Hardy's (69) study of dysentery in Georgia, New Mexico, and Puerto Rico, 9.1 convalescent or asymptomatic carriers were found for each current case of dysentery. It is significant that of 380 carriers found, only two were under the care of a physician. The potential source of infection is enormous; therefore, the actual incidence of dysentery in a community is a reflection of the opportunity for its dissemination (49).

The carrier contaminates the water, milk, and food supply. The carrier rate in the Italian civilian population during the war was 6 per cent and accounted in part for the continued reinfection of the American troops (58). Flies carry the bacilli in a mechanical manner on their feet and proboscises, but epidemics do occur in the absence of flies during the winter.

A solid immunity to dysentery is acquired with difficulty, possibly because of the variety of antigenic types, perhaps from inadequate stimulation of the body as a whole from organisms in localized ulcerations in the intestines, or it may be that the dysentery bacilli are poor antigens. The Flexner group of dysentery bacilli is the most common cause of bacillary dysentery in this country (74) and even in the Orient. The exotoxin-producing Shiga group occurs in Italy, the Near East, and the Orient. The Boyd group occurs in India and Egypt (29); the Sonne group is found in the United States and Europe. It should be emphasized, however, that strains of any one of the four types can be isolated in any diagnostic laboratory in this country. For more specific information about clinical dysentery and its epidemiology, the student should consult the monograph by Davison (10, 11) and the books by Manson-Bahr (48) and Felsen (24).

Biologic Products. An antitoxin to the exotoxin of the Shiga bacillus has been produced but is not available commercially. Antibacterial serums are ineffective. Polyvalent and monovalent typing serums for the more common types of *Shigella* can be obtained.

Mixed bacterial vaccines have been studied for years but have not proved practical because of the inherent toxicity of the somatic O antigens and the bulk of material required in order to include the various antigenic types (55).

Treatment. Chloramphenicol, chlortetracycline, and oxytetracycline (36) are reasonably effective therapeutic agents. Sulfadiazine (52, 62) and streptomycin are also effective but resistant strains which can initiate new epidemics develop readily (5, 71). The combined treatment in which a sulfonamide is given concurrently with an antibiotic delays the development of resistance. Chronic dysentery is resistant to treatment but the combination of oral and intramuscular streptomycin has been used with some success (65).

Prevention. The prevention of shigellosis is reasonably satisfactory in communities with an efficient public health department. The pasteurization of milk and milk products and the chlorination of water prevent major epidemics. Water may be recontaminated after it has been chlorinated, and a cross-connection between a water and a sewer line, which occurs too frequently in this country, usually results in an epidemic of dysentery rather than typhoid, probably because at the present time the convalescent and carrier rates for dysentery are higher than those for typhoid.

The carrier is the chief source of shigellosis and scrupulous personal cleanliness on the part of all food handlers is absolutely necessary. Fly control is more effective in reducing shigellosis than salmonellosis, but DDT alone is not effective and must be accompanied by good community housekeeping to eliminate the man-made breeding places (70).

The use of lactic acid milk has proved satisfactory in preventing dysentery and other types of intestinal infections in young infants (11).

Active immunization to the more common types of *Shigella* with the specific nontoxic polysaccharides would be more desirable.

THE ALKALESCENS-DISPAR GROUP

This group of organisms has always caused confusion in the laboratory (1). They are in general nonmotile, and since they do not ferment lactose and do not form gas from other carbohydrates, on preliminary study they are logically classified with the *Shigella*. They usually produce mild to moderately severe attacks of dysentery, although they can cause pyelitis and bacteremia (60). When studied in more detail, both biochemical reactions and antigenic structure show their relationship to *E. coli* (44). Both motility and the ability to ferment lactose has been induced in some strains by manipulations in the laboratory (7).

Most investigators agree that the Alkalescens-Dispar strains do form an antigenic group and that they are intermediate in evolution between the *Escherichia* and the *Shigella* (7, 14, 16, 18, 19, 21, 34, 44).

Tables 5 and 6 show the antigenic relationship between these organisms and *E. coli* and their corresponding biochemical reactions.

Table 5. The O Antigenic Schema for the Alkalescens-Dispar Group °

O Groups	O Antigen	Relationship to E. coli O Groups	Earlier Designations
1	1a 1a, 1b	Identical with 1a 1a, 1b	*B. alkalescens* or Alkalescens Type I
2	2	strong relationship with 25 and other groups	Alkalescens Type II or *S. tieté*
3	3	strong relationship with 25 and other groups	*S. ceylonensis* B or *S. dispar* Type II or Alkalescens Type III (2-193)
4	4	strong relationship with 4	*S. madampensis* or *S. dispar* I
5	5	identical with 2a	None
6	6	identical with 9	*S. dispar* Type III
7	7	identical with 7	None
8	8	identical with 81	None

* From Frantzen (34), and Ewing, Taylor, and Hucks (19).

Table 6. Biochemical Reactions of Members of the Alkalescens-Dispar Group
(Edwards and Ewing, 1951)

Cultures	Glucose Mannitol Maltose Arabinose Xylose	Lactose Rhamnose	Sucrose	Dulcitol	Salicin	Indol M. R.	Inositol, Adonitol Simmons' Citrate V. P., Urea Motility
01	A	—	—	A	—	+	—
02	A	V	V	—	(A)	+	—
03	A	(A)	(A)	A or (A)	—	+	—
04	A	(A)	(A)	—	—	+	—
05	A	V	(A)	V	—	+	—
06	A	A	—	—	—	+	—
07	A	A	A	(A)	—	+	—
08	A	(A)	—	A	—	+	—

A   = Acid production within 24 hours.
(A) = Acid production after 48 hours or longer.
— = No reaction (carbohydrates 30 days).
V   = Variable.

REFERENCES

1. Andrewes, F. W.   Lancet, 1:560, 1918.
2. Arkwright, J. A.   J. Path. & Bact., 24:36, 1921.
3. Barksdale, W. S., and Ghoda, A.   J. Immunol., 66:395, 1951.
4. Boyd, J. S. K.   J. Hyg., 38:477, 1938.
5. ——— J. Path. & Bact., 58:237, 1946.
6. Branham, S. E., and others.   J. Immunol., 73:199, 1954.
7. Carpenter, P. L., and Stuart, C. A.   J. Immunol., 64:237, 1950.
8. Chantemesse, M. M., and Widal, F.   Bull. Acad. nat. méd., 19:522, 1888.
9. Dack, G. M., and Petran, E.   J. Infect. Dis., 55:1, 1934.
10. Davison, W. C.   Medicine, 1:389, 1922.
11. ——— Am. J. Dis. Child., 49:72, 1935.
12. Dold, H.   Deutsche med. Wchnschr., 42:811, 1916.
13. Dubos, R. I., and Geiger, J. W.   J. Exper. Med., 84:143, 1946.
14. Edwards, P. R., and Ewing, W. H.   A Manual for Enteric Bacteriology, Atlanta, Ga., U.S. Public Health Service, 1961.
15. Erlandson, A. L., and Mackey, W. H.   J. Bact., 75:253, 1958.
16. Ewing, W. H.   J. Bact., 57:633, 1949; 58:497, 1949.
17. ——— J. Lab. & Clin. Med., 36:471, 1950.
18. ——— and Bruner, D. W.   Am. J. Clin. Path., 17:1, 1947.
19. ——— and others.   Pub. Health Rep., 65:1474, 1950.
20. ——— and Johnson, J. G.   Can. J. Microbiol., 7:303, 1961.
21. ——— J. Bact., 66:333, 1953.
22. ——— and Tanner, K. E.   J. Bact., 69:89, 1955.
23. Fastier, L. B.   J. Immunol., 62:399, 1949.
24. Felsen, J.   Bacillary Dysentery, Colitis and Enteritis, Philadelphia, W. B. Saunders Co., 1945.
25. Ferguson, W. W., and Henderson, N. D.   J. Bact., 54:179, 1947.
26. Flexner, S.   J. Exper. Med., 8:514, 1906.
27. ——— Bull. Johns Hopkins Hosp., 11:231, 1900.
28. Floyd, T. H.   J. Bact., 70:621, 1955.
29. ——— J. Bact., 71:525, 1956.
30. Formal, S. B., and Baker, E. E.   J. Immunol., 70:260, 1953.
31. ——— and Lowenthal, J. P.   Proc. Soc. Exper. Biol. & Med., 92:10, 1956.
32. ——— and others.   J. Bact., 82:284, 1961.
33. ——— and others.   J. Bact., 85:119, 1963.
34. Frantzen, E.   Acta path. et microbiol. Scandinav., 28:103, 1951; 27:236, 1950.
35. Freter, R. J.   Exper. Med., 104:411, 1956.
36. Garfinkel, B. T., and others.   J.A.M.A., 151:1157, 1953.
37. Gerber, D. F., and Watkins, H. M. S.   J. Bact., 82:815, 1961.
38. Goebel, W. F.   J. Exper. Med., 85:499, 1947.
39. ——— and others.   J. Exper. Med., 81:315, 1945.
40. Grigoriew, A. W.   Woennomedicinsky J., Tl, 71:73, 1891.
41. Halbert, S. P., and Gravatt, M.   J. Immunol., 61:271, 1949.
42. Jeter, W. S., and Wynne, E. S.   J. Bact., 58:429, 1949.
43. Johnson, R. B.   J. Immunol., 74:286, 1955.
44. Kauffmann, F.   Acta path. et microbiol. Scandinav., 26:879, 1949.
45. Kruse, W.   Deutsche med. Wchschr., 26: 637, 1900; 29:49, 201, 1903.
46. Le Brec, E. H., and Formal, S. B.   J. Immunol., 87:562, 1961.
47. Lovell, R.   J. Path. & Bact., 32:79, 1929.
48. Manson-Bahr, P.   The Dysentery Disorders, Baltimore, Williams & Wilkins, 1943.
49. Mosley, W. H.   J.A.M.A., 182:1307, 1962.
50. Okabe, K.   J. Immunol., 81:285, 1958.
51. Olitsky, P. K., and Kligler, I. J.   J. Exper. Med., 31:19, 1920.
52. Ravenel, S. F., and Smith, D. L.   South. M. J., 34:504, 1941.
53. Robertson, H. C., Jr.   South. Med. J., 56:662, 1963.
54. Ross, S., and others.   J.A.M.A., 143:1459, 1950.
55. Shaughnessy, H. J., and others.   J.A.M.A., 132:362, 1946.
56. Shiga, K.   Zentralbl. f. Bakt., 1 Abt., 23:599, 1898; 24:817, 870, 913, 1898; 42:132, 1909.
57. Smolens, J., and others.   J. Immunol., 52:41, 1946.
58. Stock, A. H., and others.   J. Infect. Dis., 81: 59, 65, 68, 72, 1947.
59. Stuart, C. A., and Rustigian, R.   J. Bact., 46:105, 1943.
60. Sutton, G. C., and Bernstein, A.   Am. J. Med., 9:422, 1950.
61. Tal, C., and Goebel, W. F.   J. Exper. Med., 92:25, 1950.
62. Taylor, G.   J. Pediat., 18:469, 1941.
63. Tee, G. H.   J. Hyg., 53:54, 1955.
64. Vaillard, L., and Dopter, C.   Ann. Inst. Pasteur, 17:463, 1903.
65. Van Gelder, D. W., and others.   Am. J. Trop. Med., 27:225, 1947.
66. Van Heyningen, W. E., and Gladstone, G. P.   Brit. J. Exper. Path., 34:202, 1953.
67. Walters, E. W., and others.   J. Bact., 67:247, 1955.
68. Watkins, H. M. S.   Ann. N.Y. Acad. Sci., 88:1167, 1960.
69. Watt, J., and Hardy, A. V.   Pub. Health Rep., 60:261, 1945.
70. ——— and Lindsay, D. R.   Pub. Health Rep., 63:1319, 1948.
71. Weil, A. J.   J. Immunol., 55:363, 1947.
72. ——— and Binder, M.   Proc. Soc. Exper. Biol. & Med., 66:349, 1947.
73. Weil, A. J., and others.   J. Immunol., 52:221, 1946.
74. ——— and Felsen, J.   J. Immunol., 74:488, 1955.
75. Wheeler, K. M., and Mickle, F. L.   J. Immunol., 51:257, 1945.
76. Winter, B. V., and others.   J.A.M.A., 180:927, 1962.
77. Zinsser, H.   Rats, Lice and History, Boston, Little, Brown & Co., 1935.

36

Klebsiella pneumoniae and Related Organisms

The extensive studies of Ørskov (39), Kauffmann (30), and Edwards and Fife (13) have shown that the nonmotile, encapsulated, strains of *Aerobacter aerogenes*, which fail to liquefy gelatin but utilize urea slowly, fit snugly into the antigenic classification of *Klebsiella pneumoniae*. Edwards and Ewing (12) have proposed the elimination of the contradictory species *Aerobacter aerogenes* by transferring the nonmotile strains which resemble *Klebsiella* in biochemical and antigenic characteristics to the *Klebsiella pneumoniae* species. Hormaeche and Edwards (24) suggest that the motile strains, and occasionally nonmotile variants of these strains which resemble the present *Aerogenes cloacae*, would be merged with this species and the related *Aerobacter liquefaciens* and subgroup *Hafnia* to form a new genus *Enterobacter* with three species, *Ent. cloacae*, *Ent. aerogenes* (motile strains from old *Aerobacter aerogenes*), and *Ent. liquefaciens*, with *Hafnia* as a subgroup. Since no official action has been taken on this proposal by the Nomenclature Committee of the International Association of Microbiological Societies, we are following the practice of Edwards and Ewing (12) in describing this organism as the *Aerobacter* group, divided into A, B, and C and the *Hafnia* subgroup (7). Subgroup A is synonymous with *A. cloacae*, subgroup B with the motile strains removed from the *Klebsiella* and merged with old *A. aerogenes*, and subgroup C with *A. liquefaciens* of Grimes and Hennerty (21a).

KLEBSIELLA PNEUMONIAE

Family: *Enterobacteriaceae* Rahn. Genus: *Klebsiella* Trevisan. Species: *Klebsiella pneumoniae* (Schroeter) Trevisan

The organism known in most clinical laboratories as *Bacillus mucosus capsulatus*, or **Friedländer's bacillus**, was isolated in 1882 by Friedländer (18) from the sputums of patients with lobar pneumonia. The bacillus can be isolated from almost any part of the body. It occurs in the nasopharynx of 1 to 5 per cent of healthy individuals (5, 25) and has been found associated with disease of the lungs and bronchi, genitourinary tract, gastrointestinal tract, liver and biliary passages, skin and appendages, vagina, uterus, and adnexa (26). Infection with *K. pneumoniae* is becoming relatively, and actually, more frequent since the introduction of sulfonamides and penicillin.

Morphology and Staining. When examined in materials obtained directly from human or animal lesions, *K. pneumoniae* appears as a coccobacillus (0.5 to 1.5 μ by 1 to 2 μ) possessing a **capsule** that often is two or three times the size of the bacillus itself (Fig. 1). The organisms often occur in pairs, and the diplobacilli may be confused easily with the

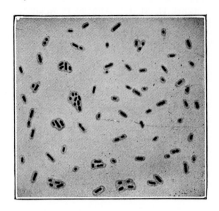

Fig. 1. *Klebsiella pneumoniae*. (From W. W. Ford. *Textbook of Bacteriology*, W. B. Saunders Co.)

diplococcal forms of the pneumococcus unless the differential gram stain is applied with care.

The **nonmotile, nonsporogenous** organism is **gram-negative.** It is decolorized easily in a thin smear, but it may appear gram-positive when a thick smear of sputum or infected material is washed inadequately with alcohol. The capsule often is easily recognizable in smears stained by Gram's method and is demonstrated easily with the usual capsule stains. Bacilli from 3 to 5 μ in length are found in cultures and filamentous forms occur in smears made from R-type colonies.

Cultural Characteristics. *K. pneumoniae* grows readily on **all the usual laboratory media,** producing, after 24 hours growth, moderate-sized grayish-white colonies with a characteristic semifluid, slimy appearance. If a wire loop is removed carefully after touching a colony, a thin string of mucoid material several millimeters long can be seen extending from the wire to the parent colony. A tentative diagnosis can be made from this observation alone. The mucoid colonies are largest on infusion media or on a simple medium containing glucose.

In **broth** the organism grows rapidly, producing a homogeneous clouding in 12 to 24 hours. A pellicle forms and is followed by the development of a profuse stringy sediment which settles to the bottom of the tube. The organism is **aerobic** but facultatively anaerobic. It grows at a pH of 6 to 7.8 over a temperature range of 12° to 43° C. with an optimum of 35° C.

Klebsiella pneumoniae ferments lactose, sucrose, salicin, inositol, and adonitol and produces **acid and gas in glucose.** Hydrogen sulfide and indol are not formed, and gelatin is not liquefied. Most strains are Voges-Proskauer-positive and methyl-red-negative, but the majority of capsular types 3 and 4 are methyl-red-positive and Voges-Proskauer-negative. *K. rhinoscleromatis* and many cultures of types 3 and 4 fail to utilize citrate in inorganic media. Although *K. pneumoniae* hydrolyzes urea, it produces ammonia so slowly that it is not confused with *Proteus* which splits urea rapidly. Noller and Hartsell (37) found that lysozyme plus circulin caused the lysis of *A. aerogenes* but not *K. pneumoniae.*

Resistance. If protected from drying, cultures remain alive for months at room temperature. The organisms are killed quickly by temperatures of 56° to 60° C. **Sulfonamides** have some inhibiting effect on *K. pneumoniae,* but **penicillin** is ineffective. Streptomycin and the broad-spectrum antibiotics are reasonably effective, but resistant strains develop within a period of days. One sulfonamide and an antibiotic, or two different types of antibiotics, should be administered simultaneously to reduce the emergence of resistant strains.

Variability. The dissociation pattern of *K. pneumoniae* is similar but somewhat more complex than that of the pneumococcus. The S forms contain the specific O antigen, while the R forms do not. Kauffmann (29) has described four colony variations for the O and four for the R depending upon the presence of a slime layer, a definite capsule, both, or neither. The material in the slime layer is antigenically related, if not identical to the capsular material (12, 56). Either a slime layer, a definite capsule, or both, can occur without the O antigen; thus only the R forms without slime, capsule, or O antigen present the true rough colony. Pickett and Cabelli (42) have described a group specific antigen (Sm) which lies beneath the capsular layer and external to the O antigen. Edwards and Ewing (12) suggest that this antigen may be analogous to the C substance of the pneumococcus.

Antigenic Structure. Since the biochemical reactions of different strains of this organism are so variable, little progress in classification was made until methods of antigenic analysis were applied to the problem.

The antigenic studies by Julianelle (27, 28) and Edwards (11) were reviewed by Kauffmann (29) in 1949 and interpreted in the light of his newly proposed antigenic classification. This author recognizes three major antigens in the *Klebsiella* group: capsular antigen (K); somatic, smooth antigen (O); and somatic rough antigen (R). The R antigen is common to all somatic O types and is not used in the classification (Table 1). To produce pure capsular agglutination, it would be necessary to absorb the serums with both O and R antigens. This difficulty is avoided by utilizing the **capsular swelling** for the differentiation of capsular types. Table 1 shows a simplified antigenic schema for the *Klebsiella* group. Capsular types 1 and 2 (old A and B) are virulent for mice and usually produce infection of the respiratory tract in man, but capsular types 8, 9, and 10 are not virulent for mice and are associated with urinary tract infections in man. The cultures from rhinoscleroma had a formula of 2a:3 (old C), while the strains from ozena were 2a, 2c, 2d:4, 6 (old D, F). Some of the O antigens are identical with some of the *Escherichia* O antigens, and some of the capsular antigens are identical with those of certain *Aerobacter aerogenes* strains. The polysaccharides of capsular type 2 (old B) are very similar chemically to those of type II pneumococci. Cross-precipitation reactions and reciprocal protection in mice are obtained with immune serums prepared from either organism. A very similar, but not identical classification, was proposed by Henriksen (22) in 1949 and Ørskov (39). There are, at the present moment, 72 known specific capsular types (12).

Table 1. **Diagnostic Klebsiella Antigenic Schema**

(Kauffmann, 1949)

GROUPS	ANTIGENS O	K	EARLIER DESIGNATION
	1	1	A—Klebsiella
	1	2	B—Klebsiella
	1	3	C—Klebsiella
1	1	7	•
	1	8	•
	1	10	•
	1	12	•
	2a	2	B—Klebsiella
	2a,2b	2	B—Klebsiella
2 A	2a	3	C—Rhinoscleroma
	2a	8	•
	(2a),2c,2d	4	D—Ozena
2 B	2a,2c	5	E—Ozena
	2a,2c	6	F—Ozena
3	3	11	•
•	•	9	•
	•	13	•
	•	14	•

Bacteriophages. Bacteriophages specific for strains in types A, B, and C have been isolated, and Edwards and his associates (14) have found two phages which will differentiate type 1 from type 2.

Bacterial Metabolites. No exotoxins are produced, and the endotoxins are not very potent. The capsular polysaccharide dissolves in tissue fluids and can be demonstrated in the urine by precipitin tests (4).

Spontaneous Disease in Animals. *K. pneumoniae* can produce epidemics of pneumonia in mice (54) and metritis in mares (11). Virulent type B strains have been isolated from soil, water, and milk (11).

Experimental Disease in Laboratory Animals. Guinea pigs and rabbits are moderately resistant to infection with *K. pneumoniae*, but mice are quite susceptible. Intraperitoneal inoculation in the mouse is the most reliable method for establishing the pathogenicity of a particular strain.

Clinical Types of Infection in Man. Lesions in almost every part of the body have resulted from infections with *K. pneumoniae.* Sinusitis, pharyngitis, meningitis, endocarditis, septicemia, peritonitis, liver abscess, and salpingitis have been reported (6, 51). Occasionally a severe form of enteritis occurs in children, which simulates bacillary dysentery (53). Pulmonary infections resembling either lobar or bronchial pneumonia frequently become chronic and present the clinical picture of pulmonary abscess, bronchiectasis, or pulmonary tuberculosis (33, 48). Manfredi and his associates (34) have shown that the physical examination and the x-ray pictures in *Klebsiella pneumoniae,* in contrast to pneumococcal pneumonia, almost always show signs of less lung volume by decreased size and expansion of the hemothorax. This is from the rapid necrosis of the lung by this organism. The very rapid progression of the disease with the high mortality is due partly to the prompt development of resistance to antibiotics (31) and partly to the dehabilitation of the patient by alcohol or chronic disease (38).

Infections of the urinary tract are not infrequent and may be spread from patient to patient by instrumentation (39). Lattimer, Seneca, and Zinsser (31) have pointed out that resistance to sulfadiazine and to nitrofurantoin develops very slowly or not at all.

Treatment. The mortality from *Klebsiella pneumoniae* in alcoholics may be as high as 70 per cent (38), a fact which led Olsson and Romansky (38) to recommend that the diagnosis be made from a gram stain of the sputum without waiting for a culture and that all patients suspected of having a *Klebsiella pneumoniae* and who have a white blood count of 5,000 or less have treatment started within minutes of admission with streptomycin and chloramphenicol or tetracycline. Fekety and his associates (17) recommend the use of colistin sulfate (Colymycin) or colistin methanesulfonate for patients who are resistant to other antibiotics. This drug, a basic polypeptide closely resembling polymyxin B, is supposed to be less toxic. Mild reversible paresthesias were observed in 27 per cent of the patients treated (17), but it can be given to azotemic patients.

A bacterial type of delayed allergy develops in many cases of chronic infection with this group of organisms, and hyposensitization with autogenous vaccine may cure some patients who have resistance to all antibiotic and chemotherapeutic agents. The slow, natural, resolution of *Klebsiella pneumoniae* may be accelerated by the administration of KI after the temperature has been reduced to a rate of not more than one degree above normal.

THE AEROBACTER GROUP

The organisms included in this group have been discussed in the introduction to this chapter. Their biochemical reactions are shown in Table 2. Practically all of the *Aerobacter* and the *Hafnia* organisms are motile, while the *Klebsiella*, by definition, are nonmotile. The majority of the *Aerobacter* C and *Hafnia* strains do not ferment lactose. Only an occasional *Aerobacter* A or B or *Klebsiella* fail to ferment lactose (50).

Sakazaka and Namioka (47) studied 170 type *A. cloacae* (*Aerobacter* A group) and established 53 O groups, 56 H antigens, and 79 serotypes. The group B and C strains have not been classified, but Eyeland and Faber (15) studied 58 cultures of the *Hafnia* group and established 21 O groups, 22 H antigens, and 43 serotypes. No phase variation was detected in the H antigens.

When these *Aerobacter* group organisms produce disease, the clinical picture and the treatment is the same as that presented above for the *Klebsiella* (35).

KLEBSIELLA RHINOSCLEROMATIS AND RHINOSCLEROMA

Rhinoscleroma is a slowly growing granulomatous tumor which begins in the external nares or upon the mucosa of the nose, mouth, pharynx, or larynx. The tumor-like masses have little effect on the health of the patient except for the disturbances arising from the exertion of mechanical pressure. The disease is rare in this country but common in southeastern Europe, India, and Central America (16, 19, 46). Biopsies of the lesions show the presence of large, swollen, mononuclear cells called "Mikulicz's cells" which are filled with gram-negative, encapsulated bacilli (Fig. 2) (36).

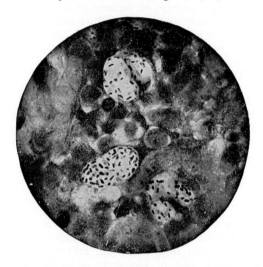

Fig. 2. Bacillus of rhinoscleroma. Section of tissue showing the microorganisms within Mikulicz cells. (From Fraenkel and Pfeiffer.)

Table 2. Simplified Schema of Biochemical Reactions of the Klebsiella-Aerobacter Group

(Edwards and Ewing, 1962)

	Klebsiella	*Aerobacter* A	*Aerobacter* B	*Aerobacter* C	*Hafnia*
Inositol (Gas)	+	−	+	+	−
Glycerol (Gas)	+	−	+	+	+
Sorbitol	+	+	+	+	−
Raffinose	+	+	+	+	−
Rhamnose	+	+	+	−	+
Lysine	+	−	+	+	+
Arginine	−	+	−	−	−
Ornithine	−	+	+	+	+
Gelatin	−	(+)	X	+	−
Motility	−	+	+	+	+

+ = Positive, 1 or 2 days
X = Late and irregular
(+) = Positive delayed
− = Negative

The bacilli grow readily on the usual laboratory media forming medium-size, white or slightly yellowish mucoid colonies after 24 to 48 hours incubation. Lactose is fermented slowly, and gas is not produced from glucose or other carbohydrates. They are methyl-red-positive, Voges-Proskauer-negative, citrate-negative, and urea-negative and do not ferment d-tartrate or mucate (32). In Kauffmann's classification they have the antigenic formula 2a:3 (old C).

The culture strains have very little, if any, pathogenicity for mice and other laboratory animals, and Reyes (46) failed to transmit the disease to laboratory animals or to man by inoculating small portions of the granulomatous tumors. The organisms from the Mikulicz cells might perhaps be isolated in the yolk sac of chick embryos by the method employed by Anderson and others (3) in 1945 for the isolation of the intracellular encapsulated organisms from the lesions of granuloma inguinale.

The disease is exceedingly chronic, and surgical treatment is very unsatisfactory. Reyes (46) has studied 200 cases and reports that the best results have been obtained with combined sulfonamide and roentgen therapy, although there is an occasional report of excellent success with **streptomycin** (49).

KLEBSIELLA OZAENAE AND OZENA

The term "ozena" is used to designate a type of atrophic rhinitis which is characterized by an unusually foul, sickening, pervasive odor. There is a lack of agreement as to the cause of the condition (10). Certain types of the disease may be due to primary infections; in others, the infection may be secondary to a metabolic or endocrine disturbance.

In 1893 Abel (1, 2) isolated an encapsulated bacillus, now called *K. ozaenae,* from patients with the disease. Julianelle (27) found that strains isolated from cases of ozena possessed capsular and somatic antigens which were quite different from those encountered in strains of *K. pneumoniae. K. ozaenae* strains have been subdivided into types D, E, and F on the basis of their capsular polysaccharides, although the somatic antigens seem to be similar (20). In Kauffmann's classification the D, E, and F strains form a subgroup of O group 2 with O antigens 2a, 2c, 2d:4; 2a, 2c:5; 2a, 2c:6 (29).

It is stated generally that *K. ozaenae* is non-pathogenic for laboratory animals but Thornell (52) isolated seven strains which were highly pathogenic for mice. Four patients have been cured with streptomycin (23).

THE PEREZ BACILLUS AND OZENA

In 1899 Perez (41) isolated a gram-negative, nonmotile, nonencapsulated bacillus from cases of clinical ozena. The organism grew readily on blood-agar plates and produced a characteristic fetid odor. Some years ago one of our students, who had clinical ozena, isolated an organism with the characteristics of the Perez bacillus from his own nose. The Perez bacillus is pathogenic for guinea pigs, rabbits and mice.

CALYMMATOBACTERIUM GRANULOMATIS AND GRANULOMA INGUINALE

The laboratory diagnosis of the venereal disease granuloma inguinale depends upon the demonstration of "Donovan bodies" in the large mononuclear cells found (Fig. 3) in the granulomatous tissues (21). These bodies have more than a superficial resemblance to the heavily encapsulated *Klebsiella* organisms which, from time to time, have been isolated from the granulomatous lesions. However, numerous attempts to reproduce the disease in man and animals by inoculation of these culture strains have resulted uniformly in failure and the etiologic relationship of the bacilli to the disease has been questioned.

In 1945 Anderson, DeMonbreun, and Goodpasture (3) isolated an encapsulated bacillus by culturing bits of tissue in the yolk sac of chick embryos. They proposed the name *Donovania granulomatis* for this organism.

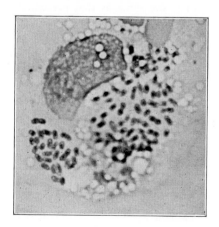

Fig. 3. *Calymmatobacterium granulomatis.* The large encapsulated organisms are concentrated in a large monocyte. (From Greenblatt, Dienst and West. *Am. J. Syph. Gonor. & Ven. Dis.,* 35:291, 1951.)

A capsular material was isolated which gave precipitin tests and fixed complement with the serums of patients having granuloma inguinale. A vaccine prepared from the organisms gave positive skin tests in patients with the disease. The skin reaction appeared 12 to 24 hours after injection and disappeared rapidly after 24 to 36 hours. The disease could not be reproduced in animals, but roosters injected with the egg yolk cultures developed precipitins and complement-fixing antibodies.

C. granulomatis has been cultured by Rake and his associates (43, 44, 45) who found that there was a morphologic and antigenic resemblance to *Klebsiella*. The cross-reaction with *K. rhinoscleroma* strain was most striking (43, 44, 45) and Packer and Goldberg (40) demonstrated cross-complement fixation with other members of the *Klebsiella* group of organisms.

Experimental infections have been produced in man with yolk sac cultures of *C. granulomatis* (8, 9). Excellent clinical results have followed treatment with either streptomycin or the broad spectrum antibiotics (9, 55, 56, 57).

REFERENCES

1. Abel, R. Zentralbl. f. Bakt., I Abt., 13:161, 1893.
2. ―― Ztschr. f. Hyg. u. Infektionskr., 21:89, 189, 1896.
3. Anderson, K., and others. J. Exper. Med., 81:25, 1945.
4. Blake, F. G. Arch. Int. Med., 21:779, 1918.
5. Bloomfield, A. L. Am. Rev. Tuberc., 4:847, 1921.
6. Botsford, T. W., and Kinney, T. D. New Eng. J. Med., 235:539, 1946.
7. Deacon, W. E. Proc. Soc. Exper. Biol. & Med., 81:165, 1952.
8. Dienst, R. B., and others. J. Bact., 54:91, 1947.
9. ―― and others. Am. J. Syph., Gonor. & Ven. Dis., 34:189, 1950.
10. Eagle, W. W. Tr. Am. Therapeut. Soc., 41:1, 1941.
11. Edwards, P. R. J. Bact., 15:247, 1928; 17:339, 1929.
12. ―― and Ewing, W. H. Identification of Enterobacteriaceae, Minneapolis, Burgess Publishing Co., 2nd ed., 1961.
13. ―― and Fife, M. A. J. Bact., 70:382, 1955.
14. ―― and others. Pub. Health Lab., 13:57, 1955.
15. Eveland, W. C., and Faber, J. E., Jr. J. Infect. Dis., 93:226, 1953.
16. Falcao, P. C. Arch. Otolaryng., 45:46, 1947.
17. Fekety, F. R., Jr., and others. Ann. Int. Med., 57:214, 1962.
18. Friedländer, C. Virchows Arch. f. path. Anat., 87: 1882.
19. Ghosh, L. M., and Panja, D. Indian M. Gaz., 80:511, 1945.
20. Gastings, W. R. O., and Snijders, E. P. Zentralbl. f. Bakt., 136:1, 1936.
21. Greenblatt, R. B., and others. Am. J. Syph., Gonor. & Ven. Dis., 35:291, 1951.
21a. Grimes, M., and Hennery, A. J. Roy. Dublin Soc. Sic. Proc., 20:(WS) 89, 1931.
22. Henriksen, S. D. Acta path. et microbiol. Scandinav., 26:436, 1949.
23. Herrell, W. E., and Nichols, D. R. Proc. Staff Meet., Mayo Clin., 20:449, 1945.
24. Hormaeche, E., and Edwards, P. R. Internatl. Bull. Bact. Nomen. and Taxon., 10:71, 1960.
25. Hyde, L., and Hyde, B. Am. J. M. Sc., 205:660, 1943.
26. Jaffe, S. A. J.A.M.A., 122:292, 1943.
27. Julianelle, L. A. J. Bact., 30:535, 1935.
28. ―― Ann. Int. Med., 15:190, 1941.
29. Kauffmann, F. Acta path. et microbiol. Scandinav., 26:381, 1949.
30. ―― Enterobacteriaceae, 2nd ed., Copenhagen, Einar Monksgaard, 1954.
31. Lattimer, J. K., and others. J.A.M.A., 170:938, 1959.
32. Levine, M. G. Am. J. Clin. Path., 21:546, 1951.
33. Limson, B. M., and others. Ann. Int. Med., 44:1070, 1956.
34. Manfredi, F., and others. Ann. Int. Med., 58:642, 1962.
35. Martin, W. J., and others. Proc. Staff Meet. Mayo Clin., 29:541, 1954.
36. Mikulicz. Arch. f. Chir., 20, 1876.
37. Noller, E. C., and Hartsell, S. E. J. Bact., 81:482, 1960.
38. Olsson, R. A., and Romansky, M. J. Ann. Int. Med., 56:801, 1962.
39. Ørskov, I. Acta path. et microbiol. Scandinav., 34:145, 1954; 35:194, 1954.
40. Packer, H., and Goldberg, J. Am. J. Trop. Med., 30:387, 1950.
41. Perez, F. Ann. Inst. Pasteur, 13:937, 1899.
42. Pickett, M. J., and Cabelli, V. J. J. Gen. Microbiol., 9:249, 1953.
43. Rake, G. Am. J. Syph., Gonor. & Ven. Dis., 32:150, 1948.
44. ―― J. Bact., 55:865, 1948.
45. ―― and Oskay, J. J. J. Bact., 55:667, 1948.
46. Reyes, E. Arch. Dermat. & Syph., 54:531, 1946.
47. Sakazaka, R., and Namioka, S. J. Med. Sci. & Biol., 13:1, 1960.
48. Smith, D. T. Trans. Am. Clin. & Climatol. A., 58:94, 1947.
49. Som, M. L., and Jaffin, A. E. J. Mt. Sinai Hosp., 15:326, 1949.
50. Stuart, C. A., and others. J. Bact., 52:431, 1943.
51. Tartakoff, S., and others. New Eng. J. Med., 235:681, 1946.
52. Thornell, W. C. Proc. Staff Meet., Mayo Clin., 21:90, 1946.
53. Walcher, D. N. J. Clin. Investigation, 25:103, 1946.
54. Webster, L. T. J. Exper. Med., 52:909, 1930.
55. Whitaker, J. C., and others. Antibiotics and Chemotherapy, 1:208, 1951.
56. Wilkinson, J. F., and others. J. Gen. Microbiol., 11:59, 1954.
57. Zises, M., and Smith, G. C. Am. J. Syph., Gonor. & Ven. Dis., 35:294, 1951.

37

Serratia marcescens and Serratiosis

Family: *Enterobacteriaceae* Rahn. Tribe: *Serrateae*. Genus: *Serratia,* Bizio. Species: *Serratia marcescens*

In the 7th edition of Bergey's Manual the genus *Serratia* was the sole genus in the new tribe *Serrateae* in the family of *Enterobacteriaceae*. There were a number of specific species in addition to *S. marcescens*. However, the extensive studies of Davis, Ewing, and Reavis (2, 4, 6) showed conclusively that the *Serratia* were closely related to the *Klebsiella* and *Aerobacter* groups of organisms. In 1962 Ewing, Davis and Johnson (5) proposed that the genus *Serratia* Bizio, type species *Serratia marcescens* be placed in the tribe *Klebsielleae* Trevisan. Only one species—*S. marcescens*—was recognized, but another subspecies was differentiated and called *S. marcescens,* var. *kiliensis* (Lehmann and Neumann, Bergey et al., Ewing et al., *comb. nov.*). Strains of this subspecies alone fail to give a positive Voges-Proskauer test. Some strains produce pink, red, or magenta pigment and some strains have capsules, but most important, **from a practical diagnostic point of view, over three fourths of the strains studied by Ewing and his associates (6) in 1959 produced no pigment at all** (11, 15).

Serratia marcescens was discovered by Bizio in 1823 and known in the older literature as *Bacillus prodigiosus* (1a). It was considered a harmless saprophyte and was often sprayed into the air to study the drifting of air currents and the settling of bacteria.

Because of, and coincidental with, the introduction of sulfonamides and antibiotics, *S. marcescens* is being isolated in the laboratory with increasing frequency.

By 1955 it was realized (14) that agglutinins frequently appeared in the blood of laboratory workers exposed to aerosols containing *S. marcescens* and sometimes actual pulmonary diseases developed. Also, allergic reactions have been reported to these aerosol exposures (14). Other reports have shown that pulmonary disease, septicemia, and even death have resulted from infection with *S. marcescens* (1, 10, 13, 17, 18). The organisms have been isolated from urine (12) and from postoperative wounds (7).

The latest development is the discovery that *Serratia* may spread in epidemic form through the hospital in a manner analogous to the spread of penicillin-resistant staphylococci (5). The strains which cause each local epidemic belong to only one or two serotypes (5). Patients with burns are particularly susceptible, and one such patient, reported by Grabar and his associates (9), developed a septicemia and died with a syndrome resembling a generalized Shwartzman reaction.

In addition to actual infections, pigmented strains may grow as secondary invaders in old abscesses and bronchiectatic pockets in the lung and produce pigment in such profusion that the sputum is stained the exact color of blood (7, 16).

In the absence of pigmentation, the identification of a culture as a *Serratia* is complicated but can be done by a series of biochemical tests (Table 1). Gale and Sonnenwirth (8) reported that their cultures have the characteristic odor of trimethylamine.

Serratia strains are readily differentiated from *Klebsiella* on the basis of their positive reactions in ornithine medium, failure to produce gas from inositol, glycerol, and cellobiose, slowness and reluctance to ferment

Table 1. The Klebsiella-Aerobacter-Serratia Division
(Based on Reactions of the Majority of Cultures)

(Edwards and Ewing, 1961)

SUBSTRATE OR TEST	Klebsiella GROUP	Aerobacter SUBGROUP A/1	Aerobacter SUBGROUP B/1	Hafnia GROUP 37° C.	Hafnia GROUP 22° C.	Aerobacter SUBGROUP C/1 37° C.	Aerobacter SUBGROUP C/1 22° C.	Serratia GROUP
Gas from glucose	+	+	+	+	+	+	+	d *
Gas from inositol	+	−	+	−	−	+	+	−
Gas from glycerol	+	−	+	+	+	d	(+)	−
Gas from cellobiose	+	+	+	+	+	d	(+)	−
Sorbitol	+	+	+	−	−	+	+	+
Raffinose	+	+	+	−	−	+	+	−
Arabinose	+	+	+	+	+	+	+	−
Lactose	+	+	+	− or x	− or x	− or x	−	− or x
Malonate	+	+	d	d	d	−	−	−
Methyl Red	−	−	−	+	−	d	d	−
Voges-Proskauer	+	+	+	d	−	d	d	+ **
Gelatin	−	(+)	x	−		+		+
Urease	+ †	d †	−	−	−	−	−	− or (+) †
Hydrogen Sulf (TSI)	−	−	−	− or x	− or x	−	−	− or x
Lysine Decarbox.	+	−	+	+	+	d	+	+
Arginine Decarbox.	−	+	−	−	−	−	−	−
Ornithine Decarbox.	−	+	+	+	+	+	+	+
Motility	−	+	+	d	+	+	+	+
Pigment	−	−	−	−	−	−	−	d

* = When gas is formed the volumes are small (10 per cent or less).

† = Urease reaction not as rapid and usually not as strong as those given by *Proteus*.

** = Occasional strains may be V-P neg.

+ = Positive in 1 to 2 days.   − = Negative.   d = different biochemical type.

x = late or irregular positive.   (+) = delayed positive reactions.

1. Subgroup A corresponds to *Aerobacter cloacae*.
2. Subgroup B corresponds to *Aerobacter aerogenes*.
3. Subgroup C corresponds to *Aerobacter liquefaciens*.

lactose, failure to utilize malonate, rapid gelatin liquefaction, motility, and the small amount of gas produced in the aerogenic cultures. They can be differentiated from the *Aerobacter* group by their failure to produce gas from inositol, glycerol, and cellobiose, reluctance to produce acid from lactose, failure to utilize malonate, and the small volume of gas produced in fermentable carbohydrates. Also, lysine decarboxylation aids in the differentiation of *Serratia* and *Aerobacter cloacae* (subgroup A) strains. *Aerobacter liquefaciens* (Grimes and Hennerty) (subgroup C) frequently forms gas from inositol, glycerol and cellobiose, while *Serratia* do not. *A. liquefaciens* produce acid from arabinose and raffinose, while the *Serratia* strains, with rare exception, do not. *A. liquefaciens* strains do not ferment adonitol where the majority of *Serratia* do so. The *Serratia* may be differ-

entiated from members of the *Hafnia* group by the failure of the *Serratia* to form gas from glycerol and cellobiose by the fermentation of sorbitol, by negative M-R and positive V-P reaction at 37 rapid liquefaction of gelatin, and by the small amounts of gas from fermented substances. The majority of *Serratia* ferment adonitol and inositol, where the *Hafnia* do not.

The methods for differentiating *Serratia* from the occasional *Proteus mirabilis*, which is both urease-negative and V-P positive, from the Proteus-Providence division, *Aeromonas* species, and from Erwineae can be obtained by consulting the *Identification of Enterobacteriaceae* by Edwards and Ewing (1961).

Over 100 cultures have been studied by Ewing, Davis, Reavis, and Johnson (4, 5, 6), and 15 O antigen group and 13 flagellar antigens have been identified. Escobar and Mc-

Clung studied 80 strains and found nine somatic O antigens and nine flagellar antigens (3).

Treatment. *Serratia* resembles the other members of the *Enterobacteriaceae* and especially the *Klebsiellae* in the rapidity with which they become resistant to a single antibiotic. Resistant strains may then become endemic hospital strains resembling penicillin-resistant strains of staphylococci.

Pulmonary infections have been treated successfully with kanamycin supplemented with sulfonamides (1). Perhaps two antibiotics should be given simultaneously to reduce the mutation rate.

REFERENCES

1. Bernard, L. A., and Sutton, W. C. Arch. Int. Med., 105:311, 1960.
1a. Bizio, Bib. Ital. Gior. lett. Sci., 30:288, 1823.
2. Davis, B. R., and others. Internat. Bull. of Bact. Nomen. & Tax., 7:151, 1957.
3. Escobar, M. R., and McClung, L. S. Bact. Proc., 1963, p. 38.
4. Ewing, W. H., and others. Int. Bull. Bact. Nomen. & Taxon., 12:47, 1962.
5. ———— Johnson, J. C., and Davis, B. R. The Occurrence of Senatra Marceseae in Noscomial Infections. Pub. Health Serv., C.D.C., Atlanta, Ga., 1962.
6. ———— and others. Studies on the Serratia Group. Pub. Health Serv., C.D.C., Atlanta, Ga., 1959.
7. Gale, D., and Lord, J. D. J.A.M.A., 164:1328, 1957.
8. ———— and Sonnenwirth, A. C. Arch. Int. Med., 109:90, 1962.
9. Graber, C. D., and others. Surg., Gynec., Obstet., 110:443, 1960.
10. Hawe, A. J., and Hughes, M. H. Brit. Med. J., 1:968, 1954.
11. Labrum, E. L., and Bunting, M. I. J. Bact., 65:394, 1953.
12. Lancaster, L. J. Arch. Int. Med., 109:536, 1962.
13. Patterson, R. H., Jr., and others. Arch. Int. Med., 90:79, 1952.
14. Reitman, M., and others. Proc. Soc. Exper. Biol. & Med., 89:236, 1955.
15. Rizki, M. T. M. J. Bact., 80:305, 1960.
16. Robinson, W., and Wolley, P. B. Lancet, 1:819, 1957.
17. Wassermann, M. M., and Seligman, E. J. Bact., 66:119, 1953.
18. Wheat, R. P., and others. Arch. Int. Med., 88:461, 1951.

38

Escherichia coli and Related Organisms

Family: *Enterobacteriaceae* Rahn. Genus: *Escherichia* Castellani and Chalmers.
Species: *Escherichia coli* (Migula) Castellani and Chalmers

When aerobic culture methods are employed, the colon bacilli are found as the dominant organisms in the feces of man and animals. The microorganism was described by Buchner (6) in 1885 and studied in detail by Escherich in 1886 (20).

Colon bacilli gain entrance to the intestinal tract shortly after birth and persist throughout life. They are present in greatest quantity in the region of the ileocecal valve and diminish in numbers upward toward the duodenum and downward as far as the rectum. Colon bacilli probably serve a useful function in the body by suppressing the growth of certain proteolytic organisms normally present in the intestines and by synthesizing appreciable amounts of vitamins (33). Certain B-complex vitamin deficiencies cannot be produced by dietary restrictions in animals unless the colon bacilli first are eliminated or suppressed by the feeding of large amounts of sulfonamides (7).

The normal flora of *Enterobacteriaceae* is not essentially different in man (87), cats and dogs (88), and the common gartersnake (57). The strains carried by a particular man or animal are individualistic, and it is difficult to implant new ones (88). Certain strains of *E. coli* produce bactericidal polypeptides, called "**colicin**," which prevent the growth of other *E. coli* strains, and many of the *Shigella,* and may account in part for the difficulty in implanting new strains (35).

Until recently the importance of *E. coli* as the etiologic agent in disease has been underestimated. Three types of disease may be produced: (1) These organisms are the most important single cause of pyelitis and pyelonephritis, and they can produce abscesses in internal organs, septicemia, endocarditis, and meningitis. (2) Certain serotypes produce a severe and often fatal type of epidemic diarrhea in infants. (3) They are the cause of sporadic, nonepidemic summer diarrhea which occurs in older children during their second and third summers of life. This type of diarrhea is caused by irritating metabolic products produced by the colon bacilli and is not a true infection.

In addition to the general physiologic effects of *E. coli* and their ability to produce disease, these organisms **are important** to the sanitarian when found in food or water **as an index of fecal contamination.**

Morphology and Staining. *Escherichia coli* is a short, plump rod, 0.4 to 0.7 μ in width and 1 to 4 μ in length (Fig. 1). Coccoid forms and short chains of organisms are found often in exudates and young cultures. **Motility** varies greatly in different cultures, some strains showing active motility, others moving sluggishly,

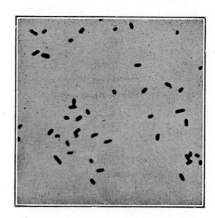

Fig. 1. *Escherichia coli.* From a smooth culture. × 1,200.

and some showing no motility whatever. **Spores are not formed** but **capsules** occur in a small percentage of the strains. The organisms are **gram-negative** and stain uniformly with the usual aniline dyes. No characteristic internal structures occur.

Cultural Characteristics. The colon bacilli are **aerobic** but facultatively anaerobic. They grow readily in 24 hours on all the usual laboratory media at temperatures ranging from 20° to 40° C. Their synthesizing powers are so well developed that the bacilli will grow in a medium consisting of inorganic salts, an ammonium salt, and glucose.

On **agar** plates surface colonies appear within 12 to 24 hours, reaching a size of 2 to 3 mm. in 48 hours. There is considerable variation in the appearance of individual colonies. The typical colony is low, convex, smooth, and colorless but rather opaque, with an entire edge. Some colonies are smaller and more dome-shaped, while others produce a typical grapeleaf-like colony. **On blood agar** a discoloration is produced in the medium immediately around the colony and **beta hemolysis** is produced by some strains. On **Endo's medium** and on **eosin methylene blue medium** colonies of *E. coli* have a peculiar metallic sheen which is seen best when they are examined with reflected light. Homogeneous clouding of **broth** is produced in 12 to 48 hours, and in 24 to 48 hours slight pellicle formation occurs and a slimy deposit collects in the bottom of the tube. **Indol** usually is formed in **peptone broth** but **gelatin is not liquefied.**

Glucose, lactose, maltose, and other sugars are fermented with the production of **acid** and **gas.** About 50 per cent of the strains ferment sucrose and have been named *E. coli communior,* while the other 50 per cent, which fail to ferment this sugar, are called *E. coli communis.* The failure to ferment sucrose has no biologic significance.

Cultures of the colon bacilli are characterized by a fetid odor not unlike that of diluted feces. The acid formed by carbohydrate fermentation is chiefly **lactic acid** with smaller amounts of **formic** and **acetic acids.** Both **carbon dioxide** and **hydrogen** are produced in approximately equal amounts.

Resistance. Colon bacilli survive for weeks in cultures stored at room temperature and for months in soil and water. Their resistance to the usual antiseptics is equal to or slightly greater than that of the micrococci. Most strains are killed in 15 to 20 minutes by a temperature of 60° C., but some survive the pasteurization process and may spoil the color

and flavor of milk. In water purification, chlorine in concentrations of 0.5 to 1 part per million is an effective bactericide for *A. aerogenes, E. coli,* and the various species of *Salmonella* and *Shigella.*

Brilliant green selectively inhibits the growth of species of *Escherichia, Aerobacter,* and *Shigella* but is less effective against *Salmonella* organisms. **Sodium desoxycholate** in the presence of **sodium citrate** inhibits the growth of *Escherichia* and *Aerobacter* with little effect on *Salmonella* or *Shigella.* Caffeine, lithium chloride, potassium tellurite, selenium salts, and tetrathionate all have a differential inhibiting action on the growth of colon bacilli and other members of the enteric group (51). These inhibiting substances are added to the selective and differential media to suppress the growth of *E. coli,* and gram-positive organisms and thus favor the growth of *Shigella* and *Salmonella.*

Variability. Under suitable conditions, *E. coli* can develop the usual M, S, and R types of colonies. Most strains of *E. coli,* when first isolated from lesions or from feces, are motile and in the S phase. The M phase is found less frequently than the S and often is less pathogenic than some of the S forms (45). A small G type colony has been studied by Colwell (10). The dissociate lacks the ability to produce gas from carbohydrates but regains this ability when it reverts to the original large form.

The biochemical reactions and antigenic structure may show variations corresponding to the colony changes, but frequently these changes cannot be correlated in any consistent manner. In one study of 132 cultures stored for two years, 59 showed changes either in biochemical properties or colony morphology, or both (71). Stuart and others (94) observed variations in 47 of 191 strains.

Interest has centered around the strains of *E. coli* known as *E. coli mutabile* since their discovery by Neisser (64) and Massini (56). These strains grow profusely in lactose broth but ferment this carbohydrate only after incubation for seven days or longer. When plated on **Endo's medium,** they grow rapidly and are colorless until small red "papillae" appear on the mother colony. Subcultures from these red papillae maintain the ability to produce red lactose-fermenting colonies, while subcultures taken from the colorless portions of the mother colony continue to produce colorless colonies which, in time, give rise to lactose-fermenting variants at a constant rate of 1 in each 100,000 cells (39). Other strains of *E. coli,* isolated by Parr and Simpson (76), show the same constant type of dissociation with the mutants acquiring the ability to grow with citric acid as the sole source of carbon. Parr's strains have been used to study some of the basic problems concerned in bacterial mutability (108). These mutable strains of E. coli usually are considered nonpathogenic, but Dulaney and Michelson (18) found this organism, in almost pure cultures, in the stools of a group of children with epidemic diarrhea. E. coli, as well as the entire family of Enterobacteriaceae, appears to be in an active state of evolution (77).

Antigenic Structure. The antigenic structure of E. coli has been studied for years by Kauffmann (46, 47), Ewing (23), and Edwards and Ewing (19). The specific serologic type is dependent upon three classes of antigen: (1) the O somatic antigens, which are not inactivated by heat at 100° C.; (2) the K somatic antigens, which occur as sheath envelopes or as capsules which act as masking antigens to inhibit O agglutination and are inactivated by heat at 100° or 121° C.; and (3) the H, or flagella, antigens which are inactivated by heat at 100° C. The K antigen, as emphasized by Kauffmann (45) is merely a convenient designation for all of the sheath or envelope antigens which inhibit agglutination of living Enterobacteriaceae in O antiserum. There are at least three varieties of K antigen based upon physical behavior. These are L, A, and B, and L can be differentiated from B by heating at 100° C., since this inactivates the binding power of L but not B. The antigenicity of B is destroyed by heat at 100° C. for one hour but 120° C. for two and one-half hours is required to inactivate the antigenicity of A (19).

By 1962, 145 O antigen groups, 86 K antigens and 49 H antigens were known (19).

In addition to these specific antigens, Duguid and his associates (17) have described **fimbrial** antigens which are not specific but have the capacity to agglutinate erythrocytes. As a further complication, Kunin (52, 53, 54) discovered a common enteric hapten in E. coli 014 which produced antibodies that would react with Salmonella, Shigella, and other Enterobacteriae. This antigen is precipitable by ethanol but not inactivated by ether, trypsin, perodontate, or phenol. It is relatively resistant to acid hydrolysis and could not be separated from the O antigen by the Boivin or Westphal methods or by Sephadex chromatography, but could be isolated by elution from DEAE cellulose with 0.1-0.2 molar NaCl in tris buffer

(54). The presence of this common hapten in E. coli 014 has been confirmed by Whang and Neter (106).

Two types of sialic acid occur on the surface of certain strains of E. coli but they are not related to the surface K antigens (15).

In addition to specific antibodies, which are frequently present in human sera, Waisbren and Brown (103) have studied a bactericidal activity of human sera against E. coli. This factor was not related to age, and its activity was heat-labile but could not be restored by the addition of fresh guinea pig complement. The immunofluorescent technic has been employed by Thompson (98) and Nelson (65) and their associates in the study of enteropathic types of E. coli. While of some value in a rapidly spreading epidemic, they are no more specific and final than a slide agglutination with the OB antiserum and is not recommended by Edwards and Ewing as a substitute for a complete serologic study, especially since other types of E. coli or even Salmonella or Shigella may be introduced during an epidemic initiated by E. coli.

E. coli in Infantile Diarrhea. Bray and Beavan (4) in this country, and Varela, Aquirre and Carillo in Mexico City independently associated a specific serologic type of E. coli with infantile diarrhea. This organism is now classified as 111:B4 and is known to be world-wide in distribution. Furthermore, one strain became resistant to neomycin and this initiated a major epidemic among children in Metropolitan Chicago and northwestern Indiana in 1960-1961 (50). A second major epidemic type was described by Giles and his associates (34) in 1949 and later identified as 055:B4. Other important types isolated from infantile diarrhea can be seen in Table 1 from Ewing.

Pathogenicity apparently depends upon certain types of O and K somatic antigens. It is not surprising, therefore, that the O antigens of some 10 serotypes of Shigella are identical with certain serotypes of E. coli (25) and that E. coli serotypes O 112 a, 112 c have the same O antigens and related but not identical K (B) antigens as Sh. dysenteriae 2 (25).

Rantz (82) studied the E. coli serotype isolated from 156 patients with urinary infections. Strains of groups 2, 4, 6, and 75 were isolated from 49.3 per cent of the urines of those patients. **About 45 per cent of the infections were acquired** in the hospital, usually following catheterization. Turck and his associates (100) studied 522 strains of E. coli isolated from patients with urinary infections, bac-

Table 1. Most Prevalent Escherichia coli Serotypes Reported in Diarrheal Disease
(Ewing, 1963)

O Antigens	K Antigens	H Antigens (and Synonyms)
26	60 (B6)	NM (Nonmotile) (E893) 11, 32
55a	59 (B5)	NM (*B*) 6, 7
86a	61 (B7)	NM (E990) 11, 34
111a, 111b	58 (B41)	NM (*a*) 2, (D433) 4, .2, 21
112a, 112c	66 (B11)	NM (Guahabara)
119	69 (B14)	NM 6 (Aberdeen) 537, 52
124	72 (B17)	NM 30
125a, 125b	70 (B15)	19 (Canioni)
125a, 125c	70	15, 21
126	71 (B16)	NM, 2 (E611) 27
127a	63 (B8)	NM (Holcomb)
128a, 128b	67 (B12)	2 (Cigleris) 789, 12
128a, 123c	67	NM 12

The simple numerical designation applied above to the K antigens is in accordance with the nomenclature recommended by Kauffmann et al., 1956, International Bulletin of Bacteriological Nomenclature and Taxonomy, 6:63, 64. For references to descriptive literature regarding these serotypes, the reader is referred to Ewing, Wallis, and Montague (23).

teremia, abscesses, pulmonary infection, and other nonenteric sources. These strains were isolated in hospitals in Seattle, Washington, Salt Lake City, Utah, and Baltimore, Maryland. Although 54 different O groups were identified, groups 1, 4, 6, and 75 accounted for 58 per cent of the groupable infections.

Bacteriophages. Bacteriophages are limited in their ability to infect strains of *E. coli* which are devoid of capsules or envelope antigens (44, 45), but some types specific for encapsulated *E. coli* have been reported (99).

Bacterial Metabolites. In the fermentation of glucose, *E. coli* produces carbon dioxide and hydrogen in approximately equal proportions. In contrast, *A. aerogenes* produces, from the same quantity of glucose, twice as much carbon dioxide as hydrogen. *E. coli* forms catalase and synthesizes vitamins of the B complex (33). Living metabolizing bacilli of some strains of *E. coli* produce a fibrinolytic substance. This material is produced most often by strains which are highly virulent for mice (109). Like other members of the enteric bacteria, the somatic antigens are **endotoxins.** A separate necrotizing factor is produced by most pathogenic strains (46).

Spontaneous Disease in Animals. Theobald Smith (91) found several strains of encapsulated *E. coli* which could produce "scours" in newborn malnourished calves. Calves could be protected by the administration of an antibacterial serum or by improving the feeding and housing conditions of their mothers (58). This is an excellent example of the **conditional pathogenicity** exhibited by *E. coli.*

Although household pets, such as cats and dogs (58), may be temporary carriers of *E. coli* strains which are pathologic for man, and an infection in an 11-month-old infant has been definitely traced to a dog, in general the strains isolated from disease states in swine, calves, and chickens have their own specific serotypes. For example, Ewing (26) identified two new serotypes (O group 138 and 138 K 8 1 (B) and 82 (B)) among strains isolated from edema disease in swine. In this instance some of the cultures were isolated in Ireland and some in the United States.

Experimental Disease in Laboratory Animals. Guinea pigs, rabbits, and mice are killed by the endotoxins of *E. coli*. Strains possessing the necrotizing toxin produce abscesses when injected subcutaneously. Pneumonitis with focal areas of necrosis results from the intratracheal injection of living or dead *E. coli* into rabbits (16). Serotype O11:B4 was found in an epidemic of diarrhea in monkeys (24, 28).

Prolonged septic arthritis has been produced in the knees of rabbits by the interarticular injection of endotoxins derived from 0:113 strain of *E. coli* (2, 3).

Clinical Types of Infection in Man. *E. coli,* as noted in the introduction to this chapter, may be associated with three different types of disease: (1) sporadic infections of the internal organs; (2) epidemic diarrhea in infants, and (3) sporadic "summer" diarrhea in older children.

Colon bacilli are the most frequent cause

of cystitis, pyelitis, and pyelonephritis and are a frequent cause of appendicitis and peritonitis. Puerperal sepsis and infections of the gall bladder, bile ducts, and liver are not infrequent. In rare instances, colon bacilli produce meningitis, septicemia (47), and endocarditis (102). Infections of the sinuses, bronchi, and lungs have become more frequent since the introduction of the sulfonamides and antibiotics.

Epidemic diarrhea, caused by certain specific serotypes of *E. coli* (Table 1) has become a scourge in hospital nurseries (4, 28, 29, 30, 34). The disease is always severe and frequently fatal. Clinical and bacteriologic relapses are the rule rather than an exception. The disease may be introduced by an attendant and transmitted by inanimate objects in the nursery. The infants show a rising titer of agglutinins or hemoagglutinins (70, 95). The same serotypes attack adults and produce diarrhea but the disease is not as severe in adults and older children as in infants. It has been reproduced in human volunteers by feeding cultures isolated during epidemics (28, 29, 67, 68, 69). The history of our knowledge of this newly dis-

covered disease has been reviewed by Neter (66, 68), Cooper (11), and Ewing and Edwards (19, 28). The methods employed in the isolation of these *E. coli* are shown in Table 2.

The nonspecific, sporadic type of diarrhea usually occurs during the child's second summer of life. In dehydrated children *E. coli* sometimes invades the jejunum and duodenum and produces irritating acids by fermentation of the lactose fraction in the ingested milk. These acids and other metabolites of *E. coli* irritate the bowel, causing violent nausea, vomiting, and diarrhea. The resulting disease is called **summer diarrhea** in the modern textbooks of pediatrics but in the older books on medicine it was labeled "Cholera Infantum." This syndrome may result in death in two to four days (13, 14).

Diarrhea of Travelers. It has been known for generations that travelers visiting Mexico, Central and South America, Europe, and Asia frequently have bouts of diarrhea which at first were attributed to changes in climate and especially changes in water. Later amoeba, *Salmonella,* and *Shigella* and still later viruses were incriminated.

Table 2. Outline of Methods for Examination of Stool Specimens in Cases of Infantile Diarrhea

(Edwards and Ewing, 1955)

| Freeze portion for virus work | Plating and enrichment media for *Salmonella* and *Shigella* serotypes | Plating media for *E. coli* serotypes blood agar MacConkey or EMB agar | Buffered glycerol-saline preservative, if specimen must be mailed |

| Test 10 or more individual colonies in *E. coli* antiserums (slide tests) | | Transfer 3 or more colonies to plain agar slants |

| Prepare dense suspensions in 0.5 per cent NaCl solution and test with *E. coli* antiserums in slide tests. If agglutination occurs, heat the suspensions (20 to 30 min., 100° C.), cool, and retest in antiserums | Biochemical Tests: *E. coli* |

Glucose	Acid and gas *
Lactose	Acid and gas **
Sucrose	Acid and gas or negative
H₂S (TSI)	Not produced
Urease	Not produced
Indol	Produced
MR test	Positive
VP test	Negative
Simmons' citrate agar	No growth †
Motility	+ or −
Stock medium	

* Some *E. coli* strains are anaerogenic.
** Certain *E. coli* strains may require more than 24 hours to produce acid from lactose.
† Occasional strains, otherwise typical, may grow on citrate agar. Usually such reactions are delayed.

Recent studies have exonerated these well-known pathogens, including the viruses (48, 49, 101). By elimination, *E. coli* came to be suspected, and clinical trials with **neomycin sulphate or phthalylsulfathiazole** as a prophylactic worked so well that we must conclude that they are probably the cause. Many South and Central American friends tell me that when they visit the United States, they have the same diarrheal disease, suggesting that we, like they, are probably immune to the local strains.

Treatment. The replacement of the depleted water and electrolytes usually effects a cure in the summer diarrhea syndrome. Chloramphenicol, the tetracyclines, and neomycin have been used with success in the epidemic diarrhea of infants (12, 13). The sporadic infections of the internal organs are treated with the same series of antibiotics but are difficult to cure since resistant strains develop with great rapidity.

The complications encountered in the treatment of pyelonephritis have been reviewed by Jackson and his associates (43).

Prevention. The summer diarrhea syndrome can be prevented by feeding the children lactic acid milk (14). The epidemic diarrhea of infants can be prevented by rigid isolation technic in the nursery.

ESCHERICHIA AURESCENS

This pigmented colon bacillus was isolated by Parr (74) in 1937 from a fecal specimen where it was the only representative of the colon group. The pigment varies from golden yellow to brown or red, depending upon the medium employed. The studies of Malligo and his associates (55) showed that the pigment was a nonwater-soluble carotenoid which was quite different from the pigment of the genus *Serratia*. The latter authors have suggested the name *Escherichia aurescens* (Parr) Comp. Nov. 1955.

PROTEUS SPECIES AND PROTEUS INFECTIONS

Family: *Enterobacteriaceae* Rahn. Tribe: *Proteeae*. Genus: *Proteus* Hauser. Type Species: *Proteus vulgaris* Hauser

In the 7th edition of Bergey's Manual, one genus, *Proteus,* is recognized in the tribe *Proteeae* with five species. These are *Proteus vul-*

garis Hauser (36), *Proteus mirabilis* Hauser, *Proteus morganii* (Winslow *et al.*) Rauss, *Proteus rettgeri* (Hadley *et al.*) Rustigian and Stuart, and *Proteus inconstans* as proposed by Shaw and Clarke (89).

Proteus inconstans is the new name for the old **Providence group.** Kauffmann suggested this name in 1951 for the intermediate bacteria described by Stuart and coworkers in 1943-46 as the 29911 paracolon bacteria (5). Ewing (21) and Edwards and Ewing (19) objected to the organisms in the Providence group being designated *P. inconstans*.

The *Proteeae* contain motile bacteria that conform to the general definition of *Enterobactericeae*. They decompose urea rapidly and actively deaminate phenylalanine to phenylpyruvic acid (38, 40). Lactose is not fermented. Two species, *P. vulgaris* and *P. mirabilis,* produce hydrogen sulfide rapidly and abundantly, liquefy gelatin, and **swarm** on moist agar media. *P. morganii* and *P. rettgeri* do not possess these peculiar characteristics. The Providence group resembles the latter two species in several respects, but they are very different from *P. vulgaris* or *P. mirabilis.* Ewing (21) has proposed genus 2 *Providencia* Kauffmann and Edwards, with two species, *Providencia alcalifaciens* (DeSalles Gomez) and *Providencia stuartii* (Buttiaux *et al.*) Ewing. This proposal has not been acted upon by the Committee on Nomenclature, so we are following the procedure used by Edwards and Ewing (19), who designated the organisms which produce gas in **adonitol** but not in **inositol** as *Providencia*, subgroup A, (*P. alcalifaciens*) and these produce gas in **inositol** but not in **adonitol** (*P. stuartii*).

The biochemical reactions of the four old recognized species are given in Table 3. The biochemical reactions of most value in identifying *Providencia* subgroup A from subgroup B are shown in Table 4.

Serologic Identification. Perch (78, 79) characterized 40 O antigenic groups and 10 flagellar groups for *P. vulgaris* and *P. mirabilis*. In 1959 Rauss and Voros (83) devised an antigenic schema for *P. morganii* which contained 29 O groups and 19 flagellar antigens and delineated 57 serotypes. The Japanese investigators Namioka and Sakazaki (62) devised a classification for *P. rettgeri* which was composed of 34 O antigenic groups, 26 flagellar antigens, and 45 serotypes. Ewing, Tanner, and Dennard (25) studied 16 antigens of the Providence group in 1954 and found 56 O antigenic groups, 28 flagellar antigenic groups, as well as several K antigens which identified 125 serologic groups. Subsequently they extended the O antigenic

Table 3. Biochemical Reactions of Proteus Cultures

(Edwards and Ewing, 1951)

	P. vulgaris	P. mirabilis	P. morganii	P. rettgeri
Indol	+	O	+	+
H₂S	+1	+	O	O
Voges-Proskauer	O2	+(O)	O	O
Simmon's Citrate	O(+)	+(O)	O	+
Glucose	++	++	++	+3
Lactose	O	O	O	O
Mannitol	O	O	O	+
Sucrose	++	++	O4	+3
Maltose	++	O	O	O
Salicin	++(O)	O(++)	O	+(O)
Urea	+	+	+	+

+ = acid production, ++ = acid and gas (bubble to 15%) production, O = no change. +(O) = usually positive, O(+) = usually negative, occasional strains positive. 1 = a rare strain may be negative, 2 = occasionally an old laboratory strain may be positive, fresh isolated cultures, negative, 3 = sometimes a bubble of gas is produced, 4 = occasional strains may be positive.

groups to 62, the flagellar antigen to 30, and the known serotypes to 156 (19). A new K antigen, designated C-antigen, was identified by Namioka and Sakazaki (63) in strains of *Proteus rettgeri, P. morganii,* and the Providence group but not in the other enteric bacterial groups.

Edwards and Ewing (19) report that members of the Providence group grow well on eosin methylene blue, SS, and MacConkey agars, producing colonies which resemble those of *Salmonella* or *Shigella*. However, in contrast to *Shigella,* Providence group cultures grow well on bismuth sulfate (Wilson, Blair) agar, producing colorless, light green or olive green colonies which occasionally are slightly dark or have a metallic sheen. There is practically no growth on brilliant green agar. In Kligler's iron agar and triple sugar iron agar (TSI) the reactions simulate those of *Shigella* except for the occasional appearance of a small amount of gas in the butt of the tubes. Although sucrose is utilized by most strains, fermentation is delayed and therefore not apparent in TSI agar.

Strains of *Proteus* are next to *E. coli* in the frequency with which they produce infections in the urinary tract. They may be even more destructive in the kidney because of the urease activity. Braude and Siemienski (2) demonstrated this in an experiment in which the urease activity was preserved by killing the *P. mirabilis* with acetone, after which the dead organisms were injected intramuscularly into rats. Extensive areas of destruction appeared in the kidneys of these rats but not in comparable control animals injected with *E. coli*.

In addition to urinary infection, *Proteus* strains have been isolated from stools in acute dysentery (37) and from the blood (1) in instances of bacteremia.

Weil and Felix (104) studied both the motile

Table 4. Subdivisions of the Providence Groups Based upon Detailed Studies with 669 Cultures

(Edwards and Ewing, 1961)

SUBDIVISIONS	NUMBER OF CULTURES	GAS +	GAS −	ADONITOL +	ADONITOL −	INOSITOL +	INOSITOL −	PER CENT OF SUBGROUP
Subgroup A	561 (84%)							
biogroup 1	490	490	0	490	0	4	486	87.1
2	28	0	28	28	0	0	28	5.0
3	20	20	0	0	20	0	20	3.6
4	24	0	24	0	24	0	24	4.3
Subgroup B	107 (16%)							
biogroup 5	101	0	101	0	101	101	0	94.5
6	6	0	6	6	0	6	0	5.5

spreading type and the nonmotile variant of *P. vulgaris.* They introduced the terms "H" (*Hauch* = film) and "O" (*Ohne Hauch* = without film) to designate the motile and the nonmotile forms. Since that time, "H" has been used synonymously with flagellar antigen and O with somatic antigen. These terms also are used to designate the type of agglutination: "H agglutination" refers to the clumping of organisms into large, soft, and loose masses resembling snow flakes, and "O" agglutination refers to the fine granular hail-stone type of clumping.

Weil and Felix (104) isolated strains of *Proteus vulgaris* from patients with typhus fever and found that the serums of the patients agglutinated particular *Proteus* strains designated X19 and X2. Since the reacting antigen is located in the body of the organism, the nonmotile OX19 and OX2 strains are used generally for agglutinating antigens. The *Proteus* organism is not the cause of typhus fever. The cross-agglutination seems to be caused by the presence of an alkali-stabile polysaccharide which is also present in *Rickettsia prowazekii* (9, 107). The agglutination of these particular strains by serums of patients with *Rickettsiae* infections is known as the **Weil-Felix reaction.**

The OX19 strain is agglutinated by the serums of patients convalescing from epidemic and endemic typhus fever and spotted fever, but not by those infected with other *Rickettsiae.* Another *Proteus* strain, OXK, isolated in 1923 by Kingsbury, gives specific reactions with serums from patients convalescing from **scrub typhus.**

Proteus morganii (Winslow and Others) Rauss. This organism was isolated by Morgan in 1906 from patients with summer diarrhea. It usually produces a disease resembling *Shigella* dysentery but may cause *Salmonella*-like fevers (37). The mortality from bacteremia in 48 cases was 64.4 per cent (1), but has been moderately reduced by antibiotic therapy (92).

ALCALIGENES FAECALIS

Alcaligenes faecalis, or *Bacillus faecalis alcaligenes,* was isolated by Petruschky (80) from stale beer. It is a normal inhabitant of the intestinal tract and on selective media produces colorless colonies which resemble those of the *Salmonella.* It is a short, plump, **gram-negative** bacillus which is **feebly motile** and possesses poorly developed peritrichal flagella (77).

It ferments none of the usual carbohydrates, does not form indol or **liquefy gelatin** and is not agglutinated by polyvalent *Salmonella* serums.

Moore and Pickett (60) have reviewed the literature and personally studied 40 strains of gram-negative rods which resemble *Alcaligenes* in failing to attack carbohydrates. They concluded that the genus *Alcaligenes* could be abandoned, since organisms with peritrichalis flagella, which fit the original description, are rarely isolated and could be logically incorporated in the genus *Acromobacter.* The more numerous *Lobotrichous* species could be included in the *Lophomonas* genus as *L. Alcaligenes.* Ikari and Hugh (41a) studied 12 strains of polar monotrichous nonfermenting bacilli and suggested the name *Pseudomonas alcaligenes.*

While usually saprophytic, either one or both of these organisms occasionally are associated with enteritis and have been isolated from the blood, meninges, liver, kidneys, biliary tract, eye, and lymph nodes (105).

BACTERIUM ANITRATUM

About 1947 an organism having the general cultural characteristics of other *Enterobacteriaceae* except for its **failure to reduce nitrates to nitrites** was isolated independently in three different laboratories (31, 32, 86, 94). Most cultures have been recovered from urinary infections, but some also have been obtained from the blood, pleural fluid, and sputum. Over 20 cases of acute and chronic meningitis have been reported (93), and 42 cases of miscellaneous infection (84). This organism is pathogenic for mice and guinea pigs (86).

The colonies when grown on deoxycholate agar plates, are mucoid and usually have a pale pink color but may be yellowish or colorless (12, 85). Citrate is utilized, but the strains are indol-negative, H_2S-negative, Voges-Proskauer-negative, and MR-negative and failed to hydrolyze urea or reduce nitrates to nitrites. The white mucoid colonies readily dissociate to flat, translucent blue gray colonies. The organisms are gram-negative and coccoid on solid media and are readily confused with *Neisseria,* but in fluid media there is a mixture of coccoid and bacillary forms. The slide agglutination technic of Cary, Lindberg and Faber (8) afford a rapid method for differentiating the diplococcal form from the *Neisseria.*

Papavassiliou (73) studied 20 strains and found that 19 were lysogenic and active against several sensitive indicator strains. The serologic studies of Mitchel and Burrell (59) confirm the previous impression that the *Mima, Herellea,* and *Moraxella* organisms are all related if not identical.

Taplin and his associates (96) have found

that at least 25 per cent of normal males carry *H. vaginicola* somewhere on the skin surface, and 10 per cent carry *M. polymorpha.*

In addition to its other activities, this organism is now appearing as a secondary infection, invading patients with severe burns. This same organism has already been discussed in the chapters on *Neisseria* and *Haemophilus.* The morphology of the organism is shown in the chapter on *Neisseria.*

EXAMINATION OF WATER FOR FECAL CONTAMINATION

It is not a practical procedure to isolate *Shigella* or *Salmonella* from samples of water. The colon bacilli, however, grow readily if present and serve as a convenient index of fecal contamination. *Aerobacter aerogenes, Aerobacter cloacae,* and *Klebsiella* occur in the feces of man and animals and would have the same significance as *E. coli* as an indication of fecal contamination. Although *Aerobacter aerogenes* is more abundant in the soil than in fecal specimens, its presence in a sample of water indicates surface water contamination and should be considered potentially dangerous (97). In practice the sanitarian tests water for the presence of gram-negative, lactose-fermenting bacilli and labels them **coliform bacteria** without attempting to classify the genera and species (75).

Salmonella have been isolated directly from sewage by Moore in England (61). He and his associates suspended strips of gauze in the flowing sewage which were periodically removed and cultured for *Salmonella.* By this method, Shearer and his associates (90) located the residence of a carrier who was causing an epidemic of typhoid fever in a small town in California.

A determination of the total number of easily cultivated organisms is obtained by adding known amounts of the water sample to nutrient agar medium and pouring two plates, one of which is incubated at 20° C. and the other at 37° C. Native water and soil organisms grow best at 20° C., while organisms of animal origin grow more rapidly at 37° C. The total count of colonies on the two plates gives some rough idea as to the number of each type present.

The **presumptive test** for the presence of coliform organisms is performed by adding 10 ml., 1 ml., or 0.1 ml., of water to each of three large tubes of lactose broth. If no acid develops in any of the tubes the possibility of fecal organisms is eliminated. The presence of acid is only a presumptive positive test, since certain yeast and gram-positive bacilli will ferment lactose.

To **confirm** the test, a sample from the tube showing the fermentation of lactose from the smallest amount of water is streaked on an eosin methylene blue plate and inoculated into brilliant green lactose bile broth. If fermentation occurs in the broth and typical colonies of *E. coli* appear on the E.M.B. plates, the test is confirmed.

To **complete the test,** typical colonies are picked from the E.M.B. plates and inoculated in lactose broth and streaked on an agar slant. If the lactose broth is fermented and smears from the slant show gram-negative bacilli morphologically consistent with *E. coli,* the test is considered completed and positive.

In addition to a reasonably low total count and the absence of coliform bacteria in the samples tested, the water must be satisfactory as to taste, odor, and color, and contain less than the following minimal amounts of chemical impurities: lead, 0.1 ppm; copper, 0.3 ppm; fluorine, 1.5 ppm; arsenic and selenium, 0.05 ppm; iron and magnesium, 125 ppm; zinc, 15 ppm; chloride and sulfate, 250 ppm; phenol, 0.001 ppm; and total solids, 500 ppm.

The standards recommended by the United States Public Health Service appear in the Manual of Recommended Water-Sanitation Practice, Pub. Health Bull., No. 296, 1946; and are summarized in Pub. Health Rep., 61:371, 1946; and in J. Am. Water Works Ass., 38:361, 1946.

The 1961 revision of the Public Health Service Drinking Water Standards includes, for the first time, limits for concentrations of radionucleids in water.

Standards for preventing contamination of water by insecticides are being studied (81).

IDENTIFICATION OF MEMBERS OF THE ENTEROBACTERIACEAE

The identification of the individual species which comprise the family *Enterobacteriaceae* requires the use of biochemical methods suggested by serologic tests or vice versa. A key to the differentiation into species or groups of species by biochemical methods is shown in Figure 2. There is enough variation in individual strains, however, to necessitate a serologic confirmation in most instances. Conversely, there is so much overlapping in antigenic structure among the *Salmonella-Shigella-Coli-Proteus* species that serologic diagnoses must be confirmed by biochemical tests.

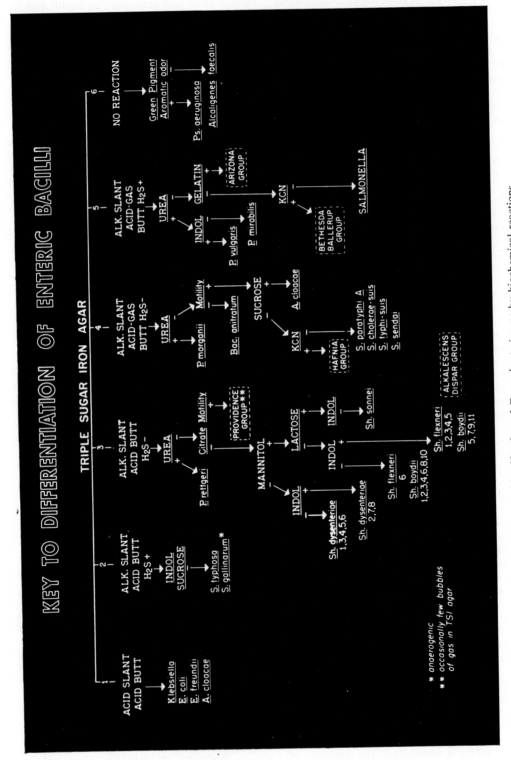

Fig. 2. Key to identification of *Enterobacteriaceae* by biochemical reactions.

622

REFERENCES

1. Abrams, H. L.   New England J. Med., 238: 185, 1948.
2. Braude, A. I., and Siemienski, J.   J. Bact., 80:171, 1960.
3. ―――― and others.   J. Immunol., 90:297, 1963.
4. Bray, J., and Beavan, T. E. D.   J. Path. Bact., 60:305, 1948.
5. Brown, G. W.   Med. J. Australia, 2:658, 1952.
6. Buchner.   Arch. f. Hyg., 3, 1885.
7. Burkholder, P. R., and McVeigh, I.   Proc. Nat. Acad. Sc., 28:285, 1942.
8. Cary, S. G., and others.   J. Bact., 75:43, 1958.
9. Castañeda, M. R.   J. Exper. Med., 62:289, 1935.
10. Colwell, C. A.   J. Bact., 52:417, 1946.
11. Cooper, M. L., and others.   J. Bact., 69: 689, 1955.
12. Daly, K. A., and others.   Arch. Int. Med., 110:580, 1962.
13. Davison, W. C.   South. M. J., 17:552, 1924.
14. ―――― Am. J. Dis. Child., 29:743, 1925; 49:72, 1935.
15. DeWitt, C. W., and Rowe, J. A.   J. Bact., 82:838, 849, 1961.
16. Dubin, I. N., and Kerby, G. P.   Arch. Path., 35:808, 1943.
17. Duguid, J. P., and others.   J. Path. & Bact., 70:335, 1955.
18. Dulaney, A. D., and Michelson, I. D.   Am. J. Pub. Health, 25:1241, 1935.
19. Edwards, and Ewing, W. H.   Identification of Enterobacteriaceae, Minneapolis, Burgess Publishing Co., 1955, 2nd ed., 1961.
20. Escherich, T.   Die Darmbakteriologie des Säuglings, Stuttgart, 1886.
21. Ewing, W. H.   Internat. Bull. Bact. Nomen. Taxon., 12:94, 1962.
22. ―――― J. Bact., 57:659, 1949; 66:333, 1953.
23. ―――― Isolation and Identification of Escherichias Coli Serotype Associated with Diarrhea Diseases, Public Health Service, C.D.C., Atlanta, Ga., 1963.
24. ―――― J. Infect. Diseases, 110:114, 1962.
25. ―――― and Tanner, K. E.   J. Bact., 69:89, 1955.
26. ―――― and others.   The Cornell Veterinarian, 48:201, 1958.
27. ―――― and others.   J. Bact., 69:549, 1955.
28. ―――― and others.   J. Infect. Dis., 94:134, 1954.
29. ―――― and others.   Studies on the Occurrence of Escherichias Coli Serotype Associated with Diarrhea Disease in the United States. C.D.C. Publication, Communicable Disease Center, Atlanta, Ga.
30. ―――― and others.   J. Infect. Dis., 94:134, 1954.
31. Ferguson, W. W., and Roberts, L. F.   J. Bact., 59:171, 1950.
32. ―――― and June, R. C.   Am. J. Hyg., 55: 155, 1952; 57:222, 1953.
33. Gant, O. K., and others.   Proc. Soc. Exper. Biol. & Med., 52:276, 1943.
34. Giles, C., and others.   Arch. Dis. Child., 24:45, 1949.
35. Halbert, S. P., and Gravatt, M. J.   Immunol., 61:271, 1949.
36. Hauser, G.   Über Fäulnissbakterien, Leipzig, 1885.
37. Havens, L. C., and Mayfield, C. R.   J. Prevent. Med., 4:179, 1930.
38. Henriksen, S. D.   J. Bact., 60:225, 1950.
39. Hershey, A. D., and Bronfenbrenner, J.   J. Bact., 31:453, 1936.
40. Hill, G. A., and others.   J. Bact., 84:191, 1962.
41. Hoffman, M. S., and others.   Proc. Staff Meet., Mayo Clin., 26:1, 1951.
41a. Hugh, R., and Leifson, E.   Internat. Bull. Bact. Nomen. and Tax., 13:133, 1963.
42. Ikari, P., and Hugh, R.   Bact. Proc., 1963, p. 41.
43. Jackson, G. G., and others.   Arch. Int. Med., 110:663, 1962.
44. Kauffmann, F.   The Diagnosis of Salmonella Types, Springfield, Ill., Charles C Thomas, 1950.
45. ―――― J. Immunol., 47:71, 1947.
46. ―――― Enterobacteriaceae, 2nd ed., Copenhagen, Einar Munksgaard, 1954.
47. ―――― and others.   Internat. Bull. Bact. Nomenclature and Taxonomy, 6:63, 1956.
48. Kean, B. H.   Ann. Int. Med., 59:605, 1963.
49. ―――― and others.   J.A.M.A., 180:367, 1962.
50. Kessner, D. M., and others.   Am. J. Hyg., 76:27, 1962.
51. Knox, R., and others.   J. Hyg., 43:147, 1943.
52. Kunin, C. M., and others.   Proc. Soc. Exp. Biol. & Med., 111:160, 1962.
53. ―――― Arch. Int. Med., 110:676, 1962.
54. ―――― Fed. Proc. Abstracts, 22 [No. 273]: 206, 1963.
55. Malligo, J. E., and others.   J. Bact., 70:498, 1955.
56. Massini, R.   Arch. Hyg., 61:250, 1907.
57. Mergenhagen, S. E.   J. Bact., 71:739, 1956.
58. Mian, K. A.   J.A.M.A., 171:1957, 1959.
59. Mitchel, P. D., and Burrell, R. G.   Bact. Proc., 1963, p. 64.
60. Moore, H. B., and Pickett, M. J.   Can. J. Microbiol., 6:43, 1960.
61. ―――― and others.   J. Hyg., 50:137, 1952.
62. Namioka, S., and Sakazaki, R.   Ann. Inst. Pasteur, 94:485, 1958.
63. ―――― and Sakazaki, R.   J. Bact., 78:301, 1959.
64. Neisser, M.   Zentralbl. f. Bakt. I Abt. Ref., Beiheft, 38:98, 1906.
65. Nelson, J. D., and others.   J.A.M.A., 176: 26, 1961.
66. Neter, E., and Shumway, C. N.   Proc. Soc. Exper. Biol. & Med., 75:504, 1950.
67. ―――― and others.   J. Exper. Med., 96:1, 1952.
68. Neter, E., and others.   Pediatrics, 12:377, 1953.
69. ―――― and others.   Proc. Soc. Exper. Biol. & Med., 82:215, 1953.
70. ―――― and others.   J. Immunol., 76:377, 1956.
71. Nyberg, C.   Centralbl. f. Bakt., 133:443, 1935.
72. Olarte, J., and Varela, G.   J. Lab. & Clin. Med., 40:252, 1952.
73. Papavassiliou, J.   J. Bact., 80:138, 1960.

74. Parr, L. W.   Proc. Soc. Exper. Biol. & Med., 35:563, 1937.
75. ———— Bact. Rev., 3:1, 1939.
76. Parr, L. W., and Simpson, W. F.   J. Bact., 40:467, 1940.
77. ———— and Robbins, M. L.   J. Bact., 43: 661, 1942.
78. Perch, B.   Acta Path. Microbiol. Scand., 25: 703, 1948.
79. ———— Om proteus grupp ens serologi (*P. vulgaris og P. mirabilis* (Summer in Anglest)), Arnold Busck, Copenhagen, 1950.
80. Petruschky, J.   Zentralbl. f. Bakt., I Abt., 19:187, 1896.
81. Pub. Health Rep., 76:781, 1961 (Advisory Committee).
82. Rantz, L. A.   Arch. Int. Med., 109:91, 1962.
83. Rauss, K., and Voros, S.   Acta Microbiol. Acad. Sci. Hungaricae, 6:233, 1959.
84. Reynolds, R. C., and Cluff, L. E.   Ann. Int. Med., 58:759, 1963.
85. Rosebury, T.   Microorganisms Indigenous to Man, New York, McGraw-Hill Book Co., 1962.
86. Schaub, I. G., and Hauber, F. D.   J. Bact., 56:379, 1948.
87. Sears, H. J., and Brownlee, I.   J. Bact., 63:47, 1952.
88. ———— and others.   J. Bact., 71:370, 1956.
89. Shaw, C., and Clarke, P. H.   J. Gen. Microbiol., 13:155, 1955.
90. Shearer, L. A., and others.   J.A.M.A., 169: 1051, 1959.
91. Smith, T.   J. Exper. Med., 48:351, 1928.
92. Spittel, J. A., and others.   Proc. Staff Meet., Mayo Clin., 29:225, 1954; 29:447, 1954.
93. Sprecace, G. A., and Dunkelberg, W. E., Jr.   J.A.M.A., 177:706, 1961.
94. Stuart, C. A., and others.   J. Bact., 36:391, 1938.
95. Stulberg, C. S., and others.   J. Immunol., 76:281, 1956.
96. Taplin, D., and others.   J.A.M.A., 186:952, 1963.
97. Taylor, C. B.   J. Hyg., 42:23, 1942.
98. Thompson, B. M., and others.   Bull. World Health Organization, 25:137, 153, 159, 1961.
99. Toft, G.   Acta path. et microbiol. Scandinav., 23:277, 1946.
100. Turck, M., and others.   J. Clin. Investigation, 41:1760, 1962.
101. Turista, Editorinz, 180:402, 1962.
102. Wallace, C. S.   Ann. Int. Med., 34:1463, 1951.
103. Waisbren, B. A., and Brown, I.   J. Immunol., 88:249, 1962.
104. Weil, E., and Felix, A.   Wien. klin. Wchnschr., 29:33, 1916; 30:1509, 1917.
105. Weinstein, L., and Wassermann, E.   New Eng. J. Med., 244:662, 1951.
106. Whang, A. Y., and Neter, E.   J. Bact., 84: 1245, 1962.
107. White, P. B.   Brit. J. Exper. Path., 14:145, 1933.
108. Zamenhof, S.   J. Bact., 51:351, 1946.
109. Zinsser, H., and Williams, W. J.   J. Bact., 58:501, 1949.

39

Pseudomonas aeruginosa and Pseudomoniasis

Family: *Pseudomonadaceae* Winslow and others. Genus: *Pseudomonas* Migula. Type species: *Pseudomonas aeruginosa* (Schroeter) Migula. Synonyms: *Bacillus pyocyaneus, Pseudomonas pyocyanea*

Gram-negative bacilli which produce water-soluble pigments are distributed widely in nature (27a) and have been brought together in the genus *Pseudomonas.* Crowell and Liston's (9) analysis of 80 bacterial strains, by the computer technic, showed that they could be divided into four large groups: Group I contained the marine species and included psychrophilic, nonproteolytic species. Group 2 was a subgeneric mesophilic group associated with *Ps. fragi.* Group 3 produced fluorescent pigment and included three subgroups: (a) psychrophilic aeruginosa-like species, (b) mesophilic *Ps. aeruginosa* species, and (c) *Ps. fluorescens.* Group 4 was a subgenetic, nonpigment-producing mesophilic group which included *Ps. ovalis* and *Ps. denitrificans* (9). The fluorescent *Pseudomonas* fall into three overlapping groups: mesophilic *Ps. aeruginosa,* **psychrophilic** *Ps. aeruginosa*-like organisms, and *Ps. fluorescens* (43).

The pigment of the *Pseudomonas* is a striking feature and is often of aid in diagnosis. The blue pigment **pyocyanine** of *Ps. aeruginosa* (17, 36) was the first reported instance of the occurrence of the phenazine nucleus as a natural produce (45). The green pigment **oxychlororaphine** of *Ps. chlororaphis,* the **fluorescence** of *Ps. fluorescens,* the purple pigment **iodinin** of *Ps. iodinum,* and the yellow pigment **phenazine-l-carboxylic** acid of *Ps. aureofaciens* are all characteristic of the species. However, non-pigment-producing strains are being isolated at an increasingly greater rate (18, 36). In

the studies of Bühlmann and his associates (5) 29 per cent of 49 strains of *Ps. aeruginosa* did not produce pyocyanin on Sabouraud's maltose agar, although all produced fluorescence.

Pseudomonas aeruginosa and *Ps. pseudomallei* are the only two species which are pathologic for man, but other members of the genus, especially psychrophilic species, have become very important vectors in the spoiling of foods handled and stored at low temperatures, such as sea food and milk (32).

Ps. aeruginosa was isolated by Gessard (22) in 1882 and named *Bacillus pyocyaneus.* This organism has been isolated from over 90 per cent of samples of sewage and from 11 per cent of human fecal specimens (39). Inapparent infections occur in a high percentage of normal individuals, as indicated by the presence of hemagglutinins but not ordinary agglutinating antibodies (21).

There seems to be little doubt that there has been both an actual as well as relative increase in infections with *Ps. aeruginosa* since the introduction of sulfonamides and antibiotics (1, 10, 14, 37, 42).

Ps. aeruginosa becomes resistant to antibiotics even more readily than *E. coli* and *Klebsiella* (10). Furthermore, it has become a hospital infection which is only a little less dreaded than antibiotic resistant *Staph. aureus,* particularly where it sets up epidemics in nurseries (1) and among patients with burns of the skin (46). In some instances these organisms have been isolated from water humidifiers, faucet aerators, sponges, and sinks (46).

For detailed information about the various types of clinical infection, the student should consult the reviews by Stanley (41) and Curtin and his associates (10) and the book by Forkner (16).

Morphology and Staining. *Ps. aeruginosa* is a small, slender rod which usually is straight but may be slightly curved, measuring about 1 to 2 μ in length and 0.5 μ in width. The organism is **actively motile** and possesses one to three polar flagella. It is **nonsporogenous** and **nonencapsulated** and stains readily with the aniline dyes. This **gram-negative** organism usually stains uniformly but under certain ill-defined conditions well-developed granules are present which stain deeply with Neisser's and Ljubinsky's stains, and, therefore, may be confused with *C. diphtheriae* unless its greater width and gram-negative character are noted.

Cultural Characteristics. *Ps. aeruginosa* is **aerobic.** Although some strains will grow anaerobically, no pigment is produced under these conditions. Excellent growth is obtained on all the usual laboratory media over a temperature range of 5° to 42° C., with an optimum at 37° C. On **plain agar,** after 24 hours incubation, large, soft, smooth, grayish, spreading colonies are produced which may become confluent and cover the entire surface of the medium. The colonies are not pigmented, but the soluble pigment produced by the organisms diffuses into the medium to produce a bright green fluorescent color which becomes darker after several days and may impart a metallic sheen to the surface growth. Gelatin is liquefied rapidly and a pellicle is formed on liquid media. Hydrogen sulfide is not produced, urea is not split, and indol not formed. False positive reactions for indol may occur with Ehrlich's reagent but not with that of Kovac. *Ps. aeruginosa* produces a small amount of acid from a number of carbohydrates (29, 30, 43) if grown in an agar base medium or peptone free broth but prefers to obtain its carbon and nitrogen from peptone, which results in an alkaline reaction that neutralizes the acid produced from the carbohydrates. In ordinary peptone base broth growth, **acid without gas** is produced from glucose but not from lactose or sucrose (18). On **blood agar** the typical pigment is not seen even when produced. The colonies of *Ps. aeruginosa* are sometimes discrete but more often spread over the plate like a swarming *Proteus;* their presence can be suspected from the **characteristic aromatic grape-like odor.**

Bühlmann and his associates (5) separated *Ps. aeruginosa* from other species of *Pseudomonas* by the type of pigment produced, growth at 42° C. in four days, failure to grow at 0 to 2° C. in one to two weeks, **breakdown of acetamide,** and virulence for white Swiss mice. However, Gaby and Logan (20) could not predict the virulence of the strain from its clinical origin or gross appearance.

Resistance. *Ps. aeruginosa* is killed by heating at a temperature of 55° C. for one hour but is somewhat more resistant to the usual chemical disinfectants than other gram-negative bacilli. The organism is resistant to penicillin and most of the broad-spectrum antibiotics. Polymyxin B is most effective, followed in order by neomycin, oxytetracycline, and streptomycin (47).

Variability. Ps. aeruginosa is an unstable organism. The usual S — R type of dissociation occurs regularly, and M types of colonies have been described by Sonnenschein (40). Hadley (24) observed colonies of *Ps. aeruginosa* which were nonpigmented, nonmotile, and nonlytic. Intermediate colonies with intricate secondary types of colonies also are formed. A new variant was described in 1949 which produced giant gelatinous colonies when grown on media containing glycerol (12). Coccoid and even branching organisms have been observed in the R colonies and in old cultures.

Antigenic Structure. The various strains are heterologous and preliminary studies by two groups of workers (33, 35) suggest that the strains in the genus *Pseudonomas* can be classified into groups by their O and H antigens. Two serologic groups were found (35). Lindberg and his associates (28) confirmed the presence of antigenic groups detectable by the agglutinin-absorption technic, but specific types must be determined by phage lyses.

Phage typing has been employed routinely for some years by Postic and Finland (38), Feary and his associates (13), Bartells and others (2), and Lindberg and his coworkers (28). Postic and Finland used 13 phage strains and identified 88.8 per cent of 161 consecutive isolations. These organisms fell into phage groups A, B, C, and D. Feary employed 12 phage types in the classification of 95 strains and found groups A, B, and C. *Ps.* 7 produced a powerful proteolytic enzyme which contributed to the virulence of the organism in experimental infections of the cornea (15). Lindberg and his coworkers studied 600 strains isolated from wound and burn infections using 45 phage types. They found that the predominant phage type, unlike the situation with *Staph. aureus,* varied from month to month.

Bacterial Metabolites. The *Pseudomonas* species **produce powerful endotoxin,** like other cell members of the *Enterobacteriaceae* (4). All pathogenic species of *Pseudomonas,* including *Ps. aeruginosa, Ps. pseudomallei, Ps. caviae,* and *Ps. reptiviora,* produce extracellular toxic substances which are antigenic and species-specific. Colling and his associates (8) found that *Ps. pseudomallei* produced two heat-labile toxins; the first was lethal but not necrotic, while the second was both lethal and necrotic. Perhaps the latter toxin accounts for the very extensive destructive abscess formation which is so characteristic of the disease pseudoglanders. Berk (3) found that the **hemolysin** (30) produced by *Ps. aeruginosa* was unusually resistant to heat, acid, and alkali, and he was not able to produce a neutralizing antibody.

A catalase, a proteinase, and occasionally a creatinase are produced (14). Gaby and Free (19) have introduced a new **cytochrome oxidase test** and evaluated the **gluconate oxidation test** (Haynes) and the oxidase test (Kovacs). The cytochrome oxidate test was the simplest and very accurate, the Haynes test was accurate but somewhat more difficult to perform, while the Kovacs test was overly sensitive since it picked up several cultures of *Alcaligenes faecalis.* This apparent crossing with *Alcaligenes faecalis* should be reinvestigated, since Moore and Pickett (34) studied 53 strains of nonpigmented gram-negative rods which failed to produce acid in Kligler's iron agar and found that 16 were really *Ps. aeruginosa* which did not produce pigment.

One should remember that the different tests studied by Gaby and Free do not differentiate between specific species within the genus *Pseudomonas.* This species separation must be done on the basis of other biochemical and cultural reactions (5).

Experimental Disease in Laboratory Animals. Rabbits, guinea pigs, mice, and goats are killed by moderate doses of virulent strains of *Ps. aeruginosa.* Other strains produce mild disease or fail to infect. The subcutaneous injection of guinea pigs or rabbits results in the development of a hemorrhagic edema at the site of the inoculation, with metastatic abscesses in the internal organs, punctuate hemorrhages in the stomach and intestines, and sometimes a nephritis.

Clinical Types of Infection. Urinary tract infections are being encountered with increasing frequency, and these occasionally eventuate in a septicemia (25, 31). Lesions of the eye (26, 41) are more rapidly destructive than those caused by the pneumococcus or gonococcus, and infections of the middle ear often persist for years.

We have seen children in our clinic with severe enteritis where the predominant organism in the stools was *Ps. aeruginosa.* A bacteremia with symptoms of a mild type of typhoid fever has been reported from China (11). Epidemics have been seen in India which resembled either salmonellosis (7) or cholera (23). *Ps. aeruginosa* has been isolated from the pharynx in a number of cases of **agranulocytic angina,** but one cannot be certain whether the organisms were the primary cause of the neutropenia or secondary invaders (41).

Ps. aeruginosa infection of the cornea is either much more frequent or much more frequently diagnosed than formerly. Not only antibiotics but local or general corticoid therapy seems to promote infection of the eye. Another new hazard is being encountered as an endocarditis in patients who have had open heart surgery (42).

Chronic ulceration of the skin is not uncommon, and infections of the lungs, valves of the heart, brain, and meninges are frequently fatal (10, 41).

Treatment. Polymyxin B ointment is frequently applied to superficial lesions. Infections of the eye can be treated locally with strong solutions of polymyxin or streptomycin. Middle ear infections may respond to polymyxin B or streptomycin solutions (6), but if they are not available, a 0.5 to 1 per cent solution of acetic acid may be used (47).

The drug of choice is the relative new one called colistin (Coly-mycin) which was introduced in 1960. It is a polypeptide antibiotic related to the polymyxin B. It seems to have fewer neurotoxic and nephrotoxic effects than polymyxin and can be used in patients with severe renal impairment (27).

Colistin is available in the form of salts, **colistin sulfate,** and **colistin methane sulfonate,** sometimes called **colistimethate.** The latter possesses, in terms of "base equivalents" only one-third as much antibactericidal activity as colistin sulfate with which the laboratory tests are usually performed, and the therapeutic dose is therefore three times higher for colistimethate than for colistin (37). Doses of colistimethate of 5 mg. per kilogram are recommended for children, although they may tolerate 7 to 10 mg. per kilogram. For adults with bacteremia or deep-seated infections more than 300 mg. per kilogram should be administered parenterally (intramuscularly), even at the risk of toxicity. In addition, local instillations should be done when possible. **In patients with brain abscesses and meningitis, 5 to 15 mg. of colistimethate should be given intrathecally every other day,** but a special shipment of **colistimethate** should be obtained from the manufacturer which **does not** contain **dibucaine,** which is included in the preparations for parenteral use.

Waisbren and Lepley (44) recommend for severe infection a combination of two therapeutic agents which seem to aid each other. These are an antibiotic, oxytetracycline, or polymyxin B, plus large doses of human gamma globulins. Presumably colistimethate could be substituted for the polymyxin B with equally good and even better results.

REFERENCES

1. Asay, L. D., and Koch, R. New Eng. J. of Med., 262:1062, 1960.
2. Barteli, P., and others. Fed. Proc., 22:324, 1963.
3. Berk, R. S. J. Bact., 84:1041, 1962.
4. Boivin, A., and Mesrobeanu, L. Compt. rend. Soc. de biol., 125:273, 1937.
5. Bühlmann, X., and others. J. Bact., 82:787, 1961.
6. Callaway, J. L. Arch. Dermat. & Syph., 55:257, 1947.
7. Chakravarti, D. N., and Tyagi, N. N. Indian M. Gaz., 72:367, 1937.
8. Colling, M., and others. J. Bact., 76:422, 1958.
9. Crowell, R. R., and Liston, J. J. Bact., 82:1, 913, 1961.
10. Curtin, J. A., and others. Ann. Int. Med., 54:1077, 1961.
11. Dold, H. Arch. f. Schiffs. u. Tropen. Hyg., 22:365, 1918; 23:472, 1919.
12. Don, P. A., and van den Ende, M. J. Hyg., 48:196, 1950.
13. Feary, T. W., and others. Proc. Soc. of Exp. Biol. and Med., 113:426, 1963.
14. Finland, M., and others. J.A.M.A., 170:2188, 1959.
15. Fisher, E., and Allen, J. H. Am. J. Ophth., 46, Part II, 249, 1958.
16. Forkner, C. E., Jr. Pseudomonas aeruginosa Infection, Grune and Stratton, New York, 1960.
17. Frank, L. H., and DeMoss, R. D. J. Bact., 77:776, 1959.
18. Gaby, W. L., and Free, E. J. Bact., 65:746, 1953.
19. —— and Free, E. J. Bact., 76:442, 1958.
20. —— and Logan, C. J. Bact., 82:149, 1961.
21. Gaines, S., and Landy, M. J. Bact., 69:628, 1955.
22. Gessard, C. Thèse, Paris, 1882; Compt. rend. Acad. d. sc., 94:536, 1882.
23. Ghosh. J. Indian M. A., 7:655, 1938.
24. Hadley, P. J. Infect. Dis., 34:260, 1924.
25. Hand, A. M. South. M. J., 47:1049, 1954.
26. Joy, H. H. Arch. Ophth., 27:1135, 1942.
27. Kirby, W. M. M., and Roberts, C. V., Jr. J.A.M.A., 177:854, 1961.
27a. Kluyver, A. J. J. Bact. 72:406, 1956.
28. Lindberg, R., and others. Fed. Proc. Abstract, 22:206, 1963.
29. Liu, P. V. J. Bact., 64:773, 1952.
30. —— J. Bact., 74:718, 1957.
31. Martin, W. J., and others. Proc. Staff Meet., Mayo Clinic, 29:562, 1954.
32. Masurovsky, E. B., and others. J. Bact., 85:722, 1963.
33. Mayr-Harting, A. J. Gen. Microbiol., 2:31, 1948.
34. Moore, H. B., and Pickett, M. J. Canad. J. Microl., 6:35, 1960.
35. Munos, J., and others. J. Bact., 57:269, 1949.
36. Neter, E., and others. J.A.M.A., 142:1335, 1950.
37. Petersdorf, R. G., and Plorde, J. J. J.A.M.A., 183:123, 1963.
38. Postic, B., and Finland, M. J. Clin. Invest., 40:2064, 1961.
39. Ringen, L. M., and Drake, C. H. J. Bact., 64:841, 1952.
40. Sonnenschein, C. Zentralbl. f. Bakt., I Abt., 104:365, 1927.
41. Stanley, M. M. Am. J. Med., 2:253, 1947.
42. Teitel, M., and Florman, A. L. J.A.M.A., 172:329, 1960.
43. Tomlin, C. E. Arch. Int. Med., 84:863, 1951.
44. Waisbren, B. A., and Lepley, D., Jr. Arch. Int. Med., 109:116, 1962.
45. Werde, F., and Stack, E. Z. Physiol. Chem., 181:58, 1929.
46. Wilson, M. G., and others. J.A.M.A., 175:1146, 1961.
47. Yow, E. M., and Townsend, E. S. Antibodies and Chemotherapeutics, 3:709, 1953.

40

Vibrio comma and Asiatic Cholera

Family: *Spirillaceae* Migula. Genus: *Vibrio* Müller. Type species: *Vibrio comma* (Schroeter) Winslow and others

No infection except plague arouses such panic as cholera. Cholera probably has been endemic in India for centuries and was formerly endemic in China and the great river valleys of India (60); it is now confined to the Bengal region of India and Pakistan, however (12). It was unknown in the western world until 1817. Between 1817 and 1875 four separate cholera epidemics of appalling magnitude occurred and spread throughout the civilized world. In 1831 Europe was invaded, and in 1832 Irish emigrants brought the infection to New York. In 1848 the disease gained entrance to this country through New Orleans and spread rapidly up the Mississippi Valley.

During the pandemic of 1883 Robert Koch (46) isolated a vibrio from cases of cholera in Egypt.

Man is the only known host for the cholera vibrio, and since the existence of chronic carriers has not been proved, the disease must be maintained by an unbroken chain of mild or inapparent infections.

Morphology and Staining. *Vibrio comma* is a small, curved or rather helicoidal-shaped organism which varies from 1 to 3 μ in length and from 0.4 to 0.6 μ in width. The degree of curvature varies from the short, comma-shaped forms to definite spirals with one or two turns. The comma-shaped organisms predominate in fecal specimens and in young cultures (Fig. 1), and the longer forms are found in older cultures. After prolonged cultivation on artificial media, the organisms may assume a distinct bacillary shape. Involution forms occur regularly when glycine is added to the medium (35), and giant globoid bodies develop in the presence of penicillin (82).

Vibrios possess terminal flagella which are thicker than those of most bacilli and seem to be anchored in the cytoplasm of the organism. *V. comma* is actively **motile** but **nonsporogenous** and **nonencapsulated,** stains readily with the aniline dyes, and is **gram-negative.**

Spheroplasts can be produced by lysozyme treatment combined with freezing and thawing (10). The cholera vibrio is one of the few bacteria which are killed and lysed by the combined action of homologous antibody and complement (59). The sequence of events is death and then lysis. The very clever studies of Freeman, Burrows, and their associates (27) have shown that the true sequence of events is the formation of spheroplasts by the action of antibody and complement. The delicate spheroplast, in the ordinary osmotic environment, dies and subsequently ruptures. Death and lysis can be prevented when osmotic protection is provided by 0.5 m. lactose in the reaction mixture.

Finkelstein and La Brec (23) have found that a rapid diagnosis can be made by the fluorescent antibody technic. Fecal samples are incubated in alkaline peptone broth, pH 8.5, for four to 10 hours. Smears are made on glass slides, from the surface growth, and stained with specific fluorescent antibody. Monospecific sera clearly distinguished the Inaba and Ogawa serotypes. El Tor strains can be detected by a group serum and by the specific serotype, which is either Ogawa or Inaba.

Cultural Characteristics. *Vibrio comma* is **aerobic** and grows poorly, if at all, under anaerobic conditions. The organism can be cultured readily on simple laboratory media at pH 6.4 to 9.6 but grows best at pH 7.8 to 8. The colonies are low, convex, translucent, flat-domed structures with entire edges which reach a size of 1 to 2 mm. after 24 hours incubation. Although maximum growth is not obtained at pH 9.2, the vibrios grow moderately well while

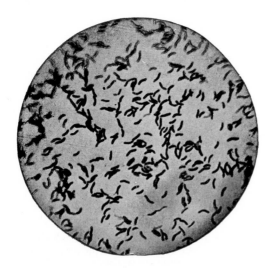

Fig. 1. Cholera vibrio. (From Fraenkel and Pfeiffer.)

the growth of the other enteric organisms is inhibited by the excess of alkali. Therefore, the selective media employed for the isolation of the cholera vibrio usually are adjusted to pH 9.2. Vibrios grow readily at temperatures between 22° and 40° C., but maximum growth is obtained at 37.5° C. Linton and Jennings (52) devised a semisynthetic medium containing glucose, casein digest, ammonium sulfate, and mineral salts which is excellent for growing vibrios for chemical analysis.

Alkaline peptone broth (pH 8.4) has been used for years as an **enrichment medium** (20, 22). In this medium vibrios grow more rapidly than the other enteric organisms and after 6 to 18 hours incubation at 37° C. form a film over the surface of the broth. Specimens which cannot be planted immediately should be preserved in Venkatraman's (73) solution consisting of 0.3 per cent boric acid and 0.37 per cent potassium chloride at pH 9.2.

Langford (48) and Smith and their associates (69) have stressed the importance of using noninhibitory rather than the standard inhibition media which worked so well with the *Enterobacteriaceae.* Landford recognized the colonies on **nutrient agar** by their chromatic greenish to red-bronze finely granular appearance when viewed with the low-power, oblique- light stereoscopic microscope. Smith and his associates (69) recognized the colonies by the cloudy peripheral zone due to gelatinase activity on **taurocholate gelatin agar** (TGA). Feley (20) found both methods excellent in his study of cholera in East Pakistan in 1962.

In many instances the vibrios are almost the only type of organism occurring in the watery stools, and no difficulty is encountered in obtaining a pure culture by direct plating on nutrient agar plates at pH 8.4. Material collected on rectal swabs or in smooth glass tubes perforated near the closed end give even better results (64). There is no production of hydrogen sulfide or decomposition of urea, but **indol is formed** and **gelatin is liquefied** in a characteristic manner (Figs. 2, 3). **Nitrates** are reduced to **nitrites,** and when sulfuric acid is added to a culture grown in nitrate-peptone broth, a red color develops. This is the classic **cholera red** or nitroso-indol reaction which once was thought to be diagnostic of cholera but now is known to be produced by any organism that produces indol and reduces nitrate.

Glucose, sucrose, and **mannitol** are among the carbohydrates which are fermented with the production of **acid without gas.** Lactose is fermented after two to eight days, while dulcitol and salacin are not fermented.

Hemolysis. *Vibrio comma* does not produce a filterable hemolysin. On blood-agar plates some strains show a clearing of the blood about the colony but this is the result of hemodigestion and is not a true hemolysis (72). The **El Tor** strains of cholera vibrios isolated by Gotschlich (36) produce a **soluble hemolysin** which can be demonstrated by exposing filtrates of broth cultures to the red blood cells of the goat (37, 62). More recent studies have shown that a number of recently isolated strains of the El Tor type did not produce hemolysis when first isolated. For this reason, other methods of separating the classical *V. comma* for the El Tor strains have been sought. Wahba and Takla used a chemical flocculation test (76) which differentiated smooth *V. comma* from smooth El Tor but was not applicable to rough strains.

Finkelstein and Mukerjee (24) found that

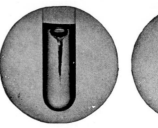

Fig. 2. Cholera vibrio. Stab culture in gelatin, three days old. (From Fraenkel and Pfeiffer.)

Fig. 3. Cholera vibrio. Stab culture in gelatin, six days old. (From Fraenkel and Pfeiffer.)

all El Tor strains would agglutinate chicken erythrocytes in slide tests while the classical *V. comma* strain would not. Fresh suspensions of agar grown vibrio cells were employed in the test. These agglutinin reactions were not the results of fimbriae or phili described in the chapter on morphology of bacteria. Other tests, such as the soda-serum-agglutinin test of Tanamal and the heat and chloroform inactivation of the agglutibility of *V. comma*, have been reviewed by Gipsen and Meyer (34).

Resistance. *Vibrio comma* dies in a few hours in fecal specimens at room temperature. Organisms from broth cultures are killed in two hours by drying on a slide but may be preserved for four years when frozen, dried, and stored in vacuo. Vibrios are destroyed readily by the usual chemical antiseptics and by the chlorination of water. The organisms are quite susceptible to heat, being killed in 10 minutes by a temperature of 55° C. Pasteurization or boiling therefore insures the safety of both milk and water. Survival in water or soil is short because of competition with other fecal organisms, but the vibrios may remain viable for four to seven days on the surfaces of fresh fruits and vegetables which have been stored in a cool, moist environment. They live only three or four days when frozen in ice.

Penicillin does not inhibit growth of the vibrios, but **sulfonamides** are moderately effective. **Streptomycin** inhibits the growth of *V. comma* in concentrations of 5 to 10 µg. per milliliter of culture fluid (64).

Variability. Variations in colony form were observed by Baerthlein (2) and Eisenberg (19). These studies on variation were continued by Balteanu (3) and later brought to completion by White (81). White described four distinct variants which can be recognized as M, S, R, and p. A different polysaccharide occurs in each of the first three variants. The S variant, isolated frequently from cases of cholera, is virulent and agglutinable in specific antiserum. The p variant is a more degenerate form of the R phase and is similar to the R except that it lacks the surface polysaccharide. The S phase is relatively stable and persists unaltered in some strains after years of subculture on artificial media.

The typical smooth (S) colony has been described in the section on cultural characteristics. The R form is somewhat larger, rougher, and flatter and may have serrated edges. In the S, R, and p colonies individual organisms have the typical comma shape.

The M or **rugose** colony is much larger and more mucoid than the other variants. Micro-scopically, large amounts of mucoid material are found between the individual cells, surrounding them in a manner which resembles a true capsule (81). There is no correlation between the capsular M variant and the virulence or immunologic type, since rugose colonies develop indiscriminately from organisms in the S, R, or p forms, but most frequently from **El Tor** strains. The capsular material is immunologically identical regardless of colony type (81). The M form of the cholera vibrio is analogous to the M variants in the *Salmonella* group in which identical polysaccharides may be found in colonies from different species. Motility, and, consequently, the H antigen, is retained in the R and p type colonies but is lost in the M variant.

Antigenic Structure. The antigenic structure of the vibrios has been investigated by Gardner and Venkatraman (32) who differentiated the various strains into O groups I, II, III, IV, V, and VI. All pathogenic strains belonged in O-group I. The H or flagellar antigens show such extensive overlapping in antigenic structure that all vibrios, whether pathogenic or not, agglutinate in anti-H serum (32).

An interesting and rather surprising byproduct of the cholera investigations during World War II was the discovery that the H antigen of *V. comma* induces a significant rise in agglutinins for *Brucella* when injected as a part of the standard cholera vaccine (17). *Brucella* agglutinins have been found in the serums of individuals more than two years after they had received their last dose of cholera vaccine (18).

Japanese workers recognized two antigenic types of *V. comma*, which they named **Inaba** and **Ogawa**. Nobéchi (57) in 1923 found a third or middle type which contained a mixture of the specific antigens of **Inaba** and **Ogawa** and called it **Hikojima**. He defined the three types in terms of O antigens A, B, C, and X, the last being common to all. Many strains were available for study during World War II, and Burrows and his associates (7, 8, 9) confirmed Nobéchi's antigenic analyses but rearranged the letters used to designate the antigens.

The O antigen is shared by *Alcaligenes faecalis* and the H antigen with *S. enteritidis*. Kauffmann (41) concluded that the cholera vibrios belonging to Gardner and Venkatraman's (32) O Group I **should not be divided into types** but **into two forms of only one type**. The Ogawa and Hikojima strains differ only qualitatively in respect to the C antigen, so these strains may be regarded as **variants** of the same O form. In practice, therefore, only two O forms have to be differentiated: **Inaba = A,** and **Ogawa = AB.** The differential diagnoses between Inaba and Ogawa required a B serum obtained by absorbing an Ogawa antiserum with an Inaba strain (Table 1).

Bacteriophage Typing.   Classical *V. comma* and El Tor strains can be separated by bacteriophage typing. Mukerjee and Guha Roy (55) identified four phage groups. Groups III and IV included all the classical *V. comma* strains but none of the El Tor strains. Groups I and II included all the *V. comma* strains but also some hemolytic and nonhemolytic El Tor strains. Takeya and Shimodori (71) confirmed the findings of Mukerjee and Guha Roy and found that none of their 83 strains were susceptible to the group IV phage. However, the highly virulent El Tor strains from the Celebes and Philippines were lysogenic. In contrast, the less virulent El Tor strains from Thailand and India did not seem to be lysogenic. The authors suggest that lysogenesis, as in diphtheria, may be related to toxicity.

Bacterial Metabolites.   Vibrios are very active biochemically. Bernheim (5) found that *V. comma* had 24 per cent more reactive amino groups than *E. coli.* In well-aerated cultures a catalase is produced and starch is rapidly hydrolyzed without acid production (40). A **lecithinase** is formed by both *V. comma* and the **El Tor** strains (22).

Burrows and his coworkers (9) found that the endotoxin increased materially the permeability of isolated strips of intestines to fluids and electrolytes. Burrows' observations have been confirmed and extended by others (34). Burnet and Stone (6) isolated a **mucinase** which caused a shredding of the intestinal epithelium. The serologic characteristics of this mucinase have been studied by Freter (28) and Chugh and his associates (11). The latter workers identified three antigenic types of mucinase. The cholera vibrios possess both of the Shwartzman fractions (49, 50, 51).

In an epidemic in South India caused by the Ogawa subtype of *V. comma,* the mortality was 45 per cent within 24 hours. This was in sharp contrast to another epidemic, caused by the Inaba subtype, where the mortality was only 31.3 per cent. Experimental studies by Mukherti (55), who injected the organisms intravenously in young rabbits, showed that the Ogawa was more virulent than the Inaba subtype and attributed the virulence to the increased amount of mucinase produced by this type. It was found that tryptophane enhanced the production of toxin.

The work of Watanabe and Felsenfeld (78) revealed that *V. comma* produced (1) nontoxic heat-labile bacterial antigens, (2) a typical endotoxin which is cell wall in origin and heat-stable, and (3) a heat-labile exotoxin-like antigen which is serologically different from the bacterial antigen.

A high yield of the toxin was obtained when the El Tor strain 17 was grown for 72 hours in a liquid medium which contained a low concentration of ferrous iron. The first type of antigen was produced by the injection of unheated, formalized bacterial cells but not by heated cells. This antibody was absorbed by unheated bacterial cells. The authors concluded that the antibody which neutralized the lethal activity of the exotoxin-like antigen was probably distinct from the antibody against the hemolytic toxin of the El Tor strain, but the possibility remains that the exotoxin-like protein may be a part of the more stable endotoxin.

Table 1. The Cholera Group of Vibrios

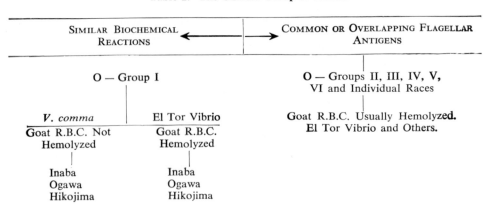

Similar Biochemical Reactions		Common or Overlapping Flagellar Antigens
O — Group I		O — Groups II, III, IV, V, VI and Individual Races
V. comma	El Tor Vibrio	Goat R.B.C. Usually Hemolyzed. El Tor Vibrio and Others.
Goat R.B.C. Not Hemolyzed	Goat R.B.C. Hemolyzed	
Inaba Ogawa Hikojima	Inaba Ogawa Hikojima	

Experimental Disease in Laboratory Animals. Metchnikoff (53) induced a fatal cholera-type disease in young suckling rabbits by contaminating the maternal teats with cultures of *V. comma*. In Koch's (46) classic experiments, a fatal infection was produced in guinea pigs by neutralizing the gastric juice with sodium bicarbonate, by introducing infected water into the stomach with a catheter, and by administering opium to prevent active peristalsis. Burrows and others (9) repeated Koch's experiments and demonstrated the multiplication of vibrios in the intestines of normal animals and a reduction in numbers in previously immunized animals. This observation led to the demonstration of agglutinins and lysins for *V. comma* in the feces of immunized guinea pigs. In humans immunized with cholera vaccine, antibodies also appear in the feces about the seventh to the tenth day after immunization, coincidental with or even before antibodies appear in the serum (9).

Fatal infection in guinea pigs can be produced by the intraperitoneal injection of virulent cultures of *V. comma* (59). The vibrios multiply in the peritoneal cavity but do not invade the blood stream, and death presumably occurs from the absorption of endotoxins. Filtrates of young, living cultures have only a slight toxicity, while heat-killed vibrios, in small amounts, produce death in guinea pigs (59).

Griffitts (38) in 1944 suspended the cholera vibrios in 5 per cent mucin and found that the intraperitoneal injection of as few as 50 organisms would produce a fatal infection in mice. Protection tests employing this technic provide a simple and satisfactory method of measuring protective antibodies in the serums of animals and man immunized with various types of vaccines (61).

Dutta and his associates (16) reproduced the clinical symptoms and the pathologic changes characteristic of cholera by feeding a toxin by mouth to eight- to 12-day old rabbits. This toxin was derived from the rabbit passage strain of Inaba 569B by the method of extraction described by Gallut (31) in 1954. In 1963 Oza and Dutta (58) found that an even more potent toxin could be produced by lysing the *V. comma* cells by the ultrasonic method.

THE PFEIFFER PHENOMENON. Pfeiffer (59) was the first to demonstrate the immunologic reaction known as **bacteriolysis.** Vibrios were introduced into the peritoneal cavity of actively and passively immunized guinea pigs, and at frequent intervals samples of the peritoneal fluid were withdrawn for examination. Within a few hours the vibrios were observed to lose their motility, become swollen and distorted, and then completely disintegrate. **Complement is necessary for bacteriolysis,** and this accessory substance is supplied automatically in the peritoneal exudates of the living animal. Immune serum, lacking complement, has no observable effect in vibrios in the test tube, but the addition of complement to the mixture results in rapid and complete lysis of the organisms. Immune serum which lacks complement will not protect chick embryos from fatal infections with *V. comma,* but the combination of complement and sensitizing antibody protects the embryo (83).

Clinical Types of Infection in Man. Mild cases of cholera cannot be distinguished clinically from mild attacks of food poisoning caused by staphylococci or members of the paratyphoid group of organisms. The diagnosis depends entirely on the isolation and identification of the vibrio. Severe cases of cholera are much more dramatic; they alarm the physician and terrify the community.

To emphasize again the variability of the disease we quote the dramatic statement of Woodward in describing the Bangkok epidemic of 1958-59: "Cholera is a medical emergency of catastrophic proportions. Ironically, the vibrio may cause human illness so subtle as to elude diagnosis and so rapid as to outdistance treatment. The physician who adopts a casual and inadequate attitude toward the patients with acute cholera will assume the role of executioner" (84).

Fortunately, in the Bangkok epidemic, the usual mortality of 50 per cent was reduced to 8 per cent by close cooperation between the physicians and the microbiologic and clinical laboratories (1).

The incubation period is short, from six or eight hours to two or three days, depending upon the size of the infecting dose. The vibrios multiply at a prodigious rate in the small intestine and, as they die, liberate endotoxins which irritate and macerate the superficial layers of the mucosa. The vibrios neither ulcerate the mucosa like the dysentery bacilli nor invade the body like the typhoid bacillus, but they alter the permeability of the intestine mucosa so drastically that enormous quantities of body fluids are poured into the lumen of the gut (7). The general intoxication is minimal and manifests itself by malaise and anorexia; there is very little fever and no mental confusion.

The onset of symptoms may be gradual, but more often it is sudden and explosive. Severe griping pains appear in the abdomen, followed by almost continuous vomiting and diarrhea. The patient may have 20 to 30 stools per day, losing liters of water. The watery stools at first contain some fecal material, but this is soon evacuated and the clear opalescent discharges contain nothing but small balls of eroded mucosa, which give the characteristic "rice water" appearance. With the excessive loss of body fluids and electrolytes, the patient exhibits symptoms of extreme dehydration. The urine is suppressed, the skin becomes wrinkled, the nose pinched, the eyeballs sunken, and the voice is weak and husky. The blood pressure falls, the heart sounds are barely audible, and the pulse becomes rapid and weak; the rate of respiration increases, and the mucous membranes become cold and cyanotic, although the rectal temperature may be normal or elevated. Thirst is intense, and severe cramplike pains develop in the extremities. The loss of fluids causes extreme hemoconcentration, slowing of the circulation, and finally coma and death.

The **diagnosis** is established by growing *V. comma* from the stools. Since agglutinins appear between the seventh and sixteenth day after the onset of symptoms, and only in those who recover, the test is of little diagnostic value.

Transmission. No chronic carriers of *V. comma* have been found. The disease apparently is transmitted by the mild cases and the early convalescents. Gilmour (33) found that 70 per cent of patients had negative cultures at the end of one week, 90 per cent after two weeks, and only a few patients harbored the organism for 20 to 25 days.

Cholera is transmitted chiefly by contaminated water and to a lesser degree by contaminated fruits and vegetables.

The formerly wide spread endemic foci of cholera in Russia, India, China and the Celebes (13, 14, 39) have been reviewed by Pollitzer (60). At the present time the classical form of the disease has disappeared from Russia and China but remains in the Bengal region of India (12). Recent epidemics in Indonesia and in the Philippines have shown conclusively that highly fatal cholera can be produced by the El Tor strains (21). Some strains of both classical *V. comma* and the El Tor type have a high degree of virulence, while others are of low virulence (56). The Ogawa subtype of *V. comma* and the "Celebes" type of El Tor (34) seems to be much more virulent than the Inaba subtype of *V. comma* and the Ubon El Tor type from Thailand (71).

Cockburn and Cassanos (12) have presented a fascinating explanation for the survival of cholera in the Bengal region. They think it survives in the water of the local village water tanks. In the hot dry weather algae grow in the stagnant water, raising the pH of the water to 9 or above for six hours each day in the summer and for four hours in winter. *V. comma* can multiply at a pH of 9.2, while *Salmonella* and most other enteric organisms cannot. Under those conditions *V. comma* not only survived in the tanks between epidemic periods but could increase in such numbers in certain periods of the year to start a new epidemic. If this theory is correct, a proper water supply for the Bengal would eliminate the last focus of classical cholera but leave unsolved the problem of the El Tor type in the Celebes.

Biologic Products. There are no antitoxic serums, and the antibacterial serums are ineffective. Heat-killed, phenolized, and living vaccines have been used with some success. Local and even generalized symptoms often follow the injection of these vaccines, and the degree of duration of the immunity is limited. The heat-killed phenolized vaccines seem to be less antigenic than live vibrio. Watanabe (78) has purified the protective lipopolysaccharide antigen and found it less toxic and more protective than the older one.

Burrows' studies suggested that the antibodies which were produced in the cells of the intestinal tract and excreted into the feces were probably more protective than the antibodies which appeared in the blood. Freter (29), of the Jefferson Medical College of Philadelphia, has prepared an oral vaccine which stimulated the formation of fecal **coproantibodies.**

Treatment. The patient with cholera dies of dehydration, demineralization, and acidosis rather than from the endotoxins produced by the vibrio. The mortality can be reduced to 5 per cent, which is no higher than that of salmonellosis, exclusive of typhoid fever, by replacement therapy with fluids, salt, and alkali. Continuous intravenous or intrasternal infusions of warm physiologic saline or Ringer's solution should be given at the rate of 60 to 100 ml. per minute until the specific gravity of the blood is reduced to the normal of 1.054 to 1.058. When the acidosis is severe and collapse is present or threatening, sodium bicarbonate (2 per cent) may be added to the infusion fluids in amounts of 100 to 300 ml. for each 1,000 ml. of the infusion fluid (64). When fluid therapy is ignored or given in inadequate amounts, the mortality may be as high as 50 to 70 per cent (79).

It is well to remember that patients may die from overhydration with symptoms of cardiac decompensation and vascular collapse. The patient already in collapse when diagnosed cannot tolerate full replacement of body fluids, but the addition of thiamine, ascorbic acid, and tetracycline to the standard fluid therapy may have remarkable beneficial results (66).

Benyajati and his associates (4) have emphasized the damage to the kidneys from hypokalemia from potassium deficiency and have suggested the addition of 10 to 20 M. eq. of potassium to each liter of saline after the initial hydration.

Sulfonamides, particularly sulfadiazine, may reduce the duration of the disease but do not reduce the number of vibrios in the stools (64). Streptomycin, when given by mouth, reduces the vibrios in the stools and shortens the days of disability (64). In general, however, results with both the sulfonamides and antibiotics have been disappointing (47).

It is comforting to learn that viruses play no role in cholera either as inciters or as intercurrent infections (1).

The protection afforded by the vaccine is not absolute, but during epidemic periods it has been found, in general, that the attack rates among the unvaccinated are approximately 10 times those of the vaccinated (*Trop. Dis. Bull.*, 43:131, 1946).

Improvement in sanitation, rather than active immunization, should be the ultimate goal. Adequate sewage disposal and proper supervision of milk and water supplies make large-scale epidemics of cholera impossible. Small outbreaks are associated with contact infections in families or other small groups. To combat this type of spread, public health education is essential, and, as shown in Fig. 4, can be accomplished even for those who cannot read.

OTHER CHOLERA-LIKE VIBRIOS

In addition to *Vibrio comma*, 33 other species are recognized in the 7th edition of Bergey's Manual. One specie, *Vibrio piscium*, causes disease in fresh water fish. Another, *Vibrio fetus*, is definitely pathogenic for cattle, sheep, and man. *V. coli* causes dysentery in swine, and *V. jejuni* causes dysentery in cattle and related animals; **these two species may produce enteritis in children** (42, 43, 54, 80).

V. fetus, *V. jejuni*, and *V. coli* are **microaerophilic.** Two species, *V. niger* and *V. spotorum*, are **strict anaerobes.** Both are found in gangrenous lesions of the mouth and lungs. One **aerobic** species, *V. sputigenus*, occurs in the human mouth and in sputum. Its relation to disease has not ben determined. A second aerobic species, *V. proteus*, has been isolated from the feces of children with severe diarrhea. A third aerobic species, *V. leonardii*, is highly pathogenic for certain species of insects. The remaining species are apparently saprophytic isolates from soil, salt and fresh water, and pickling brines.

VIBRIO FETUS INFECTION IN ANIMALS AND MAN

Vibrio fetus was isolated from cases of infectious abortion in cattle by Theobald Smith (68) in 1918. It is now recognized only to brucellosis as a cause of economic loss to the farmer. This infection is truly a venereal disease in cattle, since the organism may be carried in the testes of the bull for life without causing signs or symptoms of disease. This vibrio not only causes recognized abortions

Fig. 4. Poster used in Shanghai, 1946, epidemic of cholera to illustrate the mechanism of dissemination. (From Reimann and others. *Am. J. Trop. Med.,* 26:631, 1946.)

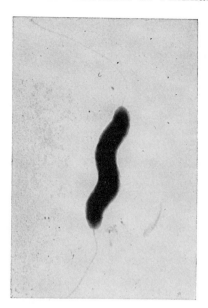

Fig. 5. Electron micrograph showing flagella arrangement of a human strain of *V. fetus.* × 13,000. (From King. *Ann. New York Acad. Med.,* 98:700, 1962.)

but reduces the conception rate of the herd. *V. fetus* causes abortion in sheep, but the ram is not involved in the transmission of the disease (25). Presumably the vibrio is transmitted by contaminated food and water.

It was not suspected that the organism was pathogenic for man until Vinzent and his associates (75) reported a case from France in 1947 and Ward (77) a case in this country in 1948. King (42) collected 17 cases of human infection with this organism and added seven new cases isolated in recent years in the United States.

In 1962 King (44) collected an additional 22 cases of *V. fetus* infection and seven others described as "related vibrios." These related vibrios may or may not be identical with *V. coli,* or *V. jejuni,* which are known to cause diarrhea in animals.

The cultural and biochemical characteristics of *V. fetus* have been reviewed by Kuzdas and Morse (45) and by King (44). The organism is a small, short, curved rod with a small flagellum at one or both ends (Fig. 5). If complete separation fails to occur after division, a long spirillum-like form occurs.

This vibrio is **microaerophilic** and requires an infusion-type medium. It fails to grow on blood agar incubated aerobically but grows well in a candle jar after subculture. It grows very poorly anaerobically and hence can be

considered a classical microaerophilic species without being adaptive to either aerobic or anaerobic condition. It shows a characteristic type of growth in thioglycollate broth if inoculated by a special technic with a capillary pipette. The growth begins at the bottom of the tube and progresses in a straight line **up one side** of the tube (Fig. 6). Both *V. fetus* and "related vibrios" from human sources grow well at 37° C. in thioglycollate broth, while *V. fetus* grows well at 25° C. but not at 42° C. The "related vibrios" grow well at 42° C. but not at 25° C.

Growth occurs on rich media on the surface of the agar if cultures are incubated under helium or nitrogen. The colonies are small and vary from transparent and convex to transparent and opaque. When the growth is scraped up, it appears tan to yellow; subsurface colonies are small, yellow, and opaque. There is no liquefaction of gelatin. Indole is not produced, and acid may or may not be produced from glucose, lactose, or sucrose without gas formation. It reduces nitrates to nitrites and gives positive oxidase or catalase test. Hydrogen sulfate is not produced in the butt of triple sugar iron agar, although a small amount can be detected by strips of lead acetate paper suspended over the slant.

Lecce (49) found that the growth of *V. fetus* strains from bovines were inhibited by

Fig. 6. Characteristic growth of *V. fetus* in thioglycollate broth. (From King. *Ann. New York Acad. Med.,* 98:700, 1962.)

0.8 glycine but the ovine strains were not. This work was extended by Fletcher and Plastridge (26). A chemically defined medium has been described by Smibert (67).

All pathogenic species of *V. fetus* are apparently members of a single sero-type. Gallut's (30, 31) studies in 1952 and 1954 indicated the presence of six antigens and six haptens (30, 31), while the reinvestigation by Reich and his associates (63) in 1961 revealed 12 antigens and four haptens. In contrast, Firehammer and Lovelace (25) and Ringen and Frank (65) would differentiate the **venereal type** of infection with *V. fetus,* which is confined to cattle, from the **oral type** of infection, which can cause abortions in both cattle and sheep. These authors believe that there are many sero-types. Presumably man could be infected by either animal type. The infection may resemble brucellosis (70) or present localized infections in one part of the body (43). In some instances the patients have been associated with animals or animals' produce, but in others no such association could be found. In the 40 cases analyzed by King (44) the diagnosis was made by blood culture in 50 per cent. In many instances the *V. fetus* infection seems to be secondary to some other serious disease. In these instances the relation to animals is distant or nonexistent (44). The infections in children have usually been enteric, and the organisms have usually not been *V. fetus* but "related vibrios" (44, 54, 80), which may be related to *V. coli* or *V. jejuni* which are known to cause dysentery in animals.

Treatment has been successful with the simultaneous administration of dihydrostreptomycin and tetracycline (69) and chloramphenicol (43).

REFERENCES

1. Abraham, A. S., and Cheever, F. S. Proc. Soc. Exp. Biol. and Med., 112:981, 1963.
2. Baerthlein, K. Berl. klin. Wchnschr., 48:373, 1911.
3. Balteanu, J. J. Path. & Bact., 29:251, 1926.
4. Benyajati, C., and others. Ann. Int. Med., 52:960, 1960.
5. Bernheim, F. Arch. Biochem., 2:125, 1943.
6. Burnet, F. M., and Stone, J. N. Australian J. Exper. Biol. & M. Sc., 25:219, 1947; 27:245, 1949.
7. Burrows, W., and others. Proc. Soc. Exper. Biol. & Med., 57:308, 311, 1944.
8. ——— and others. J. Infect. Dis., 79:159, 168, 1946.
9. ——— and others. J. Infect. Dis., 81:157, 261, 1947.
10. Chatterjee, B. R., and Williams, R. P. J. Bact., 85:838, 1963.
11. Chugh, M. L., and others. J. Bact., 71:722, 1956.
12. Cockburn, T. A., and Cassanos, J. G. Pub. Health Rept., 75:791, 1960.
13. DeMoor. C. E. Meded. D.V.G. Ned-Ind., 28:320, 1938.
14. DeVogel, W. Th. Bull. Office Internat. d'hyg. pub., 32:556, 1940.
15. Doorenbos, W. Rev. d'hyg. et de méd. preventive, 58:595, 675, 736, 1936; 59:22, 105, 1937.
16. Dutta, N. K., and others. J. Bact., 78:594, 1959.
17. Eisele, C. W., and others. Proc. Soc. Exper. Biol. & Med., 61:89, 1946.
18. ——— and others. J.A.M.A., 135:983, 1947.
19. Eisenberg, P. Zentralbl. f. Bakt., I Abt., 56:1, 1912.
20. Feley, J. C. J. Bact., 84:866, 1962.
21. Felsenfeld, O. Bull. Wld. Hlth. Org., 28:289, 1963.
22. ——— J. Bact., 48:155, 1944.
23. Finkelstein, R. A., and LaBrec, E. H. J. Bact., 78:886, 1959.
24. ——— and Mukerjee, S. Proc. Soc. Exp. Biol. and Med., 112:355, 1963.
25. Firehammer, B. D., and Lovelace, S. A. Am. J. Vet. Rec., 22:447, 1961.
26. Fletcher, R. D., and Plastridge, W. N. J. Bact., 85:992, 1963.
27. Freeman, B. A., and others. Proc. Soc. Exp. Biol. and Med., 113:675, 1963.
28. Freter, R. J. Infect. Dis., 97:238, 1955.
29. ——— To be published.
30. Gallut, J. Ann. Inst. Pasteur, 83:449, 1952.
31. ——— Ann. Inst. Pasteur, 86:561, 1954.
32. Gardner, A. D., and Venkatraman, K. V. J. Hyg., 35:262, 1935.
33. Gilmour, C. C. B. Bull. World Health Organ., 7:343, 1952.
34. Gipsen, R., and Meyer, F. H. Am. J. Trop. Med. and Hyg., 8:72, 1959.
35. Gordon, J., and Gordon, M. J. Path. & Bact., 55:63, 1943.
36. Gotschlich, F. Egypt. Sanit. Dept. Sci. Rep., p. 17, 1906.
37. Greig, E. D. W. Indian J. M. Research, 2:623, 1914-15.
38. Griffitts, J. J. Pub. Health Rep., 59:1374, 1944.
39. Gurkripal, S., and Ahuja, M. L. Indian J. M. Research, 41:285, 1953.
40. Jennings, R. K. J. Bact., 49:163, 1945.
41. Kauffmann, F. Acta path. et microbiol. Scandinav., 27:283, 1950.
42. King, E. O. J. Inf. Dis., 101:119, 1957.
43. King, S., and Bronsky, D. J.A.M.A., 175:1045, 1961.
44. King, E. O. Ann. N.Y. Acad. Med., 98:700, 1962.
45. Kuzdas, C. D., and Morse, E. V. Am. J. Vet. Research, 17:331, 1956.
46. Koch, R. Deutsche med. Wchnschr., 9:615, 743, 1883; 10:63, 111, 191, 221, 725, 1884.
47. Lahiri, S. C. Brit. M. J., 1:500, 1951.
48. Lankford, C. E. J. Microbiol. Soc. Thailand, 3:10, 1959.
49. Lecce, T. G. J. Bact., 76:312, 1958.
50. Linton, R. W. Bact. Rev., 4:261, 1940.
51. ——— and others. Indian J. M. Research, 22:659, 1934-35.

52. ———— and Jennings, R. K. Arch. Biochem., 3:419. 1944.
53. Metchnikoff, E., and others. Ann. Inst. Pasteur, 10:257, 1896.
54. Middlekamp, J. N., and Wolf, H. A. J. Pediat., 59:318, 1961.
55. Mukerjee, S., and Guha Roy, V. K. J. Bact., 81:830, 1961.
56. Mukherti, A. J. of Med., 82:381, 1959.
57. Nobechi, K. Bull. Office Internat. d'hyg. pub., 25:72, 1933.
58. Oza, N. B., and Dutta, N. K. J. Bact., 85: 497. 1963.
59. Pfeiffer, R. Ztschr. f. Hyg. u. Infektionskr., 11:393, 1892; 18:1, 1894.
60. Pollitzer, R. Cholera, WHO Monograph Series No. 43, Geneva, 1959.
61. Ranta, L. E., and Dolman, C. E. Canad. J. Pub. Health, 35:473, 1944.
62. Read, W. D. B., and others. Indian J. M. Research, 30:183, 1942.
63. Reich, C. V., and others. J. Bact., 82:210, 1961.
64. Reimann, H. A., and others. Am. J. Trop. Med., 26:631, 1946.
65. Ringen, L., and Frank, F. W. J. Bact., 86: 344, 1963.
66. Smadel, J. E. Pub. Health Report, 78:699, 1963.
67. Smibert, R. M. J. Bact., 85:394, 1963.
68. Smith, T. J. Exper. Med., 28:701, 1918.
69. Smith, H. C., and others. J. Inf. Dis., 109: 31, 1961.
70. Spink, W. W. J.A.M.A., 163:180, 1957.
71. Takeya, K., and Shimodori, S. J. Bact., 85: 957, 1963.
72. Van Loghem, J. J. Zentralbl. f. Bakt., I. Abt., 57:289, 1910; 67:410, 1912.
73. Venkatraman, K. V., and others. Indian J. M. Research, 29:419, 681, 1941.
74. Verwey, W. F. J. of Infec. Dis., to be published.
75. Vinzent, R., and others. Bull. Acad. nat. med., 131:90, 1947.
76. Wahba, A. H., and Takla, V. Bull. Wld. Hlth. Org., 26:306, 1962.
77. Ward, B. Q. J. Bact., 55:113, 1948.
78. Watanabe, Y., and Felsenfeld, O. J. Bact., 82:43, 1961; 85:31, 1963.
79. Watten, R. H., and others. J. Chm. Invest., 38:1879, 1959.
80. Wheeler, W. E., and Borchers, J. J. Dis. Child., 101:60, 1961.
81. White, P. B. J. Path. & Bact., 46:1, 1938; 50:160, 1940.
82. ———— J. Gen. Microbiol., 4:36, 1950.
83. Wilson, A. T. J. Exper. Med., 84:293, 1946.
84. Woodward, T. E. Pub. Health Rept., 76: 323, 1961.

41

Brucella melitensis, Br. abortus, Br. suis and Brucellosis

Family: *Brucellaceae* fam. nov. Genus: *Brucella* Meyer and Shaw. Type species: *Brucella melitensis* (Hughes) Meyer and Shaw

Brucellosis is primarily a disease of goats, cows, and swine; man contracts the infection either by direct contact with these animals or by the consumption of milk and milk products.

A contagious form of abortion in cattle was known to exist in England prior to 1567 (16). In 1861 Marston (56), in the Mediterranean area, contracted a febrile disease, and his description of his own case makes it almost certain that he was suffering from brucellosis. A febrile disease prevalent on the island of Malta was known as Malta Fever. In 1887 Bruce (10) isolated a small gram-negative organism from British soldiers stationed on Malta and later named it *Micrococcus melitensis*. Hughes (47) wrote the first monograph on the subject in 1897 and suggested the name **undulant fever.** In the same year that Hughes' monograph appeared, Bang (3), in Denmark, isolated a gram-negative rod from cows which had aborted and named it *Bacillus abortus*. The third member of the group, which also is bacillary in shape, was recovered from the fetuses of aborting swine by Traum (102) in the United States of America.

In 1918 and again in 1923 Alice Evans (24, 25) published reports which contained convincing evidence that *Micrococcus melitensis* from goats and *Bacillus abortus* from cows could not be differentiated morphologically or by their cultural and biochemical reactions but that there were antigenic differences which could be shown by agglutinin absorption tests. Traum's organism from swine was indistinguishable from Bang's bacillus by the agglutinin absorption technic, but a study of other characteristics revealed that they were not identical (43). Meyer and Shaw (63) confirmed Evans' observations and suggested the generic name *Brucella* in honor of David Bruce.

Keefer (51) isolated *Brucella* from the blood of a patient in Maryland who never had had any direct or indirect contact with goats. Subsequent reports by Gage and Gregory (30), Huddleson (42), Carpenter and Merriam (14), and others established the fact that *Brucella abortus* infection was a widespread and relatively common disease in the United States of America.

Indeed, the disease is world wide as shown in Spink's (93) book and by the report of *Br. suis* in rodents in Kenya, Africa (64, 66) and in Caribou in the Arctic Circle in Alaska (17).

Morphology and Staining. In tissues and exudates the three species of *Brucella* always are seen as very small coccobacilli. In the first isolates they appear either entirely coccoid in shape or as mixtures of coccoid and bacillary forms (Fig. 1). In subcultures *Br. suis* is predominantly bacillary, *Br. abortus* changes gradually to the bacillary form, while some strains of *Br. melitensis* may maintain their coccoid characteristics. Huddleson's (45) studies showed that the width of all three species varied from 0.4 to 0.8 μ; the length of *Br. melitensis* varied from 0.4 to 2.2 μ, *Br. abortus* from 0.4 to 2.5 μ, and *Br. suis* from 0.6 to 3 μ. Capsules were described by Evans and Maitland, whose observations were confirmed

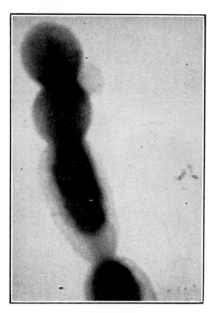

Fig. 1. Electron micrograph of *Brucella melitensis*. Bacillary and coccoid forms with clear cell wall about bacillary form. × 20,000. (Courtesy of Dr. Gordon Sharp.)

by Huddleson (46) and Mickle (68). The organism stains rather faintly with the usual aniline dyes, occasionally showing bipolar bodies. It is **gram-negative, nonsporogenous, and nonmotile.**

By using smears of known brucella organisms on glass slides the presence of specific antibodies in the sera of patients could be detected by the indirect fluorescent technic (4).

Cultural Characteristics. The organisms are aerobic and grow best at 37° C. on media adjusted to a pH of 6.6 to 6.8. *Br. abortus* **requires an atmosphere of 10 per cent CO_2 for primary isolation** and for a variable number of subcultures. The colonies are round, hemispherical, smooth, and opaque, with a whitish or dull cream color.

In most acute cases of brucellosis the bacilli can be grown from the blood without difficulty if planted in **rabbit's blood meat infusion broth** or **liver infusion broth.** In **poured blood-agar plates** the colonies resemble those of the viridans type of streptococci (79). In primary isolations from subacute and chronic cases, the organisms rarely grow on solid media, and growth in broth often is insufficient to cloud the medium. More elaborate procedures are required to obtain cultures from chronic infections because of the intracellular location of

the organisms or the presence of antibodies or other inhibiting substances in the blood.

Pickett and Nelson (73) remove inhibiting substances and free the intracellular organisms by washing the citrated blood of the patient with distilled water. The centrifuged residue is then planted in broth. Braun and Kelsh (9) have criticized all methods which require prolonged cultivation in broth because growth in broth favors dissociation. These investigators add 0.1 ml. of a heparin solution (100 USP units) to 1 ml. of freshly drawn blood from the patient.

Kuzdas and Morse (55) have described a method for the isolation of brucella from aborted fetuses, milk, water, soil, and manure. They employ Albimi brucella agar to which they add polymyxin B, actidione, circulin, and crystal violet. Calderone and Pickett (12) found that tubed egg yolk medium was superior to five-day embryonated eggs and Albimi's brucella agar. Gerhardt (31) has reviewed the literature on the nutrition of *Brucella*.

After isolation, subcultures can be maintained on almost any type of medium, and many *abortus* strains lose their requirement for increased CO_2. Stock cultures will grow in chemically defined synthetic media containing glycerol, lactic acid, DL asparagine (or glutamic acid or histidine), thiamin HC1, nicotinic acid, Ca pantothenate, biotin, and mineral salts (32). The addition of 0.03 parts of iron per million parts of medium is required for maximal growth. The iron-deficient organisms produce almost no catalase, but, in contrast to the catalase deficient tubercle bacilli, these organisms have an increased degree of invasiveness for experimental animals (103).

Biochemical Reactions. The original discovery by Huddleson and Abell (43, 44) that certain aniline dyes inhibited specifically each of the three species has been extended by Pickett and Nelson (74, 75) and others to certain biochemical reactions which differentiate, with a fair degree of accuracy, the three species. To obtain the consistent results, shown in Table 1, smooth strains as determined by colonial morphology and nonagglutininability in acriflavine must be employed and the organisms must be grown in a well-buffered medium free of peptone.

It has been known for 30 years that *Brucella* utilized glucose but failed to show acid in the conventional tests, presumably because of alkali produced by deamination of the amino acids in peptone. *Br. abortus* oxidizes glucose, inositol, mannose, and rhamnose but not maltose or trehalose. *Br. melitensis* oxidizes glu-

Table 1. Biochemical Characteristics of Brucella Species [*]

	abortus	*melitensis*	*suis*
CO_2 Requirement	+	−	−
Glucose	+	+	+
Inositol	+	−	−
Mannose	+	−	+
Rhamnose	+	−	−
Maltose	−	−	+
Trehalose	−	−	+
Urea **	−	−	+
Carbamate	−	+	−
Thionin 1:800	+†	−	−
Basic Fuchsin 1:200	−‡	−	+
Crystal Violet 1:400	−	−	+
Pyronine 1:8000	−	−	+
Azure A 1:1000	+	−	+
Safranin 1:200	−	−	+
Nitrite Sensitivity	−	+	−

[*] Table constructed from data contained in publication of Pickett and Nelson (73, 75).

** The medium of Rustigan and Stuart must be employed. Those of Christensen, Fergerson and Hook are not satisfactory.

† = zone of inhibition greater than 4 mm.

‡ = zone of inhibition less than 4 mm.

cose but not other carbohydrates. *Br. suis* oxidizes glucose, mannose, maltose, and trehalose but not inositol or rhamnose.

Urea is hydrolyzed rapidly by *Br. suis* and slowly, if at all, by *Br. melitensis* and *Br. abortus*. Sodium diethyldithiocarbonate in a 1:200 dilution gives a negative carbamate test with *Br. abortus* and *Br. suis* but a positive test with *Br. melitensis* (75).

The various dyes used for inhibition are shown in Table 1. Azure A resembles thionin in inhibiting *Br. abortus,* and safranin resembles fuchsin, crystal violet, and pyronine in inhibiting *Br. suis.* Since there is some irregularity in the degree of inhibition by the various dyes, all should be used (75). The *suis* strains from Denmark are much more susceptible to the dye than *suis* strains from America, so one-half of the concentration of dye should be employed (Fig. 2).

All three species decompose both nitrates and nitrites, and nitrite accumulation is in the order *Br. abortus* > *Br. suis* ≧ *Br. melitensis*, but the results are not sufficiently distinctive to separate the species. On the other hand, nitrite toxicity was definitely greatest for *Br. melitensis* (75).

American strains of *Br. suis* produce H_2S in abundance and *Br. abortus* to a lesser extent, while *Br. melitensis* and Danish strains of *Br. suis* produce only traces (101). All strains produce catalase, with *Br. suis* being the most active and *Br. abortus* the least active (42). Ammonia is produced in varying amounts. No indol is formed, and the methyl red and Voges-Proskauer tests are negative.

A few strains were studied by Pickett and Nelson (75) which seem to be true *Brucella* intermediates both by antigenic analyses and biochemical tests. The discovery of the intermediate lends support to the theory that the three species may have evolved from a common ancestor.

The very thorough studies of Meyer and her associates (65, 67) on the oxidative metabolic patterns of *Brucellae* have revealed that *Br. melitensis* has only one type, *Br. abortus* three types, and *Br. suis* three types. The new species *Br. neotomae,* isolated by Stoenner and Lackman in 1957 (100) from the desert wood rat *Neotoma lepida* (Thomas) showed a single distinctive metabolic pattern (65, 66). However, the new species *Br. intermedia,* described by Renoux (82) was found to be a

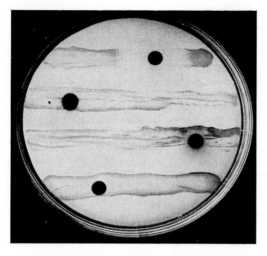 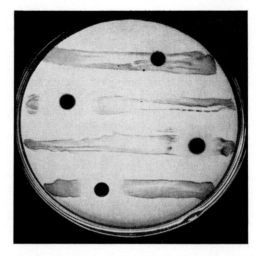

Fig. 2. Two dye-tablet differential plates. Left, *Br. abortus;* right, *Br. suis.* Top to bottom, thionin, fuchsin, crystal violet, pyronine. For best results, the prepared plates are inoculated, the dye tablet deposited, and then held at 4° C. for 14 to 16 hours before incubation. (From Pickett, Nelson, Hoyt, and Eisenstein. *J. Lab. & Clin. Med.,* 40:200, 1952.)

mixture of the known species. Among 25 strains classified as *Br. intermedia* by Renoux, 13 were identified as *Br. abortus,* 10 as *Br. melitensis,* and 1 as *Br. suis.*

Resistance. *Brucella* organisms are killed readily by the usual antiseptics or by the pasteurization of milk and milk products. They remain viable in refrigerated milk for 10 days, Roquefort cheese for two months, and refrigerated butter for four months. The organism has been grown from hog spleens after exposure for 30 days to temperatures of − 10° F. and after 45 days in a meat-curing brine (44). Penicillin has no bacteriostatic effect, but **chlortetracycline, oxytetracycline, chloramphenicol, neomycin, streptomycin** and the **sulfonamides** all inhibit the growth of the organisms in the test tube and in experimental disease in mice (93). Resistant forms develop and clinical relapses occur, making it desirable to treat with two of these therapeutic agents simultaneously.

Variability. *Brucella* shows the usual S-to-R dissociation phenomenon, although the change in colony form is gradual. Long bacilli and even filamentous forms occur in R colonies. There is a gradual and finally a complete loss of specific agglutinability as the organisms change from the S to R form. The R forms agglutinate spontaneously in physiologic saline and in serums of normal individuals and probably are identical with the strains formerly called "paramelitensis." The encapsulated M

forms occur spontaneously (46, 68) and can be induced at will (6). Braun observed that the serum of naturally resistant animals shifted the forms from S to R while that of susceptible animals favored the R to S dissociation. Braun and his associates (7, 8) have studied the phenomenon of dissociation in detail. When the S form is grown in broth cultures, alanine accumulates to toxic concentrations and is replaced by the alanine-resistant R form. When colonies of different types are stained for 15 seconds with a 1:2,000 aqueous solution of crystal violet and examined by transmitted light with a dissecting microscope, the mucoid colonies are a **light bluish red,** the rough colonies **deep violet reds,** the nonsmooth **red to blue-red,** and the smooth **blue-green** (105).

In 1946 Hall and Spink (36) isolated a "G" type microcolony from the blood of a patient with brucella endocarditis who had been treated with streptomycin. These organisms were resistant to streptomycin but were stimulated to growth by sublethal concentrations of the antibiotic. This colony variant had the biochemical and cultural characteristics of *Br. abortus* and maintained this identity for over seven years of subculturing in the laboratory. In later studies (95) "G" colonies were isolated from 11 of 14 cultures of *Br. abortus* and the variants were shown to have a reduced pathogenicity for mice. These "G" colonies bred true for several generations when incubated aerobically but reverted to the large colonial form when grown in an atmosphere of 10 per cent CO_2.

Bacteriophage. The presence of a bacteriophage capable of lysing strains of *Brucella* was reported by Pickett and Nelson in 1950 (74) and confirmed by Parnas and his associates in 1958 (72) but was not generally accepted until Stinespring and Braun (99) confirmed the work of Fomicheya (27) and Drozhevkina (15) in Russia.

This phage, whose host-propagating strain is R 19, lyses only smooth and intermediate strains of *Br. abortus.* Rough or mucoid strains of *Br. abortus* (53) and all strains of *Br. suis* and *Br. melitensis* were resistant. Mc-Duff and his associates (60) found that the phages, in the electromicrographs, had polygonal heads approximately 65 μ in diameter and wedge-shaped tails of 16 μ. Jones (49) reported that strains of atypical *Br. melitensis* isolated from cows in England by Brinley Morgan were lysed by this bacteriophage. Jones' observations were later confirmed by Meyer (65), who showed by her method of oxidative metabolic patterns that these strains were actually *Br. abortus.* In 1962 Jones and his associates (50) observed that the appearance of white colonies that were rough and not sticky were phage-resistant while white sticky colonies carried the phage and on replating gave rise to both white and blue-gray colonies.

Antigenic Structure. There are four recognized species of *Brucella: Br. melitensis, Br. abortus,* and *Br. suis,* and the new species *Br. neotomae,* which was isolated from the desert wood rat by Stoenner and Lackman (100) in 1957. The protein part of the nucleoprotein (45) is group-specific and apparently closely related to, if not identical with, the nucleoproteins of *Bord. pertussis* and *Bord. bronchiseptica* (71). Studies of freshly isolated S strains of *Brucella* by agglutinin absorption have shown that all three species of *Brucella* contain two antigens, designated as A and M (93). *Br. abortus* contains about 20 times as much A as M, while *Br. melitensis* has approximately 20 times as much M as A (69) which makes possible the differentiation of *Br. abortus* from *Br. melitensis; Br. suis,* having an intermediate antigenic pattern, is more difficult to characterize by agglutinin absorption (Fig. 3). The fractions isolated by Huddleson and his associates (45) were not antigenic but a polysaccharide studied by Wise and Craig (106) induced complement-fixing antibodies in rabbits and man.

Foster and Ribi (28) found that both the immunizing and endotoxic components were found in the isolated cell walls. Isolated protoplasm of the cells, without cell wall, had little immunizing capacity. An aqueous ether extract of the cell wall possessed immunizing potency which was superior to that of the whole dead cell, cell wall, and protoplasm.

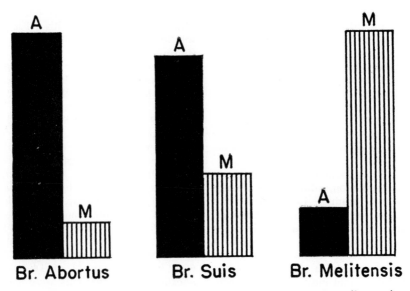

Fig. 3. Diagnostic representation of the antigenic structure of *Brucella* species. (From Miles. *Brit. J. Exper. Med.,* 20:63, 1939.)

The relationship between the protective antigen and toxin in this extract remains unresolved.

The serums of patients with active *Brucella* infections usually contain agglutinins (93), but the titers may be very low, very high, high with a prozone, or negative. Some of the negative tests result from the presence in the serum of a heat-labile blocking antibody reacting as a univalent nonagglutinating antibody. *Brucella* shares a common antigen with *V. comma* (18) and *Past. tularensis* (29). In questionable diagnoses one should inquire about a history of recent vaccination for cholera to eliminate the first possibility and should always perform a simultaneous agglutination with *Past. tularensis* to eliminate the second. The cross-titers to the nonspecific agent are almost always significantly lower (80).

Abernathy, Price, and Spink (1) have discussed the clinical significance of the "blocking antibody" in serum from patients with chronic brucellosis. This antibody accounts for the characteristic **prozone** and in some instances the failure to obtain a positive agglutination test even when the organisms have been isolated from the patients. The nature of the blocking antibody has been investigated by Glenchur, Zinneman, and Hall (33, 34). In acute cases of brucellosis in man and experimental animals classical agglutinating antibodies are present alone. As the disease becomes chronic, the blocking antibodies appear. These new antibodies are found at first in the slow moving gamma globulin but shift in a few weeks to the beta globulin (Ch. 13, Fig. 12).

Bacterial Metabolites. No exotoxins are produced, but the immunizing antigen (**endotoxin**) from the S form of *Brucella* is very toxic and varies in amount in the different species as indicated: *melitensis>suis>abortus* (22). Ammonia is formed in varying amounts, with *Br. suis* producing the greatest amount of **urease, catalase** (45), and **nitrates.**

Spontaneous Infection in Animals. Brucellosis is endemic in many herds of goats, cattle, and swine. Other animals, such as sheep, horses, mules, deer, buffaloes, dogs, rabbits and chickens, may acquire the disease from contact with infected herds (45). It has been estimated that 20 per cent of the herds in the United States of America are infected, resulting in about 5 per cent of all adult female cattle having the infection. The infection rate among swine is from 1 to 3 per cent. Although exact figures are not available, *Brucella* infection in animals is world-wide (93). Except for abortion, infection in animals usually produces few symptoms and almost never causes death; apparently healthy cows may secrete the organisms in their milk. The animals probably are infected by the ingestion of food which has been contaminated with *Brucella*. Young heifers are remarkably resistant to infection either through natural exposure or by the injection of large doses of virulent organisms. With the first pregnancy, however, they become very susceptible to spontaneous infection.

Diseased animals usually, but not always, have a high titer of agglutinins in their serums and antibodies in their milk which can be demonstrated by the **ring test.** The isolation and slaughter of infected animals have resulted in many herds being freed of brucellosis.

Experimental Disease in Laboratory Animals. Monkeys, which can be infected readily with *Br. suis* or *Br. melitensis* and occasionally with *Br. abortus,* develop an undulating type of fever, but the disease is seldom progressive. Lesions are present in the lymph nodes and spleen at necropsy (45). The intrapleural, subcutaneous, or intravenous injection of *Brucella* into guinea pigs results in an infection which progresses at first but then slowly regresses as agglutinins and complement-fixing antibodies appear. The animals become hypersensitive to the proteins of the *Brucella* organisms, and this **allergy** persists for months after recovery (6). When direct inoculations of media fail to give growth, cultures occasionally can be obtained by **guinea pig passage.** Blood, spinal fluid, and ground-up lymph nodes or other tissues should be inoculated intraperitoneally, whereas tissues likely to be contaminated should be introduced subcutaneously. After two or three weeks, agglutinins may appear in the serum and if these animals are killed, cultures can be made from the blood and spleen in the usual manner. Rabbits show good antibody production but are infected less easily than guinea pigs. Mice and rats are relatively resistant.

The inoculation of the chorioallantoic membrane of the developing chick embryo causes death of the embryo within a few days. The organisms grow **intracellularly,** *Br. melitensis* electing the ectodermal cells whereas *Br. abortus* and *Br. suis* prefer to multiply in cells of mesodermal origin such as the vascular endothelium (35).

Spink and Anderson (94) showed that the administration of cortisone to mice so reduced their resistance that a rapidly fatal fulminating disease resulted. The attenuated strain, *Br. abortus* 19, was made more virulent, but severe necrosis of the liver was not produced, as it was when virulent strains of *Br. abortus* were inoculated.

Clinical Types of Infection in Man.   Man is very susceptible to *Brucella* infection, as shown by the numerous cases resulting from accidental infections in the laboratory (62, 90). Fortunately, the majority of naturally acquired infections are subclinical as evidenced by the discovery of agglutinins and positive brucellergen skin tests in relatively large percentages of various populations (61, 89, 98).

In North Carolina 11.3 per cent of healthy university students (61) had either positive skin tests or serum agglutinins; in Tennessee 28 per cent had positive skin tests and 15 per cent agglutinins (48); in the groups tested in Iowa 10 to 25 per cent had positive skin tests; among students in Kansas 29 per cent had aggutinins (87); and in Minnesota 18 per cent of the samples from the blood bank contained agglutinins (97). These immunologic reactions almost certainly represent subclinical infections and not a response to the ingestion of dead *Brucella* in pasteurized milk, since McCullough and others (59) found that the ingestion of large doses of heat-killed *Brucella* failed to stimulate either agglutinins or allergy.

Brucellosis can be divided clinically into three types—the acute, subacute, and chronic forms—and all three types of the disease are produced by any of the three species of *Brucella* (2).

Acute brucellosis usually begins insidiously after an incubation period of 10 to 14 days. After drinking contaminated milk, the incubation period may be as short as four days or occasionally as long as 30 days (46, 90). In the experiments on human volunteers conducted by Morales-Otero in Puerto Rico (70), two patients developed the disease 10 to 17 days after drinking cultures and in six patients clinical manifestations appeared 10 to 16 days after the organisms were rubbed into the abraded skin.

Acute cases of brucellosis usually recover spontaneously after one to three months. The typical undulating type of fever described by Hughes on the Island of Malta is seen only occasionally in this country. Blood cultures generally are positive during the first two or three weeks of the disease and become negative as the patients develop agglutinins, complement-fixing antibodies, and opsonins. During relapses, which are characteristic features of this disease, the blood cultures again may become positive, even when antibodies are present in high titer. Positive skin tests to heat-killed vaccines develop in most patients, and skin tests with brucellergen become positive between the third and sixth weeks of the disease. When this **allergy** develops, it usually persists for many years (90, 91).

Subacute brucellosis may follow the acute phase of the infection and may be more or less severe than the primary infection. Blood cultures are positive less frequently, but antibodies usually are found and the patient shows hypersensitivity to the organism.

The chronic form of the disease may last from one to 20 years. The symptoms are mild but persistent and disabling. Blood cultures rarely are positive except during very acute exacerbations of the disease. Two types of chronic brucellosis can be recognized, although some cases cannot be classified in either category. The **hypersensitive type** shows evidences of good to excellent antibody production and also a marked degree of **allergy.** The **anergic type** typically shows a negative skin test to the organism, and antibodies in the blood cannot be demonstrated. The diagnosis can be established only by culturing the organism from the blood, bile, stools or lymph nodes (76, 79) or from the materials obtained by punch biopsy of the liver (26).

Local and focal lesions may occur in the **skin** (46), **mouth** (78), **eyes** (86), **lungs** (104), **lymph nodes** (5), **spleen** (96), **biliary tract** (2), **vertebrae** (96), **joints, meninges and brain** (90), **urinary tract** (1), **male genitalia** (89), and **female genitalia** (13). Many of the fatal cases of brucellosis have resulted from infection of the **valves of the heart,** giving rise to a subacute type of bacterial endocarditis (96).

In rare instances abortions have been described in women and *Brucella* have been cultivated from their placentas (13).

Pulmonary infections are being recognized with greater frequency (81, 85). The hazard of slaughtering swine that are infected with *Br. suis* has been emphasized by Harris and his associates (38).

The mortality among British soldiers stationed on the Island of Malta was about 2.3 per cent. In this country the mortality of reported infections is about 2 per cent, most of the fatal infections having been caused by *Br. suis*. The most dangerous infections are those in which there is an endocarditis or meningoencephalitis.

More information about the world-wide distribution of brucellosis and its diagnosis and treatment can be found in Spink's book (93).

Biologic Products. Convalescent human serum has been administered intrathecally for the treatment of *Brucella meningitis* (77).

Huddleson and his associates (45) have two biologic products called **brucellin** and **brucellergen.** Brucellergen is used for the preliminary skin test, and brucellin for desensitization. Neither of these products is capable of producing immunity in man or animals, but both of them may stimulate the production of agglutinins, complement-fixing antibodies, and opsonins in patients who already have a hypersensitivity. In order to evaluate the immune status of the patient, it is important to carry out the serologic studies before skin tests with vaccines, brucellergen, or brucellin are performed.

Transmission. Brucellosis occurs in areas where abortions of cattle or swine are endemic or where raw milk and milk products from infected herds of goats and cows are consumed. Direct invasion through the intact intestinal mucosa is unquestionably the most common route of infection. However, stockyard workers, farmers and veterinary surgeons frequently are infected through the skin by contact with the living or dead tissues of infected animals.

Airborne infections have been demonstrated experimentally for the monkey (62) and the guinea pig (84). In one epidemic in a swine-slaughtering plant in Iowa, 128 employees developed brucellosis over a period of nine months. Airborne infection was suspected, and Harris and his associates succeeded in isolating virulent *Br. suis* from the air of the slaughter room (38).

Spink (91) reported in 1957 a case history of 4 veterinarians who accidentally infected themselves with the attenuated strain 19 of *Br. abortus* which was being used as a prophylactic vaccine in cows. Two were infected by sticking the needle through the skin and two by squirting the vaccine into their eyes.

Treatment. Treatment with antibiotics has been reviewed by Shaffer, Kucera and Spink (86), Schirger and his associates at the Mayo Clinic (85), Martin and others (57), Kelly and others (52) and Spink (92). While tetracycline and streptomycin and even sulfonamides may cure acute cases of brucellosis, the subacute and chronic cases require more vigorous treatment. Spink's (92) clinical observation of the advantage of combined treatment with tetracycline and streptomycin has been confirmed in tissue culture experiments by Richardson and Holt (83), who showed that streptocmycin and tetracycline had an inhibiting synergistic effect on the intracellular growth of *Brucella.*

The initial doses of the antibiotics should be small to avoid the chance of a Herxheimer-like reaction. In patients who have developed a tuberculin-like allergy to brucella protein or even to the endotoxin itself, the sudden death of many bacilli may liberate enough reactive antigen to precipitate shock. This type of reaction has been observed not infrequently by Spink (92). The symptoms of shock can be relieved by the prompt administration of large doses of corticoid hormones. However, the corticoid therapy should be limited to a 72-hour period because of the accelerating effect of corticoids on brucella infections (54, 95).

One or more relapses are not unusual in cases of brucellosis and should not discourage either the patient or the physician. Retreatment is given with the same drug combination. If the relapsing patient has a very large positive skin test to Huddleson's brucellergen, hyposensitizing doses of Huddleson brucellin would do no harm and might accelerate recovery if given simultaneously with the antibiotics.

Very good results were obtained in many cases of subacute and chronic brucellosis, before the introduction of antibiotics, by the administration of Huddleson's brucellin (37, 89, 90). The degree of hypersensitization was determined by the intracutaneous injection of Huddleson's **Brucellergin.** Depending upon the size of the reaction after 24 hours, the hyposensitizing dose of brucellin was calculated (90).

Prevention.   The pasteurization of milk and milk products would protect most individuals from brucellosis, except those whose occupation brings them in direct contact with infected animals or cultures. Obviously it is advisable to detect, isolate, and eventually slaughter animals infected with brucellosis.

Active immunization of cattle, goats, and swine would be indicated if and when a suitable immunization agent is available. This also applies to active immunization of stockyard workers, farmers, veterinary surgeons, and laboratory workers who handle cultures of *Brucella* (40).

The immunity in brucellosis seems to depend upon a combination of classical antibacterial antibodies, and the tissue type of immunity dependent upon trained monocytes such as one finds in tuberculosis (41, 88).

The attenuated strain of *Br. abortus* known as 19 seems to be relatively effective in immunizing cattle but is too virulent for immunizing man (91) and not effective in the immunization of swine (88). The most hopeful lead for immunizing man and certain animals comes from the brilliant studies of Herzberg and Elberg (39, 40, 58). These investigators developed a streptomycin-dependent strain which would grow to a limited extent in animal tissues. The resulting immunity, however, was no better than that obtained by the inoculation of a relatively large amount of heat-killed organisms (23). A reversed mutant, from the dependent to the independent state in respect to streptomycin, has been obtained. This strain persists longer in the tissues and produces a more solid immunity in mice and guinea pigs. Immunization of goats with this vaccine protected 90 to 94 per cent of the animals from infection and abortion (19, 20). This reversed mutant of *Br. melitensis* from streptomycin dependence to independence is now known as the *Rev. 1 Br. melitensis* vaccine (58). An analogous reverse mutant from *Br. suis* has been derived by Simon and Berman (88) with the hope it will be effective in the immunization of swine.

REFERENCES

1. Abernathy, R. S., and others.   J.A.M.A., 159:1534, 1955.
2. Amoss, H. L., and Poston, M. A.   J.A.M.A., 93:170, 1929.
3. Bang, B.   J. Comp. Path. & Therap., 10: 125, 1897.
4. Biegeleisen, J. Z., Jr., and others.   J. Immunol., 88:109, 1962.
5. Bloomfield, A. L.   Am. Rev. Tuberc., 45: 741, 1942.
6. Braude, A. I.   J. Infect. Dis., 89:87, 1951.
7. Braun, W. J.   J. Bact., 51:327, 1946; 52: 243, 1946.
8. ———— and others.   J. Bact., 62:45, 1951.
9. ———— and Kelsh, J.   Proc. Soc. Exper. Biol. & Med., 85:154, 1954.
10. Bruce, D.   Practitioner, 39:161, 1887; 40: 241, 1888.
11. ———— and others.   Mediterranean Fever Commission Report, London, 1905-1907. Quoted from Duncan, J. T., and others. A System of Bacteriology in Relation to Medicine, London, 5:386, 1930.
12. Calderone, J. G., and Pickett, M. J.   Am. J. Med. Tech., 27:333, 1961.
13. Carpenter, C. M., and Boak, R.   J.A.M.A., 96:1212, 1931.
14. ———— and Merriam, H. E.   J.A.M.A., 87: 1269, 1926.
15. Drozhevkina, M. S.   Ahur. Microbiol. Epidemiol. Immunobiol., 28:1221, 1957.
16. Edwards, J. T.   Vet. Rec., 33:721, 739, 1921.
17. Edwards, S.   Alaska Med., 1:41, 1959.
18. Eisele, C. W., and others.   Ann. Int. Med., 28:833, 1948.
19. Elberg, S. S., and Faunce, W. K., Jr.   Bull. World Health Org., 26:421, 1962.
20. ———— and Faunce, W. K., Jr.   Bull. World Health Org., 26:421, 1962.
21. ———— and Faunce, W. K., Jr.   J. Bact., 73:211, 1957.
22. ———— and others.   J. Immunol., 67:1, 1951.
23. ———— and others.   J. Bact., 69:643, 1955.
24. Evans, A. C.   J. Infect. Dis., 22:580, 1918.
25. ———— Pub. Health Rep., 38:1948, 1923.
26. Fogel, R., and Lewis, S.   Ann. Int. Med., 53:204, 1960.
27. Fomicheva, and others.   Ahur. Microbiol. Epidemiol. Immunobiol., 27:57, 1956.
28. Foster, J. W., and Ribi, E.   J. Bact., 84:258, 1962.
29. Francis, E., and Evans, A.   Pub. Health Rep., 41:1273, 1926.
30. Gage, E. E., and Gregory, D. A.   J.A.M.A., 87:848, 1926.
31. Gerhardt, P.   Bact. Rev., 22:81, 1958.
32. ———— and others.   J. Bact., 59:777, 1950.
33. Glenchur, H., and others.   J. Bact., 85:363, 1963.
34. ———— and others.   J. Immunol., 86:421, 1961.

35. Goodpasture, E. W., and Anderson, K. Am. J. Path., 13:149, 1937.
36. Hall, W. H., and Spink, W. W. Proc. Soc. Exp. Biol. & Med., 64:403, 1947.
37. Harris, H. J. J.A.M.A., 131:1485, 1946.
38. Harris, M. M., and others. Pub. Health Rep., 77:602, 1962.
39. Herzberg, M., and Elberg, S. S. J. Bact., 66:585, 600, 1953.
40. ——— and Elberg, S. S. J. Bact., 69:432, 1955.
41. Holland, J. J., and Pickett, M. J. J. Exper. Med., 108:343, 1958.
42. Huddleson, I. F. J.A.M.A., 86:943, 1926.
43. ——— and Abell, E. J. Bact., 13:13, 1927.
44. ——— and others. J. Am. Vet. M. A., 36:16, 1932.
45. ——— Brucellosis in Man and Animals, New York, The Commonwealth Fund, Oxford University Press, 1939.
46. ——— J. Am. Vet. M. A., 96:708, 1940.
47. Hughes, M. L. Mediterranean, Malta or Undulant Fever, London, Macmillan & Co., 1897.
48. Johnson, C. W., and Bent, M. J. South. M. J., 42:62, 1949.
49. Jones, L. M. Bull. World Health Org., 23:130, 1960.
50. ——— and others. J. Bact., 83:860, 1962.
51. Keefer, C. S. Bull. Johns Hopkins Hosp., 35:6, 1924.
52. Kelly, P. J., and others. J.A.M.A., 174:347, 1960.
53. Kessel, R. W. I., and Braun, W. J. Bact., 81:503, 1961.
54. ——— and others. Bact. Proc., 1963, p. 69.
55. Kuzdas, C. D., and Morse, E. V. J. Bact., 66:502, 1953.
56. Marston, J. A. Great Brit. Army Med. Dept. Repts., London, 1861.
57. Martin, W. J., and others. Proc. Staff Meet., Mayo Clinic., 35:717, 1960.
58. McCamish, J., and Elberg, S. S. Am. J. Path., 40:77, 1962.
59. McCullough, N. B., and others. Pub. Health Rep., 64:1613, 1949.
60. McDuff, C. R., and others. J. Bact., 83:324, 1962.
61. Menefee, E. E., Jr., and Poston, M. A. Am. J. M. Sc., 197:646, 1939.
62. Meyer, K. F., and Eddie, B. J. Infect. Dis., 68:24, 1941.
63. ——— and Shaw, E. B. J. Infect. Dis., 27:173, 1920.
64. Meyer, M. E. Bact. Proc., 1963, p. 41.
65. ——— J. Bact., 82:950, 1961.
66. ——— and Cameron, H. S. Bull. World Health Org, 28:499, 1963.
67. ——— and Cameron, H. S. J. Bact., 82:387, 396, 401, 1961.
68. Mickle, W. A. J. Infect. Dis., 66:271, 1940.
69. Miles, A. A. Brit. J. Exper. Path., 20:63, 1939.
70. Morales-Otero, P. M. Puerto Rico J. Pub. Health & Trop. Med., 5:144, 1929.
71. Parfentjev, I. A., and others. J. Bact., 53:597, 603, 613, 1947.
72. Parnas, J. J. Bact., 82:319, 1961.
73. Pickett, M. J., and Nelson, E. L. J. Bact., 61:229, 1951.
74. ——— and Nelson, E. L. J. Hygiene, 48:500, 1950.
75. ——— and Nelson, E. L. J. Bact., 68:63, 1954; 69:333, 1955.
76. Poston, M. A. Pub. Health Rep., 53:7, 1938.
77. ——— and Smith, D. T. New England J. Med., 215:269, 1936.
78. ——— and Menefee, E. E., Jr. New England J. Med., 219:796, 1938.
79. ——— J. Lab. & Clin. Med., 26:1961, 1941.
80. ——— Proc. Soc. Am. Bacteriologists, 1951, p. 80.
81. Raman, S. J., and others. J.A.M.A., 170:1665, 1959.
82. Renoux, G. Arch. Inst. Pasteur Tunis., 37:23, 1960.
83. Richardson, M., and Holt, J. N. J. Bact., 84:638, 1962.
84. Rosebury, T., and others. Experimental Air-Borne Infection, Williams and Wilkins Co., Baltimore, 1947, p. 147.
85. Schirger, A., and others. Ann. Int. Med., 52:827, 1960.
86. Shaffer, J. M., and others. J. Immunol., 70:31, 1953.
87. Sherwood, N. P., and others. J. Kansas M. Soc., 51:6, 1950.
88. Simon, E. M., and Berman, D. T. J. Bact., 83:1347, 1962.
89. Simpson, W. M. Tice's Practice of Medicine, 4:99, 1952.
90. Smith, D. T. Chapter on Brucellosis in Nelson's Loose Leaf System of Medicine, New York, Thomas Nelson and Sons, 1948.
91. Spink, W. W. Ann. Int. Med., 47:861, 1957.
92. ——— J.A.M.A., 172:697, 1960.
93. ——— The Nature of Brucellosis, Univ. of Minnesota Press, Minnesota, 1956.
94. ——— and Anderson, D. Proc. Soc. Exp. Biol. & Med., 99:466, 1958.
95. ——— and Anderson, D. Proc. Soc. Exp. Biol. & Med., 99:470, 1958.
96. ——— and Hall, W. H. M. Clin. North America, 29:343, 1945.
97. ——— and Anderson, D. J. Lab. & Clin. Med., 35:440, 1950.
98. ——— and others. Am. J. Clin. Path., 24:496, 1954.
99. Stinespring, W. R., and Braun, W. J. Bact., 78:736, 1959.
100. Stoenner, H. G., and Lackman, D. B. Am. J. Vet. Research, 18:947, 1957.
101. Thomsen, A. Acta path. et microbiol. Scandinav., Suppl. 21, 1934.
102. Traum, J. U.S. Dept. of Agric. Repts., Bur. Animal Indus., 1914, p. 30.
103. Waring, W. S., and others. J. Bact., 66:82, 1953.
104. Weed, L. A., and others. J.A.M.A., 161:1044, 1956.
105. White, P. G., and Wilson, J. B. J. Bact., 61:239, 1951.
106. Wise, B., and Craig, H. W. J. Infect. Dis., 70:147, 1942.

42

Pasteurella tularensis and Tularemia

Family: *Brucellaceae* fam. nov. Genus: *Pasteurella* Trevisan. Species: *Pasteurella tularensis* (McCoy and Chapin) Bergey and others

Tularemia, a disease primarily of rabbits, hares, rodents, and birds, is transmitted from animal to animal by flies, fleas, lice, and ticks. At present, the disease in man is known in North America, Europe, Russia, and Japan and probably will be found in other parts of the world. In the United States 2,000 to 3,000 human cases are reported each year, with a mortality rate of approximately 5 per cent. Man is an accidental and a terminal host.

Francis (31) reports that Martin, an ophthalmologist, recognized the clinical disease in Arizona in 1907. The organism, first described by McCoy in 1911 and isolated by McCoy and Chapin (43) in 1912 from a "plague-like disease" of ground squirrels in Tulare County, California, was named *Bacterium tularense* in honor of the county in which it was discovered. McCoy, however, did not associate the infection with the clinical disease in man. Isolated instances of human infection were recorded by Vail and by Wherry and Lamb (65) in 1914 but the series of investigations started by Francis in 1919 has provided us with most of our basic knowledge of both the organism and the clinical disease. Francis contributed the name "tularemia" to indicate the ability of the organism to invade the blood and produce a generalized infection.

Morphology and Staining. *Pasteurella tularensis* is extremely pleomorphic (Fig. 1). Large numbers of minute coccoid forms occur in the cytoplasm of the hepatic cells of experimentally infected mice. Smears from the bone marrows of infected rabbits show both coc-

coid and small, short, bacillary forms. Morphologically recognizable forms, however, are found only rarely in the tissues of patients dead of tularemia.

In cultures, both ovoid and bacillary forms are present with average sizes of 0.2 to 1 μ in width and 1 to 3 μ in length. Careful studies of prepared smears from cultures reveal that dumbbell, bean-shaped, L-shaped, spermatozoon-like, and knobby globoid forms occur frequently and bizarre and coccoid bodies often are present (Fig. 2). The studies of Hesselbrock and Foshay (35) indicate that these structures occur in young, actively growing cultures and are different from the classic involution forms encountered so frequently in old, dying cultures of bacteria. Foshay and his associates (25) have demonstrated a series of small, coccoid forms which show gradations in size between easily visible organisms and those which were small enough to pass through Berkefeld filters having diameters of 300 to 350 mμ, as determined by filtration through Elfords' gradocol membranes. The viability of these minute forms was checked by mouse inoculation. These minimal reproductive units are shown in the electron micrographs of Eigelsbach and others (18), measurements from the photographs showing organisms from 100 to 300 μ in size.

Capsules on the coccoid forms of the organisms have been described but the investigations of Hesselbrock and Foshay indicate that these structures are **not true capsules** but **extremely thick cell walls.** Division by binary fission has not been observed. **Budding** is the chief method of reproduction (35).

Past. tularensis stains rather faintly with the usual aniline dyes and is definitely **gram-negative.**

Yager and his associates (69) have prepared an antibody for use in the fluorescent anti-

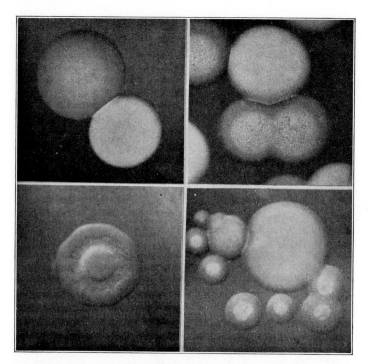

Fig. 1. *Pasteurella tularensis* colony variations. 1, smooth blue $Schu_4$ colony and smooth dense, buff $Schu_2$ virulent colonies. 2, two gray viscous $Schu_2$ relatively avirulent colonies at bottom. 3, single Schu NS_5 virulent colony. 4, large 38S, and several dwarf 38NS avirulent colonies. All colonies × 100. (From Eigelsbach, Braun, and Herring. *J. Bact.,* 61:557, 1951.)

body technic by injecting the organism into chickens. Antibodies prepared in rabbits and monkeys gave cross-reactions with enteric bacteria and with *V. comma*. The antibody produced in chickens did cross with *Pseudomonas* species, but these antibodies could be removed by absorption with *Pseudomonas* bacilli.

Cultural Reactions. *Past. tularensis* is a strict **aerobe.** It will grow over a temperature range of 24° to 39° C., with maximum growth attained at a temperature of 37° C. at a pH of about 6.9. Since phosphate ions inhibit the growth of the organism, sodium hydroxide should be used to adjust the pH of the medium.

The organism was isolated originally by McCoy and Chapin (43) on a rather dry egg yolk medium. Francis (29) found that the **cystine** of egg yolk was essential for growth of the organism and devised a medium containing blood, glucose, and cystine which has remained standard for many years. **Sodium thioglycollate** can replace cystine in solid (55) or liquid media (59), provided there are traces of cystine in the other ingredients (61).

Several investigators have described chemically defined media for the growth of *Past.* *tularensis* but growth was not comparable in luxuriance with that obtained on natural media. Nagle and his associates (48) have devised a chemically defined medium which gave optimal growth with several virulent strains.

After a 24 to 48 hour incubation period, small, smooth, opaque colonies with a butter-like consistency appear on blood-glucose-cystine or cysteine media (Fig. 3). An organism which produces growth on plain agar or in plain bouillon media is not *Past. tularensis.*

In 1941 Buddingh and Womack (9) found that *Past. tularensis* grew in the cells of the chorioallantoic membrane, embryo, and yolk sac of the chick embryo. Later studies have shown that the growth is most luxuriant in the yolk sac and least in the embryo. Indeed, the organisms grew equally as well in the yolk sac of dead as in living embryos (39, 54). *Past. tularensis* oxidizes **glucose, maltose,** and **mannose,** producing **acid without gas. Lactose, sucrose, xylose, mannitol, salicin, inulin, sorbitol,** and **rhamnose** are **not** oxidized. Irregular results were obtained with glycerol, levulose, and dextrin.

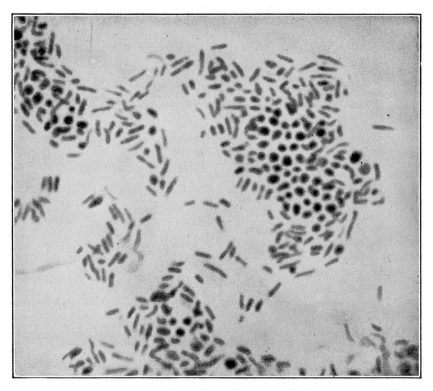

Fig. 2. *Pasteurella tularensis.* From culture on glucose cystine agar, showing coccoid and bacillary forms in the same field. Approx. × 5,000. (From Army Medical Museum. Courtesy of Edward Francis, U.S.P.H.S.)

Resistance. The organisms do not survive long in old cultures and therefore should be transferred every three or four days. Lyophilized cultures may be viable after four years. In 1932 Francis reported his studies on the preservation of viable organisms in animal tissues. When spleens of infected guinea pigs were preserved in pure undiluted neutral glycerin, viable organisms were found to persist for one month at room temperature, six months at 10° C., and six years at − 14° C. Virulence can be preserved indefinitely by semiannual injections of guinea pigs with infected glycerinated spleens which have been kept at − 14° C.

A 1 per cent solution of tricresol acting for two minutes disinfects emulsions of infected splenic tissue. Organisms from cultures are destroyed in 24 hours by 0.1 per cent formalin. A temperature of 56° to 58° C. kills organisms from cultures or in splenic pulp in approximately 10 minutes. The infected tissues of game birds and animals can be rendered harmless by thorough cooking.

The **sulfonamides** and **penicillin** are not effective in the treatment of experimental tularemia.

Chloramphenicol and the tetracyclines inhibit the growth of *Past. tularensis* in test tubes and delay the death of infected mice (40, 51). In contrast, streptomycin is bactericidal and is therefore the drug of choice in therapy (3, 44, 56).

Variability. Virulent cultures contain a variety of colonial forms, some of which are highly virulent while others are of low virulence (Fig. 1). The colonial forms can be correlated with the acriflavine reaction, acid agglutination, virulence, and immunogenic potency (17), although staining with crystal violet seems to be the best method for differentiating smooth from nonsmooth strains (47). The nonsmooth strains have little, if any, virulence. While an occasional smooth strain is found with a low degree of virulence in general, there is a good correlation between smooth colonial morphology, virulence, immunogenicity, and the ability to multiply in the tissues of white mice (47).

There is available for vaccination purposes

antigen or antigens seem to be concentrated in the cell wall of the organism but the purest preparations of cell walls contain at least four, and possibly six, different antigens (50). The studies of Larson and his associates (41, 50, 57) illustrate the complexity of the subject. The cell wall antigens induce immunity in mice, without agglutinins, in a period of 24 to 72 hours, while the same material produced agglutinins in guinea pigs and rabbits without inducing immunity. The agglutinin titer is certainly not directly related to immunity (31a), since high titers may be present in mice and rabbits (8) and also in man for several days before death.

Vosti and his associates (63) have shown that the number of precipitin lines, measured by agar gel diffusion, paralleled measurement by other serologic methods. However, vaccination with killed organisms, which gives detectable agglutinins, does not give lines in the agar gel; hence the presence of a single line has diagnostic importance. In more than one-half of the instances the precipitin line appeared before agglutination. A specific line designated D seems to be related to immunity. Patients who seem to recover, but without the

Fig. 3. Cultures of *Past. tularensis* on glucose cystine agar. Left is inoculated with heart blood of guinea pig; note presence of colonies. Right is inoculated with heart blood of mouse; note absence of colonies. (From Army Medical Museum. Courtesy of Edward Francis. U.S.P.H.S.)

a new mutant which has limited multiplying ability but excellent immunogenic capacity (16). This strain was isolated from a vial of the Russian vaccine strain (49) and was characterized as a dense colony which appears blue in color, in contrast to the less immunogenic colonies, which were less dense and gray colonies (Fig. 4).

Antigenic Structure. There appears to be only one antigenic type of *Past. tularensis*, although individual strains may be of high, medium, or low virulence. The immunizing

Fig. 4. Two colony variants found in U.S.S.R. live tularemia vaccine. The more dense colonies appeared blue and the less dense gray when illuminated with oblique light. Both variants were virulent and were designated BV and GV. Animals studied showed that BV was more antigenic, and this is now the LVS vaccine. (From Eigelsbach and Downs. *J. Immunol.*, 84:415, 1961.)

appearance of the D line, frequently relapse, and one patient who had two relapses without a D line in his serum did not relapse after its appearance. Carlisle and his coworkers (10) studied antigens prepared by sonic vibration and found six antigens could be identified by agglutination and four more by hemagglutination. The six were identified with cell wall antigen, while the four detected by hemagglutination were polysaccharides and seemed to be from the interior of the cell.

A soluble specific polysaccharide was isolated by Foshay, in 1936 (23) which produced an immediate wheal type reaction when injected into the skin of convalescent patients. Young goats produced precipitins but not agglutinins when injected with this polysaccharide. Immunity in rats can be correlated with the precipitin titer but not with the agglutinin titer (8, 26). Erythrocytes sensitized with this polysaccharide agglutinate in serums from immune animals (68). The more recent studies of Ormsbee (50), Bell (6), and Larson (41) indicate that the carbohydrate alone is not the essential immunizing antigen, although it might be a part of a complex antigen.

There is probably a common protein antigen which is shared by *Past. tularensis* and members of the genus *Brucella*. The serums of rabbits immunized against either organism may agglutinate the other in low titers. Agglutinin absorption removes the common agglutinin but not those responsible for species specificity (30). Patients with tularemia may have agglutinins in low titers for *Brucella* and vice versa, but this rarely causes difficulty in the clinical laboratory if both tests are performed simultaneously, because of the higher titer produced by the organism initiating the infection. Agglutinins have been found in the serums of man 20 years after an initial infection, and in an area where both tularemia and brucellosis are endemic an occasional patient will be seen who has high titers to both antigens (30, 52). We have interpreted such results as evidence of infection with both organisms in sequence (52).

Foshay introduced three types of skin tests which are useful in the diagnosis of tularemia. The **polysaccharide skin test,** just described, gives an immediate wheal type of reaction after 30 minutes if the patients' tissues contain antipolysaccharide antibodies. **Foshay's antibody serum test** also gives an immediate wheal type of reaction in 30 minutes if the patients' tissues contain an excess of polysaccharide from the invading organism. A positive test can be rendered negative by injecting immune serum into

the patient (23, 24). The test is performed by the intracutaneous injection of 0.04 ml. of serum obtained from a goat which has been immunized to *Past. tularensis.* An equal amount of normal goat serum is injected into the skin of the other arm as a control.

Foshay's bacterial protein antigen is a test for **allergy.** The bacterial proteins, which are moderately reactive when injected into normal individuals, are treated with nitrous acid until they no longer produce reactions. After the first week of infection the intracutaneous injection of 0.1 ml. of Foshay's bacterial antigen produces a delayed type of reaction which reaches its maximum in 48 to 72 hours and persists for five to six days.

The **tularensis polysaccharide test** is **negative** during the first week or so of the infection but becomes **positive** when sufficient antibodies have been produced by the patient to more than neutralize all the polysaccharides in the tissues. The **bacterial protein test** becomes **positive** between seven and 10 days after infection and usually remains positive for life although dying patients may become **anergic** and consequently give a negative test. **Foshay's antibody serum test** (23) usually becomes **positive** in three to five days after the onset of symptoms, before the bacterial protein antigen test is positive and long before the appearance of agglutinins. This test can be rendered negative by the injection of immune serum, as noted before, but in many instances it remains positive for years after recovery, probably indicating the persistence of *Past. tularensis* in the body for many years. It is difficult to visualize an immune mechanism which adequately controls the organism and yet permits a sufficient production of soluble polysaccharides to render the test positive.

Bacterial Metabolites. No **exotoxin** is produced by *Past. tularensis,* but proteins and lipoproteins of dead organisms are definitely toxic when injected into man or animals. However, some tolerance to the endotoxins developed in experimental tularemia in man (34).

In 1955 Flemming and Foshay (21) reported that virulent strains possess citrulline ureidase, while avirulent strains do not. This observation was confirmed by Marchette and Nicholes (42) in 1961, who noted a high level of this enzyme in the tick bourne strain from the rabbit while it was low or absent from a strain isolated from the rodent (*Microtus montanus*).

Weinstein and his coworkers (64) reported that the rate of piruvate oxidation was directly related to strain virulence, whereas the "endogenous respiration" was inversely correlated with virulence. The authors concluded that quantitative differences in the tricarboxylic acid cycle could modify the expressed virulence observed in various strains. Turning from the organism to the host we see that aconitase and fumarase activity of the liver tissue of rats infected with *Past. tularensis* was reduced by more than 33 per cent. The administration of cortisone prevented the fall of the aconitase activity for 48 hours but had little effect on the fumarase levels (66).

Spontaneous Infection in Animals. Spontaneous infections have been observed in the following animals: ground squirrels in California and Utah; wild rabbits and hares throughout the United States (Fig. 5); wild rats of Los Angeles; wild mice of California; quail, grouse, and pheasants in Minnesota; sheep in Idaho; beavers in Utah; wild rabbits in Japan, Norway, and Canada; water rats in Russia; and wood ticks in California, Montana, and Minnesota (27, 28). Severe and fatal disease has been reported in foals (12).

Larson (40) has introduced an **Ascoli-like test** by which the diagnosis of tularemia can be made from the decomposed tissue of animals found dead in the fields. The disease is transferred from animal to animal by the bites of flies, fleas, lice, ticks, and mosquitoes. The most important fly in the transmission of the disease is the deer fly, *Chrysops discalis*. Three species of ticks are of major importance both in maintaining the disease in animals and in transmitting the infection to man. These are the wood tick (*Dermacentor andersoni*), the dog tick (*D. variabilis*), and the lone star tick (*Am-*

blyomma americanum) (3, 36). The ecologic studies of Jellison and his associates (38) suggest that there are two distinct types of tularemia in the United States: the common virulent form, which is tickborne from the rabbit, and the low virulent form of rodents, which is contracted from water. The enzyme studies of Marchette and Nicholes (42) confirm the presence of the two forms of tularemia in this country. In the tick the organisms are transmitted via the ovaries to the eggs, through the larvae and nymph stages and finally the adult ticks, which transmit the infection (6, 33). Ticks which have been feeding on grouse often carry strains of *Past. tularensis* which are less virulent than those carried by ticks which have become infected from rabbits (33). There is no evidence that naturally acquired infections occur in rabbits kept under domestic conditions.

Experimental Disease in Laboratory Animals. A single *Past. tularensis* organism of a highly virulent strain can produce a fatal infection in the mouse, rabbit, guinea pig, or hamster. The susceptibility of the monkey is similar to that of man. Ten viable organisms of a virulent strain may produce systemic diseases in human volunteers when introduced intradermally (56). The dose for pulmonary or systemic tularemia in man by aerosol was 10 to 50 organisms (56).

One bacillus from a virulent strain of *Past. tularensis* can kill a guinea pig. Bacilli from avirulent strains are readily phagocytized or destroyed. Bacilli from virulent strains are phagocytized by polymorphonuclear leukocytes and by monocytes. They are not destroyed by phagocytin derived from PMN's, but the num-

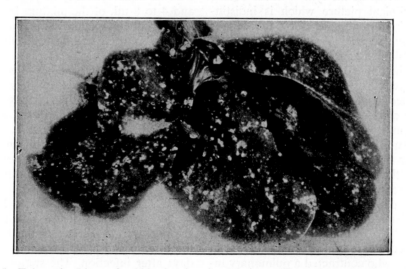

Fig. 5. Tularemia. Liver of rabbit showing focal lesions. (From Army Medical Museum. Courtesy of Edward Francis. U.S.P.H.S.)

ber is drastically reduced by 72-hour sojourn in the living cells. The bacilli are not destroyed as rapidly in the monocytes as in the PMN's; however, there is still some doubt whether the PMN or the monocyte is the most susceptible to infection (60). Rats, cats, sheep, goats, dogs, and chickens are more resistant. Cows, hogs, foxes, and pigeons are insusceptible (15).

Clinical Types of Infection in Man. Six clinical types of tularemia have been described: ulceroglandular, oculoglandular, glandular, typhoidal, pulmonary, and ingestion.

The **ulceroglandular** type is the most prevalent form of the infection and has the best prognosis. The organisms are retained at the site of the local lesion for a period of days, perhaps as a result of the mechanical effects of the local inflammation, which allows time for the development of immune bodies by the patient. The primary lesion usually occurs on the fingers or hands as the result of contact with the blood of infected birds or animals. There usually is a macroscopic scratch or cut but the organism may be able to invade the unbroken skin. After three or four days a local papule appears which develops into an open ulcer by the seventh to eighth day. At the time the ulcer appears, extensive infection in the regional lymph nodes has occurred. The rare case in which ulceration of the lymph nodes occurs paints a clinical picture which is indistinguishable from that caused by the fungus *Sporotrichum schenckii.*

The **oculoglandular type** is caused by the spattering of a drop of infected blood into the eye or by wiping the eye with a contaminated finger. There is local ulceration of the conjunctivae with swelling of the regional lymph nodes (58, 65). The prognosis is almost as favorable in this type of infection as in the ulceroglandular form.

Among the 62 cases of laboratory acquired tularemia from Fort Detrick the most common type was pulmonary, presumably from accidental inhalation of aerosols containing *Past. tularensis* (11, 62). Aagaard (1) reported a case in a graduate student in bacteriology who contracted a pulmonary infection after a rabbit sneezed in his face, and Fillmore (22) reported a case in a nurse

whose only known exposure was to a patient with pulmonary tularemia. Occasionally there is a pericarditis (45).

In some cases of ulceroglandular and oculoglandular tularemia, the organisms filter through the lymph nodes to cause the clinical picture of **septicemia** (39, 55) or **meningitis** (14).

The other forms of the disease are rare but frequently fatal because generalized invasion of the body and an overwhelming infection occur before the immune mechanism can be mobilized.

The clinical features of tularemia have been reviewed by Foshay (24), Pullen and Stuart (53), Saslaw and his coworkers (56), Allison (3), Ven Metra and Kadull (62). Ashburn and Miller (4) reported the necropsy findings in a patient who died of a laboratory infection and reviewed the necropsy findings in 72 other cases of tularemia.

Although the **diagnosis** frequently is obvious from the patient's case history, in many instances the history is inadequate or even misleading. The organism cannot be identified in smears from the lesions and will not grow in the media used for the routine culturing of blood but can be cultured, however, on the blood-glucose-cystine medium (55). Guinea pigs can be infected with exudates and tissues without difficulty. Blood from the patient should be diluted with an equal quantity of physiologic saline and 4 to 8 ml. of the mixture injected intraperitoneally into a guinea pig. *Past. tularensis* can be cultured without difficulty from the infected pig.

The dangers of handling infected animals and virulent cultures of *Past. tularensis* should be emphasized. **Many laboratory workers have become infected and a large number have died of tularemia.** The routine laboratory should limit its diagnostic efforts to the use of the Foshay skin tests and serologic examinations for agglutinins. A formalized culture of a virulent strain or a living, avirulent culture should be used for the agglutination test. The skin tests usually are positive by the end of the first week of the disease and agglutinins appear 10 to 14 days after infection. The sputum often contains *Past. tularensis* even when the patient has no pulmonary lesions. Mice should be injected intraperitoneally with sputum which has been emulsified in physiologic saline (39, 40).

An agglutinin titer of 1:20 or 1:40 is inconclusive but rising titers in successive tests are diagnostic. Titers of 1:2560 or 1:5120 in the third and fourth weeks of the disease are not at all unusual.

Transmission. Rabbits are the chief reservoir of infection, and many clinical cases follow the bite of a fly or tick which can be traced to direct contact with the carcass of a diseased animal.

Tularemia may develop following the bites of animals or reptiles that do not have the disease but do have the organisms in their mouths as the result of feeding on dead infected rabbits. Tularemia of this type has been reported following the bite of cats, dogs, skunks, opossums, foxes, and nonpoisonous snakes (46).

Waterborne epidemics of tularemia have been reported from Russia and Turkey and in one instance from this country (37). *Past. tularensis* has been found in streams of water where there were epidemics of tularemia among beavers and in ponds in Canada (7). The number of organisms present in water suggests that they might be growing in the cystine-containing mud and water (28).

Treatment. Although chloramphenicol (51) and chlortetracycline (67) produce remissions in this disease, the most satisfactory drugs have been streptomycin and dihydrostreptomycin. One gram per day is probably enough for the mild cases; the severe ones should receive 0.5 g. every six hours until the temperature approaches normal (5, 13). ACTH therapy should be considered in critically ill patients to alleviate symptoms from allergy to tularensis protein while the antibiotics are eliminating the organism.

A tentative diagnosis based on the case history or on the presence of a positive skin test or even a suspicion of tularemia justifies the use of streptomycin. One should not wait for a positive culture or the presence of agglutinins in the blood before starting treatment. Streptomycin does not inhibit the development of agglutinins (5, 26) if given after the development of symptoms from a naturally acquired infection, although it may

do so with early treatment of an experimental infection.

Prevention. Rabbits caught by dogs and cats should be incinerated or buried. Hunters should be very suspicious of "lazy" rabbits which are killed easily, and rubber gloves should be worn while cleaning and dressing animals.

Since one attack of the disease makes one immune for life, active immunization is theoretically possible.

Foshay's killed vaccine has received a thorough study by Saslaw and his associates in an Ohio prison (56) and by Van Metre and Kadull at Fort Detrick where it was used in an attempt to prevent accidental infection (62). The dead vaccine was a failure in preventing infection although the resulting disease may have been less severe.

A new approach to immunization began in Turkey in 1940 (32), where it was shown that a live strain of low virulence gave better immunity than killed organisms from a highly virulent strain. The Russians developed this vaccine in animals and then applied it to man (2, 16, 49). Eigelsbach and Downs (16) isolated a high immunogenic mutant from the Russian vaccine. The dense colonies seen in Figure 4 appeared to be blue in the original fresh growth and were designated BV since they were virulent for the mouse but not for the guinea pig. This new vaccine is known as **LVS** (live vaccine strain). Guinea pigs and monkeys have been successively immunized by aerosol vaccination (16, 19) and Eigelsbach considers it safe for man (19). A few of Saslaw's volunteers in Ohio received the LVS vaccine by intradermal inoculation and developed a significant degree of immunity to challenge with virulent *Past. tularensis* in aerosol.

REFERENCES

1. Aagaard, G. N. Minnesota Med., 27:115, 1944.
2. Aleksandrov, N. I., and others. Voyenno-Meditsinskiy Zhurnal, #12, 134, 1958.
3. Allison, F., Jr. South. Med., 52:1019, 1959.
4. Ashburn, L. L., and Miller, S. E. Arch. Path., 39:388, 1945.
5. Atwell, R. J., and Smith, D. T. South. M. J., 39:858, 1946.
6. Bell, J. F. J. Infect. Dis., 76:83, 1945.
7. Bow, M. R., and Brown, J. H. Canad. M. J., 50:14, 1944.

8. Buchele, L., and Downs, C. M.   J. Immunol., 63:135, 1949.
9. Buddingh, G. J., and Womack, F. C., Jr. J. Exper. Med., 74:213, 1941.
10. Carlisle, H. N., and others.   J. Immunol., 89: 638, 1962.
11. Charkes, N. D.   J. Immunol., 83:213, 1959.
12. Claus, K. D., and others.   J. Bact., 78:294, 1959.
13. Corwin, W. C., and Stubbs, S. P.   J.A.M.A., 149:343, 1952.
14. David, J. K., Jr., and Owens, J. N.   Am. J. Dis. Child., 67:44, 1944.
15. Downs, C. M., and others.   J. Immunol., 56: 217, 229, 245, 1947.
16. Eigelsbach, H. T., and Downs, C. H.   J. Immunol., 87:415, 1961.
17. ——— and others.   J. Bact., 61:557, 1951.
18. ——— and others.   J. Bact., 52:179, 1946.
19. ——— and others.   J. Bact., 84:1020, 1962.
20. ——— and others.   Proc. Soc. Exp. Biol. & Med., 108:732, 1961.
21. Fleming, D. E., and Foshay, L.   J. Bact., 70: 345, 1955.
22. Fillimore, A. J.   Arizona Med., 8:27, 1951.
23. Foshay, L.   J. Infect. Dis., 59:330, 1936.
24. ——— Medicine, 19:1, 1940.
25. ——— and Hesselbrock, W. H.   J. Bact., 49: 233, 1945.
26. ——— Am. J. Med., 2:467, 1947.
27. ——— Postgrad. Med., 4:315, 1948.
28. ——— Ann. Rev. Microbiol., 4:313, 1950.
29. Francis, E.   Hyg. Lab. Bull., No. 130, 1922.
30. ——— and Evans, A.   Pub. Health Rep., 41: 1273, 1926.
31. ——— J.A.M.A., 84:1243, 1925; 91:1155, 1928.
31a. Gordon, A.   J. Immunol., 90:209, 1963.
32. Gotschlich, E., and others.   Turk. Ztschr. Hyg. v. Exp. Biol., 2:145, 1940.
33. Green, R. G.   Am. J. Hyg., 38:282, 1943.
34. Greisman, S. E., and others.   J. Clin. Med., 42:1064, 1963.
35. Hesselbrock, W. H., and Foshay, L. J.   Bact., 49:209, 1943.
36. Hopla, C. E.   South. Med., 53:92, 1960.
37. Jellison, W. L., and others.   Pub. Health Rep., 65:1219, 1950.
38. ——— and others.   Tularemia and Animal Population. Ecology and Epizoology. Ann. Mid-West Wildlife Conference. Toronto, Canada, Dec. 6, 1960.
39. Larson, C. L.   Pub. Health Rep., 60:587, 863, 1049, 1945.
40. ——— J. Immunol., 62:425, 1949; 66:249, 1951.
41. ——— and others.   J. Immunol., 73:221, 1954.
42. Marchette, N. J., and Nicholes, P. S.   J. Bact., 82:26, 1961.
43. McCoy, G. W., and Chapin, C. W.   J. Infect. Dis., 10:61, 1912.
44. McCrumb, F. R., Jr., and others.   Trans. Assoc. Amer. Phycns., 70:74, 1957.
45. Meredith, H. C.   Ann. Int. Med., 32:688, 1950.
46. Meyer, K. F.   Cecil's Textbook of Medicine, 7th ed., Philadelphia, W. B. Saunders, 1947, p. 274.
47. Moody, M. E., and Downs, C. M.   J. Bact., 70:297, 305, 1955.
48. Nagle, S. C., Jr., and others.   J. Bact., 79: 566, 1960.
49. Olsuf, E. Y., N. G., and others.   J. Hyg. Epidemiol. Microbiol. Immunol., 3:138, 1959.
50. Ormsbee, R. A., and others.   J. Immunol., 74:351, 359, 1955.
51. Parker, R. T., and others.   J.A.M.A., 143: 7, 1950.
52. Poston, M. A., and Smith, D. T.   Proc. Soc. Am. Bacteriologists, p. 80, 1951.
53. Pullen, R. L., and Stuart, B. M.   J.A.M.A., 129:495, 1945.
54. Ransmeier, J. C.   J. Infect. Dis., 72:86, 1943.
55. ——— and Schaub, I. G.   Arch. Int. Med., 68:747, 1941.
56. Saslaw, S., and others.   Ann. Int. Med., 107: 689, 702, 1961.
57. Shepard, C. C., and others.   J. Immunol., 75:7, 1955.
58. Siniscal, A. A.   Am. J. Ophth., 29:698, 1946.
59. Snyder, T. L., and others.   J. Bact., 52:241, 1946.
60. Stefanye, D., and others.   J. Bact., 81:470, 1961.
61. Tamura, J. T., and Gibby, I. W.   J. Bact., 45:361, 1943.
62. Van Metre, T. E., and Kadull, P. J.   Ann. Int. Med., 50:621, 1959.
63. Vosti, K. L., and others.   J. Clin. Invest., 41: 1436, 1962.
64. Weinstein, I., and others.   J. Bact., 83:1010, 1962.
65. Wherry, W. B., and Lamb, B. H.   J. Infect. Dis., 15:331, 1914.
66. Woodward, J. M., and Miraglia, G. J.   Proc. Soc. Exp. Biol. & Med., 106:333, 1961.
67. Woodward, T. E., and others.   J.A.M.A., 139: 830, 1949.
68. Wright, G. G., and Feinberg, R. J.   J. Immunol., 1952.
69. Yager, R. H., and others.   Proc. Soc. Exp. Biol. & Med., 105:651, 1960.

43

Pasteurella pestis and Plague

Family: *Brucellaceae* fam. nov. Genus: *Pasteurella* Trevisan. Species: *Pasteurella pestis* (Lehmann and Neumann) Holland

The history of epidemic diseases has no more terrifying chapter than that of plague (35). Sweeping time and again over large areas of the civilized world, its scope and mortality were often so great that all forms of human activity were temporarily paralyzed. In the reign of Justinian almost 50 per cent of the entire population of the Roman Empire perished from the disease. The "black death" which swept over Europe during the fourteenth century killed about 25 million people. Smaller epidemics, appearing in numerous parts of the world during the sixteenth, seventeenth and eighteenth centuries, have claimed innumerable victims. In 1893 plague appeared in Hong Kong. During the epidemic which followed, *Pasteurella pestis,* now recognized as the etiologic agent of the disease, was seen in smears by Kitasato (39) but isolated and identified by the Swiss bacteriologist Yersin (84). The organism was found in the pus of afflicted individuals and could be demonstrated in enormous numbers in the cadavers of victims. This evidence was strengthened by accidental infections with laboratory cultures which occurred in Vienna in 1898.

Plague is primarily a disease of rats and wild rodents and is transmitted from animal to animal by the bites of infected fleas, with man serving only as an accidental host. The pneumonic type of plague can develop, however, and the disease can be spread from man to man by droplet infection without the assistance of an insect vector. Figure 1 shows the geographic distribution of *Past. pestis.* In some areas of the world the rat is the important carrier; in other areas the infection is carried by wild rodents, but there are regions where both rats and wild rodents harbor and disseminate the infection.

Between 1900 and 1951, 523 cases of plague were diagnosed in the United States and 65 per cent of the infected patients died (46). Plague has been reported in 13 of the far western states and in Texas, Louisiana, and Florida. A reservoir among wild rodents has been discovered in every area in the United States where plague has been found in man.

The improbability that plague bacilli can be eliminated from the vast reservoir of wild rodents is a problem of major importance to the epidemiologist, since he always will be confronted with the possibility that the plague bacillus will spread from the wild rodents to the rats living in the denser populated areas in the central and eastern parts of the United States.

Morphology and Staining. *Pasteurella pestis* is a short, plump rod, 0.5 to 0.7 μ in width and 1.5 to 1.75 μ in length. The bacilli usually appear singly or in pairs but occasionally in short chains of three or more organisms. **Pleomorphism** is extreme in old cultures (Figs. 2 and 3), and these bizarre forms can be induced within 24 to 48 hours by cultivating the organisms on plain agar to which 3 per cent sodium chloride has been added.

Past. pestis has a **capsule** in the animal body and in young cultures. The organism is **nonsporogenous** and **nonmotile.**

The bacillus is **gram-negative** and shows **polar staining.** This irregular staining is seen best in smears which have been dried in the air and fixed with alcohol. The polychrome

PLAGUE

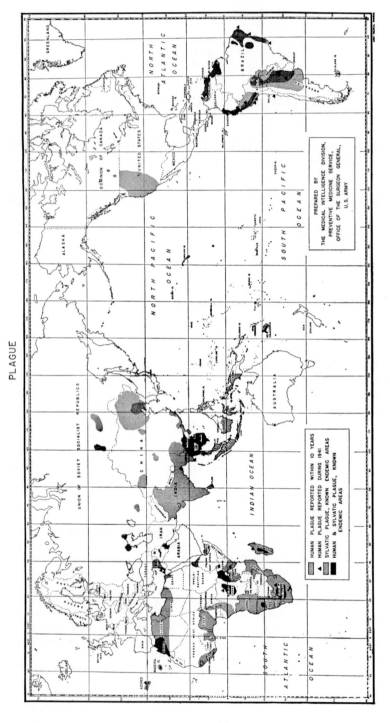

Fig. 1. Geographic distribution of plague.

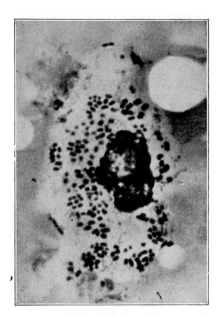

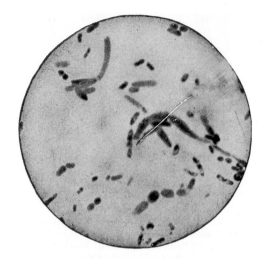

Fig. 3. *Pasteurella pestis* showing involution forms. (From Zettnow.)

Fig. 2. *Pasteurella pestis* in monocyte from mouse lung. Giemsa stain. × 1,500. (From Meyer. *J. Immunol.,* 64:139, 1950.)

stains are excellent for demonstrating the organism in sections of tissue.

Cultural Characteristics. *Past. pestis* is **aerobic** but **facultatively anaerobic.** It will grow on media containing bile salts, and media containing both bile salts and gentian violet facilitate the isolation of cultures from contaminated tissues (52). Blood-agar plates are more suitable for primary isolation than plain agar and the organisms will grow satisfactorily under ordinary atmospheric conditions even from very small inocula.

The temperature range for growth is extreme, varying from 0° C. to 43° C. The growth is five times as profuse at 28° to 29° C. as at 37° C. but good growth, particularly on blood agar occurs at 37° C. Fairly good growth occurs between pH 6.6 and pH 8.0 but the optimal range lies between pH 7.2 and pH 7.4 (84).

The temperature of incubation has a profound effect on the virulence of the organisms. When cultured at 5° C., the organism has very little virulence but subsequent incubation of the growth cultures at 37° C. restores the virulence (58). However, cultivation at 37° C. promotes the rapid multiplication of avirulent mutants (42) which will in time take over the cultures. The pH of cultivation is of importance also for virulence. A toxic product which appears when the culture is grown at pH 6 is absent from cultures grown at pH 6-8 (12).

On plain agar or on blood agar after 24-hour incubation the colonies are small, round, glistening, transparent, and colorless and resemble closely colonies of *E. coli* and *Staph. albus.* However, the addition of oxgall to blood agar produces a differential medium on which *Past. pestis* can be identified after 48 hours growth at 28° C. as translucent, granular and dentate, while *E. coli* and *Staph. albus* remain round and smooth (Figs. 4, 5) (48).

Some strains of *Past. pestis* will grow in an amino acid medium without the addition of vitamins, while others require nicotinic acid or thianin or both (7, 24). Growth is accelerated by glucose, glycine, hematin and cozymase (71).

Nitrates are reduced to **nitrites; indol is not produced; gelatin and coagulated serum are not liquefied.**

Acid without gas is produced from **glucose, maltose, mannitol,** and **salicin** after seven to 14 days' incubation. An occasional strain, however, fails to oxidize maltose. **Lactose** and **sucrose** are not oxidized. The oxidation of **glycerin** has been used to separate the **continental race** of *Past. pestis* from the **oceanic race.** The continental race which **oxidizes glycerin** occurs in the central Asiatic plateau, Mongolia, and Manchuria, while the oceanic race, which **does not oxidize glycerin,** occurs in India, Indochina, Java, Japan, Ceylon, Arabia, Madagascar and California. Of the 27 South African strains which have been studied, 23 have been found to belong to the oceanic and four to the continental race (53).

Resistance. *Past. pestis* is killed in 15 minutes by 0.5 per cent phenol or a temperature

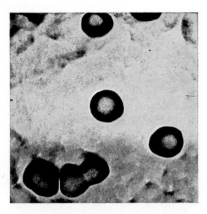

Fig. 4. Colonies of *Pasteurella pestis* growing on blood agar base medium. The colonies resemble those of staphylococci. (From Markenson and Ben-Efraim. *J. Bact.,* 85:1443, 1963.)

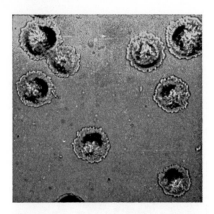

Fig. 5. Colonies of *Pasteurella pestis* grown on oxgall medium. Note the fried egg appearance. Staphylococci on this medium resembles *Past. pestis* on blood agar, as seen in Figure 4. (From Markenson and Ben-Efraim. *J. Bact.,* 85:1443, 1963.)

of 55° C. Direct sunlight destroys the organism in four to five hours and on simple drying in the air the bacilli become nonviable in two to three days. This apparently delicate organism, however, is remarkably well adapted for survival under natural conditions. In pus or sputum from patients, organisms may live for eight to 14 days. They remain viable in putrefying blood of experimentally infected animals for 100 days, and in cadavers for weeks or months. They are preserved by ice and snow for 40 days and by blood for years in sealed tubes when stored in the ice chest.

Pneumonic plague is spread by droplet infection. The survival of plague bacilli in these droplets was studied by Teague and Barber (81) in connection with the Manchurian epidemic of pneumonic plague. The bacilli contained in the droplets expelled by coughing die in a few minutes if the air is dry but survive much longer in an atmosphere saturated with moisture. The humid air in the log huts of the Manchurian trappers provided an ideal environment for the propagation of pneumonic plague.

Some strains of *Past. pestis* are inhibited by **penicillin,** but this antibiotic has not proved useful in therapy (45). **Sulfonamides,** particularly sulfadiazine and sulfamerazine, lower the mortality in experimental animals and patients (67, 68). **Streptomycin** has given the best results in experimental animals (55) and in patients (45). **Chloramphenicol** and **tetracycline** have been found to be effective therapeutic agents in the treatment of both bubonic and pneumonic forms of plague (51).

Variability. The investigation of Eisler and his associates (27) have shown that *Past. pestis* isolated directly from a bubo in man has both

smooth and rough colonies. There are usually more smooth than rough colonies, but both are virulent. In time, on artificial cultivation, both smooth and rough colonies become avirulent but virulence is maintained longer by the rough than the smooth forms (Figs. 6, 7) (26).

Antigenic Structure. There is one antigenic type of *Pasteurella pestis,* but this antigenic structure is complex. Crumpton and Davies (23) identified 10 antigens in the avirulent Tjiwidej strain. Later studies by Lawton and his associates (41) showed that virulent strains had 18 different antigens which could be differentiated in agar gel preparations. Five of these antigens were specific for *Past. pestis,* 2 for *Past. pseudotuberculosis,* and the remaining 11 were common to both organisms. The V or W antigen is not produced by most avirulent strains (17). Strain M.23 is a very good producer of these antigens and was utilized by Lawton and his associates (42) to make and analyze the VW complex. The V antigen was found to be a protein with a molecular weight of 90,000, while W was a lipoprotein with a molecular weight of 145,000. The V antigen induced antibodies in rabbits which would protect mice, but the W antigen did not.

A surface **envelope antigen** is present on virulent strains and usually is absent from avirulent strains.

The envelope antigen is a protein which has been isolated in crystalline form by Baker and his associates (5). Large amounts of this antigen can be obtained by growing strain A 1122 in a casein hydrolyzate mineral glucose medium (28). This protein is antigenic, and the anti-

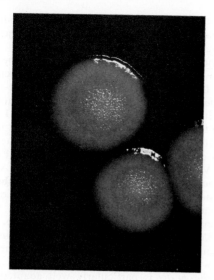

Fig. 6. Smooth form of *Past. pestis* strain 53. (From Eisler, Kubik, and Preston. *J. Bact.*, 76:41, 1958.)

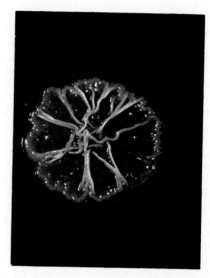

Fig. 7. Rough form of *Past. pestis* strain 53. (From Eisler, Kubik, and Preston. *J. Bact.*, 76:41, 1958.)

bodies can be measured as agglutinins, precipitins, or complement-fixing or mouse-protecting antibodies (20, 68, 78). The adsorption of the purified envelope protein on tannic-acid-treated erythrocytes provides an antigen for the hemagglutinin test which is more delicate than the agglutinin or precipitin reactions. This test has been used to measure antibodies in experimental animals (21) and in patients after vaccination with plague vaccines and after recovery from plague (63).

A pure polysaccharide was isolated by Chen and Meyer (21) and utilized in a delicate hemagglutinin test. Although the polysaccharide is antigenic, it has no protective action in experimentally infected animals. Water-soluble heat-labile antigens were extracted from the tissues of rodents dying from *Past. pestis, Past. pseudotuberculosis, Past. multocida,* and *Past. tularensis* and tested against their corresponding antiserums in a precipitin test. Cross-reactions were observed between all of these *Pasteurella,* but a specific diagnosis could be made if the serums were previously absorbed to remove the common cross-reacting antigens (40).

For more details concerning these fascinating and practical antigenic studies the student should consult the review by Pollitzer (68), Girard (30) and the papers from the Army Medical Service Graduate School (1, 63) and from the George Williams Hooper Foundation (8, 21, 28, 56, 57).

Bacteriophages are active against *Past. pestis.* One potent strain studied by Lazarus and Gun-

nison (43) lysed all the *Past. pestis* strains tested, most strains of *Past. pseudotuberculosis* and some strains of *Salmonella* and *Shigella* but none of *Past. multocida.* In the original experiment the organisms were incubated at 37° C., but later studies have shown that when the cultures are incubated at 20° C. *Past. pestis* is lysed but *Past. pseudotuberculosis* is not (44).

Bacterial Metabolites. Cultures of *Past. pestis* produce a **catalase** and a **ribonuclease** (83). **A spreading factor** appears in cultures and a **coagulase** is produced which is specific for rabbit plasma but not for the plasma of mice, men, and guinea pigs. **Fibrinolysin is not formed** (38).

No true exotoxin is produced by *Past. pestis* but the endotoxin is intermediate in its characteristics between a true exotoxin and a typical endotoxin. It is less toxic than true exotoxin but resembles them in producing a good antitoxin which will protect animals against multiple lethal doses of toxin. The guinea pig is particularly susceptible to the toxin, and antitoxin will protect it against infection with living organisms. The antitoxin protects mice and other animals against the toxin but not against virulent organisms. A concentrated antitoxin might be of value in treating patients with pneumonic plague. Ajl and his associates (2) have reported that the purified toxin splits diphosphopyridine-nucleotide (DPN), and this effect is inhibited by nicotinamide and specific antitoxins (31).

Another toxic surface antigen known as the

"pH 6 antigen" develops when virulent or avirulent strains are incubated at pH 6 and 37° C. This antigen is not found at pH 7 to pH 8. The presence of the antigen is shown by a pronounced decrease in electrophoretic mobility of the cell (6). This antigen (1) agglutinates red blood cells, (2) produces primary inflammation reactions in the skin, and (3) has a cytotoxic effect on monocytes. This latter characteristic recalls the classical work of Cavanaugh and Randall (19), who showed that non-encapsulated, but potentially virulent plague bacilli were phagocytized and destroyed by polymorphonuclear leukocytes but when ingested by monocytes, multiplied in the cytoplasm, acquired capsules, killed the cells, and after liberation were resistant to phagocytes by either PMN or monocytes (Figs. 1 and 2, Chap. 18). The pH of the cytoplasm of the monocyte may be as low as pH6 which would be a good environment for the development of the "pH 6 antigen."

Virulence. A very complex series of characteristics are required for the virulence of a culture of *Past. pestis* (13, 14, 16, 80). Some of the virulence factors can be seen in Table 1 from Burrows Publication (16). In general, virulent strains of plague have (1) an envelope protein antigen; (2) VW virulence antigens, of which V is more important (19, 41), the V having been identified as a protein and the W as a lipoprotein; (3) ability to grow as a hemain containing pigmented colonies on a defined medium; (4) calcium ++ dependence (13, 14, 34); and (5) purine independence (16). To these should be added the endotoxin which has some of the characteristics of an exotoxin since it stimulates the production of antigen (1) and (6) the "pH 6 antigen" which appears in cultures incubated at 35° C. at a pH below 6.7. This toxin (a) agglutinates red blood cells, (b) is cytotoxic for monocytes and (c) produces primary inflammatory lesions when injected intracutaneously (12).

The toxins of *Past. pestis* are quite specific since they inhibit the respiration of mitochondria from the heart of susceptible species such as the mouse but not those from the refractory rabbit (61). The importance of **Pesticin I and II** in the virulence of the organism has not been settled. The resistance factor found in the organs of normal mice and guinea pigs by Eisler and Von Metz (26) may not be active in vivo.

Spontaneous Disease in Animals. Bubonic plague is a natural disease in rats and other rodents, but the form which occurs in wild rodents usually is called **sylvatic plague.** No one knows whether the disease originated in the rat and spread to his country cousins or whether the wild rodents were the original hosts. *Pasteurella pestis* is particularly well adapted for survival in a rodent population by virtue of its secondary host, the rat flea. The infection is spread by the bite of the flea and rarely, if ever, by cannibalism. Thirty-two species of fleas have been infected by allowing them to feed on guinea pigs in the terminal stage of *Past. pestis* septicemia and at least 13 species of North American fleas can transmit the infection (29, 53). The mechanism of the transmission of plague by the flea has been investigated by Bacot and Martin (4) for the rat and by Douglas and Wheeler (25) for the wild rodents of the western states. If the flea bites another host immediately after a blood meal, while there is blood on its mouth parts, the infection can be transmitted, but if this does not occur, the flea is noninfective for four to 18 days after feeding. The plague bacilli multiply enormously in the proventriculus of the flea, forming an obstructive mass; subsequently the flea bites a new victim and regurgitates infected blood into the

Table 1. Some Representative Avirulent Strains Deficient in One or More Virulence Determinants

(From Burrows. Ann. New York Acad. Sc., 88:1125, 1960)

ONE DEFICIENCY			TWO DEFICIENCIES			THREE DEFICIENCIES
F1−	VW−	P−	F1−VW−	F1−P−	VW−P−	F1−VW−P−
M17	M15	M14	M16	M18	M32	M33
M23	A1122	EV76	14	M19	JAVA	TRU.
	Tjiwidej	Harbin		M29	O17	
	Soemedang	Elizabeth			O20	
		M7				

Strains are "+" for all other determinants; for example, M14 is F1+VW+P−PU+.
F1 = Envelope antigen. VW = antigen giving resistance to phagocytosis by PMN's.
P = Pigmented colonies with requirement for iron for virulence.
PU = Purine independence.

wound. Many fleas die from the obstruction after five to 50 days, but in others the clot dissolves and the fleas are able to feed freely and live their normal life span as carriers of plague. Eskey and Haas (29) found fleas infective for one to five months. Pirie's studies in South Africa (64) indicate that the flea is the key to the persistence of plague in a rodent population.

If a disease is to persist, some victims must survive to perpetuate the species and some carrier mechanism must be provided to preserve the infecting organism between epidemics. The mortality is never quite 100 per cent even in the most violent epizootic in rodents and the survivors are immune. McCoy (50) found some rats in the San Francisco area and some squirrels from the surrounding valleys which were quite resistant to experimental infection, suggesting a spontaneous immunization from mild or subclinical infection. McCoy's observations have been confirmed and extended by Meyer and his associates. They found resistant squirrels in areas where there had been no known sylvatic plague for a number of years and have demonstrated the presence of inapparent or latent sylvatic plague in the ground squirrels of central California (54).

Fluctuations in the virulence of *Past. pestis* occur from time to time. It is common observation that relatively avirulent strains often are isolated near the end of an epizootic (64). These strains are antigenically and culturally indistinguishable from virulent bacilli and theoretically might regain their virulence under natural conditions.

Experimental Disease in Laboratory Animals. Wild rats and guinea pigs are extremely susceptible to *Past. pestis;* three to 50 organisms initiate a septicemia in 24 to 48 hours and death in two to eight days. The lymph nodes enlarge and become surrounded by bloody, edematous tissue, while the centers of the nodes show early necrosis. The spleen is dark red in color and greatly enlarged and usually contains minute, necrotic foci. Extensive lesions are found in the lungs of animals which survive more than five days. Mice are almost as susceptible as rats. The rabbit is somewhat more resistant; and dogs, cats, pigs, cattle, sheep, goats and horses are very resistant. Different species of monkeys vary in their susceptibility, some being quite as susceptible as man while others are about as resistant as the rabbit.

Pasteurella pestis often will penetrate the unbroken skin of a guinea pig, and this technic can be used to isolate plague bacilli from material heavily contaminated with other organisms.

Guinea pigs are inoculated readily by the bite of an infected flea and the most effective method of determining whether infected fleas remain in a particular area is to expose a cage of guinea pigs.

Clinical Types of Infection in Man. *Pasteurella pestis* infections produced in man can be classified into three clinical types which are known as **bubonic, septicemic,** and **pneumonic plague.**

The **bubonic** form is most common. The infected fleas usually bite on the lower extremities, and the plague bacilli spread rapidly through the lymphatics and enlarge the lymph nodes in the groin. These enlarged nodes are known as **buboes.** In these buboes the plague bacilli multiply at an enormous rate, causing local necrosis and abscess formation. The organisms escape from the nodes, invade the blood stream and produce a generalized infection. Blood cultures on the first, second, or third days of the disease may be positive in 75 per cent of the patients (36). Secondary foci develop in various parts of the body, such as the spleen, lungs, and meninges.

A gross invasion of the blood stream accompanied by small hemorrhages in the skin and mucous membranes is called **septicemic plague.**

Pneumonic plague develops when the bacilli are breathed into the lungs in droplets of moisture. The bacilli spread rapidly throughout the lymphatics until the entire lung is involved in a hemorrhagic, pneumonic process and the patient dies of suffocation. Cyanosis, of course, is extreme in the latter stages of the disease and probably accounts for the name **black death** which was applied to the plague which spread over Europe in the fourteenth century. The mucoid, bloody sputum is filled with plague bacilli which are coughed out in droplets of moisture but apparently are not expelled by ordinary breathing or talking. When the atmospheric conditions are favorable—e.g., saturated with moisture—the disease spreads directly from man to man at an appalling rate. In the Manchurian epidemic of pneumonic plague in 1910 to 1912 there were 60,000 deaths.

The mechanism by which epidemics of

bubonic plague are converted into those of pneumonic plague is not well understood. Secondary pneumonia incidental to the septicemia occurs frequently and from time to time patients begin to cough out droplets of moisture containing plague bacilli. If all of the associated conditions are satisfactory, the primary pneumonic form of the disease becomes established.

Castellani and Chalmers (18) estimated that about 2.5 per cent of the cases of bubonic plague, originating from the rat flea, develop into the highly fatal pneumonic form.

Sylvatic plague, transmitted by the flea of wild rodents, differs in some details from the classic plague transmitted by the rat flea. The fleas usually bite on the upper extremities, and the original buboes may be in the axillae rather than in the groin. Furthermore, the plague of sylvatic origin frequently changes over to the pneumonic variety. The Manchurian epidemic of pneumonic plague started from wild rodents and in the Los Angeles epidemic of 1923-24, all but five of the 23 fatal cases were of the pneumonic type. The **diagnosis** can be made from smears of the sputum or material from buboes, or the plague bacilli can be cultivated from the blood or local lesions.

Immunity develops rather rapidly in those who survive the first seven days of the disease, but the agglutinin titers remain low and no great excess of protective antibodies appear in the serums of such patients. Since serums of normal individuals will not agglutinate the plague bacillus, a titer of 1:10 or higher is diagnostic. After recovery from plague the patient is permanently immune, and according to the investigations of Jawetz and Meyer (38) and Bhatnagar and Shrivastava (9, 10), the immunity appears to be more of a tissue immunity than a humoral one. Antibodies to the envelope antigens, however, apparently assist the mononuclear phagocytes in their ingestion of the bacilli.

Transmission. The great epidemics of plague in man have been preceded by epidemics of plague in the rat. The two epidemics usually overlap so that the streets are filled with dead rats and the houses with victims of plague. As the rats die, the in-

fected but hungry fleas are forced to seek man for food. Three species of rats live in close association with man: the common gray sewer rat, *Rattus norvegicus;* the black house rat and ship rat, *R. rattus;* and the Egyptian rat, *R. rattus alexandrinus.* The Indian rat flea, *Xenopsylla cheopis,* is the most efficient distributor of plague, although it is readily transmitted by the common rat flea of Europe and North America, *Nosopsyllus fasciatus.*

The black rat is the most dangerous, since it prefers to nest in the attics of houses and, when dead of plague, leaves its fleas free to invade the household. The gray rat lives in sewers, barns, and rubbish heaps and rarely nests above the first floor of dwellings. It is believed that the black rat arrived in Europe in the ships of the returning Crusaders. Certainly it proved an excellent host for plague during the great epidemic of the Middle Ages. Later the fiercer gray rat invaded from the north and almost completely destroyed the black rat (86). It has been suggested that this shift in the type of rat probably had more to do with the disappearance of plague from Europe than any other one factor.

Creel (22) has emphasized the importance of exterminating the rats in this country, not only because they are potential hosts for plague but also because of the severe economic losses occasioned by their depredations. According to Creel's calculations, the rat population equals the human population, and, estimating the annual cost of feeding a rat at one-half a cent per day, the economic loss through wanton destruction is in excess of $167 million each year.

Sylvatic plague occurs in many parts of the world as shown in Figure 1. The wild rodents rarely cause extensive epidemics but afford a constant source of reinfection for rats. The most important rodent hosts are the gerbil in South Africa, the tarbagan in Transbaikalia, the spermophile in Russia, and the ground squirrels in our western states. The rodents most often infected with plague bacilli in the western United States are various species of ground squirrels, chipmunks, tree squirrels, flying squirrels, marmots, prairie dogs, wood rats, water rats and mice, hares and rabbits, and badgers (29, 53).

It is usually assumed that the pandemic of plague which followed the epidemic in Hong Kong in 1894 reached San Francisco in 1900 and then spread from the rats of San Francisco to the rodents in the western mountains. This theory has been questioned by Meyer (53) who hints that the infiltration of plague into the rodents may have antedated the arrival of Columbus and the rat.

The absence of a major epidemic of plague in this country should be credited to the energetic work of the United States Public Health Service under the able leadership of Rupert Blue, McCoy, Curry, Wherry, and their successors.

Biologic Products. A number of different kinds of vaccines have been employed for inducing active immunity. Haffkine's vaccine, which has been used in India since 1898 (33), is a heat-killed product. A single dose of a living attenuated strain gives more immunity than do several injections of heat-killed antigen. The living vaccine used by the French in Madagascar has effectively reduced the incidence and mortality from plague but is not uniformly successful in either. The studies of Payne and his associates (63) in Madagascar in 1956, using the new hemagglutinin technic for the detection of (a) antibacterial antibodies and (b) antitoxin revealed that only a small amount of antibacterial antibodies and even less antitoxin was induced by a single injection of living vaccine. Something was accomplished, however, since fewer of the vaccinated contracted plague, and more survived with or without antibiotic therapy. The survivors had much higher titers of both antibacterial and antitoxic antibodies than the survivors who had not been previously vaccinated. Repeated doses of living vaccine over a period of years gives a much better antibody response and presumably a more effective immunity.

Bacteriophage preparations are ineffective in therapy (66).

Treatment. Sulfadiazine is as good as, or superior to, antiplague serum (75) in the treatment of bubonic plague. In one series the mortality was reduced from 80 per cent

to 21 per cent (49); in another, from 50 per cent to 18 per cent (36); and in a third, from 85 per cent to 6 per cent (67). Sulfadiazine should be administered by mouth to all household contacts.

Streptomycin is more effective than sulfadiazine, and 0.25 g. intramuscularly every four hours for two to three days usually effects a cure. Patients with the septicemic form of bubonic plague and patients with pneumonic plague should receive 0.5 g. every four hours for two days followed by 0.25 g. every four hours until the fever subsides. Penicillin is not effective.

Chlortetracycline in doses of 500 mg. daily cured two cases of bubonic plague (46). The drug was given intravenously for two days and by mouth for the next four to five days.

Chloramphenicol and oxytetracycline have been used with success in pneumonic plague in Madagascar by McCrum and his associates (51). The initial dose was 500 mg. orally and 500 mg. intravenously, repeated after three hours. Two grams per day, in divided doses, were given on subsequent days until the temperature approached normal. Good results were obtained when the treatment was started prior to the twentieth hour after the onset of symptoms. Cortisone given in doses of 300 to 400 mg. failed to relieve toxemia in patients treated late in the disease (15, 51).

Various types of combined therapy such as sulfadiazine-serum; sulfadiazine-streptomycin; sulfadiazine-streptomycin-serum seem to be more effective than treatment with one drug alone (36). The most logical type of treatment for septicemia and pneumonic plague would be streptomycin in the smaller dose regimen (0.25 mg.) combined with chloramphenicol or one of the tetracyclines and supplemented by serum therapy.

The importance of early treatment cannot be overemphasized. We agree with Karl Meyer that therapy should be instituted as soon as the diagnosis is suspected without waiting for laboratory confirmation (15).

Prevention. The elimination of rats from areas of endemic plague is highly desirable but difficult to accomplish. The various methods of poisoning rats has been reviewed in detail by McCrumb (51). The anticoagulant known as **Warfarin** is very slow in acting but quite effective and very safe for man. This seems best for eliminating rats in plague-free areas or in interepidemic periods. The more rapid but more dangerous poisons, such as **sodium fluoracetate,** arsenic, **red squill,** and alphanaphthylthiourea ("ANTU"), are more effective in the emergency of an active epidemic of plague. The prevention of infected rats from entering new areas requires a rigid quarantine against all rats. Ships from ports infected with plague are held in quarantine for seven days and their cargoes treated with hydrocyanic gas. All ships are provided with large, circular metal shields, which surround the hawsers that connect the ship to the dock to prevent rats from either boarding or leaving the ship.

Gordon and Knies (32) have outlined the procedure which proved successful in aborting epidemics of plague in North Africa during World War II. The primary attack was directed against the flea rather than the rat since the wholesale poisoning of rats may disseminate plague through the dispersal of the starving fleas. A circle some 200 yards in diameter was drawn around the focal spot of plague, and working from the periphery inward, the whole area was treated thoroughly with sprays and powders containing DDT.

An infection can be prevented in healthy individuals in the environment of a patient with plague by the prophylactic administration of 3 g. of sulfonamide daily (43, 45). Active immunization becomes apparent within seven to 10 days after the introduction of plague vaccine so that the sulfonamides should be continued for this length of time. Individuals who have received no vaccine during the previous four months should have a reimmunizing dose.

BACTERIA OF THE HEMORRHAGIC SEPTICEMIA GROUP

Historically, the bacillus of chicken cholera is extremely interesting, since it was with this microorganism that Pasteur carried out some of his fundamental researches upon immunity

and succeeded in immunizing chickens with attenuated cultures (62). He found that rabbits with chronic infections could serve as carriers and initiate new epidemics in chickens. It was also with this bacillus that Pasteur was first able to demonstrate the existence of a free toxin which could be separated from the bacteria by filtration.

For many years it was assumed that the bacillus of chicken cholera, *B. avisepticus;* of swine plague, *B. suisepticus;* of hemorrhagic septicemia in cattle, deer, and horses, *B. bovisepticus;* and of snuffles and septicemia in rabbits, *Bacterium lepisepticum* were all different species of organisms with specific animal hosts. It was also assumed that man was immune. Extensive studies during the past 20 years have demonstrated that both assumptions were incorrect. There are only three species responsible for all of the hemorrhagic septicemic infections in animals. These are *Past. pseudotuberculosis* of guinea pigs, rabbits, and mice; *Past. hemolytica* from pneumonia in cattle or sheep (59); and *Past. multocida,* which includes all the original species mentioned before. Both **Past. multocida and Past. pseudotuberculosis are pathogenic for man** (3). Schipper (76) collected reports of 55 cases of infection with *Past. multocida,* and Needham (59) added 11 more cases diagnosed in one clinic in 1947. Approximately one half of the human cases followed the bite of animals—cats 21, dogs four, rabbit one, panther one—or resulted from exposure to cattle, pig, or rabbit carcasses. It is probable that many human infections other than those associated with local lesions from animal bites have been incorrectly diagnosed as influenza, since the symptoms resemble those of influenza and the organism has a superficial resemblance to *H. influenzae.*

Past. pseudotuberculosis will be discussed first since it is related antigenically to *Past. pestis.*

PASTEURELLA PSEUDOTUBERCULOSIS

Pasteurella pseudotuberculosis Pfeiffer (Eisenberg) Topley and Wilson

This organism, isolated from guinea pigs by Malassez and Vignal in 1883, appears either as a small coccoid form 0.8 by 0.8 to 2 μ or as rod form 0.6 μ wide and 1.5 to 6 μ long. It is **gram-negative** and **nonsporogenous** and is nonmotile at 37° C. but **motile when grown at 18° to 26° C.** It is **aerobic** but facultatively anaerobic and grows readily on either plain agar or blood agar, forming after 24-hour incubation circular, 0.5 to 1 mm. umbonate, granular, translucent, grayish-yellow, butyrous colonies. *Past. pseudotuberculosis* does **grow on bile media. Indol is not formed, milk is not coagulated, but nitrates are reduced to nitrites; H₂S and NH₃ are formed, catalase is produced, methyl red test is positive, and the Voges-Proskauer is negative. Acid** but no gas is formed from glucose, maltose, mannitol, salicin, arabinose, xylose, rhamnose, and glycerol. Lactose, dulcitol, sucrose, and raffinose are not oxidized.

Past. pseudotuberculosis causes spontaneous disease in guinea pigs, rabbits, mice, pigeons, turkeys, and canaries and is infectious for mice, wild rats, dogs, cats, monkeys, and horses.

Serums prepared against nonencapsulated strains of *Past. pestis* will agglutinate *Past. pseudotuberculosis,* but serums prepared against *Past. pseudotuberculosis* will not agglutinate virulent strains of *Past. pestis* grown at 37° C. because the capsule envelope protects the somatic antigen (9). **Bacteriophage** activity suggests an antigenic relationship not only with *Past. pestis* but also with certain strains of *Salmonella* and *Shigella* (43). If, however, the tests are performed at 20° C. *Past. pestis* is lysed by the plague phage but *Past. pseudotuberculosis* is not. Schütze (77) established serologic groups by agglutination.

A powerful **endotoxin** is produced by a few strains of *Past. pseudotuberculosis* (57). Some of the strains that formed endotoxin belonged to Schütze's group I and some to group III (44).

Past. pseudotuberculosis can be differentiated from *Past. pestis* by (a) more rapid growth on simple media, (b) motility when grown at 20° C., (c) inability to form indol, and (d) failure to infect white rats. *Past. pseudotuberculosis* grows readily on deoxycholate citrate agar and produces a urease while *Past. pestis* does neither (82). Specific antipseudotuberculosis serum fails to agglutinate virulent *Past. pestis* grown at 37° C. but agglutinates heatkilled *Past. pseudotuberculosis.*

Past. pseudotuberculosis can produce severe and even fatal infections in man. Meyer (57) collected 14 cases from the literature. Reimann (72) found that the symptoms and anatomic changes simulated those caused by typhoid and paratyphoid fever, tularemia and tuberculosis. *Past. pseudotuberculosis* is more resistant to penicillin than *Past. multocida* and more resistant to streptomycin than *Past. pestis.* One patient recovered following treatment with sulfathiazole (79).

PASTEURELLA MULTOCIDA

Pasteurella multocida (Lehmann and Neumann) Rosenbusch and Merchant

The original strain was isolated from deer by Hueppe (37) in 1886. The subject was restudied by Schütze (77), who compared 230 strains described by 17 authors from numerous animal hosts. *Past. multocida* is a **nonmotile, nonsporogenous gram-negative** ellipsoidal rod with characteristic bipolar staining. It grows readily on plain or blood agar, forming small translucent colonies. **Indol is formed, nitrates are reduced to nitrites, H₂S is produced, and catalase synthesized. It does not grow on bile media and does not hemolyze blood agar, and milk is not coagulated. Lactose, maltose, raffinose, rhamnose, adonitol, dextrin, inulin, and glycerol are not oxidized. Acid** without gas is formed from **glucose, sucrose, fructose, sorbitol, galactose, and mannose, and sometimes from mannitol, xylose, and trehalose.**

Past. multocida is found very frequently in the upper air passages of normal cattle, horses, swine, sheep, fowl, dogs, cats, and rats (76). Less frequently it occurs in the intestinal tract of normal animals (69). An exchange of strains or a sudden change in food or environment may precipitate an acute epidemic. The magnitude of the host range and varying degrees of pathogenicity for specific animals are shown in Table 2. Man is bitten more frequently by rats than by any other animal, with the possible exception of the dog, and yet there are no reports of *Past. multocida* infections from rat bites (76).

Rosenbusch and Merchant (74) divided *Past. multocida* strains into three groups on the basis of sugar oxidations (Table 3) and agglutination reactions. Their results have been confirmed in whole (47) or in part (76) by other investigators.

The type II strains are more often rod-shaped and are rarely coccobacillary. All of the known human strains belong to type II but with this exception **any one of the three types can be found in an animal host.** Little and Lyon (47) have demonstrated that immune serum for passive immunization must be trivalent, and **bacterins** must contain representatives of all three types to be effective.

Strains of low virulence often show crossagglutination with serums of other types, suggesting that the somatic antigens are identical, although the envelope antigens probably differ in the three types. Pirosky (65) isolated four different glycolipoid antigens and found that

Table 2. Strain Origin and Range of Infectivity of Pasteurella multocida

STRAIN ORIGIN	MICE	ALBINO RATS	RABBITS	GUINEA PIGS	FOWL	CAT	DOG	HORSE	MAN
Avian	++++		++++	+	++++			+	+
Cattle, Sheep, Camels, Buffaloes, Reindeer and Elephants	++		++++	+	chicken −			−	++
Porcine	++++		++++	++++	++++				++
Norway Rats	++++	++++	++++	++++	+++	+++	+++		−?
Mice			++++	++++	pigeon −				
Feline	++++		++++	++++					++
Rabbits			++++						+
Human	++++		++++	+	pigeon +−		−		++

Table 3. Types of Pasteurella

	Pasteurella multocida			Pasteurella haemolytica
	Type I	Type II	Type III	
Lactose	−	−	−	+
Xylose	−	+	+	+
Arabinose	+	−	+	±
Dulcitol	+	−	+	±

one appeared to be related to the Vi antigen of *S. typhosa* while another reacted with anti-O serums of certain *Salmonella*. There are no serologic cross reactions between *Past. multocida* and *Brucella*, *Past. tularensis* and *H. influenzae* (76).

No **exotoxins** have been demonstrated, but powerful **endotoxins** are present in some strains. *Past. multocida* is usually much more sensitive to **penicillin** than to **streptomycin** (70, 76) and has been used to cure experimental infections in mice (59), ducks (70) and clinical infection in man (59, 85).

PASTEURELLA HAEMOLYTICA

Pasteurella haemolytica, Newsom and Cross

This species was differentiated from *Past. multocida* by Newsom and Cross (60) in 1932 because it differed from that species by showing **hemolysis on blood agar, oxidation of lactose, and maltose, no indol formation and the absence of cross-agglutination,** with *Past. multocida* strains. Rifkind and Pickett (73) restudied the subject in 1954 and concluded that *Past. haemolytica* could be readily distinguished from *Past. multocida* since the former grows readily on MacConkey's agar and is indol-negative,

while the latter does not grow on MacConkey's agar and is indol-positive. All isolates have been from pneumonia in sheep and cattle.

Biberstein and his associates (11) have described two different types of colonies in strains isolated from the blood of lambs in California. *Past. hemolytica* is "avirulent for rabbits." There are no reports of human infections with this organism but they may be expected to appear as clinical laboratories develop more interest in the *Pasteurella* group of organisms.

Three other species are recognized in Bergey's Manual. These produce disease in birds: *Past. septicaemia* in young geese, *Past. anatipestifer* in ducklings, and *Past. pfaffi* in canaries.

REFERENCES

1. Ajl, S. J., and others. J. Bact., 70:158, 1955.
2. ————— and others. Federation Proc., 15: part I, 581, 1956.
3. Allott, E. N., and others. J. Path. & Bact., 56:411, 1944.
4. Bacot, A. W., and Martin, C. J. J. Hyg., Plague Supp., 423, 1914; 23:98, 1924.
5. Baker, E. E., and others. J. Immunol., 68: 131, 1952.
6. Ben-Efraim, S., and others. J. Bact., 81: 704, 1961.
7. Berkman, S. J. Infect. Dis., 71:201, 1943.

8. Bhagavan, N. V., and others. Proc. Soc. Exper. Biol. & Med., 91:353, 1956.
9. Bhatnagar, S. S. Indian J. M. Research, 28:1, 1940.
10. ——— and Shrivastava, D. L. J. Hyg., 44:307, 1946.
11. Biberstein, E. L., and others. J. Bact., 76:445, 1958.
12. Bichowsky-Slomnicki, L., and Ben-Efraim, S. J. Bact., 86:101, 1963.
13. Brubaker, R. R., and Surgalla, M. J. J. Bact., 84:539, 1962.
14. ——— and Surgalla, M. J. J. Bact., 84:615, 1962.
15. Burmeister, R. W., and Tigertt, W. D. Ann. Int. Med., 56:789, 1962.
16. Burrows, T. W. Ann. N.Y. Acad. Sc., 88:1125, 1960.
17. ——— and Bacon, G. D. Brit. J. Exper. Path., 41:38, 1960.
18. Castellani, A., and Chalmers, A. J. Manual of Tropical Medicine, 3rd ed., London, Ballière, Tindall and Cox, 1919.
19. Cavanaugh, D. C., and Randall, R. J. of Med., 83:348, 1959.
20. Chen, T. H., and others. J. Immunol., 68:147, 1952.
21. ——— and Meyer, K. F. J. Immunol., 72:282, 1954; 74:501, 1955.
22. Creel, R. H. Pub. Health Rep., 28: No. 27, 1913.
23. Crumpton, M. T., and Davies, D. A. L. Proc. Roy. Soc. London SRR. B., 145:109, 1956.
24. Doudoroff, M. Proc. Soc. Exper. Biol. & Med., 53:73, 1943.
25. Douglas, J. R., and Wheeler, C. M. J. Infect. Dis., 72:18, 1943.
26. Eisler, D. M., and von Metz, E. J. of Med., 91:287, 1963.
27. ——— and others. J. Bact., 76:41, 1958.
28. Englesberg, E., and Levy, J. B. J. Immunol., 67:438, 1954.
29. Eskey, C. R., and Haas, V. H. Pub. Health Bull., No. 254, page 1, 1940.
30. Girard, G. Ann. Rev. Microbiol., 9:253, 1955.
31. Goodner, K., and others. J. Infect. Dis., 96:82, 1955.
32. Gordon, J. E., and Knies, P. T. Am. J. M. Sc., 213:362, 1947.
33. Haffkine, W. M. Lancet, 2:103, 1898.
34. Higuchi, K., and Smith, J. L. J. Bact., 81:605, 1961.
35. Hirsch, A. Handb. d. histor-geograph. Pathologie, Stuttgart, 1881.
36. Huang, G. H., and others. Am. J. Trop. Med., 28:361, 1948.
37. Hueppe, F. Berl. klin. Wchnschr., 23:794, 1886.
38. Jawetz, E., and Meyer, K. F. J. Infect. Dis., 73:124, 1943; 74:1, 1944.
39. Kitasato, S. Lancet, 2:428, 1894.
40. Larson, C. L., and others. J. Immunol., 67:289, 1951.
41. Lawton, W. D., and others. J. of Med., 84:475, 1960.
42. ——— and others. J. Immunol., 91:179, 1963.
43. Lazarus, A. S., and Gunnison, J. B. J. Bact., 53:705, 1947.
44. ——— and Nozawa, M. M. J. Bact., 56:187, 1948.
45. Link, V. B. Pub. Health Rep., 65:696, 1950.
46. ——— Pub. Health Monograph No. 26, 1955.
47. Little, P. A., and Lyon, B. M. Am. J. Vet. Research, 4:110, 1943.
48. Markenson, J., and Ben-Efraim, S. J. Bact., 85:1443, 1963.
49. Mathur, W., and Goyal, R. Indian M. Gaz., 80:383, 1945.
50. McCoy, G. W. Am. J. Hyg., 1:182, 1921.
51. McCrum, F. R., Jr., and others. Am. J. Med., 14:284, 1953.
52. Meyer, K. F., and Batchelder, A. J. Infec. Dis., 39:383, 1926.
53. ——— Am. J. Trop. Med., 22:9, 1942.
54. ——— and others. J. Infect. Dis., 73:144, 1943.
55. ——— Ann. Int. Med., 29:326, 1948.
56. ——— J. Immunol., 64:139, 1950.
57. ——— Bacterial & Mycotic Infections of Man, 2nd ed., Edited by R. J. Dubos, Philadelphia, J. B. Lippincott Co., 1952, p. 473.
58. Naylor, H. B., and others. J. Bact., 81:649, 1961.
59. Needham, G. M. Proc. Staff Meet., Mayo Clinic, 23:361, 1948.
60. Newsom, I. E., and Cross, F. J. Am. Vet. M. A., 80:711, 1932.
61. Packer, L., and others. J. Bact., 78:658, 1959.
62. Pasteur, L. Compt. rend. Acad. d. sc., 90:239, 1880.
63. Payne, F. E., and others. J. Immunol., 77:24, 1956.
64. Pirie, J. H. H. Rep. S. African Inst. M. Res., 3:109, 1927; 13, 1936.
65. Pirosky, I. Comp. rend. soc. de biol., 128:346, 1938.
66. Platzer, R. F. U.S. Navy M. Bull., 46:1674, 1946.
67. Pollitzer, R. Acta Trop., 6:30, 1949.
68. ——— Plague, World Health Organization, Monograph Series No. 22, Geneva, 1954.
69. Pritchett, I. W., and others. J. Exper. Med., 51:249, 1930.
70. Queen, F. B., and Quorthop, E. R. J. Am. Vet. M. A., 108:19, 101, 1946.
71. Rao, M. S. Indian J. M. Research, 27:75, 617, 833, 1939.
72. Reimann, H. A. Am. J. Hyg., 16:206, 1932.
73. Rifkind, D., and Pickett, M. J. J. Bact., 67:243, 1954.
74. Rosenbusch, C. T., and Merchant, I. A. J. Bact., 37:69, 1939.
75. Ruegsegger, J. M., and Gilchrist, H. Am. J. Trop. Med., 27:683, 1947.
76. Schipper, G. J. Bull. Johns Hopkins Hosp., 81:333, 1947.
77. Schütze, H. A System of Bacteriology in Relation to Medicine, London, 4:446, 1929.
78. Seal, S. C. J. Immunol., 71:169, 1953.
79. Snyder, G. A. C., and Vogel, N. J. Northwest Med., 42:14, 1943.
80. Surgalla, M. J. Ann. N.Y. Acad. Sci., 88:1136, 1960.
81. Teague, O., and Barber, M. A. Philippine J. Sc., Sec. B., 7:257, 1912.
82. Thal., E., and Chen, T. H. J. Bact., 69:103, 1955.
83. Woodward, G. E. J. Biol. Chem., 156:143, 1944.
84. Yersin, S. Ann. Inst. Pasteur, 8:662, 1894.
85. Zeller, W. W., and Lepper, M. H. Am. J. Med., 9:701, 1950.
86. Zinsser, H. Rats, Lice and History, Boston, Little, Brown & Co., 1935, p. 197.

44

Bacillus anthracis and anthrax (Milzbrand, Charbon)

Family: *Bacillaceae* Fischer. Genus: *Bacillus* Cohn. Species: *Bacillus anthracis* Cohn *emend.* Koch

Anthrax is primarily a disease of herbivorous animals, particularly cattle and sheep and to a lesser extent horses, hogs, and goats. Dogs and other carnivora are relatively immune to spontaneous infections. Man possesses an intermediate degree of susceptibility, being more resistant than the herbivora and more susceptible than the dog.

Anthrax is an old disease which has plagued cattle and sheep-raising countries for centuries. It is relatively uncommon in England and America but a scourge in Austria, Hungary, Germany, France, and the eastern countries. No quarter of the globe is entirely free of anthrax. Minor epidemics occur in cattle in this country almost every year and 2,447 cases developed in man between 1919 and 1949 (69).

Up to a certain point, the history of the anthrax bacillus is the history of bacteriology. The bacillus is so large that it was seen in unstained preparations of blood by Davaine and Rayer (14) in 1850 and by Pollander (47) in 1855. In 1857 Brauell (6) succeeded in infecting animals with blood containing these anthrax rods. The size of the organism and its facility of growth made possible the classic studies of Koch (31), who, in 1877, cultured the bacillus in the aqueous humor of the ox's eye, described its life cycle, and reproduced the disease in experimental animals. Finally, Pasteur and his associates (44) attenuated the bacillus by cultivation at a temperature of 42° to 43° C., thus changing the "virus" into a "vaccine" and giving the first convincing evidence of the practical application of **active immunization** against a bacterial disease.

Morphology and Staining. The anthrax bacillus is a straight rod, 5 to 10 μ in length and 1 to 3 μ in width. When examined in smears from the blood or tissues of an infected animal the organisms usually are found singly or in pairs (Fig. 1). Their ends appear square, and the corners are often so sharp that the bacilli in the chains are in contact at these points, leaving an oval chink between the organisms. The appearance of a chain of anthrax bacilli has been not inaptly compared with a rod of bamboo. Well-defined **capsules** surround the organism as they grow in the blood or tissues of the infected animal. The capsules seem to surround an entire chain and not the individual bacillus. Virulent, but not avirulent, strains develop capsules when grown on a medium or in an atmosphere which contains an excess of CO_2 (11, 63).

There are two minor exceptions to this statement (64). A few strains which become encapsulated and produce mucoid colonies in CO_2 are of low virulence, presumably because they have a reduced capacity to produce toxin. And there are a few strains which are encapsulated and produce mucoid colonies in the air and under CO_2 but are completely avirulent. Presumably these strains lack either the ability to produce toxin or lack some other factor essential for virulence.

Spores are formed in cultures, in the soil and in material from dead animals, but not in the blood or tissues of living animals. Free sporulation occurs where there is a reduction in calcium ions and an abundance of free oxygen. The spores are oval in shape, develop near the middle of the bacillus (Fig. 2) and are not wider than the body of the organism. They do not stain by Gram's method but can be demonstrated easily by any of the usual spore stains. Spores usually have antigens which are not present in the vegetative cell. However, an at-

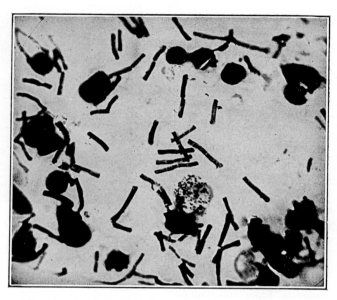

Fig. 1. *Bacillus anthracis.* In smear of spleen of animal dead of anthrax.

tempt to separate *B. anthracis* from the closely related species *B. cereus* by an antigenic analysis of their respective spores failed (34).

Cultural Characteristics. Maximal growth of the organism is obtained at pH 7.0 to 7.4 under **aerobic conditions,** but sparse growth occurs in the absence of oxygen. The optimal temperature for maximal growth is 37° C., but growth does not cease until temperatures as low as 12° C. and as high as 45° C. are reached. By continued cultivation the organisms may become adapted to either a low or high temperature and eventually attain luxuriant growth. The bacilli grow readily on simple laboratory media, producing in 24 hours large, raised, opaque, grayish white, plumose colonies 2 to 3 mm. in diameter and possessing an irregular, fringe-like edge (Fig. 3). Tangled masses of long hair-like curls can be seen with a colony microscope. The colony is membranous in consistency and emulsifies with difficulty. The bacilli will grow on a synthetic medium containing thiamin, glucose, amino acids, and mineral salts (7).

Milk is coagulated and peptonized, gelatin liquefied slowly, but **indol and H₂S are not formed. Lactose is not oxidized** but **acid without gas is formed from glucose.**

Neither morphology nor the usual cultural characteristics will differentiate *B. anthracis* from non-motile strains of *B. cereus* (9). Highly virulent strains of anthrax are easily detected by the rapidity with which small numbers kill mice, but some strains of *B. anthracis* may have

no more virulence for mice than other strains of *B. cereus.* However, animals immunized against anthrax are as susceptible as normal animals to infection with *B. cereus* (12). Leise and his associates report (36) that (1) lack of motility, (2) absence of hemolysis, (3) susceptibility to gamma bacteriophage, and (4) the "string of pearls" reaction clearly separate both virulent and avirulent *B. anthracis* from *B. cereus* and other aerobic spore formers. The "string of pearls" reaction is most dramatic. This was described first by Jensen and Kleemeyer (24) who showed that the incubation of a culture of *B. anthracis* on the surface of a solid medium containing five to 10 units of penicillin per milliliter of medium for three to six hours causes the development of spherules which resemble a string of pearls. Other aerobic spore-bearers do not give this type of reaction to penicillin under these conditions. This is true of strains of *B. cereus* which showed serologic reactions to *B. anthracis* (66).

Resistance. Because of its property of spore formation, the anthrax bacillus is extremely resistant to its chemical and physical environment. The vegetative forms themselves are no more resistant than most other nonsporulating bacteria, being destroyed by a temperature of 54° C. in 30 minutes. Anthrax spores may be kept in a dry state for many years without losing their viability (58). While there are variations in the resistance of different strains of anthrax spores, all races display an extremely high resistance to heat. Dry heat at 140° C. re-

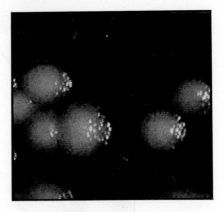

Fig. 4. Virulent strain of *B. anthracis.* Organism develops smooth colony when grown in the presence of excess CO_2. (Courtesy of Dr. Kenneth L. Burdon.)

Fig. 2. *Bacillus anthracis.* From pure culture on agar.

quires three hours to kill. Live steam at 100° C. kills them in five to 10 minutes. Boiling destroys them in about 10 minutes. Destruction of anthrax spores in furs, hides, and brushes is difficult. Blue (5) states that for brushes the best method is soaking for four hours in 10 per cent formalin solution at 110° F. Hair and bristles may be sterilized in the autoclave at 15 pounds for three hours, but this ruins many materials.

Spores may retain their viability after exposure to 5 per cent carbolic acid for 40 days or

may be destroyed by the same solution in two days. Corrosive sublimate, 1:2,000, kills most strains in 40 minutes. Direct sunlight destroys anthrax spores within six to 12 hours.

Experimental anthrax infections in mice have been treated with sulfonamides, penicillin, and streptomycin. When used in maximal doses, **sulfonamides** saved 5 per cent, **penicillin,** 58 per cent, and **streptomycin,** 92 per cent of the infected animals (41).

Variability. Both virulent and avirulent strains of *B. anthracis* give rise to rough colonies when grown on ordinary laboratory media (Fig. 3) without an excess of CO_2. Usually, the virulent strains develop capsules and produce smooth colonies (Figs. 4 and 5) when grown

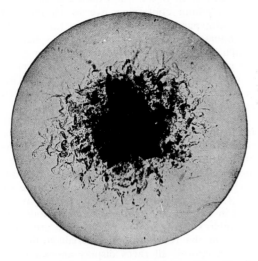

Fig. 3. Anthrax colony on gelatin. (Guenther)

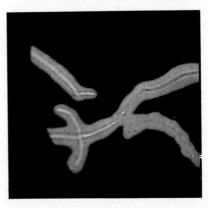

Fig. 5. Capsule formation in cultures of *B. anthracis.* Virulent but not avirulent strains develop capsules when grown in the presence of excess CO_2. (Courtesy of Dr. Kenneth L. Burdon.)

in an excess of CO_2 (11, 63). The rare exceptions have been discussed by Thorne (64). The nonvirulent strains, which are rough in the absence of CO_2, remain unencapsulated and rough in its presence. There are, however, a few avirulent strains which are encapsulated and smooth when grown in either air or in CO_2 (64). Other spontaneous variations in colony morphology have been described by Nungester (43).

The attenuated strains which Pasteur obtained by cultivating the organism at a temperature of 42° to 43° C. were asporogenous. The essential change, however, was not in the loss of the ability to form spores, since some asporogenous races are highly pathogenic. Virulence depends upon the presence of a capsule or the ability of the organism to form one when introduced into the animal body. While separate races of anthrax bacilli may vary considerably in their degree of virulence, a single individual strain remains fairly constant in this respect if dried and preserved upon threads or kept in sealed tubes in a cold, dark place. Virulence is usually, but not always, increased by animal passage.

Antigenic Structure. The capsular substance of the anthrax bacillus is **not a polysaccharide but a polypeptide** of high molecular weight composed exclusively of **d (—) glutamic acid.** This substance is not specific for anthrax but is found in smaller amounts in *B. subtilis* and related nonpathogenic, sporebearing, aerobic bacilli (65). The bodies of the bacilli contain a **polysaccharide** which consists of glucosamine and galactose attached to a molecule of acetic acid. The presence of both antigens can be demonstrated in the tissues of animals dead of anthrax by means of specific precipitin tests. The d (—) glutamic acid capsule is not a normal constituent of the animal body. Animals, however, which have been immunized against anthrax acquire the ability to destroy the capsular substance (13). The tissues of a naturally immune animal such as the dog also possess this ability to destroy or inhibit the production of the capsular material, after which the organism is phagocytized and destroyed.

The antibodies produced by the injection of heat-killed, encapsulated bacilli into rabbits will protect mice but not guinea pigs, rabbits, sheep, or monkeys. However, Watson and his associates (67) extracted an immunizing antigen from the edema fluid of infected animals. Gladstone (18) succeeded in obtaining an immunizing antigen in cultures by adding sodium bicarbonate and a protein fraction from plasma.

These observations were confirmed by others (70). The increased CO_2 from the sodium bicarbonate seems to be essential for the elaboration of the protective antigen. Using a nonproteolytic mutant of *B. anthracis,* Wright and his associates (3, 70) succeeded in obtaining relatively large yields of the protective antigen by growing the organisms in a protein-free medium made of glucose, thiamin, sodium bicarbonate, calcium, iron, leucine, isolucine, methionine, proline, phenylalanine, and histidine. Later investigation (70, 71) modified the medium by reducing the amount of ferrous sulfate, adding adenosine or L-alanine and cultivating under anaerobic conditions with constant agitation. The yield of the protective portion was increased fivefold by this modification. The protective antigen could be precipitated by alum and has been used to immunize rabbits, guinea pigs, monkeys, and man (3). The protective antigen elaborated by the nonproteolytic mutant of the vollum strain protected rabbits from both stock strains and fresh strains collected from various parts of the world (3). McGann and her associates (39) demonstrated that the protective antigen could be measured by either complement fixation or by agar gel diffusion.

The Ascoli Test. The anthrax bacillus in the animal body is encapsulated and contains a specific polypeptide. It is probable that material of this nature constitutes the heat-stable antigen obtained by Ascoli (2) from the extracts of organs of animals dead of anthrax for use in his diagnostic precipitin test. These extracts give a precipitate with antianthrax serum. Ascoli's precipitin reaction is helpful in making a rapid diagnosis when the work has to be done with putrid material from dead animals, with hides or with tissues preserved in formalin or alcohol. To make the extract, a small piece of the spleen is boiled in 5 to 10 ml. of saline, cooled, filtered clear and layered on the antiserum. A zone of precipitate occurs at the junction of the extract and antiserum in positive tests. Suitable controls should be run at the same time. The ordinary antianthrax therapeutic serum may not have a high precipitin content. The serum most useful in Ascoli's test is prepared by immunizing animals (rabbits) against encapsulated anthrax bacilli. Contrary to previous reports, Leonard and Thorne (37) have found that the D-glutamyl polypeptide from the capsule of *B. anthracis* is not antigenic for the rabbit. One must assume that the somatic carbohydrate protein complex or some other antigen explains the reliability of the Ascoli test.

Bacteriophage. McCloy (38) has described a strain of bacteriophage which is specific for *B. anthracis*. Brown and his associates (8) reported in 1955 that certain strains of bacteriophage from *B. cereus* would infect strains of *B. anthracis*. Buck and his associates (10) isolated phages from 25 of 246 *B. anthracis* strains collected from various parts of the world. A total of 9 phage growths were found among the 246 strains. These phages lysed *B. anthracis* alone and did not cross to other species except in two instances when one strain of *B. megaterium* and *B. subtilis* W23S were lysed. However, these two cultures were negative to the more reliable "string of pearls" test. The crossing of specie lines was noted previously by Yoder and Nelson (72), who observed them with *B. anthracis* and *B. thuringiensis*. The genetic basis for the bacteriophage type has been reviewed by Anderson (1).

Bacterial Metabolites. Neither classical exotoxins nor classical endotoxins have been found in cultures of *B. anthracis*. Clinical evidence of toxemia, however, which is obvious in man and in some experimental animals, suggests that a toxin may be found in the animal body. This theory is supported by the observations of Cromartie and his associates (13) in this country and Smith and his co-workers in England (56). A toxic factor is known to develop in the edema fluid of a local lesion in an animal susceptible to anthrax. One of the factors in this fluid is a **leukotoxin,** which is a part of the old "Aggressin." This toxin is highly selective since it inhibits the chemotaxis of leukocytes from susceptible animals such as the horse, sheep, and man but does not inhibit chemotoxin of resistant animals like the hog and dog (25). The specificity of the action on the leukocytes of susceptible species can be demonstrated by the rapidity with which antiserum neutralizes this inhibiting effect.

In the section on antigenic structure it was noted that Wright and his associate had isolated the "protective factor" which is not toxic. Thorne and his associates (61) reported that the culture fluid, before filtration through fritted glass filters, was highly toxic, while the protective factor in the filtrate was not. This suggested that the toxin consisted of two components and one of them was the protecting antigen. They succeeded in isolating the accessory factor by eluting it from the glass filter with an alkaline buffer. The accessory factor when purified was not toxic but a mixture of the protective and accessory factor was toxic. The specificity of the reaction was demonstrated by neutralizing the effect with *B. an-*

thracis antiserum. This work was confirmed and extended by Stanley and Smith (57) in England and Beal and his associates in this country (4). The extension consisted of isolating a second factor from the fritted glass filter which was the factor that caused local edema of the skin and subcutaneous tissue as originally described by Watson and his associates (67). However, this third toxic factor was not lethal for animals.

One of the most striking characteristics of the action of the crude toxin, after intravenous injection, was the rapid development of alkaline phosphatemia. This factor was found in crude extract of cultures of some variants of *B. cereus* and *B. thuringiensis*. All three of these species are known to produce lecithinase, but the investigations of Slein and Logan (54) have shown that lecithinase is not the cause of this phenomenon. The alkaline phosphatemia seems to be released by some other factor from the centers of ossifying bone. This phosphatemia response can be prevented by mixing the factor with antiserum before injection (54).

Spontaneous Disease in Animals. Herbivorous animals acquire the infection by the ingestion of spores which probably enter the body through microscopic cuts or abrasions of the oral or intestinal mucosa. When a pasture has been contaminated with anthrax spores, it may remain a source of infection for 20 to 30 years. Although it is impossible to determine the moment of infection in a case of spontaneous anthrax, it is certain that the duration of the disease is only a few days. The infected animals remain asymptomatic until a few hours before death. The longhaired Algerian sheep have a relatively high resistance to anthrax in contrast to the European varieties which are very susceptible. The mortality in herbivorous animals is usually about 80 per cent.

Experimental Disease in Laboratory Animals. Mice, guinea pigs, and rabbits are very susceptible and die with septicemia two to four days after infection. Dogs and swine are more resistant and develop local lesions resembling the local lesions characteristic of anthrax in man (13).

Normal rats are very susceptible to death from anthrax at six days of age but increase their resistance one and a half times each day from the sixth to the thirty-first day. Germ-free rats are much more resistant than normal rats but they also acquire resistance with age (60). The blood of the guinea pig (29) and the monkey (28) in the terminal stage of experimental anthrax contains toxin. Monkeys could be killed with toxin or protected from death with antiserum (30). The same investigators found that the injection of 10^{-11} spores killed monkeys in 2 hours, while the injection of 10^{-10} spores required 20 or more hours to produce death, suggesting that a fatal dose of toxin was present, at least potentially, in the 10^{-11} dose but not in the 10^{-10} dose. In the latter instance the bacilli had to germinate and grow to produce the additional toxin to cause death.

Immunity seems to be in part antitoxic and in part antibacterial (27, 30). Klein and his coworkers (29) found that guinea pigs immunized with alum precipitated protective antigen had the resistance to infection increased by 1,600 times, and when death did occur, the number of bacilli per milliliter of blood at death was decreased by 75 per cent. The critical period in the antibiotic treatment of experimentally infected guinea pigs seems to be 1/300 of the terminal number of bacilli per milliliter of blood. Beyond this number the animals usually die, even when treated with adequate doses of antitoxins (26).

In experimental **wool-sorters disease** in *Rhesus* monkeys the initial change in the lungs is a symmetrical widening of the upper two-thirds of the mediastinum. If treated early, the animals could be cured with penicillin but one animal died with a penicillin-resistant strain of anthrax (49).

Clinical Types of Infection in Man.   Anthrax in man usually is acquired by accidental cutaneous inoculation, but the bacilli or spores also may be inhaled or ingested. In some instances the source of the infection is difficult to detect, as in the fatal case of a worker in the piano key industry who acquired anthrax from contact with elephant tusks (51). Plotkin and his associates (46) studied an epidemic from contaminated goat's hair in a textile mill in New Hampshire. Four of the cases were by inhalation, and four were cutaneous (40a).

Cutaneous inoculation usually occurs through small abrasions or scratches upon the skin in men who habitually handle live stock, and in butchers or tanners of hides. Infection occurs most frequently upon the hands and forearms. The primary lesion, often referred to as a **malignant pustule,** appears within 12 to 24 hours after inoculation and at first resembles an ordinary small furuncle. Soon, however, its center

shows a vesicle filled with serosanguineous, later seropurulent, fluid. This may change into a black central necrosis surrounded by an angry red edematous areola. Local gangrene and a general systemic infection occasionally may lead to death within five or six days. More frequently, however, especially if prompt treatment is given, the patient recovers. The **early diagnosis** of the condition is best made bacteriologically by **finding the bacilli in the local discharge.**

The pulmonary infection known as **"wool-sorter's disease"** occurs in persons who handle raw wool, hides, or horse hair by the inhalation of spores. The disease is rare in this country, although anthrax spores have been recovered from the air of a clothing mill where the workers were developing the cutaneous form of the disease (20). The spores, once inhaled, develop into the vegetative forms which travel along the lymphatics into the lungs and pleura. The disease manifests itself as a violent irregular pneumonia which in the majority of cases leads to death. The bacilli in these cases often can be found in the sputum before death.

Infection through the alimentary canal may occur rarely in man from ingestion of uncooked meat of infected animals. The clinical picture that follows is one of violent enteritis with bloody stools and great prostration. Death is the rule. The diagnosis is made by the finding of the **bacilli in the feces.**

Transmission.   During and since World War I anthrax infection of the skin from shaving brushes has been recognized both in England and America (23, 59).

Treatment.   Gold (19) has treated 116 patients with cutaneous anthrax since 1933, with the loss of but one patient giving a mortality rate of 0.8 per cent. The one pulmonary case in the series was treated late and died. He treated 21 patients with anti-anthrax serum, 56 with sulfonamides, and 40 with penicillin or with the broad spectrum antibiotics. The total dose of penicillin varied from 980,000 to six million units in two to seven days; chlortetracycline varied from 4.5 g. in 24 hours to 20.5 g. in eight days; chloramphenicol varied from 2.5 g. in two days to 24.75 g. in seven days; oxytetracycline varied from 3 g. in three days to 29.5 g. in eight days; tetracycline varied from 10 g. in five days to 14 g. in 10 days; erythromycin ranged from 3.2 g. in 90 hours to 5.6 g. in seven days.

The importance of toxin in the death of experimental animals would suggest that antiserum, which is both antitoxic and antibacterial, should be given along with antibiotics in all generalized anthrax infections. The Russians have recommended it routinely in generalized infection for some years (52).

Prevention.   Animals with known or suspected anthrax should be isolated and their carcasses buried deeply to prevent the spread of the spores to new pastures. Wool, horsehair, and hides coming from areas where endemic anthrax is present should be sterilized. The spores on hair and wool can be destroyed by boiling for three hours or with steam under pressure. Hides and skins which cannot be boiled should be sterilized by treatment with a dilute hydrochloric acid-salt mixture at 40° C. for a period of six hours.

Active immunization is the only known method of preventing anthrax in herbivorous animals in areas where the pasture land is already contaminated with spores. Pasteur's famous attenuated living anthrax vaccine was effective but difficult to maintain at a desired level of virulence. It was ineffective if the virulence dropped too low and produced clinical disease in the vaccinated animals if it increased. Pasteur's vaccine has been superseded by the Carbazoo-R living spore vaccine made from a nonencapsulated strain of anthrax (45). In 1957 Jackson, Wright and Armstrong (22, 50) compared the relative value of alum precipitated protective antigen with the Carbazoo-R living spore vaccine in animals. The Carbazoo-R living vaccine gave good protection but caused some local disease in the animals. The protection from the alum precipitated protective antigen was 100 per cent after one month but dropped to 52 per cent in three and one-half months. The experiment of Klein and his associates with guinea pigs in 1962 (30) suggested that both materials should be used simultaneously. Live spore vaccine gave a 10- to 15-fold increase in resistance, and the alum precipitated protective antigen gave 1000-fold increase in resistance, while both together produced the astonishing figure of 100,000,000-fold increase in resistance (28).

OTHER AEROBIC SPORE-BEARING BACILLI

Gram-positive, aerobic, spore-bearing species are abundant in the soil and water. In the 7th edition of Bergey's Manual 25 species are recognized. Seventeen species are found as saprophytes in soil and water (21). Several produce antibiotics, but only one is in clinical use. This is polymyxin made by *B. polymyxa*. Six species produce disease in insects, and several of these are used to control harmful insects. One species, *B. cereus*, has a limited ability to produce disease in animals, and one species, *B. anthracis*, is highly virulent for man and herbivorous animals. *B. subtilis* from air and dust is a common laboratory contaminant and may appear in clinical specimens as a secondary contaminant of wounds.

The species and varieties of the genus *Bacillus* has been studied in detail by Fitz-James and Young (17), who found that they could be divided into groups A, B, C, D, and E on the basis of the DNA-P/spore. Except for *B. thuringiensis*, the DNA-P/spore tends to be a multiple of the amount found in the smallest spores which are in group A. *B. subtilis* is characteristic of the group.

B. subtilis is a gram-positive straight rod, 2 to 8 μ long and 0.7 μ wide, which grows in long chains (Fig. 6). Spores are formed which occur slightly nearer one pole than the other (25a). The organism is actively motile only in young cultures. Gelatin is liquefied. On gelatin and agar the bacilli grow as a dry corrugated pellicle. Microscopically, the colonies are irregularly round with fringed edges and made up of interlacing threads. There is a tendency to confluence. The bacillus is found in brackish water, infusions of vegetable matter, etc. Species which have a *B. subtilis*-like DNA base composition, such as *B. natto*, *B. subtilis* var. *atterrimus*, are readily transformed. *B. brevis* and *B. stearothermophilus* could not transform *B. subtilis* while *B. polymyxa* transforms *B. subtilis* at a reduced rate (40). Transduction with bacteriophage has been observed by Thorne (62). Bacteriophage for *B. subtilis* is readily isolated from soil by growing soil organisms in a suitable medium and then adding a streptomycin resistant strain of *B. subtilis* along with a bactericidal dose of streptomycin (48).

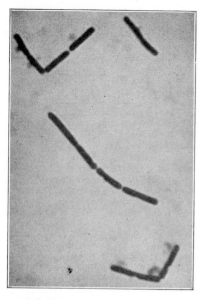

Fig. 6. *Bacillus subtilis*. (From Bartholomew and Mittwer. *J. Gen. Microbiol.,* 5:39, 1951.)

B. subtilis is frequently isolated from old sinuses or chronically infected wounds, and there are some reports of the isolations from meninges and from the blood stream (68).

B. cereus and *B. megaterium* are sometimes called the "large cell species," since they are definitely larger than *B. anthracis* and *B. subtilis*. The immunologic specificity of the spores is different from that of the cell substance (15, 32). The small cell species of aerobic sporebearers can be separated into four main types by antigenic studies of either spores or cell substance (53). Molnar has shown that *B. cereus* and *B. megaterium* have a phosphatase but this is not a part of the toxin (42). The toxin resembles that of *B. anthracis*, which has two parts which are not toxic alone but toxic when combined. But there is no cross protection from immunization with toxin of *B. anthracis* and *B. cereus* (12).

The insect pathogen strain such as *B. thuringiensis* will kill mice when given in large doses (12), but no evidence has appeared to suggest that they could infect man. This, however, is no excuse for carelessness in handling such potent biologic agents.

For more details concerning the differentiation of the aerobic spore-bearers from *B. anthracis* and from other bacilli, the student should consult the publications of Nathan Smith (55), Burdon (11), Evans and Wardlaw (16), and Lamanna (33, 34, 35).

REFERENCES

1. Anderson, E. S. Brit. Med. Bull., 18:64, 1962.
2. Ascoli, A. Ztschr. f. Immunitätsforsch. u. exper. Therap., 11:103, 1911.
3. Auerback, W., and Wright, G. G. J. Immunol., 75:129, 1955.
4. Beall, F. A., and others. J. Bact., 83:1274, 1962.
5. Blue, R. Pub. Health Rep., 34:993, 1919.
6. Brauell. Arch. f. Path. u. Anat., 11:132, 1857.
7. Brewer, C. R., and others. Arch. Biochem., 10:65, 1946.
8. Brown, E. R., and others. J. Bact., 69:590, 1955.
9. ———— and others. J. Bact., 75:499, 1958.
10. Buck, C. A., and others. J. Bact., 85:1423, 1963.
11. Burdon, K. L., and others. J. Bact., 43:717; 44:163, 1942; 71:25, 1956.
12. ———— and Wende, R. D. J. Inf. Dis., 107:224, 1960.
13. Cromartie, W. J., and others. J. Infect. Dis., 80:1, 14, 1947.
14. Davaine, and Rayer. Bull. Soc. de biol., 1850, p. 141.
15. Doak, B. W., and Lamanna, C. J. Bact., 55:373, 1948.
16. Evans, D. G., and Wardlaw, A. C. J. Gen. Microbiol., 7:397, 1952; 8:481, 1953.
17. Fitz-James, P. C., and Young, I. E. J. Bact., 78:743, 755, 765, 1959.
18. Gladstone, G. P. Brit. J. Exper. Path., 20:189, 1939; 27:394, 1946.
19. Gold, H. Arch. Int. Med., 96:387, 1955.
20. Gordon, M. A., and others. A.M.A. Arch. Indust. Hyg. & Occup. Med., 10:16, 1954.
21. Hueppe, F., and Wood, G. C. Berl. klin. Wchnschr., 16:347, 1889.
22. Jackson, F. C., and others. Am. J. Vet. Res., 18:771, 1957.
23. Jacobsohn. Month. Bull. New York City Dept. Health, 14: Nos. 3, 7, 1923-24.
24. Jensen, J., and Kleemeyer, H. Zentr. Bakteriol. Parasitenk, Abt. I Orig., 159:494, 1953.
25. Kashiba, S. Biken's J., 2:97, 1959.
25a. Kawata, T., and others. Jap. J. Microbiol., 7:23, 1963.
26. Keppie, J., and others. Brit. J. Exper. Path., 36:15, 1955.
27. Klein, F., and others. J. Bact., 85:1032, 1963.
28. ———— and others. J. Bact., 88:15, 1962.
29. ———— and others. Science, 133:1021, 1961.
30. ———— and others. Science, 138:1331, 1962.
31. Koch, R. In Cohn's Beitr. z. Biol. d. Pflanz., 2:277, 1877.
32. Lamanna, C. J. Infect. Dis., 67:193, 205, 1940.
33. ———— Internat. Bull. Bacteriol. Nomenclature and Taxonomy, 4:133, 1954.
34. ———— and Eisler, D. J. Bact., 79:435, 1960.
35. ———— and Jones, L. J. Bact., 85:532, 1963.
36. Leise, J. M., and others. J. Bact., 77:655, 1959.
37. Leonard, C. G., and Thorne, C. B. J. Med., 87:175, 1961.
38. McCloy, E. W. J. Hyg., 49:114, 1951.
39. McGann, V. G., and others. J. Immunol., 86:458, 1961.

40. Marmor, J., and others. J. Bact., 85:461, 1963.
40a. Matz, M. H., and Brugsh, H. G. J.A.M.A., 188:635, 1964.
41. Miller, E. S., and others. J. Immunol., 53:371, 1946.
42. Molnar, D. M. J. Bact., 84:147, 1962.
43. Nungester, W. J. J. Infect. Dis., 44:73, 1929.
44. Pasteur, L., and others. Compt. rend. Acad. d. sc., 92:1881.
45. Personeus, G., and others. Am. J. Vet. Research, 17:153, 1956.
46. Plotkin, S. H., and others. Am. J. Med., 29:992, 1960.
47. Pollander. Vrljschr. f. Deutsche Med., 8:103, 1855.
48. Romig, W. R., and Brodetsky, A. M. J. Bact., 82:135, 1961.
49. Sawer, W. D., and Gochenour, W. S. Am. Rev. Resp. Dis., 87:614, 1963.
50. Schlingman, A. S., and others. Am. J. Vet. Research, 17:256, 1956.
51. Seidman, R. M., and Wheeler, K. M. J.A.M.A., 135:837, 1942.
52. Shliakov, E. N. J. Microbiol. Epidemiol. Immunobiol. (USSR), 28:748, 1957. (Translation) (Pergamon, N.Y.).
53. Sievers, O. J. Bact., 43:305, 1942.
54. Slein, M. W., and Logan, G. F. J. Bact., 83:359, 1962; 85:369, 1963.
55. Smith, N. R., and others. U.S. Dept. Agric. Misc., Pub. 559, 1946. Monograph No. 16, 1952.
56. Smith, H., and others. Brit. J. Exper. Path., 34:471, 1953.
57. Stanley, T. L., and Smith, H. J. Gen. Microbiol., 26:49, 1961.
58. Surmont, H., and Arnould, E. Ann. Inst. Pasteur, 8:817, 1894.
59. Symmers, D., and Cady, B. W. J.A.M.A., 77:2120, 1921.
60. Taylor, M. J., and others. Am. J. Path., 38:625, 1961.
61. Thorne, C. B. Ann. N.Y. Acad. Sc., 88:1024, 1960.
62. ———— J. Bact., 83:106, 1962.
63. ———— and others. J. Bact., 65:472, 1953.
64. ———— and others. J. Bact., 79:450, 1960.
65. Tomcsik, J., and Ivanovics, G. Ztschr. f. Immunitätsforsch. u. exper. Therap., 93:196, 1938.
66. ———— and Schwei, Z. Z. Path. Bakt., 22:144, 1959.
67. Watson, D. W., and others. J. Infect. Dis., 80:121, 1947.
68. Weinstein, L., and Colburn, C. G. Arch. Int. Med., 86:585, 1950.
69. Wolff, A. H., and Heimann, H. Am. J. Hyg., 53:80, 1951.
70. Wright, G. G., and others. J. Bact., 83:515, 1962.
71. ———— and others. J. Immunol., 72:263, 1954; 73:387, 1954.
72. Yoder, P. E., and Nelson, E. L. J. Insect Pathol., 2:198, 1960.

45

Anaerobic Bacilli and Wound Infections

CLOSTRIDIUM PERFRINGENS AND ANAEROBIC BACTERIA ASSOCIATED WITH TRAUMATIC INJURIES

Family: *Bacillaceae* Fischer. Genus: *Clostridium* Prazmowski

Gram-positive anaerobic, spore-bearing bacilli, classified in the genus **Clostridium,** include both pathogenic and saprophytic species (Table 1). Our knowledge of these organisms began with the dawn of bacteriology when Pasteur in 1861 investigated a bacillus which produced butyric acid when grown under anaerobic conditions. Later in 1877 Pasteur (66) identified the first pathogenic species *Cl. septicum* (*Vibrion septique*). After this auspicious beginning, progress continued at a slow but steady rate until World War I, when the frequency of gas gangrene infection of wounds stimulated a vast amount of research. These investigations slowed after World War I but received a second major stimulus with World War II. The literature on *Clostridia* is voluminous and even monographs and reviews are too numerous to be discussed in this text, but some of the more important collections of literature are listed at the bottom of this page.

Anaerobic organisms, including the *Clostridia,* lack cytochrome, cytochrome oxidases, catalase and peroxidase (47). Investigations indicate that all bacteria produce hydrogen peroxide (H_2O_2) when grown in the presence of oxygen. In the absence of catalase and peroxidase this substance accumulates in sufficient concentration to kill the organism. Oxygen itself is not harmful to anaerobes; they can be grown in its presence if an effective reducing agent, such as sodium thioglycollate, is added to the medium.

The **pathogenic** *Clostridia* **are characterized by their ability to produce powerful exotoxins.** They fall naturally into three groups: the **gas gangrene organisms,** which infect only when the tissues have been traumatized and devitalized; *Cl. tetani,* which produces an insignificant local infection but general intoxication when introduced into the tissues under certain specific conditions; and the *botulinum* species, which do not invade the body but synthesize exotoxins in certain food products which **poison** after ingestion.

The gas gangrene infections will be discussed in this chapter, and tetanus and botulism food poisoning in subsequent chapters.

Many anaerobic spore-bearing bacilli are normal inhabitants of the intestinal canal of man and animals. Soils fertilized with natural

LITERATURE ON CLOSTRIDIA

Weinberg, M., and Seguin, P. La gangrène gaseuse, Paris, 1918; Hall, I. J. Infect. Dis., 27: 576, 1920; 30:445, 1922; Heller, H. H. J. Bact., 6:445, 521, 1921; Douglas, S. R., Fleming, A., and Colebrook, L. M. Med. Res. Council (Great Britain) Spec. Rept. Ser., No. 57, 1920; Smith, L. DeS. Introduction to the Pathogenic Anaerobes, Chicago, Univ. of Chicago Press, 1955; Spray, R. S. J. Bact., 32:135, 1936; McCoy, E., and McClung, L. S. Bact. Rev., 2:47, 1938; Weinberg, M., Nativelle, R., and Prévot, A. R. Les microbes anaérobies, Paris, Masson et Cie., 1937; Danielson, I. S. Tr. New York Acad. Sc., II, 9:297, 1947; Prévot, A. R. Manuel de classification et détermination des bactéries anaérobies, Paris, Masson et Cie., 1948; McClung, L. S. Ann. Rev. Microbiol., 10:173, 1956; Smith, L. De S. Bact. Rev., 13:233, 1949; van Heyningen, W. E. Bacterial Toxins, Springfield, Ill., Charles C Thomas, 1950. MacLennan, J. D. Bact. Rev. 26: 177, 1962.

Table 1. Relative Pathogenicity of Clostridial Species

Organism	Man	Mouse	Guinea Pig	Rabbit	Pigeon
Group I					
Cl. perfringens	+++	++++	++++	++	++++
Cl. novyi	++	++++	++++	++++	++++
Cl. septicum	++	++++	++++	++++	++++
Cl. chauvoei	—	+++	+++	+++	—
Cl. fallax	+		+−		
Cl. histolyticum	+	++	++	++	
Cl. bifermentans	—		—	—	
(Sordelli type)	+	+++	+++	+++	
Cl. bifermentans	0	0	0	0	—
Cl. sporogenes	—		—	—	
Cl. lentoputrescens	—	—		—	
Cl. tertium	—			—	
Cl. butyricum	—			—	
Cl. capitovale	—		+−	—	
Cl. cochlearium	—	—		—	0
Cl. sphenoides	—		—	—	
Cl. multifermentans	—		—	—	
Group II					
Cl. tetani	++++	++++	++++	+++	
Group III					
Cl. parabotulinum	++++	++++	++++	+++	++++
Cl. botulinum	++++	++++	++++	++	+

manures contain many more of these organisms than virgin or desert soils (36). Since it has been shown that *Cl. perfringens* can grow and multiply in the soil (73), it would not be surprising if all *Clostridia* possess this capacity.

Wound infections are characterized by a mixed flora, and primary cultures rarely yield a single species. **Stained smears** of secretions usually show the presence of **gram-positive cocci,** and often of **gram-negative bacilli** of the coliform types, in addition to the large **gram-positive rods** which are characteristic of the *Clostridia*. In the studies of gas gangrene made during World War I single species of *Clostridia* were found in about 40 per cent of the cases while two or more species were present in 60 per cent (Table 2). The average number found per case in World War II varied from 2.56 to 2.84 (36, 71, 78). One highly pathogenic species may be accompanied by another highly pathogenic one, such as *Cl. perfringens* and *Cl. tetani,* or by one or more species which have little if any primary pathogenicity. It is essential, therefore, that plating methods be employed and colonies of varying morphology be isolated for detailed study (Table 3).

Stock cultures of *Clostridia* usually grow readily on ordinary laboratory media when incubated under anaerobic conditions, but richer media and meticulous care are required for primary isolation. Chopped meat and milk media have been used for many years for obtaining primary mixed cultures. Most, but not all, species form spores readily in these media. Those which form spores are easily purified by heating to 80° C. for one hour to kill the vegetative forms and associated aerobic bacteria . The resistant spores are then streaked on suitable media and incubated under anaerobic conditions. **Brewer's thioglycollate broth** is probably the best medium for obtaining initial mixed cultures.

Primary isolation is often effected by plating on blood and egg agar, Wilson-Blair medium, or McClung's egg-yolk medium (44, 45). More or less characteristic surface colonies are found on the first two of these media. The deep colonies in the Wilson-Blair medium as employed by Lyons and Owens (34) appear black after eight to 16 hours incubation if the organism is *Cl. perfringens, Cl. multifermentans, Cl. tertium, Cl. novyi, Cl. sphenoides, Cl. septicum, Cl. bifermentans* or *Cl. sporogenes.* Colonies of

Table 2. Incidence of Clostridial Flora of Gas Gangrene

PER CENT OF CASES

ORGANISM	MACLENNAN (36) (146 CASES)	STOCK (78) (25 CASES)	SMITH AND GEORGE (71) (110 CASES)
Cl. perfringens	56	80	39
Cl. novyi	37	48	32
Cl. septicum	19	4	
Cl. histolyticum	6		
Cl. tetani	13	8	4
Cl. bifermentans	4	20	54
Cl. sporogenes	37	72	54
Cl. tertium	30	8	3
Cl. multifermentans			5
Cl. butyricum	13	4	3
Cl. capitovale	5		3
Cl. fallax	1	4	3
Cl. cochlearium	9	4	2
Cl. putrificum	19		2
Cl. regulare			2
Cl. sphenoides	3		2
Cl. paraputrificum			1
Cl. hastiforme	3		
Cl. tetanomorphum	2		

Table 3. Biochemical Reactions of Clostridial Species

ORGANISM	GLUCOSE	LACTOSE	SUCROSE	MALTOSE	SALICIN	LIQUE-FACTION GELATIN	LIQUE-FACTION SERUM	MILK
Group I								
Cl. perfringens	+	+	+	+	−	+	−	Stormy
Cl. novyi	+	−	−	+	−	+	−	Acid
Cl. septicum	+	+	−	+	+	+	−	Acid
Cl. chauvoei	+	+	+	+	−	+	0	Acid
Cl. fallax	+	+	+	+	+	−	−	Acid
Cl. histolyticum	−	−	−	−	−	+	+	Digested
Cl. bifermentans	+	−	−	+	+ −	+	+	Digested
Cl. sporogenes	+	−	−	+	−	+	+	Digested
Cl. lentoputrescens	−	−	−	−	−	+	+	Digested
Cl. tertium	+	+	+	+	+	−	−	Acid
Cl. butyricum	+	+	+		+	−	−	Stormy
Cl. capitovale	+	−	−	−	−	+	+ −	Acid
Cl. cochlearium	−	−	−	−	−	−	−	No change
Cl. sphenoides	+	+	+ −	+	+	−	−	Acid
Cl. multifermentans	+	+	+	+	+	−	−	Stormy
Group II								
Cl. tetani	−	−	−	−	−	+	−	No change
Group III								
Cl. parabotulinum	+	−	− +	+	+	+	+	Digested
Cl. botulinum	+	−	+ −	+	−	+	−	No change

anaerobic streptococci, aerobic spore bearers and *Cl. fallax, Cl. histolyticum* and *Cl. tetani* remain colorless. Even though the colonies may appear characteristic, they should be replated at least once before being considered pure. Some species are rapidly motile and tend to produce spreading colonies. This tendency can be reduced by using plates with a relatively dry surface, as suggested by Reed (67), or by increasing the agar from 1.5 or 2 per cent to 4 or 6 per cent, although colony morphology is altered considerably by the increased agar content. The addition of 0.12 per cent of sorbic acid to beef liver infusion medium made without K_2HPO_4 inhibits catalase-producing organisms while allowing the growth of catalase-negative *Clostridia.* The lecithinase-producing facultative anaerobic bacilli can be differentiated from the lecithinase-producing *Clostridia* by plating on an egg yolk medium to which 0.02 per cent of sodium azide has been added (25, 46).

Forget and Fredette (14) recommend the sodium azide selective medium for primary isolation. Kaufman and Weaver (28) found that the addition of 0.004 per cent neutral red to liver veal agar results in the development of zones of golden yellow fluorescence about colonies of *Clostridia* at 18 to 24 hours with ordinary light.

Final identification is made by a study of the morphology of the colony, size, shape, and location of the spores, presence or absence of hemolysis on blood agar, proteolytic effect on serum and gelatin, sugar fermentations (72), and neutralization of toxin by specific antitoxin. Atypical reactions are not infrequent in respect to indol formation, reduction of nitrate, hemolysis on blood agar, hydrogen sulfide formation, and even the fermentation of certain sugars (72). Some of these variations are inherent in the strain but others are conditioned by the medium. Table 3 shows the chief biochemical reactions of selected species.

The student should remember that toxin-producing *Clostridia* are frequently isolated from wounds which never develop into clinical cases of gas gangrene even when no specific therapy is employed. The **oxidation-reduction potential of normal tissues is too high for the growth of** *Clostridia* and must be reduced by damage to the tissues and to the blood supply before the organism can multiply and produce the toxins. After proper conditions have been established for survival and toxin formation, some species can invade the tissues while others remain localized. Van Heyningen (82) has correlated the presence or absence of invasion with the effect of normal serum on the proteinases produced by the organisms. The *kappa* toxin (collagenase) of *Cl. perfringens* and the main proteinases of *Cl. histolyticum, Cl. feseri* and *Cl. septicum* are not inhibited by normal serum, but the proteinases of

Cl. novyi, Cl. sporogenes, Cl. tetani and *Cl. botulinum* are inhibited.

CLOSTRIDIUM PERFRINGENS AND GAS GANGRENE

Family: *Bacillaceae* Fischer. Genus: *Clostridium* Prazmowski. Species: *Clostridium butyricum* Prazmowski. *Clostridium perfringens* Veillon and Zuber. (*B. welchii, B. aerogenes capsulatus*)

Cl. perfringens is the organism most frequently found in gas gangrene. It was present in about 72 to 80 per cent of the cases of gas gangrene studied during World War I and World War II (79). It has been associated consistently with civilian cases of gas gangrene and generally is considered the most important etiologic factor in this disease. It must be remembered, however, that the bacillus frequently is present in wounds which never develop gangrene. *Cl. perfringens* was discovered independently in three countries. It was discovered in the United States in 1892 by Welch and Nuttall (88), who named it *Bacillus aerogenes capsulatus.* In 1893 Fraenkel (15) isolated a similar organism in Germany from several cases of gaseous phlegmons. He called it *B. phlegmonis emphysematosae* but soon recognized that he was working with the same bacillus previously described by Welch. In the German literature, however, this organism still is referred to as the Fraenkel bacillus. In 1897, without having heard either of Welch's or Fraenkel's work, the organism was described again by Veillon and Zuber (84) in France and called by them *B. perfringens. B. welchii, B. aerogenes capsulatus, Fraenkel bacillus* and *B. perfringens* all refer to the same organism (Fig. 1).

Morphology and Staining. *Cl. perfringens* is a short, plump, spore-bearing **gram-positive** bacillus, occurring singly or in pairs. Chains are not formed as a rule. It is **nonmotile** and has a **capsule.**

Cultural Characteristics. It grows best under strictly **anaerobic** conditions, but its requirements for anaerobiosis are less rigid than those of *Cl. tetani.* It grows well in media containing tissue, such as cooked meat medium, after all the air has been expelled by simple boiling. With milk, boiling is not always sufficient to obtain good growth, and it is best to put milk tubes in anaerobic jars. The majority of strains do not form **spores** readily. Alkaline sugar-free media, rich in protein, such as alkaline egg, are necessary to demonstrate spore

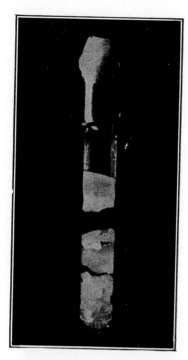

Fig. 1. *Clostridium perfringes*. Culture in dextrose infusion agar showing fragmentation of the medium by gas after 24 hours' incubation of 37° C.

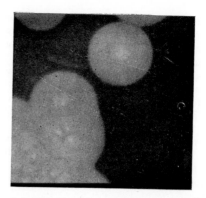

Fig. 2. *Clostridium perfringens A*. (From McClung and Toabe. *J. Bact.*, 53:139, 1947.)

formation with the majority of strains. The spore of *Cl. perfringens* is large, oval, and central or subterminal. It is the most active fermenter in the saccharolytic group and ferments all the common sugars with the production of large amounts of gas. Lactic and butyric are the two acids most frequently formed, the latter often giving cultures a characteristic odor. Glucose agar sometimes is fermented to such an extent that the plug is blown out of the tube (Fig. 1). In wounds, *Cl. perfringens* ferments the muscle sugar, producing gas in the tissues and, for this reason, commonly is called the "gas" bacillus. The crepitation thus produced is characteristic of gas gangrene and indicates the extent of the infection. Gelatin is liquefied and blackened but indol is not formed from broth, and coagulated serum is not liquefied or blackened.

Acid and **gas** are formed from glucose, fructose, galactose, mannose, maltose, lactose, sucrose, xylose, trehalose, raffinose, starch, glycogen, and inositol. Mannitol is not fermented and the action on inulin and glycerol is variable.

Variability. Verder (85) has described five distinct colony types of *Cl. perfringens*. Among these, the smooth types resemble colonies of smooth motile varieties of *Salmonella*. The rough colonies are of a spreading type, with finely fimbriated edges or deep corrugations. The morphology of the organisms varies considerably. Henderson (19) found that the S—R variation in *Cl. perfringens* is accompanied by a loss of the specific O antigen.

Antigenic Structure. The capsular material is a polysaccharide and heat-stabile. Although all strains produce the same exotoxins, precipitin reactions with extracts of capsular substance and agglutinations with intact bacilli show that the strains are heterologous (19, 64). *Cl. perfringens* type A, which causes gas gangrene in man, has a heat stable (O) antigen but no heat-labile (L) antigen, although *Cl. perfringens* types B, C, and D, which produce gas gangrene in animals, have both O and L antigens (19).

The Russian investigators have found 65 serologic groups (9). American workers at-

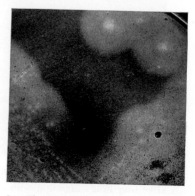

Fig. 3. *Clostridium perfringens B*. (From McClung and Toabe. *J. Bact.*, 53:139, 1947.)

tempted a classification by means of agar gel diffusion but found extensive cross-reaction between types A-F, type E, however, produced a unique antigen which might be the 101A toxin. The unique antigens of types D and F have not been identified, but the antigen common to type B and C could be due to *delta* toxin and the antigens common to B and D might be the *epsilon* toxin (12).

Bacterial Metabolites. Pathogenic strains of *Cl. perfringens* usually produce hyaluronidase (43) and a mucopolysaccharide (81), but its most important metabolites are **exotoxins.**

The *alpha* toxin is produced in the greatest amounts by the strains pathogenic for man. This toxin is hemolytic, necrotizing and lethal and has been identified as **lecithinase C,** a highly specific phosphatase (57, 90). Specific antitoxin is an antilecithinase C which com-

petes with the substrate lecithin in the tissues. Fortunately, the union between antitoxin and lecithinase C is firmer than that between the enzyme and the substrate (82). Roth and Pillemer (68) have obtained the most potent toxin, and toxoids have been prepared (81).

Considerable amounts of *theta* toxin are produced by *Cl. perfringens.* This toxin is hemolytic and lethal for experimental animals. It is serologically related to the streptolysin O of hemolytic streptococci and to the tetanolysin of *Cl. tetani.* The *alpha* toxin is a "hot-cold" hemolysin, while the *theta* toxin is not (82). Although neutralized by commercial antigasgangrene serum, this hemolysin is of minor importance in gas gangrene. The *theta* toxin has been purified by Roth and Pillemer (68), who suggest that it is an enzyme.

The *kappa* toxin is a proteolytic enzyme or more specifically a **collagenase** which digests

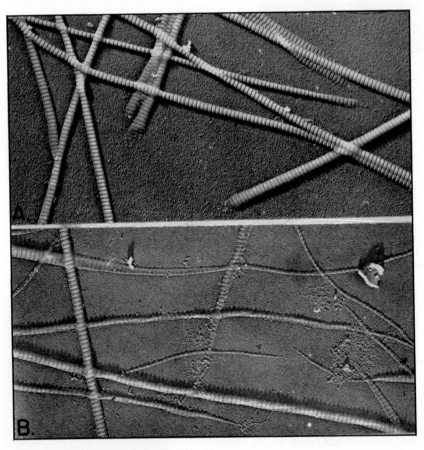

Fig. 4. Effect of collagenase on collagen fibrils. A, Collagen fibrils. × 18,300. B, Collagen fibrils after four hours digestion with collagenase. Note tapering and thinning without loss of axial periodicity. × 19,000. (From Gross. *Ann. New York Acad. Sc.,* 56:674, 1953.)

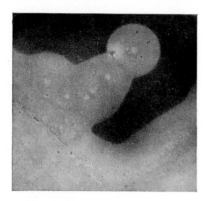

Fig. 5. *Clostridium perfringens C.* (From Mc-Clung and Toabe. *J. Bact.*, 59:139, 1947.)

the collagen of the subcutaneous tissues and muscles. Relatively pure preparations have been prepared by Bidwell and van Heyningen (6) and Mandl and his associates (41) (Fig. 4). Subcutaneous injections produce hemorrhage, necrosis and edema, while intravenous injections result in massive hemorrhages in the lungs (60). Collagenase probably plays a definite role in facilitating the spread of the infection in man. The toxin is neutralized by anti-collagenase but not by antilecithinase, the antitoxin of the *alpha* toxin (60). This toxin is not inhibited by normal serum and does attack collagen.

Type D strains, which produce enterotoxemia in sheep and goats, have an E toxin in the form of a relatively nontoxic prototoxin. This prototoxin is converted into a true toxin presumably by digestive proteolytic enzymes. The toxin-toxoid produces much higher antitoxin titer in sheep than the prototoxin-toxoid (70).

Fredette and his associates (16) have been studying, for some years, another toxin produced by the human type A strains. This is known as the "bursting factor" and is not lethal or hemolytic but acts as an "aggressin" to potentiate infection. This toxin was practically overlooked for years because it adhered to and did not pass Berkfeld, Mandel, and Seitz filters. Fredette, Forget, and Vinet (16) found that it passed through fritted glass filters. Its local edematous effect is on the muscle fiber.

Spontaneous Disease in Animals. *Cl. perfringens* type B (*Cl. agni*), shown in Figure 3, causes dysentery in lambs; type C (*Cl. paludis*), shown in Figure 5 is associated with the disease of sheep known as "struck"; and

type D (*Cl. ovitoxicus*), shown in Figure 6 causes an infectious enterotoxemia of sheep. These varieties are indistinguishable morphologically and culturally from *Cl. perfringens* type A, which causes gas gangrene in man but may be differentiated by antigenic analyses and by the type of exotoxins which they produce (Table 4).

Two new types have been added to the four original Wilsdon types. Type F has been found to produce a necrotic enteritis in man (31, 92). This disease was originally recognized in Germany by Jeckelin (37) when it was called "Darmbrand" or "fire in the bowel." It is possible that this clinical syndrome may be initiated in man by other animal strains of *Cl. perfringens* (23).

Experimental Disease in Laboratory Animals. Guinea pigs and pigeons are the most susceptible laboratory animals, although rabbits can be infected. The animals usually die in 12 to 48 hours. At necropsy, the skin at the site of the injection is tense and has a dark red or purplish color. The muscles and subcutaneous tissues are brawny, indurated, and crepitant from the presence of minute bubbles of gas. Upon incision, a thin, watery, blood-stained fluid flows out, accompanied by gas which smells like hydrogen sulfide.

When C^{14}-labeled exotoxin is given intravenously to rabbits and mice it disappears rapidly from the blood and fixes to the liver (72 per cent), lungs (15 per cent), kidney (8 per cent) or spleen (5 per cent). The radioactivity is concentrated in the mitochondrial fraction (11).

Oakley and Warrack (62) have described a rapid and economical routine for typing strains of *Cl. perfringens* by protecting mice

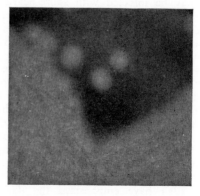

Fig. 6. *Clostridium perfringens D.* (From Mc-Clung and Toabe. *J. Bact.*, 53:139, 1947.)

Table 4.   Toxins of Human and Animal Types of Cl. perfringens

	Wilson's Type	Alpha	Beta	Gamma	Delta	Epsilon	Eta	Theta	Iota	Kappa	Lambda	Mu	Nu
Gas Gangrene in Man *Cl. perfringens* (*B. welchii*)	A	+++	−	−	−	−	(V)	V	−	++	−	V	+
Dysentery in Lambs *Cl. perfringens* (*B. agni*)	B	+	+++	+	+	++	−	+	−	−	+++	+	+
"Struck" Disease of Sheep *Cl. perfringens* (*B. plaudis*)	C	+	+++	+	++	−	−	+	−	+	−	−	+
Enterotoxemia of Sheep *Cl. perfringens* (*B. ovitoxicos*)	D	+	−	−	−	+++	−	+	−	V	V	V	+
Dysentery in Lambs, Calves *Cl. perfringens*	E	+	−	−	−	−	−	+	++	+	+	−	+
Enterotoxemia of Man *Cl. perfringens* (*B. enterotoxious*)	F	+	+	+	−	−	−	−	−	−	−	−	+

V = variable; (V) = variable, rare.

with specific antitoxins. Antitoxins for types A, B, C, D, and E are available commercially (76).

Clinical Types of Infection in Man. *Cl. perfringens* is a normal inhabitant of the intestinal tract of man and animals but is harmless until it gains entrance to the body through a perforation in the intestine. Surprisingly few cases of gas gangrene, however, follow the rupture of the appendix. Heavily manured soil usually contains an abundance of *Cl. tetani, Cl. perfringens,* and other spore-bearing Clostridia. Any wound contaminated by soil, or materials which have been in contact with the soil, may be infected with spore-bearing anaerobes. Evidences of toxemia usually precede the development of gas in the tissues contiguous to the wound, and a rapidly progressive anemia results from the hemolytic action of the toxin. Infection with *Cl. perfringens* may occur in the absence of a technical "wound." A patient in our clinic with intractable bleeding from the nose was treated by packing the nose tightly with sterile cotton. *Cl. perfringens* spores, presumably inhaled in dust before the nose was packed, found favorable anaerobic conditions for development and produced a rapidly fatal infection. Berggren and his associates (3a) have emphasized the danger of fatal *Cl. perfringens* infection from parenteral injections without proper sterilization of the skin.

CLOSTRIDIUM SEPTICUM

Genus: *Clostridium* Prazmowski. Species: *Clostridium septicum* (Macé) Ford (*Vibrion septique*)

Cl. septicum was first described in 1877 by Pasteur (66), who isolated it from the blood of a cow dead three days and from the blood of a horse dead one day, both animals having died presumably of anthrax. Although this organism is a bacillus, Pasteur called it a vibrio because it is extremely motile in animal exudates and looks slightly curved when in motion. Koch (30) in 1881, while studying the etiology of anthrax, isolated an organism which he called the bacillus of malignant edema. Koch considered his organism identical with Pasteur's *Vibrion septique,* although the bacillus of malignant edema had marked proteolytic properties, which Pasteur did not mention in his description of the organism. Much confusion has arisen from this controversy. Most workers now consider that Pasteur was working with a strictly saccharolytic organism which was identical with what now is called *Cl. septicum.* The bacillus of malignant edema of Koch is believed to belong to the proteolytic group and is identified fairly definitely with *Cl. sporogenes.*

Cl. septicum has been isolated from milk. Meyer (53) in 1915 reported the isolation of typical organisms from two cases of symptomatic anthrax in hogs. Herbivorous animals are subject to infections with *Cl. septicum*, both in the presence and the absence of demonstrable wounds, whereas infections in man seem to occur only as the result of wounds.

Cl. septicum, according to Weinberg and Seguin (87), occurred in 12 per cent of the wounds examined by them.

Cl. septicum is a slender, **motile, gram-positive** bacillus with slightly rounded ends. It is a strict **anaerobe** and forms **spores** readily in most media. The spore is **oval,** occurring either **centrally** or **subterminally,** at the end of 24 to 48 hours. It has **no capsule.** It ferments the common sugars with the exception of sucrose, and produces a loose clot in milk in one to four days. Gelatin is liquefied, but coagulated serum is not attacked. *Cl. septicum* is **hemolytic.** The organism is pathogenic for guinea pigs, mice, pigeons and rabbits. It invades the blood stream, producing a septicemia. The occurrence of long filamentous forms in the livers of guinea pigs dying of *Cl. septicum* infections is characteristic and is of value in identifying the organism.

Cl. septicum gives a green fluorescence when grown on a medium containing bile salts, such as that of MacConkey. Fluorescence is not produced by *Cl. feseri* and *Cl. novyi*.

Antigenic Structure. Strains of *Cl. septicum* can be differentiated into four groups by means of their O antigens and each group can be subdivided into specific types by H-agglutination. There is some cross-reaction between the O, but not the H, antigens of *Cl. septicum* and *Cl. chauvoei* (10, 18).

Moussa's (56) study showed that *Cl. septicum* could be classified into six groups by means of two somatic and five flagellar antigens, certain of which are shared with some but not all strains of *Cl. chauvoei*, and that the spore antigens were identical. These observations led Moussa to suggest that *Cl. septicum* and *Cl. chauvoei* are so closely related and that they might be considered as type A and B of a single species.

Bacterial Metabolites. Powerful soluble **exotoxins** are produced by all strains of *Cl. septicum*, even those which have lost the ability to infect animals. Culture filtrates may contain as much as 300 to 400 L.D.$_{50}$ units for the mouse. This toxin is **hemolytic,** and the work of Bernheimer (4, 5) shows that its lethal effect is directly proportional to its hemolytic action. It is possible that some strains may produce an additional hemolysin

or small amounts of a nonhemolytic toxin (82).

Moussa (55) has characterized four distinctive toxins, the most powerful one was Bernheimer's oxygen-stable hemolysis which Warrack named the alpha toxin.

CLOSTRIDIUM CHAUVOEI

Genus: *Clostridium* Prazmowski. Species: *Clostridium chauvoei* (Arloing *et al.*) Holland. (*Bacillus-anthracis symptomatici,* Rauschbrand, Charbon symptomatique, *Sarcemnysematis bovis, Clostridium feseri*)

Symptomatic anthrax, referred to as "quarter-evil" or "blackleg," is an infectious disease occurring chiefly among sheep, cattle, and goats. **The disease has never been observed in man.** It formerly was confused with true anthrax because of a superficial similarity between the clinical symptoms of the two maladies (2). Bacteriologically, the two microorganisms are in entirely different classes.

Symptomatic anthrax is distributed widely. Infection is usually acquired through the agency of the soil in which the bacillus is present, in the form of spores which may retain their viability for several years.

Morphology and Staining. The bacillus of symptomatic anthrax has rounded ends and is about 4 to 6 μ long and 0.5 to 0.6 μ wide. It usually occurs singly and never forms long chains. In its vegetative form the bacillus is **actively motile** and possesses numerous flagella. In artificial media it forms **spores** which are **oval,** broader than the rod itself, and placed very close to the end of the bacillary body, giving the bacillus a racket-shaped appearance (Fig. 7).

It is stained readily with the usual aniline dyes but is decolorized easily by Gram's method of staining. Von Hibler, however, claims that if the bacillus is stained carefully, it is **gram-positive**—at least when taken from the animal body. It also is gram-positive in young cultures.

Cultural Characteristics. The organism is a **strict anaerobe.** The bacillus was first obtained in pure culture by Kitasato (29) under anaerobic conditions, but it is easily cultivated upon the usual laboratory media, all of which are more favorable after the addition of glucose, glycerin, or nutrose. In all media there is active gas formation and a **foul, sour odor** due to butyric acid; the bacillus grows equally well on slightly acid or slightly alkaline media.

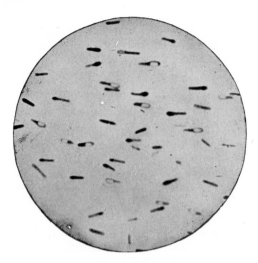

Fig. 7. *Clostridium chauvoei.* (From Zettnow.)

Surface colonies upon **agar plates** are circular and consist of a slightly granular compact center, from which emanates a thinner peripheral zone which microscopically can be shown to be composed of a tangle of fine threads.

In **agar stabs** at 37.5° C. growth appears within 18 hours, rapidly spreading as a diffuse, fine cloud from the line of stab. Gas formation, especially near the bottom of the tube, rapidly leads to the formation of bubbles and later to extensive splitting of the medium. In **gelatin stab cultures** growth is similar to that in agar stabs, though less rapid. **Liquefaction** is produced in **gelatin** stab cultures.

Cl. chauvoei ferments glucose, maltose, lactose, and sucrose with the production of acid and gas. It does not ferment mannitol or salicin. Indol is not produced.

Bacterial Metabolites. According to the investigation of Leclainche and Vallée (33), the bacillus of symptomatic anthrax produces an exotoxin. This toxin is not formed to any extent in ordinary broth but is produced in large quantities in broth containing blood or albuminous animal fluids.

The best medium for obtaining toxin, according to the same authors, is the bouillon of Martin (49) consisting of equal parts of veal infusion and a peptone solution obtained from the macerated tissues of the stomachs of pigs.

The toxins in the filtrates of cultures of *Cl. chauvoei* were reinvestigated in 1923 and 1925 by Kojima and Bassett. The review of their work by Robertson indicates that there are two toxins in these filtrates, a lethal toxin

and a hemolytic toxin. These toxins are destroyed by a heat at 52° C. in 30 to 60 minutes. Such bacteria-free filtrates as the "agressin" obtained by Schöbl in filtrates of fluid from infected tissues are antigenic and are useful for the prophylactic immunization of animals which may be exposed to infection.

Pathogenicity. Symptomatic anthrax bacilli are pathogenic for cattle, sheep, and goats. By far the largest number of cases and possibly the only spontaneous ones appear among cattle. Mice and guinea pigs are very susceptible to experimental inoculation; horses are only slightly susceptible; dogs, cats, rabbits, and birds are immune. Man appears to be absolutely immune. Spontaneous infection results from the entrance of infected soil into abrasions or wounds, usually of the lower extremities. Infection depends to some extent upon the relative degree of virulence of the bacillus—a variable factor in this species. Twelve to 24 hours after inoculation there appears at the point of entrance a soft, puffy swelling which on palpation emits an emphysematous crackling. The emphysema spreads rapidly, often reaching the abdomen and chest within a day. The course of the disease is extremely acute, the fever is high, and the general prostration is extreme. Death may result within three or four days after inoculation.

At necropsy the swollen area is found to be infiltrated with a thick, blood-tinged, and foamy exudate. Subcutaneous tissue and muscles are edematous and crackle with gas. The internal organs show parenchymatous degeneration and hemorrhagic areas. Immediately after death, few bacilli are found in the blood and internal organs, but they are demonstrable in enormous numbers in the edema fluid surrounding the central focus.

If carcasses are allowed to lie unburied for some time, the bacilli will be distributed generally and the entire body will be found bloated with gas, the organs filled with bubbles. Practically identical conditions are found after experimental inoculation.

Prevention. Active immunization against the bacillus of symptomatic anthrax was accomplished first by Arloing and his collaborators (2), who inoculated cattle with tissue-extracts of infected animals. Ryff and Lee (69) suggest that good immunity is obtained with heat-killed vaccines, or bacterins, but the immunity is primarily antibacterial, and not antitoxic. Local trauma or mixed infection may allow the survival of *Cl. chauvoei* for a sufficient length of time to kill the animal with its exotoxins.

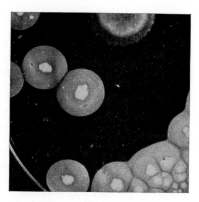

Fig. 8. *Clostridium novyi A.* (From McClung and Toabe. *J. Bact.*, 53:139, 1947.)

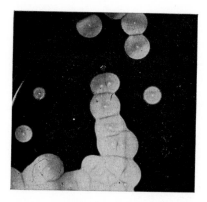

Fig. 9. *Clostridium novyi B.* (From McClung and Toabe. *J. Bact.*, 53:139, 1947.)

CLOSTRIDIUM NOVYI

Genus: *Clostridium* Prazmowski. Species: *Clostridium novyi* (Migula) (*B. oedematiens*)

Cl. novyi resembles *Cl. septicum* in that they both produce primary infections of animals which in turn contaminate the soil, thereby furnishing a source for human infections.

The organism was isolated by Novy (58) in 1894 from guinea pigs with "malignant edema." Weinberg and Seguin (87) found this bacillus in 34 per cent of the wounds studied. In Europe the French name *B. oede-·matiens* is used for *Cl. novyi*. This organism is a **strict anaerobe**. It is a **large, gram-positive bacillus** resembling *B. anthracis* in appearance and is only **sluggishly motile**. It forms chains in culture and after two or three days often shows curved forms. Filaments are not formed in the animal body. **Oval subterminal spores** are readily formed in all media. It ferments most of the common sugars except **lactose,** which serves to differentiate this organism from *Cl. septicum* and *Cl. chauvoei*. It forms a loose clot in milk in three or four days, liquefies gelatin, but does not attack coagulated serum.

Types of Cl. novyi. Scott, Turner, and Vawter suggested three types, and Oakley and Warrack (63) have named a fourth. Type A causes gangrene in man; type B, gas gangrenous disease in sheep; type C, osteomyelitis in water buffaloes; and type D, bacillary hemoglobinuria in cattle.

Bacterial Metabolites. Hydrogen peroxide is produced, and the colonies become black in color when planted on blood-agar which contains benzidine (17). This reaction differen-tiates *Cl. novyi* from the other sporulating anaerobes.

The studies of Oakley, Warrack, and Clarke (59) indicate that there are three types of *Cl. novyi* and six types of exotoxin. Type A (Fig. 8) produces *alpha, gamma, delta* and *epsilon* toxin; type B (Fig. 9) produces *alpha, beta* and *zeta;* and type C is nontoxigenic. *Alpha* is the classic toxin and culture filtrates may contain 600 to 1,200 mouse M.L.D. per milliliter (35). The nature of the *alpha* toxin is unknown. The *beta* and *gamma* toxins are lecithinase C; the *epsilon* toxin is a **lipase** or a **lecithinase-lipase.** The *delta* and *zeta* are **hemolytic.** The characteristic reaction is a non-hemorrhagic, gelatinous edema in the muscles and degenerative changes in the spleen and kidneys (65). A specific antitoxin has been prepared and is usually included in polyvalent gas gangrene antitoxins.

Pathogenicity. Spontaneous infections have been observed in guinea pigs, cattle, horses, and hogs. Infections can be induced in rabbits and mice as well as the naturally susceptible species.

In human infections massive edema and toxemia are the most striking symptoms. In contrast to *Cl. perfringens* infections, there is little, if any, gas, and the serosanguineous necrosis characteristic of *Cl. septicum* infections is absent.

OTHER CLOSTRIDIA

Cl. fallax. *Cl. fallax* was discovered during World War I by Weinberg and Seguin (87). It is a much less important factor in gas gangrene than the members of the saccharolytic group already described and usually is associated with other pathogenic anaerobes. Wein-

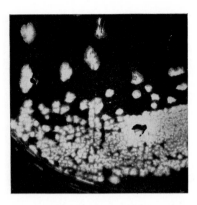

Fig. 10. *Clostridium sporogenes.* (From Mc-Clung and Toabe. *J. Bact.,* 53:139, 1947).

berg and Seguin (87) cite one case in which it invaded the blood stream and caused death.

Cl. fallax is an **anaerobic gram-positive bacillus** resembling *Cl. septicum* in appearance. It has a **capsule** and is **slightly motile. Spores are not formed readily** in most culture media but do occur on coagulated serum. The spores are **eccentric** to **subterminal.**

Cl. fallax coagulates milk slowly but does not liquefy gelatin or coagulated serum. *Cl. fallax* is not hemolytic and is only slightly pathogenic; virulence is lost quickly on artificial cultivation (76).

Cl. sporogenes. *Cl. sporogenes* was described by Metchnikoff (52) in 1908. This organism, next to *Cl. perfringens,* was found most frequently in wound cultures. Weinberg and Seguin (87) isolated it in 27 per cent of their cases. *Cl. sporogenes* was the anaerobe usually responsible for the foul odor of wounds. According to most authors, the pathogenicity of this organism is negligible. Weinberg and Seguin (87) claim to have isolated a few toxigenic strains, but it is possible that they may have been mixed with members of the saccharolytic group. *Cl. sporogenes* is a **gram-positive, anaerobic** bacillus, **actively motile,** forming **oval subterminal spores** readily in all media and in the animal body. It is **intensely proteolytic,** liquefying gelatin and coagulated serum and digesting and blackening meat. Most strains of *Cl. sporogenes* are not hemolytic. It does not produce a soluble toxin and is not pathogenic for laboratory animals unless injected in large quantities (Fig. 10).

A study of 25 strains by Mandia and Bruner (48) revealed that 18 belonged to group I and three to group II and that one was related antigenically to *Cl. histolyticum.* Specific cul-

tural requirements are being investigated (80).

Cl. histolyticum. This organism was discovered in 1916 by Weinberg and Seguin (87), who isolated it from eight wound cultures. Like *Cl. sporogenes,* it is **intensely proteolytic** and is of interest chiefly because of the striking lesions it produces in the animal body. It is a **gram-positive, anaerobic, motile bacillus** with **rounded ends.** Sporulation takes place in all media, different strains varying in the time required for spore formation. The **spores are large and oval** and occupy a **terminal position.** Although little gas is produced, this gives a nauseating odor. Gelatin and coagulated serum are liquefied. Two to three milliliters of the whole culture injected intramuscularly into guinea pigs result in such a rapid digestion of the tissues that the bone may be exposed within 12 to 24 hours. The picture is most striking, since one of the characteristics of *Cl. histolyticum* infection is that the animal appears well in spite of a tremendous local lesion.

The toxins of *Cl. histolyticum* have been studied by Bard and McClung (3) and Oakley and Warrack (61). The *alpha* toxin is the chief necrotizing agent, the *beta* toxin is a collagenase and the *gamma* toxin is a cysteine-activated proteinase. Both *beta* and *gamma* enzymes attack gelatin (41, 42). The gelatinase of *Cl. histolyticum* is serologically specific (42). A *delta* toxin was added by MacLennan, Mandel, and Howes (39) and an *epsilon* toxin by Bowen (7) and Howard (20). The *gamma* and *delta* toxin are proteases while the epsilon toxin is hemolytic. The latter is an oxygen-labile hemolysin which is related serologically to streptolysin-O, and to the *theta* toxin of *Cl. perfringens* and the toxins of *Cl. novyi* and *Cl. septicum.*

A study of various strains of *Cl. histolyticum* by MacLennan (40) revealed that a few produced maximum amounts of proteolytic enzymes with minute traces of the toxic *delta* toxin. Webster and his associates (86) have shown that at least nine and probably more proteolytic enzymes are present in crude culture filtrations (43). These proteolytic enzymes are being used now to produce **enzymatic debridement** in third-degree burns (21, 22, 80).

Cl. bifermentans. This organism was isolated by Tissier and Martally in 1902. It occurs normally in feces and soil but was isolated from cases of gas gangrene in World War II in four instances by MacLennan (36), 20 by Stock (78), and 54 by Smith and George (71). Surface colonies on blood agar are small, transparent, and hemolytic. It is a **gram-**

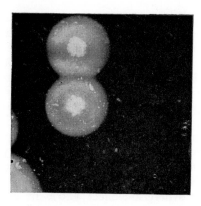

Fig. 11. *Clostridium bifermentans.* Toxogenic Sordelli type. (From McClung and Toabe. *J. Bact.,* 53:139, 1947.)

positive rod, with **central** to **eccentric spores** which do not swell the rod; it is **motile in cultures less than 24 hours old.** Milk is digested slowly, indol is formed, hydrogen sulfide is produced, and acid and gas are formed from glucose, mannose, and maltose. **Lactose and sucrose are not fermented,** but gelatin and blood serum are liquefied and blackened. Some strains kill rabbits in 24 hours; some produce local edema, while others have no effect. Mice are susceptible to the spores (79a). Toxigenic strains kill mice, guinea pigs and rabbits (Fig. 11) and are sometimes referred to as *Cl. sordelli* or *Cl. bifermentans-sordelli.* Some strains produce a lecithinase C which is related antigenically to the lecithinase C of *Cl. perfringens* (54). A medium for maximum growth is under investigation (74, 77).

There is a difference of opinion in the current literature whether *bifermentans* and *sordelli* are two types of one species or two different species (11, 13, 37).

Cl. hemolyticum. This organism was isolated in Nevada in 1926 by Vawter and Records (83) from the livers of cows dead of bacillary hemoglobinuria. A similar, but not identical, organism was isolated from the same type of disease in cattle in Chile by Sordelli and his associates (77). The exotoxin produced is a lecithinase C which is serologically related, if not identical with, the *beta* toxin of type B of *Cl. novyi* (3, 24, 75). Antibacterial immunity is induced with formalized vaccines or bacterins, but the immunity lasts only six months. Treatment with specific antitoxin is indicated (76).

Cl. tertium. *Cl. tertium,* first described as *Bacillus aero-tertius* by Bulloch and others, was recovered from cases of gas gangrene dur-

ing World War II in 30 instances by MacLennan (36), eight by Stock (78), and three by Smith and George (71). It is **microaerophilic** or facultatively aerobic. The colonies are rather large and raised, with irregular borders but without precipitate or luster on egg medium (Fig. 12). The **gram-positive** rods are moderately thick and contain **oval terminal spores which swell the rod.** Glucose, lactose, sucrose, maltose and salicin are fermented but gelatin and serum are not liquefied. It is non-pathogenic.

Cl. lentoputrescens. *Cl. lentoputrescens* was first discovered in 1889 by Bienstock in the intestine of a cadaver. It is **gram-positive anaerobic, motile,** forming **terminal oval spores** in all media. It is **actively proteolytic,** producing a foul odor. No pathogenic strains have been isolated. It has been studied by Tissier and Martally, who found it in putrid meat. Klein worked with a similar organism which he called *B. sporogenes cadaveris.* Hibler considers *Cl. lentoputrescens* and *B. sporogenes cadaveris* to be the same.

A proteolytic *Clostridium* labeled *Cl. putrificum* was isolated from cases of gas gangrene in World War II in 19 instances by MacLennan (36) and in two by Smith and George (71). This organism is listed in the seventh edition of Bergey's Manual as a synonym of *Cl. lentoputrescens.*

Cl. butyricum. Although the discovery of this organism is officially credited to Prazmowski, it is very probable that it is identical with Pasteur's *Vibrion butyrique.* It is commonly isolated from milk and cheese, is present in soils rich in humus and was recovered from 13 cases of gas gangrene by MacLennan (36), four by Stock (78), and three by Smith and George (71) during World War II.

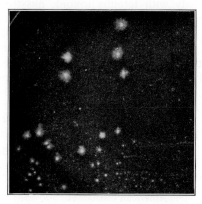

Fig. 12. *Clostridium tertium.* (From McClung and Toabe. *J. Bact.,* 53:139, 1947.)

Cl. butyricum is a large, straight or slightly oval rod which is **gram-positive, anaerobic,** and **motile** with **oval, subterminal spores.** The organism stains gram-negative upon aging. It forms acid and gas from the common sugars and produces stormy fermentation in milk, but does not form indol, reduce nitrates, or liquefy blood serum. It is not pathogenic for guinea pigs, rabbits, or man.

SURGERY AND BACTERIOLOGY IN THE MANAGEMENT OF TRAUMATIC WOUNDS

The handling of traumatic wounds was improved materially as the result of the experiences gained by surgeons during World War I. The first step in eliminating infection in such wounds was accomplished by débridement—that is, excision or removal of all the devitalized and contaminated tissues, together with foreign bodies such as bits of projectiles and clothing. This careful mechanical cleansing of the wound has proved even more effective in the treatment of traumatic wounds in the civilian population. Both smears and cultures should be made of the material removed from the wounds.

In World War II the mortality from wounds was reduced to one-twentieth of that reported for World War I, in spite of the fact that the wounds, in general, were more severe. The difference can be accounted for by the availability of **sulfonamides** and **penicillin, plasma,** and **blood** (32).

If the patient has not been immunized previously with tetanus toxoid, **passive immunization** with **tetanus antitoxin** should be given as soon as the skin tests for sensitivity have been completed and repeated after two weeks if the wound has not healed or if further operative interference is undertaken. Immunized patients should receive a "booster" dose of **tetanus toxoid. Polyvalent gas gangrene** antitoxin should be administered as soon as the diagnosis of gas gangrene has been made either by clinical observation or laboratory studies. For specific serum treatment of infected wounds, the prompt identification of *Cl. perfringens, Cl. novyi,* and *Cl. septicum* is most important.

Penicillin (1), bacitracin, chloramphenicol, oxytetracycline, and chlortetracycline are active against the vegetable forms of the organisms (89). Penicillin and bacitracin have a synergistic effect (26). In general, chemotherapy has been less useful than polyvalent gas gangrene antitoxin and **almost useless unless** preceded by prompt and effective surgery (21) (Table 5). The student should consult Meleney's book (50) on surgical infection and his article (51) on the use and abuse of antibiotics in surgical infection.

An entirely new therapeutic agent is available for infection with anaerobic organism, especially the *Clostridia.* This is hyperbaric pressure. When a patient is exposed to two or three times atmospheric pressures of oxygen, the oxygen penetrates areas which are usually anoxic and destroys obligate anaerobic organisms (8).

Active immunization in animals and man has been induced by the injection of formalized toxoids made from the toxins of *Cl. perfringens* and *Cl. novyi* (81). Good titers of antitoxin were obtained after two doses, followed by a third booster dose three to nine months later. The local reactions were no more severe than those following the injection of the corresponding toxoids of tetanus and diphtheria. Admixtures of the two toxoids produce immunity to both toxins simultaneously. Perhaps polyvalent toxoids can be prepared which will produce an active immunity to all of the organisms in the gas gangrene group.

Table 5.   Incidence of Gas Gangrene Related to the Interval between Wound Infliction and Medical Attention

(Langley and Winkelstein)

	WOUNDING AND DRESSING	WOUNDING AND SURGERY	INCIDENCE PER 1,000
American Casualties	12 min.	1.0 day	8
Free French Casualties	18 min.	1.5 day	12.3
Prisoners of War Casualties	340 min.	3.75 day	51.9

REFERENCES

1. Altemeier, W. A., and others. Arch. Surg., 55:668, 1947.
2. Arloing, and others. Le charbon symptomatique du boeuf, Paris, Asselin et Houzeau, 1887.
3. Bard, R. C., and McClung, L. S. J. Bact., 56:665, 1948.
3a. Berggren, R. B., and others. J.A.M.A. 188:1044, 1964.
4. Bernheimer, A. W. J. Exper. Med., 80:309, 321, 333, 1944.
5. ——— J. Gen. Physiol., 30:337, 1947.
6. Bidwell, E., and van Heyningen, W. E. Biochem. J., 42:140, 1948.
7. Bowen, H. E. Yale J. Biol. Med., 25:124, 131, 1952.
8. Brommelkamp, W. H., and others. Surgery, 49:299, 1961.
9. Bychenko, B. D., and others. J. Microbiol. Epidemiol. Immunobiol., 30:106, 1959.
10. Defaalla, E. N., and Soltys, M. A. Brit. J. Exper. Path., 32:510, 1951.
11. Ellner, P. D. J. Bact., 82:275, 1961.
12. ——— and Bohan, C. D. J. Bact., 83:284, 1962.
13. ——— and Green, S. S. J. Bact., 86:605, 1963.
14. Forget, A., and Fredette, V. J. Bact., 83:1217, 1962.
15. Fraenkel, E. Zentralbl. f. Bakt., 13:13, 1893.
16. Fredette, V., Forget, A., and Vinet, G. J. Bact., 83:1177, 1962.
17. Gordon, J., and McLeod, J. W. J. Path. & Bact., 50:167, 1940.
18. Henderson, D. W. Brit. J. Exper. Path., 15:166, 1934.
19. ——— J. Hyg., 40:501, 1940.
20. Howard, J. G. Bull. J. Exp. Path., 34:564, 1953.
21. Howes, E. L., and others. J. Bact., 79:191, 1960.
22. ——— and others. Surg., Gynecol. & Obstet., 109:177, 1959.
23. Jarkowski, T. L., and Wolf, P. L. J.A.M.A., 181:845, 1962.
24. Jasmin, A. M. Am. J. Vet. Research, 8:289, 1947.
25. Johansson, K. R. J. Bact., 65:225, 1953.
26. Johnson, B. A., and Meleney, F. L. Ann. New York Acad. Sc., 53:42, 1950.
27. Kaufman, L., and Weaver, R. H. J. Bact., 76:119, 1960.
28. ——— and Weaver, R. H. J. Bact., 79:292, 1960.
29. Kitasato, S. Ztschr. f. Infektionskr., 6:1, 11, 1889.
30. Koch, R. Mitt. a.d.k. Gsndhtsamte., 1:53, 1881.
31. Koslowski, L., and others. Klin. Wchnschr., 29:29, 1951.
32. Langley, F. H., and Winkelstein, L. B. J.A.M.A., 128:783, 1945.
33. Leclainche, E., and Vallée, H. Ann. Inst. Pasteur, 14:590, 1900.
34. Lyons, C., and Owens, C. R. J. Bact., 43:685, 1942.
35. MacFarlane, M. G. Mechanisms of Microbiol. Pathogenicity, Cambridge, Cambridge University Press, 1955, p. 57.
36. MacLennan, J. D. Lancet, 2:63, 94, 123, 1943; 1:203, 1944.
37. ——— Bact. Reviews, 26:177, 1962.
38. ——— and Macfarlane, B. G. Lancet II, 301, 1945.
39. ——— and others. J. Gen. Microbiol., 18:1, 1958.
40. ——— Trans. N.Y. Acad. Sci., 16:14, 1953.
41. Mandl, I., and others. J. Clin. Investigation, 32:1323, 1953.
42. ——— and Zaffuto, S. J. Gen. Microbiol., 18:13, 1958.
43. McClean, D., and others. Lancet, 1:355, 1943.
44. McClung, L. S., and others. J. Bact., 51:751, 1946.
45. ——— and Toabe, R. J. Bact., 53:139, 1947.
46. ——— Am. Rev. Microbiol., 10:173, 1956.
47. McLeod, J. W. Acta path. et microbiol. Scandinav., Suppl., 3:255, 1930.
48. Mandia, J. W., and Bruner, D. W. J. Immunol., 66:497, 1951.
49. Martin, L. Ann. Inst. Pasteur, 12:26, 1898.
50. Meleney, F. L. Treatise on Surgical Infections, New York, Oxford University Press, 1948.
51. ——— Surg., Gynec. & Obst., 92:370, 1951.
52. Metchnikoff, E. Ann. Inst. Pasteur, 22:419, 1908.
53. Meyer, K. F. J. Infect. Dis., 12:458, 1915.
54. Miles, E. M., and Miles, A. A. J. Gen. Microbiol., 4:22, 1950.
55. Moussa, R. S. J. Bact., 76:538, 1958.
56. ——— J. Path. Bact., 77:341, 1959.
57. Nagler, F. P. O. Brit. J. Exper. Path., 20:473, 1939.
58. Novy, F. G. Ztschr. f. Hyg., 17:209, 1894.
59. Oakley, C. L., and others. J. Gen. Microbiol., 1:91, 1947.
60. ——— and others. J. Path. & Bact., 60:495, 1948.
61. ——— and Warrack, G. H. J. Gen. Microbiol., 4:365, 1950.
62. ——— and Warrack, G. H. J. Hyg. Comb., 51:102, 1953.
63. ——— and Warrack, G. H. J. Path. Bact., 78:543, 1959.
64. Orr, J. H., and Reed, G. B. J. Bact., 40:441, 1940.
65. Pasternack, J. G., and Bengston, I. A. Pub. Health Rep., 55:775, 1940.
66. Pasteur, J. F., and Joubert, L. Bull. Acad. de med., Paris, 6:781, 1877.
67. Reed, G. B. Bacterial and Mycotic Infections of Man, Ed. Dubox, R. J., 2nd ed., Philadelphia, J. B. Lippincott Co., 1952, p. 392.
68. Roth, F. B., and Pillemer, L. J. Immunol., 70:533, 1953; 75:50, 1955.
69. Ryff, J. F., and Lee, A. M. J. Am. Vet. M. A., 111:283, 1947.
70. Schuchardt, L. F., and others. J. Med., 80:237, 1958.
71. Smith, L. DeS., and George, R. L. J. Bact., 51:271, 1946.
72. ——— Bact. Rev., 13:233, 1949.
73. ——— and Gardner, M. V. J. Bact., 58:407, 1949.
74. ——— and Douglas, H. C. J. Bact., 60:9, 1950.
75. ——— J. Bact., 65:222, 1953.

76. Smith, L. DeS., Introduction to the Pathogenic Anaerobes, Chicago, University of Chicago Press, 1955.
77. Sordelli, A., and others. Comp. rend. Soc. de biol., 106:142, 1931.
78. Stock, A. H. Med. Bull. of Mediterranean Theater of Operations, 2:159, 1944.
79. ———— J. Bact., 54:169, 1947.
79a. Taylor, W. J., and Novak, M. V. J. Bact., 61:571, 1951.
80. Thoma, R. W., and Peterson, W. H. J. Bact., 60:39, 1950.
81. Tytell, A. A., and others. J. Immunol., 55:233, 1947.
82. van Heyningen, W. E. Bacterial Toxins, Springfield, Ill., Charles C Thomas, 1950.
83. Vawter, L. R., and Records, E. J. Am. Vet. M. A., 68:494, 1926.

84. Veillon, A., and Zuber, A. Arch. de méd. exper. et d'anat. path., 10:517, 1898.
85. Verder, E. Proc. Exper. Biol. & Med., 30:547, 1933.
86. Webster, M. E., and others. J. Bact., 83:602, 1962.
87. Weinberg, M., and Seguin, P. La gangrène gazeuse, Paris, Masson et Cie., 1918.
88. Welch, W. H., and Nutall, G. H. F. Bull. Johns Hopkins Hosp., 3:81, 1892.
89. Willich, G. Ztschr. f. Hyg. u. Infektionskr., 134:573, 1952.
90. Zamecnik, P. C., and others. J. Exper. Med., 85:381, 1947.
91. ———— and Lipmann, F. J. Exper. Med., 85:395, 1947.
92. Zeissler, J., and Rassfeld-Sternberg, L., Brit. M. J., 1:267, 1949.

46

Clostridium tetani and Tetanus

Family: *Bacillaceae* Fischer. Genus: *Clostridium* Prazmowski. Species: *Clostridium tetani* (Flügge) Holland

Lockjaw or tetanus, though a comparatively infrequent disease, has been recognized as a distinct clinical entity for many centuries. The infectious nature of the disease, however, was not demonstrated until 1884, when Carlo and Rattone produced tetanus in rabbits by the inoculation of pus from the cutaneous lesion of a human case (6). Not long after Nicolaier (35) succeeded in producing tetanic symptoms in mice and rabbits by inoculating them with soil. From the lesions produced at the point of inoculation, Nicolaier described a bacillus which may have been *Clostridium tetani* but which he was unable to isolate in pure culture. In 1889 Kitasato (23) definitely solved the problem of etiology by isolating, from cases of tetanus, pure cultures of bacilli with which he was able to reproduce the disease in animals.

Kitasato succeeded because of his use of anaerobic methods and his elimination of nonspore-bearing contaminants by means of heat. The tetanus bacillus occurs in the superficial layers of the soil and is of especial frequency in the earth of cultivated and manured fields, probably because of its presence in the feces of some of the domestic animals.

Morphology and Staining. The tetanus bacillus is a slender rod 2 to 5 μ in length and 0.3 to 0.8 μ in breadth. The vegetative forms, which occur primarily in young cultures, are slightly **motile** and possess numerous **peritrichal flagella.** After 24 to 48 hours incubation, the length of time depending somewhat on the nature of the medium and the degree of anaerobiosis, the bacilli develop **spores** which are char-

acteristically **located at one end,** giving the bacterium the diagnostic drumstick appearance. As the cultures grow older the spore-bearing forms completely supersede the vegetative ones (Fig. 1).

The tetanus bacillus is stained easily by the aniline dyes and is **gram-positive** after 24 hours incubation, but may appear as gram-negative after that time. Flagella staining is successful only when very young cultures are employed.

Cultural Characteristics. *Clostridium tetani* is an **obligate anaerobe** which loses its ability to produce toxin when adapted to aerobic growth. The deleterious effect of oxygen can be neutralized and growth obtained in the presence of air if a low oxidation-reduction potential is established in the medium. For example, excellent growth is obtained in media containing thioglycollic acid. The value of cooked meat depends upon its content of unsaturated fatty acids which take up oxygen and glutathione, which brings about a negative oxidation-reduction potential corresponding to an Eh of about −0.2 volts (25). The organism's requirement

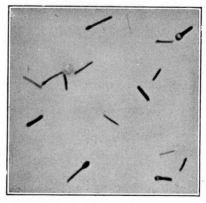

Fig. 1. *Clostridium tetani.* Gram stain. × 1,200. From culture 72 hours old, showing spores.

for mechanical anaerobiosis is less demanding when grown in symbiosis with aerobic bacteria or in the presence of fresh sterile tissue. Dedic and Koch (12) have reported that *Cl. tetani* grows readily under aerobic conditions when 4 μg. of cobalt (CO^{++}) per milliliter of medium is added.

The bacilli grow best at 37° C. at a pH of 7.0 to 7.5 and fail to grow at a pH below 6.4 or above 9.2. The addition of glucose to the medium stimulates the growth of pure cultures, although there is no detectable evidence of fermentation of this or other carbohydrates. *Cl. tetani* can be grown in a synthetic medium but requires **vitamins** (thiamin, nicotinic acid, riboflavin, pyridoxine, pantothenic acid, biotin, and folic acid), **amino acids** (arginine, histidine, tyrosine, valine, leucine, isoleucine and tryptophane), **purines** and **pyrimidines** (adenine and uracil), and **oleic acid** (30, 31).

Growth in gelatin or agar media is accompanied by the production of carbon dioxide and methylmercaptan, the latter being responsible for the characteristic unpleasant odor of putrefying organic material.

Amino acids and carbon compounds are dehydrogenated and the energy requirements are met by the direct reduction of amino acids such as glutamic and aspartic acids to carbon dioxide, ammonia, acetic, and butyric acids (7, 18, 37).

On agar, at 37.5° C., growth appears within 48 hours. Colonies on agar plates present a rather characteristic appearance, consisting of a compact center surrounded by a loose meshwork of fine filaments not unlike the medusahead appearance of *B. subtilis* colonies, but more delicate, translucent, and fern-like. In agar stabs fine radiating processes grow out in all directions from the central stab and tend to give the culture the appearance of a fluff of cotton. Blood agar is **hemolyzed.** On fresh blood agar the growth spreads over the surface like a delicate sprig of maidenhair fern. **Milk** is a favorable culture medium and is not coagulated.

The **germination of spores** occurs only at an oxygen tension lower than that of normal tissues. The failure of spores to germinate in normal tissues and the role played by necrotic tissue in forming a favorable nidus for the development of tetanus spores in the body are thus explained.

Resistance. The vegetative forms of the tetanus bacillus have no greater resistance to heat or chemical agents than the vegetative forms of other microorganisms. Tetanus spores, however, will resist dry heat at 80° C. for about one hour and live steam for about five minutes. Five per cent carbolic acid kills them in 12 to 15 hours, and 1 per cent bichloride of mercury in two or three hours. Direct sunlight diminishes their virulence and eventually destroys them. Protected from sunlight and other deleterious influences, tetanus spores may remain viable and virulent for many years.

Penicillin has some inhibitory effect on the growth of the organism and large doses reduce the mortality in experimental animals (36).

Variability. Smooth and rough colonies and motile and nonmotile variants have been observed. Isolated colonies of the motile form of the organism often can be obtained only by adding inhibiting chemicals to the medium or by increasing the agar to 6 per cent (19).

Antigenic Structure. Nine of the ten antigen types are recognized by their specific flagellar antigens (27). Type VI has no flagella. All strains have a common O antigen and a second O antigen is shared by types II, IV, V, or IX (45). Fortunately, all strains produce the same antigenic type of toxin which can be neutralized by a single antitoxin.

Bacterial Metabolites. *Cl. tetani* produces a **fibrinolysin** and a **hemolysin.** This hemolysin, discovered and named "**tetanolysin**" by Ehrlich (14), is destroyed rapidly by oxidation upon exposure to air (34) and can be absorbed by a suspension of red blood cells. The hemolysin is antigenic, giving rise to a specific antihemolysin when injected into animals. Neither of these metabolites, however, is of sufficient potency to render the bacillus pathogenic. By definition, the organism is strictly a saprophyte and can grow only in dead or damaged tissue; but growing in this isolated nidus, it elaborates a powerful **exotoxin** which may kill the patient.

EXOTOXIN. Virulent strains of *Cl. tetani* produce a powerful neurotoxin which is liberated in the medium partly by diffusion and partly by autolysis (46).

Miller and her associates (30) have measured the amount of newly formed intracellular exotoxin by inoculating the bacillary bodies directly into animals and learned that antitoxin exerted equivalent protective action against both intracellular and extracellular toxin. Miller (30) also reported that histidine in peptide form is necessary for toxin formation and toxigenic strains have an enzyme which hydrolyses histidine peptides. This peptidase resembles mammalian carnosinase in its action spectrum and also in that it is activated by manganese or zinc and inhibited by cysteine.

The neurotoxin was crystallized by Pillemer and his associates in 1946 (39). The crystalline toxin is a simple protein of about the same molecular weight as human serum albumin (39), and each milligram of nitrogen corresponded to 75,000,000 M.L.D. units. The crystalline toxin is very unstable and changes spontaneously into a highly antigenic toxoid even at 0° C. The authors suggest that the toxin molecules condense through their toxic groups.

Human beings are extremely susceptible to the tetanus neurotoxin, and cases of general and sometimes fatal tetanus have occurred in men who were only scratched by a needle which had been used for the injection of the toxin into a horse. Man is said to be as susceptible as the horse. The hen is extremely resistant to the toxin—approximately 360,000 times more resistant than the horse, and cold-blooded animals are completely insusceptible (16).

The inoculation of an animal with tetanus toxin always is followed by a definite period of incubation of from 8 to 24 hours before the toxic spasms set in. The site of injection, species of animals, and amount of toxin injected influence the length of the incubation period. This period may be shortened, but never eliminated entirely, by increase of the dose. When the toxin is injected subcutaneously, spasms begin first in the muscles nearest the point of inoculation and gradually spread until all the muscles are involved. Intravenous inoculation, however, usually results in general tetanus of all the animals. The toxin is destroyed by the acid of the gastric juice and by proteolytic enzymes in the gastrointestinal tract.

It was assumed that man and animals were immune to oral feeding. The observations of Lamanna (24) that guinea pigs could be killed by feeding 600,000 intraperitoneal doses is of theoretical value but of no practical importance.

Tetanus toxin is a selective neurotoxin which acts upon the nerve cells of the cerebrospinal axis although it, like the botulinus toxin, also paralyzes the cholinergic motor fibers to the iris of the eye (50, 51). The nerves in the medulla oblongata are most susceptible to the toxin (50), which probably explains the generalized convulsions seen in the disease.

There has been considerable controversy for many years about the route by which the toxin reaches the central nervous system after being produced in a peripheral lesion on an extremity. Meyer and Ranson (28) believed it traveled by way of the motor nerves, while Abel and his associates (1) thought it traveled by way of the blood stream. Bayliis (3) and G. Payling Wright (51) have presented convincing

evidence that it can travel to the central nervous system through the lymph spaces along the nerve trunks, although the possibility of some reaching the medulla oblongata from the blood stream cannot be eliminated. The toxin is believed to act on the synthesis and liberation of acetylcholine (47).

ANTITOXIN. Tetanus toxin is an excellent antigen but, unfortunately, such a potent toxin that it is difficult to give a dose that does not produce symptoms. When treated with formalin, the toxin is converted into a **toxoid** which is nontoxic but still antigenic (41). Commercial antitoxin is produced in both horses and cows, the latter for the benefit of individuals sensitive to horse serum. For immunization purposes toxoid is used for the initial injections followed by the adminitration of toxin after some antitoxin has been made by the animal.

The American unit of antitoxin is **ten times the least quantity of antitetanic serum necessary to save the life of a 350-g. guinea pig for 96 hours against the official test dose of a standard toxin furnished by the Hygienic Laboratory of the Public Health and Marine Hospital Service** (42). The test dose for the guinea pig is about 100 M.L.D. Each unit of tetanus antitoxin will neutralize approximately 1,000 M.L.D. of toxin and is, therefore, about ten times the size of the unit of diphtheria antitoxin.

Tests conducted under the auspices of the League of Nations showed that equivalent protection could be obtained with one German unit, 66 American units, or 3,750 French units. The new International Standard is one-half the American unit.

Clinical Types of Infection in Man. The comparative infrequency of tetanus infection is in marked contrast to the wide distribution of the bacilli in nature. Introduced into the animal body as spores and free from toxin, they often may fail to incite disease, easily falling prey to phagocytosis and other protective agencies before the vegetative forms develop and toxin is formed (46a). The nature of the wound and the simultaneous presence of other microorganisms seem to be important factors in determining whether or not the tetanus bacilli shall proliferate. Deep lacerated wounds in which there has been considerable tissue destruction, and in which chips of glass, wood splinters, or grains of dirt have become embedded are particularly favorable for the development of these organisms (11). The injuries of compound fractures and of gunshot wounds easily supply these conditions. In addition to its occurrence following trauma, tetanus has been observed after childbirth, and isolated cases have been reported in which it has followed diphtheria and ulcerative lesions of the throat, perforation of the intestines, and even the application of plaster of Paris casts which contained tetanus spores (33).

A definite **period of incubation** elapses between the time of infection with tetanus bacilli and the development of the first symptoms. In acute cases in man this may last from five to seven days, in the more chronic ones from four to five weeks (8). The first symptoms usually consist of headache and general depression, followed rather rapidly by difficulty in swallowing and in opening the mouth, due to spasms or trismus of the masseters. There is slight stiffness of the neck, which makes it difficult for the patient to bring the chin forward on the chest. There develops spasm of the muscles of the cheeks, gradually resulting in a drawing up of the tissues about the mouth to give a curious and characteristic expression, the so-called *risus sardonicus*. The spasms extend gradually to the trunk and back, with the development of opisthotonos after several days. Increased difficulty in swallowing may ensue and may be accompanied by involuntary evacuation of urine and feces. The localization of the symptoms follows to some extent the location of the injury. Occasionally, tetanus may occur in the newborn, developing soon after birth.

Treatment. The success of treatment depends directly upon the speed of treatment and indirectly upon the quantity of damaged tissue at the site of infection. It is known that antitoxin will not neutralize toxin which has already become attached to cells; hence a small dose of antitoxin or a large dose of penicillin (2) may be effective when administered a few hours after the injury, while much larger doses fail to save the patient when given days later. The greater the degree of damage to the tissue, the more suitable medium is provided for the growth of the bacilli and the synthesis of exotoxin. Deep penetrating wounds and areas which are relatively avascular afford anaerobic conditions which favor the growth of the organism.

During the past five years the emphasis in prophylaxis has shifted from the almost universal use of tetanus antitoxin to the use of active immunization and antibiotic treatment.

Bardenwerper (2) has emphasized the danger of serum sickness, which is always disagreeable and sometimes serious when followed by neuritis or encephalitis. He estimates that 2 million doses of tetanus antitoxin were being given annually in this country and that 15 to 30 per cent of the patients developed serum sickness. The risk of immediate and fatal anaphylaxis is reported to occur in 1 in 100,000 serum administrations. This includes patients where a preliminary skin sensitivity test was not performed as well as where the skin reaction was misinterpreted. One death occurred from the intracutaneous injection of 0.1 ml. of a 1:10 dilution of the tetanus antitoxin (5). **Epinephrine and a sterile syringe should always be available when foreign serum is being injected into the skin subcutaneously, intramuscularly, or intravenously.** When possible, the therapeutic serum should be given in an extremity, so that a tourniquet could be applied if a reaction occurs.

The wound should be cleaned, bleeding stopped, and dead tissue cut away. Patients who have been actively immunized in the past 20 years should receive 0.5 ml. of tetanus toxoid immediately after the injury (17). Antitoxin need not be administered, since there is evidence that in a few days antitoxin levels of 0.2 to 30 units will appear in the patient's serum (43, 48) and the accepted level for protection against tetanus in only 0.01 to 0.05 units (42). Definite evidence of reduced death rates was found in three hours in immunized rabbits following a booster injection, although measurable antitoxin was not present in the serum until after two days (21). If the wound is massive and the patient not seen unil 48 hours or more after the injury, however, 1,200,000 units of benzathine penicillin should be given intramuscularly. When the patient has not been immunized before and if the wound is a penetrating or mascerating lesion, then both penicillin and 50,000 to 100,000 units of antitoxin should be administered. In a day or so after the initial injection of penicillin, tetanus toxoid should be started as the first of three doses for active immunization.

The prognosis depends, to a major degree, upon the severity and time of onset of the original symptoms (Table 1). Perlstein (37) has reported that in patients who develop generalized spasms in 24 hours after the onset of symptoms have a mortality of 80 per cent, regardless of the method of treatment. In contrast, those patients requiring more than five days for the development of general symptoms usually have a mortality of less than 10 per cent with the same type of therapy.

If the initial wound is small, it should be excised, but if it is too large to excise or if the lesions are multiple, they should be drained and kept clean by irrigation with undiluted hydrogen peroxide or 1:4,000 dilution of potassium permanganate. After the initial intracutaneous skin test has been performed with a 1:10 dilution of normal horse serum (see Chapter 16) and found negative, then 40,000 units of tetanus antitoxin are given intravenously and another 40,000 units intramuscularly. The intravenous dose is diluted in 250 ml. of physiologic saline to which 1 ml. of 1:1,000 dilution of epinephrine has been added (37). **Intrathecal injection of tetanus antitoxin is dangerous and useless** (49).

After administering the antitoxin and penicillin the problem becomes one of preventing death from (1) convulsions or (2) asphyxia. Crandell and Whitcher (10) recommended secobarbital (seconal) or pentobarbital (Nembutal) for psychic sedation;

methocarbamol (Robaxin) for skeletal muscular relaxation; and chloropromazine (Thorazine) to potentiate the sedative-relaxant effect. The airway must be kept open by aspiration and, if necessary, by tracheotomy (44). The least active immunization has been done in the South, which has only 24 per cent of the population but 63 per cent of the deaths from tetanus (20).

Active Immunization. Death from tetanus cannot always be prevented by the most active treatment but the disease could be practically eliminated if all individuals were actively immunized (13, 19a, 40). Only five deaths from tetanus occurred in the Armed Forces during World War II between 1942 and 1945 (26). Two of the three received no proven immunization, and one did not get a booster injection at the time of injury. In contrast, there were 2,574 deaths among civilians in the United States during the same years (2). The possibility of a direct attack on the bacillus by forcing oxygen on the bacillus in the hyperbaric chamber is being investigated.

In 1936 Bergey and Etris (4) introduced in this country tetanus toxoid for active immunization of human beings. They first used a preparation detoxified with 0.3 per cent formaldehyde (41). This was soon followed by the refined alum precipitated toxoid. Their work, as well as that of Jones and Moss (22), Cowles (9), and Evans (15), showed that after three injections of the toxoid human beings developed from 0.01 to 0.1 unit or more of tetanus antitoxin per milliliter of serum. The antitoxic titer of the blood usually remains high for at least a year. It is rapidly recalled by a subsequent single subcutaneous injection.

Table 1. Effect of Incubation Period on Mortality

INCUBATION PERIODS (DAYS)	RECOVERIES	DEATHS	MORTALITY (PER CENT)	MORTALITY BEFORE THE INTRODUCTION OF SEROTHERAPY, ACCORDING TO BRUNNER (PER CENT)
1 to 5	3	7	70	90
5 to 10	20	7	29	70
10 to 12	7	1	13.3	—
Over 12	15	1	6.6	—

From Langley and Winkelstein. J.A.M.A., 128:783, 1945.

In World War II the entire military personnel of the American forces were actively immunized with tetanus toxoid. When injured, the patient was given immediately a booster dose of toxoid which increased the antitoxin content of the blood to an adequate level to afford protection and only 12 cases of tetanus developed between 1942 and 1945 (26).

Most pediatricians give a mixture of diphtheria and tetanus toxoids combined with pertussis vaccine to all infants. Consequently, a large proportion of ex-soldiers and children have had tetanus toxoid sometime in the past.

The remainder of the populations should be actively immunized with tetanus toxoid containing a small amount of diphtheria toxoid. The three doses can be given over three months or over two years. Children require a booster dose after four years, and adults after five years (43). Individuals showing undesirable local immediate or delayed allergic reaction can be actively immunized and have their immunity boosted by 0.1 ml. doses, containing 12 Lf units per milliliter, if this dose is given intracutaneously (43).

REFERENCES

1. Abel, J. J., and others. Bull. Johns Hopkins Hosp., 56:84, 317, 1935; 57:343, 1935; 59: 307, 1936; 62:522, 610, 1939.
2. Bardenwerper, H. W. J.A.M.A., 179:763, 1962.
3. Bayliis, J. H., and others. J. Path. & Bact., 64:33, 47, 1952.
4. Bergey, D. H., and Etris, S. J. Immunol., 31:363, 1936.
5. Buff, B. H. J.A.M.A., 174:1200, 1960.
6. Carlo, and Rattone. Gior. Accad. med. Torino, 1884.
7. Clifton, C. E. J. Bact., 44:179, 1942.
8. Courtois-Suffit, and Giroux. Military Med. Manuals, London, University of London Press, 1918.
9. Cowles, P. B. Yale J. Biol. & Med., 9:409, 1936.
10. Crandell, D. L., and Whitcher, C. E. J.A.M.A., 172:15, 1960.
11. Creite. Centralbl. f. Bakt., Abt I, Orig., 37:312, 1904.
12. Dedic, G. A., and Koch, O. G. J. Bact., 71: 126, 1956.
13. Edsall, G. J.A.M.A., 171:412, 1959.
14. Ehrlich, P. Berl. klin. Wchnschr, 1898.
15. Evans, D. G. Lancet, 2:316, 1943.
16. Fildes, P. A System of Bacteriology in Relation to Medicine, London, 3:228, 1929.
17. Filler, R. M., and Ellerbeck, W. J.A.M.A., 174:1, 1960.
18. Guggenheim, K. J. Bact., 47:313, 1944.
19. Hayward, N. J., and Miles, A. A. Lancet, 2:116, 1943.
19a. Heath, C. W., and others. Am. J. Pub. Health, 54:769, 1964.
20. Houston, A. N., and others. South. Med. J., 53:700, 1960.
21. Ipsen, J. J. Immol., 86:50, 1961.
22. Jones, F. G., and Moss, J. M. J. Immunol., 30:115, 1936; 33:183, 1937.
23. Kitasato, S. Deutsche med. Wchnschr., 31: 1889.
24. Lamanna, C. Science, 131:1100, 1960.
25. Lepper, E., and Martin, C. J. Brit. J. Exper. Path., 11:137, 140, 1930.
26. Long, A. P., and Sartwell, P. E. Bull. U.S. Army M. Dept., 7:371, 1947.
27. MacLennan, J. D. Brit. J. Exper. Path., 20: 371, 1939.
28. Meyer, H., and Ransom, F. Arch. f. exper. Path. u. Pharmakol., 49:369, 1903.
29. Miller, P. A. J. Bact., 77:733, 1959.
30. ——— and others. J. Bact., 79:95, 1960.
31. Mueller, J. H. J. Bact., 43:763, 1942.
32. ——— J. Immunol., 47:15, 1943; 56:143, 1947.
33. Murray, E. G. D., and Denton, G. D. Canad. M. A. J., 60:1, 1949.
34. Neill, J. M. J. Exper. Med., 44:227, 1926.
35. Nicolaier, A. Deutsche med. Wchnschr., 10: 842, 1884.
36. Novak, M., and others. Proc. Soc. Exper. Biol. & Med., 70:573, 1949.
37. Perlstein, M. A., and others. J.A.M.A., 173: 1536, 1960.
38. Pickett, M. J. J. Biol. Chem., 151:203, 1943.
39. Pillemer, L., and Robbins, K. C. Ann. Rev. Microbiol., 3:265, 1949.
40. Presse, E. New Engl. J. Med., 239:50, 1948.
41. Ramon, G. Ann. Inst. Pasteur, 38:1, 1924.
42. Rosenau, M. J., and Anderson, J. F. U.S. Pub. Health Serv. Bull., No. 43, 1908.
43. Ruegsegger, J. M. Arch. Int. Med., 106:410, 1960.
44. Smith, D. T., and Pryor, W. W. Ann. Int. Med., 32:728, 1950.
45. Smith, L. D. S. Introduction to Pathogenic Anaerobes, Chicago, University of Chicago Press, 1955.
46. Stone, J. L. J. Bact., 67:110, 1954.
46a. Vaillard, L., and Rouget, J. Am. Inst. Pasteur, 6:385, 1892.
47. van Heyningen, W. E. Bacterial Toxins, Springfield, Ill., Charles C Thomas, 1950.
48. Volk, V. K., and others. Pub. Health Reports, 78:264, 1963.
49. Wainwright, J. Arch. Surg., 12:1062, 1926.
50. Wright, E. A. J. Immunol., 71:41, 1953.
51. Wright, G. P. Mechanism of Microbial Pathogenicity, Cambridge, Cambridge University Press, 1955, p. 78.

47

Clostridium botulinum, Clostridium parabotulinum, and Food Poisoning

Family: *Bacillaceae* Fischer. Genus: *Clostridium* Prazmowski. Species: *Clostridium botulinum* (van Ermengem) Holland

The original case of botulinus food poisoning was described by van Ermengem (48) in 1896 and was caused by toxin produced in a pickled ham. However, meats are less commonly infected with the organism than canned vegetables (21), but both meat and fish, either canned or smoked, may be the source of poisoning.

The original strain of *Clostridium botulinum* described by van Ermengem was not proteolytic. However, the organisms which produce the type A toxin are always proteolytic.

Most of the type B strains from the United States, England and Europe are **ovolytic** and **proteolytic.** The **nonovolytic** type B, which corresponds to the original organism isolated by van Ermengem, has not been found in this country and is relatively rare even in Europe (31). Bergey has classified the proteolytic strains as *Clostridium parabotulinum* A or B. The disease is called **botulism** regardless of whether it is caused by the toxin of *Cl. botulinum* or *Cl. parabotulinum.*

Different strains produce antigenically distinguishable neurotoxins which have been labeled A, B, C, D, and E. Each antitoxin is specific for its own toxin. Type E occurs naturally in fresh and salt water and is associated with poisoning from smoked and canned fish (21, 24). The other types occur naturally in virginal soils but not in cultivated soils which have been fertilized with human or animal manure. This suggests that *Cl. botulinum* cannot successfully compete with the normal flora of the intestinal tract of man or animals or even survive in soil which contains organisms from the intestinal tract (24). *Cl. difficile* does occur in the intestinal tract of normal infants, however, and has been isolated from lesions in a few patients. Although the strains isolated from lesions in man would kill guinea pigs, Smith and King (40) doubt if this organism has a primary pathogenicity for man.

Morphology and Staining. *Clostridium botulinum* is a **gram-positive** rod with rounded ends, 3 to 8 μ in length and 0.5 to 0.8 μ in thickness. The bacilli occur either singly or grouped in very short chains. Involution forms are numerous on artificial media. The bacillus is **slightly motile** and possesses from four to eight flagella. **Spores** are formed, more regularly in glucose gelatin of alkaline pH. The spores are **oval** and **situated near the end of the bacillus,** rarely in the center. Spores are formed at 20° to 25° C. and usually are absent at higher temperatures.

The multilayered spores of *Cl. botulinum,* type E, have been studied by Takagi and his associates (45) using the ultrathin section technic.

Cultural Characteristics. The bacillus is a **strict anaerobe** and is easily cultivated under anaerobic conditions on the usual meat-infusion media. It grows most readily at **temperatures about 25° C.** and less luxuriantly at temperatures of 35° C. and over. The bacillus is extremely susceptible to the reaction of the medium, growing only in substrates which are neutral or moderately alkaline.

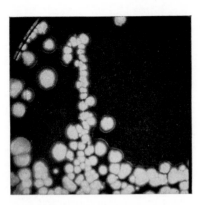

Fig. 1. *Clostridium parabotulinum.* A and B type colonies. (From McClung and Toabe. *J. Bact.,* 53:139, 1947.)

Cl. botulinum grows less readily than the *Cl. parabotulinum* strains. On glucose-sheep-blood agar plates surface colonies are dull and granular with serrated edges (Figs. 1 and 2). *Cl. botulinum* produces gas with a butyric acid odor, while *Cl. parabotulinum* gives a putrid odor. With *Cl. botulinum* no change occurs in milk; cooked meat, Löffler's serum, and coagulated serum and egg white are not liquefied. The liquefaction of gelatin begins slowly by the seventh day and is not complete until the third week. In contrast, *Cl. parabotulinum* digests milk, egg, and meat and liquefies serum and gelatin promptly. *Cl. botulinum* produces acid and gas from glucose, fructose, maltose, sucrose (33), dextrin, glycerol, adonitol, and inositol. Lactose, xylose, and salicin are not fermented. *Cl. parabotulinum* usually ferments salicin and fails to ferment sucrose.

Resistance. The heat resistance of the spores of types A and B of *Clostridium botulinum* is greater than that of any other anaerobes. Esty (11, 12) and Meyer (30) found that the heat resistance of the spores of 112 strains of this organism varied from three to 110 minutes when heated at 105° C. in a phosphate solution at pH 7.0. The maximum survival times of spores in this solution were 330 minutes at 100° C., 110 minutes at 105° C., 33 minutes at 110° C., 11 minutes at 115° C. and four minutes at 120° C. The spores of type C are less resistant to heat.

Antigenic Structure. The proteolytic species appear to possess a common O antigen, but the various types of *Cl. botulinum* have been subdivided into specific types of flagellar antigens (27, 28, 39). Nontoxigenic strains and nontoxigenic dissociates may have an antigenic structure identical with toxigenic strains. Among

the 26 strains studied by Mandia in 1951 all organisms having the formula H:5, 8, 10 produced toxins (27).

Bacterial Metabolites. The significant metabolite is a very potent exotoxin (23) which is a large molecule containing both a hemagglutinin and an exotoxin. Commercial antitoxins contain both antitoxin and antihemolysin but the two are not identical. The toxin is always type-specific, but there is reciprocal neutralization of hemolysin between type A and B and between C and D, though E is independent of the others (24). When treated with proteolytic enzymes the size of the molecule is reduced and the hemagglutinin is destroyed, but the smaller size molecule is now much more toxic (3, 29). This partial digestion of the toxin may result from proteolytic enzymes (35, 38) made by the organism or may occur at the gastro-duodenal junction in the intestines of man. This increased potentiation after ingestion is particularly important with type E toxin (13, 16). Type C has been subdivided into two types, $C\alpha$ and $C\beta$; the antitoxin prepared against the $C\alpha$ toxin is specific for the homologous toxin, while antitoxin against $C\beta$ toxin neutralizes both $C\alpha$ and $C\beta$ toxins (36).

Type A is the predominant organism found in the soils of the Rocky Mountains and Pacific Coast states but also occurs in Europe (32). Type B occurs most frequently in the central and eastern United States and, to a lesser extent, in England. Both varieties of type C occur in the United States, South Africa and Australia. Type D is found in South Africa (40) and type E in Russia (15, 20) and occasionally in the United States.

Type A toxin from *Cl. parabotulinum* was isolated in crystalline form in 1946 by Lamanna

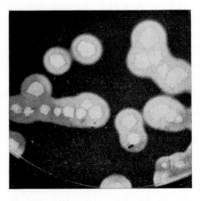

Fig. 2. *Clostridium parabotulinum.* C and D type colonies. (From McClung and Toabe. *J. Bact.,* 53:139, 1947.)

and his associates (25, 26) and by Abrams and his coworkers (1). This toxin has a molecular weight of 900,000 and is 15,000 times as toxic as aconitine, the most toxic drug known. The mouse M.L.D. per gram is 2.4×10^8. The toxin is a globulin-like protein which is not destroyed by ordinary proteolytic enzymes. This may explain why it is toxic by ingestion. The toxin is destroyed by heating at 80° C. for 30 minutes (35).

Type B toxin was isolated in amorphous form by Lamanna and Glassman (25) in 1947. It is as toxic as type A on the basis of weight, but since its estimated molecular weight is only 60,000, it is only one-tenth as toxic per molecule.

The toxin acts at the myoneural junctions and produces death by respiratory paralysis resembling that caused by curare (2, 7, 43). It apparently interfere with the **release** but **not the synthesis** of acetylcholine.

During the studies on bacterial warfare between 1942 and 1944, crystalline toxin was produced in quantities. It is somewhat disconcerting to contemplate the effects of introducing the toxin, by air, into the food and water supply of an enemy (37).

Spontaneous Disease in Animals. A number of characteristic paralytic diseases of birds and mammals are due to these toxins which the animals ingest with their food. The best known examples are **grass** or **fodder sickness** of horses (47), **silage disease** in cattle, **limberneck** in chickens (8, 17), **lamziekte** of cattle (46) in South Africa and **duck sickness** (22) in this country (Table 1).

The toxin is potent for monkeys, rabbits, guinea pigs, cats, and various birds. Many animals are lost each year in Australia from type C toxin, and it has been estimated that at least 50,000 head of cattle die each year in South Africa from eating carrion infected with types C or D botulinum toxins (42). The most susceptible animals seem to be mice, guinea pigs

Table 1. Botulism Intoxication

Cl. botulinum and *Cl. parabotulinum,* Gram Positive Anaerobic Bacillus (Subterminal Spores)
Classification Based on Toxin Production (Toxin Type Specific)

TOXIN TYPE	PROTEOLYSIS OF COAGULATED EGG WHITE	SUSCEPTIBILITY TO TOXIN	DISTRIBUTION IN NATURE	GEOGRAPHIC AREA
A	Ovolytic	Man Chickens	Soil Inadequately preserved foods Wounds	Cosmopolitan frequently found in England, Rocky Mts., Pacific Coast states
B	Ovolytic (Nevin type)	Man Chickens *	Soil Inadequately preserved foods Wounds	Cosmopolitan frequently found in central and eastern states, but specifically isolated
B	Nonovolytic (van Ermengem)	Man Chickens *	Soil Inadequately preserved foods Wounds	Cosmopolitan frequently found in central and eastern states, but specifically isolated
C	Nonovolytic	Fowls Ducks (wild water fowls) *	Stagnant alkaline mud	United States, South Africa, Australia
D	Nonovolytic	Cattle Horses Sheep	Soil Carrion	South Africa
E	Nonovolytic	Man Fish	Soil Fish	Russia, United States, Canada, Alaska

Courtesy Dr. Karl F. Meyer and associates.

* To a lesser degree.

and monkeys. Rabbits, cats, dogs, and rats are relatively resistant. The reasons for these differences in susceptibility are not known.

It has been assumed that the organism has no invasive power and did not elaborate its toxins in the animal body. However, several investigations have shown that detoxified spores injected into animals may germinate, grow in the tissues and produce a fatal toxemia (6, 18, 41). There is one report of a wound infection in man with type A *Cl. parabotulinum* which proved fatal (19).

Clinical Types of Intoxication in Man.

Most cases of botulism in Europe result from eating smoked, salted or spiced meats or fish; the mortality rate is about 25 per cent. American cases follow the ingestion of **home, not commercially, canned vegetables and fruits,** and the mortality rate is about 70 per cent. Botulism has not been associated with fresh foods, cooked or raw. Between 1899 and 1949 there were 483 outbreaks of botulism in the United States and Canada, involving 1,319 individuals and resulting in 851 deaths (34).

Surprisingly small amounts of contaminated food may cause severe symptoms and even death. One patient died after tasting a small spoonful of spoiled corn and another from a single pod of string beans (9). Symptoms may appear as early as two hours or as late as three days after the ingestion of toxin. Beginning with weakness, lassitude, and some headache the patient soon develops blepharoptosis, mydriasis, impaired light reflex, diplopia and sometimes photophobia. Involvement of pharyngeal muscles causes thickness of speech and difficulty in chewing and swallowing (9). The patients are usually constipated and may vomit, but consciousness is maintained until near the end which comes usually between the third and seventh day. Death is usually due to paralysis of the muscles of respiration and may be delayed or prevented by the use of a respirator. The temperature is normal or subnormal and the paralytic symptoms must be differentiated from those of methyl alcohol and belladonna poisoning, poliomyelitis, cerebrospinal syphilis and diphtheritic paralysis.

If some of the original contaminated food is obtained, the organism can sometimes be identified by isolation, or the type of toxin determined by neutralization test with known antitoxin. In the early stages of intoxication there may be sufficient exotoxin in the patient's blood to be detected by guinea pig inoculation. From 2.5 to 5 ml. of the patient's blood, injected intraperitoneally in a guinea pig, may produce characteristic salivation and paralysis in 24 to 48 hours (37).

Treatment. Large doses, 100,000 units or more, of polyvalent antitoxin, made against type A or B toxin, should be administered intravenously as soon as the cause of illness is suspected. Skin tests for sensitivity to horse serum should be performed and the antitoxin should not be given more rapidly than 1 ml. per minute (10).

Prevention. The facts cited in the preceding paragraphs make it imperative that all people in the habit of preparing canned food should be thoroughly aware of the possibilities of contamination and know that *Cl. botulinum* spores may be present on fruit, vegetables and other materials before they are preserved. The cook should realize that food may be contaminated with *Cl. botulinum* without being changed in any way in its gross appearance and that the slight rancid odor, which sometimes indicates its presence, may not be apparent. Canned food, sausages, and preserved meat should be thoroughly sterilized, and no home-canned preparations be consumed until they are recooked (33). Warnings such as this have indeed reduced the number of deaths from home canned vegetables, but deaths continue to be reported in the medical journals (44).

The controls for the canning industry set up by Karl Meyer and his associates (30) protected the population of the United States from botulinum poisoning from commercially canned products for 40 years. However, a break came in 1963 when there were several cases of botulinus intoxication from canned tuna fish. All of the infected cans came from one run in one cannery when defective lids were used by mistake (21).

Effective toxoids have been prepared for man from type A and B (49). These are effective even when combined (14). Three doses of 0.5 ml. given two weeks apart give effective immunity. Titers of 0.02 units of type A and 1.005 units of type B antitoxin in the serum are considered an adequate protective level. The first-year booster, after primary immunization, gave 500 times the normal level of antitoxin in the blood, and the titer remained above the minimal level for at least two years (14).

Ducks and pheasants have been actively immunized by a toxoid made from type C (4). A toxoid has been prepared from type D for animals (5). Type E toxin has been potentiated by digestion with trypsin until it had a specific activity of 45,000,000 LD_{50} per milligram nitrogen. This purified toxin could be converted into a toxoid for the immunization of mice, guinea pigs, and presumably man (13).

REFERENCES

1. Abrams, A., and others. J. Biol. Chem., 164: 63, 1946.
2. Ambache, N. J. Physiol., 108:127, 1949.
3. Bonventre, P. F., and Kempe, L. L. J. Bact., 79:24, 1960.
4. Boroff, D. A., and Reilly, J. R. J. Bact., 77: 142, 1959.
5. Cardella, M. A., and others. J. Bact., 79: 372, 1960.
6. Coleman, G. E., and Meyer, K. F. J. Infect. Dis., 31:662, 1922.
7. Davies, J. R., and others. J. Physiol., 120: 618, 1953.
8. Dickson, E. C. J.A.M.A., 65:492, 1915.
9. ———— Monogr. Rockefeller Inst. M. Research, July 31, 1918, No. 8.
10. ———— and Howitt, B. M. J.A.M.A., 74: 718, 1919.
11. Esty, J. R. Am. J. Pub. Health, 13:108, 1923.
12. ———— and Meyer, K. F. J. Infect. Dis., 31: 650, 1922.
13. Fiock, M. A., and others. J. Bact., 82:66, 1961.
14. ———— and others. J. Immunol., 88:277, 1962.
15. Geiger, J. C. J.A.M.A., 117:22, 1941.
16. Gerwing, J., and others. J. Bact., 81:819, 1961.
17. Graham, R., and Schwarze, H. J. Bact., 6:69, 1921.
18. Hall, I. C. J. Bact., 50:213, 1945.
19. Hampson, C. R. J. Bact., 61:647, 1951.
20. Hazen, E. L. Proc. Soc. Exper. Biol. & Med., 50:112, 1942.
21. Johnston, R. W., and others. Pub. Health Rep., 78:561, 1963.
22. Kalmbach, E. R. Science, 72:658, 1930; 75: 57, 1932.
23. Kempner, W. Ztschr. f. Hyg., 26:481, 1897.
24. Lamanna, C. Science, 130:763, 1959.
25. ———— and Glassman, H. N. J. Bact., 54: 575, 1947.
26. ———— and others. Science, 103:613, 1946.
27. Mandia, J. W. J. Immunol., 67:49, 1951.
28. McClung, L. S. J. Infect. Dis., 60:122, 1937.
29. Meyer, E. A., and Lamanna, C. J. Bact., 78: 175, 1959.
30. Meyer, K. F., and others. J. Infect. Dis., 31: 501, 541, 556, 1922.
31. ———— and Gunnison, J. B. J. Infect. Dis., 45:106, 119, 1929.
32. ———— and Dubovsky, B. J. J. Infect. Dis., 31:559, 1922.
33. ———— California & West. Med., 44:385, 1936.
34. ———— and Eddie, B. Ztschr. f. Hyg. u. Infektionskr., 133:255, 1951.
35. Pappenheimer, A. M., Jr. Advances in Protein Chem., 4:123, 1948.
36. Pfenninger, W. J. Infect. Dis., 35:347, 1924.
37. Rosebury, T., and Kabat, E. A. J. Immunol., 56:7, 1947.
38. Sakaguchi, G., and Sakaguchi, S. J. Bact., 78:1, 1959.
39. Schoenholz, P., and Meyer, K. F. J. Immunol., 10:1, 1925.
40. Smith, L. D. S., and King, E. O. J. Bact., 84:65, 1962.
41. Starin, W. A., and Dack, G. M. J. Infect. Dis., 36:383, 1925.
42. Sterne, M., and Wentzel, L. M. J. Immunol., 65:175, 1950.
43. Stover, J. H., and others. Proc. Soc. Exper. Biol. & Med., 84:146, 1953.
44. Sutherland, H. P. J.A.M.A., 172:1266, 1960.
45. Takagi, A., and others. J. Bact., 80:37, 1960.
46. Theiler, A., and others. 11th and 12th Reps. Vet. Res. South Africa, 1927.
47. Tocher, J. F., and others. Vet. Rec., 3:37, 75, 1923. Quoted from R. T. Hewlett, A System of Bacteriology in Relation to Medicine, London, 3:373, 1929.
48. Van Ermengem, E. Centralbl. f. Bakt., 19: 443, 1896.
49. Wright, G. G., and others. J. Immunol., 84: 384, 1960.

48

Miscellaneous Bacteria of Medical Importance

In addition to the organisms described in the preceding chapters, there are many other bacteria which are of importance in medicine. Some of these are nonpathogenic but influence the state of health of human beings, some are of doubtful pathogenicity, others are pathogenic but fortunately are sporadic and rarely encountered. However, infection with *Listeria monocytogenes* and the *Bacteroides* species of anaerobes are being encountered with increasing frequency.

LACTOBACILLI AND DENTAL CARIES *

Family: *Lactobacillaceae* Winslow and others. Tribe: *Lactobacilleae* Winslow and others. Genus: *Lactobacillus* Beijerinck. Species: *Lactobacillus acidophilus* (Moro) Holland

LACTOBACILLI

These microorganisms are gram-positive, pleomorphic, nonsporing, nonmotile (for exception, see 65) rods. They are microaerophilic, facultative-anaerobic, homo- and heterofermentative, and catalase-negative (13, 195). They tolerate and produce acid, giving a pH range as low as 3.0 and 4.0 in vigorous cultures (144). The lactobacilli grow poorly on routine laboratory media and may produce pigment in some instances. In old cultures they sometimes lose their staining characteristics.

This group of microorganisms, strictly

speaking, cannot be called pathogenic, but their intimate association with dental caries makes them important in terms of disease. Although they have been recovered from patients with diarrhea and from certain lesions of the intestinal tract, their role beyond that of opportunists is yet to be demonstrated. There is evidence of beneficial functional and metabolic effects of these organisms in the flora of the human intestinal tract (13) and the vagina.

Lactobacilli are widely distributed in nature, existing in both parasitic and saprophytic states (143). The parasitic type may be recovered from the oral cavity of caries-susceptible humans and from human and animal fecal matter when lactose and dextrin diets are consumed. The saprophytic type may be recovered from a wide variety of dairy products.

This is a heterogenous group of microorganisms, and they have been historically associated with Doderlein's bacillus, the Boas-Oppler bacillus (103), and Moro's *L. acidophilus*.

Morishita (103) attempted to show that the *L. acidophilus* of the intestinal strains were different organisms from the cultivable mouth strains, but other investigators (63, 142) could find no acceptable basis for separation of the two groups.

Methods used for classification have included historic relationships, ecology, morphology, cultivable characteristics, and, more recently, physiology, serology, and electrometric studies (116). Recent investigation by Rogosa and Sharpe (138) on classification of the lactobacilli underlines the difficulty of differentiation of species among the heterofermentative group as opposed to the homofermentative group. In spite of refinements at

* Lactobacilli and Dental Caries prepared by Grover C. Hunter, Jr., D.D.S., M.S., Professor and Head, Department of Oral Pathology and Periodontology, University of North Carolina School of Dentistry, Chapel Hill, North Carolina.

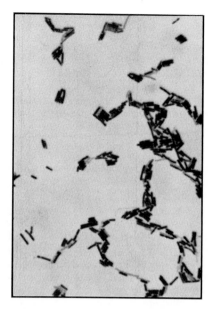

Fig. 1. Oral lactobacilli. Note tendency of organisms to form packets of parallel bacilli. × 1,150.

standardization in methods, the present classification leaves much to be desired (69).

Morphology and Cultivation. Lactobacilli may vary in shape from short plump rods, singly or in chains or palisade arrangement as in some mouth strains (Fig. 1), to long slender rods, singly or in chains, as seen in intestinal strains. *L. bifidus* exhibits a branched or Y-shaped appearance.

The organisms' ability to tolerate acid has been helpful in separating them from other bacteria of the oral flora. Serum agar medium under anaerobic and CO_2 conditions was found to stimulate growth and development of oral strains (136). A modification of Kulp's tomato peptone agar was devised by Hadley (59) to facilitate culturing for salivary counts by adjusting the final pH of the medium to 5.0 with lactic acid.

Surface colonies have been described as "smooth," "rough," "fried egg," and "ground glass" by various writers (173). Some of them are flat, grayish, and almost translucent. There is considerable variation in size. Deep colonies have been described as Y and X types, presenting considerable variation in growth design (195). Some strains produce turbidity in liquid or semisolid media, whereas others do not.

Oral lactobacilli may be grown from an inoculum of saliva from susceptible individuals by spreading a diluted sample on tomato juice

agar which has been prepared to give a final pH of 5.0. The plates are incubated at 37° C. for 72 hours, and colonies of lactobacilli are easily identified by morphologic characteristics. The colonies on tomato juice agar appear pinpoint in size, some larger than others, and may be white, dome-shaped, and shiny or, in contrast, flat, transparent and dull, or at times rust-brown in color (Fig. 2). Other variations may also occur. Colonies of yeasts, staphylococci, and *G. tetragena,* which sometimes grow concomitantly on this medium, may be separated from colonies of lactobacilli by their different morphologic characteristics. Colonies of streptococci are not as easily differentiated from lactobacilli, and smears may be necessary to establish positive identification. For detailed technic and quantitative estimation of colonies, refer to the work of Hadley (59).

Metabolism. Vitamin requirements of oral strains for maximum acid production include many of the B-complex group (84). The heterofermentative types require thiamin, whereas the homofermentative ones do not (62). A change in cultivable strains from the heterofermentative to the homofermentative type of metabolism was shown to be accompanied by a loss in thiamin requirement (26). Changes in fermentative characteristics were also shown to be associated with washing the organisms in 0.85 per cent NaCl solution (68). Fermentation reaction changes have been linked to

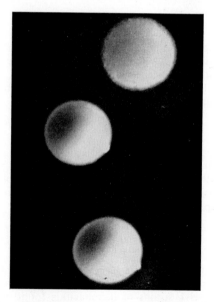

Fig. 2. Colonies of oral lactobacilli. Grown on tomato juice agar. Note two smooth colonies at bottom and one rough colony at top. × 20.

changes in immunologic specificity. These findings are not surprising in view of the present biologic concept of continuous variation and adaptation in bacterial species. Dunn and others (35) studied the amino acid requirements of 23 lactic acid bacteria and found that the number of amino acids essential for the microorganisms varied from 2 to 15 and that certain amino acids inhibited four of the strains.

Antigenic Structure. The lactobacilli are quite complex. Williams (193) did antigenic analysis by agglutinin absorption of nine strains of oral lactobacilli resulting in four distinct antigenic components (A, B, C, D). Orland (115) found major antigens (A, Ab, C, E, F, G, H, Fl) in respective strains and observed that these major antigens were rather stable. Harrison (61) found some correlation between morphology and fermentation groups within immunologic groupings. Serology seems at the present time to be promising in helping to clarify some of the issues of classification in this group of microorganisms. Williams and Franck (194) made an antigenic analysis of five strains of heterofermentative lactobacilli of human oral origin and found evidence of the presence of six major antigens and two minor antigens; cross-reactions between strains under study and the antisera of homofermentative lactobacilli were observed only in unadsorbed antisera, and none were observed where monospecific antibodies were employed.

L. CAUCASICUS

Isolated in pure culture by Beijerinck in 1889 from kefir, where it occurs symbiotically with yeasts, this organism is a gram-positive, nonmotile rod, thin and variable in size, which may occur singly or in chains (13).

L. BULGARICUS

Originally isolated from yoghurt by Grigoroff in 1905, this organism is primarily saprophytic, heat-resistant, anaerobic on fresh isolation, and nonpathogenic (13, 155).

L. CASEI

Isolated by Orla-Jensen, 1919, this microorganism is one of the most common homofermentative strains of lactobacillus found in the oral cavity (23, 140). It is also the more common lactic-acid-producing rod found in milk and milk products (13).

L. FERMENTI

Isolated by Beijerinck in 1901, this is one of the most common heterofermentative strains of lactobacillus found in the oral cavity (23, 140). It is widely distributed in fermenting plant or animal products, such as fermenting dough, milk and tomato products, and wine (13).

L. BIFIDUS

This parasitic lactobacillus was isolated by Tissier in 1900 from feces of nurslings. It is a strict anaerobe on isolation but may become microaerophilic on cultivation. Morphologically it is similar to that of other lactobacilli except that it often is branched or bifurcated and club-shaped. Williams and others (192) studied the antigenic components of eight strains of *L. bifidus* and suggested that the unbranched aerobic derivatives of the branched strains be designated *L. parabifidus*. Rogosa and Sharpe (138) have suggested the rejection of *L. bifidus* because its properties are inconsistent with the genus definition.

L. ACIDOPHILUS

Isolated by Moro in 1900 from feces of nurslings, this organism has been given great attention by investigators in dental caries. Rogosa and others (141), however, found its frequency distribution to be only 10.5 per cent of the cultivable oral strains of lactobacilli. *L. acidophilus* has undoubtedly been used in the literature to cover a group of biologically related strains and is a good representative of the whole group (70). *L. acidophilus-odontolyticus* was isolated from carious dentin by McIntosh, James, and Lazarus-Barlow (96) and classified by them into strains I and II. Rodriguez (137) also classified this organism into types I, II, and III, but his classification did not coincide with that of McIntosh, James, and Lazarus-Barlow. It is probably identical with *L. acidophilus* and deserves no separate treatment.

DENTAL CARIES

Antony van Leeuwenhoek in 1675 was probably the first to examine microorganisms from tooth scrapings under a magnifying lens, but nearly two centuries elapsed before the dental plaque was related to the carious process by Ficinus in 1847. Microorganisms were reported found in the dentinal tubuli of carious tooth lesions in 1867 by Leber and Rottenstein. Bacteria within the tubuli of carious dentin and in

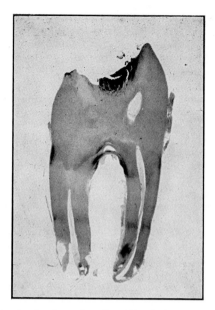

Fig. 3. Section of molar. The dark areas represent areas of decay. × 6.

dento-bacterial plaques have been demonstrated in stained laboratory sections by many since that time (Figs. 3, 4, 5, 6, and 7).

Following the stimulus of Miller's chemico-parasitic theory in 1883, and Black's (7), Miller's (102) and Williams's contributions to the dental plaque theory, investigations into the identity, nature, and physiology of the micro-organisms involved have occupied the interest of investigators for the past half century (22, 24, 31). Many microorganisms were observed to be associated with caries, including strepto-

Fig. 4. Dento-bacterial plaque. Note growth of organisms on the surface of the enamel. (From Col. Joseph L. Bernier, Armed Forces Institute of Pathology. *The Management of Oral Diseases,* C. V. Mosby Co.)

cocci, staphylococci, yeasts, leptothrix, actinomyces, and others, but by far the most numerous and intensive investigations centered around the parasitic lactobacilli (18, 19, 20, 72, 73, 74, 95, 96, 136, 137, 173).

Gies and Kligler (45) recovered among other organisms *L. acidophilus* from dentobacterial plaques on carious tooth surfaces. The next sequence in development was the association of large numbers of *L. acidophilus* on carious tooth surfaces to the carious process itself (20).

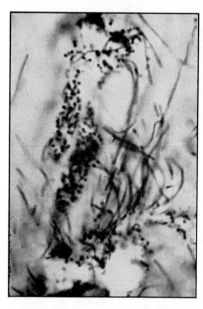

Fig. 5. Organisms on surface of decayed dentin. Both specific and nonspecific organisms grow in decayed areas. (From Kronfeld's *Histopathology of the Teeth and Their Surrounding Structures,* 4th ed., Lea and Febiger.)

Later, cultures of *L. acidophilus* from activated saliva were found to be correlated with caries activity on a clinical basis. The capability of *L. acidophilus* to develop a low pH concentration in the local dentobacterial plaque was inferred by investigators in studies of cultivable oral lactobacilli and from later solubility studies on enamel (167). Bibby (6), from his studies, asserted that not all types of dentobacterial plaques were harmful and that some were actually protective. He suggested that the role of saliva as an influencing factor in caries should not be neglected. His work intensified the search for the bacteria associated with the so-called harmful plaques. Blayney and others (9) found positive correlation between direct bacterial smears from affected teeth and cul-

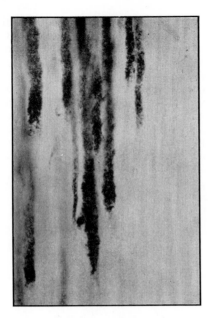

Fig. 6. Bacteria growing in tubules of dentin. Only certain tubules have been infected. × 657.

tures of *L. acidophilus* grown from activated saliva from the same mouths. An entirely different flora was found associated with noncarious plaques.

The quantitative interest in oral lactobacilli led to the devising of laboratory culture counts from samples of activated saliva in an attempt to assess the caries activity of the individual (18). Jay and others (73) in the experimental feeding of candy to a group of institutionalized children found a significant correlation between lactobacillus counts and caries activity, and also a significant predictability pattern of future dental caries activity in those children with consistently high salivary lactobacillus counts. Although these findings have been confirmed by many studies in the last two decades (9, 12, 71, 111, 168) there have been exceptions (49, 88).

What the total count of lactobacilli per milliliter of activated saliva actually means has not been elucidated. Clinically high counts (above 10,000) have been shown to be significantly correlated with high caries activity and with high carbohydrate intake by susceptible individuals. Lactobacilli, on the other hand, can be recovered sporadically from clinically immune patients, but the total counts in these instances are usually low (19). This laboratory analysis has been extremely useful in assessing the needs of susceptible individuals with a view to some form of caries control. Snyder et al.

(161) evaluated various laboratory tests recently and found that lactobacillus counts were more valid on a group rather than an individual basis. Massler (91) on the basis of the recent work of Keyes and Fitzgerald (39, 78) has suggested control of decay in patients with rampant lesions by removing all carious matter at the first appointment and replacement with zinc oxide and eugenol as temporary fillings. Such a procedure, along with dietary control measures, reduces oral lactobacillus counts in these mouths dramatically. Restorations can then be placed with some assurance of positive caries control. It is suggested that lactobacillus counts be done periodically on these patients with severe caries problems.

In addition to total salivary counts of lactobacilli, various colorimetric tests have been devised and evaluated. The Snyder test is one of the best known (160). A chemical test was devised by Fosdick and others (41) by measuring the increase in calcium of a saliva glucose-enamel mixture after four hours incubation at 37° C. Dreizen and others (34) found that the buffering capacity of the saliva was a reliable test for caries susceptibility. Rapp (128) has recently devised a test which is based on the rate of activity of reductase enzymes in the saliva and can be read in 15 minutes by the dentist.

The discovery of *L. acidophilus* agglutinins

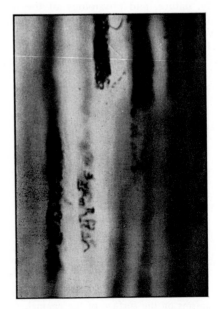

Fig. 7. Bacteria in tubules. High power of Figure 6 showing filaments and bacilli resembling those in Figure 1. × 1,150.

in the blood serums of caries-immune individuals suggested the possibility of developing an antigenic approach to caries control (38, 73), but the development of valid human skin tests and a suitable vaccine has not yet been attained (52, 72). Wilson and Green (196) made studies on the blood types and Rh factors in caries-immune and caries-susceptible individuals, with results that are suggestive of possible relationships in this area of immunology. Much more investigation will be necessary before such relationships are enlightening.

Boyd and Drain (10) noted the arrest of caries in 28 well-controlled diabetic children, 82 per cent of whom had an active caries history prior to dietary control. A diabetic diet is extremely low in carbohydrate, the natural substrate of lactobacilli. Although this linkage was not noted by Boyd and Drain at the time, it was suggestive to others; consequently a dietary control program devised by Jay and others (75) came into reality. This method of control, however, is not practicable for use on a population basis, although it is extremely valuable in selected individual cases.

Other control measures have included periodic prophylaxis, and the use of acid inhibitors in mouthwashes and toothpastes which would have retention power in the dentobacterial plaques (40). These control measures, however, have yet to be demonstrated as having statistical clinical effectiveness. Another approach using fluorides topically and in communal water supplies to enhance the defense of the teeth themselves has of late been shown to be the most promising of control measures on a wide population basis.

The mass of past experimental and clinical evidence is suggestive of an important role for the parasitic lactobacilli, at least in the initiating phase of the disease, although other organisms such as streptococci are of significance in the advancing lesion of caries (64, 66). Recent investigations in experimental caries in rodents by Keyes (78), and Fitzgerald and Keyes (39) are suggestive of the possible infectious and transmissible nature of dental caries, with the alimentary tract as a probable source of infection; however, the etiologic role was ascribed to streptococci. Lactobacilli are present in the intestinal tract of most individuals during infancy. They may persist in the flora of the mouth throughout life, may completely disappear, or may appear sporadically from time to time at different age levels (18). The inability of investigators to implant lactobacilli in the mouths and intestinal tracts of immune individuals is indirectly suggestive. Furthermore, lactobacilli have been demonstrated to be the organisms showing the most significant increase in the oral flora during caries development.

That bacteria are involved in some ways in the carious process may be inferred from experimental work on germ-free, caries-susceptible rats. Too few projects in the past have been directed toward a fundamental understanding of the dynamics of the entire flora of the oral cavity. Further knowledge will be necessary before assigning the precise role, large or small, to the parasitic lactobacilli in the complex etiologic pattern of the disease (11, 12, 52, 123, 143).

LEPTOTRICHIA

The name *Leptothrix buccalis* was originally employed by Robin in 1853 for the filamentous forms which he had seen in wet mounts of tooth scrapings because of their morphological similarity to the aquatic algae organism in the genus *Leptothrix* (Kutzing). Later studies showed that at least two and possibly more rods or filamentous forms were being called *Leptothrix buccalis* (46). These organisms were placed in the order *Actinomycetales* in the 1923 edition of Bergey's Manual but eliminated from the seventh edition.

Gilmore, Howell, and their associates (46) have restudied this organism and concluded that the name *Leptotrichia buccalis,* Trevisan, 1819 should be used for the organisms described by Thjøtta *et al.* They also propose that the organisms described by Kligler in 1915 as *Leptothrix buccalis* be renamed *Bacterionema matruchotii* (Mendel, 1919) *comb. nov.* and placed in the family *Actinomycetaceae.* The serologic studies of Schmidt and Richardson (149) on 42 freshly isolated strains justified the inclusion of the organisms in the *Actinomycetaceae.*

LISTERIA MONOCYTOGENES AND LISTERELLOSIS

Family: *Corynebacteriaceae* Lehmann and Neumann. Genus: *Listeria* Pirie. Type Species: *Listeria monocytogenes* (Murray and others) Pirie

This "Cinderella" of the bacterial species (107) was isolated from a laboratory epidemic in domestic rabbits as recently as 1926 by Murray, Webb and Swann (106). A characteristic feature of the disease was a specific increase in the mononuclear leukocytes of the circulating blood.

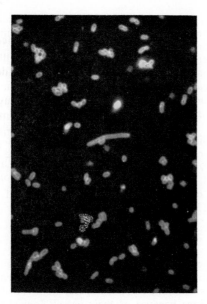

Fig. 8. Fluorescent staining of pure culture of *L. monocytogenes.* Note the mixture of bacilli and coccobacilli. (From Eveland. *J. Bact.,* 85:1448, 1963.)

The host range for this organism includes man and 35 other mammals, 15 fowls, two species of ticks, fish, and crustaceans (54). It has been found in stream water, sewage, and silage (55). The ability of the organisms to grow as well as survive in soil at temperature of 4° C. probably explains the wide range of infection (182, 189).

The organism is a small, **gram-positive, non-encapsulated, nonsporogenous** rod 0.4 to 0.5 μ by 0.2 to 2 μ, with rounded ends and a straight or slightly curved body. The larger forms may be mistaken for diphtheroids, but the shorter coccoc bacilli can be confused with cocci. (Fig. 8) (37). When grown at room temperature, the organism is motile and has peritrichous flagella which are developed most readily at 20° C. incubation. Nonflagellated mutants develop and occasionally mutate back to flagellated motile forms (80). It is aerobic but **facultatively anaerobic** and grows best at 37° C. on media enriched by liver extract or blood.

In semisolid agar containing glucose a granular type of growth appears along the line of the stab (151, 152). On sheep liver extract agar the colonies are small, circular, smooth, viscid, and slightly flattened. They appear transparent by transmitted light and milk-white by reflected light. The **zone of hemolysis** which occurs around colonies grown on blood agar results

in an appearance which is not unlike that of a colony of hemolytic streptococci. This soluble hemolysin is not definitely related to virulence of the organism (48, 109). Unfortunately, not all isolations show the hemolytic zone about the colonies (54). Gray has found that young (18- to 24-hour-old) colonies have a distinctive blue-green color when viewed by reflected light. This color is seen most readily on colorless medium but can be detected at the base of the colonies even though the colonies are black on potassium tellurite plates (54). A new selective and enrichment medium has been described by Gray (53), but the most significant discovery was the ability of the organism to regain "cultivatability" by incubating extracts of silage (55) or extracts of pus or tissues at 4° C. The mechanism of rejuvenation remains a complete mystery, but the facts are that the organisms which can be stained in smears from tissues will not grow on primary culture but do grow after 4 or 5 days at 4° C. or sometimes only after being held at this temperature for 30 to 50 days.

This organism produces acid without gas rapidly from glucose, salicin, and trehalose and slowly and variably from maltose, lactose, and sucrose. It does not oxidize xylose, mannitol, or inositol. It is catalase-positive, but indol and hydrogen sulfide are not produced. All cultures give off a penetrating, unpleasant acid odor.

Patterson (118) studied 54 strains isolated from various animals and from man and found four types with three H antigens and three O antigens. Robbins and Griffin (135) have designated the O somatic antigens as I, II, III, IV, and V and the flagellar H antigens as a, b, c, and d. Cross-agglutinations occur as a result of common H antigens. Colonies of nonmotile organisms without H antigens occur spontaneously. There is no relation between antigenic types, host specificity, or geographical distribution. Seeliger (152) confirmed the work of Patterson and distinguished two subtypes in type IV. Smith and Metzger (156) demonstrated capsule formation in *L. monocytogenes.* Metzger and Smith (101) found five serotypes by agar gel diffusion which corresponded to the types determined with "O" and "H" agglutinations. Type 4b and type 1 were found most frequently in the first 100 strains isolated in this country (80). Sword and Pickett (169) succeeded in classifying 127 of 149 strains with eight phage types.

Seeliger and Sulzbacher (153) and later Welshimer (190) found a cross-reaction antigen shared by *Staphylococcus aureus* and some type of *L. monocytogenes*. This resulted in patients with proven infection with staphylococci showing agglutinin titers up to 160 with *L. monocytogenes*. Netter and his associates (108) have found an explanation for this phenomenon. *Staphylococcus aureus, L. monocytogenes,* and *B. subtilis* may share a common Rantz antigen. By proper absorption the cross-reaction antibody can be eliminated.

The spontaneous disease in animals is characterized by the production of multiple, small, necrotic foci in the internal organs and the development of a marked increase in the number of mononuclear cells in the blood. Stanley (164) isolated a lipid component from the organism which stimulated the production of monocytes in animals. Girard and Murray (47) confirmed this work and extended it by showing that animals stimulated with this lipid made more antibodies to unrelated antigens injected at the same time.

L. monocytogenes, when instilled into the eye of the rabbit or guinea pig, produces a marked local purulent conjunctivitis and keratitis (104), and the reaction is used to differentiate it from *Erysipelothrix insidiosa* and other organisms. Gray and his associates (57) have reported that both ocular instillation and oral administration produces subsequent abortions in pregnant rabbits and guinea pigs. The isolation of *L. monocytogenes* from the cervix of lactating cows (56) may explain why raw milk may be a source for the infection of pregnant women. The organism causes multiple necrotic foci in the internal organs of young animals and not infrequently a meningitis. The disease in man was believed to be limited largely to meningitis (76, 125), until recently when the work of Seeliger (152) and others in Germany showed that it frequently caused abortions and stillbirths in women. In many instances the women gave a history of drinking raw milk from the cow or the goat. Abortions and stillbirths have been reported in cows, sheep, horses, rabbits, and guinea pigs following infection with *L. monocytogenes* (57).

This disease is being recognized with increasing frequency. More than three-fourths of the 1500 cases in the literature were diagnosed between 1957 and 1962 (54). The first cases in man were instances of meningitis in children, with more than half of the first 270 cases being in children less than one month old. But septicemia and other generalized infections occur without meningitis. The isolation of *L. monocytogenes* from the cervix of some women in England who were repeated aborters (129) emphasizes the importance of this organism as a cause of abortion. Children may be born alive but infected, and in one instance the disease spread in a nursery to other children (177). Veterinarians often get pustular or papular skin lesions from handling aborted bovine species (54). Old, debilitated patients are also subjected to terminal infections with *L. monocytogenes*.

Tetracycline, chloramphenicol, penicillin, and streptomycin have all been used in therapy with varying success. Two antibiotics supported with sulfonamides have been recommended (191).

Relationship to Infectious Mononucleosis in Man. This disease also is known as **acute benign lymphoblastosis** and **glandular fever** (90, 122, 132, 163). Characteristically it is a disease of children and young adults and often occurs in epidemic form.

The disease is characterized by the presence in the blood of increased numbers of large mononuclear cells, particularly large and somewhat atypical lymphocytes. Patients and experimental animals infected with *Listeria monocytogenes* show an increase in mononuclear cells but do not have the heterophile antibodies. Most investigators believe that the classical type of infectious mononucleosis is caused by an unknown virus.

A protozoan disease, toxoplasmosis, must be differentiated from listerellosis. This disease also causes fever, general lymph node enlargement and increases in large mononuclear cells, but it fails to develop the heterophile antibodies to sheep cells. Recent studies have shown that from 3 to 7 per cent of clinical cases of infectious mononucleosis are in fact cases of toxoplasmosis (132).

ERYSIPELOTHRIX INSIDIOSA AND ERYSIPELOID

Family: *Corynebactericceae* Lehmann and Neumann. Genus: *Erysipelothrix* Rosenbach. Type Species: *Erysipelothrix insidiosa* (Trevisan) Langford and Hansen

Erysipelothrix insidiosa was isolated by Koch in 1880 (83) from mice which had been injected with putrefying blood. In 1882 Löffler (89) cultured the organism from the blood vessels of the skin of a pig which had died of swine erysipelas. Four months previously Pasteur and Thuillier (117) had recovered the same or a similar organism from pigs dying of **rouget**. Finally, Rosenbach (145) isolated the organism from **erysipeloid** infection in man.

The organism is widely distributed in nature,

occurring in the surface slime on both fresh and salt water fish. It is the cause of a common disease of swine known as swine erysipelas and, less frequently, it has been found in polyarthritis in sheep, joint ill in lambs, and infection in horses, cattle, turkeys, and peacocks (146). Small doses of the organisms, when given intravenously, regularly produce arthritis in rabbits, and the arthritis is made worse by treatment with cortisone (51).

Man acquires the infection by contact with fish, infected animals, or animal products, such as meat, hides, bones and manure (78). An epidemic has been reported in a button factory where infected bones from hogs and cattle were being processed (93).

The organism is a **nonsporogenous, nonencapsulated, nonmotile, gram-positive** rod, 0.2 to 0.3 μ wide and 0.5 to 1.5 μ long. It occurs both singly and in chains. The R form of the organism is long and filamentous and frequently shows so much branching that at one time it was classified among the actinomycetes. The organism can be stained by the fluorescent method (30).

It is **micro-aerophilic** when first isolated and grows best in a band a few millimeters below the surface of a semisolid tube of agar. The optimal temperature is between 30° and 37° C., with limiting temperatures of 15° and 44° C. On **blood-agar plates,** the S form colonies are minute (0.1 mm.), round, convex, amorphous, water-clear, and glistening. The colonies are soft and emulsify easily. The R form is somewhat larger (0.2 to 0.4 mm.) and resembles miniature colonies of anthrax with curled filaments and fimbriated edges. On gelatin slants the S form remains confined to the line of inoculation, but the R form spreads out to form either a diffuse cloud or definite branches resembling the bristles of a test tube brush. A **hemolytic** zone is produced around the colonies of organisms grown on agar containing 10 per cent horse blood. Cultures can be maintained in nutrient tryptose broth medium adjusted to pH 7.6 with 0.5 N NaOH (172, 182).

Sugar fermentations are irregular, but **acid without gas** usually is formed in **glucose** and **lactose** but not in rhamnose, mannitol, sucrose, and salicin.

The organisms are killed in 15 minutes by a temperature of 55° C. but are highly resistant in meats, surviving from one to three months after salting, pickling, or smoking. They are not destroyed by putrefaction but live for months in buried cadavers and in the bones of animals dying of generalized infections.

Watts (181) studied 43 strains isolated from various sources and found that 38 belonged to one antigenic type and five to another. In addition to the specific heat-stabile antigen, there are two heat-labile antigens which are present in different proportions in the two types and which explain the occurrence of cross-reactions. Gledhill (50) found four serologic types among 31 strains. Agglutinins appear in the blood of man and animals during convalescence, and **antibacterial serum** has been produced in horses and is used for the treatment of both man and animals.

A variety of clinical symptoms develops in swine with spontaneous infections. Some animals die in two to four days with **acute septicemia;** more commonly, reddish to purplish rhomboid spots known as "diamonds" appear on the skin; less frequently a chronic form of infection develops with local **arthritis** or **endocarditis.**

Mice, pigeons, and rabbits are infected readily with freshly isolated cultures. Guinea pigs are resistant and can be used to differentiate *Erysipelothrix insidiosa* from *Listeria monocytogenes.* Like *L. monocytogenes* infections, rabbits inoculated with sublethal doses of the organism display an increase in the circulating monocytes.

Occasionally a rapidly fatal **septicemia** with or without **endocarditis** is observed in man (81). The most frequent type of infection is subacute and develops on the fingers or hands. The skin lesions are red and edematous and often show superficial vesicles filled with slightly cloudy fluid. The regional lymph nodes are enlarged, and an associated arthritis sometimes occurs.

Spontaneous healing requires about 30 days, but the course of the disease can be shortened substantially by the administration of **sulfonamides** or **penicillin.**

Ehrlich (36) reported the recovery of a patient who had extensive, bullous skin lesions over the body and was critically ill before the administration of penicillin. An excellent Kodachrome photograph of this patient's lesions is shown in his article.

Penicillin is superior to chlortetracycline and streptomycin in the treatment of spontaneously infected animals, particularly turkeys (58, 126) but not as effective as antiserums for the treatment of infected swine (197).

Passive immunization in swine with immune serum affords protection for about two weeks. Pasteur and Thuillier (117) attentuated the organism by passing it through rabbits and then employed the living culture as a "vaccine." Later, living virulent cultures mixed with antiserum were used for active immunization. Good immunity lasting for eight to 12 months is obtained by both methods, but, unfortunately, the living organisms in the vaccine sometimes produce local lesions which serve as foci for dissemination of the disease. This disease may be confused with actinobacillosis (3, 4, 82, 87, 130, 134, 158, 170).

NONSPOROGENOUS ANAEROBIC BACILLI

Necrobacillosis, Bacteroidosis

A number of **anaerobic** or **microaerophilic** bacilli are found in necrotic lesions of man and animals. Some occur alone in the tissues, but in most instances they are present along with a variety of other bacilli and cocci. The necrotic nature of the lesions and the foul odor may suggest the incorrect clinical diagnosis of infection with spore-bearing anaerobes.

The first known organism of this type was isolated by Löffler (89) from calf diphtheria and named *B. necrophorus*. This bacillus has had many names.

In 1896 Vincent (180) described a fusiform bacillus associated with spirochetes in gangrenous lesions of the throat and other tissues (see page 749). The name "fusiform" is such an excellent descriptive term that the organisms have been subjected to few attempts to modify its nomenclature. It has been called *Fusiformis fusiformis* (Topley and Wilson), *Bacterium fusiformis* (Jordan and Burrows), and *Fusobacterium fusiforme* (Veillon and Zuber) Hoffman (Bergey).

A third group of nonsporulating anaerobes was found in patients with gangrenous appendices by Veillon and Zuber in 1898 (179). They were named *B. ramosus, B. serpens, B. fragilis, B. furcosis,* and *B. fusiformis*. The last name obviously is synonymous with *Fusibacterium fusiforme*. Topley and Wilson include all these species under the generic name *Fusiformis*, and in Bergey's Manual they are classified in the tribe *Bacteroides*.

The most recent addition to this group of nonsporulating anaerobes is an organism isolated by Oliver and Wherry (112) in 1921. As this organism grows on blood agar, it synthesizes a black pigment which is not melanin, as suggested by the specific name of the organism, but is a derivative of hemoglobin (150). The bacillus has been called *Ristella melaninogenica* and *Haemophilus melaninogenicus*. Topley and Wilson place it in the genus *Fusi-*

formis. In the seventh edition of Bergey's Manual, it is listed as *Bacteroides melaninogenicus* (Oliver and Wherry) Roy and Kelly.

The history of the organisms, now classified in the tribe *Bacteroides*, and the type of infections which they produce was reviewed in 1952 by McVay and Sprunt (98) and by King and his associates (79). The importance of these organisms in obstetrics and gynecology was emphasized by Carter and his coworkers (25), who reported the results of their study of 153 patients.

Bacteroidosis continues to be a serious disease. McHenery and his associates (94) reported 11 instances of bacteremia in 1961, and Tynes and Frommyer (176) 25 in 1962. The latter reviewed the literature and found the mortality was 81 per cent before sulfonamides, 64 per cent with sulfonamides, 50 per cent with penicillin, streptomycin, and sulfonamides, and 33 per cent with multiple broad-spectrum antibiotics. Penicillin and streptomycin alone or in combination are not usually very effective. Tetracycline is favored by most authors (94, 176). Perhaps tetracycline plus another broad-spectrum antibiotic and sulfonamide should be used.

Family: *Bacteroidaceae* Breed and others, fam. nov. Genus: *Sphaerophorus* Prévot. Species: *Sphaerophorus necrophorus* (Flügge) Prévot

Organisms of this type occur as normal inhabitants of the mouth, vagina, and intestinal tract of man and a variety of animals. In the intestinal tract of man they may be even more numerous than *E. coli* (86).

Sphaerophorus necrophorus (*Bacteroides* species) is a **nonsporogenous, nonencapsulated, nonmotile, gram-negative** rod, 0.5 to 1.5 μ in width. The rods are very pleomorphic, varying from a few microns to long filaments 80 to 100 microns in length. The organism is a strict **anaerobe** and grows best at 37° C. Primary cultures can be obtained by cultivation in Brewer's (14) **thioglycollate broth** or deep tubes of meat media sealed with paraffin. The addition of 30 per cent ascitic fluid to the medium accelerates multiplication, and good growth is obtained in 24 to 48 hours (159). Large quantities of a foul-smelling gas are produced. Pure cultures can be obtained by streaking ascitic fluid or blood-agar plates and incubating under anaerobic conditions. After 48 hours incubation on ascitic fluid-agar plates, the colonies attain an average diameter of 1 mm. but are somewhat smaller on blood agar.

The colonies are smooth and convex, with entire edges, and are white, gray, or yellow in color. Many strains exhibit a complicated method of multiplication, with the development of pleuropneumonia-like forms (33).

Bacteroides fragilis and related species are not pleomorphic. They can be cultivated by the same methods but usually produce less gas. William Smith and Ropes (159) found that the septicemias produced by the nonpleomorphic species were somewhat less severe than those caused by the pleomorphic strains.

The organisms in this group are killed readily in 20 minutes by a temperature of 60° C.

The most important metabolic product is a **necrotizing endotoxin** (5).

The study of the antigenic structure of these organisms is far from complete. Many species are heterologous (29) but the 73 strains studied in Rettger's laboratory fell into four serologic groups (86, 188).

Spontaneous infections occur in rabbits, cattle, sheep, horses, and mules. In animals these organisms initiate specific types of infections known as "calf diphtheria," "grease heel," and "foot rot." Necrotizing lesions of the skin and metastatic abscesses of the joints, liver, lungs, and brain are not unusual.

Subcutaneous abscesses can be produced in rabbits, guinea pigs, and young mice. Rabbits injected intravenously with the organism may develop multiple metastatic abscesses, or they may die of cachexia without obvious lesions.

Necrobacillosis or **bacteroidosis** probably is a much more frequent infection of man than would be suggested by a review of the literature (29). By employing anaerobic methods of cultivation in all patients suspected of having an infection of this type, Smith and Ropes discovered that 20 instances of this disease occurred over a four-year period in one hospital. Almost any part of the body, such as the ears, tonsils, vagina, uterus, lungs, liver, joints, peritoneum, brain, and meninges may be infected. Septicemia is not uncommon (17, 159), and organisms belonging to this group have been isolated from cases of puerperal sepsis (60) and from ulcerative colitis (29).

Surgical drainage and antibiotic therapy (25, 97, 127, 147) offer the best chance of recovery. Although the previously reported cases of meningitis usually were fatal, four of the five patients in Smith and Ropes' series recovered following early surgical drainage, repeated lumbar punctures, and intravenous administration of fluids and blood, supplemented by tetracycline and sulfadiazine therapy.

Family: *Bacteroidaceae* Breed and others, fam. nov. Genus: *Fusobacterium* Knorr. Species: *Fusobacterium fusiforme* (Veillon and Zuber) Hoffman

Fusobacterium fusiforme is a nonsporogenous, nonencapsulated, nonmotile, gram-negative rod, 0.5 to 1 μ in width and 8 to 16 μ in length. The ends taper to a sharp point. The organisms often are paired, end to end, and various stages of transverse division can be seen in almost every preparation. Although the organism is gram-negative, gram-positive granules and bands frequently are seen in the larger forms. The bacillus is anaerobic and grows best between 35° and 37° C. at a pH ranging from 6.8 to 8.0 (114). It grows well in serum or ascitic broth, and in symbiosis with cocci and other bacilli, but is somewhat difficult to isolate and maintain in pure culture. Small, grayish white colonies appear on ascitic agar or blood-agar plates which have been incubated under anaerobic conditions for 48 to 72 hours. Gas is not formed, and no odor is produced by this species, although *Fusobacterium nucleatum* Knorr does develop a rather sour disagreeable odor. Acid without gas is formed from glucose, fructose, and sucrose, but the fermentation of lactose is variable (67).

Omata (113) has found that *F. nucleatum* requires pantothenate and purines for growth, and both Omata (114) and McCarthy and Snyder (92) have described a selective medium for isolation.

Weiss and Mercado (186) extracted type-specific protein-like substances from this group of organisms and found evidence for the existence of a group-specific polysaccharide. Some progress has been made toward an antigenic classification of the fusiform bacilli by Varney (178), Pesch and Schmitz (120), Spaulding and Rettger (162), Hine and Berry (67), Weiss and Mercado (186) and Kelley (77).

We agree with Tunnicliff and Hammond (175) that the large, motile, fusiform bacillus which is found regularly in the lesions of Vincent's angina and trench mouth is a form of *Bor. buccalis* (157). The small fusiform bacilli are nonmotile, are not destroyed by arsenicals, and have no generic relationship to the spirochetes. They are, however, fellow symbionts in the fusospirochetal symbiotic disease. In 20 years of observation we have never seen a clinical infection in which fusiform bacilli were the only organisms present. Animals have not been infected with pure cultures. However, Murphy and his associates (105) reported in 1963 a patient who developed a fusobacterium septicemia following a human bite. The patient recovered after treatment with penicillin and chloramphenicol. A more detailed discussion of the pathogenesis of fusospirochetal symbiosis will be found in Chapter 51, page 749.

Family: *Bacteroidaceae* Breed and others, fam. nov. Genus: *Bacteroides* Castellani and Chalmers. Species: *Bacteroides fragilis* (Veillon and Zuber) Castellani and Chalmers. *Bacteroides melaninogenicus* (Oliver and Wherry) Roy and Kelly

Bacteroides melaninogenicus is a **nonsporogenous, nonencapsulated, nonmotile, gram-negative** bacillus, 0.8 μ in width and 1 to 3 μ in length. It grows readily on the surface of ascitic or blood-agar plates in symbiosis with other organisms but is difficult to isolate and maintain in pure culture. As the organism grows on blood agar, a black pigment is produced which, after four to five days, gives the colony a characteristic black color. Unfortunately, the organisms frequently die before the diagnostic color is well developed, which, in part, accounts for the difficulties encountered in obtaining and perpetuating pure cultures. Serros and Mattman (154) reported that the addition of 5 per cent laked blood to tryptose agar is superior to cooked meat or whole blood media for the isolation and maintenance for pure cultures (Fig. 9). Both hematin and vitamin K are essential for growth (43, 44), and its ability to hydrolize native collagen perhaps

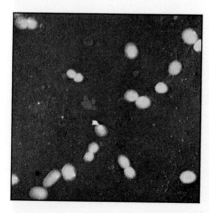

Fig. 9. *Bacteroides melaninogenicus.* Electron micrograph showing coccobacilli and dense internal granules. × 12,000. (From Senos and Mattman. *J. Bact.,* 70:483, 1955. Electron micrograph by A. R. Taylor of Parke Davis Laboratories.)

explains its secondary role in necrotic mixed fusospirochetal infections.

Oliver and Wherry (112) isolated the organism from the mouth, feces, and urine and from some infected wounds. Weiss (187) has reported that it is found almost constantly in sputum from cases of fusospirochetal symbiotic types of pulmonary abscess. We have had no difficulty in confirming Weiss's observations.

Burdon (21) isolated the organisms from the blood of several cases of puerperal sepsis. In pure culture the organism is essentially nonpathogenic and will not kill mice or rabbits, although it does produce local inflammatory edema and necrosis when injected intracutaneously into rabbits (187).

STREPTOBACILLUS MONILIFORMIS

Family: *Bacterioidaceae* fam. nov. Breed Murray Smith. Genus: *Streptobacillus* Levaditi and others. Species: *Streptobacillus moniliformis* Levaditi and others

This pleomorphic gram-negative bacillus has been described in the literature under several names: *Haverhillia multiformis*, *Streptothrix ratti*, *Actinomyces muris*, *Asterococcus muris*, and *Actinomyces muris ratti*. In Bergey's Manual, sixth edition, 1948, this organism was listed in the appendix attached to the description of the genus *Haemophilus*.

Streptobacillus moniliformis occurs normally in the mouths of wild rats and may be introduced into the tissues of man by the bite of this animal (8, 15, 148). It also is the cause of an epidemic milk-borne disease known as **Haverhill fever,** after the town of Haverhill, Massachusetts, where the first outbreak was reported in 1926 by Place and his associates (124). In the same year the organism was isolated and identified independently by Parker and Hudson and by Levaditi. A more extensive outbreak, in which 86 individuals were infected, occurred in Massachusetts in 1934 (124). It has been assumed that the milk becomes contaminated from infected cows or by rats drinking from uncovered cans of milk. The strains recovered from patients infected by the bites of rats have been shown to be identical with the strains cultured from individuals who acquired their disease by drinking infected milk (32).

The name "rat-bite fever" is somewhat ambiguous, since wild rats also carry a spirochete, *Spirillum minus*, which, when introduced into a human by a bite, initiates a disease with the same general clinical characteristics as that produced by *Streptobacillus moniliformis* (32). In a few instances both organisms have been introduced simultaneously by the same bite (2).

Streptobacillus moniliformis is a **nonsporogenous, nonencapsulated, nonmotile gramnegative,** pleomorphic rod, 0.4 to 0.6 μ in width and from 1 to 30 or 40 μ in length. Coccobacillary, bacillary, branching, and clubshaped cells are found in cultures. Pleuropneumonia-like organisms are found associated with most strains isolated from rats and man.

The organism is a **facultative anaerobe** which is isolated best on a medium containing serum or ascitic fluid, incubated in the presence of 10 per cent CO_2.

The bacillus will grow on the chorio-allantoic membrane of the developing chick embryo but usually invades the joints, where it multiplies primarily in the cells of the synovial membranes (16). Mice are susceptible to experimental infection.

In man the disease begins within a few days following the introduction of the organism by the bite of the rat. An irregular type of fever develops which may persist for weeks or months. Early in the disease a morbilliform-like eruption appears on the skin of the extremities and there is a more or less severe generalized **arthritis.** The organisms usually are easier to isolate from the blood than from the original wound. Specific agglutinins appear in the blood 10 to 75 days after infection and persist for months after the patient has made an apparently complete recovery (15). **Penicillin** in large doses is moderately effective if administered early in the disease.

BARTONELLA BACILLIFORMIS AND OROYA FEVER

Order: *Rickettsiales.* Family: *Bartonellaceae* Gieszczykiewicz, 1939. Genus: *Bartonella* Strong, Tyzzer and Sellards, 1915. Species: *Bartonella bacilliformis* Strong, Tyzzer and Sellards, 1915

In the seventh edition of Bergey's Manual *Bartonella bacilliformis* which causes disease in man, and the somewhat similar organisms

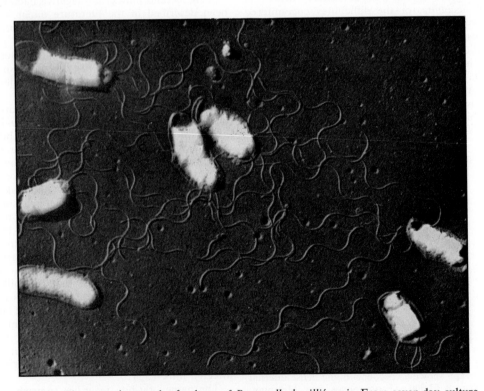

Fig. 10. Electron micrograph of culture of *Bartonella bacilliformis.* From seven-day culture. Note cell wall and terminal flagella apparently originating from protoplasts. $\times$ 15,000. (From Peters and Wigand. *Z. tropenmed. u. Parasitol.,* 3:313, 1952.)

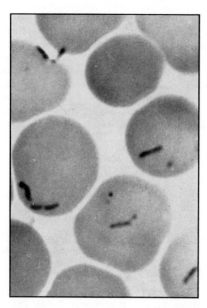

Fig. 11. *Bartonella bacilliformis.* Human blood stained with Giemsa stain. × 3,000. (From Wigand, Peters, and Urtega. *Z. Tropenmed. u. Parasitol.,* 4:539, 1953.)

from animals, *Haemobartonella, Eperythro-zoon,* and *Grahamella,* have been brought together with the *Rickettsiaceae* and the *Chlamydiaceae* in the order *Rickettsiales* of the class *Microtatobiotes.* This classification has not met universal approval. Peters and Wigand (121) suggest that *Bartonella bacilliformis* and *Grahamellae talpae* should be classified with the small bacteria since both are larger than *Rickettsia* and can be cultivated on artificial media. *Bartonella bacilliformis* has a definite cell wall, with *lophotrichous* flagella attached to one end of the rod (Figs. 10, 11). The animal erythrocyte parasites, *H. muris,* and *E. coccoides* are filterable and resemble the *Chlamydiaceae* and the pleuro-pneumonia organism in size. Their morphology (Figs. 12 and 13), plasticity, and lack of cell walls suggest the pleuropneumonia organism, but they cannot be classified with them since they have not been cultivated on artificial media.

From ancient times the inhabitants of certain areas in Peru have suffered from a disease characterized by fever, anemia and a nodular warty eruption. Many of the natives have died from this disease. The infection manifests itself as two distinct clinical diseases: **Verruga peruviana,** in which the eruption is the predominant symptom, and **Oroya fever,** which is characterized by fever and severe anemia. The

argument as to whether or not the diseases were separate entities or different manifestations of the same disease apparently was settled in 1885 by Daniel Carrión, a medical student in Lima, who inoculated himself with blood from a patient with a verruga nodule. He died, presumably of Oroya fever, 23 days later, and the infection often is referred to as **Carrión's disease** in recognition of his martyrdom. Subsequent bacteriologic and transmission investigations have indicated that the two diseases actually are different manifestations of the same infectious process.

In 1905 Barton found a small coccobacillus in or on the **red corpuscles,** and sometimes outside the cells, in the blood of patients with Oroya fever. Strong in 1913 named the organism *Bartonella bacilliformis.* In 1926 Noguchi cultivated the bacillus from the blood of patients with Oroya fever (110).

Under natural conditions *Bartonella bacilliformis* grows on the erythrocytes of man but in the cytoplasm of his tissue cells. The organisms vary in size from minute coccoid bodies to short rods, 0.25 to 0.5 μ in width and 1 to 3 μ in length. When grown in culture, they are **nonsporogenous, nonencapsulated, motile, gram-negative** rods. They are **obligate aerobes** and grow best at a temperature of 28° C. in semisolid agar containing fresh rabbit serum and rabbit hemoglobin, with or without the

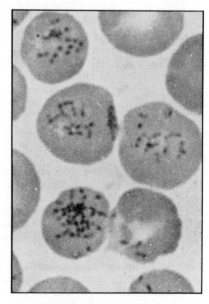

Fig. 12. *Haemobartonella muris.* Blood of Syrian hamster stained with Giemsa stain. × 3,000. (From Wigand and Peters. *Z. Tropenmed. u. Parasitol.,* 3:437, 1952.)

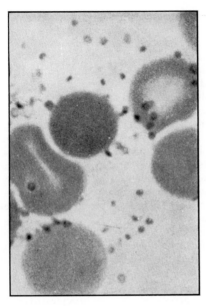

Fig. 13. *Eperythrozoon coccoides.* Mouse blood stained with Giemsa stain. × 3,000. (From Wigand and Peters. *Z. Tropenmed. u. Parasitol.,* 3:461, 1952.)

addition of fresh tissue. They also can be cultured in the chorioallantoic fluid and yolk sac of the developing chick embryo.

With pure cultures, Noguchi (110) produced atypical Oroya fever but typical verrucal lesions in several species of monkeys.

The mortality from the Oroya fever form of the infection varies from 18 to 95 per cent, with an average of 40 per cent. The mortality from the verrucal form of the disease, however, is very low (99). A permanent immunity follows recovery from either form of the disease, and convalescent serums contain complement-fixing and agglutinating antibodies which react with strains of *Bartonella bacilliformis* isolated from both types of the infection. Complement-fixation tests with strains isolated from different patients suggest that there is only one antigenic type (131).

Under natural conditions the infection is transmitted to man by the bite of *Phlebotomus verrucarum* in Peru and by *P. colombianum* in Colombia (184, 185).

Neoarsphenamine and arsenic-antimony compounds do not affect *Bartonella bacilliformis* but do eliminate *H. muris* and *E. coccoides* from the blood of animals. Patients with *Bartonella bacilliformis* infections have been cured with penicillin (100), streptomycin (1), chloramphenicol (119). The tetracycline antibiotics

are effective in Murine bartonellosis (165, 166). DDT, when used properly, eliminates the sand flies and prevents the disease (27).

Related organisms which parasitize the red cells of animals include *Haemobartonella muris, H. canis, Grahamella talpae,* and *Eperythrozoon coccoides.*

A detailed discussion of these parasites of red blood cells can be found by consulting other references (121, 174, 184, 185).

REFERENCES

1. Aldana, G. L., and others. Arch. peruanos patol. y. clin. Lima, 2:323, 1948.
2. Allbritten, F. F., and others. J.A.M.A., 114: 2360, 1940.
3. Bayne-Jones, S. J. Bact., 10:569, 1925.
4. Beaver, D. C., and Thompson, L. Am. J. Path., 9:603, 1933.
5. Beveridge, W. I. B. J. Path. & Bact., 38: 467, 1934.
6. Bibby, B. G. J. Dent. Res., 11:855, 1931.
7. Black, G. V. Practitioner, 7:546, 1886.
8. Blake, F. G. J. Exper. Med., 23:39, 1916.
9. Blayney, J. R., and others. J. Dent. Res., 15:326, 1935.
10. Boyd, J. D., and Drain, C. L. J.A.M.A., 90: 1867, 1928.
11. Boyle, P. E. Kronfeld's Histopathology of Teeth and Their Surrounding Tissues, 4th ed., Philadelphia, Lea and Febiger, 1955.
12. Bradel, S. F., and Blayney, J. R. J.A.D.A., 27:1601, 1940.
13. Breed, R. S., and others. Bergey's Manual of Determinative Bacteriology, 7th ed., Baltimore, The Williams and Wilkins Co., 1957.
14. Brewer, J. H. J.A.M.A., 115:598, 1940.
15. Brown, T. McP., and Nunemaker, J. C. Bull. Johns Hopkins Hosp., 70:201, 1942.
16. Buddingh, G. J. J. Exper. Med., 80:59, 1944.
17. Buhler, V. B., and others. Am. J. Clin. Path., 12:380, 1942.
18. Bunting, R. W., and others. Dental Cosmos., 68:931, 1926.
19. ——— and others. J.A.D.A., 16:224, 1929.
20. ——— and Palmerlee, F. J.A.D.A., 12: 381, 1925.
21. Burdon, K. L. J. Infect. Dis., 42:161, 1928.
22. ——— and Scherp, H. W. J. Dent. Res., 30:766, 1951.
23. Burnett, G. W., and Scherp, H. W. Oral Microbiology and Infectious Disease, Baltimore, The Williams and Wilkins Co., 1962, 2nd ed.
24. Canby, C. P., and Bernier, J. L. J.A.D.A., 23:2083, 1936.
25. Carter, B., and others. Obs. & Gyn., 1:491, 1953.
26. Coolidge, T. B. J. Infect. Dis., 88:241, 1951.
27. Corradetti, A. Rendic. 1st Super. San., 12: 561, 1949.
28. Custis, D. L., and others. Arch. Path., 38: 332, 1944.
29. Dack, G. M. Bact. Rev., 4:227, 1940.
30. Dacres, W. G., and Groth, A. H. J. Bact., 78:298, 1959.

31. Davies, E. F., and Nemes, J. L. Oral Surg., Oral Med., and Oral Path., 8:526, 1955.
32. Dawson, M. H., and Hobby, G. Proc. Third Internat. Congress Microbiol., New York, Sect. 1, 177, 1940.
33. Dienes, L., and Smith, W. E. J. Bact., 48:125, 1944.
34. Dreizen, S., and others. J. Dent. Res., 25:213, 1946.
35. Dunn, M. S., and others. J. Biol. Chem., 168:1, 23, 1947.
36. Ehrlich, J. C. Arch. Int. Med., 78:565, 1946.
37. Eveland, W. C. J. Bact., 85:1448, 1963.
38. Fish, E. W., and Maclean, I. H. Dent. Cosmos., 76:837, 1934.
39. Fitzgerald, R. J., and Keyes, P. H. J.A.D.A., 61:25-33, 1960.
40. Fosdick, L. S., and others. J. Dent. Res., 32:486, 1953.
41. ——— and others. Dent. Cosmos., 24:1275, 1937.
42. Garrod, L. P. British M. J., 2:1529, 1955.
43. Gibbons, R. J., and MacDonald, J. B. J. Bact., 80:164, 1960.
44. ——— and MacDonald, J. B. J. Bact., 81:614, 1961.
45. Gies, W. J., and Kligler, I. J. J. Allied Dent. Socs., 10:141, 242, 445, 1915.
46. Gilmore, M. N., and others. Bact. Rev., 25:131, 1961.
47. Girard, K. F., and Murray, E. G. D. Canad. J. Biochem. & Physiol., 32:1, 1954.
48. Girard, K. F., and others. J. Bact., 85:349, 1963.
49. Glass, R. L. Oral Surg., 5:210, 1952.
50. Gledhill, A. W. J. Path. & Bact., 57:179, 1945.
51. Goldie, W., and Collins, D. H. J. Path. & Bact., 71:425, 1956.
52. Gordon, S. M. Dental Science and Dental Art, Philadelphia, Lea and Febiger, 1938.
53. Gray, M. L. J. Bact., 59:443, 1950.
54. ——— Ann. N.Y. Acad. Sc., 98:686, 1962.
55. ——— Science, 132:1767, 1963.
56. ——— and McWade, D. H. J. Bact., 68:634, 1954.
57. ——— and others. Proc. Soc. Exper. Biol. & Med., 89:163, 175, 1955.
58. Grey, C. G. Vet. Med., 42:74, 177, 216, 1947.
59. Hadley, F. P. J. Dent. Res., 13:415, 1933.
60. Harris, J. W., and Brown, J. H. Bull. Johns Hopkins Hosp., 40:203, 1927.
61. Harrison, R. W., and others. J. Infect. Dis., 65:255, 1939.
62. ——— J. Infect. Dis., 70:77, 1942.
63. ——— and Opal, Z. Z. J. Dent. Res., 23:1, 1944.
64. Harrison, R. W. J.A.D.A., 37:391, 1948.
65. ——— and Hansen, P. A. J. Bact., 59:444, 1950.
66. Hemmens, E. S., and others. J. Dent. Res., 25:195, 1946.
67. Hine, M. K., and Berry, G. P. J. Bact., 34:517, 1937.
68. Hodge, E. A., and others. J. Infect. Dis., 88:237, 1951.
69. Hoffman, H. Ann. Rev. Microbiol., 11:195, 1957.
70. Howitt, B. J. Infect. Dis., 46:351, 1930.
71. James, P. M. C., and Parfitt, G. J. J. Brit. Dent. Assoc., 97:83, 1954.
72. Jay, P., and others. J. Dent. Res., 12:429, 1932.
73. ——— and others. J.A.D.A., 19:265, 1932.
74. ——— and others. J.A.D.A., 23:846, 1936.
75. ——— and others. Dietary Program for the Control of Dental Caries, Ann Arbor, The Overbeck Co., 1955.
76. Julianelle, L. A. Ann. Int. Med., 14:608, 1940.
77. Kelly, F. C. J. Infect. Dis., 74:93, 1944.
78. Keyes, P. H. Arch. Oral Biol., 1:304, 1960.
79. King, A. B., and others. Ann. Int. Med., 37:761, 1952.
80. King, E. O., and Seeliger, H. P. R. J. Bact., 77:122, 1959.
81. Klauder, J. V., and others. J.A.M.A., 122:938, 1943.
82. Klinger, R. Centralbl. f. Bakt., I Abt., Orig., 62:191, 1912.
83. Koch, R. Investigations into the Etiology of Traumatic Infective Disease, London, New Sydenham Soc., 1880.
84. Koser, S. A., and others. J. Dent. Res., 30:532, 1951.
85. Leifson, E., and Palen, M. I. J. Bact., 70:233, 1955.
86. Lewis, K. H., and Rettger, L. F. J. Bact., 40:287, 1940.
87. Lignières, J., and Spitz, G. Bull. Soc. Cent. Med. Vet., 20:487, 546, 1902.
88. Lilly, C. A. J. Nutr., 5:175, 1932.
89. Löffler, F. Arb. a. d. Reichsgsndhtamt., 2:421, 1884; 1:46, 1886.
90. Longcope, W. T. Am. J. Med. Sc., 164:781, 1922.
91. Massler, M. N. Zeal. Dent. J., 58:272, 1962.
92. McCarthy, C., and Snyder, M. L. J. Bact., 86:158, 1963.
93. McGinnis, G. F., and Spindle, F. Am. J. Pub. Health, 24:32, 1934.
94. McHenry, M. C., and others. Arch. Int. Med., 107:572, 1961.
95. McIntosh, J., and others. Brit. J. Exper. Path., 9:260, 1925.
96. ——— and others. J. Brit. Dent. Assoc., 43:728, 1922.
97. McVay, L. V., Jr., and others. J.A.M.A., 140:1150, 1949.
98. ——— and Sprunt, D. H. Ann. Int. Med., 36:56, 1952.
99. Merino, C. Rev. Med. peruana, 18:329, 1945.
100. ——— J. Lab. & Clin. Med., 30:1021, 1945.
101. Metzger, J. F., and Smith, C. W. Proc. Soc. Exper. and Med., 110:903, 1962.
102. Miller, W. D. Dent. Cosmos., 25:1, 337, 1883; 44:425, 1902.
103. Morishita, T. Proc. Soc. Exper. Biol. & Med., 25:654, 1928.
104. Morris, M. C., and Julianelle, L. A. Am. J. Ophth., 18:535, 1935.
105. Murphy, R., and others. Arch. Int. Med., 111:51, 1963.
106. Murray, E. G. D., and others. J. Path. & Bact., 29:407, 1926.
107. ——— Trans. Roy. Soc. Canada, 47:15, 1953.
108. Neter, E., and others. Proc. Soc. Exper. Biol. and Med., 105:131, 1960.

109. Njokv-Obi, A. N., and others. J. Bact., 81:1, 1963.
110. Noguchi, H. J. Exper. Med., 43:851, 1926; 44:543, 697, 715, 729, 1926; 48: Supplement No. 2, 1-53, 1928.
111. Noyes, H. J. Dent. Res., 15:327, 1935.
112. Oliver, W. W., and Wherry, W. B. J. Infect. Dis., 28:341, 1921.
113. Omata, R. R. J. Bact., 77:35, 1959.
114. ——— and Disraely, M. N. J. Bact., 72: 677, 1956.
115. Orland, F. J. J. Infect. Dis., 86:63, 1950.
116. ——— Int. Dent. J., 4:123, 1953.
117. Pasteur, L., and Thuillier. Compt. rend. Acad. d. sc., 97:1163, 1883.
118. Patterson, J. S. J. Path. & Bact., 51:427, 1940.
119. Payne, E. H., and Urteaga, O. Antibiotics and Chemotherapy, 1:92, 1951.
120. Pesch, K. L., and Schmitz, L. Zentralbl. f. Bakt., 136:476, 1936.
121. Peters, D., and Wigand, R. Bact. Reviews, 19:150, 1955.
122. Pfeiffer, E. Jahrb. f. Kinderh., 29:257, 1889.
123. Pincus, P. Brit. Dent. J., 76:231, 1944.
124. Place, E. H., and Sutton, L. E. Arch. Int. Med., 54:659, 1934.
125. Poston, M. A., and others. J. Pediat., 11: 515, 1937.
126. Prier, J. E., and Alberts, J. O. J. Bact., 60:139, 1950.
127. Rantz, L. A. J.A.M.A., 147:124, 1951.
128. Rapp, G. W. Ill. Dent. J., 31:290, 1962.
129. Rappaport, F., and others. Lancet, I., 1273, 1960.
130. Ravant, P., and Pinoy. Presse med., 19:49, 1911.
131. Reese, J. D., and others. J. Immunol., 65: 355, 1950.
132. Remmington, T. S., and others. Arch. Int. Med., 110:744, 1962.
133. Rettger, L. F., Levy, M. N., Weinstein, L., and Weiss, J. E. *Lactobacillus acidophilus* and Its Therapeutic Application, New Haven, Yale University Press, 1935.
134. Ristic, M., and others. Am. J. Vet. Res., 17:555, 1956.
135. Robbins, M. L., and Griffin, A. M. J. Immunol., 50:237, 247, 1945.
136. Rodriguez, F. E. J.A.D.A., 17:1711, 1930.
137. ——— Milit. Dent. J., 5:199, 1922.
138. Rogosa, M., and Sharpe, M. E. J. Applied Bact., 22:329, 1959.
139. ——— and others. J. Bact., 54:13, 1947.
140. ——— and others. J. Bact., 65:681, 1953.
141. ——— and others. J. Dent. Res., 29:658, 1950.
142. Rosebury, T., and others. J. Bact., 18:395, 1929.
143. ——— and others. Arch. Path., 38:413, 1944.
144. ——— and others. J. Dent. Res., 12:430, 1932.
145. Rosenbach, F. J. Ztschr. f. Hyg. u. Infektionskr., 58:343, 1909.
146. Rosenwald, A. S., and Dickinson, E. M. Am. J. Vet. Res., 2:202, 1941.
147. Rubin, S. H., and others. Ann. Int. Med., 35:468, 1951.
148. Schottmuller, H. Dermat. Wchnschr., 58: 77, suppl. 1914.
149. Schmidt, J. M., and Richardson, R. L. J. Bact., 83:584, 1962.
150. Schwabacher, H., and others. J. Gen. Microbiol., 11:109, 1947.
151. Seastone, C. V. J. Exper. Med., 62:203, 1935.
152. Seeliger, H. P. R. Listerosis. Hafner Publishing Co., Inc., New York, 1961.
153. ——— and Sulzbacher, F. Canadian J. Microbiol., 2:220, 1956.
154. Serros, G., and Mattman, L. H. J. Bact., 70:483, 1955.
155. Sherman, J. M., and Hodge, H. M. J. Bact., 40:11, 1940.
156. Smith, C. W., and Metzger, J. F. Path. Microbiol. (Basel), 25:499, 1962.
157. Smith, D. T. Oral Spirochetes and Related Organisms in Fuso-Spirochetal Disease. Williams & Wilkins Co., Baltimore, 1932, pp. 14-20.
158. Smith, T. J. Exper. Med., 28:333, 1918.
159. Smith, W. E., and Ropes, M. W. New England J. Med., 232:31, 1945.
160. Snyder, M. L., and Clark, M. K. J. Dent. Res., 29:298, 1950.
161. Snyder, N. S., et al. J.A.D.A., 65:30, 1962.
162. Spaulding, E. H., and Rettger, L. F. J. Bact., 34:535, 549, 1937.
163. Sprunt, T. B., and Evans, F. A. Bull. Johns Hopkins Hosp., 31:410, 1920.
164. Stanley, N. F. Australian J. Exper. Biol. & Med., 27:123, 1949; 28:117, 1950.
165. Stanton, A. T., and Fletcher, W. J. Hyg. 23:347, 1925.
166. Stanton, M. F., and others. Proc. Soc. Exper. Biol. & Med., 74:705, 1950.
167. Stephan, R. M. J. Dent. Res., 17:251, 1938; 24:202, 1945; 26:15, 1947.
168. Stralfors, A. J. Dent. Res., 27:576, 1948.
169. Sword, C. P., and Pickett, M. J. J. Gen. Microbiol., 25:241, 1961.
170. Thompson, L., and Willius, F. A. J.A.M.A., 99:298, 1932.
171. ——— J. Bact., 26:221, 1933.
172. Tiffany, L. D., and Wheaton, R. B. J. Bact., 68:258, 1954.
173. Tilden, E. B., and Svec, M. J. Dent. Res., 29:659, 1950; 31:831, 1952.
174. Topley, W. W. C., and Wilson, G. S. The Principles of Bacteriology and Immunity, 3rd ed., Baltimore, Williams & Wilkins Co., 1946.
175. Tunnicliff, R., and Hammond, C. J. Infect. Dis., 61:26, 1937.
176. Tynes, B. S., and Frommeyer, W. B., Jr. Ann. Int. Med., 56:12, 1962.
177. van Gelder, D. W., and others. J.A.M.A., 169:559, 1959.
178. Varney, P. L. J. Bact., 13:275, 1927.
179. Veillon, A., and Zuber, A. Arch. de méd. expér. et d'anat. path., 10:517, 1898.
180. Vincent, H. Ann. Inst. Pasteur, 10:488, 1896.
181. Watts, P. S. J. Path. & Bact., 50:355, 1940.
182. Webb, R. A. Lancet, 2:5, 1943.
183. Weed, L. A. Am. J. Clin. Path., 38:537, 1962.
184. Weinmann, D. Tr. Am. Philosophical Soc., 33:243, Pt. III, 1944.
185. ——— Bacterial and Mycotic Infections of Man, 2nd ed., Dubos, R. J., ed., Philadelphia, Lippincott, and Co., 1952, p. 608.

186. Weiss, C., and Mercado, D. G. J. Exper. Med., 67:49, 1938.
187. Weiss, C. Surgery, 13:683, 1943.
188. Weiss, J. E., and Rettger, L. F. J. Bact., 33:423, 1937.
189. Welshimer, H. J. J. Bact., 79:456, 1960.
190. ——— J. Bact., 80:316, 1960.
191. ——— and Winglewish, N. G. J.A.M.A., 171:1319, 1959.
192. Williams, N. B. J. Infect. Dis., 82:31, 1948; 92:121, 1953.
193. ——— J.A.D.A., 37:403, 1948.
194. ——— and Franck, E. B. J. Dent. Res., 36:361, 1957.
195. Wilson, G. S., and Miles, A. A. Topley and Wilson's Principles of Bacteriology and Immunity, 4th ed., Baltimore, Williams & Wilkins Co., 1955.
196. Wilson, R. M., and Green, G. F. Proc. Soc. Exper. Biol. and Med., 112:149, 1963.
197. Woodbine, M. Bact. Rev., 14:1616, 1950.

THE SPIROCHETES

49

The Spirochetes

Order: *Spirochaetales*

Spirochetes are slender, undulating, cork-screw-like, relatively flexible, filamentous organisms. They are ubiquitous, occurring in nature in soil, water, and decaying organic materials and in and upon the bodies of plants, animals, and man. Some of the spirochetes are **saprophytes,** some are **commensals,** and others are **pathogens,** causing a number of very serious and severe diseases of human beings and of the lower animals. Among the pathogens are the spirochetes which cause diseases in man, such as **syphilis, yaws, relapsing fever** and **hemorrhagic jaundice;** other spirochetes cause various septicemias in birds and mammals (4, 19).

Leeuwenhoek described the appearance and motility of spirochetes in his own feces and his own mouth (6). The first disease-producing spirochete was discovered by Obermeier (15) in 1873 in the blood of patients with relapsing fever. *Treponema pallidum* was not discovered until 1905, and the discoverers, Schaudinn and Hoffmann (17), believed the organism was a protozoan.

Nature of Spirochetes. Those who are best qualified to express opinions on the nature of spirochetes have not agreed as to whether the organisms are bacteria or protozoa. The spirochetes have characteristics common to both groups of microorganisms and individual properties distinguishing them as a class. It is the present belief that spirochetes are more closely related to the bacteria than to the protozoa.

General Characteristics of Spirochetes. The most important general features of these organisms are the following (14).

Morphology. The spirochetes have short or long spirals with the coils in three dimensions. The size varies greatly, from 2 to 500 μ in length. The organisms are unicellular. Some forms have an elastic axial filament, but in the small forms the existence of this filament could not be demonstrated until the technic of electron micrography was developed and perfected (20). The cell body usually is cylindrical and round on cross-section. The spirals are relatively fixed but are somewhat extensible. The number of spirals in some forms has diagnostic importance. The distance between the crests of the spirals, the amplitude or distance from the crest of the spiral to the midline, and the pitch or sharpness of angle of the spirals are superimposed upon these fundamental spirals. Except in *Spirochaeta plicatilis,* there is no cell wall, but a thin elastic membrane is present. The existence of a nucleus, comparable to that in bacilli, is suggested by certain structures seen in electron micrographs (2). Thin sections of *Treponema microdenium* made by Listgarten and his associates (12) shows that this organism has an axial filament made of two fibrils approximately 150 Å. in diameter, and these fibrils are located between an external envelope approximately 140 Å. in thickness and an internal protoplastic cylinder.

Flexibility. All spirochetes are more flexible than bacteria, but flexibility of these organisms varies with different species. Zinsser and Hopkins (22) found an organism in the testis of the rabbit so inflexible that the name *Treponema rigidum* was proposed for it. The pathogenic spirochetes are all very flexible.

Spore and Granule Formation. The spirochetes do not form resistant endospores. In old cultures, in some lesions, and in the eggs of insect vectors only minute granular forms can be found. Most of these granules are nonviable (16), but the possibility of minute viable spirochetes which might be mistaken for granules has not been eliminated.

Filtrability. Infectious filtrates of spirochetes of the relapsing fever types and the leptospiral types have been obtained by various observers. These organisms, either in a granulated form or in a spiral form, pass through Berkefeld V and N filters. This question involves the physics of filtration as much as the form and nature of the organism. A slow passage through a filter by growth along the channels has been demonstrated for *Treponema pallidum*.

MOTILITY. Spirochetes are motile. They progress by sinuous and rotating movements of the body. Some of them have delicate terminal filaments. Noguchi (14) believed that the essential structure of a *Treponema* consisted of a spring-like axial filament and a layer of contractile protoplasm enclosed in a delicate protoplast. He believed that the axial filament was a kind of intracellular flagellum. Noguchi did not illustrate the axial filament, and most observers for the next 40 years denied its existence. The first electron micrographs failed to show axial filaments but did reveal thread-like appendages resembling flagella. Subsequent studies have confirmed Noguchi's conclusions. External flagella are not found on organisms examined directly from living man or animals. However, after tryptic or peptic digestion for 10 minutes, three axial filaments can be seen in the body of *T. pallidum*, and eight to 12 in *Bor. recurrentis*. After 20 minutes digestion, the filaments are freed from the body and appear as flagella (1, 3, 20). The contractile material in the *Leptospira* is wound around the outside of the organism (3, 20). The organism *Spirillum minus*, which causes rat-bite fever, resembles a spirochete in many ways but has a tuft of flagella at each end.

DIVISION. Spirochetes usually divide by transverse fission, but they may have a more complicated method of reproduction. In the large free-living spirochete studied by Williams (21) the most common mode of division was by transverse fission, but sometimes the organism folded back upon itself in such a manner that a fusion of protoplasm occurred at certain specific locations. This fusion was followed by the development of a large cyst-like structure. After a period of time numerous short spirochetes emerged from the cyst and gradually grew to a size characteristic of the species. Large bodies of this type have been seen in electron micrographs of *Treponema* by a number of observers (5, 16), in *Bor. duttonii* (3, 20) and in *Leptospira* (2), but the emergence of young forms has not been observed. Spherical bodies similar to those developing spontaneously in cultures of treponemes can

be produced by reducing the osmotic pressure in the median containing the spirochetes (10).

RESISTANCE. Resistance to the solvent or lytic action of saponin and bile varies with the different species, but since the same variations are found among the bacteria, this property has no special differential significance. Resistance to plasmolysis and plasmoptysis is the same as that observed for bacteria. The range of resistance to heat is within that of the bacteria. Most of the spirochetes are killed at 60° C. in one half-hour. Since these organisms do not form endospores, their resistance to injurious substances and physical agents is similar to that of the nonsporogenous bacteria.

Susceptibility to chemotherapeutic agents is notable among the organisms in this group, and the spirochetes differ from the bacteria in being especially susceptible to destruction by arsenic, antimony, bismuth, mercury compounds, and penicillin when they are within the bodies of animals.

STAINING REACTIONS. Some spirochetes stain readily with the ordinary aniline dyes, but most of the pathogenic varieties are difficult to stain. Such stains as those of Wright, Giemsa, and the ones based upon Romanowsky's method give the best results. Spirochetes which can be stained by Gram's method are **gram-negative**. Impregnation of the organisms with silver nitrate, followed by reduction of the silver in the organism, is a procedure of great utility in the demonstration of spirochetes in tissue and smears. The Levaditi method usually is applied to tissues; the Fontana-Tribondeau method is employed in staining smears.

The pathogenic spirochetes, 0.1 to 0.2 μ in thickness, are seen best in the living state by darkfield illumination. **Darkfield illumination** is and should be a routine procedure in the examination of material for spirochetes.

CULTIVATION. Geiman (9) has reviewed the nutritional requirement and metabolism of the spirochetes which can be cultivated. The *Leptospira* and many of the free-living forms are aerobic and can be cultivated without much difficulty. The *Borrelia* are anaerobic or microaerophilic. They survive and multiply slowly in Noguchi's ascitic fluid—rabbit kidney medium and in embryonated eggs (1a). Nonpathogenic *Treponema* from the mouth or genitalia can be cultivated under anaerobic conditions by Noguchi's and other methods (14). Investigators agree that the pathogenic *Treponema* from syphilis, yaws, and pinta have not been cultivated.

Hardy, Lee, and Nell (11) succeeded in

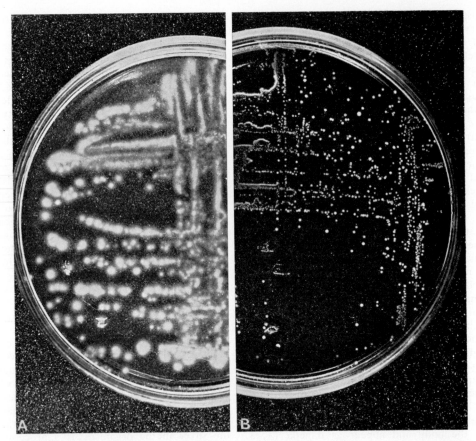

Fig. 1. A, diffuse colonies of Kazan A strain of *Treponema pallidum* on 0.7 per cent agar after eight days of incubation. B, rhizoid and discrete round colonies of the Reiter strain of *T. pallidum* on 0.7 per cent agar after eight days of incubation. (From Hardy, Lee, and Nell. *J. Bact.,* 86:616, 1963.)

cultivating 14 strains of treponemas and one of *Borrelia vincenti* in colony form on agar plates inoculated under ordinary atmospheric conditions but incubated anaerobically (Fig. 1). All strains produced diffused colonies in the depth of the agar, and eight *Treponema* strains also produced discrete colonies with surface growth (Fig. 2 and 3). A firm jelly agar, Iongar, No. 2, with a final agar concentration of 0.7 per cent, was essential for growth in a rich medium which was clear and contained 10 per cent rabbit serum but no red blood cells.

Nomenclature. A primary classification can be based on habitat, parasitism, and pathogenicity, although parasites, commensals, and saprophytes occur in the same genus.

The classification of spirochetes summarized from the seventh edition of Bergey's Manual, is as follows:

1. *Spirochaeta.* Nonparasitic, with flexible, undulating body. Protoplast wound spirally around a well-defined axial filament. Motility by creeping motion. Primary spiral permanent. Free-living in fresh or sea water slime. Type species: *Spirochaeta plicatilis* Ehrenberg.

2. *Saprospira.* Spiral protoplasm without evident axial filament. Motility active and rotating. Free-living in marine ooze. Type species: *Saprospira grandis* Gross.

3. *Cristispira.* Flexous cell bodies in coarse spirals, 28 to 120 microns in length. Characterized by a crista or by a thin membrane of varying prominence on one side of the body. Found in the intestinal tracts of mollusks. Type species: *Cristispira balbianii* (Certes) Gross.

4. *Borrelia.* Length 8 to 16 μ. Coarse, shallow, irregular spirals. Some are patho-

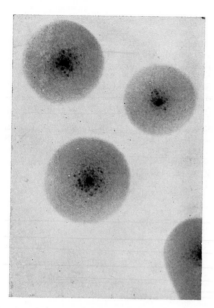

Fig. 2. Round colonies of Reiter *Treponema* after seven days incubation. × 30. (From Hardy, Lee, and Nell. *J. Bact.,* 86:616, 1963.)

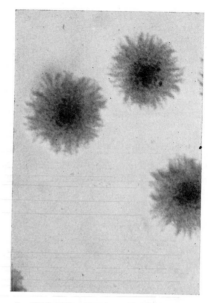

Fig. 3. Rhizoid colonies of Reiter *Treponema* after seven days incubation. × 30. (From Hardy, Lee, and Nell. *J. Bact.,* 86:616, 1963.)

genic for man, other mammals, and birds. Generally hematophytes are found on mucous membranes. Type species: *Borrelia anserina* (Sakharoff) Bergey and others.

5. *Treponema.* Length 3 to 18 μ. Protoplasm in acute, regular, or irregular spirals. Pathogenic and parasitic for man and animals. Type species: *Treponema pallidum* (Schaudinn and Hoffmann) Schaudinn.

6. *Leptospira.* Finely coiled organisms 6 to 20 μ in length. Spirals 0.3 μ in depth and 0.4 μ in amplitude. In liquid medium one or both ends are bent into a semicircular hook. Type species: *Leptospira icterohaemorrhagiae* (Inada and Ido) Noguchi.

In this classification there is no place for the spiral organism which causes rat-bite fever. This organism was called *Spirochaeta morsus-muris* by its discoverer. It is a small rigid spiral form with tufts of flagella at each end. English authorities, particularly, regard this organism as predominantly bacterial and have named it *Spirillum minus*. Bayne-Jones (1) considers the organism to be more closely related to the spirochetes. Other similar organisms have been found in the stomach contents and intestines of animals, and for these the generic name *Spirella* was proposed by

Dubosq and Lebailly (7) in 1912. In 1928 Noguchi (14) applied this name to the rat-bite fever organism.

Artifact Spirochetes. Many mistakes have been made by those unfamiliar with the appearance of blood, pus, and cultures under darkfield illumination in identifying as spirochetes wavy filamentous structures of heterogeneous origin. Forms extraordinarily like spirochetes are given off by red corpuscles in a drop under a coverglass (18). Fibrin filaments may resemble spirochetes. Cilia (13), bacterial flagella (8), and numerous pieces of cellular débris often have a deceptive spirochetal appearance. They usually can be distinguished from spirochetes by repeated **controlled** observations.

REFERENCES

1. Bayne-Jones, S. New York State J. Med., 27:1113, 1927.
1a. Bradfield, J. R. G., and Cater, D. B. Nature, 169:944, 1952.
2. Czekalowski, J. W., and Eaves, G. J. Bact., 67:619, 1954.
3. ——— Eaves, G. J. Path. & Bact., 69:129, 1955.
4. Davis, G. E. Ann. Rev. Microbiol., 2:305, 1948.
5. DeLamater, E. D., and others. Am. J. Syph., Gonor. & Ven. Dis., 35:164, 1951.
6. Dobell, C. Antony van Leeuwenhoek and His "Little Animals," New York, Harcourt

Brace and Co., 1932, pp. 225 and plate XXIV facing p. 239.

7. Dubosq, O., and Lebailly, C.   Compt. rend. Acad. d. sc., 154:535, 1912.
8. Florence, L.   J. Bact., 6:371, 1921.
9. Geiman, Q. M.   Ann. Rev. Microbiol., 6: 299, 1952.
10. Hardy, P. H., Jr., and Nell, E. E.   J. Bact., 82:967, 1961.
11. ——— and others.   J. Bact., 86:616, 1963.
12. Listgarten, M. A., and others.   J. Bact., 85: 932, 1963.
13. May, H. G., and Goodner, K.   Tr. Am. Micr. Soc., 45:302, 1926.
14. Noguchi, H.   The spirochetes, in The Newer Knowledge of Bacteriology and Immunology.

Chicago, University of Chicago, 1928, Chap. 36, pp. 452-497.
15. Obermeier, O. H. F.   Centralbl. f. d. med. Wissensch., 11:145, 1873.
16. Rose, N. R., and Morton, H. E.   Am. J. Syph., Gonor. & Ven. Dis., 37:17, 1952.
17. Schaudinn, F., and Hoffmann, E.   Arab. a. d. k. Gsndhtsamte., 22:526, 1905.
18. Schulitz, E. W.   J. Lab. & Clin. Med., 8:2, 1923.
19. Stavitsky, A. B.   Bact. Rev., 12:203, 1948.
20. Swain, R. H. A.   J. Path. & Bact., 69:117, 1955.
21. Williams, M. A.   Bacteriol. Proc., p. 36, 1956.
22. Zinsser, H., and Hopkins, J. G.   J. Bact., 1:489, 1916.

50

Treponema pallidum and Syphilis

Family: *Treponemataceae* Robinson. Genus: *Treponema* Schaudinn. Species: *Treponema pallidum* (Schaudinn and Hoffmann) Schaudinn

SYPHILIS

Syphilis is an infectious disease with protean manifestations caused by a spirochete, *Treponema pallidum.* Under natural conditions syphilis occurs only in man, and the infection usually is transmitted from one human being to another by direct contact, generally through sexual intercourse.

Beginning about 1936, a major effort was made to control syphilis in the United States. Moderate success was being obtained before the introduction of penicillin therapy in 1945. The combination of control measures and penicillin therapy reduced the number of cases of primary and secondary syphilis by 85 per cent between 1947 and 1955. Unfortunately, the rapid elimination of federal and state funds for control measures forced the abandonment of organized control programs. This was followed by the elimination of routine serologic tests for syphilis in many clinics and hospitals. This period of neglect is now bearing bitter fruit. Syphilitic psychotics in tax-supported mental institutions still cost $50 million per year (9). The low point in the incidence of new infections was reached in 1955, with a rise beginning in 1956. From 1959 to 1963 each year has shown a 50 per cent increase in incidence over the previous year (Fig. 1). The most rapid increase has been in homosexuals and in teenagers. Between 1956 and 1960 there was an increase of more than 130 per cent in the 15 to 19 year age group (27). About 124,000 cases of syphilis of all ages were reported in 1962. It is known that general practitioners and specialists (22), outside of well-organized hospitals and clinics, report only from 10 per cent to 50 per cent of the actual cases seen. Moore (60) has estimated that the actual increase of syphilis is between 75,000 and 100,000 each year. Many patients never consult a physician, and others are not treated for one reason or another, leading Moore to estimate that there are 1,200,000 individuals in the United States who need treatment for syphilis at the present time.

After the return of Columbus' sailors to Europe in about 1494, syphilis became almost epidemic and was one of the great scourges of the next century. There is disagreement among authorities about the origin of this sudden explosion. Some (38) believe that syphilis had been smouldering in the population for centuries and became epidemic about the time Columbus' sailors returned from the New World. Others believe that syphilis evolved in the New World and was introduced into Europe by the returning sailors (37). Hudson (38) supports the Old World origin. He believes that treponematosis originated thousands of years ago in the villages of hot, humid Africa. The original disease was not venereal and probably resembled *yaws,* which is still prevalent in Africa. He assumed that the disease was transformed into a dry, nonvenereal type of infection resembling bejel when transferred to the hot, dry deserts of North Africa and Arabia. Yaws or bejel was transformed into syphilis by sexual promiscuity in urban cities. However, history teaches that, though sexual promiscuity was common in the great cities of Mesopotamia and in the

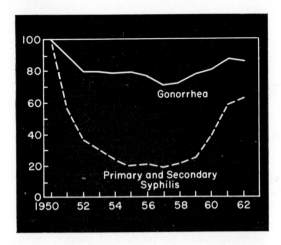

Fig. 1. Graph showing the increase of syphilis in the teen-age population from 1956 to 1962. (From Brown. *Med. Tribune,* Jan. 25, 1963.)

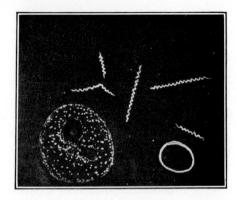

Fig. 2. *Treponema pallidum.* Diagrammatic sketch of appearance of this spirochete under dark-field illumination, drawn to scale in comparison with a red corpuscle and a leukocyte.

Roman cities and even in the Christian cities of the Middle Ages, recognized epidemics of syphilis did not appear in Europe until Columbus returned to Spain. On the other hand, there is convincing evidence that osseous lesions characteristic of yaws and syphilis are present in the skeletons of Indians (20) who died long before Columbus discovered America (37, 73). A mild treponematosis of South and Central America, known as *Pinta,* could have evolved into the venereal disease syphilis in the New World. A rereading of Hudson's 1963 report suggests the possibility that treponematosis did originate with man in tropical Africa and migrated with man to Asia and over the Bering Strait to America. In the cities of Mexico and Peru, it could have evolved into venereal syphilis, which became in time a mild disease for the Indians but reverted to a virulent disease when contracted by the new race of men represented by Columbus' sailors.

The contagiousness of syphilis was apparent to those who contracted it, and in the eighteenth and nineteenth centuries John Hunter, Ricord, and other physicians (48) proved that syphilis was infectious by inoculating men with material from syphilitic sores. *Treponema pallidum* was discovered in 1905 by Schaudinn and Hoffmann (81).

Morphology and Staining. *Treponema pallidum* is delicate in form and resistant to staining by the methods usually employed for staining bacteria. It is readily visualized by the darkfield technic (Fig. 2), or by coating the organism with reduced silver nitrate after the method of Fontana-Tribondeau. It was demonstrated first in tissue sections by Levaditi's silver impregnation method (Fig. 3). Other methods of staining have been described by Campbell and Rosahn (14) and Beamer and Firminger (4).

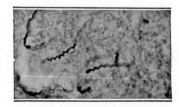

Fig. 3. *Treponema pallidum.* Photograph of section of liver, congenital syphilis, stained by Levaditi method.

Deacon and his associates (24) found that *T. pallidum* could be identified by smears on slides by the new fluorescent antibody technic. Later studies by Edwards (28) have shown that the method is about as accurate as a darkfield and had the advantage that slides may be made in the jungles in any part of the world and mailed to a central laboratory for staining. By appropriate absorption of the testing serum the various species of *Treponema* can be identified (25). This should make it possible to identify the *Treponema* of yaws, pinta and bejel by the staining technic (28).

Treponema pallidum has a cylindrical flexible body 5 to 20 μ in length and about 0.2 μ in diameter. The ends are pointed and sometimes prolonged in delicate terminal filaments. The body is coiled in 8 to 14 regular, rigid, sharp spirals, with a spiral amplitude of about 1 μ (Fig. 2). Living organisms rotate rapidly but progress slowly. The rotation continues as the organism bends into S and circular shapes without losing its coiled shape. Noguchi (65) attributed its motility to a coiled, contractile axial filament which functioned as an "internal flagellum." The beautiful electron micrographs of Swain (85) (Fig. 4A) reveal an outer periplast which covers the entire organism. Neither axial filament nor flagella are visible. After 20 minutes of tryptic digestion the periplast is dissolved to reveal three twisted axial filaments (Fig. 4B). Peptic digestion is more rapid and reveals the filaments in seven to eight minutes. The fibrils, 14 to 17 μ in diameter, may become detached from the body at one end to spread out on the film to simulate flagella (94).

Multiplication is usually by transverse fission, with a division time of 30 hours (46) calculated from direct enumeration of organisms in experimental chancres in rabbits. The division time for the cultural form of the nonpathogenic Reiter strain of *Treponema* averaged 10 hours. There may be a more complicated life cycle in the multiplication of *T. pallidum*. Hardy and Nell (31) have shown that the cyst-like structures can be produced by reducing the osmotic pressure in the medium. This makes less likely, but does not eliminate, the possibility that the cysts are a part of a complicated life cycle. *T. pallidum* is not filterable in the usual meaning of this term, although they may grow through the pores of a filter. Heat-resistant endospores are not produced. *T. pallidum* cannot be differentiated morphologically from *T. pertenue* or from such nonpathogenic spirochetes of the mouth and genitalia as *T. microdentium* or *T. mucosum.*

Cultural Characteristics. There is general agreement among investigators that the pathogenic treponemas, *T. pallidum, T. pertenue,* and *T. carateum,* have not been cultivated. The organisms are anaerobic, and although they grow readily in the tissues of man and in the testicles of the experimentally inoculated rabbit, they do not grow in tissue cultures, in embryonated eggs, or in artificial media, even when the latter are under anaerobic conditions.

The cultured *Treponema,* such as the strains isolated by Noguchi, Zinsser (95) Nichols, Reiter, and Kazan, were originally isolated from syphilitic lesions but were probably contaminating saprophytes. They are anaerobes and require a rich medium (3, 76).

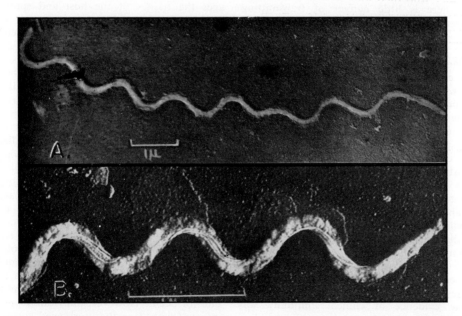

Fig. 4. Electron micrographs of *T. pallidum*. A, *T. pallidum* from exudate of primary chancre. B, *T. pallidum* after 20 minutes tryptic digestion which revealed three axial filaments in body of organism. With more digestion the filaments became free at one end and spread out on the film to simulate flagella. (From Swain. *J. Path. & Bact.,* 69:117, 1955.)

The Reiter strain has been grown in a chemically defined medium consisting of 13 amino acids, uracil, biotin, nicotinic acid, and pantothenic acid. Choline, riboflavin, and thiamin were stimulative but not necessary for growth (83). Colonies have been grown from some of these treponema and from *Borrelia vincenti* (Chap. 49, Figs. 1, 2, and 3) by the new technic described by Hardy, Lee, and Nell (32).

Resistance. These delicate organisms are immobilized and killed by contact with oxygen, saponin, distilled water, soap, mercuric ointment, and other common bactericidal agents. Carpenter, Boak, and Warren (15) found that *T. pallidum* in infected testicular tissue of rabbits was destroyed by a temperature of 39° C. in five hours, of 40° C. in three hours, of 41° C. in two hours, and of 41.5° C. in one hour. These observations form a rational basis for the treatment of syphilis with fever, whether induced by malaria or high frequency electric currents (15).

They may live for six to 24 hours in testicular tissues of the rabbit when stored at 25° C. or for 10 to 13 days at room temperature in sealed tubes (86). When frozen at −80° C. and kept in a frozen state, some of the organisms remain viable and infectious for years (88).

Since *T. pallidum* dies in three days in blood stored in the refrigerators of blood banks, there is little danger of transmitting the disease by a routine blood transfusion from banked blood, although the infection may be transmitted by fresh blood.

Antigenic Structure. Information concerning the antigenic structure of *T. pallidum* is incomplete, primarily because of the difficulty in obtaining enough treponemas free of tissue proteins for chemical study. Limited studies have shown the presence of protein, polysaccharides, and two different lipids (23). Although clinical evidence of immunity had been demonstrated in experimentally infected rabbits and in man, nothing was known about the nature of this immunity, and it was assumed, until about 1950, that the classical type of antibodies associated with immunity in bacterial diseases was absent in syphilis. The first breakthrough on this problem was achieved by Nelson and Mayer (62) in 1949 when they described the "treponema pallida immobilization test" (TPI). The serum of patients showing evidence of clinical immunity was able to stop the motility of living *T. pallidum* obtained from primary experimental testicular lesions in rabbits. The improved methods of harvesting and freeing the living treponema

from rabbit tissue protein supplied the material with which precipitins (80), agglutinins (12, 30), and complement-fixing antibodies (71) have been demonstrated. In the presence of complement the treponemas are not only immobilized but are eventually killed. With the immobilization test (TPI) there are cross-reactions between *T. pallidum* from different patients and between *T. pallidum* and *T. pertenue,* but none between the nonpathogenic cultured strains of *Treponema,* such as the Reiter, Kazan and S26. There was no cross-immobilization with *T. cuniculi,* which causes venereal spirochetoses in rabbits, or with pathogenic *Leptospira* or *Borrelia* (62).

THE WASSERMANN REACTION. The complement-fixation test for syphilis introduced by Wassermann and his associates in 1906 uses a nonspecific lipoid antigen and measures an antibody known as **reagin** which is not a protective. The nonspecific antigen is distributed widely in mammalian tissues and even in some plants. The cultivated strains of nonpathogenic *Treponema* also contain an antigen which will react with the reagin (71). Although the reagin is not a protective antibody and is measured with a nonspecific antigen, this antibody is produced by practically every patient who becomes infected with *T. pallidum.* Sachs, Klopstock, and Weil (79) suggested in 1925 that an infection with *T. pallidum* damages the tissues of the host and splits off a lipoidal fraction which, acting as a hapten, combines with the protein of the treponema and then stimulates the production of antibodies (reagin) which can be measured in the complement-fixing reaction with the lipoid antigen. Eagle (26) induced reagin-like antibodies in normal rabbits by the intravenous injection of floccules produced by mixing Kahn's antigen suspension in serum from a patient with syphilis. Affleck and Allen (1) demonstrated the same phenomenon with cardiolipin antigen, and Fowler and Allen (29) with synthetic substitutes for lecithin and cardiolipin. The experiments in man, reported by Magnuson and his associates (48) in 1956 support this theory. The investigators found that the injection of heat-killed *T. pallidum* into normal human volunteers did not stimulate the production of either reagin antibodies or TPI antibodies. Presumably in the absence of damage to tissue the haptenic combination did not occur. However, individuals previously infected with *T. pallidum* showed an increased titer of TPI (protective) antibodies, suggesting an anamnestic reaction. After treatment with penicillin, the TPI antibody may disappear more rapidly or more slowly than the reagin antibody (67).

In clinical infection with *T. pallidum* the reagin antibody appears several weeks before the specific TPI antibody but gradually disappears with time and may be absent in late cases when the TPI is present in good titer. A more specific antigen for the Wassermann test was described by Portnoy and Magnuson (71) in 1955. The treponemas were extracted with a sodium desoxycholate-citrate-sodium mixture and the lipoid material removed by treatment with acetone followed by ether. This antigen measures a treponema complement-fixing antibody (TPCF) which is different from the TPI or the reagin and may correspond to one of the two agglutinating antibodies (52) present in the serum of syphilitics. This test becomes positive early in the disease, like the Wassermann, but does not persist in the late stages of disease as does the TPI. Electrophoretic studies (91) have shown that the Wassermann reagin is concentrated in the slow moving gamma globulin, the TPI in the fast-moving gamma globulin, while the agglutinating antibody is distributed in more than one fraction, suggesting that more than one type of agglutinating antibody is present (52).

McLeod and Garson's studies (54) suggest that the **treponema protein complement-fixing test (TPCF)** and the **fluorescent treponema antibody (FTA)** measure essentially the same type of specific antibody. The cost of maintaining living *T. pallidum* for the fluorescent test stimulated Kent and his associates (42) to utilize the common antigen in the Reiter treponema. This worked quite well when the nonpathogenic treponema was treated with a solution of dilute hypochloride.

ALLERGIC REACTIONS. The destructive lesions in late syphilis seem to be analogous to those in tuberculosis, which are known to be the result of hypersensitivity (84). Patients with destructive lesions usually give strong local dermal reactions 24 to 48 hours after the intracutaneous injection of "organic luetin" which is prepared by extracting mature syphilomas from the testicles of rabbits (90), or of *T. pallidum*, **freed of tissue by centrifugation and preserved with 1 per cent formalin** (50). **This latter preparation is called "treponemin."**

Clinical observations suggest that some strains of *T. pallidum* are more virulent than others and that some are more neurotropic than viscerotropic, but this variation may be in the patient rather than in the spirochete. Rabbits do show varying degrees of resistance to homologous and heterologous strains of *T. pallidum* (87).

TOXINS. Neither exotoxins nor endotoxins have been demonstrated and the minimal amount of reaction to the primary infection suggests the absence of toxins.

Experimental Infection in Laboratory Animals. Most animals are resistant to infections with *T. pallidum.* Metchnikoff and Roux (55) infected a female chimpanzee in 1903, and Nicolle (64) infected a Macacus monkey in the same year. The rabbit is the most useful experimental animal (7), and Brown and Pearce (8) succeeded eventually in reproducing nearly all of the clinical forms of syphilis by appropriate methods of inoculation. Only two virulent treponemas are required to initiate an experimental infection in this animal (46). Since virulent *T. pallidum* cannot be grown on artificial media, the testicle of the rabbit functions as a test tube for the preservation and multiplication of strains of *T. pallidum*. Virulence and specificity is maintained in rabbit passage strains. Men accidentally or deliberately inoculated with *T. pallidum* strains which had been maintained for over 40 years in rabbits, developed typical syphilitic lesions.

Rats and mice develop asymptomatic infections after inoculation. Lesions are not produced in the internal organs, although the organisms persist in the tissues for months. The infection is not entirely harmless, however, since mice infected in this manner have a significantly reduced life expectancy (75).

Experimental Infection in Man. Magnuson and his associates (48) reviewed the previous attempt of deliberate inoculations of man with material from infectious syphilis and accidental inoculations with passage strains in rabbits (19). They also inoculated 62 human volunteers with the Nichols strain. The 50 per cent infectious inoculum for nonsyphilitic subjects were 57 organisms. The five patients with untreated latent syphilis were resistant to superinfection. Previously treated and untreated patients in various stages of syphilis tended to react in a manner characteristic of the particular stage of their immunologic maturity (90). The development of gummatous lesions in two of the previously well-healed patients demonstrates that the particular type of allergy productive of gummas may persist for years, in spite of treatment (48).

Clinical Types of Infection in Man. There are many analogies between syphilis and tuberculosis, although one is caused by a spirochete and the other by a bacterium. Both diseases are extremely prevalent, protean in their manifestations, and inherently chronic. *T. pallidum,* even more than *Myco. tuberculosis,* approaches the condition of ideal parasitism in which the invading organism lives unharmed in the host and produces little, if any, reaction. The spirochete of syphilis has an advantage over the bacillus of tuberculosis in its method of transmission. The early lesions of syphilis are superficial and highly infectious, while the late destructive lesions are not infectious and, therefore, undesirable from the standpoint of the parasite.

[PRIMARY SYPHILIS.] The primary lesions develop on the genitalia in about 95 per cent of the cases, and on the mucous membranes of the mouth and the nipples of the breast, in most of the remaining 5 per cent. The **incubation period** varies from 10 to 90 days, with an average time of three weeks. During the incubation period the organisms not only multiply locally but also invade the lymphatics and blood stream and are well distributed throughout the entire body before the appearance of the local lesion. The patient may be **infectious by contact** even before there is a recognizable local lesion.

The typical local primary lesion is circumscribed, indurated, superficially ulcerated, relatively avascular, and painless. It is frequently called a **Hunterian chancre** in honor of John Hunter, or a **hard chancre,** to distinguish it from the chancroid caused by infection with *H. ducreyi.* The primary lesion, unfortunately, is not always characteristic or detectable and may be so insignificant that it is overlooked by the patient. Thus, in the female the chancre may be located on the cervix of the uterus, and in the male it occasionally occurs in the urethra, where it cannot be seen by a casual inspection. Infections have been produced in rabbits without the development of observable local lesions, and presumably similar infections occur also in man. The regional lymph nodes usually are swollen, hard, and rubbery.

A clinical diagnosis of primary syphilis always should be confirmed by the demonstration of the spirochetes in the secretions from the lesion (Fig. 5). It is most impor-

tant that the specimen be examined before the administration of arsenicals or penicillin, because the treponemas usually disappear from the local lesion within six to 24 hours after the first treatment.

No detectable antibodies appear during the incubation period of the disease or even during the early days after the appearance of the chancre. Usually within 10 days and always within 30 days after the appearance of the primary lesion an antibody appears in the serum; it can be detected by any one of the various serologic tests for syphilis.

Fig. 5. *Treponema pallidum.* Photograph of India ink preparation from chancre.

The primary lesion invariably heals, even without treatment, within a period of 10 to 40 days. The mechanism by which the spirochetes in the local lesion are destroyed is not understood, but it is presumed to be of the nature of a local tissue immunity rather than a humoral immunity, because an unhindered multiplication of the organisms in the skin and the mucous membranes preparatory to the explosive onset of the **secondary lesions** occurs simultaneously with the elimination of the spirochetes from the local lesion.

[SECONDARY SYPHILIS.] Following the healing of the primary lesion, the patient is asymptomatic for a period varying from two to six months, with an average of three months, before the appearance of **multiple secondary lesions** in the skin or mucous membranes or both. Often secondary manifestations develop concurrently with the healing of the primary lesion. The patient may have some constitutional symptoms at the time, such as fever, headache, and malaise, but the symptoms are minimal in view of the multiplicity of the lesions and the enormous numbers of spirochetes present in each individual area. Usually there is a generalized enlargement of the lymph nodes at this time. Lesions also disappear without treatment and with minimal scar formation after intervals of three weeks to three months, but may recur after a latent period of 3 to 12 months. In some instances, latent periods alternate with recurrences for as long as four years, although the latent periods become materially lengthened and the recurrences correspondingly shortened. During the period of secondary recurrences the serologic tests for syphilis practically always are positive. **Meningovascular syphilis,** particularly the meningeal form, not infrequently develops during this secondary phase.

TERTIARY OR LATE LATENT SYPHILIS. After an interval of about four years the mucosal and cutaneous recurrences no longer appear, but lesions of the cardiovascular and nervous systems make their appearance. Lesions in these systems are indolent and slowly progressive and stimulate no violent tissue reaction. This is sometimes described as the **anergic type** of reaction.

In other patients, in the late stages of syphilis, granulomatous, destructive tumor-like masses known as **gummas** develop in the **skin, bones, nervous system,** and occasionally other organs and tissues. Although actually very slow in evolution, requiring weeks or months, their development is rapid when compared to the still slower evolution of the disease in the cardiovascular and nervous systems. The destructive nature of the gumma is attributed to the development of **hypersensitivity** to the spirochetes, although it is not known why the patient suddenly should develop this hypersensitivity to the spirochetes with which he has been living peacefully for years. It has been suggested that a constitutional factor is involved and that certain individuals inherit the ability to react in this manner while others do not. During the late latent periods of syphilis, the serologic tests may be positive in only 60 to 70 per cent of the patients, although the spinal fluid may be positive when the blood serum is negative. Even the spinal fluid may be negative in 5 to 10 per cent of clinical cases of **paresis** and up to 30 per cent of clinical cases of **tabes dorsalis.**

In a surprising number of cases, nature finally effects a "cure." In Bruusgaard's (10) series of 2,181 untreated cases in Oslo, Norway, not less than 64.6 per cent passed through the whole course of their disease without being seriously inconvenienced and 27.9 per cent were symptomatically, if not biologically, cured. The only other study resembling that of Bruusgaard's is the one which was carried out in Macon county, Alabama (82). Nonsyphilitic controls of the same age were included in this study. Among the 159 Negro males with untreated or inadequately treated syphilis who were living 20 years later, 14.5 per cent showed evidence of late syphilis. Approximately half of these had cardiovascular disease and the remainder were about evenly divided between neurosyphilis and osseous syphilis (68).

ACQUIRED IMMUNITY. The nature of the acquired immunity in syphilis is still a mystery. Most syphilologists assume that it is a local cellular or tissue immunity and that humoral antibodies contribute little, if anything, to the recovery. The studies of Turner and his associates (88) with rabbits and the human inoculations with living and dead treponema by Magnuson and his co-workers (18, 47, 48) suggest that humoral antibodies of the TPI type play a significant role in immunity.

The immunity to syphilis, like that to tuberculosis, is slow in developing and of a relative, rather than an absolute, nature. It is more effective in preventing the entrance of new treponemas than in eliminating those already present in the tissues.

CONGENITAL SYPHILIS. Pregnancy may produce some subtle change in the immunity of the woman with latent syphilis, which results in the mobilization of the treponemata and their passage through the placenta to the embryo in utero. The pregnant woman also transmits those reacting substances which give positive serologic tests for syphilis but transmits no protective antibodies at all or only in amounts insufficient to prevent the development of enormous numbers of spirochetes in the tissues of the unborn child. Some of the infants die in utero and are expelled as **miscarriages;** others are born dead —**stillbirths.** The living child may display obvious evidence of syphilis at birth or develop signs of syphilis during the first few weeks or months of life. In some instances the manifestations of congenital syphilis are delayed until late in childhood when the patient may develop **Hutchinson's teeth, interstitial keratitis, eighth nerve deafness, saddle nose, sabre shins,** and a variety of other manifestations.

If the mother has received adequate treatment during pregnancy, the child will be born free of syphilis even though the mother has a positive serologic test for syphilis, as does the blood from the umbilical cord. When the infant is apparently healthy, it is advisable to delay treatment for a number of weeks or until a series of quantitative serologic tests demonstrates whether the tests remain positive or gradually decrease. In the latter instance the positive reactions were from reacting substances passively transferred to the infant and specific treatment is not indicated. It has been estimated that about 1 to 2 per cent of all infants born in the United States at the present time have congenital syphilis.

Serologic Tests for Syphilis. The evolution of the serologic test for syphilis is one of the most interesting stories in the field of immunology. In 1906 Wassermann applied the principle of Bordet's complement-fixation to the diagnosis of syphilis. Unable to cultivate *T. pallidum,* he used as an antigen extracts from the livers of syphilitic stillborn infants which contained great numbers of spirochetes. Later, when the supply of stillborn infants was depleted, it was learned that extracts of normal spleens and other organs could be substituted for the original antigen. For many years an alcohol extract of the lipids of the cow's heart has been used as an antigen in the complement-fixation test. A group of so-called precipitin or flocculation tests, such as the **Kline, Kahn, Mazzini** and **Eagle,** were introduced later as supplements or substitutes for the original Wassermann test.

These serologic tests for syphilis do not establish or exclude automatically the diagnosis of syphilis and always should be correlated with the clinical data. In most laboratories, a battery of precipitin tests is performed, such as the Kahn, Kline, and Mazzini, because in a particular patient one

test may be positive while the others are negative. Quantitative serologic tests for syphilis should be performed routinely in those patients receiving active therapy so that the rate of antibody decrease can be available to the clinician who is treating the case. The **cardiolipin antigen** appears more specific than any of the older types of antigens (43).

BIOLOGIC FALSE POSITIVE REACTION FOR SYPHILIS. Since the lipoidal antigen which stimulates the production of the reagin antibody is nonspecific in nature, it is not surprising that false complement-fixation and flocculation tests are encountered in a number of diseases unrelated to syphilis. The incidence of such reactions is shown in Table 1 (58). The highest percentages of false reactions occur in malaria and leprosy. Those occurring after acute infections usually disappear spontaneously after a few months. The presence of 20 per cent of false reactions in lupus erythematosus is of great importance particularly because the reaction may occur early in the disease before L.E. cells appear in the blood and before there are any diagnostic signs or symptoms (5, 6, 59). Harvey (33) has observed the appearance of Hashimoto's thyroiditis as well as lupus erythematosus in patients who were asymptomatic at the time the biologic false Wassermann was discovered.

Neurath, Volkin, Craig, and associates (63) succeeded in fractionating the serum so that the specific antibodies were obtained in one fraction and those responsible for the biologically false reaction in another. The methods of choice at the present time are the treponema immobilization test (TPI), *Treponema pallidum* immune adherence test (TPIA) (56), and the complement-fixation test (TPCF) which uses an antigen from virulent treponema. The margin of error with the TPI is less than 2 per cent (59). Failure of *T. pallidum* to stain with methylene blue gives results comparable to the TPI test (77).

The rapid plasma reagin test for syphilis with unheated plasma or serum introduced by Portnoy for rapid screening of migrant workers has been combined with Brewer's method of visualizing flocculation by adding carbon particles to the antigen and observing

Table 1. Approximate Incidence of Biologically False Positive Reactions
in Various Nonsyphilitic Conditions

(Moore and Mohr)

Disease	Approximate Incidence of BFP * Reactions, Per cent	Disease	Approximate Incidence of BFP * Reactions, Per cent
1. Malaria	100	12. Infectious hepatitis	10
2. Leprosy	60	13. Subacute bacterial endocarditis	5
3. Relapsing fever	30	14. Chancroid	5
4. Rat-bite fever	20	15. Scarlatina	5
5. Typhus	20	16. Measles	5
6. Vaccinia	20	17. Chickenpox	5
7. Pneumonia, "atypical"	20	18. Tuberculosis, advanced	3 to 5
8. Lymphogranuloma venereum	20	19. Pneumonia, pneumococcal	2 to 5
9. Infectious mononucleosis	20	20. Lupus erythematosus (disseminated or discoid)	20
10. Leptospirosis	10	21. Rheumatoid arthritis	5
11. Trypanosomiasis	10		

* BFP = biologically false positive.

the reaction of the mixture on a special card (72).

Transmission. *Treponema pallidum* is a strict parasite to which all races of human beings appear to be susceptible, although there are racial and individual differences in reaction to the organism. Nearly all syphilitic infections are acquired by sexual contact, kissing, or abnormal sexual practices, leaving only 0.01 per cent for the truly accidental infections from household contacts, common drinking cups, eating utensils, clothing, linens, barber shops, and beauty parlors. Syphilis may be considered an **occupational disease** for nurses, midwives, dentists, and physicians.

Syphilis still is very prevalent, as shown by the experience of the Selective Service Boards during World War II. Positive serologic evidence of syphilis was found in 4.53 per cent of the first 1,895,778 men examined. The most striking differences were found between the whites and Negroes, the percentage being 25.23 per cent in the Negro and only 1.74 per cent in the whites. The whites who lived in areas where there was a large Negro population had a percentage considerably higher than the average for all whites (92).

As noted in the introduction, syphilis is increasing rapidly in the population but most rapidly in homosexuals and teenagers from 15 to 19 years. In a typical city like Rich-mond, Virginia, the incidence of syphilis has increased fourfold between 1958 and 1962 (49). There are many causes for the reappearance of massive syphilitic infection. Among the more important are (1) public apathy, (2) elimination of funds for adequate control measures, (3) modifications of the clinical picture of syphilis, (4) promiscuous use of penicillin for minor, non-syphilitic disease (49, 78), (5) inadequate teaching about syphilis in medical schools (41), and (6) increasing sexual promiscuity among teenagers.

Treatment. The so-called immune and convalescent serums are ineffective in the treatment of syphilis.

Mercury, bismuth, and the arsenicals served mankind faithfully as therapeutic agents for many generations but have now been completely replaced by **penicillin.** This antibiotic is more efficient in eliminating the spirochetes and does not have the toxicity which is inherent in the heavy metals (5, 13). More frequent **Jarisch-Herxheimer reactions** occur, however, following the beginning of penicillin treatment. This phenomenon is assumed to be an allergic reaction which is precipitated by the sudden release of antigen from the spirochetes that are killed by penicillin. Such reactions may be fatal when they occur in patients with syphilis of the cardiovascular or central nervous system (13). **Chlortetracycline** (66), **chloramphenicol** (74) and **oxytetracycline** may be as effective as penicillin in eliminating spirochetes from the primary and secondary lesions, but since they are more expensive and more toxic, they should not be substituted for penicillin except in patients who have developed a hypersensitivity to penicillin (57). **Cortisone** seems of value when applied locally to the lesions of interstitial keratitis (21).

However, the systemic use of cortisone may be dangerous since experiments in rabbits have shown that cortisone alters the tissue reaction in such a manner that there is a reduction in the TPI antibodies and an increase in spirochetemia (53).

Prevention.   All attempts at active immunization with dead or attenuated cultures of *Treponema pallidum* have failed.

Congenital syphilis can be completely eliminated by treating the mother adequately with penicillin during pregnancy (61).

Theoretically, local cleansing with soap followed by the application of mercurial ointments will prevent the development of primary infection, but in practice this method of prophylaxis has not been very satisfactory. One large dose of penicillin taken by injection (70) or by mouth within a few days after exposure should prevent infection. This method of prevention is being studied.

The prevention of acquired syphilis remains basically a problem of education, supplemented by a constant, unremitting effort to diagnose, isolate, and treat until noninfective every newly acquired case of syphilis.

BEJEL, YAWS, AND PINTA

It is difficult to evaluate the relationship between **syphilis, bejel, yaws,** and **pinta,** but clinical, pathologic, and biologic evidence indicates that they all are caused by organisms belonging to the same family tree. Some investigators have suggested that the latter three are attenuated forms of syphilis, while others believe that all four organisms evolved independently from a common saprophytic ancestor.

These three spirochetal infections are limited strictly to specific geographic areas. **Bejel is found in Arabia among the Bedouin Arabs; yaws, or frambesia tropica,** occurs exclusively in the tropics; while **pinta** is endogenous in Mexico, Cuba, and the West Indian Islands,

Central America, and tropical South America.

Bejel, yaws, or pinta cannot be classified as a venereal disease. Bejel and yaws occur primarily in children but pinta attacks all age groups.

The treponemas found in the lesions are morphologically indistinguishable from *T. pallidum,* and, although none of these have been cultivated, all of them can infect rabbits. Positive reactions are obtained in serologic tests employing the patient's serum and the antigen commonly used for the detection of syphilis, although in pinta the appearance of these reacting substances is delayed. In most cases of pinta the tests are negative during the primary stage, positive in 50 per cent of patients with secondary lesions, and almost always positive in the late reactions to the infection.

Bejel.   This disease is the most difficult to differentiate from syphilis, and at least one investigator believes that it is an unusual form of congenital syphilis (11). A similar, if not identical, nonvenereal treponematosis has been reported from India (39), Bosnia, and Gambia, West Africa (6). The experimental inoculation of human volunteers carried out by Akrawi (2) in Iraq indicates that Bejel is an attenuated form of syphilis.

Mucous patches are very common in bejel (38) and cardiovascular lesions occur with some frequency (36), but involvement of the central nervous system is rare.

Yaws.   Castellani (16, 17) discovered the etiologic agent of yaws in 1905 and named it *Treponema pertenue.* Both primary and secondary lesions of yaws are more severe and persistent than those of syphilis, and, in contrast to syphilis, scar formation develops at the site of the secondary infection. The lesions are granulomatous or wart-like with a granular surface simulating that of a raspberry; hence the name "frambesia." The general appearance of the skin lesions is quite different from that of syphilis, although some of the individual lesions may appear identical. Destructive areas in the bones occur in about 15 per cent of the cases, but cardiovascular and neurologic manifestations are rare (34). Latent periods alternating with recrudescences are as characteristic of yaws as of syphilis. Partial but incomplete reciprocal immunity has been found between yaws and syphilis (44).

Pinta.   This disease is caused by *T. carateum* Brumpt (*Treponema herrejoni* León y Blanco). The primary lesion is a nonulcerating, squamous, erythematous patch on the skin which, after four of five months, may assume a lichenoid or psoriasiform appearance. Following a latent period of four to five months, secondary lesions appear about the initial lesion and on the skin of other parts of the body, such as the palms of the hands and the soles of the feet. Pinta thus resembles yaws in having a predilection for the palmar surfaces of the body but not for the mucous membranes (69). Some areas of the skin are depigmented, while others are hyperpigmented, and many become pink, brown or blue in color. These varicolored patches obviously suggested the name "pinta" for the disease. Lesions in the bones have not been observed, but cardiovascular involvement has been reported (69). There is no evidence of cross immunity between syphilis and pinta, patients with syphilis having been infected experimentally with the treponemas of pinta (45).

Transmission. In all three diseases numerous treponemas are present in both primary and secondary lesions, and transmission is usually accomplished by direct contact. The fly *Hippelates pallipes* can transmit *T. pertenue* from a sore on a patient's skin to a raw spot on the back or testicle of a rabbit. *T. pertenue* survives for hours and even may multiply in the diverticulum of the fly (44). *Simulium* flies have been incriminated in the transmission of pinta, but the evidence is not entirely conclusive.

Treatment. All three diseases respond readily to treatment with arsenicals. Penicillin therapy heals the primary and secondary lesions of yaws even more rapidly than arsenical therapy (35). Presumably, penicillin also would be effective in the treatment of bejel and pinta.

Prevention. Prompt diagnosis, isolation, and treatment with arsenicals or penicillin should materially reduce the incidence of bejel, yaws, and pinta.

VENEREAL SPIROCHETOSIS OF RABBITS

The occurrence of a spirochete indistinguishable from *Treponema pallidum* in a natural venereal disease of rabbits was reported by Ross in 1912 and by Bayon in 1913. The organism is identical morphologically with the spirochete of syphilis and was called *Treponema cuniculi* by Noguchi in 1928 (65).

In the rabbit the lesions produced by this organism are slightly elevated and superficial, but not indurated, scaly areas about the genitalia (93). The organism has none of the invasiveness of *Treponema pallidum* and does not produce a generalized infection. Its oc-

currence in animals used for experimental studies of syphilis might lead to confusion if the examinations were limited to morphology alone. Rabbits with natural venereal spirochetosis do not give positive Wassermann reactions but do develop antibodies which immobilize *T. cuniculi* (40).

Intratesticular inoculation in rabbits will differentiate *Treponema cuniculi* from *T. pallidum* but not from *T. pertenue* (51).

REFERENCES

1. Affleck, M. N., and Allen, R. H. Am. J. Syph., 38:567, 1954.
2. Akrawi, F. Brit. J. Ven. Dis., 25:115, 1949.
3. Barban, S. J. Bact., 68:493, 1954.
4. Beamer, R., and Firminger, I. Lab. Invest., 4:9, 1955.
5. Beerman, H., and others. Arch. Int. Med., 87:287, 424, 1951.
6. —— and others. Arch. Int. Med., 97:215, 1956.
7. Bertarelli, E. Centralbl. f. Bakt., 41:320, 1906.
8. Brown, W., and Pearce, L. J. Exper. Med., 33:553, 1921.
9. Brown, W. J. South. Med. J., 56:840, 1963.
10. Bruusgaard, E. Arch. f. Dermat. u. Syph., 157:309, 1929.
11. Butler, C. S. Am. J. Clin. Path., 9:1, 1939.
12. Cain, R. M. Canad. J. Pub. Health, 44:61, 1953.
13. Callaway, J. L., and others. South. M. J., 43:412, 1950.
14. Campbell, R. E., and Rosahn, P. D. Yale J. Biol. & Med., 22:527, 1950.
15. Carpenter, C. M., and others. J. Exper. Med., 56:751, 1932.
16. Castellani, A. Brit. M. J., 2:1280, 1905.
17. —— J. Hyg., 7:558, 1907.
18. Chesney, A. M. Immunity in Syphilis, Medicine, 5:463, 1926; published also in Medical Monographs, Vol. XII, Baltimore, 1927.
19. —— Medicine, 5:463, 1926.
20. Cole, H. N., and others. Arch. Dermat., 71:231, 1955.
21. Crane, G. W., Jr., and McPherson, S. D., Jr. Am. J. Syph., 35:525, 1951.
22. Curtis, A. C. J.A.M.A., 186:46, 1963.
23. D'Alessandro, G., and others. Riv. 1st sieroterap. ital., 24:134, 1949.
24. Deacon, W. E., and others. Proc. Soc. Exper. Biol. & Med., 96:477, 1957.
25. —— and Hunter, E. F. Proc. Soc. Exper. Biol. & Med., 110:352, 1962.
26. Eagle, H. J. Exper. Med., 55:667, 1932.
27. Editorial: J.A.M.A., 183:1104, 1963.
28. Edwards, E. A. Pub. Health Reports, 77:427, 1962.
29. Fowler, E., and Allen, R. H. J. Immunol., 88:591, 1962.
30. Hardy, P. H., Jr., and Nell, E. E. J. Exper. Med., 101:367, 1955.
31. —— and Nell, E. E. J. Bact., 82:967, 1961.
32. —— and others. J. Bact., 86:616, 1963.

33. Harvey, A. McG. J.A.M.A., 182:513, 1962.
34. Helfet, A. J. J. Bone & Joint Surg., 26:672, 1944.
35. Hill, K. E., and others. Lancet, 2:522, 1946.
36. Hoff, H., and Shaby, J. A. Tr. Roy. Soc. Trop. Med. & Hyg., 33:549, 1940.
37. Holcomb, R. C. Bull. Hist. Med., 10:148, 1941.
38. Hudson, E. H. Ann. Int. Med., 58:1037, 1963.
39. Iswariah, J. A., and Nair, V. G. J. Indian M. A., 7:651, 1938.
40. Kahn, A. S., and others. Am. J. Hyg., 53:296, 1951.
41. Kampmeier, R. H. J.A.M.A., 183:1094, 1963.
42. Kent, J. F., and others. Proc. Soc. Exper. Biol. & Med., 109:584, 1962.
43. Kline, B. S. Am. J. Clin. Path., 16:68, 1946.
44. Kumm, H. W. Rept. of Jamaica Yaws Commission, 1935.
45. León y Blanco, F. Rev. de med. trop. y parasitol., bacteriol., clín. y lab., 6:13, 1940.
46. Magnuson, H. J., and others. Am. J. Syph., 32:1, 1948.
47. ——— and Thompson, F. A., Jr. J. Immunol., 67:35, 1951.
48. ——— and others. Medicine, 35:33, 1956.
49. Manson, R. C., and Trice, E. R. South. M. J., 56:705, 1963.
50. Marshak, L. C., and Rothman, S. Am. J. Syph., 35:35, 1951.
51. McLeod, C., and Turner, T. B. Am. J. Syph., 30:442, 455, 1946.
52. ——— and Stokes, P. S. Pub. Health Rep., 70:379, 1955.
53. ——— and Magnuson, H. J. J. Immunol., 76:373, 1956.
54. McLeod, C. P., and Garson, W. Pub. Health Reports, 77:446, 1962.
55. Metchnikoff, E., and Rous, E. Ann. Inst. Pasteur, 1903-1905.
56. Miller, J. N., and others. J.A.M.A., 163:112, 1957.
57. Moore, J. E. Am. J. Syph., 35:101, 1951.
58. ——— and Mohr, C. F. J.A.M.A., 150:468, 1952.
59. ——— and Lutz, W. B. J. Chron. Dis., 1:297, 1955.
60. Moore, M. B., Jr. J.A.M.A., 186:831, 1963.
61. Nelson, N. A., and Struve, V. R. J.A.M.A., 161:869, 1956.
62. Nelson, R. A., Jr., and Mayer, M. M. J. Exper. Med., 89:369, 1949.
63. Neurath, H., and others. Am. J. Syph., 31:347, 1947.
64. Nicolie, C. Ann. Inst. Pasteur, 17:636, 1903.
65. Noguchi, J. I. The Newer Knowledge of Bacteriology and Immunology, Chicago, 1928, p. 478.
66. Olansky, S., and others. Am. J. Syph., 34:436, 1950.
67. ——— and others. Brit. J. Ven Dis., 32:104, 1956.
68. ——— and others. J. Chronic Dis., 4:177, 1956.
69. Pardo-Castello, V., and Ferrer, I. Arch. Dermat. & Syph., 45:843, 1942.
70. Plotke, F., and others. Am. J. Syph., 35:246, 1951.
71. Portnoy, J., and Magnuson, H. J. J. Immunol., 75:348, 1955.
72. ——— and others. Pub. Health Reports, 77:645, 1962.
73. Riverius, L. Urol. & Cutan. Rev., 50:510, 1946.
74. Romansky, M. J., and others. Am. J. Syph., 35:234, 1951.
75. Rosahn, P. D. Arch. Dermat. & Syph., 66:547, 1953.
76. Rose, N. R., and Morton, H. E. Am. J. Syph., 36:1, 17, 1952.
77. Rosenau, B. J., and Kent, J. F. Proc. Soc. Exper. Biol. & Med., 91:579, 1956.
78. Rosenblum, B. F. Pub. Health Reports, 78:611, 1963.
79. Sachs, H., and others. Deutsch. med. Wchnschr., 51:589, 1925.
80. Saurino, V. R., and DeLamater, E. D. Am. J. Syph., 36:353, 1952.
81. Schaudinn, F., and Hoffmann, E. Arb. a. d. k. Gsndhtsamte., 22:527, 1905.
82. Schuman, S. H., and others. J. Chronic Dis., 2:543, 1955.
83. Steinman, H. G., and others. J. Bact., 67:597, 1954.
84. Stokes, J. H., and others. Modern Clinical Syphilology, 3rd ed., Philadelphia, W. B. Saunders Co., 1944.
85. Swain, R. H. A. J. Path. & Bact., 69:117, 1955.
86. Tucker, H. A., and others. Arch. Int. Med., 83:77, 197, 1949.
87. Turner, T. B. Am. J. Hyg., 23:431, 1936; 25:477, 1937.
88. ——— J. Exper. Med., 69:867, 1939.
89. ——— and others. J. Clin. Invest., 18:471, 1939.
90. Urbach, E., and Beerman, H. Am. J. Syph., 31:192, 1947.
91. Vannier, W. E. Proc. Soc. Exper. Biol. & Med., 91:514, 1956.
92. Vonderlehr, R. A. J.A.M.A., 120:1369, 1942.
93. Warthin, A. S. J. Infect. Dis., 30:592, 1922.
94. Watson, J. H. L., and others. J. Bact., 61:455, 1951.
95. Zinsser, H., and others. J. Exper. Med., 21:213, 1915.

51

The Spirochetes of Relapsing Fever, Vincent's Angina, and Other Diseases

The genus *Borrelia* contains the spirochetes which cause relapsing fever in man and a corresponding spirochetosis in fowls. It also includes *Bor. vincentii* and *Bor. buccale,* members of the symbiotic group of organisms which causes Vincent's angina and fusospirochetal symbiotic disease.

There are marked differences between the genera *Borrelia* and *Treponema*. The *Borrelia* are larger and longer and are characterized by loose irregular coils which form, disappear, and re-form as the organism progresses. The treponemas, on the other hand, are much smaller and possess fixed, rigid, and tightly wound coils. The *Borrelia* are easily stained by strong aniline dyes, such as gentian violet and carbolfuchsin, and by Giemsa and Wright stains. With the exception of the species in the *Borrelia* belonging to the fusospirochetal symbionts, these organisms are blood parasites. Some of them have become adapted to arthropod hosts as well as to man and animals and are transmitted by such vectors. They are difficult to isolate and retain their virulence when cultured on artificial media. Morphologically similar, but apparently nonpathogenic, spirochetes have been identified in the blood of sheep, horses, and bats and in the alimentary tracts of fish and insects. *Bor. theileri* is associated with a benign type of infection of cattle in South Africa.

RELAPSING FEVER

Family: *Treponemataceae* Robinson. Genus: *Borrelia* Swellengrebel. Species: *Borrelia duttonii, novyi,* and *recurrentis*

The microorganism causing relapsing fever was observed first by Obermeier (38) in 1873 in the blood of patients suffering from this characteristic type of fever. Since his time, extensive studies by other observers have proved beyond question the etiologic connection between the disease and the organism.

Morphology and Staining. The spirochete of Obermeier is a delicate spiral thread from 8 to 20 μ in length and about 0.3 μ in thickness. While this is its average size, according to some observers it may be considerably longer, its undulations varying from 4 to 10 or more in number. Compared with the red blood cells among which they are seen, the microorganisms may vary from one-half to 9 or 10 times the diameter of a corpuscle. In fresh preparations of the blood very active corkscrew-like motility and definite lateral oscillation are observed. In stained preparations no definite cellular structure can be detected, the cell body appearing homogeneous except in degenerated individuals, in which irregular granulation or beading has been observed.

Spores are not produced. Structures resembling flagella have been stained (20). The electron micrographs of Swain (57) in Figures 1 and 2 indicate that they are axial filaments originating in the interior of the organism.

Cultivation. Novy and Knapp (36) succeeded in keeping the microorganisms alive and virulent in the original blood for as long as 40 days. Norris, Pappenheimer, and Flournoy (35) obtained positive evidence of multiplication of the spirochetes in fluid media (Fig. 3). They obtained their cultures by inoculating a few drops of infected rat blood into 3 to 5 ml. of citrated human or rat blood, but attempts at cultivation for a third generation failed. Noguchi (33) in 1913 cultivated the spirochete of Obermeier in ascitic fluid containing a piece of sterile rabbit's kidney and a few drops of citrated blood (34, 64). The spirochete was cultured in the developing chick embryo by Levaditi (21), McKercher (24), and Oag (37); Bohls and others (2)

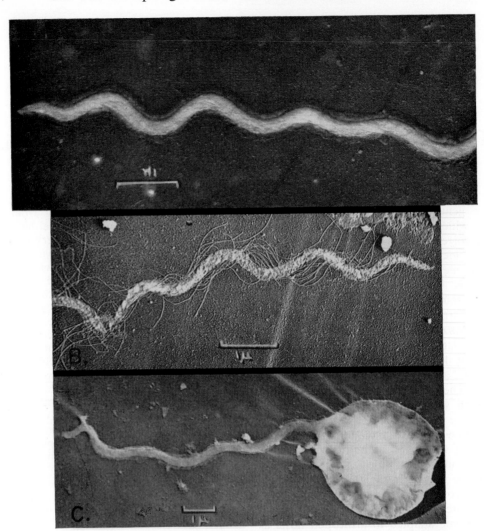

Fig. 1. *Borrelia duttoni.* A, From blood of infected mouse. Note sheath-like outer coat, and absence of flagella. B, After exposure to distilled water the outer surface disappears and the fibrils can be seen. C, An encysted form of the spirochete. (From Swain. *J. Path. & Bact.,* 69:117, 1955.)

have isolated it directly from human blood by this method.

The various species of *Borrelia* known to infect man, together with their vectors, are shown in Table 1. We wish to thank Dr. Gordon E. Davis for supplying the data for the table.

Pathogenicity. Inoculation with blood containing these spirochetes produces disease in monkeys, rats, mice, and Chinese hamsters. Attempts to transmit the disease experimentally to dogs and rabbits so far have been unsuccessful. The subcutaneous inoculation of monkeys is followed after two to four days by an abrupt rise of temperature, which may last several days. During this time the spirochetes can be found in the blood of the animals. The temperature subsides after a day or more and returns rapidly to normal. As a rule, the paroxysms are not repeated. Occasionally, however, two or three attacks may supervene before immunity is established (46). In rats the spirochetes may be found in large numbers in the blood, and the animals show symptoms of systemic infection. The attack lasts from four to five days, at the end of which time the

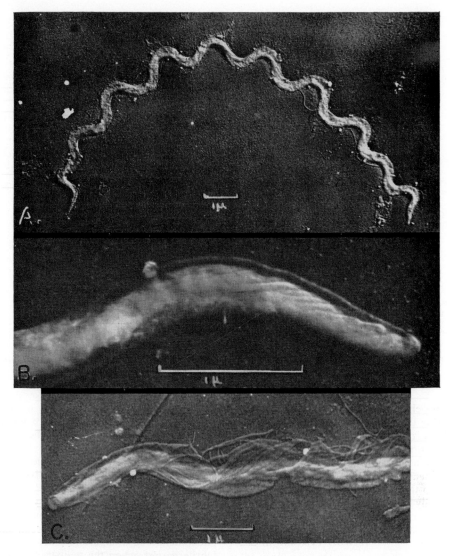

Fig. 2. Electron micrographs of Borrelia. A, *Bor. recurrentis* (Obermeieri) from blood of an infected mouse. A single filament has become detached. After tryptic digestion for 10 minutes numerous wavy filaments appeared which simulated flagella. B, *Borrelia* sp. from a case of gingivitis. C, Similar spirochetes after 10 minutes tryptic digestion. Note disappearance of cell wall and release of fibrils. (From Swain. *J. Path. & Bact.*, 69:117, 1955.)

microorganisms again disappear. Occasional relapses have been observed even in these animals. Except for splenic enlargements, gross pathologic changes are not found.

In man the disease caused by the spirochete of Obermeier and allied organisms, commonly known as "relapsing fever," is prevalent in eastern Europe, India, Africa, Panama (3, 19), and most of the warmer countries. It has, from time to time, been observed epidemically in Europe, especially in Russia, and a few epi-

demics have occurred in the United States (11). The disease comes on abruptly, beginning usually with a chill accompanied by a sharp rise of temperature and generalized pains. With the rise of temperature, which often exceeds 104° F., there is great prostration and occasionally delirium. Early in the disease the spleen becomes palpable and jaundice may appear. Rose colored spots resembling the exanthemata of typhus and hemorrhagic smallpox may develop on the skin of the body and trunk (26).

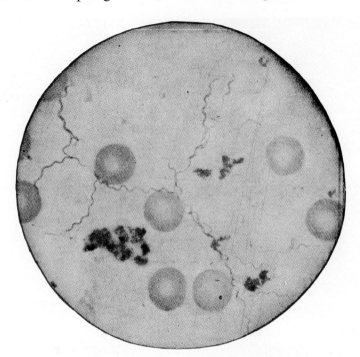

Fig. 3. Spirochete of relapsing fever. (From Norris, Pappenheimer, and Fluornoy. *J. Infect. Dis.,* 3:266, 1906.)

The spirochetes are detected easily in the blood during the persistence of the fever, which usually lasts from 3 to 10 days (Fig. 4). At the end of this time the temperature usually drops as suddenly as it rose, and the general symptoms disappear rapidly. After a free interval of from one to three weeks, a relapse may occur, which usually is less severe and of shorter duration than the original attack. Two, three, or even four attacks may occur, but the disease is seldom fatal. When patients do succumb, however, the autopsy findings are not particularly characteristic. Apart from the marked enlargement of the spleen, which histologically shows changes indicating simple hyperplasia and a slight enlargement of the liver, there are few observable lesions (1).

Immunity. Both syphilis and yaws are characterized by relapses, but relapsing fever, as the name indicates, exhibits this immunologic phenomenon to a superlative degree. After the febrile period, when the temperature returns to normal and the organisms disappear from the blood, agglutinins and lytic and spirocheticidal antibodies appear. The spirochetes are not eliminated completely during the afebrile period, and the survivors are able to alter their antigenic structure in such a way that they can multiply in the presence of the antibodies formed to the antigens liberated during the previous febrile attack. By the time they have multiplied sufficiently to be demonstrated in ordinary blood smears, a relapse occurs. Antibodies are produced to this newer antigenic type and the spirochetes again are driven from the blood. *Bor. duttonii* is such a plastic spirochete antigenically that Cunningham and his associates (5) were able to identify nine different serologic types. After a particular type once has

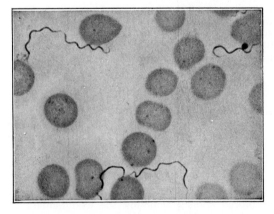

Fig. 4. Spirochete of relapsing fever. (Courtesy of Dr. G. N. Calkins.)

Table 1. Relapsing Fever Spirochetes

AREA	SPECIES	VECTOR
Europe	Bor. recurrentis (obermeieri) Bor. hispanica	Pediculus corporis O. erraticus (marocanum)
Africa	Bor. duttonii Bor. marocanum Bor. crocidurae Bor. merionesi Bor. recurrentis (kochi, rossi, berbera, aegyptium)	O. moubata O. erraticus O. erraticus O. erraticus Pediculis corporis
Middle East	Bor. persica Bor. microti	O. erraticus (papillipes) O. tholozani
India	Bor. recurrentis (carteri)	Pediculus corporis O. crossi
USSR	Bor. persica Bor. caucasica Bor. latyschewi ?	O. tholozani O. verrucosus O. tartarowskyi O. neerensis
North America	Bor. novyi Bor. turicatae Bor. parkerii Bor. hermsii not named	? * O. turicata O. parkeri O. hermsi O. talaje
British Columbia	Bor. hermsii	O. hermsi
Central and South America	Bor. venezuelensis (neotropicalis) not named	O. rudis (venezuelensis) O. talaje
Mexico	Bor. turicatae Bor. dugesii	O. turicata O. dugesi

* The origin of Bor. novyi is unknown. In its present form it is not transmitted by O. turicata.

appeared and stimulated the production of antibodies, it does not reappear, at least during that particular infection (5, 29). New infections may occur two to six months later as the result either of a disappearance of antibodies or of an infection with a new type of spirochete. Native populations in endemic areas usually have fewer relapses than visitors and eventually may become completely immune, indicating that even the great versatility of the spirochete is finally conquered by the greater adaptability of the human body. A mechanical basis for the persistence of spirochetes is suggested by the observations of Sergent and Richard (47) and Schuhardt and Hemphill (45), who found the organisms in the brains of experimentally infected guinea pigs and rats.

Zarafonetis and others (65) reported that animals infected experimentally with Bor. recurrentis and Spirillum minus and **patients with relapsing fever often give a positive Weil-Felix reaction with Proteus OXK but not with OX19.** Specific complement-fixation tests are somewhat more reliable than agglutination tests (56).

Transmission. Relapsing fever is perpetuated in nature by a tick-animal cycle. Various species of the soft tick Ornithodoros are the chief insect vectors. In West Africa the host is the shrew mouse, in Panama the monkey Leontocebes geoffroyi, in Texas the armadillo and opossum, and in California the squirrels and chipmunks. The spirochetes can be transmitted transovarially to the offspring for many generations (6, 7, 8). The infection is not transmitted by the bite of the tick but by contamination of the wound with coxal secretions, saliva and feces. There is no specific host relationship between the kind of tick and the species of spirochete.

Tick-borne relapsing fever is necessarily an endemic disease. True epidemics occur only when an anthropod vector such as the body louse *Pediculus corporis,* is in intimate and constant contact with man. Epidemic relapsing fever of Europe, particularly Russia, is transmitted by the louse, but even in areas of tick-borne disease the infection can be introduced into a population infested with lice and then become epidemic. An epidemic of relapsing fever began in Tunisia in 1944 and swept over most of North Africa during 1945 and 1946. In the Sudan, between September, 1945, and June, 1946, 600 to 900 cases occurred each week (10).

Treatment. If diagnosis is not made until near the end of the first febrile attack, it may be wise to wait for the next relapse before giving treatment since **some very severe and occasionally fatal reactions have been seen, presumably from the toxic effect of rapidly destroyed spirochetes.**

Penicillin G has been found effective both in experimental animals (43, 63) and in patients with louse-borne relapsing fever (16). Chlortetracycline has been reported as more effective than penicillin. Terramycin (oxytetracycline) is supposed to be more effective than penicillin in the treatment of Arabian relapsing fever, caused by *Bor. persica.*

Prevention. Immune and convalescent serums are ineffective, and prophylactic vaccination with killed cultures has not proved satisfactory. A direct attack on the inset vector with DDT is recommended.

FUSOSPIROCHETAL SYMBIOTIC DISEASE

In general, Koch's postulates should be satisfied before an organism is accepted as the cause of a particular disease. In practice, however, the requirement that the disease be reproduced in an experimental animal necessarily has been modified to include accidental or experimental infections in man. There is no place in Koch's scheme, however, for diseases caused by the symbiotic action of two or more organisms unless a further modification be made to provide for the acceptance of various groups of symbionts as infectious units. Swine influenza is a classic example of such a situation, since the disease is caused by combined action of the swine influenza virus and the bacillus *Haemophilus suis* (48). Both organisms have

been isolated in pure culture, but neither by itself will reproduce the typical disease. A gangrenous infection of the skin caused by staphylococci and streptococci has been described by Meleney (30), and Smith and others (54) have reported an infection in rats resulting from the symbiotic action of a gram-positive coccus and a gram-negative bacillus. A number of other examples have been described or suspected.

To this test list should be added the new observation that an oral diphtheroid stimulates the growth of *Bor. vincentii* in culture (31).

The most complicated symbiotic infectious unit is illustrated in the disease known as **Vincent's angina** or identified by the more comprehensive term **fusospirochetal disease.** This infection is caused by fusiform bacilli and spirochetes acting in symbiosis with vibrios and cocci. The spirochetes and fusiform bacilli never occur alone in progressive lesions, and the disease cannot be reproduced with these two organisms unless the other members of the unit are present.

The first comprehensive descriptions of this infection were published by Vincent (61, 62) in 1896 and 1898, although Plaut (41) and others had noted the association of fusiform bacilli in ulcerating lesions of the tonsils (Fig. 5). Castellani's (4) bronchial spirochetosis, which for a time was regarded as a tropical spirochetosis, is caused by the same symbiotic unit previously mentioned. Photographs of the organisms found in the secretions from lesions almost invariably show the presence of fusiform bacilli, vibrios, and cocci accompanying the spirochetes.

These fusospirochetal symbionts are normal inhabitants of the gums, but their numbers increase enormously when the local tissue resistance is reduced either by trauma or by deficiencies of certain vitamins, such as niacin and ascorbic acid. They are found either as primary or secondary invaders in many infections of the oropharynx, bronchi, and lungs, and less frequently in the intestinal tract, genital regions, and skin. Any organ or tissue of the body, including the brain, may be infected by metastases from the local lesions (17, 18, 42, 49, 50, 53).

Morphology and Staining. The fusiform bacilli are long or short, straight or slightly curved rods with sharply pointed ends. In the process of division by fission, the two organisms separate slowly and often are found in pairs attached end to end by a short delicate filament. They vary in size from 3 to 10 μ in length, and 0.3 to 0.8 μ in width. They are **gram-negative** but stain so faintly by Gram's method that the smaller ones frequently are

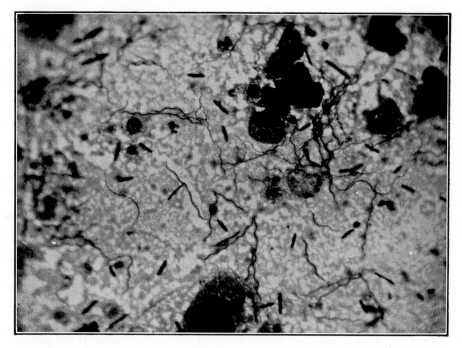

Fig. 5. Throat smear from Vincent's angina showing fusiform bacteria and spirochetes. (Courtesy of Stella Zimmerman, Syracuse University School of Medicine.)

unrecognizable. When stained with the stronger aniline dyes, such as gentian violet or carbolfuchsin, the bacilli are found to contain deeper staining granules and bands which are superimposed upon a faintly staining background. *Fusobacterium nucleatum* and *Fusobacterium polymorphium* have been studied with the electron microscope by Hampp and his associates (14).

Borrelia buccalis and *Bor. vincentii* stain faintly with gentian violet and carbolfuchsin and with the stains of Giemsa and Wright. *Treponema microdentium* and *T. mucosum* are as difficult to stain as *T. pallidum* but can be stained easily with the silver nitrate method of Fontana-Tribondeau.

These actively motile treponemas which are demonstrated readily by the darkfield microscope cannot be differentiated morphologically from *T. pallidum* or *T. pertenue*.

The **vibrios** are **gram-negative** and appear identical morphologically and culturally with those found in the normal mouth.

Cultivation. The organisms in this symbiotic unit are **anaerobic.** Since no spore-formers are present in the unit, all are killed readily by a temperature of 60° C. for one hour. The streptococci and vibrios often become adapted to aerobic growth after a number of transfers but the essential fusiform bacilli and spirochetes are **obligate anaerobes.** They are difficult to isolate and maintain in pure culture, but they grow readily in mixed cultures and in Vaselinesealed meat infusion broth tubes to which ascitic fluid has been added. The anaerobic streptococci grow fairly well on the surfaces of bloodagar plates when incubated at 37° C. under anaerobic conditions. Fusiform bacilli and vibriosis may be isolated by the same method, but success more often is the result of persistence rather than skill (Fig. 6). Varney (60) has been more successful than most investigators in isolating and classifying the fusiform bacilli.

DeAraujo and his coworkers (9) have found serologic differences between *Fusobacterium polymorphium* and *Fusobacterium fusiforme* (*L. buccalis*). This is not surprising, since some cultures of fusiform in morphology, motility, and specific susceptibility to arsenicals are identical with *Bor. buccale.* However, the authors state that the proper name should be *Leptotrichia buccalis* as suggested by Omata and Braumberg (39).

Noguchi (33) was the first to isolate *T. microdentium, T. mucosum,* and *Bor. vincentii* by using his ascitic-fluid-rabbit kidney technic which had been devised originally for the isolation of *T. pallidum.* Smith (52) and Proske

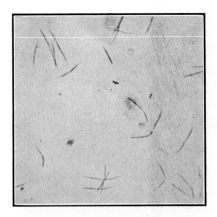

Fig. 6. *Fusiform bacilli.* Pure culture. Gentian violet stain. × 800. (From Smith. *J. Infect. Dis.,* 46:303, 1930.)

and Sayers (42) isolated several strains of *T. microdentium* by Noguchi's method. In 1947 Hampp (12) succeeded in growing the smaller oral treponemata, *Borrelia vincentii,* and the cultural strains of *T. pallidum* in sufficient quantity for immunologic studies. The culture requirement of *Bor. buccale, Bor. vincentii* and *Treponema microdentium* have been studied by Hampp and Nevin (13). Oral vibrios and spirochetes are usually associated with fusiform bacilli, spirochetes, and cocci in the oral flora. New methods of isolating *S. sputigenum* has been published by MacDonald and his associates (22, 23). Mashimo and Ellison (28) described a method by which both *S. sputigenum* and *Vibrio sputorium* can be isolated.

Relation of Fusiform Bacilli to Spirochetes. The constant association of fusiform bacilli and spirochetes naturally suggested the possibility that they were merely different morphologic forms of the same organism. Tunnicliff (58) reported the transformation of pure cultures of fusiform bacilli into spirochetes, but Varney (60) and other observers found no evidence of this transformation. The problem was reinvestigated by one of us (50, 52). The medium-sized and small fusiform bacilli isolated by Varney have no resemblance at any time to spirochetes, but the large fusiform bacillus, which is found in large numbers in smears from cases of Vincent's angina and trench mouth, probably is not a bacillus at all but a morphologic variant of *Borrelia buccalis.* We have observed individual organisms, presumably from pure cultures, slowly coil to resemble *Borrelia buccalis* and then straighten out again to appear as fusiform bacilli (Fig. 7). We exchanged cultures with Tunnicliff and are convinced that her ob-

servations were correct. This large fusiform bacillus or spirochete is destroyed readily by arsenicals while the true fusiform bacilli are unaffected.

Metabolites. Neither exotoxins nor endotoxins have been demonstrated, but it is probable that **proteolytic enzymes** are produced by some of these organisms since rapid necrosis and liquefaction of tissues is a striking characteristic of both spontaneous and experimental infections.

Antigenic Structure. Varney (60) isolated 18 strains of fusiform bacilli and separated them into four groups by specific agglutination reactions.

Experimental Infection in Laboratory Animals. Abscesses are produced readily in guinea pigs, rabbits, dogs, and mice by subcutaneous or intrabronchial injections of the fusospirochetal symbiotic mixture. The experimental lesions are characterized by local gangrene and a fetid odor. Severe spontaneous infections with these organisms occur in guinea pigs deprived of ascorbic acid and in dogs on diets deficient in niacin. If the animals are not moribund, spontaneous recovery takes place when the missing vitamin is restored to the diet.

Pure cultures of spirochetes, fusiform bacilli, and vibros fail to infect experimental animals. The anaerobic streptococci, when introduced in large numbers, produce small, transitory, self-limiting infections. However, mixtures made from pure cultures of *T. microdentium,* a small fusiform bacillus, a vibrio, and an anaerobic streptococcus reproduce the typical disease in guinea pigs (50, 52). The mixture is non-infectious when the symbiotic unit is disturbed

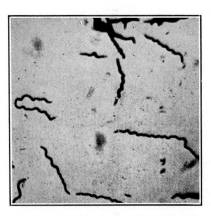

Fig. 7. *Borrelia buccale.* Pure culture. Fontana stain. × 1,000. This form appeared in subcultures from the fusiform bacilli shown in Figure 6. (From Smith. *Oral Spirochetes and Related Organisms,* Williams & Wilkins Co.)

by the inactivation of *Treponema microdentium* with small amounts of neoarsphenamine. Proske and Sayers (42) isolated in pure culture a number of strains of spirochetes, fusiform bacilli, vibrios and cocci from the sputum or lungs of patients with fusospirochetal symbiotic disease. The minimal number required to reproduce the disease was the same as that just described. Thus, in a modified form, Koch's postulates have been fulfilled; the disease has been reproduced in animals with a **mixture made from pure cultures** and the organisms have been recovered in pure culture from the experimental disease. The presence of another symbiotic group, in which bacteriodes species are an essential element, has been reported by MacDonald and his associates (22).

Although pure cultures of fusiform bacilli have not infected experimental animals, they may be able to infect man under certain specific conditions and produce multiple small necrotic lesions throughout the body. Tynes and Utz (59) in 1960 collected from the literature 53 cases where the fusobacteria have been isolated from the blood of patients.

Clinical Types of Infection in Man. The most commonly recognized form of the infection is that which occurs on the tonsils. The tonsil is congested and erythematous for 12 to 24 hours but soon is covered with a grayish-white pseudomembrane resembling that caused by the diphtheria bacillus. In another 24 to 48 hours the mucous membrane becomes gangrenous and the breath fetid. There may be a rapid ulceration of the tonsillar tissue resulting in a deep "punched out" ulcer which often has been diagnosed erroneously as syphilitic.

Not infrequently a redness or congestion develops in the entire oral cavity, accompanied by edema and pseudohypertrophy of the gums. This form of the disease, known since World War I as **trench mouth,** usually is sporadic but occasionally becomes epidemic in schools, orphanages and military units. During the first seven to 10 days the pulmonary forms of the disease are indistinguishable from those caused by the ordinary pyogenic cocci. A metabolic product of the organism then begins to necrotize the pulmonary tissues, and after several weeks the patient presents the clinical and anatomic picture of **pulmonary gangrene, pulmonary abscess,** or **bronchiectasis** (Fig. 8) (51).

Transmission. The source of the infection is the patient's own mouth. The disease usually is sporadic and not contagious. Occasionally, however, a physician contracts an infection of the tonsils or lungs while treating a patient with

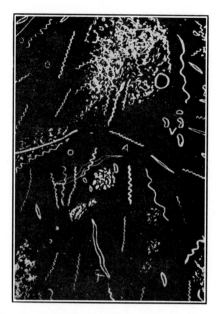

Fig. 8. Fusospirochetal symbiotic organisms. Found in patient with chronic bronchiectasis. (From Smith. *Oral Spirochetes and Related Organisms,* Williams & Wilkins Co.)

Vincent's angina and, in rare instances, epidemics of trench mouth occur.

Treatment. Penicillin apparently is even more effective than the arsenicals (53). Primary tropical ulcers, which are caused by these symbiotic organisms, also respond to treatment with penicillin (40).

Prevention. Good oral hygiene is the best preventive measure; this necessitates an adequate supply of vitamins in the diet as well as the mechanical cleansing of the teeth.

SPIROCHETOSIS OF FOWLS

Species: *Borrelia anserina* (Sakharoff) Bergey and others

This disease was recognized by Sakharoff (44) in 1891 among the geese of the Caucasus and was studied in some detail by Marchoux and Salembeni (27) in 1903 and Sreenivasan and Sankaranarayan (55) in 1945. This spirochetosis is prevalent in North and South Africa, India, the Middle East, Russia, Europe, Australia, Java, Brazil, and Argentina. Epidemics occur in chickens, turkeys (Fig. 9), ducks, grouse, and canaries. Pigeons and guinea fowls are rather resistant, but many other species can be infected experimentally. The disease is usually transmitted by the tick, *Argas persicus.*

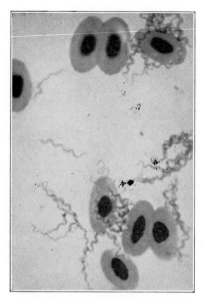

Fig. 9. *Borrelia anserina.* Smear of turkey's blood. (From McNeil, Hinshaw, and Kisling. *J. Bact.,* 57:191, 1949.)

This infection was recognized in the United States in 1945 when Hoffman (15) isolated *Borrelia anserina* from turkeys in California. A second outbreak in California turkeys was studied in great detail by McNeil, Hinshaw, and Kissling (25). Circumstantial evidence suggests that culicine mosquitoes and not ticks were responsible for the California epidemics.

The onset of the disease is sudden with fever, diarrhea, and prostration. Spirochetes are demonstrated easily in the circulating blood by staining blood smears with Giemsa's stain or with dilute carbolfuchsin.

The spirochetes remain viable in blood stored at 0° C. for three weeks (55) and in the tissues of birds for 31 days when stored at 32° F. (25). **Cultivation** is difficult, although it was grown by Noguchi in 1912 in his ascitic fluid-fresh rabbit kidney medium. Other investigators have used rabbit serum and Tyrode's solution. More consistent results have been obtained by inoculating embryonated eggs (19). Agglutinins are produced by the infection and birds which recover are immune. There may be more than one antigen type (27).

A single dose of 10,000 units of **penicillin** will cure infected turkeys but streptomycin is ineffective (25). **Active** immunization with vaccines prepared with spirochetes grown in chick eggs has been used successfully in Brazil (32) and may find use in this country if the infection spreads.

REFERENCES

1. Anderson, T. R., and Zimmerman, L. E. Am. J. Path., 31:1083, 1955.
2. Bohls, S. W., and others. Proc. Soc. Exper. Biol. & Med., 45:375, 1940.
3. Calero, C. Am. J. Trop. Med., 26:761, 1946.
4. Castellani, A. Lancet, 1:1384, 1906.
5. Cunningham, J., and others. Indian J. M. Research, 22:105, 595, 1934.
6. Davis, G. E. Pub. Health Rep., 54:1345, 1939.
7. ———— Tick Vectors and Life Cycles of Ticks, A.A.A.S., No. 18, 1942, pp. 67-76.
8. ———— Ann. Rev. Microbiol., 1:305, 1948.
9. DeArajo, Wilson, C., and others. J. Bact., 86:837, 1963.
10. Epidemiological Information Bulletin, 2:929, 1946.
11. Francis, E. Tr. A. Am. Physicians, 47:143, 1932.
12. Hampp, E. G. J. Am. Dent. A., 34:606, 1947.
13. ———— and Nevin, T. A. J. Bact., 77:800, 1959.
14. ———— and others. J. Bact., 79:716, 1960.
15. Hoffman, H. A., and others. J. Am. Vet. M. A., 108:329; 109:481, 1946.
16. Ingraham, H. S., and Lapenta, R. G. U.S. Nav. M. Bull., 46:1719, 1946.
17. Kelly, F. C. J. Infect. Dis., 74:93, 1944.
18. Kline, B. S., and Berger, S. S. Arch. Surg., 18:481, 1929.
19. Knowles, R., and others. Indian M. Research Mem., 22:1, 1932.
20. Leifson, E. J. Bact., 60:678, 1950.
21. Levaditi, C., and others. Ann. Inst. Pasteur, 80:9, 1951.
22. MacDonald, J. B., and others. J. Infect. Dis., 98:15, 1956.
23. ———— and others. J. Bact., 77:558, 1959.
24. McKercher, D. G. J. Bact., 59:446, 1950.
25. McNeil, E., and others. J. Bact., 57:191, 1949.
26. Manson-Bahr, P. H. Manson's Tropical Diseases, Baltimore, Williams & Wilkins Co., 1940.
27. Marchoux, E., and Salembeni, A. Ann. Inst. Pasteur, 17:665, 1903.
28. Mashimo, P. A., and Ellison, S. A. J. Bact., 78:636, 1959.
29. Meleney, H. E. J. Exper. Med., 48:65, 1928.
30. Meleney, F. L. Ann. Surg., 91:287, 1930; 95:961, 1931; 101:997, 1935.
31. Nevin, T. A., and others. J. Bact., 80:783, 1960.
32. Nobrega, P., and Reis, J. Arq. Inst. biol. São Paulo, 12:87, 1941.
33. Noguchi, H. J. Exper. Med., 16:199, 620, 1912; 17:89, 1913.
34. ———— The Newer Knowledge of Bacteriology and Immunology, Chicago, University of Chicago Press, 1928, Chap. 36, pp. 452-497.
35. Norris, C., and others. J. Infect. Dis., 3:266, 1906.
36. Novy, F. T., and Knapp, R. E. J. Infect. Dis., 3:291, 1906.
37. Oag, R. K. J. Path. & Bact., 51:127, 1940.
38. Obermeier, O. H. F. Centralbl. f. d. med. Wissensch., 11:145, 1873.
39. Omata, R. R., and Braumberg, R. C. J. Bact., 80:737, 1960.

40. Pinkerton, J. McL. J. Trop. Med., 50:243, 1947.
41. Plaut, H. C. Deutsche med. Wchnschr., 20: 920, 1894.
42. Proske, H. O., and Sayers, R. R. Pub. Health Rep., 48:839, 1212, 1934.
43. Richardson, A. P., and others. J. Pharmacol. & Exper. Therap., 85:23, 1945.
44. Sakharoff, M. N. Ann. Inst. Pasteur, 5:564, 1891.
45. Schuhardt, V. T., and Hemphill, E. C. Science, 103:422, 1946.
46. ——— and Wilkerson, M. J. Bact., 62:215, 1951.
47. Sergent, A., and Richard, H. Arch. Inst. Pasteur d'Algérie, 20:293, 298, 1942.
48. Shope, R. E. J. Exper. Med., 64:47, 791, 1936.
49. Smith, D. T. Am. Rev. Tuberc., 15:352, 1927; 16:584, 1927.
50. ——— Oral Spirochetes and Related Organisms in Fusospirochetal Disease, Baltimore, Williams & Wilkins Co., 1932.
51. ——— Arch. Surg., 21:1173, 1931.
52. ——— J. Infect. Dis., 46:303, 1930.
53. ——— J. Thoracic Surg., 17:72, 1948.
54. ——— and others. J. Bact., 20:361, 1930.
55. Sreenivasan, M. K., and Sankaranarayan, N. S. Indian Vet. J., 21:325, 1945.
56. Stein, G. J. J. Exper. Med., 79:115, 1944.
57. Swain, R. H. A. J. Path. Bact., 69:117, 1955.
58. Tunnicliff, R. J. Infect. Dis., 3:148, 1906; 8:316, 1911; 33:147, 1923; 53:280, 1933; 55: 380, 1934.
59. Tynes, B. J., and Utz, J. P. Am. J. Med., 29: 879, 1960.
60. Varney, P. J. Bact., 13:275, 1927.
61. Vincent, H. Ann. Inst. Pasteur, 10:488, 1896.
62. ——— Bull. et mém. Soc. méd. d. hôp. de Paris, 15:244, 1898.
63. Williamson, J., and Lourie, E. M. Brit. M. J., 1:828, 1946.
64. Wolman, B., and Wolman, M. Ann. Trop. Med. & Parasitol., 39:82, 1945.
65. Zarafonetis, C. J. D., and others. J. Immunol., 52:189, 1946.

52

The Leptospira Group—Infectious Jaundice
(Weil's Disease) and Other Leptospiroses

Order: *Spirochaetales*. Family: *Treponemataceae* Robinson. Genus: *Leptospira* Noguchi. Type Species: *Leptospira icterohaemorrhagiae* (Inada and Ido) Noguchi

The medical and economic importance of the leptospiroses has been underestimated in this country. Physicians rarely consider the possibility of a leptospiral infection unless the patient is jaundiced, not realizing that this sign is absent in 50 per cent of classic cases of Weil's disease and in 80 to 90 per cent of infections with the other leptospira.

Weil (65) described in 1886 an infectious disease characterized by fever, jaundice, and petechial hemorrhages, although it was not until 1915 that Inada and Ido (35) of Japan isolated *Leptospira icterohaemorrhagiae,* the etiologic agent.

The reservoir of leptospiral infection seems to be in the *Muridae* in whom they produce mild or asymptomtaic infection (3). The leptospira settle out, however, and colonize in the renal tubule cells (62, 63), where they are protected from the circulating antibodies and are in a favorable location for discharge into the urine (45). The carrier state may persist longer than the antibodies, since it has been established that leptospiras may be isolated from the urine of dogs and other animals when antibodies cannot be detected in their sera (26).

The organisms do not live long in the concentrated acid urine, but when the urine is diluted with natural waters, they remain viable and infectious for weeks or months (3). The extent of their colonization of the carrier species is illustrated by Roth's (54) study which showed that 57.4 per cent of 650 striped skunks, *Mephitis mephitis,* collected in Louisiana were carrying virulent forms of five major serogroups (14).

The large domestic animals and man are usually terminal hosts and more often show clinical symptoms. Dogs, swine, cows, horses, and, to a lesser degree, sheep and goats may become infected and may die. Man may be a temporary renal carrier for a few weeks or months but not longer than a year. In contrast, the convalescent dog is the chief carrier of *L. canicola,* swine for *L. pomona* (67, 68), and cattle for *L. grippotyphosa* (10). Cattle may also be infected with *L. pomona* and in turn infect water, which in one case infected nine children in two families (17).

In 1962 Galton (26) reported that 60 leptospiral serotypes or subserotypes had been recognized or provisionally classified. This does not include some 35 other strains which have been described but not officially accepted.

The 13 major serologic groups of *Leptospira* are shown in Table 1 with their distribution and their hosts. Eleven types have been isolated from animals in this country: *L. icterohaemorrhagiae, L. canicola, L. pomona* (67, 68,) *L. hebdomadis, L. autumnalis, L. pyrogenes, L. grippotyphosa* (31), *L. ballum, L. hyos, L. bataviae* (Roth et al 1962), and *L. australis A.* (4). Six of these serotypes are known to produce disease in man: *L. icterohaemorrhagiae, L. canicola,*

Table 1. Leptospires, Distribution, and Hosts

ORGANISM	DISTRIBUTION	COMMON HOST
L. icterohaemorrhagiae	Japan, Germany, England, U.S.A., the World	Rat, mouse, dog, skunk, fox, raccoon (14)
L. hebdomadis	Japan, Italy, Eastern Asia, U.S.A. (24)	Field mice, dog, cattle, skunk (24)
L. autumnalis *	Japan, Eastern Asia, U.S.A.	Field mice, dog, cat, goat
L. bataviae	Indonesia, Belgian Congo, Eastern Asia, U.S.A. (52)	Rat, cat, field mice
L. australis	North Queensland, Italy, Malaya, Brazil, U.S.A. (4)	Field rat, dog, bandicoot, raccoon, opossum, fox (4)
L. pyrogenes	Indonesia, Japan, Italy, Malaya, U.S.A. (54)	Dog, nutria
L. canicola	Netherland, Denmark, England, U.S.A., World-wide	Dog, jackal, pig, horse, cattle, sheep
L. grippotyphosa	Russia, Germany, Israel, Malaya, Netherland, U.S.A.	Goat, horse, skunk (field mice), dog (54)
L. pomona	North Queensland, Indonesia, Europe, Asia, South America, U.S.A.	Pig, cat, cattle, horse, dog
L. sejro	Denmark, Europe, Switzerland	Field mice, cattle, dog, horse, pig
L. ballum	Denmark, Holland, Yugoslavia, Czechoslovakia, Portugal, Canada, U.S.A., Puerto Rico (54)	House mouse, opossum, pig, skunk (54)
L. andamana	Andaman Islands, Finland	Not known
L. hyos	Argentina, Queensland, Malaya, France, Italy, Switzerland, U.S.A. (54)	Pigs, cattle, horse, skunk (54)

* Identified as the cause of U.S.A. pretibial or Fort Bragg Fever.
Data computed from studies of Schlossberger and Brandis (57), Wolff (66), Rothstein and Hiatt (55), Alston and Broom (3).

L. pomona, L. hebdomadis (L. mimigeorgia) (24, 25), L. autumnalis (28), L. australis A (4).

Morphology and Staining. The spirochetes of the genus *Leptospira* are tightly coiled, thin, flexible organisms, 7 to 20 μ long and 0.10 to 0.2 μ in diameter. The individual spirals are composed of 12 to 18 regular small primary spirals. The terminal third of the body of the spirochete is more flexible than the middle portion and usually is bent to form a hook. The organism is motile, progressing by an undulatory movement and by a rapid spinning on the long axis. During this spinning motion one end may be curved in a hook while the other end remains straight (Fig. 1). The organism then progresses slowly in the direction of the straightened end. Often both ends are hooked, usually in opposite directions, while the organism spins rapidly on its long axis.

Leptospirae in smears can be stained by the silver nitrate method of Fontana-Tribondeau and in tissues by the technic of Levaditi. The individual coils of the organisms are so closely wound that the precipitated silver salt usually obscures them and the organisms appear as straight or slightly curved rods. The individual turns in the organisms can be seen in the dark field and have been delineated in electron micrographs. The electron micrographs of Czekalowski and Eaves (20) show clearly the presence of internal granules which may be nuclei

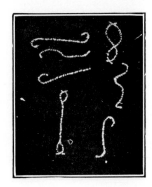

Fig. 1. *Leptospira icterohaemorrhagiae.* Diagrammatic sketch of appearance of organisms in darkfield.

but are certainly not spores. Multiplication is usually by fission, but some organisms develop rather large cyst-like structures at one end, which suggest a more complicated method of reproduction. The organisms have no flagella, and motility apparently depends upon the presence of a rather rigid axistyle. This structure lies outside the membrane enveloping the cytoplasmic cylinder (Fig. 2) but may be released from it by treatment with sodium desoxycholate (Fig. 3) (21). The axistyles end subterminally in knob-like processes suggesting blepharoplasts.

Cultivation. The leptospirae are **aerobic** and grow best at pH 7.2 at a temperature of 25°

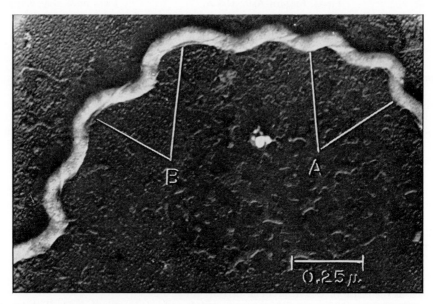

Fig. 2. *L. icterohaemorrhagiae.* The protoplasmic cylinder (A) is wound helically around the axistyle (B). × 75,000. (From Czekalowski and Eaves. *J. Path. & Bact.,* 69:129, 1955.)

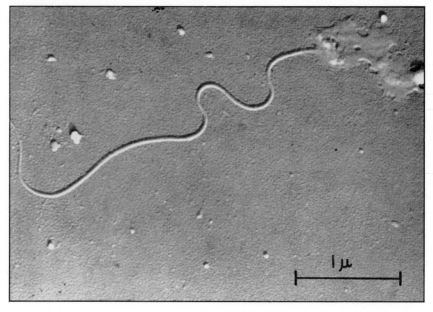

Fig. 3. *L. leeds.* The cytoplasmic cylinder has been dissolved by treatment with sodium deoxycholate and the axistyle released. × 25,000. (From Czekalowski and Eaves. *J. Path. & Bact.,* 69:129, 1955.)

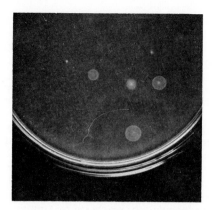

Fig. 4. *Leptospira canicola* colonies 16 days after inoculation, showing morphological variations of young colonies. (From Stalheim and Wilson. *J. Bact.*, 86:482, 1963.)

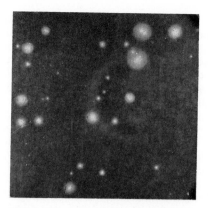

Fig. 6. *Leptospira autumnalis* colonies 30 days after inoculation; note the morphological variations among colonies. (From Stalheim and Wilson. *J. Bact.*, 86:482, 1963.)

to 30° C. The Japanese workers used Noguchi's ascitic fluid medium to isolate their first cultures (35). Noguchi (48) later introduced a simpler medium composed of physiologic saline, fresh rabbit serum, rabbit hemoglobin and 0.2 per cent agar. Leptospira will grow in a simple medium consisting of salts, thiamine, asparagine, and rabbit serum albumin but the rabbit albumin cannot be replaced by a mixture of the amino acids known to occur in the albumin (59). Other studies with *L. pomona* (36) have shown a requirement for fatty acids. Colonies of some of the more common *Leptospira* are shown in Figures 4, 5, 6, and 7. *L. biflexa* produces almost invisible colonies when grown in Cox's medium, but the colonies can be made sharp and clear by treatment with oxidase reagent (30). Leptospirae grow rapidly on the

membranes of the developing chick embryo and kill the embryo in less than seven days (15, 46). Contaminated material may be injected into young guinea pigs (60), hamsters, or into two-day-old baby chicks (33) and pure cultures obtained from the blood after the development of a leptospiremia.

Pseudoleptospira, probably arising from red cells, appear frequently in specimens of human blood **making it difficult to diagnose leptospiroses by direct darkfield examination.**

Resistance. At room temperature leptospirae remain viable in defibrinated blood for seven days and in infected guinea pig livers, stored in the refrigerator, for 26 days. Adapted strains live in culture media for weeks without transfer (47). They withstand freezing but are destroyed in 30 minutes at temperatures of 50°

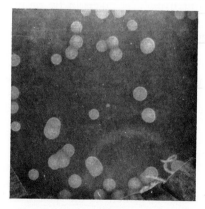

Fig. 5. *Leptospira grippotyphosa* colonies 24 days after inoculation, showing mature colonies except for one delayed colony near center. (From Stalheim and Wilson. *J. Bact.*, 86:482, 1963.)

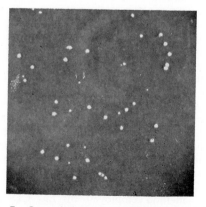

Fig. 7. One of the stable variants picked from a plate similar to Figure 6. (From Stalheim and Wilson. *J. Bact.*, 86:482, 1963.)

to 55° C. The organisms cannot be cultured in a medium which is even slightly acid; they are readily destroyed by gastric juice and are dissolved by both trypsin and bile, but not by a 10 per cent solution of saponin.

Penicillin may have some effect on the clinical disease if given early (2), although it did not prevent infection in a laboratory worker even when 6 million units were given by mouth over three days beginning one hour after the accidental infection (11). *Chlortetracycline* or *oxytetracycline* may be somewhat more effective (3).

Antigenic Structure. Definite antigenic differences occur between the suprophytic *L. biflexa* and the pathogenic species. It should be noted that the pathogenic *L. icterohaemorrhagiae* may be isolated from water which has been contaminated by the urine of rats carrying *Leptospira*.

The studies of Rothstein and Hiatt (55, 56) and others (57, 66) suggest that leptospira contain two major antigenic components. The first is a surface antigen, probably a protein polysaccharide complex which is a type-specific antigen. The second is a somatic antigen, which is a lipopolysaccharide, and is genus-specific. Two and possibly three antigens occur in the surface layers, which may explain the overlapping serologic relationships among the spirochetes of this genus and also the presence of serologic biotypes within a single species. The Schüffner-Mochtar agglutination-lysis method, employing living leptospira, has been used almost exclusively for the detection of serotypes (27, 29). The test is carried out both before and after reciprocal agglutinin absorption with other strains. Heat-killed (33) and formalin-killed cultures (34) are more convenient than living cultures for agglutination reaction but are somewhat less specific. The complement-fixation test employing sonically disrupted leptospiral antigens (58) is specific for closely related groups of *Leptospira*. Human O erythrocytes can be sensitized with extracts of *Leptospira* to give a hemagglutinin reaction (16). The same extract could be used to sensitize sheep erythrocytes, which would then be hemolyzed in the presence of homologous rabbit antiserum and complement (19). Other methods of diagnosis utilize the **immune adherence** method (41) or the fluorescent antibody technic. Galton (25) has published the serodiagnostic method employed by the CDC, and Lang and Morse (38) the variety of cross reactions encountered among the *Leptospira*.

Metabolites. Neither exotoxins nor endotoxins have been demonstrated, but hemolysins are produced by cultures of certain strains of pathogenic *Leptospira* (1). The hemolysin is soluble, nondialyzable, thermolabile, and oxygen-stabile and is produced by certain specific serotype strains.

Experimental Infection in Laboratory Animals. Rats and mice are not suitable for experimental infection because they may be immune or have a spontaneous infection at the time of inoculation. Young guinea pigs and young golden hamsters (9, 39) are most susceptible. The inoculation of blood, tissues, spinal fluid or other exudates may be made by the intraperitoneal, intracutaneous, or subcutaneous routes (6). Fever begins about 24 hours following inoculation, reaches a maximum on the fourth to fifth day, and then falls to normal or subnormal. Jaundice appears as the fever declines, and death occurs between the seventh and twelfth days after inoculation. Characteristic lesions containing numerous leptospira are found in the liver and kidneys. Virulence is increased by serial passage in guinea pigs.

Clinical Types of Infection in Man. All types of pathogenic *Leptospira* may produce mild clinical or subclinical infection without jaundice and all types may produce severe or fatal infection with jaundice, but in general *L. icterohaemorrhagiae* is most severe and most frequent icteric; *L. autumnalis* and *L. australis A* and *B* are less severe and less icteric; while *L. canicola, L. pomona,* and *L. hebdomadis* are milder and usually without icterus (3). The incubation period varies from 9 to 19 days with an average of 10 days. *Leptospira icterohaemorrhagiae* may enter the body through an abrasion on the skin but usually is taken in by mouth with food or water which has been contaminated by the urine of infected animals. While jaundice is a characteristic feature of typical cases of Weil's disease, mild cases usually do not present this symptom. The mortality varies from 4 to 48 per cent but was 10.2 per cent in the 452 cases studied in Holland (5).

Fiedler divides Weil's disease into three stages: an initial period of two or three days, with fever, followed by a second stage of three days, during which icterus, edema of the liver, enlargement of the spleen, and skin hemorrhages occur. The defervescent period starts on the seventh day and initiates convalescence. Inada describes it as follows (35): The onset is initiated by chills and fever, intestinal disturbances, headache.

muscular pains, hyperemia of the conjunctivae, and albuminuria. In this stage death
is rare, and during this time the spirochetes
are circulating freely in the blood. Blood
injected during this period into guinea pigs
produces a typical reaction. From this time
on, according to Inada, the infectivity of the
blood decreases. From the seventh to the
thirteenth day, the icteric period which
covers a little less than a week, the symptoms
decrease, and the jaundice and hemorrhages
into the skin appear, together with great
weakness, neural and cardiac symptoms
(62). The two stages merge into each other,
and the second period is the one during
which death is most common. In cases dead
at this time the spirochetes have disappeared
from the blood, and antibodies can be
demonstrated by the Pfeiffer test. During the
second stage, the spirochetes are present in
the urine and can be found by the darkfield.
As antibodies develop, the spirochetes disappear from the blood and from the liver.
This may occur early in the course of the
disease.

Permanent immunity usually follows an
attack of leptospirosis and appears to be primarily humoral. L. pomona produces meningitis in a high percentage of cases but
rarely causes jaundice. In a recent epidemic
in this country 30 persons developed meningitis after swimming in water contaminated
by swine (7, 8). Gseld (32) has reported the
development of iridocyclitis as a late complication of L. pomona infection which is
known colloquially in Switzerland as "swine-
herd's disease." Beeson and his associates
(7) found a similar case in an abattoir
worker in Atlanta, Georgia.

Following the stimulating work of Karl
Meyer and his associates in California (42,
43, 44), clinical cases of L. canicola infections in man are being recognized with
greater frequency in this and other countries
(13, 18, 61, 62).

The clinical syndrome described by
Daniels and Grennan (22) in 1943 as pretibial fever or Fort Bragg Fever was characterized by malaise, fever, splenomegaly,
leukopenia, and a rash on the fourth day of
the disease. The infectious agent was transmitted to guinea pigs by Tatlock (63) and
maintained in serial passage in these animals
and in embryonated chick eggs until 1952,
when Gochenour and his associates (27, 28)
isolated a strain of L. autumnalis from the
animals and showed that convalescent serum
from the soldiers infected in 1942 to 44
contained specific agglutinating and protective antibodies for this leptospira.

More details about the clinical course of
Leptospirosis can be found in the publica-
tions of Coggins (17) Ammon (4), and
Edwards and Domm (23).

Transmission. *Leptospira icterohaemorrhagiae* has been found in 4 per cent of the
rats in New York, in 10 per cent of those
in Philadelphia, in 30 per cent of those in
England and in 40 per cent of those in
Holland (5, 50). The field vole is the reservoir of infection in the Orient. *L. canicola* is
present in 25 per cent of the dogs in northern
California (51), and dog catchers and
veterinary surgeons are infected not infrequently by contact with these animals (44).

It may be considered an occupational disease of young adult males who work in wet
areas where rats are common. Fish cleaners
and poultry dressers often are infected, as
well as sewer workers, tunnel diggers, barge
men, sugar cane cutters and workers in rice
fields. One instance of a water-borne epidemic has been reported (37).

Treatment.   Although the antibiotics
chlortetracycline (40) and oxytetracycline
are reasonably effective in curing experimentally infected animals, their effect in man
has been equivocal unless administered very
early in the disease (11).

Prevention.   The complete eradication of
infected rats, mice and voles is desirable but
not yet practical. Food and water should be
protected from contamination, and rubber
boots should be worn by those working in
damp places where the water may have been
contaminated with urine from infected rats.

Heat-killed vaccines have been used
among the coal miners in Japan for many
years with considerable success (64), but
they have not been used in this country
probably because of occasionally severe local
or general reactions.

Olitzki and others (49) found that calves
could not be immunized with formalin-
treated cultures of L. bovis but could be immunized against L. bovis with living cultures
of L. grippotyphosa. Brunner and Meyer
(12) obtained excellent immunity in puppies

and dogs against *L. canicola* and *L. ictero-haemorrhagiae* with a vaccine inactivated by shell-freezing and lyophilization but not with formalized cultures.

REFERENCES

1. Alexander, A. D., and others. Proc. Soc. Exper. Biol. & Med., 91:205, 1956.
2. Alston, J. M., and Broom, J. C. Brit. M. J., 2:719, 1944.
3. ―――― and Broom, J. C. Leptospirosis in Man and Animals, E. and S. Livingston, Ltd., Edinburgh and London, 1958.
4. Ammons, J., and others. South. M. J., 52: 900, 1959.
5. Ashe, W. F., and others. Medicine, 20:145, 1941.
6. Beamer, P. B. North Carolina M. J., 11: 566, 1950.
7. Beeson, P. B., and others. J.A.M.A., 145: 229, 1951.
8. ―――― and Hankey, D. D. Arch. Int. Med., 89:575, 1952.
9. Borg-Petersen, C. Acta path. et microbiol. scandinav., 27:726, 1950.
10. Bernkopf, H., and others. J. Infect. Dis., 80: 53, 1947; 83:232, 1948.
11. Broom, J. C., and Norris, T. S., Jr. Lancet, 1:721, 1957.
12. Brunner, K. T., and Meyer, K. F. J. Immunol., 64:365, 1950.
13. Campbell, A. M. G., and others. Brit. M. J., 1:336, 1950.
14. Carbrey, E. A., and others. Pub. Health Report, 78:355, 1963.
15. Chabaud, A. Bull. Soc. path. exot., 32:483, 1939.
16. Chang, R. S., and McComb, D. E. Am. J. Trop. Med., 3:481, 1954.
17. Coggins, W. J. J.A.M.A., 181:1077, 1962.
18. Correia, M. O. A., and Alyes Meira, J. An. paulist. de med. e cir., 58:431, 1949.
19. Cox, C. D. Proc. Soc. Exper. Biol. & Med., 90:610, 1955.
20. Czekalowski, J. W., and Eaves, G. J. Bact., 67:619, 1954.
21. ―――― and Eaves, G. J. Path. & Bact., 69: 129, 1955.
22. Daniels, W. B., and Grennan, H. A. J.A.M.A., 122:361, 1943.
23. Edwards, G. A., and Domm, B. M. Medicine, 39:117, 1960.
24. Galton, M. M. Pub. Health Report, 75:917, 1960.
25. ―――― and others. Leptospirosis. Method in Laboratory Diagnosis. U.S. Dept. of Health Education and Welfare, Pub. Health Service, Atlanta, Ga., 1960.
26. ―――― Ann. New York, Acad. Sc., 98:675, 1962.
27. Gochenour, W. S., Jr., and others. Proc. Soc. Exper. Biol. & Med., 74:199, 1950.
28. ―――― and others. Pub. Health Rep., 67: 811, 1952.
29. ―――― and others. Am. J. Pub. Health, 43: 405, 1953.
30. Goldberg, H. S., and Armstrong, J. C. J. Bact., 77:512, 1959.
31. Goldberg, E. E. Ann. Int. Med., 41:1245, 1954.
32. Gseld, O. Ergebn. inn. Med. u. Kinderh., 1: 367, 1949.
33. Hoag, W. G., and others. Proc. Soc. Exper. Biol. & Med., 83:490, 1953; 83:712, 1953.
34. Howarth, J. A. Am. J. Vet. Research, 17: 789, 1956.
35. Inada, R., and others. J. Exper. Med., 23: 377, 1916; 26:341, 1917.
36. Johnson, R. C., and Gary, N. D. J. Bact., 85:976, 1963.
37. Jorge, R. Bull. Office Internat. d'hyg. pub., 24:88, 1932.
38. Lang, R. W., and Morse, E. V. J. Immunol., 82:471, 1959.
39. Larson, C. L. Pub. Health Rep., 56:1546, 1941; 58:10, 1943; 59:522, 1944.
40. Liebowitz, D., and Schwartz, H. J.A.M.A., 147:122, 1951.
41. Linscott, W. D., and Boak, R. A. J. Immunol., 86:471, 480, 1961.
42. Meyer, K. F. Ann. Int. Med., 23:361, 1948.
43. ―――― and Brunner, K. T. Acta trop., 7:1, 1950.
44. ―――― and others. Am. J. Pub. Health, 29: 347, 1939.
45. Miller, N. G., and Wilson, R. B. J. Bact., 84:569, 1962.
46. Morrow, G., and others. Science, 88:384, 1938.
47. Noguchi, H. J. Exper. Med., 25:755, 1917.
48. ―――― The New Knowledge of Bacteriology and Immunology, Chicago, 1928, U. Chicago Press, Chapter XXXVI, pp. 452-497.
49. Olitzki, L., and others. J. Infect. Dis., 84:15, 1949.
50. Raven, C. J. J. Infect. Dis., 69:131, 1941.
51. Rosenbaum, H. D. Arch. Int. Med., 78:521, 1946.
52. Roth, E. E., and others. Pub. Health Report, 77:583, 1962.
53. ―――― and others. Pub. Health Report, 78: 727, 1963.
54. ―――― and others. Pub. Health Report, 78: 994, 1963.
55. Rothstein, N., and Hiatt, C. W. J. Immunol., 77:257, 1956.
56. ―――― J. Immunol., 79:276, 1957.
57. Schlossberger, H., and Brandis, H. Leptospira. Ann. Rev. Microbiol., 8:133, 1954.
58. Schneider, M. D. Proc. Soc. Exper. Biol. & Med., 85:32, 1954.
59. Schneiderman, A., and others. Proc. Soc. Exper. Biol. & Med., 82:53, 1953.
60. Schuffner, W. Centralbl. f. Bakt., Abt. I, Orig., 145:341, 1940.
61. Spink, W. W. Minnesota Med., 35:525, 1952.
62. Sutliff, W. D., and others. Ann. Int. Med., 39:134, 1953.
63. Tatlock, H. J. Clin. Invest., 26:287, 1947.
64. Wani, H. Ztschr. f. Immunitätsforsch. u. exper. Therap., 79:1, 1933.
65. Weil, A. Deutsche med. Wchnschr., 39:209, 1886.
66. Wolff, J. W. Symposium on the Leptospiroses. Med. Sci. Pub. No. 1, U.S. Gov. Printing Office, Washington, D.C., 1953.
67. Yager, R. H., and others. J. Am. Vet. M. A., 117:202, 1950.
68. ―――― and Gochenour, W. S., Jr. Am. J. Pub. Health, 43:411, 1953.

53

Spirillum minus and Rat-Bite Fever

Order: *Pseudomonadaceae* Orla-Jensen. Family: *Spirillaceae* Migula. Genus *Spirillum* Ehrenberg. Species: *Spirillum minus* Carter

Rat-bite fever is an infectious disease caused by an organism resembling a spirochete, *Spirillum minus* (*Spirochaeta morsus muris*), usually contracted from the bite of a rat (24).

In 1840 Wilcox, in Louisiana, gave the first scientific account of a case of rat-bite fever (29). The modern period of study dates from Miyake's monograph on *Rattenbisskrankheit* in 1900 (18). Miyake is credited with the introduction into general usage of the Japanese name of the disease, "sodoku" (from *so*, a rat, and *doku*, poison). The disease is of frequent occurrence in Japan, but cases have been reported from nearly every part of the world. Bayne-Jones (2, 3) collected 75 case reports of the disease from medical publications in the United States over the 90-year period 1840 to 1930. Since then additional reports have been published, notably the study of a case and of the organism by Francis (10) in 1932.

The reviews of Brown and Nunemaker (7), Beeson (5), and Watkins (28) indicate that this infection is being recognized with greater frequency in this country. Infections with this spirillum must be differentiated from the fever produced by *Streptobacillus moniliformis* (*Actinomyces muris ratti*), which also is transmitted by the bite of a rat (7, 15).

Futaki and his associates discovered the cause of rat-bite fever in 1916 and named the organism *Spirocheta morsus muris*. Robertson has identified this organism with *Spirillum minus*, discovered by Carter in the blood of a rat in India in 1887 (8). The name *Spirillum minus* has been widely adopted. Bayne-Jones, however, thinks this assignment of the organism to the group of spirilla and vibrios is unsatisfactory and that, on the basis of resemblance to the spirochetes, it should be classified with them. For flagellated spirochetes of this type, Dubosq and Lebailly (9) proposed the genus *Spirella*, and in Noguchi's discussion of the characteristics of the organism in 1928, the name *Spirella morsus muris* was used for the organism of rat-bite fever (20).

Morphology. *Spirillum minus* is a spiral organism of 3 to 5 μ long, approximately 0.2 μ thick, with pointed ends. Bayne-Jones has seen only one flagellum at each end, but Adachi (1) and Zuelzer (30) have described tufts of flagella at each pole. Short and long forms occur simultaneously in the blood of an infected animal. The body is relatively rigid and twisted in one to four angular spirals with crests about 1 μ apart. It displays an extremely rapid darting to-and-fro motion with a spinning around the long axis (Fig. 1).

The spirillum is **gram-negative.** Giemsa's and Wright's stains are most useful for the demonstration of the organism in blood films. Silver impregnation methods, such as that of Fontana-Tribondeau, stain the flagella. Darkfield illumination of a drop of blood containing the organism is the best method for demonstrating its rapid motility, spiral structure, and flagella.

Cultivation. Although there have been a few reports of successful cultivation of the organism, particularly by Futaki and his associates (13) and by Joekes (16), it is probable that this spirillum has never been cultivated. Proof that the organism produces rat-bite fever has been provided by experimental inoculation of man with blood containing the organism.

The definite diagnosis of rat-bite fever should be based upon demonstration of the *Spirillum* by laboratory tests. These are, in order of value:

1. Inoculation of white mice and guinea pigs with the patient's blood, exudate from the initial lesion, serum expressed from exanthematous patches, material aspirated from lymph nodes or ground-up pieces of tissue excised from lesions. These animals are susceptible, develop infection from inoculation with very few organisms, and pass through characteristic stages of the disease, with the spirilla in their

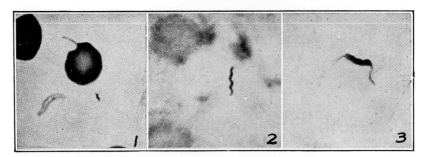

Fig. 1. *Spirillum minus.* 1, in blood of guinea pig. Short form. Wright's stain. × 1,500. 2, in blood of white mouse. Long form. (Army Med. Museum 50281. Courtesy of Edward Francis. U.S.P.H.S.) 3, in blood plasma of guinea pig. Flagellum at each end stained by Fontana-Tribondeau silver method. (Army Medical Museum 50417. Courtesy of Edward Francis. U.S.P.H.S.)

blood. White mice often harbor this organism (10, 11, 12). It is necessary to determine that these animals are free from spirilla before inoculations are made. Inoculations of mice should be controlled by injection of the same material into guinea pigs.

2. Examination of blood and exudate from lesions by darkfield illumination and stains. The organism rarely has been detected with certainty in the blood of man but may be found in material from the lesions. Wright's and Giemsa's stains are satisfactory. The flagella can be demonstrated best by the use of the Fontana-Tribondeau silver stain.

3. Immobilization test. The mixture of a patient's serum with blood of a mouse or guinea pig containing the spirilla may cause the organism to lose its motility. This is a confirmatory test but is often negative, uncertain and subject to error.

Clinical Infection in Man. In a case uncomplicated by mixed or secondary infection, the wound of the rat bite heals promptly. After an incubation period of 5 to 14 days (average 13 days, with occasional long incubation periods of six weeks or more), the site of the wound swells and becomes purplish and painful. A chancre-like indurated ulcer with a black crust may develop at this site and on the broader parts of the body may reach a diameter of 5 to 10 cm. The regional lymphatics are inflamed, and the adjacent lymph nodes become enlarged and tender. The development of the local lesion is accompanied by malaise and headache and a sharp rise of temperature, usually with a chill. After this, periods of fever alternate with afebrile periods. The temperature rises abruptly to 103° to 104° F., remains elevated for 24 to 48 hours, and falls rapidly to normal within about 36 hours. The intervening afebrile periods last from three to nine days. In untreated

cases this relapsing type of fever may continue for weeks or months, gradually subsiding. Within the first week of the beginning of the fever the characteristic skin rash usually appears. This is a purplish maculopapular eruption on the skin of the arms, legs, and trunk, and occasionally on the face and scalp. The skin lesions do not ulcerate. They fade somewhat during the afebrile periods but reappear, with new patches of eruption, during the paroxysms of fever. In addition to the cardinal symptoms, such as recurrent inflammation at the site of infection, a relapsing type of fever and the characteristic skin eruption, there are numerous minor symptoms.

The untreated disease tends to end in recovery after several months, but there are reports of infections prolonged for 4 to 20 years. The mortality has been estimated at 10 per cent, but this figure is too high, since many fatalities were due to secondary pyogenic infection. Death should be rare in uncomplicated cases properly treated with penicillin and arsenicals.

The Wassermann reaction is usually negative when syphilis can be excluded.

There are very few recorded autopsies of cases of rat-bite fever. The local lesion, which is a granuloma without suppuration, shows necrosis of the epithelium and dense round cell infiltration of the corium. Similar round cell infiltration with dilated vessels occurs in the lesions of the skin eruption. Lesions in the organs are chiefly those associated with a long-continued febrile disease.

Transmission. Rat-bite fever is primarily a disease of wild rats, transmissible to rats, various other animals, and man by the bite of an infected animal. Fleas and other insects are not vectors, and there is no record of transmission of the disease from man to man by contact, excreta, or fomites. Cases attributed to the bites of cats, ferrets, and weasels have been reported.

The incidence of the disease in rats is not definitely known. Parmanand (21) found 2 to 11 per cent of the rats in Bombay infected, while Knowles and Das Gupta (17) found that of 23 rats in Calcutta approximately 21 per cent were infected.

The infecting organism is carried into the wound of the bite by the teeth or by material from the rat's mouth or lips falling on the surface of the wound. The *Spirillum* has not been found in the saliva of rats. It may get into the mouth and on the teeth from blood from injured gums, lesions in the mouth, infectious conjunctival exudate (19, 4) which drains through the lacrimal ducts, or exudate from pulmonary lesions. When several persons have been bitten by an infected rat, often only the first victim will be found to have the disease.

Rat-bite fever begins as a wound infection. As this wound may be infected with organisms other than *Spirillum minus,* other forms of rat-bite fever occur. A variety of cocci, bacilli, and streptothrices have been found in these conditions (25, 6). Severe and fatal infections, usually of a pyogenic and septicemic nature, have been due to these accompanying or secondary microorganisms.

A disease of chickens, characterized by diphtheritic lesions of the buccal mucosa, was studied by Mathey (17a) in 1956, who demonstrated that the etiologic agent was *Spirillum pulli* nov. sp.

REFERENCES

1. Adachi, K.   J. Exper. Med., 33:647, 1921.
2. Bayne-Jones, S.   New York State J. Med., 27:1113, 1927.
3. ———— Internat. Clin., 41st ser., 3:235, 1931.
4. ———— and Lerner, M. L.   Arch. Ophth., 4:858, 1930.
5. Beeson, P. B.   J.A.M.A., 123:332, 1943.
6. Blake, F. G.   J. Exper. Med., 23:39, 1916.
7. Brown, T. McP., and Nunemaker, J. C.   Bull. Johns Hopkins Hosp., 70:201, 1942.
8. Carter, H. W.   Scient. Mem. Med. Off. India, 1887, Part 3, p. 45 (cited by Robertson).
9. Dubosq, O., and Lebailly, C.   Compt. rend. Acad. d. sc., 154:535, 1912.
10. Francis, E.   Tr. A. Am. Physicians, 47:143, 1932.
11. ———— J.A.M.A., 99:70, 1932.
12. ———— Pub. Health Rep., 51:976, 1936.
13. Futaki, K., and others.   J. Exper. Med., 23:249, 1916; 25:33, 1917.
14. Hata, S.   München. med. Wchnschr., 59:854, 1912.
15. Haynes, E.   J. Bact., 53:802, 1947.
16. Joekes, T.   Lancet, 2:1225, 1925.
17. Knowles, R., and Das Gupta, B. M.   Indian J. M. Research, 63:493, 1928.
17a. Mathey, W. J.   Am. J. Vet. Research, 17:742, 1956.
18. Miyake, H.   Mitt. a. d. Grenzgeb. d. Med. u. Chir., 5:231, 1899-1900.
19. Mooser, H.   J. Exper. Med., 39:589, 1924; 42:539, 1925.
20. Noguchi, H.   The Newer Knowledge of Bacteriology and Immunology, Chicago, 1928, p. 497.
21. Parmanand, M. J.   Indian J. M. Research, 12:609, 1925.
22. Rhees, H.   J. Bact., 23:211, 1932.
23. Robertson, A.   Ann. Trop. Med. & Parasitol., 24:367, 1930.
24. Ruge, H.   Rattenbissfieber. In Mense's Handb. d. Tropenkrankheiten, 5 (Part I):621, 1929.
25. Schottmüller, H.   Dermat. Wchnschr., 58:77, 1914.
26. Solomon, H., and others.   Arch. Int. Med., 38:391, 1926.
27. Stühmer, A.   Arch. f. Dermat. u. Syph., 158:98, 1929.
28. Watkins, C. G.   J. Pediat., 28:429, 1946.
29. Wilcox, W.   Am. J. M. Sc., 26:245, 1840.
30. Zuelzer, M.   Centralbl. f. Bakt., I Abt., 85:154, 1920.

THE PLEUROPNEUMONIA GROUP
OF ORGANISMS

54

Pleuropneumonia, Pleuropneumonia-Like Organisms, and L-Type Forms of Bacteria

Order: *Mycoplasmatales* Freundt. Family: *Mycoplasmataceae* Freundt. Genus: *Mycoplasma* Nowak. Type Species: *Mycoplasma mycoides* (Borrel and others), Freundt

This group of microorganisms are characterized by the absence of a cell wall (Fig. 1). Their recognition was delayed because they could not be stained or grown by the methods usually employed for the study of bacteria. In the seventh edition of Bergey's Manual a new order, *Mycoplasmatales,* was created for these organisms. They are intermediate in size between bacteria and viruses. In size of reproductive unit, filterability, and complex method of reproduction they resemble the *psittacosis* group of organisms, but they can be cultivated in cell-free media such as bacteria.

Fifteen species of *Mycoplasma* are recognized in Bergey's Manual. Fourteen of these are classified as parasitic to pathogenic and one, *M. laidlawii,* as saprophytic. More recently Adler and his associates (1) isolated another saprophytic species from the infraorbital sinus of a chicken.

The recognized parasitic and pathogenic species are associated with disease in birds, mammals, and man. The avian species is *Mycoplasma gallinarum*. Rats have *M. pulmonis* and *M. arthritidis;* mice have *M. neurolyticum*. Dogs have *M. canis, M. spumanis,* and *M. maculosum*. Swine have *M. hyorhinis*. Cows have *M. mycoides* and *M. bovigenitalium* and sheep have *M. agalactiae*.

The human species are: *M. hominis* type 1 and 2; *M. salivarium;* and *M. fermentans*. Three strains of four PPLO organisms iso-

lated from the nasal pharynx of normal individuals were found, by complement fixation, to be closely related to *M. hominis* type 1, and one was related to *M. salivarium* (96). A large series of strains have been isolated from the oropharynx of Navy recruits by Organic (79).

A new, highly pathogenic species for man, has been isolated (11, 17, 35, 66) and identified as the transmissible agent of Eaton which causes most clinical cases of primary atypical pneumonia. The name *Mycoplasma pneumoniae* has been suggested for this new species (16).

The pleuropneumonic organisms have a predilection for the mouth, genitalia, lungs, and joints. The original bovine species, for which the group was named, infected the lungs, pleura, and joints (5, 6, 7, 78), while the second bovine species is apparently limited to the genital tract. The caprine species produce pleuropneumonia, septicemia, and infection of the lactating glands. Two of the dog species are limited to the throat and vagina, while the third has been isolated only from the vagina and semen. In rats one species produces pulmonary disease and another arthritis (46). The mouse species occurs in the conjunctiva, nasal mucosa, and lung, and the swine species in the nose, lungs, and pleura. The avian specie, or species, causes sinusitis and pulmonary disease in chickens and turkeys.

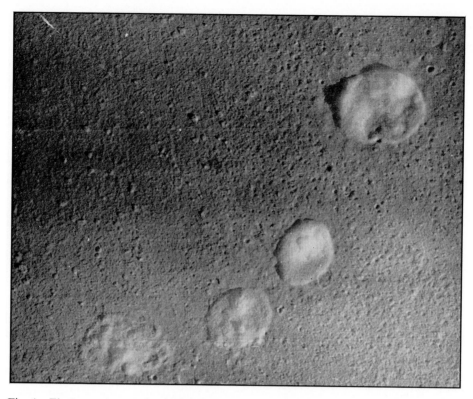

Fig. 1. Electron micrograph of PPLO. Note the obvious plasticity of the organism and the lack of a definite cell wall. × 20,000. (From Morton, Lecce, Oskay, and Coy. *J. Bact.*, 68:697, 1954.)

Among the human species, *M. salivarium* is found only in the mouth, pharynx and saliva, and *M. hominis* type 1 and 2 occur in the male and female genitalia in the absence of lesions or in association with nongonorrheal urethritis. *M. fermentans* is found in the normal genital tract and in association with fusiform bacilli or spirochetes, while the new species, *M. pneumoniae*, produces a characteristic type of pneumonia.

The first member of this group of organisms (PPO) was isolated in 1898 by Nocard (78) from an infectious disease of cows known as pleuropneumonia. In 1935 Klieneberger (48) isolated typical pleuropneumonia-like organisms (PPLO) from rats and from laboratory cultures of *Streptobacillus moniliformis*. By 1942 she isolated the same type of organisms from the joints of rats with an infectious arthritis. The organisms isolated directly from the rats by Klieneberger (50); from mice by Sabin (85, 86) and from the genital tract of man by Dienes and Edsall (21, 25) as well as the saprophytic species (51, 87) are called pleuro-pneumonia-like organisms or PPLO. The organisms isolated by Klieneberger from stock cultures of *Streptobacillus moniliformis* were found by Dienes and his associates (22, 23, 27) and later by Klieneberger and Noel (51, 52) to be dissociated forms of bacteria which are usually designated as L-forms or L-phase organisms.

A sharp distinction has been drawn between (a) the primary pathogens of cattle, sheep, and goats (PPO); (b) the PPLO organisms which have been isolated from man, dog, swine, rats, mice, fowls, sewage, and manure; and (c) the L-phase of organisms of bacteria. The relation between these three types of organisms will be discussed at the end of this chapter.

What is known, at the present time, about these organisms is presented in the same

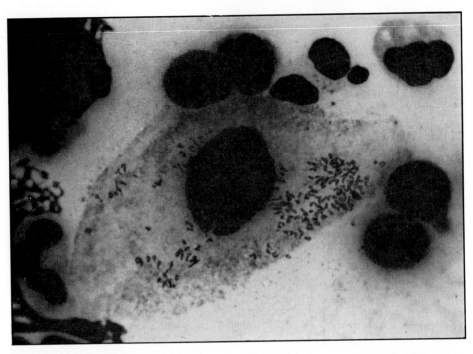

Fig. 2. PPLO in cytoplasm of cell. The cell is from the urethra of a patient with nongonococcal urethritis. Colonies of PPLO were grown from cells of this type which contained organisms. (From Shepard. *J. Bact.,* 73:162, 1957.)

order as employed for bacterial and spirochetal diseases, although our information is incomplete and often limited to a single observation on a single species.

Morphology and Staining. The PPO, PPLO, and L-forms are gram-negative when stained by Gram's method as one would expect in the absence of a cell wall (Fig. 1). The absence of a cell wall also makes the organism so plastic and fragile that very special methods have been devised by Dienes (24, 25) and Klieneberger (49) for staining them. Both PPLO and L-form have been studied by Edwards and Foch (39) in thin sections of tissue culture cells. Both multiple budding and multinuclear division was seen, but a splitting plate is not formed, as with bacteria, in the process of division. The morphology should be studied in the cells of the infected host, in tissue culture cells, and in colonies on artificial media. Shepard (89) found *M. hominis* growing as minute rods and cocci in the cytoplasm of epithelial cells from the male urethra (Fig. 2). The organism has the same appearance when grown in HeLa cells (89), with round to oval basophilic bodies of approximately 330 μ in size. They were usually single but frequently in pairs

and occasionally in short chains of three to four elements. Similar minute cocco-bacillary bodies were found in chick embryos infected with the Eaton agents (*M. pneumoniae*) (16). When the Eaton agent was grown in human amnion cells, the microcolonies of these organisms appeared in the cytoplasm and could be stained by the May Grunwald-Giemsa method (Fig. 3) (35).

The original *M. mycoides* from pleuropneumonia of cows was grown in fluid serum medium and described as coccoid, branched and unbranched filaments (59). *M. hominis* grown by Dienes are shown in smear preparations in Figures 4 and 5. The filaments seen in Figure 5 were considered artifacts by Dienes (26, 28), but the investigations of Weibull and Lundin (100) with *M. hominis* showed that floating organisms in a fluid medium could be photographed as primary filamentous. They became more spherical when fixed and stained, although if fixed with formalin they remained in the filamentous phase. Under the same condition of cultivation the saprophytic *M. laidlawii·* were always coccoid and L-forms of proteus were spherical but connected with filaments. The electron micrographs published by Dienes (28) in 1953 showed no morpho-

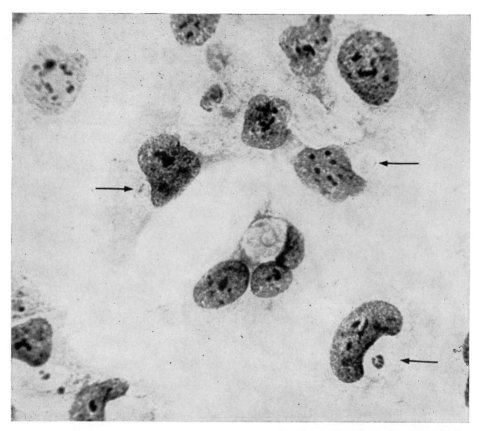

Fig. 3. Infection of human amnion cells at eight days. Microcolonies of the organisms can be seen in the cytoplasm. The colony in the center is surrounded by three nuclei. Colonies were stained a light pink by May-Grunwald-Giemsa method. × 1,100. (From Eaton, Farnham, Levinthal, and Scala. *J. Bact.*, 84:1330, 1962.)

logic difference in the reproduction of L-phase organisms and the naturally occurring PPLO isolated from man (15).

Weibull and Lundin (100) measured the size of *M. agalactiae* which had been grown in liquid medium and found the organism to vary from 0.2 to 0.6 μ. Even the smallest, 0.2 μ, was much larger than the diameter found by filtration which ranges from 0.12 to 0.25 μ. Recent studies by Morowitz and his associates (71) showed that forms which passed a 0.1 μ filter could be cultivated.

Cultural Characteristics. A good basal medium to which 10 per cent horse serum or 20 to 30 per cent ascitic fluid has been added is essential for the cultivation of this group of organisms (64). The serum or ascitic fluid supplies certain essential growth factors but also serves to increase the osmotic pressure to protect these delicate organisms from rupturing their cytoplasmic membranes.

When grown on semisolid agar enriched with ascitic fluid or horse serum the colonies are umbonate with dense centers and fringe-like peripheries (73, 74). The organisms in the center of the colonies grow into the medium, while the growing fringes are relatively flat on the surface (25, 29). Individual colonies vary from 20 to 200 μ. Some grown on certain media may be as small as 12 μ, and occasional strains reach a size of 60 μ. The smaller colonies have the central core without the surface fringe (89). Only the larger colonies are visible with the naked eye. A good hand lens is required for the colonies of medium size, and the low power of the microscope is needed for the smaller colonies. Shepard found both large and small colonies in the cultures of urethral discharges from patients with nongonococcal urethritis. The smaller ones, which he described as T-colonies, were associated with clinical symptoms

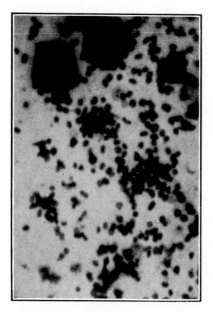

Fig. 4. Pleuropneumonia-like organisms. From young colonies which have been slightly disturbed and stained with Giemsa's stain following agar fixation. × 3,000. (From Dienes. *J. Bact.,* 50:441, 1945.)

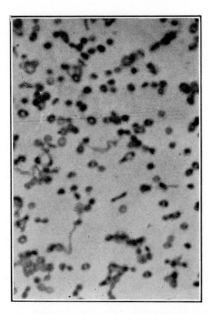

Fig. 5. Pleuropneumonia-like organisms. From a human strain grown in broth and stained with Giemsa's stain. Note the slightly elongated ring-like organisms and a few typical bipolar rod-shaped forms. The filaments are artefacts. × 3,000. (From Dienes. *J. Bact.,* 50:441, 1945.)

in the patient (89a) and cytoplasmic effect in HeLa cells. Shepard's observations on colony formations have been confirmed by Ford (41). Ford pictures the large colony and the T-colony as shown in Figure 6. The distinctive colony of the Eaton agent (*M. pneumoniae*) on artificial media is shown as Figure 7 (11). A darkfield microphotograph of a colony of *M. hominis* (15) is shown in Figure 8. The individual organisms resemble those found in the human urethral cell (Fig. 2) and the HeLa cell culture (89), and the Eaton agent (*M. pneumoniae*) in monkey kidney cells (17, 18).

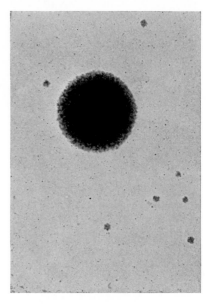

Fig. 6. Note the large-colony type of PPLO in the upper part of the figure and several of the small "T-strain" type in the lower part of the figure. (From Ford. *J. Bact.,* 84:1028, 1962.)

The Eaton agent (*M. pneumoniae*) produces a soluble hemolysin which is easily detected when guinea-pig red cells are overlaid on the plate after the appearance of definite colonies of the PPLO. A clear zone (beta hemolysis) appeared (Fig. 9) within 24 hours after the red cells were introduced (94). *M. hominis* type 1 and the Navel strain of PPLO, which did not produce plaques with the guinea-pig red cells, did produce plaques with horse erythrocytes after four or five days. The other human strains, which were not *M. pneumoniae,* produced alpha type plaques with horse red cells in two to three days.

Cultivation in Chick Embryo. The bovine or goat pleuropneumonia organism produces

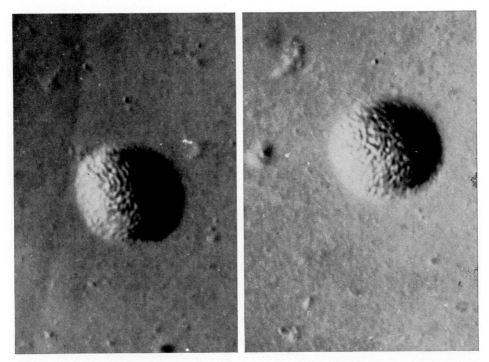

Fig. 7. Colonies of *Mycoplasma pneumoniae* (Eaton agent). Note granular appearance. The organisms grew down into the agar beneath the surface colony. (From Chanock, Hayflock, and Barile. *Proc. Nat. Acad. Sc.,* 48:41, 1962.)

areas of edema and plaques on the chorioallantois (90, 95) and later kills the embryos. The highly virulent PPLO strain isolated from the joint fluid of a goat by Yamamoto, Adler, and Cordy (103) killed the embryos when inoculated on the chorioallantois, amniotic cavity, or yolk sac. The PPLO strains originally isolated from a man with meningitis grew readily in the yolk sac. Keller and Morton (54) found that strains of PPLO isolated from the human genitourinary tract grew in the allantoic fluid but did not harm the embryos. PPLO strains from the respiratory tract of turkeys were most frequently fatal when inoculated into the yolk sac, although a few strains were found which grew profusely in the yolk sac without injuring the embryos (103). These observations suggest the use of the yolk-sac method of inoculation as a test of pathogenicity for PPO, PPLO, and L-phase organisms.

Cultivation in Tissue Cultures. Sabin (86) observed intracellular multiplication of the mouse PPLO type B when grown on minced-mouse-embryo tissue in Tyrode's solution. It was discovered recently that up to 75 per cent of standard tissue cell lines were already infected with PPLO organism (4, 80, 83). However, there seems to be no deleterious effect from these PPLO infections. In contrast, cytoplastic effects were produced in the HeLa cells by "T" type *M. hominis* (89) and in human amnion cells by the Eaton agent (*M. pneumoniae*) (35).

Resistance. The PPLO organisms from goats die in 30 days when stored in serum broth at 37° C. If grown aerobically, however, and then sealed with vaseline, the organisms remain viable for 22 months at 37° C. but less than five months at 0°, 6°, 12°, and 25° C. The PPLO organisms in infected tissues may be preserved by lyophilization (86). The microorganisms of agalactia are killed by 50° C. in 10 minutes. Most of the pleuropneumonia-like organisms are destroyed at 45° C. in 15 minutes.

The PPLO and L-phase organisms are no more resistant to hydrogen peroxide, phenol, and ultraviolet light than ordinary bacteria, but they are much more susceptible to the deleterious action of soaps (53). These organisms are resistant to sulfonamides, penicillin, thallium acetate (58) and erythromycin (84).

Tetracycline in a concentration of 2.5 μ

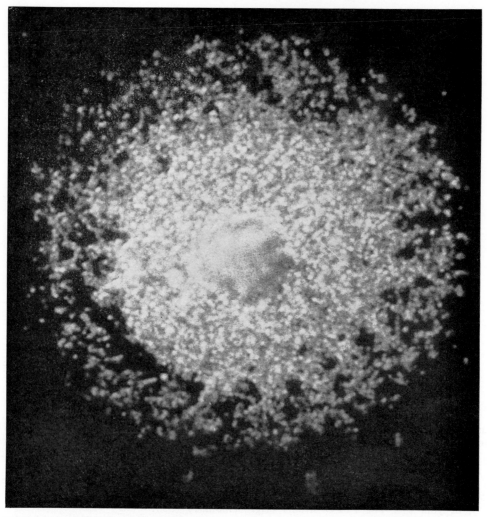

Fig. 8. Darkfield photomicrograph of an unstained human genital PPLO colony prepared by hot water fixation, showing minimal size particles calculated to be approximately 160 mμ. (From Clark, Fowler, and Brown. *J. Bact.,* 81:500, 1961.)

per milliliter of medium eliminated PPLO from tissue cultures (10). Kanamycin and streptomycin also eliminates these organisms from tissue culture cells (41, 80).

The avian type PPLO was sensitive to the action of certain polyene antifungal antibiotics at the following concentrations: Filipin, 0.5 μg. per milliliter, amphotericin B, 3 μ per milliliter, and fungi-chromin, 10 μg. per milliliter of medium (56).

Antigenic Structure. Complement fixation was the original procedure for studying antigenic relations in this group of organisms, but now other procedures, such as agglutination, latex fixation, indirect fluorescent antibody test, gel diffusion (96), direct and indirect hemagglutinins, and hemagglutinin inhibition test (98) are employed. Gel diffusion, as might be expected, showed both specific and common antigens in all strains. Strains of *M. mycoides* from cows are apparently all identical (50, 95). The strains isolated from goats show a compact immunogenic group (86).

M. hominis from urethritis in man has two serologic types, 1 and 2. Type 1 is not pathogenic for mice, while type 2 produces localized abscesses after subcutaneous inoculation. *M. salivarium* is serologically distinct from the *M. hominis* 1 and 2, and *M. fermentans* is different from both. The Eaton agent (*M.*

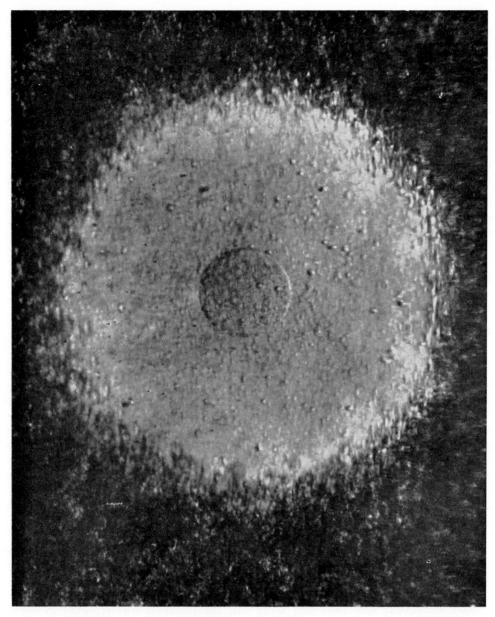

Fig. 9. Beta-hemolytic plaque produced by *Mycoplasma pneumoniae*. × 200. (From Somerson, Taylor-Robinson, and Chanock. *J. Hyg.*, 77:122, 1963.)

pneumoniae) differs serologically from the other three human species (96).

Complement fixation is a practical method for identifying antigenic relationships. For example, three of four strains isolated from the nasal pharynx of normal individuals were found to be *M. hominis* type 1, while the fourth was antigenical *M. salivarium* (96). Several PPLO strains were isolated from HeLa cell lines, and most were found to be antigenically similar to *M. hominis* type 1, but one strain was type 2 (4). Another tissue culture isolate seemed to be identical with *M. gallinarum*.

Bacterial Metabolites. The carbohydrate metabolism of *M. mycoides* has been discussed by Rodwell (82) and the amino acid metabolism of human strains has been investigated by Smith (93). Glucose is oxidized by the avian strain *M. gallisepticum* (variant of *M. gallinarium* or new species) but not by *M. gallinarium* (4). Glucose and other sugars are oxidized by *M. mycoides, M. pulmonis, M. neurolyticum, M. fermentans,* and *M. laidlawii* but not by other species. *M. mycoides* produces a soluble toxin which kills rabbits, but it is not known if this is an endotoxin or exotoxin (78). Sabin (85) identified an exotoxin from *M. neurolyticum* which infects mice. For more details about these intriguing but elusive organisms the students should consult the reviews (30, 31, 32) by Dienes and Weinberger (27), Edwards and Freundt (37), Freundt (42), Madoff (64), Whitelock (101), Morton (75), and Klieneberger-Nobel (51).

MYCOPLASMA PNEUMONIAE AND PRIMARY ATYPICAL PNEUMONIA IN MAN

Family: *Mycoplasmataceae,* Freundt. Genus: *Mycoplasma* Nowak. Species: *Mycoplasma pneumoniae*

During World War II a peculiar type of pneumonia appeared in endemic form in army camps and in many schools and colleges. The incubation period was longer than either typical bacterial or typical viral infections. The incubation period varied from five to 25 days, with an average time of 13 days (47). Since it was not as highly infectious as influenza virus pneumonia, it did not rapidly exhaust the susceptible individuals and was thus able to persist in a college or army camp for several years where new students or recruits were being added periodically. While many patients were extremely ill, and a few died, very extensive pulmonary infections, with rales and x-ray changes could be found in asymptomatic subjects.

The most striking laboratory finding was the appearance of cold agglutinins for human red cells and for the M G streptococcus. In 1944, Eaton, Meiklejohn, and VanHenrick (34) transmitted the infectious agent to cotton rats, hamsters, and chicken embryos, with filtrates from bronchial secretions from patients with primary atypical pneumonia. No side effects which could be identified

were produced by the infecting agent. After 13 years of transmission Liu and Eaton (60, 61) demonstrated organisms in the animal tissues with the new fluorescent antibody technic and identified specific antibodies in the serum of convalescent patients. Although indirect evidence concerning the infectious agents was supplied by Marmion and Goodburn (66), direct evidence for the pleuropneumonia etiology was furnished by Chanock and his associates (11, 14). The intracellular microcolonies found by Eaton and his associates (35) in human amnion cells are shown in Figure 3. The gross colony formation on artificial media is seen in Figure 7 (11) and the beta hemolytic effect (18) by Somerson and his coworkers (94) in Figure 9.

There is general agreement among the investigators who have done most of the work on this organism that it should be named *Mycoplasma pneumoniae* (16).

During 1960 and 1961, 161 of 238 marines of Camp Lejeune with pneumonia were found to be infected with this specific pleuropneumonia organism. The organism was grown in monkey kidney tissue culture in some 14 of 17 of these recruits. Approximately 44 per cent of the recruits were infected at some time in their three months' training period, as shown by antibodies in their serum (12). However, only one in 30 had an infection which could be diagnosed clinically as pneumonia. The direct fluorescent antibody test was more efficient in detecting infections with *M. pneumoniae* than the cold agglutinin, although those positive to the cold agglutinins usually had more severe infections which lasted longer.

The symptoms, signs, and clinical course of the infection was reported in detail by Mufson and his associates (77) in 1961.

M. pneumoniae is susceptible to both streptomycin and tetracycline, and tetracycline in relatively large doses has proven reasonably effective in therapy for man (13).

Since one attack seems to give permanent immunity, there is a theoretical possibility that a vaccine might be effective. Some progress has been made with an attenuated culture (19).

PLEUROPNEUMONIA-LIKE ORGANISMS FROM MAN AND ANIMALS

Family: *Mycoplasmataceae,* Freundt. Genus: *Mycoplasma,* Nowak. Species: *Mycoplasma hominis* type 1 and 2 (Freundt), *Mycoplasma salivarium* Edwards, *Mycoplasma fermentans* (Edwards)

Man. Pleuropneumonia-like organisms have been isolated so frequently from the oral cavity (29, 36) and from the male and female urinary tract (14, 51, 67) in the absence of inflammation to suggest that certain strains of PPLO are a part of the normal flora of the body. There is very good evidence that the genital strains are transmitted by copulation (72, 89a).

Most of these oral and genital strains produce rather large colonies, 200 to 600 μ, which are readily detected with a hand lens. A much smaller colony type isolated from the mouth and genital tract is only 10 to 20 μ and requires the use of the low power of the microscope (29). The colony consists of a central core without the usual surface fringe. Shepard (68) calls this the T-form colony. The organism which gives rise to this type of colony can be seen in the cytoplasm of cells from the urethra (Fig. 2) (89). The T-form colony comprised 86 per cent of all the PPLO isolations from 74 patients with nongonococcal urethritis at Camp Lejeune, North Carolina (89, 89a).

The best proof of the pathogenicity of some of the PPLO strains for man is furnished by the isolation of the organism from the blood of three children with purpura (9) and from the blood of the febrile patient studied by Slingerland and Morgan (91). These authors isolated a PPLO organism from each of nine blood cultures taken on the second and third day of fever. After antibiotic therapy the PPLO organism and the fever disappeared simultaneously. PPLO organisms have been isolated fairly frequently from a clinical type of disease, known as **Reiter's syndrome,** which is characterized by conjunctivitis, nonspecific urethritis, arthritis, and occasionally skin lesions (24, 57). A PPLO strain isolated from the genitourinary tract of a patient, with Reiter's Syndrome, grew well in the cytoplasm of tissue cultures of human synovial cells (26). The organism disappeared and the symptoms subsided in two patients after treatment with streptomycin and in seven additional patients after treatment with oxytetracycline (57).

PLEUROPNEUMONIA OF CATTLE, SHEEP, AND GOATS

Order: *Mycoplasmatales* Freundt. Family: *Mycoplasmataceae* Freundt. Genus: *Mycoplasma* Nowak. Species: *Mycoplasma mycoides* (Borrel and others), Freundt

With the exception of North America, western Europe, and India (99) pleuropneumonia exists in an endemic form in cattle throughout the world. The disease appeared in the United States in 1843 but was eliminated after considerable difficulty. Bovine pleuropneumonia is a highly infectious disease which spreads rapidly through herds of cattle, producing pulmonary consolidation and pleural effusion, killing some animals and rendering the survivors immune. The infectious agent is present in the serous exudates of pleurae and infected joints, but the subcutaneous injection of such exudates into normal animals does not result in pleuropneumonia. The animals develop local inflammatory lesions and may or may not die of cachexia. Those which recover are immune both to reinoculation and to the spontaneous disease. Meyer (70) studied a strain which produced polyarthritis regularly in calves when lymph from the infected joints was injected into the subcutaneous tissues of the tail, but the organisms cultured from this material had no such selective localization. All other animals, including man, apparently are completely resistant to infection with the original exudates and to cultures grown in bovine serums. Dujardin-Beaumetz (33), however, has reported that cultures grown in horse or sheep serum broth become highly infectious for sheep and goats but not for other animals. It has been assumed that the disease spreads from animal to animal by means of droplet infection.

Pleuropneumonia of goats occurs in various parts of Europe, Asia, and Africa and is almost always fatal (62). The clinical disease resembles that in cows, and the cultural characteristics of the organisms are similar. The goat strains share a common antigen with the bovine strains and have been classified as *M. mycoides* var. *capri* (36). The highly virulent organism isolated from goats in California by Cordy, Adler, and Yamamoto (103), and labeled a PPLO, may be a true PPO.

The PPO organisms of sheep and goats in

Italy, France, Switzerland, and Algeria diminish or destroy the lactating ability of the females. This explains the local name for the disease agalactia, although the infection is generalized, with local lesions in the skin, eyes, joints, breasts of females, and scrotum of males. Some animals die early, before the development of local lesions. In lactating females the breasts become swollen, then nodular, and finally atrophic. The microorganisms can be isolated from the blood in the early days of the disease and later from the lacteal secretions, milk, and joint exudates. Both exudates and cultures reproduce the disease when injected intravenously, subcutaneously, intracutaneously, and intra-articularly.

Prevention. Attenuated or formalized cultures have been used to immunize cows against *M. mycoides* and sheep and goats against *M. agalactiae*. *M. mycoides* has been attenuated by repeated passage in embryonated eggs (90). *M. agalactiae* has been grown in chick embryos and the infected tissues then treated with formalin and used for the immunization of sheep and goats (63). Zavagli (104) immunized sheep by injecting infected milk which had been treated with formalin and following this injection with one containing living organisms. He succeeded in protecting 95 per cent of the vaccinated sheep from spontaneous infections.

PLEUROPNEUMONIA OF FOWLS

Family: *Mycoplasmataceae* Freundt. Genus: *Mycoplasma* Nowak. Species: *Mycoplasma gallinarum* Freundt

Strains of PPLO have been isolated from the upper respiratory tract of normal fowls and from fowls with catarrh, but these would not infect birds after experimental inoculation. However, other strains isolated by Roekel and his associates and by Markham and Wong (65) from upper respiratory tract infections in fowls and sinus infection in turkeys could be passed in chick embryos and the passage strain reproduced the disease in fowls. The PPLO organisms picked up by Herick and Eaton (44) in chick embryos, by blind passage of material from patients with "virus" pneumonia, agglutinated erythrocytes. Antiserum produced in rabbits and serum from a high proportion of the hens in the hatchery, prevented this hemagglutination. It is apparent that some of the PPLO from fowls have little or no pathogenicity, while others are definitely pathogenic.

Strains isolated by Fahey and Crawley (40) in 1954 oxidized glucose and other sugars and may be a different species. The strains isolated by Edwards and Kanarer in 1960 were named by the author *M. gallisepticum* (39). This strain, or species, also oxidizes glucose (43).

THE L-PHASE ORGANISMS FROM BACTERIA

The L-phase dissociate has been isolated from species of bacteria representing 16 genera. These are *Bacillus, Bacteroides, Clostridium, Azotobacter, Escherichia, Salmonella, Shigella, Proteus, Haemophilus, Neisseria, Pasteurella, Streptobacillus, Vibrio, Streptococcus, Staphylococcus,* and *Corynebacterium.* The L-phase organisms develop from the "large body" (Fig. 19 in Chap. 3) produced by certain strains under specific conditions. The large bodies occur regularly in stock strains of *Streptobacillus moniliformis* and in an occasional freshly isolated strain of other genera. They can be induced in many strains by exposure to a large amount of penicillin. However, penicillin did not cause the formation of large bodies or L-phase organisms in species of *Streptococcus, Staphylococcus* or *Corynebacterium.* Dienes and Sharp (31) succeeded in producing both large bodies and L-phase organisms by growing certain strains of these genera on a medium in which the NaCl was increased above 0.26 M. Some of the large bodies segment and revert back to the size characteristic of the species, many degenerate, and only about 1 per cent develop into L-phase-colonies (68, 69).

The use of penicillin to induce the formation of L-phase organisms was introduced by Dienes (28) in 1947 and applied first to *H. influenzae.* The bacteria are seeded heavily on blood-agar plates, and one or more shallow troughs are cut into the agar without cutting through the medium. One drop of a solution containing 2,000 units of penicillin per milliliter is introduced into each trough. *Serratia marcescens* is inoculated at the periphery of the plates, which then are sealed with paraffin. Some are incubated at 30° C. and some at 37° C. The plates are opened after three or four days, and the area about the trough is examined with a hand lens or microscope for the appearance of the colonies of L-phase organisms. There is a complete inhibition of bacterial growth for 2 to 3 mm. about the trough; farther out the bacilli are found growing as filaments, and still farther out as normal

H. influenzae. Dienes (28) has observed that only those strains of bacteria that exhibit the globoid or large body type of reproduction are capable of giving rise to colonies of L-phase organisms; however, this organism has not been isolated from all strains exhibiting the globoid type of reproduction. Other agents, such as bacteriophage or antiserums (26), which inhibit or prevent the growth of the normal form of bacteria, may induce the appearance of L forms. Such PPLO forms were isolated from apparently pure cultures of *N. gonorrhoeae* by plating the cocci on media containing sulfadiazine (8).

Whether obtained from broth cultures or by direct plating, colonies of L-phase organisms are transferred to fresh plates of solid media by cutting out a square of agar containing colonies, inverting it on the plate, and distributing the organisms by pushing the agar square over the surface of the medium. The surface of the agar should be kept moist by inserting in the cover of the petri dish filter paper moistened with water.

Medill and O'Kane (69) devised a synthetic medium composed of glucose, a mixture of mineral salts, nicotinamide, and a mixture of 15 amino acids. The strains of *Proteus* employed in the experiments grew readily in the synthetic medium. When agar and penicillin were added, L-phase colonies were isolated and subcultured readily in the synthetic medium. They did not grow on natural media without the addition of serum, and the authors suggest that the stimulation of growth of L-phase organisms by serum or plasma is caused by a detoxification of inhibitory substances in natural media rather than by supplying nutrients.

There are apparently several steps in the evolution of the L-phase organisms, especially if the change was initiated by exposure to penicillin (28). Some L-phase mutants revert back to normal-size organisms as soon as the penicillin is removed from the medium. Others are stable in the L-phase on solid media but revert back when subcultured in broth. These strains produce rather large colonies, up to 200 to 600 μ, and retain some of the biochemical and antigenic traits of the parent strain. Dienes (28) has described a final step in which a form was obtained which would grow floating on the surface of broth without reverting to the bacillary form.

PPLO organisms isolated from the genitourinary tract of man are reported to mutate back to *Streptococcus faecalis, Proteus mirabilis,* and *Alcaligenes faecalis* (76) and to

Corynebacterium (102). Paul Smith and his associates (92) also reported the conversion of supposedly fixed strains of PPLO to diphtheroids, and serologic relations were demonstrated between the PPLO and the bacteria. These diphtheroids were different from the ordinary oral and air diphtheroids. McKay and Taylor (67) reported that PPLO from fowls reverted to *Haemophilus gallinarum.*

Sharp (88) found that there was no trace of muramic acid in the L-forms from staphylococci and streptococci, but some persistence of this cell wall material may explain the persistence of endotoxin in L-phase *S. paraptyphi* at a level of 1:5.5 to 1:9 in comparison with that found in the parent bacillus (20).

Altenbern (2) has studied the colony forms when *P. mirabilis* is cultured on penicillin-containing medium. Both large colony 3B and small colony 3A types were found. The 3B reverts rather readily to bacilli in the absence of penicillin while the 3A, which is changed in size and other characteristics, is much more difficult to revert. If this small colony type 3A became "fixed" in this physiologic state, would it be a PPLO?

PLEUROPNEUMONIA-LIKE ORGANISMS IN MAMMALIAN CELL TISSUE CULTURE LINES

In 1956 Robinson and associates (81) found that tissue cell lines were frequently contaminated with PPLO organisms, although there was no cytopathic effect or influence on the growth of the cells. These results were confirmed by subsequent studies of other investigators (3, 10, 45, 80). Barile and his associates (3) showed that 72 per cent of cell lines grown in the presence of penicillin were infected with PPLO's. These workers also demonstrated that they could isolate PPLO's from 101 of 102 cultures in which the PPLO had been demonstrated by fluorescent antibody (10, 16).

The association of PPLO's with penicillin in the medium suggests infection with L-form bacteria rather than true PPLO, and Holmgren and Campbell (45) demonstrated the conversion of a contaminating gram-negative rod to an L-form by the addition of polymixin to the media. In contrast to these results, Clark and his associates (16) have isolated and identified *M. hominis* 1 and 2 from tissue culture lines. Growth of the PPLO was inhibited by specific antiserum. This leaves the possibility that tissue culture cell lines may be infected by either true PPLO or L-forms of bacteria.

Cell lines may be freed from PPLO or L-forms by treatment with 100 μg. of kanamycin per milliliter of media for a period of three weeks (80), or 2.5 μ of tetracycline (10) per milliliter or by antiserum (80).

RELATION OF PPO, PPLO, AND L-PHASE ORGANISMS

In morphology and mode of reproduction all three forms belong together. The presence of PPLO organisms which are highly pathogenic for goats, mice, rats, chickens, and turkeys suggests that no useful purpose is achieved by separating the PPO from the PPLO. The presence of saprophytic, commensal and opportunist strains is analogous to bacteria.

The status of the L-phase organisms is still controversial. Tulsane and Bringmann (97), Dienes and Weinerger (27), and Dienes believe that the PPLO represent stabilized L-phase mutants. Edward (36) and Klieneberger-Nobel (52) are reluctant about accepting this conclusion because of certain differences in cultural reactions, serologic tests, and the failure to demonstrate pathogenicity for any of the L-phase organisms.

Dienes (32) reviewed the subject again in 1960 and emphasized the fact that the L-forms produced, or selected, by laboratory manipulations of the bacterial environment are poorly adapted to live in this form. Therefore, it is not possible, at the present time, to decide for or against the theory that PPLO forms are L-phase organisms which have become "fixed" in the PPLO phase.

REFERENCES

1. Adler, H. E., and others. J. Bact., 82:239, 1961.
2. Altenbern, R. A. J. Bact., 81:586, 762, 1961.
3. Bailey, J. S., and others. J. Bact., 82:542, 1961.
4. Barile, M. F., and others. J. Bact., 84:130, 1962.
5. Bordet, J. Ann. Inst. Pasteur, 24:161, 1910.
6. Borrel, P., and others. Ann. Inst. Pasteur, 24:168, 1910.
7. Bridré, J., and Donatien, A. Ann. Inst. Pasteur, 39:925, 1925.
8. Brown, T. M., and Hayes, G. S. J. Bact., 43:82, 1942.
9. Carlson, H. J., and others. Am. J. Dis. Child., 81:193, 1951.
10. Carski, T. R., and Shepard, C. C. J. Bact., 81:626, 1961.
11. Chanock, R. M., and others. Proc. Nat. Acad. Sc., 48:41, 1962.
12. ——— J.A.M.A., 175:213, 1961.
13. ——— Proc. Soc. Exper. Biol. & Med., 110: 543, 884, 1962.
14. ——— and others. Science, 140:662, 1963.
15. Clark, H., and others. J. Bact., 81:500, 1961.
16. ——— and others. J. Bact., 85:111, 1963.
17. Clyde, W. A., Jr. Proc. Soc. Exper. Biol. & Med., 107:715, 1961; 112:905, 1963.
18. ——— Science, 139:55, 1963.
19. Couch, R. B., Cate, T. R., and Chanock, R. M. J.A.M.A., 187:442, 1964.
20. Dasinger, B. L., and Suter, F. Proc. Soc. Exper. Biol. & Med., 111:399, 1962.
21. Dienes, L., and Edsall, G. Proc. Soc. Exper. Biol. & Med., 36:740, 1937.
22. ——— J. Infect. Dis., 65:24, 1939.
23. ——— Proc. Soc. Exper. Biol. & Med., 42: 773, 1939.
24. ——— and Smith, W. E. Proc. Soc. Exper. Biol. & Med., 50:99, 1942.
25. ——— and others. New England J. Med., 238:509, 563, 1948.
26. ——— and others. J. Bact., 59:755, 1950.
27. ——— and Weinberger, H. J. Bact. Rev., 15:245, 1951.
28. ——— J. Bact., 48:125, 1944; 50:441, 1945; 66:274, 280, 1953.
29. ——— and Madoff, S. Proc. Soc. Exper. Biol. & Med., 82:36, 1953.
30. ——— Bacteriol. Proc., p. 84, 1956.
31. ——— and Sharp, J. T. J. Bact., 71:208, 1956.
32. ——— Ann. New York Acad. Sc., 79:356, 1960.
33. Dujardin-Beaumetz, E. Ann. Inst. Pasteur, 20:449, 1906.
34. Eaton, M. D., and others. J. Exper. Med., 79:649, 1944.
35. ——— and others. J. Bact., 84:1330, 1962.
36. Edward, D. G. ff. J. Gen. Microbiol., 4:4, 1950; 10:27, 1954.
37. ——— and Freundt, E. A. J. Gen. Microbiol., 14:197, 1956.
38. ——— and Kanarek, A. D. Ann. New York Acad. Sc., 79:696, 1960.
39. Edwards, G. A., and Foch, F. J. Bact., 79: 267, 1960.
40. Fahey, J. E., and Crawley, J. F. Canad. J. Comp. Med. Vet. Sci., 18:13, 1954.
41. Ford, D. K. J. Bact., 84:1028, 1962; 85: 699, 1963.
42. Freundt, E. A. The Mycoplasmataceae (the pleuropneumonia group of organism) Morphology, Biology and Taxonomy. Copenhagen, Munksgaard, 1958.
43. Gill, J. W. J. Bact., 83:213, 1962.
44. Herick, W. van, and Eaton, M. D. J. Bact., 50:47, 1945.
45. Holmgren, N. B., and Campbell, W. E., Jr. J. Bact., 79:869, 1960.
46. Howell, E. V., and Jones, R. S. Proc. Soc. Exper. Biol. & Med., 112:69, 1963.
47. Jordon, W. S., Jr. Am. J. Hyg., 50:315, 1949.
48. Klieneberger, E. J. Path. & Bact., 40:93, 1935.
49. ——— J. Hyg., 39:260, 1939.
50. ——— J. Hyg., 38:458, 1938; 40:204, 1940; 42:480, 1942.

51. Klieneberger-Nobel, E. Pleuropneumonia-like organism (PPLO) Mycoplasmataceae. New York, Academic Press Inc., 1962.
52. ———— Biol. Rev., 29:154, 1954.
53. Keller, R., and others. J. Gen. Microbiol., 7:313, 1952.
54. ———— and Morton, H. E. J. Bact., 67:129, 1954.
55. Laidlaw, P. P., and Elford, W. J. Proc. Roy. Soc., London, s.B., 120:292, 1936.
56. Lampen, J. O., and others. J. Bact., 86:945, 1963.
57. Leberman, P. R., and others. J. Urol., 68:399, 1952.
58. Lecce, J. G., and Morton, H. E. J. Bact., 67:62, 1954.
59. Ledingham, J. C. G. J. Path. & Bact., 37:393, 1933.
60. Liu, C. J. Exper. Med., 106:455, 1957.
61. ———— and Eaton, M. D. J. Exper. Med., 109:545, 1959.
62. Longley, E. O. Colonial Research Publications, No. 7, London, H. M. Stationery Office, 1951.
63. Lopez, and Lopez. Bull. Acad. Vet. Fr., 25:23, 1952.
64. Madoff, S. Ann. New York Acad. Sc., 79:383, 1960.
65. Markham, F. S., and Wong, S. C. Poult. Sci., 31:902, 1952.
66. Marmion, B. P., and Goodburn, G. M. Nature, 189:247, 1961.
67. McKay, K. A., and Taylor, T. R. E. Canad. J. Comp. Med., 18:7, 1954.
68. Medill, M. A., and Hutchinson, W. G. J. Bact., 68:89, 1954.
69. ———— and O'Kane, D. J. J. Bact., 68:530, 1954.
70. Meyer, K. F. Trans. Dept. Agri. Govt. Vet. Bacteriologist for 1908-1909, Pretoria, p. 159.
71. Morowitz, H. J., and others. J. Bact., 85:134, 1963.
72. Morton, H. E., and others. J. Dent. Research, 30:415, 1951.
73. ———— and others. J. Syph., 35:361, 1951.
74. ———— and others. J. Bact., 68:697, 1954.
75. ———— Ann. New York Acad. Sc., 98:670, 1962.
76. Moustardier, G., and others. Ann. Inst. Pasteur, 85:520, 1952.
77. Mufson, M. A., and others. J.A.M.A., 178:369, 1961.
78. Nocard, M. E., and others. Ann. Inst. Pasteur, 12:240, 1898.
79. Organick, A. Clin. Res., 10:295, 1962.
80. Pollock, M. E., and others. Proc. Soc. Exper. Biol. & Med., 105:10, 1960; 112:176, 1963.
81. Robinson, L., and others. Science, 124:1147, 1956.
82. Rodwell, A. W. Ann. New York Acad. Sc., 79:499, 1960.
83. Rothblat, G. H., and Morton, H. E. Proc. Soc. Exper. Biol. & Med., 100:87, 1959.
84. Rubin, L., and others. Am. J. Syph., 38:472, 1954.
85. Sabin, A. B. Science, 88:575, 1938.
86. ———— Bact. Rev., 5:1, 1941.
87. Seiffert, G. Zentralbl. f. Bakt., Abt. I, Orig., 140:168, 1937.
88. Sharp, J. J. J. Bact., 86:692, 1963.
89. Shepard, M. C. J. Bact., 75:351, 1958.
89a. ———— and others. J.A.M.A., 188:729, 1964.
90. Sheriff, D., and Piercy, S. E. Vet. Record, 64:1, 1952.
91. Slingerland, D. W., and Morgan, H. R. J.A.M.A., 150:1309, 1952.
92. Smith, P. F., and others. Proc. Soc. Exper. Biol. & Med., 96:550, 1953.
93. ———— Ann. New York Acad. Sc., 79:543, 1960.
94. Somerson, N. L., and others. Am. J. Hyg., 77:122, 1963.
95. Tang, F. F., and others. J. Path. & Bact., 42:45, 1936.
96. Taylor-Robinson, D., and others. J. Bact., 85:1261, 1963.
97. Tulasne, R., and Bringmann, G. Rev. Immunol., 16:325, 1952.
98. Tully, J. G. Proc. Soc. Exper. Biol. & Med., 114:704, 1963.
99. Walker, J. A System of Bacteriology in Relation to Medicine, Medical Research Council, London, 7:322, 1930.
100. Weibull, C., and Lundin, B. J. Bact., 84:513, 1962; 85:440, 1963.
101. Whitelock, O. V. St. Biology of the Pleuropneumo-like Organism. Ann. New York Acad. Sc., 79: Art. 10, 1960.
102. Whittler, R. G. Fed. Proc., 15: (part I) 622, 1956.
103. Yamamoto, R., and others. J. Bact., 69:472, 1955.
104. Zavagli, V. Bull. Off. Int. Epizoot., 36:336, 1951.

THE RICKETTSIAE AND THE BEDSONIA

55

The Rickettsiales

Order: *Rickettsiales* Buchanan and Buchanan. Family: *Rickettsiaceae* Pinkerton. Family: *Chlamydiaceae* Rake

In the seventh edition of Bergey's Manual the rickettsial and the psittacosis organisms are grouped together in the order *Rickettsiales*. Although unrelated serologically or in any other way, these two groups of organisms have in common a susceptibility to antibiotics, a larger size, and metabolic enzyme systems which set them apart from the viruses. It must be re-emphasized that, although the rickettsial and psittacosis agents may be grouped together for purposes of classification, the organisms of these two groups are entirely distinct. This is exemplified by the modes of transmission of these diseases. Thus, all rickettsia require an insect vector for the maintenance of the disease cycle, but no such vector is necessary for agents of the psittacosis group. The generic name *Bedsonia* as a synonym for the psittacosis group will be used in this text.

The generic name *Rickettsia* was suggested by da Rocha-Lima in honor of Dr. Howard Taylor Ricketts who, at the age of 39, died of typhus fever in Mexico City during the course of his investigation of the disease. Ricketts in 1909 found bacillary bodies in the blood of patients with Rocky Mountain spotted fever and in 1910, together with Wilder, described similar organisms in blood smears of patients and in smears of lice that had fed on patients with typhus fever. The species name *prowazekii,* for the *Rickettsia* causing typhus fever, also was suggested by da Rocha-Lima in honor of von Prowazek, another martyr of the disease, who had conducted his investigations in Serbia in 1913.

An adjustment has been made between the pathogenic rickettsia of ticks and mites and their natural animal host so that no violence is done to either. However, disease is produced when the rickettsiae are introduced into a new host, such as man, monkey, or guinea pig, by the bite of the arthropod vector. A new arthropod host for a pathogenic rickettsia may also suffer disease and death. Zinsser calls attention to the fact that the body lice of man, which transmit epidemic typhus fever, die even more frequently than the men from whom they acquire their infection. The *Rickettsiaceae* fall naturally into several groups: (1) the Typhus group, (2) the Spotted Fever group, (3) Q Fever, and (4) Trench Fever. The diseases, their distribution and vectors are shown in Table 1.

Rickettsiae are coccobacilli up to 2 μ in length and 0.3 μ in width, nonmotile and gram-negative (Fig. 1). More commonly these organisms are stained by the Giemsa, Macchiavello, or Castañeda methods. Growth seems best in cells slowly metabolizing. They grow in laboratory-reared lice and ticks, tissue cultures, and in the yolk sacs of the embryonated egg, the latter being the method of choice. Rickettsiae are susceptible to inactivation by heat, drying, and chemical agents but can be readily preserved at low temperatures. A notable exception to the above is *C. burnetii,* the agent causing Q fever. This organism is much more resistant to inactivation by heat or drying than are the other rickettsia. It has persisted for months in tick feces in the dust of dairy farms and barn yards. In one instance straw contaminated by dust containing *C. burnetii* was

Table 1. Rickettsial Diseases

GROUP	DISEASE Type	DISEASE Agent	GEOGRAPHIC DISTRIBUTION	NATURAL CYCLE Arthropod	NATURAL CYCLE Mammal	TRANSMISSION TO MAN
TYPHUS	Endemic	*R. typhi* (*R. mooseri*)	World-wide	Flea	Small rodents	Infected flea feces into broken skin.
	Epidemic	*R. prowazekii*	World-wide	Body louse	Man	Infected louse feces into broken skin.
	Brill's disease		U.S.A. Europe	Recurrence years after original attack of epidemic typhus.		
	Scrub	*R. tsutsugamushi*	Asia, Australia Pacific Islands	Trombiculid mites	Small rodents	Mite bite
SPOTTED FEVER	Rocky Mountain spotted fever	*R. rickettsii*	Western Hemisphere	Ticks	Small wild rodents; dogs	Tick bite
	African tick fever	*R. conorii*	Mediterranean and Africa			
	Rickettsial-pox	*R. akari*	North Atlantic Seaboard States, Russia	Blood-sucking mite	House mouse	Mite bite
Q FEVER		*C. burnetii*	World-wide	Ticks	Small mammals, cattle, sheep	Inhalation of dried infected material
TRENCH FEVER		*R. quintana*	Europe Ethiopia Mexico	Body louse	Man	Infected louse feces into broken skin.

(From Smadel, *Diagnostic Procedures for Virus and Rickettsial Diseases.* Am. Pub. Health Ass., New York, 1956, p. 513.)

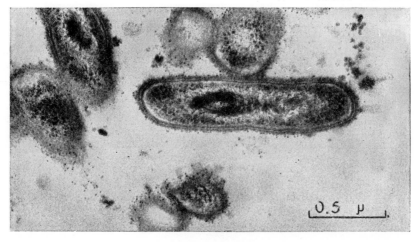

Fig. 1. Section of *Coxiella burnetii*. Note the double-walled limiting membrane and the cytoplasmic structures. × 47,000. (Courtesy of Drs. Robert L. Anaker and Kazue Fukushi.)

used to pack machinery shipped to Switzerland and subsequently small epidemics of Q fever appeared in workers who unpacked this machinery. All of the rickettsiae are susceptible to broad-spectrum antibiotics, such as tetracycline, chloramphenicol, and chlortetracycline.

No exotoxins are produced by rickettsia, but endotoxins are present; large doses kill mice in a few hours. Thus factor is species-specific and can be neutralized by specific antiserum.

Antigenically, rickettsial antigens induce agglutinating, complement-fixing, and neutralizing antibodies. Most rickettsia contain an antigen also found in certain strains of *Proteus.* Thus, serum from patients convalescent from rickettsial injections may agglutinate *Proteus* organisms of strains *X19, OX2,* or *OXK.* These antibodies against the proteus antigen will not neutralize or protect against the rickettsial organisms themselves. The agglutination of *Proteus* strains with serum from patients with rickettsial diseases is called the **Weil-Felix reaction.**

BEDSONIA

The psittacosis organisms, formerly referred to as "the large viruses," are classified by Bergey in the family *Chlamydiaceae.*

These agents are responsible for such diseases as **psittacosis, lymphogranuloma venereum, trachoma,** and **inclusion conjunctivitis.** The organisms are small, gram-negative coccoid bodies which are obligate intracellular parasites. These organisms infect many species of birds, including parrots, pigeons, turkeys, ducks, canaries, sparrows, etc. Ornithosis refers to agents recovered from nonpsittacine sources, reserving psittacosis for those proven to come from psittacine birds.

These organisms, unlike the viruses, are susceptible to antibiotics both *in vitro* and in clinical disease. They are 300 to over 1 μ in size and stain basophilic with methylene blue dyes and in this respect are similar to the Rickettsia (Fig. 2).

Man is the sole host for trachoma, inclusion conjunctivitis, and lymphogranuloma venereum. In the laboratory all of these agents can be cultivated in the yolk sac of the embryonated eggs or in tissue cultures. Psittacosis can be propagated in a number of animals, including mice.

Trachoma, lymphogranuloma, and inclusion conjunctivitis can be transmitted to apes and monkeys but not to birds.

The psittacosis group of organisms resembles rickettsiae in their susceptibility to the broad spectrum antibiotics.

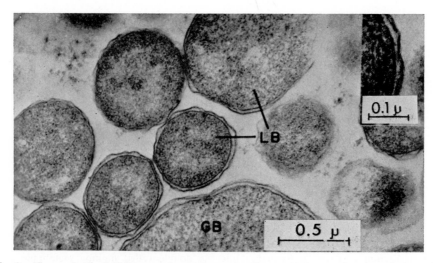

Fig. 2. "Large Bodies" (LB) seen in sections of yolk sac 48 hours after inoculation with a trachoma agent. A part of a "Giant Body" (GB) is seen at bottom. Insert shows cell wall at high magnification. × 45,000. (Courtesy of Professor Yukihito Mitsui, Tokushima University School of Medicine.)

There is a common heat-stable antigen to which the patient develops a complement-fixing antibody. The presence of this antigen suggests a common ancestor for the groups, but the antibodies afford no cross-immunity. The specificity of the various species is demonstrable by animal inoculation, protection tests, toxin neutralization, and other refined serologic methods.

Also included with the order *Rickettsiales* are the more complex organisms of the *Bartonella* group. Although these agents parasitize red blood cells, they are relatively large size (1 to 3 μ), and some can be grown in the absence of living cells, setting them apart from both the rickettsial and psittacosis groups.

RELATION OF RICKETTSIAE AND BEDSONIA TO BACTERIA

The phylogenetic position of the rickettsia in relation to bacteria seems clearer from recent studies. On the basis of cell wall analysis of *R. mooseri,* the major components of bacterial cell wall, amino acids and oligosaccharides, have been isolated (4). Twelve amino acids have been identified, but diaminopimelic acid was not found. In addition to polysaccharides, a small amount of ribonucleic acid was isolated. In addition to these analytical studies, Smadel (5) demonstrated binary fission by *R. rickettsia* and *R. tsutsugamushi* organisms in rat fibroblasts viewed under the phase contrast microscope. Thus, on the basis of the above evidence, it seems clear that rickettsia are members of the bacterial group of organisms, although they have certain special characteristics of their own. The situation in regard to the psittacosis group is less clear. Cell-wall analyses are not yet complete, but the published studies report both muramic acid and *d*-alanine present (3). Electron micrography indicates that binary fission is the mode of reproduction or multiplication of these organisms (1).

Thus, on the basis of cell-wall analyses and type of division, both the rickettsia and the psittacosis group appear related to the bacteria and are distinct from the "true" viruses. There is, as indicated earlier, no evidence of a relationship between the rickettsia and psittacosis group. From the phylogenetic standpoint it appears that the rickettsia and psittacosis group followed separate evolutionary pathways but both originated from some bacterial ancestor. Obviously, the term "viruses"—or even the qualifying phrase "large viruses"—now is no longer applicable to the Psittacosis group.

With regard to the intracellular parasitism of rickettsia and bedsonia, the following comments by Moulder (2) are most appropriate:

It is seldom recognized that the evolution of an organism capable of growing and multiplying only in another living cell depends upon the operation of two different lines of selection. One line involves the loss of ability to grow extracellularly, and the mechanism here is undoubtedly the occurrence of mutations that reduce the biosynthetic competence of the organism. The other line is concerned with the gain of the ability to survive and multiply within another living cell. Intracellular parasites are often looked down on as metabolic weaklings lacking something required for growth outside of the cells, while few stop to think that their more robust extracellular cousins lack something required for life inside the cell. The ability to grow intracellularly is a highly restricted property among microorganisms, and we know next to nothing of its biochemical basis.

REFERENCES

1. Jenkins, Howard M.   J. Bact., 80:639, 1960.
2. Moulder, James W.   The Psittacosis Group as Bacteria, New York, John Wiley and Sons, Inc., 1964.
3. Perkins, H. R., and Allison, A. C.   J. Gen. Microbiol., 30:469, 1963.
4. Schaechter, M., and others.   J. Bact., 74:822, 1957.
5. Smadel, J. E.   J. Immunol., 84:1, 1960.

56

The Typhus Group of Rickettsioses

These rickettsiae cause **epidemic typhus, Brill's disease,** and **murine typhus.** Although the organisms producing these clinical entities are closely related antigenically, they vary so much in their epidemiology and prognosis that each will be discussed as a separate disease. Scrub typhus is sufficiently distinct to warrant a separate chapter.

EPIDEMIC TYPHUS

(Classic Typhus, European Typhus)

Family: *Rickettsiaceae* Pinkerton. Genus: *Rickettsia* da Rocha-Lima. Type Species: *Rickettsia prowazekii* da Rocha-Lima

For centuries the louse-borne epidemic form of typhus fever has been one of the greatest killers of mankind, especially as an aftermath of war, when it attacks the cold and hungry. The disease was first recognized in a monastery near Salerno in 1083, but it was Fracastorius (22) who gave the first precise clinical description in his famous book *De Contagione* published in 1546. Typhus fever was introduced into the Americas by the Spanish explorers, where it ravished the Indian population and even now persists in endemic form in mountainous areas in Mexico, Central and South America. Typhus was a major factor in the wars of the seventeenth and eighteenth centuries culminating in Napoleon's disaster in Russia in 1812 (29, 44). Zinsser (91) claims that Napoleon's retreat from Moscow "was started by a louse." There were few major outbreaks between the end of the Napoleonic Wars and the beginning of World War I. During 1915, in less than six months, 150,000 Serbians, including 30 per cent of

all Serbian physicians, died of typhus (74). The mortality at the height of the epidemic was from 60 to 70 per cent. Between 1918 and 1922 some three million Russians died of typhus fever. During World War II, incipient epidemics of typhus threatened military operations in Northern Africa and Italy but were quickly eliminated by modern control measures (2, 3, 55, 87).

True to form, typhus appeared again among the North Koreans and the Chinese armies in 1951.

It is of some practical as well as historical interest to recall that typhus fever and typhoid fever were not clearly differentiated clinically until 1837, when Gerhard (25) in Philadelphia pointed out the clinical and pathologic differences between the two diseases. Even now in some parts of Europe typhoid fever is called "typhus abdominalis."

Morphology and Staining. The *rickettsiae* found in the typhus fever are small coccobacillary forms 3.0 to 0.5 μ long and 0.3 μ wide, but occasionally bacillary forms 2 μ in length are observed (Figs. 1, 2).

When stained by Gram's method they are found to be gram-negative, but since they are almost invisible, they are usually stained by the Giemsa, Castañeda, or Macchiavello methods. With Giemsa's stain the organisms are blue or purple, while they appear red with Macchiavello's stain, giving a striking contrast to the blue staining cytoplasm of the infected cells.

Studies in the electron microscope show a clearly defined double-walled limiting membrane with amorphous masses of cytoplasmic material. Cell wall analysis shows a protein and polysaccharide composition similar to bacterial cell walls (68).

Cultural Characteristics. The rickettsiae are obligate **intracellular parasites,** and their

Fig. 1. Air-dried, shadowed, preparation of *R. mooseri* showing cell walls surrounded by the central, shrunken cytoplasm. (From Schaechter and others. *J. Bact.*, 74:822, 1957.)

oxygen needs, pH and osmotic pressure requirements are the same as those of their host cells. Zinsser found that rickettsiae grow more profusely in resting or slowing metabolizing cells than in those with an active metabolism (95). In tissue cultures they multiply most rapidly at 32° C. but will grow equally well at 37.5° C. (56) in Maitland's medium where the cells are surviving rather than actually growing (94). The rickettsiae which cause typhus fever multiply only in the cytoplasm of the host cells, while the rickettsiae which produce spotted fever grow in both cytoplasm and nucleus.

In the earlier studies laboratory-reared lice and ticks were used as living test tube cultures (24), but obviously complete sterility could not be maintained. Zinsser and Castañeda (93) obtained a fair yield of the rickettsiae which causes murine typhus from peritoneal washings of experimentally infected rats, provided the animals had been previously treated with x-rays. The embryonated hen's egg was inoculated by Zia (89)

in 1934, but he obtained only a sparse growth on the chorio-allantoic membrane. In 1938 Cox (14) inoculated the yolk sac and found that pathogenic rickettsiae of all types **grew in abundance in cells which line the yolk sac** (15). Fertile eggs were incubated at 39° C. for five to six days, inoculated with the rickettsiae, and then incubated at 32° C. for three to seven days. Since Cox's discovery, cultured rickettsiae have been available in relative abundance for antigenic studies and for the preparation of vaccines.

Yields of rickettsiae in tissue culture are far below those obtained in embryonated eggs. Efforts to increase this yield by irradiation with Co^{60} (81) and by centrifugation of rickettsiae onto cultured cells (83) have been only partly successful. Centrifugation apparently facilitates infection by bringing

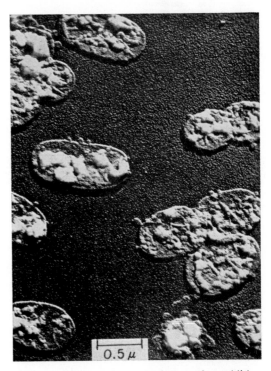

Fig. 2. Sample taken 10 minutes after addition of 1 per cent sodium deoxycholate to a suspension of *R. mooseri*. Residual masses of cytoplasmic material are seen. The globular structures protruding from the surface of the cell walls may represent the extrusion of cytoplasmic material. (From Schaechter and others. *J. Bact.*, 74:822, 1957.)

Fig. 3. T-1824-albumin escape into the skeletal musculature following rickettsial toxin injection. Posterior view of lumbosacral and hind-limb musculature. The specimen at the top is the control; that on the bottom is from a mouse sacrificed 80 minutes after toxin. The darker musculature of the toxemic mouse is due to the escape of the blue azoprotein into the tissues. (From Wattenberg and others. *J. Immunol.,* 74:147, 1955.)

the organism into contact with the cell rapidly, avoiding inactivation of the rickettsiae in the supernate fluid.

Resistance. The rickettsiae in general are easily destroyed by heat, drying, and chemical agents. Although they die in a few hours when stored at room or incubator temperature, they survive in infected tissues for several months when suspended in glycerin at 0° C. (75). Topping found that the organisms could be preserved for at least five months if the infected tissues were macerated, suspended in sterile skimmed milk, and lyophilized. The tissues showing the number

of viable organisms after lyophilization were the brain for *R. prowazekii,* testicular washings for *R. typhi,* and the spleen for *R. rickettsii* or *C. burnetii.*

Under certain exceptional conditions rickettsiae may survive in nature for more than one year. The dried feces of fleas containing *R. typhi* have infected human volunteers after 165 days (4). Dried louse feces (73) containing *R. prowazekii* are often infectious for months (2).

Bacterial Metabolites. Preliminary studies indicate that rickettsiae contain small quantities of carbohydrate, carbohydrate-protein complexes, nucleic acid, and lipids (13). Isolated organisms can metabolize glutamate (33) and contain considerable amounts of glutamic-aspartic transaminase and small quantities of alanine-glutamic transaminase (30).

Adenosine triphosphate can be formed through oxidative phosphorylations, and this compound (ATP) appears to be a prerequisite for all biologic systems (6). Serine can be formed (47). *R. prowazekii* and *R. mooseri* can incorporate trace amounts of isotope labelled amino acids (23), and Bovarick (7) has shown that acetate 1-C^{14} can be incorporated into lipid. Thus, rickettsiae are capable of carrying out several important synthetic reactions.

Rickettsial suspensions have toxic properties which cannot be separated from the infective particles and these are endotoxins. No exotoxins have been found. These toxins, first described by Clarke and Fox (12), produce two easily demonstrable reactions: (1) generalized hemoconcentration in animals and (2) hemolysis of rabbit erythrocytes. Mice inoculated intravenously with suspensions of rickettsiae develop vasoconstriction after about 30 minutes, followed by increased vascular permeability, edema, and death. Mouse erythrocytes are not lysed by the toxin. The altered permeability of mouse vascular system is illustrated in Fig. 3, a photograph taken 80 minutes after toxin and a dye were injected into the mouse on the bottom (78). Toxin injections into rabbits produce intravascular hemolysis with hypotension and death (52). Unlike most endotoxins, the typhus toxin is readily neutralized in vitro by species-specific antiserums (5) and in vivo, provided the antiserum is given prior to or simultaneously with the toxin.

Antigenic Structure. Antigenic studies have been performed with rickettsiae which were grown in the yolk sac of embryonated chick eggs and then purified by differential centrifugation. Each species of rickettsia has specific antigens which induce in man, or the experimentally infected animals, specific antibodies which can be measured as agglutinins, complement-fixing antibodies, or protective antibodies. Repeated washing and centrifugation is necessary to produce this particulate antigen which is specific but expensive (66).

In the process of centrifuging the rickettsiae, a soluble antigen is recovered which is quite active in the complement-fixation test and not nearly as expensive as the particulate antigen. However, the soluble antigen is group-specific not species-specific. It will differentiate the rickettsiae of the typhus fevers from those of the spotted fevers but will not differentiate between endemic and epidemic typhus species.

An **erythrocyte-sensitizing substance** (ESS) was isolated from the typhus rickettsia by Chang and his associates (11) in 1953. Suspensions of infected yolk sac were centrifuged and the supernate discarded. The sedimated rickettsiae were extracted with ether, after which the aqueous phase, which contained both particulate and soluble antigens, was extracted with heat and alkali. After absorption on human O erythrocytes, the altered erythrocytes agglutinate in the presence of specific antiserum from patients and animals. The ESS is group-specific but more sensitive than any of the other serologic tests. It is also much less expensive. The ESS has certain characteristics which suggest that it may be a haptenic derivative of the group-specific soluble substance, since it does not precipitate or fix complement in the presence of specific antiserum. It is also distinct from the rickettsial agglutinogen of the antigen of *Proteus OX19*. The ESS hemagglutinin will differentiate the typhus group from the spotted fever group of rickettsia.

Weil-Felix Reaction. The typhus rickettsiae and most of the spotted fever rickettsiae share a common antigen with one or another of certain strains of the *Proteus bacillus*. The serum of patients infected with these rickettsiae may agglutinate one or another of the *Proteus* strains such as *Proteus OX19, OX2,* or *OXK*. However, the antibodies induced by these common antigens afford no protection against the specific rickettsiae.

During World War I, in 1915, Weil and Felix (79) isolated from the urine of a typhus patient in Rumania an organism belonging to the *Proteus* group which was agglutinated by the serum of the patient and the serums from nine other typhus cases. The following year they isolated another strain, designated *Proteus X19,* which was agglutinated to a much higher titer by the serums of patients with typhus fever. Several other strains were isolated and dissociated into H and O types, after which it was learned that the O antigens gave more specific reactions. Castañeda (10) demonstrated in 1934 the presence of a common carbohydrate antigen in *Proteus OX19* and *R. prowazekii*. Patients with typhus fever do not always develop an appreciable titer, and patients previously immunized with vaccines but who contract typhus fever usually have lower titers to *Proteus OX19* than many vaccinated patients (45). Confusion may arise from the fact that proteus infections will also cause a significant rise in titer to *Proteus OX19* and must be differentiated from that of rickettsial infections.

The origin of this proteus antigen is not known. It is conceivable but hardly likely that the original rickettsiae in insects developed from a free-living proteus in the intestines. It is more likely that this is another example of a biologic accident, of which there are so many examples among the pneumococci, where unrelated organisms and even other organic materials happen to possess a common chemical group. It seems probable that the proteus antigens were acquired by a distant ancestor of the present rickettsial species, since nearly all react with one or another or all three of the proteus antigens.

Spontaneous Disease in Animals. Epidemic typhus occurs as a natural disease in man and his two associates, the human body louse *Pediculus humanus corporis,* and the human head louse *Pediculus humanus* *capitis.* Proof that the body louse could transmit typhus was furnished by Nicolle, Comte and Conseil (50) in 1909 and promptly confirmed by American workers (1).

Experimental Disease in Laboratory Animals. A mild type of typhus can be produced in monkeys by inoculating them with the blood of a patient or macerated bodies of infected lice (51), or by the bite of infected lice. The animal almost never dies and only occasionally develops a skin rash (1).

Typhus was transmitted to the guinea pig by Nicolle, Conseil, and Conor (51) in 1911 and since that time it has become the animal of choice for experimental work. If the patient is in the first week of the disease, 4 to 5 ml. of whole blood should be injected into the peritoneum of several male guinea pigs. Subsequent to the seventh day of the disease the patient may have antibodies in the serum, which will prevent the transfer of the rickettsiae. The blood should be allowed to clot, after which the serum is removed for serologic studies. The clot is ground with an equal volume of sterile skimmed milk or nutrient broth, and 4 or 5 ml. of the clot suspension are inoculated into the peritoneum of two or more male guinea pigs. A few animals will show evidence of illness and may die in the first 24 hours after inoculation, presumably from the toxic effect of the large volume of inoculated blood. If they survive the first 48 hours, they remain well, although after 12 to 24 days daily temperature readings will reveal a characteristic febrile reaction of 40° to 40.5° C., which persists for some three to seven days. After the temperature returns to normal, the guinea pig is immune and cannot be reinfected. Blood, spleen, or brain from the febrile guinea pigs can be used to infect new animals, which now and in subsequent transfers usually show the characteristic febrile rise in seven to nine days. The guinea pigs do not develop scrotal swelling or skin rash. If some of the infected brain is inoculated into the yolk sac of an embryonated egg, within three to five days smears of the yolk will show an abundance of *Rickettsia prowazekii.*

The white rat and white mouse develop only inapparent infection after inoculation with blood from typhus patients, and the disease cannot be maintained by subinoculation. However, fatal infection will develop in white mice after intraperitoneal inoculation if the animals are first treated with rather large doses of x-rays (35), or the disease may be maintained in nonirradiated white mice by the intranasal inoculation of rich suspensions of *R. prowazekii* (16). Other rodents such as the cotton rat (66), the South African gerbil, and two species of Egyptian gerbils (72) have been used successfully for experimental studies.

Clinical Types of Infection in Man. The patient becomes sick from five to 21 days after the bite of an infected louse. The onset may be either extremely abrupt or gradual, but as a rule it closely resembles that of a severe case of influenza. The main points of the following description were taken from a study by George C. Shattuck on cases observed during the Serbian epidemic.

The temperature rises rapidly, often to 103° to 104° F., with chills, great depression, weakness, and pains in the head and limbs. The eruption appears on the fourth or fifth day after the onset, and, except in times of epidemic, it is extremely difficult to make the diagnosis in the pre-eruptive stage. The rash usually appears first on the shoulders and trunk, extending secondarily to the extremities, the backs of the hands and feet, and sometimes to the palms and soles. It becomes more abundant during the subsequent second and third days, but it is seen very rarely on the face and forehead. The rash at first is composed of pink spots which disappear on pressure, but the spots soon become purplish, more deeply brownish red, and finally fade into a brown color. Hemorrhagic centers, which may develop later, persist for considerable lengths of time. There are no eruptions on the mucous membranes of the mouth and pharynx. Fresh flea bites sometimes are hard to distinguish from the typhus eruption.

The heart usually beats rapidly and may become irregular. The blood pressure is apt to be low, and Shattuck believes that myocardial weakness often occurs. Epistaxis is common at the height of the disease. Bronchitis often develops during the later stages, and cough is present almost regularly. Neural symptoms of various kinds are important accompaniments of the disease. In many cases a state of lethargy, resembling that of typhoid fever, is present. There may be twitching of the muscles during this stage of stupor. Delirium occurs in all but the very mild cases. The most constant and troublesome subjective symptom is the very severe headache.

The leukocyte count is increased only rarely and ranges in number from 3,000 to 15,000, the average being between 5,000 and 7,000. Differential counts show approximately normal percentages.

The most common complications are parotitis, suppurative otitis media, and mastoiditis. A peculiar gangrene of the extremities, especially of the feet, is associated particularly with cases occurring during the cold weather. This gangrene probably is associated with the vascular changes incident to the localization of the rickettsiae. Bronchitis is almost a regular complication and albuminuria is common.

The case fatality rate varies from epidemic to epidemic and may be as high as 7 per cent or as low as 15 per cent.

The lesions of typhus fever are caused primarily by the acute reactions in the blood vessels, with damage to the vessels and perivascular inflammation resulting in thromboses, hemorrhages and focal areas of necrosis.

Immunologic Response. The Weil-Felix agglutination with *Proteus OX19* becomes positive about the fourth or fifth day of the disease, reaches its peak about the fifteenth day, and declines rapidly after the sixtieth day. *Proteus OX2* is also agglutinated but never in a significant titer. Serums of normal individuals often have a low titer for *Proteus OX19* and *OX2,* and patients infected with *Proteus vulgaris* and *P. mirabilis* may have a high titer (49). A *Proteus OX19* agglutinin titer of 1:160 or above—or even one less than 1:160, which doubles its original value as the disease progresses—may be considered positive for a rickettsial disease. *Proteus OX19* **agglutination does not differentiate between epidemic typhus, endemic typhus and spotted fever.**

Rickettsiae from chick eggs after treatment with formaldehyde and purification by differential centrifugation were used for agglutination reactions. Agglutinins for rickettsia appear about the same time as agglutinins for *Proteus OX19* and reach a higher titer in 15 or 20 days. They also decline precipitously after the sixtieth day. The serum agglutinates the rickettsiae of murine typhus but in a lower titer.

Complement-fixing antibodies (57) appear in the second week of the disease, reach a high titer by the third week, and decline after the sixtieth day. Cross-reactions were sometimes obtained when rickettsiae of the murine type were used as the antigen but always in a lower titer.

The curve for neutralizing antibodies follows very closely that for the rickettsiae agglutinins but remains high for a long time after the detectable antibodies have declined. It is unfortunate that the neutralization test is so laborious and expensive that it cannot be used routinely. **All strains of R. prowazekii are apparently identical; one attack of epidemic typhus fever usually gives permanent immunity to both epidemic and murine typhus but not to spotted fever.** Occasionally there is a recrudescence of the disease after a number of years (see Brill's disease, page 789).

In addition to the erythrocyte sensitization method (ESS) described previously, a new immunologic method employs fluorescent antibody (26). In this technic labeled anti-human globulin is reacted with the patient's sera. The sera are then exposed to the rickettsial antigens, and the degree of staining of organisms by the test serum is measured.

Direct comparisons of the CF, Weil-Felix, and ESS methods in the diagnosis of typhus (28) indicate that the CF is probably the most sensitive, particularly when increased amounts of antigen are used. The ESS is more prone to nonspecific reactions and becomes negative in months whereas the CF remains positive for years.

A major problem in the serodiagnosis of rickettsial diseases is that exposure to one species antigen may affect all subsequent antibody response (the doctrine of "original antigenic sin"). Thus, an individual infected initially with epidemic typhus and then subsequently infected with murine typhus may show a higher CF titer against the epidemic typhus than the current infecting agent. This could lead to an erroneous diagnosis of Brill's disease (27).

Transmission. Both the body louse, *Pediculus corporis,* and the head louse, *P. capitis,* can transmit the infection, but the former is a much more important vector. The rickettsia multiplies in the intestinal lining cells of the louse (61), which then becomes infectious within four to six days, but reaches its maximum infectiousness between the eighth and the eleventh days. Infected lice invariably die, a fact which Zinsser (92) feels is an indication that the louse is a comparatively recent host of rickettsial disease, since all the other arthropod vectors are unharmed by these organisms. Since the louse always deposits feces when it feeds, it is thought that man acquires the infection by contamination of the wound by the infected feces.

Zinsser believed that the original infection may have been a disease of rodents which became adapted to man and that a man-to-man cycle was set up with the louse as the vector. Such an adaption is suggested by the high mortality rate in man as compared with the almost negligible mortality in experimentally inoculated rats. An important factor in the spread of typhus fever pertains to the high degree of parasitism developed by the louse. Since the louse is quite sensitive to changes in temperatures, it not only leaves the feverish body of an infected patient but also migrates from a body cooling off in death. Although the louse is the natural vector of the disease, infection occasionally occurs by way of the respiratory tract by inhalation of organisms contained in louse feces or by way of the conjunctival sac (62).

The mysterious reappearance of epidemic typhus fever in an area which had been free of the disease for many years raised the problem of where and how the organisms survive in interepidemic periods. Unlike the arthropod vectors of other rickettsial diseases, the louse does not become a carrier, and there are no animal reservoirs. Zinsser believed that man might be the natural reservoir and that Brill's disease (p. 789) was a recrudescent typhus. Murray and Snyder (45) confirmed Zinsser's hypothesis

by isolating seven strains of *R. prowazekii* from patients ill from Brill's disease. They also showed that lice became infected when fed on the patients. The final proof was supplied by Price (60) in 1955, when he isolated *R. prowazekii* from lymph nodes of two individuals who came to this country from Russia more than 20 years previously. These patients were not ill at the time the nodes were removed but did have specific complement-fixing and toxin-neutralizing antibodies to *R. prowazekii.*

Biologic Products. A rickettsial vaccine prepared by the yolk sac method of Cox has proved to be of value as an immunizing agent against epidemic typhus. An opportunity for a field test of the vaccine occurred in Egypt and was carried out by the Cairo unit of the American Typhus Commission (19). The authors reported the findings on 61 patients who had been diagnosed as typhus fever cases and who had received one or more doses of the Cox vaccine previously. The only death in this vaccinated group occurred in a patient who had received a single dose of vaccine three days before the onset of his illness. In most instances the disease was mild, especially in those who had received two or more doses of vaccine at least three weeks before the onset of the illness, but the reporters feel that vaccination during the incubation period is worthwhile.

Treatment. Excellent nursing case is essential in the treatment of typhus fever. Hyperimmune rabbit and horse serums are expensive and of little value except in the early stages of the disease (69, 70). Specific treatment with para-aminobenzoic acid (PABA) reduces the severity and duration of the disease but is not nearly as effective as the new antibiotic, chloramphenicol (54). There were no deaths in 21 consecutive cases of epidemic typhus treated in Bolivia although the death rate was 28 per cent in the 50 controls (53).

Oxytetracycline, chlortetracycline, and erythromycin also are effective against epidemic typhus as well as in other rickettsial infections. Rickettsia may, however, develop resistance to the above drugs including chloramphenicol as well as to *p*-aminobenzoic acid (80, 82, 84).

Cortisone has little or no effect on antibody development in infected animals, but it increases the susceptibility of animals to rickettsial infections as well as altering the course of the infections (85, 86).

Prevention. The prevention of epidemic typhus is accomplished best by louse-killing measures, but active immunization with vaccines also is important (21). The use of the insecticide DDT completely replaced the older methods of louse control, such as hot baths and steam treatment of clothing, which were expensive and had no lasting effects. Dusting of clothing with 10 per cent DDT in pyrophillite not only killed the lice but also prevented their return for periods up to a month. Brilliant results were obtained with such measures in the 1943-44 Naples epidemic. Body lice resistant to DDT appeared in Korea in 1951 (31). Cox's formalinized rickettsial vaccine was used routinely in the American troops which were sent overseas (88). Although some 64 cases developed in vaccinated individuals, there were no deaths in an epidemic in which 13 of 41 unvaccinated British soldiers died of the disease (32 per cent) (62). Laboratory-reared lice were fed on patients who had not been vaccinated and on those who developed the disease even though previously vaccinated. It was found that the lice fed on the vaccinated had only 10 *R. prowazekii* per milliliter of blood while the unvaccinated had 2,300 per milliliter of blood (71).

Certainly the vaccine should be given to soldiers and to laboratory personnel who are working with either the disease or the rickettsiae. However, it is not an entirely harmless procedure, since many individuals are allergic to egg antigens. Severe allergic reactions developed in about two of every 1,000 soldiers vaccinated, and there were a few deaths (76). Individuals with a history of allergy to egg should be given a preliminary skin test with the vaccine.

Successful vaccination with a vaccine made from *R. prowazekii* does not protect the individual from a spontaneous infection with *R. typhi*, the etiologic agent of murine typhus (58).

Vaccination effects a long lasting immunity. A single booster dose of 1 ml. given as long as five or six years after the two primary doses resulted in a maximum antibody increase. A second booster dose given either seven days or seven weeks later gave no additional antibody response (46). The authors suggest that the primary immunization doses should be given at intervals of two to four weeks rather than 7 to 10 days.

BRILL'S DISEASE

Brill noted in New York City in 1898 the occurrence of a febrile, eruptive disease which resembled a mild form of typhus fever (9). The patients had not been in contact with human body lice, but all were immigrants from southeastern Europe and most of them gave a history of having epidemic typhus many years before. The disease is not confined to New York City but occurs chiefly in the cities of the northeastern part of the country. Anderson and Goldberger (1) transmitted the infection to monkeys and found that the convalescent animals could not be reinfected with blood from patients with classic epidemic typhus.

For years Brill's disease was confused with endemic murine typhus. Zinsser (90) felt that these cases were different clinically from the endemic typhus found in the southeastern states and succeeded in isolating three strains which seemed to him to be identical with *R. prowazekii* and different from *R. typhi*, the cause of murine typhus (93). Zinsser's hypothesis was supported by the complement-fixation studies of Plotz (57) in 1943 and the more elaborate investigation of Murray and his associates (45) in 1951. The latter investigators infected lice by feeding them on patients with Brill's disease and later recovered and identified *R. prowazekii*. These studies suggest that man may function as a reservoir for typhus. A man in a louse-infested community may suffer a recrudescence of classic typhus, or Brill's disease, infect his own lice, and thus initiate a new epidemic.

The high incidence of potential carriers of epidemic typhus rickettsiae in emigrants from eastern Europe emphasizes the importance of Brill's disease. Schaefer and his associates (63) found 22 per cent with antibodies to typhus, while not one in a group of 60 controls born in the United States or Canada had antibodies.

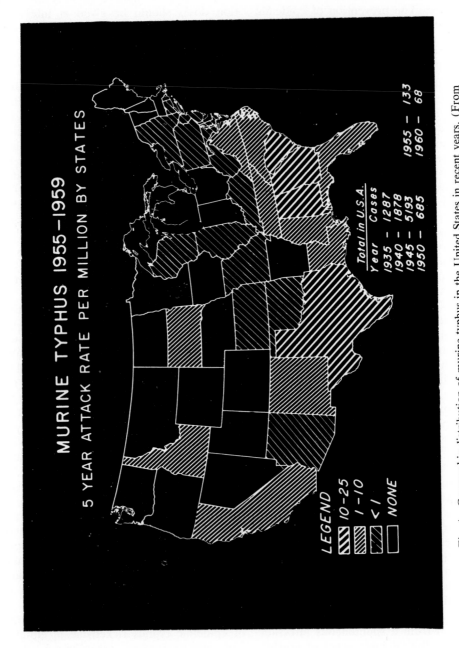

Fig. 4. Geographic distribution of murine typhus in the United States in recent years. (From Smadel. *Ann. Int. Med.*, 51:426, 1959.)

Chlortetracycline produced a dramatic cure in one patient with a severe attack of Brill's disease (64). In this instance the patient had had, 30 years before in Europe, a primary attack of epidemic typhus.

MURINE TYPHUS

Genus: *Rickettsia* da Rocha-Lima. Species: *Rickettsia typhi* (Wolbach and Todd) Philip. (Endemic Typhus, Flea-borne Typhus, Urban or Shop Typhus)

Murine or endemic typhus occurs in western Europe, central Africa, Asia, southern United States (34) and along the western coast of South America. Over 36,000 cases were reported in the United States between 1913 and 1944, of which 95 per cent occurred in eight southern states (59). Fox and others (20) found in their 1949 studies with the complement-fixation technic that 12 to 16 per cent of individuals in certain areas of the South were already immune to murine typhus, presumably from a previous clinical or subclinical infection.

Murine typhus is in general a much milder disease than epidemic typhus, with an average mortality of about 3.5 per cent. The attack rate of typhus for the years 1953-57 is shown in Figure 4. The total cases, fatalities, and mortality rate for the years 1935-57 is given in Figure 5. The significance of the fact that the mortality has remained constant even after the introduction of antibiotic therapy is unknown. Murine typhus frequently occurs with few or no skin lesions and thus the diagnosis may be missed.

Smadel (67) suggests that the recent decline in murine typhus is due in part to better rodent control but also the wide use of insecticides in agriculture. There are, however, some serologic data which indicated that *R. typhi* exists in a number of wild animals (43) which, if confirmed, will mean that complete eradication of this disease may not be possible.

Between 1910 and 1930 endemic typhus in the southern states was usually called Brill's disease and not differentiated from the true Brill's disease of Philadelphia, New York, and Boston. The epidemiologic studies of Maxcy (36) and his associates between 1926 and 1929 showed that the disease in the South was not associated with lice but occurred under circumstances where a mite, flea or tick could be the vector; the flea was proven to be the vector by Dyer, Rumreich and Badger (17, 18) in 1931.

In Mexico both epidemic and murine typhus are endemic at the present time (65, 77). The colloquial name "tabardillo," from the mantle-like spotted rash, goes back to the time of the siege of Granada but is used in Mexico for both epidemic and murine typhus.

Experimental Disease in Laboratory Animals. Monkeys, donkeys, cats, squirrels, deer, mice, voles, gerbils, white mice, and rats and guinea pigs can be infected with *R. typhi*. This organism can be transmitted indefinitely in white rats, in contrast to *R. prowazekii,* which dies out after a few passages (39). The rats do not die but harbor the rickettsiae in their brains for several months. X-ray treatment of white rats and cotton rats increases the yield of rickettsiae from the tissues. Intranasal inoculation of large doses of *R. typhi* produces fatal pneumonitis in mice, rats, rabbits, dogs, and sheep.

The guinea pig is the most useful animal for the isolation of *R. typhi* from patients. When male guinea pigs are inoculated intraperitoneally with the patient's blood by the method described for the recovery of *R. prowazekii* (Fig. 6), the febrile response is less striking, but there is usually a marked scrotal swelling like that first noted by Neill (48). The rickettsiae multiply in abundance in the cytoplasm of the serosal cells over the testes. This response is known as the **Neill-Mooser reaction,** the swollen cells as **Mooser cells** (38, 40) and the intracytoplasmic rickettsiae as **Mooser bodies.** This same reaction is occasionally produced by *R. prowazekii* and occasionally absent after infection with *R. typhi,* especially in very hot weather, and in general is not as reliable as the complement-fixation test in differentiating *R. typhi* from *R. prowazekii.* Mooser's contributions to our knowledge of both epidemic and endemic typhus during a 20-year period were reviewed in 1946 (41). The evidence

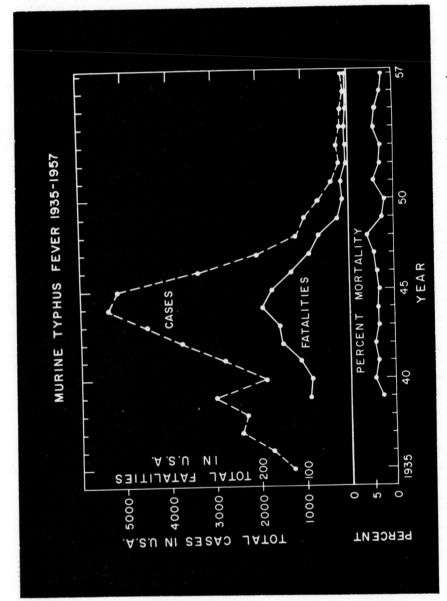

Fig. 5. Murine typhus in the United States in recent years: total number of cases, number of deaths, and per cent mortality. (From Smadel. *Ann. Int. Med.,* 51:427, 1959.)

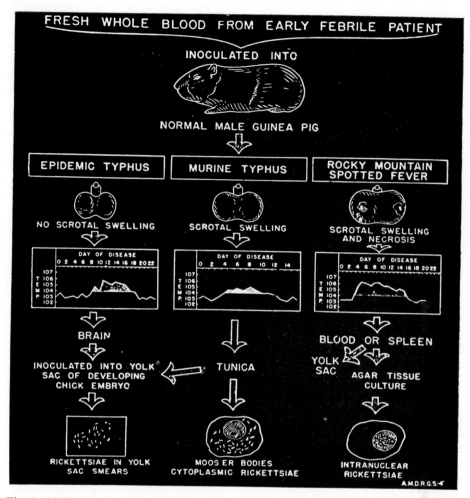

Fig. 6. Method for isolating rickettsiae. (From Smadel. *Diagnostic Procedures for Virus and Rickettsial Diseases,* American Public Health Association.)

for prior discovery which would justify the name *R. mooseri* rather than *R. typhi* for the etiologic agent of endemic typhus was published in 1948 (42).

Clinical Types of Infection in Man. After an incubation period varying from six to 14 days, most patients become ill suddenly with fever, chills, headache, and prostration. The temperature rises step-like to reach a maximum usually between the fifth and eighth days, but wide daily variations in temperature are the rule. According to Maxcy (36), one of the most characteristic features is the almost uniform 14-day duration of the illness, 86 per cent of his 94

patients reaching normal between the twelfth and the sixteenth days.

The eruption, which appears about the fifth day but occasionally as early as the second day, usually begins as a few spots which come on the abdomen or flexor surfaces of the forearms and, within 24 hours, becomes generalized. The rash rarely involves the palms of the hands, the soles of the feet, or the face. Maxcy emphasizes the irregularity of the eruption in almost all of its features, such as size, color, shape, and distribution. In severe cases the rash becomes petechial. Other characteristic symptoms are a hacking type of cough and nausea with vomiting; mental symptoms, such as nervousness, dullness, or occasionally delirium. Convalescence often is prolonged for a month or more.

In general, the symptoms are somewhat less severe than those seen in epidemic typhus. The rash is often less extensive and of shorter duration, and occasionally is missing. There is less severe involvement of the myocardium, kidneys, and central nervous system, and the complications are milder or absent. The mortality ranges from 1 to 4 per cent, with the fatal attacks occurring almost exclusively in the aged and debilitated patients (37).

Immunologic Response. Patients with murine typhus develop agglutinins to *Proteus OX19* and *OX2* at about the same time and to the same degree as those having epidemic typhus. **Agglutinins are produced to both** *R. typhi* **and** *R. prowazekii* **but those to** *R. typhi* **appear several days sooner and reach an appreciably higher titer. Complement-fixing antibodies to washed** *R. typhi* **appear between the tenth and fourteenth day and reach a maximum about the twenty-fifth day.** Little if any reaction occurs when washed *R. prowazekii* are used as the antigen. When a soluble antigen from *R. typhi* is used in the complement-fixation test, there is a marked degree of cross-reaction between the serums of patients with epidemic and murine typhus. The surprising observation was made by Plotz and Wertman (58) and others that **individuals who contract murine typhus after being previously immunized against epidemic typhus will give a higher complement-fixing titer with the epidemic antigen.** Smadel (66) suggests that this may be an anamnestic reaction to the common antigen shared by the two species of rickettsiae. Fortunately, the agglutinins are higher for the specific infection.

All strains of *R. typhi* **seem to be identical immunologically and patients who have recovered from murine typhus are immune to epidemic typhus but not to spotted fever.**

Transmission. The rat flea *Xenopsylla cheopis* is the vector of endemic typhus. Dyer, Rumreich, and Badger (17) found infected fleas in nature on rats trapped in Baltimore, and later Dyer and others (18) transmitted the infection from rat to rat by means of the rat flea. The rickettsiae can remain infective in the flea for at least 52 days after the last feeding (18). Multiplication of rickettsiae in the flea was demonstrated by Dyer and others (18), who showed that two days after feeding, half a flea was noninfectious for a guinea pig, while after three days, $\frac{1}{32}$ of a flea was infective, and by the eleventh day, 1/128,000 of a flea would reproduce the disease. Rickettsiae also have been found in nature in other insects, including the cat flea *Ctenocephalides felis* (32) and even a chicken flea *Echidnophaga gallinacea* removed from a rat (8). Many insects, such as lice, bedbugs, and ticks, have been infected experimentally.

An alternation may have occurred in the past when *R. typhi* was introduced into a population harboring an abundance of lice so the rickettsiae could be transmitted from man to man by the louse for generations. Zinsser (92) thought this might have happened since *R. prowazekii* infection is much more often fatal for both man and louse than is *R. typhi* for man and flea.

Biologic Products. An effective rickettsial vaccine has been prepared from *R. typhi* grown in embryonated chick egg by Cox's method. A single adequate dose of a fluid vaccine seems to be as effective as multiple smaller doses, but the vaccine should be repeated each year. Individuals suspected of being allergic to egg proteins should be given a preliminary skin test with the vaccine before vaccination.

Treatment. Treatment with para-aminobenzoic acid shortens the course of the disease, but chlortetracycline and chloramphenicol are much more effective.

Prevention. The prevention of endemic typhus, like that of plague, is dependent upon rat control and mass ratproofing of buildings and proper disposal of garbage and rubbish. The United States Public Health Service has set up a typhus fever control unit which cooperates with local units if the latter comply by enacting suitable ordinances, providing money and personnel, and agreeing to extend and maintain the program.

Active immunization by injections of rickettsial vaccine is advisable to provide protection to laboratory and field workers engaged in typhus work.

REFERENCES

1. Anderson, J. F., and Goldberger, J. Hygienic Lab. Bull., No. 86, 1912, Washington, D.C.
2. Bayne-Jones, S. Rhode Island M. J., 30:423, 1947.
3. ——— Symposium on Rickettsial Diseases, American Association for the Advancement of Science, Dec., 1946, Boston, 1948.
4. Blanc, G., and Baltazard, M. Bull. Soc. path. exot., 33:25, 1940.
5. Bengtson, I. A., and others. Nat. Inst. Health Bull., 183:25, 1945.
6. Bovarick, M. R. J. Biol. Chem., 220:353, 1956.
7. ——— J. Bact., 80:508, 1960.
8. Brigham, G. D. Pub. Health Rep., 56:1803, 1941.
9. Brill, N. E. Am. J. M. Sc., 139:484, 1910.
10. Castañeda, M. R. J. Exper. Med., 60:119, 1934; 62:289, 1935.
11. Chang, R. Shi-Man, and others. J. Immunol., 70:215, 1953.
12. Clarke, D. H., and Fox, J. P. J. Exper. Med., 88:25, 1948.
13. Cohen, S. S., and others. J. Immunol., 65:465, 1950.
14. Cox, H. R. Pub. Health Rep., 53:2241, 1948.
15. ——— Science, 94:399, 1941.
16. Durand, P., and Giroud, P. Compt. rend. Acad. d. Sc., 210:751, 1940.
17. Dyer, R. E., and others. Pub. Health Rep., 46:334, 1931.
18. ——— and others. Pub. Health Rep., 47:131, 987, 1932.
19. Ecke, R. S., and others. Am. J. Trop. Med., 25:447, 1945.
20. Fox, J. P., and others. Am. J. Hyg., 49:321, 1949.
21. ——— Am. J. Trop. Med., 5:464, 1956.
22. Fracastorius, H. De contagionibus et contagiosis morbis et eorum curatione, libre tres, Venice, 1546. Translated by Wright.
23. Fujita, K., and others. Jap. J. Med. Sc. & Biol., 12:387, 1957.
24. Fuller, H. S., and others. Pub. Health Rep., 64:1287, 1949.
25. Gerhard, W. W. Am. J. M. Sc., 19:289, 1837.
26. Goldwasser, R. A., and Shepard, C. C. J. Immunol., 82:383, 1959.
27. ——— and others. J. Immunol., 83:491, 1959.
28. Hersey, D. F. J. Immunol., 79:409, 1957.
29. Hirsch, A. Handbook of Geographical and Historical Pathology, Translated by Creighton, London, New Sydenham Society, Vol. 1.
30. Hopps, H. E., and others. J. Bact., 71:708, 1956.
31. Hurlbut, H. S., and others. Science, 115:11, 1952.
32. Irons, J. V., and others. Am. J. Trop. Med., 24:359, 1944.
33. Karp, A. J. Bact., 67:450, 1954.
34. Love, G. J., and Smith, W. W. Pub. Health Rep., 75:429, 1960.
35. Liu, P. Y., and others. J. Exper. Med., 73:669, 1941.
36. Maxcy, K. F. Pub. Health Rep., 41:1213, 1926; 44:1735, 1929.
37. Miller, E. S., and Beeson, P. M. Medicine, 25:1, 1946.
38. Mooser, H. J. Infect. Dis., 43:241, 261, 1928.
39. ——— and others. J.A.M.A., 97:231, 1931.
40. ——— Acta trop., Suppl. 4, Reinhardt, Basel, 1945.
41. ——— Schweiz. med. Wchnschr., 76:877, 1946.
42. ——— Am. J. Trop. Med., 28:841, 1948.
43. Morlan, H. B., and others. Pub. Health Rep., 65:57, 1950.
44. Murchison, C. A Treatise on the Continued Fevers of Great Britain, 3rd ed., London, Longmans, Green and Company, 1884.
45. Murray, E. S., and Snyder, J. C. Am. J. Hyg., 53:22, 1951.
46. ——— and others. J. Immunol., 68:207, 1952.
47. Myers, W. F., and others. Bact. Proc., 122, 1959.
48. Neill, M. H. Pub. Health Rep., 32:1105, 1917.
49. Nelson, C. T. J. Lab. & Clin. Med., 32:360, 1947.
50. Nicolle, C., and others. Compt. rend. Acad. d. sc., 149:486, 1909.
51. ——— Compt. rend. Acad. d. sc., 152:1632, 1911.
52. Paterson, P. Y., and others. J. Immunol., 72:12, 1954.
53. Payne, E. H., and Knaudt, J. A. Proc. 4th Internat. Cong. Trop. Med. & Malaria, Washington, D.C., May 10-18, 1948.
54. ——— and others. J. A. Trans. Roy. Soc. Trop. Med. & Hyg., 42:163, 1948.
55. Philip, C. B. Symposium on Rickettsial Diseases, American Association for the Advancement of Science, Dec., 1946, Boston, 1948.
56. Pinkerton, H., and Hass, G. M. J. Exper. Med., 56:131, 1932.
57. Plotz, H. Science, 97:20, 1943.
58. ——— and Wertman, K. Proc. Soc. Exper. Biol. & Med., 59:248, 1945.
59. Pratt, H. D. Ann. New York Acad. Sc., 70:516, 1958.
60. Price, W. H. J. Bact., 69:106, 1955.
61. Ricketts, H. T., and Wilder, R. M. J.A.M.A., 54:1304, 1910.
62. Sadusk, J. F. Yale J. Biol. & Med., 21:211, 1949.
63. Schaefer, G. L., and others. Ann. Int. Med., 42:979, 1955.
64. Schoenbach, E. B. J.A.M.A., 139:450, 1949.
65. Silva-Goytia, R. Rev. d. Inst. salub. y enferm. trop., 5:241, 1944.
66. Smadel, J. E. Diagnostic Procedures for Virus and Rickettsial Diseases. Am. Pub. Health Assoc., N.Y. City, 1956, p. 513.
67. ——— Ann. Int. Med., 51:421, 1959.
68. Schaechter, M., and others. J. Bact., 74:822, 1957.
69. Snyder, J. C. Symposium on Rickettsial Diseases, American Association for the Advancement of Science, Dec., 1946, Boston, 1948.
70. ——— and Anderson, C. R. Science, 95:23, 1942.
71. ——— and others. Am. J. Hyg., 49:340, 1949.
72. ——— Proc. Soc. Exper. Biol. & Med., 59:110, 1945.
73. Starzyk, J. Compt. rend. Soc. de biol., 123:1221, 1936.

74. Strong, R. P., and others. Typhus Fever with Particular Reference to the Serbian Epidemic, Cambridge, Harvard University Press, 1920.
75. Topping, N. H., and Shepard, C. C. Ann. Rev. Microbiol., 1:333, 1947.
76. Untract, S., and Ratner, B. Ann. Allergy, 8:699, 1950.
77. Varela, G., and Zozaya, J. Rev. d. Inst. salub. y enferm. trop., 6:11, 1945.
78. Wattenberg, L. W., and others. J. Immunol., 74:147, 1955.
79. Weil, E., and Felix, A. Wien. klin. Wchnschr., 29:33, 974, 1916.
80. Weiss, E. H., and others. J. Bact., 73:421, 1957.
81. ———— and Dressler, H. R. J. Bact., 75:544, 1958.
82. ———— and Dressler, H. R. Am. J. Hyg., 71:292, 1960.
83. ———— and Dressler, H. R. Proc. Soc. Exper. Biol. & Med., 103:691, 1960.
84. ———— and Dressler, H. R. J. Bact., 83:409, 1962.

85. Whitmore, C. E. J. Bact., 74:417, 1957.
86. ———— J. Bact., 74:425, 1957.
87. Zarafonetis, C. J. D. Symposium on Rickettsial Diseases, American Association for the Advancement of Science, Dec., 1946, Boston, 1948.
88. ———— and others. J. Immunol., 53:15, 1946.
89. Zia, S. Am. J. Path., 10:211, 1934.
90. Zinsser, H. Am. J. Hyg., 20:513, 1934.
91. ———— Rats, Lice and History, Boston, Little, Brown & Co., 1935.
92. ———— Immunity in Rickettsial Diseases in Virus and Rickettsial Diseases. Harvard Symposium Volume, Cambridge, Harvard University Press, 1940, p. 872.
93. ———— and Castañeda, M. R. J. Exper. Med., 56:455, 1932.
94. ———— and others. J. Exper. Med., 69:179, 1934.
95. ———— and Schoenbach, E. B. J. Exper. Med., 66:207, 1937.

57

The Spotted Fever Group of Rickettsioses

In this group are included the following organisms and their diseases: (1) Rocky Mountain spotted fever, *R. rickettsii*, (2) boutonneuse fever (probably identical to African tick-bite fever, Kenya tick typhus, and Indian tick typhus), *R. conorii*, (3) rickettsialpox, *R. akari*, (4) North Queensland tick typhus, *R. australis*, (5) maculatum disease, (6) Siberian tick typhus, *R. sibericus*. The above divisions were based on the spotted fever toxin neutralization test in mice reported by Bell and Stoenner (4) and are supported by various previous studies using other serologic technics (7, 17, 28, 31, 35). Note that the casual agent of maculatum disease has not been named as yet. **All organisms of the spotted fever group are characterized by growing in the nuclei as well as in the cytoplasm of cells.** Most of the rickettsia grouped above are tick-borne and are classified in some texts as "tick-borne typhus group." An obvious exception is that of rickettsialpox, which has as its vector the mouse mite. Neither the "spotted fever" nor "tick-borne" types of classification are entirely satisfactory and should be superseded by serologic groups (A, B, C), as has been done with the arbo viruses.

ROCKY MOUNTAIN SPOTTED FEVER

(American Spotted Fever)

Family: *Rickettsiaceae* Pinkerton. Genus: *Rickettsia* da Rocha-Lima. Species: *Rickettsia rickettsii* (Wolbach) Brumpt

This disease was recognized as a clinical entity in Idaho as early as 1899 (19). By 1947 cases had been reported from all of the states except Maine, Vermont, Rhode Island, and Kansas (47). A focus has existed on Long Island, New York, since 1912 (30), and several are known in western Canada. About 480 cases are reported each year in the United States and 663 in Brazil, although the actual number must be considerably greater.

About 1905 two physicians of Boise, Idaho, transmitted the infection to two volunteers in series by the bite of a tick which they removed from one of their patients (6). Howard Taylor Ricketts (38) infected monkeys and guinea pigs with blood from patients in 1906. Later in the same year, Ricketts (38) and King (24) independently demonstrated that the wood tick *Dermacentor andersoni* was the primary vector in the Rocky Mountain area (37). However, in the eastern states the dog tick *D. variabilis* is the vector. The history of the disease was reviewed in detail by Wilder (49) in 1950.

Spontaneous Disease in Animals. The rickettsiae are transmitted in the tick transovarially and by copulation. The organism occurs in all tissues, and larvae and nymphs as well as adult ticks are infectious. The ticks are not injured by the presence of the rickettsiae. The larvae and nymph feed on small rodents, small carnivores, and even birds, while the adult ticks prefer larger animals, such as deer, cattle, dogs, and man. Inapparent infections are produced in animals. The variety of ticks capable of harboring *R. rickettsii* and their choice of animal hosts has been reviewed by Steinhaus (45). The animal reservoirs and their ticks in Brazil were studied by Travassos (48) and those of South Africa by a joint team of Office of International D'Hygiène Publique/World Health Organization (22).

Experimental Disease in Laboratory Animals. Monkeys are quite susceptible to *R. rickettsii* and often die of the infection. A rash frequently develops over the face, lower back, and thighs, and the scrotum may become swollen and the ears necrotic.

White mice are relatively resistant, but white rats are moderately susceptible. Rabbits develop fever and may show lesions of the ear and scrotum but rarely die of the infection.

The guinea pig is the experimental animal of choice. Fresh blood collected from the patient during the first week of the disease, or ground clots of blood collected during the second week, is injected intraperitoneally into male guinea pigs by the method described for the isolation of *R. prowazekii.* A sharp febrile rise to 105° or 106° F. occurs after three or four days; the scrotum becomes swollen and necrotic, and the animals frequently die. Rickettsiae are found in the nuclei as well as the cytoplasm of cells in agar tissue cultures which have been infected from blood, scrotal tissues, or spleen. The guinea pigs which survive are immune, and their serum contains protective antibodies. Rabbits and monkeys develop agglutinins to *Proteus OX19,* but guinea pigs do not.

Clinical Picture. The incubation period of spotted fever varies from three to 12 days, and the onset of symptoms is characterized by severe chills, headache, and pains in the joints and muscles. Fever of 104° to 105° F. is usual, and higher temperatures are not uncommon. The most characteristic clinical feature is the rash, which appears from the second to the fifth day after the onset and is noticed first on the peripheral parts of the body, such as the wrists, ankles, forehead, palms of the hands, and soles of the feet. The location and progression of the rash are important features of the differential diagnosis of this infection from typhus, in which the rash begins over the trunk and spreads peripherally (32).

In severe cases the rash becomes hemorrhagic. The spleen usually is enlarged, and the white blood count is elevated to 12,000 or 15,000. Agglutinins for *Proteus OX19* may appear as early as the fifth day, and the titer rises with convalescence. Complement-fixing antibodies using *R. rickettsii* antigens also appear.

In the fortunate patient the disease usu-ally lasts for two to three weeks and the fever comes down by lysis; the doomed patient usually dies in the second week of his illness. The main lesions are in the vascular endothelium, and the resulting proliferation and inflammation lead to vascular disturbances, such as hemorrhages and thromboses. The convalescence is very slow in severe cases, and months may be required for complete recovery.

The mortality rate is quite variable and depends upon such factors as the strain of the infecting organism and the age of the patient. It was the variability in mortality rate which led to some confusion originally as to whether or not there were different types of spotted fever. Thus a mortality of 70 to 80 per cent was observed in cases acquired on the west side of the Bitter Root River in Montana, a mortality of 5 per cent in the Snake River Valley, and about 25 per cent in cases acquired in the eastern part of the United States (18). Topping (47) compared the case fatality rates of cases in the west (Montana and Idaho) over the 10-year-period 1930 to 39 with those in two eastern states, Maryland (1930 to 39) and Virginia 1933 to 39. The over-all case fatality rate in the western states was 28.1 per cent and 18.4 per cent in the eastern states. However, in the east almost half of the patients were less than 15 years of age, an age group in which the mortality is significantly lower than in the older age groups. When the ages are taken into account, the mortality rates did not differ significantly.

In the clinical description of epidemic typhus and Rocky Mountain spotted fever it is stated that the rash begins on the body in typhus and spreads peripherally, while the reverse is true of spotted fever. This is true of the typical case; but in the majority of cases of endemic typhus and spotted fever which we have seen in our hospital the differentiation could not be made by inspecting the rash, and we have resorted to guinea pig inoculation, isolation of rickettsia, or serologic methods.

Serology. The organisms of the spotted fever group have a soluble cross-reacting group antigen and specific particulate antigens.

Agglutinins to proteus may begin to appear 8 to 10 days after onset of the disease but a four-fold rise in titer usually cannot be found for two or three weeks. Complement-fixing antibodies appear somewhat later.

The rickettsial toxin neutralization test in mice is most important in the serologic differentiation of these organisms and may well be used in diagnostic studies when the conventional tests are indefinite. A standardized toxin suspension of organisms is prepared and its LD_{50} determined. Toxin is mixed with antiserum, so that final toxin-antiserum mixture contains two LD_{50} toxin doses (sufficient to kill 100 per cent of control mice). Mixtures are incubated one hour, and 0.5 cc. inoculated intravenously into mice. Titration end points are read at 24 hours (3, 4).

Fluorescent antibody staining has been described for detecting R. rickettsii in individual ticks (42). The erythrocyte-sensitizing substance (ESS) tests are positive in spotted fever, but it is a **group**-reactive substance.

Epidemiology and Transmission. The disease is transmitted by the bite of an infected tick, usually the wood tick Dermacentor andersoni or the dog tick D. variabilis. The cycle of infection in nature goes from animal hosts, such as dogs, field mice, and rabbits, to ticks. Ticks may transmit the infection to their progeny. The role of the rabbit tick, which will not bite man, is probably considerable in keeping an infectious cycle going in rabbits and dogs.

It is a fortuitous circumstance that the tick must feed (bite) for several hours before the infection is transmitted. This apparently is due to some factor in blood needed to activate the rickettsia and was first described by Spencer and Parker (44) as the **reactivation** phenomena. The precise nature of the activation process is unknown. The reactivation process takes longer in the spring than in midsummer.

The two major areas of infection in the United States are in the Rocky Mountains and middle Atlantic States (Fig. 1), with the attack rate in Virginia of 66 cases and in Wyoming 150 cases per million persons (43). In the years 1953-57 seven states

(Maine, Vermont, Rhode Island, Connecticut, Michigan, Wisconsin, and Minnesota) reported no cases. Maine and Vermont have never reported a case. The total cases, fatalities, and percentage of fatalities for the years 1935-57 are shown in Figure 2. Note that, unlike typhus, the per cent fatality showed a marked decline with the advent of antibiotic therapy.

Treatment. Good nursing care is as essential in spotted fever as in typhus fever. Harrell (15) has shown that in severe cases there is a rapid progressive drop in the serum albumin, which must be replaced promptly by intravenous injection of serum or whole blood.

The broad-spectrum antibiotics, especially chlortetracycline, have been used widely and successfully. With the use of these drugs the mortality should be about 7 per cent or less. Widespread use of these antibiotics should ameliorate the disease so that it might not be recognizable. Moreover, antibiotics may delay or reduce the immune response (27).

Prevention. Spotted fever can be prevented only by the avoidance of ticks, which means that sheep herders and ranchers, whose occupation requires exposure in tick-infested regions, should wear protective clothing such as high boots, leggings and tightly buttoned shirts. No repellent has been found to be satisfactory, and since it is very difficult to prevent ticks from crawling on the body in spite of protective clothing, the body should be inspected frequently. In highly infested areas the yolk sac vaccine (5) should be administered annually to those most likely to become infected. The adult dose consists of two injections, 10 days apart, of 2.0 ml. each; children should receive half of this amount.

In the eastern United States almost half the patients are children, probably because of their close association with dogs. The infection is so sporadic in occurrence that it is doubtful whether an active immunization program would be of practical value, although it has been suggested. More important is the education of the public to be aware of the dangers of infection by dog ticks. In the summer months especially,

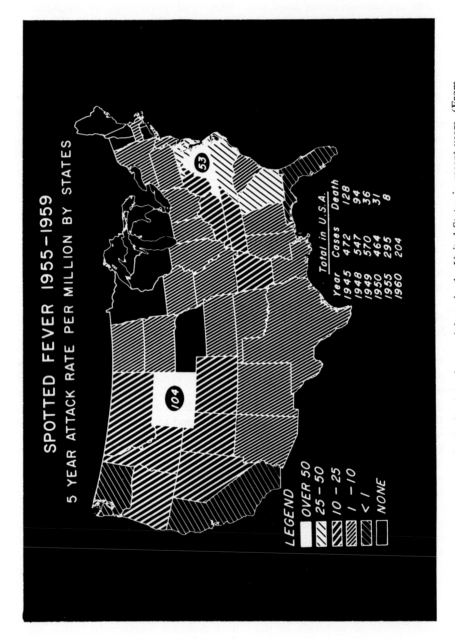

Fig. 1. Geographic distribution of spotted fever in the United States in recent years. (From Smadel. *Ann. Int. Med.,* 51:422, 1959.)

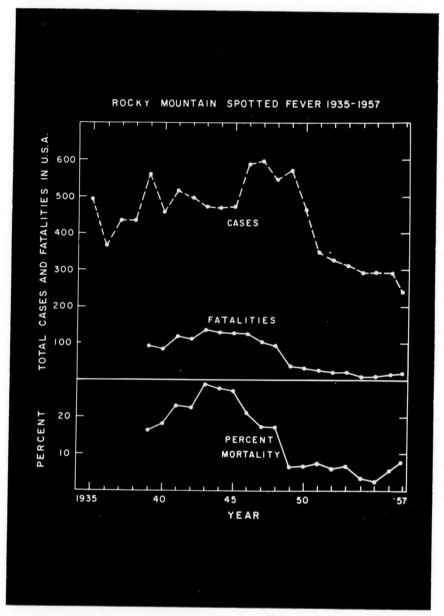

Fig. 2. Spotted fever in the United States in recent years: total number of cases, number of deaths, and per cent mortality. (From Smadel. *Ann. Int. Med.,* 51:422, 1959.)

children should be inspected by their parents at least three times a day and any ticks which are found should be removed. Fortunately, a tick has to be attached some hours before the rickettsiae are activated, so that infection may be prevented by their early removal. Ticks should be removed by forceps or by protecting the fingers with a piece of paper.

RICKETTSIALPOX

Genus: *Rickettsia* da Rocha-Lima. Species: *Rickettsia akari* Huebner, Jellison and Pomerantz

This disease was first recognized in New York by Sussman (46) and Shankman (41) in 1956. The etiologic agent was identified by the brilliant work of Huebner and others (20) of the U.S. Public Health Service and their colleagues. They discovered the vector to be the mouse mite (*Allodermanyssus sanguineus*) and the animal reservoir the house mouse. About 200 cases are reported in the United States each year, mostly in New York City, but infections have been found in Philadelphia, Boston, and Cleveland. *R. akari* has been isolated from patients in Moscow (50) and from a wild field mouse in Korea (21).

The etiologic agent *Rickettsia akari* has been isolated from the blood of patients and from pools of mites *Allodermanyssus sanguineus* which are parasites of the house mouse *Mus musculus*. One strain of *R. akari* has been recovered from the blood of a wild house mouse trapped on the premises where cases of the disease had occurred. These observations established **the house mouse as the animal reservoir and the house mouse mite as the vector of the disease.**

Wild house mice trapped in nonepidemic area, albino mice, and guinea pigs are easily infected but the monkey is apparently completely resistant. Albino mice show evidence of illness by the sixth day and frequently die between the ninth and thirteenth days after infection. Either brain or spleen may be used for new inoculations. Male guinea pigs inoculated intraperitoneally with blood from patients or tissues from infected mice develop fever of a remittent type after four to six days which lasts for three to five days. Scrotal swelling, without necrosis, occurs about the fourth or fifth day after inoculation. Animals which have recovered are immune to *R. akari* and partially immune to *R. rickettsii*.

The organism grows quite well in both the yolk sac and amniotic sac of embryonated eggs. **They resemble *R. prowazekii* or *R. typhi* in morphology and staining reactions but like *R. rickettsii* grow in the nucleus as well as the cytoplasm of cells.**

Clinical Types of Infection in Man. The name rickettsialpox was suggested by Huebner, Stamps and Armstrong (20) because of the superficial resemblance of the lesions to those of chickenpox.

The onset of the disease is sudden with chills, sweats, headache, backache, and often photophobia. An examination of the skin usually reveals on arm, leg and body a red papule accompanied by enlarged and tender regional lymph nodes, which the patient knows has been present for five to seven days (2). The rash appears three or four days after the onset of fever and is maculopapular, discrete, and erythematous but soon develops vesicles in the summit of the papules. There is no pattern to the number or distribution of the lesions, which may vary from two or three to several hundred and may involve any part of the skin except the palms and soles. The fever rises to 103° to 104° F. and persists for about one week. The vesicular papules dry to a black crust and fall off after five to ten days without leaving scars on the skin. There is a neutropenia with a relative lymphocytosis and occasional monocytosis (13).

The original red papule caused by the bite of the mite evolves into a vesicle, which may resemble the vesicle of vaccinia, and then a black eschar which disappears after three to four weeks. Thus this local lesion is the first to appear and the last to disappear. Biopsy specimens show essentially the same cellular changes which are found in the eschars of scrub typhus and boutonneuse fever (8). No fatal cases have been reported.

No agglutinins to *Proteus OX19, OX2* and *OXK* have been found in the sera of convalescent patients, but the sera fix complement with *R. akari* and give cross-complement-fixing reactions with the soluble antigens of *R. rickettsii*.

Treatment. Treatment with chlortetracycline (39) or with oxytetracycline induces prompt recovery (40).

Prevention. Greenberg and others (14) pointed out that rickettsialpox is a domiciliary disease and believe that excellent mouse harborages are provided by the accumulations of garbage and trash in the large incinerators when they are not fired too frequently. They advised that constant attention be paid to the matter of avoiding the accumulation of rubbish and food scraps, especially in incinerators such as those used in large housing developments.

BOUTONNEUSE FEVER, SOUTH AFRICAN TICK-BITE FEVER, KENYA TICK TYPHUS, ABYSSINIAN TICK TYPHUS, AND INDIAN TICK-BITE FEVER

Genus: *Rickettsia* da Rocha-Lima. Species: *Rickettsia conorii* Brumpt

Recent serologic studies indicate that boutonneuse fever (12), South African tick-bite fever, (10) Kenya tick typhus (7, 16, 17), Indian tick typhus (23), and Abyssinian tick typhus have the same etiologic agent, *R. conorii*, and that the relatively minor differences in clinical and epidemiologic features represent strain rather than species differences (4). The diseases occur in countries adjacent to the Mediterranean Sea, including Spain, France, Italy, Greece, and all of Africa, and in India. The tick vectors vary depending on the locale, and in most instances the animal hosts are unidentified.

Clinical Types of Infection. The course of these infections is very similar with the possible exception of Indian Tick Typhus, which usually does not have an eschar. Following an incubation period of one or two weeks, during which time the eschar develops at the site of the tick bite, the disease begins with the onset of fever to 104° F., headache, chills, and lymphadenopathy. After one or two days of these nonspecific symptoms a discrete maculopapular rash which disappears on pressure covers the body. Later the rash becomes papular and hemorrhagic and cannot be obliterated by pressure. The eschar is present in about 80 per cent of cases as a 2 to 5 mm. wide uicer with a necrotic black center surrounded by an area of erythema. The eschar may be the only manifestation of infection. The disease lasts one to two weeks and has few constitutional symptoms other than prostration; its mortality is about 1 per cent.

Proteus agglutinins and complement-fixing antibodies appear during convalescence. *R. conorii* can be isolated from the blood of patients during the acute phase of the disease by the intraperitoneal inoculation of guinea pigs. Scrotal swelling with adhesion of the tunica vaginalis, fever, and the appearance of extra and intranuclear rickettsia in stained smears are positive tests.

Treatment. These diseases respond to the broad spectrum antibiotics. Improvement can be expected in two to three days.

NORTH QUEENSLAND TICK FEVER

In 1946 Andrews, Bonnin and Williams (1) described a new clinical entity in North Queensland. The disease was mild, resembling in this respect flea-borne murine typhus, but the patients had local eschars and enlarged regional lymph nodes like those seen in the more severe disease known as "scrub typhus." The patient's serums collected during convalescence did not agglutinate *Proteus OXK* but did agglutinate *OX19* and *OX2;* usually the *OX19* titer was higher than the *OX2,* but sometimes the reverse was true (9).

The infection is transmitted by *Ixodes halocytus.* Several strains of rickettsiae have been isolated from patients. They grow quite well in the yolk sac of embryonated eggs and in agar slant tissue cultures, where rickettsiae are found in the nucleus as well as the cytoplasm of cells. The reaction in the scrotum of guinea pigs after intraperitoneal injection resembles that of murine typhus rather than the more severe reaction of American spotted fever.

Because of the mild symptoms, the high *Proteus OX19* titers and the murine typhus-like reaction in the scrotum of guinea pigs (36), **the disease was named North Queensland tick typhus** under the impression that this was a new typhus-like rickettsiosis (11). **However, thorough immunologic and serologic studies (29) in 1948 indicate that this is a new rickettsial disease and a new member of the spotted fever group.**

The infection can be expected to respond to therapy with chlortetracycline and chloromycetin.

SIBERIAN TICK-BITE TYPHUS
(Far Eastern Typhus)

Since 1940 a rickettsial disease has been recognized in central Asia, central Siberia, and in the maritime provinces of the Far East (6). It occurs in the spring and summer months, and the vectors are *D. nuttali, D. silvarium,* and *H. concinna.* The infection is passed transovarially in the tick. Rickettsiae have been isolated from the suslik, a type of ground squirrel (33).

Within two or three days after the bite of an infected tick a local lesion which is accompanied by regional lymphadenitis appears in 75 per cent of cases (34). The local lesion subsides in three to four days and is practically well when the generalized symptoms of headache, fever, and nausea develop. A typical rickettsial rash appears about the third day of fever starting on the upper extremities and extending over the entire surface of the skin. The fever falls by lysis between the eighth and fourteenth day after which convalescence is rapid. The mortality is low or absent.

A positive Weil-Felix test to *Proteus OX19* develops during the first week and may reach a titer of 1:6,400 during the second week. Agglutinins for *Proteus OX2* may appear even earlier than those to *Proteus OX19,* but the maximum titer is never over 1:25 to 1:400. Sometimes agglutinins to *Proteus OXK* are demonstrable in low titers late in the disease.

The tick vector, the course of the disease, and serologic studies by Bell and Stoenner (4) place this organism in the spotted fever group but as a distinct entity. There is, however, a one-way cross-reaction with the maculatum rickettsia.

MACULATUM DISEASE

Maculatum disease is an experimental rickettsial disease in guinea pigs induced by the injection of a new species of rickettsia isolated from the cattle tick *Amblyomma maculatum.* The name, maculatum disease, was introduced by Parker, Kohls, Cox, and Davis (31) who studied the disease in 1939. Infected ticks have been found in Texas, Georgia and Mississippi, but the ticks which transmit Rocky Mountain spotted fever in these areas do not harbor the maculatum rickettsiae and vice versa.

The disease does not occur, or has not been recognized, in man or cattle.

A mild febrile infection, with scrotal swelling but no necrosis, is produced in male guinea pigs. Occasionally the scrotum swells in the absence of fever, but the animals never die of the infection. After recovery they are immune to the maculatum disease and have varying degrees of resistance to other rickettsia. Guinea pigs vaccinated against spotted fever are not protected from maculatum disease.

The serologic studies of Lackman and Parker (25) and Lackman and Gerloff (26) in 1949 show that this rickettsia is related antigenically to Rocky Mountain spotted fever but differs from all other known members of the spotted fever group.

REFERENCES

1. Andrews, R., and others. M. J. Australia, 2:251, 1946.
2. Barker, L. P. J.A.M.A., 141:1119, 1949.
3. Bell, E. J., and Pickens, E. G. J. Immunol., 70:461, 1953.
4. ———— and Stoenner, H. G. J. Immunol., 84:171, 1960.
5. Cox, H. R. Pub. Health Rep., 54:1070, 1939.
6. ———— Bacterial and Mycotic Infections of Man, Philadelphia, J. B. Lippincott Co., 1948, p. 493.
7. Craddock, A. L. East African M. J., 36:580, 1959.
8. Dolgopol, V. B. Am. J. Path., 24:119, 1948.
9. Editorial: North Queensland tick typhus, Bull. U.S. Army M. Dept., 7:4, 1947.
10. Freyche, M. J., and Deutschman, Z. W. H. O. Rep., 3:161, 1950.
11. Funder, J. F., and Jackson, A. V. M. J. Australia, 2:258, 1946.
12. Golinevitch, H. Arch. Inst. Pasteur, 37:13, 1960.
13. Greenberg, M. Am. J. Med., 4:866, 1948.
14. ———— and others. Am. J. Pub. Health, 37: 860, 1947.
15. Harrell, G. T. Medicine, 28:333, 1949.
16. Heisch, R. B., and others. East African M. J., 34:459, 1957.
17. ———— and Harvey, A. E. C. East African M. J., 36:116, 1959.
18. Holmes, W. H. Bacillary and Rickettsial Infections. New York, Macmillan Co., 1940.
19. Huebner, R. J. Bact. Rev., 14:245, 1950.
20. ———— and others. Pub. Health Rep., 61: 1605, 1946.
21. Jackson, E. B., and others. Am. J. Hyg., 66: 301, 1957.
22. Joint OIHP/WHO study-group on African Rickettsioses, World Health Organization, Technical Reports Series, No. 23, Geneva, World Health Organization, 1950.
23. Kalra, S. L. Indian J. M. Res., 47:477, 1959.
24. King, W. W. Pub. Health Rep., 21:863, 1906.
25. Lackman, D. B., and Parker, R. R. Pub. Health Rep., 63:1624, 1948.
26. ———— and Gerloff, R. K. Pub. Health Rep., 64:1342, 1949.
27. ———— and Gerloff, R. K. Pub. Health Lab., 11:97, 1953.
28. ———— and Pickens, E. G. Bact. Proc., page 51, 1953.
29. Lundford, C. G., and Cook, I. M. J. Australia, 1:463, 1957.
30. Miller, J. K. Ann. Int. Med., 33:1398, 1950.
31. Parker, R. R., and others. Pub. Health Reports, 66:455, 1951.
32. Peterson, J. C., and others. J. Pediat., 30: 494, 1947.
33. Petjaev, E. D. Trop. Dis. Bull., 44:515, 1947.
34. Plotz, H., and others. Proc. Soc. Exper. Biol. & Med., 55:173, 1944.
35. ———— First Inter-American Congress on Typhus Fever, Mexico City, 1945.
36. ———— M. J. Australia, 1946, 2:263, 1946.
37. Howard Taylor Ricketts, 1870-1910, Chicago, University of Chicago Press, 1911, p. 333.
38. Ricketts, H. T. J.A.M.A., 47:33, 358, 1906.
39. Rose, H. M. Am. J. Med., 9:300, 1950.
40. ———— Practice of Medicine, Meakins, ed., 6th ed., St. Louis, C. V. Mosby Co., 1956, p. 460.
41. Shankman, B. New York State J. Med., 46: 2156, 1946.

42. Shepard, C. C., and Goldwasser, R. A. Am. J. Hyg., 72:120, 1960.
43. Smadel, J. E. Arch. Int. Med., 51:421, 1959.
44. Spencer, R. R., and Parker, R. R. Pub. Health Rep., 38:333, 1923.
45. Steinhaus, E. A. Insect Microbiology, Ithaca, New York, Comstock Publishing Company, 1946.
46. Sussman, L. N. New York Med., 2:27, 1946.

47. Topping, N. H. Pub. Health Rep., 54:1143, 1939, 56:1699, 1941; 58:757, 1943.
48. Travassos, J. Studies on Rickettsial Diseases in Brazil. VI Dept. of State, U.S. Gov. Printing Office, Washington, D.C., 1948.
49. Wilder, R. M. Arch. Path., 49:479, 1950.
50. Zdrodovskii, P. F., and Golinevich, E. M. in Uchenie o rikkelsiakh i rikketsiozakh, Medgiz, Moscow, 1956.

58

Tsutsugamushi Rickettsioses

(Scrub Typhus Mite-Borne Typhus, Japanese River Fever, Tropical Typhus)

Family: *Rickettsiaceae* Pinkerton. Genus: *Rickettsia* da Rocha-Lima. Species: *Rickettsia tsutsugamushi* (Hayashi) Ogata

Tsutsuga signifies disease and *mushi* means mite. Several species of trombiculid mites (chiggers) spread the disease to man from infected rodents, particularly field moles. There is an eschar at the site of the mite bite and serologically the organisms are distinct from both the typhus and spotted fever rickettsia; thus the name "typhus" should not imply any relation of this organism, *R. tsutsugamushi,* to the classical typhus rickettsia. This disease is very widespread in the Orient (Japan, China, and all of southern and southeastern Asia, including India) and in most South Pacific Islands, including Australia. About 6,000 cases appeared in U.S. troops in these areas in World War II. These cases antedated the specific antibiotic therapy, but a recent follow-up of 16 cases which had severe or grave scrub typhus and did not die showed no evidence of residual damage from the disease (4). Chloramphenicol has reduced the mortality from a previous 5 to 35 per cent to less than 1 per cent and shortened the febrile period from three weeks to two days.

Morphology and Staining. In morphology and staining *R. tsutsugamushi* resembles the other rickettsiae except that it is somewhat less pleomorphic, showing usually **diplococcal forms or short rods with dark-staining bipolar bodies.**

Cultural Characteristics. *R. tsutsugamushi* grows well in the yolk sac of the embryonated chicken egg and in various cell types in tissue culture (3, 7). Tissue cultured cells can be cleared of infection by treatment with chloramphenicol (8). The multiplication of the Rickettsia in mouse M. B. III cells in culture (2) is shown in Figure 1. The rickettsia grow in the cell cytoplasm. Figure 2 is an electron micrograph of a thin section of *R. tsutsugamushi.*

Antigenic Structure. There are many heterologous antigenic types (11), with only a few showing partial cross-immunity in protection tests. There is no cross-immunity with other known kinds of rickettsia.

Metabolites. A specific **endotoxin** is produced by some strains as they grow in embryonated eggs (12). **The antitoxin against this toxin is strain-specific;** it is absent

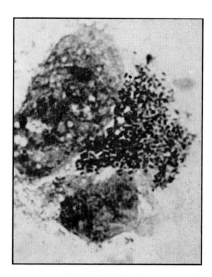

Fig. 1. *Rickettsia tsutsugamushi.* MB III cell with many organisms 72 hours after infection. × 1,275. (From Bozeman, Hopps, Danauskas, Jackson, and Smadel. *J. Immunol.,* 76:475, 1956.)

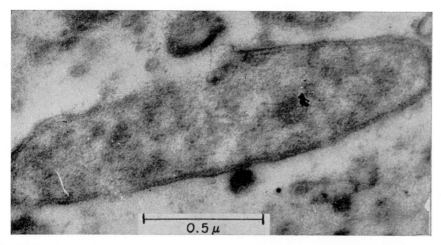

Fig. 2. Section of *R. tsutsugamushi* in a rat fibroblast cell. Limiting membranes surround the organism except for the torn portion. (From Schaechter and others. *J. Bact.*, 74:822, 1957.)

from serums of animals convalescent from epidemic and murine typhus and absent also from the serums of animals immune to other strains of *R. tsutsugamushi,* although such serums may contain neutralizing and complement-fixing antibodies against their homologous organisms.

Spontaneous Disease in Animals. Not much is known about the spontaneous disease in rodents. The larvae of *Trombicula akamushi* transmit the disease in Japan and those of *T. deliensis* in New Guinea and Burma.

The rickettsia *R. tsutsugamushi* can be maintained by transovarial passage, but the usual cycle involves mites and a vertebrate host. The potential capacity of other mites as vectors is discussed in the monograph of Johnson and Wharton (10).

Experimental Disease in Laboratory Animals. Rats, guinea pigs, rabbits, gerbils, and monkeys are all susceptible to experimental infection, but the animal of choice is the white mouse. Mice may be inoculated by the intranasal (6), subcutaneous, intravenous, or intraperitoneal routes (5).

There is marked variation in virulence even of freshly isolated strains, and some infect mice only occasionally, regardless of the dose or route of inoculation.

Clinical Types of Infection in Man. The incubation period is usually 7 to 14 days but may be prolonged to 21 days. About 60 per cent of patients develop a **character-istic eschar** where they have been bitten by the infected mites. This lesion is found most often on the ankles and legs but may be present on any part of the body. There is some generalized enlargement of the lymph nodes, with those nearest the eschar being the largest.

The onset of symptoms occurs some days after the appearance of the local lesion and may be gradual and insidious but is more often sudden and violent, with chills, headache, orbital pain, severe malaise, vomiting, and prostration. There is a step-like rise in the temperature while the pulse rate remains relatively low.

A characteristic red macular, or maculopapular rash may appear between the fifth and eighth day over the trunk and spread to the arms and legs. The rash may be present in as few as 7 per cent or as many as 85 per cent of patients and usually disappears after a few days without leaving scars. The fatalities occur about the end of the second week and are attributable in about equal numbers to circulation failure, encephalitis, and secondary bacterial pneumonia. The fever usually subsides during the third week, after which convalescence is slow, often being prolonged for months (1).

The **mortality** varies with the age of the patient, the locality and possibly other factors. It is often as low as 3 per cent in children and as high as 44 per cent in individuals over 50 years of age. The mortality in American soldiers varied from 0 to 25 per cent (9).

Immunologic Response. Agglutinins to *Proteus OXK* **usually appear about the end of the second week of the disease but not in very high titers.** Titers above 1:160 are diagnostic, but rising titers in serial samples of serums may be diagnostic even though the final titer is less than 1:160. Permanent immunity may develop for the particular strain which infected the patient while the individual remains susceptible to other strains. **There is no cross-immunity between tsutsugamushi fever and the other rickettsioses.**

Biologic Products. Antigens for complement-fixation and agglutinin tests may be obtained from rickettsiae grown in the yolk sac or in agar tissue cultures; or they may be prepared by the method of Fulton and Joyner (6) from the lungs of infected cotton rats. The most effective vaccines are made from the rickettsiae grown by the agar-tissue-culture method.

Treatment. There is no specific serum therapy. Treatment with chlortetracycline, oxytetracycline, and chloramphenicol is usually successful. Smadel and his associates (15) had no deaths in 69 consecutive patients treated with chloramphenicol in an area where the usual death rate was 5 to 7 per cent.

Prevention. Clothing designed to prevent access of mites to the skin should be worn in infected areas (10). The clothing can be made much more protective if treated with the **insect repellent dimethylphthalate** (16).

Smadel and his coworkers have shown that prophylactic oral doses of chloramphenicol (13, 14) will prevent the development of symptoms after spontaneous infections. The infection is suppressed, not cured, and symptoms appear when the drug is discontinued. Intermittent treatment, however, which allows the development of symptoms in the drug free intervals, does result in cure. Formalized vaccines made from tissue cultures or from yolk sac rickettsia have failed to protect. Immunization can be accomplished if living virulent organisms are injected and intermittent treatment with chloramphenicol is given after symptoms appear (15).

REFERENCES

1. Blake, F. G., and others. Am. J. Hyg., 41: 243, 1945.
2. Bozeman, F. M., and others. J. Immunol., 76:475, 1956.
3. Cohen, Z. A., and others. J. Exper. Med., 109:271, 1959.
4. Eisom, K. A., and others. Ann. Int. Med., 55:784, 1960.
5. Fletcher, W., and others. Part II, Tr. Roy. Soc. Trop. Med. & Hyg., 23:57, 1929.
6. Fulton, F., and Joyner, L. Lancet, 2:729, 1945.
7. Hopps, H. E., and others. J. Immunol., 82: 161, 1959.
8. ———. J. Immunol., 82:172, 1959.
9. Irons, E. N., and Armstrong, H. E. Ann. Int. Med., 26:201, 1947.
10. Johnson, D. H., and Wharton, G. W. U.S. Nav. M. Bull., 46:459, 1946.
11. Shishido, A., and others. Jap. J. M. Sc. Biol., 12:391, 1959.
12. Smadel, J. E., and others. Proc. Soc. Exper. Biol. & Med., 62:138, 1946.
13. ——— and others. J. Clin. Investigation, 28:1196, 1949.
14. ——— and others. Am. J. Hyg., 51:216, 229, 1950.
15. ——— Am. J. Med., 17:246, 1954.
16. Welt, L. G. Am. J. Trop. Med., 27:221, 1947.

59

Q Fever

Family: *Rickettsiaceae* Pinkerton. Genus: *Coxiella* Philip. Species: *Coxiella burnetii* (Derrick) Philip

This rickettsiosis presents certain striking contrasts to those discussed in the preceding chapters. The disease is only occasionally transmitted to man by the bite of an arthropod vector, there is no skin rash, and agglutinins to proteus organisms fail to appear.

The infection may be acquired from the ingestion of raw milk (28) or by the inhalation of dust from infected dairy barns and lambing sheds (24). To emphasize the difference of this organism from other rickettsia, a new genus and species name is given, *Coxiella burnetii* (see below).

About 100 cases of Q fever have been reported from California each year from 1952 to 1955 (45). Recent developments suggest that the infection may be spreading eastward. Kitze (22) in Wisconsin and Reed and Wentworth (40) in Ohio have found large numbers of cattle infected with *C. burnetii*. These findings and others indicate that the normal movement of cattle will continue to spread the infection (26). Increasing infection should appear in wool sorters and people who process domestic animal materials and two such cases have recently been reported: a woman who is employed as a comber of goat hair in Philadelphia (43), and a butcher in Baltimore (33). These and other recent studies show that Q fever not only is more widespread in the United States than previously thought but now is present in 35 states and certain to spread further (6, 27, 49).

This rickettsiosis was recognized by Derrick (15) of Brisbane, Australia in 1935 and given the name "Q" fever for "query" and not because it was discovered in Queensland as many subsequent writers have assumed (17).

The etiologic agent was isolated by the Australian workers from both the blood and urine of patients and named *Rickettsia burnetii*. In 1938 Davis and Cox (13) reported the isolation of a rickettsia from the wood tick *Dermacentor andersoni* in Montana. Since later studies showed that rickettsia was filterable, the name *Rickettsia diaporica* was suggested (12). The identity of *R. burnetii* and *R. diaporica* was established by the work of Dyer (16) in this country and Burnet and Freeman (7, 8) and others in Australia (46). Finally, because of the resistance of this organism to physical (19) and chemical agents and other characteristics a new generic name *Coxiella*, after H. L. Cox, was created and the etiologic agent of Q fever was renamed *Coxiella burnetii* (36).

Morphology and Staining. *C. burnetii* is very pleomorphic; it usually appears as a bipolar rod 0.25 μ to 0.5 μ long but varying from large forms resembling small bacteria to minute granules which pass Berkefeld N filters or collodion membranes with pore diameters of 500 μ. It resembles the other rickettsiae in staining reactions and in pictures made with the electron microscope (Figs. 1, 2).

Cultural Characteristics. *C. burnetii* grows well in the yolk sac of embryonated eggs and in tissue cultures of strain "L" mouse fibroblasts and chicken fibroblasts (42). Purification of the organisms can be accomplished by density gradient centrifugation (41) and by cellulose exchange column

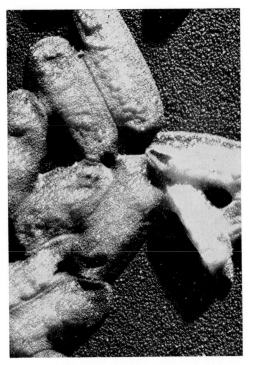

Fig. 1. *C. burnetii* purified by density-gradient sedimentation. × 42,000. (From Ribi and Hoyer. *J. Immunol.,* 85:314, 1960.)

sage has been demonstrated in some species and is suspected in all. There is a varied animal reservoir, which includes the bandicoots in Australia and sheep, goats, and cows in this and other countries. The animals suffer little inconvenience from the infection and do not carry the rickettsiae very long in their blood; however, the udders of sheep (21), cows, and goats remain infected for years, and milk and milk products become an important means of transmission (20, 23). Placentas of infected animals are heavily contaminated with *C. burnetii.*

Experimental Infection in Laboratory Animals. Monkeys, mice, and cows can be infected with *C. burnetii,* but the animal of choice is the guinea pig. Blood drawn from patients during the febrile period, sputum, urine, spinal fluid, or tissues removed at necropsy can be injected intraperitoneally in guinea pigs. When a febrile response appears, the animals are sacrificed, and the enlarged spleen is emulsified and reinoculated

(18). *C. burnetii* has been shown to possess several enzyme systems (11), folic acid (29) and to synthesize serine (34).

Antigenic Structure. All strains of *C. burnetii* are antigenically identical but vary considerably in virulence. The complement-fixation test is a standard procedure (2), although it may be replaced to some extent by the capillary agglutination test (25), which is cheaper, easier to perform, and more sensitive.

C. burnetii is unique among rickettsia in that treatment of aqueous suspensions of the organism with ethyl ether does not cause the release of soluble antigens (35). Certain antigenic fractions contribute to the hypersensitivity reactions seen with the vaccine (1).

Spontaneous Disease in Animals. Various species of ticks belonging to the family *Ixodidae* and a few of the family *Argosidae* are involved in the maintenance of *C. burnetii* in nature (46). Transovarial pas-

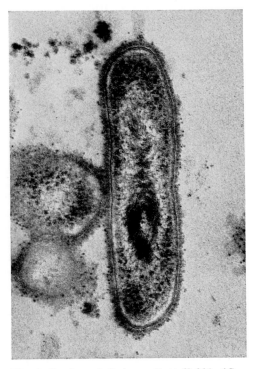

Fig. 2. Section of *C. burnetii.* × 63,000. (Courtesy of Drs. Robert L. Anacker and Kazue Fukushi.)

in other guinea pigs. Rickettsia are rarely seen in the splenic tissue until after several passages. Guinea pigs die of the infection if the dose is sufficiently large, but those which recover have complement-fixing antibodies in their sera and resist reinoculation with homologous and heterologous strains. **There is no cross-immunity between** C. burnetii **and the other rickettsiae.**

Isolation experiments should not be attempted in routine laboratories because of the danger of infection not only for those immediately in contact with the animals but for the entire laboratory personnel. **The complement-fixation test introduced by Bengtson in 1941** (3, 4) **is a reliable diagnostic method** (44).

Clinical Types of Infection in Man. Q fever is an acute febrile disease, with malaise and headache being prominent symptoms. The mild cough, generalized muscle aches, and patchy infiltration of the lungs may suggest mild influenza or primary atypical pneumonia (14). There are no skin lesions, and the disease is rarely fatal. Autopsy of fatal cases shows bronchopneumonia as the major finding. This infection may simulate other diseases, and one case suggested acute lymphoma (39). Hepatic involvement is not uncommon, simulating a granulomatous process (38).

Antigenic Response. Patients do not develop proteus agglutinins, but the sensitive capillary agglutinin test of Luoto is positive during convalescence (25). Complement-fixing antibodies in a titer of more than 1:20 are diagnostic.

Transmission. Q fever is a **place** disease contracted by inhalation of dried tick products or other material contaminated by C. burnetii. Ingestion of unpasteurized contaminated milk accounts for some infections, but the disease is rarely transmitted from patient to patient or by tick bites.

Treatment. Chloramphenicol and broad-spectrum antibiotics are effective.

Prevention. Pasteurization of milk is certainly indicated, but more important methods must be found to control air contamination by infected materials. Vaccines have been developed from formalized suspensions (5) and with soluble antigens separated by ultrasonic vibration (10).

TRENCH FEVER

Family: *Rickettsiaceae* Pinkerton. Genus: *Rickettsia* da Rocha-Lima. Species: *Rickettsia quintana* Schmincke

This disease was unknown until 1915. The development of trench warfare in World War I forced millions of soldiers to live under conditions favorable to the spread of lice. Most of the armies of both sides became infested with these arthropods. The disease was believed to have originated in Russia but soon spread to all the armies, infecting at least 1,000,000 men. With the exception of influenza, trench fever was the most prevalent disease in World War I. There were no deaths, and the only available pathologic material was biopsies of the skin lesions. These showed inflammation in the walls of the small blood vessels resembling those seen in spotted fever. Wolbach (50) stained rickettsial-like bodies in the cytoplasm of endothelial cells found in the inflamed areas.

The clinical picture was dramatic. The onset was sudden with fever, chilly sensations, headaches, dizziness, postorbital pain, nystagmus, conjunctivitis, and severe pains in the back and legs. The pulse was rapid, the spleen became enlarged, and several crops of erythematous macules or papules appeared over the skin of the chest, abdomen, and back. About one half of the patients had only one febrile attack while the other half had from one to eight relapses. Most patients recovered in five to six weeks, but some were ill for several months and a few for more than one year (48).

There are no specific serologic tests, and the only method by which the organism can be isolated is to feed lice on the patient. Later a suspension of the lice is inoculated into monkeys. Treatment with chloramphenicol is effective (30). The infection is rarely fatal.

Epidemiologic investigations incriminated the body louse, *Pediculus humanis,* var. *corporis.* Laboratory-reared lice, when fed on patients, developed rickettsial-like bodies in the cells of their gut, and these same bodies appeared in their feces. The lice were not injured by the infection, which persisted for the remainder of the arthropod's life. The infection, however, was not transmitted to the larvae through the egg. Human volunteers developed typical trench fever 14 to 30 days after being bitten by an infected louse. The immunity acquired from an infection persisted for a period of months after which the patient was susceptible to a new infection (9, 47).

The disease could not be transmitted to any of the ordinary laboratory animals.

Trench fever disappeared after World War I, only to reappear in Yugoslavia near the end of World War II. Mooser and his associates (31, 32) established strains of *R. quintana* in laboratory-reared lice and have maintained them by passage from louse to louse by either rectal injections or intracelomic injections. Mooser transmitted the infection to nine human volunteers by the bite of the infected lice. Accidental infections occurred in a bacteriologist and two members of his family during this period of experimentation. The louse is not infectious until five to 10 days after feeding on a patient.

OTHER RICKETTSIOSES

In the seventh edition of Bergey's Manual Philip (37) has assigned the organism found in rickettsial diseases of animals to the tribe *Ehrlichieae* and distributed them among three genera: (1) *Ehrlichia,* (2) *Cowdria,* and (3) *Neorickettsia.*

Organisms resembling *Rickettsia* but confined to insects have been classified in the tribe *Wolbachieae,* which includes three genera: (1) *Wolbachia,* (2) *Symbiotes* gen. nov., and (3) *Rickettsiella* gen. nov. These first two genera are very commonly found in insects and apparently do no harm to the host. The genera *Rickettsiella* is pathogenic for insects, and *Rickettsiella papilliae* is the etiologic agent of blue disease of beetle larvae (37).

REFERENCES

1. Anacher, R. L., and others. J. Immunol., 89: 145, 1962.
2. Berge, T. O., and Lennette, E. H. Am. J. Hyg., 57:125, 1953; 57:144, 1953.
3. Bengtson, I. A. Proc. Soc. Exper. Biol. & Med., 46:665, 1941.
4. —— Pub. Health Rep., 1941, 56:327, 1941.
5. Berman, S., and others. J. Bact., 81:749, 1961.
6. Braun, J. L. Pub. Health Rep., 77:171, 1962.
7. Burnet, F. M., and Freeman, M. M. J. Australia, 1:296, 1938.
8. —— and Freeman, M. M. J. Australia, 2:887, 1939.
9. Byam, W., and Lloyd, L. L. Proc. Roy. Soc. Med., Section on Epidemiology and State Medicine, 13:1, 1919.
10. Colter, J. S., and others. J. Immunol., 76: 270, 1956.
11. Consigli, R. A., and others. Bact. Proc., 183-184, 1960.
12. Cox, H. R., and Bell, E. J. Pub. Health Rep., 54:2171, 1939; 55:110, 1940.
13. Davis, G. E., and Cox, H. R. Pub. Health Rep., 53:2259, 1938.
14. Denlinger, R. B. Ann. Int. Med., 30:510, 1949.
15. Derrick, E. H. M. J. Australia, 2:281, 1937.
16. Dyer, R. E. Pub. Health Rep., 54:1229, 1939.
17. —— Am. J. Pub. Health, 39:471, 1949.
18. Hoyer, B. H., and others. Science, 127:859, 1958.
19. Huebner, R. J., and others. Pub. Health Rep., 64:499, 1949.
20. Jellison, W. L., and others. Pub. Health Rep., 63:1712, 1948.
21. —— and others. Pub. Health Rep., 65: 395, 1950.
22. Kitze, L. Am. J. Hyg., 65:239, 1957.
23. Lennette, E. H. Practice of Medicine, ed. Meakins, St. Louis, C. V. Mosby Co., 1956, p. 469.
24. Luoto, L., and Huebner, R. J. Pub. Health Rep., 65:541, 1951.
25. —— J. Immunol., 71:226, 1953; 77:294, 1956.
26. —— Am. J. of Pub. Health, 49:334, 1959.
27. —— Pub. Health Rep., 75:135, 1960.
28. Marmion, B. P., and Stoker, M. G. P. Brit. M. J., 2:809, 1958.
29. Mattheis, M. S., and others. J. Bact., 85:37, 1963.
30. Mooser, H., and Weyer, F. Proc. Soc. Exper. Biol. and Med., 83:699, 1953.
31. —— and others. Schweiz. Zeit. f. allg. Path. v. Bakt., 12:476, 1949.
32. —— and others. Schweiz. Zeit. f. allg. Path. v. Bakt., 11:513, 1948.
33. Morbidity and Mortality Weekly Reports. 7: 19, 1958.
34. Myers, W. F., and Paretsky, D. J. Bact., 82: 761, 1961.
35. Ormster, R. A., and others. J. Immunol., 88: 741, 1962.
36. Philip, C. B. Am. J. Hyg., 37:301, 1943.
37. —— Canad. J. Microbiol., 2:261, 1956.
38. Picchi, J., and others. Ann. Int. Med., 53: 1065, 1960.
39. Ramos, H. S., and others. Ann. Int. Med., 47:1030, 1957.
40. Reed, C. F., and Wentworth, B. B. J. Am. Vet. M. A., 130:458, 1957.
41. Ribi, E., and Hoyer, B. H. J. Immunol., 85: 314, 1960.
42. Roberts, A. N., and Downs, C. M. J. Bact., 77:194, 1959.
43. Shuman, C. R., and Galloway, J. A. Penn. Med. J., 61:1376, 1958.
44. Smadel, J. E. Diagnosis of Viral and Rickettsial Infections, New York, Columbia University Press, 1949, p. 117.
45. —— Ann. Int. Med., 51:421, 1959.
46. Smith, D. J. W. Australian J. Exper. Biol. & Med., 18:103, 1940; 19:133, 1941; 20:213, 1942.
47. Strong, R. P., and others. Trench Fever, Report of Commission, Medical Research Committee, American Red Cross, London, University Press, 1918.
48. Swift, H. F. Trench Fever, Harvey Lect., Series XV, 1919-1920, Philadelphia, Lippincott Co., p. 58.
49. Weiner, D., and others. Pub. Health Rep., 76:257, 1961.
50. Wolbach, S. B. The Rickettsial Disease, Boston, Harvard University Press, 1940.

60

The Psittacosis Group of Organisms or Bedsonia

(Psittacosis, Lymphogranuloma Venereum, Trachoma, Inclusion Conjunctivitis)

Family: *Chlamydiaceae*

The recent studies of the chemistry of the cell wall, electron microscopy of infected cells, the metabolism of the purified particles, and the action of antibiotics **place these organisms with the bacteria** albeit as a group having rather specialized properties which go along with obligate intracellular parasitism. The previous designations of these organisms as "viruses" or "large viruses" is untenable and confusing. The scientific name adopted by Bergey, *Chlamydiaceae,* has not been received with enthusiasm. The question, then, is raised as to what to call these organisms. The usual designation is that of the "Psittacosis group." There are many reasons, however, to adopt the name *Bedsonia,* suggested by Meyer in honor of Sir Samuel Bedson who did much pioneer work in this field. The term *Bedsonia* would compare favorably with *Rickettsia* and is easily pronounced. We are in agreement with this completely and will use both the terms "bedsonia" and "psittacosis group" to refer to these organisms.

The rickettsia and bedsonia, although having a common, remote bacterial ancestor have evolved separately and are quite distinct from each other. The most obvious distinction is that of the insect vector present in the life cycle of all rickettsia and absent in bedsonia. There are other differences. The rickettsia have a high-energy-producing mechanism not found in any bedsonia—namely, the ability to aerobically oxidize glutamate with the generation of ATP (13). Serologically, the bedsonia are unrelated to the rickettsia, but all of the psittacosis group have certain common antigens. One antigen induces a delayed tuberculin-like skin allergy, another feature not present in rickettsia.

In the psittacosis group per se there are some differences which allow these organisms to be divided tentatively into two subgroups (Table 1).

Morphology and Staining. The psittacosis group of organisms show great variation in the size of individual particles from 200 mμ to over a micron. The individual

Table 1. Physiologic Subgroups within the Psittacosis Group

CHARACTER	PHYSIOLOGICAL GROUP	
	A (Trachoma, inclusion conjunctivitis, lymphogranuloma venereum, mouse and hamster pneumonitis)	B (Psittacosis, human pneumonitis, mouse pneumonitis, feline pneumonitis, meningo pneumonitis)
INCLUSION		
Morphology	rigid	diffuse
Carbohydrate matrix	+	0
DRUG SUSCEPTIBILITY		
Sulfanilamide	+++	0
d-Cycloserine	+++	+

Gordon, F. B., and Quan, A. L. *Bact. Proc.,* p. 148, 1962.

813

particles have a dense center and double-walled limiting membrane. Purified preparations of organisms can be divided into large and small particle types (Fig. 1), but chemical analysis indicates that the composition of both types is similar (119). Electron microscopy (53, 66, 67, 93) reveals that the small particles have a dense central body but the large bodies do not. This observation, correlated with the chemical analysis of both types of particles, suggests that one particle may be transformed into another. The small particle is probably the stable infective form and the large particle a transitional vegetative form. The particles divide by binary fission (7, 118). Cell infection probably occurs within an hour after addition of the organism, and multiplication begins in 12 to 15 hours. As the log phase of growth begins, organisms lie in cytoplasmic vesicles which eventually constitute the large (2-12 μ) basophilic cell inclusions characteristic of the bedsonia.

Cultivation. The organisms of psittacosis have been propagated in eggs for years

(10, 16, 62, 103, 105). Trachoma virus was isolated and grown in the egg by T'ang (120) in 1957 and confirmed by others (25, 49). More recently it has been grown in chick embryo explants and tissue cultures of various cell types (38, 40, 99). The virus of inclusion conjunctivitis has also been grown in embryonated eggs (50, 59).

One feature of the bedsonia infections is **latency** in which the organism may persist in infected cells for long periods without apparent damage to the host cell (6, 29, 45). The latent state appears to involve an interruption in the maturation phase of the organism after it has entered the cell. This can be accomplished readily by exposing the cells to various antibiotics or drugs which affect bedsonia maturation or by nutritional deficiencies (89). The latent state may be reversed and the infection reactivated by correcting the deficiency or by adding an antagonist, such as penicillinase, to the antibiotic.

Metabolic Properties and Effects of Antibiotics. Various antibiotics inactivate bed-

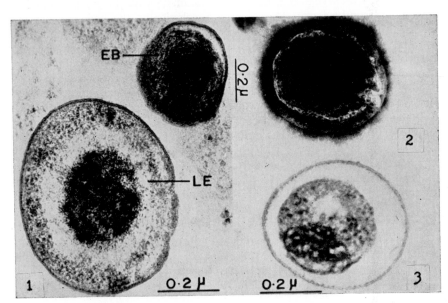

Fig. 1. An intermediate form (LE) seen in sections of yolk sac 72 hours after infection with a trachoma strain ("Mita"). A nucleoid is in the center. A mature elementary body (EB) in the right upper corner of the same preparation suggests a filamentous arrangement of the nucleoid. × 90,000.

Fig. 2. A purified elementary body of negative staining technic. × 75,000.

Fig. 3. An elementary body in methacrylate section. The limiting membrane is clearly separated from the remainder of the structure. × 100,000.

(Courtesy of Professor Yukihiko Mitsui, Tokushima University School of Medicine.)

sonia at different levels of activity, but streptomycin is effective on both maturing and fully formed particles (100). Chlortetracycline and tylosin tartrate interrupt the maturation process of the organism and also inactivate extracellular particles (100). Sulfonamides divide the bedsonia into two groups (Table 1) (135) and prevent multiplication of group A organisms without killing them. Sulfa probably interferes with the endogenous synthesis of folic acid by the drug-sensitive organisms (20, 21). Penicillin and D-cycloserine interfere with cell-wall synthesis (55, 132). Under penicillin bedsonia became large irregularly shaped bodies (spheroplasts) which, after treatment with penicillinase, are fully infective (90). The inhibition effect of D-cycloserine (19) is due to the inhibition of the D-alanine dipeptide which is a portion of the cell-wall mucopeptide. Since this dipeptide is a well-demonstrated major component of bacterial cell walls, the action of D-cycloserine is further evidence of the homology of the bacteria and the bedsonia.

Since a major and distinctive component of bacterial cell walls is muramic acid, demonstrations of this compound in the psittacosis group would be very significant. The identification of muramic acid from the organisms of psittacosis, trachoma, feline pneumonitis, and mouse pneumonitis has been reported by Allison and Perkins (2, 96) and by Jenkins (57).

The cell-wall analysis by Jenkins (57) showed small amounts of carbohydrate, large amounts of lipid, and various amino acids, including lysine. Diaminopimelic acid was not present. The main pathway of lysine synthesis in bacteria is via diaminopimelic acid. The bedsonia do not contain DAP but do have DAP carboxylase (27).

Serology. Most of the important antigens of the bedsonia reside in the cell wall, as is the case with bacteria (58, 109). These organisms have an endotoxin-like substance which, as is also true of the rickettsia, are like exotoxins in that they are highly specific and can be neutralized by specific antitoxins (73, 104). Antisera will neutralize both the toxic and infective properties. Adsorption of antiserum with cell-wall fractions removes both toxic and infective neutralizing proper-

ties. Cell wall fractions act as specific antigens in the complement-fixation test.

The heat-stable, ether-extractable, complement-fixing antigen is **group-specific** and cannot be used for identification of specific organisms. In addition to the tests above, the fluorescent antibody technic has been adapted to psittacosis, lymphogranuloma, and trachoma organisms (91). Both microscopic and capillary tube agglutination tests have been described (74). Patients convalescent from psittacosis group infections form only small amounts of neutralizing and antitoxin antibody, so that clinical tests for these antibodies are not practical.

PSITTACOSIS—ORNITHOSIS

(Parrot Fever)

Order: *Rickettsiales.* Family: *Chlamydiaceae* Rake. Genus: *Miyagawanella* Brumpt. Type Species: *Miyagawanella lymphogranulomatis* Brumpt. Species: *Miyagawanella psittacii* (Lillie) Moshkovsky, *Miyagawanella ornithosis* Rake

A severe febrile disease obviously contracted from parrots was recognized in Switzerland, France, and Germany in the last two decades of the nineteenth century (106). World-wide interest in this infection dates from 1929-30, when over 700 cases were found in 12 different countries (81) including the United States. Psittacosis causes endemic disease in the parrots of South America (4, 95, 110), in parrots and parakeets of Australia (17), and in parrot and parakeet aviaries in this country. The ornithosis organism has been found in pigeons (113), canaries, finches, sparrows, ducks, chickens, petrels (46), herring gulls (98), willets, and nonpsittacine birds (80). Turkeys have a very virulent type of psittacosis which can infect men (9, 75, 80). Infection has been discovered in the opossum (108); in cattle (79, 140); a pneumonitis in sheep (76); and enzootic abortion of ewes (84, 115). The spread of these agents to cattle and other animals was reviewed by Gerloff and Lackman (39).

Between 1945 and 1951 an average of 28 cases of psittacosis per year was reported. Since that time there has been a rapid increase in reported cases, reaching a total of 444 in 1954 (5a). Some of the increase can be attributed to the relaxation of quarantine regulations for psittacine birds, and some to the increased incidence of infections from turkeys; the latter accounting for nearly one-half of the cases found in 1954. The source of the infection in young children, reported from Palestine in 1956, has not been determined (30).

Since 1954 there has been a steady decline in the number of cases of psittacosis in the United States, from 563 cases (3 deaths) in 1954 to 79 cases (no deaths) in 1962. The total number of cases per year since 1958 has been less than 200 (88).

Spontaneous Disease in Animals. In parrots the spontaneous disease is characterized by apathy, shivering weakness, diarrhea, and respiratory symptoms. At necropsy, multiple areas of necrosis are found in the liver and spleen and occasionally in the lungs. Inapparent or subclinical infections do occur in birds of the psittacine group and even more frequently in nonpsittacine birds, leaving healthy carriers of the organism (80). Inapparent carriers occur less frequently in mammalian infections.

Experimental Infection in Laboratory Animals. The white mouse is the most susceptible laboratory animal and may be infected by the intraperitoneal, intravenous, subcutaneous, intranasal, and intracerebral routes or by feeding. The mouse should be inoculated with sputum, blood, or tissues from patients suspected of having this type of infection (82). The guinea pig has a low-grade febrile response after the intraperitoneal injection of most strains of psittacosis organism but develops a rapidly fatal infection when injected by any route with the human strains of the Louisiana (32) or California types of the human psittacosis organism (82).

Clinical Types of Infection in Man. The classic picture of psittacosis or ornithosis in man is characterized by an abrupt onset with chills, fever, headache, backache, and prostration. The cough at first is nonproductive, but later in the disease tenacious mucoid sputum is produced. The leukocyte count is normal or low. As with many other pulmonary diseases the x-ray shadows show changes which are much greater than those anticipated from the physical signs.

Children are readily infected but rarely develop severe illness. Women have this disease about twice as often as men, probably because many women raise birds and many live in close association with birds in the home. The most severe cases are in patients who are over 40 years of age. For decades the mortality in the diagnosed cases was about 20 per cent, but with the recognition of mild and ambulatory infections it is now as low as 9.3 per cent. At necropsy a mononuclear infiltration is found in the lungs, microscopic areas of focal necrosis in the liver, degenerative changes in the parenchyma of the kidneys, and hemorrhages and capillary thrombi in the adrenals (11, 64, 114).

Diagnosis is suggested by the clinical history, particularly contact with sick birds. A positive diagnosis requires either isolation of the organism or a rise in complement-fixing antibodies.

Transmission. The respiratory tract is the primary portal of entry in most instances. The feces, urine, nasal discharges, and soiled feathers from sick, dying or even latently infected birds may travel a considerable distance through the air before losing their infectivity. Handling sick or dead birds increases the probability of infection. Laboratory workers exposed to the organisms may contract the disease. A severe case of psittacosis resulted following the opening in the laboratory of a package which contained a crushed vial of lyophilized bedsonia (43).

The infection may spread directly from patient to attendant. In Buenos Aires in 1945 there were 26 such infections with 13 deaths (69). In the Louisiana epidemic in 1943 there were eight deaths in 19 recognized infections among nursing attendants (128). In rare instances the patient becomes a carrier. Karl Meyer has followed one patient who continues to excrete organisms in his sputum 10 years after his initial infection.

Treatment. Sulfonamides, particularly sulfadiazine, reduce the severity of the disease. Penicillin is useful in preventing secondary infections with gram-positive cocci but it is doubtful whether it is as effective as the sulfonamides against the bedsonia. Chlortetracycline and oxytetracycline are most effective in therapy and can reduce the mortality to 2 per cent (33, 75).

Prevention. It would be desirable, although impractical, to eliminate all parrots and parakeets from the homes and all pigeons from the eaves of houses and barns. Certainly each patient should be strictly isolated and the case reported to the proper authorities so that epidemiologic investigations could be initiated. Although vaccines have been attempted (35, 107, 130), their value and effectiveness is dubious.

LYMPHOGRANULOMA VENEREUM

(Lymphogranuloma Inguinale, Durand-Nicolas-Favre Disease, Climatic Bubo, Tropical Bubo, Esthiomene, Paradenitis)

Family: *Chlamydiaceae* Rake. Genus: *Miyagawanella* Brumpt. Type Species: *Miyagawanella lymphogranulomatis* Brumpt

Vague reports of a venereal disease known as tropical bubo appeared from time to time throughout the eighteenth century. The first definitive description was published by Durand, Nicolas, and Favre (28) in 1913. The disease now has been recognized in many countries throughout the world, and there are indications which suggest that its prevalence is increasing (54). The disease occurs more commonly in Negroes than in whites and is found, or at least is recognized, more frequently in males than in females (116).

Durand's description of the disease was followed by those of Phylactos, Frei (36), and Hellerström (51). Frei introduced his diagnostic skin test in 1925; Hellerström and Wassén in 1930 transmitted the disease to monkeys by intracerebral inoculation; and Levaditi (63) produced infection in mice by the same route. Rake and others (103) succeeded in cultivating the organism in the yolk sacs of embryonated chick eggs.

There is only one antigenic type and man is the sole natural host. **Lymphogranuloma** venereum should not be confused with granuloma inguinale, which is caused by *Granulomatis donovani.*

Experimental Infection in Laboratory Animals. Mice (31, 63) and monkeys are most susceptible to experimental infection, but rabbits, squirrels, marmots, rats, cats, dogs, and sheep can be infected. Fowls, pigeons, rice birds, and parakeets cannot be infected even by intracerebral injections (82). Monkeys cannot be infected by the intravenous or intranasal routes but develop disease analogous to that observed in man when the organism is introduced intracutaneously, intraperitoneally, intraocularly, intrapreputially or into the tissues of the lymph nodes, intestines, or rectum.

The disease has been transmitted experimentally from man to man by intraurethral inoculations (51), and human volunteers have been infected by material from experimentally infected monkeys (131).

Clinical Types of Infection in Man. The disease usually is spread by genital contact, but the organism may enter the body through the mouth or conjunctivae. The importance of such extragenital infections has not been appreciated generally. The **incubation period** is seven to 12 days, and the primary lesion, a small painless papule in the genital region, is followed by the enlargement of one or more lymph nodes, called **buboes,** in the groin (44). These buboes may or may not suppurate, but they usually persist for months unless adequately treated. In addition to adenitis, elephantiasis of the vulva and stricture of the rectal ampullae are common complications in the female. Occasionally infections of the throat and other parts of the body have been observed (141). The patient is infectious as long as the exudate persists. One attack apparently produces immunity for life, and reinfections have not been observed.

It has been known for many years that headache is a common symptom in lymphogranuloma venereum infections, but its significance was not recognized until von Haam and D'Aunoy (129) in 1936 isolated the organism from the spinal fluids of two acutely ill patients, and there appeared other reports of meningoencephalitis complicating lymphogranuloma venereum infections (8,

101, 111, 141). These studies and others have established the neurotropism of the organism and added weight to the concept that this infection is bacteremic in nature.

The complement-fixation test becomes positive between the tenth and twenty-first days of the infection, appearing somewhat earlier than the **Frei test.**

A positive complement-fixation test in a 1:40 dilution of serum is accepted as evidence of infection, provided the clinical findings are consistent.

The Frei Test. A positive Frei test may be elicited by the intracutaneous injection of sterile pus from a bubo, an emulsion of infected mouse brain (42), or a suspension from the yolk sac of the chick embryo. The reaction becomes positive within 24 to 48 hours and persists for four to eight days. When hypersensitivity is developed to this antigen, it apparently persists for the rest of the patient's life. A positive Frei test, therefore, is interpreted in the same manner as a positive tuberculin test, in that it does not differentiate between an active infection and an infection which has been healed for many years. The skin test does give cross-reaction with infections due to other bedsonia but has not been detected in other infections (102). The new skin test developed by Barwell (5) is specific for lymphogranuloma venereum and does not cross with infections caused by other bedsonia. The infected yolk sac is treated with 0.02 normal HCl, which destroys the complement-fixing antigens. A control made from normal, uninfected yolk sac should be used to eliminate reaction from coincidental sensitivity to egg yolk. The positive skin test appears later than the complement-fixing antibodies and may be negative when the latter is positive (102).

Transmission. The mechanism of transmission is obvious. The disease is more prevalent in tropical countries, in the Mediterranean area, in southern and eastern ports, and in the colored races. There is no evidence of racial susceptibility or climatic influence, but there is a good correlation with unfortunate social conditions.

Biologic Products. The Frei antigen for skin testing can be prepared by sterilizing pus aspirated from an unopened bubo. At the present time the material used most

commonly is marketed under the trade name of Lygranum.

Treatment. MacCallum and Findlay (72) demonstrated the beneficial effect of sulfonamides on the course of experimental infections in mice. Since that time the sulfonamides have been used in the treatment of human infections. Chlortetracycline and oxytetracycline are effective in the therapy of early cases (102).

Prevention. Since man is the sole source of the organism, this infection theoretically could be controlled. It should be a reportable disease in every state, and the state or local board of health should supply adequate diagnostic facilities, including the complement-fixation test. Free treatment should be provided for individuals financially unable to employ a private physician.

TRACHOMA

(Granular Conjunctivitis)

Family: *Chlamydiaceae* Rake. Genus: *Chlamydia* Rake. Type Species: *Chlamydia trachomatis* Rake

Currently about 400 million people are afflicted with Trachoma, an infection recognized by Hippocrates and for the past decade or so the world's leading cause of blindness (replacing smallpox). The disease is not widespread in the United States, but in 1962 some 460 cases were reported from nine states (87). Nevada had 389 cases and Oregon 60.

A major advance was made in 1957 when T'ang and associates (120) reported the isolation of the organism in the yolk sac of embryonated eggs. Although experiments of this type had been done for more than 20 years (139), T'ang's studies represented the first successful isolation. These findings have been confirmed in many laboratories (25, 49), and the organism has been grown in various tissue culture systems (38, 40, 99). The reasons for the years of unsuccessful experiments followed by sudden success using the same technics is not clear, but Jawetz and associates (56) have found that eggs exhibit a seasonal insusceptibility possibly related to the intermittent production of some inhibitor or the presence of some interfering organism. The disease is limited to man in nature, but various primates can be infected by conjunctival inoculation (26). The name "trachoma" is derived from a Greek word which means "rough," referring to the pebble-like appearance of the infected conjunctivae.

Clinical Types of Infection in Man. The incubation period may be as short as five to seven days, with either mild or severe symptoms at onset. Mild cases occur most often in children, where a slight ptosis of the upper eyelid is accompanied by a follicular hypertrophy of the upper tarsal conjunctivae. The upper lids must be everted to reveal the lesion. When the onset is more acute, there is infiltration, papillary hypertrophy, and marked conjunctival inflammation, accompanied by superficial reddening of the cornea and often swelling of the lids and enlargement of the periauricular lymph nodes. Regardless of the mode of onset, the disease may progress over a period of months or years to pannus formation, corneal ulceration, and cicatrization resulting in partial or complete blindness (12). Secondary bacterial infection is a complication occurring in about half of the cases seen in the United States but in nearly all cases in the Orient and Middle East. Recurrences often occur after apparent healing, indicating that an effective immunity does not develop (125). Thygeson (125) suggests that the destructive lesions may be caused by a type of endotoxin analogous to that which the organism of lymphogranuloma venereum and some strains of the psittacosis are known to produce. For demonstration of inclusion bodies, the superficial exudate should be wiped away, and epithelial cells removed for examination by gentle scraping and stained with Giemsa's stain. **The inflammation and inclusion bodies are most numerous in the upper tarsal conjunctivae in trachoma and in the lower conjunctivae in inclusion conjunctivitis** (15). There is striking evidence of damage to the epithelial cells which contain the inclusion bodies of trachoma in contrast to those which contain inclusion bodies of inclusion conjunctivitis (124, 137). Although the subepithelial infiltration is mononuclear in type, the exudate contains chiefly polymorphonuclear cells,

even in cases where there is no secondary infection. This is in sharp contrast to the findings in epidemic keratoconjunctivitis and herpes simplex virus infections where the exudate is predominantly mononuclear.

Transmission. The infection is transmitted directly from eye to eye by fingers or fomites, although the fly may be an important mechanical vector (136, 138). A recent investigation by Lyons (71) shows that the fly is an important mechanical vector in the Near East. There is no evidence of a subclinical infection or transmission by a symptomless carrier.

Treatment. The treatment of trachoma was revolutionized by the introduction of sulfonamide therapy (34, 61, 68). In early cases cures may be obtained in a period of weeks without the complication of scarring. In more chronic cases plastic surgery is needed after prolonged treatment with sulfonamides (97). Chlortetracycline can be used locally and systemically. After chlortetracycline therapy the organism can no longer be transmitted to baboons (70), and the clinical results seem to be as good if not better than those obtained with sulfonamide therapy (127). Chloramphenicol (81) and oxytetracycline have also produced rapid and dramatic cures. Topical applications of cortisone may reactivate a healing lesion (126).

Prevention. Poverty and malnutrition contribute markedly to the frequency and severity of trachoma. Improvement in dietetic and hygienic condition, early diagnosis, and thorough treatment should eliminate this ancient curse of mankind.

INCLUSION CONJUNCTIVITIS

(Inclusion Blenorrhea, Para Trachoma, Swimming Pool Conjunctivitis)

Family: *Chlamydiaceae* Rake (1956). Species: *Chlamydia oculogenitale* Rake (1956)

A benign nonbacterial form of conjunctivitis in the newborn was described by Morax (85, 86) in 1903 and, in 1909, inclusion bodies, resembling those of trachoma, were found in the epithelial cells of the conjunctivae (112, 117). The disease in the adult is usually sporadic but may be epidemic following the accidental contamination of unchlorinated swimming pools (60, 122). The reservoir of infection is the cervical canal of certain females (47). No symptoms are produced in the female, but a moderately severe urethritis occurs when the infection is transferred to the male urethra (52). The eyes of the newborn infant are infected during passage through the birth canal, and the eyes of adults may be infected by fingers contaminated with vaginal or ocular discharges.

The disease has been transferred to apes, baboons, and some species of monkeys by inoculation of urethral discharge (37, 65). The cervix of the female baboon has been experimentally infected with the organism of inclusion conjunctivitis (14), but the urethra of the male baboon could not be infected.

Recently Jones and associates (59) reported the successful isolation of this organism in the yolk sac of embryonated eggs, and this has been confirmed by Hanna and associates (50). Isolation of the organism of inclusion conjunctivitis in eggs, however, is much more difficult than isolations of trachoma.

The **inclusion bodies in man are morphologically identical with those found in trachoma, and the early lesions are very similar except that the lower lid is more involved and there is no evidence of necrosis in the epithelial cells.** The incubation period is five to 12 days. The initial reaction may be as severe as in trachoma, but pannus, necrosis, and scarring are not seen. Spontaneous cures occur after two or three months, although a year or more may elapse before all evidence of infiltration disappears. The disease in adults is usually less severe at onset than in the infant but a longer period is required for complete healing. Inclusion conjunctivitis must be differentiated from epidemic keratoconjunctivitis, which is caused by a virus (see Chapter 69).

The relation of trachoma to inclusion conjunctivitis has become an especially intriguing problem since Braley (14) succeeded in infecting the cervical canal of baboons with trachoma. The absence of cytoplasmic damage in epithelial cells containing inclusion bodies was observed by Thygeson (124).

Lindner (65) suggests that the organism of inclusion conjunctivitis was derived from trachoma in a manner analogous to the derivation of vaccinia from variola virus except that in this instance the trachoma was introduced and propagated in the cervical canal of the human female rather than in another animal. The failure of the inclusion conjunctivitis organism to acquire any of the characteristics of trachoma, even after serial transfers in 40 human subjects (1), does not necessarily conflict with this theory.

Treatment. Sulfonamide therapy usually effects a cure in 5 to 10 days in both the infant and adult (121). A 5 per cent sulfathiazole or sulfadiazine ointment is effective in the infant (122, 123), but irregularly successful in adults. This should not be used because of the high incidence of sensitization. Penicillin therapy has been disappointing (125), but oxytetracycline and other broad-spectrum antibiotics are effective. Topical applications of cortisone may reactivate a subsiding infection (94).

Prevention. The silver nitrate or penicillin drops applied to the conjunctivae of the newborn to prevent gonorrheal ophthalmia do not prevent infection with the organism of inclusion conjunctivitis. Nurses, pediatricians, obstetricians, and gynecologists should be aware of the dangers of contracting the infection. The proper chlorination of the waters of swimming pools will prevent epidemics from this source.

ANIMAL TYPES OF BEDSONIA

Mouse Pneumonitis. *Miyagawanella bronchopneumoniae* Moshkovsky.

This organism is latent in many stocks of laboratory mice and may be activated and recovered when other infectious materials are injected into mice for diagnostic studies. It is related to both psittacine and ornithocine strains as shown by protection and toxin neutralization. This organism shows selective localization in the lungs (78, 92).

Feline Pneumonitis. *Miyagawanella felis,* Rake. Isolated by Baker (3) in 1942, this organism has a predilection for the lungs, causing epidemics among cats and symptoms resembling influenza or distemper. It is pathogenic for cats, mice, hamsters, and embryo chicks; its toxin is not neutralized by antitoxin from other species of the psittacosis-lympho-granuloma group (78).

Sporadic Bovine Encephalomyelitis. This disease was described by McNutt and Waller (77) in 1940. The elementary bodies can be grown in embryonated eggs and then adapted to Swiss mice, cotton rats, and Rhesus monkeys. The organism is widely disseminated among herds and usually produces unapparent infections. Severe infection and death occurs only under exceptional conditions (79, 133, 134). Neutralizing antibodies to the Lansing strain of poliomyelitis do occur in bovine serum (18, 48), but this virus is not the cause of the antibodies (133).

Enzootic Abortion in Ewes. This disease was described by Stamp and his associates (115) in Scotland in 1949 and studied in some detail by Monsur and Barwell (84). Apparently one attack confers immunity. The organism has been isolated in chick embryo cultures. It is pathogenic for guinea pigs but shows cross-neutralization of toxins with other types (83).

Infectious Conjunctivitis in Animals and Birds. These agents grow in the conjunctival cells of their respective host species and are the apparent cause of epidemic conjunctivitis. *Colesiota conjunctivae* Rake (22, 24) is pathogenic for sheep, cattle, and goats. A similar infection occurs in swine and responds to sulfonamide therapy (24).

One form of ocular roup (23) in the domestic fowl is caused by *Colesiota conjunctivae-gallii* (Coles) Rake.

REFERENCES

1. Allen, J. H. Am. J. Ophth., 27:833, 1944.
2. Allison, A. C., and Perkins, H. R. Nature, 188:796, 1960.
3. Baker, J. A. J. Exper. Med., 79:159, 1944.
4. Barros, E. La psittacose durante el decennio 1929-1939, Buenos Aires, Buffarini, 1940.
5. Barwell, C. F. Brit. J. Exper. Path., 33:268, 1952.
5a. Bauer, T. J. J.A.M.A., 158:1407, 1955.
6. Bedson, S. P. Brit. J. Exper. Path., 19:353, 1938.
7. ——— and Gostling, J. V. T. Brit. J. Exper. Path., 35:299, 1954.
8. Beeson, P. B., and others. Proc. Soc. Exper. Biol. & Med., 62:306, 1946.
9. Benedict, A. A., and O'Brien, E. J. Immunol., 76:293, 1956.
10. Beveridge, W. I. B., and Burnet, F. M. Medical Research Council Special Report, Series No. 256, London, 1946.
11. Binford, C. H., and Hauser, G. H. Pub. Health Rep., 59:1363, 1944.
12. Bland, J. O. W. J. Path. & Bact., 56:161, 1944.
13. Bovarnick, M. R. Ann. New York Acad. Sc., 98:247, 1962.
14. Braley, A. E. Arch. Ophth., 22:393, 1939.
15. ——— Arch. Ophth., 24:681, 1940.
16. Burnet, F. M., and Rountree, P. M. J. Path. & Bact., 40:471, 1935.
17. ——— M. J. Australia, 1:545, 1939.
18. Chang, T. W., and Wenner, H. A. Proc. Soc. Exper. Biol. & Med., 78:659, 1961.
19. Ciak, J., and Hahn, F. E. Antibiotics Chemotherapy, 9:47, 1959.
20. Cohn, J. I., and Moulder, J. W. J. Infect. Dis., 103:199, 1958.
21. ——— Ann. New York Acad. Sc., 98:234, 1962.
22. Coles, J. D. W. A. Rep. Direct. Vet. Serv. and An. Ind. Un. South Africa, 17 Report, 1931, p. 175.
23. ——— Onders J. Vet. Sc. and Indust., 14:469, 1940.
24. ——— Arch. Ophth., 25:101, 1941.
25. Collier, L. H., and Sowa, J. Lancet, 1:993, 1958.
26. Dawson, C., and others. Proc. Soc. Exper. Biol. & Med., 106:898, 1961.
27. Dewey, D. L., and others. Biochem. J., 58:523, 1954.
28. Durand, M., and others. Bull. et mém. Soc. méd. d. hôp. de Paris, 35:274, 1913.
29. Early, R. J., and Morgan, H. R. J. Immunol., 53:251, 1946.
30. Ephrati-Elizur, E., and Bernkopf, H. J. Infect. Dis., 98:45, 1956.
31. Findlay, G. M., and others. Tr. Roy. Soc. Trop. Med. & Hyg., 32:183, 1938.
32. Fite, G. L., and others. Pub. Health Rep., 61:1100, 1946.
33. Fitz, R., and others. Am. J. M. Sci., 229:252, 1955.
34. Forster, W. G., and McGibony, J. R. Am. J. Ophth., 27:1107, 1944.
35. Francis, R. D., and others. Proc. Soc. Exper. Biol. & Med., 66:184, 1947.
36. Frei, W. Klin. Wchnschr., 4:2148, 1925.
37. Fritsch, H., and others. Arch. f. Ophth., 76:547, 1910.
38. Furness, G. J. Gen. Microbiol., 23:613, 1960.
39. Gerloff, R. K., and Lackman, D. B. Am. J. Pub. Health, 44:323, 1954.
40. Gordon, F. B., and others. Science, 131:733, 1960.
41. ——— and Quan, A. L. Bact. Proc., p. 148, 1962.
42. Grace, A. W., and Suskind, F. H. Proc. Soc. Exper. Biol. & Med., 32:71, 1934.
43. Green, T. W. J.A.M.A., 144:237, 1950.
44. Greenblatt, R. B. Pub. Health Serv. Ven. Dis. Info. Sup., 19:1, 1943.
45. Greenland, R. M. J. Infect. Dis., 108:287, 1961.
46. Haagen, E., and Mauer, G. Zentralbl. f. Bakt. Abt. I. Orig., 143:81, 1938.
47. Halberstadter, L. Berl. Klin. Wchnschr., 46:1839, 1909.
48. Hammon, W. McD., and others. J. Immunol., 57:285, 1947.
49. Hanna, L., and others. Science, 130:1339, 1959.
50. ——— and others. Science, 132:1660, 1960.

51. Hellerström, S. C. Acta dermat.-venereol., Supp. I, 5:224, 1929.
52. Heymann, B. Berl. Klin. Wchnschr., 47:663, 1910.
53. Higashi, N., and others. Ann. New York Acad. Sc., 98:100, 1962.
54. Howard, M. E., and Strauss, M. J. New England J. Med., 212:323, 1935.
55. Hurst, E. W., and others. Brit. J. Pharm. Chemotherapy, 8:297, 1953.
56. Jawetz, E. W., and others. J. Immunol., 89:80, 1962.
57. Jenkins, H. M. J. Bact., 80:639, 1960.
58. ———— and others. J. Immunol., 86:123, 1961.
59. Jones, B. R., and others. Lancet, 1:902, 1959.
60. Julianelle, L. A. Proc. Soc. Exper. Biol. & Med., 36:617, 1937.
61. ———— and Smith, J. E. Am. J. Ophth., 25:317, 1942.
62. Lazarus, A. S., and Meyer, K. F. J. Bact., 38:121, 1939.
63. Levaditi, C., and others. Ann. Inst. Pasteur, 48:27, 1932.
64. Lillie, R. D. Nat. Inst. Health Bull., No. 161, Washington, D.C., 1933.
65. Lindner, K. Arch. f. Ophth., 78:345, 1911.
66. Litwin, J. J. Infect. Dis., 105:129, 1959.
67. ———— and others. J. Infect. Dis., 109:251, 1961.
68. Loe, F. J.A.M.A., 111:1371, 1938.
69. Loizaga, N. S., and Averbach, S. Rev. med. y cien. afines, Mexico, 7, 297, 379, 461, 543, 1945.
70. Lyons, F. M. Rev. internat. du trachome, 27:126, 1950.
71. ———— Rev. internat. du trachome, 30:341, 1953.
72. MacCallum, F. O., and Findlay, F. M. Lancet, 2:136, 1938.
73. Manire, G. P., and Myer, K. F. J. Infect. Dis., 86:241, 1950.
74. Mason, D. M. J. Immunol., 83:661, 1959.
75. McCulloh, A. Texas J. Med., 51:817, 1955.
76. McKercher, D. G. Science, 115:543, 1952.
77. McNutt, S. H., and Waller, E. F. Cornell Vet., 30:437, 1940.
78. Manire, G. P., and Meyer, K. F. J. Infect. Dis., 86:226, 233, 241, 1950.
79. Menges, R. W., and others. Am. J. Hyg., 57:1, 15, 1953.
80. Meyer, K. F., and Eddie, B. Proc. Soc. Exper. Biol. & Med., 30:484, 1933.
81. ———— Medicine, 21:175, 1942.
82. ———— Viral and Rickettsial Diseases of Man, T. M. Rivers, 2nd ed., Philadelphia, Lippincott Co., 1952, p. 440.
83. Meyer, K. F. The Dynamics of Virus and Rickettsial Infections, eds. Hartman, Horsfall, and Kidd. New York, The Blakiston Co., Inc., 1954, p. 461.
84. Monsur, K. A., and Barwell, C. F. Brit. J. Exper. Path., 32:414, 1951.
85. Morax, V. Ann. d'ocul., 129:346, 1903.
86. ———— Bull. et mém. Soc. franç. d'opht., 46:5, 1933.
87. Morbidity and Mortality Weekly Report. 11:27, 1962.
88. ———— 11:2, 1963.
89. Morgan, H. R., and Boder, J. C. J. Exper. Med., 106:39, 1957.
90. Moulder, J. W., and others. J. Infect. Dis., 98:229, 1956.
91. Nichols, R. L., and McComb, D. E. J. Immunol., 89:545, 1962.
92. Nigg, C., and Eaton, M. D. J. Exper. Med., 79:497, 1944.
93. Officer, J. E., and Brown, J. J. Infect. Dis., 107:283, 1960.
94. Ormsby, G. Am. J. Ophth., 35:1811, 1952.
95. Parodi, A. S., and Silvetti, L. M. Prensa méd. Argent., 33:529, 1946.
96. Perkins, H. R., and Allison, A. C. J. Gen. Microbiol., 30:469, 1963.
97. Pines, N. Proc. Roy. Soc. Med., 40:129, 1947.
98. Pollard, M. Proc. Soc. Exper. Biol. & Med., 64:200, 1947.
99. ———— and others. Proc. Soc. Exper. Biol. & Med., 104:223, 1960.
100. ———— and Tanami, Y. Proc. Soc. Exper. Biol. & Med., 107:508, 1961.
101. Rajam, R. V. Brit. J. Ven. Dis., 12:237, 1936.
102. Rake, G. Diagnostic Procedures for Virus and Rickettsial Diseases. New York, Am. Pub. Health Assoc., 1956, p. 453.
103. ———— and others. Proc. Soc. Exper. Biol. & Med., 43:332, 1940.
104. ———— and Jones, H. P. J. Exper. Med., 79:463, 1944.
105. ———— and Jones, H. P. J. Exper. Med., 75:323, 1942.
106. Ritter, J. Deutsches Arch. f. klin. Med., 25:53, 1879-80.
107. Rivers, T. M., and Schwentker, F. F. J. Exper. Med., 60:211, 1934.
108. Roca-García, M. J. Infect. Dis., 85:275, 1949.
109. Ross, M. R., and Jenkins, H. M. Ann. New York Acad. Sc., 98:329, 1962.
110. Roubakine, A. Epidemiological Rep. League of Nations, 9:141, 1930.
111. Sabin, A. B., and Aring, C. D. J.A.M.A., 120:1376, 1942.
112. Schmeichler, L. Berl. Klin. Wchnschr., 46:2057, 1909.
113. ———— and others. J. Exper. Med., 78:189, 1943.
114. Sprunt, D. H., and Berry, G. P. J. Infect. Dis., 58:129, 1936.
115. Stamp, J. T., and others. Vet. Records, 62:251, 1949.
116. Stannus, H. S. A Sixth Venereal Disease, London, Bailliere, Tindall and Cox, 1933.
117. Stargardt, K. Arch. f. Ophth., 69:525, 1909.
118. Swain, R. H. A. Brit. J. Exper. Path., 36:507, 1955.
119. Tamura, A., and Higashi, N. Virology, 20:596, 1963.
120. T'ang, F. F., and others. Chinese M. J., 75:429, 1957.
121. Thygeson, P. Arch. Ophth., 25:217, 1941.
122. ———— and Stone, W., Jr. Arch. Ophth., 27:91, 1942.
123. ———— J.A.M.A., 119:407, 1942.
124. ———— Am. J. Ophth., 29:1499, 1946.
125. ———— Viral and Rickettsial Infections of Man, T. M. Rivers, 2nd ed., Philadelphia, Lippincott Co., 1952, p. 465.
126. ———— Diagnostic Procedures for Virus and Rickettsial Diseases, New York, Am. Pub. Health Assoc., 1956, p. 413.

127. Trabone, V. Rev. internat. du trachome, 27:137, 1950.
128. Treuting, W. L., and Olson, B. J. Pub. Health Rep., 59:1331, 1944.
129. von Haam, E., and D'Aunoy, R. J.A.M.A., 106:1642, 1936.
130. Wagner, J. C., and others. J. Immunol., 54:35, 1946.
131. Wassén, E. Acta path. et microbiol. Scandinav., Supp. XXIII, 1935, p. 1.
132. Weiss, E. J. J. Infect. Dis., 87:249, 1950.
133. Wenner, H. A., and others. J. Infect. Dis., 94:284, 1954.
134. ———— Psittacosis Diagnosis Epidemiology and Control, Ed. Beaudette, F. R., New Brunswick, New Jersey, Rutgers University Press, 1955, p. 22.
135. Wenner, H. A. Adv. in Virus Res., 5:40, 1958.
136. Wilson, R. P. Ann. Rep. Mem. Ophth. Lab. 4th (1929), Giza, Cairo, 1930, p. 63.
137. Wilson, R. P. Ann. Rep. Mem. Ophth. Lab. 11th, (1936), Giza, Cairo, 1937, p. 117.
138. ———— Ann. Rep. Mem. Ophth. Lab. 14th, (1939-44), Giza, Cairo, 1945, p. 38.
139. Wright, R. E. Brit. J. Ophth., 21:198, 1937.
140. York, C. J., and Baker, J. A. J. Exper. Med., 93:587, 1951.
141. Zarafonetis, C. J. D. New England J. Med., 230:567, 1944.

THE VIRUSES

61

Physical, Morphologic, and Chemical Properties of Viruses

Viruses are infectious agents which, in size, adjoin and extend downward from the protozoa and bacteria. Some are barely visible in the light microscope, but most lie far beyond the range of this instrument. The virus diseases, some of which have been known for centuries while others still being recognized from time to time, rival in importance other infectious conditions of man, animals, and plants. Many deadly and costly human virus diseases—smallpox, yellow fever, and, more recently, poliomyelitis—are subject to control by immunization and other measures, and a measles vaccine is ready for distribution. In contrast, others, principally influenza and the common cold, levy a great annual toll in morbidity and mortality and constitute a heavy economic burden. Among the costly animal diseases are hog cholera; leukosis of chickens, now the major cause of losses in the poultry industry in this country; and foot and mouth disease, which thus far can be eradicated only by the slaughter of affected cattle. Increasing attention is being directed toward the possible role of viruses in the etiology of cancer (see Chap. 75). To the group of virus-induced neoplasms, consisting principally for many years of malignant conditions only of fowls—avian leukosis and fowl sarcoma—have been added numerous virus-induced tumors of mammals. These include mammary carcinoma in mice and the carcinomas arising in warts induced in rabbits by the papilloma virus. The most recent contribution to the knowledge in this field has been the recognition of a broad spectrum of leukemias and other virus-induced tumors in the mouse. Tumors caused by viruses occur also in plants. Insect diseases may be of much economic importance either because of de-struction of commercially valuable organisms, such as silkworm jaundice and sacbrood of bees, or, conversely, because of the control of harmful insects, examples of which are the spruce budworm and spruce sawfly. Much loss is suffered because of the many plant virus diseases.

Though diseases caused by viruses have long been known clinically, the existence of the agents and their possible nature have been realized only within the past few decades. It has been scarcely a century since the pathogenic protozoa, bacteria, yeasts, and molds were even suspected of being causative agents of disease, and most of these etiologic agents have been cultured apart from the host and studied individually. Among the many well-known diseases, however, there were some which were believed to be infectious in origin but in which the suspected agent could not be recovered. It was not until about 70 years ago that evidence was seen of a group of entities which did not respond to investigative methods previously used and which lay in a size range beyond that of the known forms. In 1892 Iwanowski (59) found that the infectious agent of tobacco mosaic could pass through an earthen filter which held back bacteria and other known agents. Beijerinck (10) in 1899 corroborated Iwanowski's findings, and within a few years many causative agents were found to display this property. The known range of hosts was extended still further when Twort in 1915 and, independently, d'Herelle (36) in 1917 discovered agents of similar properties which parasitized and destroyed bacteria. More recently there have been found agents in this same category which parasitize some of the fungi, an example of which is the actinophage (87).

Such infectious agents came to be known first as "filterable" viruses or, with time, simply as viruses. The agents parasitizing bacteria are the **bacteriophages.** Since the place of viruses in the biologic scale has not yet been fully established, a rigid definition of the agents is not possible. The ability to traverse earthen filters, the criterion first serving to separate viruses from other infectious agents, indicates a **smallness of size** fully substantiated in subsequent work (Table 1).

A second general, differentiating criterion, thus far valid, is that the agents are **obligate parasites** multiplying only within living susceptible cells. Neither smallness of size nor obligate parasitism is unique to viruses, however, for the pleuropneumonia-like organisms —125 to 250 mμ in diameter (see Chap. 1) —are filterable but grow on artificial medium. The malaria protozoan is an example of a nonfilterable, relatively large, intracellular parasite which has not been grown in the absence of cells.

As will be seen, the viruses constitute an exceedingly large and heterogeneous group of agents of highly diverse properties. Although a comprehensive definition has not yet been formulated, viruses may be regarded as infectious agents in the size range between 250 mμ and 17 mμ and growing only in living cells. The basic constituent is nucleic acid, always in association with protein and, in some of the larger entities, with nonnucleic-acid carbohydrate and lipid.

In ultimate significance, knowledge gained in the study of viruses is of importance beyond that concerned with etiology of disease. Constitutionally and physically viruses vary widely in complexity, but in comparison with other analogous entities, such as cells, protozoa, and bacteria are all of extreme simplicity. Nevertheless, the respective agents are definitive biologic units manifesting the fundamental property of **reproduction.** Except for this capacity, the smallest and simplest viruses approach closely the characteristics of large molecules. Indeed, in some definitions the agents have been designated as nucleoprotein macromolecules, but this is an unwarranted simplification detracting from full appreciation of the total spectrum of viral characteristics. No matter how simple, viruses still exhibit the basic property of organisms to effect their own reproduction under suitable conditions.

It is in the correlations of viral constitution and architecture with their behavior as the simplest microorganisms that investiga-

Table 1.   Sizes of Representative Viruses of Man, Animals, Plants, Insects, and Bacteria

Virus	mμ	Virus	mμ
Fowl pox	264 x 332	Canine hepatitis	82
Canary pox	263 x 311	Equine encephalomyelitis	50
Vaccinia	284 x 222	Yellow fever	22
Molluscum contagiosum	240 x 303	Poliomyelitis	30
Rabbit fibroma	244 x 283	Coxsackie	24
Herpes simplex	120	Mouse encephalomyocarditis	30
Rabies	125	Foot and mouth disease	27
Influenza virus A	100	Vesicular stomatitis	68 x 175
Mumps	170	Reovirus	65
Newcastle disease	170	*Tipula* iridescent	130
Fowl plague	120	*Antheraea mylitta*	30
BAI strain A leukosis	120	*Sphinx ligustri*	15
Rous sarcoma	120	Silk worm jaundice (polyhedrosis)	40 x 288
Mouse leukemia (Friend)	100	Fir shoot roller (granulosis)	50 x 262
Mouse leukemia (Gross)	100	T$_2$ bacteriophage	80 x 100—111 *
Mouse mammary cancer	100	T$_7$ bacteriophage	50
Rabbit papilloma	50	øX174 bacteriophage	25
Human papilloma	50	F$_2$ bacteriophage	25
Polyoma	45	Tobacco mosaic	17 x 300
Adeno, type 5	75	Tomato bushy stunt	25
Avian adeno-like (GAL)	100	Tobacco necrosis	17

* The respective values for the T$_2$ bacteriophage of *E. coli* indicate width of head, length of head, and length of tail.

tions of the agents can be most fruitful. At the most primitive structural level, viruses consist only of nucleic acid and protein in uniform amounts and arrangement. The matter is further simplified by knowledge that nucleic acid is the determinative component responsible for establishment of viral relationship with the cell and for direction of cellular processes resulting in virus synthesis and elaboration. Cell infection has been induced by both deoxyribonucleic acid (DNA) and ribonucleic acid (RNA) isolated from a wide variety of agents (25, 40, 43, 58, 64, 95, 117), including plant viruses and representative animal agents of the papova, arbor, and nanivirus groups (see Table 2). Viruses are thus the most promising models not only for characterization as infectious agents but for synthesis of a primitive unit with the fundamental behavior of "living" matter. Thus far cellular functions have been indispensable for virus synthesis, but progress has been made (25, 81) in the disclosure of mechanisms of virus assembly. Protein molecules derived by degradation of tobacco mosaic virus can be reassembled into typical rods in the absence of cells, and suitable incorporation of specific nucleic acid in the protein structure results in rods of characteristic size and infectious properties.

Finally, information in this field has practical as well as theoretical implications. There

Table 2. Virus Groups of Various Host Categories with Indication of Virus Particle Structure (Helical, Cubic or Complex) and Kind of Nucleic Acid [Deoxyribonucleic Acid (DNA) or Ribonucleic Acid (RNA)]

1. Plant (RNA)
   - A. Rods (helical)
   - B. Near-spherical (cubic)

2. Insect
   - A. Polyhedrosis
     - a. Nuclear (rods, DNA, helical)
     - b. Cytoplasmic (cubic, RNA)
   - B. Granulosis (rods, DNA, helical)
   - C. Cytoplasmic (cubic, DNA)

3. Bacteriophage
   - A. Tailed (complex, DNA)
   - B. Near-spherical (cubic, DNA or RNA)

4. Animal and Man
   - A. Pox viruses (complex, membrane, DNA)
     - a. Smallpox; vaccinia; rabbit, monkey, mouse (ectromelia) and cow pox
     - b. Ungulate pox-contagious pustular dermatitis of sheep (orf); horse, goat, swine and sheep pox
     - c. Avian pox-fowl, canary
     - d. Myxomalike-rabbit myxoma, rabbit and squirrel fibroma
     - e. Molluscum contagiosum and monkey tumor
   - B. NITA viruses (complex, membrane, DNA)
     - a. Herpes simplex, B virus, pseudorabies, virus III, varicella and zoster
     - b. Inclusion viruses of man, guinea pig, mouse and pig
     - c. Avian viruses-infectious laryngotracheitis; parrot, pigeon and cormorant diseases

   - C. Adenoviruses (simple, cubic, DNA) Human, chimpanzee, simian, mouse, fowl (GAL) and canine hepatitis
   - D. Papova (simple, cubic, DNA)
     - a. Papilloma of man, rabbit and other animals
     - b. Polyoma of mice; rat virus and K virus
     - c. SV40
   - E. Myxoviruses (complex, membrane, RNA)
     - a. Influenzas of man, swine and horse; fowl plague
     - b. Paramyxoviruses - mumps, Newcastle disease, Sendai
     - c. Measles, canine distemper, rinderpest
   - F. Tumor viruses (complex, membrane, RNA)
     - a. Avian agents of many interrelated strains causing myeloid or erythroid leukemias, lymphomatosis, sarcomas and other tumors
     - b. Mouse agents of many strains causing myeloid or lymphoid leukemias and other tumors
   - G. Arborviruses (RNA) Equine encephalomyelitis, yellow fever, dengue, St. Louis encephalitis, Jap B encephalitis and many others (see Chap. 74)
   - H. Naniviruses (simple, cubic, RNA) poliomyelitis, Coxsackie, ECHO, enteroviruses (cattle, swine, monkeys, cats, birds), foot-and-mouth disease, mouse encephalomyelitis, encephalomyocarditis, Mengo
   - I. Not grouped Rabies, REO viruses, rubella, infectious hepatitis, vesicular stomatitis, various viruses of fowls and fish

is the potentiality that with sufficient knowledge of biochemical cell-virus interrelationships, it may be possible to **treat** virus diseases by chemical interruption of the processes of virus synthesis and effect. This is of particular importance in virus-induced tumors, in which there is frequently an enduring intracellular relationship with protection of the agent from adverse environmental immunologic influences.

The literature on viruses and virus diseases is very large. Nevertheless, it is important to realize that, though much is known about the filterable agents, virology as a biologic science is in a highly stimulating state of change and progress in the most varied directions. By virtue of their peculiar properties, as will be indicated, viruses are susceptible to study not only by the conventional approaches of microbiology but possibly even more so by other basic technics, particularly those of the physicist, chemist, and the geneticist. Because of the diversity of interests, the literature is badly scattered, and the magnitude of total information has hampered the preparation of comprehensive texts. Adequate contact with the field can be maintained only by examination of the numerous current reports. Some texts, however, provide the background and citations of the literature necessary for undertaking the more detailed study of viruses. Among the older references are the lengthy work *Virus Diseases of Man* by van Rooyen and Rhodes (114) and *General Virology* by Luria (67). A current text is *Principles of Animal Virology* by Burnet (21). Extensive reviews are in three volumes of *The Viruses* (22) edited by Burnet and Stanley. Virus-induced insect diseases were described by Steinhaus in *Principles of Insect Pathology* (109) and, more recently, in a review by Smith (107). Plant diseases were discussed in the book *Plant Viruses and Virus Diseases* by Bawden (7). Virus-induced tumors have been considered in a book by Gross (45). Valuable sources of information and references are numerous reviews in *Advances in Virus Research, Annual Review of Microbiology, Progress in Animal Virology, Annual Review of Biochemistry,* and others by specialists in the different fields. The basis for technics of virus isolation, cultivation, titration, and identification by cul-

tural and serologic characteristics were described in *Diagnostic Procedures for Virus and Rickettsial Diseases* (39) and a review by Schmidt and Lennette (94). It should be emphasized that, although much of virology is well established and factual, there are many areas of controversy and confusion. There is no substitute for consultation of original reports.

Despite the present considerable knowledge of the chemical, physical, and biologic characteristics of viruses, criteria are not yet sufficient for more than a beginning classification of the agents. It has been customary, most frequently, to group viruses in relation to the host parasitized—namely, animal viruses, insect viruses, bacteriophages, or plant viruses. Individual agents and groups of agents in these categories exhibit certain distinctive or related characteristics in various aspects of constitution, morphology, pathogenesis, and numerous biologic properties which are useful for purposes of discussion and correlation. Intensive work with agents causing disease in vertebrates has resulted in enough information to permit a partial but informative grouping (5). The list in Table 2, though not exhaustive, will be convenient for purposes of reference in discussion of the agents. More details are given in other chapters dealing with the individual virus diseases.

In Table 2 plant viruses are divided only with respect to shape. Insect agents are grouped with respect to cell-virus relationships. In some insect diseases (12, 13, 107, 109) large polyhedral or inclusion bodies are found in the nucleus, and in others, in the cytoplasm. Virus particles in the two types of polyhedrosis differ in shape and, thus far, in kind of nucleic acid. In granulosis rod-shaped particles are in granules or capsules in the cytoplasm; and in other diseases virus particles are elaborated free in the cytoplasm. The animal and human viruses are grouped (5) in relation to various aspects of structure, composition, and different immunologic and biologic properties. Group types of nucleic acid have been indicated in the table, but this is a generalization, since direct identification of nucleic acid has not been made in every agent listed. The suffix "NITA" signifies nuclear inclusion type A; "nani" means dwarf; and "arbor" designates arthropod-borne viruses. Cell-agent relationships in the processes of synthesis of representative viruses of the major groups are described in Chap. 62.

VIRUS PURIFICATION

Study of many fundamental properties of viruses is critically dependent on obtaining the agents in purified preparations (8, 71, 96). Since viruses grow only in the presence of living cells, it has been necessary to devise the means for separating the agents from the host cells. The basic method is that of fractional centrifugation of virus-containing materials at alternate low- and high-speed spinning with instruments affording high gravitational fields (71, 90, 93, 108). Factors influencing the outcome are concentration of virus in the source material and the complexity of the materials from which the agents must be separated. Some agents, particularly plant viruses, can be purified by chemical precipitation and fractionation.

When virus is to be obtained from diseased tissue, the material may be ground with sand or special instruments and extracted in saline or other suitable medium. Preliminary extract clarification can be effected by low-speed centrifugation, filtration with celite, filtration through earthen filters, or a combination of all. The extracts are then centrifuged at speeds and gravitational fields adequate for sedimentation of the agents. Large volumes of extracts or virus-containing fluids can be handled for clarification and fractionation by use of constant-flow instruments such as the Sharples Supercentrifuge (112). In the fractionation sequence, the sedimented virus is resuspended and dispersed in suitable medium and then spun at low speed to eliminate aggregated nonviral material. High- and low-speed sequences are repeated until the desired homogeneity has been obtained.

Bacteriophages can be purified easily by centrifugal fractionation of lysates of bacteria cultivated in broth or synthetic media (1, 86, 100). Influenza, Newcastle disease, mumps, and various other viruses can be propagated in chick embryos and appear in high concentration in the choriallantoic fluid, from which they are readily isolated (8). Many agents can be obtained from tissue culture fluid. Complex procedures are needed for some agents, such as the poliovirus (92, 93). The purification process includes precipitation of the virus from tissue culture fluid at the isoelectric point, elution of the agent from precipitated extraneous material in alkaline buffers, and final ultracentrifugal fractionation by sedimentation through a sucrose or other density gradient (19). Virus purification can be effected also by electrophoresis (90).

PHYSICAL CHARACTERIZATION AND MEASUREMENT OF HOMOGENEITY

The smallness of the agents and many of their properties have made possible examinations (8, 62, 71, 90) by physical and chemical methods (13, 25, 63, 64) developed initially for the study of proteins and various macromolecular materials. Approximations of size can be made by **ultrafiltration** with collodion membranes (41). Many physical characters of viruses, such as size, shape, and density, and the purity of the preparations can be studied by sedimenting the agents in an **analytical ultracentrifuge** in which the descent of the virus can be followed optically during spinning. Further physical studies have been made by means of **electrophoresis** in the Tiselius apparatus or by **diffusion, viscosity, x-ray diffraction,** and other methods. Of the greatest importance from the viewpoint of actual knowledge of virus morphology and structure is micrography of the agents with the **electron microscope.**

Analytical ultracentrifugation, as most often employed (71, 90), is a technic designed for quantitative measurement of rate of virus sedimentation which is a function of the density, size and shape of the virus particles and of the viscosity and density of the suspending medium (65). In the analytical ultracentrifuge the material sedimenting can be watched and photographed by the ultraviolet absorption method (102, 111) of Svedberg (Fig. 1), or by the Schlieren or Rayleigh optical technics (71, 90). The character of the descending boundary gives evidence of the homogeneity or purity of the preparation, as shown in Figure 1. A mate-

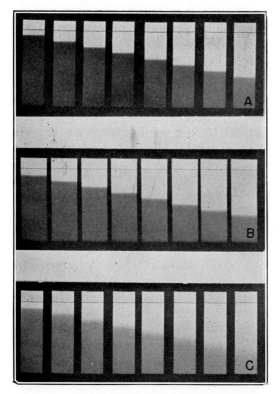

Fig. 1. Sedimentation diagrams. A, sedimentation diagram of the T$_2$ bacteriophage of *E. coli*. The interval between pictures was 2½ minutes, and the ultracentrifugal field was 7,270 g. B, sedimentation diagram of equine encephalomyelitis virus (Western strain). The interval between exposures was 2½ minutes, and the ultracentrifugal field was 17,000 g. C, sedimentation diagram of human influenza virus A (PR8 strain). The successive photographs were taken at intervals of 2½ minutes, and the ultracentrifugal field was 7,270 g.

rial consisting of particles uniform in size, shape, and density gives a single sharp boundary. If a preparation contains two homogeneous materials differing in these properties, two sharp boundaries may be seen. If the sedimentation properties of the individual particles vary, there will be either no boundary or a diffuse one. The rate of descent of the sedimenting boundary is constant under standard conditions and is a value used to calculate virus size.

Density of viruses in the wet or hydrated state under natural conditions is a property difficult to investigate (65, 96). Knowledge of this attribute, however, is essential for in-terpretations of the significance of sedimentation diagrams, size calculations from sedimentation velocity data, estimation of water content, and interpretation of morphologic and structural data (18). Since rate of sedimentation is dependent on particle density in relation to that of the suspending medium, it is theoretically possible to learn particle density by estimate of sedimentation rate in mediums of different densities. For this purpose solutions of bovine serum albumin (103) of high molecular weight and low solution osmotic pressure have been used with certain agents. Examples of density values obtained in this way are: swine influenza virus, 1.100; rabbit papilloma virus, 1.133; BAI strain A (myeloblastosis) avian tumor virus (98), 1.059. The applicability of various materials to the study of plant and other viruses has been reviewed in detail (65).

Dry density, or its reciprocal, partial specific volume (90), is generally determined by weighing relatively large amounts of highly purified virus in pycnometers. A procedure requiring but small quantities of virus not necessarily of high purity has been developed (97) by sedimenting influenza and other viruses in heavy water, D$_2$O.

With both dry and wet densities known, water content can be calculated. The values for the swine influenza virus are 43.3 per cent by volume; for the papilloma virus, 58 per cent; and for the avian BAI strain A virus, 80 per cent, which may bear on intense distortion effects on the agent seen on drying (18).

Electrophoresis is the phenomenon of migration of charged particles, molecules or ions, in an electrical field (90, 105). Viruses, like proteins, are amphoteric (82), possessing an electric charge which is either positive or negative, depending on the pH of the suspending medium, and, except in few instances, are susceptible to study by this means. The rate and manner of migration is related to electric charge on the entities and is independent of size, shape, and density. Electrophoresis thus provides a sensitive criterion of homogeneity or purity of virus preparations distinct from sedimentation data. As mentioned before, electrophoresis may be useful for virus purification (90).

MORPHOLOGY AND STRUCTURE

Contemporary knowledge and concepts of virus morphology and structure have been developed by correlation of information gained by a variety of methods, including examination by **x-ray diffraction, electron microscopy, and chemical analysis.** A notable contribution of x-ray diffraction studies was the initial evidence that some viruses, particularly the rod-shaped tobacco mosaic virus and the spherical tomato bushy stunt agent, were of relatively simple structure and consisted of uniformly arranged subunits. X-ray diffraction patterns have provided a detailed picture of the shape and structure of these virus particles together with evidence of the number and arrangement of the subunits.

Studies by x-ray diffraction (24, 62) are limited greatly by the requirement for rather large amounts of virus in crystalline state. Many agents are not simple in constitution or structure and do not form crystals. Of much more simple and general applicability are the methods for direct examination of virus particles with the electron microscope (49, 110, 122, 125). The theoretical limit of resolution with this instrument is about 0.5 Å, or 0.05 mμ. Primarily because of the low electron-absorbing capacities of viruses, however, the limits of resolution with objects of this sort without special treatment are about 10 mμ. Great reduction in the limit has been effected by improvements in the technics of preparation for examination, and now structures as small as about 2 mμ can be observed. Electron micrographs are usually taken at magnifications up to about 40,000, and enlargements can be made photographically to useful magnifications, in some instances, as great as 1,000,000.

The image in an electron microscope (85, 122, 125) is formed by a beam of electrons, brought into focus by the action of magnetic lenses. Electron micrography differs in several ways from micrography with light. Images are formed as the result, principally, of the differential absorption of electrons by the various parts of the object. Color is absent, and the image cast on the photographic plate is dark where electrons are not ab-

sorbed and lighter where the electrons are absorbed. Growing usefulness of the electron microscope has been related to the development of a variety of procedures for increasing differential electron absorption by viruses and surrounding medium. Some technics have been designed for study of particles separate from associated cells, but others permit examination of cells together with related viruses. In the latter field progress in morphologic virology has advanced parallel with improvements in the means for study of cell ultrastructure.

In the beginning viruses were examined in **untreated** preparations (122, 125) dried on exceedingly thin collodion membranes. Some evidence of size and shape was revealed, as well as indications of internal structure, particularly of the larger agents. A marked advance was development of the **"shadow"** technic whereby virus particles could be observed (4, 122) in high contrast and with a three-dimensional effect. Particles deposited on a collodion membrane in the conventional manner were held at an angle to a source of vaporizing metal in a vacuum chamber. In this way a coat of metal—platinum, gold, chromium, or other—was deposited on the surface of the particles exposed to the flow of metal vapor, but not on the opposite particle side nor on the film shielded by the particles. Thus a "shadow" behind the particles was formed, and much was revealed concerning the shape of the agents. However, a disturbing influence in this and other procedures was distortion of the particles attending drying, especially in the presence of salt. Some of this difficulty could be avoided by freezing and drying the particles before coating (122). Much of the effect can be eliminated, also, by drying virus on an agar plate (18) into which water and salt diffuse at the same time.

Concurrently, there were being developed procedures for study of cell structure (14) at the electron microscopic level. Technics for **ultrastructural study** were devised (85) on the same principles as those employed for conventional histology. Very small bits of tissue were fixed, dehydrated in alcohol, and embedded in a material hardening to a consistency suitable for cutting sections of a suitable thinness—20 mμ, more or less. Con-

Table 3. **Morphologic Features of Representative Viruses of Man, Animals, Plants, Insects, and Bacteria**

Virus	Symmetry	Size of Capsid mμ	Number of Capsomeres
Tipula iridescent	Cubic	130	812
Adenovirus	Cubic	70-75	252
Gal (Gallus adeno-like)	Cubic	95-100	252
Infectious canine hepatitis	Cubic	82	252
Herpes simplex	Cubic	120	162
Wound tumor	Cubic	?	92
Polyoma	Cubic	45	42
Warts	Cubic	50	42
Turnip yellow mosaic	Cubic	28-30	32
øX174	Cubic	23-25	12
Tobacco mosaic	Helical	300 x 17	2, 130
Mumps	Helical	170 (diameter)	
Newcastle disease	Helical	170 (diameter)	
Sendai	Helical	170 (diameter)	
Influenza	Helical	90-100 (diameter)	
T-even bacteriophage	Complex	80 x 100 (head)	
Contagious pustular dermatitis (Orf)	Complex	260 x 160	
Vaccinia	Complex	284-222	

trast in micrographs was enhanced by tissue fixation with osmium tetroxide, which stains protein, lipid, and nucleic acid, and the use of stains consisting of salts of the heavy metals, such as those of lead and uranium. These same procedures showing ultrastructure of the cells disclosed elements not only of virus-particle structure but of the relationship of the agents to the cells in the processes of infection and formation of virus (14, 76, 88). Refinements of the methods have resulted in the development of **ultracytochemical** technics (15, 37, 38, 42) for identification of virus constituents with stains and for study of specific enzyme activity effects on particle components at the ultrastructural level.

The most recent technic is that of **negative staining** (20, 54, 121). Employed earlier in the study of very small organisms with the the light microscope, the principle consists in the preparation of a film in which the object is embedded in an opaque material. For electron microscopy of viruses, particles are mixed with potassium phosphotungstate, for example, and spread on a carbon film. Phosphotungstate pervades all of the particle surface interstices and outlines the contour to yield a negative electron microscopic image of the particle. Fine details of surface structure are revealed, and phosphotungstate may penetrate damaged, incomplete, or treated particles to show also some characteristics of internal structure. Negative staining has disclosed elements of architecture and particle shape not apparent by other methods employed for electron microscopy.

In their morphologic aspects, viruses are particulate entities which occur in a large variety of shapes and sizes (Tables 1, 3). Many viruses causing disease in plants and insects are rods of highly symmetrical shape and uniformity of size and consist only of protein and nucleic acid. Numerous agents —some causing diseases in plants, higher animals, and insects as well as some bacteriophages—are essentially or nearly spherical and are composed also of protein and nucleic acid. Many near-spherical agents affecting plants and higher animals are so uniform in size and shape that they can array or pack themselves in true three-dimensional crystals. Rods can form paracrystals in which the particles are arrayed in a two-dimensional pattern. In contrast, many agents are of complex constitution containing lipid and, some, carbohydrate in addition to that bound specifically in nucleic acid. Ultrastructural studies have effected a degree of correlation between composition (Table 4) and physical structure (Table 3), which in turn are related largely but not entirely to mechanisms of virus syn-

Table 4. Constitution of Representative Viruses and of Certain Biologically Associated Materials

	Lipid				Carbo-hydrate		Nonlipid			
	Total	Phospho-lipid	Choles-terol	Neutral fat	Total	Total	Protein	Carbo-hydrate	Nucleic DNA	Acid RNA
1. Tobacco mosaic					2.5	100	94.2	1.8	0	5.8
2. Tomato bushy stunt					5-6	100	85	5-6	0	15
3. Turnip yellow mosaic							63		0	37
4. Poliomyelitis						100	78		0	22
5. Adenovirus (type 2)						100	87		13	0
6. Papilloma	1.ɔ				6.5	98.5	90		8.7	0
7. Equine encephalomyelitis (Eastern strain)	54.1	35.0	13.8	9.6	4.0	53.0	49		0	4.4
8. Influenza (PR8)	23.4	11.3	7.0	5.1	12.5	77.5	69	7.3	0	1
9. BAI strain A	35					63			0	2.2
10. Vaccinia	5.7	2.2	1.4	2.2	2.8	94	89		5.2-5.6	0
11. Herpes	22	22					70		6.5	0
12. T$_2$ bacteriophage	2.6	0	0	2.6	13.6	97.4	50	13.1	45	0
13. T$_7$ bacteriophage	1				16.6	99-100	48.6		41.1	0
14. f$_2$ bacteriophage										25
15. *Escherichia coli*	7.75	7.75	0	0	12.5	92.3	67.9	12.5	5.2	19
16. Polyhedral virus (silkworm)						100	86		14	0
17. Polyhedral body (silkworm)						100	99.4-100		0.6	0
18. *Tipula* iridescent	5	5				95	82		12.4	0
19. *D. pudibunda*						100	93			7

thesis and final assembly of the "mature" form of the agents. Moreover, apparent constitutional simplicity is not always paralleled by morphologic simplicity, as exemplified by the morphology and constitution of the tailed bacteriophages. These agents contain only protein and DNA, but the protein is of demonstrable ultrastructural and antigenic complexity.

In the study of virus architecture, the problem of determining the composition of the components, demonstrating the manner of arrangement or packing of the components to form the particles, and determining the interrelationships of the different kinds of components in the particle arises. Thus, in viruses consisting only of protein and nucleic acid the question of the manner in which the protein components could be arranged to form the different-shaped particles in relation to the nucleic acid has been studied. Two principal types of highly uniform arrangement have been observed: (a) **helical** symmetry, exhibited by many rod-shaped particles, and (b) **cubic** symmetry, shown by near-spherical agents. In the simplest structural arrangement the particle consists of an external shell, the **capsid,** made up of distinct components, termed **capsomeres,** enclosing a central region designated as the

core. Other agents are of **complex symmetry** and of widely varying characteristics. Many, such as herpes and myxoviruses, consist of an inner body, **nucleoid** (14), enclosed in a relatively large membrane structure. In some instances the nucleoid closely resembles and may correspond to the capsid-capsomere-core structure of the simplest agents and may exhibit elements of helical or cubic symmetry. Other viruses exemplified by members of the pox group are much more complex.

The characteristics of helical symmetry displayed by the tobacco mosaic virus have been determined in much detail by correlations of findings by x-ray diffraction (24, 62), electron microscopy (20, 54), and chemical analysis (25, 63, 64, 70). Figure 2 is an electron micrograph of metal-shadowed tobacco mosaic virus showing the typical rods of about 300 mμ length and 17 mμ diameter. Treatment of the virus with detergent (46) partly dissolved the protein and showed that the rod consisted of a protein sheath enclosing a core (Fig. 3). That the core was RNA was shown by treatment with ribonuclease which dissolved the nucleic acid. X-ray diffraction showed (24, 62), further, that the subunits of the sheath were arranged in a regular array in the form of a helix wound around the nucleic acid. Chemical

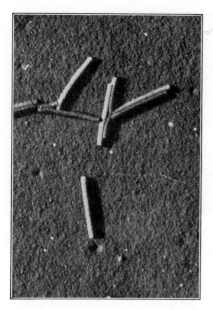

Fig. 2. Tobacco mosaic virus, shadowed. The virus is 17 mμ by 300 mμ. × 55,000. (Courtesy of Dr. Robley C. Williams.)

and RNA components are present, some of the reassembled rods are of the same structure and length of the initial virus and display of the infectious properties as the native agent.

No other rod-shaped virus has been studied as extensively as that of the tobacco mosaic, but the same principle of structure has been demonstrated for tobacco rattle virus (25, 80). It has been postulated that the relationships of protein and nucleic acid will probably be the same in principle in all rod-shaped agents, with variations in the details of length of rod, radius of the ribonucleic acid spiral, and association of the nucleic acid with the protein components. Tobacco rattle virus is about 25 mμ in diameter, and the infectious rods are 179 to 192 mμ in length, with a hollow center about 5 mμ diameter. It has not been demonstrated that the capsomeres are all of identical constitution.

Like some plant agents, many insect disease viruses are rods (12, 13, 107, 109), but, unlike plant viruses, contain protein and *DNA* instead of RNA. Insect virus rods

analysis indicated that the protein was made up of identical molecules (6). Correlation of all data led to the conclusion that the virus is a hollow rod consisting of 2,130 identical protein molecules—capsomeres—of 18,000 molecular weight wound in a spiral around a single strand of RNA with a molecular weight of 2.2×10^6. Negatively stained virus (54) (Fig. 4) shows not only the helical array of capsomeres forming the sheath —capsid—but a cross-section of a rod fragment with the central hollow. The pitch of the spiral is 2.3 mμ, with 49 capsomeres for each three turns of the helix. The hole through the center is 4 mμ in diameter. From the amount of nucleic acid per rod and the molecular weight of the nucleotides, it can be calculated that three nucleotides are combined with each protein molecule, as suggested in the diagram of Figure 5 (62).

The rods can be broken down into the protein and RNA components by appropriate treatment (6, 90), and reassembly of the protein components can be effected to result in rods of helical-sheath structure like the original, except that the rods are of widely differing lengths. When both protein

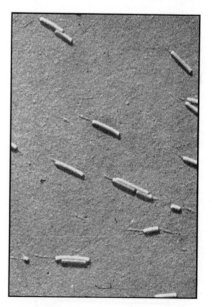

Fig. 3. Tobacco mosaic virus with protein sheath partially dissolved showing projecting internal rods of ribonucleic acid. × 44,000. (Courtesy of Dr. R. G. Hart, Virus Laboratory, University of California.)

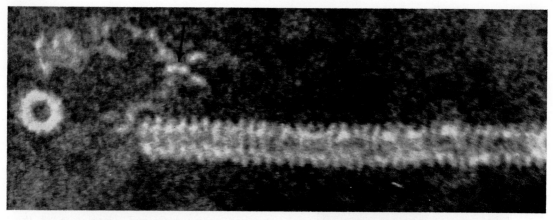

Fig. 4. Negatively stained tobacco mosaic rod showing periodic arrangement of capsomeres along the axis. Cross section of rod shows central hollow. Some capsomeres are free (arrow). × 700,000. (From Horne and Wildy. *Virology,* 15:348, 1961.)

occur in two different cell relationships—in **polyhedral bodies** in the nucleus and in **granules** synthesized in the cytoplasm. In both cases, the rods are similar in appearance, 20 to 70 mμ in width and 200 to 400 mμ in length. Rod-shaped particles, as exemplified by the nuclear polyhedral virus of *Bombyx mori* (silkworm) (Fig. 6) have been obtained from polyhedral bodies of the gypsy moth,

nun moth, yellow-striped army worm, alfalfa caterpillar, California oakworm, tent caterpillar, and spruce budworm. Rods of the granule diseases like those of *Cacoecia murinana* Hüb (fir-shoot roller) (Fig. 7) occur in the variegated cutworm, the buckeye caterpillar, the omnivorous looper, and salt marsh caterpillar. Rods from nuclear polyhedroses are sheathed in a primary "in-

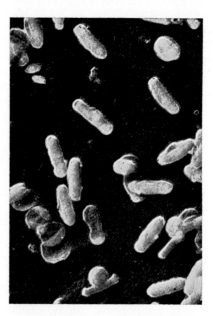

Fig. 5. Schematic representation of tobacco mosaic virus structure with ribonucleic acid helix associated in the ratio of three nucleotides to each protein subunit (capsomere). (From Klug and Caspar. *Adv. Virus Res.,* 7:225, 1960.)

Fig. 6. Polyhedral virus of *Bombyx mori* Linn. (silk worm) showing some infectious rods ensheathed in membranes and others outside membranes. Some membranes are empty. × 50,000. (Courtesy of Dr. G. Bergold.)

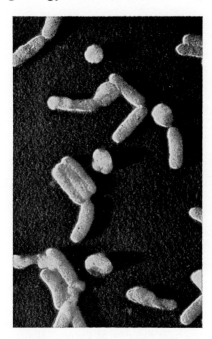

Fig. 7. Virus rods of the capsular disease of *Cacoecia murinana* Hüb. × 50,000. (Courtesy of Dr. G. Bergold.)

timate" membrane (Fig. 8A) closely applied to the particle (12, 107). The membrane, about 2 mμ thick, peels off the rod, which then may show evidence of helical arrangement of surface units. The structure of the intimate membrane itself is not known. In contrast, the granulosis virus rod still ensheathed in the membrane may exhibit apparent helical structure (Fig. 8B), but whether this is related to the membrane per se or to the rod has not been determined.

The fundamental studies with tobacco mosaic virus showed the manner in which identical protein molecules—capsomeres—could be packed in a symmetrical fashion about nucleic acid in a rod-shaped particle. A variety of plant viruses, particularly the agent of tomato bushy stunt, were known early to be of essentially spherical shape and highly uniform in size and shape—so much so that many readily formed crystals (Fig. 9). Some of the animal agents—wart, polio, and Coxsackie viruses—showed the same symmetry and likewise were crystallizable.

From these data on tobacco mosaic and tomato bushy stunt viruses (23), it was postulated (24, 27, 54, 62) that most or all

spherical or nearly spherical viruses would consist of symmetrically situated subunits or capsomeres arranged in some manner about the nucleic acid. Regular packing of such subunits into a particle limited by a symmetrical shell could be accomplished in only a restricted number of ways (24, 27), namely, at symmetrically situated points at the surface of bodies with the characteristics of cubic symmetry. Such bodies are the tetrahedron (4 faces), dodecahedron (12 faces), and icosahedron (20 faces). Subsequent work has substantiated these views and has shown that essentially all nearly spherical viruses are either of true icosahedral shape or spheres of icosahedral distribution of specific numbers of subunits arranged in various groupings at the surface.

The surface of the icosahedron (Fig. 10B) is made up of 20 faces consisting of equilateral triangles which form 12 vertexes and 30 edges at the junction of the points or bases of the respective triangles. The properties of symmetry of the regular icosahedron are described in terms of rotational characteristics. On an axis through opposite vertexes and the center, the body can be rotated in five positions (360°), each showing the same surface pattern. Similarly, rotation on axes through opposite faces or through opposite edges yields three and two positions, respectively, of the same appearance. The icosahedron is thus characterized as of 5:3:2 symmetry.

Virus particles have been observed with various numbers and distributions of capsomeres in this type of symmetry. Thus, one capsomere at each vertex would result in a total of 12, which is a possible distribution for øX174 phage. Or one may be at each vertex and one between on each edge resulting, in 12 plus 30, or 42 capsomeres (polyoma and papilloma viruses). Capsomeres might also be distributed at each vertex, with two or more between on the edge and others in symmetrical array on the faces of the triangles. With such arrangement the number of capsomeres can be calculated with the formula $10 (n - 1)^2 + 2$, where $n =$ the number of subunits along one edge joining the bases of a pair of triangles. Variations thus far observed are indicated in Table 3. This formula is applicable only when capso-

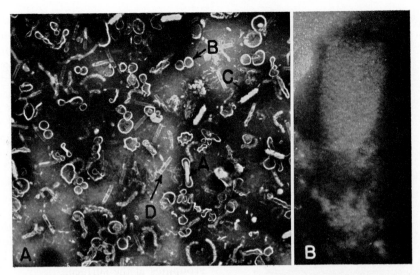

Fig. 8. A, negatively stained virus from nuclear polyhedral body of *Bombyx mori* Linn. treated with weak alkali showing (A) rod developmental membrane breaking and folding back; (B) spheres formed by freed membrane; (C) free rod with surface of helical appearance on high magnification; and (D) empty intimate membranes. × 21,600. B, negatively stained virus rod from a granulosis disease of *Pieris brassicae* Linn. (cabbage butterfly of Europe) showing appearance of helical structure. × 400,000. (From Smith. *Adv. Virus Res.,* 9:195, 1962.)

meres occur at each vertex of a regular icosahedron or at each vertex plus one or more additional capsomeres along each edge and others on the faces. Different numbers of capsomeres can be arranged, also, to yield the series 32, 122, ... (24). In addition, there are several classes of icosahedra which might yield other numbers not yet observed. For practical purposes, however, the evidence indicates that most of the agents can be regarded as having regular icosahedral symmetry. This does not mean that the particles will always be of icosahedral **shape,** but only that capsomere arrangement will conform to icosahedral *symmetry.*

It should be borne in mind, further, that apparently unit capsomeres may consist of combined smaller subunits. Moreover, capsomere interrelationships in the capsid may be of two types. In a hypothetical icosahedron with capsomeres only at the vertexes, each capsomere is ringed with five others. With other members of the series capsomeres at the vertexes are ringed by five, as before, but capsomeres on edges or faces are contiguous with six, thus forming combinations of surface pentagons and hexagons.

As determined by x-ray diffraction or, most frequently, by negative staining, many viruses exhibit the characteristics of cubic symmetry. The agents included in this category in this discussion are those in which the capsid is the external shell consisting of uniformly arrayed capsomeres without evidence of a separate membrane peripheral to the layer of capsomeres. Most of such agents are members of large groups already classified on the basis of other criteria as listed in Table 2. These are insect viruses occurring in cytoplasmic polyhedral inclusion bodies and others occurring free in the cytoplasm; animal viruses of the adeno, papova, nani— polio, ECHO, Coxsackie—and REO virus groups; plant agents of spherical or nearly spherical shape; and nearly spherical bacteriophages. As already mentioned, some with more complex total particle structure, including peripheral membranes, have been classified as either helical or cubic. The membrane-enclosed nucleoid sometimes has structure resembling the capsid of the simplest particles. In other agents the nucleoid contains flexible helical strands with the general capsid appearance of rod-shaped plant viruses. Though the evidence indicates that nucleic acid is the critical component of virus particles, this does not seem a good reason to ignore other well-defined parts of

Fig. 9. Tobacco necrosis virus. An electron micrograph of single crystals of a strain of tobacco necrosis virus showing the arrangement of the individual virus particles making up the crystals. × 90,000. (After Smith, Markham, and Wyckoff. *Nature, London*, 161:760, 1948.)

many particles which exhibit properties characteristic of the individual agents.

An elegant demonstration of cubic symmetry with actual icosahedral shape was accomplished early with the large *Tipula* iridescent insect virus (124). This agent develops in the cytoplasm of fat-body cells and becomes oriented in crystalline array in the cell (107). Virus particles frozen-dried and double-shadowed (124) with metal at different angles revealed (Fig. 10A) shadows similar to those produced by double-shadowing a model icosahedron (Fig. 10B). The agent is the largest—120 mμ diameter—of the isometric viruses thus far studied, and has 812 capsomeres in the capsid. This could be formed with 10 capsomeres along each edge and 28 on each face. Figure 11 is a nega-

Fig. 10. A, *Tipula* iridescent virus from *Tipula paludosa* Meigen (crane fly). Virus particle frozen-dried and double-shadowed with metal shows hexagonal contour and shadows similar to those cast by icosahedral model in B. × 100,000. B, double shadows cast by model icosahedron lighted in same orientation as virus particle in A. (From Williams and Smith. *Biochim. et Biophys. Acta,* 28:464, 1958.)

tively stained capsid in which there is no core. The capsomeres are hollow and hexagonal in shape and measure 8.5 × 14 mμ. As will be seen, such empty capsids are frequently found in preparations of "spherical" viruses and are regarded as developmental

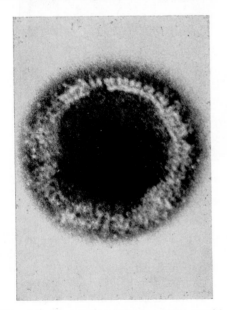

Fig. 11. Negatively stained empty capsid of *Tipula* iridescent virus showing hexagonal-shaped, hollow capsomeres (812 capsomeres per capsid). × 300,000. (From Smith. *Adv. Virus Res.,* 9:195, 1962.)

forms of the agents. The hollow capsomere feature is likewise a characteristic demonstrable in a variety of agents.

The *Tipula* iridescent virus contains lipid, 5.2 per cent, in addition to DNA and protein. Suitable treatment of whole particles or particles in thin sections (107) results in the digestion of the outer shell, indicating the protein nature of this part of the agent. Pepsin had no effect on the core; trypsin and deoxyribonuclease acting together, but not separately, removed the core, showing that this structure consists of deoxyribonucleoprotein. Chemical analyses of the degradation products showed that the cores were about 30 per cent DNA and 60 to 65 per cent protein.

Virus particles differing greatly in size from *Tipula* iridescent agent are found (12, 106) in polyhedral inclusion bodies in the cytoplasm. One of these from *Antheraea mylitta,* a large silkworm moth, is 30 mμ in diameter and displays cubic symmetry as seen by negative staining. Another virus from the privet hawk moth, *Sphinx ligustri,* is still smaller, 12 to 15 mμ diameter, and forms microcrystals (106). The particle is so small that the shape has not been determined; it may be either spherical or of cubic symmetry.

Members of the adenovirus group (Table

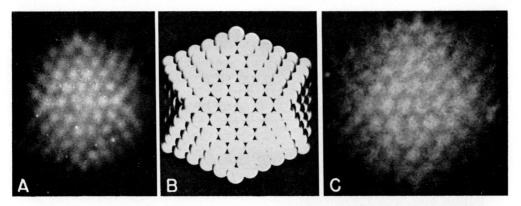

Fig. 12. A, negatively stained particle of adenovirus, type 5, showing icosahedral symmetry with six capsomeres along triangle edges and six capsomeres on each triangle face. Each capsomere on vertices is associated with five other capsomeres and each unit on triangle edges is surrounded by six capsomeres. × 550,000. B, photograph of icosahedral model with 252 units oriented as adenovirus particle in A. (From Horne, Brenner, Waterson, and Wildy. *J. Molec. Biol.,* 1:84, 1959.) C, negatively stained infectious canine hepatitis virus (ICH) particle with 252 capsomeres in the same arrangement as in the adenovirus particle. × 625,000. (From Davies, Englert, Stebbins, and Cabasso. *Virology,* 15:87, 1961.)

2) thus far studied have 252 capsomeres (Table 3). This is illustrated with a human adenovirus (50) Fig. 12A) and the infectious canine hepatitis (ICH) virus (33) (Fig. 12C). That the arrangement of the surface units or capsomeres of the two virus particles is icosahedral is shown by comparison with the model constructed of balls in Figure 12B. Six capsomeres are on each edge and six on each of the 20 faces.

The surface arrangement of pentagons and hexagons is easily seen in the model (Fig. 12B). The capsomeres have been obtained in purified preparation (118). The gallus adeno-like (GAL) virus (104) also belongs to this group (69). All of these agents contain DNA in the core.

Viruses with 162 capsomeres are agents of herpes and varicella, NITA viruses, described later.

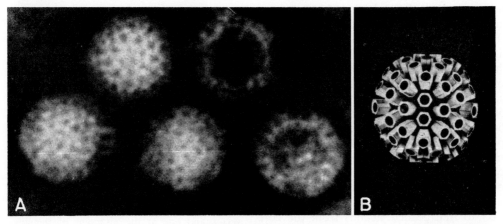

Fig. 13. A, reovirus particles, 60 mμ diameter, negatively stained show capsids with 92 capsomeres, one at each vertex, two on each triangle edge and one for each face as illustrated in model in B. Capsomeres are hollow and hexagonal- or pentagonal-shaped. One capsid, upper right, is empty. × 580,000. (From Vasquez and Tournier. *Virology,* 17:503, 1962. Courtesy Dr. W. Bernhard.) B, model illustrating arrangement of 92 capsomeres. (From Wildy and Watson. *Cold Spring Harbor Symposia on Quant. Biol.,* 27:25, 1962.)

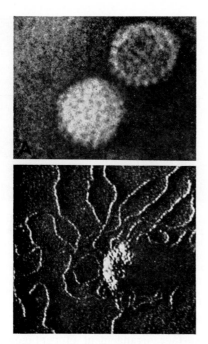

Fig. 14. A, negatively stained wound tumor virus of sweet clover and other plants. Particles are 60 mμ in diameter, and capsids are constructed of 92 capsomeres. One capsid is empty. × 346,000. B, disintegrated wound tumor virus particle shows ribonucleoprotein strands freed from capsid. × 118,000. (From Bils and Hall. *Virology,* 17:123, 1962.)

Members of the 92-capsomere type agents are the wound tumor virus (16) of plants and an animal REOvirus (115) not yet classified (89) with other large groups. The REOvirus is shown in Figure 13A together with a model for comparison in Figure 13B. The capsomeres appear to be elongated, hollow units of hexagonal or pentagonal shape. It is suggested that each capsomere consists of five or six subunits arranged about the hollow space, yielding a total of approximately 540 smallest discernible subunits. Wound tumor agent has the same appearance, Figure 14A. The nucleic acid of both agents is RNA. The shell of the wound tumor virus disintegrates progressively (Fig. 14B) to free beaded strands from the core (16). These are 3 mμ thick, a size indicating that the strands represent ribonucleoprotein. In both agents the capsomeres are arranged with four along each edge and one in each of the 20 faces.

Agents of the papova group (73)—papilloma, polyoma, and SV40 viruses—contain DNA and are about 45 mμ in diameter. Micrographs of negatively stained polyoma virus particles (Fig. 15A) indicate (120) that the capsid is constructed of 42 capsomeres (Fig. 15B) arranged in icosahedral symmetry, each having a hollow axial space. The capsomeres are distributed one at each vertex and one at the midpoint of the edges between the vertexes. Specimens of rabbit papilloma virus examined in thin sections and in negatively stained preparations (123) show ghost particles with only an external wall and an empty center. Such particles are demonstrable also with negatively stained polyoma virus, in which the external wall consists of a ring of capsomeres, and the center is occupied by phosphotungstate as illustrated for *Tipula* iridescent (Fig. 11), REOvirus (Fig. 13A), and wound tumor virus (Fig. 14A).

Small spherical RNA viruses, such as

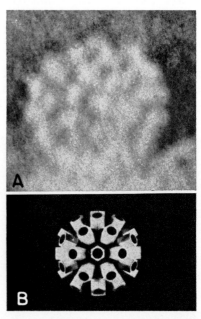

Fig. 15. A, negatively stained polyoma virus, 42 mμ diameter, with 42 capsomeres, one at each vertex and one at the midpoint of the edges as illustrated by the model in B. × 950,000. (From Wildy, Stoker, MacPherson, and Horne. *Virology,* 11:444, 1960.) B, model illustrating arrangement of 42 capsomeres. (From Wildy and Watson. *Cold Spring Harbor Symposia on Quant. Biol.,* 27:25, 1962.)

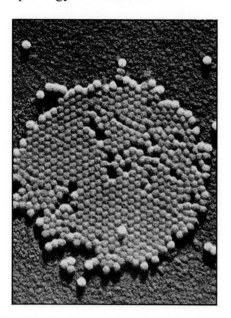

Fig. 16. Purified poliomyelitis virus MEF-1. × 74,000 (Courtesy Dr. C. E. Schwerdt and Dr. R. C. Williams, Virus Laboratory, University of California.)

those of the nanivirus group, and plant and some insect viruses have been studied by conventional electron micrography, negative staining, and x-ray diffraction. The appearance of purified poliovirus shadowed with metal (122) is shown in Figure 16, and Figure 17 is a micrograph of crystals of the agent (92). X-ray studies (62) have indicated cubic symmetry for tomato bushy stunt, turnip yellow mosaic, southern bean mosaic, tobacco ring spot, polio, and Coxsackie viruses, but the number of capsomeres has not been determined by this method. Chemical and physical analyses of tomato bushy stunt virus indicate (48, 78) that the protein constitutional subunits are of about 60,000 molecular weight, suggesting that the shell or capsid consists of 120 protein molecules. These might be distributed in pairs to yield a shell of 60 paired molecules, which is compatible with icosahedral symmetry (see p. 836). Negatively stained poliovirus (Fig. 18) exhibits an isometric capsomere arrangement (51), but the number of units is not clear. Turnip yellow mosaic virus is unusual in structural appearance. Particles negatively stained show an array (79) suggesting the presence

of 32 capsomeres, which has likewise been regarded as compatible with x-ray diffraction data. This number, however, does not fit the series of capsomere distribution observed with other agents of cubic symmetry.

Some bacteriophages are tadpole-shaped particles, as described later, but others, such as T_7 bacteriophage of *E. coli* (Fig. 19), are nearly spherical (60). However, application of the freeze-drying technic gives evidence that agents of this sort frequently have hexagonal shapes, and a very short nub or protrusion which may be regarded as a tail. Whether all bacteriophages have tails or not is of much importance in view of current concepts of attachment to and parasitism of their host cells (see p. 865).

Negative staining of one of the smallest bacteriophages—øX174—revealed evidence of cubic symmetry (68, 113). The agent, which is 25 mμ diameter and contains DNA, seems to be constructed (Fig. 20) of 12 capsomeres arranged with one at each vertex of an icosahedron as indicated by the model in Figure 20 C. It is notable, however, that the apparently individual capsomeres revealed in the micrograph may not represent the ultimate units but may be composed of a num-

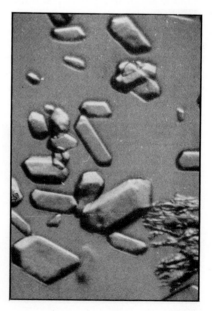

Fig. 17. Crystals of poliomyelitis virus. × 800. (Courtesy Dr. F. L. Schaffer and Dr. C. E. Schwerdt, Virus Laboratory, University of California.)

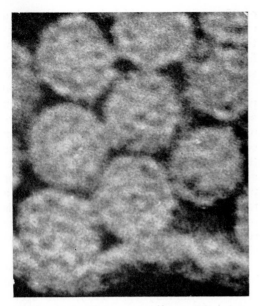

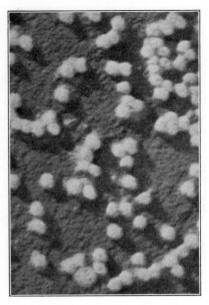

Fig. 18. Negatively stained poliovirus, 30 mμ diameter, suggesting capsomere arrangement with icosahedral symmetry. Number of capsomeres undetermined. $\times$ 760,000. (From Horne and Nagington. *J. Molec. Biol.,* 1:333, 1959.)

Fig. 19. T$_7$ bacteriophage of *E. coli.* $\times$ 48,500. (From Kerby, Gowdy, Dillon, Dillon, Csáky, Sharp, and Beard. *J. Immunol.,* 63:93, 1949.)

ber of still smaller entities. There is evidence that each capsomere of this bacteriophage may be made up of five smaller subunits.

In the foregoing there have been considered only the simplest viruses, consisting of protein and nucleic acid and not enclosed in separate complex membranous structures. Many animal viruses—pox, herpes, and myxoviruses and murine and avian tumor agents—consist of a nucleoid located in a surrounding substance, all enclosed within a peripheral limiting membrane. In some of these agents, particularly those of the herpes group, the external structure of the nucleoid resembles that of the capsid of viruses with cubic symmetry. Nucleoids of membrane-enclosed myxoviruses do not show this structure, but breaking of the nucleoid shell frees

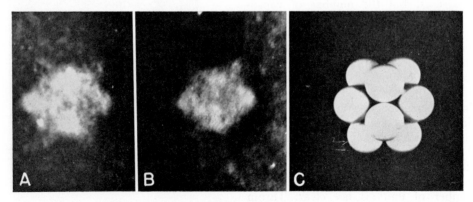

Fig. 20. A and B, negatively stained øX174 bacteriophage, 25 mμ diameter, in two orientations suggesting icosahedral symmetry of particle constructed of twelve capsomeres with one capsomere at each vertex as illustrated in model of C. $\times$ 1,000,000. (From Tromans and Horne. *Virology,* 15:1, 1961.)

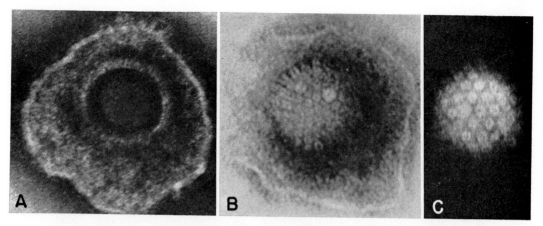

Fig. 21. A, negatively stained herpes virus illustrating whole particle with external envelope and outline of empty internal capsid. B, another whole particle illustrating intact capsid consisting of hollow, hexagonally or pentagonally shaped capsomeres. C, free capsid showing hexagonal packing of capsomeres. Number of capsomeres is 162. × 250,000. (From Wildy, Russell, and Horne. *Virology,* 12:204, 1960.)

flexible helical-shaped strands, providing the basis for classification of these agents with viruses of helical symmetry. Murine and avian tumor viruses are still different; nucleoids do not show capsid structure, nor are the strands released on disintegration of the nucleoids. Greater complexity is shown by the pox virus group and by a variety of oddly shaped individuals, including vesicular stomatitis and equine abortion viruses and the tailed bacteriophages. The complexity of some of these agents can be correlated with mode of assembly of the mature particles, particularly those formed in association with cellular membrane systems (Fig. 21).

Herpes, a DNA virus (11), appears first in the nucleus (see Fig. 24 in Chap. 62), where there are assembled particles notable in thin sections as dense central bodies enclosed in a single membrane. An additional membrane or double membrane is acquired in association with the nuclear membrane (see p. 879), possibly while the particle is within the nucleus or on passage of the particle from the nucleus into the cytoplasm. Negative staining (119) reveals spheroidal particles (Fig. 21A), with approximately centrally placed nucleoids which are sometimes empty. Intact nucleoids, however, exhibit a surface structure (Fig. 21B) which, on examination of the isolated body (Fig. 21C), displays typical capsid morphology with hollow, angulated surface capsomeres.

The number of capsomeres arranged with cubic symmetry is estimated as 162. The viruses of varicella (3), avian laryngotracheitis (28), and equine herpes are essentially identical in appearance with herpes.

Myxoviruses—influenza, mumps, Newcastle disease, fowl plague, Sendai, measles, canine distemper, and rinderpest (Table 1) —are, like the agents of the herpes group, spheroidal particles of variable size and shape, as exemplified by mumps virus (116) (Fig. 22). The influenza virus consists of an essentially spherical nucleoid surrounded by material enclosed in a well-defined peripheral membrane. The initial stages of influenza and fowl plague virus synthesis occur in the nucleus (see p. 870), electron microscopically invisible components traverse the cytoplasm, and the mature particles are assembled by budding of the cytoplasmic membrane (see p. 871). Thus, the outer membrane and material enclosing the nucleoid are derivatives of the cell membrane. The external membrane is well formed, and, as shown by negative staining (53), an array of spike-like projections extend out from the surface (Fig. 23A). In this respect the surface of the virus particle resembles the cell surface (57) from which it was budded (Fig. 23B). Influenza-virus disintegration by ether treatment results in breakdown of the peripheral membrane to yield small bodies (Fig. 24A) with the appearance of mem-

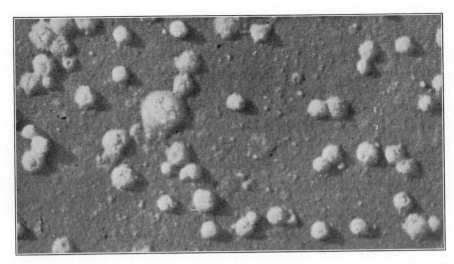

Fig. 22. Mumps virus. × 28,600. (From Weil, Beard, Sharp, and Beard. *J. Immunol.,* 60: 561, 1948.)

brane fragments folded—porcupine-like— into spherical shapes from which radiate the spikes shown in Figure 23A. The nucleoid shows no evidence of capsid or capsomere structure, but disruption of the nucleoid releases coiled, flexible strands (Fig. 24B) closely resembling the rigid helix observed in tobacco mosaic virus (Fig. 4). It is conceived that the strands constitute a helical arrangement of protein subunits in combination with ribonucleic acid. Formation of the nucleoid could be accomplished by coiling the strand, as suggested (54) in Figure 24C.

An analogous flexible, helical strand derived from mumps virus is negatively stained (52) in Figure 25A, and a corresponding strand from Sendai virus is in Figure 25B. A cross-section (Fig. 25A) shows that the mumps strand, like the tobacco mosaic virus rods, is hollow.

From the particles of influenza (57) and fowl plague (91) viruses two antigens have been isolated. One, the s or g antigen, corresponds to the helical inner material of the nucleoid (Fig. 24B) consisting of nucleoprotein, and the other, the HA antigen, is

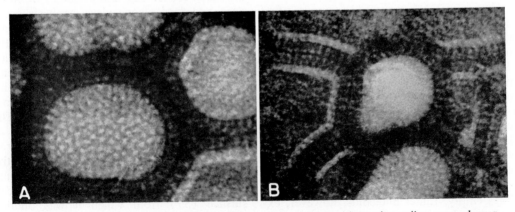

Fig. 23. A, negatively stained intact influenza virus particles illustrating spikes arrayed over surface of peripheral membrane or envelope. × 450,000. (From Hoyle, Horne, and Waterson. *Virology,* 13:448, 1961.) B, virus particle in center and lower edge mixed with cell-membrane fragments illustrating alignment of respective virus and cell-membrane spikes in agglutination of cell fragments. × 350,000. (From Hoyle, Horne, and Waterson. *Virology,* 17:533, 1962.)

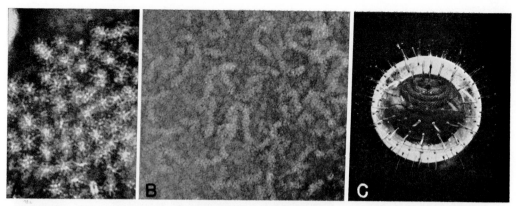

Fig. 24. A, negatively stained components from hemagglutinin fraction of ether-disintegrated influenza virus. Spikes on components resemble those of virus particle outer envelope, and components may represent fragments of disintegrated virus membrane. × 200,000. B, negatively stained helical-shaped strands of ribonucleoprotein from nucleoid of ether-disintegrated influenza virus present in soluble antigen fraction. × 200,000. (From Hoyle, Horne, and Waterson. *Virology*, 13:448, 1961.) C, schematic model suggesting possible arrangement of components comprising myxovirus particles. Transparent envelope with spike array encloses coiled ribonucleoprotein component in nucleoid (capsid). (From Horne and Wildy. *Virology*, 15:348, 1961.)

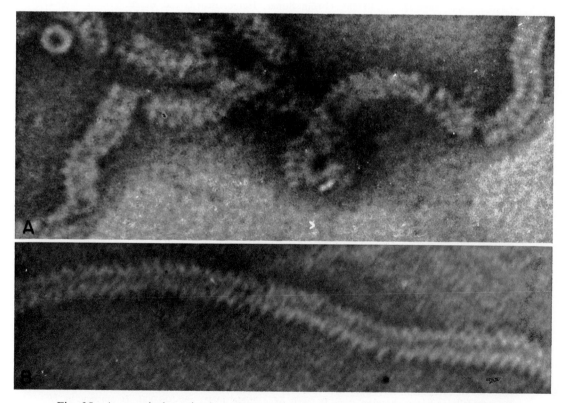

Fig. 25. A, negatively stained portions of flexible helical strands probably of ribonucleoprotein from disrupted mumps virus. Strands are hollow, as indicated by cross section viewed at upper left. × 600,000. B, negatively stained helical strand from Sendai virus. × 600,000. (From Horne and Waterson. *J. Molec. Biol.*, 2:75, 1960.)

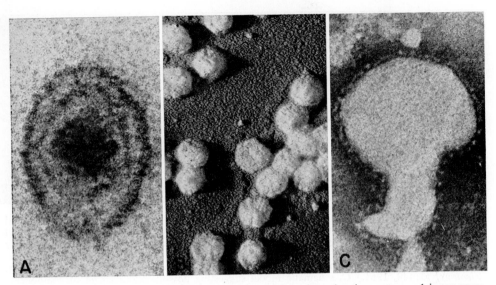

Fig. 26. A, thin section of BAI strain A avian tumor virus showing outer and inner membranes and nucleoid containing dense circular images with open centers which may represent cross sections of coiled hollow strands. × 368,000. B, same virus dried on agar, fixed with osmium vapor and metal-shadowed showing spheroidal shape of agent. × 50,000. C, same virus negatively stained showing distortion due to drying effects. Spicules are arrayed about peripheral membrane surface. × 240,000. (From Bonar, Heine, Beard, and Beard. *J. Nat. Cancer Inst.,* 30:949, 1963.)

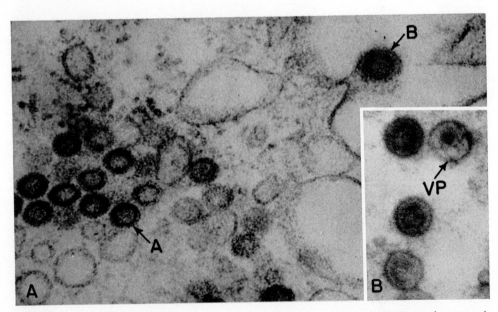

Fig. 27. A, thin section of portion of mouse mammary carcinoma cell illustrating type A particles in cytoplasm (A) and virus particle budding (B) from cell membrane. × 106,000. B, extracellular virus showing type B form of particle (VP). × 106,000. (Courtesy of Drs. M. L. Lyons and D. H. Moore.)

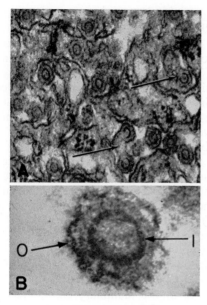

Fig. 28. A, thin section of megakaryocyte cytoplasm from mouse infected with Moloney leukemia virus illustrating budding (arrows) of type A particles from membranes of cytoplasmic channels. × 53,000. (From Dalton, Law, Moloney, and Manaker *J. Nat. Cancer Inst.*, 27:747, 1961.) B, thin section of extracellular virus particle type C budded from cytoplasmic membrane of Friend mouse leukemia cell illustrating nucleoid of low density enclosed in inner (I) and outer (O) membranes. × 228,000. (From de Harven and Friend. *J. Biophys. & Biochem. Cytol.*, 7:747, 1960.)

physical properties of the agent (see p. 829). Similar pleomorphism is shown by particles prepared by negative staining (Fig. 26C), but particles fixed with osmic acid before treatment with phosphotungstate are spherical. The RNA of the virus is situated in the nucleoid, but there is no evidence that the arrangement is either of helical or cubic symmetry. The nucleic acid may be distributed in filaments or in the form of granules. As in the case of the influenza virus (Fig. 23A), the particles of the BAI A strain show (Fig. 26C) the presence of a surface array of spikes, the function of which is not known. As will be seen, the BAI strain A, but no other avian tumor virus, exhibits adenosinetriphosphatase activity localized at the region of the spikes. It is possible that the enzyme activity is associated with the material corresponding to that of the spikes (see p. 873). This is not certain, however, because the Rous sarcoma virus has spikes but no enzyme activity.

Viruses causing neoplastic conditions in mice (45) may vary considerably in morphology from one disease to another and within a single disease in relation to conditions of synthesis. Among the malignancies,

associated with disruption products of the external membrane (Fig. 24A). The HA antigen displays the hemagglutinating properties of the agents.

Avian tumor viruses (9) are also formed by cell-membrane budding (see p. 871) and resemble in some features the agents of the myxovirus group. Of variable size, the particles seen in thin sections (14, 18) in Figure 26A contain an essentially centrally placed nucleoid embedded in an amorphous material of low electron density surrounded by a peripherally situated membrane. An inner membrane is likewise visible. Particles of the BAI A strain A agent (see Chap. 75) dried on agar and fixed with osmic acid before shadowing with metal are spheroidal in shape (Fig. 26B). The virus is very susceptible to distortion when dried in the presence of salt and gives rise to varied tadpole and sperm shapes, a behavior related to the

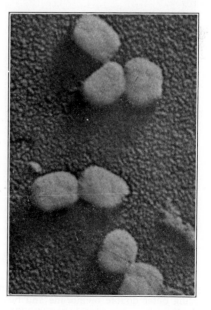

Fig. 29. Vaccinia virus. × 40,500. (From Sharp, Taylor, Hook, and Beard. *Proc. Soc. Exper Biol. & Med.*, 61:259, 1946.)

other than those induced by the polyoma agent (see Chap. 75), are carcinoma of the mouse breast and a variety of leukemias, most of which involve lymphoid cells. Another is a myeloid leukemia associated with green coloration of the lymph nodes, and a third type is a "blast" leukemia of uncertain nature but not involving the lymphoid system.

Membrane-enclosed virus or virus-like particles of two types (14, 74) occur in mouse mammary carcinoma. One, the "A" particle (14), is found in the cytoplasm in the Golgoi region (see p. 874) between and about vesicles or vacuoles. The particle (Fig. 27A) consists of a spheroidal, centrally placed nucleoid of relatively very low electron density immediately surrounded by a thin covering of high density. The nucleoid and dense membrane are surrounded by a thin region of low density bordered peripherally by an outer membrane. Particles of just this structure do not occur outside the cell. Particles of type "B" (14), in contrast, bud from the external cell membrane (Fig. 27B) in a manner similar in principle to the formation of avian tumor viruses. After budding, such particles attain different sizes,

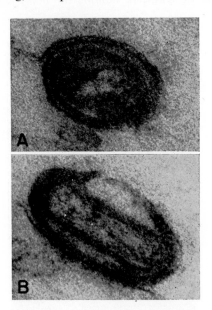

Fig. 30. Thin-sectioned vaccinia virus particles illustrating outer double membrane and biconcave discoid character of nucleoid. × 131,000. (From Morgan, Ellison, Rose, and Moore. *J. Exper. Med.,* 100:301, 1954.)

are globular in shape and contain a relatively small, very dense nucleoid (Fig. 27B) usually eccentrically situated. The nucleoid is enclosed in a closely fitting membrane of high density lying in a material of very low density. The whole particle is surrounded by a thin, dense membrane with the appearance of a double wall. A definitive relationship between types "A" and "B" has not been established, but it would appear that type "B" formed by cell membrane budding and occurring outside the cell is the infectious agent of mouse mammary cancer. Negatively stained "B" particles exhibit a spike array (84) about the periphery similar to that of the avian tumor viruses.

Two types of particles (Fig. 28) occur likewise in the mouse leukemias (14, 30, 32, 35, 84), an "A" type similar to "A" particles of mouse mammary carcinoma and a third type, "C," not present in the mammary cancer. In mouse leukemia virus particles may be assembled in two situations, and the morphology of the agent is related to the locus of formation (30, 32). Virus of type "C" is assembled, as in the avian tumors, at the external membrane of the malignant elements, such as the lymphoblasts in lymphatic leukemia or the blast cells in the Friend disease. Budding from the blast cells of the Friend leukemia (35) (see p. 873) is essentially the same as that seen in the avian diseases, with the difference that the mature extracellular particle is not quite like the chicken tumor viruses. The mature particle is bounded by a peripheral membrane enclosing material of relatively low density (Fig. 28B). The nucleoid is enclosed in a well-defined inner membrane somewhat more dense than that in the avian tumor virus particles. A major difference from the chicken agents is in the nucleoid, which in the mouse viruses is of relatively low density (compare Fig. 28B with Fig. 26A). Particles resembling "C" virus budding from the cell membrane are seen in some instances budding from intracytoplasmic membrane systems of megakaryocytes.

Megakaryocytes are the cells most often seen to be involved in the formation of virus particles in the mouse leukemias (32). Elaboration of the particles in these cells occurs also by budding, but the process in-

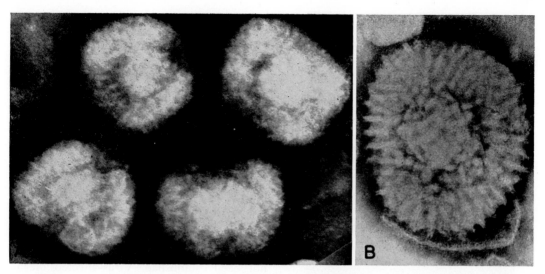

Fig. 31. A, negatively stained structures from vaccinia virus preparations probably representing nucleoids separated from enveloping membranes (see text). Surface markings faintly shown. × 120,000. (From Nagington and Horne. *Virology,* 16:248, 1962.) B, structure as in A with clearly shown tubular formations in surface of nucleoid. × 180,000. (From Dales. *J. Cell. Biol.,* 13:303, 1962.)

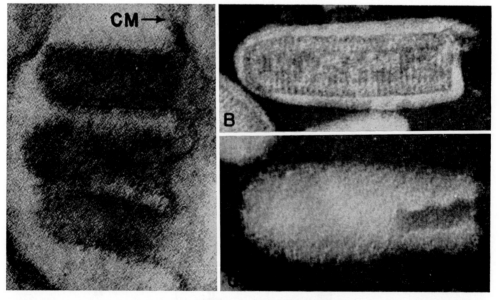

Fig. 32. A, thin section of vesicular stomatitis virus rods budding from cell membrane (CM). × 233,000. B, negatively stained vesicular stomatitis virus shows striated (helical) structure after partial removal of outer coat. C, intact particle shows hollow in rod and faint spicules arrayed at particle surface. × 340,000 (From Howatson and Whitmore. *Virology,* 16: 466, 1962.)

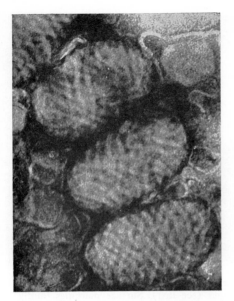

Fig. 33. Negatively stained structures from preparation of contagious pustular dermatitis (ORF) virus which probably represent nucleoids with envelopes removed. Structures show crisscross strands or tubules in surface comparable with tubules in surface of vaccinia virus nucleoids. × 143,000. (From Nagington and Horne. *Virology,* 16:248, 1962.)

volves cytoplasmic membrane systems enclosing vacuoles usually in the Golgi region (Fig. 28A). Often the particles resemble "A" type observed in mouse mammary carcinoma, but there may be considerable difference, as can be seen by comparing Figure 28A with Figure 27A. In the Friend leukemia (35) the particles liberated into the vacuolar spaces are somewhat irregular in contour and are surrounded by a very thin but definite membrane enclosing a more or less dense nucleoid which may also be irregular in outline. As in the case of mouse mammary carcinoma, a clear relationship between particles formed by the external cell membrane and those arising from intracellular membranes in the megakaryocytes has not been established. Virus-affected megakaryocytes display no attributes of malignant cells. It is possible that particles formed in megakaryocytes are derivatives of the respective leukemia agents but are aberrant forms related to imperfect systems of formation in association with intracytoplasmic membranes. As will be mentioned later, the structure and properties of avian tumor

PHAGE T4

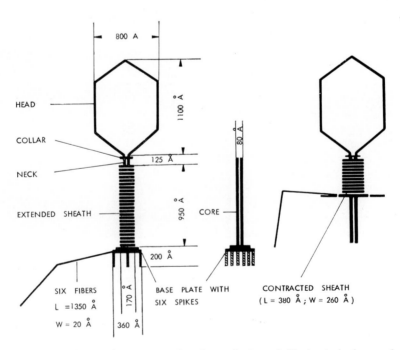

Fig. 34. Diagram illustrating structural units and size of T_4 bacteriophage of *E. coli.* (Courtesy of Dr. E. Kellenberger.)

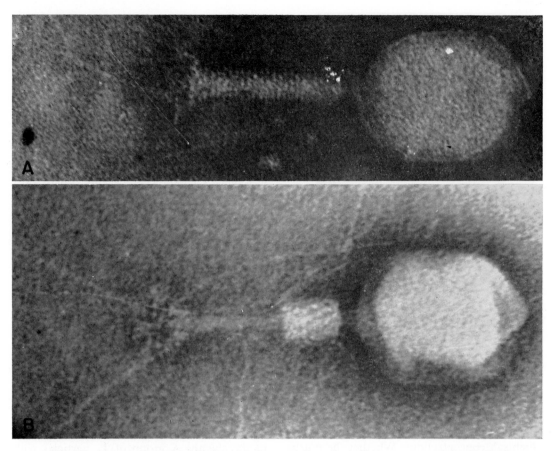

Fig. 35. Negatively stained T₂ bacteriophage of *E. coli*. A illustrates extended tail sheath, membrane surrounding head contents, and the tail-plate and fibers. B shows sheath contracted. × 500,000. (From Brenner, Streisinger, Horne, Champe, Barnett, Benzer, and Rees. *J. Molec. Biol.,* 1:281, 1959.)

viruses may depend greatly on properties of the cell in which they are elaborated.

Pox viruses responsible for a variety of diseases—small pox, vaccinia, fowl pox, molluscum contagiosum, and rabbit fibroma —are large brick-shaped particles (101) (Fig. 29) containing DNA and are synthesized in the cytoplasm (see p. 869). All are enclosed in a membrane seemingly with a double wall, and partial digestion of vaccinia with pepsin (34), for example, reveals the presence of internal structure. Thin sections of the particles show (75) (Fig. 30) that the internal structure consists of a biconcave mass or nucleoid evident also in negatively stained particles (77) (Fig. 31A). Negative staining shows that the particle surface is made up, in part, of hollow filaments arranged (29) as seen in Figure 31B.

Insofar as comparative studies have been made—vaccinia (75, 77), fowl pox (75), rabbit fibroma (14), and molluscum contagiosum (55)—all agents of the pox group exhibit similar morphologic attributes.

An odd shape for an animal virus is that of vesicular stomatitis (56). The particle is rod-shaped, round at one end (Fig. 32), and square across the other. A portion of the particle is hollow, the opening extending from the square end. The virus is assembled by budding from the cell membrane (Fig. 32A). In negatively stained preparations (Fig. 32B) there is a suggestion of helical structure.

An apparently tadpole-shaped animal virus is the cause of equine abortion (99). There have been reports (31) that certain murine leukemia viruses are of similar shape,

Fig. 36. Metal-shadowed T_2 bacteriophage of *E. coli* after treament with hydrogen peroxide and alcohol illustrating contracted sheaths and tail fibers. $\times$ 40,000. (From Kellenberger and Arber. *Ztschr. Naturforsch.,* 10B:688, 1955.)

and it has been noted that avian tumor viruses may also show tadpole- and sperm-shaped forms when the particles are dried under conditions conducive to distortion by high salt concentrations. Whether the murine viruses are really tadpole-shaped has not yet been unequivocally determined.

The ORF agent responsible for contagious pustular dermatitis of sheep and man (77) is of unusual structure (Fig. 33). Some negatively stained particles consist of an envelope of irregular outline enclosing an inner cylindrical structure—nucleoid—with convex ends. Such particles are thus similar in principle to other agents surrounded by a limiting membrane, particularly the pox viruses. Conspicuous in the surface of the inner structure—corresponding to a capsid—are bands wound spirally about the particle. In the micrograph the bands appear to cross one another, but this could be due to manifestations of bands running in a single direction on both sides of the particle. The bands are about 7 to 9 mμ in width and appear to be hollow. Particles which appear to be developmental forms of the agent are also in evidence. Some are bounded by a membrane filled with an amorphous material

similar in appearance to that seen in developing particles of vaccinia virus in the cell cytoplasm (see p. 869). Other particles are like this form but show a beginning orientation of material inside the membrane into strand forms resembling the bands in the cylindrical body. The recently studied virus (44) causing milker's nodules exhibits essentially the same structure as the ORF agent.

The most complex structure is exhibited thus far by the intensively studied tailed bacteriophages (54). These agents consist of a head piece of apparanely hexagonal shape and an attached tail, as illustrated in the diagram of T_4 in Figure 34 and the negatively stained particles of T_2 of *E. coli* in Figure 35. The head is bounded by a thin membrane enclosing electron-dense material containing DNA. The tail consists of a thin, hollow core enclosed in a sheath and terminated by an end plate armed with six fibers. The sheath is contractile (Figs. 34, 35B). As will be seen, the fibers and tail plate are involved in bacteriophage attachment to the host cell. Tailed bacteriophages are actually syringes; attachment to the host cell (see p. 865) is followed by digestion of the cell wall, penetration by the tip of the core, and injection of DNA attended by contraction of the sheath. A group of T_2 particles with contracted sheaths and extended fibers produced by treatment with hydrogen peroxide and alcohol are shown in Figure 36. Stretched tail sheaths (Fig. 35A) exhibit helical arrangement of components. Negatively stained purified preparations of tails (54) show the hollow core with cogwheel protrusions corresponding to the helically arranged subunits seen in the lengthwise stretched sheaths. This morphologic complexity is paralleled by complexity of composition indicated by chemical and antigenic analysis described later.

COMPOSITION

Various principles of virus constitution were discussed in relation to particle morphology. Inspection of Table 4 reveals large differences between the agents, but further consideration shows that the differences reflect group rather than individual virus characteristics. Intimate interrelationships between certain aspects of constitution and virus particle structure were also demonstrated. In addition, correlations were evident between constitutional-architectural interrelationships and virus function and activity. It is an ultimate objective in virology to understand the exact nature of biochemical virus-host cell interaction resulting in disease, and this can be approached only by establishment of the basis for interpretations of virus activity in terms of chemical constitution.

Although studies to correlate virus constitution with function have progressed steadily since initial isolation of tobacco mosaic virus in 1935, relatively few agents have been intensively investigated at the fundamental constitutional level. Most detailed information has been accumulated with plant viruses and some bacteriophages. Nevertheless, data gained with these models have provided the basis for enlightening extrapolations to less well-studied viruses.

From Table 4 it is evident that viruses vary greatly in constitutional complexity, and this is reflected largely, but by no means completely, in the architectural aspects of the virus particles. Comparison of composition with physical evidence of particle structure shows at once that the results of chemical analysis alone are not equally informative for all agents. Instead, constitution is interpretable only in the light of knowledge of physical structure. In addition, as will be illustrated later (Chap. 62), both structure and constitution are related in many instances to the mechanisms of virus particle assembly.

For purposes of discussion of virus constitution, it is expedient to divide viruses into two groups related primarily to particle architecture—that is, agents which are structurally simple and others of morphologically demonstrable complexity. Plant viruses are the classic models of simple structure, and, from the results of recent studies, a variety of other agents, including animal viruses of the nani, adeno, papova and some insect virus groups, are of comparable simplicity. In contrast, representative examples of the pox, NITA, and myxovirus categories as well as avian and murine tumor viruses are both structurally and constitutionally com-

plex. In contrast, bacteriophages are simple in that they contain only protein and nucleic acid, but they may be highly complex in structure and protein component distribution.

Constitutionally and structurally simple viruses exhibit a principal feature in common; namely—with present information— these agents contain only protein and nucleic acid. They differ strikingly, however, in the kind of nucleic acid and in the relative arrangements of protein and nucleic acid. Ribonucleic acid only is a component of all plant viruses, some animal disease agents, and a few bacteriophages (66, 83), whereas other simple animal viruses contain only DNA. A major advance has been the demonstration that the protein component of sufficiently well-studied simple agents is not a collection of different protein molecules but consists of an orderly arrangement of identical protein molecules or subunits (25, 64, 70). Studies of tobacco mosaic virus with carboxypeptidase resulted in the liberation of only one amino acid, threonine, which thus showed that this amino acid was the terminal group of the polypeptide chains constituting the protein components. The amount of threonine liberated in correlation with other analytical data and x-ray findings indicated the presence of 2,130 identical molecules of helical arrangement, as already described. Complete analyses have revealed the kind and number of other amino acids constituting the individual protein molecules. The total number of amino acids per polypeptide chain was 158. Such intensive studies have not been made with other rod-shaped viruses, but morphologic evidence indicates that those examined exhibit the same subunit structure and are thus similar in principles of protein constitution to tobacco mosaic virus.

Knowledge of viruses of cubic symmetry is not as advanced as that of tobacco mosaic virus, but enough is known to indicate that the principles of protein constitution are the same as those found for the helical agents examined. In bushy stunt virus the terminal polypeptide chain group determined by hydrazinolysis was leucine, and the number of amino acid residues indicated a protein molecular weight of 48,000, approximately three-fold that of the corresponding unit in tobacco mosaic virus. Disruption of the agent with detergent yielded units of about 60,000 molecular weight. The equivalent molecular weight of the total bushy stunt protein is about 7.5×10^6. A subunit molecular weight of 48,000 would suggest the presence of about 162 polypeptide chains, which is the number demonstrated by negative staining in other agents of the regular icosahedral series. X-ray studies (23) indicated 60 subunits, but it is notable that x-ray estimates with icosahedral viruses do not conform to electron microscopic determinations. The equivalent protein molecular weight of tobacco mosaic virus is about 37×10^6. Thus the ratio of 162 units of 48,000 molecular weight to 2,130 polypeptide chains of 18,000 molecular weight is similar to the ratio of the respective equivalent protein molecular weights of the two agents.

Another principle of protein substructure is suggested by turnip yellow mosaic virus. Electron microscopy demonstrated 32 subunits or capsomeres, whereas constitutional analysis indicated a polypeptide molecular weight of about 20,000. The equivalent total protein molecular weight of the virus is 3.2×10^6 which would account for about 160 such protein molecules. This would suggest an aggregate of five protein subunits per physically demonstrable capsomere. Morphologic evidence obtained by electron microscopy indicated the possibility of such constitutional complexity, since the capsomeres in this agent, as well as those of other viruses, show ring (or pentagonal or hexagonal) shapes, hollow in some instances, possibly representative of capsomere subunits. Information is not available to indicate whether all polypeptide chains are alike or whether two or more different molecules comprise the protein component.

Much less is known about the constitutional aspects of other helical and icosahedral agents than about the viruses just mentioned. For several reasons considered during the past decade, it would appear that all constitutionally and structurally simple viruses are assembled by the same principles. Morphologically the shell—presumably protein—of the icosahedral viruses appears to

consist of variable numbers of similar capsomeres each of which, however, may consist of either one or more than one of the same or different kinds of polypeptide chains. That the number of differences is severely restricted may be judged by absolute amounts of nucleic acid per particle, which is a limiting factor in the coding (26) of polypeptide chain synthesis from amino acids.

The foregoing account was concerned with agents consisting of uniformly and constantly distributed subunits in association only with nucleic acid. In such material chemical analyses serve to reveal the nature of the subunit. With some viruses of apparently simple constitution, however, there is evidence of structural complexity which lessens the significance of such analyses. Notable examples in this category are at least some rod-shaped viruses. As already observed, nuclear polyhedrosis and cytoplasmic granular rods are ensheathed in a thin membrane which would complicate the significance of component analyses. Only one demonstrably icosahedral virus, *Tipula* iridescent, contains lipid which conceivably might complicate the analyses, depending on whether the lipid is associated with capsomere or other protein.

The significance of analytical data derived in the studies of structurally and constitutionally complex viruses is quite different from that concerned with the simple agents. Most of the complex agents—pox viruses, herpes, myxoviruses, and avian and murine tumor viruses—consist of a nucleoid enclosed in a surrounding material bounded by an external membrane. In herpes, for example, the nucleoid exhibits structure comparable to the capsids and capsomeres of the simple agents. Furthermore, the nucleoid is the locus of the nucleic acid component. Thus, the complex agents contain a nucleoid and an additional enveloping material lacking in the simple viruses. The distinction between envelope and nucleoid is evident from the mechanism of virus particle assembly. In this process myxoviruses and the avian and murine tumor agents—except polyoma virus—are completed by budding from the cell membrane. The herpes nucleoid or capsid originating in the cell nucleus may acquire an envelope either from membrane in the cell cytoplasm or by final assembly by budding from the cell membrane.

With these agents it is evident that the envelope represents cellular components incorporated in the particles. The extent of alteration of cell membrane under the influence of the virus constituents is not known. Nevertheless, some attributes of the cell are demonstrable in some cases. Influenza virus, for example, contains precipitins specific to the host cell. The BAI strain A avian tumor virus acquires adenosinetriphosphatase activity (9) when it is budded from cells with the enzyme in the cell membrane, but virus budded from cell membranes without membrane adenosinetriphosphatase is enzyme-free (37, 38). Herpes virus contains the enzyme for the same reason (42). The BAI strain A agent contains chicken tissue and Forssman antigens derived from the cell. Cartilage fibers may be included in virus budded from chondrocytes, and particles from cells actively liberating collagen have wrinkled membranes, as if deformed by inclusion of collagen (47). The envelope of the pox viruses is of a different origin. The nucleoid and envelope are synthesized simultaneously in the cell cytoplasm.

Further evidence of protein constitutional complexity is the multiplicity of antigenic and other properties. Agents of the influenza group, for example, exhibit two antigens, one associated with the nucleoid material and the other with the envelope, which also possesses the hemagglutinin properties of the particles (91). The influenza viruses likewise contain the enzyme neuraminidase (72). Most demonstrably complex are the large, tailed bacteriophages (64). In the head section are protein, polyamines, and nucleic acid. In the tail contractile protein, phage lysozyme, tail core, tail plate, tail fibers, and adenosinetriphosphatase have been identified.

From these considerations, it is plain that total protein and amino acid analyses disclose little evidence of the basic-unit constitutional characteristics. In order to effect the same correlation of constitution with structure and function, it is necessary to fractionate the agents into their individual separate components.

Nucleic acid analyses (Table 5) yield information of relatively equal significance for all viral agents. From morphologic and other evidence it would appear that nucleic acid, whether RNA or DNA, is virus-specific and represents no additives of host cell material. In consequence, the amount and kind of nucleic acid is a specific viral characteristic, regardless of nature of assembly or adventitious enveloping or associated substance.

As noted in Table 5, the proportion of nucleic acid varies greatly from one agent to another. A different perspective emerges, however, with calculations of the absolute amounts of nucleic acid per individual virus particle (2). It then becomes evident that the nucleic acid content of most RNA viruses varies but little about the value of approximately 2×10^6 molecular weight. The lowest value, 1.5×10^6, is that of tobacco necrosis, and the highest in the comparable range is 3.1 for foot and mouth disease. A notable exception (17) to the relative uniformity is the BAI strain A avian tumor agent, with a molecular weight of 9.6×10^6. A like value was obtained for the Rous sarcoma virus.

In tobacco mosaic virus the RNA is disposed in a single-stranded helix consisting of 6,390 nucleotides. Other helical plant viruses contain similar amounts of RNA, probably arranged in the same manner. In tobacco mosaic virus three nucleotides are associated with each protein subunit or capsomere. Neither chemical nor structural protein-nucleic acid relationships are known in agents other than rods. It has been determined, however, that nucleoprotein occurs in chains or "helix" formations in some complex agents such as the myxoviruses (Figs. 25, 26), closely similar to those constituting the tobacco mosaic virus rod (Fig. 4). Chains of nucleoprotein are demonstrable in the icosahedral wound tumor virus (Fig. 15), but the relation to other particle components is not known.

The nucleic acid content of DNA viruses (2) is usually much greater than in those with RNA, and the range is broad (Table 5). It is likely that DNA is double-stranded in most DNA agents, as in the rabbit papilloma agent. In the øX174 bacteriophage, in contrast, DNA seems to be single-stranded.

Table 5. Nucleic Acid Content of Viruses (2)

GROUP	VIRUS	SHAPE	(mμ)	NUCLEIC ACID PER CENT	NUCLEIC ACID MOL. WT. (x 10^{-6})
		RNA			
Rodlike plant viruses	Tobacco mosaic	Rod	300 x 17	5.8	2.2
	Tobacco rattle	''	180 x 25	5.0	2.7
	Potato X	''	600 x 10	5.7	2.6
Spherical plant viruses	Turnip yellow mosaic	Sphere	22	37	2.0
	Southern bean mosaic	''	25	20	1.9
	Tomato bushy stunt	''	25	15	2.1
	Tobacco necrosis	''	17	18	1.5
Spherical vertebrate viruses	Poliomyelitis	''	30	22	1.75
	Foot and mouth	''	27	40	3.1
	Encephalomyocarditis	''	30	30	2.10
Arborvirus	Equine encephalitis	''	50	4.4	2.2
Myxovirus	Influenza	Spheroid	100	1.0	2.3
	Fowl plague	''	120	1.8	2.7
Avian tumor	BAI strain A	''	120	2.2	9.6
Insect cytoplasmic	*Dasychira pudibunda*	Sphere	40	7	2.5
	Sphinx populi	''	80	0.9	2.6
		DNA			
Large phage	T2, T4, T6		100 x 80 (head)	45	126
	T1, T3, T7	Prismatic + tail	50 x 45 (head)	41	35
			45 x 45 (head)	45	60
	Salmonella P22		50 x 45 (head)	40	35
Small phage	øX174	Sphere	25 diameter	25	1.7
Insect nuclear	*Bombyx mori*		288 x 40	14	76
	Lymantria dispar	Rod	300 x 30	16	56
	Aporia crataegi		220 x 50	9	58
Insect cytoplasmic	*Tipula* iridescent	Icosahedral	130 diameter	12.4	156
Pox virus	Vaccinia	Brick	284 x 222	5.2-5.6	156
	Cowpox			7.2	156
Adenovirus	Adenovirus type	Icosahedral	75 diameter	13	66
Animal tumor	Rabbit papilloma		50 diameter	8.7	7

Protein-DNA patterns have not been clearly distinguished, but essentially tubular or strand-like structures occur in the surface or superficial substance of nucleoids in pox viruses such as vaccinia and ORF. Questions concerning molecular multiplicity of DNA in the respective agents of high DNA content continue under study. In some viruses RNA is known to occur as a single chain or molecule. All of the DNA of the T_2 phage, with a molecular weight of about 130×10^6, is demonstrable as a single strand of 49 ± 4 μ length (61).

Concepts of the significance of virus constitution have matured rapidly since the discovery that nucleic acid is the specific essential component (25, 43, 64, 95). As will be discussed further in Chap. 62, it has been shown that initiation of the infectious process and specific virus synthesis of some agents can be induced by nucleic acid alone. This was accomplished first with RNA isolated from tobacco mosaic virus and subsequently with the RNA of a variety of both plant and animal viruses. It had been realized for some time that only DNA of the tailed bacteriophages entered the parasitized bacterium. Recognition of the phenomenon was extended more recently to DNA animal viruses of the papova group—

rabbit papilloma (58) and polyoma agents (40), for example—and infection is transmitted also by the single-stranded DNA of the øX 174 bacteriophage.

Such findings effect much clarification of the functional significance of nucleic acid composition and provide the basis for judgements relative to the role of ancillary components of protein and lipid. It would appear that materials enclosing nucleic acid serve two principal purposes: (1) to protect nucleic acid during exposure to adverse environmental conditions inside or outside the cell and (2) partly to influence specificity of host-cell parasitization. It is unlikely that transmission by free nucleic acid is a significant factor under natural conditions, and nucleic acid must be conserved in the process of transfer from one cell to another and also under the varied conditions of virus uptake by the cell. In some cases nucleic acid alone can make its way into the cell, but in others whole virus particles are taken up. Virus membrane or sheath influence on specificity of host cell infection is indicated by the broader spectrum of hosts parasitized by nucleic acid than by whole virus particles.

REFERENCES

1. Adams, M. H. Bacteriophages, New York, Interscience Publishers, 1959.
2. Allison, A. C., and Burke, D. C. J. Gen. Microbiol., 27:181, 1962.
3. Almeida, J. D., Howatson, A. F., and Williams, M. G. Virology, 16:353, 1962.
4. Anderson, T. F. Cold Spring Harbor Symp. Quant. Biol., 18:197, 1953.
5. Andrewes, C. H. Adv. in Virus Res., 9:271, 1962.
6. Ansevin, A. T., and Lauffer, M. A. Nature, London, 183:1601, 1959.
7. Bawden, F. C. Plant Viruses and Virus Diseases, 4th ed., New York, The Ronald Press Company, 1964.
8. Beard, J. W. J. Immunol., 58:49, 1948.
9. ——— Adv. in Cancer Res., 7:1, 1963.
10. Beijerinck, M. W. Zentralbl. Bakt., Abt. II, 5:27, 1899.
11. Ben-Porat, T., and Kaplan, A. S. Virology, 16:261, 1962.
12. Bergold, G. H. Adv. in Virus Res., 1:91, 1953.
13. Bergold, G. H. In The Viruses, Burnet, F. M., and Stanley, W. M., eds., New York, Academic Press Inc., 1959, vol. 1, p. 505.
14. Bernhard, W. Cancer Res., 20:712, 1960.
15. ——— Cold Spring Harbor Symp. Quant. Biol., 27:67, 1962.
16. Bils, R. F., and Hall, C. E. Virology, 17:123, 1962.
17. Bonar, R. A., and Beard, J. W. J. Nat. Cancer Inst., 23:183, 1959.
18. ——— Heine, U., Beard, D., and Beard, J. W. J. Nat. Cancer Inst., 30:949, 1963.
19. Brakke, M. K. Adv. in Virus Res., 7:193, 1960.
20. Brenner, S., and Horne, R. W. Biochim. et Biophys. Acta, 34:103, 1959.
21. Burnet, F. M. Principles of Animal Virology, 2nd ed., New York, Academic Press Inc., 1960.
22. ——— and Stanley, W. M. The Viruses, New York, Academic Press Inc., 1959, vols. 1, 2, and 3.
23. Caspar, D. L. D. Nature, London, 177:475, 1956.
24. ——— and Klug, A. Cold Spring Harbor Symp. Quant. Biol., 27:1, 1962.
25. Colter, J. S., and Ellem, K. A. O. Ann. Rev. Microbiol., 15:219, 1961.
26. Crick, F. H. C., Barnett, L., Brenner, S., and Watts-Tobin, R. J. Nature, London, 192:1227, 1961.
27. ——— and Watson, J. D. Nature, London, 177:473, 1956.
28. Cruickshank, J. G., Berry, D. M., and Hay, B. Virology, 20:376, 1963.
29. Dales, S. J. Cell Biol., 13:303, 1962.
30. Dalton, A. J. Fed. Proc., 21:936, 1962.
31. ——— Haguenau, F., and Moloney, J. B. J. Nat. Cancer Inst., 29:1177, 1962.
32. ——— Law, L. W., Moloney, J. B., and Manaker, R. A. J. Nat. Cancer Inst., 27:747, 1961.
33. Davies, M. C., Englert, M. E., Stebbins, M. R., and Cabasso, V. J. Virology, 15:87, 1961.
34. Dawson, I. M., and McFarlane, A. S. Nature, London, 161:464, 1948.
35. de Harven, E., and Friend, C. J. Biophys. Biochem. Cytol., 7:747, 1960.
36. d'Herelle, F. Compt. rend. Acad. d. sc., 165:373, 1917.
37. de The, G., Becker, C., and Beard, J. W. J. Nat. Canter Inst., 32:201, 1964.
38. ——— Heine, U., Sommer, J. R., Arvy, L., Beard, D., and Beard, J. W. J. Nat. Cancer Inst., 30:415, 1963.
39. Diagnostic Procedures for Virus and Rickettsial Diseases, 2nd ed., New York, American Public Health Association, 1956.
40. Di Mayorca, G. A., Eddy, B. E., Stewart, S. E., Hunter, W. S., Friend, C., and Bendich, A. Proc. Nat. Acad. Sc., 45:1805, 1959.
41. Elford, W. J. In Doerr, R., and Hallauer, C. Handbuch der Virusforschung, Erste Hälfte, Wien, Julius Springer, p. 126, 1938.
42. Epstein, M. A., and Holt, S. J. Nature, London, 198:509, 1963.
43. Fraenkel-Conrat, H. In The Viruses, Burnet, F. M., and Stanley, W. M., eds., New York, Academic Press Inc., 1959, vol. 1, p. 429.
44. Friedman-Kien, A. E., Rowe, W. P., and Banfield, W. G. Science, 140:1335, 1963.
45. Gross, L. Oncogenic Viruses, International Series of Monographs on Pure and Applied Biology, New York, Pergamon Press, 1961, vol. 11.
46. Hart, R. G. Proc. Nat. Acad. Sc., 41:261, 1955.

47. Heine, U., de The, G., Ishiguro, H., Sommer, J. R., Beard, D., and Beard, J. W. J. Nat. Cancer Inst., 29:41, 1962.
48. Hersh, R. T., and Schachman, H. K. Virology, 6:234, 1958.
49. Hillier, J. Ann. Rev. Microbiol., 4:1, 1950.
50. Horne, R. W., Brenner, S., Waterson, A. P., and Wildy, P. J. Mol. Biol., 1:84, 1959.
51. ———— and Nagington, J. J. Mol. Biol., 1:333, 1959.
52. ———— and Waterson, A. P. J. Mol. Biol., 2:75, 1960.
53. ———— Waterson, A. P., Wildy, P., and Farnham, A. E. Virology, 11:79, 1960.
54. ———— and Wildy, P. Virology, 15:348, 1961.
55. Howatson, A. F. Brit. Med. Bull., 18:193, 1962.
56. ———— and Whitmore, G. F. Virology, 16:466, 1962.
57. Hoyle, L., Horne, R. W., and Waterson, A. P. Virology, 13:448, 1961.
58. Ito, Y., and Evans, C. A. J. Exper. Med., 114:485, 1961.
59. Iwanowski, D. Bull. Acad. Imp. Sc. (St. Petersburg), n.s. 35:67, 1892.
60. Kerby, G. P., Gowdy, R. A., Dillon, E. S., Dillon, M. L., Csáky, T. Z., Sharp, D. G., and Beard, J. W. J. Immunol., 63:93, 1949.
61. Kleinschmidt, A. K., Lang, D., Zacherts, D., and Zahn, R. K. Biochim. Biophys. Acta, 61:857, 1962.
62. Klug, A., and Caspar, D. L. D. Adv. in Virus Res., 7:225, 1960.
63. Knight, C. A. In The Viruses, Burnet, F. M., and Stanley, W. M., eds., New York, Academic Press Inc., 1959, vol. 2, p. 127.
64. Kozloff, L. M. Ann. Rev. Biochem., 29:475, 1960.
65. Lauffer, M. A., and Bendet, I. J. Adv. in Virus Res., 2:241, 1954.
66. Loeb, T., and Zinder, N. D. Proc. Nat. Acad. Sc., 47:282, 1961.
67. Luria, S. E. General Virology, New York, John Wiley & Sons, Inc., 1953.
68. MacLean, E. C., and Hall, C. E. J. Mol. Biol., 4:173, 1962.
69. Macpherson, I., Wildy, P., Stoker, M., and Horne, R. W. Virology, 13:146, 1961.
70. Markham, R. In The Viruses, Burnet, F. M., and Stanley, W. M., eds., New York, Academic Press Inc., 1959, vol. 2, p. 33.
71. ———— Adv. in Virus Res., 9:241, 1962.
72. Mayron, L. W., Robert, B., Winzler, R. J., and Rafelson, M. E., Jr. Arch. Biochem. & Biophys., 92:475, 1961.
73. Melnick, J. L. Science, 135:1128, 1962.
74. Moore, D. H., Lasfargues, E. Y., Murray, M. R., Haagensen, C. D., and Pollard, E. C. J. Biophys. Biochem. Cytol., 5:85, 1959.
75. Morgan, C., Ellison, S. A., Rose, H. M., and Moore, D. H. J. Exper. Med., 100:301, 1954.
76. ———— Rifkind, R. A., and Rose, H. M. Cold Spring Harbor Symp. Quant. Biol., 27:57, 1962.
77. Nagington, J., and Horne, R. W. Virology, 16:248, 1962.
78. Niu, Ching-I, Shore, V., and Knight, C. A. Virology, 6:226, 1958.
79. Nixon, H. L., and Gibbs, A. J. J. Mol. Biol., 2:197, 1960.
80. ———— and Harrison, B. D. J. Gen. Microbiol., 21:582, 1959.
81. ———— and Woods, R. D. Virology, 10:157, 1960.
82. Northrop, J. H., and Kunitz, M. J. Gen. Physiol., 7:729, 1925.
83. Paranchych, W., and Graham, A. F. J. Cell & Comp. Physiol., 60:199, 1962.
84. Parsons, D. F. J. Nat. Cancer Inst., 30:569, 1963.
85. Pease, D. C. Histological Techniques for Electron Microscopy, New York, Academic Press Inc., 1960.
86. Putnam, F. W. Adv. Prot. Chem., 8:175, 1953.
87. Reilly, H. C., Harris, D. A., and Waksman, S. A. J. Bact., 54:451, 1947.
88. Rose, H. M., and Morgan, C. Ann. Rev. Microbiol., 14:217, 1960.
89. Sabin, A. B. Science, 130:1387, 1959.
90. Schachman, H. K., and Williams, R. C. In The Viruses, Burnet, F. M., and Stanley, W. M., eds., New York, Academic Press Inc., 1959, vol. 1, p. 223.
91. Schäfer, W. Bacteriol. Rev., 27:1, 1963.
92. Schaffer, F. L., and Schwerdt, C. E. Proc. Nat. Acad. Sc., 41:1020, 1955.
93. ———— and Schwerdt, C. E. Adv. in Virus Res., 6:159, 1959.
94. Schmidt, N. J., and Lennette, E. H. Prog. Med. Virology, 3:1, 1961.
95. Schramm, G. Ann. Rev. Biochem., 27:101, 1958.
96. Sharp, D. G. Adv. in Virus Res., 1:277, 1953.
97. ———— Beard, D., and Beard, J. W. J. Biol. Chem., 182:279, 1950.
98. ———— and Beard, J. W. Biochim. et Biophys. Acta, 14:12, 1954.
99. ———— and Bracken, E. C. Virology, 10:419, 1960.
100. ———— Hook, A. E., Taylor, A. R., Beard, D., and Beard, J. W. J. Biol. Chem., 165:259, 1946.
101. ———— Taylor, A. R., Hook, A. E., and Beard, J. W. Proc. Soc. Exper. Biol. & Med., 61:259, 1946.
102. ———— Taylor, A. R., McLean, I. W., Jr., Beard, D., and Beard, J. W. J. Biol. Chem., 156:585, 1944.
103. ———— Taylor, A. R., McLean, I. W., Jr., Beard, D., and Beard, J. W. J. Biol. Chem., 159:29, 1945.
104. Sharpless, G. R. Ann. New York Acad. Sc., 101:515, 1962.
105. Smith, I. Chromatographic and Electrophoretic Techniques, 2nd ed., New York, Interscience Publishers, 1960.
106. Smith, K. M. Virology, 5:168, 1958.
107. ———— Adv. in Virus Res., 9:195, 1962.
108. Steere, R. L. Adv. in Virus Res., 6:1, 1959.
109. Steinhaus, E. A. Principles of Insect Pathology, 1st ed., New York, McGraw-Hill Book Co., Inc., 1949.
110. Swerdlow, M., Dalton, A. J., and Birks, L. S. Analytical Chem., 28:597, 1956.
111. Taylor, A. R., Sharp, D. G., Beard, D., and Beard, J. W. J. Infect. Dis., 72:31, 1943.
112. ———— Sharp, D. G., McLean, I. W., Jr., Beard, D., and Beard, J. W. J. Immunol., 50:291, 1945.

113. Tromans, W. J., and Horne, R. W. Virology, 15:1, 1961.
114. van Rooyen, C. E., and Rhodes, A. J. Virus Diseases of Man, 2nd ed., New York, Thomas Nelson & Sons, 1948.
115. Vasquez, C., and Tournier, P. Virology, 17:503, 1962.
116. Weil, M. L., Beard, D., Sharp, D. G., and Beard, J. W. J. Immunol., 60:561, 1948.
117. Weil, R. Cold Spring Harbor Symp. Quant. Biol., 27:83, 1962.
118. Wilcox, W. C., Ginsberg, H. S., and Anderson, T. F. J. Exper. Med., 118:307, 1963.
119. Wildy, P., Russell, W. C., and Horne, R. W. Virology, 12:204, 1960.
120. ———— Stokes, M. G. P., Macpherson, I. A., and Horne, R. W. Virology, 11:444, 1960.
121. ———— and Watson, D. H. Cold Spring Harbor Symp. Quant. Biol., 27:25, 1962.
122. Williams, R. C. Adv. in Virus Res., 2:183, 1954.
123. ———— Kass, S. J., and Knight, C. A. Virology, 12:48, 1960.
124. ———— and Smith, K. M. Biochim. et Biophys. Acta, 28:464, 1958.
125. Wyckoff, R. W. G. Electron Microscopy, New York, Interscience Publishers, Inc., 1949.

62

Biologic Phenomena of Virus Diseases

Most agents causing disease are physiologically and reproductively independent of host processes. In contrast, viruses are totally dependent on the living cell for manifestation of physiologic activity, and the influences responsible for cell disorder and virus replication are exerted at the fine biochemical level of cell constitution.

In many respects diseases resulting from virus infection exhibit no distinguishing principles of host and immunologic response, and there is evident a distinct continuity of many basic biologic phenomena of virus diseases and conditions caused by other organisms. Viruses outside the cell are subject to host self-protective influences operative in bacterial diseases, but once the agents are inside cells, disease induction and virus replication are regulated by cell-virus interaction. The special features of virus diseases are thus additive to the phenomena of other microorganismal parasitization. For these reasons, special procedures can and must be applied to the study of the characteristics of the virus-cell interaction. Electron microscopy reveals many ultrastructural features of cell involvement by virus, and since viruses are of relatively simple constitution, the problems of cell-virus interaction can be approached with purely biochemical methods. Nevertheless, the more conventional procedures of light microscopic histopathology provide the basis for correlation of the grosser aspects of disease with the processes occurring at the molecular level.

PATHOGENESIS

The course of the induction of virus infection varies broadly, and uniformity is seen only in the basic principles leading to the development of the process. Under natural conditions there must occur, first, **contact** of the virus with the susceptible cell. In the higher multicellular organisms this involves **introduction of the agent** into the tissues of the intact host and transport to the site of specific cell or cells. There, secondly, the virus or **representative constituents** of it must **enter the cell.** Finally, the process of **cell-virus interaction** must be established.

Transmission from one host to another under natural conditions may be simple or complex. The spread of some agents is effected by mechanical transfer (126). Transmission may occur by **contact** of various sorts: with injured **superficial cells** of the skin—warts—or leaf surfaces—tobacco mosaic; by **grafting** diseased plant tissue to healthy hosts; or, in animals, through the **respiratory tract,** directly to the cells affected—respiratory epithelium in influenza—or to remote sites in the parotid glands or testes—mumps—or skin and mucous membranes—measles. The **digestive tract** is the portal of entry of poliomyelitis virus, for example, and for many viruses responsible for insect diseases. Transmission of some diseases is dependent on **insect vectors**—as yellow fever and equine encephalomyelitis (mosquitos), louping ill virus of sheep (ticks), and sandfly fever (flies). Most plant viruses are carried principally by sucking insects (11), aphids, leaf hoppers, and thrips. Multiplication of virus may occur in the insects concerned which may constitute **reservoirs** by passage of virus to succeeding generations through the egg. Avian and mouse tumor viruses may be passed through the egg, and other viruses pass from mother to child in utero (12).

Cell susceptibility is of vital significance in virus diseases. The principal determining factors are **genetic constitution** with respect to **species** and **cell type** and host age at the time of exposure. Degrees of species and cell specificity vary greatly. Various papilloma viruses are species-specific, as are some plant and insect viruses. Less host specificity is seen with other agents such as equine encephalomyelitis and vaccinia viruses. Broad ranges of cell-type susceptibility are observed also: smallpox and measles affect skin and mucous membranes, and mumps affects the parotid gland and testes. Neither host nor cell specificity is unchangeable, however, since both may be altered under experimental conditions. Usually newborn or young animals are more susceptible to infection than older individuals. The route of exposure is important in many cases. Viruses are sometimes grouped according to the tissue most affected—**neurotropic, dermotropic,** or **viscerotropic**—and those which affect several types of tissue are **pantotropic** agents.

GENERAL PATHOLOGY

The clinical and pathologic effects of virus invasion are variable. Disease symptoms may be entirely lacking, though virus multiplication is in progress. Some viruses cause only sharply circumscribed **local** lesions without spread other than mechanical extension to contiguous cells. In most cases, however, systemic disease is associated with widespread involvement of susceptible tissues. The clinical outcome is governed by the nature of the lesions, by the extent of involvement of critical tissues, and, in some diseases, by infection with **secondary bacterial invaders** (107).

Effects on individual parasitized cells vary from rapid degeneration, or necrosis, to continued, uncontrolled cell proliferation. Bacteria infected by some bacteriophages disintegrate or lyse after a period of minutes. There may be extensive necrosis of affected cells in higher organisms. Molluscum contagiosum and warts are processes of limited epithelial hyperplasia. Warts in rabbits, however, after several months' standing, may undergo carcinomatous changes that lead to invasive, eroding tumors (101). *Condyloma acuminatum* in man may likewise progress to an eroding, malignant, carcinomatous

process (15). At the extreme of the agents causing hyperplasia, mouse mammary carcinoma virus (53), and the fowl sarcoma, avian leukosis (5, 7), and mouse leukemia viruses (108) induce continuing cell multiplication. Nearly perfect states of symbiosis between virus and cell may be established in some neoplasms. Some viruses may be present in **latent** infections without outward evidence of disease.

INCLUSION BODIES

Morphologic evidence of cell-virus interaction was first revealed by light microscopy by the presence of certain structures of diagnostic specificity termed **inclusion bodies** (44). These are structures of various sizes and appearance occurring within the cytoplasm or nucleus of diseased cells. Both intranuclear and cytoplasmic inclusion bodies may be seen in the same cell in multiple infections (116). Much of the significance of some specific inclusion bodies had been learned before development of the electron microscope, as in fowl pox (125), molluscum

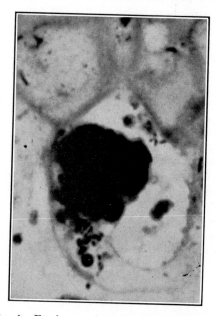

Fig. 1. Fowl pox virus. An inclusion body of fowl pox in an epidermal cell of chicken skin. Mitochondria are also present in the cell. × 2,200. (From Goodpasture, in T. M. Rivers. *Filtrable Viruses,* Williams and Wilkins Co.)

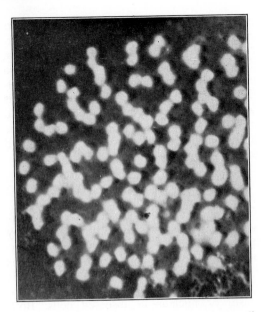

Fig. 2. Inclusion body of mouse ectromelia (mouse pox). × 12,000. (From van Rooyen and Rhodes. *Virus Diseases of Man,* Thomas Nelson and Sons.)

Fig. 3. Polyhedral body of *Prodenia praefica* Grote (yellow-striped army-worm) treated with sodium hydroxide and showing the bundles of virus rods lying in the remains of the polyhedral body. Each bundle consists of several virus particles lying side by side. × 7,500. (From Hughes. *J. Bact.,* 59: 189, 1950.)

contagiosum (119), and some of the insect diseases (9, 111, 112).

Fowl pox inclusion bodies are relatively large structures found in the cell cytoplasm (Fig. 1), enveloped in a lipid-like membrane. Such bodies contain thousands of virus particles, as illustrated in the electron micrograph of an ectromelia (mouse pox) inclusion body (Fig. 2). Inclusion bodies of molluscum contagiosum (119) are as large as 24 to 27 μ in width and 30 to 37 μ in length and can be picked out of epithelial cell cytoplasm with microneedles. Evidence of the character of these inclusion bodies and the particles contained within them is described in a following section (see Figs. 12 and 13). Classic examples of inclusion bodies (112) occur in the polyhedral diseases of certain insects. The intranuclear polyhedra in silkworm jaundice are highly refractive, crystal-like bodies of five to eight faces, 0.5 to 15 μ in diameter, and enclose numbers of specific bacilliform virus particles (Fig. 3). Polyhedral bodies in the cytoplasm of many lepidopterous larvae contain not rods but nearly-spherical particles or particles of cubic symmetry demonstrable in ultrathin sections of the polyhedron (110).

Another form of inclusion bodies occurs in granulosis diseases affecting insects. Individual granules occurring in cell cytoplasm are uniform, egg-shaped bodies 0.2 to 0.3 μ in diameter (Fig. 4). The granules contain one or more bacilliform virus particles (Fig. 5).

ULTRASTRUCTURAL CELL-VIRUS RELATIONSHIPS

In early studies inclusion bodies were not seen in all diseases of known viral etiology. Electron micrography corroborated these findings and revealed the true state of affairs. Many viruses develop without inclusion-body formation, and most of the morphologically demonstrable components and organelles of the cell are involved by one or another of the agents. Thin sections of virus-infected cells not only have shown mere association of virus with the cell but have provided information relative to the mode of cell invasion, course of particle assembly, and release of the agents. Cell

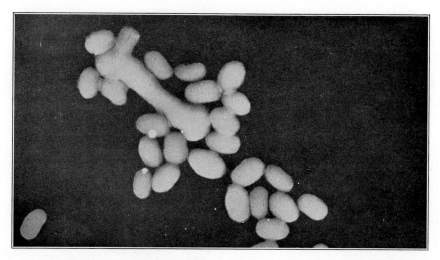

Fig. 4. Virus capsules of *Cacoecia murinana* Hüb. (fir-shoot roller). × 25,000. (From Bergold. *Ztschr. Naturforsch.*, 3b, 38, 1948.)

types affected by viruses vary greatly in the proportions and characteristics of nuclear and cytoplasmic structures. Correlations of light and electron microscopic structural aspects of different cells have been effected in the textbook *Histology* by Ham and Leeson (54).

Fig. 5. A single capsule of *Cacoecia murinana*, like those of Figure 4, splits open, showing the virus rod and the groove in which it was enclosed. × 100,000. (Courtesy of Dr. G. Bergold.)

Principles of cell involvement in the synthesis, elaboration, and liberation of viruses of the principal groups listed in Table 2 in Chapter 61 are illustrated schematically in Figure 6. Some DNA agents—nuclear insect polyhedrosis, the papova, adeno, and herpes viruses—are synthesized in the nucleus; and other DNA viruses—insect granulosis, cytoplasmic free insect virus particles, and pox viruses—are elaborated in the cytoplasm. Only one group of RNA agents—myxoviruses—are presently known to involve both the nucleus and cytoplasm, and all other RNA viruses are assembled in the cytoplasm. There is thus, at the moment, no correlation between either virus particle architecture or kind of nucleic acid and the cell loci of virus formation.

Bacteriophages added to cultures of sensitive bacteria are quickly adsorbed (117) to the host surface. Efficiency of adsorption may be influenced by various factors (2, 95). Individual bacteria can adsorb enough phage practically to cover the surface (65). Inactive phage, produced as by ultraviolet irradiation, is likewise adsorbed and kills the host but without virus elaboration. Adsorption of tailed phages occurs by contact of the tailpiece and fibers (3, 65) (Fig. 35 in Chap. 61) with the surface of the host (Fig. 7). A tiny portion of the cell wall at the point of contact is dissolved. The terminal part of the tail penetrates the cell

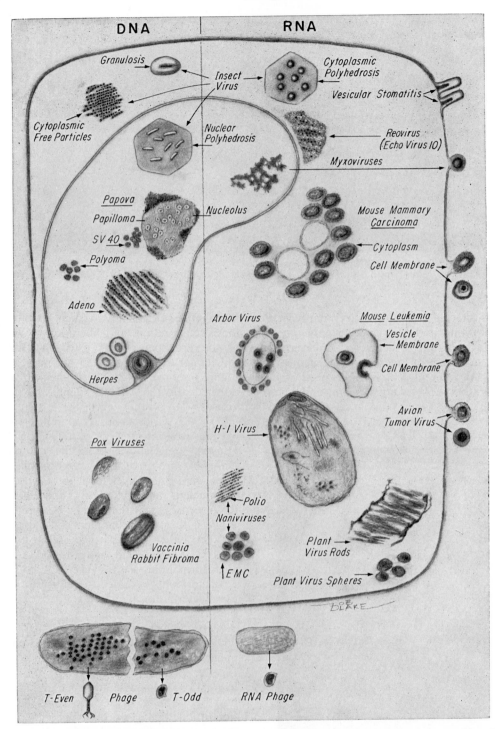

Fig. 6. Diagrammatic illustration of cell-virus relationships in the synthesis and assembly of various categories of plant, insect, animal, and bacterial viruses. Drawing was not made to relative or absolute scales. Relative position of cell organelles and loci of virus formation are schematic.

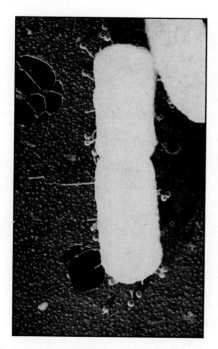

Fig. 7. Bacteriophage adsorbed to host bacterium showing empty head structures after expulsion of head-contents (DNA) into host. (Courtesy of Drs. T. F. Anderson, F. Jacob, and E. Wollman.)

At the beginning there is no evidence of phage-like bodies, but after a time there is condensation of the DNA, and electron-dense rounded forms appear in the ill-defined vacuolar spaces. These then acquire the appearance of the phage head which becomes enveloped in the head membrane. The inner tail units, the outer tail sheath, the terminal tail plate, and the tail fibers are then added. The completed phage is liberated in a "burst" of the bacterium.

An example of plant virus-cell association is illustrated in Figure 10, showing a mass of tobacco mosaic virus in a tobacco leaf cell. Virus rods are aligned lengthwise and also end to end and are often associated with chloroplasts. There was no evidence of involvement of the cell nucleus.

Polyhedral inclusion bodies are formed in different ways. In the nuclear polyhedroses (112) the nucleus swells, and the chromatin first clumps and then spreads into a network. Virus rods appear near the center and later collect in groups near the nuclear margin where they are enveloped in inclusion-body

wall, and the DNA contents of the phage head pass through the patent tailpipe into the intracellular substance of the bacterium.

Morphologic evidence of the sequence of events is demonstrable by electron micrography (65). Figure 35A in Chap. 61 is the "normal" T_2 bacteriophage with sheath extended and covering the tail spike. In Figure 7, phage is attached to the bacterium, and the heads are empty, showing that the electron-dense DNA has passed into the cell. By contrast, bacteriophage altered by treatment with hydrogen peroxide and alcohol (Fig. 36 in Chap. 61), can still adsorb to the bacterial host but is unable to empty the head contents into the cell as illustrated in Figure 8. The micrograph shows the electron dense heads still containing DNA.

Changes in the bacterium infected with T_2 phage are illustrated in Figure 9. Within one minute the cell nucleoids begin to break down and migrate to the cell center. Vacuoles forming at the cell margins contain strands with the appearance of DNA fibrils.

Fig. 8. Adsorption of T_2 bacteriophage to host cell after oxidation of the phage. (See Fig. 38, Chap. 61). The micrograph shows contraction of tail sheaths, but the electron-dense heads indicate that DNA remains in the heads. × 20,000. (From Kellenberger and Arber. *Ztschr. Naturforsch.*, 10B:688, 1955.)

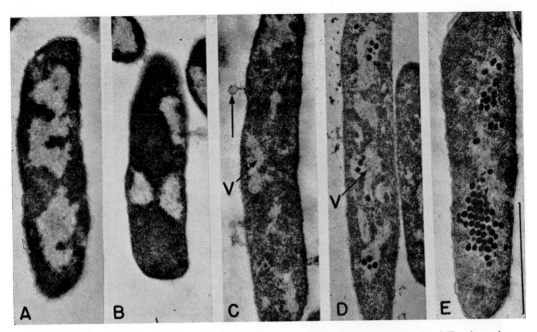

Fig. 9. Thin section electron micrographs showing different steps of growth of T_2 phage in *E. coli*. Time after infection: A, 0 minutes; B, 2 to 4 minutes; C, 10 minutes; D, 14 minutes; and E, 40 minutes. V = vacuoles. Arrow in C indicates attached phage ghost. × 24,500. (From Kellenberger. *Adv. Virus Res.,* 8:2, 1961.)

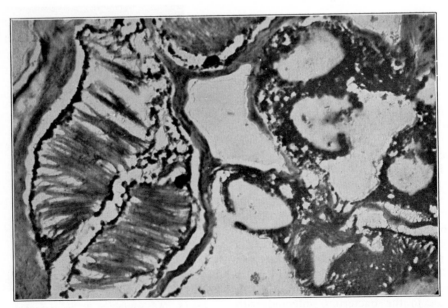

Fig. 10. Tobacco mosaic virus within a cell. Electron micrograph of a portion of a thin section of a tobacco leaf cell containing, at the left, masses of strands or fibers of the virus rods. × 7,500. (Courtesy of Dr. R. W. G. Wyckoff.)

material. The nucleus fills the cell, with the inclusions arranged at the periphery. The polyhedra are freed by cell burst. Virus rods in nuclear polyhedrosis are closely ensheathed individually by a thin intimate membrane (Fig. 8A in Chap. 61). One or more rods may occur together, and the group is enclosed in another—developmental—membrane.

A relatively small number of recognized insect virus diseases show no evidence of inclusion bodies. Instead, the *Tipula* iridescent virus, for example, is elaborated (111) in enormous numbers free in the cytoplasm without invasion of the nucleus. The very large agent (see p. 838) of cubic symmetry forms crystalline arrays in the cell with an appearance somewhat similar to that of some cytoplasmic nani viruses described later.

Members of the pox virus group exhibit striking similarities to one another in morphologic relationship to the host cell and particle elaboration, as shown by studies on vaccinia (27, 28, 30, 78, 85, 86, 93), fowl pox (78), molluscum contagiosum (39), and rabbit fibroma (10, 43). Events in cell parasitization and virus formation exhibit principles entirely different from those observed with bacteriophage. The whole vaccinia virus particle is taken up by the cell (27, 30), and virus formation occurs rapidly in the cytoplasm.

Studies of these large viruses afford physical evidence of the sequence of cell-virus interactions known by biologic investigations to occur in the processes of infection and elaboration of virus. These events are (1) **adsorption** to susceptible cells, (2) **penetration** into the cell, (3) **eclipse** period in which the mature or extracellular form of virus is not demonstrable, (4) **synthesis** and elaboration of infectious agent, and (5) **liberation** of virus particles. Successive stages are indicated schematically in Figure 11 and

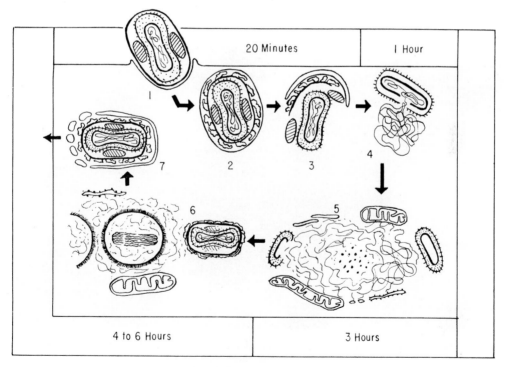

Fig. 11. Diagrammatic interpretation of vaccinia virus uptake and replication. Virus particle (1) taken up by cell reaches cytoplasm (2), and external membrane ruptures (3) to free nucleoid in about 20 minutes. In an hour, nucleoid ruptures (4), freeing DNA, and in 3 hours, mass of viroplasm forms (5) to give rise to complete and incomplete virus particles (6). Complete particles then escape from cell (7) in a period of 4 to 6 hours. (Modified from Dales. *J. Cell. Biol.,* 18:51, 1963.)

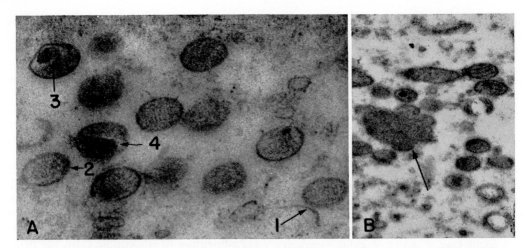

Fig. 12. A, developmental stages of vaccinia virus in cytoplasm of chick embryo chorio-allantoic membrane cell. Earliest stage (1) is sickle-shaped segment of outer particle membrane. At (2) outer membrane is complete, and at (3) there is beginning condensation of nucleoid which is of larger size at (4). × 46,000. (From Morgan, Ellison, Rose, and Moore. *J. Exper. Med.,* 100:301, 1954.) B, molluscum contagiosum virus in cytoplasm of cell showing same forms as vaccinia virus in A. In addition, arrow indicates mass of dense viroplasm with beginning particle membranes. At upper right is a particle with characteristic pox virus nucleoid (see Figure 32, Chap. 61). × 22,000. (From Dourmashkin and Bernhard. *J. Ultrastructural Res.,* 3:11, 1959.)

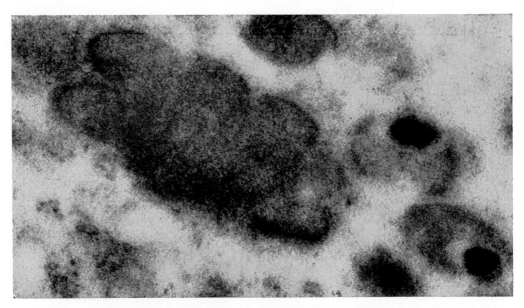

Fig. 13. Molluscum contagiosum virus developing in cell showing dense viroplasm with peripheral developing particle membranes and more advanced particles with immature dense nucleoids at the right. × 85,000. (From Dourmashkin and Bernhard. *J. Ultrastructural Res.,* 3:11, 1959.)

illustrated by micrographs in Figures 12 and 13.

Vaccinia virus particles are engulfed by pinocytosis and then remain briefly intact but shortly begin to disintegrate by focal disruption of the peripheral membrane. This is followed by cytoplasmic collections of fibrogranular, amorphous, electron-dense material—**viroplasm**—in which the new agent is synthesized. There appear first sickle-shaped external membrane segments. With growth of the membranes to the closed spheroidal form, granular material is enclosed, filling the body. The nucleoid or internal structure begins as a tiny, very dense, eccentrically located body without differentiated structure. As a final step, the dense material differentiates and occupies most of the spheroid to yield finally the fully formed particle (Fig. 30 in Chap. 61).

Optical examinations of vaccinia-infected areas show Feulgen-positive cytoplasmic masses indicating that the viroplasm contains DNA. Ferritin-conjugated antibody localizes (85, 86) at the external membrane of particles in process of formation in the cytoplasm. Vaccinia virus labeled with radioactive thymidine (27) was taken up by the cell, and autoradiographs showed the labeled DNA located in the masses of viroplasm.

Cells infected with fowl pox (78), molluscum contagiosum (39), and rabbit fibroma (10) viruses showed phenomena essentially identical with those with vaccinia under like conditions. A thin section through a mature molluscum contagiosum inclusion body (76) is seen in Figure 14. The body is separated from the surrounding cytoplasm by a wall-like structure within which lie the virus particles. Figure 2 shows an inclusion body with contained virus particles in ectromelia (mouse pox).

Myxovirus elaboration (82, 83, 84, 103) illustrates morphologic principles deviating from those observed with the pox viruses. One phase of synthesis of some myxoviruses, influenza and fowl plague, involves the nucleus (83, 103), and final assembly occurs by **budding** at the cell membrane with addition of virus-particle components (61). Unequivocal evidence of the mechanism of cell invasion is not available. Adsorption of virus to the cell membrane (103) is rapid, but the mechanism of entry into the cell is not

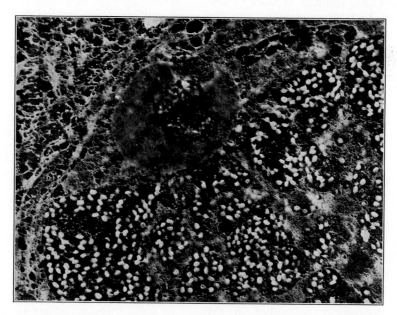

Fig. 14. Inclusion body of molluscum contagiosum. Electron micrograph of a thin section of a portion of a cell and inclusion body. The cell nucleolus is the dense body above the center, and the cell cytoplasm is to the left. The virus particles lie in locules separated by septa. × 7,000. (From Melnick, Bunting, Banfield, Strauss, and Gaylord. *Ann. New York Acad. Sc.*, 54:1214, 1952.)

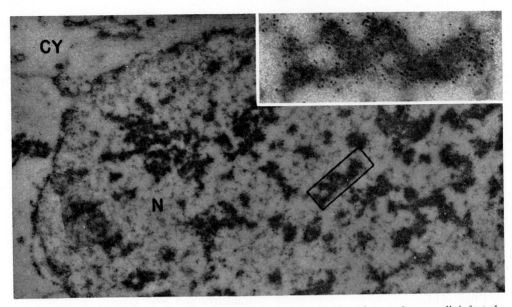

Fig. 15. Portion of nucleus (N) of chick embryo chorioallantoic membrane cell infected with influenza virus showing results of reaction with anti-influenza virus ferritin-conjugated immune serum. Fine ferritin granules are attached to dense, irregular, randomly distributed masses containing influenza virus antigen. CY = cytoplasm. × 26,000. Inset is higher magnification of area indicated. × 97,000. (From Morgan, Hsu, Rifkind, Knox, and Rose. *J. Exper. Med.,* 114:833, 1961.)

entirely clear (62). Intimate contact of the respective cell and virus surfaces can be seen with negative staining, and intact particles of influenza (28) and Newcastle disease (88) virus have been found both in the cytoplasm and in vacuoles of the cell. Whether this is a specific invasion mechanism is still obscure. Newcastle disease virus synthesis occurs only in the cytoplasm.

Morphologic evidence of the virus is quickly lost in the cytoplasm. Virus determinative material, RNA or ribonucleoprotein, reaches the nucleus where the first stages of myxovirus elaboration occur (83, 103). The myxoviruses contain two antigens: an s antigen consisting of virus RNA and protein (Fig. 24B in Chap. 61), and a hemagglutinating antigen (Fig. 24A in Chap. 61), associated with non-RNA particle components (see p. 847). Within three hours after infection, the s antigen was found with fluorescent antibodies in the nucleus. Electron micrographs of influenza virus-infected cells (83) showed dispersed dense material in the nucleus, with attached ferritin-conjugated antibody (Fig. 15).

Hemagglutinin demonstrated by fluorescent antibodies was formed only in the cytoplasm sometime after appearance of the s antigen in the nucleus. Thus the two components were synthesized in nuclear and cytoplasmic loci, respectively, but there has been no morphologic evidence of the cytoplasmic component. Final assembly occurs only at the cell membrane where the particle is completed by the process of budding (Fig. 16). Budding is associated with incorporation of cell membrane into the virus particle, and the membrane near budding virus particles contains the virus antigen.

Chick embryo chorioallantoic membrane cells infected with large doses of influenza virus do not synthesize the agent as usual, but many cell membrane fragments are formed (84). These may represent **incomplete virus particles** which react with ferritin-conjugated antibody (Fig. 17).

In some respects, agents of avian tumors and leukemias and of murine leukemias resemble the myxoviruses. The mechanism of cell invasion is not known, but these RNA agents are assembled by budding either at

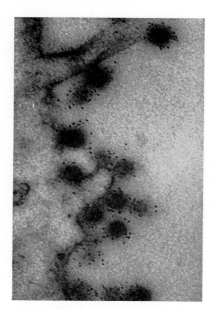

Fig. 16. Segment of chick embryo chorio-allantoic cell infected with influenza virus with membrane-budding virus particles. Reaction with ferritin-conjugated antibody as for Figure 15 showing attachment of ferritin particles to surface of virus particles. × 78,000. (From Morgan, Hsu, Rifkind, Knox, and Rose. *J. Exper Med.*, 114:825, 1961.)

densation of the nucleoid occurs after the particle is freed. Such processes occur in naturally induced neoplasms, including fibroblastic sarcomas (57), chondroma and epithelial cells of kidney tumors (58), and myeloblasts and erythroblasts of myeloid and erythroid leukemias as well as other chicken cell types. Such particles are budded, also from pancreas (56, 127) and liver cells (37) without evidence of neoplasia in the organs.

An interesting and important feature of virus assembly by cell membrane budding is the incorporation of components with the properties of the host cell. This principle was demonstrable with influenza virus which could be precipitated (69) with anti-host-cell immune serum. BAI strain A avian tumor virus (5) contains chick and Forssman antigens and is neutralized by immune serums against these antigens (40). There is evidence that the same agent assembled by chondrocytes or collagen-forming cells may contain cartilage fibrils or collagen-related material, respectively (58).

the cell membrane or at membranes associated with cytoplastic structures. A major difference from the myxoviruses with present knowledge is lack of any evidence of nuclear involvement in virus formation. There is no evidence of cell-virus association except the formation of buds.

As already illustrated (Fig. 26A in Chap. 61), avian tumor virus particles exhibit a dense, central nucleoid in a spheroidal body enclosed in a peripheral membrane (5, 10, 14). Budding occurs at the external cell surface by thickening and increase in density of a locus in the membrane, attended by the appearance of an inner curve of high density, enlargement of the whole, and shedding of the particle by rupture of the final attaching pedicle (5, 14, 36, 57). The principles of the process are illustrated in the budding of the Friend murine leukemia virus (Fig. 18) (34), which are essentially identical with those of avian tumor virus formation. In newly formed avian tumor virus particles, the nucleoid is of low density and homogeneous in appearance (36, 58), but final con-

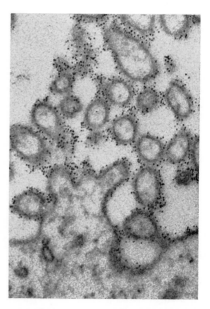

Fig. 17. Cytoplasmic membrane fragments from chick embryo chorioallantoic cells after high-dose infection with influenza virus. Fragments, interpreted as possible incomplete forms of virus, react with ferritin-conjugated antibody. Surfaces of fragments heavily tagged with ferritin granules. × 63,000. (From Morgan, Hsu, and Rose. *J. Exper. Med.*, 116:553, 1963.)

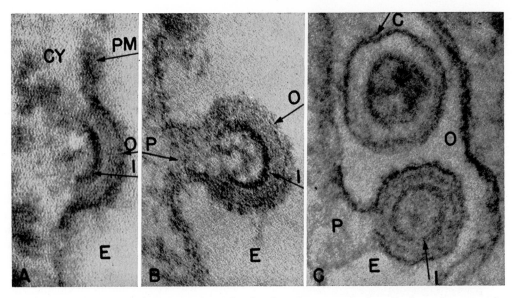

Fig. 18. Budding of Friend mouse leukemia virus from neoplastic cell. A, early stage of bud formation in cell membrane (PM) with cell cytoplasm (CY) at left. Dense inner sickle-shaped image (I) is beginning inner virus membrane, and (O) is outer membrane continuous with cell membrane extending into extracellular space (E). × 390,000. B, advanced budding with same structures attached to cell by pedicle (P). × 270,000. C, particle with complete inner membrane (I) still attached by pedicle (P). A completed particle of C type (C) is free in extracellular space (E). × 260,000. (From de Harven and Friend. *J. Biophys. & Biochem. Ultrastruct. Cytol.,* 7:747, 1960.)

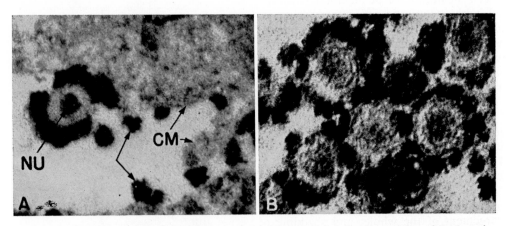

Fig. 19. Ultracytochemical demonstration of adenosinetriphosphatase activity of BAI strain A avian tumor virus and origin of enzyme from cell membrane incorporated in virus particle. A, a single virus particle with typical nucleoid (NU) with peripheral dense deposit of lead phosphate resulting from enzyme reaction. Deposit (arrows) at cell membrane (CM). Virus particle is extracellular. × 120,000. (From de Thé, Ishiguro, Heine, Beard, and Beard. *J. Nat. Cancer Inst.,* 30:1267, 1963.) B, virus particles sedimented from blood plasma of chicken with myeloblastic leukemia showing heavy deposits of lead phosphate around each particle. × 170,000. (From de Thé, Becker, and Beard. *J. Nat. Cancer Inst.,* 32:201, 1964.)

More direct evidence is the incorporation of the enzyme adenosinetriphosphatase in the BAI strain A virus budded from cells with the enzyme in the surface membrane (Fig. 19) (36). Other cell types of growths caused by the same agent contain no enzyme of this kind, and virus particles budded from them are enzyme free. HeLa cell membranes are enzyme positive, and the herpes virus budded from these cells has adenosinetriphosphatase in the particles in the same way (42) as the avian tumor virus. Thus it can be seen that, in the instances mentioned, host material contributes directly to virus particle components. This mechanism differs from the processes of synthesis responsible for basic virus-specific components, such as the capsids and capsomeres of simple viruses of the helical and cubic-symmetry categories.

Viruses are associated with a large variety of murine neoplasms. Most prominent are the leukemias (32, 34, 38, 53, 108) of lymphoid, myeloid, and stem cell origin. All exhibit essentially the same principles of cell-virus relationship. Mechanisms of cell invasion have not been disclosed, but the morphologic aspects of virus liberation from the cells is well known. In all of the **primary cells** affected—lymphoblasts, myeloblasts, and stem cells—the virus is assembled at the cell surface by budding, Figure 18, in the same way as the avian tumor viruses. A different relationship is seen with the megakaryocytes (32, 34) in all of the leukemias examined. Virus is not budded from the external membrane of these cells—which do not themselves become neoplastic—but from the membranes enclosing a system of intracellular intercommunicating channels different in these elements from the usual components of endoplasmic reticulum and the Golgi apparatus (Fig. 20; see also Fig. 28 in Chap. 61).

In mouse mammary carcinoma two types of virus-cell relationship occur in the same —carcinoma—cells (10, 38, 77). In one process the virus is elaborated by budding at the external cell membrane (Fig. 27A in Chap. 61), as in the case of the leukemias, but the particles found in the extracellular

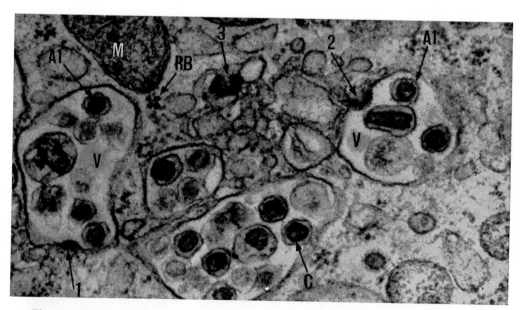

Fig. 20. Virus particles budding from cytoplasmic, vesicular (V) membranes of mega-karyocyte in mouse of Friend type of leukemia. Budding occurs by same principles as from external cell membrane of leukemic cells and successive stages of bud formation are indicated at (1, 2, and 3). There are two Al type particles (Al) with inner and outer membranes and relatively electron-lucent nucleoids and a type C particle (C) with single membrane and electron-dense nucleoid. Particles vary in shape and size. M = mitochondrion, and RB = ribosomes. × 60,000. (From de Harven and Friend. *J. Ultrastructural Res.,* 7:747, 1960.)

spaces are different in appearance (Fig. 27B in Chap. 61). A central dense nucleoid is eccentrically located in a spheroidal, bulbous body of low density, and the particle is enclosed in a limiting peripheral membrane. A different process occurs in the cytoplasm of the same cells. Cytoplasmic particles (Fig. 27A in Chap. 61) are distributed about the membranes of vacuole-like structures and are sometimes in aggregates in inclusions visible in the light microscope. Avian and murine tumor viruses may be grouped in relation to both particle morphology (see p. 848) and assembly process (10, 31).

A different virus causing tumors in mice and also in rats and hamsters is the polyoma agent described later.

Another surface-cell-membrane budding virus is the agent of vesicular stomatitis already described (Fig. 32 in Chap. 61).

Arbor viruses, as exemplified by Western (80) and Venezuelan (89) strains of equine encephalomyelitis, represent another group of RNA agents synthesized in the cell cytoplasm. The manner of cell invasion is not known, but many of the agents can be transmitted by RNA (20) isolated from purified virus or from infected tissues. Elaboration of Western equine encephalomyelitis virus appears to occur entirely in the cytoplasm without specific changes in the nucleus. Cells (Fig. 21) develop open clefts and vacuoles lined by single or laminated membranes (80). Discrete dense bodies become arrayed about the vacuolar membranes. Assembly of the virus particles takes place by passage through the vacuolar membrane, at which time the dense particle acquires an outer membrane. Virus particles of finished appearance pass into the vacuoles. They may be liberated from the cell either by rupture of the vacuoles through the cell surface or may pass through the cell membrane and acquire the outside coat. Extracellular particles are illustrated in Figure 21B.

Cell-virus relationships with several nani viruses have been studied—polio (45), Coxsackie (79), and ECHO 9 (97) and 19 (91), encephalomyocarditis and Mengo viruses (29). All are formed and assembled in the cytoplasm without morphologic evidence of specific nuclear involvement.

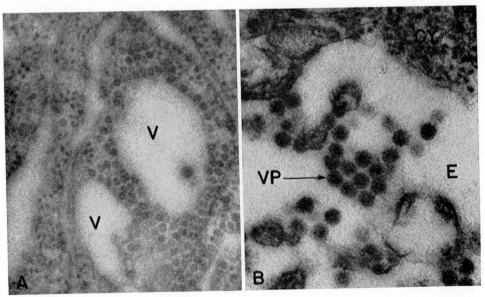

Fig. 21. A, elaboration of Western strain equine encephalomyelitis virus in cell cytoplasm. Cytoplasm of infected cells undergoes pronounced vacuolization. Immature virus particles are dense bodies arrayed outside vacuole (V) wall. (Particles mature by passage through wall and collect in vacuoles.) × 85,000. B, mature virus particles (VP) in space (E) outside cell (CY). Dense nucleoids enclosed in indefinite membrane. × 100,000. (From Morgan, Howe, and Rose. *J. Exper. Med.,* 113:219, 1961.)

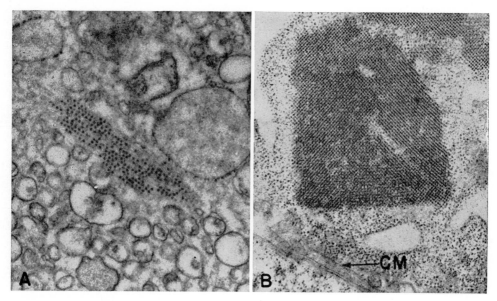

Fig. 22. A, portion of cytoplasm of cell infected with ECHO type 9 virus. Cytoplasm is highly vesiculated and shows small dense particles—virus precursors—in crystalline array sectioned linear to interspersed fibrils. × 38,000. (From Rifkind, Godman, Howe, Morgan, and Rose. *J. Exper. Med.,* 114:1, 1961.) B, crystalline array of Meno virus particles in cell cytoplasm. CM = cell membrane. × 45,000. (From Dales and Franklin. *J. Cell. Biol.,* 14:281, 1962.)

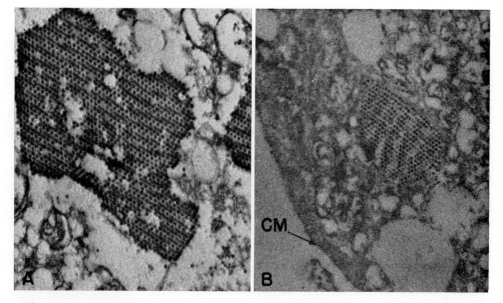

Fig. 23. A, crystalline array of poliovirus particles in cell cytoplasm. Cell shows marked disruptive disturbance of cytoplasm. × 60,000. (From Fogh and Stuart. *Virology,* 11:308, 1960.) B, crystal formation of Coxsackie virus in cell cytoplasm. Marked vacuolization and destruction of cytoplasm. CM = cell membrane. × 40,000. (From Morgan, Howe, and Rose. *Virology,* 9:145, 1959.)

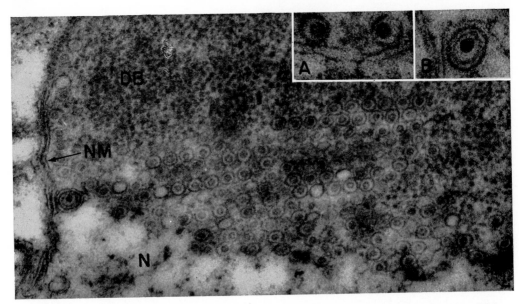

Fig. 24. Portion of nucleus (N) of cell infected with herpes virus. Nucleus contains widely scattered dense bodies (DB). Linear arrays of circular images representing membrane enclosing dense center or empty are in body of nucleus and distributed about periphery beneath nuclear membrane. One particle enclosed in three membranes is in nucleus near nuclear membrane. × 44,000. Inset A is higher magnification of simple particle with single membrane, and B is particle with mature appearance in nucleus. (From Morgan, Rose, Holden, and Jones. *J. Exper. Med.,* 110:643, 1959.)

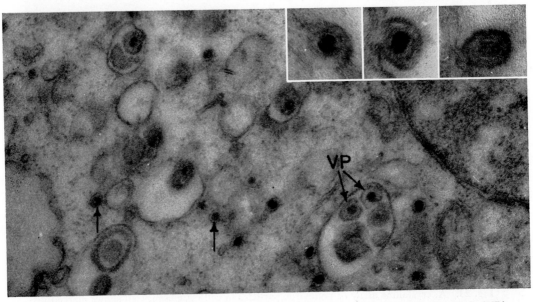

Fig. 25. Assembly of herpes virus in cytoplasm showing completed virus particles (VP) collected in vacuoles and immature particles (arrows) free in cytoplasm. × 52,000. Insets illustrate budding of immature particles through vacuole membrane to form complete particle inside vacuole. × 100,000. (From Epstein. *J. Cell. Biol.,* 12:589, 1962.)

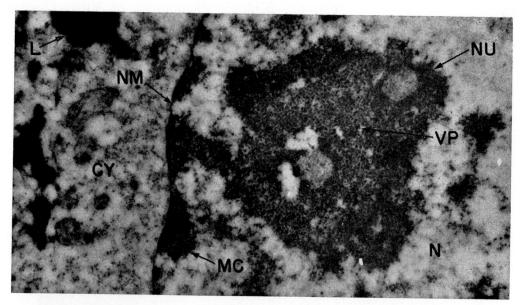

Fig. 26. Portion of cytoplasm (CY) and nucleus (N) of rabbit papilloma cell showing formation of rabbit papilloma virus. Marked changes in the nucleus with striking margination of chromatin (MC) against nuclear membrane (NM). Virus (VP) consisting of dense centers surrounded by less dense material are developing in the body of the nucleolus (NU). Cytoplasm contains dense lipid (L) bodies. × 30,000. (From Stone, Shope, and Moore. *J. Exper. Med.,* 110:543, 1959.)

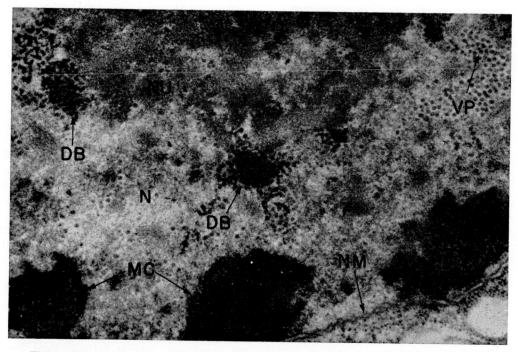

Fig. 27. Monkey kidney cell 10 days after infection with SV40 virus. Nucleus (N) shows margination of chromatin (MC) and distinct nuclear membrane (NM). Nucleolus (NU) composed of finely granular substance. At periphery of nucleolus are clusters of coarse, very dense granules (DB). A few virus particles (VP) are in the nucleoplasm. × 36,500. (From Granboulan, Tournier, Wicker, and Bernhard. *J. Cell. Biol.,* 17:423, 1963.)

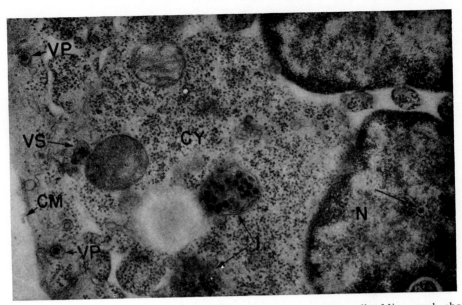

Fig. 28. Adsorption and transfer of adenovirus type 7 in HeLa cells. Micrograph shows portion of nucleus (N) and cytoplasm (CY) two hours after exposure to virus. Two single virus particles (VP) are in vesicles near cell membrane (CM), and one or two particles are in a larger vesicle (VS) in the cytoplasm. Two large membrane-enclosed inclusions (I) are packed with particles. The small clump of dense material (arrow) in the nucleus may be remains of a virus particle. × 20,400. (From Dales. *J. Cell. Biol.,* 13:303, 1962.)

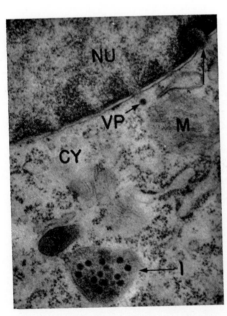

Fig. 29. Portion of cell nucleus (NU) and cytoplasm (CY) two hours after infection with adenovirus type 7. An inclusion (I) contains virus particles. A single virus particle (VP) is free in the cytoplasm near the nucleus and a mitochondrion (M). Another particle resembling virus (arrow) lies close to an invagination of the nuclear membrane. × 31.700. (From Dales. *J. Cell. Biol.,* 13:303, 1962.)

With ECHO 9 virus, (Fig. 22A), both nuclear and cytoplasmic alterations occur very soon after infection (97). The cytoplasm becomes highly vesiculated and the nucleus markedly distorted, lobulated, and collapsed. Virus forms in association with cytoplasmic masses of finely granular material, with which are often associated fibrils or filament-like structures. In these masses, which are analogous to the collections of finely granular cytoplasmic masses in cells elaborating pox viruses, virus particles are assembled in linear and crystalline array (Fig. 22A). Virus leaves the cell after death and disintegration of the element. In a variety of studies, including immunofluorescence and ultrastructural examinations, there has been no evidence of specific involvement of the nucleus in particle formation.

Cells infected with ECHO virus 19 (91) showed similar changes in the nucleus and vesiculation of the cytoplasm. The agent was formed in distinct crystalline arrays in the cytoplasm. Similar crystals were found in cells infected with Mengo (Fig. 22B) (29), polio (Fig. 23A) (45), and Coxsackie (Fig. 23B) (79) viruses. Mengo virus elaboration was associated with cytoplasmic inclusions consisting of granular or fibrillar aggregates in crystalline-like array. That such material was virus precursor was suggested by formation of Mengo virus crystals within the inclusion structures. Differences were observed (29) in the formation of encephalomyocarditis virus. In this case the same marked changes occurred in the nucleus and cytoplasm, but crystalline arrays of particles were not seen in the cytoplasm.

In the foregoing sections animal disease agents assembled by cytoplasmic processes and with the exception of some myxoviruses, without specific involvement of the nucleus were considered. Three other groups of agents—NITA (herpes), adeno, and papova viruses—containing DNA are synthesized in the nucleus.

The mechanisms of herpes virus invasion of the host cell are not known. Virus formation begins with the appearance (41, 87) of groups or masses of small dense bodies about 20 mμ in diameter throughout the nu-

cleus (Fig. 24) but not associated with the nucleolus. Forms appear with dense centers surrounded by a single membrane, and empty membranes of the same size are also seen. With increase in number, the single-membrane-covered particles are scattered at random and immediately beneath the nuclear membrane, and become arrayed in lines arranged in lattice-like formation (Fig. 24).

A second membrane (87) may be added in the nucleus, and some particles adjacent to nuclear membranes may be enclosed in three membranes. Virus appears in the cytoplasm as individual single-membrane particles like those in the nucleus. In the cytoplasm there occur also numerous small vesicles or vacuoles possibly derived either from the Golgi apparatus or endoplasmic reticulum (41). Clear evidence is shown that the "immature" virus particles become associated with the vesicles or vacuoles and bud through the walls to yield double- or triple-membraned particles characteristic of

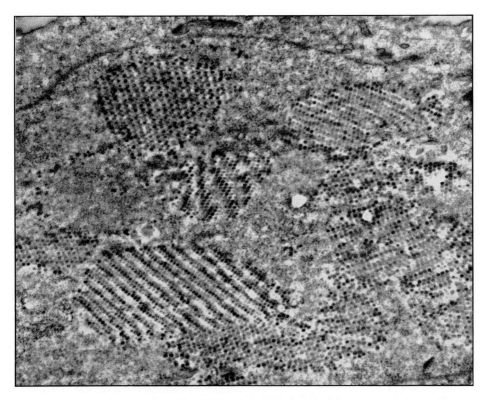

Fig. 30.   Adenovirus particles (RI-APC Group, see text) arranged in crystalline structure as they occur in the nucleus of a HeLa cell. × 16,800. (From Morgan and others. *J. Biophys. & Biochem. Cytol.*, 2:351, 1956.)

the extracellular virus (Fig. 25). Other immature particles may be assembled in the same form by budding through the surface cell membrane. Such particles exhibit adenosinetriphosphatase activity when the cell membrane contains the enzyme (42). Laryngotracheitis virus (25) induces nuclear changes resembling those in herpes infection.

The **papova viruses**—human and rabbit papilloma and polyoma and SV 40 agents—are assembled in the nucleus. Elaboration of the rabbit papilloma virus (114) occurs in the body of the nucleolus. Masses of dense chromatin are deposited in contact with the nuclear membrane (Fig. 26) and in strands about the nucleolus. In the nucleolus appear small, very dense bodies, and in the terminal stages virus particles spread through the nucleus. Papilloma cells die and disintegrate in a mass of desquamated, keratinized elements, and large amounts of virus are located in the debris (4).

Polyoma (10) and SV 40 (51) agents seemed to develop in association with chromatin either close to or separated from the nucleolus. Particles of SV 40 virus (Fig. 27) were adjacent to the periphery of the nucleolus and also enclosed occasionally in walled structures in the nucleus. Particles appeared later in the cytoplasm, lying outside vacuolar walls before cell disintegration. A relationship between the nucleolus and polyoma virus formation was not clear (10). The agent appears throughout the nucleus in very large numbers.

Adenoviruses thus far studied (13, 26, 28, 81) develop also in the nucleus. Particles outside the cells have been seen closely applied to the cell surface in membrane indentations (Fig. 28) and individual particles seem to traverse the cell membranes to appear in the cytoplasm enclosed in vacuole-like structures (26). Such structures approach the nucleus, and particles are seen in apposition to the membrane (Fig. 29). Some appear in invaginations of the membrane, and others are within the nucleus.

Initial changes in the nucleus (81) are the appearance in the chromatin mass of small, scattered collections of reticular network. Dense-body precursors of virus particles appear at the boundaries of the reticular collections, and particles characteristic of the virus soon become arrayed in crystalline formations (Fig. 30) or scattered individually through the nucleus. Virus particles escape into the cytoplasm by rupture of the nuclear membrane.

Little evidence has been seen of mitochondrial involvement in specific processes of virus formation. The H-1 virus, isolated from a human epidermal carcinoma (118), causes mongoloid deformities in newborn hamsters. Cellular changes were observed in Küpffer cells, chondrocytes and renal interstitial cells. A virus of 75 mμ diameter and structure resembling that of rabbit papilloma virus (Fig. 31) was present in cytoplasmic gray bodies or occasionally free in the cytoplasm near ruptured gray bodies (16). Such structures were wall-enclosed and contained few or large numbers of virus particles. Possible involvement of mitochondria is illustrated in Figure 31, which shows, below, a normal mitochondrion and, above, a like organelle with dense bodies with the appearance of virus.

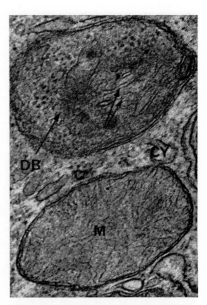

Fig. 31. Portion of cytoplasm (CY) of hamster kidney tubule cell infected with H1 virus. Lower structure (M) is mitochondrion with cristae of normal appearance. Upper structure contains dense virus precursor bodies (DB). That structure with dense bodies is mitochondrial derivative is indicated by remnants of cristae (arrow). (From Chandra and Toolan. *J. Nat. Cancer Inst.,* 27: 1405, 1961.)

BIOCHEMICAL INTERACTIONS IN VIRUS SYNTHESIS

As in many other aspects of virus study, bacteriophages have served as productive models for investigating the problems of cell alteration and the phenomenon of virus synthesis at the biochemical level. Many investigations have been made with the T system (35) of bacteriophages active against a single strain, B, of *E. coli*. The range of host-virus relationships with bacteriophage (72) extends, as with animal and plant viruses, from rapid necrosis or lysis of the bacterium to a state approaching enduring symbiosis without perceptible change in the host cell. In these relations there are thus two categories of phages: **virulent** ones which regularly induce lysis and others, called **temperate,** which are able to establish a sym-

biotic or "lysogenic" state with the host cell, as described later.

Lysis of bacteria may be seen with the light microscope. In a mixture of phage and bacteria the organisms may suddenly swell and disappear. Electron micrography of such preparations reveals the cell fragments and debris with interspersed characteristic phage particles. If a mixture of a large amount of phage with a heavy suspension of bacteria is spread on an agar plate, the surface of the agar may remain entirely clear, because all bacteria have been lysed. A mixture of an appropriate number of phage particles with the bacterial suspension will give a surface bacterial growth that shows the presence of clear regions or **plaques** that differ in size and appearance with different phages and hosts (Fig. 32). Under suitable conditions, the plaque count is closely related to the number of bacteriophage par-

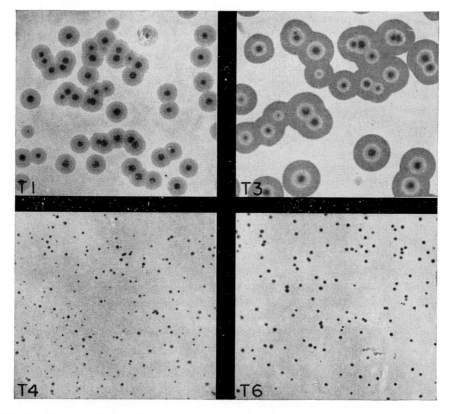

Fig. 32. Plaques of some of the bacteriophages of the T series of *E. coli* obtained by seeding phage with susceptible bacterial host cells on an agar surface. (From Demerec and Fano. *Genetics,* 30:119, 1945.)

ticles counted by electron microscopy (75). Plaque characteristics provide criteria for selection of mutants in genetic studies mentioned later.

Much evidence has been obtained of the biochemical events attending phage invasion (17, 18, 19, 70, 96). About 80 per cent of phage protein, identified by methionine labeled with radioactive S^{35}, remained outside the infected host. In contrast, practically all phage DNA entered the cell, since little of the phage phosphorus labeled with P^{32} could be identified in the outside medium.

Inside the cell there was complete breakdown, and processes leading to cell division and other metabolic functions ceased. Synthesis of DNA, a prominent constituent of the bacterium, was halted. After a brief lag period, synthesis of DNA resumed at a high rate but was directed to the formation of virus and not cell DNA. That cell functions were not merely modified but were completely revised has been shown by the radical alterations in synthetic processes (18, 19). Virus was able to initiate entirely new metabolic functions not present in the normal bacterium. Whereas DNA formed by the cell ordinarily contains cytosine, phage DNA contained the unique pyrimidine 5-hydroxymethyl cytosine, which required a new enzyme for production. The magnitude of functional changes was indicated by demonstration of approximately 24 new proteins consisting of new enzymes and specific phage proteins constituting structural parts of the phage (see p. 852).

Studies on the metabolic processes and products concerned with the synthesis of viruses causing disease in plants, animals, and insects (17, 18, 19, 70) have been limited by the complexities of the systems and the availability of suitable materials for investigation. As already mentioned, many of these agents can be transmitted with isolated and purified nucleic acid (20, 47, 70, 105).

A variety of studies have revealed some of the events occurring in the cell after infection with pox viruses (19), particularly vaccinia. Particles reach the cytoplasm intact, but within one to two hours the outer virus membrane undergoes partial destruction—uncoating—which is accomplished by a newly formed cytoplasmic enzyme (64). Uncoating enzyme may be induced by a single virus particle. When many virus particles are taken up, not all are uncoated, and the uncoating process is terminated after about six hours. Heat-inactivated virus may be taken up, with resulting cell death, but neither uncoating nor synthesis occurs (55). Reactivation and vaccinia virus synthesis can be accomplished by another, heterologous virus—such as ectromelia—present in the cell before the inactivated virus was adsorbed.

Marked changes occur in DNA synthesis (19). Nuclear DNA synthesis is suppressed, but the rate of cytoplasmic DNA synthesis is increased 500 to 600 per cent. Virus DNA is formed *de novo* and is not derived from host DNA. Ultrastructural studies of H^3-thymidine-labeled virus (27) showed that the label first associated with the virus nucleoid was located in the viroplasm, and later a few newly formed mature particles contained labeled nucleic acid. Fluorescent antibody studies showed the presence of viral antigen synthesized in the masses of viroplasm. Virus protein and DNA synthesis begin about two and three hours after infection, respectively, and the processes are complete in about three hours more. This is in striking contrast to the even rates in the formation of nuclear DNA agents, the adenoviruses (52).

Isolated RNA from myxovirus agents has thus far not been infectious. Much work with fowl plague virus (103) has not revealed violent changes in cell metabolism. The virus antigen—the s antigen associated with RNA—appears first in the nucleus as demonstrated by fluorescent or ferritin conjugated antibodies (see Fig. 15). In undisturbed infection the s antigen and RNA are synthesized in the nucleus and are transported to the cytoplasm. The hemagglutinating—HA—antigen is formed only in the cytoplasm and appears shortly after the s antigen. Both antigens are brought together and assembled in virus particles by budding at the cell membrane.

Cell involvement by arbor virus only in the cytoplasm (123) was confirmed biochemically by demonstration of virus RNA limited almost exclusively to cytoplasmic cell fractions. With equine encephalomyelitis, there was no evidence of the need for new enzyme for synthesis of RNA. Inhibition of protein synthesis in the early period of infection prevents formation of cytoplasmic infectious RNA, and interference later affects assembly of mature virus.

Infection with poliovirus is associated with decrease in RNA synthesis in the host cell nucleus (33). Virus RNA is formed in the cytoplasm, where virus is evident by ultrastructural examination. Inhibition of protein synthesis within two hours after infection interferes with both protein and virus RNA formation. The protein—enzyme—necessary for RNA replication is formed early and continues to act without further increase. Cytoplasmic virus RNA and protein, once formed, are quickly incorporated into virus particles.

In Mengo virus infection assembly of mature agent (46) begins within two and one-half hours and reaches the maximum after six to seven hours, when most of the virus is released. With infection, RNA synthesis in the nucleus quickly ceases. Cytoplasmic RNA synthesis begins at about three hours and increases to six to seven hours, corresponding to the growth and increase in virus. Changes in cell ultrastructure paralleled the metabolic alterations. Use of labeled uridine (29) showed that primary labeling occurred in the cytoplasm rather than in the nucleus and was concentrated in the late stages in cytoplasmic structures corresponding to virus crystals. Comparable studies showed similar findings with the Maus-Elberfield and encephalomyocarditis viruses (103).

Infection with adenoviruses (49, 52, 124) results in cessation of cell multiplication, but synthesis of protein, RNA, and DNA continues, with consequent increase in cell size to approximately double that of the control in 36 hours. Although infection is established within one hour after exposure to virus, intracellular virus was found only after 13 to 14 hours. When DNA synthesis was inhibited with 5-fluorodeoxyuridine, RNA, soluble nucleotide, and protein synthesis continued. Addition of inhibitor up to seven hours after infection suppressed virus DNA formation completely. If the inhibitor was added after seven hours, virus was formed in amounts increasing with the longer intervals after the seven-hour period. Reversal of inhibition before seven hours was followed by virus formation in the usual course, and reversal thereafter resulted in virus synthesis but after a delay of one to eight hours. Thus for the first seven hours after infection, DNA synthesis was not necessary for virus formation occurring in the interval of seven to fourteen hours after infection. This suggests the possible accumulation in the first seven hours of other materials required for later virus DNA synthesis. Intracellular virus began to appear about eight hours after DNA synthesis was initiated, and DNA was synthesized concurrently with virus maturation.

Most of the knowledge of host-virus interactions with the papova, herpes, and RNA tumor virus has been obtained by ultrastructural investigations. In rabbit papillomatosis a specific arginase (99) is formed. Studies on synthesis of BAI strain A chicken tumor virus by avian myeloblasts suggests (115) that soluble RNA is precursor to virus nucleic acid.

GENETIC PHENOMENA

Viruses constitute the source of the simplest materials of natural origin thus far available for investigation of genetic phenomena. The biologic consequences of genetic expression have long been studied in varied organisms, with particular attention during recent years to viruses, especially the bacteriophages. The most recent work (8, 19, 24, 73, 74, 98) has been concerned with the direct approach to mechanisms at the molecular level. A major advance bearing on the phenomena of virology, as well as other genetic systems, was development of the Watson-Crick concept of DNA structure (67). As a result, correlations have been effected between DNA structure and function which have afforded a basis for devising relatively simple cell-free systems for clarification of the directive processes of nucleic acid and protein synthesis.

In most instances DNA consists of a helical array of two polynucleotide strands containing the bases adenine, thymine, guanine, and cytosine. The bases are joined by hydrogen bonds in pairs, always of thymine-adenine and guanine-cytosine. Bacteriophage øX174 provides an instance of single-stranded DNA. In contrast, ordinary RNA is a single strand of nucleotides with the bases adenine, guanine, cytosine, and uracil (105, 113). Synthetic processes in the replication of DNA, RNA, and protein are directed by coding effects (24, 113) of one or the other or both types of nucleic acid, dependent on the relative numbers of kinds and the sequential distribution of nucleotides in the polynucleotide chains. It is the concept that the coding unit for incorporation of a single amino acid into a polypeptide chain consists of a unit of three nucleotides (24).

The basic material determining the direction and character of synthetic processes in the cell per se is DNA. One mechanism for DNA synthesis thus far known is dependent on the action of a polymerase acting in the presence of a pre-existing primer DNA and all four deoxyribonucleoside triphosphates. Polymerases differ somewhat in activity in relation to the source, and polymerase in bacteriophage-infected cells, for example, is not the same as that in the uninfected host. DNA produced in the system is indistinguishable thus far from the primer DNA, indicating that the new DNA is a replica of the bacteriophage-derived primer nucleic acid providing the directive template. The state of primer DNA is not known; it may act as a double strand or as single strands unwound from the helix. Some evidence indicates the single-strand state; the single strand of øX174 is more active as a primer than the double strand from other sources.

There is evidence that protein synthesis is directed by DNA in processes involving RNA (122). It is conceived that an RNA intermediate in protein synthesis is formed as a complementary template on DNA catalyzed by action of an RNA polymerase. Such nucleic acid is termed "messenger" RNA since it migrates from the site of synthesis to attachments on ribosomes, where protein formation occurs. Amino acids are brought to "messenger" RNA on ribosomes by another type of ribonucleic acid, "transport" RNA. In protein synthesis amino acids are selectively transported to ribosomes and incorporated into polypeptide chains in the order dictated by the "code" in "messenger" RNA attached to the ribosome.

The manner of coding of amino acid incorporation has been studied in the preparation of polypeptide chains (90, 113) mediated in cell-free systems by synthetic polyribonucleotides. This is accomplished with an enzyme, polynucleotide phosphorylase, in extracts of bacteria and animal and plant cells, a polynucleotide primer and Mg^{++} being necessary for the reaction. In such a system ribopolynucleotides are synthesized, with the character determined by the RNA base, adenine, guanine, cytosine, or uracil, added to the reaction medium. In the presence only of uracil, polynucleotides consisting of chains containing only polyuridylic acid are formed. Pure polynucleotides with other bases could be synthesized, as could random mixtures of all.

The synthetic polynucleotides were capable of directing polymerization of amino acids in specific ways (90). A polynucleotide sequence of uridylic acids only constituted the code for incorporation of phenylalanine into a polypeptide chain containing only this amino acid. A sequence consisting of polycytidilic acids specified polypeptide chains of proline. Experiments with polynucleotide chains of single-base nucleotides or suitable mixtures revealed the codes for each amino acid and showed that the code consisted of sequences of triplicate nucleotides. The results indicated the kinds of nucleotide in each triplicate but not the sequence of the arrangement. For most of the amino acids two or more codes could effect incorporation.

Correlations of these sequences of synthesis from reduplication of DNA through "messenger" and "transport" RNA afford a basis for interpretations of genetic phenomena in virus-cell reactions with the DNA agents. Less is known of some aspects of the possible processes occurring in infections with RNA viruses. Whereas the reactions concerned with protein synthesis may be the same in principle as those related to DNA agents, mechanisms for replication of virus RNA lack clarification (113). On the one hand, it is possible that virus RNA may function as a template for synthesis of a complementary RNA strand to direct replication of virus RNA, but, on the other, studies on poliovirus RNA synthesis (33) have revealed the intracellular presence of virus RNA and no evidence of a different or complementary RNA. Furthermore, virus RNA can attach to ribosomes and direct synthesis of agent-specific protein, as demonstrated with RNA from tobacco mosaic and polio viruses. It would thus appear that virus RNA provides all information necessary for its own replication and services, as well as "messenger" RNA in the direction of virus-protein synthesis. There is evidence that the processes of virus RNA synthesis are separate from those of cellular RNA formation, and that virus RNA synthesis is not dependent on DNA. Cellular RNA synthesis can be inhibited without prevention of virus RNA formation.

The state of nucleic acid capable of inducing infection and virus replication has not been clarified in all cases. It is known, however, that the total tobacco mosaic virus RNA strand is required to transmit infection and that a single break in the chain destroys infectious capacity (105). Less definitive results with RNA animal viruses have also suggested the requirement for a complete chain for infectiousness. In these instances the molecular weight of nucleic acid was in the range of 2×10^6. DNA of the large T_2 bacteriophage of 130×10^6 molecular weight has been obtained as a single strand which was $49 \pm 4 \mu$ in length as measured directly in electron micrographs (68). Isolated T2 DNA may induce infection of *E. coli* protoplasts.

Numerous virus genetic phenomena had been recognized before development of the field of biochemical genetics. The phenomenon known as **transformation** is one concerned with the extracellular transfer of genetic material from one bacterial strain to another (see Chap. 19). Transformation has been observed also with viruses in the well-known Berry-Dedrick phenomenon (66), which was the first evidence of genetic interaction between viruses. A phenomenon analogous to transformation is that of **transduction,** in which heritable changes (73, 74) are brought about, for example, in bacteria (host cell) under the influence of bacteriophage (virus) in the induction of the state of ly-

sogeny. Genetic material intrinsically incorporated in the phage is transferred from one host to another and is integrated in the new host genome. In this process, many heritable characteristics, such as colony morphology or antigenic constitution, may be transferred. A striking instance is that pertaining to the transduction of virulence from a virulent strain of *Corynebacterium diphtheriae* to a nontoxigenic strain (Chap. 27). The heritable characteristics are manifested only with persistence of the lysogenic state.

Virus variation and mutation are of frequent occurrence (8). Certain variations and mutations are spontaneous, occurring as the result of recombinations and rearrangement of genetic factors inherent in the virus. Such mutants may be recognized and propagated by selection of proper conditions. Some mutations are hereditary, or **genotypic,** involving the virus genetic substance, and others are **phenotypic,** not heritable but may be maintained in a stable state by arrangement of conditions. This is the sort of change which takes place in many conditions of adaptation, for example, to a new host as in the chick embryo culture of many viruses. A striking adaptation occurs in the passage of hog cholera virus to rabbits. In such transfers profound alterations may be seen in the pathogenicity and virulence of the agents. In the new host the agent may become stabilized with respect to its cultural and pathogenic or infectious behavior. A classic example of variation or mutation is the fixation of rabies virus in the rabbit. These properties are of great value in carrying out studies on the agents and in the preparation of vaccines.

Variation under natural conditions frequently occurs and is of much importance as an epidemiologic factor from the point of view of both host morbidity and mortality and for the survival of the virus. A characteristic of some viruses is the frequency with which new strains occur under natural conditions. This phenomenon has been extensively studied in the instance of the agent of influenza, and the evidence indicates that it may be of importance in the recurrence of epidemics or repeated attacks in the individual.

Much clarification of the processes involved in mutation has been effected by experimental **mutagenesis** (8, 19, 105) which can be produced both in vivo and in vitro. A variety of agents are effective in their action on virus-infected host cells, including ultraviolet light and X-rays, use of purine and pyrimidine nucleic acid analogs, and alkylating agents, such as the mustards, epoxides, ethyleneimines, and alkyl esters of sulphonic acid. Among the base analogs active on T_4 bacteriophage are 5-bromodeoxyuridine, 5-bromouracil, 2-aminopurine, and 2,6-diaminopurine. Incorporation of the analogs into DNA seems to result in transitions of nucleotide pairs such that one purine may be exchanged for another purine and one pyrimidine for another. Proflavine and nitrous acid cause change in base composition of DNA in the phages. The production of mutants with these materials has been of great value in the mapping of genetic changes in the rII region of T_4 bacteriophage.

The classic demonstration of mutagenesis in vitro was that of the influence of nitrous acid on the isolated RNA of tobacco mosaic virus (19, 105). Reaction of nitrous acid with the RNA resulted in transformation of purine and pyrimidine amino groups to hydroxy groups. Change in a single base in the chain of more than 6,000 nucleotides of tobacco mosaic virus RNA was sufficient to induce mutation. Mutations similar in principle have been produced by treatment of influenza, Newcastle disease, and polioviruses.

A phenomenon responsible for extensive biologic mutagenesis is that of genetic **recombination** (8, 72, 73). When a susceptible bacterium, for example, is exposed to two unrelated phages, both may attach, but infection and reproduction can be established by only one of the viruses. Inhibition of one or the other is termed **mutual exclusion.** In contrast, when the same bacterium is exposed to two related phages, such as T_2 and T_4, the same cell may produce both kinds of particles. If the two phages are very closely related, as a pair of mutants of the same agent, the cells may produce particles like the originals or particles with properties indicating a combination of the genetic characteristics of the infecting mutants.

Among the recombinants of T_4 phages

there occur a group of closely related mutants designated (8, 98) as **rII** which have been employed to construct a map reflecting the internal structure of the genetic moiety—gene—responsible for the mutants. It was shown that rII mutants were defective in genetic structure, and that the defect was located in a minute region, rII, of the genetic map—that is, in the DNA polynucleotide chain. The functional genetic units are aligned along a linear array. In the rII region of the total phage genetic array alone, about 400 mutants have been observed and genetically located in relation to one another on the map (8). The rII region contains two distinct genetic segments or cistrons.

Chemically or physically induced, as well as spontaneous, mutants are found in the rII region (8). The number of spontaneous mutants was greater than that of the experimentally induced, but the latter corresponded to the same points of linear array as the former. Mutants thus appear to be due to damage or alteration of individual nucleotides or sequence of nucleotides in the polynucleotide chain of phage DNA, in the same way as the effect of nitrous acid, for example, alters the RNA of tobacco mosaic virus.

Recombination occurs with other viruses, including those causing disease in man and animals, but suitable models are not available for work such as that with phage. Nevertheless, many instances have been observed. Transformation of rabbit fibroma-myxomatosis viruses—Berry-Dedrick transformation (66)—has been mentioned. Recombination occurs between a strain of vaccinia and rabbit pox, two DNA animal viruses. The most extensive work with animal viruses has been that with various strains of the RNA influenza agents.

LYSOGENY, CARRIER STATE, AND INTERFERON

Numerous instances of lysogeny (8, 72, 73, 74) occur in nature, and other like states have been established by bringing appropriate phages and host cells together experimentally. In lysogeny the host cell is presumably infected by the same mechanisms as those involving virulent phages, but the bacterium is not lysed. Instead, the phage genetic material becomes integrated with the genome of the host cell in the **prophage** state. With host cell proliferation, there is parallel increase in prophage, which is thus transmitted continuously through cell progeny. Such cells lyse only rarely under ordinary conditions. Lysis does occur at very low rates, however, and the existence of the lysogenic state is demonstrable by mixture of the liberated phages with a different and susceptible strain of host cells.

Lysogeny results in a variety of phenomena related to the integration of phage genetic material with the bacterial chromosome. **Bacteria bearing prophages are immune** to infection by homologous or mutant phages. Mutant phages may inject their DNA into the bacterium, but the DNA cannot be established as prophage and is diluted out in the course of bacterial multiplication. Multiple lysogeny can be established, however, by infection with a nonrelated temperate phage. Lysogenic bacteria may also be as sensitive to lysis by an unrelated virulent phage as a nonlysogenic host. **Temperate phages may be excluded by the virulent agents;** that is, a lysogenic bacterium bearing a temperate phage may produce only the virulent agent to which it is exposed. Genetic material may confer new, heritable properties on the chromosomes of the bacterium. A prominent example already mentioned (Chap. 27) is the conversion or transduction of nontoxinogenic strains of *Corynebacterium diphtheriae* to toxinogenic strains by establishment of lysogeny. This property of the bacterium is then dependent on the continued presence of the phage and is a heritable character only as long as the state of lysogeny persists. Other alterations in the characteristics of various hosts may be detected by changes in colony morphology or in antigenic and metabolic properties.

Although lysis of lysogenic bacteria seldom occurs naturally, development of phage maturation and lysis can be **induced** by a variety of means. Massive lysis can be induced by treatment with ultraviolet light, x-rays, gamma rays, nitrogen mustard, and other chemicals. Most of the inducing agents are also mutagens or carcinogens.

Phenomena superficially resembling those of the bacteriophage lysogenic systems have been observed in cell-virus relationships with other agents causing infections of plants and animals. In intact organisms the processes may be of the character designated as **latent infections,** in which virus is present in the host without manifestation of disease. There are numerous instances of virus isolation from apparently undiseased individuals by means of tissue culture. Monkey kidney cell cultures (21) are an unusually rich source of agents present without apparent influence on the initially isolated cells. Such cultures have yielded adenoviruses, **foamy** agents causing cytopathogenic changes and the SV or Simian viruses. One of these, SV40, was present in kidney cultures from rhesus and cynomologous monkeys without evidence of infection but caused marked cytopathic changes in like cultures from the heterologous species, the grivet monkey. The agent is of special interest since it induces tumors —fibrosarcomas—in newborn hamsters.

Analogous phenomena at the cellular level in tissue culture are manifested as the **carrier** state (48), in which viruses ordinarily causing cell alterations may be associated with cells without evidence of pathogenicity. Carrier cultures can be derived with many agents under a variety of conditions. Some cell lines may be susceptible to infection but do not respond with cell processes leading to notable alteration, as in the instance of chick embryo tissues infected with vaccinia virus or MCN cells infected with Newcastle disease virus. Although not all MCN cells liberated virus, the characteristics of the whole culture were changed. Selected variants of susceptible cells may likewise support virus synthesis and liberation without cytopathic changes. Such variants may be selected by cloning cells not dying in infected cultures. The factors responsible for such persistence of viral infection are not clearly known. There has been no evidence that the carrier state bears any resemblance in principle to lysogeny in the bacteriophage system.

Recent work (59, 121) suggests that a factor promoting the carrier state is the occurrence of **interferon.** It has long been known that cell infection by some viruses suppressed or prevented further infection by other filterable agents. The phenomenon— known as **interference**—was observed first in diseases of plants. In the early work with these hosts it appeared that interference occurred only between related agents, and the phenomenon was employed as a means for differentiating and classifying plant viruses.

Among animal viruses (59) Hoskins found that a neurotrophic strain of yellow fever virus protected against a related viscerotropic strain of the agent. In contrast, viscerotropic virus did not affect the course of the disease caused by the neurotropic strain. Findlay and McCallum showed, further, that both the viscerotropic and pantropic yellow fever viruses protected mice against the Rift Valley fever agent which is related to the yellow fever virus. A variety of principles are evident in the occurrence of the phenomenon. In some instances the effect occurred in only one direction; that is, one of the agents interfered with the other, but the latter did not affect the behavior of the former. In other cases the effect was reciprocal. The effect might be demonstrable between two derivatives of an agent—**auto-interference**—between related viruses—**homologous** interference—and between unrelated agents—**heterologous** interference. Not all combinations of viruses exhibited interference, since two or more viruses may occupy and multiply in the same cell. Exclusion was not dependent on multiplication of the interfering agent but was affected within a few hours under suitable conditions also by virus inactivated by heat or ultraviolet light. The findings suggested that interference was an intracellular phenomenon not related either to entry of the excluded virus into the cell or to exit of the synthesized agent.

A recent advance was the discovery that interference was associated with the elaboration and liberation by the test cell of a new material, interferon (59, 121). Interferon released by chick chorio-allantoic cells treated with heat-inactivated influenza virus interfered with infection by influenza virus of fresh membrane cells treated with the material. Interference was exhibited also by cells elaborating interferon. A large number of viruses either active or inactivated by heat or ultraviolet light are capable of stimulating cells to elaborate interferon. Interferon acts inside the cell and does not neutralize extracellular virus or infectious nucleic acid. Interferons are not all alike but differ in relation to the virus system involved and may exhibit host-cell specificity.

In its fundamental influence, interferon acts to increase the resistance to viral infection of cells treated with it or elaborating it and may be of importance as a factor in virus immunity or in the processes of recovery from infection. Evidence of parallelism between interferon formation and recovery has been found with several viruses. Virus-infected cells may be maintained (50) in culture for long periods under conditions conducive to continuous interferon formation (Fig. 33). Analogous conditions may exist in the intact animal in the case of mice infected before birth with lymphocytic choriomeningitis virus. Such mice resist lethal doses of the agent given after birth. In clinical tests (106) interferon produced with influenza virus in monkey kidney cell cultures depressed local response to vaccinia in man and has been used with good effect in the treatment of vaccinia virus keratitis.

Interferons are not recognizable as virus components. The materials are heat-stable and stable over a wide range of pH and behave as proteins of low molecular weight subject to digestion by a variety of proteolytic enzymes. One product had a molecular weight of 25,000 and contained a trace of carbohydrate and no nucleic acid.

The mechanism of action of interferon is not known but appears to be concerned with some stage of intracellular virus synthesis. There is no interference with adsorption, penetration, or integration of nucleic acid. There is no effect, either, on liberation of formed virus. It would thus appear that the influence is on the processes of viral nucleic acid and protein synthesis.

Although the mechanisms of interferon effects are unknown, recent work has suggested a unifying principle possibly responsible for occurrence of the materials. This is the hypothesis (100) that formation of interferon is stimulated by exposure of cells to nucleic acid, DNA or RNA, derived from sources "foreign" to the test cells. Support of the hypothesis has been demonstrated by action of RNA from chicken tissue to induce

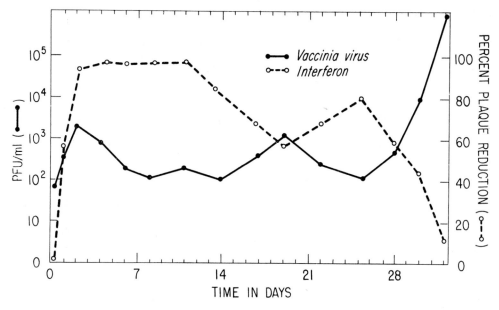

Fig. 33. Inverse relationship between interferon concentration in culture fluid and elaboration of vaccinia virus in tissue culture. (From Glasgow and Habel. *J. Exper. Med.,* 115:503, 1962.)

interferon active against infection of mouse cells with vaccinia virus. Interference with the same virus occurred also after mixture of mouse RNA with chick cells exposed to the vaccinial agent. The approach has much promise in possibly effecting a solution to the origin and action of interferon.

METABOLIC FACTORS AND ENZYMES

Despite repeated studies, none of the viruses has shown evidence of independent metabolic activity. Vaccinia virus (109) contains copper, biotin, and riboflavin. Several enzyme activities—phosphatase, catalase, and lipase—were associated with vaccinial elementary bodies, but there has been no agreement that the respective enzymes are essential constituents of the agent.

Influenza virus contains the enzyme neuraminidase (19, 71) with the capacity to act at the linkage of n-acetylneuraminic acid with oligosaccharides of host-cell receptor sites. Enzyme activity is expressed biologically by irreversible changes in red blood cells agglutinated by the agent and by physi-

cal and chemical changes in the molecular structure of substrates from egg white and other materials. Action of the viral enzyme on the red blood cells is similar to the activity of the receptor-destroying enzyme from filtrates of *Vibrio comma.* The enzyme appears to be associated with the surface structures, perhaps the peripheral array of spikes (Fig. 23A in Chap. 61) of the virus particles, and may be of importance in the processes of cell parasitization.

A strong adenosinetriphosphatase activity (5) is associated with the BAI strain A virus responsible for avian myeloblastosis, and ultracytochemical studies demonstrated the enzyme in the surface structures of the virus particle (Fig. 19). The presence of the enzyme in the virus was dependent on enzyme in the cell surface budding the virus particle. The same virus budded from cells without membrane enzyme does not exhibit the activity. Herpes virus forming in cell membranes with adenosinetriphosphatase activity likewise contains the enzyme (42). These findings serve to reveal the origin but do not explain possible function of the enzyme in the processes of infection or cell activity.

Enzymes such as trypsin, chymotrypsin,

carboxypeptidase, ribonuclease, ficin, and cathepsin did not affect vaccinia virus in the pH range of virus stability, but papain at pH 5.5 and pepsin at pH 2.0, where the virus was inactivated, induced digestion. The respective nucleases, however, digest DNA or RNA separated from the protective capsids and envelopes of the various agents and destroy the infectious properties of nucleic acid isolated from plant and other agents transmitted by nucleic acid.

VIRUS INFECTIVITY AND TITRATION

Viruses can be recognized unequivocally only by virtue of their capacity to cause infection in susceptible cells or hosts, in contrast to most bacteria and other organisms, which can be identified and enumerated by the simple cultural methods already described in earlier chapters. A fundamental problem in virology, then, is the titration (63) of infectious capacity, for no studies involving quantitative information about virus amount or activity can be made before the proper procedures have been established. Titration is accomplished by administration of suitable dilutions of test material into susceptible hosts and the calculation, by one method or another, of an end point or potency level. Advantages are afforded by the use of the embryonated chick egg for such agents as those of influenza, Newcastle disease, and mumps. Titration of viruses such as the pox group can be accomplished by counting the number of lesions or pocks occurring on inoculated chick embryo chorio-allantoic membrane.

Tissue cultures are indispensable in the titration of agents such as the poliomyelitis, equine encephalomyelitis, and other cyto-pathogenic viruses (23, 92). Massive cultures of HeLa, monkey kidney, or other cells are prepared on a plane surface after mixing with dilutions of virus. Localized cell death or change is revealed in plaques, one for each center of activity or infectious unit (Fig. 34). In this manner the number of infectious virus units can be estimated on the basis of the number of plaques and the dilution of material mixed with the cells.

The pattern of titration or infectivity results in intact organisms is a summation of the reaction of the host and the properties of the virus in question (6). Administration of most viruses in a series of graded doses in the proper dose range results in an incidence of 100 per cent positive inoculations with the largest amount and 0 per cent with intermediate incidences between. Ordinarily, when incidence (in per cent positive) is plotted against dose (in logarithms), the result is a sigmoid curve.

The titration end point with many viruses is estimated from incidence data as the 50 per cent end point (6), or that dilution which will cause infection by half the number of inocula and no infection by the other half. This point is calculated by the method of Reed and Muench as applied to viruses.

The above methods are based on **quantal,** or all-or-none, response, which is noted as incidence in per cent in relation to dose in logarithmic units. Another procedure is based on the latent period, or the time elapsing between administration of the inoculum and the appearance of disease; this is a **continuous variate** response. This type of response is particularly useful (6) in the study of the tumor-inducing viruses and those causing rabbit papillomatosis, Rous sarcoma, myeloblastic leukosis, and also in the study of the chemical carcinogens. The relations employed are those of the latent period, or some function of it, to the logarithm of dose. The linear relations thus described may be as useful as or more so than those of the quantal response.

The actual number of virus particles required to cause infection varies greatly (63), not only with different agents but also with the same agent under different conditions. A single bacteriophage particle may be sufficient to cause infection. Most viruses are relatively highly infectious, and infection can be established by one or small numbers of particles. In contrast, an average of about 90 million rabbit papilloma virus particles are required to give the 50 per cent end point in the rabbit under the conditions of inoculation, whereas 26 million particles of the BAI strain A virus of myeloblastic leukosis are needed to infect 50 per cent of the chicks injected.

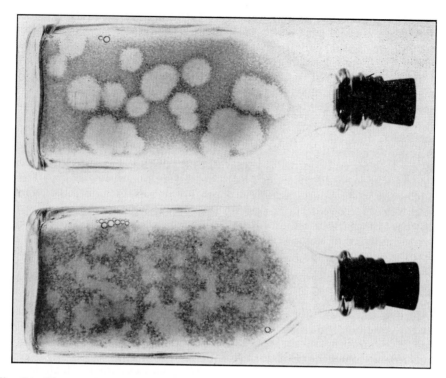

Fig. 34. Plaque tritration of viruses in monolayer cell cultures in convenient disposal bottles. The upper bottle shows plaques of poliovirus (type 3) six days after seeding and the lower one plaques of echo virus (type 6') eight days after seeding. (Courtesy of Drs. G. D. Hsuing and J. L. Melnick.)

VIRUS CULTIVATION

It is frequently necessary to cultivate viruses apart from the normal hosts. Sometimes this can be accomplished by adaptation of the agents to less expensive or more convenient **new hosts,** which are useful for virus titration and production of virus for study, as in the adaptation of vaccinia virus to the rabbit. Tissue culture has attained the status of an indispensable means for the study of viruses (23, 92, 104). This has been due in part to a much needed simplification of the procedures and to the use of antibiotics in culture fluids to control bacterial infection, which eliminates most of the formerly tedious discipline required for definitive results. Use has been made of cells layered in plasma clots or in sheets in culture tubes and flasks. Tissue culture has been applied to studies on virus morphology and reproduction as well as immunity and virus titration, and for the isolation of the agents

undemonstrable by other technics. Various recently developed lines of cells are highly susceptible to the action of many viral agents, and the possibilities for their further usefulness for isolation, identification, and titration of viruses yet unknown are extensive. Tissue culture can be applied on large productive scales, such as utilization of cultures of monkey kidney cells for the growth, titration, identification, and serology of the poliomyelitis virus and the preparation of vaccines from the resultant virus. The application of "sheet" cultures to the titration of poliomyelitis, equine encephalomyelitis, and other cytopathogenic viruses has been mentioned.

Of great value has been the use of the embryonated chicken egg. Some of the agents—vaccinia and laryngotracheitis of the fowl, and others—dropped through a hole in the shell onto the chorio-allantoic membrane yield local lesions and accumulation of virus. The viruses of equine encephalomyelitis and Newcastle diseases kill the embryos. Influenza, mumps, and Newcastle disease viruses are inoculated into the chorio-allantoic sac. Embryo culture provides a source of several viruses—equine, encephalomyelitis, influenza, yellow fever, and laryngotracheitis—for the preparation of vaccines on a large scale. Whereas some of the agents reach only relatively low concentrations in the tissues of the natural host, the amounts in the embryo or in the chorio-allantoic fluid may be exceedingly great. The viruses of influenza in 42 hours, mumps in five days, and Newcastle disease in 36 to 38 hours reach titers of nearly a billion infectious units per milliliter of chorio-allantoic fluid. Embryos are useful in the isolation of some viruses from infected hosts. Virus-cell relations can be studied in isolated bits of chorio-allantoic membrane. A valuable preparation frequently employed for study of influenza virus multiplication is the de-embryonated egg consisting of the chorio-allantoic membrane attached to the shell after the embryo has been taken out.

HEMAGGLUTINATION

A number of viruses, particularly those of influenza, Newcastle disease of chickens, and mumps, possess strongly the capacity to agglutinate red blood cells of the chicken, guinea pig, and man (1). Other agents give the reaction in a different way—such as vaccinia, smallpox, and mouse pox (ectromelia) in a second group; Japanese, St. Louis and Russian encephalitis, and others in a third group. Hemagglutination of the influenza virus is due to adsorption of virus particles at specific receptor sites on red blood cells and binding together of the cells through the virus which can attach to more than one cell (see Fig. 23B in Chap. 61). The reaction with the fully active virus is reversible. Agglutination occurs rapidly at 0° C. Exposure of the aggregated cell masses to 37° C. causes dispersion of the cells, in the process of which the virus is freed or **eluted** and returned to suspension. The extent of hemagglutination is related to virus concentration, and the reaction constitutes a rapid and convenient means for measurement of virus amount.

Agglutination and elution cause no changes in the virus and have therefore been employed as a means for concentration and purification of the agents by repeated agglutination and elution—as, for example, for the preparation of influenza vaccine. Elution is effected, under proper conditions, by enzymatic—neuraminidase—action of the agent on the receptor areas. Inactivation does not change the adsorbing capacity but does destroy the enzyme. Virus receptors on the red cell surface can be destroyed by other enzymes including the "receptor destroying enzyme" (RDE) present in the culture fluids of *Vibrio comma*. Hemagglutination does not occur in the presence of specific virus serum, which provides a well-established basis for clinical diagnosis and study.

IMMUNITY AND IMMUNOLOGIC PHENOMENA

Some viruses exhibit a high degree of host or species, and even cell, specificity. Consequently, some hosts are naturally immune or highly resistant to infection, and, conversely, such hosts may provide an unsuitable medium for invasion by, and propagation of, the agents. Such a relation, however, may not be unchangeable, for the hog cholera virus, long considered to be species specific for swine, has been passed to the rabbit. Numerous instances of adaptation, variation, and mutation have indicated a broader range of tolerance between viruses and hosts than once thought. Great differences may be observed in the natural resistance or susceptibility of different species of susceptible animals—as in the instance of vaccinia virus, to which rabbits are much more highly susceptible than guinea pigs. Natural resistance or susceptibility of individuals may vary widely among a population of relatively highly susceptible hosts. Host susceptibility and resistance, as well as the properties of the virus, influence the character of the response to virus infection. The influence of genetic constitution was shown experimentally in studies of encephalitis in mice. In some instances age may be an influencing factor: young mice are more susceptible than older animals to equine encephalomyelitis, and three-day-old chicks are far more susceptible to myeloblastic leukosis virus than older ones. Nutritional disturbances may decrease susceptibility, and cell injury may increase the ability of some agents to invade the host cell, as was found in the instance of chicken tumor viruses.

Resistance may be acquired actively as the result either of disease or vaccination. Infection with some agents is followed by a long-lasting immunity to reinfection, as in smallpox, yellow fever, hog cholera, vaccinia, measles, and mumps. Other agents, such as influenza and common cold viruses (22), do not produce lasting immunity. In certain other diseases, such as the chicken tumors and the various papillomas, high degrees of immunity to reinfection may be present in the animal supporting tumors; these lead to the death of the host while the viruses remain in quantity in the proliferating cells.

Active immunization with vaccines of different sorts is of great value in the control of some virus diseases of man and animals. Several principles of vaccination or types of vaccine are employed with success. Fully active and virulent virus may be used in association with a modifying procedure. Laryngotracheitis virus, virulent by respiratory inoculation, is introduced in the membrane of the cloaca of the fowl. Virulent hog cholera virus is given to swine at one point subcutaneously, while hyperimmune serum is given at another point simultaneously.

Using another principle, virus is employed which is fully active but which has become attenuated for the host concerned. Examples are the yellow fever, measles (60), and poliomyelitis viruses (94). Another method of vaccination with active virus is the use of immunologically related agents: cowpox or vaccinia virus, cultured in the calf, is employed for the vaccination of man against smallpox, and pigeon pox virus protects chickens against fowl pox. In all of these instances, the resultant immunity is related to the multiplication of virus in the vaccinated host.

Inactivated virus vaccines have not been of generally outstanding value, to some extent though by no means wholly because of the difficulties of obtaining preparations of sufficient virus concentration. However, completely inactivated virus in sufficient concentration may be effective in some instances. High resistance to equine encephalomyelitis is induced in man and horse with chick-embryo-cultured virus inactivated with formalin. Another vaccine of this type is the influenza virus cultured in the chick embryo and concentrated either by hemagglutination and elution or by centrifugation. Poliomyelitis virus grown in monkey kidney cultures and inactivated with formalin (102) was employed until it was replaced recently by live virus vaccine (94).

Major factors in acquired immunity are the humoral antibodies (104). These antibodies, found in blood serum in the gamma globulin fraction, possess in varying degree the capacity to neutralize virus activity, to agglutinate the respective agents in suitable concentration in vitro, to precipitate certain soluble antigens associated with some viruses, and to fix complement under proper conditions of virus and serum concentration.

In certain of the diseases protection against reinfection can be accounted for largely on the basis of the neutralizing antibodies. Under such conditions, the portals of entry into the body and the tissues to be affected are so separated that the antibodies in the blood stream and tissues have an opportunity to destroy the agents before they reach the susceptible cells and establish infection. Immune bodies are not effective in animals with virus tumors, since the infected cells maintain their integrity in continuous proliferation and provide the virus inside them with constant protection from antibody. Passive immunity can be conferred temporarily by the administration of specific immune serum, but the procedure is of but little value in the treatment of virus diseases after infection has occurred. Convalescent serum may lessen the severity of measles, but the modified disease may not result in durable immunity.

Immunologic reactions in virus diseases—neutralization, complement fixation, etc.—are valuable in diagnostic and epidemiologic studies (104), in the identification and differentiation of viruses, in the determination of immunologic or antigenic relationships between viruses, and in testing the potencies of antiserums. The methods are simply those of virus titration, in which immune serum is mixed with various dilutions of virus or various dilutions of serum are mixed with a given amount of virus, and the effect is determined by animal test or in tissue culture.

Agglutination and complement-fixation reactions are obtained with virus and immune serums when the two materials are present in suitable amounts. These reactions, like the neutralization test, are of value in diagnostic, epidemiologic, and virus identification investigations. In the agglutination reaction with viruses, as with bacteria, the serum acts on the virus particles causing agglomeration, and the flocs fall out of suspension. The complement-fixation reaction requires less antigen, and extracts of diseased tissues may be employed in some instances. Precipitin reactions involving "soluble" antigens present in virus-diseased tissue have been observed in association with several viruses. These reactions are analogous to the precipitin reactions associated with the soluble products and toxins of bacteria as distinguished from the agglutination reaction which involves the whole bacterial or virus particle.

THERAPY OF VIRUS DISEASES

Progress and potentialities of the application of chemotherapy to treatment of virus diseases have been recently reviewed (19, 20). Antibiotics and other drugs have been notably deficient in activity on the outcome of infections by filterable agents with the exception of the psittacosis group the members of which are no longer classed with the viruses. In contrast, however, much has been learned of the very significant influence of a large variety of materials on the processes of virus-host interaction at the cellular level. This has been effected through the rapidly increasing investigation of basic biochemical phenomena manifest in the reactions in the various stages of virus synthesis and elaboration. The outstanding advances thus far have been made with viruses and cells in tissue cultures, but some of the findings have

been applicable in practical usefulness with promising results.

Many virus diseases are subject to much control by prophylactic measures of vaccination which are effective in the prevention of infection. Immunologic processes also exert controlling influences on the progress of numerous diseases, but only after damage to infected cells. In contrast, virus-induced neoplastic conditions are not affected by the usual immunologic processes, since viruses are protected inside the growing cells beyond reach of immune bodies. Administration of antibodies has been of dubious usefulness in the control of developed virus disease.

At the cellular level in vitro the outcome of infection can be markedly influenced by a variety of inhibitors acting in critical stages of elaboration of the different virus types. The elaboration of DNA agents, vaccinia, adenovirus, and pseudorabies is inhibited by mitomycin C and halogenated pyrimidines, including 5-fluorodeoxyuridine and 5-bromodeoxyuridine, all of which are inhibitors of DNA synthesis. Synthesis of RNA viruses is not affected, except to some extent in the instance of the RNA REO virus.

Actinomycin D inhibits DNA-dependent RNA synthesis and, consequently, inhibits processes of virus formation dependent on continued elaboration of RNA critical for virus synthesis. Action of the antibiotic is not related to the DNA or RNA type virus but only on the requirement for processes involving essential DNA or RNA synthesis. Thus, vaccinia virus synthesis is inhibited, while that of the RNA Mengo virus is not. Influence of actinomycin D differs with various RNA agents; Mengo, polio, and Newcastle disease viruses are not inhibited, but REO virus and influenza are.

Influences are exerted also by inhibitors of protein synthesis, the antibiotic puromycin and amino acid analogues such as *p*-fluorophenylalanine. The former has a reversible effect on polio and Mengo virus synthesis, and the latter influences formation of fowl plague virus hemagglutinin and poliovirus.

A potent and selective inhibitor is 2-(α-hydroxybenzyl)-benzimidazole, the action of which is limited to influence on synthesis of poliovirus and some enteroviruses. Other agents thus far studied were not affected. Guanidine inhibits multiplication of some enteroviruses, and its action is associated with occurrence of mutants resistant to the action of the drug.

Several materials act to interfere with virus formation at the level of final maturation or assembly. Among these are the basic dyes. Proflavine interrupts maturation of bacteriophage and poliovirus. Isatin β-thiosemicarbazone prevents formation of mature vaccinia virus.

The occurrence of natural inhibitors of the interferon group has been discussed.

Although it is evident that much progress is being made in simple cell-virus systems, conditions in the intact host present obstacles of a different order of magnitude to practical application of the knowledge. Nevertheless, a basis has been established for expansion of directed comprehensive studies in the field. Optimism for intensifying the work is stimulated by some promising results. The use of interferon in limiting the vaccinial infectious process in the intact host has been mentioned. Herpes virus keratitis in rabbits has been controlled by topical applications of 5-iododeoxyuridine, and measures of success attend such treatment of the human disease. These positive results have been meager, but it must be realized that the problems of the viruses are highly complex, are manifest at the finest biochemical level of cell physiology itself, and must be expected to vary widely in relation to the individual agents.

REFERENCES

1. Anderson, S. G. in The Viruses, Burnet, F. M., and Stanley, W. M., eds., New York, Academic Press, Inc., 1959, vol. 3, p. 21.
2. Anderson, T. F. Ann. Rev. Microbiol., 4:21, 1950.
3. ———— Cold Spring Harbor Symp. Quant. Biol., 18:197, 1953.
4. Beard, J. W. Cancer Res., 16:279, 1956.
5. ———— Adv. in Cancer Res., 7:1, 1963.
6. ———— Sharp, D. G., and Eckert, E. A. Adv. in Virus Res., 3:149, 1955.
7. Becker, C., Beaudreau, G. S., Castle, W., Gibson, B. W., Beard, D., and Beard, J. W. J. Nat. Cancer Inst., 29:455, 1962.
8. Benzer, S. Harvey Lect., 56:1, 1960-61.
9. Bergold, G. H. Adv. in Virus Res., 1:91, 1953.
10. Bernhard, W. Cancer Res., 20:712, 1960.

11. Black, L. M. in The Viruses, Burnet, F. M., and Stanley, W. M., eds., New York, Academic Press Inc., 1959, vol. 2, p. 157.
12. Blattner, R. J., and Heys, F. M. Prog. Med. Virology, 3:311, 1961.
13. Bloch, D. P., Morgan, C., Godman, G. C., Howe, C., and Rose, H. M. J. Biophys. Biochem. Cytol., 3:1, 1957.
14. Bonar, R. A., Heine, U., Beard, D., and Beard, J. W. J. Nat. Cancer Inst., 30:949, 1963.
15. Buschke, A., and Loewenstein, L. Klin. Wchnschr., 2:1726, 1925.
16. Chandra, S., and Toolan, H. W. J. Nat. Cancer Inst., 27:1405, 1961.
17. Cohen, S. S. in The Viruses, Burnet, F. M., and Stanley, W. M., eds., New York, Academic Press Inc., 1959, vol. 1, p. 15.
18. ———— Fed. Proc., 20:641, 1961.
19. ———— Ann. Rev. Biochem., 32:83, 1963.
20. Colter, J. S., and Ellem, K. A. O. Ann. Rev. Microbiol., 15:219, 1961.
21. Committee on Tissue Culture Viruses and Vaccines. Science, 139:15, 1963.
22. Conference on Newer Respiratory Diseases. Am. Rev. Resp. Dis., 88:1, 1963.
23. Cooper, P. D. Adv. in Virus Res., 8:319, 1961.
24. Crick, F. H. C., Barnett, L., Brenner, S., and Watts-Tobin, R. J. Nature, London, 192:1227, 1961.
25. Cruickshank, J. G., Berry, D. M., and Hay, B. Virology, 20:376, 1963.
26. Dales, S. J. Cell Biol., 13:303, 1962.
27. ———— J. Cell Biol., 18:51, 1963.
28. ———— and Choppin, P. W. Virology, 18:489, 1962.
29. ———— and Franklin, R. M. J. Cell Biol., 14:281, 1962.
30. ———— and Siminovitch, L. J. Biophys. Biochem. Cytol., 10:475, 1961.
31. Dalton, A. J. Federation Proceedings, 21:936, 1962.
32. ———— Law, L. W., Moloney, J. B., and Manaker, R. A. J. Nat. Cancer Inst., 27:747, 1961.
33. Darnell, J. E., Jr. Cold Spring Harbor Symp. Quant. Biol., 27:149, 1962.
34. de Harven, E., and Friend, C. J. Biophys. Biochem. Cytol., 4:151, 1958.
35. Delbruck, M. Biol. Rev., 21:30, 1946.
36. de Thé, G., Becker, C., and Beard, J. W. J. Nat. Cancer Inst., 32:201, 1964.
37. ———— Ishiguro, H., Beard, D., and Beard, J. W. J. Nat. Cancer Inst., 31:717, 1963.
38. Dmochowski, L. Prog. Med. Virol., 3:363, 1961.
39. Dourmashkin, R., and Bernhard, W. J. Ultrastructure Res., 3:11, 1959.
40. Eckert, E. A., Sharp, D. G., Beard, D., Green, I., and Beard, J. W. J. Nat. Cancer Inst., 16:593, 1955.
41. Epstein, M. A. J. Cell Biol., 12:589, 1962.
42. ———— and Holt, S. J. Nature, 198:509, 1963.
43. Febvre, H. in Tumors Induced by Viruses: Ultrastructural Studies, Dalton, A. J., and Haguenau, F., eds., New York and London, Academic Press Inc., 1962, vol. 1, p. 79.
44. Findlay, G. M. in Doerr, R., and Hallauer, C. Handbuch der Virusforschung, Erste Hälfte, Wien, Julius Springer, p. 292, 1938.

45. Fogh, J., and Stuart, D. C., Jr. Virology, 11:308, 1960.
46. Franklin, R. M., and Baltimore, D. Cold Spring Harbor Symp. Quant. Biol., 27:175, 1962.
47. Gierer, A., and Schramm, G. Nature, 177: 702, 1956.
48. Ginsberg, H. S. Prog. Med. Virology, 1:36, 1958.
49. ———— Perspectives in Virology, 2:58, 1961.
50. Glasgow, L. A., and Habel, K. J. Exper. Med., 115:503, 1962.
51. Granboulan, N., Tournier, P., Wicker, R., and Bernhard, W. J. Cell Biol., 17:423, 1963.
52. Green, M. Cold Spring Harbor Symp. Quant. Biol., 27:219, 1962.
53. Gross, L. Oncogenic Viruses, International Series of Monographs on Pure and Applied Biology, New York, Pergamon Press, 1961, vol. 11.
54. Ham, A. W., and Leeson, T. S. Histology, 4th ed., Philadelphia, Montreal, J. B. Lippincott Co., 1961.
55. Hanafusa, H. Cold Spring Harbor Symp. Quant. Biol., 27:209, 1962.
56. Heine, U., de Thé, G., Beard, D., and Beard, J. W. J. Nat. Cancer Inst., 30:817, 1963.
57. ———— de Thé, G., Ishiguro, H., and Beard, J. W. J. Nat. Cancer Inst., 29:211, 1962.
58. ———— de Thé, G., Ishiguro, H., Sommer, J. R., Beard, D., and Beard, J. W. J. Nat. Cancer Inst., 29:41, 1962.
59. Hilleman, M. R. J. Cellular and Comparative Physiology, 62:337, 1963.
60. ———— Stokes, J., Jr., Buynak, E. B., Weibel, R., Halenda, R., and Goldner, H. Am. J. Pub. Health, 52:44, 1962.
61. Hoyle, L. Cold Spring Harbor Symp. Quant. Biol., 27:113, 1962.
62. ———— Horne, R. W., and Waterson, A. P. Virology, 17:533, 1962.
63. Isaacs, A. Adv. in Virus Res., 4:111, 1957.
64. Joklik, W. K. Cold Spring Harbor Symp. Quant. Biol., 27:199, 1962.
65. Kellenberger, E. Adv. in Virus Res., 8:1, 1961.
66. Kilham, L. Adv. in Virus Res., 7:103, 1960.
67. Kit, S. Ann. Rev. Biochem., 32:43, 1963.
68. Kleinschmidt, A. K., Lang, D., Zacherts, D., and Zahn, R. K. Biochim. Biophys. Acta, 61:857, 1962.
69. Knight, C. A. J. Exper. Med., 83:281, 1946.
70. Kozloff, L. M. Ann. Rev. Biochem., 29: 475, 1960.
71. Laver, W. G. Virology, 20:251, 1963.
72. Luria, S. E. General Virology, New York, John Wiley & Sons, Inc., 1953.
73. ———— Ann. Rev. Microbiol., 16:205, 1962.
74. ———— Science, 136:685, 1962.
75. ———— Williams, R. C., and Backus, R. C. J. Bact., 61:179, 1951.
76. Melnick, J. L. Ann. New York Acad. Sc., 61:754, 1955.
77. Moore, D. H., Lasfargues, E. Y., Murray, M. R., Haagensen, C. D., and Pollard, E. C. J. Biophys. Biochem. Cytol., 5:85, 1959.
78. Morgan, C., Ellison, S. A., Rose, H. M., and Moore, D. H. J. Exper. Med., 100:301, 1954.
79. ———— Howe, C., and Rose, H. M. Virology, 9:145, 1959.
80. ———— Howe, C., and Rose, H. M. J. Exper. Med., 113:219, 1961.
81. ———— Howe, C., Rose, H. M., and Moore, D. H. J. Biophys. Biochem. Cytol., 2:351, 1956.
82. ———— Hsu, K. C., Rifkind, R. A., Knox, A. W., and Rose, H. M. J. Exper. Med., 114:825, 1961.
83. ———— Hsu, K. C., Rifkind, R. A., Knox, A. W., and Rose, H. M. J. Exper. Med., 114:833, 1961.
84. ———— Hsu, K. C., and Rose, H. M. J. Exper. Med., 116:533, 1962.
85. ———— Rifkind, R. A., Hsu, K. C., Holden, M., Seegal, B. C., and Rose, H. M. Virology, 14:292, 1961.
86. ———— Rifkind, R. A., and Rose, H. M. Cold Spring Harbor Symp. Quant. Biol., 27: 57, 1962.
87. ———— Rose, H. M., Holden, M., and Jones, E. P. J. Exper. Med., 110:643, 1959.
88. Mussgay, M., and Weibel, J. Virology, 16: 506, 1962.
89. ———— and Weibel, J. Virology, 16:52, 1962.
90. Nirenberg, M. W. Scientific American, 208: 80, 1963.
91. Núñez-Montiel, O., and Weibel, J. J. Biophys. Biochem. Cytol., 8:291, 1960.
92. Pereira, H. G. Adv. in Virus Res., 8:245, 1961.
93. Peters, D. in Fourth International Conference on Electron Microscopy, Berlin, Sept. 10-17, 1958, Bargmann, W., Peters, D., and Wolpers, C., eds., Springer-Verlag, Berlin-Göttingen-Heidelberg, 1960, vol. 2, p. 552.
94. Plotkin, S. A., Carp, R. I., and Graham, A. F. Ann. New York Acad. Sc., 101:357, 1962.
95. Puck, T. T. Cold Spring Harbor Symp. Quant. Biol., 18:149, 1953.
96. Putnam, F. W. Adv. Prot. Chem., 8:175, 1953.
97. Rifkind, R. A., Godman, G. C., Howe, C., Morgan, C., and Rose, H. M. J. Exper. Med., 114:1, 1961.
98. Riley, M., and Pardee, A. B. Ann. Rev. Microbiol., 16:1, 1962.
99. Rogers, S., and Moore, M. J. Exper. Med., 117:521, 1963.
100. Rotem, Z., Cox, R. A., and Isaacs, A. Nature, 197:564, 1963.
101. Rous, P. Harvey Lect., 31:74, 1935-36.
102. Salk, J. E. J.A.M.A., 169:1829, 1959.
103. Schäfer, W. Bact. Rev., 27:1, 1963.
104. Schmidt, N. J., and Lennette, E. H. Prog. Med. Virology, 3:1, 1961.
105. Schramm, G. Perspectives in Virology, 2: 38, 1961.
106. Scientific Committee on Interferon. Lancet, 1:873, 1962.
107. Shope, R. E. Harvey Lect., 31:183, 1935-36.
108. Sinkovics, J. G. Ann. Rev. Microbiol., 16: 75, 1962.
109. Smadel, J. E., and Hoagland, C. L. Bact. Rev., 6:79, 1942.
110. Smith, K. M. Virology, 5:168, 1958.
111. ———— Adv. in Virus Res., 9:195, 1962.

112. Steinhaus, E. A.   Principles of Insect Pathology, 1st ed., New York, McGraw-Hill Book Co., Inc., 1949.
113. Stevens, A.   Ann. Rev. Biochem., 32:15, 1963.
114. Stone, R. S., Shope, R. E., and Moore, D. H. J. Exper. Med., 110:543, 1959.
115. Sverak, L., Beaudreau, G. S., and Beard, J. W.   J. Nat. Cancer Inst., 29:355, 1962.
116. Syverton, J. T., and Berry, G. P.   J. Exper. Med., 86:145, 1947.
117. Tolmach, L. J.   Adv. in Virus Res., 4:63, 1957.
118. Toolan, H. W.   Science, 131:1446, 1960.
119. van Rooyen, C. E.   J. Path. & Bact., 46:425, 1938.
120. Wagner, R. R.   Am. Rev. Resp. Diseases, 88:404, 1963.
121. ———— Bacteriol. Rev., 27:72, 1963.
122. Watson, J. D.   Science, 140:17, 1963.
123. Wecker, E., and Richter, A.   Cold Spring Harbor Symp. Quant. Biol., 27:137, 1962.
124. Wilcox, W. C., and Ginsberg, H. S.   Virology, 20:269, 1963.
125. Woodruff, C. E., and Goodpasture, E. W. Am. J. Path., 6:713, 1930.
126. Yarwood, C. E.   Adv. in Virus Res., 4:243, 1957.
127. Zeigel, R. F.   J. Nat. Cancer Inst., 26:1011, 1961.

63

Poxviruses of Man and Animals

SMALLPOX AND VACCINIA

Class: *Microtatobiotes* Phillip. Order: *Virales* Breed, Murray, Hitchens. Smallpox, *Poxvirus variolae;* vaccinia, *Poxvirus officinale.*

The disease smallpox is so closely associated with vaccinia virus, the virus used to vaccinate against smallpox, that it is convenient to consider these agents together. Many of the world's cases of smallpox occur in vaccinated persons, and in those persons the clinical course may be modified considerably. In fact, a point deserving great stress is that vaccination against smallpox with vaccinia virus affords **varying degrees of protection** rather than absolute protection. Vaccination materially reduces the death rate from about 30 per cent in unvaccinated individuals to from 5 to 17 per cent in vaccinated persons, depending on number of vaccinations, size of scar, and time between vaccination and exposure. Besides reduction in death rate, vaccination reduces the incidence of **blindness.** Obviously, vaccination does not afford complete protection against smallpox, but it does do three very important jobs: (1) it reduces the mortality; (2) it makes the disease much less severe, particularly in preventing blindness; and (3) it limits the spread of the disease.

The following pages will be concerned with four distinct viruses: (1) **smallpox** (variola) virus, which causes classic smallpox; (2) **alastrim,** a stable variant of smallpox virus which causes the relatively mild disease alastrim; (3) **cowpox,** a virus which causes a natural disease in cows and which is antigenically related to smallpox virus to the extent that infection with cowpox protects against smallpox; and (4) **vaccinia,** a virus of uncertain origin. It was not until recently that it occurred to scientists to compare vaccinia with smallpox and cowpox. Surprisingly, it differed from both (48). At present, then, the origin of vaccinia virus is obscure. Jenner's initial material was probably cowpox, so vaccinia may be cowpox virus altered by many passages. On the other hand, smallpox virus may have contaminated Jenner's material and a virus variant selected which is now known as vaccinia. Since it is possible by appropriate animal passage to convert smallpox, alastrim, or cowpox viruses to vaccinia, the question is actually academic.

History. The name "smallpox" was used to differentiate this disease from the "large pox" or syphilis and is the term used universally although some writers use the synonym "variola." Smallpox probably first appeared in Central Africa and was known in Egypt no later than 1160 B.C. (Rameses V died of smallpox); likewise, it was described in China about 1000 B.C. Descriptions written at the time of the Crusades showed smallpox to be spreading rapidly in Europe and Asia (43). Smallpox was unknown in the New World until introduced by Europeans, and it is with some truth that the conquest of the New World can be partly attributed to smallpox. The American Indians were decimated by this disease, and many villages were wiped out and tribes depleted by the virus.

Ironically, smallpox indirectly contributed to the spread of syphilis. In the nineteenth century it was common practice to maintain vaccinia virus by inoculating susceptible persons with material (virus) obtained from other vaccinated persons. In some instances the suppliers were syphilitics in the early stages of the disease, and thus the spirochete was passed along with the virus.

Many early attempts were made to combat smallpox by inoculating dried smallpox virus into susceptibles. This was usually done by passing a needle and thread through a pustular lesion and allowing the thread to dry for several months, after which the needle and thread would be passed through the skin of the susceptible person. Many of these persons developed a mild infection, but others died. Even worse, the infected individuals spread the fully virulent virus to all their contacts. Isolation of cases is very difficult so that control by quarantine is essentially impossible.

Smallpox has killed millions of people and blinded millions of others. It should rank as the most dangerous infectious disease in the world today, despite the effective control in many countries. Likewise, the discovery of protection or vaccination with cowpox (or vaccinia virus) ranks with the greatest of medical discoveries. Many honors were accorded Jenner, and there is a story (possibly apocryphal) that the Tsar of Russia was so enthusiastic he changed the name of the first child vaccinated in Russia to "Vaccinoff." As might also be expected,

vaccination raised a storm of controversy which rages even today. Opponents raise the question of violation of personal liberty (partly valid) and claim the dangers or complications outweigh the advantages (completely invalid, in this writer's opinion).

Morphology. These viruses have a characteristic brick shape and measure about 320×230 mμ in size (Figs. 1, 2) (84). The particle consists of a triple-layered membrane composed of two thin protein layers separated by a middle layer of indefinite structure, probably lipid (38). In the center of the particle is a **deoxyribonucleic acid** nucleoid which on section has a rather distinctive dumbbell shape. These virus particles are identical with the "elementary bodies" or "Paschen bodies" which make up the large part of the intracytoplasmic inclusion bodies found in virus-infected tissues (81). The inclusions are **acidophilic,** vary in size from 2 to 10 μ and are formed by collections or colonies of the virus particles as the virus replicated in the cell cytoplasm. The inclusions were first described in 1892 by Guarnieri (52) and are frequently called **Guarnieri bodies.**

Growth and Cultivation. Virus enters the tissue cell by phagocytosis or pinocytosis. About four to six hours after virus infection,

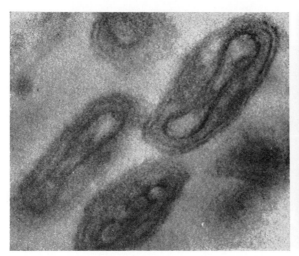

Fig. 1. A thin section micrograph of several vaccinia particles showing the double-walled limiting membrane and the dumbbell-shaped DNA-containing dense central body. $\times$ 150,000. (Courtesy of Dr. J. R. Overman.)

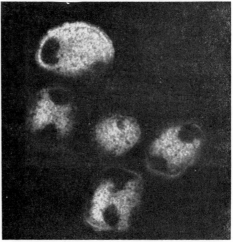

Fig. 2. Vaccinia particles negatively stained with phosphotungstic acid. Theoretically this acid stains only "empty" spaces. $\times$ 66. (Courtesy of Dr. J. R. Overman.)

new virus particles begin to form, and the completed particles are released nine or ten hours after infection (29). Release of virus from cells tends to be slow, prolonged and incomplete. Thus, Overman and Tamm (78) and others (54) showed that in tissue culture only about 10 per cent of newly formed virus is released into the supernate.

These viruses, in general, infect most simian species (53), the rabbit skin and eye, the chorioallantoic membrane of the chicken egg, and various cells in tissue culture. The virus growth on the chorioallantoic membrane produces discrete white dense pocks; this represents infection by a single virus infectious unit. Overman and Tamm (76, 77, 79), demonstrated that a single virus particle is capable of causing virus infection but in most instances the ratio of

particles to infectious units is in the range of 4:1 or 6:1. Variola virus causes small dense white lesions on the chorioallantoic membrane measuring about 1 mm. in diameter or less whereas the discrete pocks of vaccinia virus measure 3+ mm. in diameter. The only other virus which can be isolated directly from humans onto the chorioallantoic membrane is herpes simplex, and its lesions are almost microscopic in size and much less dense than either vaccinia or variola. The type of lesions on the chorioallantoic membrane can serve to differentiate variola, vaccinia, and herpes simplex viruses (Fig. 3).

Both vaccinia and variola virus infect the rabbit eye. Inoculation of pustular contents from smallpox patients onto the scarified cornea of the rabbit eye (Paul's test) pro-

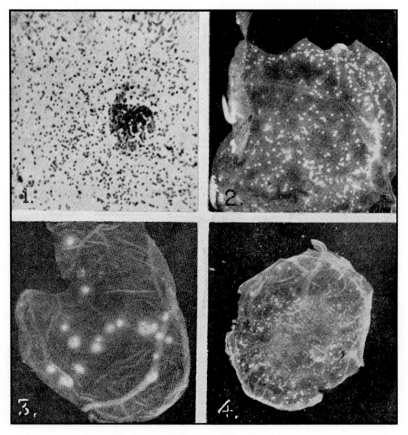

Fig. 3. Variola, vaccinia, and herpes simplex. 1, smear from skin lesion of variola showing elementary bodies. Gutstein stain. × 1,400. (Courtesy of A. W. Downie.) 2, variola on chorioallantoic membrane after three days. 3, vaccinia on chorioallantoic membrane after three days. 4, herpes simplex on chorioallantoic membrane after three days. (From Kempe. *Fed. Proc.,* 14:468, 1955.)

duces discrete white opaque lesions in 48 hours, and Guarnieri bodies can be found on histologic examination. Paul's test can be positive in alastrim, but in this disease the results are frequently negative.

In general, vaccinia virus readily produces infection of many animals by various routes of inoculation, whereas variola and alastrim on primary isolation tend to be quite restricted in their pathogenicity to the monkey, the chorioallantoic membrane, and the rabbit eye. Thus, variola usually requires a number of rabbit passages before it will infect the rabbit skin.

Vaccinia virus can be produced by suitable animal passage from variola, alastrim, or cowpox virus. Interestingly, passage of these viruses on the chorioallantoic membrane does **not** lead to a vaccinia type of virus strain.

Resistance. These viruses are among the most resistant to complete inactivation, and virulent smallpox virus has been recovered from dried human scabs over a year old. The virus is destroyed by heating to 60° C. for one hour.

Vaccinia virus appears less resistant to heat inactivation than smallpox virus. This is of great importance, since the virus vaccine must not be allowed to stand at room temperature for more than one week and at 40° C. for more than five weeks. Actually, it seems poor practice to allow vaccine to remain at room temperature for more than a few hours, since growth of bacterial contaminants is always a distinct possibility with calf lymph preparations. Dried (lyophilized) virus remains viable at room temperature for at least a month and thus can be used in the tropics with greater facility.

Antigenic Structure. Antigenic relationships in this group of viruses have been studied by Downie and MacDonald (30), who immunized fowls and used their serum in the "inhibition of complement-fixation tests." They found a close relationship between various strains of variola, alastrim, and vaccinia. Cowpox strains, isolated from the cow in the not too distant past, were easily differentiated from the variola-alastrim-vaccinia strains and seemed closer to ectromelia or mousepox. Gispen's (48)

study of the soluble antigens from these viruses by the double diffusion technic in an agar gel showed two major precipitation zones, I and III, in variola major, variola minor (alastrim), vaccinia, neurovaccinia, and rabbit pox. The major precipitation zone, I, was absent in cowpox and ectromelia.

A nucleoprotein antigen (NP), which constitutes at least half of the organism, has been isolated from vaccinia virus (93, 94). Antibodies to this antigen can be produced in rabbits, but they will not protect against infection. The viruses of variola and vaccinia agglutinate red blood cells (17). Only certain fowls have agglutinable red blood cells, and the proportion varies with the breed (96). There are probably two distinct hemagglutinins found in vaccinia virus grown in the chick chorioallantois; one is a soluble hemagglutinin component which can be separated from the virus unit, and the other is closely associated with that unit (46). An antihemagglutinin antibody has been found in the serum of patients with smallpox (24). Hyperimmune serum also contains an X agglutinin (28, 93) the significance of which is unknown (92). The vaccinia hemagglutinin is related to the lipid content of the virus particle and functions by a mechanism completely different from the myxovirus hemagglutinin.

The virus particles can be agglutinated and their soluble products precipitated. This soluble material can also be used for the complement-fixation test (28, 50, 80) or for absorbing the protective antibodies from hyperimmune sera, but the specific antigen which is responsible for immunity is as yet unknown. Monkeys and rabbits convalescent from vaccinia are resistant to variola and vice versa, but many workers believe that variola is less effective in protecting against vaccinia than vaccinia is against variola (13, 14, 50).

There is no evidence of toxin formation. One or more of the antigens in vaccinia produce a delayed type of sensitivity of the skin of the immunized subject to the elementary bodies (55), and this sensitivity may persist longer than immunity, causing complications in interpreting the results of revaccination (7). The lesions in the purpuric type of smallpox suggest that some strains of the virus have at least one of the Shwartzman antigens, as is borne out by experiments showing that vaccinia will prepare the skin of rabbits.

Clinical Disease. SMALLPOX IN NONIMMUNE SUBJECTS. Following an incubation period of 10 to 12 days, the disease begins with various nonspecific symptoms, including fever, chills, and headache lasting three to four days prior to the appearance of the rash. The macular-papular rash begins on exposed parts of the body and is composed initially of discrete lesions. After a day or so the rash becomes progressively more confluent, spreads to all parts of the body, and becomes vesicular in nature. It is characteristic of smallpox that **most** of the lesions in any given area of the body will be in the same stage of development. Five to six days after the onset of fever the vesicles begin to change to pustules which heal with scar tissue formation. Usually, death will occur within 10 days of the onset of fever.

In addition to this classic case of confluent smallpox, there are two other important clinical types. In discrete smallpox, which has the lowest mortality and fewest complications, the lesions never progress to the confluent state. Hemorrhagic (or "toxic," or "black") smallpox is characterized by bleeding into the skin in the prodromal stages, with death frequently occurring prior to the onset of a rash (86).

During the recovery stage the pustules crust over and eventually fall off. It should be noted that these crusts contain viable virus and thus the patient may remain infective for prolonged periods after his life is no longer in danger.

Complications of smallpox include bacterial infection of skin, eyes, and lungs and virus invasions of central nervous system with encephalitis. Ocular involvement occurs in about 20 per cent of cases of confluent smallpox, and 20 per cent of these are due to direct effect of the virus and 80 per cent to secondary bacterial infection (90). Special care of the eyes with antibiotic therapy should reduce the incidence of blindness following smallpox.

The over-all mortality rate in smallpox is about 30 per cent, but it may be as low as 5 per cent in the discrete type and as high as 100 per cent in the hemorrhagic type.

SMALLPOX IN THE PARTIALLY IMMUNE. Vaccination frequently only modifies rather than prevents this disease; however; it also markedly reduces the mortality and morbidity. Unfortunately, it also can change the clinical picture so that diagnosis may be extremely difficult. In general, the rash is discrete, but what lesions there are go through the usual vesicular-pustular stages. Frequently the rash is absent and only the nonspecific symptoms of fever, chills, headache, and muscle pain are present. The course of the disease may last three or four days. Smallpox without a rash and lasting only a day or so has been called "contact fever" and appears related to the "toxemic" phase of smallpox which occurs very early in the disease. The infectiousness of persons with modified smallpox is debatable. In the "contact fever" type or **variola sine eruption** the transmissibility seems low. Conybeare (25, 26) reported seven cases of modified smallpox without any spread to contacts, but in these cases all the contacts had been vaccinated. At present it is safest to consider any case of smallpox to be fully infectious.

ALASTRIM. This mild form of smallpox is characterized by discrete lesions with a low mortality. It may be difficult to differentiate alastrim from smallpox. It is important to note that alastrim "breeds true" and does not give rise to smallpox by spontaneous mutations.

Diagnosis. Diagnosis is based on the following: (1) the clinical picture and history of exposure, (2) microscopic examination of skin scrapings for Paschen bodies, (3) isolation of virus on the chorioallantoic membrane of the embryonated egg, collecting the contents of pustules or vesicles and injection into the rabbit testicle or dropping onto the scarified rabbit cornea (Paul's test), (4) complement-fixation and/or neutralization tests on convalescent sera, and (5) if available, electron microscope studies of vesicle fluid to demonstrate typical brick-shaped particles.

Treatment. No specific treatment is yet available, but reports of the activity of 5-iodo-2′-deoxyuridine against vaccinia virus suggest that this compound should be studied for possible clinical effectiveness (21, 59, 60). The control of secondary infection is most important in smallpox, with particular attention directed to the eyes.

In a more recent study oral semicarbazone compound (N-methylisatin β-thiosemicarbazone) was administered to 1,100 smallpox contacts in which only three cases of smallpox developed, while in a group of 1,126 controls 78 developed smallpox (36). Another significant development in smallpox prevention is that of seroprophylaxis in smallpox contacts. Kempe's method combines that of vaccination and hyperimmune gamma globulin given as soon as possible after exposure to smallpox. Results indicate a marked reduction in case incidence over vaccination alone.

VACCINATION AND VACCINIA VIRUS

Vaccine Preparation. Vaccine virus used for smallpox vaccination today is usually prepared from calf lymph but may be prepared from infected chorioallantoic membranes or tissue culture.

CALF LYMPH VACCINE. This is the standard vaccinia virus used in most parts of the world and is derived from various sources including Jenner's original stock, local strains of smallpox virus, and alastrim virus. Whatever their source, they have been passed in calves many times until the "vaccinia" characteristics are well established and irreversible. There is no evidence that vaccinia virus derived from local strains of smallpox produces better immunity against these local strains than virus derived from alastrim or Jenner's stock. After a vaccinia seed is established in cows, occasional human passages are made to maintain human pathogenicity. Thus, vaccinia virus may be passed 24 consecutive times in calves and then inoculated into a human. Virus from this human vaccination site would then be taken back to the calf for another series of passages.

Calf lymph vaccine is prepared as follows. A healthy calf is scrubbed with soap and antiseptic and the thorax and upper abdomen shaved. The shaved area is again washed with soap and antiseptic. With great attention to sterile technic, a scalpel blade is dipped into stock vaccinia seed and a number of very superficial cuts are made into the skin of the prepared area. These cuts should not be deep enough to cause bleeding. About five days after inoculation the animal is sacrificed, and the skin is cleaned again and dried with a sterile towel. The vesicles are scraped with a special spoon and the pulp weighed. The pulp is then suspended in a glycerol solution and stored at −10° C. Obviously, the above method cannot result in bacteriologically sterile material, although the bacterial count may be very low.

CHORIOALLANTOIC MEMBRANE VACCINE. This vaccine is prepared by dropping seed virus on the chorioallantoic membrane of embryonated chicken eggs 12 days old. The eggs are incubated for three days and the chorioallantoic membranes removed and extracted for virus by grinding. The extracted membranes are then diluted in glycerol and stored at −10° C. This vaccine is relatively cheap and can be made completely free of contaminating bacteria. There is no reason why the CAM vaccine should not replace calf lymph vaccine except for the natural reluctance to abandon a time-tested method (20, 57).

MISCELLANEOUS. Tissue culture vaccine can be used, but in general the virus yield is lower than in either calf lymph or CAM vaccine. Likewise, loss of human virulence appears to occur more frequently with tissue culture passage. It is possible to use various animals in place of calves, which are sometimes difficult to obtain. Thus in southeastern Asia buffalo have been used for many years with good success.

Vaccination Technic. The four specific methods of vaccination are (1) multiple pressure, (2) scratch, (3) intradermal, and (4) jet. The skin should be cleansed with soap and water, alcohol, or acetone. The most widely used technic is that of multiple pressure by which the needle point is pressed through a drop of vaccine with the needle shaft almost parallel to the skin surface. About 10 to 30 pressures are made in an area about one-quarter inch in diameter. The needle point should break the superficial cell layers but should not cause bleeding.

A slight redness at the pressure site should be the maximal immediate reaction. After vaccination the remaining lymph should be allowed to dry on the skin and then should be covered with a plain band-aid or no covering at all. Plastic cup protectors over the vaccination sites are contraindicated.

Note that before applying the lymph virus the skin must be perfectly dry, and any materials used to clean the skin area must have been removed or allowed to evaporate.

The other methods described are not widely used. The scratch method consists of dropping the virus onto a single one-quarter inch long scratch in the skin made with a sterile needle. The intradermal method consists of inserting a needle through a drop of vaccine into the epidermal layer of the skin. The jet method involves skin inoculation by vaccine under high pressure utilizing a special instrument.

Note also that no special area of the skin is indicated. The usual site is the upper part of the deltoid but any area can be used. The back is sometimes of value in children.

There are certain specific contraindications to vaccination: (1) any systemic illness, (2) any skin rash, (3) patients taking large doses of cortisone, (4) the first trimester of pregnancy, and (5) any adverse environmental factors. In regard to the last, inquiry should always be made as to whether any of the specific reasons against vaccination exist in the patient's environment, such as whether he has any brothers, sisters, children, etc., who might contract the virus from the patient and who should not be exposed to vaccinia virus even indirectly.

It is not often emphasized that there are specific indications for vaccination besides the obvious. Persons should not allow excessive intervals to elapse between vaccinations, since primary reactions in older people tend to be quite severe. Therefore, vaccination at 5 to 10 year intervals should be given to all persons, regardless of their exposure to smallpox. The incidence of primary reactions in revaccinated persons increases very markedly when the interval between vaccinations is 20 years or greater (16).

Vaccination Reactions. There are four possible reactions following vaccination: (1) primary, (2) secondary (accelerated), (3) immediate, and (4) negative (no reaction).

Since the primary and secondary reactions are clear-cut and easy to interpret, the more controversial **immediate** and **negative** reactions will be discussed first to emphasize their importance. These reactions are sources of much confusion among many medical personnel, and, although completely definitive answers are not possible for all the questions these reactions can raise, it is possible to outline the salient facts and present a logical and scientific basis for interpretation. Prior to a more detailed discussion, the following generalizations should be made. First, the truly negative reaction is very uncommon (12, 44). Second, the immediate reaction should not be called the immune reaction, since it does not necessarily depend on immunity at all, let alone a high degree of immunity (28, 37).

The negative (no reaction) to vaccinia virus usually indicates poor vaccine or poor technic in cleaning the skin or making the multiple pressures. It may be due to a poor choice of vaccination area, in which the skin may be rougher or more keratinized than usual. Finally, a few individuals do not respond well or at all to vaccinia virus without being immune to smallpox virus. Easton (35) reported a case of a soldier who had been vaccinated 10 times in one year and failed to react to vaccinia virus each time but subsequently died of smallpox. Moreover, one cannot judge that because several persons in a group responded to a given lot of vaccine all such persons should have so responded. It is clear that if the level of immunity is low, a vaccinia preparation of very low infective titer can induce a primary whereas it may be inactive against a higher (but not necessarily high) level of immunity. That is to say, then, that a very infective vaccine may induce primaries or secondaries where a less infective lot will fail.

If an individual fails to react, the following steps should be taken. A new potent lot of vaccine should be obtained. A new area of the skin should be chosen, possibly the back but certainly an area where the skin is soft and pliable. The multiple pressure method should be repeated and if it brings no results, first the single cut or scarification method and then the intradermal method should be used. If calf lymph had been used, CAM vaccine should be used, or vice versa. If no "take" can be produced by any method, the patient should be warned that he may still be susceptible to smallpox.

The immediate (or allergic reaction) is described as an area of erythema surrounding a small papule appearing eight to 72 hours after vaccination. No vesicle forms, and the reaction may disappear in a few hours. This reaction does **not** indicate successful vaccination, and the same measures discussed above should be taken to insure a true immune response to vaccinia virus. The immediate reaction can be elicited by heat-killed virus.

The primary reaction to vaccinia is that in which the papule develops into a vesicle and then to a pustule which scabs over and heals with a scar. This lesion should show vesicle formation in five days and a pustule in nine to 10 days and should begin healing with scab and scar formation by 12+ days.

The secondary reaction (accelerated, modified, or vaccinoid) shows vesicle formation in three days, early pustulation, and scab formation. The whole reaction may take only a week, and pustule formation does not always occur. A good general rule is that some definite lesion should be present seven days after vaccination, and this will serve to distinguish immune reactions from the immediate reaction which will never show a lesion persisting as long as seven days.

In summary, only primary and secondary responses are indicative of a vaccination "take," and one of these responses **must** be present. If the only reaction seen is of the three day or immediate type or if no reaction is produced, then a series of steps should be taken to produce a live virus reaction. The series of steps outlined (new skin area, new lot vaccine, new methods, etc.) will almost certainly result in either a primary or secondary reaction. The minimum objective evidence of a "take" is a lesion at the vaccination site **seven days after vaccination.**

Complications of Vaccination. In general, it should be emphasized that smallpox vaccination is one of the safest of all medical procedures. From the standpoint of both safety and effectiveness it has undergone more thorough and prolonged testing than virtually any disease-controlling procedure. From time to time individuals arise to protest vaccination on various grounds (infringement of personal liberties, danger, etc.), but clearly the case against vaccinia is weak. The following complications may occur.

GENERALIZED VACCINIA. Following vaccination a few unusually susceptible individuals develop a severe disease which progresses to death (12). There is usually a generalized pock eruption which is indistinguishable clinically from variola (Fig. 4). We know of one fatal case which resulted from the vigorous rubbing of a nonimmune child with a rough towel which had just been used by his older brother who had been vaccinated a week previously. **Individuals with eczema or other types of atopic eruptions are particularly susceptible to a severe form of vaccinia either from their own vaccination or from that of playmates** (39, 41, 45, 83). The lesions may be clinically indistinguishable from Kaposi's varicelliform eruption, which may be caused by the virus of herpes simplex (45). Excellent clinical results have been reported following the use of tetracycline (39, 83) and chloramphenicol (41), but the effects were due to suppression of the secondary infection. To maintain perspective in regard to the frequency of generalized vaccinia following vaccination, one should recall that there were only 45 cases and three deaths among the five million people vaccinated in New York City in 1947 (51). Of the 45 cases of generalized vaccinia, 38 had a pre-existing dermatitis. The two deaths were in babies under one year of age who contracted the virus from vaccinated persons, and a third death was due to a secondary bacterial infection following vaccination. There were, in addition, 45 cases which showed central nervous symptoms (see below), of which four died. Autopsies on these four failed to show histopathology of post-infection encephalitis. It is of interest that vaccination indirectly accounted for three deaths in five million vaccinated persons, whereas smallpox virus in the same epidemic accounted for five deaths.

POSTVACCINAL ENCEPHALITIS. This is a rare complication but one with a high mor-

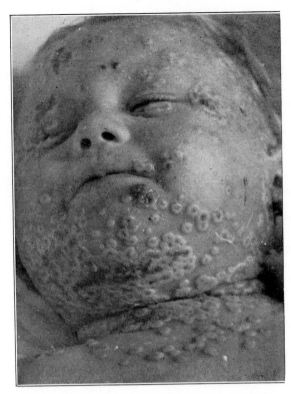

Fig. 4. Eczema vaccinatum (From Perry andMartineau. *J.A.M.A.*, 141:657, 1949.)

tality in some series. There were 110 deaths among the 222 cases collected by Conybeare (27) from England and Wales during the years 1927 to 1946. In contrast to this, in the New York series of five million vaccinations, there were four deaths and two patients with severe residual symptoms, but it is questionable whether the deaths which occurred were from the post-vaccinal encephalitis (51).

TETANUS. Formerly an occasional complication, tetanus has almost completely disappeared since viable tetanus spores have been eliminated from the vaccine and the practice of covering the vaccinated area with a celluloid shield or other types of plastic dressings has been discontinued.

PROGRESSIVE VACCINIA OR VACCINIA NECROSUM. This is a very rare complication but usually a fatal one. There is a slow but unrelenting progression from the original site of inoculation over a period of weeks and months. The infected areas of skin become gangrenous, and satellite lesions appear at a distance on the skin, in bones, and in internal organs. This type of reaction has been observed when there is a defect in the immune mechanism, such as agammaglobulinemia (3, 61), or in patients who have had prolonged treatment with cortisone (75). The injection of gamma globulin may save those with a defect in gamma globulin production (64), but not necessarily those with cortisone intoxication (75).

TREATMENT OF VACCINAL COMPLICATIONS. In general, most complications of vaccination fall into two groups, bacterial and viral. Contamination of the vaccination lesion with various bacteria may occur, and of these, tetanus has been a serious problem in the past. This usually followed covering of the vaccination site with some sort of protective shield. Such a covering is absolutely contraindicated. All vaccinations should be observed for possible pyogenic infections, and the possibility of septicemia should be kept in mind.

Since vaccination is tantamount to deliberately inducing a viral infection, the viral complications, in general, will not respond to antibacterial therapy. There are certain indications for possible use of gamma globulin, one being the **vaccinia necrosum** indicated above.

Other possible uses of gamma globulin are (62, 63, 66): (1) as a prophylactic in individuals with dermatitis who are exposed to vaccinated persons, (2) in smallpox contacts (in addition to vaccination), (3) at the time of vaccination to reduce possibility of complications in cases in which the danger seems unusually great, and (4) in the treatment of corneal ulcers. The use of gamma globulin in the treatment of vaccinia encephalitis is debatable.

Schedule for Vaccination. Children should be vaccinated soon after birth or at least before the fifth month of life. Complications are minimal at this age. Vaccination should be repeated routinely every seven years thereafter and at any time before traveling into an area where smallpox might be endemic. It has been reported that vaccination during pregnancy does not increase the incidence of still births, abortions, or congenital malformation (6), but McArthur's (72) observations indicate that damage may be done if the vaccination is done in the first two or three months of pregnancy. Vaccination is contraindicated in patients with eczema or other types of chronic skin disease and in patients anticipating an elective operative procedure.

MOLLUSCUM CONTAGIOSUM

Poxvirus mollusci

This disease is confined to man, and the etiologic agent has not been transmitted to animals. Although known as a clinical entity since 1817, it was regarded as a neoplasm until Lipschütz (68) in 1907 described inclusion bodies resembling those seen in smallpox (67). For many years the infectious agent was thought to be a protozoan parasite, until the studies of Goodpasture and Woodruff (49) demonstrated the similarity of the inclusion bodies to those found in fowlpox. Studies employing the electron microscope revealed the brick shaped appearance of the

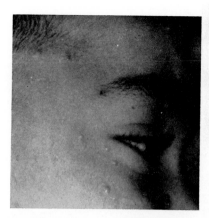

Fig. 5. Molluscum contagiosum lesions on the face. (From Neva. *Arch. Int. Med.,* 110:720, 1962.)

virus and its size, which varies from 290 to 380 mμ in length and from 190 to 250 mμ in width (15, 85, 95, 97). A study of thin sections showed a developmental cycle (2) resembling that of smallpox. Mitchell (73) demonstrated complement-fixing antibodies in three of 14 patients, employing a heat-stable antigen extracted from ground up lesions. Recent attempts to isolate the virus of molluscum contagiosum in tissue culture apparently have been successful. Cytopathic effects were produced, but continued serial propagation was not accomplished (23, 74).

This contagious disease of the skin is worldwide in distribution and is encountered most frequently in children and young adults. The lesions occur on the face, lips, arms, legs, buttocks, genitalia, or scalp, but rarely on the mucous membranes of the mouth and never on the soles and palms. The lesions, which vary in number from one to 50, are characterized by slightly elevated pearly white painless nodules which usually have small central depressions (Fig. 5). Microscopic sections show a series of radially branching masses of epithelial cells which are separated by fibrous septa (Fig. 6).

The incubation period has been estimated by various investigators at as low as 14 and as high as 50 days. In the human experiments performed by Juliusberg (58) in 1905, the lesions appeared 50 days after the intracutaneous injection of filtered extracts of ground up tissue. The disease occurs in southeastern United States at a rate of one

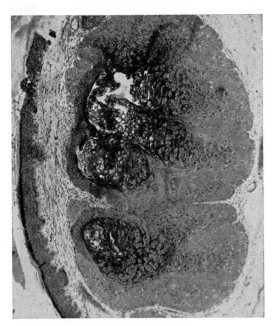

Fig. 6. Section of biopsy of typical skin lesion of molluscum contagiosum. × 18. (From Neva. *Arch. Int. Med.,* 110:720, 1962.)

case in each 500 to 1,700 admissions to dermatology clinics (4).

The lesions can be cured by excision or curettage. If this is not desirable the application of the resin of podophyllum, as described by Barefoot in 1956, will effect a cure (4). A mixture of podophyllum and salicylic acid produces more inflammation but gives a more rapid cure. Some patients become sensitized to podophyllum during treatment.

POX DISEASE OF BIRDS

Poxvirus avium

The avian pox viruses of chickens, turkeys, pigeons, and canaries are related antigenically and are regarded as variants of one species (32). The lesions are more proliferative and tumor-like than those of variola and the mammalian pox diseases. The inclusion bodies, or Bollenger bodies, are large compact structures which can be freed from the cell by tryptic digestion. The brick shaped virus bodies are somewhat larger than those of vaccinia, measuring about 332 x 264 mμ (15).

The disease in chickens is of considerable economic importance. The infection may be confined to the head, where wart-like nodules appear on the comb, wattles, and skin of the head; or to the mouth, with the appearance of adherent yellow, cheesy-like membrane production; or the mucous membranes of the eye and nose, with a watery or muco-purulent discharge. This last type is often referred to as "roup." Only one or any combination of these three types of disease can occur in a single bird (34).

The clinical picture and the pathologic lesions in canary pox are somewhat different from fowlpox, but the viruses are closely related (18). Pigeons are resistant to fowlpox, but pigeon pox produces a mild disease in fowls, with subsequent immunity against fowlpox. The vaccine is prepared by suspending dried pigeon pox crusts in glycerolated saline (33). Beaudette (5) has reported the successful vaccination of pullets at the fourth or fifth month of age with virulent fowlpox virus.

POX DISEASES OF MAMMALS

Cowpox. *Poxvirus bovis* is a mild disease in its natural host, with lesions confined to the teats and udders. A somewhat more severe disease occurs when man acquires an infection from the cow. Cowpox in man is somewhat more severe than vaccinia. The contents of the vesicles in man and in the skin of the rabbit are often blood-stained. The lesions on the chorioallantoic membranes of embryo chicks may be hemorrhagic, and the embryos usually die.

Generalized infection in an eczematous child and demyelinating encephalomyelitis has resulted from cowpox infections (98). Cows are readily infected with vaccinia from man, and the infection may spread from cow to cow and back to man. Among 36 strains isolated in Holland from cows or associated humans, 28 were typical cowpox strains and eight were vaccinia (32).

The cultivations on the chorioallantoic membrane of the chick embryo may result in the appearance of a stable mutant (31) which is less virulent for the embryo and no longer produces hemorrhagic lesions in the skin of rabbits. This mutability and its proven pathogenicity for a variety of hosts is the chief support for the theory that vaccinia may have been derived as a mutant from cowpox (32).

Mouse Pox (Ectromelia). *Poxvirus muris* was discovered by Marchal (71) in a colony of mice at Hampstead, England, in 1930. The disease may appear as an acute epidemic, with visceral lesions and a high mortality. It also produces chronic infections characterized by edema and necrosis of the feet and tail. In some stocks of mice it persists as an asymptomatic infection until something occurs to precipitate an epidemic of the visceral type of disease. It can be grown in tissue cultures or on the chorioallantoic membranes of embryo chicks.

Burnet and Boake (19) noted the resemblance between mouse ectromelia and vaccinia and suggested the name "mouse pox." Both viruses agglutinate fowl erythrocytes, but the virus of mouse pox also agglutinates the erythrocytes of the mouse. Vaccination with vaccinia virus produces some immunity but not as solid an immunity as vaccination with the mouse pox virus. Fenner (42) has used this infection as a working model to elucidate the pathogenicity of variola in man.

This virus resembles that of cowpox in its affinity for mesoblastic tissue and, like the latter, induces the formation of large acidophilic inclusion bodies in the cytoplasm of epithelial cells. The mouse pox virus shares some common soluble antigens with both vaccinia and variola but resembles cowpox by failing to show the major precipitation zone I (48).

Sheep Pox. This is an acute febrile disease with a rather low mortality. It is characterized by an eruption on the more exposed parts of the body which at first is vesicular but later becomes pustular. The virus can be grown on the chorioallantoic membrane of the embryo chick. There is one report that vaccinia virus protects sheep against sheep pox (47). Studies made in the Sudan suggest that sheep pox and goat pox are unrelated antigenically. Neither cross infections nor cross-immunity could be established (8).

Goat Pox, Horse Pox, and Swine Pox. Very little is known about these diseases. The nature of the inclusions and the size of the viruses suggest that they belong to the mammalian group of pox viruses. Swine are susceptible to vaccinia, and such infection must be differentiated from true swine pox (32).

Rabbit Pox. This highly infectious and frequently fatal disease of laboratory rabbits is now believed to be a mutant of vaccinia (32, 88).

MYXOMATOSIS AND FIBROMATOSIS OF RABBITS

Poxvirus myxomatis

The viruses found in these two diseases are antigenically related, but they are not related to vaccinia. Fenner (42) has summarized the

evidence for including these agents in the pox group of viruses.

Myxomatosis of Rabbits. Discovered in the native rabbits of South America by Sanarelli in 1898 (89), this disease is mild in its native host but almost always fatal when transferred to domestic rabbits of European origin. Following inoculation, tumor masses appear at the local site, in other subcutaneous areas, in lymph nodes, and in the spleen. Rivers (87) found that the virus destroyed epithelial cells but stimulated the proliferation of connective tissue cells. The myxoma virus has been cultivated on the chorioallantoic membrane of the chick embryo. The virus is brick-shaped, about the same size as vaccinia, and contains the same type of dense pepsin-resistant central body (40).

This virus was introduced into Australia in 1950 with the hope that it would destroy the enormous and destructive population of wild rabbits of European ancestry. The virus is apparently transmitted from rabbit to rabbit in Australia and South America in a mechanical manner by the bite of mosquitoes. In France and England the spread, particularly during the winter months and over long distances, is attributed to birds and to the rabbit flea.

Fibromatoses of Rabbits. This disease was discovered in wild cotton tail rabbits in the United States by Shope (91) in 1932. The disease could be transmitted both to wild and domestic rabbits. The virus stimulates the connective tissue to produce a fibroma. The disease is self-limiting, and the fibromas undergo spontaneous retrogression. If, however, tar is inoculated intramuscularly the fibromas persist, and a transformation into a fibrosarcoma may occur (1).

Recovery from fibromatoses gives considerable immunity against myxomatoses, and the occasional animal which survives myxomatoses is immune to fibromatoses (65). Berry and Dedrick (10) in 1936 and Berry (11) in 1940 apparently transformed the fibromatosis virus into the myxomatosis virus by inoculating a mixture of heat-inactivated myxomatous virus and a living fibromatous virus.

CONTAGIOUS PUSTULAR DERMATITIS OF SHEEP AND GOATS AND THE VIRUS OF MILKERS' NODES

The viruses found in these two diseases are about the same size as the pox viruses. They infect man as well as their natural host (22, 56).

Pustular dermatitis has been transferred from

sheep to human volunteers. After recovery, the volunteers were immune to reinfection (82). Human serum from patients with pustular dermatitis showed no cross-reactions with antibodies by complement fixation (70).

The viruses of pustular dermatitis or of milkers' nodes are not related antigenically to vaccinia (9, 69), but more study will be required to differentiate them from some of the less well known pox viruses of mammals.

REFERENCES

1. Andrewes, C. H., and Ahlström, C. G.   J. Path. & Bact., 47:87, 1938.
2. Banfield, W. G., and others.   Proc. Soc. Exper. Biol. & Med., 77:843, 1951.
3. Barbero, G. J., and others.   Pediatrics, 16:609, 1955.
4. Barefoot, S. W.   South. M. J., 49:1270, 1956.
5. Beaudette, F. R.   J. Am. Vet. M. A., 115:232, 1949.
6. Bellows, M. T., and others.   Pub. Health Rep., 64:319, 1949.
7. Beneson, A. S.   J.A.M.A., 143:1238, 1950.
8. Bennett, S. C. J., and others.   J. Comp. Path. & Therap., 54:131, 1944.
9. Berger, K.   Zentralbl. Bakt., 162:363, 1955.
10. Berry, G. P., and Dedrick, H. M.   J. Bact., 31:50, 1936.
11. ———— Proc. 3rd Congr. Microbiol., N.Y., 1940, p. 343.
12. Bigler, J. A., and Slotkowski, E. L.   Pediatrics, 7:24, 1951.
13. Blaxall, F. R.   Chap. Smallpox, A System of Bacteriology in Relation to Medicine, London, Her Majesty's Stationery Office, 7:84, 1930.
14. Bohls, S. W., and Irons, J. V.   Am. J. Pub. Health, 32:300, 1942.
15. Boswell, F. W.   Brit. J. Exper. Path., 28:253, 1947.
16. Broom, J. C.   Lancet, 1:364, 1947.
17. Burnet, F. M., and Stone, J. D.   Australian J. Exper. Biol. & M. Sc., 24:207, 1946.
18. ———— and Lush, D.   Brit. J. Exper. Path., 17:302, 1936.
19. ———— and Boake, W. C.   J. Immunol., 53:1, 1946.
20. Cabasso, V. J., and others.   Am. J. Pub. Health, 44:194, 1954.
21. Calabresi, P., and others.   Nature, 197:767, 1963.
22. Cawley, E. P., and others.   South. M. J., 46:21, 1953.
23. Chang, T. W., and Weinstein, L.   J. Invest. Derm., 37:433, 1961.
24. Collier, W. A., and others.   Ztschr. Hyg. u. Infektionskr., 131:555, 1950.
25. Conybeare, E. T.   Lancet, 1:813, 1939.
26. ———— Lancet, 1:1125, 1939.
27. ———— Monthly Bull. Ministry Health, 7:72, 1948.
28. Craige, J., and Wishart, F. O.   Canad. Pub. Health J., 27:371, 1936.
29. Dales, S., and Siminovitch, L.   J. Biophys. & Biochem. Cytol., 10:475, 1961.
30. Downie, A. W., and MacDonald, A.   J. Path. & Bact., 62:389, 1950.
31. ———— and Haddock, D. W.   Lancet, 1:1049, 1952.
32. ———— and Dumbell, K. R.   Ann. Rev. Microbiol., 10:237, 1956.
33. Doyle, T. M., and Minett, F. C.   J. Comp. Path. & Therap., 40:247, 1927.
34. ———— Vet. Rec., 9:62, 1929.
35. Easton, J. H. L.   Public Health, London, 58:110, 1945.
36. Editorial.   J.A.M.A., 187:145, 1964.
37. Edsall, G.   Lancet, 1:887, 1947.
38. Epstein, M. A.   Brit. J. Exper. Path., 39:346, 1958.
39. Esplin, B. M.   Ann. Int. Med., 35:1346, 1951.
40. Farrant, J. L., and Fenner, F.   Australian J. Exper. Biol. & M. Sc., 31:121, 1953.
41. Fasal, P.   J.A.M.A., 144:759, 1950.
42. Fenner, F.   Nature, 171:562, 1953.
43. Fields, A.   The Merck Report, 1950, p. 24.
44. Findlay, F. M.   J. Roy. Micro. Soc., 56:213, 1936.
45. Fries, J. H., and Borne, S.   J. Allergy, 20:222, 1949.
46. Gillen, A. L., and others.   J. Immunol., 65:701, 1950.
47. Gins, H. A., and Kunert, H.   Deutsche tierärztl. Wschr., 45:257, 1937.
48. Gispen, R.   J. Immunol., 74:134, 1955.
49. Goodpasture, E. W., and Woodruff, C. E.   Am. J. Path., 7:1, 1931.
50. Gordon, M. H.   Med. Res. Council, Special Report, Series No. 98, London, His Majesty's Stationery Office, 1925.
51. Greenberg, M.   Am. J. Dis. Child., 76:492, 1948.
52. Guarnieri, G.   Arch. per le sc. med., 16:403, 1892.
53. Hahon, N.   Bact. Rev., 25:459, 1961.
54. ———— and Friel, J. J.   J. Bact., 83:837, 1962.
55. Hooker, S. B.   J. Infect. Dis., 45:255, 1929.
56. Horgan, E. S., and Haseeb, M. A.   J. Comp. Path. & Therap., 57:1, 1947.
57. Irons, J. V., and others.   Am. J. Pub. Health, 43:25, 1953.
58. Juliusberg, M.   Deutsche med. Wchnschr., 31:1598, 1905.
59. Kaufman, H. E., and others.   Arch. Ophth., 67:583, 1962.
60. ———— and Maloney, E. D.   Proc. Soc. Exper. Biol. & Med., 112:4, 1963.
61. Kempe, C. H.   Fed. Proc., 14:468, 1955.
62. ———— Pediatrics, 26:176, 1960.
63. ———— and others.   Pediatrics, 18:177, 1956.
64. Kozinn, P. J., and others.   Pediatrics, 16:600, 1955.
65. Ledingham, J. C. G.   Brit. J. Exper. Path., 18:436, 1937.
66. Lewis, H. M., and Johnson, F. C.   Arch. Dermat., 75:837, 1957.
67. Lipschütz, B.   Arch. f. Dermat. u. Syph., 136:438, 1921.
68. ———— Wien. klin. Wchnschr., 20:253, 1907; 40:1101, 1927.
69. Lloyd, G. M., and others.   Lancet, 1:720, 1951.
70. MacDonald, A.   J. Path. & Bact., 63:758, 1951.
71. Marchal, J.   J. Path. & Bact., 33:713, 1930.
72. McArthur, P.   Lancet, 2:1104, 1952.
73. Mitchell, J. C.   Brit. J. Exper. Path., 34:44, 1953.

74. Neva, F. A.   Arch. Int. Med., 110:720, 1962.
75. Olansky, S., and others.   J.A.M.A., 162:887, 1956.
76. Overman, J. R., and Tamm, I.   J. Immunol., 76:228, 1956.
77. ———— and Tamm, I.   Proc. Soc. Exper. Biol. & Med., 92:806, 1956.
78. ———— and Tamm, I.   Virology, 3:173, 1957.
79. ———— and Sharp, D. G.   J. Exper. Med., 110:461, 1959.
80. Parker, R. F.   in Diagnostic Procedures for Virus and Rickettsial Diseases, New York, Am. Pub. Health A., 1948, p. 84.
81. Paschen, E.   München. med. Wchnschr., 53: 2391, 1906.
82. Pask, V. M., and others.   M. J. Australia, 2: 628, 1951.
83. Perry, F. G., and Martineau, P. C.   J.A.M.A., 141:657, 1949.
84. Peters, D.   Zeitschrift für Naturforschung, 126:11, 1957.
85. Rake, G., and Blank, H.   J. Invest. Dermat., 15:81, 1950.
86. Ramachandra, R. A., and others.   J. Indian M. A., 35:296, 1960.

87. Rivers, T. M.   Proc. Soc. Exper. Biol. & Med., 24:435, 1926-27.
88. Rosahn, P. D., and others.   J. Exper. Med., 63:379, 1936.
89. Sanarelli, G.   Zentralbl. Bakt., 23:865, 1898.
90. Sen, K.   Indian Med. Gaz., 80:181, 1945.
91. Shope, R. E.   J. Exper. Med., 56:793, 803, 1932; 63:33, 43, 173, 1936; 65:219, 1937.
92. Smadel, J. E.   Viral and Rickettsial Infections of Man, Philadelphia, Lippincott Co., 1952, p. 414.
93. ———— and Hoagland, C. L.   Bact. Rev., 6: 79, 1942.
94. ———— Arch. Path., 34:275, 1942.
95. Strauss, M. J., and others.   Proc. Soc. Exper. Biol. & Med., 72:46, 1949.
96. Suzuki, S., and others.   Zentralbl. Bakt., 162: 405, 1955.
97. Van Rooyen, C. E., and Rhodes, A. J.   Virus Diseases of Man, New York, Thomas Nelson & Sons, 1948.
98. Verlinde, J. D.   Tijdschr. v. diergeneesk., 76: 334, 1951.

64

Rabies

(Hydrophobia, Lyssa, Tollwut, Rage, Rabbia)

Rabies has been a well-documented human disease since about 2000 B.C. Certain codes of ancient Mesopotamia include scales of fines to be imposed on mad dog owners whose animals have bitten persons of various social standing (e.g., 40 shekels if a citizen was bitten and died, 15 shekels if the victim was a slave). Two points about rabies are thus illustrated: the infection is transmitted by bite of infected dogs (animals), and disease control depends on control of infected animals. Since those early times rabies has spread to all parts of the world (except Australia), and if absent in some area, it is, nevertheless, an ever-present threat.

Rabies is unique among microbial infections in several respects. First, it is the only infectious disease of man which carries a mortality of 100 per cent. There has never been a reasonably well-documented human case of recovery from rabies. This fact plus the terrifying manner in which victims die make hysteria and panic co-problems in rabies control. Second, the very long incubation period of 30 to 90 days makes feasible post-exposure immunization and development of high antibody levels in the patient before the onset of clinical symptoms. In no other infectious disease is post-exposure immunization of value. This lengthy incubation period is comparable to leprosy, but in the latter case no post-exposure immunization is possible as yet.

Until recent years the presence of rabies virus infection widely distributed in animals such as dogs, cats, squirrels, and foxes, was balanced by the knowledge that in these lower animals, as in man, infection was invariably fatal. Thus, one could derive some small comfort from the absence of carriers and the knowledge that, by and large, only sick animals carried the virus. Unfortunately, this situation is not entirely correct. Bat rabies is a variant of common street rabies. Usually the bats so infected are sick and eventually die, but there is clear evidence that some bats may harbor the virus and that a true carrier state exists (5, 12, 19). Bat rabies is not at present a major problem in the United States in regard to mortality (five deaths reported to date) but is a definite public health problem and is of increasing concern to the laity due to widespread newspaper publicity (6).

The general rabies situation in the United States has improved in the past 25 years so that the yearly death rate has decreased from between 40 and 50 to between five and ten deaths per year. Primarily, this is a result of pre-exposure rabies vaccination of dogs and other pets.

As indicated, rabies is an ancient disease which probably had its beginnings in Asia and spread rapidly to Europe. It was probably unknown in North and South America until imported from Europe. At present it is absent in Australia and kept rigidly under control in England and other countries by strict quarantine laws. In England, for example, animals to be imported must be kept in quarantine for six months. During that period rabies will be apparent in most but not all animals. Thus, constant vigilance is the key factor in rabies control.

The major problem in rabies at present is that of vaccination, particularly post-exposure vaccinations. The factors involved are exceedingly complex and require for understanding a broad knowledge of rabies virus infections in all its aspects.

Morphology and Staining of Virus and Negri Body. The virus is round or oval, about 140 to 250 mμ in size and relatively stable (9). The virus can be preserved in 50 per cent glycerol in the refrigerator for about one year, and in normal saline at 20° C. it remains active for one or two weeks. The virus stores well in the frozen state.

The Negri body is the inclusion body found in rabies infected nerve cells (21). It is of very great diagnostic importance and thus will be described in some detail.

This cell inclusion is round or oval in shape and varies from 0.25 to 20+ μ in size. The smallest forms are present early in infection. The inclusions stain red with a definite purplish tendency but, in addition, have a very characteristic internal structure of basophilic granules, sometimes forming a ring of granules around a large central granule. The inclusions are always intracytoplasmic and never are in the nucleus. Several inclusions may be found in a single nerve cell. There is general unanimity on the diagnostic specificity of the Negri body. It should be pointed out that various eosinophilic inclusions may occasionally be found in animal brains. Some can be produced experimentally, but these almost never contain the dark basophilic granules characteristic of the true Negri body. Inclusions are usually sought for in impression smears of brain or cord material stained with Giemsa's or Seller's stain.

The incidence of Negri bodies in infected animals varies. They are present in most infected dogs and mice but may be absent in a considerable per cent of human autopsy material. Thus, about 90 per cent of infected dogs develop Negri bodies in the brain or cord tissue. If present, the Negri body is diagnostic; if absent, further studies are indicated. Busson (4) reported on absence of Negri bodies in more than 58 per cent of humans dead of rabies following antirabies vaccination; thus, vaccine treatment may inhibit Negri body formation (Fig. 1).

Negri bodies are found in bats and in human brain material from victims of bat rabies. In some recent studies, however, one human brain contained intracytoplasmic in-

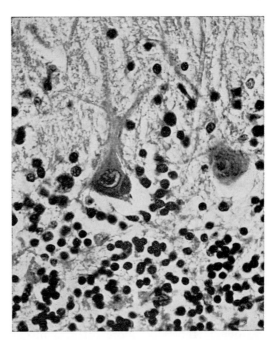

Fig. 1. Negri body in the cytoplasm of a Purkinje's cell of the cerebellum. Patient was a white male bitten on the finger by a rabid dog 62 days before death. × 556. (From Erickson, Marcuse, and Halpert. *J.A.M.A.*, 155:823, 1954.)

clusions not characteristic of Negri bodies in the presence of extensive encephalitis (14); rabies virus was isolated from this patient's brain tissue and from the bat which bit her. The situation in regard to the incidence of Negri bodies in infected bats in the United States is not clear, but recent studies show that at least some bat brains infected with rabies virus may not have demonstrable Negri bodies.

Antigenic Structure. Surveys of rabies virus indicate only a single antigenic strain exists. Rabies virus isolated from bats is identical antigenically to other animal strains (2, 16). Serologic studies of infected animals are of no value, since most animals die before significant antibody levels can be attained. Vaccination with attenuated or dead virus gives rise to complement-fixing and neutralizing antibodies. Fluorescent antibody technics have been applied successfully to tissues infected with rabies virus infected tissues (8, 11).

Natural Infection in Animals. In nature rabies virus infects all mammals, and many other animals can be experimentally infected, including chickens, pigeons, sparrows, and other birds. Rabid birds have been found in nature. Rabid wolves are particularly dangerous, since their bite is unusually severe, resulting in almost certain virus inoculation. In the United States the animals most involved are dogs, foxes, cattle, skunks, and squirrels. The virus in nature has a variable incubation period and is called "street" virus. Following passage to laboratory animals via intracerebral inoculation the virus becomes "fixed" and the incubation period decreases to a constant five or six days. Fixed virus differs from street virus in several other respects: it does **not** usually produce Negri bodies, it has less virulence for nonneural tissue, and it has a more rapid growth rate.

Animals infected with street virus under natural conditions develop either "furious" or "dumb" rabies or, more often, a mixed clinical picture. "Furious" rabies is the typical "mad dog" syndrome. Following a bite from an infected animal the incubation period in dogs will last three to seven weeks. Usually the picture will be that of furious rabies, though some dogs may show the typical dumb or paralytic picture, and many will show a mixed type of infection with features of both furious and paralytic types. A typical mixed syndrome would begin with restlessness, loss of appetite, and nervousness. A tendency to snap and bite appears along with running for no apparent reason, sometimes staggering, and a distinct change in the tonal quality of the bark. Also well known is the change in food habits; the dog often eats dirt or wood. This, of course, is the stage when the animal is most dangerous and should not be touched except by experienced (and well-protected) persons. Many dogs also show excessive salivation. Following this excitement stage paralysis appears, soon followed by coma and death. Death occurs from 3 to 11 days after onset of symptoms. Many variants of the disease are seen: dogs may develop only paralysis and die without any excitatory symptoms, or sudden death may occur without any signs of illness. Virus may be secreted in the saliva three or five days prior to the onset of symptoms, so if the biting dog remains well for seven or eight days, no risk of rabies is present.

Experimental Animal Infections. The first animal used in laboratory studies was the rabbit, although Zenke (32) had made demonstration of the transmissibility of rabies by inoculating dogs with saliva from rabid dogs in 1804. In 1879 Galtier (10) established rabies in rabbits, which are most convenient animals for this type of research since they are cheap, do not ordinarily bite, and usually develop the dumb or paralytic form of the disease conducive to ease in handling the animal. Pasteur (22) began his experiments leading to rabies vaccine in 1881 using dogs and rabbits. Mice are very widely used in experimental work at present. Initial studies were made by Remlinger (27) in 1908, but it was the work of Hoyt and Jungeblut (13) in 1930 which demonstrated the particular value of this animal.

Besides the low cost, mice are about **10 times more** susceptible to rabies than rabbits. They can be infected by less virus given by any route and can develop rabies after a dog bite or even by eating an infected cadaver. Mice develop furious rabies with street virus and paralytic rabies with fixed virus. Following I.C. inoculation with extracts of rabid dog brain, mice will show tremors and convulsions in 6 to 8 days but may survive up to 21 days. The finding of Negri bodies in the brains of these mice may be possible as early as five days after inoculation. Symptoms of disease in mice inoculated for rabies diagnosis are insufficient evidence, and Negri bodies **must** be observed in brains of sick mice. If the first mouse passage is negative, a second passage should be done where suspicion of rabies is strong.

In recent years rabies virus has been grown in fertile hen's eggs and duck's eggs and in various tissue culture systems, including chicken embryo and embryonic hamster kidney tissues.

Clinical Infection in Man. In the years 1955-60 there were a total of 33 rabies deaths in the United States, for a straight average of 6.6 per year. Since rabies is relatively characteristic, there are probably few cases unrecognized and unreported, and these figures are accurate indications of the case incidence. In 1960 only two cases were reported. In contrast, the years 1938 to 1942 had a total of 163 cases, for an average of 32.6 per year. This decline in incidence is encouraging, but since every animal bite—and there are hundreds of thousands of these—carries the **risk** of rabies, the problem is far from solved.

Table 1 shows some of the ranges in incubation period found in man. Various factors may influence the incubation period, the most important of which is the site of the bite. Thus, Webster (31) gives the following incubation periods: face, 30 days; arm, 40 days; and leg, 60 days. Much depends on the severity of the bite, suggesting that the amount of virus inoculated is a factor. It is of interest to note that antirabies vaccine treatment tends **to shorten** the incubation period, and hyperimmune serum tends to lengthen it, although precise data are not available. It is quite clear, however, that severe bites about the head are followed by the shortest incubation period, so that prompt and vigorous treatment is mandatory. Head and face bites carry the highest mortality despite treatment.

Table 1. **Incubation Period of Rabies in Man**

Days	Per Cent of Cases
30	20
30-90	48
90-150	30
<15	rare but reported
>150	rare but reported

Range: 10 days to 200+ days

The symptoms and signs of rabies begin with a prodrome of fever and headache lasting two to four days. About 80 per cent have pain at the site of the wound, or the bite may itch or tingle. The central nervous system complex of symptoms then appears and is basically that of widespread excitation and stimulation of all parts of the nervous system, usually involving, in order, the sensory system, the motor system, the sympathetics, and mental systems. The patient complains of sounds, light, or drafts (sensory), and examination may then show increased reflexes and muscle spasms (motor) along with dilation of the pupils and increased perspiration and lacrimation (sympathetic).

Mental changes include fear of death, anger, irritability, and depression. Paralysis may occur late, and death may supervene at any stage. The spasm of the throat muscles induced by contact with water or the thought of drinking is common and is responsible for the term **hydrophobia.** Death usually occurs 6 to 10 days after onset of symptoms.

Although no documented case of recovery from human rabies has been reported, it is apparent that some of the paralytic reactions to rabies vaccine may conceivably have been due to rabies infection. Unless the patient's saliva has been inoculated into mice for possible virus recovery (which is rarely done), the rabies symptoms would be considered due to the vaccine. It may well be true that 100 per cent of rabies infections of man are fatal, but this degree of absoluteness seems remarkable in medical science, where there is almost always some exception to the rule.

Diagnosis and Treatment. Diagnosis is based on virus recovery in mice. Treatment is symptomatic.

RABIES PROPHYLAXIS IN MAN

This enormous problem involves several aspects, which include (a) estimating risk of infection, (b) vaccine development and evaluation, (c) the problem of human allergic reaction to the vaccine per se, (d) pre-exposure immunization and control of rabies in animals, and (e) human rabies prophylaxis.

The basic difficulty in rabies lies in two facts: (1) it is not possible to determine whether or not a rabid animal has or has not succeeded in inoculating the rabies virus during the course of the bite, and (2) no controlled studies of rabies vaccine in man are possible. When the mortality rate is 100 per cent, one cannot withhold vaccine to establish a control group. With these two facts in mind, we will now explore the five major problem areas listed above.

Estimating the Risk of Infection. In order to transmit rabies, the virus must be inoculated through the skin into the tissue. The only significant way this can be accomplished in nature is by a bite, **providing the**

virus is present in the saliva. The percentage of rabid dogs which excrete virus in the saliva is less than 100. The actual percentage varies by study but has been shown to range from 50 to 75 per cent (30). The amount of virus present in the salivary glands likewise has varied from "detectable" to titers of 10^5 infectious doses. Immediately, therefore, we are faced with the impossibility of determining whether the individual bitten by a rabid dog is at risk of rabies or not. To compound this problem, it is clear that the nature of the bite is important. Thus, "deep" bites are more apt to result in rabies than "superficial" bites. Likewise, clothing tends to filter out the virus to a significant degree, but, of course, to what **precise** degree one cannot say.

There are other factors, but, given only those listed above, it is obvious that in the case of any animal bite one has only limited courses of action. The animal should be observed, and if it remains well, it can be assumed the animal did not have rabies and that the bite could not have transmitted rabies virus. If the animal dies within 12 to 14 days, the brain can be examined, and if rabies virus is **not** found, again one can assume that the bite did not transmit the virus. If rabies virus is found in the dog brain, one **must** assume that the virus not only was in the saliva but that the bite was made in such a way that virus was introduced into the wound.

Obviously, many persons given antirabies treatment received this unnecessarily, but there is no way to determine which of these fall into that small group who actually were at risk.

Vaccine Development and Evaluation. As indicated above, fixed virus does not multiply in nonneural tissue. Pasteur, noting the long incubation period, felt that it might be possible to develop resistance (antibodies) to infection by injecting some fixed virus as soon after exposure to street virus as possible.

Without a very definite knowledge of the factors involved, Pasteur (23) used rabbit spinal cord infected with fixed virus and dried for 1 to 14 days. This resulted in a living, attenuated strain of fixed virus which he then used as antigen to inject subcuta-neously into his first human subject, Joseph Meister, a 9-year-old boy who had been severely bitten by a rabid dog. Meister lived and thus became famous in medical history and was later employed as a concierge at the Pasteur Institute, but, ironically, he later committed suicide. In the next year Pasteur had treated about 2,500 persons, with a total of 12 deaths or treatment failures (24). This success aroused the greatest possible interest, and the general reaction was favorable. Since then, intense efforts have been made to improve the quality and safety of the vaccine.

The types of vaccines used along with their advantages and disadvantages are listed in Table 2. With the development of the duck embryo vaccine, it seemed that the allergic reaction problem had been solved, since more than 50,000 doses had been administered without neuropathies. Recently, however, a case of dorsolumbar myelitis has been reported following the duck egg vaccine (26). This report emphasizes the fact that, although these embryo vaccines do not contain large amounts of nervous tissue, they do contain some. The incidence of neurologic side effects is directly related to the amounts of neural tissue they contain (29).

The goal has been to increase specific antigenic response to the virus while simultaneously decreasing the vaccine content of nervous tissue antigens which give rise to the serious and sometimes fatal complication of allergic encephalitis. Unfortunately, as the nervous tissue content is reduced, the virus content tends to decrease, so that the specific viral antigen content seems contingent on a certain content of nervous tissue. There is now rather clear evidence that the living "attenuated" strains of the rabies virus, such as Flury, do **not** multiply when injected subcutaneously, so that the degree of antibody response depends on the amount of virus antigen injected. The trend has been not to inactivate these strains, more in order to guard against losing some important viral antigens than for safety's sake, since the Flury strain is safe for human use as a live virus vaccine (28). Thus, the living rabies vaccines are not comparable to the attenuated polio or measles vaccines with which the virus multiplies in the patient, usually

Table 2. Rabies Vaccines

Type of Vaccine	Virus	Advantage	Disadvantage
Original Pasteur—rabbit cord	Living		Virus reversion, dangerous, used only in France
Semple—rabbit cord	Dead—phenol killed	Very antigenic, safe, effective	Very allergenic
Flury (HEP) hen's egg	Usually living	Less antigenic than Semple *	Less allergenic than Semple —few CNS reactions
Duck's egg	Dead	Comparable to Flury	Allergic reactions comparable to Flury or even fewer

* Results of comparative studies of Flury and duck's egg versus Semple vary. None show the duck's egg or Flury to be superior antigenically to the Semple; some (1, 7) show them to be inferior.

producing a mild infection. Since the attenuated polio or measles vaccine virus multiplies in the host, the resultant antigenic stimulus is very great, in contrast to that with the attenuated live virus rabies vaccine.

Efforts to completely eliminate nervous tissue from vaccine by growing rabies virus in tissue culture are in progress, but, again, virus titers are disappointingly low (17, 18).

In regard to vaccine evaluation for effectiveness in preventing rabies, the situation again leaves much to be desired. Controlled field studies in humans are not possible, and the animal studies are not truly comparable. For example, if one wishes to expose an animal to rabies virus in order to test a vaccine, injecting virus by needle tends to be too severe a challenge for post-exposure immunization. And, of course, using biting animals as inoculating agents is completely unpredictable and uncontrolled.

Vaccine evaluation tests at present involve injecting the vaccine and determining the time of appearance and amount of antibody produced. Good vaccines should produce enough antibody to protect mice against subsequent challenge by 1,000 LD_{50} of rabies virus injected intracerebrally (Habel's Test).

Problem of Human Allergic Reaction to Rabies Vaccine. Rabies vaccine is given in daily injections for a total of 14 to 21 days. Since these are essentially repeated doses of foreign protein, it is easy to see that allergic reactions may develop, particularly during the later injections. These reactions include hives, skin lesions, and reactions resembling serum sickness, some of which can be very severe. A second type of reaction is that involving the patient's own brain or spinal cord tissue. Nervous tissue from all animals have certain antigens in common. Thus, nervous tissue extracts of rabbit cord can induce antibodies in humans which may react with nervous tissue of the human brain or spinal cord. This may result in a demyelinating encephalitis or myelitis which may be fatal or lead to paralysis. This complication occurs in about 1:2,000 to 1:7,000 cases of antirabies vaccine treatments. The search to find ways to eliminate these allergic reactions is a major reason for the effort to find new improved rabies vaccine, above and beyond the goal of improving the specific virus antigenicity.

Pre-exposure Immunization and Rabies Control in Animals. Since rabies has a very long inoculation period, it is clear that elimination of the disease from all animals in the world would be an impossible goal. Obviously, any wild animals sick with the disease should be killed, but at the present time almost all of the rabies exposures in the United States come from dog bites, and most control measures are aimed at dogs. The bat rabies problem will be discussed separately.

The most successful approach has been that of pre-exposure immunization. Thus, besides receiving distemper and other prophylactic immunization, many states now require all dogs to be given rabies vaccines as a part of their routine care. Usually this vaccine has been either the Flury or duck embryo virus, which results in good rabies protection lasting about three years. Booster shots at intervals of two or three years are necessary. As with **any** vaccine, protection is not assured, and vaccinated dogs may develop rabies in a small percentage of cases.

The above program is adequate for pets but does not help prevent rabies in wild or unowned dogs. These animals are a constant menace and, in this writer's opinion, should be eliminated. All dogs should have owners, and dog owners should be legally responsible for the dog's care and immunizations. Unfortunately, laws controlling wild and pet dogs are of varying stringency, and many states have large unowned dog populations. Many animal societies oppose systematic efforts to destroy unowned dogs or cats on "humane" grounds.

Pre-exposure immunization is of value to humans who may because of their work be high risks for rabies. These include veterinarians, farmers, mailmen, speleologists, etc. Obviously no person can afford to have repeated courses of the 14 to 21 daily injections and thus pre-exposure immunization is mandatory in some occupational groups.

Human Rabies Prophylaxis. Human rabies treatment following an animal bite consists of three steps. (1) The bite area should be thoroughly washed with soap and water, including some mild antiseptic, such as Zephiran. Some states **require** use of nitric acid in and on the wound. This is unfortunate, since studies indicate that soap will do as good a job and the acid will leave bad scars. (2) Vaccine injections should be begun if indicated. (3) **Hyperimmune rabies antiserum** is indicated in face and neck bites. This consists of serum from horses or mules immunized against rabies virus and having a high titer of rabies antibodies. Anaphylactic and serum sickness reactions are calculated risks, and the patient must be tested for serum sensitivity. Antirabies gamma globulin has been prepared from both animal and human sera. If human antirabies serum is used, no danger of anaphylaxis or serum sickness will be present; however, this serum is not generally available. Note that serum must be given **within** 72 hours of the bite.

The indications for treatment under various circumstances are summarized in Table 3. Each case must have careful scrutiny by the physician and the decision as to what to do should follow the recommendations of the WHO Committee. If the physician does not follow this chart and if the regimen he prescribes is incorrect, a malpractice suit may ensue.

BAT RABIES

Bat rabies is a definite but minor problem in the United States at present, except for the fact that in some areas the general public concern may be quite serious. That bats could be infected with and transmit rabies was first described by Carini (5) in 1911, but for many years this disease was thought to be limited to vampire bats, which transmit the virus to cattle. The habitat of the vampire bat ranges from Uruguay to Mexico and is not found in the United States. In the areas populated by vampire bats a number of human cases appeared, characterized by paralysis and death without muscle spasm, convulsions, or "hydrophobia." These cases were shown to be rabies both by appearance of Negri bodies in the brain and by virus isolation and neutralization tests using specific antirabies antiserum. Further studies showed that insectivorous and other bats in Central and South America also carried rabies virus, possibly infected in fights with vampire bats. It is now clear that some migratory bats indigenous to the United States are infected with rabies, probably spread into them from sources in Mexico. Some nonmigratory bats are now infected, and it is conceivable that the bat may become an important wildlife reservoir spreading the virus to dogs and various wild animals. It should be noted, however, that up to the present time the rabies-infected bat in Central and South America has not been implicated as a virus source for any large epizootics in dogs.

The incidence of rabies in bats in the United States is now being determined, and reports are conflicting. In Trinidad, a hotbed of bat rabies, the infected bats have constituted about 3.8 per cent of animals studied (25). A study by Bell (3) in Montana in 1957 found three of 127 bats infected (2.4 per cent). In another series in Arizona the incidence of rabies was 13 out of 522 bats examined (2.2 per cent) (20).

Bats usually become sick and die from the

CONDITION OF ANIMAL

NATURE OF EXPOSURE	AT TIME OF EXPOSURE	DURING OBSERVATION PERIOD OF 10 DAYS	RECOMMENDED TREATMENT
I. No lesions; indirect contact only	Rabid	—	None *
II. Licks			
(1) Unabraded skin	Rabid	—	None *
(2) Abraded skin and abraded or unabraded mucosa	(a) Healthy	Healthy	None
	(b) Healthy	Clinical signs of rabies or proved rabid	Start vaccine at first signs of rabies in animal
	(c) Signs suggestive of rabies	Healthy	Start vaccine immediately; stop treatment if animal is normal on fifth day after exposure †
	(d) Rabid, escaped, killed, or unknown	—	Start vaccine immediately
III. Bites			
(1) Simple exposure	(a) Healthy	Healthy	None
	(b) Healthy	Clinical signs of rabies or proved rabid	Start vaccine at first signs of rabies in animal
	(c) Signs suggestive of rabies	Healthy	Start vaccine immediately; stop treatment if animal is normal on fifth day after exposure †
	(d) Rabid, escaped, killed, or unknown: or any bite by wolf, jackal, fox or other wild animal	—	Start vaccine immediately
(2) Severe exposure (Multiple or face, head, or neck bites)	(a) Healthy	Healthy	Hyperimmune serum immediately; no vaccine as long as animal remains normal
	(b) Healthy	Clinical signs of rabies or proved rabid	Hyperimmune serum immediately; start vaccine at first signs of rabies in animal
	(c) Signs suggestive of rabies	Healthy	Hyperimmune serum immediately, followed by vaccine; vaccine may be stopped if animal is normal on fifth day after exposure
	(d) Rabid, escaped, killed, or unknown: any bite by wild animal	—	Hyperimmune serum immediately, followed by vaccine

Note: To be effective, hyperimmune serum must be given within 72 hours of exposure. Dose: 0.5 ml. per kilogram of body weight. These indications apply equally well whether or not the biting animal has been previously vaccinated.

* Start vaccine immediately in young children and patients where a reliable history cannot be obtained.

† Alternative treatment would be to give hyperimmune serum and not start vaccine as long as animal remained normal.

infection, but it is clear that some bats may become more or less permanent carriers. Some bat carriers excrete virus, so that this animal appears unique in this regard. Likewise, some bats sick with rabies recover to become carriers. In the years 1951-58 there were a total of 92 rabies deaths in the United States, of which three were bat connected. Thus, bat rabies is a minor problem compared to rabies contracted from terrestrial animals. Since 1958 only two more bat rabies deaths have been reported (15). It is important to note that of the five rabies deaths reported only **one** resulted from an unprovoked attack by the bat; the others occurred in persons who handled sick bats.

Insectivorous bats are one of this country's most valuable wild animals, and some species may eat their weight in insects in 24 hours. It is, therefore, unthinkable to even consider measures to wipe out the bat population.

Bat rabies infection in man may produce either the paralytic or rabid type of disease. Negri bodies may be present or absent, and brain tissue should be extracted for virus isolation. Fortunately, bat rabies virus is antigenetically identical to all other strains, so that the usual rabies vaccines are effective. Treatment failures have occurred in bat rabies just as in rabies transmitted by other animals.

It is fitting to conclude this chapter with one single admonition. **Handle any sick animal pet with great care, and never, under any circumstances, handle a sick wild animal unless this is a part of your job.**

REFERENCES

1. Anderson, G. R., and others. Am. J. Hyg., 71:158, 1960.
2. Bell, J. A., Hadlow, W. J., and Jellison, W. L. Pub. Health Rep., 70:991, 1955.
3. —— and others. Pub. Health Rep., 72: 16, 1957.
4. Busson, B. Zentralbl. Bakt., Abt. 1, Orig., 115:135, 1930.
5. Carini, A. Ann. Pasteur Inst., 25:843, 1911.
6. Clough, P. W. Ann. Int. Med., 25:1330, 1960.
7. Dean, D. J., and Sherman, I. Pub. Health Rep., 77:705, 1962.
8. Etcheborne, M., Bernal, P. G., and Leyton, G. R. J. Immunol., 84:6, 1960.
9. Galloway, I. A., and Elford, W. J. J. Hyg., 36:532, 1936.
10. Galtier, V. Compt. rend. Acad. Sc., 89:444, 1879.
11. Goldwasser, R. A., and Kissling, R. E. Proc. Soc. Exper. Biol & Med., 98:219, 1958.
12. Haupt, H., and Rehaag, S. Ztschr. Infektionskr. Haustiere, 22:104, 1921.
13. Hoyt, A., and Jungeblut, C. W. J. Infect. Dis., 47:418, 1930.
14. Humphrey, G. L., Kemp, G. E., and Wood, E. G. Pub. Health Rep., 75:317, 1960.
15. —— and others. Pub. Health Rep., 75: 317, 1960.
16. Hurst, E. W., and Pawan, J. L. J. Path. & Bact., 35:301, 1932.
17. Kissling, R. E. Proc. Soc. Exper. Biol. & Med., 98:223, 1958.
18. —— and Reese, D. R. J. Immunol., 91: 362, 1963.
19. Lima, E. Brazil-Med., 48:38, 1931.
20. Maddy, K. T. Arizona Med., 15:344, 1958.
21. Negri, A. Ztschr. Hyg. Infektionskr., 43:507, 1903.
22. Pasteur, L., and others. Compt. rend, Acad. Sc., 92:159, 1881.
23. —— Compt. rend. Acad. Sc., 101:765, 1885.
24. —— Compt. rend. Acad. Sc., 103:777, 1886.
25. Pawan, J. L. Ann. Trop. Med. & Parasit., 30:101, 1936.
26. Prussin, G., and Katabi, G. Ann. Int. Med., 60:114, 1964.
27. Remlinger, P. Compt. rend. Soc. Biol., 65: 385, 1908.
28. Ruegsegger, J. M., and Sharpless, G. R. Ann. Int. Med., 110:754, 1962.
29. Shiraki, H., and others. World Neurology, 3:125, 1962.
30. Webster, L. T. Rabies, New York, The Macmillan Co., 1942.
31. Webster, W. J. Rabies and Antirabic Treatment in India, Govt. of India Press, Simla, 1944.
32. Zinke, G. G. Neue Ansichten der Hundswuth, ihrer Ursachen and Folgen, nebst einer sichern Behandlungsart der von tollen Thieren gebissenen Menschen, Jena, C. E. Gabler, 1804.

65

The Herpetic Viruses in Man

(Varicella, Herpes Zoster, Herpes Simplex, and Herpes B Virus)

These viruses characteristically produce vesicular lesions in the skin and mucuous membranes. They can occasionally involve nervous tissue and other visceral structures. The virus particles are round or slightly brick-shaped and are smaller than the pox viruses. The cytopathic effect of this group is characterized by intranuclear inclusions and multinucleated giant cells. Most evidence supports the presumption that they are DNA viruses. They are highly contagious, and epidemiologic studies suggest a latent or carrier state.

VARICELLA— HERPES ZOSTER

(Varicella = Chickenpox; Herpes Zoster = Shingles)

Clinical Types of Infection (21). Varicella is an epidemic disease of children characterized by an incubation period of 14 to 17 days (12) followed by a short prodrome of mild constitutional symptoms and then the development of a vesicular eruption first appearing over the trunk and then the face, neck, and extremities. The rash occurs in crops, so that one area may contain several lesions in various stages of development—macule, papule, vesicle, or crust. The lesions rapidly evolve to the crusted stage, which may persist for several weeks, although scarring is minimal. Rarely is the chickenpox lesion hemorrhagic or bullous. Complications are uncommon and consist of secondary pyogenic infections, encephalitis, and varicella pneumonia. The encephalitis is rarely fatal (5 per cent) but can leave residual damage (1). The viral pneumonia is more commonly seen in adults and carries with it a guarded prognosis (9). A predisposing factor is a tendency of skin lesions to occur more frequently at sites of irritation. The association of severe or fatal attacks with leukemias has been noted, as well as the observation that varicella developing in the setting of corticosteroid therapy is a more serious and even fatal disease (14).

Herpes zoster, epidemiologically and experimentally related to varicella, is an endemic disease of uncertain incubation period seen primarily in adults and characterized by a localized, usually unilateral, vesicular eruption restricted in distribution to the sensory dermatome served by a single or neighboring group of dorsal root ganglia. The location is most commonly on the trunk, but it can involve cervical and fifth cranial nerve distributions (17). The eruption is commonly associated with pain, which may persist in a distressing degree following evolution of the vesicles (post-herpetic neuralgia). Occasionally changes in protein content and cell count of the cerebrospinal fluid are noted, as are neurologic complications (8). Rarely a generalized vesicular eruption will occur, presenting features of varicella and zoster in the same patient. Not infrequently a history of preceding trauma in the area of the eruption can be elicited. As with varicella, severe attacks occur in the setting of leukemia (26).

Varicella-Zoster Virus. The similar, if not identical, nature of the viruses causing varicella and herpes zoster is based on epidemiologic and experimental observations. Numerous outbreaks of chickenpox following exposure to a case of herpes zoster have been documented (10). The infectious

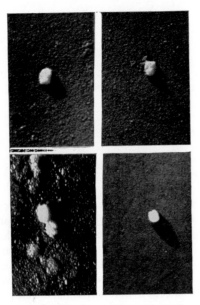

Fig. 1. Varicella-herpes zoster. Organisms from varicella vesicle in two upper frames are from herpes zoster in two lower frames. × 17,240. (From Rake, Blank, Coriell, Nagler, and Scott. *J. Bact.,* 56:293, 1948.)

nature of varicella was experimentally established by the transmission of the disease to susceptible children through inoculation of vesicular fluid (33). Zoster vesicular fluid will produce chickenpox in susceptible children, although all attempts to transmit illness to adults or children who have previously had varicella have been negative (3). Histologically both viruses produce the same pathologic changes, intranuclear acidophilic inclusion bodies. Electron microscopic studies of the vesicular fluid in both diseases have demonstrated indistinguishable viral bodies averaging 210 by 243 mμ (Fig. 1) (25). Isolation of the viruses in human embryonic tissue culture has revealed identical cytopathic effects—intranuclear inclusions and multinucleated giant cells (39). One unusual feature of the growth of these viruses in tissue culture is the inefficiency with which infected cells release biologically active virus, in that progressive cytopathic effect occurs in a contiguous sheet, and passage of virus to fresh tissue cultures is best accomplished by transferring infected cells (38). Antigenically the viruses of both illnesses appear identical in that natural antibody from both illnesses cross-reacts equally with antigens derived from the other (derived from either vesicle fluid or tissue culture) by complement-fixation, neutralization, or fluorescent antibody technics (37, 40). One interesting observation is that the antibody response in herpes zoster is more rapid and of greater intensity than in varicella (34). These findings, coupled with the clinical observation that many adult patients with herpes zoster give a previous history of childhood varicella, have led to the theory that adult herpes zoster is the result of provocation of a latent varicella virus in a partially immune host.

Epidemiology (11). Varicella occurs as a fluctuating endemic disease with sporadic peaks of "epidemics" occurring every two to three years in a population of mixed susceptibility. Most cases are seen during the winter and spring months. Attack rates are highest around age 6, and about 70 per cent of persons give a history of chickenpox by age 20. Transplacental infection of the foetus has been described, and adult chickenpox is not rare. Epidemiologic evidence has demonstrated that the disease is airborne (13) and that the period of communicability probably exists for at least 24 hours before the rash appears and not much longer than 5 days after the onset of the rash (35). Second attacks of varicella occur with great rarity, if at all. However, varicella does not protect against herpes zoster. Since herpes zoster is not a reportable disease, its epidemiology is not clearly defined. Most evidence indicates sharp contrasts to varicella in that it is primarily a sporadic disease of adults without seasonal predilection.

Treatment and Prevention. There is no specific treatment for varicella. Occasionally secondary bacterial infections require antibiotics. Steroids are contraindicated in varicella, with the possible exception of varicella pneumonia. Prevention of the disease with pooled gamma globulin is unsuccessful, although modification of the disease has been suggested (28). Quarantine of house cases is outmoded, although patients who develop varicella in a hospital setting should be carefully isolated because of the increased population of steroid-treated susceptible patients.

Similarly, there is no specific therapy for

herpes zoster. Treatment is symptomatic, and steroids are of questionable value. The multiplicities of regimens recommended for herpetic neuralgia speak against any one effective treatment.

HERPES SIMPLEX

Herpesvirus hominis
(Herpes Labialis, Herpes Febrilis, Herpetic Gingivostomatitis, Herpes Progenitalis, and Eczema Herpeticum)

Clinical Types of Infection in Man (21). Herpes simplex virus infections characteristically produce a localized vesicular eruption of the skin and mucous membranes. These infections can be categorized as primary and recurrent. The primary disease occurs in young children about one year of age, several months after disappearance of measurable maternally transferred antibodies. As judged from serologic conversions, the primary infection is much more often asymptomatic than not (4). When clinical illness occurs, it is most commonly an acute gingivostomatitis. However, other less common primary manifestations include acute vulvovaginitis, acute conjunctivitis, and a generalized vesicular eruption such as Kaposi's varicelliform eruption. The latter develops in the setting of pre-existing atopic eczema or chronic dermatitis. Least common is invasion of the central nervous system and other visceral structures usually seen in neonatal infants. Following recovery patients may experience recurrent exacerbations of herpetic infection. These exacerbations most commonly present as localized vesicular eruptions about the mouth commonly referred to as "fever blisters" or "cold sores." Less common sites for recurrent disease are the genitalia (herpes progenitalis) and cornea (recurrent dendritic keratoconjunctivitis). A variety of nonspecific stimuli has been associated with the recurrence of these lesions. As the name implies, one of the most common is fever. In addition, sunburn, trauma, menstruation, section of the fifth cranial nerve for tic douloureux, psychiatric stresses, and allergic reactions have been cited. There is rarely any mortality associated with herpes virus infections, with the exception of neonatal en-

cephalitis and occasionally the generalized cutaneous disease. The recurrent corneal infection can lead to markedly diminished visual acuity.

Herpes Simplex Virus. The virus can be readily isolated from vesicular fluid. The first successful transmission (22) was to the cornea of the rabbit, where small vesicles followed by shallow dendritic ulcers of the epithelium not unlike those seen in man were produced. Intracerebral inoculation of rabbits, guinea pigs, and mice, especially sucklings (20), will produce encephalitis. Virus dropped on the chorioallantoic membrane of the embryonated chicken egg will produce discrete, small, gray pocks (6). Recently a wide variety of animal and human cells in tissue culture has been shown to support multiplication of virus (31, 36). The characteristic pathologic lesion is an eosinophilic intranuclear inclusion body, seen in both animals and tissue culture. Some strains in tissue culture also produce a multinucleate giant cell or syncytium (16, 32). Electron microscopy of infected cells has suggested that complete virus begins with the intranuclear development of a dense core, which then becomes surrounded by a double membrane. The virus then crosses the cytoplasm in a vacuole derived from the nuclear membrane, which in turn fuses with the cytoplasmic membrane to release the virus (23). Electron microscopy of purified virus has revealed a central polyhedral core (775 Å.) surrounded by an iscohedral capsid (1050 Å.) in which there are 162 capsomeres. These structures in turn are surrounded by an envelope 1800 Å. in diameter (42). Chemical analysis of the virus reveals that it contains DNA (24). The virus is not very stable in that infectivity is lost rapidly on exposure to heat, and it is rapidly inactivated by ultraviolet light. Although antigenic analysis of strains of herpes simplex virus has revealed some variations (2), no marked strain differences have been noted (5).

Epidemiology. Herpes simplex virus is world-wide in its distribution. It is primarily a disease of man. In some studies more than 90 per cent of newborn children have measurable antibodies in their cord blood, although higher socioeconomic groups have a tendency to a lower incidence (4). It is presumed that the virus is transmitted by contact. Neutralizing and complement-fixing antibodies rapidly develop following the first attack. Occasionally herpes virus may be recovered from the saliva late in convalescence despite the presence of circulating antibody (4). Indeed, it is characteristic that those patients who have recurrent attacks of herpetic infection have pre-existing high titers of neutralizing antibody in their sera. In addition, these patients have demonstrated a delayed hypersensitivity skin reaction to intracutaneous injection of inactivated virus (27). In vitro it is also possible to construct a persistent infection of tissue culture by using antibody which markedly retards but never eliminates spread of virus (41). These observations have led to the hypothesis that herpes virus exists as a latent infection following the acute attack and that a variety of stimuli for unexplained reasons is associated with a relapse.

Treatment. The recent observation that 5-iodo-2-deoxyuridine inhibited multiplication of herpes virus in tissue cultures (15) leads to the experimental and clinical observation that superficial herpetic keratoconjunctivitis in man could be benefited by topical application of this compound (18). The cutaneous application of this compound has given conflicting results (7). It should be stressed that herpetic infections of the cornea can become much worse when topical cortisone is administered. There is no consistently effective therapy for the prevention of the recurrent illness.

HERPETIC INFECTIONS OF ANIMALS

Other members of the herpetic group of viruses have been found in monkeys, rabbits, and swine. Those types found with rabbits and swine have not presented a problem with man. However, the herpes virus associated with monkeys has been transmitted to man, most commonly by the bite of a monkey and has resulted in a fatal ascending myelitis (30). This type, known as *Herpesvirus simiae* (herpes B virus), experimentally produces skin and mucous membrane lesions in the monkey (29). Many normal monkeys have neutralizing antibodies in their sera for this virus (19). The virus can be isolated on the chorioallantoic membrane of the embryonated chicken egg and a variety of cells in tissue culture will support the growth of this virus. The cytopathic effect is that of intranuclear inclusions, and antigenically it is related to herpes virus hominis, although antibodies to herpes virus hominis will not protect against herpes virus simiae infections.

REFERENCES

1. Applebaum, E., and others. Am. J. Med., 15:223, 1953.
2. Ashe, W. K., and Scherp, H. W. J. Immunol., 91:658, 1963.
3. Bruusgaard, E. Brit. J. Dermat., 44:1, 1932.
4. Buddingh, G. J., and others. Pediatrics, 11: 595, 1953.
5. Burnet, F. M., and Lush, D. J. J. Path. & Bact., 48:275, 1939.
6. ———— and Williams, S. W. M. J. Australia, 1:637, 1939.
7. Burnett, J. W., and Katz, S. L. J. Invest. Derm., 40:7, 1963.
8. Carter, A. B. Brit. M. J., 1:987, 1951.
9. Fitz, R. H., and Meiklejohn, G. Am. J. M. Sc., 232:489, 1956.
10. Garland, J. New England J. Med., 228:336, 1943.
11. Gordon, J. E., and Ingalls, T. H. Am. J. M. Sc., 244:362, 1962.
12. ———— and Meader, F. M. J.A.M.A., 93: 2013, 1929.
13. Habel, K. Am. J. M. Sc., 209:75, 1945.
14. Haggerty, R. J., and Eley, R. C. Pediatrics, 18:160, 1956.
15. Herrman, E. C., Jr., and others. Proc. Soc. Exper. Biol. & Med., 103:625, 1960.
16. Hoggan, M. D., and Roizman, B. Am. J. Hyg., 70:208, 1959.
17. Kass, E. H., and others. New England J. Med., 246:167, 1952.
18. Kaufman, H., and others. Arch. Ophth., 68: 235, 1962.
19. Keeble, S. A., and others. J. Path. & Bact., 76:189, 1958.
20. Kilbourne, E. D., and Horsfall, F. L., Jr. J. Immunol., 67:321, 1951.
21. Krugman, S., and Ward, R. Infectious Diseases of Children, St. Louis, C. V. Mosby Co., 1958, p. 22.
22. Lowenstein, A. Klin. Monatsbl. Augenheilk., 64:15, 1920.
23. Morgan, C., and others. J. Exper. Med., 110: 643, 1959.
24. Pen-Porat, T., and Kaplan, A. S. Virology, 16:261, 1962.
25. Rake, G., and others. J. Bact., 56:293, 1948.
26. Rodnan, G. P., and Rake, G. W. New England J. Med., 254:472, 1956.
27. Rose, H. M., and Malloy, E. J. Immunol., 56:287, 1947.
28. Ross, A. New England J. Med., 267:369, 1962.

References

925

29. Sabin, A. B. Brit. J. Exper. Path., 15:321, 1934.
30. —— and Wright, A. M. J. Exper. Med., 59:115, 1934.
31. Scherer, W. F., and Syverton, J. T. Am. J. Path., 30:1057, 1954.
32. Scott, T. F., and others. J. Immunol., 86:1, 1961.
33. Steiner, W. Wien. Med. Wchnschr., 25:306, 1875.
34. Taylor-Robinson, D., and Rondle, C. J. Brit. J. Exper. Path., 40:517, 1959.
35. Thompson, F. H. Lancet, 1:397, 1919.

36. Weinstein, H. J., and others. Proc. Soc. Exper. Biol. & Med., 92:535, 1956.
37. Weller, T. H., and Coons, A. H. Proc. Soc. Exper. Biol. & Med., 86:789, 1954.
38. —— and Wilton, H. M. Am. J. Dis. Child., 86:644, 1953.
39. —— and others. J. Exper. Med., 108:843, 1958.
40. —— and Wilton, H. M. J. Exper. Med., 108:869, 1958.
41. Wheeler, C. E. J. Immunol., 84:394, 1960.
42. Wildy, P., and others. Virology, 12:204, 1960.

66

Measles

The three types of viral infections discussed in this chapter are measles (rubeola), rubella (German measles), and exanthem subitum. They are not caused by related viruses but are grouped together because they are clinically characterized by a moderately long incubation period and prodromal respiratory symptoms followed by the developments of a generalized maculopapular rash. Man is the sole host. Measles is one of the most contagious infectious diseases in that recurrent epidemics are almost continuous and at least 90 per cent of the population has had the disease by the age of 20. The virus has been fairly well characterized, and an effective living attenuated vaccine is now available. German measles is less contagious and is a mild disease which is a cause of concern primarily because of its association with increased congenital defects in children born to mothers who have contracted the disease in the first trimester of pregnancy. The virus has only recently been isolated. Exanthem subitum occurs characteristically in late infancy between 10 months and 2 years and produces a short, sharp febrile attack which disappears before the appearance of the skin rash. The virus as yet has not been characterized.

MEASLES

Clinical Types of Infection (27, 34). Measles is a highly contagious acute illness primarily of young children characterized by an incubation period of 10 to 14 days. This is followed by the prodromal stage, which consists of the onset of fever, malaise, conjunctivitis, rhinitis, and tracheobronchitis lasting from 2 to 4 days. The temperature, which is low at first, increases day by day and frequently reaches 104° or 105° F.

before the skin eruption appears. It is during this period that Koplik's spots, pathognomonic of measles, appear on the buccal mucous membranes opposite the molars. These are small, irregular, bright red spots in the center of which is a bluish white speck. Following the prodromal stage, the rash appears as an erythematous maculopapular eruption first noticed on the forehead behind the ears and the upper part of the neck. From here it spreads to involve the face, trunk, and extremities. The fever usually subsides rapidly between the second and third day following the onset of the rash which begins to fade by the third day but may leave a transient brownish discoloration of the skin.

Complications occur occasionally. The most common is secondary bacterial infection, manifested as otitis media and less commonly as pneumonia. The most serious complication is encephalitis, which occurs approximately once in 1,000 cases. Characteristically it appears several days following the rash. Its clinical course is extremely variable and unpredictable. Mortality rates of 10 per cent have been reported, and residual brain damage in 25 per cent of such cases is also noted (3).

Measles Virus. The first attempt to reproduce disease in man was that of Home (20) in Edinburgh in 1759. Blood taken from the arm of patients infected with measles was collected on cotton and placed on wounds made in the arms of normal individuals. Measles of a modified or mild type resulted. In 1905 Hektoen (18) succeeded in producing the disease in two medical students by the subcutaneous injection of blood taken from measles patients on the fourth day of the disease. Anderson and Goldberger (1) in 1911 transmitted measles to monkeys, and their work was confirmed convincingly by Blake and Trask (8) in 1921. *Macaca rhesus* monkeys were inoculated intratracheally with filtered and unfiltered washings from patients in the early eruptive stages, and histologic examinations of the lesions which developed in the skin and mucous membranes during the course of the infection were practically identical with those found in human measles. The infection was transmitted successfully from monkey to monkey, and it was shown that one attack of experimental measles can confer immunity upon the monkey. Rake and his associates (34) showed that serial passage in egg was accompanied by diminished virulence, and Stokes (37) successfully transmitted the disease after 66 egg passages. In 1954 Enders and Peebles (13) reported the primary isolation of measles virus in tissue cultures of renal epithelial cells of human and later monkey origin. The cytopathic effect in tissue culture was characterized by the development of multinuclear giant cells or syncitia which on staining revealed inclusion bodies within the syncitial nuclei and cytoplasm. Attempts to isolate virus in other cell lines both of human and nonhuman origin had been for the most part unsuccessful. After repeated passage in renal epithelium of human or primate origin, however, it became possible to transfer the virus to other cell lines (12). Of considerable interest was the demonstration that measles virus was capable of replicating in the blood leukocytes (5). One strain of virus known as the "Edmonston strain" was passed to human amnion cells, where, in addition to giant cells, an increasing number of refractile fusiform and stellate cells (spindle cells) was noted. Transfer of this strain to chicken embryo tissue culture cells eventually yielded a strain which produced the spindle cell cytopathology and from which was derived the attenuated living vaccine virus (14). Laboratory-adapted virus grows relatively slow to moderate titers (6), and the supernatant yields a specific complement-fixing antigen. In addition, the measles virus causes hemagglutination of monkey red blood cells which can be specifically inhibited by antibody (33). Electron microscopic studies of the fine structure of measles virus particles

revealed them to be 120 to 150 mμ in diameter and to consist of a well-defined outer membrane from the surface of which there were short projections and an inner component which presented a whorled appearance (39). Antigenic analysis of the virus has shown it to be homogenous. One interesting observation is the immunologic relationship between the viruses of measles and canine distemper (24). The virus is sensitive to heat (6) and is rapidly inactivated (11) by ether and trypsin. The available evidence suggests that it is an RNA virus and that it probably belongs in the myxovirus group (24).

Epidemiology (4). Measles is perhaps the most infectious of all the specific human diseases. People of all races and of all ages are infected readily by even casual exposures. In most civilized countries measles is a childhood disease, merely because most adults are immune as a result of previous childhood infection. The disease is more severe in adults than in children, and during the winter of 1916 extensive epidemics occurred in the Army camps among young Army recruits from rural areas. Mortality from secondary streptococcal pneumonia which followed measles was as high as that attained during the influenza epidemic the following year. When measles first appeared among aboriginal populations, it swept through them with a violence that was unknown to more civilized nations in which the disease had been endemic for centuries. Such was the great epidemic in the Fiji Islands in 1874 and those which occurred in the South Sea Islands and among the American Indians (15, 31). In isolated communities everyone may become immunized by infection and the virus disappears. This results in a new generation which is universally susceptible to the disease. Such a situation developed on the island of Tahiti, where the disease disappeared after the 1929 epidemic and did not reappear until 1951. Practically every individual under the age of 22 contracted the disease, and many died (21). The disease is transmitted primarily by the respiratory route. The virus can be demonstrated in abundance in the nasopharyngeal secretion during the prodromal period and for approximately 32 hours after the appearance of the rash. In addition, the virus has been isolated from the conjunctivae, blood, and urine (35). The incidence of the disease is usually highest in the second, third, and fourth years of life. Its problems vary from time to time and place to place, but in large cities it is common for it to show a biennial peak. There is no evidence for a persistent carrier state or latent virus infections. However, cases of measles virus pneumonia without rash have been noted (35). Interesting contributions to the understanding of the epidemiology of the disease were made with serologic studies of different populations (7). Only a small part of a city population acquired antibodies prior to the school age. After a person has entered school, the rate of acquisition was rapid, and within three years 90 per cent of the population acquired antibodies. Later conversions nearly totaled 100 per cent, although some individuals in older age groups gave negative reactions.

Prevention and Specific Prophylaxis. The value of rigid quarantine in this disease is open to question. If the infant's mother has had measles, sufficient antibody is usually passed through the placenta to protect the child for four to six months. Older children may be protected by passive immunization with pooled gamma globulin (38). The disease may be prevented if larger amounts are given very shortly after exposure. Smaller amounts given up to 11 days after exposure may modify the disease. The recommended dosage of gamma globulin for modifying measles is 0.02 to 0.05 ml. per pound body of weight. For prevention of the disease it is recommended that 0.1 ml. per pound of body weight be given (27).

Active Immunization (23). Active immunization is now possible through the development of the Edmonston strain of measles virus which upon adaptation to chick embryo tissue culture cells demonstrated a decrease in virulence for monkeys (14). Administration of this virus to susceptible children has resulted in an excellent serologic response and protection for at least three years from naturally acquired measles. The vaccine resulted in a relatively high incidence of fever and exanthematous reactions, although inoculated children appeared strikingly well. Attempts to modify these reactions to the vaccine have been accomplished by the simultaneous administration of gamma globulin, which reduces but does not eliminate the incidence of fever or rash (28, 29). Following intramuscular administration of the vaccine, virus cannot be recovered from the throat or blood and is, therefore, nontransmissible. Although the serologic response is slightly diminished by the simultaneous administration of gamma globulin, the duration of effective immunity appears equal.

RUBELLA

Clinical Types of Infection in Man (27). Rubella is an acute infectious disease of children and young adults characterized by an incubation period of 16 to 18 days followed by a mild prodromal period of 1 to 5 days consisting of low-grade fever, headache, malaise, mild conjunctivitis, rhinitis, pharyngitis, and bronchitis. One striking characteristic is the post-auricular lymphadenopathy and occasional cervical and generalized adenopathy. The prodromal period is followed by a rash which is more discreet than that of measles and is an erythematous maculopapular eruption appearing first on the face and then the trunk and extremities. Characteristically, the rash very rapidly evolves over a three-day period, by which time it is practically gone. Complications are very uncommon and consist of arthritis, encephalitis, and purpura. The biggest cause of concern is the development of rubella during the first trimester of pregnancy, which has been associated with an increased risk of congenital malformations (16) estimated at 18 per cent as compared with approximately 5 per cent in a controlled group (22). These congenital manifestations most commonly consist of cataracts, deafness, cardiac malformations, and abnormalities of the central nervous system.

The Virus. Hiro and Tasaka (19) transmitted the infection to children by subcutaneous injections of filtered nasal washings obtained during the prodromal stages. Anderson (2) and Krugman and Ward (26) infected human volunteers by spraying their throats with nasal washings collected from patients during the first 24 hours of their

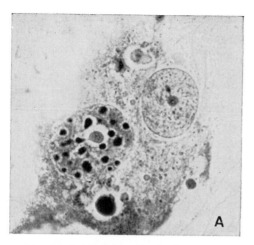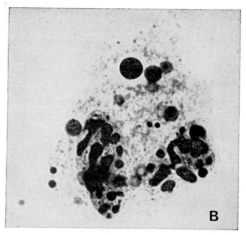

Fig. 1. Cytopathic effect in human amnion cell tissue culture produced by rubella virus. (From Weller and Neva. *Proc. Soc. Exper. Biol. & Med.*, 111:215, 1962.)

rash. Habel (17) reproduced the disease in monkeys by injections of blood obtained from patients during the height of the febrile disease. Recently a virus has been isolated in tissue culture from patients with characteristic rubella (31, 35, 39). Positive specimens were obtained from the throat, blood, and urine. The cytopathic effect in primary amnion tissue cultures was characterized by aggregation of basophilic material in small and later large clumps as well as prominent eosinophilic inclusion bodies in the cytoplasm (Fig. 1). In addition, the presence of virus can be detected by its ability to interfere with the normal progressive tissue culture infection of an Echo virus type 11. This major advance in the understanding of rubella should clarify more exactly the relationship between rubella and congenital malformations as well as open the way to a preventive vaccine.

One attack of the disease produces permanent immunity. Immune mothers pass antibodies to the fetus, and the child is protected for four to six months. Ordinarily no treatment is indicated unless the patient is pregnant. If the exposure date is known, an attempt should be made to prevent the disease by injection of gamma globulin, although evidence for the prevention of the disease with gamma globulin prophylaxis is not great. Those studies which used the larger amount of gamma globulin gave the best evidence for prevention of the disease (29).

EXANTHEM SUBITUM

(Roseola Infantum, Roseola Subitum, Pseudo-Rubella, Rose Rash of Infants)

This acute exanthematous disease occurs almost exclusively in infants and young children and was probably confused with rubella until differentiated in 1910 by Zahorsky (47) in the United States. This infection occurs most often about the twelfth month of life, and is recognized frequently in hospitals and institutions. There must be many subclinical cases, because sporadic infection occurs singly in families with several children. The incubation period varies from seven to 17 days (10). The onset is sudden, with temperatures of 104° to 106° F., and is frequently accompanied by convulsions. The fever is remittent in type and disappears by crisis after three to five days but is followed by a rash which appears in 2 to 24 hours after the fever subsides. A fine macular rash is typical, but maculopapules may occur and there may be erythematous spots and streaks on the soft palate (9). There is usually some enlargement of the lymph nodes and a relative if not absolute lymphocytosis.

The virus is present in the blood of patients by the third, but not on the first day of fever. A febrile disease was produced in monkeys with blood taken on the third day and, after recovery, the animals were immune to a second injection (25).

REFERENCES

1. Anderson, J. F., and Goldberger, J.   J.A.M.A,. 57:1612, 1911.
2. Anderson, S. G.   J. Immunol., 62:29, 1949.
3. Appelbaum, E., and others.   Am. J. Dis. Child., 77:25, 1949.
4. Babbott, F. L., Jr., and Gordon, J. E.   Am. J. M. Sc., 228:334, 1954.
5. Berg, R. B., and Rosenthal, M. S.   Proc. Soc. Exper. Biol. & Med., 106:581, 1961.
6. Black, F. L.   Virology, 7:184, 1959.
7. —————— Am. J. Dis. Child., 103:242, 1962.
8. Blake, F. G., and Trask, J. D.   J. Exper. Med., 33:385, 1921.
9. Clemens, H. H.   J. Pediat., 26:60, 1945.
10. Cushing, H. B.   Canad. M.A.J., 17:905, 1927.
11. DeMaeyer, E., and Enders, J. F.   Proc. Soc. Exper. Biol. & Med., 107:573, 1961.
12. Enders, J. F.   Am. J. Dis. Child., 103:282, 1962.
13. —————— and Peebles, T. C.   Proc. Soc. Exper. Biol. & Med., 86:277, 1954.
14. —————— and others.   Am. J. Dis. Child., 103: 335, 1962.
15. Gafafer, W. M.   Isis, 24:90, 1935.
16. Gregg, N. McA., and others.   M. J. Australia, 2:122, 1945.
17. Habel, K.   Pub. Health Reports, 57:1126, 1942.
18. Hektoen, L.   J. Infect. Dis., 2:238, 1905.
19. Hiro, Y., and Tasaka, S.   Monatschr. f. kinderh., 76:328, 1938.
20. Home, I.   Medical Facts and Experiment, Edinburgh, 1759.
21. Horstmann, D. M.   Meakin's Practice of Medicine, St. Louis, C. V. Mosby Co., 1956, p. 244.
22. Ingalls, T. H.   Am. J. Dis. Child., 93:555, 1957.
23. International Conference on Measles Immunization.   Am. J. Dis. Child., 103:211, 1962.
24. Karzon, D. T.   Ann. New York Acad. Sc., 101: Art. 2, 527, 1962.
25. Kempe, C. H.   J. Pediat., 37:561, 1950.
26. Krugman, S., and Ward, R. J.   J. Pediat., 44: 489, 1954.
27. —————— and Ward, R. J.   Infectious Diseases of Children, St. Louis, C. V. Mosby Co., 1958, p. 114.
28. —————— and others.   Am. J. Dis. Child., 103: 353, 1962.
29. —————— New England J. Med., 269:195, 1963.
30. McCrumb, F. R., and others.   Am. J. Dis. Child., 103:350, 1962.
31. Ordman, C. W., and others.   J. Clin. Invest., 23:541, 1944.
32. Parkman, P. D., and others.   Proc. Soc. Exper. Biol. & Med., 111:225, 1962.
33. Peries, J. R., and Chany, C.   Compt. rend. Acad. Sc., 251:820, 1960.
34. Rake, G. J.   J. Pediat., 23:376, 1943.
35. Robbins, F. C.   Am. J. Dis. Child., 103:266, 1962.
36. Sever, J. L., and others.   J.A.M.A., 182:663, 1962.
37. Stokes, J., and others.   J. Pediat., 22:1, 1943.
38. —————— and others.   J. Clin. Invest., 23:531, 1944.
39. Waterson, A. P., and others.   Virology, 15: 379, 1961.
40. Weller, T. H., and Neva, F. A.   Proc. Soc. Exper. Biol. & Med., 111:215, 1962.
41. Zahorsky, J.   Pediatrics, 22:60, 1910.

67

The Myxovirus Group

This group of viruses has the property of agglutinating red cells of various animals due to the viral affinity for mucin, a component of many cell surfaces. The term **myxovirus** is derived from the Greek word meaning "mucin" or "mucous." The viruses of the myxogroup are presented in Table 1. The **myxoviruses** contain ribonucleic acid (RNA) and are ether-sensitive viruses. All grow well in embryonated eggs on either amniotic or allantoic inoculation and have some animal pathogenicity; all grow in one or more cell lines in tissue culture and all have soluble (S) and virus (V) antigens. The soluble antigen is identical to the ribonucleoprotein core. The virus (V) antigens are present in the substance of the particle and cannot be separated from it. The standard test for **myxoviruses** is the hemagglutination-inhibition test. The hemagglutinin of this group is distinctly different from the **ARBO** virus hemagglutinin, and these two virus groups actually have no significant common features other than that both are RNA viruses.

INFLUENZA

Myxovirus influenzae

Influenza, derived from the Italian word *influenza* meaning "influence," is estimated to have directly or indirectly caused the

Table 1. Myxovirus Group

| | | | SEROLOGIC CROSS REACTIVITY | | | | | | | | | |
| | | | INFLUENZA | | | PARA-INFLUENZA | | | | | | |
VIRUS	TYPES	DISEASE	A	B	C	1	1a	2	3	4	MUMPS	NDV
	A Human Classic (PR8, 1933) A-1 (A-Prime, 1947) A-2 (Asian, 1957)	Epidemic flu	+	0	0							
	Animal Swine, horse, duck, fowl											
M. influenzae	B Human		0	+	0							
	Classic (B-1 or Lee, 1940) B-2 (1954) B-3 (1962)	Epidemic flu										
	C Human (1947)	Minor resp.	0	0	+							
	1 (Hemadsorption virus 2)	Croup	0	0	0	+	+	+	+	0	+	0
	1a (Sendai, Hemagg. virus Japan, HVJ)	Infantile pneumonia				+	+	+	+		+	+
M. parainfluenzae	2 (Croup-associated, CA)	Croup				0	+	+	+			
	3 (Hemadsorption virus 1)	Croup; bronchiolitis				+	0	+				
	4 (M 25)	Minor resp.							+			
	5 (SA)	?										
M. parotitis	1 (Mumps)	Mumps					+		+		+	+
M. multiforme	1 (Newcastle disease virus, NDV)	Pneumonia in chickens					+				+	+

931

death of 20 million persons in 1918-1919 and induced clinical disease in about one billion people or one half of the world's population. On the basis of this single pandemic it is easy to see why influenza is of great concern to everybody. Moreover, pandemics and epidemics occurred at regular intervals prior to and after the 1918-1919 catastrophe and outbreaks are certain to continue.

The 1918 pandemic had a rather singular feature in that the death rate was abnormally high in the 25-to-40-year age group even though the case incidence, as usual, was highest in persons 5 to 20. Fatalities were lowest in children and highest in elderly persons, which is the usual course of events. The question is, then, what caused the unusually high death rate in the young adult group? It is true that secondary bacterial infections were important, but no organisms selectively affect this age group. Various experimental studies show that the primary pathology of influenza virus infections is destruction of respiratory tract epithelium. In a significant number of cases this lesion very probably was the principal cause of death, and secondary bacterial infections or the presence of bacteria were incidental. Since the case incidence was highest in the younger age groups, the death rate should have been highest, but it was not. Francis' theory (16) would afford the best explanation. The older persons possessed some latent immunity, and, although they frequently died subsequent to the influenza infection, the actual case incidence was the lowest for all age groups. The young persons had little immunity, so the case incidence was highest, but their high, innate physiologic resistance prevented an otherwise high mortality. The middle age group thus presented the situation of relatively low viral immunity and low physiologic resistance, making for an unusually great mortality.

It is important to point out that in 1918-1919 the incidence of pneumonia was higher even in the older age groups than that observed in subsequent epidemics of influenza, despite the fact that there is evidence for believing that the population had been exposed to a virus similar to the pandemic strain prior to 1918. If true, this would suggest that the strain was able to overcome some immunity, and this is one characteristic of increased virulence. Thus, the 1918-1919 catastrophe most probably can be explained as follows: a virus of unusual virulence presented a new antigenic mosaic to a population relatively unprepared to cope with it.

The specific virus responsible for the 1918-1919 pandemic has never been recovered, but later serologic studies on sera obtained then showed that the virus was a type A strain and closely related antigenically to swine influenza and the PR8 strain.

During the pandemic of 1889 Pfeiffer (39) isolated a bacterium which was thought to be the etiologic agent and was named *Haemophilus influenzae,* but this organism was found in 1918-1919 in only a small percentage of cases. In 1933, Smith, Andrewes, and Laidlow (45) isolated a virus which has subsequently been proven to be the cause of human influenza. This isolate, the PR8 strain, is the prototype strain of type A influenza viruses. In 1943 a very closely related strain, Weiss, caused a widespread epidemic. A major variant of the PR8-Weiss strain occurred in 1940 with the appearance of the Hickcox strain and this mutated to the well-known FM1 virus which caused a 1947 pandemic. These strains are known as A-1 or A' influenza viruses and have caused epidemics and pandemics in 1947, 1950, 1951, 1952, 1953, 1955, and 1956. In 1957 a second major mutation occurred with the appearance of the A-2 virus (Asian, or A-Jap) and this resulted in one of the largest pandemics in recent history in 1957-1958. Type A epidemics and pandemics tend to occur in two- to three-year cycles, an occurrence rate about double that of influenza B epidemics.

The B prototype strain was isolated in 1940 (15), and this virus or variants of it have caused relatively minor epidemics and pandemics about every four to six years, the last major pandemic occurring in 1962. As with the type A virus, the B strains have changed their antigenic structure over the past 20 years, and Francis (17) has suggested their division as follows: B1 subgroup, prototype B/Lee/40. This is the strain originally isolated. The B2 subgroup represented by B/Great Lakes/1739/54, isolated in 1954 and is comprised of strains causing epidemics in 1950 to 1956. The sharp outbreak of B influenza which occurred in 1961-1962 was caused by a new mutant distinct from both B1 and B2 subgroups (37, 41).

The type C viruses were isolated in 1947, are distinct both antigenically and in their growth characteristics from the type A and B, and cause infections with limited spread and of mild character.

Morphology. Influenza virus is a spherical particle with an average diameter of 120 mμ varying from 80 to 180 mμ. The outer membrane is 10-15 mμ thick, covered by a series of projections 8-10 mμ long. The inner component is a helical ring of ribonucleoprotein (RNA) which is identical to the soluble complement-fixing antigen. Filamentous forms of virus are formed but have a low degree of infectivity. Both spherical and filamentous forms of virus develop at the surface of the infected cell (24, 51). Incomplete or noninfectious virus is formed under certain conditions. Morphologic studies of incomplete virus show the particles to be of variable size and flatter than normal, and the dense center of ribonucleoprotein is absent (5).

Cultivation. The influenza viruses grow readily in embryonated eggs and reach maximum concentrations in the allantoic and amniotic fluids. The embryo may or may not survive the infection. Even large amounts can be grown if the embryo and yolk sac are removed and the virus is incubated with the living chorioallantoic membrane (4). By ultracentrifugation the virus in the chorioallantoic fluid has been concentrated and the relatively pure virus has been studied for its chemical, physical, and biologic characteristics. The results of these studies can be found in the reports of Beard and others (2, 3), Stanley (46), and Wyckoff (52).

Strains of influenza virus have been propagated in cultures of human embryonic tissues, with cytopathogenic effects accompanying the viral growth (38). Other studies show that primary isolation of virus from throat washings may be accomplished in monkey kidney tissue culture (48).

Primary isolation of virus from patients, however, is accomplished much more readily in the embryonated egg than in tissue culture (29, 31).

Resistance. The virus remains viable when stored at $-70°$ C. for long periods. It resists freezing and drying when suspended in chorio-allantoic fluid or tissue extracts. It is inactivated quickly by 5 per cent phenol, but it resists 0.1 per cent phenol for one month. It is killed by formalin and a variety of other agents (14). Propylene glycol vapor inactivates virus which has been suspended in air (40). Since the sulfonamides and penicillin do not inhibit the virus, this makes possible its direct isolation from nasal secretions by primary culture in embryonated eggs (9). ACTH has no effect on mice infected with the virus of influenza (33), but cortisone increases their susceptibility (30).

Viral Metabolites. Certain strains of living influenza virus are toxic, and this toxic activity is said to be destroyed when the virus is killed by heat or formalin (21). The toxicity is firmly associated with the virus particle and cannot be separated from it. Mice injected intravenously with large amounts of virus may die in 24 hours. Pathologic examination shows necrosis of liver and spleen, but viral studies show no virus multiplication occurs.

Antigenic Structure. Influenza viruses have complement-fixing antigens which are type- but not strain-specific. Thus, antiserum to one strain of type A influenza virus reacts to a common soluble A antigen from all type A strains but not to soluble antigen from B and C type viruses. As indicated, all influenza viruses have a hemagglutinin, and antibody to this hemagglutinin is strain-specific. In other words, the antigenic structure of the hemagglutinin of all type A viruses varies to some degree, and antibody to hemagglutinin can distinguish one type A strain from another. This strain difference is more apparent in the hemagglutination-inhibition test than in the complement-fixation test (28). The virus neutralization test performed in eggs or tissue culture is quite specific but expensive and laborious.

One of the most important characteristics of influenza virus is its unusual ability to change (mutate) to a new antigenic structure. In fact, antigen variation **within types** of influenza virus is so great that isolation of strains currently causing a given epidemic must be accomplished and used as the diagnostic antigen for **that epidemic** to insure serologic diagnosis.

Influenza virus is comprised of many antigens which are quite variable in forming the virus antigenic pattern. Influenza A virus has at least 18 such components and yet is serologically distinct from Type B virus. Of these 18 components some may be the major antigen(s) in one given epidemic, whereas others take predominance at other times (Fig. 1). Since 1931 there have been five major antigenic pattern changes in Influenza A virus alone. Given so many antigens, it is felt that the final antigenic structure in an epidemic strain is determined by the immunity pattern of the population. Antibodies to various components suppress the virus variants, some of which are "selected" or allowed to spread widely because they possess a pattern least affected by the current immune state of the population. In 1947 the A strain pattern contained major antigens, 12, 13, 14, which persisted until 1951-1953 (26). After the epidemic virus infections in 1947, these

strains appeared sporadically but were unable to initiate widespread disease. In 1951-1953 components 16 and 17, which were previously minor antigens, became major components, along with other antigenic changes, and waves of influenza began to recur. Francis (16) has proposed the "doctrine of original antigenic sin," meaning that the antigenic mosaic first presented to the individual dominates his future antibody pattern. Antibody to swine influenza is the basic pattern of persons over 30 years of age, and this supports the concept that a virus antigenically similar to swine influenza was the responsible agent in 1918. In children antibody to A-prime virus is most characteristic, and these serums are deficient in classic A and swine antibodies. The aim of total protection by vaccines would be to supply individuals with stimuli for antigenic patterns not characteristic of their age group. The fundamental question today is whether the antigenic variation is infinite or finite and whether or not it is predictable. There is some reason to believe that major antigenic variation is limited and that vaccines prepared with certain dominant patterns will

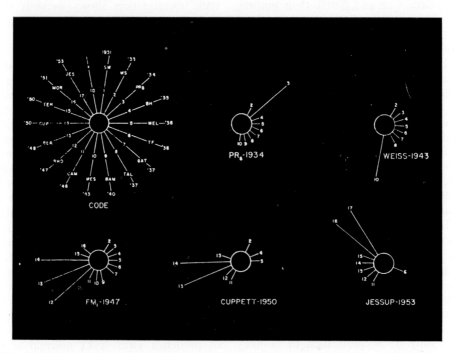

Fig. 1. Influenza virus antigens. Changes in the antigenic patterns of Type A influenza virus from 1934 to 1953. (From Jenson and Francis. *J. Exper. Med.,* 98:619, 1953.)

protect against all possible strains of virus.

Hemagglutination (HA) and Hemagglu-tination-inhibition (HI). Hirst (22) and McClelland and Hare (35) almost simultaneously reported that influenza virus suspensions caused the agglutination of red blood cells and that this hemagglutination could be blocked or inhibited by specific antibody. The nature and significance of these reactions have been studied intensively over the past 20 years (1, 6, 7, 8, 10, 18, 20, 23, 25, 34, 45).

The mechanism of hemagglutination is based on the presence of an enzyme, neuraminidase, which is a part of the surface of the myxovirus particle and which acts on red cell receptors forming a "bridge" between red cells. The cells are then brought together in a lattice type of structure. During the virus attachment to the receptor site, the receptor is destroyed, and the virus particle then elutes from the red cell surface. The eluted virus is unaffected and can be used to reagglutinate fresh cells; the cells which have had their receptors destroyed, however, are inagglutinable by the same virus. The red cell receptor is a type of sialic acid (specifically, N-acetylneuramic acid or **NANA**) incorporated into a protein-polysaccharide complex. The evidence for this is that the red cell receptors can be removed by periodate and trypsin as well as by virus. Active, infective, and heat-inactivated virus particles are all capable of agglutination, but heat-inactivated particles will not elute from the receptor or destroy it.

Besides specific antihemagglutinin antibody, certain mucoid materials found in many animal fluids or tissues will inhibit virus hemagglutination. Obviously, these nonspecific inhibitors must be removed from test serum before the specific antibody level can be determined. Intensive study of these inhibitors has revealed three principal types: (1) the **alpha** (Francis) inhibitor, which is heat-stable but is destroyed by RDE, trypsin, or periodate (the active part of this inhibitor being **NANA**); (2) the **beta** (Chu) inhibitor, a heat-labile alpha globulin not destroyed by RDE or periodate but removed by trypsin; and (3) the **gamma** (Belyavin) inhibitor, which inactivates active A-2 virus, is heat-stable, is not destroyed by RDE but

is destroyed by periodate (11, 19). Receptor-destroying enzyme (RDE) is an enzyme prepared from cholera vibrio filtrate which acts on nonspecific inhibitors in the manner described.

The hemagglutination-inhibition test is performed in the following manner. A stock suspension of virus is serially diluted, and to these dilutions are added red cells. The virus-cell suspension is allowed to settle, and the hemagglutinin titer of the stock suspension is determined. The stock suspension is then diluted to contain four hemagglutinating units of virus. (One hemagglutinating unit is equal to the dilution of the last tube in the titration series causing unequivocal agglutination. If the titer of the stock suspension was 1:1024, the dilution to contain four hemagglutinating units would be 1:256 in a serial twofold series). The above step is called the "unit titration." Next, the serum to be tested is diluted in series, and to each serum dilution is added a volume of diluted stock virus containing four hemagglutinating units. The serum-virus mixture is incubated, and red cells are added and allowed to settle. The highest dilution of serum completely inhibiting agglutination of four units of virus is the H-I titer. Serum may need to be treated to remove the non-specific inhibitors described above.

Clinical Types of Infections in Man. Influenza has been described as follows:

A kind of fever, in general slight, but sometimes not a little fatal to old men and children who had weak lungs, raged throughout all this country. At once and at the same time, innumerable persons were seized with a wandering kind of shiver and heaviness in the head; presently also came on a pain therein and also in the joints and back; several however, were troubled with a universal lassitude. Immediately a very great and acrid defluxion from the eyes, nostrils and fauces, and very often falling upon the lungs, which occasion almost perpetual sneezings, and commonly a violent cough.

This description made by John Huxham (50), an English country doctor, in 1743 emphasizes, as pointed out by C. H. Stuart-Harris (47), that epidemics come and go but the clinical picture of influenza remains remarkably constant.

The onset of uncomplicated influenza is characteristically abrupt, although occasionally there are a few days of mild malaise before the onset of symptoms. The characteristic symptoms are anorexia, fever, and headache, sometimes accompanied by injection and burning of the eyeballs, and mild sore throat. Pains in the back and somatic muscles, particularly in the calves of the legs, may be quite severe. The temperature rises sharply to 101° or 104° F., persists for two or three days, and then gradually returns to normal, leaving the patient extremely exhausted.

Serious complications of influenza virus infection may occur as a result of secondary bacterial infection, or in a relatively small percentage of cases the damage to the respiratory epithelium by the virus per se may be so great as to cause death. The Asian epidemic in 1957 resulted in widespread recognition of influenzal-staphylococcal pneumonia developing primarily in persons having some underlying cardiorespiratory disease (Table 2). The per cent of various bacteria involved in secondary pulmonary infections is given in Table 3, where it is evident that the predominant organism was the staphylococcus (43). Generally, the patients with the influenza-staphylococcal syndrome presented with a picture of typical uncomplicated influenza. This was followed by clinical improvement lasting one to four days. Then there was a sudden exacerbation of the respiratory symptoms characterized by fever, pleural pain, and bloody sputum. Response to antibiotics was variable.

The fatal influenza uncomplicated by sec-

Table 3. Bacteriologic Findings in Fatal Cases of Influenza in Which Virus Was Demonstrated in the Lung *

1937-1950

TOTAL CASES, 143

Bacterial (75%)		Abacterial (25%)
Staphylococci	80	
Pneumococci	6	
Beta-hemolytic streptococci	2	
H. influenzae	1	
E. coli	7	
Alpha streptococci	1	
Unknown	2	
TOTAL	108	35

* From Rogers. *Am. Rev. Resp. Dis.,* 83:61, 1961.

ondary bacterial infection arose in patients with underlying cardiorespiratory disease. The typical influenza syndrome progressed rapidly to severe respiratory failure characterized by dyspnea and cyanosis. Pleural pain was absent (42). These patients failed to respond to antibiotics, and five out of six died. No bacteria could be recovered from lung tissue or visualized on histologic sections.

Diagnosis cannot be made on clinical grounds in any individual case, and it should be stressed that a large percentage of influenza virus infections are inapparent. Serologic determinations of influenza virus antibody levels done with acute and convalescent sera are the most reliable diagnostic criteria. Either the hemagglutination-inhibition or complement-fixation test may be used. The complement-fixation test is less specific than the H-I and therefore better, in general, for diagnostic purposes. Moreover, serum used in the complement-fixation test does not need to be treated with RDE, trypsin, or periodate, which may destroy small amounts of antibody. The hemagglutination-inhibition test is used when a more precise definition of the influenza virus subgroups is desired (28). The rapid diagnosis of influenzal infection can be accomplished by fluorescent antibody staining, although this method is less sensitive than serologic tests or virus isolation. The fluorescent method is type-specific rather than strain-specific (32).

Table 2. Underlying Disease in Fatal Cases of Abacterial Influenza †

TOTAL, 35

Underlying disease		Status unknown
Rheumatic heart disease	13	
ASCVD *	1	
"Myocarditis"	1	
"Normal"	2	
TOTAL	17	18

* ASCVD—arteriosclerotic heart disease.
† From Rogers. *Am. Rev. Resp. Dis.,* 83:61, 1961.

Treatment. The virus of influenza is not susceptible to any known therapeutic agents. The administration of sulfonamides or penicillin, beginning with the onset of symptoms, usually will reduce or eliminate the danger of secondary bacterial infections but has no effect on the course of the uncomplicated disease (49). Another handicap is man's inherent difficulty in producing permanent immunity.

Prevention. Recent experiments with influenza vaccines give variable results in their ability to protect. Vaccines against virus A, A-1, and A-2 ranged from 40 to 95 per cent effective, with an average of 78 per cent; against B and B-1 the range was 63 to 96 per cent, with an average of 90 per cent (12, 13, 36). Virus is grown in embryonated eggs, concentrated by centrifugation, and inactivated with formalin. Recommended dosages are given subcutaneously in the following amounts: 1.0 ml. for adults, 0.5 ml. for children six to 12 years old, and 0.2 ml. for children less than six years. Previously vaccinated persons get one dose; those not previously vaccinated get two or three doses several weeks apart. The current vaccines are polyvalent and contain A-1, A-2 (Asian), and B types of viruses, although use of vaccines containing five to six virus strains have been recommended (27). Live attenuated virus vaccines have been tested in Russia and appear to be effective (53, 54).

Despite the apparent optimism in the above description of influenza vaccine, there are serious problems in these programs. It is not entirely clear whether virus strains other than the one involved in any given epidemic are of any value as vaccine antigens. In other words, is the virus strain derived from the current epidemic the only important antigen in a polyvalent vaccine? This question relates to the theoretical question previously discussed as to whether influenza antigens are finite or infinite: Will the virus as it mutates repeat old antigenic patterns? There are marked differences of opinion on whether vaccines made with classic A and A-1 virus conferred any immunity against the Asian A-2 pandemic. A further question might be raised as to the relation of antibody induced by the vaccine to protection of the individual from infection. Thus, Rose vaccinated over 3500 men with a monovalent A-2 vaccine and found 60 to 80 per cent reduction (compared to controls) in respiratory infection during the Asian epidemic; however, the vaccinated group showed no rise in hemagglutination-inhibition antibody to A-2 virus.

Again, the central question is whether the effective antigen is the current epidemic virus strain. If it is this antigen, and **only** this antigen, then the influenza immunization program is faced with a series of "crash" vaccine production crises. The 1957 "crash" program was essentially a failure. Only 15 to 20 million doses out of a goal of 60 to 80 million were ready for distribution at the peak of the epidemic. This was due to difficulties in adapting the A2 strain to grow in eggs in sufficient titer to make a potent vaccine. Distribution of vaccine raises further problems, particularly in educating people to the need for the vaccine and particularly to the need for speed in getting serum antibody levels built up. In a study of the 1957 epidemic in some American cities (44) less than 25 per cent of the population accepted influenza vaccine. Most persons interviewed in this study did not believe they would become infected with the Asian virus and that, if they did, it would not be a more serious disease than the common cold. By the time the production and distribution methods were solved, the pandemic was too far along to be affected greatly. The solution to the problems of influenza virus vaccination is one of the most important in modern virology.

PARAINFLUENZA VIRUSES

Myxovirus parainfluenzae

This group of viruses differs from the influenza viruses in the following respects: (1) filamentous forms of virus do not occur, (2) growth in embryonated eggs does not occur except with the parainfluenza 1a (Sendai) virus, and (3) giant cell formation in infected tissue cultures occurs. The parainfluenza group shows serologic cross-reactions with mumps and Newcastle disease virus but not with influenza viruses.

The first virus of this group to be isolated was the 1a (Sendai) virus recovered from cases of pneumonitis in children in Japan in 1953 (67). Since this is the only virus of this group which grows readily in embryonated eggs, it was suggested that this agent constitutes a fourth type of influenza virus and be designated influenza virus group D. However, this agent is serologically distinct from all types of influenza viruses and definitely related to the other parainfluenza agents. The parainfluenza types 1 and 3 were previously known as the "hemadsorption viruses" (71), named after the tissue culture reaction by which they were first demonstrated. In this reaction red cell suspensions are added to infected tissue culture cell sheets. The infected culture cells adsorb the erythrocytes, and this test can be used to type new isolates or detect antibody. The hemadsorption method is particularly valuable in detecting viruses which grow in tissue culture without producing cytopathic effects. The parainfluenza virus type 2 was originally isolated in monkey kidney tissue culture from children with croup and was referred to as the Croup-Associated (CA) virus (56). The SA virus was isolated from hamsters inoculated intracerebrally with allantoic fluid from eggs incubated for seven days after inoculation with nasal washings from a patient suffering from an acute upper respiratory infection (70).

The relation of these agents to respiratory disease is well established, but their relative importance is not entirely clear. An epidemic of parainfluenza 2 (CA virus) in 31 children was characterized by a mild upper respiratory syndrome, with cough and coryza in 10 from which virus was isolated. Only one of 31 children had croup (65). In studies of patients hospitalized with croup, a large percentage of cases were caused by parainfluenza 2 virus (61, 63, 66). In adults parainfluenza viruses were the causative agents of mild respiratory disease in 4.5 per cent of naval recruits (69). Surveys of parainfluenzal antibody in adults and children have given results shown in Table 4.

The high incidence of Sendai antibodies and the low incidence of isolation of this virus may be due to serologic cross-reactions

with Sendai to mumps (59, 62) and infectious mononucleosis (60). Parainfluenza 1 and 3 likewise cause a wide variety of clinical manifestations, including croup, pneumonia, bronchiolitis, pharyngitis, and mild febrile disease, and account for about 6 per cent of these infections (57, 58). Parainfluenza 3 has been repeatedly isolated from cattle with mild respiratory disease (55). Type 4 virus has been isolated from children with minor respiratory infections (64).

Table 4. Per Cent Antibody to Parainfluenza Virus *

| | PARAINFLUENZA TYPE | | | |
	1	1a (Sendai)	2	3
American adults	84	76	22	100
American children	32	44	21	69
Italian adults	74	81	28	97
Italian children	44	52	10	92

* Adapted from La Placa and Moscovici. *J. Immunol.,* 88:72, 1962.

ANIMAL INFLUENZA VIRUS INFECTIONS

Coincidentally with the 1918 pandemic of human influenza a new acute respiratory disease was recognized in swine in Iowa (72), and this infection has been reported each year since in the United States and more recently in Europe. This disease suddenly appears in swine herds in the fall and winter, and the explosive outbreaks mimic human influenza. Shope demonstrated that the disease is caused by a symbiosis of a bacillus, *Haemophilus influenzae suis,* and a virus, the swine influenza virus. The virus has a complicated life cycle entering the lungworm of the pig and passing to the ova of these worms, which subsequently may be eaten by an earthworm (a passive intermediate host) which then may be ingested by a pig again, releasing virus into the swine (76, 77).

The relationship between swine and human influenza has been the basis of much speculation, the question raised being whether a mutant of the swine virus initiated the 1918-1919 pandemic in humans or whether the human virus took refuge in the swine. Swine influenza virus is a type A virus similar to the human PR8 strain. Recent studies indicate that several animals may be infected with type A human influenza virus. Thus, human A-2 virus will infect swine (79), and two new related strains, A-equi-prague-56 (78) and A-duck-57 Czechoslovakia (74), have been isolated from horses and ducks, respectively. Fowl plague, an influenza-like disease of fowl which has been recognized since 1880, is caused by a virus very similar to human type A influenza strains (75). Subsequent to the recent A-2 pandemic, antibodies were found to this virus in 51 of 288 horses, but swine antibodies were absent (73). Thus, the possibility of an animal reservoir for human influenza virus exists, but the precise relationship of the human and animal infections is yet to be determined.

REFERENCES

INFLUENZA

1. Ackermann, W. W.   J. Exper. Med., 93:635, 1951.
2. Beard, J. W.   J. Immunol., 58:49, 1948.
3. ———— South. M. J., 37:313, 1944.
4. Bernkopf, H.   Proc. Soc. Exper. Biol. & Med., 72:680, 1949.
5. Birch-Anderson, A., and Paucker, K.   Virology, 8:21, 1959.
6. Burnet, F. M.   Virus or Organism, Cambridge, Mass., Harvard University Press, 1945.
7. ———— and others.   Brit. J. Exper. Path., 27:228, 1946.
8. ———— and others.   Lancet, 1:807, 1946.
9. Cabasso, V. J., and others.   Proc. Soc. Exper. Biol. & Med., 78:791, 1951.
10. Carlisle, H. N., and Elrod, R. P.   Proc. Soc. Exper. Biol. & Med., 72:223, 1949.
11. Cohen, A., and Belyavin, G.   Virology, 13:58, 1961.
12. Davenport, F. M.   Am. Rev. Resp. Dis., 83:146, 1961.
13. ———— J.A.M.A., 182:11, 1962.
14. Dunham, W. B., and MacNeal, W. J. J.   Immunol., 49:123, 1944.
15. Francis, T., Jr.   Science, 92:405, 1940.
16. ———— Ann. Int. Med., 39:203, 1953; 43:534, 1956.
17. Francis, T., Jr.   in Rivers, T. M., and Horsfall, F. L., Jr., Viral and Rickettsial Infections of Man, Philadelphia, J. B. Lippincott Co., 1959, p. 643.
18. Ginsberg, H. S., and Horsfall, F. L., Jr.   J. Exper. Med., 90:475, 1949.
19. Gottschalk, A., and Fazekas de St. Groth, S.   J. Gen. Microbiol., 22:690, 1960.
20. Green, R. H., and Woolley, D. W.   J. Exper. Med., 86:55, 1947.
21. Henle, W., and Henle, G.   Proc. Soc. Exper. Biol. & Med., 59:179, 1945.
22. Hirst, G. K.   J. Immunol., 45:293, 1942.
23. ———— J. Exper. Med., 91:161, 177, 1950.
24. Horne, R. W., and others.   Virology, 11:79, 1960.
25. Hurst, E. W., and Stacey, M.   Brit. J. Exper. Path., 31:410, 1950.
26. Jensen, K. E., and Francis, T., Jr.   J. Exper. Med., 98:619, 1953.
27. ———— and others.   J.A.M.A., 172:1230, 1960.
28. ———— Am. Rev. Resp. Dis., 83:120, 1961.
29. Kalter, S. S., and others.   Proc. Soc. Exper. Biol. & Med., 100:367, 1959.
30. Kass, E. H., and others.   J. Lab. & Clin. Med., 37:780, 1951.
31. Lennette, E. H.   Am. Rev. Resp. Dis., 83:116, 1961.
32. Liu, C.   Am. Rev. Resp. Dis., 83:130, 1961.
33. Loosli, C. G., and others.   J. Lab. & Clin. Med., 36:956, 1950.
34. Magill, T. P.   J. Exper. Med., 94:31, 1951.
35. McClelland, L., and Hare, R.   Canad. Pub. Health J., 32:530, 1941.
36. Meiklejohn, G.   J.A.M.A., 179:544, 1962.
37. Moffet, H. L., and others.   J.A.M.A., 182:96, 1962.
38. Mogabgab, W. J., and others.   J. Immunol., 76:314, 1956.
39. Pfeiffer, R.   Deutsche med. Wchnschr., 18:28, 1892.
40. Robertson, O. H., and others.   Science, 94:612, 1941.
41. Robinson, R. Q., and others.   Proc. Soc. Exper. Biol. & Med., 112:658, 1963.
42. Rogers, D. E., and others.   Tr. Asian Am. Phys., 71:260, 1958.
43. Rogers, D. E.   Am. Rev. Resp. Dis., 83:61, 1961.
44. Rosenstock, I. M.   Am. Rev. Resp. Dis., 83:171, 1961.
45. Smith, W., and others.   Lancet, 2:66, 1933.
46. Stanley, W. M.   J. Exper. Med., 79:255, 267, 1944.
47. Stuart-Harris, C. H.   Am. Rev. Resp. Dis., 83:56, 1961.
48. Takemoto, K. K., and others.   Proc. Soc. Exper. Biol. & Med., 89:308, 1955.
49. Thalmann, W. G., and others.   J.A.M.A., 144:1156, 1950.
50. Thompson, T.   Ann. of Influenza in Great Britain 1510-1837, Sydenham Society, London, 1852.
51. Valentine, R. C., and Isaacs, A.   J. Gen. Microbiol., 16:195, 1957.
52. Wyckoff, R. W. G.   Science, 101:129, 1945.
53. Zhdanov, V. M., and Ritova, V. V.   J. Hyg. Epid. (Praha), 3:472, 1959.
54. ———— and Soloviev, V. D.   Am. Rev. Resp. Dis., 83:178, 1961.

PARAINFLUENZA

55. Abinanti, F. R., and others.   Am. J. Hyg., 71:52, 1960.
56. Chanock, R. M.   J. Exper. Med., 104:555, 1956.
57. ———— and others.   J.A.M.A., 169:548, 1959.

58. Chanock, R. M., and others. in Perspectives in Virology, Pollard, M., ed., Minneapolis, Burgess Publishing Company, 1961, vol. 2, pp. 126-239.
59. DeMeio, J. L., and Walker, D. L. J. Immunol., 78:465, 1957.
60. ———— and Walker, D. L. Proc. Soc. Exper. Biol. Med., 98:453, 1958.
61. Gardner, P. S., and others. Brit. M. J., 1: 1077, 1960.
62. ———— J. Hyg., 58:283, 1960.
63. Hilleman, M. R., and others. J.A.M.A., 180: 445, 1962.
64. Johnson, K. M., and others. Am. J. Hyg., 71:81, 1960.
65. Kapikian, A. Z., and others. J.A.M.A., 183: 324, 1963.
66. Kim, H. W., and others. Pediatrics, 28:614, 1961.
67. Kuroya, N., and others. Yokohama M. Bull., 4:217, 1953.
68. La Placa, M., and Moscovici, C. J. Immunol., 88:72, 1962.
69. Miller, L. F., and others. J.A.M.A., 185:92, 1963.

70. Schultz, E. W., and Habel, K. J. Immunol., 82:274, 1959.
71. Vogel, J., and Shelokov, A. Science, 126: 358, 1957.

ANIMAL INFLUENZA

72. Gibson, J. I. Proc. 22nd Annual Meeting, U.S. Livestock Sanitary Assoc., Chicago, p. 192, 1918.
73. Kaplan, M. M., and Payne, A. Bull. WHO, 20:465, 1959.
74. Koppel, Z., and others. Bull. WHO, 20:435, 1959.
75. Schafer, W. in Perspectives in Virology, New York, John Wiley and Sons, 1955, p. 20.
76. Shope, R. E. J. Exper. Med., 54:349, 373, 1931; 62:561, 1935; 64:47, 791, 1936.
77. ———— J. Exper. Med., 74:49, 1941.
78. Tumova, B., and Fiserova-Sovinova. Bull. WHO, 20:445, 1959.
79. Wallace, G. D., and Kissling, R. E. Bull. WHO, 20:455, 1959.

68

Mumps

Myxovirus parotitidis

Mumps or infectious parotitis was described accurately by Hippocrates (7), and he recognized several complications, including orchitis. The origin of the word "mumps" is obscure but probably comes from one of several uses of this word in archaic or Chaucerian English meaning "a lump" or "to sulk." Another possible derivation is from the Dutch word *mommelen,* "to mumble." Whatever the origin, the name "mumps" is firmly entrenched in English medical terminology.

This disease has a world-wide distribution and is most common in children from the ages of 5 to 15 years. The clinical picture of mumps is remarkably uniform, as is the mumps virus particle itself. Thus, there is only a single serologic type, and the physical and biologic properties of the virus do not vary much either from year to year or in geographic location. The number of cases varies year to year, with more major outbreaks occurring in cycles of 8 to 10 years. In 1960 about 200,000 cases of mumps were reported in the United States, compared, for example, with about 440,000 cases of measles in the same year. Mumps, however, is not a reportable disease, and 14 of the 50 states failed to report in 1960.

The virus etiology of mumps was established by Johnson and Goodpasture (9) in 1934. Filtrates of saliva were injected into Stensen's duct of the rhesus monkey, producing a typical mumps parotitis.

Morphology. Mumps virus particle is spherical with an average diameter of 170 mμ (22) but with a large variation in particle diameter ranging from about 90 to over 200 mμ. It has about the same resistance to inactivation as influenza virus and can be stored at $-70°$ C. for months or lyophilized. Sterile neutralized skim milk aids in preserving mumps virus infectivity, and virus-milk suspensions can be shipped without freezing. As is true with most viruses, infected tissue can be placed and held in 50 per cent glycerin for two weeks or more at room temperature, and the virus then can be isolated successfully. Infectivity is destroyed by formalin, but antigenicity is retained.

Cultivation. Initially the virus was isolated from humans by injecting filtered saliva into the rhesus monkey parotid gland duct. The gland becomes swollen in six or seven days, with the most marked enlargement at the eighth or ninth day. Virus for passage and mumps complement-fixation antigen can be isolated from extracts of the gland. Other than the parotitis and low-grade fever, monkeys show no other signs of the disease. Monkeys cannot be infected by exposure to human cases. Mumps research lagged from 1934 to 1945 when Habel (5) and Levens and Enders (15) succeeded in growing the virus in the embryonated egg. Mumps virus grows without prior adaptation after intracerebral inoculation of newborn hamsters (14), producing a fatal encephalitis, and the hamster strains have been adapted to newborn mice (13). Recently mumps virus has been grown in various tissue culture systems, including chick embryo amnion (4) and monkey kidney cells (21). Mumps virus has been recovered from human saliva, cerebrospinal fluid, urine (21), blood (11, 18), testes (8), milk (12), and thyroid tissue (3).

Pathology. Histologic studies of infected parotid tissue reveal perivascular infiltration, focal degeneration of acinar epithelium, interacinar edema with serofibrinous, and cell exudates in the region of acini, ducts, and vessels as the primary lesion (10). The cells found are lymphocytes and mononuclear lymphocytes; polymorphonuclear cells are not present. In the parotid gland and in the testes scattered patchy reaction is the rule. Necrosis may follow in areas distal to a vascular reaction severe enough to cause occlusion of the vessel. Studies of a fatal meningo-encephalitis in hamsters (16) failed to show evidence of direct neuronal necrosis by the virus. The hamster brains showed most marked vascular reactions in the mid-brain, but involvement of meningeal vessels was also present. The best-documented case (1) of human death from mumps infection followed a severe meningo-encephalitis, and the pathologic studies showed a type of lesion and distribution very similar to that found in newborn hamsters. In the human case, unfortunately, virus isolation from the brain tissue was not done. Because of the late appearance of meningo-encephalitis in humans and the lack of autopsy and virus studies, some workers postulated that the central nervous system lesions were due to a reaction of mumps virus and its antibody. The implication was that the mumps virus particle did not have the capacity per se to cause brain tissue changes. The studies in newborn hamsters, however, clearly show this concept to be incorrect (16, 17). Interestingly, in embryonated eggs the virus grows without producing any discernible lesions, and, in fact, many of the inoculated eggs will hatch normal embryos despite the prolific virus growth.

Antigenic Structure. Mumps virus is of a single antigenic type and cross-reacts with hemadsorption viruses 1a (Sendai) and 4 and Newcastle disease virus. Both soluble (S) and virus particle (V) antigens have been found (6). Antibody levels as measured by hemagglutination-inhibition (H-I), complement-fixation (CF), or neutralization tests in eggs correlate with immunity, the H-I and CF tests being most widely used. Persons convalescent from mumps develop a tuberculin type of skin sensitivity to the virus, appearing two to three months after infection and usually persisting for life (2). There is evidence to indicate that some per-

sons may lose the skin sensitivity but retain neutralizing antibody (20). The skin test may be of great help diagnostically, since it should be negative during the acute disease. If positive, the acute disease in question is not mumps. The skin test reaction is redness and/or induration of 15 mm. or more in diameter, appearing 24 to 48 hours after intradermal inoculation of the skin test antigen. The two essential criteria are (1) the antigen must be injected intradermally (subcutaneous injection is useless) and (2) the reaction must be 15 mm. or more in diameter.

Hemagglutinin and Hemagglutination Inhibition (H-I). A hemagglutinin is associated with the virus particle (15) and is comparable to the influenza virus hemagglutinin. Virus-infected egg chorio-allantoic fluid or amniotic fluid agglutinates chicken cells, and this agglutination can be specifically blocked or inhibited by mumps virus antibody. Sera to be tested for mumps antibody should be treated with **cholera** filtrate to reduce nonspecific inhibitors. Since the mumps hemagglutinin is somewhat weaker than that of influenza virus, the cell suspension used is half as concentrated, and the test must be read earlier and more carefully. Mumps virus-agglutinated cells tend to revert to negative on standing, particularly in higher dilutions of virus.

Clinical Infection in Man. Mumps is transmitted by droplet infection from close contact. Persons infected may transmit the disease from six days prior to onset of parotitis to nine days thereafter; however, the period of greatest communicability is probably much shorter. Transmission of mumps infection is notoriously erratic, and contact by no means insures infection. The factors involved in mumps infection are obscure. The incubation period is unusually long, being 18 to 21 days in most cases.

PAROTITIS. Swelling of the parotid gland is the most common clinical feature. This may be preceded or accompanied by a redness of the orifice of Stensen's duct, which, if present, is a valuable diagnostic sign. This sign, however, is frequently absent. Parotitis may be accompanied by fever, congestion of upper respiratory tract, and pain in the gland. Salivatory stimulants (such as the sight of a pickle) may cause pain. The gland size is at its maximum in two days, and swelling may persist for 7 to 10 days. The white blood count is normal. All the salivary glands may be enlarged to some extent. Presternal edema is an unusual physical sign thought to be due to blockage of lymphatics in upper chest and neck by the swollen glands.

ORCHITIS. Testicular swelling may occur sometimes, with pain severe enough to require narcotics. The testicular involvement is usually unilateral, but bilateral swelling is not uncommon. Some unilateral testicular atrophy may follow, but bilateral atrophy is extremely rare. Sterility following mumps is rare because of the unilateral involvement and the patchy character of the lesion (23). Previous reports of sterility were based on low sperm counts during convalescence, but if sperm counts are done several months after recovery, sperm activity is almost always normal. Atrophy of one testicle may occur, but this alone will not affect fertility.

Orchitis is more apt to occur in persons 15 years of age or older.

MENINGO-ENCEPHALITIS. This complication occurs in about 10 per cent of cases, depending on criteria used. Thus, many persons with no significant central nervous system symptoms may show increased mononuclear cells in the spinal fluid. The usual picture is that of aseptic meningitis with fever, headache, stiff neck, and a CSF cell count of 15 to 60 mononuclear cells. The meningo-encephalitis may follow parotitis by several days or may be the presenting complaint without parotitis. At Duke two cases had as presenting complaint severe, deep coma of sudden onset without parotitis or any other manifestation of mumps (19). Symptoms usually last one or two days, and recovery is quite rapid once it begins. Deaths are very rare, and only a few of the cases reported may actually have been due to mumps virus. Most deaths from mumps reported are not documented and are errors in diagnosis or are due to some other

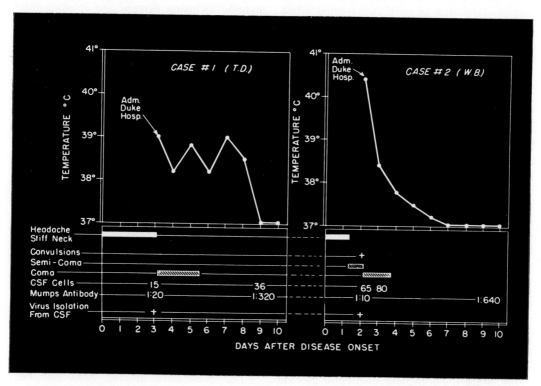

Fig. 1. Salient clinical and laboratory findings in two cases of sudden coma induced by mumps virus. (From Overman. *Am. J. Med.,* 26:957, 1959.)

cause, with mumps infection being coincidental.

THYROIDITIS.   Mild pain and swelling of the thyroid gland may occur, but thyroid activity is not affected. Chronic thyroiditis following mumps is not yet established (3).

OTHER COMPLICATIONS.   Pancreatitis is often talked about but rarely proved. Diabetes following mumps probably does not occur. **Deafness** in children may occur. **Oophoritis** is rare.

SUBCLINICAL INFECTIONS.   Mumps infection without any clinical signs is common (based on antibody studies) and may constitute 30 to 50 per cent of all cases. Persons having asymptomatic mumps are just as immune as those who had a clinical infection. It is worth noting that mumps infection of one parotid gland is just as immunogenic as bilateral involvement.

Treatment.   Treatment is symptomatic. In cases of severe orchitis cortisone may be considered, particularly if the pain is unusually severe. Use of cortisone in meningoencephalitis is not recommended. Laboratory studies show that in cortisone-treated adult hamsters mumps virus yields are many times greater in brain extracts than in nontreated controls (17).

Prevention.   A formalin-killed mumps virus vaccine has been tested but, due to the general mild nature of the disease, is not recommended. Antibody levels after inactivated virus do not persist long, and frequent boosters would be needed. It should be noted that most persons who say they have never had mumps actually have good mumps antibody titers because of subclinical infections. As increased travel is reducing the incidence of susceptible individuals and increasing the chance of childhood infection, fewer adult cases of mumps are being reported. During World War I thousands of cases occurred in recruits mostly from rural areas, but no such problem existed in World War II. Gamma globulin made from pooled plasma is of no value in the prevention of mumps. Gamma globulin made from plasma of persons convalescent from mumps has not been sufficiently tested to be of proven value. Since the convalescent mumps gamma globulin is very expensive and of questionable value, it is not recommended.

OTHER VIRUS DISEASES OF THE SALIVARY GLANDS

Guinea pigs, hamsters, rats, and mice have a latent virus disease of their salivary glands characterized by gigantic enlargement of the nuclei and the presence of intranuclear inclusions. The fetus is more susceptible than the young animals even when the mother has immune bodies (24, 25, 26, 29, 32).

Man has a corresponding disease of the salivary glands with a virus which infects the fetus in utero. There are now 64 fatal cases on record, with all but nine occurring in stillbirths and infants (34). Margaret Smith (31) has isolated from human salivary gland and renal tissue extracts two viruses which caused characteristic intranuclear inclusions in cultures of human uterine wall.

Usually this virus infection is confined to the salivary gland in the dormant or latent form. When it becomes disseminated, the salivary gland virus infection is called **cytomegalic inclusion disease** and is often fatal.

The classical infection occurs in infants and is characterized by a progressive infection leading to death in a few weeks. The clinical syndrome includes enlargement of the spleen and liver, with jaundice, enteritis, and cerebral calcification. Another form is characterized by pneumonia, nausea, vomiting, diarrhea, and death. The disease is contracted from the mother, who may have an asymptomatic viremia during pregnancy. Diagnosis is made by virus isolation from liver biopsy, urine, or other body fluids or tissue. A serologic diagnosis can be made with the complement-fixation or neutralization tests (28, 30, 33).

The virus has a DNA core and varies from 100 to 500 mμ in size (27). It grows in tissue cultures of various human cells but has no animal pathogenicity. It is ether-sensitive.

NEWCASTLE DISEASE VIRUS

(*Myxovirus multiforme*)

The Newcastle disease virus has been known for many years. Humans become infected from handling infected chickens, and the clinical manifestations include conjunctivitis, headache, preauricular lymphadenopathy, and a respiratory infection simulating influenza. The infection does not spread readily from human to human, and most cases have been in poultry raisers or dealers, veterinarians, and virologists.

The virus is typical of the myxovirus group with respect to size, chemical composition, hemagglutinin, and growth in embryonated eggs. This virus is described in greater detail in Chapter 76.

LYMPHOCYTIC CHORIOMENINGITIS

Lymphocytic choriomeningitis is a natural disease of mice caused by a virus about 50 mμ in diameter. It grows in minced chick embryo tissue cultures and in embryonated eggs and will infect monkeys, mice, guinea pigs, and hamsters. The virus does not produce cellular destruction in HeLa tissue culture (41). It is transmitted to man through the respiratory tract, probably in dust (35), but may be transferred from rodent to rodent by arthropod vectors. It is introduced here because of the difficulty encountered in differentiating the human infection from mumps meningo-encephalitis without parotitis. In both instances the cells in the spinal fluid are predominantly lymphocytes.

The virus of lymphocytic choriomeningitis was discovered accidentally in a monkey by Armstrong and Lillie (37) in 1934 and later identified by Traub (42) as a natural infection in albino mice. Rivers and Scott (40) recovered the virus from the spinal fluid of a patient diagnosed as having Wallgren's (43) aseptic meningitis, and Lépine and others (38) transmitted the disease from mice to man and from man to man by the intramuscular inoculations of infected blood. Apparently about 9 per cent of the benign cases of aseptic meningitis are caused by this virus, although 11 per cent of 1,248 samples of human serums collected at random showed neutralizing antibodies to the virus (36).

Pseudolymphocytic choriomeningitis virus was recovered from mice inoculated intracerebrally with spinal fluid from two patients with acute aseptic meningitis (41). Recent studies (1957) indicate that this virus is not a new or distinct entity but is, in fact, ectromelia virus, which contaminated the original studies (39).

REFERENCES

Mumps

1. Donohue, W. L. J. Pediat., 19:42, 1941.
2. Enders, J. F., and others. J. Exper. Med., 84:341, 1946.
3. Eylan, E., and others. Lancet, 1:1062, 1957.
4. Gresser, I., and Enders, J. F. Proc. Soc. Exper. Biol. & Med., 107:804, 1961.
5. Habel, K. Pub. Health Rep., 1945.
6. Henle, G., and others. J. Exper. Med., 88:133, 1948.
7. Adams, F. The Genuine Works of Hippocrates, New York, Wood, 1891, v. 1, p. 294.
8. Hook, E. W., and others. J. Infect. Dis., 84:230, 1949.
9. Johnson, C. D., and Goodpasture, E. W. J. Exper. Med., 59:1, 1934.
10. ———— and Goodpasture, E. W. Am. J. Path., 12:495, 1936.
11. Kilham, L. Proc. Soc. Exper. Biol. & Med., 69:99, 1948.
12. ———— J.A.M.A., 146:1231, 1951.
13. ———— and Murphy, H. W. Proc. Soc. Exper. Biol. & Med., 80:495, 1952.
14. ———— and Overman, J. R. J. Immunol., 70:147, 1953.
15. Levens, J. H., and Enders, J. F. Science, 102:117, 1945.
16. Overman, J. R., and others. Arch. Path., 55:457, 1953.
17. ———— and Kilham, L. J. Immunol., 71:352, 1953.
18. ———— Arch. Int. Med., 102:354, 1958.
19. ———— Am. J. Med., 26:957, 1959.
20. Tucker, D. N., and Overman, J. R. J. Lab. & Clin. Med., 52:446, 1958.
21. Utz, J. P., and Szwed, C. F. Proc. Soc. Exper. Biol. & Med., 110:841, 1962.
22. Weil, M. L., and others. J. Immunol., 60:561, 1948.
23. Werner, C. A. Ann. Int. Med., 32:1066, 1950.

Diseases of the Salivary Glands

24. Andrewes, C. H. Brit. J. Exper. Path., 11:23, 1930.
25. Kuttner, A. G., and Wang, S. H. J. Exper. Med., 60:773, 1934.
26. Lucas, A. M. Am. J. Path., 12:933, 1936.
27. Luse, S. A., and Smith, M. G. J. Exper. Med., 107:623, 1958.
28. Nelson, J. S., and Wyatt, J. P. Medicine, 38:223, 1959.
29. McCordock, H. A., and Smith, M. G. J. Exper. Med., 63:303, 1936.
30. Rowe, W. P., and others. Am. J. Hyg., 67:57, 1958.
31. Smith, M. G. Proc. Soc. Exper. Biol. & Med., 92:424, 1956.

32. Thompson, J.   J. Infect. Dis., 58:59, 1936.
33. Weller, T. H., and others.   Virology, 12:130, 1960.
34. Wyatt, J. P., and others.   J. Pediat., 36:271, 1950.

LYMPHOCYTIC CHORIOMENINGITIS

35. Armstrong, C.   Harvey Lect., 36:39, 1940-41.
36. ——— and Wooley, J. G.   J.A.M.A., 109:410, 1937.

37. ——— and Lillie, R. D.   Pub. Health Rep., 49:1019, 1934.
38. Lépine, P., and others.   Compt. rend. Soc. de Biol., 124:422, 1937.
39. MacCallum, F. O., and others.   Brit. J. Exper. Path., 20:260, 1939; 38:120, 1957.
40. Rivers, T. M., and Scott, T. F. M.   Science, 81:439, 1935.
41. Scherer, W. F., and Syverton, J. T.   Am. J. Path., 31:31, 1955.
42. Traub, E.   Science, 81:298, 1935.
43. Wallgren, A.   Acta paediat., 4:158, 1925.

69

Adenoviruses

For many years a variety of acute respiratory diseases have been attributed to viruses, but the specific etiologic agents were not found. In the general population these infections occurred sporadically, but at military installations large epidemics were quite common. During World War II the U.S. Commission on Acute Respiratory Diseases investigated this problem, and the syndrome became known as "ARD" in the United States and "febrile catarrh" in England. The clinical picture was variable. Some cases were characterized by insidious onset of fever, sore throat, and cough, with respiratory symptoms soon predominating. Others had fever, sore throat, cough, and laryngitis but few if any pulmonary signs or symptoms. Some cases resembled a common cold, and still others demonstrated pharyngitis with mucopurulent exudate on the tonsils or throat from which neither hemolytic streptococci nor any other bacterial organism could be isolated consistently. Filtered throat washings from patients produced the disease in volunteers and conferred a homologous immunity. No immunity to the common cold or to primary atypical pneumonia followed, however. On the basis of a number of these experiments, it was postulated that the etiologic agent was a virus but attempts to isolate a specific agent in experimental animals and chick embryos were unsuccessful. Recently a new group of viruses was isolated in tissue culture from human tonsils, adenoids, and other specimens and these have been established as the causative agents in ARD as defined by the U.S. Commission of Respiratory Diseases in their wartime studies (4, 5, 6, 7).

Morphology. Adenovirus particles extracted from infected tissue and purified are roughly spherical and have a diameter of about 70 mμ, sometimes showing a depressed center, as seen in Figures 1 and 2 (9, 10, 26). Negative staining of the particles by phosphotungstic acid show that they are not actually round but are regular icosahedrons with 252 surface units each 70 Å. in diameter (11). The virus crystals are strongly Feulgen-positive (2), indicating that the virus contains deoxyribonucleic acid. On thin section the virus particle is seen to have a dense central body measuring 20-40 mμ (15), and recent evidence indicates that the virus nucleic acid is concentrated in this body and is surrounded by the 252 virus protein subunits (27).

Reaction to Physical and Chemical Agents. The viruses are resistant to ether. They are heat-inactivated at a temperature of 56° C. for 30 minutes and are likewise destroyed at pH ranges of 2 and below and 10 or above. The virus is inactivated by chlorine concentrations sufficient to kill coliform bacteria. Antibiotics are not effective against these viruses.

Cultivation and Host Range of Susceptibility. The virus was first recovered from tissue cultures of human tonsillar and adenoid tissue (23). Cells growing from fragments of tissue in culture media showed degenerative changes after a number of days, and the supernatant fluid then produced cytopathogenic changes in HeLa cell tissue cultures (10). In other studies throat washings from military personnel suffering from clinical ARD were inoculated into cultures of human tracheal epithelium and, after four passages, maintained and studied in HeLa cells. After growth is well established in HeLa cultures almost complete cell degeneration can be expected in two to seven days for most virus types.

The nomenclature of these viruses is

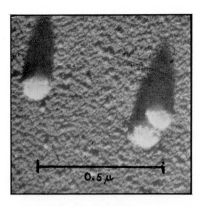

Fig. 1. Adenovirus type 4 (RI-67). Virus purified from extracts of HeLa cell cultures. × 72,000. (From Hilleman and others. *Proc. Soc. Exper. Biol. & Med.,* 89:587, 1955.)

somewhat confusing. Rowe, Huebner, and coworkers (23) initially called their agents "adenoid-degenerating" or "AD" viruses, later adapting the name adenoidal-pharyngeal-conjunctival or "APC" for the same organisms, since their strains came from and primarily affected these tissues. The strain Hilleman (9) isolated produced a somewhat different clinical syndrome, although they were closely related to the Rowe-Huebner viruses serologically, and were given the name "RI-67" (Respiratory Illness). Recently the name "adenoviruses" has been adopted by mutual agreement to designate the entire group.

Attempts to propagate the virus in eggs and animals have failed for the most part;

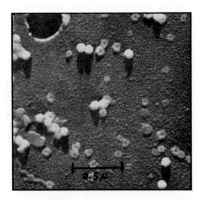

Fig. 2. Adenovirus type 6. Spherical and "doughnut shape" particles. × 24,500. (From Hilleman and others. *Proc. Soc. Exper. Biol. & Med.,* 89:587, 1955.)

however, latent infections of rabbits by type 5 Adenovirus have been demonstrated (17). The virus also induces tumors in the hamster cheek pouch. Adenoviruses of human origin are readily grown in cells derived from human and animal tissue, but viruses of simian origin may grow better in simian cells.

Cytopathic effects in cell cultures may be due either to a toxic protein which can be separated from the particle (8, 18) or to the consequences of virus growth in the cell which are later changes than those produced by the toxic protein.

The site of virus growth is intranuclear, but fluorescent antibody studies show that synthesis of virus antigenic material precedes formation of fully infectious particles (3).

Antigenic Structure. On the basis of virus neutralization tests performed in tissue culture, 18 human and 5 simian virus types have been isolated and studied (24). The tests are performed with rabbit antisera and are highly specific, with few cross-reactions. Type 7 strains are exceptional in that the behavior in neutralization tests is non-uniform, so that subgroups 7 and 7a have been made (16). With human sera the neutralization test is less specific (28).

The complement-fixing activity of adenoviruses is associated with a soluble antigen which can be removed from the intact particle (19, 25) and probably is a surface material of the particle (29).

Other antigens and serologic methods described recently include a hemagglutinin for mammalian red cells (13, 21), indirect hemagglutination (22) and gel-diffusion precipitation (20).

Clinical Infection in Man. Infection with these agents is very widespread in all populations studied, as indicated by the presence of neutralizing antibodies. Thus, in children five to 11 months of age more than 50 per cent show antibodies to one or more types, and in the 16 to 34 year group this figure approaches 100 per cent (12). A variety of clinical syndromes are produced, and it appears that certain virus types are associated with rather distinct disease entities (Table 1).

Nonbacterial acute pharyngitis and pharyngoconjunctival fever are acute upper

Table 1. Adenovirus Infections

DISEASE	TYPES	REMARKS
Acute Respiratory Disease (ARD) including adenovirus pneumonia	4, 7, 14, 7a	Military recruit populations, with few outbreaks in civilian populations
Epidemic keratoconjunctivitis	8	Usually in adult industrial workers
Pharyngoconjunctival fever including nonbacterial pharyngitis and minor respiratory disease	3, 7, 7a, 1, 2, 5, 6, 10	Adults and children in sporadic and small epidemic outbreaks
Epidemic and endemic infections	3, 4, 7, 8	Prevalent epidemic types
	1, 2, 5, 6	Types producing sporadic or inapparent infections
	1, 2, 3, 5	Prevalent types in children less than 3 years old

respiratory tract infections characterized by sore throat, fever, and headache, with physical findings of red, edematous pharynges, and enlarged tonsils and adenoids. A tonsillar exudate may be present, with some cervical lymphadenopathy. In some instances a marked conjunctivitis is present, and virus may be isolated from conjunctival swabs (12). Adenovirus types 1, 2, 3, and 5 have been isolated from patients with this syndrome. This form of infection is most prevalent in young children, but adults may be affected. The infectiousness is high and rather explosive, but relatively localized epidemics result. In young children the predominant types seem to be 1, 2, and 5, whereas type 3 apparently affects all age groups but again children predominate.

Acute respiratory disease (ARD) of military recruits is an acute infection characterized by cough, hoarseness, fever, chills, and, on occasion, pulmonary infiltration as evidenced by x-ray.

This syndrome is more often seen in adults, particularly in military populations, and might be thought of as a viral pneumonia in contradistinction to the adenovirus pharyngitis described above. At present, type 4 (RI-67) strain appears to cause this type of disease more often than other types of adenovirus (14). Symptomatically and by clinical and laboratory studies this syndrome is similar to primary atypical pneumonia, but, unlike the latter disease, cold agglutinins do not develop. The severity of this infection may be judged by the fact that approximately 25 per cent of the military personnel

infected with type 4 virus required hospitalization. Types 7 and 14 may produce a similar clinical picture.

Epidemic keratoconjunctivitis (EKC) is an acute nonfollicular conjunctivitis which is accompanied by corneal lesions which are subepithelial without superficial ulceration. The incubation period is thought to be five to seven days. Infection usually starts in one eye and is characterized by redness and swelling of the conjunctiva with a bacteria-free seromucoid discharge. Occasionally a nasal catarrh is present, which may be accompanied by mild systemic symptoms. The preauricular lymph node on the affected side is usually swollen and tender. In uncomplicated cases the disease lasts two to four weeks and is followed by complete recovery. The corneal lesions may persist for an extended period and by so doing reduce visual acuity significantly. The disease was first described by Fuchs in 1889, and epidemics have occurred throughout the world. Transmission experiments indicated a viral etiology and present evidence shows that type 8 adenovirus is the etiologic agent. Jawetz (14) studied serums from cases in various parts of the world and found a very high incidence of Adenovirus type 8 neutralizing antibody in a rising titer as compared to control serums.

An entirely distinct virus reported isolated from EKC by Saunders and propagated in mice has an uncertain status and the original agent may be lost.

Epidemiology. Studies indicate that the distribution of adenoviruses is quite widespread and serums from individuals in many countries contain specific neutralizing antibodies for these agents. Spread of the diseases induced by adenoviruses appears to be primarily by contact, and present indications are that infections are most widespread during the winter months.

Treatment. Treatment is symptomatic. Antibiotics appear not to affect the course of the disease, and these infections do not seem to predispose to secondary bacterial infection.

Prevention. Preliminary studies with a formalin-inactivated trivalent vaccine composed of types 3, 4, and 7 adenovirus indicate a possibility of reducing the incidence of ARD in military populations (1).

REFERENCES

1. Bell, J. A., and others. J.A.M.A., 161:1521, 1956.
2. Block, D. P., and others. J. Biophys. & Biochem. Cytol., 3:1, 1957.
3. Boyer, G. S., and others. J. Exper. Med., 109:85, 1959.
4. The Commission on Acute Respiratory Diseases. Am. J. Pub. Health, 36:439, 1946.
5. ——— Medicine, 26:441, 1947.
6. ——— J. Clin. Investigation, 26:957, 1947.
7. ——— J. Clin. Investigation, 26:974, 1947.
8. Everett, S. F., and Ginsberg, H. S. Virology, 6:770, 1958.
9. Hilleman, M. R., and others. Am. J. Pub. Health, 45:203, 1955.
10. ——— and others. Proc. Soc. Exper. Biol. & Med., 89:587, 1955.
11. Horne, R. W., and others. J. Molec. Biol., 1:84, 1959.
12. Huebner, R. J., and others. New England J. Med., 251:1077, 1954.
13. Hull, R. N., and others. Am. J. Hyg., 63:204, 1956.
14. Jawetz, E., and others. Proc. Soc. Exper. Biol. & Med., 92:91, 1956.
15. Morgan, C., and others. J. Biophys. & Biochem. Cytol., 3:305, 1957.
16. Pereira, H. G., and Kelly, B. Proc. Soc. Exper. Biol. & Med., 50:755, 1957.
17. ——— and Kelly, B. Nature, 180:615, 1957.
18. ——— Virology, 6:601, 1958.
19. ——— and others. Nature, 180:895, 1959.
20. Pereira, M. S., Pereira, H. G., and Allison, A. C. Lancet, 1:551, 1959.
21. Rosen, L. Virology, 5:554, 1958.
22. Ross, E., and Ginsberg, H. S. Proc. Soc. Exper. Biol. & Med., 98:501, 1958.
23. Rowe, W. P., and others. Proc. Soc. Exper. Biol. & Med., 84:570, 1953.
24. ——— and others. Proc. Soc. Exper. Biol. & Med., 97:465, 1958.
25. ——— and others. J. Exper. Med., 108:713, 1958.
26. Tousimis, A. J., and Hilleman, M. R. Virology, 4:499, 1957.
27. Valentine, R. C. Fourth International Conference on Electron Microscopy, Berlin, September, 1958.
28. Wenner, H. A., and others. J. Infect. Dis., 101:275, 1957.
29. Werner, G. H. J. Bact., 72:568, 1956.

70

Rhinoviruses and the Common Cold

(Rhinoviruses; Respiratory Syncytial Viruses)

The common cold is a syndrome of mild, never serious, but irritating and debilitating symptoms which tends to make the patient miserable for one to two weeks and which costs the United States more than $1 billion per year in wages, days lost from work, and medications (12a). The etiologic agent was shown to be a virus in 1915 by Kruse (6), and since that report intensive efforts have been made to isolate this agent.

In 1946 the common cold research unit was established in England by the British Medical Research Council, and laboratories were established in Salisbury, England. This unit has excellent isolation facilities, and patients who volunteer for the experiments are transported gratis to Salisbury, where they are fed and housed at the government's expense. Thus, with these, and other facilities in the United States, it has been possible to test the new viruses isolated in various parts of the world for their ability to produce colds.

Table 1 lists most of the viruses now implicated in the common cold syndrome. The major problem at present is to determine the relative importance of these various agents and to define clearly which virus groups are most often responsible for this disease. The newest agents are the Salisbury viruses (now renamed **rhinoviruses**) which were isolated by Andrewes and his colleagues (1, 10, 13). Interestingly, the Salisbury viruses tend to require a more acid pH and lower tissue culture temperature (91° F.) than most viruses and it appears that these are the conditions which exist at the surface of the nasal mucous membranes (14).

The rhinoviruses have been classified as a subgroup of the picornaviruses (formerly enteroviruses), and these agents grow in embryonic-human kidney cells, fetal-human diploid fibroblasts, and primary monkey kidney cells. It has been suggested that the virus strains which grow in the monkey kidney cells be designated "M" strains and those that grow in human cells only be called "H" strains. The rhinoviruses at present seem to account for common colds in 5 per cent of children and 10 to 25 per cent of adults (8).

A recent study at Children's Hospital in Washington (5) showed that about 35 per cent of respiratory illnesses were caused by parainfluenza 1 and 3, influenza A, and adenoviruses. Added to this may be 10 per cent estimated disease caused by the respiratory syncytial virus. The RS virus causes some typical colds, but also over 50 per cent of the cases of bronchiolitis and pneumonia in infants are due to the RS virus (5).

The agents responsible for the common cold now seem to be definitely identified in part, and with present methods it seems likely that this aspect of the problem will be solved in the near future. The problem of **prevention** of these diseases, however, is still a major one, although there is evidence that a quantitative relationship exists between antibody level and occurrence of infection with rhinoviruses, which offers encouragement to the development of an effective vaccine for rhinovirus diseases (8).

Clinical Types of Infection in Man. The typical cold has a short incubation period of 24 to 48 hours and a sudden onset with congestion of the nasopharynx, sneezing, and copious watery discharges from nasal and conjunctival mucous membranes. The temperature is elevated slightly, and the patient

Table 1. Viruses which Cause Infections which May Simulate the Common Cold Syndrome

	TYPES	NUCLEIC ACID	SIZE	ETHER RESIST- ANCE	GROWTH	INFECTION
Influenza	3	RNA	90-120	0	Eggs & T.C.	Epid. resp. only
Adenovirus	23	DNA	70-80	+	T.C.	Epid. & endemic resp.
Echo Types 11 & 20	32	RNA	20-30	+	T.C.	Mild resp.
Coxsackie A21 (Coe)	30	RNA	20-30	+	Animals & T.C.	Mild resp.
Rhinoviruses including Salisbury strains & Echo 28,* Giles & Bastianni	30+	RNA	20-30	+ †	T.C.**	Common Cold
Para-influenza (Sendai, Hemadsorption (HA) and Croup Assoc. (CA))	5	RNA	90-180	0 ††	T.C. & Mice	Mild resp. inc. croup and pneumonia
Reovirus (inc. former Echo 10)	3	RNA	70	+	T.C.	Colds in apes, human disease?
Respiratory Syncytial (chimpanzee coryzal agent)	1?	RNA	90-140	0	T.C.	Minor resp., bronchiolitis and pneumonia
SA (12) (parainfluenza 5)	1	RNA	100?	0	T.C.	?

  * Identical to JH and 2060 virus strains.
  † Can be differentiated from enteroviruses by its lability at pH 3.0-5.0 (3).
  ** Standard culture system in a human diploid cell strain (4).
  †† Unusually unstable even at 4° C.

feels uncomfortable but not ill enough to remain in bed. Therefore the victim of a cold usually remains ambulatory and consequently spreads the virus to many other individuals. After 24 to 48 hours the copious watery discharge ceases and is replaced by a thick mucoid or mucopurulent one which is filled with bacteria, usually of the type which the individual was carrying before he developed the cold. Sinus infection, otitis media, mastoiditis, bronchitis, and occasionally pneumonia develop as sequelae of the common cold.

The idea that colds result from rainy weather or sudden drops in the temperature is firmly fixed in the popular mind. While such changes may reactivate a smoldering bacterial infection in the nasopharynx and give rise to sporadic colds, epidemic colds do not develop unless the virus is introduced into the community at the same time. In Paul and Freese's (9) investigations of the bacteriology and epidemiology of colds in the Arctic community of Spitsbergen, it was noted that an epidemic of colds involving almost the entire population appeared shortly after the arrival of the first ship in the spring.

The clinical syndrome of a cold can be produced by an acute bacterial infection of the upper respiratory tract or by the reactivation of a residual infection in the nasopharynx. These "colds" usually do not produce much congestion of the mucous membranes and are rarely transmitted to others (2, 11).

Transmission. It is very difficult to prevent the spread of virus colds, even by isolation of the infected individuals, because the patient may transmit the infection for some hours before the appearance of clinical signs of the disease (7). Individuals with colds should be excluded from contact with infants, and school children should be kept at home during the first few days of the infection. Colds are particularly dangerous as "catalyzing agents" during epidemics of diphtheria, measles, poliomyelitis, meningitis, and epidemic pneumonias.

Treatment. There is no specific treatment for colds, but the secondary infections may be controlled with antibiotics. The antihistaminics often reduce the amount of swelling in the nasal mucosa and improve the breathing, but there is no evidence that they materially affect either the duration or severity of colds.

Prevention. Acquired immunity to the virus of the common cold is poor in quality and of short duration and since there are many antigenic types of the virus, the average individual has two or three viral colds each year. There is as yet no acceptable vaccine. A trial with triethylene glycol vapor did not reduce colds among office workers.

The individual who has frequent, recurring, nontransmissible colds which are precipitated by chilling, wetting the feet, or sudden drops in temperature may have these colds reduced in frequency and in duration by autogenous or stock vaccines. However, such vaccines afford no protection against viral colds.

RESPIRATORY SYNCYTIAL (RS) VIRUS

This virus was first isolated from a colony of chimpanzees with a cold syndrome and was named the chimpanzee coryza agent (CCA) (20). Recently it has been recovered from infants and children with croup and pneumonia (15, 16). In adult human volunteer experiments (19) this virus produced a typical "cold" lasting about a week and characterized by nasal discharge, sneezing, malaise, minimal pharyngitis, and cough, all without fever. The incubation period is three or four days. Possibly 10 per cent of respiratory illness in hospitalized children is due to this virus (17, 18, 21).

The virus is 90 to 140 mμ in size, has an RNA core, and is ether-sensitive. It was initially isolated in Chang's liver cells but grows well in Hep-2 and rhesus monkey kidney cells. It is not related antigenically to any other known group of viruses.

REFERENCES

THE COMMON COLD

1. Andrewes, C. H., and others. Lancet, 2:546, 1953.
2. Fabricant, N. D. Eye, Ear, Nose & Throat Monthly, 25:615, 1946.
3. Hayflick, L., and Moorhead, P. S. Exper. Cell Res., 25:484, 1961.
4. Ketler, A., and others. Proc. Soc. Exper. Biol. & Med., 110:821, 1962.
5. Knight, V., and others. Ann. Int. Med., 55:507, 1961.
6. Kruse, W. München. med. Wchnschr., 61:1547, 1914.
7. Long, P. H., and others. Bull. Johns Hopkins Hosp., 51:278, 1932.
8. Mufson, M. A., and others. J.A.M.A., 186:578, 1963.
9. Paul, J. H., and Freese, H. L. Am. J. Hyg., 17:517, 1933.
10. Roden, A. T. Proc. Soc. Exper. Biol. & Med., 51:271, 1958.
11. Sargent, F., and others. Am. J. Hyg., 45:29, 1947.
12. Shultz, E. W., and Habel, K. J. Immunol., 82:274, 1959.
12a. Statistical Bull., Metropolitan Life Ins. Co., 28:6-7 (Nov.), 1947.
13. Tyrrell, D. A. J., and Bynoe, M. L. Lancet, 2:931, 1958.
14. ——— and Parsons, R. Lancet, 1:239, 1960.

RESPIRATORY SYNCYTIAL (RS)

15. Chanock, R. M., and others. Am. J. Hyg., 66:281, 1957.
16. ——— and Finberg, L. Am. J. Hyg., 66:291, 1957.
17. Kapikian, A. Z., and others. Am. J. Hyg., 75:570, 1961.
18. Knight, V., and others. Ann. Int. Med., 55:507, 1961.
19. Kravetz, H. M., and others. J.A.M.A., 176:657, 1961.
20. Morris, J. A., and Blount, R. E., Jr. Proc. Soc. Exper. Biol. & Med., 92:544, 1956.
21. Parrott, R. H., and others. J.A.M.A., 176:653, 1961.

71

Picornaviruses and Enteroviruses

This group of viruses named picorna (*pico,* small and *rna,* ribonucleic acid) includes a number of agents previously classified as "enteroviruses" and other recently isolated viruses, such as the rhinoviruses. The viruses now classified as picornaviruses are given in Table 1.

Table 1. Classification of Picornaviruses *

A. *Picornaviruses of Human* *Origin*	*Size*	*Inactiva- tion pH*
1. Enteroviruses		
a) Polioviruses	20-30	<2
b) Coxsackieviruses A	20-30	<2
c) Coxsackieviruses B	20-30	<2
d) Echoviruses	20-30	<2
2. Rhinoviruses	15-30	<6
3. Reoviruses †	70	<2
4. Unclassified		
B. *Picornaviruses of Lower* *Animals*		

  * Panel for Picornaviruses (38).
  † Reoviruses not included by the Panel for Picornaviruses but placed in this table (by J.R.O.) as a possible addition to this group of viruses and for purposes of discussion.

The characteristics of picornaviruses may be listed as follows: (1) small size, (2) ether-insensitive, and (3) containing RNA cores. The characteristics of the enterovirus subgroup (besides those named) are: (1) inhabit the gastrointestinal tract including the nasopharynx, (2) exhibit cationic stabilization to heat inactivation, (3) size of about 28 mμ, and (4) comprised of multiple antigenic types. It is also true that all enteroviruses are relatively resistant to acid pH, a feature which readily distinguishes the rhinoviruses from the enteroviruses. The cationic stabilization criterion is based on the observation that high concentrations of certain ions, such as magnesium, make enteroviruses

more resistant to inactivation at 50° C. for one hour. Cationic stabilization has been reported for reoviruses (60). Thus, since reoviruses exhibit cubic symmetry, have an RNA core, are ether-resistant, show cationic stabilization, and are found in the human gastrointestinal tract, they seem to fit the picornavirus group, despite their relatively large size. The reovirus hemagglutinin is not temperature-variable, and certain characteristics of the reoviruses hemagglutination reaction suggest that it is not a typical enterovirus (28). Among viruses accepted as enteroviruses, however, there are clear-cut differences in the nature of the hemagglutinin.

The rhinoviruses are considered separately (Chap. 70) from the enteroviruses, since the former are primarily etiologic agents of respiratory diseases and have not been implicated in central nervous system infections so characteristic of the enteroviruses.

POLIOMYELITIS

Poliomyelitis is undoubtedly an ancient disease. A skeleton unearthed in Cairo and dating about 3700 B.C. showed a marked shortening of the left leg compatible with that found in this disease. In addition, an Egyptian stele of about 1500 B.C. depicts a priest with a withered leg, the foot of which lies in the typical equinus position. Subsequent medical literature, however, fails to record cases of paralysis which could be construed as poliomyelitis, and this disease seems to have disappeared until the middle of the nineteenth century. Perhaps the vast majority of cases were inapparent infections, as is still true in parts of Africa and Asia.

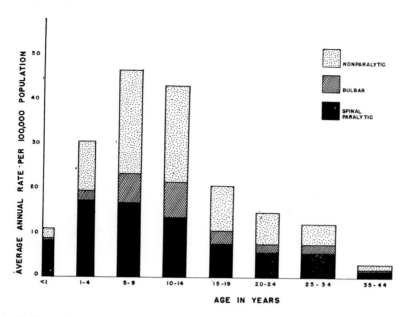

Fig. 1. Poliomyelitis and age. Poliomyelitis morbidity rates by age and by type of disease, Massachusetts, 1948-1952. (From Dauer. *Ann. New York Acad. Sc.*, 61:943, 1955.)

Even today poliomyelitis in its worst epidemics cannot be compared to the havoc wreaked by plague, typhus, yellow fever, malaria, and smallpox. It is understandable, then, that physicians occupied with such dramatic and fearful diseases may have given little attention to instances of paralysis affecting occasional children or young adults who, except for the loss of use of a limb, were otherwise in good health.

The first modern epidemics were described by Swedish and English physicians. Badham (3) in England published a paper in 1836 entitled *Four Remarkable Cases of Suddenly Induced Paralysis in the Extremities* and the syndrome described in these children is much as we know it today. Heine (17) in 1840 published a classical description of the disease, and Medin (33) in 1890 reported an epidemic of 44 cases, probably the first instance of an outbreak large enough to attract attention. In honor of their early work, poliomyelitis is sometimes called the Heine-Medin disease. Epidemics then became more frequent and widespread, and Wickman's (63) systematic studies from 1907 to 1913 strongly indicated that the disease was infectious. He recognized several

clinical syndromes, including spinal, bulbar, encephalitis, meningitis, and abortive.

Since the beginning of the present century epidemics have occurred in many nations throughout the world, but principally in those of the temperate zones and where the standards of public health and sanitation have been relatively high. Apparently exposure to the virus in infancy tends to result in subclinical infections, so that virtually all children in tropical countries are immune at an early age and paralytic poliomyelitis is almost unknown. Fecal contamination of water supplies and anal-oral transference of virus resulting from over-all unhygienic habits provides continuous exposure of these individuals from childbirth on producing and maintaining high levels of immunity. Conversely, when exposure to the virus is delayed until late childhood or beyond, paralytic or even fatal disease is more apt to occur (Fig. 1, Table 2), and there appears to be a direct relationship between advances in public sanitation and the shift of peak incidence of infection from infants to older children and to adults. It would seem essential, then, that a program of mass exposure of children to poliovirus via vaccination be developed in countries maintaining high sanitary standards, and such a program is now underway.

Table 2. Per Cent Deaths per Reported Cases of Paralytic Poliomyelitis in Various Age Groups

(Dauer)

Age	Massachusetts 1948 to 1952	Minnesota 1946	Maryland 1945 to 1951
1	2.8	——	5.9
1 to 4	1.0	3.3	2.8
5 to 9	3.4	7.1	4.3
10 to 14	4.2	11.1	5.5
15 to 19	4.3	11.1	11.1
20 to 24	10.0	14.3	7.1
25 to 34	14.3	20.0	14.3

Morphology. The virus is a spherical particle, with a diameter of about 28 mμ for the Lansing and MEFI (51, 52) strains, and the size is generally quite uniform. The type 3 or Leon strain appears to be somewhat larger (47). Chemical analysis reveals that the particles are nucleoproteins of the RNA type and that the nucleic acid constitutes 20 to 25 per cent of the total mass. There is evidence that the particle RNA core is surrounded by a series of 60 protein subunits (10, 18).

Resistance. Poliovirus is quite stable, and virus in tissue extracts or fecal suspensions stored in sealed ampules at $-70°$ C. retain their viability for years (34). Survival of the virus in feces at room temperature is variable, but it may retain its infectivity for weeks. Oxidizing agents, 0.05 p.p.m. chlorine, and iodine rapidly inactivate the virus, and, in contrast to other viral agents, it is not well preserved by lyophilization. It is relatively resistant to ether, and advantage is taken of this characteristic to recover the virus from stools by treating the fecal material with ether, which destroys most other intestinal organisms. Unfortunately, poliovirus and the "C" or Coxsackie viruses and ECHO viruses have similar resistance to chemical agents, in addition to a similar size, and stool extracts for the one agent are likely to contain the others.

Cultivation and Host Range of Infection. The only known reservoir of infection is man, although chimpanzees experimentally infected may become symptomless carriers for some days. Landsteiner and Popper (27) in 1909 first demonstrated that a filterable agent from a human case of poliomyelitis would cause paralysis if injected intraperitoneally into monkeys. Subsequent studies have shown that monkeys of various species are susceptible to the virus by almost all routes of inoculation (24, 57). Oral inoculation with virus is accomplished readily.

Progress in research was given great impetus by Armstrong (1, 2), who in 1939 adapted the Lansing strain to cotton rats and subsequently to white mice by intracerebral inoculation. More recently, type 3 (Leon) and type 1 (Mahoney) viruses have been adapted to mice by intraspinal inoculation (29, 30).

Possibly the single most significant advance in poliovirus research was made by Enders, Weller, and Robbins (13) in 1949, when they demonstrated virus growth in cultures of human embryonic extraneural tissue. Previously Sabin and Olitsky (46) reported growth of virus in tissue culture of human embryonic brain and spinal cord, but the titer was low relative to that obtained recently. Enders found the Lansing strain grew well in human embryonic skin, muscle, and intestinal mucosa, and in human foreskin obtained postnatally. Subsequently, poliovirus has been grown in a variety of human and animal tissues in vitro producing in them a characteristic change in the morphology of the cultivated cells, generally referred to as a cytopathogenic (C-P) effect (41, 50, 53, 62) (Figs. 2, 3). Moreover, initial isolation of virus from human sources can be accomplished in such cultures (23). At present, cells from monkey kidney and those from a human carcinoma of the cervix (HeLa) are most widely used for virus cultivation, typing, and serologic testing.

The successful adaptation of type 2 MEF$_1$ strain to the embryonated egg and to suckling hamsters has supplied still further tools for poliomyelitis research (36, 42).

Clinical Infection in Man. Poliomyelitis, although having involvement of the central nervous system as its most striking feature, is primarily a systemic disease. The incubation period generally is from seven to 14 days, with limits of three and 30 or more days. Clinical manifestation can be divided into

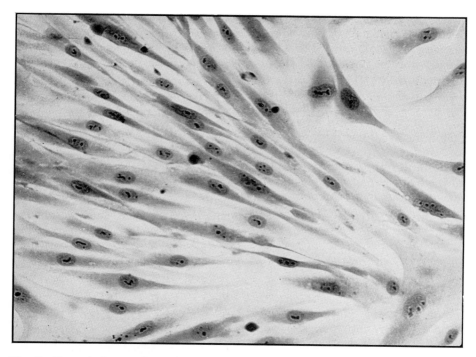

Fig. 2. Normal tissue culture. Human fibroblastic growth in tissue culture after 13 days incubation. × 250. (Courtesy of Dr. J. S. Syverton.)

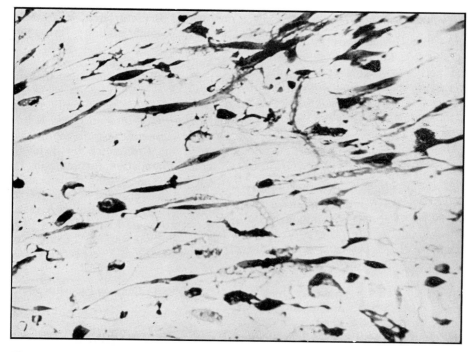

Fig. 3. Poliovirus-infected tissue culture. A culture similar to that in Figure 2, three days after inoculation with type 3 poliovirus. Note widespread cellular destruction which is referred to as the cytopathogenic (C-P) effect of the virus. × 250. (Courtesy of Dr. J. S. Syverton.)

three stages; the systemic, preparalytic, and the paralytic. The first stage is characterized by pharyngitis, malaise, fever, headache, nausea, and occasional vomiting. The disease may progress no further, in which case it is referred to as "abortive poliomyelitis." However, after a temporary diminution of symptoms lasting a day or so, an exacerbation of the acute syndrome may recur, with return of fever, giving the so-called biphasic fever curve. In this phase the acutely ill patient is hyperirritable and anxious and may exhibit signs of vasomotor disturbances, such as profuse sweating. Muscle pain is prominent, associated with some spasm, and stiffness of the neck and back may be present. Again, the disease may terminate without further progression and may be called "preparalytic" or "nonparalytic" poliomyelitis. Finally, evidence of muscle weakness and paralysis in a rather patchy distribution occurs and the stage of "paralytic poliomyelitis" is developed. The paralysis is of the flaccid type **without** sensory involvement. If muscles of respiration and those of the throat involved in swallowing are affected, the syndrome is referred to as bulbar or bulbospinal poliomyelitis.

Paralysis is found most often in the lower extremities, but virtually any muscle group may be affected. Immunization with diphtheria or pertussis vaccine appears to predispose the injected extremity to paralysis, and such immunizations are not advisable during the summer months when poliomyelitis is most prevalent (58). There does not, however, appear to be any such contraindications for poliovirus vaccine injections during an epidemic.

Serologic studies indicate that the majority of infections are inapparent or abortive and that the disease is about as common in the general population as is measles.

Probably 80 to 85 per cent of all poliovirus infections never progress to the paralytic stage (34). Of cases suspected or provisionally diagnosed as poliomyelitis by physicians, a significant number ultimately turn out to have some other disease. In 1,000 hospital admissions for suspected poliomyelitis at the Southwestern Poliomyelitis Respiratory Center the final case distribution was as follows (54):

	CASES	PER CENT
Nonpoliomyelitis	151	15
Nonparalytic poliomyelitis	258	26
Paralytic poliomyelitis	591	59

Many diverse diseases may simulate poliomyelitis, among which are mumps, other viral and bacterial meningitides, infectious neuronitis, central nervous system tumors, and hysteria. A large percentage of cases of meningoencephalitis cannot yet be ascribed to a specific etiologic agent, although some of these may yet wall into the ECHO (enteric cytopathogenic human orphan) and/or Coxsackie groups of viral agents (11).

Pathology. Despite the systemic nature of the infection, pathologic changes are found only in the central nervous system. In fatal cases lesions are found mainly in the anterior horn cells of the spinal cord, particularly in the cervical and lumbar enlargements. Lesions in the brain are so characteristically located that the disease can be readily differentiated from other neurotropic virus infections. Brain lesions are found in the motor cells of the pons and medulla and in the vestibular nuclei. In the cortex the motor and premotor areas may be damaged, but visual and auditory areas are not involved.

Antigenic Structure. Early work with strains of poliovirus indicated that antigenic differences existed. Initially there appeared to be two distinct types, until Bodian (6) and others (22) demonstrated a third type by cross-immunity tests in monkeys. Subsequently, the Committee on Typing of the National Foundation for Infantile Paralysis began large-scale typing of 100 strains and confirmed the existence of type 1 (prototype Brunhilda), type 2 (prototype Lansing) and type 3 (prototype Leon) viruses (Table 3). The distribution was 85, 12 and 3 per cent for types 1, 2, and 3 respectively.

Table 3. **Common Poliovirus Strains**

TYPE 1	TYPE 2	TYPE 3
Brunhilda	Lansing	Leon
Mahoney	MEF$_1$	Saukett
Frederick	MV	
HoF	Yale-SK	

More recent epidemiologic studies show the virus type distribution to be as follows: type 1, 81; type 2, 1; and type 3, 18 per cent (32). The ascendancy of type 3 over type 2 has important implications in live vaccine immunizations, since, although type 3 tends to lose its genetic marker, it must be included in any vaccine program. Neutralization tests, whether performed in animals or tissue culture appear quite type-specific, but complement-fixation tests are much less so, and antibodies with one type cross-react with the other two, indicating that this test is group- not type-specific. Neutralizing antibodies persist for years following infection, but complement-fixing antibodies disappear in a matter of weeks. Reports of a type 4 poliovirus have not been substantiated.

Transmission and Pathogenesis. Spread of the virus of poliomyelitis may occur in various ways, and the relative importance of each is yet to be determined. However, certain facts indicating the possible sources of the virus have been established and may be summarized as follows:

1. The virus is present in the stools before and during the acute phase of the disease and may continue to be present for some weeks thereafter, irrespective of whether the case is subclinical or clinical.

2. Virus is present in the nasopharynx for several days before and after onset of the disease.

3. Healthy carriers of the virus over a period of years (as exemplified by typhoid carriers) have not been demonstrated.

The question in regard to transmission is whether spread of virus is from case to case, in the manner of respiratory diseases, or whether temporary carriers disseminate the virus to many susceptible persons, as in enteric diseases. Further study is needed to resolve this question. It is clear that the large majority of cases occur during the summer months, the case incidence falling markedly during the winter. If poliomyelitis were primarily a respiratory disease it would seem likely that the greater incidence would occur in the winter. On the other hand, several epidemics have shown that a large percentage of all clinical cases had direct and intimate contact with persons having clinical poliomyelitis, which would, of course, suggest the case-to-case mode of transmission (8, 9).

Various investigators have suggested transmission by arthropod vectors which may carry the virus mechanically from the source to the patient. Thus, virus has been isolated from flies (35) and cockroaches (56). Mosquitoes have been implicated on theoretical grounds, but experimental studies have not supported this theory. In addition, food and milk have been under suspicion as virus carriers. From present evidence it would appear that, although these are possible sources, none are major factors in the spread of the virus.

Once the virus enters the susceptible human host, the subsequent course of events is likewise in doubt. It seems clear that viral multiplication does occur in cells lining the alimentary tract, particularly in the oropharynx (21) and in the intestine (44). Recently, a viremic stage has been demonstrated in infected humans and chimpanzees (19, 20, 61). In addition, virus has been demonstrated in peripheral nerve tissue associated with the alimentary tract, and progression of virus along nerve tracts toward the central nervous system has been found (14, 59). At present the route by which the virus enters the central nervous system has not been clearly defined. Both of the above may be operative.

Finally, the factors involved in producing paralysis need more definitive data. One factor seems to be exercise and fatigue, since activity of muscle groups tends to increase the likelihood of paralysis of that muscle. One patient, quoted by Sabin (44), remarked: "The muscles I used are the muscles I lost." Paralysis or lack of it also may be influenced by variations in neurotropism of the virus as well as by variations in host resistance.

Treatment. Treatment is entirely nonspecific, and no chemotheraputic or antibiotic agent has been shown to be of any value whatsoever. Measures to relieve the pain of muscle spasm, improve respiration if impaired, and rehabilitate paralyzed limbs in so far as possible are described in various recent texts. Treatment with gamma globulin after clinical infection is present, is of no value.

Control and Immunization. Search for an effective and safe vaccine has been sought for many years. Two large studies by Brodie (7) from 1934 to 1935 (25) and Kolmer from 1934 to 1937 utilized virus from extracts of monkey brain or cord tissue. Brodie's vaccine was treated with formalin, and this material injected intradermally. Kolmer's vaccine contained live virus which was thought to be of low virulence for man as a result of its passage in monkeys. Unfortunately, a number of cases of poliomyelitis developed from this vaccine, and further studies were discontinued.

The discovery of poliovirus growth in monkey kidney tissue culture solved two major problems: **(1) It produced virus in high titer relatively free of extraneous proteinaceous material.** Virus relatively uncontaminated with extraneous material is more uniformly and predictably inactivated by formalin. Extracts of cord or brain material contain virus in much lower titer and have very great amounts of nonviral protein. **(2) It produced virus in a medium free of nervous tissue** and thus eliminated the possibility of producing allergic encephalitis.

Salk (49) has developed and tested a vaccine which contains all three types of poliovirus grown in monkey kidney tissue culture and inactivated by formalin. Field trials have shown that this vaccine is safe and apparently confers significant immunity. Neutralization tests with serums from vaccinated subjects indicate good levels of protective antibodies one to two years after vaccination, particularly when the first two injections are given at three-week intervals and the third after an interval of seven months. Paul (39) recently reviewed the indications for poliomyelitis vaccination with the Salk vaccine.

The obvious disadvantage of killed vaccine is the necessity for multiple primary vaccinations and subsequent booster doses. A reasonably large percentage of the population can be persuaded to take a single immunization but the number who will follow this with successive doses falls precipitously, even though these additional doses are essential for adequate protection. Live, attenuated poliovirus vaccine would solve this problem to a large extent, since it would induce a mild infection which would confer the immunity of a natural infection but without the risk of paralysis. Sabin (43) and others (26) have succeeded in attenuating all three types of poliovirus, proving that neurotropism is not an essential characteristic of this virus. Large studies in the United States (4, 48) and many foreign countries have proven the over-all effectiveness and safety of these vaccines in approximately 100 million persons. The advantages of live attenuated vaccine may be listed as follows: (1) ease of administration (oral vs. parenteral), (2) duration of protection without booster doses, and (3) a higher degree (approaching 100 per cent) of effectiveness. The disadvantages are: (1) the necessary interval or delay between administration of different types of virus, (2) the danger of mutation to virulent types, and (3) the danger of accidental contamination by other living microorganisms, particularly viruses.

In regard to the interval between types of virus, it has been shown that when all three poliovirus types are given together in a single dose, interference occurs and certain virus types grow to the exclusion of others. Usually type 2 becomes dominant, and the growth of types 1 and 3 is markedly reduced. It is possible that this problem could be overcome by suitable balance of the individual types in a single dose. The recommended schedule is for type 1 to be followed by types 3 and 2; the interval between virus types should be six weeks (a minimum of four weeks).

The danger of mutation is a problem in several respects. One of the important advances in attenuated poliovirus vaccine was the observation by Dubes and Wenner (12) that growth of virus in tissue cultures at low temperatures of incubation favors growth of attenuated particles. By this and other technics strains of type 1 and type 2 have been attenuated, and these have been genetically stable. These strains have certain biologic characteristics (markers) which allow them to be identified and separated from the nonattenuated strains. These genetic markers include growth rate in stable as opposed to unstable (freshly isolated) cell lines, morphology of plaques, inhibition by cysteine, elution rates from ion-exchange resins, and

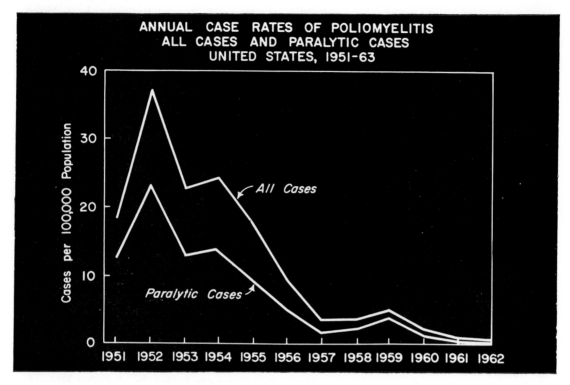

Fig. 4. Incidence of poliomyelitis in the U.S.A. since 1951. (From various U.S. Public Health Service Publications.)

growth at different temperatures. Thus, if attenuated types 1 and 2 are given a subject and virus isolations made on the individual's stools, the vaccine types 1 and 2 remain stable, keep their markers, can be shown to be still attenuated by neurovirulence tests in monkeys, and thus can be distinguished from the wild types 1 and 2. One of the most important genetic markers is the ability to grow at various temperatures. Thus, an attenuated strain will grow well at 23° and 37° C. but little or not at all at 40° C. Virulent, wild-type strains grow well at 37° C. and 40° C. but not at 23° C. This is the **reproductive capacity, temperature** (rct) of a given virus (31). Unfortunately, attenuated type 3 strains have had a facility for reverting to wild type during a single human intestinal passage. This not only makes this virus impossible to follow but makes it dangerous both for the recipient and for his associates. Recently Plotkin and associates (40) have attenuated a type 3 strain designated WM-3 which appears to be genetically

stable. This may replace the previously used Leon, Chat or W-Fox, all of which mutate to wild types after intestinal passage.

In general, the safety of the attenuated virus vaccine is well established and the cases of polio-like illness in subjects receiving oral vaccine have been very few in many millions (45).

The danger of contamination of the poliovirus vaccine by unwanted viruses present in monkey kidney tissue is very real, and one such agent, SV-40, has been isolated from many batches of living (and a few killed) vaccine (55). The significance of this and other extraneous viruses is difficult to assess. It seems likely, however, that this aspect of the problem can be solved by using a human diploid cell line for virus growth if such appears indicated (16). As yet, SV-40 has not been shown to cause disease in man, although it is oncogenic for newborn hamsters (15) and induces proliferative changes in various tissue culture cells (5).

It should be noted that a definite fall in

the yearly polio incidence began in 1953, long **before** any significant field trials with any vaccine, live or dead (Fig. 4). It seems doubtful that vaccine would have had any significant effect prior to 1956 or 1957. In 1952 the United States had 57,879 reported cases, dropping to 15,140 in 1956. Periodic fluctuation of poliomyelitis has been observed for many years.

Other control measures to prevent spread of the disease include isolation of diagnosed cases for several weeks, with particular care and attention directed to disposal of fecal material from the patient. Children should avoid overexertion and elective tonsillectomies during the poliomyelitis "season," and pertussis-diphtheria immunizations should be postponed. Use of gamma globulin for passive immunization appears to be of questionable value for mass inoculation but may be indicated in cases where exposure of an individual to an inordinately large amount of virus may have occurred. Pregnancy predisposes to paralytic disease, and vaccine should be administered early in pregnancy as a routine precaution (37).

REFERENCES

1. Adamson, J. D., and others. Canad. M.A.J., 61:339, 1949.
2. Armstrong, C. Am. J. Pub. Health, 40:1296, 1950.
3. Badham, J. London Med. Gaz., 17:215, 1836.
4. Barr, R. N., and others. J.A.M.A., 170:893, 1959.
5. Black, P. H., and Rowe, W. P. Proc. Soc. Exper. Biol. & Med., 114:721, 1963.
6. Bodian, D., and others. Am. J. Hyg., 49:234, 1949.
7. Brodie, M. Proc. Soc. Exper. Biol. & Med., 32:300, 1935.
8. Casey, A. E. J.A.M.A., 120:805, 1942.
9. ———— and others. J.A.M.A., 129:1141, 1945.
10. Chaney, J., and others. Virology, 15:269, 1961.
11. Davis, David C., and Melnick, J. L. Proc. Soc. Exper. Biol. & Med., 92:839, 1956.
12. Dubes, G. R., and Wenner, H. A. Virology, 4:275, 1957.
13. Enders, J. F., and others. Science, 109:85, 1949.
14. Faber, H. K. Pediatrics, 17:278, 1956.
15. Girardi, A. J., and others. Proc. Soc. Exper. Biol. & Med., 109:649, 1962.
16. Hayflick, L., and Moorhead, P. Exper. Cell Res., 25:484, 1961.
17. Heine, J. Beobachtungen über Lähmungszustände der untern Extremitäten und deren Behandlungen, Stuttgart, 1840.
18. Horne, R. W., and Nagington, J. J. Molec. Biol., 1:333, 1959.
19. Horstmann, D. M. Proc. Soc. Exper. Biol. & Med., 79:417, 1952.
20. ———— and McCollum, P. W. Proc. Soc. Exper. Biol. & Med., 82:434, 1953.
21. Kessel, J. F., and Moore, F. J. Am. J. Hyg., 41:25, 1945.
22. ———— and Pait, C. F. Am. J. Hyg., 51:76, 1950.
23. Kibrick, S., and others. J. Immunol., 75:391, 1955.
24. Kling, C., and others. Bull. Acad. de méd., Paris, ser. 3, 102:158, 1929.
25. Kolmer, J. A. Am. J. Pub. Health, 26:126, 1936.
26. Koprowski, H. South African M. J., 29:1134, 1955.
27. Landsteiner, K., and Popper, E. Ztschr. f. Immunitätsforsch. u. exper. Therap., 2:377, 1909.
28. Lerner, A. M., and others. Virology, 19:58, 1963.
29. Li, C. P., and Habel, K. Proc. Soc. Exper. Biol. & Med., 78:233, 1951.
30. ———— and Schaeffer, M. Proc. Soc. Exper. Biol. & Med., 82:477, 1953.
31. Lwoff, A., and Lwoff, M. Comp. rend. Acad. sc., 246:190, 1958.
32. Magoffin, R. L., and others. J.A.M.A., 175:269, 1961.
33. Medin, O. Verhandl. d. X. Internat. med. Cong., 2:Abt. 6, 37, 1890.
34. Melnick, J. L. J. Infect. Dis., 79:27, 1946.
35. ———— and Paul, J. R. J. Exper. Med., 78:273, 1943.
36. Moyer, A. W., and others. Proc. Soc. Exper. Biol. & Med., 81:513, 1952.
37. Paffenbarger, R. S., Jr., and Wilson, V. O. Ann. New York Acad. Sc., 61:856, 1955.
38. Panel for Picornaviruses. Science, 141:152, 1963.
39. Paul, J. R. J.A.M.A., 162:1585, 1956.
40. Plotkin, S. A., and others. Proc. Soc. Exper. Biol. & Med., 107:829, 1961.
41. Robbins, F. C., and others. J. Immunol., 69:673, 1952.
42. Roca-Garcia, Manuel, and others. Proc. Soc. Exper. Biol. & Med., 81:519, 1952.
43. Sabin, A. B. J.A.M.A., 162:1589, 1956.
44. ———— Science, 123:1151, 1956.
45. ———— J.A.M.A., 183:268, 1963.
46. ———— and Olitsky, P. K. Proc. Soc. Exper. Biol. & Med., 34:357, 1936.
47. ———— and others. Proc. Soc. Exper. Biol. & Med., 85:359, 1954.
48. ———— and others. J.A.M.A., 173:1521, 1960.
49. Salk, J. E. J.A.M.A., 151:1081, 1953.
50. Scherer, W. F., and others. J. Exper. Med., 97:695, 1953.
51. Schwerdt, C. E., and Schaffer, F. L. Ann. New York Acad. Sc., 61:740, 1955.
52. Selzer, G., and Polson, A. Biochem. et Biophys. Acta, 15:251, 1954.
53. Smith, W. M., and others. Northwest Med., 49:368, 1950.
54. Spencer, W. A. Treatment of Acute Poliomyelitis, 3rd ed., Springfield, Illinois, Charles C Thomas, 1956.
55. Sweet, B. H., and Hilleman, M. R. Proc. Soc. Exper. Biol. & Med., 105:420, 1960.

56. Syverton, J. T., and others. Federation Proc., 11:795, 1952.
57. Trask, J. D., and Paul, J. R. J. Exper. Med., 73:453, 1941.
58. Trueta, J. D., and others. Ann. New York Acad. Sc., 61:883, 1955.
59. Verlinde, J. D., and others. Arch. ges. Virusforsch., 6:175, 1955.
60. Wallis, C., and Melnick, J. L. Virology, 16: 504, 1962.
61. Ward, R., and others. J. Clin. Investigation, 25:284, 1945.
62. Weller, T. H., and others. J. Immunol., 69: 645, 1952.
63. Wickman, I. Beiträge zur Kenntnis der Heine-Medinischen Krankheit, Berlin, 1907.

72

Coxsackie Virus, Echo Virus, Reoviruses, and the Aseptic Meningitis Syndrome

COXSACKIE VIRUS

During screening studies of human stools for poliovirus Dalldorf and Sickles (10) in 1948 recovered an infectious agent from patients residing in Coxsackie, New York, who had developed muscular weakness during a poliomyelitis outbreak of the year. Extracts of these stools when injected into suckling mice produced a fatal disease, and after it was established that this was a heretofore unknown virus, the name Coxsackie or C virus was given to this group of organisms (8, 9).

Subsequent studies have shown that Coxsackie viruses can be divided into subgroup A (24 types) and subgroup B (6 types). These subgroups have distinct complement-fixing antigens and also differ in their tissue pathology; group A viruses produce degeneration of skeletal muscle as their only specific lesion, whereas group B viruses generally spare the skeletal muscle but produce inflammatory lesions in the brain, heart (smooth muscle degeneration), liver, pancreas, and fat pads (20). In man these viruses produce diseases associated with the central nervous system, heart, pleura, and respiratory tract. Certain strains, A-7 and A-9, produce a polio-like syndrome with flaccid paralysis.

Morphology. The virus is a spherical particle having a diameter of 20 to 30 mμ (Fig. 1). Virus suspensions are relatively stable and can be stored at $-20°$ to $-70°$ C. for months without loss of infectivity (19). Virus in infected tissues likewise is well preserved in 50 per cent glycerol. It is unaffected by antibiotics and the more com-

Fig. 1. Clusters of Coxsackie A virus purified from infected mouse tissues. (From Breese and Briefs. *Proc. Soc. Exper. Biol. & Med.,* 83:119, 1953.)

mon antiseptics, such as Lysol, and is ether-resistant. The virus has been crystallized (17) (Fig. 2).

Cultivation and Host Range of Infection. All strains of virus are pathogenic for newborn mice by intracerebral or intraperitoneal inoculation; however, resistance to infection increases with age, and a decrease in mortality begins to appear in mice 5 to 10 days after birth (3). Signs of disease appear 2 to 10 days after inoculation and are manifested by weakness, paralysis, and death. Strains of virus differ considerably in the disease elicited. Thus, some strains may produce disease in mice as old as 15 to 20 days, yet with other strains recovery rates even in newborn animals may be considerable.

Chimpanzees and monkeys can be infected, but the disease produced is inapparent. In chimpanzees, for example, the

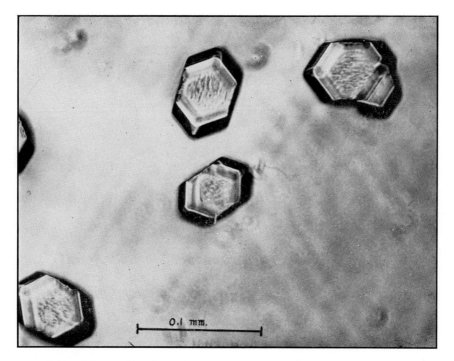

Fig. 2. Crystals of Coxsackie virus. (From Mattern and DuBuy. *Science,* 123:1037, 1956.)

only outward sign of infection is fever, but virus can be recovered from the blood and pharynx, and these animals excrete virus in the feces for several weeks after exposure (19). One strain of Coxsackie, Easton-10, has been adapted to the embryonated egg, and some strains of both group A and B produce cytopathogenic effects in HeLa tissue culture as well as in other cell culture systems (6, 23) (Figs. 3, 4).

Antigenic Structure. At present 24 types of Coxsackie virus fall into two immunologic groups, A and B. In general C viruses have been named for the geographic area in which they were first isolated; e.g., Conn.-5; Easton (Conn.)-10; Texas-13; Ohio-1; etc. (2, 5, 18). These viruses are now designated by number. Group A contains types 1 to 19, with types 1 to 10 being most prevalent, and Group B, types 20 to 24.

Serologic classification of these viruses is based on neutralization and complement-fixation tests. The latter is not type-specific, and human serums to strains of group A or B virus show complement-fixing antibody to virus strains of both groups. With mouse immune serum, however, complement-fixing antibodies do not exhibit a heterotypic response. It must be emphasized that Coxsackie virus has not been shown to cross-react with other known viral agents.

Virus neutralization presents a special problems, since susceptibility changes so rapidly with the age of the mice (1). One method has been to vaccinate the mothers, which then transfer a solid type specific immunity to the litter. More conventional neutralization tests in mice are widely used, as are cross-protection tests in chimpanzees.

In human infection both neutralizing and complement-fixing antibodies appear early, but neutralizing antibodies seem to precede the complement-fixing antibodies. Rises in titer of neutralizing antibodies seem more readily demonstrable when a constant amount of virus is set up against varying dilutions of serum than when serum is constant and virus is varied.

Recent experiments have demonstrated that Coxsackie B1, B3, B5, A21 (Coe virus), A20 and A24 agglutinate human erythrocytes (11, 21).

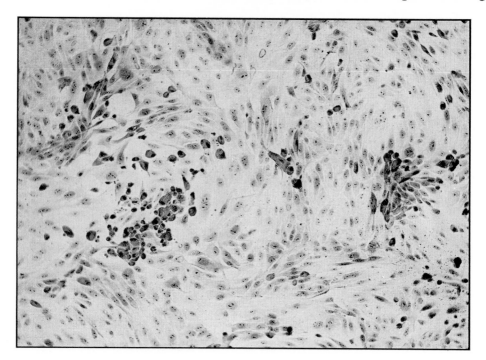

Fig. 3. Coxsackie virus B_2. Cytopathic effect of virus on culture of trypsinized monkey kidney cells 24 hours after inoculation of virus. $\times$ 105. (From Enders. *Ann. Int. Med.*, 45:331, 1956.)

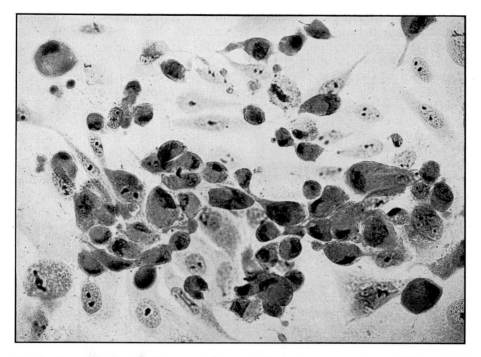

Fig. 4. Coxsackie virus B_2. Focus of injured cells from Figure 3. Note crescentric pyknotic nuclei and intense eosinophilic staining of cytoplasm. $\times$ 430. (From Enders. *Ann. Int. Med.*, 45:331, 1956.)

Clinical Infection in Man. These viruses are the causative agents of several different clinical entities which are summarized in Table 2.

Herpangina is an acute febrile illness epidemic during the summer months and most often affecting children five years of age or younger. Age incidence varies, however, and persons over 18 years of age have contracted the disease. Most characteristic is the appearance of vesicles or ulcers on the fauces, tonsils, soft palate, and pharynx. Generalized symptoms include anorexia, vomiting, and prostration. In most cases the disease lasts but two or three days. Group A virus can be isolated from throat swabs and feces. Neutralizing antibodies can be demonstrated in high titer in convalescent serum (4, 12, 13).

Pleurodynia, likewise, is an acute febrile disease characterized by pleuritic pain which may be extremely severe. The old name "Devil's grip" may be most appropriate in such instances. Generalized symptoms include headache and malaise. The disease may last a few days or several weeks, but there are no sequelae. Group B Coxsackie viruses can be recovered from the throat or feces (13).

Summer grippe is characterized by a gradual onset of fever, headache, malaise, sore throat, and vague generalized pains. Group B (Conn.-5) virus has been isolated (7, 15).

Aseptic meningitis. This syndrome is characteristically caused by B strains. The infections have a seasonal incidence, with most cases occurring in August, September, and October, thus coinciding with the "polio season." Weakness or paralysis of muscle groups is **not** characteristic of Coxsackie aseptic meningitis outbreaks or epidemics. Although muscle weakness and flaccid paralysis may occur in a few instances, particularly with Coxsackie A7 and A9 strains, the general **lack of muscle involvement** may be said to still be an important clinical feature of Coxsackie infections, differentiating it from poliomyelitis (12).

Myocarditis and pericarditis. Group B strains cause some of the cases of epidemic myocarditis of the newborn. Janett (14) reported 10 cases with six deaths. Four cases came to autopsy and showed typical Coxsackie myocarditis, and strain B3 was isolated from three nonfatal cases and from the myocardium of one fatal case. Infantile pericarditis has been observed in epidemics of pleurodynia, and Coxsackie B virus has been isolated from pericardial fluid in one case (16).

Treatment. Antibodies are of no value, and only general nonspecific supportive therapy is indicated.

Epidemiology. As indicated, the Coxsackie viruses are world wide in distribution. In addition to humans, virus isolations have been made from sewage and flies. No natural animal reservoir of infection has been demonstrated. The incidence of antibodies in the general adult population is high, and gamma globulin preparations are effective in neutralizing most Coxsackie types.

Spread of infection probably involves contact, direct and by droplets, and fecal dissemination. Frequently outbreaks of the disease involve all members of a family. In herpangina many subclinical cases develop

Table 1. Coxsackie Virus Infections

DISEASE	CLINICAL FINDINGS	AGE GROUP	VIRUS GROUP
Herpangina	Oropharyngeal ulcers or vesicles	<5 years	A (2, 3, 4, 5, 6, 8, 10)
Pleurodynia	Pleuritic pain	Adults (63%) Children (37%)	B (1, 2, 3, 4, 5)
"Grippe"	Fever-URI	Children and young adults	A, B (all types)
Aseptic meningitis	Stiff neck, rash, fever	Young adults	A (2, 4, 7, 9) All B types
Myocarditis and peri- carditis	Acute cardiac failure	Infants	B (2, 3, 4, 5)
Paralysis	Flaccid paralysis	Adults	A7, A9, B3, B4, B5
Rash	Fever, mouth lesions	Children	A (2, 4, 9, 16)

along with those having overt illness; however, outbreaks of pleurodynia are not accompanied by so large an incidence of inapparent infections. There does not appear to be a true carrier state following C virus infections.

ENTERIC CYTOPATHOGENIC HUMAN ORPHAN VIRUSES (ECHO)

ECHO viruses were first isolated during screening studies of human stools for polioviruses and were called "human orphans" because they did not appear to be associated with any specific diseases. To date 32 ECHO types have been described, and although they fit into the enterovirus category, they are a more diverse group of agents than either the polioviruses or Coxsackie viruses. ECHO viruses have been recovered from many animals. There are, for example, a series of simian viruses (SV) totaling 33 types, some of which are ECHO-like while others are related to adenoviruses, reoviruses, and hemadsorption or parainfluenza viruses. The SV-40 vaculating agent is one of the SV series.

Physical and Biologic Properties. The ECHO viruses have all the general characteristics of picorna and enteroviruses. ECHO viruses have the following distinctive features: (1) They are not pathogenic for experimental animals. ECHO 9 is an exception, since it produces fatal paralysis in suckling mice after passage in tissue culture. Some other ECHO viruses produce pathologic lesions in experimental animals. (2) All ECHO viruses grow well in tissue culture. The cell lines usually used are monkey kidney and human amnion. Growth in HeLa cells is poor. (3) All ECHO virus agglutinate human type O erythrocytes. (4) ECHO viruses have soluble and virus antigens. The usual test for identification is the virus neutralization test performed in tissue culture.

Clinical Diseases. ECHO viruses cause a number of specific syndromes both in epidemic and endemic proportions.

Epidemic Diarrhea of Infants and Newborns. Various virus groups inhabit and grow in the gastrointestinal tract, including poliovirus, Coxsackie, ECHO, and reo-

viruses. Some types of these viruses have been isolated from infants and children with some form of diarrheal disease. In addition, it is well established that certain strains of *E. coli, Shigella, Salmonella,* and *Shigella* in combination with viruses, likewise play a role in summer diarrheal infections.

In a study in 1955-1956 by Ramos-Alvarez and Sabin (30) the agents listed accounted for about 80 per cent of summer diarrheas in Cincinnati. In 1955, for example, viruses accounted for the majority of cases, whereas pathogenic *E. coli,* pathogenic *E. coli* plus ECHO 12 and ECHO 18, *Salmonella* only, *Shigella* only, and *Shigella* in combination with ECHO 11 and Coxsackie were implicated in a few cases each. *Salmonella* was not found in association with any enteroviruses. Coli types 0.111 B4 and 0.55 B5 were found in 80 per cent of the cases caused by pathogenic *E. coli,* with 20 per cent divided among seven other serotypes.

Recent studies of epidemic diarrhea in nurseries have demonstrated the presence of ECHO 18 and a rise in antibodies to this virus in the infected children (25). A number of these epidemics, however, were due to reoviruses, previously considered to be part of the ECHO group (30).

Aseptic Meningitis. Epidemics of aseptic meningitis have been described as due to types 2, 4, 6, 9, and 16 with other types causing endemic cases. Clinically the ECHO form of meningitis cannot be distinguished from Coxsackie infections. Both viruses have seasonal case incidence, with most cases occurring in the summer. Certain ECHO types (e.g., 9) may cause a flaccid paralysis or muscle weakness. As with Coxsackie infections, paralysis is an unusual feature of ECHO infections (26). A new ECHO virus implicated in many cases of aseptic meningitis is type 30, also known as the Bastianni virus, which is the prototype. Other viruses which fall into this serologic group are the Giles, PR-17 and the Price viruses. In 1960 the Giles virus was the most common cause of aseptic meningitis (24, 27, 28).

Rash. Many ECHO infections include an exanthem in the syndrome, and the rash may be of epidemic proportions (29). In

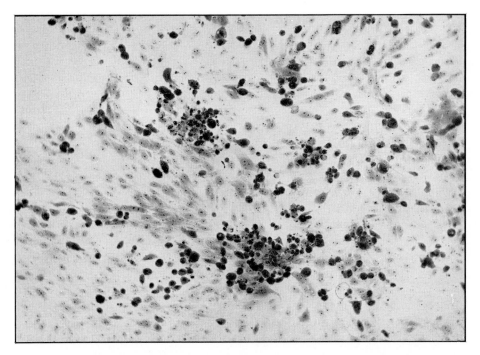

Fig. 5. Echo virus type 6. Focus of cytopathic effect in monkey kidney cell cultures four days after virus inoculation. × 105. (From Enders. *Ann. Int. Med.*, 45:331, 1956.)

general, the patients have had a morbilli form rash lasting one to three days. Rash alone is common, although some patients in Minnesota showed fever and aseptic meningitis.

Fever and Respiratory Disease. Outbreaks of mild upper respiratory infections, many identical to the common cold syndrome, have been described. The ECHO 10 agent has been the cause of many such illnesses but, because of its large size, has been removed from the ECHO group and is now classified as a reovirus (31). Similarly, ECHO 28 is now classified as a rhinovirus (32). ECHO types 11 and 20 also cause a mild respiratory disorder and remain in the ECHO group.

REOVIRUSES

(Respiratory-enteric)

The reoviruses are comprised of three types, one of which was previously classified as ECHO 10, but these agents have been removed from the ECHO category and now form a new subgroup of the picornaviruses. They are about 72 mμ in size (36) and inhabit both the respiratory and gastrointestinal tracts. They have been recovered from cases of respiratory infection and mild febrile illness (35), and various outbreaks of enteritis and diarrhea (30) in children and have been isolated from cattle (34) and simian hosts (37).

All reoviruses have the capacity to multiply in suckling mice and produce clinical and pathologic manifestations similar to those caused by Coxsackie viruses (33, 36).

THE ASEPTIC MENINGITIS SYNDROME

This syndrome was given its intriguing name by Wallgren (38) in 1925, and his initial criteria were as follows: (1) acute onset with obvious signs of meningitis, (2) CSF changes of nonbacterial meningitis (increases in monocytic cells, slight to moderate increase in protein, little or no change in sugar),

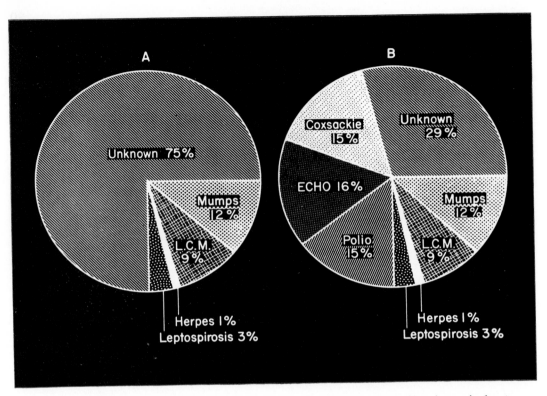

Fig. 6. Etiology of aseptic meningitis in 1953 as contrasted to 1956. The change is due to the discovery of the Coxsackie and Echo virus groups. (Data for 1953 from Adair, Gould, and Smadel. *Ann. Int. Med.,* 39:675, 1953; data for 1956 from Davis and Melnick. *J. Lab. & Clin. Med.,* 51:97, 1958.)

(3) absence of bacteria in CSF by stain or culture, (4) benign, short course (aseptic meningitis is not invariably "benign"), (5) absence of conditions predisposing to meningitis (e.g., absence of mastoiditis or middle ear infection), and (6) absence of epidemic disease in the community. This final criterion is not valid, for aseptic meningitis frequently occurs in epidemic proportions. Figure 6 shows the reduction in the incidence of aseptic meningitis due to unknown causes from 75 per cent in 1950 to 29 per cent in 1960 due to the discovery of the Coxsackie and ECHO virus groups.

One of the ever-present dangers is the assumption during an epidemic of viral meningitis that all cases are indeed viral. Thus, when during this type of situation a case of meningococcal or pneumococcal meningitis appears, a spinal tap may be neglected, possibly leading to a disastrous result. The cardi-

nal clinical signs and symptoms of aseptic meningitis are stiff neck, fever, and headache, which of course may be symptoms and signs of many diseases. CSF changes are therefore of great importance in separating the viral from the nonviral cases. Some infections which may simulate viral aseptic meningitis are given in Table 2. Viruses implicated in aseptic meningitis and their incidence are given in Table 3.

It should be noted that influenza and hepatitis viruses, although sometimes causing symptoms referable to the central nervous system, do not cause aseptic meningitis. Likewise, none of the rickettsia cause this syndrome, and the cerebrospinal fluid in rickettsial infections is normal. Poliovirus usually causes a meningitis and myelitis; poliovirus encephalitis is uncommon but has grave prognostic significance when present.

The CSF changes in Table 2 are only

Table 2. Typical CSF Findings in Infectious Meningoencephalitis

	RANGE CELLS	TYPE CELLS	SUGAR Mg/%	PROTEIN mg/%	ORGANISM
NORMAL	0	0	45-60	15-45	0
Bacterial	2000-10,000+	PMN	15-30	500-1000	+
Virus	0-600 *	Mono	N	60-100	0
TB	200-2000	Mono	<15	500-1000	+
Syphilis	0-100	Mono	N	60-100	0
Leptospiral	100-300	Mono	N	50-60	0

Tumor—variable, usually only a sl. inc. protein

Fungus—quite variable but organisms present

* Counts of 1000-3000 occur in a significant number of cases, particularly with LCM virus.

Table 3. Virus Aseptic Meningitis

	PER CENT		
Primarily encephalitic	INCIDENCE	DEATHS	PERMANENT DAMAGE
Mumps	12%	0	0
Chicken pox	1:600	5-10%	5-10%
Measles	1:1000	15-30%	30%
Equine (U.S. only)	Uncommon	Variable-low	Variable
Polio	Very low	High	High
Rabies	Very low	100%	—
Herpes simplex	1%	High	?
LCM	5-10%	Very low	Very low
Primarily meningitic			
Polio *	15%	Uncommon	1-5%
Coxsackie	15	0	Low
ECHO	16	0	Low
Leptospiral	3%	Very low	Low
Unknown	29		

* A myelitis can occur without increased cells in CSF, particularly in children.

generalizations, and great variability can be found in individual cases. However, it is generally true that the cell count in viral infections is low (15-600), the sugar normal, and the protein only slightly increased relative to the changes found in bacterial meningitis. A few cases of a low CSF sugar level in viral meningoencephalitis have been reported. The protein is rarely increased more than 2+. In Coxsackie and lymphocytic choriomeningitis cell counts of 1,000-3,000 have been reported. Finally, although the characteristic cell in virus infections is the monocyte, the early, initial response may be of polymorphonuclear cells, shifting gradually to polys over a period of several days. Arbo viruses usually show an initial high polymorphonuclear response in the cerebrospinal fluid.

REFERENCES

COXSACKIE

1. Beeman, E. A., and others. Am. J. Hyg., 55:83, 1952.
2. ———— and Huebner, R. J. J. Immunol., 68:663, 1952.
3. Cheever, F. S., and others. J. Exper. Med., 92:153, 1950.
4. Cole, R. M., and others. Am. J. Pub. Health, 41:1342, 1951.
5. Contreras, G., and others. J. Immunol., 69:395, 1952.
6. Crowell, R. L., and Syverton, J. T. J. Immunol., 74:169, 1955.
7. Curnen, E. C. Bull. New York Acad. Med., 26:335, 1950.
8. Dalldorf, G. J. Exper. Med., 94:65, 1951.
9. ———— and others. J. Exper. Med., 89:567, 1949.
10. ———— and Sickles, G. M. Science, 108:61, 1948.
11. Goldfield, M., and others. Proc. Soc. Exper. Biol. & Med., 96:788, 1957.

12. Huebner, R. J., and others.   New England J. Med., 247:249, 1952.
13. Hummeler, K., and others.   J.A.M.A., 156:676, 1954.
14. Janett, S. N., and others.   J. Pediat., 48:1, 1956.
15. Kilbourne, E. D.   Federation Proc., 9:581, 1950.
16. Kogan, H., and Bernkopf, H.   Ann. Paediat., 189:44, 1957.
17. Mattern, C. F. T., and DuBuy, H.   Science, 123:1037, 1956.
18. Melnick, J. L.   Ann. New York Acad. Sc., 56:587, 1953.
19. ————— Ann. Rev. Microbiol., 5:309, 1951.
20. Pappenheimer, A. M., and others.   J. Exper. Med., 92:169, 1950.
21. Rosen, L., and Kern, J.   Proc. Soc. Exper. Biol. & Med., 107:626, 1961.
22. Syverton, J. T., and others.   J.A.M.A., 164:2015, 1957.
23. Weller, T. H., and others.   J. Immunol., 71:92, 1953.

Echo

24. Cooney, M. K., and others.   Am. J. Hyg., 75:301, 1962.
25. Eichenwald, H. F., and others.   J.A.M.A., 166:1563, 1958.

26. Faulkner, R. S., and Ozeri, R. L.   New England J. Med., 263:551, 1960.
27. Klemman, H., and others.   J.A.M.A., 187:90, 1964.
28. Lennette, E. H., and others.   Proc. Soc. Exper. Biol. & Med., 110:769, 1962.
29. Prince, J. T., and others.   J.A.M.A., 167:691, 1958.
30. Ramos-Alvarez, M., and Sabin, A. B.   J.A.M.A., 167:147, 1958.
31. Sabin, A. B.   Science, 130:1387, 1959.
32. Tyrrell, D. A., Jr., and Chanock, R. M.   Science, 141:152, 1963.

Reoviruses

33. Dalldorf, G.   Ann. New York Acad. Sc., 67:209, 1957.
34. Rosen, L., and Abinanti, F. R.   Am. J. Hyg., 71:250, 1960.
35. ————— and others.   Am. J. Hyg., 71:266, 1960.
36. Sabin, A. B.   Ann. New York Acad. Sc., 67:250, 1957.
37. ————— Science, 103:1387, 1959.

Aseptic Meningitis

38. Wallgren, A.   Acta Paediat., 4:158, 1925.

73

The Hepatitis Viruses

Viral hepatitis is characterized by degenerative changes in the parenchymal cells of the liver resulting in varying degrees of impairment of liver function. This clinical syndrome may be found in two diseases caused by viruses which, although presumably related, have certain biologic attributes readily differentiating them. Infectious hepatitis (I.H. or Virus Hepatitis A) has been recognized for many years, and occurs endemically and epidemically. Virus is present in the stools of infected persons and spread of the disease is via the anal-oral route. Serum hepatitis (S.H. or Virus Hepatitis B) infects only when injected by needle into the susceptible host. The increased use of blood plasma and other parenteral therapy has resulted in a concomitant rise in the incidence of serum hepatitis. Clinically the two infections are indistinguishable.

INFECTIOUS HEPATITIS
I.H.

(Epidemic Jaundice, Catarrhal Jaundice, Virus Hepatitis A)

For over two centuries liver disease in epidemic form has been recognized, particularly in military installations in time of war. In fact, another of the many synonyms of this disease is "Epidemic Jaundice of Campaigns." There is some reason to believe that I.H. was recognized in ancient Greece, since Hippocrates described jaundice accompanied by fever "which is soon cured," but the first recorded epidemic occurred in Minorca in 1745. During recent wars the disease has become a major problem. The Federal troops during the Civil War reported over 40,000 cases. Extensive epidemics have been re-ported in campaigns throughout the world and seriously interfered with military operations during World War II. In 1943 between 35 and 40 per cent of the Air Corps personnel in Sicily were stricken during a three-month period, and the Fifth Army in 1944 to 1945 reported an attack rate of 13 per 1000 cases during one peak period.

The disease was first recognized as being infectious in nature by Cockayne (6) in 1912, and he coined the term "infective hepatitis." In addition, Cockayne's clinical description of this disease was excellent, and he was the first to note a relationship between infectious hepatitis and acute yellow atrophy of the liver. Cockayne stated, "Sporadic and epidemic catarrhal jaundice and acute yellow atrophy of the liver are due in the great majority of cases to the same cause, a specific organism of unknown nature" (6).

The inability of many investigators to recover bacterial organisms in this disease suggested that the causative agent may be a virus. This was confirmed during World War II by inoculation of human volunteers (32). Duodenal contents, blood, serum, and feces, all filtered and treated to insure bacteriologic sterility, were obtained from patients in the acute stage of the disease and either fed or injected into volunteers (4, 11, 21). Transmission experiments of this type showed that virus was present in the blood prior to and during the onset of jaundice. Virus was excreted in the feces for weeks after the onset of the disease and likewise could be detected in the blood for a similar period. Urine and nasopharyngeal washings from patients do not appear to be infective.

The virus causes disease only in man. Many attempts to propagate the agent in every conceivable animal have failed, or at least failed of confirmation, when such was reported. Special zoologic expeditions have been sent to trap exotic animals in order to test their susceptibility to this virus, but none were susceptible hosts.

The various reports of isolation of hepatitis virus in tissue culture systems, although certainly indicative of the isolation of some viral-like agent, do not provide clear, definitive and irrefutable proof that these isolates are, in fact, the specific agents which cause either human infectious or serum hepatitis. Rightsel and associates (30) reported isolation of a virus in the Detroit-6 (human epithelial cell) which was about 18 mμ in size, stable to 60° C. for 30 minutes, produced hepatitis in volunteers, comprised at least three serotypes and gave promise as an immunizing agent (3, 31). It is significant that these results have not been reported as readily reproducible by other laboratories. Another agent, A-1 virus, isolated by O'Malley, Meyer and Smadel (27) in rabbit kidney cells appeared to be much larger (about 100 mμ) and was inactivated at 56° C. for 30 minutes. This virus was isolated from icterogenic human plasma; sera of patients convalescent from **serum** hepatitis neutralized this virus, whereas sera from cases of infectious hepatitis did not. A third agent was isolated by Davis (7) in human lung epithelial cells. The inoculum came from stool extracts of children with infectious hepatitis. The agent was relatively heat-stable (survived 60° C. for 40 minutes) but was not associated with a hemagglutinin.

A fourth isolate named the DA virus was isolated from a fatal case of infectious hepatitis (14, 16, 17). Agar overlay primate cells were inoculated with human whole blood. The virus isolate had properties which placed it in the myxovirus group, was relatively heat-labile (titer dropped on heating to 56° C. for 15 and 50 minutes), and agglutinated chicken cells; sera from infectious hepatitis cases inhibited this viral hemagglutinin.

In view of the above diversity of agents and the problems of viral orphans in general, the initial comment on this subject made in the eleventh edition of this text is still applicable—namely, "in view of the many pitfalls in hepatitis research, careful study will be necessary to evaluate these findings."

Antigenic Structure. Detailed knowledge is not available. Cross-immunity tests indicate an antigenic difference between infectious hepatitis (I.H.) and serum hepatitis viruses (S.H.). In fact, previous infection with S.H. virus has been reported to predispose to I.H. virus infection. It is well established that one attack of infectious hepatitis confers considerable immunity and second attacks are uncommon. In human volunteer experiments infection with one strain of I.H. virus stimulated definite immunity to this strain and partial immunity to a second strain of I.H. (10, 24, 25). The protective effect of gamma globulin in I.H. indicates generally good levels of immunity in the adult population and confirms the impression that this disease is quite widespread, probably to about the same extent as poliomyelitis. Data on strain variation of I.H. is unavailable.

Clinical Infection in Man (Table 1). The disease is best understood in terms of the liver pathology (Kaufman, N., personal

Table 1. Salient Features of Infectious and Serum Hepatitis

	INFECTIOUS HEPATITIS	SERUM HEPATITIS
Age	Children	All ages
Season	Winter	All year
Geographic area	Rural or suburban	All areas
Average incubation period	25 days	100 days
Onset	Acute or insidious	Insidious
Fever	May be high or low	Absent or **low** grade
Clinical syndrome	Indistinguishable	
Viremia	Present	Present
Virus in stools	Present	Absent
Route of infection	Oral or parenteral	Parenteral **only**
Carrier state	Prolonged fecal excretion of virus	Very prolonged viremia
Immunity Homologous Heterologous	Present Absent	Uncertain Absent
Gamma globulin	Effective	Not effective
Contagiousness	Contagious	Not contagious

communication). Early changes show necrosis of liver cells principally in the center of the liver lobule. More advanced stages include widespread necrosis of liver parenchyma and cellular infiltrations in response to dying cells, but a large percentage of the liver may be damaged in the absence of clinical jaundice.

A small proportion of the cases will die of a diffuse, massive liver necrosis (acute yellow atrophy) (19). In the vast majority there is complete healing of the liver parenchyma (20). There may be various degrees of persistent and permanent liver damage (2). Cirrhosis develops when necrosis is submassive, so that the patient survives and healing occurs but the liver is not restored to its normal architecture. The most characteristic type of cirrhosis believed to follow viral hepatitis is post-necrotic cirrhosis which is characterized by a shrunken liver, with broad scars and nodules of regenerated liver parenchyma of varying size from small through large. Microscopically this is reflected in irregular and coarse cicatrization. The scars surround and separate liver nodules composed of groups of regenerated parenchymal lobules as well as apparently uninvolved liver tissue. This type of cirrhosis is not pathognomonic for viral hepatitis but may follow other types of extensive liver injury produced, for example, by certain chemicals.

Other types of cirrhosis are believed to be a result of a smoldering inflammation. One of these has been termed post-hepatitic cirrhosis (9). Whether this is necessarily the result of a viral infection is not clear. In this type the liver is uniformly coarsely nodular, and microscopically narrow bands of fibrous tissue extend between portal areas. This results in individual lobules or small groups of lobules being surrounded by scar tissue.

Another type, which presents a finely granular appearance and may belong in this category, is pericholangiolitic biliary cirrhosis (22) or cholangiolitic cirrhosis (33).

These types of cirrhosis are not to be confused with Laennec's or nutritional cirrhosis, which grossly presents a finely uniform nodularity. The nodules are separated by narrow bands of connective tissue. The appearance varies with the stage of cirrhosis. Microscopically, bands of fibrous tissue encroach into the lobule and extend into the central area, as well as connect portal areas. The result is a pseudolobule formation, marked distortion of lobular architecture, and loss of the central veins. There is nodule formation, but there are no intact groups of normal appearing lobules. The parenchymal cells contain varying amounts of lipid.

The incubation period is 10 to 40 days, with an average of 25. This is a most important aid in distinguishing this disease from serum hepatitis. The clinical picture is quite variable. Probably the majority of cases are inapparent, and many may be characterized only by very mild constitutional symptoms. Most patients sick enough to be seen by physicians give a history of fever, anorexia, nausea, vomiting, and some abdominal distress, with the onset being either slow or abrupt. Jaundice usually appears on the fifth to seventh day of the illness. Posterior cervical lymphadenopathy is common, and splenomegaly may be present. During the preicteric phase only liver tenderness may be found. Some patients may have fever of 104° F., chills, and pain so severe in the right upper quadrant as to cause splinting of the right chest region, simulating right lower lobe pneumonia with pleurisy. At the end of the preicteric stage, symptoms may subside somewhat but reappear with the onset of jaundice. At this stage the liver becomes enlarged and tender. The icteric stage may last one to 10 weeks. Laboratory findings reveal a leukopenia with a relative lymphocytosis, often including many atypical cells which are similar to those found in infectious mononucleosis. Diagnosis is based on the clinical history and liver function tests. A few patients' serums contain a substance which agglutinates sheep red cells. It may be distinguished from other similar agglutinins by its absorbability on boiled guinea pig kidney. However, this test has little or no diagnostic value. It is positive in only a small percentage of the cases and, even when positive, may not be specific. Various skin tests, as described in the literature, are of no value.

Virtually every type of possible serologic

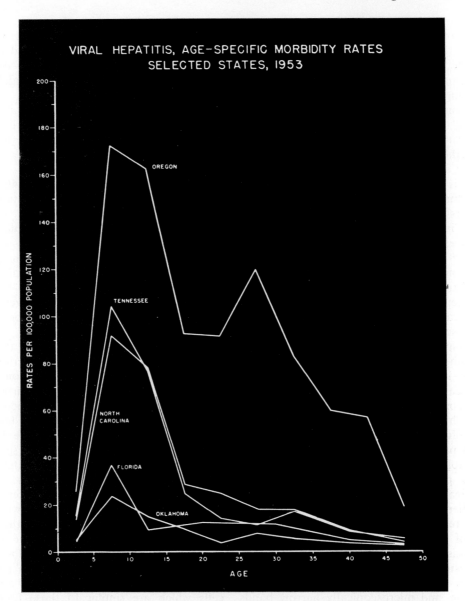

Fig. 1. Relation of age to incidence of infectious hepatitis. (From Sherman and Eichenwald. *Ann. Int. Med.*, 44:1049, 1956.)

approach has been tried in an effort to find a test for hepatitis with very little success (12). Recent experiments have used day-old chick erythrocytes (13). The prognosis is good, and the death rate is only about 1 per 1,000. In some individuals, however, a progressive infection may occur to the point of acute yellow atrophy of the liver, coma, and death. Others may subsequently develop hepatic cirrhosis. Convalescence in the group of patients sick enough to be hospitalized may be prolonged, and relapses are not uncommon.

Transmission.   Infectious hepatitis is primarily a disease of children and adolescents. In this age group the majority of infections are mild or inapparent in contrast to the more severe disease which frequently occurs when older persons are affected (Figs. 1, 2). Women in the postmenopausal phase of life

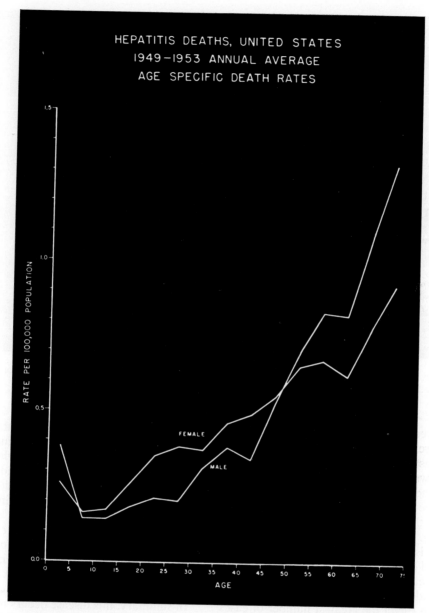

Fig. 2. Relation of age and mortality in infectious hepatitis. (From Sherman and Eichenwald. *Ann. Int. Med.,* 44:1049, 1956.)

seem particularly vulnerable to this virus and
have a relatively high mortality rate. Since
the virus is in the feces and since many cases
are associated with unsanitary living conditions, fecal dissemination would appear to be
the most important mode of virus spread.
In some instances spread of disease is associated with person-to-person contact, but
well-documented epidemics arising from

contamination of drinking water (26), milk
(29), and food (23) have been reported.
Neefe and Stokes (26) investigated an epidemic at a children's summer camp in which
350 of 572 (61 per cent) developed hepatitis over a 13-week period. Of these 255
had clinical jaundice, and 95 had hepatitis
(by laboratory studies and nonspecific symptoms) but without jaundice. In most cases

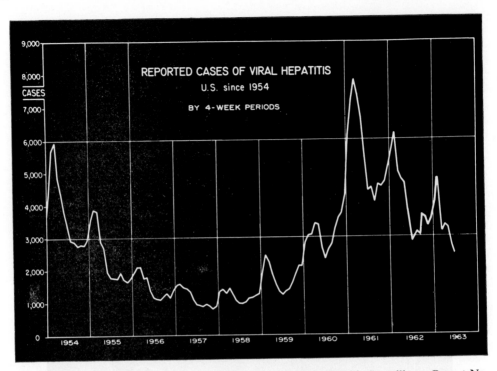

Fig. 3. Cases of viral hepatitis from 1954 to 1963. (From Hepatitis Surveillance Report No. 16, U.S.P.H.S., Department of Health, Education and Welfare.)

clinical recovery occurred in 24 to 48 hours, and there were no deaths. A well in the camp was fecally contaminated and samples of this water produced hepatitis in volunteers. One of the children developed hepatitis three days after arriving at the camp and was thought to be the original source of the virus. The incidence in temperate zone climates is highest in the fall and winter, but cases and even epidemics appear sporadically at any season. In tropical countries a seasonal tendency is less marked. During World War II in Egypt the greatest number of cases appeared in August and September. The frequency of cases in the winter months would suggest respiratory spread, but virus appears rarely in nasopharyngeal washings in the relatively few experimental studies on record. Generally there is a preponderance of cases in rural as opposed to urban areas. Anderson found a four times greater incidence in rural areas in Iceland than in metropolitan areas in a study of 19 outbreaks of this disease (1). Other modes of transmission which have been implicated

have been flies, mosquitoes, and rats. On the battlefield flies may assume plague conditions, particularly in front lines where fecal pollution of ground and unburied corpses are commonplace. Several epidemics in World War II were related to fly infestation under these conditions. Finally, in regard to carrier states, fecal carriers appear to exist. Virus may remain in the blood for several weeks, but the duration of the viremia is not comparable to that found in serum hepatitis. There is, of course, no animal reservoir.

In summary, this disease occurs most often in situations where persons are living in close quarters with communal feeding and restricted hygienic facilities, and where opportunities for fecal spread of virus to clothes, food, water, bedding, and so forth, are relatively good.

Treatment. Present concepts of treatment are reviewed by Chalmers (5), but briefly they include adequate, palatable diet and bed rest until the patient is asymptomatic. Ward activity is permitted for symptom-free patients, even though jaundice may still be present. Use of corticosteroids may be of value in certain cases, but caution is advised, since the relapse rate appears higher in these cases (8, 15). Antibiotics are of no value.

Prevention. Control consists mainly of isolation of clinically recognized cases, with care to sterilization of any objects which may be contaminated with the patient's feces. Since the virus has a blood stream phase, all needles and syringes must be autoclaved. In all large or prolonged outbreaks possible fecal contamination of food and water must be considered. Institutional outbreaks may be controlled to some extent by injections of gamma globulin in exposed individuals. This is indicated particularly in exposed persons whose general physical condition is poor.

Studies of the efficacy of gamma globulin in an institution for mentally defective children, an environment with a high rate of infectious hepatitis, showed very marked reduction in **icteric** attack rates as compared to controls (18). Interestingly, the attack rate in subclinical hepatitis was not reduced, paralleling the effect of gamma globulin in measles. Another important observation was that 0.06 ml. of gamma globulin per pound of body weight was a much more effective dose in children and adults than smaller amounts.

The main control measure is protection against virus contamination of water supplies. In this regard it is important to note that at least three epidemics have occurred via chlorinated water supplies (28). The incidence of **all** cases of hepatitis (mostly infectious hepatitis, however) in recent years is given in Figure 3.

SERUM HEPATITIS
S.H.

(Homologous Serum Jaundice, Postvaccinal Hepatitis, Virus Hepatitis B)

Although this disease has been most prominent in the past 20 years, when parenteral therapy has been used with increasing frequency, there is reason to believe that serum hepatitis occurred many years ago. Various reports of hepatitis following injections of arsphenamine, smallpox vaccinations, and patients' visits to diabetic clinics would suggest, in retrospect, the disease as we know it today.

In 1938 jaundice was found in a small group of individuals who had received injections of measles convalescent serum (54). This observation was followed by reports of jaundice which developed subsequent to the administration of vaccines containing human serums (39, 51). The disease also has been produced by the injection of plasma and whole blood (34, 35, 40, 50). The most important stimulus to the investigation of the disease was the appearance of jaundice in military personnel who had received yellow fever vaccine containing human serum as a stabilizing agent. During World War II several million American troops received the vaccine, and at least 28,000 cases of serum hepatitis (55) resulted. The resistance of the virus to physical and chemical agents is similar to that of infectious hepatitis virus. There is no known method of treating whole blood or plasma which will render it free of virus without making such materials unusable for parenteral therapy. Ultraviolet irradiation of plasma does not inactivate all the virus (43). This agent very possibly is killed by boiling or dry heat, but since so many variables may be present, these technics are not dependable. All needles and syringes and any accessory equipment used in parenteral therapy which might be contaminated by the blood of any patient and which subsequently will be used on other patients should be autoclaved.

Many attempts to propagate serum hepatitis virus in the laboratory in animals, embryonated eggs, and tissue culture have been made without success, and all of the available information about this virus has been obtained in human volunteer experiments. The size of the virus is estimated at 26 mμ or less (42). Information regarding antigenic structure is meager, and it is uncertain whether homologous immunity follows infection with serum hepatitis virus.

In one study 10 men having had well-documented serum hepatitis were challenged with virus-contaminated yellow fever vaccine and did not develop clinical hepatitis. No liver function tests were done. In 10 controls this lot of vaccine produced three cases of serum hepatitis. Convalescent serum hepatitis serum mixed with contaminated vaccine caused serum hepatitis in one of 10 persons, indicating a lack or low level of neutralizing antibodies in this experiment (49). In a study by Neefe and others (46), nine persons who had recovered from S.H. contracted from various source materials were inoculated with a proven icterogenic human plasma, along with nine controls. In the control group eight out of nine developed typical S.H., whereas none of the experimental group became sick. However, five of nine of the latter group showed some changes in the liver function tests in the absence of clinical disease. Considering the vagaries of S.H. and the small size of the samples, no definite conclusion is possible. In summary, there is suggestive evidence that some homologous immunity may exist, but definitive studies are lacking. The prolonged viremic carrier state suggests that little immunity exists and/or that the virus is a weak antigen (47, 52).

Clinical Infection in Man. The clinical disease cannot be differentiated from that of infectious hepatitis. In serum hepatitis the incubation period is from 60 to 150 days, with an average of about 90 days. This feature correlated with a history of needle injection, particularly in regard to receiving blood plasma, are the essential diagnostic criteria. Helpful but not diagnostic points are: (1) serum hepatitis tends to have a more insidious onset than infectious hepatitis; and (2) the fever is low-grade, rarely high. It is well to keep in mind the high incidence of serum hepatitis in dope addicts who habitually pass around unsterilized needles and syringes.

Treatment. Treatment is identical for serum hepatitis and infectious hepatitis. Stool precautions are not necessary in the case of serum hepatitis.

Transmission. In general, transmission is accomplished only when virus is injected into a susceptible host. After infection, virus is present in the blood for weeks prior to the onset of clinical hepatitis and remains for years after recovery. During this carrier period the patients may be entirely well.

Two exceptions to the above mode of transmission, however, cannot be disregarded. MacCallum and Bauer (41) produced hepatitis in two individuals after intranasal inoculation of serum taken from a case of S.H. on the seventh day of illness. Icterogenic yellow fever vaccine given intranasally may have caused a third case. Findley and Martin (38) reported three cases of S.H. following intranasal inoculation using serum obtained either preicterically or early in the icteric stage of S.H. following yellow fever inoculation.

Of blood products, pooled human blood plasma is most apt to contain the virus, and the plasma virus titer has been shown to be 1×10^4 infectious units per milliliter or higher in one pool (43). This pool produced hepatitis in 53 per cent of a large group of persons inoculated with it. Whole blood taken during the acute stage of S.H. has had titers of 1×10^6 per milliliter infectious units (36). Since plasma is pooled from many persons routinely, the chance that it will contain some virus is great. The incidence of S.H. following plasma infusion is 5 to 20 per cent, but, after whole blood alone, which is never pooled, the rate is only 1 to 3 per cent. In addition to whole blood and plasma, virus has been found in (1) human fibrinogen, (2) human thrombin, and (3) Cohn's Fraction IV. **Human gamma globulin** (37, 44) **and albumin preparations do not contain live virus, presumably because it is inactivated or lost during the preparation of these materials.** Transplacental transmission of S.H. has been claimed.

One of the most striking features of S.H. is the very prolonged viremia (45, 48, 53). Virus has been found in the blood as early as 87 days before the onset of symptoms, and several symptomless carriers have been reported. One individual, for example, gave no history of any disease accompanied by jaundice but was shown to have carried the virus in his blood for at least five years (53). He was a habitual blood donor and transmitted the disease to a number of unwitting recipients. Blood banks refuse donors who have a history consistent with hepatitis, but obviously the history alone is insufficient. At the present time there is no practical method to screen out all possible carriers, and the use of blood and plasma remains a calculated risk insofar as viral hepatitis is concerned.

The virus has not been demonstrated in the feces, urine, or nasopharyngeal washings as tested by feeding filtrates of these materials to volunteers. Moreover, oral ingestion of infected serum fails to cause hepatitis. It must be kept in mind, however, that until this agent can be isolated and studied in the laboratory, few, if any, of the experimental results described can be called definitive.

Prevention. Only measures which prevent the virus from gaining access to the body via a parenteral route are effective. Gamma globulin is not effective in this disease.

REFERENCES

INFECTIOUS HEPATITIS

1. Anderson, L. S. Lancet, 1:778, 1947.
2. Baggenstoss, A. H. J.A.M.A., 165:1099, 1957.
3. Boggs, J. P., and others. J.A.M.A., 177:678, 1961.
4. Cameron, J. D. S. Quart. J. Med., 12:139, 1943.
5. Chalmers, T. C., and others. J. Clin. Investigation, 34:1163, 1955.
6. Cockayne, E. A. Quart. J. Med., 6:1, 1912.
7. Davis, E. V. Science, 133:2059, 1961.
8. Evans, A. S., and others. Ann. Int. Med., 38:1134, 1953.
9. Gall, E. A. Am. J. Path., 36:241, 1961.
10. Havens, W. P., and others. Proc. Soc. Exper. Biol. & Med., 57:206, 1944.
11. ———— J. Exper. Med., 84:403, 1946.
12. Havens, W. P. New England J. Med., 259:1202, 1958.
13. ———— Arch. Int. Med., 106:327, 1960.
14. Hsiung, G. D., and others. J. Immunol., 88:284, 1962.
15. Huber, T. H., and Wiley, A. T. Ann. Int. Med., 42:1011, 1955.
16. Isacson, P., and others. J. Immunol., 88:300, 1962.
17. ———— and others. J. Immunol., 88:291, 1962.
18. Krugman, S., and others. J.A.M.A., 174:823, 1960.
19. Lucke, B. Am. J. Path., 20:471, 1944.
20. ———— Am. J. Path., 20:585, 1944.
21. MacCallum, F. O., and Bradley, W. H. Lancet, 2:228, 1944.
22. MacMahon, H. E. Lab. Invest., 4:243, 1955.
23. Murphy, W. J., and others. Am. J. Pub. Health, 36:169, 1946.
24. Neefe, J. R., and Stokes, J. J.A.M.A., 128:1063, 1945.
25. ———— and others. Am. J. M. Sc., 210:561, 1945.
26. ———— and others. Am. J. Med., 1:3, 1946.
27. O'Malley, J. P., and others. Proc. Soc. Exper. Biol. & Med., 108:200, 1961.
28. Poskanzer, D. C., and Beadenkopf, W. G. Pub. Health Rep., 76:745, 1961.
29. Read, M. R., and others. Am. J. Pub. Health, 36:367, 1946.
30. Rightsel, W. A., and others. Science, 124, 226, 1956.
31. ———— and others. J.A.M.A., 177:671, 1961.
32. Voeght, H. München med. Wchnschr., 89:76, 1942.
33. Watson, C. J., and Hoffbauer, F. W. Ann. Int. Med., 25:195, 1946.

SERUM HEPATITIS

34. Apley, J., and Wallis, H. R. E. Brit. M. J., No. 4543, p. 197, 1948.
35. Beeson, P. B., and others. Lancet, 1:814, 1944.
36. Drake, M. E., and others. Proc. Soc. Exper. Biol. & Med., 80:310, 1952.
37. ———— and others. J.A.M.A., 152:690, 1953.
38. Findlay, G. M., and Martin, N. H. Lancet, 1:679, 1943.
39. ———— and MacCallum, F. O. Proc. Roy. Soc. Med., 31:799, 1938.
40. Grossman, E. B., and others. J.A.M.A., 129:991, 1945.
41. MacCallum, F. O., and Bauer, D. J. Lancet, 1:622, 1944.
42. McCollum, R. W. Proc. Soc. Exper. Biol. & Med., 81:157, 1952.
43. Murray, R., and others. J.A.M.A., 157:8, 1955.
44. ———— and Ratner, F. Proc. Soc. Exper. Biol. & Med., 83:554, 1953.
45. ———— and others. J.A.M.A., 154:1072, 1954.
46. Neefe, J. R., and others. Am. J. Med., 1:3, 1946.
47. ———— Medicine, 27:279, 1948.
48. ———— and others. J.A.M.A., 154:1066, 1954.
49. Oliphant, J. W. Pub. Health Reports, 59:1614, 1944.
50. Rappaport, E. M. J.A.M.A., 128:932, 1945.
51. Soper, F. L., and Smith, H. H. Am. J. Trop. Med., 18:111, 1938.
52. Stokes, J. S. Am. J. M. Sc., 225:349, 1953.
53. ———— and others. J.A.M.A., 154:1059, 1954.
54. Report. Annual Rep. Chief Med. Officer, Ministry of Health, London, 1938.
55. Report. J.A.M.A., 119:1110, 1942.

74

Arthropod-Borne Virus Diseases of Man

(ARBO Viruses)

This group of viral agents has the distinctive feature that all are transmitted to man by the bite of an insect vector. The most common vectors are the mosquito, *Aedes aegypti*, for yellow fever and dengue, but other arthropods such as ticks (Colorado tick fever) and flies (sandfly fever) may be more or less specific vectors for certain viruses. These viruses have the ability to multiply in the arthropod vector and to infect them for the life of the insect; however, no transovarial transfer of virus occurs to any significant degree. The cycle for these infections is clear in tropical climates, where the arthropod vector is present year round, but in temperate climes a reservoir not yet clearly defined must exist. Some warm- or cold-blooded animal must carry the virus through the winter and then produce a viremia for the spring crop of insects. If no winter reservoir is present, then the virus must be reintroduced into the temperate climates each year, possibly by migratory birds.

All of these viruses are small, ranging in size from 20 to 50 mμ. The diseases associated with this group of viruses are characterized, for the most part, by central nervous system involvement, so that encephalitis has been almost synonymous with arthropod-borne virus. This is an oversimplification, since a number of these viral agents cause a primarily systemic disease. Classification of the arthropod-borne viruses is difficult. The only logical system appears to be that arising from the work of Clarke, Casals, Olitsky, Sabin, Theiler, Smithburn, and others (1-15), which groups together those viruses which share common antigens, based principally on the hemagglutination-inhibition reaction (Table 1).

Table 1. Serologic Classification of Principal Arthropod-borne Viruses Associated with Human Infections

I. SEROLOGIC GROUP A

Primarily encephalitic infections
1. Eastern Equine Encephalomyelitis
2. Western Equine Encephalomyelitis
3. Venezuelan Equine Encephalomyelitis

Type of human disease not established
1. Semliki Forest Virus
2. Sinbis Virus

II. SEROLOGIC GROUP B

Primarily systemic infections
1. Yellow Fever
2. Dengue Fever
3. West Nile Fever
4. Ilheus Fever
5. Zika Fever

Primarily encephalitic infections
1. St. Louis Encephalitis
2. Japanese B Encephalitis
3. Russian Spring and Summer Encephalitis (Louping Ill (?))
4. Murray Valley Encephalitis

Type of human disease not established
1. Nitaya Virus
2. Uganda S Virus
3. Louping Ill Virus

III. SEROLOGIC GROUP C

A group of Brazilian Viruses. Disease characterized by fever and headache.

IV. UNGROUPED (Not related to Group A and B or to each other)
1. Colorado Tick Fever
2. Sandfly Fever (Two distinct serologic types)
   Neapolitan
   Sicilian

V. MISCELLANEOUS

Includes California, Bunyamera and Bwamba groups.

The hemagglutinin of these viruses is prepared by extracting infected suckling mouse brains with acetone and ether. The hemagglutinin is identical with the virus particle, agglutinates erythrocytes from newly hatched chickens, and is very sensitive to pH, limited to a range of pH 6.4 to 6.8. The hemagglutination is permanent, and no virus elution occurs. Inhibition of hemagglutination by lipid is quite marked, and these lipoprotein inhibitors must be removed from serum, brain, or other tissues used (7). It should be noted that the hemagglutinin associated with these viruses is quite different from that of the influenza-mumps (myxovirus) hemagglutinin. The complement-fixation test is commonly used for diagnostic purposes, although the definitive test is the virus neutralization test performed in mice or tissue culture. Immunofluorescent technics have been applied to these viruses (8, 10).

Hammon has suggested that the name of this group be the **ARBO** (rather than "arbor," which implies a plant virus), and this designation will be used in this text. The principal cycles of infection for **ARBO** viruses are summarized in Figure 3.

SEROLOGIC GROUP A ARTHROPOD-BORNE VIRUSES

EQUINE ENCEPHALOMYELITIS

These viruses, which characteristically produce disease in horses, are easily differentiated as a group from other viruses causing encephalomyelitis by their high degree of pathogenicity for the nervous system of guinea pigs and rabbits (41, 43).

A viral encephalomyelitis of horses and mules has been known in Europe for many years as Borna disease (28). A similar, though more acute, disease occurs in the United States, Canada, South America, Australia, and eastern Asia, where epizootics due to this virus are of great economic importance to the livestock industry. In 1931 Meyer, Haring, and Howitt (35) reported the isolation of a virus from affected California horses, and subsequently Meyer (36) suggested that the disease might be transmitted to man.

In Massachusetts in 1938 a number of patients became ill with a bizarre type of encephalitis which appeared concurrently with an epidemic of encephalomyelitis among horses. Fothergill and others (20) and Webster and Wright (50) established the diagnosis in man by isolation of the eastern type of virus (E.E.E.) from brain tissue. Howitt (26, 27) then reported the isolation of the Western type of virus (W.E.E.) from the brain tissue of a fatal human case in California.

In 1961 in the United States there were 27 cases (3 deaths) of W.E.E. and 1 case of E.E.E., and in 1962 there were 17 (1 death) cases of W.E.E. and no cases of E.E.E. (13). Most of the above cases occurred in Texas.

Morphology. The equine viruses are about 50 mμ in diameter, with a 30 mμ core (38) of ribonucleic acid (RNA). Infectious RNA has been extracted from the whole virus particles (51).

Cultivation. The virus can be grown in the embryonated hen's egg (26). Both the eastern and western viruses grow well in HeLa cell tissue cultures, producing marked cytopathogenic changes in those cultures (42) (Figs. 1, 2).

Spontaneous Infection in Animals. No other virus disease studied thus far has been shown to have such a broad spectrum of susceptible animals and birds. Although attention to the disease resulted from the observation of infection in horses, in which it causes a highly fatal infection known to the laymen as the **blind staggers, forage poisoning, or botulism,** the horse probably is not the primary host, for the virus has been found in a wide variety of wild and domestic animals and birds (49).

This group of viruses is probably maintained in nature in wild birds (23, 30, 45) or transferred to nestlings by mites (37), although it can be transmitted by mosquitoes (17, 23, 24) and is probably transmitted by mosquitoes from birds to both horses and man (33). The eastern encephalomyelitis has been recognized as an unapparent infection in horses (32) and as a spontaneous paralyzing disease of Philippine monkeys (31).

Experimental Infection in Laboratory Animals. Many animals, such as guinea

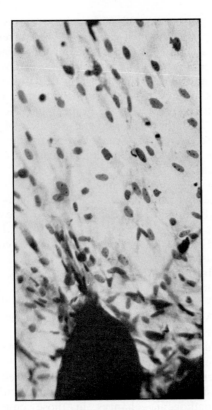

Fig. 1. Cytopathic effect of equine virus. Normal Rhesus monkey testicular tissue culture. × 100. (From Smith and Evans. *J. Immunol.,* 72: 353, 1954.)

pigs (18), rats, mice, monkeys, rabbits, goats, and calves are susceptible to infection with the virus (34, 44). Sheep, dogs, and cats are resistant to the western but not to the eastern type of virus (21). Among the susceptible birds are pigeons, geese, blackbirds, vultures, storks, and ducks (40). After inoculation, chickens and turkeys may carry the virus in the blood without having any symptoms (48).

Clinical Types of Infection in Man. The disease in both men and horses occurs during the summer and fall and is related directly to the prevalence of mosquitoes. The **western** infection occurs most frequently in rural areas and affects both adults and children, whereas **eastern** equine encephalomyelitis is primarily a disease of children. The onset of symptoms is sudden, with high fever, irritability, convulsions, cyanosis, vomiting, drowsiness, and muscular twitch-

ings. All the signs of increased intracranial pressure are present, and spinal fluid examination shows an elevated total protein and a pleocytosis as high as 2,000 cells, predominantly polymorphonuclear in type but later changing to a mononuclear cell predominance.

Deaths occur early in the severely ill, and mental and neurologic residual effects may persist in some who recover. The mortality rate in E.E.E. is more than 50 per cent in symptomatic patients, whereas in W.E.E. it ranges from 5 to 15 per cent.

In man neutralizing antibodies occur in the serum as early as six to eight days after onset. The neutralization test is remarkably specific in this disease, which makes it an excellent laboratory diagnostic adjunct (52).

The virus shows considerable pantropism, attacking tissues of both ectodermal and

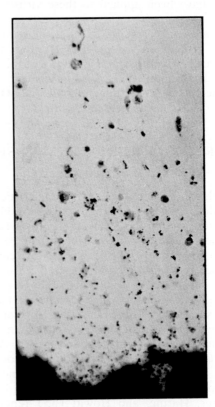

Fig. 2. Cytopathic effect of equine virus. Rhesus monkey testicular culture five days after inoculation with Western equine encephalomyelitis virus showing destruction of most of the cells. × 100. (From Smith and Evans. *J. Immunol.,* 72:353, 1954.)

mesodermal origin. Focal areas of nerve cell destruction, infiltration with polymorphonuclear leukocytes and microglial cells, perivascular cuffing, thrombosis, and frequently neuronophagia are the essential features of this meningoencephalitis (19).

Transmission. Kelser (29) showed that the disease could be transmitted to guinea pigs and horses by infected *Aedes aegypti* mosquitoes. Since that time numerous insects have been shown capable of transmitting the infection, including the tick *Dermacentor andersoni* (47), mites, *Liponyssus sylviarum* (39, 25), and bugs, *Triatoma sanguisuga* (22). *Culex tarsalis* probably is the most important vector of western equine encephalomyelitis. The virus has been isolated from ectoparasites of chickens and birds, and it is possible that the latter provide the reservoir for the mosquito. *Aedes* probably is the vector of the eastern type of the disease (Fig. 3).

Biologic Products. An excellent vaccine for active immunization of horses and mules has been made by formalinizing the virus cultured in the chick embryo (16). The vaccine also has been used successfully in immunizing laboratory workers.

Hyperimmune rabbit serum has been shown to immunize animals passively (53).

Treatment. There is no specific treatment for equine encephalomyelitis.

Prevention. Active immunization of horses not only reduces the occurrence of the disease in these animals but also should reduce the incidence of human infections. Insect control measures should be of value. Laboratory workers handling the virus should be immunized with the vaccine.

Venezuelan Equine Encephalomyelitis

The virus causing the Venezuelan type of equine encephalomyelitis is immunologically distinct from the two types which cause the disease in the United States (54, 57). The virus is highly infectious for man, and in several small laboratory epidemics, two patients died of the infection (55).

The incubation period is only three or four days, and the symptoms resemble those of grippe, with generalized aching, malaise, and severe and persistent headache. Specific neu-

tralizing antibodies appear in the serum during convalescence (56).

SEROLOGIC GROUP B ARTHROPOD-BORNE VIRUSES WHICH CAUSE PRIMARILY SYSTEMIC DISEASES

Yellow Fever

The virus of yellow fever is present in scattered areas over equatorial Africa and South America, where it is maintained by a **forest mosquito-indigenous monkey cycle.** Sporadic cases in woodsmen and hunters occur from time to time, but the classic form of epidemic yellow fever does not develop until the **Aedes aegypti-man cycle** is established. These epidemics began coincidentally with the development of the slave trade between Africa and South America, the first one definitely identified being in Yucatan in 1648 (65). The evidence for an African and a South American origin is equally convincing, although the susceptibility of the South American marsupials favors a South American origin or an origin before the time of the separation of the two continents.

During the seventeenth and eighteenth centuries the disease was endemic in parts of equatorial Africa, South America, and the islands of the Caribbean Sea, from whence it spread periodically during the summer months to the coastal cities of the United States as far north as New York, and to New Orleans, and thence up the Mississippi River. Epidemics also occurred in Spain. The disappearance of the disease in the temperate zone with the arrival of cold weather was noted in 1848 by Josiah Nott (77), who advanced the hypothesis that yellow fever was transmitted by insects. Carlos Finlay observed that the disease disappeared with the disappearance of the mosquitoes and specifically incriminated the *Aedes aegypti* in 1881 (68). Finlay's theory was ignored until it was revived by Carter in 1900 (64).

The growing importance of the disease resulted in the appointment, in 1900, of the American Army Commission for the study of yellow fever, which was headed by Reed, Carroll, Agramonte, and Lazear (80). The courage, self-sacrifice, and scientific accuracy which characterized the work of these men has made the chapter of yellow fever one of the most brilliant in the annals of American scientific achievement. It will be reviewed in some detail. Their work was facilitated considerably by the experiences of Gorgas and others, who had demonstrated that ordinary sanitary regulations failed to limit, in any way, the spread of yellow fever. The commission investigated and soon eliminated *B. icteroides,* described by Sanarelli (81) as the etiologic agent in yellow fever. They then proceeded to investigate the possibility of the mosquito host, beginning their work in August, 1900. Various species of mosquitoes of the genus *Aedes,* then called *Stegomyia,* were allowed to bite nonimmune human volunteers after they had obtained blood meals from patients with yellow fever. The first nine experiments were negative, but the tenth, of which Carroll was the subject, was successful. Four days after being bitten by the infected insect, Carroll became ill with a severe attack of yellow fever, which not only endangered his life but also left residual effects from which he died several years later. On September 13, 1900, Lazear, while working in the yellow fever wards, noticed that an *Aedes* mosquito had settled on his hand, but he deliberately allowed the insect to drink its fill. Five days later he became ill with yellow fever and died after a violent and short illness. After five more successful experiments in which all possible contacts were used, the commission made a series of conclusions.

Yellow fever is acquired, under natural conditions, only by the bite of the female *Aedes aegypti* mosquito (*Stegomyia fasciata*). It is necessary that the infecting insect has attained her blood meal from a yellow fever patient within the first three days of the disease, and an interval of at least 12 days must elapse before it can infect another human. A blood meal from patients after the fifth day of the disease does not seem to render the mosquito infectious. Experiments by the commission to ascertain whether the power of infecting was transmitted transovarially from the mosquito to the next generation were negative, and their findings were confirmed subsequently by Bauer and Hudson (60, 61).

The results of the American Commission were duplicated by Guiteras (72, 73) and Marchoux (75). These observers found that infection could be produced experimentally by the injection of blood and blood serum taken from a patient during the first three days of the disease but not after the fourth day and that 0.1 ml. of serum sufficed for an infection. They also confirmed the observations of Carroll that the virus of the disease could pass through coarse Berkefeld and Chamberland filters.

In 1925, under the auspices of the International Health Division of the Rockefeller Foundation, the subject was reinvestigated in West Africa. The monkeys native to this area of Africa were found to be completely resistant to infection by the yellow fever virus, but the disease could be transmitted to the Asiatic monkey, *Macaca mulatta,* which made possible an extensive investigation of the nature of the virus (89). These results were confirmed in West Africa by Mathis and others (76) and subsequently in South America.

The next major advance was made by Theiler (90), who modified the naturally viscerotropic virus into one with neurotropic properties by passing the infectious agent through the brains of a series of mice. The neurotropic virus retained its immunologic identity but failed to infect either monkey or man when given subcutaneously. The modified virus, however, was still capable of producing encephalitis in monkeys if introduced intracerebrally. The last step to be accomplished was the adaptation of the neurotropic virus to tissue culture (74, 88). After repeated transfers in tissue culture through many generations a strain known as 17-D was stabilized. Because of the depression of its neurotropism and viscerotropism without alteration of its immunizing properties, it could be used for the immunization of man. The virus vaccine in use at the present time is a frozen and dried emulsion of infected chick embryos which is rehydrated with physiologic saline just before use. This vaccine has been used to immunize more than two million individuals in South America, many others in Africa and in the American Army during World War II.

The list of martyrs to yellow fever is a long one and cannot be presented here. It includes soldiers, nurses, attendants, technicians, and physicians. Some died from naturally acquired infections while studying the disease, some were deliberately infected, and others were infected accidentally in the laboratory. Sawyer (82) pays a tribute in his review of 1930 to Adrian Stokes, Noguchi, Alexander Young, Paul Lewis, and Theodore Hayne, all of whom lost their lives from infections contracted in the course of their investigations of this dreaded disease.

Morphology. Electron microscope studies of infected rhesus monkey livers reveal spherical particles measuring 56 to 61 mμ in diameter packed in the cytoplasm (62, 63).

Cultivation. The virus grows in Maintland minced chick embryo tissue culture (91) and in cell lines of human appendix and conjunctiva tissues (67). Cytopathic effects were produced only in appendix cells. The virus also grows in chick fibroblasts, producing plaques in agar overlay preparations.

Resistance. The virus is very unstable in watery or saline suspensions, and relatively large amounts of protein (10 per cent) must be taken to maintain viability. It can be preserved by lyophilization.

Antigenic Structure. The various strains isolated from different parts of Africa and South America seem to be antigenically identical. The virus employed for active immunization may be used as the antigen to demonstrate precipitins, complement-fixing, and neutralizing antibodies in convalescent serums.

Spontaneous Infection in Animals. The monkeys indigenous to Africa and South America are susceptible to infection and maintain the virus in the forest mosquito-monkey cycle. The disease is mild, the period of viremia is short, and recovery is followed by the appearance of protective antibodies in the serum and a permanent immunity. The mildness of the disease in contrast to that in Asiatic monkeys suggests a long period of adaptation to the virus.

Experimental Infection in Laboratory Animals. The Asiatic monkey, *Macaca mulatta,* is very susceptible to experimental infections and develops a rapidly fatal disease following inoculation with blood from a patient with yellow fever. Extensive necrosis of the liver is found at necropsy with intranuclear inclusion bodies (59). A fatal encephalitis is induced by the intracerebral inoculation of the virus.

Birds, cold-blooded animals, *Carnivora, Chiroptera,* and most rodents are resistant to the parenteral inoculation of the virus. Among the moderately susceptible animals are the peccary, anteater, armadillo, sloth, and all of the marsupials (92). Mice develop encephalitis following intracerebral inoculation, and after a number of such passages, the naturally viscerotropic virus becomes neurotropic and loses its ability to produce lesions in the liver of man or monkey, although it remains infectious for the monkey when introduced intracerebrally.

A neurotropic strain adapted by the French workers is used for dermal vaccination in French Equatorial Africa. The virus is preserved in dried mouse brain and mixed with gum arabic immediately before vaccination (78).

Clinical Types of Infection in Man. After the bite of an infected mosquito there is a short **incubation period** of three to six days, followed by the rapid development of fever with severe gastrointestinal symptoms, jaundice, vomiting of blood, albuminuria, and often delirium. The jaundice is moderate, but the prostration is profound, and a decisive conclusion to the illness is reached quickly. The patient dies between the fifth and sixth days of the disease or begins to show striking improvement at this time; convalescence may be prolonged. Some cases simulate influenza virus infections, and many are unapparent. Over-all case mortality is about 5 per cent or less; in those cases which develop clinical jaundice the mortality is much higher. The virus is present in the blood of the patient for a few hours preceding the onset of symptoms and for the first three or four days of the disease. One attack produces an immunity which persists for life. In certain endemic areas in West Africa the entire adult population was found to be immune to yellow fever, which at first was assumed to be due to a racial immunity until it was determined that they had a mild form of yellow fever previously.

At first the symptomatology is related to the general virus infection, but the development of severe liver damage very quickly changes the picture to that of fulminating hepatic insufficiency.

Transmission. Yellow fever occurs in two epidemiologic patterns. The first is the classic or urban pattern described by the Army Commission and is a cycle of man to female *Aedes aegypti* mosquito then back to man. The mosquito takes her blood meal during the first three days of the illness, while there is a marked viremia, and 12 days pass before she can transmit the infection by a bite. The virus multiplies in the mosquito (93) and persists for the life of the insect without harm. The female culicine feeds in the late afternoon and evening. The second pattern is that of the jungle type of yellow fever. The virus has been isolated from a number of species, *Haemogogus, Aedes leucocelaenus* in South America and *Aedes simsoni* in Africa (85, 92). This pattern occurs in areas where colonial outposts border the jungle. Epidemics in the monkeys may serve as a source of this virus and offer a constant threat if a vector of this type of infection might bring it into an area where the *Aedes aegypti* could then start an epidemic on the classic pattern.

Treatment. There is no specific treatment for yellow fever. Although a permanent immunity is produced by injections of the vaccine, convalescent serums containing neutralizing antibodies for the virus have no significant effect on the course of the disease.

Prevention. The destruction of the *Aedes aegypti* mosquito eliminated classic or urban yellow fever from Havana, the Panama Canal Zone, and most of South America. It was not necessary to eliminate all of the Aedes mosquitoes throughout the entire country, but only in certain key areas where the infection was kept going by a constant supply of nonimmune individuals from the surrounding area. For example, the eradication of yellow fever from Guayaquil resulted

in the disappearance of the disease from the entire west coast of South America.

Unfortunately, the disease can spread back from the forest mosquito to man and hence to new areas. Soper traced such an epidemic from its point or origin in the Amazon basin in 1933 through Brazil to Rio de Janeiro in 1938 (87). The last case of classic yellow fever in Panama was reported by Gorgas (71) in 1903), but an investigation (66) in 1950 revealed that the infection is increasing in monkeys and is spreading slowly to man. The existence of jungle yellow fever made imperative the development of a method for vaccination.

ACTIVE IMMUNIZATION. The attenuated and modified virus strain 17-D is used for active immunization. This vaccine, although containing living virus, is entirely innocuous. The immunity conferred by this vaccine is effective for five years (58, 69, 70). During 1941 and 1942, several million doses of yellow fever vaccine were used by the armed forces of the United States. During 1942, 26,771 cases of postvaccinal jaundice appeared, an incidence of 18 per 1,000 vaccinated persons. At first it was suspected that the virus had become active and was producing a modified form of yellow fever. However, it soon was noted that all the cases of jaundice were limited to individuals who had received certain lots of vaccine. Investigations of the preparation and history of certain lots of vaccine suggested that the jaundice-producing factor was associated with the particular batch of human serum used as a stabilizing agent for the vaccine. Although the pooled serums used for the dilutions came from supposedly normal individuals, the epidemiologic data were so convincing that the serum factor was eliminated in subsequent vaccine production, and no more cases of postvaccinal jaundice developed (94).

Diagnosis. The diagnosis of yellow fever can be established with a fair degree of accuracy by the examination of a microscopic section of the liver. In primitive communities with inadequate transportation facilities, a specimen of hepatic tissue obtained by means of a punch biopsy can be preserved in formaldehyde and shipped to a central laboratory for diagnosis. Soper and his associates (86) of the International Health Division of the Rockefeller Foundation introduced the practice of collecting such specimens from the livers of all persons dying with a febrile disease of less than 11 days' duration regardless of the clinical diagnosis. Following the introduction of this relatively simple and innocuous procedure, many thousands of specimens have been examined, and yellow fever has been detected in regions where it was not suspected previously.

Since neutralizing antibodies apparently persist indefinitely in the blood of patients recovered from yellow fever, the neutralization test using mouse-adapted virus can be used to test the serums of individuals of various ages in a community. By such a method it is possible to estimate at what date yellow fever was last present in that area (83, 84).

Perlowagora and Hughes (79) reported the use of a sensitive and specific globulin antigen for use in the complement-fixation test in yellow fever. With this antigen, they showed that antibodies are formed regularly following yellow fever infection but not following yellow fever vaccination.

DENGUE FEVER

Dengue fever is analogous to yellow fever in its host reservoir and mode of spread. The disease is maintained in a forest mosquito-indigenous monkey cycle in various (102) parts of the tropics. The *Aedes aegypti* can be infected from man who has acquired the infection from a forest mosquito, *Aedes scutellaris* or *Aedes albopictus*, after which major epidemics may spread to the temperate zones during the summer months. The common mosquito, *Culex fatigans*, does not transmit the disease (96, 99). In contrast to yellow fever, there are several antigenic types of the virus of which the Hawaiian type shows the best cross-immunity. This type has been used by Sabin (98) and Schlesinger (100) for the preparation of vaccines.

The virus, as measured by filtration, is 17 to 25 mμ. It occurs in enormous amounts in the serum of man during the first 24 hours of the disease, and 1 ml. of blood may contain a million M.I.D. doses for man (99). The nasal instillation of 1 ml. of this serum produced typical attacks of dengue fever in some human volunteers. Symptoms resemble those of measles more than those of yellow fever. As in measles, the patients have photophobia, conjunctivitis, alterations in the sense of taste, enlargement of cervical and other lymph nodes, and the common but not universal development of a maculopapular or scarlatiniform skin rash. Late in the disease a second type of skin rash, which is petechial in nature, develops on mucous membranes of the mouth, and on the wrists, fingers, and dorsum of the feet. The symptoms may be very mild or very severe, but the mortality is very low. Immunity to the invading strain is apparently permanent.

The virus cannot be grown directly in the embryonated egg. After propagation the virus for 101 passages by intracerebral inoculation in mice, Sabin and Schlesinger (98) could grow the modified virus in the embryonated egg. This living but modified virus produced in human volunteers mild infections with a fine macular rash. Specific antibodies developed following the vaccination (100). Vaccination with living attenuated Type II virus has been accomplished by Schlesinger. In these experiments an anamnestic response to yellow fever was observed, suggesting the possibility of broad-spectrum immunization to all viruses of this serologic group (101).

There is no specific treatment. The disease can be prevented by vaccination with the egg culture virus or by the elimination of mosquitoes. The mosquito vector must take its blood meal during the first three days of the disease and cannot transmit the infection until after an 11-day incubation period. There is no hereditary transmission by mosquitoes but the inoculated insects probably remain infectious for life (95, 97, 102, 103).

WEST NILE FEVER

This small virus, 21 to 31 mμ as measured by filtration technics, but 38 to 40 mμ according to electron photomicrographs (106), was isolated from the blood of an African native in 1940 by Smithburn and his associates (107, 108). Its natural insect vector is unknown, but Philip and Smadel (105) found that *Aedes albopictus* could transfer the disease from hamster to hamster. Monkeys can be infected and are probably the host reservoir in Africa. In Egypt a cycle in man, presumably with mosquitoes as the vector, has been established. The disease is so common that Melnick and his associates found both neutralizing and complement-fixing antibodies for the virus in the serums of 70 per cent of the population over four years of age.

Clinically, this is a mild disease, characterized by fever, lymphadenopathy, and rash associated with malaise, headache, and pain in the chest and back. The acute stage lasts only a few days, but convalescence is slow. The virus can be recovered from the blood during the acute phase by inoculations of mice, hamsters, or eggs. Only one antigenic type exists, but the cross-reactions with other viruses of this group must be considered (104).

The virus can be isolated by the inoculation of serum intracerebrally in Swiss mice or by direct culture in the embryonated chick egg. The West Nile virus shares a common antigen with the yellow fever virus (41) and its antibodies afford some protection against the Japanese B and St. Louis viruses. The virus grows well in HeLa cultures (42).

Table 2. Morbidity and Mortality in U.S. of St. Louis Encephalitis, 1961 *

AGE	CASES	DEATHS
0-4	0	
5-9	1	
10-19	5	
20-29	5	1
30-39	4	1
40-49	4	
50-59	5	1
60-69	4	
70+	12	4
Unknown	3	
TOTAL	43	7

* From Encephalitis Surveillance Section, Communicable Disease Center, U.S. Public Health Service.

SEROLOGIC GROUP B ARTHROPOD-BORNE VIRUSES WHICH CAUSE PRIMARILY ENCEPHALITIC DISEASES

ST. LOUIS ENCEPHALITIS

In Cincinnati, Ohio, and Paris, Illinois, during the summer of 1932 there occurred many cases of encephalitis which at first were thought to be instances of encephalitis lethargica of the von Economo type. The following year in St. Louis County, Missouri, more than 1,000 cases of encephalitis were reported; and studies of this epidemic by Muckenfuss, Armstrong, and McCordock (122) and Webster and Fite (127, 128) showed conclusively that the encephalitis was caused by a filtrable virus which was indistinguishable clinically from that which had caused the previous outbreak in Paris, Illinois. The same disease reappeared in St. Louis in 1937, and since that time outbreaks have occurred in other western states (116, 121, 131).

In 1961 in Florida a discrete outbreak of St. Louis Encephalitis occurred in the Tampa Bay area. There were 24 cases, with seven deaths. In the country as a whole in 1961 there were 43 cases summarized in Table 2. Note the increased mortality in the older groups. In 1962 in the same Florida area a major outbreak of more than 200 cases occurred, with at least 28 deaths. Virus

was isolated from mosquitoes, but although antibody was found in some mammals and birds in the area, no virus isolations were made in over 1,400 animal specimens tested (115). The yearly incidence of E.E.E., W.E.E., and St. Louis Encephalitis in the United States for 1955-1961 is given in Table 3.

Morphology. The virus is 20 to 33 mμ in size, as determined by ultrafiltration.

Cultivation. The virus can be grown in media containing minced embryonic mouse tissue (125), in embryonated hen's egg (120), and in tissue cultures of the Ehrlich ascites carcinoma of mice and HeLa cells (42, 112).

Resistance. The virus is resistant to glycerin and freezing; frozen mouse brain emulsions retain their virulence for several months. The virus resists 1 per cent phenol for 25 days if kept cold, and 0.1 per cent

Table 3. Incidence of Encephalitis in the United States, 1955-1961 *

YEAR	W.E.E.	E.E.E.	S.L.E.
1955	37	15	107
1956	47	15	563
1957	35	5	147
1958	141	2	94
1959	14	36	118
1960	21	3	21
1961	27	1	43

* From Encephalitis Surveillance Section, Communicable Disease Center, U.S. Public Health Service.

formalin inactivates it in 12 hours at room temperature (109). Its pH stability range of 8.4 to 8.8 is similar to that of the virus of Japanese B encephalitis (114).

Antigenic Analysis. The viruses causing St. Louis encephalitis and Japanese B encephalitis are related serologically, although they can be distinguished from each other (113, 126).

Spontaneous Infection in Animals. In endemic areas, the serums of many wild animals and birds are found to contain neutralizing antibodies, indicating a wide range of contact with the virus (117). Experimental inoculations of such animals usually result in the development only of subclinical infections and the appearance of antibodies.

Experimental Infection in Laboratory Animals. Mice, inoculated intracerebrally, develop coarse tremors and convulsions, and death usually occurs on the fourth to sixth day. *Macacus rhesus* monkeys are susceptible to infection by intracerebral and intraperitoneal inoculations of suspensions of brain tissue from cases of encephalitis. After a short febrile period the monkeys show excitability and develop muscular weaknesses and tremors, but they recover. *Cebus* and Java monkeys and rabbits are refractory to infection.

Clinical Types of Infection in Man. After an incubation period of 4 to 21 days, there is a sudden onset of headache and high fever, muscular rigidity and tremors. In patients who survive, the severe acute phase lasts from seven to 10 days, and recovery is both rapid and complete. The spinal fluid, which usually is under slightly increased pressure, shows a pleocytosis of 50 to 250 mononuclear cells.

Complement-fixing antibodies appear after the first week of the disease and may aid in confirming the clinical impression (110).

The serums of 82 per cent of the convalescents show neutralizing antibodies, as demonstrated by mouse protection tests (129). Wooley (130) examined normal human serums collected from different parts of the United States and found that 30 per cent of the samples contained neutralizing antibodies for the virus. The disease is not confined to the United States, for neutralizing antibodies also have been found in serums obtained in various regions of Africa (124).

The histopathologic picture of affected brain tissue shows a nonsuppurative inflammatory process with perivascular infiltration by mononuclear cells. Neuronophagia is seen in some of the areas of focal accumulations of cells.

Transmission. The epidemic in St. Louis began in July and ended abruptly in October. At first the disease had a rural distribution, and the cases appeared to be concentrated near small streams, ponds and areas where open sewage was draining. The epidemiologic data pointed to an insect vector, but the early investigations failed to substantiate this hypothesis. However, evidence has been accumulating that an insect is involved in the transmission of the infection (Fig. 3). Hammon and Reeves (118), studying the mosquito *Culex dorsalis* in the Yakima Valley, Washington, isolated three strains of the St. Louis virus and proved that the mosquito was capable of transmitting the disease experimentally. He recovered the virus from naturally infected *Aedes* caught in California. Further, the virus was isolated from mites (*Liponyssus sylviarum*) found in the nests of yellow-headed blackbirds (111, 119, 123).

Biologic Products. There is no commercial vaccine available for active immunization. A mouse brain vaccine has been used experimentally.

Treatment. The therapy of St. Louis encephalitis is entirely symptomatic.

Prevention. At the present time mosquito control methods appear to be the only method by which the infection can be prevented.

JAPANESE B ENCEPHALITIS

(B Encephalitis, Summer Encephalitis)

This virus was designated B by the Japanese to distinguish it from the undiscovered A virus which was supposed to be the etiologic agent of von Economo's encephalitis.

For many years, summer outbreaks of an acute encephalitis have occurred in the Japa-

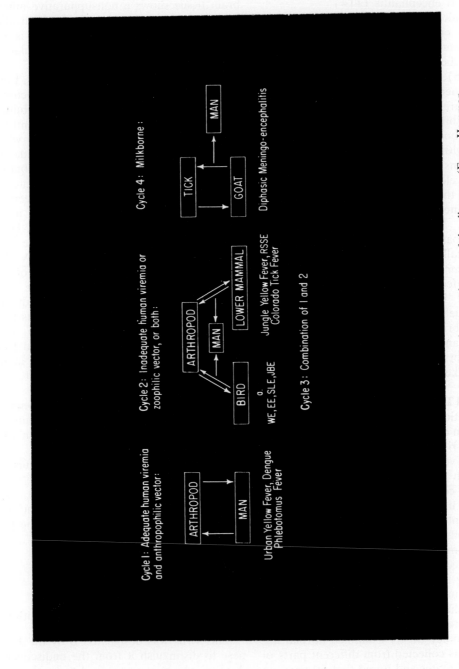

Fig. 3. Epidemiologic patterns of ARBO viruses and some of the diseases. (From Hammon. *Pub. Health Reports*, 76:806, 1961.)

nese Islands. The epidemic of 1924, though centered in the region of the Inland Sea, covered a wide area and accounted for 4,000 deaths among 6,000 reported cases. It was during this last epidemic that the clinical studies by Kaneko and Aoki (147) differentiated this entity. The virus was isolated by Takaki (162) and by Taniguchi and others (163). Since 1924 outbreaks have occurred annually (136, 149, 155).

Japanese B encephalitis also has occurred in Siberia, Korea, the Ryukyu Islands, Formosa, China, Manchuria, and the Maritime Krais (90, 92). In 1945 an outbreak of the disease occurred among natives on Okinawa (149) and U.S. military personnel (141, 155, 158). There were over 5,000 cases, with more than 2,000 deaths in Korea in 1949 (143).

Morphology. By ultracentrifugation and filtration methods the virus has been estimated to be 20 to 30 mμ in size.

Cultivation. The virus can be grown in a medium containing minced chick embryo brain (148) or in the embryonated hen's egg (137, 142, 161) and in tissue cultures of HeLa cells (42, 132).

The virus hemagglutinin was demonstrated in the brains of infected mice by Sabin and Bueschner (156).

Resistance. The virus may be preserved in 50 per cent buffered glycerin for three months, or for a year when frozen in a gastight container in solid CO_2.

Antigenic Analysis. The viruses of St. Louis, West Nile, and Japanese B encephalitis possess common antigens.

Spontaneous Infections in Animals. Mitamura and others (151) reported the presence of the virus in the blood of dogs. Sabin (155) found neutralizing antibodies in the serums of native Okinawan horses, cows, and goats, but not in the serums of chickens. Subsequent investigations which have confirmed those of Sabin show that almost 100 per cent of swine in Korea and Okinawa have neutralizing antibodies (135, 143). In Japan during 1935 and 1947 epidemics of abortions in swine, caused by congenital encephalitis, occurred simultaneously with epidemics of encephalitis in horses and man (133).

Experimental Infection in Laboratory Animals. Inoculation of infected material intracerebrally into mice (157), monkeys, and sheep results in a nonsuppurative meningoencephalitis. Rabbits and guinea pigs are refractive to the virus inoculated in this manner. Horses and pigs, inoculated intravenously, die with an encephalitis, and the virus has been demonstrated in the blood of horses, three and six days after inoculation (150, 164). Hammon and others (139) demonstrated that the virus persisted in the blood of chickens one to seven days after inoculation.

Clinical Infections in Man. Following an **incubation period** of six to eight days, the infection begins with headache, high fever, and subsequent delirium, coma, and paralysis. Normal children have been observed to become severely ill while playing and to develop, within six hours, nuchal rigidity, disassociated eye movements, and a variety of neurologic signs. Although the onset is acute, the subsequent course may be subacute or chronic. Mental and personality changes occur frequently. The pathologic picture is similar to that of louping ill, and the lesion of the Purkinje cells in the cerebellar cortex is the prominent pathologic finding in Japanese B encephalitis (165).

The clinical impression may be confirmed either by the isolation of the virus or by the demonstration of specific antibodies in the patient's serum. The complement-fixing antibody appears early in the infection and subsequently disappears, whereas the neutralizing antibodies may persist for five years. A significant rise in antibody titer is regarded as evidence of the disease. On Okinawa the serums of normal adults were found to contain neutralizing antibodies but rarely complement-fixing antibodies (149, 153).

Transmission. Japanese B encephalitis resembles St. Louis encephalitis in that both host and the vector may be different in different areas (138, 153). In any event, the isolation of the Japanese B encephalitis virus from *Culex tritaeniorhynchus* and *Culex pipiens* var. *pallens* has been reported by Inada (146) and Petrischeva and Shubladse (152). These observations have been confirmed by Hammon and his associates (140) who found that an eight-day interval is necessary after the mosquito feeds on infected mice before she can transmit the disease. The persistence of the virus in experimental hibernating mosquitoes suggests that the virus can pass through the winter in these insects (144). Hamsters have been infected by eating food containing the virus (159), but there is evidence of a rodent reservoir infected with the Japanese B virus.

Many other mosquitoes, including *C. quinquefasciatus,* have been shown to be capable of transmitting the infection experimentally (145). The virus was not isolated from *C. quinquefasciatus* in the Okinawan outbreak in 1945, although this mosquito was present in large numbers before and during the epidemic.

Biologic Products. In 1942 a mouse brain vaccine was developed which consisted of a formaldehyde-inactivated 10 per cent suspension of mouse brain (154). Subsequently Smadel, Randall, and Warren (160) reported that a vaccine against Japanese B encephalitis had been prepared from infected chick embryos. This vaccine, which is stabilized by lyophilization, is now in use by the U.S. Army. Such vaccines are effective in stimulating the production of neutralizing antibodies in man and resistance to infection in mice (134).

There is no specific **treatment** for Japanese B encephalitis, but supportive measures will aid in reducing the mortality.

Prevention is accomplished by vaccination and enforcement of mosquito control measures (83).

RUSSIAN SPRING AND SUMMER ENCEPHALITIS

(Woodcutter's Encephalitis, Forest-Spring Encephalitis, Tick-borne Encephalitis, Vernoaestival (Vernal) Encephalitis)

In certain forested areas of northern Russia and Siberia from April through July an encephalitis occurs which was not differentiated from other types of encephalitis until 1935 (168). The infection is transmitted by the bite of infected ticks (*Ixodes persulcatus* and others) and occurs chiefly among human males frequenting the tick-infested areas in this region. Silber (174) reported that the causative agent was a virus.

Morphology. The virus is about 20 mμ in size, as estimated by ultrafiltration studies.

Resistance. The virus can be preserved in 50 per cent buffered glycerin or by maintaining it at $-70°$ C.

Antigenic Analysis. There is little antigenic relationship between the virus causing Russian spring-summer encephalitis and those causing St. Louis encephalitis and Japanese B encephalitis (167). Casals and Webster (166) reported that the virus of Russian spring-summer encephalitis perhaps is identical with that of louping ill, a tick-borne disease of sheep.

Spontaneous Infection in Animals. In the endemic areas, the virus has been found in blood samples collected from rodents such as field mice, rats, moles, squirrels, hamsters, chipmunks, porcupines, and rabbits (170, 176). Such infected animals seldom show any symptoms of the infection.

Experimental Infection in Laboratory Animals. Intracerebral inoculations of the virus into mice results in an encephalitis. Subsequent passage of the virus by intraperitoneal inoculation of mice results regularly in death of the animal. Such behavior distinguishes the virus from Japanese B encephalitis virus and other encephalitis-producing viruses in which intraperitoneal injections of mouse-passed virus do not cause death.

Clinical Types of Infection in Man. After an incubation period of 8 to 18 days following the bite by an infected tick, the patient has an acute onset of an illness which is characterized by headache, cervical pain, fever, nausea and vomiting, and vertigo and coma (172, 175, 177). Muscle paralysis, if it appears, occurs most commonly on the second or third day of the disease. The virus occurs in the blood and spinal fluid during the acute phase of the illness (177). The spinal fluid shows a pleocytosis of 40 to 200 cells, most of which are lymphocytes. The acute symptoms last from two to 10 days and the mortality rate varies from 2 to 30 per cent in nonvaccinated patients. Neutralizing antibodies may be demonstrated in the serums about one month after the onset of the disease and persist for many years (175). Approximately 20 per cent of the patients have neurologic residual effects such as paralysis and atrophy of the muscles of the neck and shoulder girdle. Histopathologic studies of brain tissues reveal perivascular infiltrations of the blood vessels and degenerative changes of the neurons of the medulla and spinal cord, which range from chromatolysis and loss of Nissl substance to complete necrosis and neuronophagia.

Transmission. The infection is transmitted by the ticks *Ixodes persulcatus, Dermacentor silvarum* and *Haemaphysalis concinna.*

Biologic Products. A mouse brain vaccine (169) and an egg vaccine (173) have been tested and found effective.

Prevention. Russian spring-summer encephalitis is rare in those endemic areas in which the forests have been cleared. The use of the vaccine has greatly reduced the morbidity and mortality (171).

LOUPING ILL

The virus of louping ill and Russian Far Eastern encephalitis are closely related antigenically and appear to have a minor antigen in common with West Nile and Japanese B viruses (41).

In the counties along the border between England and Scotland, there exists a tick-borne encephalomyelitis of sheep. The disease, which occurs in the spring and fall, has a mortality among lambs and yearlings of approximately 50 per cent. The survivors usually are immune.

Pool and his associates (184) produced the disease in sheep and swine by the intracerebral inoculation of emulsions of infected brain tissue. Gordon and others (183) found that the virus was present in the blood during the febrile stage of the infection and that the infection could be transmitted to cattle, monkeys, and mice. The virus can be grown in tissue cultures or on the chorioallantoic membrane of 10-day-old chicks. The natural infection is transmitted by the tick, *Ixodes ricinus* (186). Filtration experiments by Elford and Galloway (182) indicate that the virus is from 15 to 20 mμ in size.

Accidental infections have occurred in laboratory workers (185), and the virus has been recovered from the spinal fluid of a shepherd who contracted the disease directly or indirectly from sheep (179). Convalescent patients and those having inapparent infections exhibit neutralizing antibodies (185) and complement-fixing antibodies (180, 181).

MURRAY VALLEY ENCEPHALITIS

In 1917 and 1918 there occurred in Australia an encephalitis with a high case fatality rate. A similar disease occurred in New South Wales in 1922 and 1926. Monkeys and sheep, cattle, and horses were found to be susceptible to inoculations of the virus. Although the disease resembled Japanese B encephalitis clini-

cally, no comparative studies were made because it was impossible to maintain the Australian virus.

A recent outbreak of encephalitis in the Murray Valley in Australia was investigated by Anderson and others and a virus isolated. Subsequent studies show the disease to be endemic in this area in a variety of animals including birds. Spread is via birds, mites, and mosquitoes. The virus is related to the virus of Japanese B encephalitis (178).

MISCELLANEOUS ARTHROPOD-BORNE VIRUSES

COLORADO TICK FEVER

Colorado tick fever, although once thought to be a rickettsial infection, now is known to be a virus disease (191, 192), and, in spite of the implication of the name, the disease is distinct from Rocky Mountain spotted fever (199). The virus causes a similar clinical picture to that of dengue and sandfly fevers but is entirely distinct immunologically (188, 193, 198). The virus kills hamsters and may be adapted to the mouse and embryonated hen's egg (197).

Recently Colorado tick fever virus has been isolated from ground squirrels and porcupines collected in Western Colorado (190). The animal of choice for laboratory isolation of the virus is the suckling mouse, where the principal lesions were found in the heart and brain (195). Heart lesions consisted of necrosis of muscle and the brain showed liquefaction necrosis of the cerebellar folia. The fluorescent antibody technic has been applied to identification of the virus in mouse brains (187).

This virus is about 20 mμ in size. It has been recovered from *Dermacentor andersoni* collected on Long Island, N.Y., although the disease has not been recognized in the East (194). A vaccine made from an egg-adapted strain protected volunteers from infection with the human strain of living virus (196). Dr. Florio and his associates have isolated the virus from the spinal fluid of a series of patients, although they had no meningeal symptoms other than headache (personal communication).

Clinically the disease is characterized by the acute onset of chills, headache, nausea, fever, and anorexia. Leukopenia is common. Clinical meningoencephalitis may occur, but in general this is a benign disease. It should be suspected in any febrile disease following exposure to ticks in the Northwestern United States (189).

SANDFLY FEVER

(Pappataci Fever, Three Day Fever)

This disease was found originally in countries bordering upon the Mediterranean, but since then it has been described in many different parts of the world, especially in the warmer climates, where epidemics occur in the summer. Although the disease has been known for a long time, it was not recognized as a separate entity until recently, since its bold character, sudden onset, and rapid defervescence led to its confusion with other diseases. The disease was studied thoroughly by an Austrian Commission (201).

The **incubation period,** as determined by the intracutaneous inoculation of the virus, is two and one-half to six days (202, 204). The disease is characterized by a fever, up to 104° F., which lasts about two or three days and is accompanied by muscular pains and generalized symptoms. Vomiting and severe gastrointestinal disturbance may be present in severe cases (205).

The virus can be demonstrated in the blood one day before and two days after the onset of fever. Recovery is followed by an immunity of at least four months.

In 1908 Doerr (200) succeeded in transmitting the disease by the bite of the sandfly. The flies were permitted to bite patients during the first 24 hours of the fever. When the infected insects were allowed to bite normal non-immunes, Doerr found that transfer of the disease was possible only after the infected blood had been in the body of the sandfly for at least four to five days, a fact which proved that simple mechanical transfer of virus was not sufficient to cause infection.

Recovery of virus from suspected cases is accomplished by intracerebral inoculation of newborn mice (203). There are two distinct immunologic types of viruses, and infection with one does not produce immunity to the other.

RIFT VALLEY FEVER

This disease, which affects chiefly sheep, cattle, and goats, occurs primarily in Kenya, Sudan, Uganda, and the French Sudan (209). Man also is susceptible, and fatal human laboratory infections have been reported (208, 211, 213).

The virus of Rift Valley fever was isolated first by Daubney and others (207), who also established its pathogenicity for man. The size of the virus has been estimated to be in the range of 23 to 35 mμ (206), and it has been grown in tissue culture (212). It is destroyed by a temperature of 56° C. for 40 minutes but survives in phenol at 40° C. for six months.

The disease can be transmitted to mice, monkeys, and ferrets but not to guinea pigs or rabbits. The routes of inoculation may be intracerebral, intraperitoneal, intranasal, intracutaneous, or subcutaneous. The laboratory animal of choice is the mouse, and infected mice usually die within 36 to 96 hours after intraperitoneal or intracerebral inoculation (214). Histopathologic studies reveal acidophilic intranuclear inclusion bodies.

In man the disease is characterized by the sudden onset of severe headaches, fever, severe aching in the muscles, bones, and joints, anorexia, malaise, and an uneventful recovery three days later, resembling, in this respect, sandfly fever (214). Most of the reported cases of the disease in man have resulted from accidental infections.

The **incubation period,** as judged by laboratory infections, is about one week (215). Sheep are **immune** after an attack of the disease, and the convalescent serums of animals and man contain relatively large quantities of neutralizing and complement-fixing antibodies. Neutralizing antibodies have been found in serums of man and animals as long as 12 years after initial attacks (214).

The mode of **transmission** of the disease is not known, but it has been shown that the virus may gain entrance through the respiratory tract or the skin (210, 214).

The isolation of the virus may be accomplished either by intracerebral or by intraabdominal inoculation of mice with serum or blood, but the blood is infectious only if it is obtained during the first few hours of the disease. The mouse inoculation technic is used to differentiate Rift Valley fever from sandfly fever and dengue, since neither of the latter viruses is infectious for this animal. Apparently only a single virus strain exists.

REFERENCES

1. Casals, J., and Brown, L. J. Exper. Med., 99:429, 1954.
2. ———— and Brown, L. Proc. Soc. Exper. Biol. & Med., 83:170, 1953.
3. Chanock, R. M., and Sabin, A. B. Am. J. Dis. Child., 84:628, 1952.
4. ———— and Sabin, A. B. J. Immunol., 70:271, 1953.
5. ———— and Sabin, A. B. J. Immunol., 73:352, 1954.

6. Clarke, D. H., and Casals, J. Proc. Soc. Exper. Biol. & Med., 88:96, 1955.
7. ——— and Casals, J. Am. J. Trop. Med., 7:561, 1958.
8. De Groat, C. J., and others. Virology, 12:317, 1960.
9. Kerr, J. A. J. Immunol., 68:461, 1952.
10. Metzger, J. F., and others. Proc. Soc. Exper. Biol. & Med., 106:213, 1961.
11. Sabin, A. B., and Buescher, E. L. Proc. Soc. Exper. Biol. & Med., 74:222, 1950.
12. Smithburn, K. C. J. Immunol., 68:441, 1952.
13. Surveillance Section, C.D.C., U.S.P.H.S.
14. Sweet, B. H., and Sabin, A. B. J. Immunol., 73:363, 1954.
15. Taylor, R. M. J. Immunol., 68:473, 1952.

EQUINE ENCEPHALOMYELITIS
(Eastern and Western)

16. Beard, J. W. J. Immunol., 58:49, 1948.
17. Chamberlain, R. W., and others. Proc. Soc. Exper. Biol. & Med., 77:396, 1951.
18. Cox, H. R., and Olitsky, P. K. J. Exper. Med., 64:223, 1936.
19. Farber, S., and Branch, C. Arch. Path., 27:647, 1939.
20. Fothergill, L. D., and others. New England J. Med., 219:411, 1938.
21. Giltner, L. T., and Shahan, M. S. J. Am. Vet. M. A., 88:363, 1936.
22. Grundemann, A. W., and others. J. Infect. Dis., 72:163, 1943.
23. Hammon, W. McD., and others. J. Immunol., 67:357, 1951.
24. ——— Bull. New York Acad. Med., 1952 (in press).
25. ——— and others. Science, 107:92, 1948.
26. Higbie, E., and Howitt, B. J. Bact., 29:399, 1935.
27. Howitt, B. F. Science, 88:455, 1938.
28. Hurst, E. W. J. Exper. Med., 59:529, 1934.
29. Kelser, R. A. J. Am. Vet. M. A., 82:767, 1933.
30. Kissling, R. E., and others. Proc. Soc. Exper. Biol. & Med., 77:398, 1951.
31. Livesey, H. R. J. Infect. Dis., 84:306, 1949.
32. Mace, D. L., and others. Bull. U.S. Army Med. Dept., 9:504, 1949.
33. Merrill, M. H., and Tenbroeck, C. J. Exper. Med., 62:687, 1935.
34. Meyer, K. F. North American Vet., 14:30, 1933.
35. ——— and others. Science, 74:227, 1931.
36. ——— and others. Am. Int. Med., 6:645, 1932-1933.
37. Miles, V. I., and others. Proc. Soc. Exper. Biol. & Med., 77:395, 1951.
38. Morgan, C., and others. J. Exper. Med., 113:219, 1961.
39. Reeves, W. C., and others. Science, 105:41, 1947.
40. Remlinger, P., and Bailly, J. Compt. rend. Soc. de biol., 123:562, 1936.
41. Sabin, A. B. Bull. New York Acad. Sc., 1952.
42. Scherer, W. F., and Syverton, J. T. Am. J. Path., 30:1075, 1954.
43. Schultz, E. W. chap. The Neurotropic Virus, Ann. Rev. Microbiol., 2:335, 1948.
44. Shahan, M. S., and Giltner, L. T. J. Am. Vet. M. A., 84:928, 1934.

45. Sooter, C. A., and others. Proc. Soc. Exper. Biol. & Med., 77:393, 1951.
46. Surveillance Section. C.D.C. U.S.P.H.S.
47. Syverton, J. T., and Berry, G. P. J. Bact., 33:60, 1937.
48. Tenbroeck, C. Arch. Path., 25:759, 1938.
49. ——— and others. J. Exper. Med., 62:677, 1935.
50. Webster, L. T., and Wright, F. H. Science, 88:305, 1938.
51. Wecker, E. Virology, 7:241, 1959.
52. Whitman, L. J. Immunol., 56:97, 1947.
53. Zichis, J., and Shaughnessy, H. J. J.A.M.A., 115:1071, 1940.

VENEZUELAN EQUINE ENCEPHALOMYELITIS

54. Beck, C. E., and Wyckoff, R. W. G. Science, 88:530, 1938.
55. Casals, J., and others. J. Exper. Med., 77:521, 1943.
56. Koprowski, H., and Cox, H. R. New England J. Med., 236:647, 1947.
57. Kubes, V., and Rios, F. A. Science, 90-20, 1939.

YELLOW FEVER

58. Anderson, C. R., and Gast-Galvis, A. Am. J. Hyg., 45:302, 1947.
59. Angulo, J. J., and others. J. Bact., 57:297, 1949.
60. Bauer, J. H., and Hudson, N. P. Am. J. Trop. Med., 8:371, 1928.
61. ——— J. Exper. Med., 48:147, 1928.
62. Bearcroft, W. G. C. J. Path. & Bact., 80:421, 1960.
63. ——— J. Path. & Bact., 83:59, 1962.
64. Carter, H. R. New Orleans M. & S. J., 52:617, 1900.
65. ——— Yellow Fever, ed. by L. A. Carter and W. H. Frost, Baltimore, Williams & Wilkins Co., 1931.
66. Courtney, K. O. Am. J. Pub. Health, 40:417, 1950.
67. Doherty, R. L. Virology, 6:575, 1958.
68. Finlay, C. An. r. Acad. de cien. méd. de la Habana, 1881.
69. Fox, J. P., and Cabral, A. S. Am. J. Hyg., 37:93, 1943.
70. ——— Am. J. Hyg., 46:1, 1947.
71. Gorgas, W. C. J. Trop. Med., 1903.
72. Guiteras, R. Rev. de méd. trop. y parasitol., bacteriol., clin. y lab., Jan. 1901.
73. ——— New York Med. J., 77:10, 1901.
74. Lloyd, W., and others. Tr. Soc. Trop. Med. & Hyg., 29:481, 1936.
75. Marchoux, and others. Ann. Inst. Pasteur, 17:665, 1903.
76. Mathis, C., and others. Compt. rend. Acad. sc., 186:604, 1928.
77. Nott, J. C. New Orleans M. & S. J., 4:563, 1848.
78. Peltier, M., and others. Ann. Inst. Pasteur, 65:146, 1940.
79. Perlowagora, A., and Hughes, T. P. J. Immunol., 55:103, 1947.
80. Reed, W., and others. Philippine M. J., October, 1900; Pub. Health Rep., 1903.
81. Sanarelli, G. Ann. Inst. Pasteur, 11:433, 1897.
82. Sawyer, W. A. Recent Progress in Yellow Fever Research, DeLamar Lecture, Johns

Hopkins Univ. School of Hyg. & Pub. Health, 1930.
83. Sawyer, W. A. Medicine, 10:509, 1931.
84. ——— and Lloyd, W. J. Exper. Med., 54: 533, 1931.
85. Shannon, R. C., and others. Science, 88: 110, 1938.
86. Soper, F. L., and others. Am. J. Hyg., 19: 549, 1934.
87. ——— Tr. Roy. Soc. Trop. Med. & Hyg., 32:297, 1938.
88. ——— and Smith, H. H. Am. J. Trop. Med., 18:111, 1938.
89. Stokes, A., and others. J.A.M.A., 90:253, 1928.
90. Theiler, M. Ann. Trop. Med., 24:249, 1930.

YELLOW FEVER

91. Theiler, M., and Smith, H. H. J. Exper. Med., 65:767, 1937.
92. ——— Yellow Fever, in Viral and Rickettsial Infections of Man, Philadelphia, J. B. Lippincott Co., 1948, p. 420.
93. Whitman, L. J. Exper. Med., 66:133, 1937.
94. Report. J.A.M.A., 119:1110, 1942; 120:51, 1942.

DENGUE FEVER

95. Ashburn, P. M., and Craig, C. F. Philippine J. Sc., 2:93, 1907.
96. Cleland, J. B., and others. M. J. Australia, 2:179, 1916.
97. Downs, W. G., and others. Suppl. Am. J. Trop. Med., 27:69, 1947.
98. Sabin, A. B., and Schlesinger, R. W. Science, 101:640, 1945.
99. ——— Dengue Fever, in Viral and Rickettsial Infections of Man, Philadelphia, J. B. Lippincott Co., 1948, p. 445.
100. Schlesinger, R. W. Am. J. Hyg., 51:248, 1950.
101. ——— Personal Communication.
102. Siler, J. F., and others. J.A.M.A., 84:1163, 1925.
103. ——— and others. Philippine J. Sc., 29:1, 1926.

WEST NILE FEVER

104. Goldblum, N., and others. Am. J. Hyg., 59:89, 1954.
105. Philip, C. B., and Smadel, J. E. Proc. Soc. Exper. Biol. & Med., 53:49, 1943.
106. Smithburn, K. C., and Bugher, J. C. J. Bact., 66:173, 1953.
107. ——— J. Immunol., 44:25, 1942.
108. ——— and others. Am. J. Trop. Med., 20: 471, 1940.

ST. LOUIS ENCEPHALITIS

109. Brodie, M. Proc. Soc. Exper. Biol. & Med., 31:1227, 1934.
110. Casals, J., and Palacios, R. J. Exper. Med., 74:409, 1941.
111. Chamberlin, R. W., and others. Am. J. Hyg., 77:221, 1959.
112. Cheever, F. S., and Dickos, J. Proc. Soc. Exper. Biol. & Med., 83:822, 1953.
113. Cox, H. R., and Fite, G. L. Proc. Soc. Exper. Biol. & Med., 31:499. 1934.

114. Duffy, C. E. Proc. Soc. Exper. Biol. & Med., 63:333, 1946.
115. Encephalitis Surveillance. Annual Summary, 1961 and 1962.
116. Hammon, W. McD. J.A.M.A., 121:560, 1943.
117. ——— and others. J. Immunol., 67:357, 1951.
118. ——— and Reeves, W. C. Am. J. Pub. Health, 35:994, 1945.
119. ——— and others. Science, 107:92, 1948.
120. Harrison, R. W., and Moore, E. Am. J. Path., 13:361, 1937.
121. Lennette, E. H. Proc. Soc. Exper. Biol. & Med., 61:206, 1946.
122. Muckenfuss, R. S., and others. Pub. Health Rep., 48:1341, 1933.
123. Reeves, W. C., and others. Science, 105: 411, 1947.
124. Smithburn, K. C., and Jacobs, H. R. J. Immunol., 44:9, 1942.
125. Syverton, J. T., and Berry, G. P. Science, 82:596, 1935.
126. Webster, L. T. J. Exper. Med., 67:609, 1938.
127. ——— and Fite, G. L. Science, 78:463, 1933.
128. ——— Proc. Soc. Exper. Biol. & Med., 31: 344, 1933.
129. ——— and others. J. Exper. Med., 62:827, 1935.
130. Wooley, J. G. Pub. Health Rep., 49:1495, 1934.
131. Report. U.S. Pub. Health Bull., No. 214, 1935.

JAPANESE B ENCEPHALITIS

132. Banta, J. E. Am. J. Hyg., 67:286, 1958.
133. Burns, K. F. Proc. Soc. Exper. Biol. & Med., 75:621, 1950.
134. Cox, H. R. Am. J. Pub. Health, 38:351, 1948.
135. Deuel, R. E., and others. Am. J. Hyg., 51:1, 13, 21, 1950.
136. Epidemic Encephalitis, Third Report of the William J. Matheson Commission for Encephalitis Research, New York, Columbia University Press, 1939, p. 159.
137. Haagen, E., and Crodel, B. Zentralbl. f. Bakt., 142:269, 1938.
138. Hammon, W. McD., and Reeves, W. C. Am. J. Pub. Health, 35:994, 1945.
139. ——— and others. Proc. Soc. Exper. Biol. & Med., 61:304, 1946.
140. ——— and others. Am. J. Hyg., 50:46, 51, 1949.
141. Hodes, H. L., and others. Proc. Soc. Exper. Biol. & Med., 60:220, 1945.
142. Howitt, B. F. Proc. Soc. Exp. Biol. & Med., 62:105, 1946.
143. Hullinghorst, R. L. J.A.M.A., 145:460, 1951.
144. Hurlbut, H. S. Am. J. Hyg., 51:265, 1950.
145. ——— and Thomas, J. I. Am. J. Trop. Med., 30:683, 1950.
146. Inada, R. Bull. Office internat. d'hyg. pub., 29:1389, 1937.
147. Kaneko, R., and Aoki, Y. Ergebn. d. inn. Med. u. Kinderh., 34:342, 1928.
148. Kawakita, Y. Jap. J. Exper. Med., 17:211, 1939.

149. Lewis, L., and others.   Arch. Neurol. & Psychiat., 57:430, 1947.
150. Meiklejohn, G., and others.   Proc. Soc. Exper. Biol. & Med., 65:359, 1947.
151. Mitamura, T., and others.   Tr. Path. Soc. Japan, 27:573, 1937; 29:72, 1939.
152. Petrischeva, P. A., and Shubladse, A. K. Arch. Dis. Sc. Biol., 59:72, 1940.
153. Sabin, A. B.   Proc. Soc. Exper. Biol. & Med., 65:127, 1947.
154. ———— J.A.M.A., 122:477, 1943.
155. ———— J.A.M.A., 133:281, 1947.
156. ———— and Buescher, E. L.   Proc. Soc. Exper. Biol. & Med., 74:222, 1950.
157. ———— and others.   J.A.M.A., 122:477, 1943.
158. ———— and others.   Proc. Soc. Exper. Biol. & Med., 65:135, 1947.
159. Schabel, F. M., Jr.   J. Infect. Dis., 88:32, 1951.
160. Smadel, J. E., and others.   Bull. U.S. Army M. Dept., 7:963, 1947.
161. Smith, M. G., and Lennette, E. H.   Proc. Soc. Exper. Biol. & Med., 41:323, 1939.
162. Takaki, I.   Ztschr. f. Immunitätsforsch. u. exper. Therap., I Mitteilung, 47:441, 1926.
163. Taniguchi, T., and others.   Jap. J. Exper. Med., 13:48, 1936.
164. Thomas, L., and Peck, J. L.   Proc. Soc. Exper. Biol. & Med., 61:5, 1946.
165. Zimmerman, H. M.   Am. J. Path., 22:965, 1946.

RUSSIAN SPRING AND SUMMER ENCEPHALITIS

166. Casals, J., and Webster, L. T.   Science, 97:246, 1943.
167. ———— J. Exper. Med., 79:341, 1944.
168. Chumakov, M. P., and Seitlenok, N. A. Science, 92:263, 1940.
169. Ovchinnikova, L. D., and others.   Problems of Virology (London), 4:56, 1959.
170. Pavloskii, E. N., and Soloviev, V. D.   Arch. di sc. biol., 59:111, 1940.
171. Pervushin, V. P.   Klin. med., 21:17, 1943.
172. Shubladze, A. K., and Serdinkova, G. V. Arch. di sc. biol., 56:2, 1939.
173. ———— J. Microbiol. Epidem., 29:1642, 1958.
174. Silber, L. A.   Arch. Sc. Biol. (Moscow) 56:9, 1939.
175. Smorodintsev, A.   Arch. f. d. Ges. Virusforsch., 1:468, 1939-40.
176. Soloviev, V. D.   Arch. di sc. biol., 56:132, 1939.
177. Warren, J.   Am. J. Trop. Med., 26:417, 1946.

MURRAY VALLEY ENCEPHALITIS

178. Anderson, S. G.   Med. J. Aust., 1:3, 1952.

LOUPING ILL

179. Brewis, E. G., and others.   Lancet, 1:689, 1949.
180. Casals, J., and Palacios, R.   J. Exper. Med., 74:409, 1941.
181. ———— J. Exper. Med., 79:341, 1944.
182. Elford, W. J., and Galloway, I. A.   J. Path. & Bact., 37:381, 1933.
183. Gordon, W. S., and others.   J. Compt. Path. & Therap., 45:106, 1932.

184. Pool, W. A., and others.   J. Comp. Path. & Therap., 43:253, 1930.
185. Rivers, T. M., and Schwentker, F. F.   J. Exper. Med., 59:669, 194.
186. Silber, L. A., and Shubladze, A. K.   Am. Rev. Soviet Med., 2:339, 1945.

COLORADO TICK FEVER

187. Burgdorfer, W., and Lackman, D.   J. Bact., 80:131, 1960.
188. DeBoer, C. J., and others.   Proc. Soc. Exper. Biol. & Med., 64:202, 1947.
189. Eklund, C. M., and others.   J.A.M.A., 157:335, 1955.
190. ———— and others.   Science, 128:413, 1958.
191. Florio, L., and others.   J. Exper. Med., 80:165, 1944; 83:1, 1946.
192. ———— and others.   J. Exper. Med., 83:295, 1946.
193. ———— and Miller, M. S.   Am. J. Pub. Health, 38:211, 1948.
194. ———— and others.   J. Immunol., 64:257, 265, 1950.
195. Hadlow, W. J.   J. Infect. Dis., 101:158, 1958.
196. Koprowski, H., and others.   Proc. Soc. Exper. Biol. & Med., 74:126, 1950.
197. ———— and Cox, H. R.   Immunol., 57:239, 255, 1947.
198. Pollard, M., and others.   Proc. Soc. Exper. Biol. & Med., 61:396, 1946.
199. Shaffer, F. C.   Colorado Med., 32:226, 1935.

SANDFLY FEVER

200. Doerr, R.   Berl. klin. Wchnschr., 45:1847, 1908.
201. ———— and others.   Wien. klin. Wchnschr., 22:609, 1909.
202. Sabin, A. B., and Paul, J. R.   J.A.M.A., 125:693, 1944.
203. ———— and Sweet, B. H.   Proc. 5th Internat. Cong. Trop. Med. Malaria, Istanbul, 1953.
204. ———— and others.   J.A.M.A., 125:603, 1944.
205. Shortt, H. E., and others.   Indian J. M. Research, 27:847, 1940.

RIFT VALLEY FEVER

206. Broom, J. C., and Findlay, G. M.   Brit. J. Exper. Path., 14:179, 1933.
207. Daubney, R., and others.   J. Path. & Bact., 34:545, 1931.
208. Findlay, G. M.   Brit. J. Exper. Path., 17:89, 1936.
209. ———— and others.   Bull. Soc. path. exot., 29:986, 1936.
210. Francis, T., Jr., and Magill, T. P.   J. Exper. Med., 62:433, 1935.
211. Kitchen, S. F.   Am. J. Trop. Med., 14:547, 1934.
212. Mackenzie, R. D.   J. Path. & Bact., 37:75, 1933.
213. Schwentker, F. F., and Rivers, T. M.   J. Exper. Med., 59:305, 1934.
214. Sabin, A. B., and Blumberg, R. W.   Proc. Soc. Exper. Biol. & Med., 64:385, 1947.
215. Smithburn, K. C., and others.   J. Immunol., 62:213, 1949.

75

Miscellaneous Diseases of Suspected Viral Etiology

INFECTIOUS MONONUCLEOSIS

This acute, infectious disease of children and young adults is characterized by changes in the blood, liver, and sometimes the central nervous system. The symptoms are usually mild, with sore throat, malaise, and some fever. The cervical lymph nodes are most often affected, but sometimes all peripheral nodes are enlarged. The spleen and liver may be palpable. A few patients have photophobia, conjunctivitis, and a skin rash.

The most characteristic finding is the change in the peripheral blood, where peculiar lymphocytes with somewhat basophilic or vacuolated cytoplasm make up 40 to 60 per cent of the total white cells. After the first week of the disease 60 to 92 per cent of the patients have agglutinins for sheep cells in a titer of 1:64 or greater. These agglutinins or heterophile antibodies are measured by the Paul-Bunnell test (3, 9).

Heterophile antibodies found in apparently normal serum can be adsorbed completely by guinea pig kidney, and those which appear after the injection of horse serum are adsorbed by guinea pig kidney and by boiled beef red blood cells. Such treatment does not eliminate the specific heterophile antibodies of infectious mononucleosis (2). Human erythrocytes which have been treated with the virus of Newcastle's disease of chickens are often agglutinated in high titer by convalescent serum from patients with infectious mononucleosis. This reaction was reported by Burnet and Anderson, but its significance is not clear.

A viral etiology is suspected but has not been proved; Wising's (12) success in transferring the infection to monkeys has not been repeated. Moreover, experimental transmission of the disease to human volunteers using various materials such as throat washings, lymph node extracts, and so forth has been unsuccessful. Epidemics of infectious mononucleosis have been reported but in each instance the epidemicity is open to serious question. Characteristically, for example, the disease does not occur in college roommates. A most provocative recent paper by Hoagland (4) proposes that transmission of the disease occurs among young men and women who indulge in kissing intimate enough to allow the intermixing of saliva. This theory would explain a number of very puzzling features of this disease. It accounts for the peak incidence in the 17-to-26-year age group and explains why dormitory spread does not occur. It also explains why the incidence is high in nurses, students, and interns, while cross infections to patients under their care are absent. Further study of this observation will be necessary to test the validity of the hypothesis (4).

There is increasing emphasis on hepatic involvement in infectious mononucleosis, particularly in differentiating this disease in which pharyngitis is such a prominent feature from acute bacterial pharyngitis. Jaundice with relatively high bilirubin levels of 10-30 mg. per cent have been reported (1, 6); however, the usual picture resembles that of mild infectious hepatitis. Liver biopsy may show definite hepatitis without jaundice or hepatic enlargement (8). There is usually an increase in the serum glutamic oxalacetic transaminase or the serum glutamic pyruvic transaminase, which may be of help in the differential diagnosis. In 48 patients with infectious mononucleosis 36 showed an increased SGP-T, whereas in 42 cases of acute bacterial tonsillitis the SGP-T was normal (7).

The mechanism of jaundice is not entirely clear. In some instances it may be a hemolytic process (11), but in most instances it is due to the liver parenchymal cell damage (5). Histologically the hepatitis of infectious mononucleosis can be differentiated from that of infectious hepatitis in that the former shows infiltrates of Downey cells and focal and minimal hepatic cell necrosis without disruption of hepatic cell plates.

It is of interest that a number of cases of toxoplasmosis mimic infectious mononucleosis and must be considered in the differential diagnosis. Of 92 college students suspected of infectious mononucleosis, significant rises in antibody titer to toxoplasma were found in 3, and toxoplasma organisms were isolated from the blood of 1 of these (10).

EPIDEMIC HEMORRHAGIC FEVER

A disease characterized by hemorrhages in the skin, mucous membranes, and internal organs was described in 1930 by Japanese physicians stationed in Manchuria (16). They believed the disease was caused by a virus and reported the infection of monkeys by the injection of emulsions of mites from field rodents, *Laelaps jettmari* Lizthum (13). The disease appeared among American soldiers in June, 1950. Although reported as a virus disease by Japanese workers, the character of the lesions and the epidemiologic evidence suggest a new species of *Rickettsia* as the etiologic agent.

The disease is typically biphasic, with a sudden onset accompanied by chills, anorexia, nausea, vomiting, and frontal headaches. Conjunctival redness, often associated with episcleral hemorrhages, appears about the seventh or eighth day, only to be followed by facial and pretibial edema, and hemorrhages in the skin and internal organs (15).

The disease seems to be transmitted by an arthropod vector, but, despite heroic efforts in the laboratory to isolate the causative agent, none has been found. Since the etiology is unknown, the placing of this disease in the virus section is merely a matter of convenience.

Renal damage of varying degree was a prominent feature of this disease, and renal insufficiency was the major cause of death in most patients. Follow-up studies showed good functional recovery in patients that survived, but a number of patients who had no overt kidney insufficiency showed some renal function abnormalities (depression of tubular function with limitation of concentrating ability) with sensitive tests in long-term follow-up (14).

CAT SCRATCH DISEASE

Cat scratch disease (or fever) characteristically follows a skin scratch by a cat. A primary lesion develops at the site of the wound and subsequently regional lymphadenitis and fever appear. The disease was first recognized by Foshay and later described by Debré (20). Hanger and Rose prepared a skin test antigen in 1945. Mollaret's (23) studies indicate that the etiologic agent may be an organism related to the psittacosis group. Although there are reports of the isolation and transmission of a filterable virus recovered from patients with this syndrome, such studies are inconclusive (24). Cat scratch disease is self-limiting and without sequelae, but it may be confused with more serious granulomatous and some neoplastic diseases. Daniels and MacMurray describe nine types of clinical syndromes (19), which are shown in Table 1. Of the 160 cases studied, 148 had contact with cats in some form or other, and in 100 of these cases the contact appeared to be quite significant.

Table 1. Manifestations of Cat Scratch Disease

	CLINICAL TYPE	DISEASE SIMULATED
1.	Ulceroglandular (with axillary mass)	Tularemia
2.	Cervical (with supraclavicular nodes and sore throat)	Infectious Mononucleosis
3.	Cervical (with pulmonary infiltration)	Tuberculosis
4.	Cervical (discrete midline mass)	Thyroglossal duct cyst
5.	Cervical (hard mass in suprasternal notch)	Malignant tumor
6.	Inguinal	Lymphogranuloma inguinale
7.	Oculoglandular	Parinaud's Syndrome
8.	Inguinal (with cutaneous lesions of erythema nodoseum)	
9.	Encephalitic	

To the above manifestations can be added erythema nodosum (27) and thrombocytopenic purpura (17, 18). Another interesting recent case is reported by Rosof (25) in which a 25-year-old male had chronic recurrent lymphadenopathy for a year and a half. Other recent reports indicate that this disease is more prevalent than previously thought (26).

The diagnosis is based on a skin test using antigen prepared from suppurative lymph nodes (the technic used for the original Frei test antigen for lymphogranuloma venereum). Pus is aspirated from the nodes, diluted 1:5 in sterile saline and homogenized in a blender. The homogenate is then heated to 60° C. for two to three hours and stored at 4° C. New lots must be standardized against a preparation of known strength. Antigen prepared from several patients should be pooled to increase the percentage of positive reactions. The test is performed by injecting 0.1 ml. antigen intradermally into the skin of the forearm. Readings are made at 24 and 48 hours. Any erythematous reaction is considered positive, induration alone is questionable, and immediate reactions are considered negative.

Experiments with cat scratch antigen in patients with known positive Frei reactions give generally negative or inconclusive result and vice versa. The specificity and value of the skin test is well established (19).

A complement-fixation test using psittacosis-lymphogranuloma venereum (bedsonia) antigens has shown positive sera in a certain number of patients with cat scratch fever, but the actual positive results vary from 20 to 70 per cent, depending on the series. Controls vary from 0 to 11 per cent positive. A recent study by Kalter (22) found 25.8 per cent positive in 130 patients and 3 per cent positive in 200 controls; the majority of patients with positive skin tests did not have complement-fixing antibodies. It should be emphasized that relatively few patients (4 to 5 per cent) with cat scratch fever show a **rise** in complement-fixing antibody, and about three-quarters show no complement-fixing antibody at all. Thus, this test has little diagnostic value compared to the skin test.

Another serologic test describes hemagglutination of rabbit red cells by pus from lymph nodes of clinical cases and the hemagglutination-inhibition by sera of patients with this disease (21).

At present writing, no definite isolation of the specific etiologic agent has been reported and confirmed. The serologic studies with both the skin test and the complement-fixation test strongly suggest that the causative agent is one of the bedsonia or psittacosis-lymphogranuloma group. They further suggest that there are several different antigenic strains and that, although the agent is similar to the bedsonia, it is not the psittacosis or lymphogranuloma organism per se.

WARTS

(Verrucae)

The virus (Fig. 1) has a size of 55 mμ when isolated from tissue and shadowed or negatively stained (40). In tissue sections the particles are smaller, because of shrinkage during embedding and measure about 46 mμ outside diameter. The particles have a dense core of 34 mμ (32, 33) and are found in intranuclear arrays simulating crystalline formation. Light microscopic studies of wart tissue describe both eosinophilic and basophilic intranuclear inclusions, but the relation of these inclusions to the site of virus formation has not been clearly defined (30, 31, 36, 37, 38). Almeida and her associates (28) recently presented strong evidence that virus growth is associated with the basophilic inclusions (Fig. 1). Filtered materials transmit the infection to man after an incubation period of weeks or months, but not to animals (34, 39).

A type which may give considerable trouble is the venereal wart or **condyloma acuminatum.** This form occurs in the genital region and, in addition to discomfort caused by the growths, offensive odors, and secretions, the growth may undergo malignant changes. For example, condyloma acuminata occurring on the glans penis may become a form of malignant papillomatosis behaving as an erosive, destructive carcinoma.

The literature concerned with the virus etiology of warts has been reviewed by

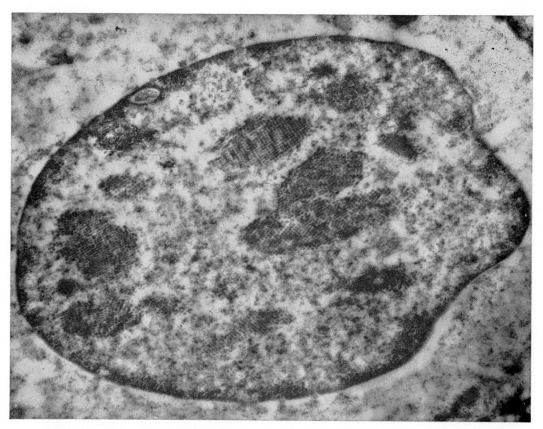

Fig. 1. Nucleus of a human skin cell in the upper stratum granulosum containing wart virus arranged in crystalline formation. × 20,200. (From Almeida and others. *J. Invest. Derm.*, 38:337, 1962.)

Findlay and more recently by Blank (29, 30). It seems likely that the various types of warts in man are caused by the same virus and that to some extent the form assumed by the growth is affected by its location on the body. The incubation period of the disease varies widely from about four weeks to five or six months.

Podophyllin is an effective therapeutic agent in the treatment of condylomata acuminata but has no effect on warts of other kinds in man.

Recently it has been shown that a large percentage of common warts disappear or decrease in size after heating the area to 45-48° C. (35). The affected area was repeatedly immersed in hot water at temperatures which did not produce skin burns. This clever approach should be easily reproducible and seems worthy of further study.

REFERENCES

INFECTIOUS MONONUCLEOSIS

1. Carr, W. P., Jr., and Scion, L. F. J.A.M.A., 181:52, 1962.
2. Davidsohn, I., and others. Am. J. Clin. Path., 21:1101, 1951.
3. Gardner, H. T., and Paul, T. R. Yale J. Biol. & Med., 19:839, 1947.
4. Hoagland, R. J. Am. J. M. Sc., 229:262, 1955.
5. —— and McCluskey, R. T. Ann. Int. Med., 43:1019, 1955.
6. Houk, V. N., and McFarland, W. J.A.M.A., 177:210, 1961.
7. Laureson, T. Danish Med. Bull., 8:40, 1961.
8. Nelson, R. S., and Darrogh, J. H. Am. J. Med., 21:26, 1956.
9. Paul, J. R., and Bunnell, W. W. Am. J. M. Sc., 183:90, 1932.
10. Remington, J. S., and others. Arch. Int. Med., 110:744, 1962.
11. Thurm, R. H., and Bassen, F. Blood, 10: 841, 1955.
12. Wising, P. J. Acta med. Scandinav., 133 (Suppl.):1-102, 1942.

EPIDEMIC HEMORRHAGIC FEVER

13. Kaskura, K., and others. J. Parasit. Soc. Jap., 34:3, 1944.
14. Rubini, M. E., and others. Arch. Int. Med., 106:378, 1960.
15. Symposium on Epidemic Hemorrhagic Fever. Am. J. Med., 16:617, 1954.
16. Urono, K. Nippon Rinsyo, 1:961, 1943.

CAT SCRATCH FEVER

17. Belber, J. P., and others. Arch. Int. Med., 94:321, 1954.
18. Billo, O. E., and Wolff, J. A. J.A.M.A., 174:1824, 1960.
19. Daniels, W. B., and MacMurray, F. G. J.A.M.A., 154:1247, 1954.
20. Debré, R., and others. Semaine d. hôp. Paris, 26:1895, 1950.
21. Dodd, M. C., and others. Proc. Soc. Exper. Biol. & Med., 102:556, 1959.
22. Kalter, S. S. Ann. Int. Med., 55:903, 1961.
23. Mollaret, P., and others. Presse méd., 59:681, 1951.
24. ———— and others. Presse méd., 59:701, 1951.
25. Rosof, B. M. J.A.M.A., 178:328, 1961.
26. Spaulding, W. B., and others. Am. J. Med., 28:504, 1960.

27. Ziegler, L. K. Clin. Proc. Child. Hosp. (Wash.), 15:71, 1959.

WARTS
(Verrucae)

28. Almeida, J. D., and others. J. Invest. Derm., 38:377, 1962.
29. Blank, H. Acta dermat.-venereol., 29:77, 1949.
30. ———— and others. J. Invest. Dermat., 16:19, 1951.
31. Bunting, H., and others. Am. J. Path., 28:985, 1952.
32. ———— Proc. Soc. Exper. Biol. & Med., 84:327, 1953.
33. Charles, A. Dermatologica, 121:193, 1960.
34. Kingery, L. B. J.A.M.A., 76:440, 1921.
35. LoCricchio, J., Jr., and Haserick, J. R. Cleveland Clinic Quart., 29:156, 1962.
36. Lyell, A., and Miles, J. A. R. Brit. M. J., 1:912, 1951.
37. Strauss, M. J., and others. J. Invest. Derm., 15:433, 1950.
38. ———— and others. J. Invest. Derm., 17:209, 1951.
39. Wile, V. J., and Kingery, L. B. J.A.M.A., 73:970, 1919.
40. Williams, M. G., and others. Nature, 189:895, 1961.

76

Virus Diseases of Plants, Insects, and Animals

The virus diseases most frequently attracting attention are those directly affecting the health of man, but many diseases of animals and plants are of utmost importance to human welfare. The total array of known virus diseases and viruses is formidable because of relatively recent advances in the discovery and demonstration of new animal (75) and human agents, such as those of the acute respiratory diseases (45) and echo groups (59), including viruses of insect diseases (11, 81). Many of the more important virus diseases of man and the domestic animals are being brought under control by newly developed vaccines. The well-recognized problems of the virus diseases in plants increase in importance with the rapidly expanding needs for agricultural products.

In addition to economic importance, virus diseases of animals are of interest for other reasons. Certain animals constitute reservoirs (60) for viruses which affect man, and many of them are widely distributed. Some —monkeys (yellow fever virus) and vampire bats (rabies virus)—occur in sparsely settled regions and are difficult to control, while others are maintained by man himself for his own use and pleasure. Every year many people must submit to a painful course of immunization against rabies carried by dogs.

The virus diseases of animals have also provided materials indispensable for many fundamental investigations on the nature of viruses (Chap. 61) and the characters and potentialities of virus diseases in general. The susceptibility of both man and animals to the same virus confers benefits as well as disadvantages, because animals may serve as test hosts for the demonstration of virus activity and for immunologic, epidemiologic, and pathologic investigations. The primary need for such studies of a virus is an animal host which is neither too expensive nor too difficult to control. Research on poliomyelitis was hampered greatly by the lack of such a suitable host, and the investigation of hog cholera has been limited because the virulent virus is so specific to swine. Experiments requiring the use of primates are even more difficult and expensive. Many of these difficulties have been resolved by use of tissue culture systems. Cancer research has been aided materially by study of virus-induced tumors in animals. The full implications of such cancer work cannot yet be judged, but it has demonstrated that at least one tumor condition of man is of virus origin (21). A variety of virus-induced tumor or hyperplastic states occur also in plants (16).

PLANT DISEASES

The importance of virus-induced plant diseases and their influence on human economy has not been generally appreciated. However, the importance of these agents in the problems of purification and studies on the nature of viruses, as already described, has broadened the area of interest in recent years. The early and continuing work has involved such plant viruses as those of tobacco mosaic (Fig. 4 in Chap. 61), tomato bushy stunt, tobacco necrosis (Fig. 9 in Chap. 61), and others. While these viruses have established the pattern of study of other viral agents, this should not distract attention from the diseases which they cause.

The plant virus diseases have been considered in detail in a book by Bawden (3), and some of the properties of representative agents of this group were described in Chapter 61. It will suffice here to call attention to a few of the more important conditions.

Plant viruses are recognized to attack only the higher angiosperm plants (with the exception of bacteriophages, which parasitize members of the phylum Thallophyta), although parasitism of other forms may have been overlooked. Virus diseases are an expensive problem in fruit trees, particularly the peach, since large orchards may be completely destroyed by peach yellows. Tobacco mosaic virus causes loss of much tobacco annually and also greatly reduces the yield of tomatoes in some sections. Curly top of the sugar beet may take whole crops. Potatoes may be similarly affected, as well as other small crops, such as lettuce and other vegetables. Cocoa trees are affected, and production of cocoa beans was affected in West Africa because of the swollen-shoot viruses.

VIRUS-INDUCED INSECT DISEASES

The principal insect virus diseases have been classified (80) and described by Steinhaus (80, 81) and others (78, 79). Considering the huge total number of the known members of this phylum, the distribution of diseases recognized to be due to viruses is relatively restricted. The better-known agents affect the lepidoptera (butterflies and moths), hymenoptera (ants, bees and wasps), and a few of the diptera (flies). Other groups—orthoptera, coleoptera, and hemiptera—are not affected. In nearly all instances, it is only the larval stage of the insect which is actively diseased; in only a few cases are the viruses now known to cause actual disease in the pupal stage, though the agents may be carried by the adult insect.

Although much is known of a few of the recognized insect virus diseases and of the characters of the etiologic agents (Chaps. 61, 62), the information is scant with the majority of the diseases. This has been an obstacle in arranging a systematic nomenclature. The insect diseases have been divided into four groups: (1) the polyhedral diseases characterized by the occurrence of nuclear polyhedral inclusion bodies (Fig. 3 in Chap. 62), (2) those showing the presence of polymorphic inclusions within the cytoplasm, (3) the granuloses characterized by granules (Fig. 4 in Chap. 62) in the cytoplasm of affected cells, and (4) those in which no inclusions are seen. The largest categories are the polyhedroses and the granuloses. It is quite evident that the known insect diseases constitute but a small part of those remaining to be studied. New ones are continually being seen (78) for the first time.

Insect viruses in most instances affect the cells of the tracheal matrix, adipose tissue, hypodermis, and blood leukocytes. The disease usually progresses within a few days to virtual liquefaction of the insect, which becomes a bag of tissue debris containing large quantities of virus. The agents, protected by the polyhedral or capsular material, are highly resistant to inactivation and most are highly infectious for the specific hosts.

There is scarcely a more fascinating story (10, 77, 80) of natural balances than that of the relation of insect viruses to their hosts and to the plant life parasitized, in many cases, specifically by these insect hosts. Recognition of these relations is by no means new; many of the diseases and effects have long been known. Silkworm jaundice as a potent economic factor in the production of silk once claimed much attention in efforts to eradicate the disease. The important aspects of insect viruses in the control of pests have been witnessed repeatedly. In 1889 and 1892 the nun moth in the process of destroying large spruce forests in Europe (77, 80) was curbed under natural conditions by a disease later found to be a virus-induced polyhedrosis. Polyhedrosis of the spruce sawfly produced a like result in the spruce forests of Canada (77). Other serious infestations which may be curbed by virus diseases in nature are due to the yellow-striped army worm and the alfalfa caterpillar, which are a menace to alfalfa; the California oakworm; the gipsy-moth, a costly pest in Massachusetts; the fir-shoot roller; and the spruce budworm. The gratifying effects of natural viral epidemics obviously suggest artificial spread of the diseases, and these possibilities have been explored. In California the economic threat of the alfalfa caterpillar may be reduced by spraying virus on fields from an airplane (77).

VIRUS-INDUCED TUMORS OF ANIMALS

A number of tumors have been known for years to be the result of infection with viruses (6). Until relatively recently, however, the neoplastic states investigated were those occurring in the fowl (7), designated as the sarcomas and avian leukosis. Work with the growths was sporadic and restricted because of the earlier reluctance of many workers to include these chicken diseases in the category of mammalian tumors. Interest was increased by discovery of the virus etiology of the rabbit papilloma (74), which progressed with time to malignant carcinoma (68, 85). Further attention was drawn to virus tumors by studies on the virus-induced mammary carcinoma in mice (15). Appreciation of the role of viruses in the induction of cancer was greatly heightened by the demonstration of filterable agents as the cause of a variety of forms of leukemia in the mouse (Fig. 1) (43) and by discovery of the tumor-inducing attributes of other agents—the polyoma (33, 82), SV40 (40) and adenoviruses types 12 (88) and 18 (46, 88). Thus, the field of virus-tumor investigation has expanded (43) from one dealing with malignancy in the bird to that involving typical neoplastic states in the higher animals. Progress has been furthered by recent studies of the character and properties of the etiologic agents in these categories of virus tumors described in Chapters 61 and 62.

Fig. 1. Typical generalized leukemia that developed in a 10-month old C57 brown male mouse. This mouse was inoculated when less than 3 hours old with C58 leukemic filtrate. Note very large peripheral lymph nodes, large mesenteric tumor, very large spleen. (From Gross. *Cancer*, 9:778, 1956.)

AVIAN SARCOMA

It has been customary (7) to consider avian neoplasms in two groups: (1) the chicken sarcomas and (2) a variety of tumors and associated hyperplastic conditions designated as the leukosis complex. With increased information, the basis for distinction between the groups has diminished. The first observed growth, tumor I or the Rous sarcoma (66), was a spindle-celled neoplasm, and other sarcomas have been of varied pathology (67), such as osteochondrosarcoma and a spindle-celled growth containing large blood sinuses. In very young chicks the Rous virus which causes solid tumors in older birds produces a disseminated hemorrhagic disease. These growths, despite their infectious nature, possess all the definitive characteristics of true malignant neoplasms.

In the early work it appeared that the sarcoma agents were specific in the induction of the respective growths and that they were likewise infectious only for birds. The Rous sarcoma virus, however, may induce erythroblastic leukemia and lymphomatosis—forms of the leukosis complex (20). More remarkable has been the demonstration that chicken sarcoma virus is infectious for the rabbit (90) and induces sarcoma (1, 84) in hamsters, mice, rats, and, most recently, in primates (63).

Evidence of the nature of avian tumor viruses has been obtained in electron micrographs of ultra-thin sections (12) and of

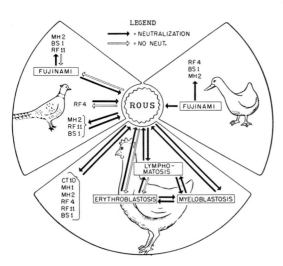

Fig. 2. Immunologic interrelationships between the chicken tumor viruses; between the various forms of avian leukosis indicated; and between the Rous sarcoma virus and avian leukosis viruses. The solid arrows indicate neutralization of the virus at the point by immune serum to the virus at the base. The open arrows signify no neutralization in tests already made. The immune serums were derived in the bird indicated. Location of the Rous virus as the apparent pivot is an artifact due to the large numbers of experiments done with the agent. Central significance of the Rous virus is not implied. (Courtesy of Dr. B. R. Burmester, Regional Poultry Research Laboratory, and Dr. W. Ray Bryan, National Cancer Institute.)

negatively stained preparations (32). All chicken tumor viruses thus far studied are morphologically indistinguishable from one another (Fig. 2).

Comprehensive studies have been made of the biologic phenomena exhibited by the Rous sarcoma virus in the chicken (18) and in tissue culture (86). These have been concerned with the problems of bioassay of virus activity and host-virus relations in the occurrence of the agent in the growths and affected tissue culture cells. In tissue cultures studies have been made of the immunologic relationships between avian tumor viruses, the kinetics of sarcoma virus elaboration, and mutation.

AVIAN LEUKOSIS

Some elements of the complex (7, 19, 34, 35) of neoplastic states in the fowl were first recognized as virus-induced by Ellermann

(34) in 1908. The neoplastic state of most importance in incidence and in economic influence is lymphomatosis, which is presently responsible for the largest losses in the poultry industry. The **visceral** type of lymphomatosis is manifested by the formation of tumors or widespread collections of primitive cells of the lymphoid type in the liver, spleen, and other viscera. Other conditions arising independently or in association with visceral lymphomatosis are **ocular** lymphomatosis, marked by collections of lymphoid cells in the iris, and **neurolymphomatosis,** characterized by localization of lymphoid cells in nerve trunks resulting in paralysis. **Osteopetrosis,** an involvement of the periosteum and not of lymphoid cells, is a disease characterized by bone overgrowth called "big leg" or marble bone. There occur also leukemias of two distinct types. One is **myeloblastosis** (7), which is characterized by the occurrence in the circulating blood of huge numbers, up to 2,000,000 per cubic millimeter, of primitive cells of myeloid origin. The other is **erythroblastosis** (7), in which smaller numbers of primitive erythroid cells, up to perhaps 500,000 per cubic millimeter, find their way into the circulation. These leukemias are profoundly malignant diseases leading rapidly to the death of the host. Less frequently observed associated neoplasms (8) are spindle-cell sarcomas and endotheliomas like those caused by the "sarcoma" viruses. The BAI strain A virus causes a high incidence of nephroblastomas closely resembling Wilms' tumor of man.

RELATION OF THE CHICKEN SARCOMAS TO THE AVIAN LEUKOSIS COMPLEX

Intensive investigations of several long-studied strains of chicken tumor viruses have been made in recent years. The results have indicated that virus-induced chicken tumors comprise a family of growths caused by a family of more or less closely related agents. Immunologic relationships are demonstrable (5) between the various strains. Furthermore, each of the different strains elicits a multiplicity of host response (7). The spectrum of tumors induced by each strain is characteristic of the strain, and the various spectrums exhibit broad overlapping. Thus, none of the strains is specific for a single growth. Qualitative and quantitative aspects of host response are strongly influenced by genetic constitution of the chicken, age at the time of exposure to the virus, and dose of the respective agents.

Avian tumor viruses are spread (19) by contact, by virus in saliva and feces, and through the egg.

PAPILLOMATOSIS

Papillomas of various forms and sizes occur (36) in many animals, such as cattle, rabbits, dogs, and fish. The most economically important are warts of cattle, which produce holes in the hides and impair their market value. Warts also occur on the teats and udders of milk cows, causing difficulties in milking. Epidermal papillomas occur about the mouth in dogs, and oral papillomas (28) occurring in the mucous membrane of the mouth cause debilitation in young puppies.

The papilloma frequently found under natural conditions in the western cottontail rabbit (67) and sometimes in the jackrabbit is the only form now important in the cancer problem. The virus extracted from the papillomas of the cottontail rabbit readily transmits the disease to other cottontail rabbits, domestic rabbits, jackrabbits, and snowshoe rabbits. The warts thus produced develop rapidly as the result of hyperplasia of the epidermal cells, giving rise to growths ranging from long thin horns to broad-based warts several inches high. With time the growth loses the orderly arrangement of cells in the base; strands of cells begin gradually to invade the deeper tissues, and finally the growths become invasive and metastasize in the fashion of typical carcinoma. Because of the character of the growth and the ready availability of the host, the rabbit papilloma has been valuable in the investigation of its tumor attributes.

One of the tantalizing problems (4, 85) of the virus-induced tumor field is the nature of association of the papilloma virus with host cells in the induction of the papillomatous and carcinomatous states and the continuation of the latter. The papilloma virus can be obtained in relatively large amounts (4) from many and in some quantity from nearly all cottontail papillomas. Little virus, in terms of infectivity, however, can be recovered from experimentally induced domestic rabbit papillomas, although the domestic rabbit growths contain virus antigen. Furthermore, once the carcinoma has been established, virus can rarely be obtained from the growth in either the domestic or cottontail rabbit except under unusual conditions, though the antigen can be carried from animal to animal by transplantation. A further change in these relations occurs after repeated transplantations, since even this antigen may be lost (69), although the carcinoma maintains its original properties as a malignant growth. These findings were paralleled by fluorescent antibody studies (57) which showed virus antigen in cottontail rabbit wart cells, much less in domestic rabbit growths and none in carcinoma not showing antigen by other methods. The amount of infectious DNA from the respective growths parallels the infectivity of virus extracted from the same tumors (47). Clarification of the possible relationships of virus or virus constituents to the various growths has not been effected.

The virus of rabbit papillomatosis has been purified (4), and some of its chemical, physical, and morphologic properties, closely similar to those of polyoma (Fig. 15 in Chap. 61) and SV40 viruses have been determined (Chaps. 61 and 62). The morphology of the virus causing papillomas in man resembles closely that of the rabbit virus. Little is known of the nature of the agents causing the papillomas in dogs and cattle. There is no immunologic relationship between the viruses causing warts in man, cattle, dogs, and rabbits (9).

MOUSE MAMMARY CANCER

Spontaneous mammary cancer in mice has been a prominent subject of study in the tumor problem (2, 5, 30, 43), particularly in the early work, from the point of view of the influence of genetic and hormonal factors. Intensive breeding experiments resulted in the development of mouse strains exhibiting high incidences of the spontaneous disease and others showing high resistance to the occurrence of tumors. In these studies it was also established that hormone stimulation exerted an outstanding influence on tumor incidence.

The participation of an entirely different factor was first recognized in 1936 (15), when it was learned that the young of highly susceptible strains of mice, when fostered immediately after birth by females of a low incidence strain, exhibited a low incidence of cancer. By this means the incidence could be reduced to 10 per cent, in contrast with the 90 per cent incidence in mice nursed by their own mothers of the cancerous strain. These and other experiments demonstrated the presence of a "milk factor," which, when taken by the sucklings, increased the incidence of cancer and in the absence of which cancer developed with only low incidence. The rates of incidence were further improved by removing the young from the uterus of the mother.

Continued investigation has shown that the milk factor possesses the properties of the viruses. Virus particles have been demonstrated in ultrathin sections (12) of the tissues of the mouse tumor (Fig. 27 in Chap. 61) and numerous physical experiments have been made to identify the infectious type particles (62). It has been evident that the occurrence of mouse mammary cancer is influenced by complex interrelations of genetic factors and hormonal influences, which provide the conditions favorable for the activity of the viral agent. The problem of unravelling these relationships and determining the implications with respect to human cancer is one of the most intensively studied problems in the tumor field at the present time. The virus has been demonstrated in wild mice (2).

MOUSE LEUKEMIAS

Certain strains of mice, Ak, for example, are particularly susceptible to development of leukemia (Fig. 1), which has long been investigated as a process possibly analogous to leukemia in man. In 1950 Gross (43) obtained evidence of the role of filterable agents in the induction of the disease. Filtered material from leukemic Ak mice regu-

larly transmitted leukemia of the lymphoid type to other strains of mice, including C3H, of naturally low incidence of leukemia. Transmission was highly conditioned by age of the recipient mouse, and significant results were obtained only in animals of a few hours age at the time of injection. Since then four other lymphoid type leukemias (43, 61) have been derived from various sources. Another type of mouse leukemia, a reticulum cell neoplasm associated with erythroblastosis, was derived by Friend (37) from a Swiss mouse carrying the Ehrlich mouse ascites tumor. It is transmissible in adult mice. An agent causing myeloid leukemia was described by Graffi and associates (42), and a virus-induced reticulum cell sarcoma (61) has been described. Some of the agents transmit disease to rats or hamsters. Immunologic experiments suggest that murine leukemia agents constitute a family of viruses analogous to the various strains of avian tumor agents (61). Morphologic properties of the murine viruses were discussed in Chapters 61 and 62. These findings, together with those derived from studies on avian leukemia, serve to increase interest in the possible relationship of viruses to the occurrence of the leukemias and Hodgkins' disease as well as other neoplastic states in man. Virus has been demonstrated in lymph nodes from cases of human leukemia (31), but efforts to demonstrate human leukemia virus by transmission experiments have not been successful.

It should be emphasized that the virus tumors are of interest not only as a part of the cancer problem but as virus diseases. Thus, not only are these available tumors susceptible to study by the classic methods of oncology in general, but, with access to the viruses themselves, studies can be made of host cell-virus relationships in the induction and maintenance of the neoplastic process.

OTHER MAMMALIAN TUMOR VIRUSES

Polyoma Virus. Inoculation of material from mice with Gross' leukemia resulted occasionally in the occurrence of parotid tumors, sarcomas, and a variety of other growths (43). Fluid from tissue cultures of such material with mouse embryo cells yielded the same and many other growths (33, 82). The causative virus—initially designated as parotid tumor virus and later polyoma virus, an agent of the papova group —was entirely different from that responsible for leukemia (Chaps. 61 and 62). Antibody studies indicate that the agent may occur with high incidence in wild mice in dense populations and in many experimental mouse colonies (71). The agent is transmissible to rats, hamsters, and rabbits. It occurs in urine, saliva, and feces and is highly contagious. There was no apparent relationship between the occurrence of tumors and presence of virus under natural conditions.

SV40 Virus. Another agent of the papova group and similar in many respects (Fig. 27 in Chap. 62) to the papilloma and polyoma viruses is the SV40 (Simian virus) agent (40). Occurring in cultures of rhesus and cynomolgus monkey kidney cells without cell pathology, the agent caused cytopathogenic changes in cultured kidney cells of the grivet monkey. The agent induces a variety of neoplasms in the hamster.

Adeno Viruses. Two types of this group of agents (70) induce tumors in hamsters and mice on inoculation into the newborn animals. Types 12 (88) and 18 (46, 88) induce sarcomas in the chest or peritoneal cavities where the agents are injected.

HEP 1 Virus. This agent was isolated from a human epidermoid carcinoma and induces a mongoloid disease on inoculation into newborn hamsters. Morphologically (24) the virus resembles the papova agents but may be elaborated in the mitochondria of affected cells (Fig. 31 in Chap. 62).

VESICULAR DISEASES OF SWINE, CATTLE, AND HORSES

In this group three principal conditions of similar pathologic and clinical characteristics occur. These economically important diseases are caused by different agents and affect different natural and test hosts (Table 1). Although diagnosis of vesicular disease per se is simple, the differential diagnosis between the three types—1, vesicular exanthema; 2, foot-and-mouth disease; and 3, vesicular stomatitis—can be effected under practical conditions by test of differential pathogenicity of the agents for various hosts as shown in Table 1.

Table 1. Host Susceptibility to the Vesicular Viruses

(Madin and Traum)

	HORSE	PIG	CATTLE	GUINEA PIG
Vesicular stomatitis	+	+	+	+
Foot-and-mouth disease	−	+	+	+
Exanthema of swine	±	+	−	−

VESICULAR EXANTHEMA OF SWINE

Until recently this was an economically very important disease (44, 53) which was observed for the first time in California in 1932. In succeeding years the disease was well distributed over the United States.

The condition is an acute, highly infectious disease of low mortality (about 5 per cent) running its course in one to two weeks and followed by complete recovery. It is characterized by the occurrence of vesicles on the snout, lips, tongue, oral cavity, sole, and interdigital spaces. Vesicles may be found also on the udder and teats of nursing sows. The incubation period is usually about 24 to 72 hours, but may vary from 12 hours to 12 days. All ages are susceptible. The disease is indistinguishable from foot-and-mouth disease and vesicular stomatitis, both of which may be seen in swine.

The agent is one of the smaller viruses, estimated as perhaps about 20 mμ in diameter. At least seven immunologically distinct strains have been identified. Aside from interhost transmission, the disease is spread largely by garbage feeding. No practical means of immunization has been developed, but control has been effected by quarantine measures, embargoes against shipping, and prompt disposal of affected pigs. The disease has not been observed in the United States since 1956.

FOOT-AND-MOUTH DISEASE

This is the really critical vesicular disease (73). It is characterized by fulminating outbreaks which are very difficult to control. In some foreign countries efforts to control the disease are not intensive, and the outbreaks run their course and disappear, only to recur when immunity has diminished and a new, susceptible animal population has been brought up. In the United States, where stringent measures are taken to avoid the disease, the danger is from sporadic outbreaks which can be traced usually to material imported from outside affected areas.

Foot-and-mouth disease occurs chiefly in cattle, pigs, sheep, and goats and more rarely in other domestic animals. Infection can be induced in a broad spectrum of hosts by experimental inoculation. The disease is highly infectious and characterized by vesicular eruption in the mucosa of the mouth and the delicate skin of the hoofs and udders. With the onset of the eruption there may be increased temperature, refusal of food, and general depression. Usually the disease is complicated by catarrhal gastroenteritis or by inflammation of the respiratory tract, which may result in the death of the animal. The disease may be transmitted from animal to animal, either by means of virus contained in the vesicular contents or through the milk. Rarely may the disease be transmitted to man.

As in the case of swine vesicular exanthema, the disease is usually mild, resulting in low mortality, although highly malignant forms have been seen. Here, again, the importance of the disease is related not to death, but to loss in weight, decrease in milk production, and other effects of disease and malnutrition. Under epidemic conditions, spread is rapid by direct transmission. Less well understood are the reservoirs of the disease between outbreaks and the basis for recurrence of epidemics. Various elements have been implicated, such as birds, rodents, man, and chronic carriers among cattle. The incubation period is about two to seven days. Convalescence is associated with an immunity of varying degree. Several strains of the virus are known, and resistance to one strain does not necessarily indicate resistance to another.

Study of the virus has been intensified in recent years (73). The agent is classified with the nani viruses, is 23 mμ in diameter, and contains RNA, and the disease is trans-missible with isolated virus RNA. The agent can be propagated in bovine kidney cell cultures, in chick embryos, and in cultures of a large variety of other cells. Despite intensive efforts, complete control of the disease by prophylactic measures has not been attained. Formalin-inactivated Al(OH)$_3$-adsorbed virus derived from tissue culture has given some promise of success. Vaccine prepared by inactivating the virus with crystal violet has been used. Efforts are being made to develop attenuated virus grown in chick embryos and tissue culture. Some measure of control has been effected in this country by supervision to prevent importation of suspected material and animals. In an epidemic there is resort to large scale slaughter, quarantine, and embargo. Because of the danger of spread by laboratory materials, research has been severely restricted. An isolated laboratory has been established on Plum Island for the study of the disease in the United States.

Vesicular Stomatitis

This occurs principally in equine animals and is characterized by the development of vesicles on the tongue and other oral mucosa (87). Two strains, Indiana and New Jersey, have been studied (38). Cattle may acquire the disease naturally, and the resulting lesions resemble those of foot-and-mouth disease, except that the feet are not usually affected. Pigs may likewise contract vesicular stomatitis naturally. There is a July to October seasonal influence on incidence in the United States, related probably to transmission by biting flies. The causative virus grows in the chick chorio-allantoic membrane and in cultures of Earle L strain cells and is a rod-shaped particle of unusual morphology elaborated by budding at the cell membrane (Fig. 32 in Chap. 61). No vaccine has been developed.

Rinderpest

This disease of cattle (64), known to the French as la peste bovine and occurring in Southern Europe, Asia, and Africa has been a serious economic scourge for centuries. Clinically it is characterized, after an incubation period of three to nine days, by catarrhal conditions of the nasal mucous membrane, with fever, conjunctival infection, profuse diarrhea, and rapid emaciation. The animals die on the tenth or eleventh day, the mortality being 15 to 75 per cent. The virus is present in blood, secretions, and intestinal contents.

Knowledge of the nature of the agent and its relationship to other agents has been markedly advanced. The virus exhibits the morphologic attributes of the myxoviruses with membrane-enclosed nucleoid containing strands of ribonucleic acid similar to those in influenza, mumps, and Newcastle disease (Chap. 61). The agent is immunologically related to the measles and canine distemper viruses and is closely similar to them in morphology and structure. Vaccines consisting of live attenuated virus cultured in the goat, rabbit, and chick embryo have given good results under proper conditions.

Equine Infectious Anemia

This serious and widespread virus-induced disease (87) of horses is analogous to malaria in man. The acute febrile condition may result quickly in death but frequently becomes chronic, and severe anemia is manifested, with associated loss of weight and general debilitation. The disease process may become quiescent for long periods without symptoms. The virus persists, however, and recrudescence of the disease may occur at any time. Animals once diseased remain virus carriers and constitute a menace to other horses. Nothing is known of the characters of the virus, and no treatment has been found effective.

Hog Cholera

The disease, limited to swine, causes large losses in many countries, including the United States (56, 76). It is characterized by an acute course, with fever, pneumonia, petechial hemorrhages in the skin, intestine, bladder, and kidney, marginal infarction of the spleen, and ulceration of the intestine. The mortality is high, and animals that recover or are chronically affected are useless for market purposes.

The causative agent is of small size, probably not greater than 30 to 35 mμ in diameter. Recovered animals are immune to reinfection for life. The virus is highly specific for swine, though infection of sheep has been reported. The virus has been passed to rabbits (51) and cultivated in pig kidney cells (52). The disease may be passed by the swine lung worm (76).

Vaccination was formerly practiced extensively by the simultaneous serum-virus method. Active virus in blood from infected pigs is injected at one site in the animal, and immune serum from hyperimmunized swine is given at another site. However, since every vaccination involves active virulent virus, a "break" may occur and result in a spread of the disease.

Vaccine consisting of virus inactivated with crystal violet has been used with some success. Adaptation of the cholera virus to rabbits has provided an attenuated live virus vaccine (25, 26), which gives much promise for the control of cholera without the hazards of the serum-virus noted previously. Vaccines consisting of fresh, frozen, or desiccated blood, spleen, and liver from rabbits infected with the leporine strain of virus have been tested under laboratory and field conditions. The results have indicated modification of the virus to complete loss of virulence for swine but with retention of high immunogenic capacity. The virus was not lethal for pigs after about the two hundredth passage in rabbits.

Bluetongue

This disease (36) occurs principally in sheep but may affect cattle and goats. Seen only in South Africa until about 1944, the disease reached the United States in 1948 and became a major hazard to the sheep industry. Here the condition is analogous to foot-and-mouth disease and is characterized "by catarrhal inflammation of the mouth, nose, and intestines, and often inflammation of the coronary bands and sensitive laminae of the hoofs. There is an excoriation of the epithelium and, later, necrosis of the buccal mucosa; the swollen and inflamed tongue and mouth take on the dirty blue color from which the disease derives its name" (36).

The disease is transmitted by biting insects —gnats, midges, sandflies, no-see-ums—of the genus *Culicoides.* The occurrence of the disease depends on conditions favorable to these insects—warm, wet weather in localities of low altitude. The etiologic agent is about 120 mμ in diameter, of which there are about four to five distinct immunologic groups. Highly effective multivalent vaccines have been developed from virus attenuated by chick embryo passage and, more recently, virus propagated in bovine kidney cells (50). However, it is not effective in newborn lambs dropped from immune mothers in the late spring and summer shortly before the optimal time for natural spread of the disease.

VIRUS DISEASES OF THE DOG

The principal canine virus diseases are distemper, infectious canine hepatitis and rabies. Rabies in dogs has been described in Chapter 64.

CANINE DISTEMPER

Distemper (39) most commonly affects young dogs, but other members of the order Carnivora, such as the weasel, ferret, mink, skunk, raccoon, dingo, fox, coyote, wolf, and binturong, are susceptible. The type of lesion produced varies with the species affected. In dogs the disease is characterized by fever, catarrhal and purulent secretions from the respiratory tract, diarrhea, and sometimes nervous symptoms due to encephalitis. Another manifestation of distemper, formerly known as "hard pad" disease, includes hardening of the foot pads and scanty nasal or eye discharge followed by convulsions and death. Because of its highly infectious nature, distemper causes severe losses in kennels and on mink and fox farms. The disease is spread by contact with infective secretions and discharges. Diseased animals are very susceptible to secondary bacterial infections with organisms of the respiratory group.

The virus, which is found in the blood of dogs during the initial febrile period and in the catarrhal secretions from the respiratory tract, may be grown in tissue culture and on the chorio-allantoic membrane of the chick embryo. Intracytoplasmic and intranuclear inclusion bodies may be found widely disseminated throughout the various tissues, but they are most abundant in the epithelial cells of the respiratory system and urinary tract. Rapid diagnosis may be made by the demonstration of inclusion bodies in the nose, bladder, or trachea. As already noted, canine distemper virus is immunologically related and morphologically similar to the agents of measles (89) and rinderpest (64). All have been classified with the myxovirus group, to which they are structurally similar (Fig. 23 in Chap. 61).

Effective vaccines have been developed (22, 29) by use of living attenuated or modified distemper virus cultured on the chorioallantoic membrane of the chick embryo or in tissue cultures of chick embryo cells. Fully virulent virus loses its lethal effect in ferrets after about 30 passages on the chorioallantoic membrane. The vacuum-dried vaccine taken up in distilled water is administered intraperitoneally to puppies. Bivalent vaccines containing the live attenuated agents of distemper and infectious canine hepatitis protect against both viruses.

INFECTIOUS CANINE HEPATITIS AND FOX ENCEPHALITIS

These conditions are considered together, since the diseases in the two hosts are caused by the same agent (22). Fox encephalitis has been known for years as a common disease of the North American silver fox, coyote, and raccoon, and epizootics of the disease tend to occur when the animals are congregated in captivity. Under such circumstances the disease appears suddenly, spreads rapidly, and subsides within a period of a month. The disease is characterized by an abrupt onset, with the picture of a generalized virus infection which particularly involves the endothelial cells of the smaller blood vessels. Subsequent symptoms are referable to the brain and spinal cord. The essential feature is hemorrhage which follows injury of the vascular system, resulting in cellular degeneration.

Canine hepatitis attracted attention only a few years ago as a distinct pathologic entity in the dog described exhaustively by Rubarth. Antibody studies have shown that the disease is of world-wide distribution. It affects puppies and young dogs particularly and causes manifestations varying from sudden death to an attack followed by recovery. In animals not dying quickly fever, apathy, malaise, keratoconjunctivitis, tachycardia, and sometimes diarrhea are observed. There may also occur hysteria and running fits. Postmortem examination shows swelling of the liver, fibrinous exudate on the surface of the liver, fluid in the abdominal cavity, and thickening of the gallbladder wall due to subserous edema. Sections of the liver reveal distension of the centrilobular sinuses, centrilobular necrosis of the liver cells, and specific intranuclear inclusion bodies in the liver cells and vascular endothelium.

Recovery from the diseases results in a high degree of immunity in both the fox and the dog. In the latter, however, the virus may remain in the blood for long periods. Transmission in the fox is apparently by way of upper respiratory secretions, and virus has been recovered from nasal washings of both sick and apparently well animals. The virus is present in the urine, respiratory secretions, and feces of affected dogs.

The diagnosis may be confused with canine distemper, but however similar these two diseases are clinically, they are very different histopathologically and serologically. Fox encephalitis is essentially a disease of the endothelial cells, and intranuclear inclusion bodies are seen easily. In canine hepatitis the intranuclear bodies in the liver cells are specific. In distemper the virus invades the cells of epithelial origin, and the inclusion bodies are intracytoplasmic. Ferrets and mink are susceptible to distemper virus but not to the virus of infectious canine hepatitis. Both neutralizing and complement-fixing antibodies are present in recovered dogs, and both, especially, the latter, are of value in diagnosis of the disease.

The virus, one of the adenovirus group (Fig. 12C in Chap. 61), has been cultivated in cultures of dog, ferret, and pig kidney cells, and much is known of the morphologic and chemical properties of the agent. Vaccines prepared with living virus attenuated by passage in pig kidney cell cultures and administered with canine distemper vaccine immunize effectively against the disease.

VIRUS DISEASE OF THE CAT

FELINE AGRANULOCYTOSIS (Cat Enteritis, Panleukopenia)

A very contagious virus-induced disease of cats is that generally known among practitioners (41) as feline enteritis but is designated more specifically, on the basis of the principal pathologic changes, as agranulocytosis. The condition is characterized clinically by depression, weakness, and dehydration. Vomiting is seen frequently and diarrhea rarely. The mortality in cats developing symptoms is about 80 to 90 per cent. Recovery is followed by a high state of immunity. Under experimental conditions the incubation period is about five days. During this period and a few days afterward, there is a profound agranulocytosis, and there is an associated hypoplasia and absence of differentiation of the myeloid elements of the bone marrow. The virus has not been grown in tissue culture (14), but an effective vaccine has been developed by use of formalin-inactivated agent in the liver and spleen from diseased kittens.

VIRUS DISEASES OF CHICKENS

NEWCASTLE DISEASE OF FOWLS

This disease, characterized by pneumonia and encephalomyelitis (65), was first discovered outside the United States but later spread widely in this country. Although the mortality is low in adult birds, the disease is debilitating and interferes both with egg production and preparation of birds for the market. Infection with the virus causes a mild conjunctivitis in man (49).

The agent is a member of the myxovirus group and has been purified and employed in numerous studies of morphology and other characteristics (72) (Chaps. 61 and 62). It grows readily in the embryonated egg and tissue cultures and is found in high concentrations in the chorio-allantoic fluid of infected embryos.

During the war Newcastle disease was investigated in this country (17, 48), principally for the purpose of the developing vaccines. In the early work, virus from diseased chick embryos was inactivated with formalin or ultraviolet light. Protection induced by inactivated virus lasted about four months, but much longer immunity was induced by recovery from infection with active virus. Subsequent work (48, 54) has resulted in the development of attenuated virus of low virulence for the chick. Such virus, grown in the chick embryo, has proved effective when administered as live virus to young chicks in large-scale procedures by spraying liquid suspensions of the virus or by dust vaccines of the agent mixed with finely ground talc (54). Virus may be administered in drinking water. The immunizing process can be undertaken at a time when the chicks are easiest to handle and when the loss is at a minimum. Vaccination against infectious bronchitis can be accomplished simultaneously by including this agent with that of Newcastle disease.

INFECTIOUS BRONCHITIS

This is a highly infectious and contagious virus-induced disease of chickens (65). A pronounced hazard in the poultry industry, it is spread by contact, with an incubation period of 18 to 36 hours. The disease is somewhat similar in its early stages to Newcastle disease and laryngotracheitis, the young birds exhibiting nasal discharge, gasping, rales, and coughing. In older birds the nasal discharge is less evident. In young chicks there is malnutrition, failure to grow, and death. In older chicks there is serious decline in egg production. Recovered birds display high immunity. There is no effective means of treatment, but the disease can be eradicated by strict isolation measures. Vaccination can be effected by use of live chick embryo virus incorporated in a dust along with attenuated Newcastle disease virus and sprayed in young chicks.

Infectious Laryngotracheitis. This is another highly contagious virus-induced respiratory disease of chickens (65). After an incubation period of six to 12 days, the disease is characterized by gasping, rales and coughing, and particularly by hemorrhagic tracheitis and the formation of a thick membrane in the trachea. The mortality is about 13 per cent. Most losses are due to failure to grow and to some decline in egg production. The disease frequently appears at the broiler age. Transmission occurs by way of the respiratory tract, and recovery is followed by a strong immunity. Vaccination is effected by inoculation of live chick embryo cultured virus by the route of the cloaca. This abnormal route of inoculation does not result in the typical disease, since immunity is developed before the virus can reach the natural areas of disease production. It is of importance to see that vaccination is effective, since the normal disease may occur in those birds which do not react to vaccination.

The virus has been cultivated in tissue culture. Morphologically it is essentially identical with the agents of herpes simplex (Fig. 21 in Chap. 61), varicella, and equine herpes virus (27).

FOWL PLAGUE

This rapidly fatal disease of chickens, turkeys, and geese is characterized by weakness, sleepiness, and violet combs (83). Death may occur after a few days, a week, or longer. The virus can be cultivated in the embryonated egg and tissue culture. The agent is a myxovirus (Chaps. 61 and 62) and has been employed for intensive studies on morphology and biochemical aspects of cell-virus relationships (72). The disease has been rarely observed in the United States.

NEUROMUSCULAR DISEASES OF RODENTS AND SWINE

These viral agents of animals have been reviewed by Melnick (58). Rodent viruses have been isolated from mice and cotton rats and fall into two antigenic groups, Theiler's encephalomyelitis viruses and the encephalomyocarditis agents which include the EMC, Mengo, MM, and Columbia SK (29). The latter are similar immunologically but are not related to Theiler's agents.

Teschen virus (55), an enterovirus of swine (13) causes encephalomyelitis in the pig. The agent readily infects swine and has been cultured in kidney and other pig cell cultures. Vaccines have been prepared by inactivation of tissue culture virus with formalin and by use of live attenuated tissue culture agent. Teschen disease does not occur in swine in this country, and importation of the virus for study is prohibited.

REFERENCES

1. Ahlström, C. G.   J. Exper. Med., 115:839, 1962.
2. Andervont, H. B.   Ann. New York Acad. Sc., 54:1004, 1952.
3. Bawden, F. C.   Plant Viruses and Virus Diseases, 4th ed., The Ronald Press, 1964.
4. Beard, J. W.   Cancer Research, 16:279, 1956.
5. ———— Ann. New York Acad. Sc., 68:473, 1957.
6. ———— Amer. Sc., 46:226, 1958.
7. ———— Adv. Cancer Res., 7:1, 1963.
8. ———— Ann. New York Acad. Sc., 108:1057, 1963.
9. ———— and Kidd, J. G.   Proc. Soc. Exper. Biol. & Med., 34:451, 1936.
10. Bergold, G. H.   Canad. J. Zoology, 29:17, 1951.
11. ———— Adv. Virus Res., 1:91, 1953.
12. Bernhard, W.   Cancer Research, 18:491, 1958.
13. Betts, A. O., Lamont, P. H., and Kelley, D. F.   Ann. New York Acad. Sc., 101:428, 1962-63.
14. Bittle, J. L., Emery, J. B., York, C. J., and McMillen, J. K.   Am. J. Vet. Research, 22:374, 1961.
15. Bittner, J. J.   Harvey Lect., 42:221, 1946-47.
16. Black, L. M.   Survey of Biol. Progress, 1:155, 1949.
17. Brandly, C. A., Moses, H. E., Jones, E. E., and Jungherr, E. L.   Am. J. Vet. Research, 7:243, 1946.
18. Bryan, W. R.   J. Nat. Cancer Inst., 16:287, 1955.
19. Burmester, B. R.   Ann. New York Acad. Sc., 54:992, 1952.
20. ———— and Walter, W. G.   J. Nat. Cancer Inst., 26:511, 1961.
21. Buschke, A., and Loewenstein, L.   Klin. Wchnschr., 2:1726, 1925.
22. Cabasso, V. J.   Ann. New York Acad. Sc., 101:498, 1962-63.
23. ———— Kiser, K. H., Stebbins, M. R., and Cooper, H. K.   Am. J. Vet. Research, 23:394, 1962.
24. Chandra, S., and Toolan, H. W.   J. Nat. Cancer Inst., 27:1405, 1961.
25. Cox, H. R.   Lancet, 2:1, 1953.
26. ———— Bact. Rev., 18:239, 1954.
27. Cruickshank, J. G., Berry, D. M., and Hay, B.   Virology, 20:376, 1963.
28. Demonbreun, W. A., and Goodpasture, E. W.   Am. J. Path., 8:43, 1932.
29. Dick, G. W. A.   J. Immunol., 62:375, 1949.
30. Dmochowski, L.   Adv. Cancer Res., 1:103, 1953.
31. ———— and Grey, C. E.   Blood, 13:1017, 1958.
32. Dourmashkin, R. R., and Simons, P. J.   J. Ultrastructural Res., 5:505, 1961.
33. Eddy, B. E.   Adv. Virus Res., 7:91, 1960.
34. Ellermann, V.   Leucosis of Fowls and Leucemia Problems, London, Gyldendal, 1921.
35. Engelbreth-Holm, J.   Spontaneous and Experimental Leukemia in Animals. London, Oliver and Boyd, Ltd., 1942.
36. Findlay, G. M.   In A System of Bacteriology, London, Her Majesty's Stationery Office, 7:252, 1930.
37. Friend, C.   J. Exper. Med., 105:307, 1957.
38. Geleta, J. N., and Holbrook, A. A.   Am. J. Vet. Research, 22:713, 1961.
39. Gillespie, J. H.   Ann. New York Acad. Sc., 101:540, 1962-63.
40. Girardi, A. J., Sweet, B. H., Slotnick, V. B., and Hilleman, M. R.   Proc. Soc. Exper. Biol. & Med., 109:649, 1962.
41. Gledhill, A. W.   Vet. Rec., 64:723, 1952.
42. Graffi, A., and Gimmy, J.   Ztschr. ges. inn. Med., 13:881, 1958.
43. Gross, L.   Oncogenic Viruses, International Series of Monographs on Pure and Applied Biology, New York, Pergamon Press, 1961, vol. 11.
44. Henderson, W. M.   Adv. Vet. Sc., 6:19, 1960.
45. Hilleman, M. R., Tousimis, A. J., and Werner, J. H.   Proc. Soc. Exper. Biol. & Med., 89:587, 1955.
46. Huebner, R. J., Rowe, W. P., and Lane, W. T.   Proc. Nat. Acad. Sc., 48:2051, 1962.
47. Ito, Y.   Cold Spring Harbor Symp. Quant. Biol., 27,387, 1962.
48. Johnson, E. P., and Gross, W. B.   Vet. Med., 46:55, 1951.
49. Keeney, A. H., and Hunter, M. C.   Arch. Ophth., 44:573, 1950.
50. Kemeny, L., and Drehle, L. E.   Am. J. Vet. Research, 22:921, 1961.
51. Koprowski, H., James, T. R., and Cox, H. R.   Proc. Soc. Exper. Biol. & Med., 63:178, 1946.
52. Lee, R. C. T.   Cornell Vet., 52:39, 1962.
53. Madin, S. H., and Traum, J.   Bact. Rev., 19:6, 1955.
54. Markham, F. S., Sylstra, A. W., Hammar, A. H., and Gingher, P.   Poultry Sc., 35:390, 1956.
55. Mayr, A.   Ann. New York Acad. Sc., 101:423, 1962-63.
56. McNutt, S. H.   Adv. Vet. Sc., 1:283, 1953.
57. Mellors, R. C.   Cancer Research, 20:744, 1960.
58. Melnick, J. L.   Ann. Rev. Microbiol., 5:309, 1951.
59. ———— Ann. New York Acad. Sc., 61:754, 1955.
60. Meyer, K. F.   Adv. Vet. Sc., 1:1, 1953.
61. Moloney, J. B.   Fed. Proc., 21:19, 1962.
62. Moore, D. H., Pollard, E. C., and Haagensen, C. D.   Fed. Proc., 21:942, 1962.
63. Munroe, J. S., and Windle, W. F.   Science, 140:1415, 1963.
64. Plowright, W.   Ann. New York Acad. Sc., 101:548, 1962-63.
65. Roekel, H. V.   Adv. Vet. Sc., 2:64, 1955.
66. Rous, P.   J. Exper. Med., 13:397, 1911.
67. ———— Harvey Lect., 31:115, 1935-36.
68. ———— and Beard, J. W.   J. Exper. Med., 62:523, 1935.

69. Rous, P., Kidd, J. G., and Smith, W. E. J. Exper. Med., 96:159, 1952.
70. Rowe, W. P., and Hartley, J. W. Ann. New York Acad. Sc., 101:466, 1962-63.
71. ——— Huebner, R. J., and Hartley, J. W. Perspectives in Virology, 2:177, 1961. Burgess Publishing Co., Minneapolis.
72. Schäfer, W. Bact. Rev., 27:1, 1963.
73. Shahan, M. S. Ann. New York Acad. Sc., 101:444, 1962-63.
74. Shope, R. E. J. Exper. Med., 58:607, 1933.
75. ——— Adv. Vet. Sc., 2:1, 1955.
76. ——— In Perspectives in Virology, New York, John Wiley & Sons, Inc., 1:145, 1959.
77. Smith, K. M. Endeavour, 10:194, 1951.
78. ——— Adv. Virus Res., 9:195, 1962.
79. ——— The Seventeenth Annual Symposium on Fundamental Cancer Research. Viruses, Nucleic Acids, and Cancer, Feb. 20, 21, and 22, 1963. The University of Texas. M.D. Anderson Hospital and Tumor Institute. Texas Medical Center: Houston, Texas.
80. Steinhaus, E. A. Principles of Insect Pathology, 1st ed., New York, McGraw-Hill Book Co., Inc., 1949.
81. ——— Insect Pathology, vol. 1, New York, Academic Press, 1963.
82. Stewart, S. E. Adv. Virus Res., 7:61, 1960.
83. Stubbs, E. L. In Biester, H. E., and Schwarte, L. H. Diseases of Poultry, 3rd ed., Ames, The Iowa State College Press, 1952, p. 669.
84. Svoboda, J. Fol. Biol., 7:46, 1961.
85. Syverton, J. T. Ann. New York Acad. Sc., 54:1126, 1952.
86. Temin, H. M., and Rubin, H. Virology, 8:209, 1959.
87. Topley and Wilson's Principles of Bacteriology and Immunity, 4th ed. Baltimore, The Williams & Wilkins Co., 2:1955.
88. Trentin, J. J., Yabe, Y., and Taylor, G. Science, 137:835, 1962.
89. Warren, J., Nadel, M. K., Slater, E., and Millian, S. J. Am. J. Vet. Res., 21:111, 1960.
90. Zilber, L. A. J. Nat. Cancer Inst., 26:1295, 1961.

MEDICAL MYCOLOGY

77

Introduction to Medical Mycology

Fungi, like bacteria, are ubiquitous. Many of the saprophytic forms play indispensable roles in the cyclical transformations of organic matter, not only in the decomposition of substances such as hemicelluloses and lignins but also in the synthesis of complex organic compounds. Their economic importance can be illustrated by the large volumes which have been written on the industrial uses of yeasts and molds.

Fungi are frequent causes of diseases in plants, but of the thousands of known species, less than 100 are capable of invading man or animals, and less than a dozen of them produce fatal infections. It is fortunate, moreover, that only a few of the fungi, the *dermatophytes,* can spread from man to man or animal to man and initiate epidemics.

A few unrelated fungi can be considered as endogenous because they can be carried by the normal individual apparently in the same manner as staphylococci, pneumococci, and meningococci. Included in this group are *Actinomyces israelii, Candida albicans,* and, perhaps, *Geotrichum candidum.* Males are attacked more frequently than females but never in a ratio greater than 3:1, in contrast to infections caused by **exogenous** fungi, where males are infected 7 to 20 times as frequently as females.

The habitat of **exogenous** fungi is somewhere in nature, and males because of their occupations are exposed to the infectious materials more intimately and frequently than are the females. The exogenous group contains many of the more pathogenic fungi, most of which have been isolated from the soil (1). Where there are concentrated sources of infection in environments, such as *Coccidioides immitis* in certain areas of the southwest (18) and *Histoplasma capsulatum* in the Mississippi Valley (14), as many as 50 to 80 per cent of the adult population can be demonstrated, by positive skin tests, to have been infected at some time during their residency in the area. Where fungi such as *H. capsulatum* (7) and *Sporotrichum schenckii* (6) have been found to contaminate heavily restricted areas, epidemics of active infection have occurred.

There is a general feeling that prolonged use of broad-spectrum antibiotics and steroid therapy, as well as nitrogen mustards and urethane, among other therapeutic regimens, predispose to latent or subclinical fungus infections. Increased susceptibility to cryptococcosis and histoplasmosis has been reported in malignant diseases of the reticuloendothelial system (3, 5, 13, 19) while mucormycosis (phycomycosis) frequently has been associated with uncontrolled diabetes mellitus (2).

The diseases produced by pathogenic fungi resemble those caused by *Mycobacterium tuberculosis* in that they evolve slowly and develop characteristic chronic infections which persist for weeks, months, and even years. The organisms grow slowly in the tissues, produce **neither endotoxins nor exotoxins,** and induce slowly developing granulomatous reactions. In most mycoses a state of **hypersensitivity** analogous to that found in tuberculosis develops. Lesions such as tissue necrosis and abscess formation often are produced as direct results of this hypersensitivity. Sensitizing antibodies, measured as agglutinins, precipitins, and complement-fixing antibodies, develop as a result of mycotic infections.

Except for *Actinomyces, Nocardia,* and *Streptomyces,* the pathogenic fungi are much larger than bacteria, and it is not surprising that a fungus was the first microorganism to be proved as an etiologic agent of a disease.

Schoenlein (17) reported that favus was caused by a fungus which later was named *Achorion schoenleinii* by Remak (15). In the same year Langenbeck (11) demonstrated yeast-like fungi in thrush. The ringworm fungi were described by Gruby (8) and Malmsten (12) as *Microsporum audouinii* and *Trichophyton tonsurans,* respectively. In 1871 Harz (9) described the fungus nature of eczema marginatum caused by the organism now known as *Epidermophyton floccosum.*

Most of the fungi which cause disease in man and animals had been isolated and identified before 1900. The slow development of medical mycology, in contrast to that of medical bacteriology, can be attributed in part to the complexity of their morphologic forms but primarily to the fact that the fungi did not produce epidemic diseases as do some of the bacteria, viruses, and rickettsiae. Since the major bacterial, spirochetal, rickettsial, and viral diseases now have been identified, the microbiologist belatedly is taking up the study of the pathogenic fungi.

The supposed difficulties of medical mycology are largely psychological. The nomenclature of mycology is neither more difficult nor more changeable than those of bacteriology or parasitology. With few exceptions, all of the fungi pathogenic for animals and man grow readily on simple laboratory media, and their striking variations in colony and microscopic morphology facilitate rather than handicap their identification and classification (4).

Classification. The fungi belong to a group of plants which lack chlorophyll. They may be single- or multi-celled; the cells contain true nuclei and have definite walls. The rudimentary plant body, Thallus, is not differentiated into roots, stems, and leaves, and reproduction takes place by means of spores, sexual and asexual. Such plants are called Thallophytes. The various divisions among these rudimentary, non-chlorophyll containing plants are characterized as follows:

Kingdom: Plantae
  Division: Schizomycota
    Subdivision: Schizomycotina
      Class: Schizomycetes—fission fungi or bacteria

Division: Mycota
  Subdivision: Myxomycotina
    Class: Myxomycetes—slime molds
  Subdivision: Eumycotina (true fungi)
    Class: Phycomycetes—water molds
      Ascomycetes—sexual spores in ascus
      Basidiomycetes—sexual spores on basidium
      Deuteromycetes—asexual spores

In the Schizomycetes only the genera *Actinomyces, Nocardia,* and *Streptomyces* are of interest to the medical mycologist. These forms are thought to be intermediate between the Eubacteriales (true bacteria) and the Eumycotina (true fungi). They are bacteria-like in size and morphology but demonstrate true branching, a characteristic of the higher fungi. There are no known pathogenic forms in the Myxomycetes. The class Phycomycetes contains the well-known bread molds *Mucor* and *Rhizopus,* which occasionally have been isolated from patients with cerebral and pulmonary mucormycosis (2). The only human pathogens belonging to the Ascomycetes are *Allescheria boydii* (*Monosporium apiospermum*) and *Leptosphaeria senegalensis,* which cause maduromycosis, and *Piedraia hortai,* the cause of black piedra. These fungi are known to have a "perfect" stage, or phase of growth which produces spores in asci. Although members of the Basidiomycetes produce poisons which are extremely toxic for man, none of these fungi initiates infection.

Almost all of the fungi pathogenic for man or animals are classified among the fungi imperfecti, so named because they have no known perfect or sexual spore development in highly specialized structures as are found among the other classes. In the imperfecti only asexual spores are produced. Such spores are formed on or from the filaments, and their methods of development, size, color, and arrangement are used for identification. Also, the type of macroscopic colony developed in culture allows a grouping into a yeast type, yeast-like type, and filamentous type. By noting the macroscopic colony type and the microscopic morphology (spore forms), the fungi can be identified readily.

The Colony. The **filamentous colony** is composed of a mat of intertwining, branching filaments. An individual filament is called a **hypha** (pl. **hyphae**), and the collective mass of hyphae is called the **mycelium.** The mycelium which penetrates the substrate is known as the **vegetative mycelium,** while the growth which projects into the air from the surface of the substrate is called the **aerial mycelium.** The aerial mycelium is designated further as **reproductive mycelium** when it produces spores which, when freed, germinate and develop other similar colonies. The entire plant is called the **thallus.**

A second type of colony, the **yeast-like type,** is composed of individual oval cells which reproduce by budding, but, in addition, there can be seen elongated, budding cells which remain attached and thus form false hyphae or **pseudomycelia.** Such colonies are characteristic of the genus *Candida.*

The third type of colony, **yeast type,** is composed only of individual oval to round, budding cells. Such colonies are bacteria-like in consistency and are characteristic of the true yeasts, *Saccharomyces* and of *Cryptococcus.*

Spores. Although fragments of hyphae, if transferred to fresh media, will germinate to produce new colonies, the fungi characteristically reproduce by definite spore forms. Those spore forms which develop from specialized cells in the mycelium as a result of nuclear fusions are called **sexual spores;** those which are derived from the mycelium or from specialized structures on the mycelium, but without nuclear fusions, are called **asexual spores.**

Sexual spores which are developed endogenously in a sac-like structure, the **ascus,** are called **ascospores,** and the fungi which produce these spores are placed in the Ascomycetes. The simplest type of ascus is found among the yeasts, in which the oval vegetative cells produce internal spores with an accompanying nuclear fusion. The cell then becomes the ascus and the spores are designated as ascospores. Among the highly organized filamentous fungi, specialized structures enclose numerous asci, each having eight ascospores.

Sexual spores developed exogenously on a specialized club-like structure, the **basidium,** are called **basidiospores,** and the fungi which produce these spores are placed

in the Basidiomycetes. The basidia, with four attached spores, are characteristic structures found in the mushrooms.

Two types of sexual spores are found in the Phycomycetes. The **zygospore** is developed as a result of the fusion of two identical cells, and the **oospore** is developed as a result of the fusion of two unlike cells.

Asexual spores which are derived directly from, or as a part of, the original hypha are called **thallospores.** One such type of spore is developed by the concentration of protoplasm into a hyphal cell, which enlarges to become wider than the other cells in the hypha. With the development of a thick protective wall, the spore becomes very resistant to environmental conditions. Such a spore is called a **chlamydospore.** All fungi produce chlamydospores in the mycelium.

Spores developed by fragmentation of hyphae into short, oblong, or rounded elements are designated as **arthrospores.** Species in the genus *Geotrichum* and *Coccidioides immitis* reproduce by this type of thallospore in culture.

Spores developed as budding processes from vegetative cells are designated as **blastospores.** Yeasts, various species of *Candida* and *Cryptococcus neoformans* reproduce by this type of thallospore.

Spores produced endogenously within a swollen structure, **sporangium,** on the end of a hypha (sporangiophore) in the Phycomycetes are designated as **sporangiospores.**

Spores developed from or on a specialized supporting structure of the mycelium are called **conidia** (singular **conidium**) and the supporting structure is known as the **conidiophore.** Such spores are found among all the Deuteromycetes and Fungi Imperfecti. The type of conidiophore plus the type and arrangement of the conidia constitute the morphologic characters by which these fungi are identified.

Methods of Studying Fungi. The general methods of bacteriology are applicable to the study of the fungi in so far as cultural technics are concerned. All of the fungi, with the exception of *Actinomyces israelii,* can be cultivated on routine bacteriologic media under aerobic conditions both at room and at incubator temperatures. Since most of the fungi are slow growing, cultures must be maintained for a week or two and should be protected against drying during this period.

The microscopic examination of cultures differs somewhat from the usual bacteriologic methods of examination. Identification of fungi is based on the type of spores produced and the arrangement of the spores on the hyphae. Smears are quite useless when prepared in the manner in which bacterial films are spread on slides, since the cell walls are crushed and the arrangement of diagnostic structures is displaced. Preparations must be made with the least possible disorganization of the fungus or by careful dissection of parts of the culture. Cultures may be examined undisturbed by placing the culture tube on the stage of the microscope and examining the growth at the top of the slant with the low power objective. Also, numerous types of culture preparations may be made for microscopic examinations, cell cultures (10), and slide cultures (4, 16). Microscopic preparations may be made by placing a portion of the colony in a drop of mounting medium on a slide, carefully teasing it with needles, and covering the preparation with a coverglass. Lactophenol-cotton blue or eosin-glycerin may be used for this purpose. Yeast and yeast-like colonies are best examined microscopically by emulsifying a bit of the culture in a drop of water on a slide and covering the preparation with a coverglass.

Clinical materials such as skin, hair, and nails should be placed on a slide with a drop of 10 per cent potassium hydroxide and covered with a coverglass. Such preparations may be heated over a low flame of a Bunsen burner and immediately examined. Sputum, pus or other exudates should be examined as **fresh preparations;** i.e., placed on a slide, coverglass added, and examined, untreated and unstained, with reduced light under the low- and high-power objectives of the microscope.

The following textbooks on medical mycology are available for a more detailed discussion of the medically important fungi:

Brumpt, E. *Précis de Parasitologie,* 5th ed., Paris, Masson et Cie., 1936, Vol. II, pp. 1571-2070.

Conant, N. F., Smith, D. T., Baker, R. D., Callaway, J. L., and Martin, D. S. *Manual of Clinical Mycology,* 2nd ed., Philadelphia, W. B. Saunders Co., 1954.

Emmons, C. W., Binford, C. H., and Utz, J. P. *Medical Mycology,* Philadelphia, Lea & Febiger, 1963.

Lewis, G. M., Hopper, M. E., Wilson, J. W., and Plunkett, O. A. *An Introduction to Medical Mycology,* 4th ed., Chicago, The Year Book Publishers, Inc., 1958.

Sabouraud, R. *Maladies du Cuir Chevelu. III. Les Maladies Crytogamiques, Les Teignes,* Paris, Masson et Cie., 1910.

REFERENCES

1. Ajello, L.   Science, 123:876, 1956.
2. Baker, R. D.   Am. J. Path., 32:287, 1956.
3. Cawley, E. P., and Curtis, A. C.   J. Invest. Dermat., 11:443, 1948.
4. Conant, N. F., and others.   Manual of Clinical Mycology, 2nd ed., Philadelphia, W. B. Saunders Co., 1954.
5. Curtis, A. C., and Grekin, J. N.   J.A.M.A., 134:1217, 1947.
6. Du Toit, C. J.   Proc. Transvaal Mine Med. Officers Assoc., 22:111, 1942.
7. Grayston, J. T., and Furcolow, M. L.   Am. J. Pub. Health, 43:665, 1953.
8. Gruby, M.   Compt. rend. Acad. d. sc., 17:301, 1843.
9. Harz, C. O.   Bull. Soc. Imp. Nat. Moscou, 44:88, 1871.
10. Henrici, A. T.   Molds, Yeasts and Actinomyces, 2nd ed., New York, John Wiley & Sons, Inc., 1947.
11. Längenbeck, B.   Neue Notizen Gebiete Natur und Heilkunde (Froriep), 12:145, 1839.
12. Malmsten, P. H.   Trans. by F. C. H. Creplin. Arch. f. Anat., Physiol. u. wissensch. Med., 1848, pp. 1-19.
13. Nichols, D. R., and Martin, W. J.   Ann. Int. Med., 43:767, 1955.
14. Palmer, C. E.   Pub. Health Rep., 60:513, 1945.
15. Remak, R.   Diagnostische und pathologische Untersuchungen, Muscardine and Favus, 7:193, 1845.
16. Riddell, R. W.   Mycologia, 42:265, 1950.
17. Schoenlein, Prof.   Arch. f. Anat., Physiol. u. wissensch. Med., 1839, p. 82.
18. Smith, C. E.   M. Clin. North America, 27:790, 1943.
19. Zimmerman, L. E., and Rappaport, H.   Am. J. Clin. Path., 24:1050, 1954.

78

Actinomycosis and Actinomycetes

Standing midway between the true bacteria and the more complex molds are a number of pathogenic organisms which have been placed in the order *Actinomycetales*. Colonies of these organisms have some gross resemblances to the hyphomycetes, usually being dry, tough, and wrinkled, and sometimes covered with a down of aerial mycelium. These mold-like fungi are characterized by a **delicate mycelium,** usually less than 1 μ in diameter and hence within bacterial dimensions. The mycelium is septate and shows a marked tendency to branch. The component parts of the mycelium often stain unevenly but do not contain recognizable nuclei.

In the *Actinomycetaceae* the mycelial filaments fragment into bacillary and coccoid forms, and some varieties under special conditions grow in diphtheroid forms. Those varieties which are anaerobic or microaerophilic, nonacid-fast, obligate parasites are placed in the genus *Actinomyces* as *A. israelii, A. bovis,* and *A. naeslundii.* Other varieties, which are aerobic, partially acid-fast or nonacid-fast, and saprophytic but facultative parasites, are placed in the genera *Nocardia* and *Streptomyces.* Whereas several species of *Nocardia* and *Streptomyces* can cause disease in man, there are only two species, *A. israelii* and *A. bovis,* in the genus *Actinomyces; A. naeslundii* is considered to be a saprophytic facultative species of *Actinomyces* (8, 17, 49).

The nonpathogenic intermediate forms can be classified according to their method of reproduction: by means of conidia produced in chain formation at the ends of hyphae (*Streptomyces*) or by means of conidia produced singly on the ends of short conidiophores (*Micromonospora*). Many classifications of the group have been proposed, but still there are differences of opinion among investigators, particularly in respect to the phylogenetic relations among these organisms. Some regard them as degraded fungi, others see them as a primary stock from which both bacteria and fungi have developed, and still others prefer to call them "higher bacteria." There is, however, a general agreement that the actinomycetes belong in an intermediate position between bacteria and fungi. The recent revision of the classification of these rudimentary forms by Waksman and Henrici (50) has become accepted generally and has been included in the seventh edition of Bergey's Manual (1957) (Table 1).

Of the other generic names which have been applied to this group, *Leptothrix* was used first for the autotrophic, free-living, filamentous, iron bacteria and should not have been applied to members of the actinomycetes or to the parasitic unbranched, filamentous, gram-positive organisms which occur frequently in the human mouth (41). *Cladothrix, Streptothrix, Oöspora, Discomyces, Actinocladothrix, Proactinomyces,* and *Cohnistrepothrix* are other generic names which, serving no useful purpose, have been discarded. A few species of *Streptomyces* cause disease in man and animals, but the vast majority are of importance because of the role they play in the economy of nature.

They are ubiquitous and quite active in bringing about changes in organic matter in the soil and water and in and upon the bodies of man and animals. The medical bacteriologist may encounter *Streptomyces* as a contaminant in culture media, as a nonpathogenic organism in feces, in sputum contaminated by saliva, and in exudates from open skin lesions. Species of *Streptomyces,*

Table 1. Classification of the Actinomycetales

(Waksman and Henrici, 1943)

I. Mycelium rudimentary or absent. Family *Mycobacteriaceae* Chester.
    A. Acid-fast organisms. *Mycobacterium* Lehmann and Neumann.
II. True mycelium produced.
    A. Vegetative mycelium fragments into bacillary or coccoid elements.
                Family *Actinomycetaceae* Buchanan.
        a. Anaerobic or micro-aerophilic, parasitic, not acid-fast.
                Actinomyces Harz.
        b. Aerobic, partially acid-fast or nonacid-fast.
                Nocardia Trevisan
    B. Vegetative mycelium not fragmenting into bacillary or coccoid elements.
                Family *Streptomycetaceae* Waksman and Henrici.
        a. Multiplication by conidia in chains from aerial hyphae.
                Streptomyces Waksman and Henrici
        b. Multiplication by single terminal spores on short sporophores.
                Micromonospora Ørskov.

however, have furnished several important antibiotics.

ACTINOMYCOSIS

Actinomycosis, caused by *Actinomyces israelii,* is a chronic suppurative or granulomatous infection characterized by the formation of abscesses, multiple draining sinuses, and the appearance of tangled mycelial masses, or "granules," in the discharges and in tissue sections.

Harz (9) first described *A. bovis* from pathologic material obtained from a case of "lumpy jaw" in cattle and named the infection actinomycosis, Israel (21) described human cases of the disease, and Ponfick (40) showed that bovine and human cases were caused by the same organism. Wolff and Israel (52) obtained pure cultures of this organism from human infections and proved their pathogenicity by inoculation of animals.

Since the Wolff-Israel fungus could be cultured only by micro-aerophilic methods, and repeated culturing by other investigators showed this to be true for the organism of both human and bovine actinomycosis (53), the micro-aerophilic *A. bovis* became established as the etiologic agent of the disease. Erickson (6) and Thompson (48), however, established two distinct species of anaerobic *Actinomyces* as the etiologic agents of actinomycosis: *A. bovis* in cattle and *A. israelii* in man. Thompson and Lovestedt (49) also described a new species, *Actinomyces naeslundii,* which was considered a

saprophyte often found in the mouth. Garrod (8) isolated this species from saliva from normal persons in 18 out of 21 specimens. Also, Buchanan and Pine (2) described a new species, *Actinomyces propionicus,* isolated from the lachrymal duct of a case of human canaliculitis.

Morphology. In tissues *A. israelii* and *A. bovis* are found as organized colonies or "granules" composed of densely packed and tangled filaments, 1 μ or less in diameter (Fig. 1). The ends of the filaments, at the

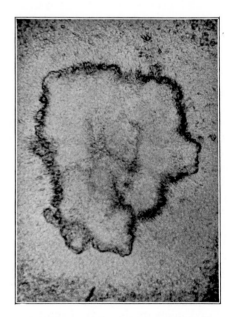

Fig. 1. *Actinomyces bovis.* Granule in pus. × 350. (From Conant and others. *Manual of Clinical Mycology,* 2nd ed., W. B. Saunders Co.)

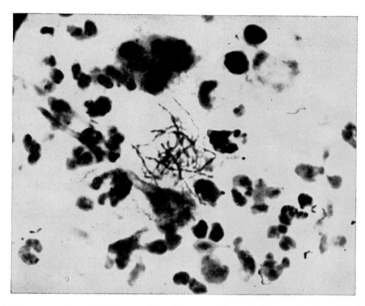

Fig. 2. *Actinomyces israelii*. Gram stain of smear of crushed granule showing gram-positive branching hyphae. × 1,300. (From Conant and others. *Manual of Clinical Mycology,* 2nd ed., W. B. Saunders Co.)

periphery of the granule, are encased in a sheath of material and resemble clubs. Pine and Overman (38) have examined sectioned granules of *A. bovis* by light and phase microscopy and ultrathin sections by electron microscopy. The hyphae tips were quite distinct within the material apparently secreted by the fungus. Chemical analysis showed this material to be a polysaccharide-protein complex. Widra (51) examined granules of *A. israelii* by histochemical technics and concluded that the substance around the tips of the hyphae was secreted by the fungus and was a highly polymerized basic protein. The granule itself is, apparently, a mycelial mass cemented by a polysaccharide-protein complex and contains about 50 per cent calcium phosphate (38).

In sections of tissue stained with hematoxylin and eosin, the filaments take the hematoxylin stain and the sheaths or clubs, if present, take the eosin stain. When granules from sputum or pus are crushed between slides and stained by Gram's method, the preparation reveals gram-positive branching filaments, short diphtheroid forms and coccoid elements (Fig. 2).

Cultural Characteristics. *Actinomyces* spp. are catalase negative, anaerobic, micro-aerophilic organisms. They may be cultured directly from uncontaminated materials in thioglycollate broth, anaerobic chopped meat medium, or in deep-shake cultures of beef infusion glucose agar at 37° C. In the latter medium, pinpoint to large-sized lobulated colonies, which appear in four to five days, are found at varying depths below the surface of the agar, but often form a band 1 to 1.5 cm. from the surface of the medium (Fig. 3).

For identification of species, colonies are picked from the above media, emulsified in sterile water, if necessary, and streaked on the surface of brain heart infusion agar plates which are incubated at 37° C. under 95 per cent nitrogen and 5 per cent CO_2. The appearance of microcolonies at 24 hours, macrocolonies at five to seven days and a negative catalase test identify the species (17, 37, 39).

Initial isolation from contaminated materials demands carefully streaked agar plates. A granule is washed several times in sterile distilled water and crushed with a glass rod in a short test tube; the resulting emulsion streaked over the agar surface. Several media have been recommended for initial isolation: beef extract-starch-blood agar (17, 19),

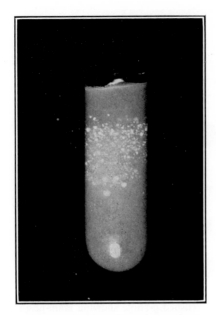

Fig. 3. *Actinomyces bovis.* Culture in shake tube of beef infusion glucose agar. pH 7.6.

brain heart infusion agar, and a synthetic maintenance medium (37, 39). Final identification of the isolate, however, is based on the criteria mentioned above when anaerobic brain heart infusion agar plates are examined.

Actinomyces israelii. At 24 to 48 hours microscopic colonies on anaerobic brain heart infusion agar plates are mycelial and spidery in appearance (Fig. 4A). Later, at five to seven days, microscopic colonies are raised, rough, and molar-tooth in appearance (Fig. 4B). Gram-stained smears reveal gram-positive branching diphtheroid forms (Fig. 4C). This species does not liquefy gelatin; a majority of the strains produce acid from glucose, xylose, and mannitol and are negative in raffinose and starch. Reduction of nitrate to nitrite is variable; starch may or may not be hydrolyzed. The species was isolated from disease in man (17, 37).

Actinomyces bovis. At 24 to 48 hours, microscopic colonies on anaerobic brain heart infusion agar plates, are smooth, round, and dew-drop in appearance (Fig. 5A). Later, at five to seven days, macroscopic colonies are convex, smooth, and entire in appearance (Fig. 5B). Gram-stained smears reveal gram-positive branching diphtheroid forms (Fig. 5C). This species does not liquefy gelatin, produces acid from glucose and starch and is negative in xylose, mannitol and raffinose. Starch is strongly hydrolyzed, while nitrates are not reduced to nitrites. The species was isolated from disease in cattle (37).

Actinomyces naeslundii. At 24 to 48 hours microscopic colonies on anaerobic brain heart infusion agar plates have a dense tangled mycelial center, with a surrounding fringe of hyphae (Fig. 6A). Later, at five to seven days, macroscopic colonies may be

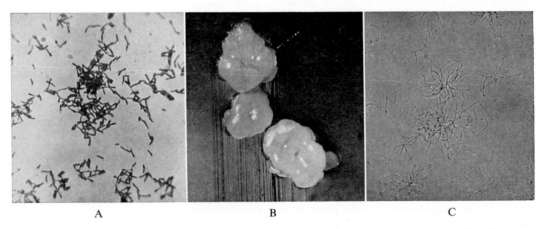

A   B   C

Fig. 4. A, *Actinomyces israelii.* Gram stain of smear from rough colony showing diphtheroid forms. × 1,200. B, *Actinomyces israelii.* Molar tooth colony on BHI agar plates, 15 days. C, *Actinomyces israelii.* Spidery colony on BHI agar plates, 24 hours. × 500. (Courtesy Mycology Unit, Communicable Disease Center, Atlanta, Georgia.)

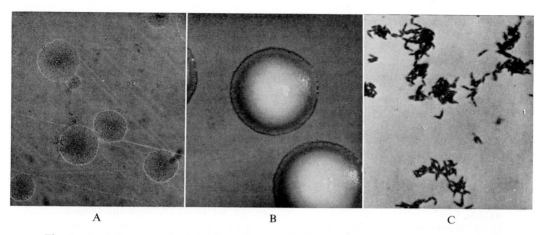

A   B   C

Fig. 5. A, *Actinomyces bovis*. Entire colony on BHI agar plate, 24 hours. × 100. B, *Actinomyces bovis*. Smooth colony on BHI agar plate, 10 days. C, *Actinomyces bovis*. Gram stain of smear from smooth colony showing diphtheroid forms. × 1,000. (Courtesy Mycology Unit, Communicable Disease Center, Atlanta, Georgia.)

convex and smooth or lobulated and rough (Fig. 6B). Gram-stained smears reveal gram-positive branching diphtheroid forms (Fig. 6C). This species does not liquefy gelatin, produces acid from glucose and raffinose, and is negative in xylose and mannitol. Acid from starch is variable. Hydrolysis of starch also is variable, while nitrate is reduced to nitrite. While *A. israelii* and *A. bovis* are obligate anaerobes, this species is a facultative aerobe. The species was isolated from mouth and saliva of man (8, 17, 49).

Actinomyces propionicus. This species is similar to *A. israelii* but differs in its metabolic and physiologic characteristics by its fermentation of glucose to form CO_2, acetic, and **propionic acids** with small amounts of lactic (DL) and succinic acids. Also, this species is a facultative aerobe. The species was isolated from human canaliculitis (2).

Resistance. *A. israelii* resists drying at room temperature for 18 to 22 days (53) or in vacuo in the refrigerator for three to four months (36). It is killed at 60° C. for one hour (3).

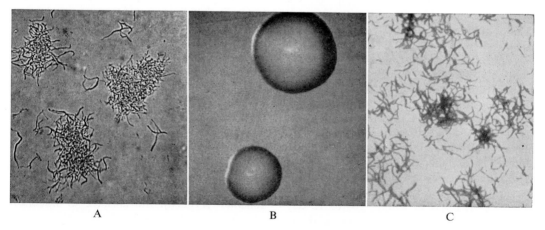

A   B   C

Fig. 6. A, *Actinomyces naeslundii*. Dense tangled mycelial colony on BHI agar plate, 24 hours. × 475. B, *Actinomyces naeslundii*. Smooth colony on BHI agar plate, seven days. C, *Actinomyces naeslundii*. Gram stain smear from smooth colony showing branching diphtheroid forms. × 900. (Courtesy Mycology Unit, Communicable Disease Center, Atlanta, Georgia.)

In vitro studies with many strains of *A. israelii* have shown degrees of variability as regards their sensitivity to penicillin, streptomycin, chloramphenicol, chlortetracycline, and oxytetracycline (7, 15, 27, 46). Penicillin and oxytetracycline have been shown to be the most active, and streptomycin the least active (7).

Fungus Metabolites. **Neither endotoxins nor exotoxins** have been demonstrated for *A. israelii.* Lactic acid, ethanol, and acetic and formic acid are formed from glucose (18). Acid phosphatase is produced by some strains (16).

Antigenic Structure. Rabbits immunized with various strains of *A. israelii* have produced agglutinins in high titer (3, 11, 44, 45). Slack and others (45) have identified two serologic groups (A and B) based on reciprocal agglutinin adsorption tests using 20 strains from human and animal sources. Attempts to sensitize animals have not been successful (5, 30, 41).

Antigenically related components exist in the cytoplasmic fractions of *A. israelii* and *Mycobacterium* species, but cell wall fractions show specificity (23, 25). Also, cytoplasmic components of *Nocardia* species are antigenically related to those of *A. israelii,* whereas certain cell wall fractions are species- and type-specific (24). Agar gel diffusion tests show *A. israelii* and *A. bovis* to be antigenically distinct, whereas *A. naeslundii* shows antigenic relationship to both of these species (22).

Experimental Infection in Laboratory Animals. Although guinea pigs and rabbits may be infected with *A. israelii,* the experiments are difficult to repeat and progressive actinomycosis is infrequent. Some success has been attained by methods employing repeated inoculations and introduction of foreign materials (calcium phosphate and salivary calculus) and by efforts to sensitize animals before inoculation. The use of gastric mucin, however, has been shown by Meyer and Verges (33) to establish infection with *A. bovis* in young, 10- to 15-day-old albino mice. Hazen and others (10) reported the hamster to be susceptible to intraperitoneal inoculation of pure culture.

Clinical Types of Infection in Man. Actinomycosis usually is differentiated into cervicofacial, thoracic, and abdominal types of infection.

Cervicofacial actinomycosis is an infection of the jaw and tissues of the face and neck, characterized by swelling and hardness with the formation of multiple abscesses which eventually break down to form draining sinuses. The sanguinopurulent drainage from the sinuses usually contains macroscopic granules of *A. israelii.* Such infections follow tooth extractions or other operative procedures in the mouth, and the disease progresses by a slow and direct extension of the infection through the tissues.

Thoracic actinomycosis is an infection of the lungs and thoracic cage. Until extension through the thoracic skin results in multiple draining sinuses, the diagnosis often is not suspected. Infection usually is confined to the hilar region and the base of the lungs. Direct extension through the tissue to the lung surface and pleura may result in an inflammatory process, with pleural thickening, empyema, and osteomyelitis of the ribs. Hematogenous spread from a primary lung infection can result in the formation of foci in tissues such as the liver, kidneys, and brain.

Abdominal actinomycosis originates in the region of the cecum and may simulate acute or subacute appendicitis. Infection by *A. israelii* should be suspected when an appendectomy wound fails to heal and irregular tender masses appear in the abdomen. Later in the disease evidence of destruction of vertebral bodies or of the formation of a psoas abscess should suggest infection by *A. israelii.* Infection extends to the abdominal skin, and sinuses from which granules may be obtained are formed. Generalized infection can occur, particularly from extension through the diaphragm to the pleural cavity.

Method of Transmission. Actinomycosis, caused by *A. israelii,* is an endogenous infection of man and animals. The fungus may be isolated from carious teeth and tonsillar crypts in the absence of infection (5, 20, 28, 29, 41, 43, 47, 49). Reports of foreign bodies in the lesions, such as particles of straw in cervicofacial infections, would seem to indicate that the fungus lives in nature and can be introduced into the body as a contaminant. *A. israelii,* however, has never been isolated from natural substrates, and it is agreed generally that when foreign bodies are found in such lesions, they probably were the means by which the fungus was inoculated deeper into the tissue from its natural oral habitat. There have been no reports of man-to-man or animal-to-man transmission. Indeed, it is difficult to infect laboratory animals with granules directly from lesions or with pure cultures, and the pathogenesis of actinomycosis is not understood thoroughly.

The possible role of "associated organisms," such as *Actinobacillus actinomycetemcomitans,* anaerobic diphtheroids, or anaerobic streptococci, in the pathogenesis of actinomycosis has been investigated by Holm (12, 13, 14). In a bacteriologic study of specimens from 650 patients with closed lesions, *A. israelii* was never found in pure culture. Such results would seem to indicate a symbiotic relationship of organisms to be necessary in actinomycosis. Also, such a relationship may be the cause of varied results in the treatment of this disease.

Treatment. Actinomycosis responds to sulfonamides and penicillin (4, 34, 42), chlortetracycline (32, 54), oxytetracycline (26, 55), isoniazid (31), and stilbamidine (34). Prolonged and vigorous treatment with penicillin, however, is the treatment of choice.

NOCARDIOSIS

Nocardiosis is a primary pulmonary infection, caused by *Nocardia asteroides,* producing protean symptoms due to metastases throughout the body, resulting in widespread systemic disease.

Nocard (90) first described an infection in cattle which was caused by an aerobic type of actinomycete named *Nocardia farcinica* by Trevisan (96). Eppinger (70) described *Cladothrix asteroides,* which he had isolated from a human case of pseudotuberculosis with meningitis and brain abscesses. Blanchard (60) in 1896 renamed this fungus *Nocardia asteroides.* More recently Gordon and Mihm (79) in 1962 reported *N. farcinica* and *N. asteroides* to be similar, if not identical, and discussed the

problem in nomenclature posed by this finding.

Morphology. Organized granules are not present in such materials as sputum, spinal fluid, or other exudates in systemic nocardiosis; only gram-positive, branching or bacillary elements may be seen (Fig. 7). The acid-fast forms may be mistaken for the tubercle bacillus.

Also, granules are not seen in tissues. Hematoxylin- and eosin-stained sections reveal only an acute inflammatory response; no organisms are seen. In gram-stained sections, however, *N. asteroides* appears as gram-positive, delicate, branching bacillary forms, 1 μ in diameter, scattered throughout areas of necrosis (Fig. 8).

Cultural Characteristics. *Nocardia asteroides* is cultured easily on all common laboratory media. From closed lesions, subcutaneous abscesses and spinal fluid cultures may be made directly on Sabouraud's glucose agar slants and brain heart infusion blood agar slants for incubation at room temperature and 37° C., respectively. Sputum and exudates from draining sinuses must be streaked carefully on agar plates of the above media for adequate separation of resulting colonies. Antibiotics should not be used in these media for the purpose of

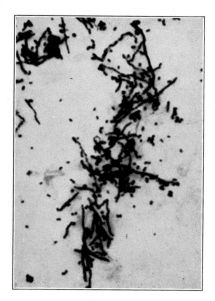

Fig. 7. *Nocardia asteroides.* Gram stain of sputum smear. × 1,524.

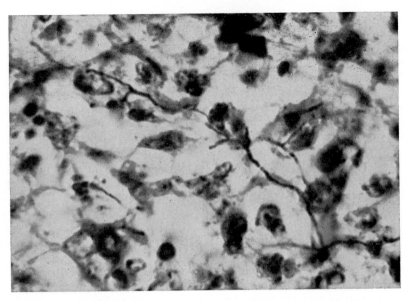

Fig. 8. *Nocardia asteroides.* Gram stain section of brain abscess showing gram-positive, branching filaments. (From Conant and others. *Manual of Clinical Mycology,* 2nd ed., W. B. Saunders Co.)

curtailing bacterial contaminants. *N. asteroides* is susceptible to most of the antibacterial substances in vitro. Since *N. asteroides* grows at 40-45° C., cultures from contaminated materials can be incubated at these temperatures to inhibit contamination (78).

On Sabouraud's glucose agar *N. asteroides* appears glabrous and somewhat granular and will vary in color from yellow to deep orange. An occasional isolate will produce a chalky white surface and have an earthy odor resembling a *Streptomyces* (Fig. 9).

Fig. 9. *Nocardia asteroides.* Culture on Sabouraud's glucose agar at room temperature for 12 days.

Microscopically the growth consists of delicate, branching hyphae, 1 μ or less in diameter, when examined in undisturbed preparations such as cell cultures. The hyphae fragment readily into bacillary and coccoid forms and in stained smears are gram-positive and partially acid-fast.

Pathogenic species of *Nocardia* and *Streptomyces* present such rudimentary morphology it is difficult or impossible to separate species on a morphologic basis. Therefore, biochemical and physiologic characteristics are used to identify these organisms.

N. asteroides does not decompose casein, tyrosine, xanthine and does not liquefy gelatin or affect litmus milk. It does utilize paraffin and will grow at 45° C. (61, 73, 75, 77, 78, 79, 80, 87).

Resistance. *N. asteroides* has been isolated from the soil, which would seem to indicate that it has a marked resistance to drying and the effects of temperature. Although some isolates are resistant to 50° C., they are readily killed at 60° C. for one hour. Salle and Jann (92) showed subtilin to be effective at a dilution of 1:1000. Strains of *N. asteroides* differ in their resistance to the inhibiting effect of penicillin. Strauss and others (95) tested the sensitivity of 10 strains of *N. asteroides* to 14 chemotherapeutic agents. They reported inhibition by chlortetracycline, chloramphenicol, oxytetracycline, and myvizone (p-formylacet-anilide thiosemicarbazone), and partial to complete inhibition was obtained with penicillin, streptomycin, diazone, and para-aminosalicylic acid. Sodium sulfadiazine was not as effective as some of the antibiotics. In vivo tests with mice showed sulfadiazine to be the drug of choice.

Fungus Metabolites. Neither exotoxins nor endotoxins have been demonstrated in species of *Nocardia*. Drake and Henrici (68) obtained a polysaccharide, a protein, and a lipoid fraction from cultures of *N. asteroides,* but they were unable to obtain a protein fraction from the medium in which the fungus had been grown. Drake (67) found that cultures of *Streptomyces* and *Nocardia* produced penicillinase.

Biochemical studies of cell-wall preparations of *Streptomyces* and *Nocardia* have shown differences in carbohydrate composition. *Streptomyces* cell walls are susceptible to lysis by lysozyme while cell walls of *Nocardia* are not affected by this enzyme (91). The difference seemed to be due to a large amount of hexosamine present in the former and a small amount of this amino sugar in the latter. On further examination of more species of *Nocardia,* Sohler and others (94) reported the carbohydrate composition of cell walls of *Nocardia* to be similar to that of the *Corynebacterium*. Avery and Blank (58) also had reported *Nocardia* to be more closely related to bacteria, *Corynebacteria,* than to true fungi on the basis of cell-wall composition.

Antigenic Structure. Since *N. asteroides* is acid-fast and is culturally and morphologically similar to *Mycobacterium tuberculosis,* several studies have been initiated to determine whether they also were antigenically similar. Early studies showed that antigens common to both organisms could be demonstrated by complement-fixation, agglutination, and precipitation tests (68). The question of cross-allergic reactions, however, seemed to be answered by Drake and Henrici (68), who showed that animals infected with *N. asteroides* reacted to skin tests with a polysaccharide, a protein, and a crude extract of powdered defatted organisms but did not react to tuberculin. Likewise, tuberculous animals with a high degree of allergy did not react to the allergens of *N. asteroides*. However, Freund and Lipton (72) demonstrated a slight tuberculin sensitivity in guinea pigs inoculated with killed *N. asteroides* in water-in-oil emulsion. Affronti (56) also reported small reactions to international standard tuberculin, PPD-S, in the skin of rabbits sensitized with PPD made from *N. asteroides*. Since the animals gave larger reactions to the homologous PPD, he considered the reaction specific.

Magnusson (86) prepared PPD, sensitin, from *Nocardia* species and reported that guinea pigs sensitized with heat-killed oil suspensions of these organisms gave larger delayed skin test reactions to the homologous PPD than to the heterologous PPD's and human tuberculin. Bojalil and Magnusson (62) reported that "sensitin" of *N. asteroides* did not give reactions in the skin of patients infected with *N. brasiliensis, N. madurae,* and tuberculosis and in healthy controls at a 0.2 gamma per 0.1 ml. dose. However, when the dose was raised to 2.0 gamma per 0.1 ml., cross-reactions occurred in tuberculous patients. Zamora and others (99) extracted polysaccharides from *N. asteroides* and *N. brasiliensis* which were species-specific in agar gel diffusion studies. Kwapinski (83) reported cytoplasmic fractions of *Nocardia* species and *Actinomyces israelii* to be serologically similar but certain cell wall fractions of *Nocardia asteroides* and *N. rubra* to be genus- and species-specific.

Experimental Infection in Laboratory Animals. Only *N. asteroides* is pathogenic for laboratory animals, and some strains have maintained their virulence for a number of years. Many strains, however, differ in their capacity to initiate infection. Drake and Henrici (68) reviewed the question of pathogenicity and found that death resulted from the injection of large doses of the organisms intraperitoneally into guinea pigs and somewhat smaller doses intravenously into rabbits. A progressive disease, however, could not be produced. Georg and others (73) reported that it was sometimes necessary to inoculate several guinea pigs before a particular isolate could be shown to be pathogenic.

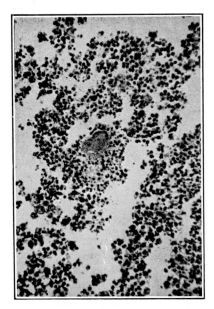

Fig. 10. *Nocardia brasiliensis.* Small granule in subcutaneous tissue. × 147.

Strauss and others (95) used mice for in vivo studies of chemotherapeutic agents against *N. asteroides* by intraperitoneal injections of the fungus with 5 per cent hog gastric mucin. Mohapatra and Pine (88) used an intravenous injection of *N. asteroides* followed by an intraperitoneal injection of 5 per cent mucin in mice for pathogenicity studies.

Clinical Types of Infection in Man. Systemic nocardiosis is not uncommon (63, 65, 66, 71, 84, 89, 97, 98). McQuown (85) has estimated that 5 per cent of the cases of tuberculosis have coexistent nocardiosis. The infection usually is pulmonary in origin and simulates tuberculosis. Hematogenous spread to the rest of the body may result in abscess formation in the subcutaneous tissue, viscera, and brain. Infection by *N. asteroides* has been found to complicate already existing debilitating disease (93). *N. asteroides* has been isolated from the sputum, subcutaneous abscesses, and spinal fluid (59, 63, 69, 74, 81, 82).

Mode of Transmission. It has been known for years that *N. asteroides* exists as a saprophyte in the soil (76). Infection by inhalation establishes systemic infection, nocardiosis. Man-to-man transmission is not known. A wide variety of animals are infected by *N. asteroides* (57), but there has been no report of animal to man transmission of this disease.

Biologic Products. The PPD's, sensitins, and the chemical fractions mentioned above may prove of value as specific skin-testing antigens or serologic antigens for diagnosis of human infections.

Treatment. Sulfadiazine is recognized as the drug of choice in the treatment of systemic nocardiosis (59, 63, 71, 93, 95).

ACTINOMYCOTIC MYCETOMA

Actinomycotic mycetoma is a localized nonmetastasizing infection of the subcutaneous tissues, usually of the extremities, producing a tumor-like lesion (mycetoma) with multiple abscess formation.

Vincent (129) in 1894 reported *Streptothrix madurae* from a case of mycetoma of the foot. This fungus is considered now to be a *Streptomyces* (*S. madurae*). Since this initial report, other aerobic actinomycetes such as *Streptomyces somaliensis, S. pelletierii* (119), *S. paraguayensis* (102), *N.*

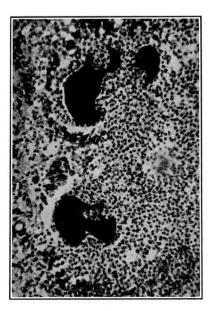

Fig. 11. *Nocardia pelletierii.* Red granules in subcutaneous tissue. × 147.

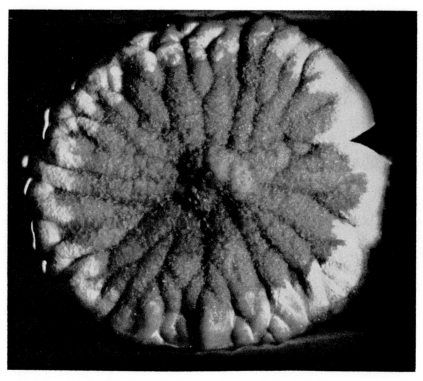

Fig. 12. *Nocardia brasiliensis.* Culture on Sabouraud's glucose agar at room temperature for 15 days.

brasiliensis, N. caviae (116) and, perhaps, *Nocardia asteroides* (106, 110) have been isolated from mycetomas (121, 122).

Morphology. In tissues or exudates from the localized subcutaneous lesion small white to yellow, red or black granules may be seen (Figs. 10 and 11). Such granules are composed of a delicate branching mycelium which may or may not have clubs on the hyphae at the periphery. In sectioned tissues the size of the granule, pigmentation, morphology, and staining reaction with hematoxylin and eosin are said to be characteristic for species identification of *S. madurae, S. somaliensis* and *S. pelletierii* (107).

Cultural Characteristics. All species of *Nocardia* are aerobic and are cultivated easily on common laboratory media at both room and incubator temperatures. They develop slow-growing, variously pigmented (cream to yellow and orange, pink to coral and brick-red, or gray to black), glabrous, wrinkled, or granular colonies some of which resemble colonies of acid-fast bacteria (Fig.

12). Pigmentation of a single strain may vary from transfer to transfer on Sabouraud's glucose agar but remains fairly constant on Czapek's agar. Some strains produce an aerial, chalky white mycelium that may be lost on subculture, subsequent colonies remaining smooth and glabrous. Some colonies may be membranous and difficult to remove from the agar surface; others are soft and granular and easily removed. Some species may have the characteristic earthy odor of species of *Streptomyces.* In liquid media they usually produce surface pellicles with the medium remaining clear.

The formation of aerial hyphae with its segmentation into spores has been one of the distinguishing morphologic features of *Streptomyces* which separated this genus from *Nocardia.* The presence of spore formation in *Streptomyces* and its absence in *Nocardia,* however, has been reported to be a fluctuating character (117, 118, 130). Species of *Nocardia* and *Streptomyces* are best identified by their biochemical and physiologic characteristics (Table 2). *Nocardia* species are characterized by fragmentation of mycelium and acid-fastness; *Streptomyces* species form chains of spores and are not acid-fast.

Resistance. *N. asteroides* will grow at 50° C., whereas the other actinomycetes fail to grow beyond 40° C. *N. brasiliensis* and *S. pelletierii* are susceptible to subtilin (1:1,000) (126). Drake (111) found *N. brasiliensis* to be partially inhibited by 10,-000 units but resistant to 1,000 units of penicillin per milliliter of agar. Gonzalez-Ochoa and others (115) reported *N. brasiliensis* to be partially inhibited by 1:50,000 and completely inhibited at 1:10,000 dilutions of DDS (4,4-di-amino-di-phenyl-sulfone). Mariat and Satre (124) tested the

effect of sulfamethoxypyridazine on the growth of aerobic actinomycetes with the following results: *N. asteroides* was inhibited by 256 μg, *N. brasiliensis* by 4 to 16 μg, *S. madurae* by 4 to 32 μg, *S. pelletierii* by 8 to 16 μg, and *S. somaliensis* by 64 to 256 μg per milliliter.

Fungus Metabolites. Neither endotoxins nor exotoxins have been demonstrated in species of *Nocardia* or *Streptomyces*. Gonzalez-Ochoa and Baranda (112) obtained a carbohydrate from the mycelium of *N. brasiliensis* which gave positive delayed skin tests in patients infected with this organism. They considered the antigen to be specific. Magnusson (120) prepared "sensitin" by a method similar to that used for tuberculin (PPD) from cultures of *N. brasiliensis* and

Table 2. Comparison of Pathogenic Aerobic Actinomycetes

SPECIES	GRANULE	FRAGMENTATION OF MYCELIUM	ACID-FAST	CASEIN	DECOMPOSITION OF TYROSINE	XANTHINE	UTILIZATION OF PARAFFIN	LIQUEFY GELATIN	UREASE
N. asteroides (Eppinger) Blanchard, 1896 Syn. *Cladothrix asteroides* Eppinger, 1890	No granule formed in systemic Nocardiosis; cause Mycetoma?	+	+	−	−	−	+	−	+
N. brasiliensis (Lindenberg) Castellani & Chalmers, 1913 Syn. *Discomyces brasiliensis* Lindenberg, 1909	Small; white to yellowish; soft; with or without clubs	+	+	+	+	−	+	+	+
N. caviae (Erikson) Gordon & Mihm, 1962 Syn. *Actinomyces caviae* Erikson, 1935 *N. otitis caviae* Snijders, 1924	Small; white to yellowish; soft; with or without clubs	+	+	−	−	+	?	?	?
S. madurae (Vincent) Mackinnon & Artagaveytia-Allende, 1956 Syn. *Streptothrix madurae* Vincent, 1894	Large (1-10 mm); white to yellowish; soft; lobulated; large clubs at periphery	−	−	+	+	−	−	+	−
S. somaliensis (Brumpt) Mackinnon & Artagaveytia-Allende, 1956 Syn. *Indiella somaliensis* Brumpt, 1906	Large (1-2 mm); yellow to brownish; hard; round; smooth border	−	−	+	+	−	−	+	−
S. pelletierii (Laveran) Mackinnon & Artagaveytia-Allende, 1956 Syn. *Micrococcus pelletierii* Laveran 1906	Large (0.3-0.5 mm); red; firm; smooth border	−	−	+	+	−	−	+	−
S. paraguayensis (Almeida) Gonzales-Ochoa, *et al.,* 1951 Syn. *Actinomyces paraguayensis* Almeida, 1940	Large (0.5 mm); black; firm; clubs at periphery	−	−	+	+	+ *	?	?	?

* Six weeks.

N. asteroides. Guinea pigs sensitized with these fungi gave a larger skin test reaction to homologous PPD. Bojalil and Magnusson (104) reported that patients with mycetoma caused by *N. brasiliensis* reacted to a skin test dose of 0.2 gamma per 0.1 ml. of the homologous PPD and did not react to the same dose of *asteroides* PPD. Bojalil and Zamora (105) reported a purified protein to be a specific skin test antigen in patients infected by *N. brasiliensis.*

Antigenic Structure. Gonzalez-Ochoa and Vazquez Hoyos (114) obtained a polysaccharide from a variety of cultures of *Nocardia* and *Streptomyces.* They reported precipitin tests to show antigenic similarities to exist between *N. asteroides* and *N. brasiliensis, N. madurae* and *N. pelletierii,* and *N. paraguayensis* and *Streptomyces* species. *N. somaliensis* antigen reacted only in its homologous serum. Schneidau and Shaffer (127), Bevis (103), and Cummins (108) have reported cross-reactions in antibody-antigen reactions between *Nocardia* and the mycobacteria. Zamora and others (131) obtained purified polysaccharides from *N. asteroides* and *N. brasiliensis* which gave specific reactions by the agar gel diffusion technic. The polysaccharide from *N. brasiliensis* precipitated only in sera of patients infected with this organism.

Experimental Infections in Laboratory Animals. Destombes and others (109) have been able to produce granules in mice and guinea pigs inoculated intraperitoneally with suspensions of *N. asteroides* and *N. brasiliensis* with and without adjuvants of paraffin oil or killed tubercle bacilli.

Clinical Types of Infection in Man. The majority of infections caused by aerobic actinomycetes are subcutaneous, suppurative tumefactions or mycetomas. Such lesions usually occur on the extremities as swollen, deformed, indurated areas accompanied by moderate pain. Multiple abscesses throughout the infected area break down to form numerous fistulas from which typical actinomycotic granules are discharged. The bones of the foot may show decalcification and small punched-out areas. The infection is unilateral, develops over months or years, and may spread by the lymphatics to involve the leg but does not metastasize.

Mycetoma of the hand and arm and of the thoracic skin has been reported. Diagnosis is established by demonstrating the actinomycotic granules and by culture.

Method of Transmission. Actinomycotic mycetoma occurs throughout the world, but the majority of infections are reported from the subtropical and tropical areas where the pathogenic aerobic actinomycetes are readily introduced into wounds of exposed feet and legs (100, 110, 123, 125, 128). Only *N. asteroides* and *N. brasiliensis* have been isolated from soil (101, 113). There is no doubt, however, that other pathogenic aerobic actinomycetes also exist as saprophytes in nature. *N. asteroides* causes infection in a variety of animals. Of the mycetoma-producing actinomycetes only *N. brasiliensis* is known to produce natural infection in an animal (101). There have been no reports of man-to-man or animal-to-man transmission of this disease.

Biologic Products. The skin test antigens and precipitating polysaccharide mentioned above might be used to establish a diagnosis of infection by *N. brasiliensis* (105).

Treatment. Chemotherapy with sulfonamides is effective when surgical intervention allows drainage of deeply affected tissues. Long-standing infection with scar tissue formation and fibrosis of considerable tissue areas is amenable only to amputation.

ERYTHRASMA

Erythrasma is a superficial infection of the skin in the axillary and occasionally in the genitocrural and pubic areas. The disease is characterized by sharply circumscribed maculopapular areas of reddish-yellowish to reddish-brown pigmentation with a non-vesiculated, unelevated serpiginous erythematous border with overlying furfuraceous scales. The affected areas give a coral-red fluorescence under the Wood's light.

The etiologic agent, *Nocardia minutissima,* appears in the furfuraceous scales as delicate branching hyphae or as bacillary and coccoid forms (Fig. 13). Sarkany and others (132) cultured, on a fetal bovine serum medium, a gram-positive rod which

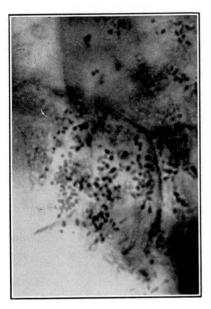

Fig. 13. Erythrasma. Skin scraping showing bacillary forms. × 1,630. (From Conant and others. *Manual of Clinical Mycology,* 2nd ed., W. B. Saunders Co.)

was nonmotile and produced acid in dextrose, sucrose, and maltose but gave no reaction in lactose. Colonies of this organism produced varying degrees of coral-red to orange fluorescence under the Wood's light for the first 96 hours of growth.

Partridge and Jackson (133) also cultured gram-positive bacilli from erythrasma and considered the organisms to belong to the genus *Bacillus*. Growth was obtained by direct culture of skin strippings onto various media. Pink-pigmented colonies developed in subculture to a glucose medium. A coproporphyrin obtained from these cultures gave a coral-red fluorescence similar to that of affected skin areas. They suggested that intertriginous areas supplied by apocrine glands might favor growth of the bacillus, which would be responsible for the scaling and red fluorescence of erythrasma.

Despite the above reports, no attempt is made to cultivate the organism; diagnosis is based on the appearance and location of the lesions and on microscopic examination of skin scrapings. The organisms can be seen in KOH preparations but are best demonstrated in stained preparations (methylene blue, Giemsa, or PAS).

TRICHOMYCOSIS

Trichomycosis is an infection of axillary or pubic hairs caused by *Corynebacterium tenuis* (134) which forms soft nodules along the hair shafts (Fig. 14). Such nodules are composed of delicate, short, branching hyphae intermixed with chromogenic cocci which, at times, give the nodules a yellow, red or black appearance. The surrounding skin is not affected. No attempt is made to culture the fungus; diagnosis is based on the appearance and location of the affected hairs and on the microscopic appearance of the nodules.

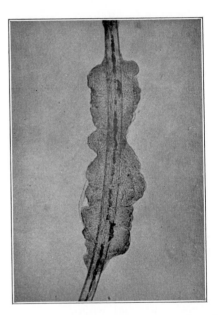

Fig. 14. Trichomycosis. Nodule extending along hair shaft. × 147. (From Conant and others. *Manual of Clinical Mycology,* 2nd ed., W. B. Saunders Co.)

REFERENCES

ACTINOMYCOSIS

1. Breed, R. S., and others. Bergey's Manual of Determinative Bacteriology, 7th ed., Baltimore, Williams & Wilkins Co., 1957.
2. Buchanan, B. B., and Pine, L. J. Gen. Microbiol., 28:305, 1962.
3. Colebrook, L. Brit. J. Exper. Path., 1:197, 1920.
4. Dobson, L., and Cutting, W. C. J.A.M.A., 128:856, 1945.
5. Emmons, C. W. Pub. Health Rep., 53:1967, 1938.

6. Erickson, D. Med. Res. Council (Brit.), Special Rept., Series #240, 1940.
7. Garrod, L. P. British M. J., 1:1263, 1952.
8. ——— Tubercle, 33:258, 1952.
9. Harz, C. O. (in Bollinger) Zentralbl. med. Wchnschr., 15:481, 1877.
10. Hazen, E. L., and others. J. Lab. & Clin. Med., 40:914, 1952.
11. Holm, P. Acta path. et microbiol., Scandinav. (Suppl. 3), 151, 1930.
12. ——— Acta path. et microbiol., Scandinav., 25:376, 1948.
13. ——— Acta path. et microbiol., Scandinav., 27:736, 1950.
14. ——— Acta path. et microbiol., Scandinav., 28:391, 1951.
15. Howell, A., Jr. Antibiotics and Chemotherapy, 3:387, 1953.
16. ——— and Fitzgerald, R. J. J. Bact., 66:437, 1953.
17. ——— Murphy, W. C., III, Paul, F., and Stephen, R. M. J. Bact., 78:82, 1959.
18. ——— and Pine, L. J. Bact., 71:47, 1956.
19. ——— and Rogosa, M. J. Bact., 76:330, 1958.
20. ——— Stephen, R. M., and Paul, F. J. Dental Res., 41:1050, 1962.
21. Israel, J. Arch. f. path. Anat. Phys., 74:15, 1878.
22. King, S., and Meyer, E. J. Bact., 85:186, 1963.
23. Kwapinski, J. B. Path. Microbiol., 23:159, 1960.
24. ——— J. Bact., 86:179, 1963.
25. ——— and Snyder, M. L. J. Bact., 82:632, 1961.
26. Lane, S. L., and others. J.A.M.A., 151:986, 1953.
27. Littman, M. L., and others. Am. J. Clin. Path., 20:1076, 1950.
28. Lord, F. T. J.A.M.A., 55:1261, 1910.
29. ——— and Trevett, L. D. J. Infect. Dis., 58:115, 1936.
30. Mathieson, D. R., and others. Am. J. Hyg., 21:405, 1935.
31. McVay, L. V., Jr., and Sprunt, D. H. J.A.M.A., 153:95, 1953.
32. ——— Ann. Int. Med., 38:955, 1955.
33. Meyer, E., and Verges, P. J. Lab. & Clin. Med., 36:667, 1950.
34. Miller, J. M., and others. J.A.M.A., 150:35, 1952.
35. Naeslund, C. Acta path. et microbiol., Scandinav., 2:110, 1925.
36. Negroni, P., and Bonfiglioli, H. J. Trop. Med. Hyg., 40:226, 1937.
37. Pine, L., Howell, A., Jr., and Watson, S. J. J. Gen. Microbiol., 23:403, 1960.
38. ——— and Overman, J. R. J. Gen. Microbiol., 32:209, 1963.
39. ——— and Watson, S. J. J. Lab. & Clin. Med., 54:107, 1959.
40. Ponfick, E. Die Aktinomykose des Menschen, Berlin, 1882.
41. Rosebury, T., and others. J. Infect. Dis., 74:131, 1944.
42. Sanford, G. E., and Barnes, R. O. Surgery, 25:711, 1949.
43. Slack, J. J. Bact., 43:193, 1942.
44. ——— and others. J. Bact., 61:721, 1951.
45. ——— and others. J. Bact., 70:400, 1955.

46. Strauss, R. E., and others. Am. Rev. Tuberc., 63:441, 1951.
47. Sullivan, H. R., and Goldsworthy, N. E. J. Path. & Bact., 51:253, 1940.
48. Thompson, L. Proc. Staff Meet., Mayo Clin., 25:81, 1950.
49. ——— and Lovestedt, S. A. Proc. Staff Meet., Mayo Clin., 26:169, 1951.
50. Waksman, S. A., and Henrici, A. T. J. Bact., 46:337, 1943.
51. Widra, A. Sabouraudia, 2:264, 1963.
52. Wolff, M., and Israel, J. Virchows Arch. f. path., Anat., 126:11, 1891.
53. Wright, J. H. J. M. Research, 13:349, 1905.
54. Wright, L. T., and Lowen, H. J. J.A.M.A., 144:21, 1950.
55. Zegarelli, E. V., and others. Oral Surg., Oral Med. & Oral Path., 5:1182, 1952.

NOCARDIOSIS

56. Affronti, L. F. Am. Rev. Tuber., 79:284, 1959.
57. Ajello, L., and others. J. Am. Vet. Med., 138:370, 1961.
58. Avery, R. J., and Blank, F. Canadian J. Microbiol., 1:140, 1954.
59. Benbow, E. P., Jr., and others. Am. Rev. Tuberc., 49:395, 1944.
60. Blanchard, R. Traité de path. générale (Charles Bouchard), 2:811, 1896.
61. Bojalil, L. F., and Cerbon, J. J. Bact., 78:852, 1959.
62. ——— and Magnusson, M. Am. Rev. Resp. Dis., 88:409, 1963.
63. Carlisle, W. K., and others. J.A.M.A., 184:477, 1963.
64. Connar, R. G., and others. J. Thoracic Surg., 22:424, 1951.
65. Cotton, R. E., and Lloyd, H. E. D. J. Path. & Bact., 79:251, 1960.
66. Cupp, C. M., and others. Ann. Int. Med., 52:223, 1960.
67. Drake, C. H. J. Bact., 51:199, 1946.
68. ——— and Henrici, A. T. Am. Rev. Tuberc., 48:184, 1943.
69. Eckhardt, K., and Pilcher, J. Texas State J. Med., 46:915, 1950.
70. Eppinger, H. Bitr. z. path. Anat., u. z. allg. Path., 9:287, 1890.
71. Freese, J. W., and others. J. Thoracic & Card. Surg., 46:537, 1963.
72. Freund, J., and Lipton, M. M. Proc. Soc. Exper. Biol. & Med., 68:373, 1948.
73. Georg, L. K., and others. Am. Rev. Resp. Dis., 84:337, 1961.
74. Glover, R. P., and others. J.A.M.A., 136:172, 1948.
75. Gonzalez-Ochoa, A. Rev. d. Inst. salub. y enferm. trop., 6:155, 1945.
76. Gordon, R. E., and Hagan, W. A. J. Infect. Dis., 59:200, 1936.
77. ——— and Mihm, J. M. J. Bact., 73:15, 1957.
78. ——— and Mihm, J. M. J. Gen. Microbiol., 20:129, 1959.
79. ——— and Mihm, J. M. J. Gen. Microbiol., 27:1, 1962.
80. ——— and Smith, M. M. J. Bact., 69:147, 1955.
81. Hager, H. F., and others. New England J. Med., 241:226, 1949.

82. Jacobson, J. R., and Cloward, R. B. J.A.M.A., 137:769, 1948.
83. Kwapinski, J. B. J. Bact., 86:179, 1963.
84. Larsen, M. C., and others. Arch. Int. Med., 103:712, 1959.
85. McQuown, A. L. Am. J. Clin. Path., 25:2, 1955.
86. Magnusson, M. Am. Rev. Resp. Dis., 86:395, 1962.
87. Mariat, F. Ann. Soc. Belge Méd. Trop., 4:651, 1962.
88. Mohapatra, L. N., and Pine, L. Sabouraudia, 2:176, 1963.
89. Murry, J. F., and others. Am. Rev. Resp. Dis., 83:315, 1961.
90. Nocard, M. E. Ann. Inst. Pasteur, 2:293, 1888.
91. Romano, A. H., and Sohler, A. J. Bact., 72:865, 1956.
92. Salle, A. J., and Jann, G. J. Proc. Soc. Exper. Biol. & Med., 60:60, 1945.
93. Saltzman, H. A., and others. Lab. Invest., 11:1110, 1962.
94. Sohler, A., and others. J. Bact., 75:283, 1958.
95. Strauss, R. E., and others. Am. Rev. Tuberc., 63:441, 1951.
96. Trevisan. I. Genere e le Species delle Bacteriaceae, Milan, 1889, 36 pp.
97. Webster, B. H. J. Am. Geriat. Soc., 10:192, 1962.
98. Weed, L. A., and others. New England J. Med., 253:1137, 1955.
99. Zamora, A., and others. J. Bact., 85:549, 1963.

ACTINOMYCOTIC MYCETOMA

100. Abbott, P. Tr. Roy. Soc. Trop. Med. & Hyg., 50:11, 1956.
101. Ajello, L., and others. J. Am. Vet. Med. A., 138:370, 1961.
102. Almeida, F. Mycopathologia, 2:940, 1940.
103. Bevis, M. L. Sabouraudia, 1:154, 1961.
104. Bojalil, L. F., and Magnusson, M. Am. Rev. Resp. Dis., 88:409, 1963.
105. ———— and Zamora, A. Proc. Soc. Exper. Biol. & Med., 113:40, 1963.
106. Brounst, G., and others. Bull. Soc. Path. Exot., 55:964, 1962.
107. Camain, R., and others. Sem. Hôp. Paris, P. et B., 33:923, 1957.
108. Cummins, C. S. J. Gen. Microbiol., 28:35, 1962.
109. Destombes, P., and others. Bull. Soc. Path. Exot., 51:815, 1958.

110. ———— and others. Sabouraudia, 1:161, 1961.
111. Drake, C. H. J. Bact., 51:199, 1946.
112. Gonzalez-Ochoa, A., and Baranda, F. Rev. Inst. Salubr. Enferm. Trop., 13:189, 1953.
113. ———— and Sandoval, M. A. Rev. Inst. Salubr. Enferm. Trop., 20:147, 1960.
114. ———— and Vazquez Hoyos, A. Rev. Inst. Salubr. Enferm. Trop., 13:177, 1953.
115. ———— and others. Gaceta Medica Mexico, 82:345, 1952.
116. Gordon, R. E., and Mihm, J. M. Ann. New York Acad. Sc., 98:628, 1962.
117. ———— and Smith, M. M. J. Bact., 69:147, 1955.
118. Jones, K. L. J. Bact., 57:141, 1949.
119. Mackinnon, J. E., and Artagaveytia-Allende, R. C. Tr. Roy. Soc. Trop. Med. & Hyg., 50:31, 1956.
120. Magnusson, M. Am. Rev. Resp. Dis., 86:395, 1962.
121. Mariat, F. Ann. Soc. Belge Med. Trop., 4:651, 1962.
122. ———— Arch. l'Institut Past., Tunis, 39:309, 1962.
123. ———— Bull. Soc. Path. Exot., 56:35, 1963.
124. ———— and Satre, J. Bull. Soc. Path. Exot., 54:63, 1961.
125. Orio, J., and others. Bull. Soc. Path. Exot., 56:161, 1963.
126. Salle, A. J., and Jann, G. J. Proc. Soc. Exper. Biol. & Med., 60:60, 1945.
127. Schneidau, J. D., Jr., and Shaffer, M. F. Am. Rev. Resp. Dis., 82:64, 1960.
128. Segretain, G., and Mariat, F. Bull. Soc. Path. Exot., 51:833, 1958.
129. Vincent, M. H. Ann. Inst. Pasteur, 8:129, 1894.
130. Williams, A. M., and McCoy, E. Appl. Microbiol., 1:307, 1953.
131. Zamora, A., and others. J. Bact., 85:549, 1963.

ERYTHRASMA

132. Sarkany, I., and others. J. Invest. Dermat., 37:283, 1961.
133. Partridge, B. M., and Jackson, F. L. Lancet 1 [part 1]:590, 1962.

TRICHOMYCOSIS

134. Crissey, J. R., and others. J. Invest. Dermat., 19:187, 1952.

79

Fungus Diseases Involving the Internal Organs

CRYPTOCOCCOSIS

(Torulosis, European Blastomycosis,
Torula Meningitis)

Cryptococcosis, caused by *Cryptococcus neoformans,* usually is referred to as "European blastomycosis" in the European literature and "torulosis" in the older American literature. The disease, however, occurs sporadically throughout the world and a defining geographic term, such as "European blastomycosis," is misleading.

Cryptococcus neoformans may infect any part of the body but has a predilection for the brain and meninges, where it produces a disease closely simulating tuberculous meningitis, brain abscess, or brain tumor. Busse (11, 12) in 1894-95 first described from Europe a localized infection caused by a *Saccharomyces* species which later became generalized. A similar yeast-like organism, *S. tumefaciens,* was isolated from a myxomatous tumor of the hip by Curtis (17). Sanfelice (71) in 1894, however, had isolated a yeast-like organism from fermenting peach juice. He was able to demonstrate pathogenicity for laboratory animals (72, 73) and, because of its "tumor-forming ability," named the yeast *Saccharomyces neoformans* (73). Later, Sanfelice (74, 75) isolated encapsulated, pathogenic yeast-like organisms from the lymph nodes of an ox and from the lungs of swine. In 1902 Weis (92) compared the so-called cancer yeasts with an isolate from milk (49) and found them to be pathogenic and to be similar organisms. Vuillemin (91) placed these fungi in the genus *Cryptococcus,* and since Benham's comparative studies (5, 6), the etiologic agent for cryptococcal meningitis has been recognized as *C. neoformans.*

The first case of meningitis was described by von Hansemann (41) in Germany, but interest in the United States dates from the monograph published by Stoddard and Cutler (84).

Morphology. Both in tissue and in culture, *C. neoformans* is a thick-walled, oval to spherical, budding cell, 5 to 15 μ in diameter (Fig. 1). The cells are surrounded by a wide gelatinous capsule which may equal or exceed the diameter of the cell itself. Identification is facilitated by emulsifying a portion of the colony, pus from abscesses, sputum, or the sediment from spinal fluid in a drop of India ink under a coverglass (Fig. 2). The presence of the large gelatinous capsule, clearly seen in such preparations, differ-

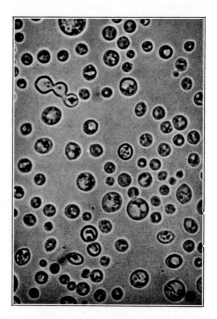

Fig. 1. *Cryptococcus neoformans.* Small round yeast-like cells from Sabouraud's agar. × 736. (From Conant and others. *Manual of Clinical Mycology,* 2nd ed., W. B. Saunders Co.)

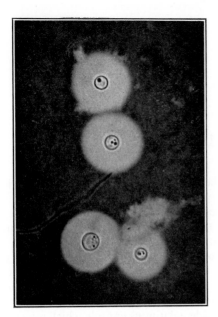

Fig. 2. *Cryptococcus neoformans.* India ink preparation of spinal fluid. × 736.

entiates this fungus from all other yeast-like organisms. In culture and in tissue this yeast-like organism reproduces by budding, and neither mycelium nor endospores are produced. Benham (74), however, has described endosporulation in a single strain which had been isolated from a spontaneous infection in a dog.

Cultural Characteristics. *C. neoformans* grows readily on all the usual laboratory media at room temperature and at **37° C.** In primary cultures from spinal fluid, blood, or tissues the colonies usually appear in two to four days, but in some isolations the growth is delayed and definite colonies cannot be detected until after 10 to 14 days' incubation. Cultured on Sabouraud's glucose agar at room temperature, white, mucoid, glistening colonies appear, which gradually develop a cream to light tan pigmentation (Fig. 3). In a liquid medium growth is confined to the bottom of the tube except in old cultures, in which a ring may be formed at the surface. In a synthetic medium *C. neoformans* synthesizes all of its growth requirement substances with the exception of thiamine (20, 69, 76).

C. neoformans does not ferment sugars, assimilate potassium nitrate (KNO_3), or re-

duce nitrates to nitrites. In carbon assimilation tests with various carbohydrates, however, positive tests are obtained with glucose, maltose, sucrose, and galactose, while lactose is negative (7, 8). A positive urease test is obtained on Christensen's urea agar (78).

Resistance. Cox and Tolhurst (15) were able to culture *C. neoformans* from spinal fluid which had been allowed to dry at room temperature for 10 months. The fungus is killed, however, when heated at 60° C. for five minutes (15, 16). At induced high temperatures to which man can be subjected (40° to 42° C.) the survival rate of cells is greatly decreased (50, 53, 54).

The effect of numerous antibiotics and chemotherapeutic agents on the growth of *C. neoformans* has been reported (47, 50, 76, 81, 83, 93). The most promising antibiotic is Amphotericin B, which has had sufficient clinical trials to have established its usefulness as a specific chemotherapeutic agent in cryptococcosis (40, 89).

Fungus Metabolites. No toxins have been demonstrated.

A polysaccharide has been obtained from the capsular material. An extracellular starch produced in liquid medium and on solid medium has been reported by Aschner, Mager and Leibowitz (4) and Mager and Aschner (60). The latter investigators also reported a polysaccharide, consisting largely of pentose, in culture filtrates (61). Hehre and others (44) isolated a crystalline amylose and a pentose containing polysaccharide

Fig. 3. *Cryptococcus neoformans.* Colony on Sabouraud's glucose agar at room temperature for 15 days.

from their cultures. Evans (27) and Evans and Kessel (28) obtained a polysaccharide which gave a positive Molisch test, positive test for pentose and hexuronic acid, and negative tests for protein and amino acids. Evans and Mehl (29) found by filter paper chromatography the polysaccharide substance to contain xylose, mannose, galactose, and uronic acid. Drouhet, Segretain, and Aubert (21), however, reported the polysaccharide to contain xylose, mannose, and uronic acid (glucuronic acid). Drouhet and Segretain (19) reported hyaluronidase to destroy the capsule, which suggests that it is hyaluronic acid in nature.

Foley and Uzman (38) used hot alkali to extract capsular material and obtained a highly polymerized polysaccharide. This material was not affected by hyaluronidase, and they could not demonstrate any effect by hyaluronidase on encapsulated cells. Einbinder and others (22) reported the capsular substance to contain 6.7 per cent hexuronic acid (glucuronic acid), 18.1 per cent hexose (glucose), and 31 per cent pentose (arabinose). Evans and Theriault (30) reported further purification of capsular substance to yield two carbohydrate fractions. One contained glucuronic acid, mannose, and xylose; the other was identified as galactose. Uzman and others (88) investigated the amino acid composition of C. neoformans somatic protein and found a high content of dicarboxylic amino acids (aspartic and glutamic acids).

Evans (33, 34, 35) has shown that an acidic polysaccharide of the cryptococcal capsule behaves as a polyvalent ion capable of reacting with a variety of cationic substances. Salvin and Smith (70) reported a soluble specific skin-testing antigen obtained from disrupted cells.

Antigenic Structure. Benham (5) has shown by agglutinin and precipitin-absorption tests that three pathogenic strains of C. neoformans were antigenically identical but a fourth strain (S. tumefaciens of Curtis) seemed antigenically different. Also, a nonpathogenic strain isolated from the feces of a normal individual showed only a slight difference antigenically from the pathogenic strains in that its antigen could absorb the antibodies from the serums prepared against three pathogenic strains. However, the antigens of these later strains could not absorb the antibodies from the serum prepared against the so-called nonpathogenic strain; that is, Benham demonstrated nonreciprocal cross-reaction. Further studies by Evans (26, 27) and Evans and Kessel (28) have demonstrated three serologic types of C. neoformans (A, B, and C) based on agglutination and precipitin tests and capsular reactions. The capsule is said to be responsible for type specificity. Capsular reaction in immune serum was demonstrated by Neill and others (55).

The capsular reaction, mentioned above, is not a quellung reaction, since no difference in size could be determined by comparison with India ink preparations, or by packed cell volumes before and after the addition of antibody to the cells (32).

Evans and others (31) have reported cross-reactions to occur in anticryptococcal serums with Candida albicans, Saccharomyces cerevisiae, trichophytin, Pneumococcus type II, and gum tragacanth.

C. neoformans caused a varied and minimal immunologic response in infected humans and animals or in immunized animals. Agglutinins and complement-fixing antibodies could not be demonstrated in patients' serums by Flu and Woensdregt (37), Shapiro and Neal (79), Heine, Lauer and Mumme (45) or Urbach and Zach (86). Rappaport and Kaplan (67), however, reported agglutinins in a human serum to a titer of 1:40, and Ramel (66) reported a positive complement-fixation test which later became negative.

Neill and others (65) have demonstrated a serologically reactive material in the spinal fluid, blood, and urine of a patient with cryptococcosis.

Vogel and others (90) have demonstrated antibody in patients' serums by the indirect fluorescent staining technic. Bloomfield and others (9) demonstrated antigen in the serum and/or spinal fluid from seven of nine patients with CNS cryptococcosis by an agglutination test with antibody-coated latex particles. Kase and Marshall (51) used the fluorescent antibody technic for the identification of C. neoformans. Tsuchiya and others (85) have described a serologic test for the rapid identification of C. neoformans.

Spontaneous Infection in Animals. Spontaneous infections have been reported in a wide variety of animals: horse, dog, cat, fox, cheetah, civet, monkey, guinea pig, ferret, pig, and dairy cattle (3, 46, 56).

Experimental Infections in Laboratory Animals. Mice, guinea pigs, and rabbits can be infected with cultures of *C. neoformans,* but the mouse seems to be the most susceptible. This animal has been useful in the study of the relationship of capsular material to virulence (42), actively acquired immunity to experimental cryptococcosis (1, 58, 59), and cutaneous anaphylactic reactions (2).

Clinical Types of Infection in Man. Cutaneous lesions appear as acneform pustules, punched-out granulomatous ulcers, subcutaneous tumors, or rather tumor-like masses which have been mistaken for myxomatous tumors (13, 39). Such lesions usually result from metastases to the subcutaneous tissues from an established systemic infection. Primary infections of the lungs may simulate tuberculosis or neoplasm (18, 68). From this primary focus (43), the organism disseminates to the rest of the body, invading the skin, bones (14), viscera, and eventually the brain and meninges.

The terminal meningitis is frequently diagnosed as tuberculous meningitis (55). Although lymphadenopathy associated with cryptococcosis may be diagnosed correctly as coexistent lymphoblastoma or sarcoidosis, it is not infrequent that an incorrect diagnosis of these two diseases is made; also, coexistent myelogenous leukemia, lymphatic leukemia, and monocytic leukemia have been reported (94).

Transmission. Cryptococcosis is a sporadic infection with a worldwide distribution. Although spontaneous infections in animals have been reported, there are no known instances of transmission from animal to man. Furthermore, there have been no reports of man-to-man transmission. Benham (5) was able to isolate from the skin and feces of normal people cryptococci which resemble those isolated from infections. Some of these strains differed from *N. neoformans* only by reduced pathogenicity, and it might be assumed that the disease is one of endogenous origin. Emmons (23) and Ajello (3), however, have isolated this fungus from the soil, and it has been isolated from pigeon dung in Washington, D.C. (25), Maryland (24), Cincinnati (48) and New York City (57). This natural habitat for *C. neoformans* would indicate its exogenous source, from which both man and animals become infected. The extent of subclinical disease is not known but must be considerable because of the possible opportunity for large population groups to become infected from these exogenous sources.

Treatment. Reports by Reeves, Butt and Hammack (68) and Marshall and Teed (62, 64) would indicate that sulfapyridine and sulfadiazine can be used successfully. In our own clinics we have seen pulmonary, cutaneous and bone cryptococcosis respond favorably to sulfadiazine therapy. Since proven cases have been known to have remissions for more than eight years, the value of any specific therapy can be judged accurately only after long periods of time. Amphotericin B is now being used with success for the treatment of cryptococcosis (10, 36, 52, 77, 82, 87).

CANDIDIASIS

Candidiasis, caused by *Candida albicans,* is endogenous in origin, since pathogenic strains have been isolated from the mouth, vagina, and intestinal tracts of normal individuals. In most instances the infections are superficial and mild, and the organism frequently is found as a secondary invader in pathologic processes initiated by other pathogenic organisms or neoplasm. Yeast-like fungi, particularly *C. albicans,* have been identified, however, as the primary etiologic agents of mycotic infections of the skin and nails, in bronchitis, pulmonary infections, thrush, vaginitis, mycotic endocarditis, meningitis, and generalized systemic infections.

Langenbeck (138) was the first to demonstrate a yeast-like fungus in the lesions of thrush. The fungus was named *Oidium albicans* by Robin (161) and *Monilia albicans* by Zopf (195). Berkhout (101) proposed the generic name *Candida* to include these fungi which developed a pseudomycelium and reproduced by budding, but before 1930 many generic names and over 100 species had

Fig. 4. *Candida albicans.* Gram stain of sputum smear showing budding cells and pseudohyphae. × 1,175.

been recorded in the literature. Publications concerning the classification of this group of fungi by Benham (100), Martin and others (148), Langeron and Guerra (139), Martin and Jones (149), Diddens and Lodder (107), and Lodder and Kreger-Van Rij (140), have resulted in a great simplification of many of the problems of classification and identification. The single genus *Candida* has been accepted generally, and the recognized human pathogenic species, to be included in this genus, have been reduced. Of these species only *C. albicans* is considered to be pathogenic, but other species are encountered in pathologic conditions. The review of the yeast-like fungi by Skinner and Fletcher (169) is an excellent summary of the information available concerning these organisms.

C. albicans, which has been isolated heretofore only from human or animal sources, has recently been isolated from soil and vegetable sources in nature (184).

Morphology. *C. albicans* is a small, oval, budding, yeast-like fungus, 2.5 × 4 × 6 μ. It develops a pseudomycelium by elongation of cells which fail to detach. In sputum, tissue, and exudates both the budding cells and fragments of pseudomycelium may be seen (Fig. 4). Typical chlamydospores serve to distinguish *C. albicans* from other species

of *Candida* (Fig. 5). There are, however, differences in ability among strains of this species to produce chlamydospores, and a variety of media have been described for this purpose (99, 106, 115, 156, 173, 176, 188). Also, *C. albicans* can be identified by pseudomycelial formation on selected media (162, 175, 189) and by pigment production in the colony (98, 147, 157, 160, 162).

Cultural Characteristics. *Candida albicans* grows readily (24 to 48 hours) at both room and incubator temperatures on Sabouraud's glucose agar. The colonies are of moderate size, smooth and pasty, and have a characteristic yeasty odor. Older colonies (giant colonies) may be honeycombed in the center and develop radial furrows (Fig. 6). There is no surface growth in broth (48 hours); glucose and maltose are fermented with acid and gas, sucrose with acid only, and lactose is not fermented. The fermentations are apt to be irregular unless conditions are carefully controlled (148, 149).

C. albicans produces a distinctive filamentous colony in two days on a streaked plate of Levine eosin-methylene blue agar at 37° C. in 10 per cent CO_2 (189). Different species of *Candida* may be identified rather accurately by (*a*) the type of colony

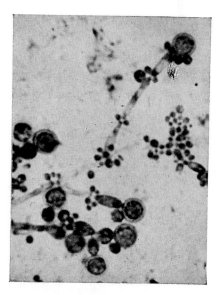

Fig. 5. *Candida albicans.* Characteristic chlamydospores from corn meal agar. × 790. (From Conant. *Am. Rev. Tuberc.,* 61:696, 1950.)

Table 1. Differential Diagnosis of Species of Candida

(Martin and others)

| | PATHOGENIC | | NONPATHOGENIC | | | | |
	C. albicans	C. tropicalis	C. pseudotropicalis	C. krusei	C. parakrusei	C. stellatoidea	C. guilliermondii
Sabouraud's agar	Creamy growth	Not characteristic	Not characteristic	Flat, dry	Creamy	Creamy	Creamy growth
Sabouraud's broth	No surface growth	Narrow surface film with bubbles	No surface growth	Wide surface film	No surface growth	No surface growth	No surface growth
Blood-agar	Medium-sized, dull gray colonies	Large, gray colonies surrounded by mycelial fringe	Colonies small, not characteristic	Colonies small, irregularly shaped, flat, or heaped	Colonies small, brilliant white	Colonies star-shaped	Medium-sized, dull gray colonies
Corn meal	Branched, tree-like mycelium with chlamydospores	Mycelium well developed, branched, bearing numerous blastospores, no chlamydospores	Mycelium poorly developed, no chlamydospores	"Crossed sticks" mycelium, no chlamydospores	Mycelium well-developed, no chlamydospores	Mycelium with large, ball-like clusters of blastospores	Mycelium well-developed, no chlamydospores
Glucose	AG	AG	AG	AG	AG*	AG	—†
Maltose	AG	AG	—	—	—	AG	—
Sucrose	A	AG	AG	—	—	—	—
Lactose	—	—	AG	—	—	—	—

* Occasionally acid only.

† Langeron and Guerra report acid and gas produced in glucose when cultured at 25° C. and held 20 days.

developed on blood-agar plates at 37° C. (10 days), (*b*) the type of growth in Sabouraud's glucose broth at 37° C. (48 hours), (*c*) development and morphology of blastospores, chlamydospores, and pseudomycelium on corn meal agar at room temperature, and (*d*) the fermentation reaction after 10 days at 37° C. in glucose, maltose, sucrose, and lactose (see Table 1).

Resistance. *Candida* species are killed in 90 minutes at 60° C. and in five minutes at 70° C. Most species withstand refrigerator temperature 5° to 10° C. for long periods of time. The usual chemical disinfectants prove to be effective fungicidal agents: Merthiolate, Metaphen, tincture of iodine and 10 per cent formalin (129). Gentian violet and methyl violet are said to be inhibitory in 1:1,000,000 dilution. The sulfonamides do not inhibit these fungi. The antibiotics Candicidin (132), Nystatin (123), and Amphotericin B (171) are inhibitory.

Fungus Metabolites. Neither endotoxins nor exotoxins have been demonstrated for organisms in this group of yeast-like fungi. Salvin (164) reported toxemia in mice inoculated intraperitoneally with a suspension of killed *C. albicans* and tubercle bacilli. Mourad and Friedman (141) also produced a toxemia in mice by intravenous injection of soluble substances obtained by sonic oscillation of *C. albicans, C. robusta* and *C. reukaufii*. However, Ekmen (109) could not demonstrate toxins from sonic extraction, mechanical disruption, or acetone-treated cells of *C. albicans*. *C. albicans* has been shown to have a capsular polysaccharide (130, 131, 152, 192). Neytcheff (155) reported polysaccharides of *C. albicans* extracted with phenol to have a minimum pyogenic activity at 0.9 mg. per kilogram and to be 55 to 580 times as potent as polysaccharides obtained from *C. tropicalis, C. krusei,* and *C. pseudotropicalis.*

Antigenic Structure. Serologic studies have shown recognized species of *Candida* to be closely related antigenically. Benham (100), Almon and Stovall (96), Stone and Garrod (172), and Martin and others (148) showed by agglutination, agglutinin absorption, complement-fixation, precipitation, and precipitin-absorption tests that cross-reactions between many species were pro-

Fig. 6. *Candida albicans.* Giant colony on Sabouraud's glucose agar at room temperature for 20 days.

nounced. Some of these species could be differentiated specifically by absorbed serums, but *C. albicans* and *C. tropicalis* seemed to be antigenically identical. Tsuchiya and others (177, 178, 179, 181) have proposed an antigenic structure for seven species of *Candida* and have reported heat-stable and heat-labile antigens based on antigenic analyses. Their type-specific sera have allowed accurate and rapid identification of species with the genus (182, 183). Gordon (113, 114) reported anti-albicans fluorescent conjugate to be specific and to differentiate *C. albicans* from *C. stellatoidea,* particularly if absorbed with *C. parakrusei*. Kaplan and Kaufman (127) reported two distinct serologic groups of *C. albicans* based on fluorescent antibody technics. Kunz (137) used fluorescent antibody to distinguish *C. albicans* and pneumocystis in the lungs of two of three premature infants who died of interstitial plasma cell pneumonia. Kunz (136) and Kemp and Solotorovsky (129) used fluorescein-labeled anti-*C. albicans* sera to detect this organism in the tissues of infected mice. Hasenclever and Mitchell (119) demonstrated two antigenic groups for *C. albicans* by agglutination and agglutinin-absorption studies. These groups (A and B) were shown to be antigenically similar to *C. tropicalis* and *C. stellatoidea,* respectively (122). Also, organisms of groups A and B differed little in their pathogenicity for rabbits and mice (122), and a study of isolates from patients did not reveal one group to be more pathogenic than the other (121). Vogel and Collins (187) reported a specific hemagglutination test to detect antibodies in anti-albicans rabbit serum.

Since *C. albicans* may be found in the mouth, intestinal tract, and vagina of many normal individuals, little diagnostic significance can be attached to the finding of a positive skin test or agglutinins. Drake (108) reported that a high percentage of serums from normal individuals contained agglutinins for *C. albicans* and advanced the hypothesis that these agglutinins occurred naturally in human serums and were independent of the presence or absence of the fungus.

Experimental Infection in Laboratory Animals. The rabbit is particularly susceptible to infection with *Candida albicans* but relatively, if not absolutely, resistant to the other species of *Candida*. Rabbits injected intravenously with 1 ml. of a 1 per cent saline suspension of *C. albicans* die in four to five days with typical abscesses in the kidneys. Rabbits having a high agglutinin titer because of previous immunization are not protected against a subsequent injection of a lethal dose of the organism. Meyer and Ordal (150) reported lesions on the chorioallantoic membrane and death of the embryo when chick embryos were inoculated with *C. albicans* and *C. stellatoidea; C. tropicalis* produced mild lesions, while no lesions were produced by *C. krusei* and *C. parakrusei.* A number of reports have shown enhancement of infection in mice with *C. albicans* when they have also received gastric mucin, alloxan, tetracyclines, and/or cortisone (97, 143, 163, 165, 168, 190). However, mice are uniformly susceptible to *C. albicans* by intravenous inoculation (110, 118, 170). Therefore, this animal has been used extensively for studies on the pathogenesis of *C. albicans* infections (95, 126, 133, 145).

The ability of *C. albicans* to produce pseudomycelium quickly upon injection into animals is said to interfere with phagocytosis and thus enhance its virulence (125, 146, 193).

Clinical Types of Infection in Man. It is difficult to evaluate the presence of *C. albicans* in cultures obtained from clinical materials. In infections of the lungs, for example, the fungus is found often as a secondary invader superimposed upon tuberculosis or a malignancy. In sprue and pernicious anemia the fungus is isolated frequently from stool specimens, but these findings merely indicate the presence in greater quantity of an organism that can be isolated from the normal intestinal tract. The fungus also may be cultured from mouth lesions which were initiated by dietary deficiencies.

The extensive use of antibiotics, particularly the tetracyclines, has resulted in candidiasis complicating the primary disease. Infection of the mucous membranes, the mucocutaneous areas (thrush, perlèche, vaginitis, and vulvovaginitis) and generalized candidiasis have been reported following the use of these antibiotics (117, 142, 159).

C. albicans, however, can produce infections of various types in which the fungus can be recognized as the primary etiologic agent. Candidiasis (thrush) of the oral mucous membranes occurs in infants (112) and elderly people with wasting diseases (102). Vaginitis, vulvovaginitis, and infection of the vaginal mucosa are not uncommon in diabetes and during pregnancy (104).

Candidiasis of the skin may follow maceration of tissue resulting from constant exposure to water (housewives or bartenders) or from friction of adjacent parts in obese patients (axillae, inframammary areas, and inguinal region). The presence of *C. albicans* in the intestinal tract may serve to infect such areas.

Bronchopulmonary candidiasis, though difficult to prove, is an infection which occurs frequently enough to be considered in a differential diagnosis of an obscure disease of the lungs and bronchi (105). Severe pulmonary candidiasis occasionally is diagnosed by exclusion and by recovery after successful therapy directed specifically against *C. albicans* (124). Such cases may simulate miliary tuberculosis.

Generalized candidiasis is rare, but *C. albicans* has been the primary cause of meningitis (111, 116, 194). Cases of endocarditis have been reported from which *C. albicans, C. parakrusei,* and *C. guilliermondii* have been isolated (135, 158).

Transmission. Since *C. albicans* is found in the mouth and intestinal tract of a high percentage of humans, the fungus may spread from such locations to cause skin and nail infections. Aspiration of material may lead to bronchopulmonary infections which eventually, though rarely, may initiate generalized infection. Such types of infection can be assumed to be endogenous in origin. Infections due to *C. albicans* can be transmitted, however. Balanoposthitis has been observed in the husbands of women with vaginitis, and cutaneous candidiasis about the nipples of nursing mothers has been caused by infants with oral thrush. Thrush frequently occurs in infants who became infected by passage through the birth canal of a mother with vaginitis (174).

Biologic Products. A vaccine for desensitization can be made from stock cultures of *C. albicans* or from autogenous cultures. Saline suspensions (1:1000 packed volume of cells) from 48-hour Sabouraud's glucose agar cultures should be heat killed in a water bath at 56° C. for two hours. Intradermal injections of 0.1 ml. of this vaccine should be read in 30 minutes for an immediate reaction and in 24 hours for the delayed tuberculin type of reaction.

Treatment. Nystatin has proved to be useful in the treatment of candidiasis (103, 153, 166, 191). Mysteclin, a preparation of Nystatin and a tetracycline, is used when antibiotic therapy is necessary and control of *C. albicans* desirable. Amphotericin B is probably the most effective antibiotic for therapy of the yeast-like fungi (134, 141, 144, 154, 171, 185, 196).

Prevention. Since candidiasis usually is endogenous in origin, it can be prevented best by personal hygienic measures.

BLASTOMYCOSIS

(North American Blastomycosis, Gilchrist's Disease)

Blastomycosis, caused by *Blastomyces dermatitidis,* may manifest itself as a slowly evolving, chronic infection of the skin, as a subacute suppurative infection of the lungs, or as a generalized systemic infection which may involve any or all organs of the body with the exception of the intestinal tract.

The organism was seen first by Gilchrist

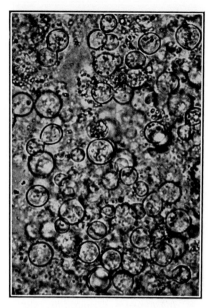

Fig. 7. *Blastomyces dermatitidis.* Budding yeast-like cells in pus. × 762.

(218) in sections of a skin lesion which resembled tuberculosis. From a second case Gilchrist and Stokes (219) cultured the fungus, and named it *Blastomyces dermatitidis. Glenospora gammeli, Blastomycoides tulanensis, Monosporium tulanense, Endomyces capsulatus, Endomyces dermatitidis,* and *Glenospora brevis* have been described as etiologic agents of North American blastomycosis, but comparative studies of cultures of these fungi have shown them to be identical with *B. dermatitidis* (199, 205).

Morphology. In sputum, pus, and exudates *B. dermatitidis* appears as large, round thick-walled cells, 5 to 15 μ in diameter, which reproduce by budding (Fig. 7). In sections of various tissues small forms measuring 2 to 5 μ in diameter have been described (270). Such small forms might be mistaken for *H. capsulatum* in tissue.

Cultural Characteristics. On blood-agar or brain-heart infusion glucose agar incubated at 37° C., the fungus develops soft, waxy, wrinkled colonies not unlike those of *Myco. tuberculosis* (Fig. 8). Microscopic examination reveals round budding forms, identical in appearance to those found in tissues or in discharges from lesions (Fig. 9). Temperature alone is responsible for the

Fig. 8. *Blastomyces dermatitidis.* Culture on blood agar at 37° C. for seven days.

yeast growth at 37° C., and, when grown on a chemically defined medium, no accessory growth factors were found to be essential for its growth (234, 253). Extensive physiologic studies on the yeast phase have been reported by Bernheim (200), and Levine and Novak (231, 232, 233). Comparative nutritional studies with yeast phase cultures of *B. dermatitidis* and *B. brasiliensis* showed no differences between these two species (217).

On Sabouraud's glucose agar at room temperature, the fungus develops a white to light brown filamentous colony (Fig. 10). Microscopic examination reveals branching septate hyphae with lateral, spherical to pyriform conidia, 5 to 8 μ in diameter (Fig. 11). If this filamentous growth is transferred to fresh media and incubation at 37° C., the fungus will revert to the tissue or yeast phase.

Antibiotics (penicillin 10 units, streptomycin 40 units, chloramphenicol 0.05 mg., cycloheximide 0.5 mg., per milliliter) are used in the medium to isolate *B. dermatitidis* from contaminated clinical materials. However, cycloheximide and chloramphenicol should not be used in cultures to be incubated at 37° C., since these two antibiotics

are inhibitory for the yeast phase at this temperature (243).

Resistance. *B. dermatitidis* is killed at 56° C. for 60 minutes, and saline suspensions of the yeast phase can be heated in this way for the preparation of vaccines. Most of the sulfonamides have no effect on the growth of the fungus, but 125 mg. per cent sulfadiazine and 175 mg. per cent sulfanilamide exert inhibiting effects (247). Penicillin does not affect *B. dermatitidis* in vitro (216, 227), but streptothricin (10 units per milliliter) and gilotoxin (1:8,000) were found to be inhibitory (216, 225). Differences in inhibitory concentrations of aromatic diamidine derivatives, reported by numerous investigators, would seem to be dependent on the technics of the tests and whether mycelial or yeast cultures were used (244). Amphotericin B inhibits growth at 0.5 mg. per milliliter (246, 268).

Fungus Metabolites.   Neither endotoxins nor exotoxins have been demonstrated.

A hemolysin against guinea pig erythrocytes occurs in the supernate of disintegrated yeast cells (252). It is destroyed by autoclaving at 15 lb. for 15 minutes but not at 60° C. for 30 minutes.

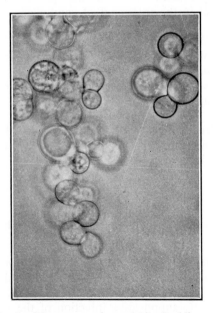

Fig. 9. *Blastomyces dermatitidis.* Budding yeast-like cells from culture on blood agar at 37° C. × 700. (From Conant and others. *Manual of Clinical Mycology,* 2nd ed., W. B. Saunders Co.)

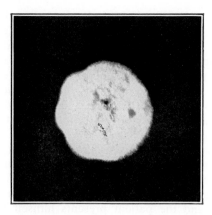

Fig. 10. *Blastomyces dermatitidis.* Colony on Sabouraud's glucose agar at room temperature for 14 days.

Lipids have been extracted from *B. dermatitidis* (212, 249, 250) and the soaps of their fatty acids have been shown to inhibit tissue enzymes (248). Carbohydrates and proteins also have been isolated (251).

Antigenic Structure. The yeast phase may be used as an antigen in the complement-fixation test with animal serums (207, 254, 256) and with human serums (239). Blastomycin, a filtrate of a filamentous culture (215), also has been used as an antigen in the complement-fixation test (254, 269) and as an antigen for collodion particle sensitization for an agglutination test (255). Soluble antigens from whole yeast cells and sonic-treated cells have been used in the complement-fixation test with animal and human serums (241). A carbohydrate obtained from the supernatant fluid of yeast cell suspensions was shown to sensitize sheep cells, which could then be used in an hemagglutination test with patients' serums (241).

Heat-killed (60° C. for one hour) saline suspensions of a 1:1,000 dilution of the yeast phase (240) and blastomycin (215, 224) elicit a positive skin test in 24 to 48 hours if animals or humans have been sensitized to the fungus or its products. These materials also will react on *Histoplasma*-infected animals or humans. Positive skin tests have been elicited in patients by the carbohydrate and protein fractions obtained from *B. dermatitidis* (251). Dyson and Evans (213) have reported a specific skin-test antigen obtained from yeast culture supernates by alcohol

precipitation. A soluble extract from sonic-treated cells, a cell-free extract from ground cells, and various carbohydrate fractions have been obtained from *B. dermatitidis* for dermal sensitivity studies and for serologic investigations (228, 229, 238). Kaufman and Kaplan (226) reported fluorescent antibody technics to distinguish common and distinct antigens of *B. dermatitidis* and *H. capsulatum.*

Spontaneous Disease in Animals. Spontaneous blastomycosis has been reported in the horse (198), sea lion (272), and dogs (245).

Experimental Infection in Laboratory Animals. Rabbits, guinea pigs, and mice can be infected experimentally, but mice are the most susceptible and, after an intraperitoneal injection of 1 ml. of a 1:200 suspension of the yeast phase, usually develop extensive infection within three weeks. Intravenous injection of the yeast phase into mice produces a rapidly fatal infection (223). This animal, therefore, has been used extensively to test drugs for in vivo activity against *B. dermatitidis* and for possible use as chemotherapeutic agents for blastomycosis. Guinea pigs inoculated intrathoracically de-

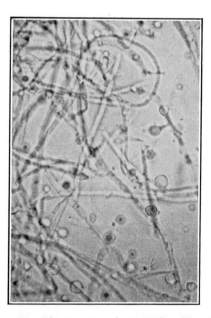

Fig. 11. *Blastomyces dermatitidis.* Mycelium and conidia from culture on Sabouraud's agar at room temperature. × 736.

velop systemic infections with early serologic findings which correlate with extent of infection (237). Experimentally infected guinea pigs held at 35° to 37° C. have minimum infection, whereas those held at 10° to 20° C. demonstrate maximum infection (206).

Clinical Types of Infection in Man. Recent reports have presented excellent clinical data derived from studies of 90 cases (230), 40 cases (202) and 35 cases (196) of North American blastomycosis. Weed (273) has discussed the salient features of this disease and has emphasized the problems of diagnosis. It is convenient to classify blastomycosis into three clinical forms: cutaneous, pulmonary, and systemic. In primary cutaneous blastomycosis, the lesions usually occur on the exposed parts of the body. The lesion, following trauma and introduction of the organism, begins as a papule or papulopustule which slowly increases in size. The regional lymphatics become involved with resulting lymphadenopathy which is characteristic of primary cutaneous infection (259, 274). On further extension the lesion becomes raised above the surrounding skin, and irregular, smooth, glistening reddish or dark-colored, wart-like papilliform elevations appear. The lesion is defined sharply from the surrounding skin by an abrupt, elevated, dark red or purple verrucous border which contains minute dermal abscesses. The diagnosis can be made by microscopic examination and culture of the small amount of pus expressed from these abscesses. The lesions usually are not painful or sensitive to pressure.

Multiple subcutaneous abscesses may occur anywhere on the body and rupture to evolve into cutaneous lesions as described. The lack of lymphadenopathy distinguishes these lesions from the primary cutaneous type; they are the result of metastases to the subcutaneous tissues from an established systemic infection.

Pulmonary blastomycosis usually begins as isolated pneumonic lesions in any part of the lung, apparently as a result of inhalation of the organism. The lesions most often are diagnosed incorrectly as either tuberculosis or neoplasm. Many patients have been sent to sanatoria for tuberculosis, and we know of several patients who underwent pneu-

monectomy because of the incorrect diagnosis of neoplasm. Occasionally the organisms invade the chest wall and produce multiple-draining sinuses. The sputum may or may not contain blood but usually contains numerous yeast-like budding *Blastomyces.* Two instances of a self-limited untreated pulmonary infection have been reported (230, 265).

Systemic blastomycosis results from a dissemination of the fungus from a pulmonary lesion. In some cases, however, no focus can be detected either in the lungs or on the skin, and the patient presents himself with involvement of the subcutaneous tissues, vertebrae, ribs, brain, or other internal organs.

Transmission. North American blastomycosis occurs within the borders of the United States and Canada. The rare patient with this disease reported elsewhere—for example in Mexico and in Europe—invariably has a history of previous residence in the United States (201, 242). The chronicity of blastomycosis allows for several years to intervene between infection and demonstrable signs and symptoms of active disease (202). The disease occurs in greatest frequency in the north central and southeastern states. The infection may be acquired at any age between two months and 80 years but is seen most often between the ages of 20 and 40. All races are susceptible, but males are infected nine times as frequently as females. In a few instances positive skin tests to blastomycin, analogous to histoplasmin and coccidioidin, have been found in normal individuals, suggesting that subclinical infections do occur. Several epidemiologic studies of blastomycosis have been reported (197, 203, 259, 260, 261, 265). Spontaneous infections have been reported in dogs, but there are no proven cases of animal-to-man transmission, despite the recent report of Schwartzman and others (258).

Since *B. dermatitidis* has been isolated from the soil, both animal and man become infected from this source (210). The infection does not spread from man to man, although a few cases have occurred as a result of a wound at the necropsy table (259). Complement-fixing antibodies have been reported in an infant whose mother had blastomycosis during pregnancy (247), but infection could not be demonstrated.

Biologic Products. Since all *Blastomyces* are identical antigenically, stock vaccines may be used for skin tests and for desensitization.

Treatment. Following the report of successful treatment of cutaneous blastomycosis with propamidine (204), systemic infections have been treated with stilbamidine and dihydroxystilbamidine (209, 214, 222, 236, 257, 254, 265). Because of the toxic effects of stilbamidine resulting in neuropathy of the trigeminal nerve, the less toxic drug dihydroxystilbamidine has been used with success (208, 235, 266, 267). However, relapses have occurred following diamidine therapy (222, 263), probably as a result of the poor immunologic status of the patients (221, 264). Amphotericin B is a very effective antibiotic in the treatment of blastomycosis and is considered now to be the drug of choice (211, 220, 221, 246, 262, 271).

SOUTH AMERICAN BLASTOMYCOSIS

(Paracoccidioidal Granuloma or Lutz-Splendore-Almeida's Disease)

South American blastomycosis, caused by *Blastomyces brasiliensis,* is a chronic granulomatous infection of the mucous membranes of the mouth, skin, lymph nodes, and internal organs. The disease has been described in several countries in South America and in Costa Rica (283, 306), Guatemala (319), Honduras (292), and Mexico (295). The one case described in the United States had a history of previous residence in Venezuela (316). The greatest number of cases, however, has been reported from Brazil.

Lutz (307) in Brazil described the first case of this disease, and he reported it as a case of paracoccidioidal granuloma because he thought the invading fungus was similar to *Coccidioides immitis.* Carini (282), in describing a similar case, reported it as blastomycosis; and Splendore (317), who was the first to report a generalized infection, named the fungus *Zymonema brasiliensis.* Da Fonseca (287, 288) thought the fungus

to be similar to *Coccidioides immitis,* but Almeida (275), by a careful comparative study of the two fungi, was able to differentiate them and named the South American organism *Paracoccidioides brasiliensis.* Moore (310, 311) described two additional species, *P. tenuis* and *P. cerebriformis,* but these species were reduced to synonymy with *P. brasiliensis* by Conant and Howell (384). The latter authors proposed that the South American organism be placed in the genus *Blastomyces* as *B. brasiliensis.* A recent review of this disease has been published by Lacaz (299).

Morphology. *Blastomyces brasiliensis* occurs in tissue, exudates and sputum as large, round, thick-walled, **multiple budding** cells, 10 to 60 μ in diameter. The entire surface of the parent cell may be covered with small buds, 1 to 5 μ in diameter, or it may show only a few larger buds, 10 to 30 μ in diameter. Single budding cells occasionally resemble the yeast-like tissue form of *B. dermatitidis* (284, 316).

Cultural Characteristics. On blood-agar or beef-infusion glucose agar at 37° C., smooth, waxy, yeast-like colonies develop which resemble those of *B. dermatitidis* (Fig. 12). Microscopically such cultures are com-

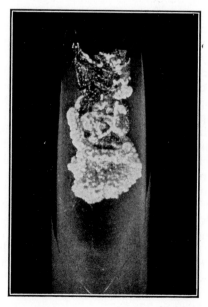

Fig. 12. *Blastomyces brasiliensis.* Growth on beef infusion glucose agar at 37° C. for 12 days.

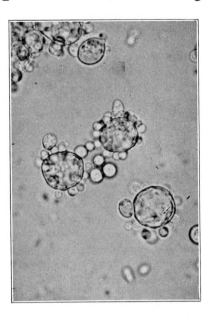

Fig. 13. *Blastomyces brasiliensis.* Multiple budding yeast-like cell from beef infusion glucose agar at 37° C. × 790. (From Conant. *Am. Rev. Tuberc.,* 61:696, 1950.)

Resistance. Saline suspensions of the yeast phase are killed readily at 60° C. for one hour. *B. brasiliensis* is inhibited in vitro by sulfadiazine (20 mg.) and sulfamerazine (50 mg.) but not by sulfanilamide, sulfapyridine, sulfathiazole, or sulfaguanidine (279). In vitro sensitivity to Gantricin differs with the strain being tested: 0.1-1.0 mg. per milliliter of medium (304). Penicillin exerts no in vitro or in vivo inhibitory effect on *B. brasiliensis* (280), streptomycin is inhibitory at a level of 5 mg. per milliliter, but is without in vivo activity (300), and tyrothricin is inhibitory in vitro at a level of 0.25 mg. per milliliter of medium (301). The aromatic diamidines have little effect on the growth of *B. brasiliensis* (302). Nystatin is inhibitory at levels of 40-50 μg per milliliter (303), while Amphotericin B is inhibitory at 0.06 to 0.24 mg. per milliliter of medium (306).

Fungus Metabolites. No exotoxins or endotoxins have been described. Filtrates of

posed of multiple-budding cells, 6 to 30 μ in diameter, with surface buds, 1 to 5 μ in diameter (Fig. 13). The ultrastructure of the yeast forms has been studied by Carbonell and Pollock (281).

On Sabouraud's glucose agar at room temperature the colonies develop slowly, reaching a diameter of 1 to 2 cm. after two or three weeks' incubation. Such colonies may be covered with a short, white, aerial mycelium which later becomes light brown in color (Fig. 14), or they may become heaped, folded, and cerebriform. Microscopically, the mycelium consists of hyphae with numerous chlamydospores, noncharacteristic hyphal swellings, and short, broad, thick-walled cells. A subculture of this filamentous phase will revert to the yeast phase if incubated at 37° C. (284).

Cultures from clinical materials are difficult to obtain because growth is very slow (one to two months) and the agar tends to dry before cultures are obtained. Almeida and Fernandez (278) were able to obtain growth within 13 days, or even in 5 days, by using a chocolate agar medium and incubating at 37° C.

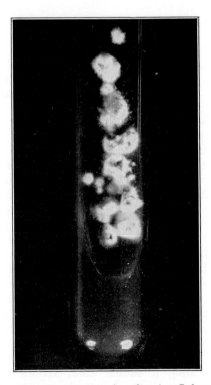

Fig. 14. *Blastomyces brasiliensis.* Colony on Sabouraud's glucose agar at room temperature for 25 days.

broth cultures contain the substance "para-coccidioidin," which has been used as a skin-testing antigen and as an antigen in the complement-fixation test.

Antigenic Structure. A filtrate of Sabouraud's broth, **paracoccidioidin,** in which 19 different strains of *B. brasiliensis* have been grown for several months, elicits a positive skin reaction in 48 hours upon intracutaneous inoculation into sensitive patients (276, 277). Such patients do not react to coccidioidin but may give a positive test to blastomycin (297). Paracoccidioidin can be used as the antigen in complement-fixation tests with the serum and spinal fluid of patients with systemic infections (296). Skin-testing antigens also can be prepared by making saline suspensions of the yeast phase grown on chocolate agar and heating at 80° C. for one half-hour on three successive days or diluting infected pus 1:10 in saline and heating at 70° C. for half an hour on three successive days (277). Also, the yeast phase growth has been used as antigen in the complement-fixation test (293). Cross-reactions occur, however, with serum from patients with North American blastomycosis (293). A filtrate of the yeast phase culture grown at 37° C. has been used successfully as a skin-testing antigen (305). A polysaccharide obtained from an autoclaved yeast cell suspension also served as an antigen in a precipitin test and in the complement-fixation test (289) and as a skin-testing antigen (291).

Experimental Infection in Laboratory Animals. Guinea pigs and mice can be infected with cultures of *B. brasiliensis.* Intratesticular injection of guinea pigs and intraperitoneal injection of mice, using the cultural yeast phase or clinical materials containing the budding forms, results in lesions similar to those produced by *B. dermatitidis.* Dissemination of infection is readily produced in mice when inoculated by the bronchopulmonary route and by intravenous injection (308). Guinea pigs and rabbits also develop systemic infections after intracardiac inoculation (285). Repeated passage of inoculum by intratesticular inoculation of guinea pigs was reported to increase the virulence of *B. brasiliensis* (290).

Clinical Types of Infection in Man. South American blastomycosis usually is classified clinically into mucocutaneous, lymphatic, visceral, and mixed types. In the **mucocutaneous** infection the fungus enters the mouth and produces ulcerative lesions on the tonsils, tongue, cheek, gums, and palate. The skin lesions about the mouth and nose usually are secondary to the spreading, vegetative, papillomatous lesions of the buccal mucosa. Such lesions are similar to yaws and mucocutaneous leishmaniasis.

The **lymphatic** type most commonly involves the glands of the neck, which may become infected by an extension of the buccal lesions, but they also occur in the absence of demonstrable lesions in the mouth. Lymphatic spread results in hard, painful glands which adhere to the skin, soften, and finally ulcerate. Massive lymphadenopathy of the mesenteric glands may be mistaken for Hodgkin's disease or a tumor, particularly when located in the ileocecal region.

Visceral infections are widespread with involvement of the spleen, liver, pancreas, kidneys, and intestines. With hematogenous dissemination the lungs and brain also are invaded.

Mixed infections include various combinations of the types just described.

Transmission. The hundreds of cases reported from Brazil would indicate that the disease is endemic in certain regions and that the fungus exists in the soil or on vegetation of some kind. Primary infections of the anal mucocutaneous junction following the use of leaves for cleansing indicate the existence of the fungus on such materials. The fungus as yet has not been isolated from soil or natural substrates, and there have been no reports of spontaneous infections in animals. An intensive epidemiologic study of the disease might reveal a situation in Brazil similar to that of coccidioidomycosis in the United States.

Treatment. South American blastomycosis, more than any other fungus infection, responds to sulfonamide therapy (298). Oliveira Ribeiro (314, 315) described the first cases which were treated successfully with sulfanilamide, sulfathiazole, and sulfadiazine; and Decourt and others (286) in

Brazil, Negroni (302), and Nino (303) in Argentina have reported cures using sulfadiazine, sulfamerazine, and sulfathiazole. The drug must be given in large doses (4 g. daily) over a period of months, and vaccine therapy may be given as a supplement to the drug. Sulfamethoxypyridazine and sulfadimethoxine in doses of 1 g. daily for the first week and maintenance doses of 0.5 g. daily until apparent cure is an effective treatment regime (294). Amphotericin B is effective in the treatment of South American blastomycosis and should be considered for those patients showing sensitivity to sulfonamides (309).

COCCIDIOIDOMYCOSIS

Coccidioidomycosis is an exogenous, dustborne infection caused by *Coccidioides immitis* (394). Two forms of the disease are known: primary coccidioidomycosis, which usually is an acute, benign, self-limiting, respiratory infection; and progressive coccidioidomycosis, which is a chronic, malignant, disseminated disease that involves cutaneous, subcutaneous, visceral, and osseous tissues.

In 1892 Posadas (381) and Wernicke (401) found the tissue form of the organism in a patient in Argentina. The second and third cases were discovered in California (385, 386). The organism was named *Coccidioides immitis* under the impression that it was a protozoan. The mycotic nature of the infection was demonstrated by Ophüls and Moffitt (374) and Ophüls (375), who isolated it in pure culture and reproduced the disease in animals. The progressive form of the disease originally was called "coccidioidal granuloma" and almost always terminated fatally. The benign primary type of the infection was described by Gifford (349), Dickson (338), and Dickson and Gifford (339).

Morphology. *Coccidioides immitis* in the tissues develops into spherical, thick-walled structures, 15 to 80 μ in diameter, which are filled with numerous small endospores, 2 to 5 μ in diameter (Figs. 15, 16). When the spherules rupture, the endospores are freed and become distributed throughout the tissues, where they increase gradually in size and develop into mature spherules which become filled with endospores. Immature cells may contain no endospores and in size

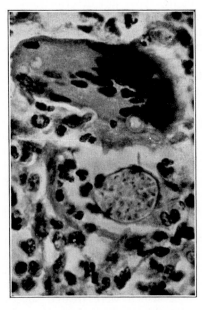

Fig. 15. *Coccidioides immitis.* Section of lung showing mature spherule and giant cell containing three immature cells. × 736.

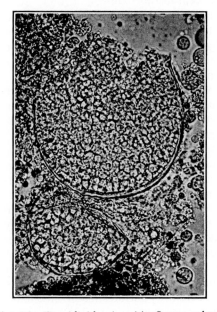

Fig. 16. *Coccidioides immitis.* Large spherules with endospores in pus. × 315 (From Smith. *Am. J. Med.,* 2:594, 1947.)

Fig. 17. *Coccidioides immitis.* Colony on Sabouraud's glucose agar at room temperature for 19 days. (From Conant and others. *Manual of Clinical Mycology,* 2nd ed., W. B. Saunders Co.)

and appearance resemble the nonbudding forms of *Blastomyces dermatitidis.* Occasional reports have described mycelium as well as spherules in the tissues and sputum of patients with coccidioidal cavities of the lungs (342, 382). In culture the organism grows as a typical mold and presents an entirely different microscopic picture, which will be described in the next section.

Cultural Characteristics. *C. immitis* grows readily on Sabouraud's glucose agar at room temperature. After four to six days' incubation, a flat membranous type colony appears, which during the course of the next week becomes covered with an abundance of cottony, aerial mycelium which at first is snow-white but gradually becomes tan to brown (Fig. 17). Microscopic examination of young cultures shows branching septate hyphae and many so-called racquet hyphae. In older cultures the hyphae broaden and break up into numerous, thick-walled, rectangular, ellipsoidal, or spherical arthrospores about 2.5 to 3 × 3 to 4 μ in size (Fig. 18). Nutritional requirements for growth and arthrospore formation have allowed abundant sporulation of this type

(350). These small arthrospores are detached easily by jarring or shaking the culture, and numerous laboratory infections have resulted from the inhalation of these detached spores (369). Cultures have been described, however, in which both the macroscopic and microscopic appearance is so atypical as to make morphologic identification impossible (347, 363, 380, 395). Such cultures are identified by mouse inoculation and the subsequent demonstration of typical endosporulating spherules. The cytology of the mycelium and spherule of *C. immitis* has been studied by means of electron microscopy (373).

The spherules, or tissue phase, have been cultivated on artificial media (331, 332, 333, 367, 368, 370, 387) and the spherule phase maintained in culture for four years (324). Physiologic studies of spherule production reveal certain amino acids and amino acid derivatives to be important for conversion from the mycelium (325).

When isolation is difficult because of overgrowth by saprophytic fungi, Sabouraud's glucose agar with penicillin, streptomycin, and cycloheximide has been recommended (338).

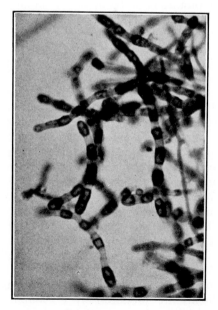

Fig. 18. *Coccidioides immitis.* Typical arthrospore formation on Sabouraud's glucose agar. × 736.

C. immitis liquefies gelatin, coagulates milk, and can utilize carbon from many sugars, alcohols, amino acids, organic acids, and amides. Peptone, amides, amino acids, nitrate ion, and ammonium ion may serve as utilizable sources of nitrogen (323). The biochemical activities of *C. immitis,* however, are not practical aids for the identification of the fungus. The fungus is identified by its characteristic arthrospore formation in culture and its spherule production when inoculated intraperitoneally into mice.

Resistance. *C. immitis* is highly resistant to drying and will live for months or years in cultures or in the soil. The fungus has been cultured from soil near Delano in the San Joaquin Valley, in San Benito County bordering the San Joaquin Valley, and in the desert near San Carlos, Arizona (341). The arthrospores produced in cultures are viable up to two months at 5° C. but are killed readily in four minutes at 60° C. (387). Spherules in exudates remained viable at temperatures of 10° to 15° C. for 110 days (389). Spherules in sputum exposed to various outdoor conditions gave positive cultures in 72 days in one instance, while viability for guinea pigs was doubtful in all conditions tested (388).

Streptothricin at 10 units per milliliter in both liquid and solid media inhibits *C. immitis,* while streptomycin has no effect on growth (387). Prodigiosin is fungistatic at a dilution of 1:500,000 and fungicidal after 48 hours at a dilution of 1:100,000 (337); protoanemonin is inhibitory at a dilution of 1:125,000 (356), bacillomycin is fungistatic at 0.005 mg. per milliliter (362), and penicillin has no effect on growth (343). Of 37 compounds tested against three strains of *C. immitis,* stilbamidine, thorazine, pyrrolidinoproprionyl phenothiazine, and pentochlorophenyl cellosolve were inhibitory in molar concentrations of 0.01 M or less (330). Nystatin is inhibitory at 100 μg. (352), and Amphotericin B inhibits at a level of 0.5 μg. per milliliter of medium (366).

Fungus Metabolites. No endotoxins or exotoxins are produced by *C. immitis.* A skin test material, **coccidioidin,** is prepared by growing for a period of three to six months a single or several strains in Long's synthetic medium with the addition of 1 per cent glucose. Such cultures are Seitz-filtered, and Merthiolate (1:10,000 final concentration) is added. The filtrate is used as a skin test material for the detection of hypersensitivity. Coccidioidin also may be used as an antigen in the complement-fixation test and precipitin reaction. However, only certain samples of coccidioidin can be used for the complement-fixation test, since many preparations are anticomplementary. To overcome the time interval of preparation (three to six months) and to obtain reproducible conditions of preparation, Ajello and others (320) found that a neopeptone dialyzate medium with agitation at 25° C. for three weeks produced a coccidioidin useful for the complementation test. This material, however, was of no value as a skin-testing antigen.

Coccidioidin is heat-stable. It resists 80° C. for 30 minutes (355) and autoclaving (396). The material which elicits the skin reaction is a polysaccharide (354, 355). McNall (372) reported an insoluble polysaccharide to contain mannose, glucose, glucosamine, and galacturonic acid. Pappagianis and others (378) found the antigenic material to contain mannose and galactose and a bound protein.

Antigenic Structure. Probably there is only one antigenic type of *Coccidioides immitis,* since coccidioidins prepared from different strains have been found to give identical skin reactions when tested on sensitive individuals (323). In the complement-fixation reaction, serums from infected patients from Texas, Arizona, and California all may fix complement with a single antigen. However, a protein carbohydrate complex similar to that mentioned above has been reported in *Histoplasma capsulatum* (390) and might be responsible for cross-reactions in serologic and cutaneous tests for coccidioidomycosis and histoplasmosis (326, 327).

Immunogenic substances reside in the cell wall of the spherule (361, 365).

Spontaneous Infection in Animals. Spontaneous infections with *Coccidioides immitis* occur in cattle, sheep, dogs, desert rodents, horses, burros, swine, monkeys, and the like (341, 371, 394, 397).

Experimental Infection in Laboratory Animals. Mice, rats, rabbits, guinea pigs, dogs, and monkeys are infected readily with *C. immitis*. Many of these animals have been used for investigations concerning the pathogenesis of coccidioidomycosis (335, 336, 357, 398) and for immunologic studies relative to the possible production of a vaccine suitable for active immunization against coccidioidomycosis (334, 346, 361, 364, 365, 376, 377, 399).

Clinical Types of Infection in Man. In certain areas in the southwestern part of the United States from 50 to 80 per cent of the population react to coccidioidin skin tests, suggesting that most cases of primary coccidioidomycosis either are completely asymptomatic or cannot be differentiated from mild nonspecific respiratory infections (322). Goldstein and McDonald (351) studied 75 soldiers who developed the primary form of coccidioidomycosis while on maneuvers in the desert during World War II. The incubation periods ranged from eight to 21 days, and the symptoms were those of bronchitis or "flu." About 19 per cent of the soldiers developed skin lesions of the erythema nodosum type, and 28 per cent had arthralgia. This form of the disease has been known for years as "valley fever," "desert rheumatism," or "desert fever."

Hypersensitivity to coccidioidin develops between the second and third weeks of the infection. The standard dose of coccidioidin is 0.1 ml. of a 1:1,000 dilution of a standardized product, and the material is injected intracutaneously. A 1:100 dilution is necessary to elicit reactions in many patients, but those who have had previous skin lesions often give severe reactions even with a 1:10,000 dilution. Precipitins and complement-fixing antibodies are absent in mild cases but appear in the more severe infections, only to disappear with recovery.

Reports by Smith and others (392) and Smith and Saito (391) describe the use of serology in coccidioidomycosis and the pattern of reactions in 39,500 serologic tests.

Progressive coccidioidomycosis or coccidioidal granuloma usually develops from the more severe cases of the primary disease, although, theoretically, it is possible for the infection to reactivate itself from an inadequately healed lymph node in a manner analogous to reinfection pulmonary tuberculosis. One should suspect the progressive form of the disease if the temperature remains elevated after the third or fourth week, if the precipitin and complement-fixation titers increase, and if new shadows appear in the parenchyma of the lungs. As the disease progresses, metastatic lesions appear in the bones, subcutaneous tissues, and internal organs. Many patients die in coma from a terminal meningitis (344).

Generalized delayed hypersensitivity to coccidioidin can be transferred in man with leukocyte extracts from sensitive donors (384). Repeated intradermal testing with coccidioidin does not create sensitivity in previously nonsensitized individuals (383).

Transmission. Coccidioidomycosis is a dust-borne respiratory infection occurring in endemic areas in the arid regions of the southwestern United States, particularly in Southern California, the San Joaquin Valley in California, the area around Phoenix and Tucson in Arizona, and in central West Texas. An occasional case has been reported from Honduras (329) and the northern states of Mexico (363). A few cases have been reported from Italy, southeastern Europe, the Hawaiian Islands (323), and France (340). The Chaco region of Argentina may prove to be a major endemic area in South America (360). There is no known man-to-man or animal-to-man transmission of the disease. There has been one report, however, of transmission from an adult monkey to its offspring (328). Animals living in the endemic areas probably are infected, as is man, by the inhalation of contaminated dust, and infected rodents may serve to indicate the extent of endemic areas.

Travel through or within an endemic area is not without hazard (359). Also, infection from fomites outside known endemic areas has been documented (321).

Treatment. No particular treatment is necessary for the cases of primary coccidioidomycosis other than assigning the patient to bed until the sedimentation rate is normal, the lungs are clear when examined by x-ray, and the complement-fixation reaction becomes negative. Most patients with the progressive form of the disease (coccidioidal granuloma) will need specific therapy, although an occasional patient recovers after a prolonged illness. At the present time Amphotericin B would seem to be the drug of choice for specific treatment of coccidioidomycosis. The chronicity of the disseminated form of the disease, however, demands withholding judgment of the final efficacy of chemotherapy (358, 366, 379, 400).

Surgery has been successful for pulmonary cavities which cause distressing symptoms (345).

Prevention. Dust-control measures, such as paving roads and runways, oiling athletic fields, and planting lawns in four of the air fields used by the Army Air Forces in World War II, have been shown by Smith and others (393) to reduce the infection rate of susceptibles by 50 to 75 per cent.

Vaccination of large nonimmune population groups moving into endemic areas would minimize the danger of dissemination following primary pulmonary infections.

HISTOPLASMOSIS

Histoplasmosis, caused by *Histoplasma capsulatum,* is an infection primarily of the reticuloendothelial system. It usually results in enlargement of the liver, spleen, and lymph nodes. Frequently a neutropenia with relative lymphocytosis is present as a result of massive infection of the bone marrow.

The organism was seen first by Darling (422) in sections of livers and spleens removed from natives of the Canal Zone who had died of a disease resembling visceral leishmaniasis. Darling named the organism *Histoplasma capsulatum* and thought it was a protozoan closely related to *Leishmania donovani.* Da Rocha-Lima (423) noted that the organisms budded and suggested that they were fungi related to the Cryptococci. Final proof of the mycotic nature of the infection was furnished by Hansmann and Schenken (441, 442) and DeMonbreun (424), who were the first to culture *H. capsulatum.*

Morphology. *Histoplasma capsulatum* is a small (2 to 4 μ), budding, oval, yeast-like organism which in the body appears to grow

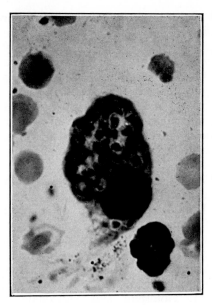

Fig. 19. *Histoplasma capsulatum.* Parasitized mononuclear cell in peripheral blood smear. $\times$ 1,540.

exclusively in the cytoplasm of endothelial and mononuclear cells (Fig. 19). The organisms are about the size and shape of *Leishmania donovani* but lack the central nuclear material and blepharoplast seen in stained preparations of these protozoa. They can be demonstrated in tissue sections by Gram's stain or, more clearly, by Giemsa's stain and the methenamine silver stain. Smears of peripheral blood, bone marrow, sputum, and exudates should be made on coverglasses and stained by the Giemsa method.

Large yeast-like forms are seen in human tissues infected with *Histoplasma duboisii* isolated from histoplasmosis in Africa (470, 500).

Cultural Characteristics. The tissue stage of *H. capsulatum* can be grown on blood agar slants at 37° C. if the tubes are sealed after inoculation (Fig. 20). The colonies, which are yeast-like, smooth, and white to cream in color, closely resemble the colonies of *Staphylococcus albus.* Microscopically the growth is composed of small, oval, single budding cells, 2 × 4 μ in size (Fig. 21).

A filamentous growth occurs on Sabouraud's glucose agar at room temperature. The growth at first is cottony and white

Fig. 20. *Histoplasma capsulatum.* Yeast-like growth on blood agar at 37° C. for five days.

but gradually becomes buff to brown with age (Fig. 22). In young cultures the branching septate hyphae bear small, 2.5 to 5 μ, smooth, round to pyriform spores on short lateral branches. In older cultures there are numerous round to pyriform, thick-walled spores (8 to 20 μ), which are covered with finger-like projections. These tuberculate spores are characteristic and diagnostic for *H. capsulatum* (Fig. 23). The filamentous cultures usually can be converted to the yeast-like form by subculturing the filamentous growth on blood-agar slants which are sealed after inoculation and incubated at 37° C. Large quantities of the yeast-like growth have been obtained by Salvin (476) by growing the organism at 37° C. in a liquid medium containing a mixture of organic nitrogen compounds; and by Campbell (407) by growing the organism on Francis' cystine blood agar. Kurung and Yegian (449) used a medium of egg-potato flour to support the yeast phase growth.

Pine (465, 466), Rowley and Pine (475), and Pine and Peacock (467) have studied the nutritional requirements for cultural maintenance of the yeast phase and conversion of yeast cells to mycelium. Northey and Brooks (461) reported that enzymatic digests of casein of technical grades stimu-

lated conversion of mycelium to yeast phase growth.

Resistance. *H. capsulatum* is killed at 55° C. for 15 minutes and by 1 to 2 per cent formalin in 24 hours. The sodium salts of sulfathiazole, sulfadiazine, and sulfamerazine inhibit growth in concentrations of 100 mg. per cent (437). Penicillin has no in vitro effect. The in vitro inhibitory effect of many common therapeutic agents (atabrine, quinine, and emetine) has been investigated (440). In one instance streptomycin stimulated growth of *H. capsulatum* in vitro but had no such effect in vivo (409, 410). Atabrine showed some inhibitory effects in in vivo tests with mice (411). Nystatin prolongs the survival time of infected mice beyond that of the untreated controls (413). Amphotericin B is inhibitory in vitro from 0.5 to 12.5 μg. per milliliter of medium (57).

Fungus Metabolites. No endotoxins or exotoxins have been demonstrated. A supernate from dissociated yeast cells shows hemolytic activity against guinea pig and hen erythrocytes (478). The hemolysin was not inactivated at 60° C. for 30 minutes but was destroyed by autoclaving at 15 lb. pressure for 15 minutes. The filtrates of broth cul-

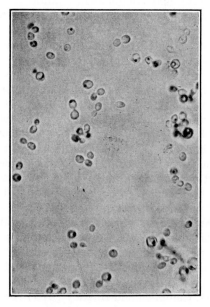

Fig. 21. *Histoplasma capsulatum.* Yeast-like cells from blood agar culture at 37° C. × 700.

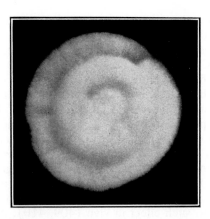

Fig. 22. *Histoplasma capsulatum.* Colony on Sabouraud's glucose agar at room temperature for 23 days. (From Conant and others. *Manual of Clinical Mycology,* 2nd ed., W. B. Saunders Co.)

tures of the mycelial phase of *H. capsulatum* contain substances which may be used to detect hypersensitivity to the organism. This material, known as **histoplasmin,** is prepared by growing the filamentous culture for two to four months in a synthetic medium. A polysaccharide and a protein have been obtained from the mycelial phase and from histoplasmin (420). Prior and Saslaw (468) and Saslaw and Campbell (489) have reported transient positive collodion agglutination tests and complement-fixation tests by repeated histoplasmin skin testing of skin-test-positive persons. A single positive skin test or repeated tests in a skin-test-negative individual had no effect on antibody titer. Edwards and Palmer (427) have reported on the geographic variation and prevalence of histoplasmin sensitivity and *Histoplasma* infection in the United States, while Edwards and Kiaer (425) have reported the incidence of infection and histoplasmin sensitivity throughout the world. A polysaccharide extract of culture filtrates of *H. capsulatum* has been shown to be comparable to histoplasmin in skin test surveys (426).

Antigenic Structure. Yeast cells and histoplasmin have been used as antigens in a complement-fixation test with serums from humans and infected and immunized animals (408, 435, 444, 477, 485, 491, 492, 499). Campbell and Binkley (413) reported frequent cross-reactions of histoplasma antigens with serums from patients with blasto-

mycosis and a few cross-reactions with serums from patients with coccidioidomycosis. Sorensen and Evans (496) precipitated an antigen by zinc and alcohol from the supernates of yeast phase cultures. This antigen proved to be specific in complement-fixation tests with serums from infected rabbits. Collodion particles sensitized with histoplasmin have been used in an agglutination test to demonstrate antihistoplasma antibodies in animal and human serums (484, 486, 487, 488). A hemagglutination test also has been reported by Norden (460). Precipitins to histoplasmin and four fractions isolated from it have been demonstrated in serums from infected rabbits (464). Salvin and Furcolow (481) used histoplasmin in a precipitin test with human serums. Precipitins could be demonstrated in the serums of patients with mild and severe acute histoplasmosis.

A histoplasmin-latex agglutination test (490), whole-cell agglutination test (418), capillary-tube agglutination test (419), and an agar gel precipitin test (443, 493) have been used to demonstrate antibody in animal or human serums.

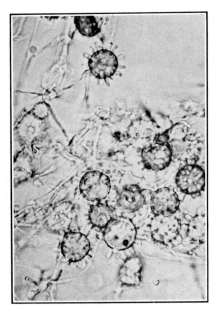

Fig. 23. *Histoplasma capsulatum.* Typical tuberculate chlamydospores from Sabouraud's agar culture. × 658. (From Smith. *Am. J. Med.,* 2:594, 1947).

Salvin and Smith (483) reported a protein-carbohydrate complex of *H. capsulatum* to contain mannose and galactose. Purified antigens have been obtained from histoplasmin by means of column chromatography on DEAE-cellulose (439).

Salvin (480) has shown mice and guinea pigs to have acquired resistance to histoplasmosis after inoculation with acetone-dried dead yeast cells and a cell-wall fraction of the yeast cells obtained by disruption in a Mickle tissue disintegrator followed by differential centrifugation (482). Knight and others (451) reported mice to show some resistance to infection after immunization with polysaccharide.

Methods for making specific fluorescent antibody for yeast phase *H. capsulatum* have been described by Kaufman and Kaplan (448).

Spontaneous Infection in Animals. Spontaneous infections have been found in the dog, mouse, rat, cat, skunk, horse, and cow (431, 452). There is no evidence, however, that man is infected by contact with animals.

Experimental Infection in Laboratory Animals. The pathogenesis of experimental histoplasmosis has been investigated in mice, hamsters, guinea pigs, and dogs (445, 472, 473, 474, 479). Intranasal, intracerebral, intraperitoneal, and intravenous routes of inoculation have been used. Ajello and Runyon (402) were able to infect mice with a single tuberculate spore.

Clinical Types of Infection in Man. Loosli (455) has published an excellent article on the clinical, epidemiologic, and laboratory aspects of histoplasmosis. Although primary cutaneous lesions have been described (421, 441), histoplasmosis essentially is a systemic infection with the small, yeast-like fungus being distributed widely in the reticuloendothelial system. Lesions on the mucosa of the nose, lips, mouth, pharynx, or larynx usually are secondary manifestations of widespread infection (458). These lesions may simulate carcinoma or tuberculosis.

In many cases primary infection may take place through the intestinal tract, with ulceration of lymphoid tissue, enlargement of the mesenteric lymph nodes, hepatosplenomegaly and generalized lymphadenopathy

suggestive of Hodgkin's disease or visceral leishmaniasis or lymphoblastoma (415).

Furcolow and Brasher (433) have described the signs and symptoms of chronic progressive (cavitary) histoplasmosis, which closely resembles the reinfection type of tuberculosis. The disease is characterized by exacerbations, with cough, profuse sometimes blood-tinged sputum, elevation of temperature and sedimentation rate, and moderate weight loss. Apical pneumonia or cavitary lesions, occasionally bilateral, are found. Progressive disease with dissemination of the fungus throughout the body occurs after varying periods of time. Other investigators also have reported this type of chronic pulmonary (cavitary) histoplasmosis (446, 456, 498, 502).

Straub and Schwarz (497) have shown that a primary complex does occur in histoplasmosis, which is essentially identical with that of tuberculosis in that there is a primary pulmonary focus with affected corresponding lymph nodes. Schwarz and others (495) also were able to demonstrate splenic calcification thought to be part of a primary infection with *H. capsulatum*.

At first the infection was thought to be a progressive, malignant, and highly fatal disease. The epidemiologic studies of Christie and Peterson (417), Palmer (462, 463) and others, however, have indicated that a benign type of self-limiting pulmonary histoplasmosis may be the most common type of infection. The evidence for such a view consists of the positive histoplasmin skin tests in tens of thousands of individuals residing in the Central Mississippi Valley. Such patients are asymptomatic, but x-ray shadows of the lung taken during the first few months of the disease show numerous small soft areas of infiltration 2 to 3 mm. in size. After three or four years these areas become calcified and simulate the calcification seen in primary pulmonary infections (436). In many instances the hilar lymph nodes are enlarged and calcified. Such patients give a markedly positive skin test to a 1:1,000 dilution of a standard histoplasmin. In endemic areas studies of a number of individuals with multiple calcified foci in their lungs have shown that the negative tuberculin, positive histoplasmin reactors far outnumber those with positive tuberculin and negative histoplasmin tests. A granulomatous ocular infection poses a problem in differential diagnosis which should include histoplasmosis. Jarvis and McCulloch (447) base their diagnosis on clinical evidence of chorioretinitis, calcified pulmonary lesions, and a negative tuberculin and positive histoplasmin skin test.

It is not known why the infection is so benign when the organism is inhaled into the lungs, or why it is so uniformly fatal when it enters the body through other routes.

Transmission. *H. capsulatum* has been isolated from animals (429, 453, 457, 471) and from soil (403, 428, 438), and several epidemics have been described (414, 416, 434, 437, 494). Such epidemics have resulted from groups having contact with a common exposure and not by direct transmission from person to person. The isolation of *H. capsulatum* from bird and bat guano in caves (432) has allowed Aspin (404) to consider histoplasmosis a spelunker's risk. Infections acquired in such areas result in a pneumonitis, with eventual development of miliary calcification in the lungs.

There is no known transmission from animal to animal or from animal to man (430). Young children frequently are infected with *Histoplasma,* the youngest reported patient being only one month of age, but 10 other cases have been reported in which the disease occurred during the first 12 months of life. Before the age of 10 years both sexes are affected equally; but in the older age groups males contract clinical infection seven times as frequently as females. Such a sex distribution suggests that the reservoir of infection is in the fields or woods, where males would naturally be more exposed, but it indicates also that the organism can be brought into the home, where infants of both sexes would be exposed equally.

Treatment. Histoplasmosis in its generalized form is a highly fatal disease, although a few spontaneous recoveries have been reported (405, 406, 450, 452, 501). Antimony compounds, sulfonamide compounds, penicillin, streptomycin, arsenicals, stilbamidine, radium, and roentgen-ray therapy have been used with little success except in a few instances, particularly with localized lesions. Amphotericin B now offers the best therapy for histoplasmosis.

Successful surgical removal of pulmonary cavities and segmental resection of coin lesions have been reported (469, 498). The use of Amphotericin B combined with the surgical removal of localized cavitary lesions offers the best management for chronic pulmonary histoplasmosis (454).

GEOTRICHOSIS

Geotrichosis, caused by *Geotrichum candidum,* may present itself as an infection of the skin and mucous membranes or as an infection of the lungs simulating chronic pulmonary tuberculosis.

In the older literature the genera *Oidium, Mycoderma,* and *Oospora* have been used interchangeably for the yeast-like fungi which form membranous colonies and reproduce by segmentation of the hyphae into rectangular arthrospores. *Geotrichum candidum,* isolated from leaf mold by Link (516), has been accepted as the type species, and the other generic names have been reduced to synonymy (507, 515). Several species of *Geotrichum* have been isolated from sputum, stools, and skin. Dodge (510) lists 10 species, some of which do not belong in the genus. *G. immitis* and *G. louisianoideum,* for example, are identical with *Coccidioides immitis.* Other species are separated on doubtful grounds because of the lack of differentiating morphologic or biologic characteristics.

Geotrichum has been isolated from the sputum of patients showing chronic bronchitis and acute or chronic pulmonary disease (513, 514, 517, 520, 521). The fungus has also been isolated from the blood stream (503, 512).

Morphology. In the sputum, *Geotrichum candidum* appears either in the form of rectangular elements (arthrospores), 4 to 6 by 8 to 12 μ in size, or as thick-walled, ovoid to rounded cells, 8 to 15 μ in diameter. The rectangular cells are characteristic for *Geotrichum,* but the rounded forms may be mistaken for *Blastomyces dermatitidis.* In the presence of both types of cells, however, *Geotrichum* is suspected.

Fig. 24. *Geotrichum candidum.* Colony on Sabourauds' glucose agar at room temperature for 10 days.

Cultural Characteristics. *G. candidum* grows quickly on Sabouraud's glucose agar at both room and incubator temperatures. Colonies become noticeable in four to five days, and in 7 to 10 days the large colony is membranous, mealy, flat and white to cream in color (Fig. 24). Despite its appearance, the consistency is soft and the yeast-like material can be picked up by a loop and emulsified readily in water. Microscopically the surface of the culture shows numerous rectangular and rounded cells (arthrospores) which have been formed by fragmentation of the hyphae (Fig. 25). In the agar the hyphae are wide, 4 to 10 μ in diameter, and tend to branch dichotomously. The arthrospores do not bud but characteristically produce germ tubes from one corner. Germ tubes—which are produced by both the rectangular and rounded cells— elongate, branch, and eventually form new colonies. A surface membrane is formed on liquid media; fermentation tests are negative for glucose, galactose, saccharose, maltose, and lactose; assimilation tests are positive for glucose, galactose, and lactose, and negative for saccharose and maltose; good growth is produced on ethanol medium; arbutin is not split (523).

A study of 55 strains allowed Carmichael (505) to propose that a single species was representative for *G. candidum.*

Resistance. *Geotrichum candidum* is killed at 56° C. for one hour. The effects of sulfonamides and antibiotics are not known. Gentian violet in high dilutions is inhibitory (508).

Fungus Metabolites. No endotoxins or exotoxins have been demonstrated. A sand-ground extract containing 7 to 14 mg. of protein per milliliter gave positive reactions in a passive cutaneous anaphylactic (PCA) test in sensitized guinea pigs (506). Extracted polysaccharides have shown *G. candidum* to yield galactose, glucose, and mannose in the proportion 1:3:2 (524).

Antigenic Structure. Fractionated cell extracts of three strains of *Geotrichum* gave similar tests in complement-fixation and precipitin studies (522). Also, Cheek and Barrett (506) reported 12 strains to be antigenically identical by agglutination and agglutinin-adsorption tests. Gel-precipitation studies by Torheim (525) showed seven differently named species of *Geotrichum* to be antigenically identical. Qualitative and quantitative precipitin reaction studies with polysaccharide antigens extracted from the above cultures also showed them to be identical (526).

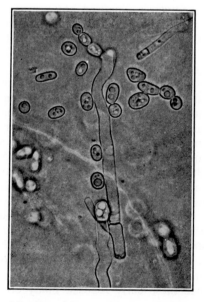

Fig. 25. *Geotrichum candidum.* Typical arthrospore formation on Sabouraud's glucose agar. $\times 658$. (From Smith. *Am. J. Med.,* 2:594, 1947.)

Clinical Types of Infection in Man. Infection of the bronchi produces symptoms similar to those of a chronic bacterial bronchitis with persistent cough. The sputum usually is white and mucoid and contains grayish flakes, but occasionally it may be blood-streaked. Medium and coarse rales may be heard at the lung bases; x-ray usually shows a diffuse peribronchial thickening (527). There is little systemic reaction, and the general health of the patient is good.

Infection of the lungs may simulate tuberculosis, with the typical signs of dullness, altered breath sounds, and fine and medium rales. The lesions may appear as smooth dense areas of infiltration with or without thin-walled cavities (518). Oral geotrichosis resembles thrush caused by *Candida albicans*.

Transmission. *Geotrichum candidum* occurs in the soil as a saprophyte. It has been isolated from the stools of normal people (504, 519) and also from the skin (504, 509, 511).

Treatment. Potassium iodide by mouth and sodium iodide intravenously have proved to be effective (514, 520).

PHYCOMYCOSIS

Phycomycosis, caused by species of *Mucor, Absidia,* and *Rhizopus,* is a rapidly fatal disease of man, in whom primarily the brain but occasionally the lungs and other organs are invaded. The disease has been reported most often in patients with uncontrolled diabetes mellitus and is characterized by intraorbital cellulitis and a meningoencephalitis, with invasion of the wall and lumen of blood vessels resulting in acute inflammation and vascular thrombosis (543).

Paltauf (554) in 1885 reported a fatal infection in a patient with involvement of the central nervous system. The fungus was not cultured but thought to be a *Mucor* because of its appearance in tissues. Lichtheim (548) in 1884, had shown, however, that *Absidia* (*Mucor*) *corymbifera* was pathogenic for the rabbit.

Since these early reports, many cases of mucormycosis in man and animals have been described in the literature. With few exceptions, cultures were not obtained, and

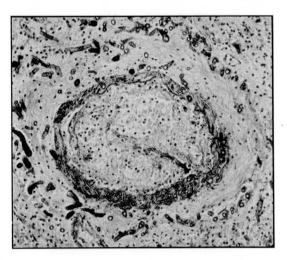

Fig. 26. Mucormycosis. Hyphae in wall and lumen of blood vessel and in pulmonary alveoli. × 150. (From Conant and others. *Manual of Clinical Mycology,* 2nd ed., W. B. Saunders Co.)

the diagnosis was based on postmortem studies of tissues. Bauer and others (530) and McCall and Strobos (550) have cultured *Rhizopus oryzae,* while Harris (544) cultured *Rhizopus arrhizus* from diabetic patients with cerebral infections. A culture of *Rhizopus rhizopodiformis* has been obtained from a cutaneous lesion of a diabetic by Baker and others (529). A peculiar type of subcutaneous phycomycosis has been described in children in Indonesia and Africa (532, 546, 558). *Basidiobolus ranarum* and *Basidiobolus* species have been isolated from some of these patients (549, 558).

Morphology. Large, broad, nonseptate, branching hyphae, 7 to 15 μ in diameter and 100 to 200 μ in length, are seen in the affected tissues, particularly in the wall and lumen of blood vessels which contain thrombi infiltrated with hyphae. The fungus can be readily demonstrated in hematoxylin- and eosin-stained sections (Fig. 26). In fresh preparations or potassium hydroxide mounts of scrapings from sinuses the fungus appears as extremely wide, nonseptate, hyaline, branching hyphae (Fig. 27).

The mycelium of the Phycomycetes differs from that of all other fungi in that it is broad, nonseptate, and coenocytic. These characteristics allowed the hyphal fragments seen in tissues to be identified with the Phyco-

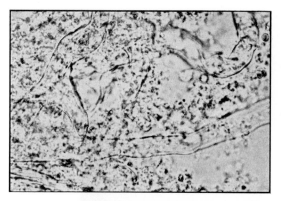

Fig. 27. *Rhizopus arrhizus*. Wide, nonseptate hyphae seen in potassium hydroxide preparation in scraping from lesion on palate.

mycetes rather than with other possible groups of fungi and the term "mucormycosis" was given to infections in which such hyphae were seen. Since fungi belonging to different genera of the Phycomycetes have been cultured from tissues in which nonseptate hyphae have been seen, the term "phycomycosis" has been adopted for diseases caused by these fungi.

Cultural Characteristics. *Absidia corymbifera* has been isolated from bovine phycomycosis, while *Rhizopus oryzae* and *Rhizopus arrhizus* have been isolated from human cases. Species of these two genera of the Mucorales grow quickly and fill the test tube or Petri dish with loose, greyish mycelium in three to four days (Fig. 28). *Absidia* and *Rhizopus* produce runners, "stolons," which attach themselves to the walls of the test tube or to the cover of the Petri dish with holdfasts, "rhizoids." The rhizoids may be seen microscopically by focusing through the test tube wall or Petri dish cover with the low-power objective (Fig. 29).

In *Absidia* the sporangiophores arise in fascicles from the arching internodes of the stolons between the rhizoid-bearing nodes. The sporangia are terminal and pyriform, the columella hemispherical with papillate apical prolongation, and the sporangiospores small.

In *Rhizopus* the sporangiophores arise in fascicles from the node of the stolon directly opposite the tuft of rhizoids (Fig. 30). The sporangia are terminal and globose, the columella hemispherical, and the sporangiospores oval or angular, smooth, or have longitudinal striations.

In *Mucor* stolons are not produced, and the sporangiophores arise directly from the mycelium. They are simple or branched and terminate in a sporangium. The sporangia are large, globose, and have an evanescent wall; the columella is continuous with the sporangiophore, and varies in shape but is never hemispheric; sporangiospores are globose to elliptical, with a smooth thin wall.

Genera and species in the Phycomycetes (Mucorales) can be differentiated only by their methods of sporulation, sexual and asexual, which occur in culture on suitable media. The three species belonging to two genera of the Mucorales mentioned above, therefore, appeared identical in tissue and were identified by isolation and a study of their cultural characteristics.

Since the species mentioned above have been, and others may yet be, isolated from cases of mucormycosis, identification of cultures from this disease can be obtained only by reference to monographs of this group of fungi (552).

Resistance. Formalin, phenol, and so forth readily kill the spores of *Mucor* and *Rhizopus*. Also, they are killed if subjected to 56° C. for one hour. They are not affected by known antibiotics.

Fungus Metabolites. The cell sap for *Rhizopus nigricans* has been reported to be highly toxic for rabbits (542). Henrici (556) reported anaphylactic reactions in rabbits when given a second injection of a toxin derived from *R. nigricans*.

Spontaneous Infection in Animals. Spontaneous infection has been reported in cattle, swine, the dog, and the horse (533, 535, 536, 538, 540, 541, 553).

Experimental Infection in Laboratory Animals. Cerebral and pulmonary mucormycosis has been produced with *R. oryzae* and *R. arrhizus* in rabbits made diabetic with alloxan (531, 537). Pulmonary infection could be established only in the acute toxic diabetic rabbit; the reaction of the chronic diabetic rabbit did not differ greatly from that of the normal animal. Alloxan-induced diabetes in mice did not increase susceptibility to intracerebral or intraperitoneal infection with *R. arrhizus* (555). *Absidia*

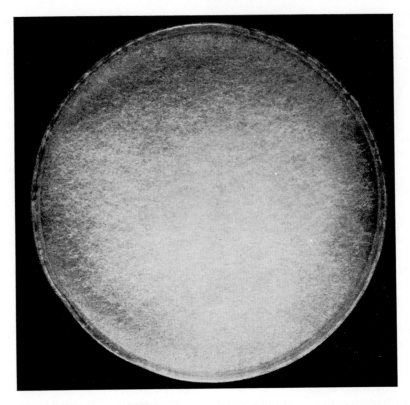

Fig. 28. *Rhizopus oryzae.* Culture on Sabouraud's glucose agar at room temperature for seven days.

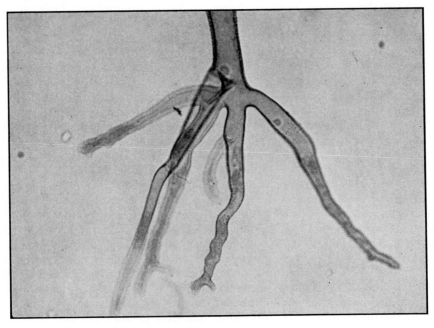

Fig. 29. *Rhizopus oryzae.* Rhizoids typical of the genus *Rhizopus.* × 450. (From Bauer and others. *Am. J. Med.,* 18:822, 1955.)

Fig. 30. *Rhizopus oryzae*. Fascicle of sporangiophores terminated by sporangia arising from tuft of rhizoids. × 32. (From Bauer and others. *Am. J. Med.*, 18:822, 1955.)

corymbifera inoculated subcutaneously in mice produced tumor-like granulomata (557), while intravenous inoculation produced death with suppurative renal lesions (536).

Chick and others (534) tested the effect of Amphotericin B on experimental infections of rabbits and on the inhibitory effect of *Rhizopus oryzae* in the pneumoderma pouch of the rat. This antibiotic was found to have considerable effect on the course of the experimental disease in these animals.

Clinical Types of Infection in Man. Cerebral mucormycosis is characterized by uncontrolled diabetes with ophthalmoplegia and meningoencephalitis. Infection with spores originates in the nasal and paranasal sinuses. Concurrent bacterial infection of these areas may aid the fungus to gain entry into the tissues, after which it spreads by invasion of the wall and lumen of blood vessels to cause thrombosis, vascular obstruction, and infarction. Extension to the brain, meninges, and orbit results in ophthalmoplegia and meningoencephalitis.

Pulmonary phycomycosis is characterized by a sudden onset, with severe chest pain, pleural friction rub, and the production of bloody sputum. Inhalation of spores results in bronchitis and pneumonia, thrombosis and infarction. Large areas of consolidation are seen in roentgenograms (528).

Transmission. Fungi belonging to the Phycomycetes are ubiquitous in nature. They occur in the soil and dust, cause rotting of fruits, readily establish growth on dead plant or animal tissues, and are constant contaminants in laboratory cultures (539). These saprophytes sporulate readily, and the spores may be inhaled to establish infection in the sinuses and bronchi of man and animals.

Several predisposing factors seem necessary to enable these fungi to establish infection. Diabetes mellitus with acidosis, leukemia, multiple myeloma, and hemochromatosis have been associated with phycomycosis (528, 543, 545, 547, 559). Chemotherapy (urethan, 6-mercaptopurine, cortisone, ACTH) and the prolonged use of broad-spectrum antibiotics also may enhance susceptibility to the disease (528, 559).

Treatment. There is no specific treatment for phycomycosis. The majority of cases have been diagnosed at necropsy. In one instance the disease was diagnosed by biopsy and culture, and the patient recovered with control of her diabetes, desensitization with autogenous vaccine, and potassium iodide therapy (544). The surgical removal of a localized intracerebral septic formation, caused by a phycomycete, resulted in complete recovery (551).

In the absence of a known specific treatment, Amphotericin B should be used in proven cases of phycomycosis.

CLADOSPORIOSIS

Cladosporiosis is an infection of the brain caused by species of dematiaceous fungi, particularly by *Cladosporium trichoides* and rarely by *Hormodendrum pedrosoi* and *Hormodendrum dermatitidis.*

Binford and others (560) in 1952 described from Maryland the first case of brain abscess caused by *Cladosporium trichoides,* which appeared in the pus and abscess wall as branching, septate, brown hyphae. King and Collette (568), in the same year, described the second case of brain abscess caused by this fungus. Two additional cases

have been described in the United States; McGill and Breuck (570) in 1956 isolated a pigmented fungus but did not identify it, whereas Riley and Mann (571) in 1960 isolated and described *C. trichoides* from their patient with brain abscess.

Fukushiro and others (565) in 1957 were able to identify *Hormodendrum pedrosoi,* which they isolated from a brain abscess in a Japanese patient who also had cutaneous chromoblastomycosis. A previous isolation of *H. pedrosoi,* which had been identified initially as *C. trichoides,* had been made from a patient seen in the Congo by Lucasse and others (569) in 1954. Recently Shimazono and others (574) have reported the isolation of *Hormodendrum dermatitidis* from a brain abscess of the second patient to be seen in Japan.

Morphology. Regardless of the species causing the brain abscess, they all appear as branching, septate, brown hyphae in the pus and tissue. Individual cells in the hyphae may assume a dumbbell shape and become swollen and rounded or the hyphae may appear moniliform. Such hyphae are seen readily in the pus when a drop of the exudate is mounted on a slide under a coverglass (Fig. 31). No special staining is necessary for tissue sections, since the brown-pigmented hyphae are easily detected. Cultures

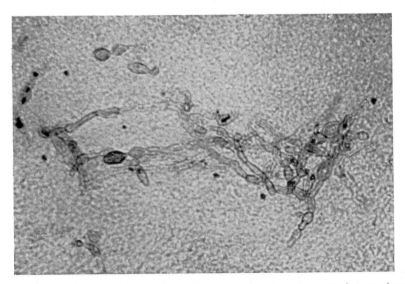

Fig. 31. *Cladosporium trichoides.* Brown hyphae and chlamydospores in pus from brain abscess. × 750.

are necessary for species identification of the fungus responsible for the infection.

Cultural Characteristics. *Cladosporium trichoides* develops an olive-gray to olive-brown colony on Sabouraud's glucose agar. The surface is velvety and develops radial folds in old cultures. The slow-spreading growth of the colony (4 cm. in two weeks) is typical of that for cultures of *Hormodendrum pedrosoi* and not of that for the rapid-growing, large, powdery colonies of saprophytic *Cladosporium* species (Fig. 32).

Sporulation is of the *Cladosporium* type, with septate conidiophores bearing long-branched chains of conidia (Fig. 33). The conidia are elliptical, 2 to 2.5 μ by 4 to 7 μ, brown, smooth-walled, and separated in the chain by the typical disjunctors seen in *Cladosporium* species.

The biochemical activity of cultures of *C. trichoides* differentiates this species from saprophytic strains. *C. trichoides* does not liquefy gelatin or Löffler's coagulated serum, coagulate milk, digest starch, or utilize tributyrine and cellulose. Saprophytic species are positive in these tests, with the exception of tributyrine and cellulose (564).

Resistance. Nothing is known about the possible susceptibility or resistance of *C. trichoides* to various antibiotics or chemotherapeutic agents. It is more thermophilic,

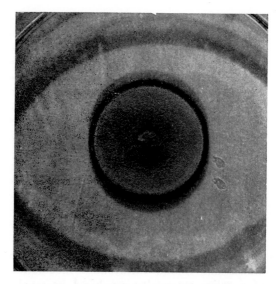

Fig. 32. *Cladosporium trichoides.* Colony on potato dextrose agar at room temperature for 14 days. (From Dr. C. W. Emmons, National Institutes of Health, Bethesda, Maryland.)

however, than other known pathogenic dematiaceous fungi. Although its optimum temperature for growth is 37°-38° C., its maximum temperature for growth is 42°-43° C. (2).

Fungus Metabolites. No exotoxins or endotoxins have been reported for *C. trichoides.*

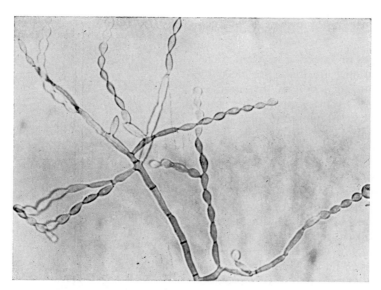

Fig. 33. *Cladosporium trichoides.* Conidiophore showing branching chains of conidia. × 690. (From Emmons and others. *Medical Mycology,* Lea & Febiger.)

Antigenic Structure. Seeliger (572) reported on the antigenic structure of some of the so-called black yeasts. *C. trichoides* antigen did not react in a precipitin test with antiserum against *Pullularia pullulans, Torula bergerii, Cladosporium werneckii,* or *Phialophora jeanselmei.* Seeliger and others (573) showed antigenic grouping of these dematiaceous fungi could be determined by serologic methods.

Spontaneous Infections in Animals. There have been no reports of spontaneous infections in animals. *C. trichoides* has been isolated only from disease of humans.

Experimental Infection in Laboratory Animals. Binford and others (560) reported *C. trichoides* to be pathogenic for the mouse and rabbit. Intravenous inoculation of a saline suspension produced brain abscesses in these animals. Duque (562, 563) also reported dissemination to the brain when mice were inoculated intraperitoneally with *C. trichoides.* Shimazono and others (574) found their isolate of *H. dermatitidis* to produce brain abscesses in mice following intravenous inoculation. Iwata and Wada (566) inoculated mice and guinea pigs intraperitoneally with their isolate of *Hormodendrum pedrosoi.* They describe fatal systemic infections in these animals with abscesses "in the liver, spleen, mesentery and other internal organs, the kidney, however, being not so much affected." No mention was made of lesions in the brain of these animals.

Clinical Types of Infection in Man. The signs and symptoms are those produced by any space-occupying lesion in the brain or may be those of a chronic meningitis. In a review of 23 cases Shimazono and others (574) found headache, drowsiness, hemiplegia and meningeal signs to be the most prominent. In 17 of these cases the patients showed loss of mobility, with 12 demonstrating hemiplegia; 14 complained of headache; 9 had fever; 8 were disoriented; 7 had meningeal signs; and 3 each had disturbance of vision, convulsive seizures, and ataxia.

Transmission. *Cladosporium trichoides* probably occurs in nature. Infection by pulmonary inhalation of spores with eventual dissemination to the brain by the blood stream is the most likely route to cerebral infection. Experimental infection of mice by intravenous inoculation of *C. trichoides* would seem to prove the above assumption. Also, an abscess in the lung has been noted in one instance of human infection from which *C. trichoides* was isolated from both the lung and the brain (567).

Treatment. There has been no report of successful therapy for this infection. Many drugs have been used without effect for the several patients whose infection had not been diagnosed until autopsy or surgical removal of the abscess. In the first case reported by Binford and others (560) the patient remained well following surgery.

REFERENCES

CRYPTOCOCCOSIS

1. Abrahams, I., and Gilleran, T. G. J. Immunol., 85:629, 1960.
2. —— and others. J. Immunol., 89:684, 1962.
3. Ajello, L. Am. J. Hyg., 67:72, 1958.
4. Aschner, M., and others. Nature, 156:295, 1945.
5. Benham, R. W. J. Infect. Dis., 57:255, 1935.
6. —— Mycologia, 27:496, 1935.
7. —— Proc. Soc. Exper. Biol. & Med., 89:243, 1955.
8. —— Bact. Rev., 20:189, 1956.
9. Bloomfield, N., and others. Proc. Soc. Exper. Biol. & Med., 114:64, 1963.
10. Boshes, L. Dis. Nervous System, 21:253, 1960.
11. Busse, O. Centralbl. f. Bakt., 16:175, 1894.
12. —— Virchows Arch. f. path. Anat., 140:23, 1895.
13. Cawley, E. P., and others. J. Invest. Dermat., 14:327, 1950.
14. Collins, V. P. Am. J. Roentgenol., 63:102, 1950.
15. Cox, L. B., and Tolhurst, J. C. Human Torulosis, Melbourne, Australia, Melbourne University Press, 1946.
16. Crone, J. T., and others. Am. J. Path., 13:863, 1937.
17. Curtis, F. Ann. Inst. Pasteur, 10:449, 1896.
18. Dormer, B. A., and others. J. Thoracic Surg., 14:322, 1945.
19. Drouhet, E., and Segretain, G. Compt. rend. Acad. sc., 228:424, 1949.
20. —— and Mariat, F. Compt. rend Acad. sc., 230:319, 1950.
21. —— and Aubert, J. P. Ann. Inst. Pasteur, 79:891, 1950.
22. Einbinder, J. M., and others. J. Invest. Dermat., 22:279, 1954.
23. Emmons, C. W. J. Bact., 62:685, 1951.
24. —— Am. J. Hyg., 62:227, 1955.
25. —— Pub. Health Reports, 75:362, 1960.
26. Evans, E. E. Proc. Soc. Exper. Biol. & Med., 71:644, 1949.
27. —— J. Immunol., 64:423, 1950.

28. ―――― and Kessel, J. F. J. Immunol., 67: 109, 1951.
29. ―――― and Mehl, J. W. Science, 114:10, 1951.
30. ―――― and Theriault, R. J. J. Bact., 65: 571, 1953.
31. ―――― and others. J. Bact., 66:287, 1953.
32. ―――― and others. Proc. Soc. Exper. Biol. & Med., 93:257, 1956.
33. ―――― Proc. Soc. Exp. Biol. & Med., 101: 760, 1959.
34. ―――― Ann. New York Acad. Sc., 89:184, 1960.
35. ―――― Fungi and Fungous Diseases, Dalldorf, G., ed., Springfield, Ill., Charles C Thomas, 1962, p. 187.
36. Fitzpatrick, M. J., and Poser, C. M. Arch. Int. Med., 106:261, 1960.
37. Flu, P. C., and Woensdregt, M. M. G. Meded. Bnrgerl. Geneesk. Dienst., Nederl. Indie, 6:1, 1918.
38. Foley, G. E., and Uzman, L. L. J. Infect. Dis., 90:38, 1952.
39. Gandy, W. M. Arch. Dermat. & Syph., 62: 97, 1950.
40. Gold, W., and others. Antibiotics Annual 1955-56, New York, Medical Encyclopedia, Inc., 1956, p. 579.
41. von Hansemann. Verhandl. d. deutsch. path. Gesellsch., 9:21, 1905.
42. Hasenclever, H. F., and Mitchell, W. O. Ann. New York Acad. Sc., 89:156, 1960.
43. Haugen, R. K., and Baker, R. D. Am. J. Clin. Path., 24:1387, 1954.
44. Hehre, E., and others. J. Biol. Chem., 177: 289, 1949.
45. Heine, J., and others. Beitr. z. path. Anat. u. z. allg. Path., 104:57, 1940.
46. Innes, J. R. M., and others. Am. J. Vet. Research, 13:469, 1952.
47. Johnson, C. W., and others. Antibiotics and Chemotherapy, 2:636, 1952.
48. Kao, C. J., and Schwarz, J. Am. J. Clin. Path., 27:652, 1957.
49. Klein, E. J. Hyg., 1:78, 1901.
50. Kligman, A. M., and Weidman, F. D. Arch. Dermat. & Syph., 60:726, 1949.
51. Kase, A., and Marshall, J. D., Jr. Am. J. Clin. Path., 34:52, 1960.
52. Kress, M. B., and Cantrell, J. R. Arch. Int. Med., 112:386, 1963.
53. Kuhn, L. R. Proc. Soc. Exper. Biol. & Med., 41:573, 1939.
54. ―――― Proc. Soc. Exper. Biol. & Med., 71: 341, 1949.
55. Levin, E. A. Arch. Int. Med., 59:667, 1937.
56. Littman, M. L., and Zimmerman, L. E. Cryptococcosis, New York, Grune & Stratton, 1956, p. 38.
57. ―――― and Schneierson, S. S. Am. J. Hyg., 69:49, 1959.
58. Louria, D. B. J. Exper. Med., 111:643, 1960.
59. ―――― and others. J. Exper. Med., 117: 509, 1963.
60. Mager, J., and Aschner, M. Proc. Soc. Exper. Biol. & Med., 62:71, 1946.
61. ―――― J. Bact., 53:283, 1947.
62. Marshall, M. J.A.M.A., 120:527, 1942.
63. ―――― Proc. Soc. Exper. Biol. & Med., 77: 775, 1951.

64. ―――― and Teed, R. W. Ann. Int. Med., 34:1277, 1951.
65. Neill, J. M., and others. J. Exper. Med., 89:93, 1949.
66. Ramel, E. Arch. F. Dermat. u. Syph., 148: 218, 1925.
67. Rappaport, B. Z., and Kaplan, B. Arch. Path. & Lab. Med., 1:720, 1926.
68. Reeves, D., and others. Arch. Int. Med., 68:57, 1941.
69. Reid, J. D. J. Bact., 58:777, 1949.
70. Salvin, S. B., and Smith, R. F. Proc. Soc. Exper. Biol. & Med., 108:498, 1961.
71. Sanfelice, F. Ann. Igiene Sperimentale, 4: 463, 1894.
72. ―――― Ann. Igiene Sperimentale, 5:239, 1895.
73. ―――― Sez. Chirurg., 2:204, 1895.
74. ―――― Centralbl. f. Bakt., 18:521, 1895.
75. ―――― Ztschr. f. Hyg., 29:463, 1898.
76. Schmidt, E. G., and others. Arch. Biochem., 26:15, 1950.
77. Seabury, J., and others. Arch. Int. Med., 102:960, 1958.
78. Seeliger, H. P. R. J. Bact., 72:127, 1956.
79. Shapiro, L. L., and Neal, J. B. Arch. Neurol. & Psychiat., 13:174, 1925.
80. Simon, J., and others. J. Am. Vet. Med. A., 122:31, 1953.
81. ―――― Am. J. Vet. Research, 60:394, 1955.
82. Smith, G. W., and others. South. M. J., 53:305, 1960.
83. Solotorovsky, M., and Bugie, E. J. J. Immunol., 60:497, 1948.
84. Stoddard, J. L., and Cutler, E. C. Rockefeller Inst. M. Research, 25:1, 1916.
85. Tsuchiya, T., and others. Sabouraudia, 2: 209, 1963.
86. Urbach, E., and Zach, F. Arch. f. Dermat. u. Syph., 162:401, 1930.
87. Utz, J. P., and others. Antibiotic Annual, 1958-59, New York, Medical Encyclopedia, Inc., 1959, p. 628.
88. Uzman, L. L., and others. J. Infect. Dis., 98:208, 1956.
89. Vandeputti, J., and others. Antibiotics Annual, 1955-56, New York, Medical Encyclopedia, Inc., 1956, p. 587.
90. Vogel, R. A., and others. J.A.M.A., 178: 921, 1961.
91. Vuillemin, P. Rev. Gen. Sc., 12:732, 1901.
92. Weis, J. D. J. Med. Res. (New Series), 2:280, 1902.
93. Whiffen, A. J. J. Bact., 56:283, 1948.
94. Zimmerman, L. E., and Rappaport, H. Am. J. Clin. Path., 24:1050, 1954.

CANDIDIASIS

95. Adriano, S. M., and Schwarz, J. Am. J. Path., 31:859, 1955.
96. Almon, L., and Stovall, W. D. J. Infect. Dis., 55:12, 1934.
97. Andriole, V. T., and Hasenclever, H. F. Yale J. Biol. & Med., 35:96, 1962.
98. Bakerspiegel, A. J. Bact., 83:694, 1962.
99. ―――― Canadian J. Microbiol., 9:909, 1963.
100. Benham, R. W. J. Infect. Dis., 49:183, 1931.
101. Berkhout, C. M. De Schimmelgeslachten Monilia, Oidium, Oospora en Torula Scheveningen, Edauw & Johannissen, 1923.

102. Boggs, D. R., and others. Arch. Int. Med., 107:354, 1961.
103. Candidiasis (Moniliasis) and Its Management with Mycostatin. Monographs on Therapy, 2:1-98, 1957.
104. Carter, B., and others. Am. J. Obst. & Gynec., 39:213, 1940.
105. Chakravarty, S., and Sandhu, R. S. Acta Tubercul. Pneumol. Scandinavica, 42:198, 1962.
106. Dawson, C. O. Sabouraudia, 1:214, 1962.
107. Diddens, H. A., and Lodder, J. Die anaskosporogenen Hefen, Zweite Hälfte, Amsterdam, N. V. Noord-Hollandsche Uitgevers Maatschappij, 1942.
108. Drake, C. H. J. Immunol., 50:185, 1945.
109. Ekmen, H. Turkish Bull. Hyg. & Exp. Biol., 22:18, 1962.
110. Fuentes, C. A., and others. Mycopath. & Mycol. Appl., 6:176, 1952.
111. Geiger, A. J., and others. Yale J. Biol. & Med., 18:259, 1946.
112. Goldman, L., and Schwarz, J. Acta Dermato Venereol., 42:314, 1962.
113. Gordon, M. A. J. Invest. Dermat., 31:123, 1958.
114. ——— Fungi and Fungous Diseases, Dalldorf, G., ed., Springfield, Ill., Charles C Thomas, 1962, p. 207.
115. ——— and Little, G. N. Sabouraudia, 2:171, 1963.
116. Halpert, B., and Wilkins, H. J.A.M.A., 130:932, 1946.
117. Harrell, E. R., and Thompson, G. R. Ann. Int. Med., 49:207, 1958.
118. Hasenclever, H. F. J. Bact., 78:105, 1959.
119. ——— and Mitchell, W. O. J. Bact., 82:570, 1961.
120. ——— and Mitchell, W. O. J. Bact., 82:578, 1961.
121. ——— and Mitchell, W. O. Sabouraudia, 2:201, 1963.
122. ——— and others. J. Bact., 82:574, 1961.
123. Hazen, E. L., and Brown, R. Proc. Soc. Exper. Biol. & Med., 76:93, 1951.
124. Hiatt, J. S., and Martin, D. S. J.A.M.A., 130:205, 1946.
125. Hill, D. W., and Gebhardt, L. P. Proc. Soc. Exper. Biol. & Med., 92:640, 1956.
126. Hurley, R., and Winner, H. I. J. Path. & Bact., 86:75, 1963.
127. Kaplan, W., and Kaufman, L. Sabouraudia, 1:137, 1961.
128. Keiper, T. W. Am. J. Med. Tech., 4:175, 1938.
129. Kemp, G., and Solotorovsky, M. J. Immunol., 86:777, 1962.
130. Kesten, H. D., and others. J. Exper. Med., 52:813, 1930.
131. ——— and Mott, E. J. Infect. Dis., 50:459, 1932.
132. Kligman, A. M., and Lewis, F. S. Proc. Soc. Exper. Biol. & Med., 82:399, 1953.
133. Kozinn, P. J., and others. Am. J. Dis. Child., 99:31, 1960.
134. Kroetz, F. W., and others. New England J. Med., 266:592, 1962.
135. Kunstadter, R. H., and others. J.A.M.A., 149:829, 1952.
136. Kunz, C. Schweiz. Z. Path., 21:892, 1958.
137. ——— Zentralbl. Bakt., 172:446, 1958.

138. Lägenbeck, B. Neue Notizen aus dem Gebiete der Natur und Heilkunde (Froriep), 252:145, 1839.
139. Langeron, M., and Guerra, P. Ann. de parasitol., 16:36, 162, 429, 481, 1938.
140. Lodder, J., and Kreger-Van Rij, N. J. W. The Yeasts. A Taxonomic Study, 1st ed., New York, Interscience Publishers, 1952.
141. Louria, D. B. Antibiotic Med. & Clin. Therapy, 5:295, 1958.
142. ——— Ann. New York Acad. Sc., 98:617, 1962.
143. ——— and Browne, H. G. Ann. New York Acad. Sc., 89:39, 1960.
144. ——— and Dineen, P. J.A.M.A., 174:273, 1960.
145. ——— and others. Sabouraudia, 2:271, 1963.
146. ——— and others. Proc. Soc. Exper. Biol. & Med., 115:93, 1964.
147. MacLaren, J. A., and Armen, D. Am. J. Clin. Path., 30:411, 1958.
148. Martin, D. S., and others. J. Bact., 34:99, 1937.
149. ——— and Jones, C. P. J. Bact., 39:609, 1940.
150. Meyer, E., and Ordal, Z. T. J. Bact., 52:615, 1946.
151. Mourad, S., and Friedman, L. J. Bact., 81:550, 1961.
152. Negroni, P. Rev. d. Inst. bact., Buenos Aires, 7:568, 1936.
153. Newcomer, V. D., and others. Antibiotics Ann., 1954-55, New York, Medical Encyclopedia, Inc., 1955, p. 686.
154. ——— and others. J. Chronic Dis., 9:353, 1959.
155. Neytcheff, S. Zentral. Bakt. Parasit. Infektionskrank. u. Hyg., 190:132, 1963.
156. Nickerson, W. J., and Mankowski, Z. J. Infect. Dis., 92:20, 1953.
157. Pagano, J., and others. Antibiot. Ann., 1957-58, p. 137, 1958.
158. Pearl, M. A. Am. Heart J., 60:345, 1960.
159. Richart, R. R., and Dummin, G. J. New England J. Med., 263:474, 1960.
160. Ridley, M. F. Australian J. Dermat., 5:209, 1960.
161. Robin, C. Histoire naturelle des végétaux parasites qui croissent sur l'homme et sur animaux vivants, Paris, J. B. Baillière, 1853.
162. Rosenthal, S. A., and Furnari, D. J. Invest. Dermat., 34:229, 1960.
163. Roth, F. J., and others. J. Immunol., 78:122, 1951.
164. Salvin, S. B. J. Immunol., 69:89, 1952.
165. ——— and others. J. Infect. Dis., 90:177, 1952.
166. Sarewiltz, A. B. Ann. Int. Med., 42:1187, 1955.
167. Seeliger, H. Ztschr. f. Hyg. u. Infectionskr., 141:488, 1955.
168. Seligmann, E. Proc. Soc. Exper. Biol. & Med., 83.
169. Skinner, C. E., and Fletcher, D. W. Bact. Rev., 24:397, 1960.
170. Solotorovsky, M., and others. Antibiotics & Chemotherapy, 4:165, 1954.
171. Sternberg, T. H., and others. Antibiotics Annual, 1955-56, New York, Medical Encyclopedia, Inc., 1956, p. 566.

172. Stone, K., and Garrod, L. P. J. Path. & Bact., 34:429, 1931.
173. Taschdjian, C. L. Mycologia, 49:332, 1957.
174. ―――― and Kozinn, P. J. J. Pediat., 50: 426, 1957.
175. ―――― and others. J. Dis. Child., 99:212, 1960.
176. Taubert, H. D., and Smith, A. G. J. Lab. & Clin. Med., 55:820, 1960.
177. Tsuchiya, T., and others. Jap. J. Exp. Med., 24:95, 1954.
178. ―――― and others. Jap. J. Exp. Med., 25: 15, 1955.
179. ―――― and others. Jap. J. Exp. Med., 25: 75, 1955.
180. ―――― and others. Yokohama Med., Bull., 7:127, 1956.
181. ―――― and others. Jap. J. Med. Sci. & Biol., 9:103, 1956.
182. ―――― and others. Mycopath. & Mycol. Appl., 10:191, 1959.
183. ―――― and others. Studies on Candidiasis in Japan. Research Committee of Candidiasis, Japan, Feb. 1961, p. 34.
184. Uden, N. van, and others. J. Gen. Microbiol., 15:151, 1956.
185. Utz, J. P., and others. Antibiotics Ann., 1957-58, New York, 1958, Medical Encyclopedia, Inc., p. 65.
186. ―――― and others. Antibiotics Ann., 1958-59, New York, 1959, Medical Encyclopedia, Inc., p. 628.
187. Vogel, R. A., and Collins, M. E. Proc. Soc. Exper. Biol. & Med., 89:138, 1955.
188. Walker, L., and Huppert, M. Am. J. Clin. Path., 33:190, 1960.
189. Weld, J. T. Arch. Dermat. & Syph., 67:473, 1953.
190. Winter, W. D., and Foley, G. E. J. Infect. Dis., 98:150, 1956.
191. Wright, E. T., and Graham, J. H. J.A.M.A., 163:92, 1957.
192. Yen, A. C. H., and Kurotchkin, T. J. J. Infect. Dis., 56:238, 1935.
193. Young, G. J. Infect. Dis., 102:104, 1958.
194. Zimmerman, S. L. J.A.M.A., 135:145, 1947.
195. Zopf, W. Die Pilze, Breslau, E. Trewendt, 1890.

BLASTOMYCOSIS

196. Abernathy, R. S. Ann. Int. Med., 51:707, 1959.
197. Ball, O. G., and others. Am. J. Hyg., 72: 231, 1960.
198. Benbrook, E. A., and others. J. Am. Vet. Med. A., 112:475, 1948.
199. Benham, R. W. Arch. Dermat. & Syph., 30:385, 1934.
200. Bernheim, R. J. Bact., 44:533, 1942.
201. Brody, M. Arch. Dermat. & Syphil., 56: 529, 1947.
202. Cherniss, E. I., and Waisbren, B. A. Ann. Int. Med., 44:105, 1956.
203. Chick, E. W., and others. Am. J. M. Sc., 231:253, 1956.
204. Colbert, J. W., and others. J. Invest. Dermat., 14:71, 1950.
205. Conant, N. F. Proc. Sixth Pacific Sc. Cong., 5:853, 1939.

206. Conti-Diaz, I. A., and Mackinnon, J. E. Ann. Fac. Med., Montevideo, 46:280, 1961.
207. Cross, F. W., and Howell, A., Jr. Pub. Health Reports, 63:179, 1948.
208. Curtis, A. C., and Bocobo, F. C. J. Chronic Dis., 5:404, 1957.
209. ―――― and Harrell, E. R. Arch. Dermat. & Syph., 66:676, 1952.
210. Denton, J. F., and others. Science, 133: 1126, 1961.
211. Derbes, V. J., and Krafchuk, J. D. Bull. Tulane Med. Fac., 17:157, 1958.
212. DiSalvo, A. F., and Denton, J. F. J. Bact., 85:927, 1963.
213. Dyson, J. E., and Evans, E. E. J. Invest. Dermat., 24:447, 1955.
214. Editorial, J.A.M.A., 154:588, 1954.
215. Emmons, C. W., and others. Pub. Health Reports, 60:1383, 1945.
216. Foster, J. W., and Woodruff, H. B. Arch. Biochem., 3:241, 1943.
217. Gilardi, G. L., and Laffer, N. C. J. Bact., 83:219, 1962.
218. Gilchrist, T. C. Johns Hopkins Hosp. Rep., 1:269, 1896.
219. ―――― and Stokes, W. R. J. Exper. Med., 3:53, 1898.
220. Harrell, E. R., and Curtis, A. C. Arch. Dermat. & Syphil., 76:561, 1957.
221. ―――― and Curtis, A. C. Am. J. Med., 27: 750, 1959.
222. ―――― and others. Ann. Int. Med., 43: 1076, 1955.
223. Heilman, F. R. J. Invest. Dermat., 9:87, 1947.
224. Howell, A., Jr. Pub. Health Rep., 62:631, 1947.
225. Johnson, J. R., and others. J. Am. Chem. Soc., 65:2005, 1943.
226. Kaufman, L., and Kaplan, W. J. Bact., 85: 986, 1963.
227. Keeney, E. L., and others. Bull. Johns Hopkins Hosp., 75:440, 1944.
228. Knight, R. A., and Marcus, S. Am. Rev. Tuberc., 77:983, 1958.
229. ―――― and others. Am. Rev. Resp. Dis., 80:264, 1959.
230. Kunkel, W. M., and others. Internat. Abstr. Surg., 99:1, 1954.
231. Levine, S., and Novak, M. J. Bact., 60:333, 1950.
232. ―――― J. Bact., 60:341, 1950.
233. ―――― J. Bact., 57:93, 1949.
234. ―――― and Ordal, I. J. Bact., 52:687, 1946.
235. Lockwood, W. R., and others. Ann. Int. Med., 57:553, 1962.
236. London, I. D. South. M. J., 49:1098, 1956.
237. Maldanado, W. E., and Felton, F. G. Am. Rev. Resp. Dis., 89: 1964.
238. Marcus, S., and others. Ann. New York Acad. Sc., 89:193, 1960.
239. Martin, D. S. J. Invest. Dermat., 4:471, 1941.
240. ―――― and Smith, D. T. Am. Rev. Tuberc., 39:275, 488, 1939.
241. ―――― J. Bact., 71:192, 1953.
242. Martinez Baez, M., and others. Rev. Inst. Salubr. Enferm. Trop., 14:225, 1954.
243. McDonough, E. S., and others. J. Lab. & Clin. Med., 55:116, 1960.

244. McMillen, S., and others. J. Invest. Dermat., 24:455, 1955.
245. Menges, R. W. Vet. Med., 55:45, 1960.
246. Newcomer, V. D., and others. J. Chronic Dis., 9:353, 1959.
247. Noojin, R. O., and Callaway, J. L. Arch. Dermat. & Syph., 47:620, 1943.
248. Peck, R. L. J. Am. Chem. Soc., 64:487, 1942.
249. ———— J. Biol. Chem., 134:403, 1940.
250. ———— and Hauser, C. R. J. Am. Chem. Soc., 60:2599, 1938.
251. ———— and others. J. Immunol., 38:449, 1940.
252. Salvin, S. B. Proc. Soc. Exper. Biol. & Med., 76:852, 1951.
253. ———— Mycologia, 41:311, 1949.
254. ———— Proc. Soc. Exper. Biol. & Med., 66:342, 1947.
255. Saslaw, S., and Campbell, C. C. Pub. Health Rep., 64:290, 1949.
256. ———— J. Lab. & Clin. Med., 33:811, 1948.
257. Schoenbach, E. G., and others. Ann. Int. Med., 37:31, 1952.
258. Schwartzman, R. M., and others. J.A.M.A., 171:2185, 1959.
259. Schwarz, J., and Baum, G. L. Am. J. Clin. Path., 21:999, 1951.
260. ———— Document. Med. Geograph. Trop., 5:29, 1953.
261. ———— and Goldman, L. Arch. Dermat. & Syph., 71:84, 1955.
262. Seabury, J. H., and Dascomb, H. E. Arch. Int. Med., 102:960, 1958.
263. Sivak, G. C., and Lick, R., Jr. J. Urol., 76:678, 1956.
264. Smith, D. T. Ann. Int. Med., 31:463, 1949.
265. Smith, J. G., and others. J.A.M.A., 158:641, 1955.
266. Snapper, I., and others. Tr. New York Acad. Sc., 14:269, 1952.
267. ———— and others. Am. J. Med., 15:603, 1953.
268. Sternberg, T. H., and others. Antibiotics Annual, 1955-56, New York, Medical Encyclopedia, Inc., 1956, p. 574.
269. Tenenberg, D. J., and Howell, A., Jr. Pub. Health Reports, 63:163, 1948.
270. Tompkins, V., and Schleifstein, J. Arch. Path., 55:432, 1953.
271. Utz, J. P., and others. Antibiotics Annual, 1957-58, New York, 1958, Medical Encyclopedia, Inc., p. 65.
272. Weaver, M., and others. J. Am. Vet. Med. A., 135:513, 1959.
273. Weed, L. A. Am. J. Clin. Path., 25:37, 1955.
274. Wilson, J. W., and others. Arch. Dermat. & Syph., 71:39, 1955.

SOUTH AMERICAN BLASTOMYCOSIS

275. Almeida, F. P. An. Fac. de med. da Univ. de São Paulo, 5:125, 1930.
276. ———— and Lacaz, C. S. Folia clin. et biol., 13:177, 1941.
277. ———— and Cunha, A. C. Arch. brasil. de med., 35:267, 1945.
278. ———— and Fernandez, M. An. Fac. de med. da Univ. de São Paulo, 20:155, 1944.
279. ———— and Forattini, O. P. Resenha clin. cient., 15:1, 1946.
280. ———— and others. O Hospital, 29:109, 1946.
281. Carbonell, L. M., and Pollock, L. Mycopathol. et Mycol. Appl., 19:184, 1963.
282. Carini, A. Rev. Soc. Sc. São Paulo, 3:120, 1908.
283. Chavarria, A. P., and others. Rev. med. Costa Rica, 16:369, 1949.
284. Conant, N. F., and Howell, A., Jr. J. Invest. Dermat., 5:353, 1942.
285. Conti-Diaz, I. A., and others. An. Fac. Med., Montevideo, 44:601, 1959.
286. Decourt, L. V., and others. Rev. Hosp. Clin., 1:247, 1946.
287. da Fonseca, O. Biol. d. Inst. clin. quir., 4:469, 1928.
288. ———— Rev. med.-cir. do Brasil, 37:124, 1929.
289. Fava Netto, C. Arg. Cir. Clin. Exper., 18:197, 1955.
290. ———— and others. Path. Microbiol., 24:192, 1961.
291. ———— and Acucena, R. Rev. Inst. Med. Trop. São Paulo, 3:161, 1961.
292. Fernandez, E. H. Rev. Med. Hondurena, 31:41, 1963.
293. Friedman, L., and Conant, N. F. Mycopath. et Mycol. Appl., 6:310, 317, 1953.
294. Gonçalves, A. P. Bol. Acad. Nac. Med., 134:81, 1962.
295. Gonzalez Ochoa, A., and Esquivel, E. Rev. med. d. Hosp. gen., 13:159, 1950.
296. Lacaz, C. S. Arch. urug. de med., cir. y especialidad., 27:167, 1945.
297. ———— Rev. Hosp. Clin., 3:11, 1948.
298. ———— O Hospital, 47:689, 1950.
299. ———— Mycopath. et Mycol. Appl., 6:241, 1953.
300. ———— and others. O Hospital, 33:693, 1948.
301. ———— and others. Rev. brasil. med., 3:356, 1946.
302. ———— and others. O Hospital, 43:163, 1955.
303. ———— and others. Rev. do Hospital las Clinicas, 10:436, 1955.
304. ———— and others. O Hospital, 53:89, 1958.
305. ———— and others. Rev. Inst. Med. Trop. São Paulo, 1:245, 1959.
306. ———— and others. Rev. Paulista Med., 54:357, 1959.
307. Lutz, A. Brasil-med., 22:121, 141, 1908.
308. Mackinnon, J. E. Tr. Roy. Soc. Trop. Med. & Hyg., 53:487, 1959.
309. Miranda, J. L., and Machado, J. Filho. O Hospital, 56:93, 1959.
310. Moore, M. Arch. Dermat. & Syph., 38:163, 1938.
311. ———— Rev. de biol. e higiene, 6:148, 1935.
312. Negroni, P. Rev. argent. dermatosif., 50:223, 1946.
313. Nino, F. L. Bol. Inst. clin. quir., 22:7, 1946.
314. Oliveira Ribeiro, D. Publ. Med., São Paulo, 22:36, 1940.
315. ———— Rev. paulista de med., 20:392, 1942.
316. Perry, H. O., and others. Arch. Dermat. & Syph., 70:477, 1954.
317. Splendore, A. Bul. Soc. path. exot., 5:313, 1912.

318. Trejos, A., and Remero, A. Rev. Biol. Trop., 1:63, 1953.
319. Valenzuela, C. T., and others. Rev. Colegio Med., Guatemala, 11:7, 1960.

COCCIDIOIDOMYCOSIS

320. Ajello, L., and others. J. Bact., 77:753, 1959.
321. Albert, B. L., and Sellers, T. F., Jr. Arch. Int. Med., 112:253, 1963.
322. Aronson, J. D., and others. Arch. Path., 34:31, 1942.
323. Baker, E. E., and others. Farlowia, 1:199, 1943.
324. Breslau, A. M., and Kubota, M. Y. J. Bact., 87:468, 1964.
325. Brooks, L. D., and Northey, W. T. J. Bact., 85:12, 1963.
326. Campbell, C. C., and Binkley, G. E. J. Lab. & Clin. Med., 42:896, 1953.
327. ——— Ann. New York Acad. Sc., 89:163, 1960.
328. Castleberry, M. W., and others. Arch. Path., 25:459, 1963.
329. Castro, A., and Trejos, A. Rev. Biol. Trop., 1(1):83, 1953.
330. Chinn, H. I., and others. Antibiotics and Chemotherapy, 4:982, 1954.
331. Converse, J. L. J. Bact., 72:784, 1956.
332. ——— J. Bact., 74:106, 1957.
333. ——— and Besemer, A. R. J. Bact., 78:231, 1959.
334. ——— and others. J. Bact., 84:46, 1962.
335. ——— and others. J. Bact., 83:871, 1962.
336. ——— and others. J. Bact., 87:81, 1964.
337. Cox, A. J., and Smith, C. E. Arch. Path., 27:717, 1939.
338. Dickson, E. C. California & West. Med., 47:151, 1937; Arch. Int. Med., 59:1029, 1937.
339. ——— and Gifford, M. A. Arch. Int. Med., 62:853, 1938.
340. Drouhet, E. Bull. Soc. Path. Exot., 54:1002, 1961.
341. Emmons, C. W. U.S. Pub. Health Reports, 57:109, 1942.
342. Fiese, M. J., and others. Ann. Int. Med., 43:255, 1955.
343. Foley, H. W., and others. Antibiotics, London, Oxford Univ. Press, 1949.
344. Forbus, W. D., and Bestebreurtje, A. M. Mil. Surgeon, 99:654, 1946.
345. Forsee, J. H., and Perkins, R. B. J.A.M.A., 155:1223, 1954.
346. Friedman, L., and Smith, C. E. Am. Rev. Tuberc., 74:245, 1956.
347. ——— and others. J. Lab. & Clin. Med., 42:438, 1953.
348. Georg, L. K., and others. Science, 114:387, 1951.
349. Gifford, M. A. Ann. Rep. Kern County Health Dept., 1935-36, p. 22.
350. Goldschmidt, E. P., and Taylor, G. W. J. Bact., 75:265, 1958.
351. Goldstein, D. M., and McDonald, J. B. J.A.M.A., 124:557, 1944.
352. Gordon, L. E., and others. Am. Rev. Tuberc., 72:64, 1955.
353. Hampson, C. R. J. Bact., 67:739, 1954.
354. Hassid, W. Z., and others. J. Biol. Chem., 149:303, 1943.

355. Hirsch, E. F., and D'Andrea, D. J. Infect. Dis., 40:634, 638, 1927.
356. ——— and Benson, H. J. Infect. Dis., 40:629, 1927.
357. Hugenholtz, P. G., and others. Am. J. Vet. Res., 19:433, 1958.
358. Hunter, R. C., Jr., and Mongan, E. S. U.S. Armed Forces Med. J., 9:1474, 1958.
359. Izenstark, J. L. South. M. J., 56:745, 1963.
360. Jorge, J. M., and others. Prensa med. argent., 33:630, 1946.
361. Kong, Y. M., and others. Sabouraudia, 2:131, 1963.
362. Landy, M., and others. Proc. Soc. Exper. Biol. & Med., 67:539, 1948.
363. Lavalle, P. Memorias. III Congreso Ibero Latino Americano de Dermatologia, p. 198, 1959.
364. Levine, H. B., and others. Tr. New York Acad. Sc., 22:436, 1960.
365. ——— and others. J. Immunol., 87:218, 1961.
366. Littman, M. L., and others. Am. J. Med., 24:568, 1958.
367. Lones, G. W., and Peacock, C. L. J. Bact., 79:308, 1960 (a).
368. ——— and Peacock, C. L. Ann. New York Acad. Sc., 89:102, 1960 (b).
369. Looney, J. M., and Stein, T. New England J. Med., 242:77, 1950.
370. Lubarsky, R., and Plunkett, O. A. J. Bact., 70:182, 1955.
371. Maddy, K. T. Vet. Med., 54:233, 1959.
372. McNall, E. G., and others. J. Invest. Dermat., 34:213, 1960.
373. O'Hern, E. M., and Henry, B. S. J. Bact., 72:632, 1956.
374. Ophüls, W., and Moffitt, H. C. Philadelphia M. J., 5:1471, 1900.
375. ——— J. Exper. Med., 6:443, 1905.
376. Pappagianis, D., and others. Am. Rev. Resp. Dis., 82:244, 1960.
377. ——— and others. J. Immunol., 86:28, 1961.
378. ——— and others. J. Bact., 82:714, 1961.
379. Perry, D. M., and Kirby, M. M. Arch. Int. Med., 105:929, 1960.
380. Plunkett, O. A., and others. Sabouraudia, 3:16, 1963.
381. Posadas, A. An. Circ. Med. Argentine, 15:585, 1892.
382. Puckett, T. F. Am. Rev. Tuberc., 70:320, 1954.
383. Rappaport, F. T., and others. J. Immunol., 84:368, 1960.
384. ——— and others. J. Immunol., 84:358, 1960.
385. Rixford, E. Occidental M. Times, 8:704, 1894.
386. ——— and Gilchrist, T. C. Johns Hopkins Hosp. Rep., 1:209, 1896.
387. Roessler, W. G., and others. J. Infect. Dis., 79:12, 1946.
388. Rosenthal, S. R., and Elmore, F. H. Am. Rev. Tuberc., 61:95, 1950.
389. ——— and Routien, J. B. Arch. Int. Med., 80:343, 1947.
390. Salvin, S. B., and Smith, R. F. J. Infect. Dis., 105:45, 1959.
391. Smith, C. E., and Saito, M. T. J. Chronic Dis., 1957.

392. Smith, C. E., and others. J.A.M.A., 160: 546, 1956.
393. ——— and others. J.A.M.A., 132:833, 1946.
394. Smith, H. Am. J. Path., 24:223, 1948.
395. Spaur, C. L. Am. J. Clin. Path., 26:689, 1956.
396. Stewart, R. A., and Kimura, F. J. Infect. Dis., 66:212, 1940.
397. Stiles, G. W., and Davis, C. L. J.A.M.A., 119:765, 1942.
398. Tabert, J. E., and others. Am. J. Path., 28: 901, 1952.
399. Vogel, R. A., and others. Am. Rev. Tuberc., 70:498, 1954.
400. Utz, J. P., and others. Antibiotics Annual, 1958-59, New York, Medical Encyclopedia, Inc., 1959, p. 628.
401. Wernicke, R. Centralbl. f. Bakt., 12:859, 1892.

HISTOPLASMOSIS

402. Ajello, L., and Runyon, L. C. J. Bact., 66: 34, 1953.
403. ——— and Zeidberg, L. D. Science, 113: 662, 1951.
404. Aspin, J. Am. Rev. Resp. Dis., 85:444, 1962.
405. Blumberg, R. W., and others. Pediatrics, 3:296, 1949.
406. Bunnell, I. L., and Furcolow, M. L. Pub. Health Rep., 63:299, 1948.
407. Campbell, C. C. J. Bact., 54:263, 1947.
408. ——— Pub. Health Rep., 64:551, 1949.
409. ——— Proc. Soc. Exper. Biol. & Med., 70: 562, 1949.
410. ——— Pub. Health Rep., 66:16, 1951.
411. ——— Pub. Health Rep., 66:570, 1951.
412. Campbell, C. C., and Binkley, G. E. J. Lab. & Clin. Med., 42:896, 1953.
413. ——— and others. Antibiotics and Chemotherapy, 4:406, 1954.
414. Campins, H., and others. J. Trop. Med., 5:690, 1956.
415. Cawley, E. P., and Curtis, A. C. J. Invest. Dermat., 11:443, 1948.
416. Chin, T. D. Y., and others. South. M. J., 49:785, 1956.
417. Christie, A., and Peterson, J. C. Am. J. Pub. Health, 35:1131, 1945.
418. Cozad, G. C. J. Immunol., 81:368, 1958.
419. ——— and Larsh, H. W. J. Immunol., 85: 389, 1960.
420. Cross, F. W., and Howell, A., Jr. Pub. Health Reports, 63:179, 1948.
421. Curtis, A. C., and Grekin, J. N. J.A.M.A., 134:1217, 1947.
422. Darling, S. T. J.A.M.A., 46:1283, 1906.
423. Da Rocha-Lima, H. Zentralbl. Bakt., 67: 233, 1913.
424. DeMonbreun, W. A. Am. J. Trop. Med., 14:93, 1934; 19:565, 1939.
425. Edwards, P. Q., and Kiaer, J. H. J. Trop. Med., 5:235, 1956.
426. ——— and others. Am. Rev. Resp. Dis., 83:528, 1961.
427. ——— and Palmer, C. E. Pub. Health Reports, 78:241, 1963.
428. Emmons, C. W. Pub. Health Rep., 64:892, 1949.
429. ——— Am. J. Pub. Health, 40:436, 1950.
430. ——— Bull. New York Acad. Med., 31: 627, 1955.
431. ——— and others. Am. J. Hyg., 61:40, 1955.
432. ——— and Greenhill, A. M. Sabouraudia, 2:18, 1962.
433. Furcolow, M. L., and Brasher, C. A. Am. Rev. Tuberc., 73:609, 1956.
434. ——— and Grayston, J. T. Am. Rev. Tuberc., 68:307, 1953.
435. ——— and others. Pub. Health Rep., 63: 169, 1948.
436. ——— Pub. Health Rep., 62:1711, 1947.
437. Grayston, J. T., and Furcolow, M. L. Am. J. Pub. Health, 43:665, 1953.
438. ——— and others. Science, 114:323, 1951.
439. Greene, C. H., and others. Proc. Soc. Exper. Biol. & Med., 105:140, 1960.
440. Hansen, A. E., and Beene, M. L. Proc. Soc. Exper. Biol. & Med., 77:365, 1951.
441. Hansmann, G. H., and Schenken, J. R. Science, 77:Suppl. No. 2002, p. 8, 1933.
442. ——— Am. J. Path., 10:731, 1934.
443. Heiner, D. C. Pediatrics, 22:616, 1958.
444. Hill, G. B., and Campbell, C. C. J. Lab. & Clin. Med., 48:255, 1956.
445. Howell, A., Jr., and Kipkie, G. F. Proc. Soc. Exper. Biol. & Med., 75:121, 1950.
446. Howson, C. R., and others. Ann. Int. Med., 44:985, 1956.
447. Jarvis, G. J., and McCulloch, C. Canad. M. A. J., 89:1270, 1964.
448. Kaufman, L., and Kaplan, W. J. Bact., 82: 735, 1961.
449. Kerung, J. M., and Yegian, D. J. Bact., 84: 577, 1962.
450. Klingberg, W. G. J. Pediat., 36:728, 1950.
451. Knight, R. A., and others. Proc. Soc. Exper. Biol. & Med., 100:356, 1959.
452. Kunstadter, R. H., and others. J. Lab. & Clin. Med., 34:1290, 1949.
453. Larsh, H. W., and others. Am. J. Hyg., 63: 18, 1956.
454. Loewen, D. F., and others. Am. J. Med., 28:252, 1960.
455. Loosli, C. G. Med. Clin. N. Am., 39:171, 1955.
456. Mankiewicz, E., and others. Canad. M. A. J., 71:386, 1954.
457. Menges, R. W., and Kinter, L. D. North Am. Vet., 32:692, 1951.
458. Moore, M., and Jorstad, L. H. Ann. Otol. Rhin. & Laryng., 52:779, 1943.
459. Newcomer, V. D., and others. J. Chronic Dis., 9:353, 1959.
460. Norden, A. Proc. Soc. Exper. Biol. & Med., 70:218, 1949.
461. Northey, W. T., and Brooks, L. D. J. Bact., 84:577, 1962.
462. Palmer, C. E. Pub. Health Rep., 60:513, 1945.
463. ——— Pub. Health Rep., 61:475, 1946.
464. Pates, A. L. Science, 108:383, 1948.
465. Pine, L. J. Bact., 68:671, 1954.
466. ——— J. Bact., 74:239, 1957.
467. ——— and Peacock, C. L. J. Bact., 75: 167, 1958.
468. Prior, J. A., and Saslaw, S. Am. Rev. Tuberc., 66:588, 1952.

469. Puckett, T. F. Am. Rev. Tubercl., 67:453, 1953.
470. Resseler, J. J. C., and others. Ann. Soc. Belge. Méd. Trop., 5:801, 1962.
471. Richman, H. North Am. Vet., 29:710, 1948.
472. Rowley, D. A., and Huber, M. J. Infect. Dis., 96:174, 1955.
473. ———— J. Infect. Dis., 97:27, 1955.
474. ———— J. Immunol., 77:15, 1956.
475. ———— and Pine, L. J. Bact., 69:695, 1955.
476. Salvin, S. B. J. Bact., 59:312, 1950.
477. ———— Proc. Soc. Exper. Biol. & Med., 66:342, 1947.
478. ———— Proc. Soc. Exper. Biol. & Med., 76:852, 1951.
479. ———— J. Infect. Dis., 94:22, 1954.
480. ———— Tr. New York Acad. Sc., 18:462, 1956.
481. ———— and Furcolow, M. L. J. Lab. & Clin. Med., 43:259, 1954.
482. ———— and Ribi, E. Proc. Soc. Exper. Biol. & Med., 90:287, 1955.
483. ———— and Smith, R. F. J. Infect. Dis., 105:45, 1959.
484. Saslaw, S., and Campbell, C. C. Proc. Soc. Exper. Biol. & Med., 68:559, 1948.
485. ———— J. Lab. & Clin. Med., 33:811, 1948.
486. ———— Pub. Health Rep., 64:424, 1949.
487. ———— Am. J. Pub. Health, 40:427, 1950.
488. ———— J. Lab. & Clin. Med., 35:780, 1950.
489. ———— and Campbell, C. C. Proc. Soc. Exper. Biol. & Med., 82:698, 1953.
490. ———— and Carlisle, H. N. Proc. Soc. Exper. Biol. & Med., 97:700, 1958.
491. Schubert, J., and others. J. Lab. & Clin. Med., 41:91, 1953.
492. ———— and others. J. Bact., 69:558, 1955.
493. ———— and others. Am. Rev. Resp. Dis., 84:845, 1961.
494. Schwarz, J., and Furcolow, M. L. Am. J. Clin. Path., 25:261, 1955.
495. ———— and others. New England J. Med., 252:887, 1955.
496. Sorensen, L. J., and Evans, E. E. Proc. Soc. Exper. Biol. & Med., 87:339, 1954.
497. Straub, M., and Schwarz, J. Am. J. Clin. Path., 25:727, 1955.
498. Sutliff, W. D., and others. Arch. Int. Med., 92:571, 1953.
499. Tenenberg, D. J., and Howell, A., Jr. Pub. Health Rep., 63:163, 1948.
500. Vanbreuseghem, R. Mycologia, 45:803, 1953.
501. Wheeler, W. E., and others. Am. J. Dis. Child., 79:806, 1950.
502. White, F. C. Am. Rev. Tuberc., 72:274, 1955.

GEOTRICHOSIS

503. Bendove, R. A., and Ashe, B. I. Arch. Int. Med., 89:107, 1952.
504. Benham, R. W., and Hopkins, A. M. Arch. Dermat. & Syph., 28:532, 1933.
505. Carmichael, J. W. Mycologia, 49:820, 1957.
506. Cheek, C. W., and Barrett, J. T. Mycopath. & Mycol. Appl., 17:47, 1962.
507. Ciferri, R., and Redaelli, P. Ann. Mycologici, 27:243, 1929.

508. Conant, N. F., and others. Manual of Clinical Mycology, Philadelphia, W. B. Saunders Co., 1944.
509. Croft, C. C., and Black, L. A. J. Lab. & Clin. Med., 23:1259, 1938.
510. Dodge, C. W. Medical Mycology, St. Louis, C. V. Mosby Co., 1935, p. 217.
511. Fisher, C. V., and Arnold, L. Univ. Illinois Bull., 33:1, 1936.
512. Kaliski, S. R., and others. J.A.M.A., 148:1207, 1952.
513. Kunstadter, R. H., and others. Am. J. Dis. Child., 79:82, 1950.
514. ———— and others. Am. J. M. Sc., 211:583, 1946.
515. Langeron, M., and Talice, R. C. Ann. de parasitol., 10:1, 1932.
516. Link. Mag. Ges. Natur. Freunde Berlin, 3:17, 1809.
517. Minton, R., and others. Ann. Int. Med., 40:340, 1954.
518. Reeves, R. J. Am. J. Roentgenol., 45:513, 1941.
519. Schnoor, T. G. Am. J. Trop. Med., 19:163, 1939.
520. Smith, D. T. J. Thoracic Surg., 3:241, 1934.
521. Thjotta, Th., and Urdal K. Acta path. et microbiol. Scandinav., 26:673, 1949.
522. Thjotta, R., and others. Acta path. et microbiol. scandinav., 28:132, 1951.
523. Torheim, B. J. Sabouraudia, 2:146, 1963.
524. ———— Sabouraudia, 2:155, 1963.
525. ———— Sabouraudia, 2:292, 1963.
526. ———— Sabouraudia, 2:303, 1963.
527. Webster, B. H. Dis. Chest, 35:273, 1959.

PHYCOMYCOSIS

528. Baker, R. D. Am. J. Path., 32:287, 1956.
529. ———— and others. Lab. Invest., 11;1091, 1962.
530. Bauer, H., and others. Am. J. Med., 18:822, 1955.
531. ———— Yale J. Biol. & Med., 28:29, 1955.
532. Blaché, R., and others. Bull. Soc. Path. Exot., 54:56, 1961.
533. Bridges, C. H., and Emmons, C. W. J. Am. Vet. Med. A., 138:579, 1961.
534. Chick, E. W., and others. Antibiotics and Chemotherapy, 8:394, 506, 1958.
535. Christiansen, M. Virchows Arch. f. path. Anat., 273:829, 1929.
536. Davis, C. L., and others. J. Am. Vet. M. A., 126:261, 1955.
537. Elder, T. D., and Baker, R. D. Arch. Path., 61:159, 1956.
538. Emmons, C. W., and Bridges, C. H. Mycologia, 53:307, 1961.
539. Garrett, S. D. New Phytologist, 50:149, 1951.
540. Gitter, M., and Austwick, P. K. C. Vet. Record, 71:6, 1959.
541. Gleiser, C. A. J. Am. Vet. M. A., 123:441, 1953.
542. Gortner, R. A., and Blakeslee, A. F. Am. J. Physiol., 34:353, 1914.
543. Gregory, J. E., and others. Bull. Johns Hopkins Hosp., 73:405, 1943.
544. Harris, J. S. Pediatrics, 16:857, 1955.

545. Hutter, R. V. P.   Cancer, 12:330, 1959.
546. Jelliffe, D. B., and others.   J. Pediat., 59: 124, 1961.
547. LeCompte, P. M., and Meissner, W. A. Am. J. Path., 23:673, 1947.
548. Lichtheim, L.   Ztschr. f. klin. Med., 7:140, 1884.
549. Lie Kian Joe, and others.   Arch. Dermat., 74:378, 1956.
550. McCall, W., and Strobos, R. R. J.   Neurology, 7:290, 1957.
551. Muresan, A.   J. Clin. Path., 13:34, 1960.
552. Naumov, N. A.   *Clés des Mucorinées.* Translated from Russian by Buchet, S., and Muraview, I., Paris, Paul Lechevalier, 1939.
553. Nielsen, N.   Virchows Arch. f. path. Anat., 273:859, 1929.
554. Paltauf, A.   Virchows Arch. f. path. Anat., 102:543, 1885.
555. Schofield, R. A., and Baker, R. D.   Arch. Path., 61:407, 1956.
556. Skinner, C. E., Emmons, C. W., and Tsuchiya, H. M.   Molds, Yeasts, and Actinomycetes, 2nd ed., New York, John Wiley & Sons, Inc., p. 128, 1947.
557. Symeonidis, A., and Emmons, C. W.   Arch. Path., 60:251, 1955.
558. Tio Tiong Hoo and others.   Dermatologia Tropica, 1:23, 1962.
559. Zimmerman, L. E.   A. J. Clin. Path., 25:46, 1955.

CLADOSPORIOSIS

560. Binford, C. H., and others.   Am. J. Clin. Path., 22:535, 1952.
561. Borelli, D.   Riv. Anat. Patol. Oncol., 17: 615, 1960.
562. Duque, O.   Am. J. Clin. Path., 36:505, 1961.
563. ——— Riv. Latinoamerica Anat. Patol., 7: 101, 1963.
564. Fuentes, C. A., and Bosch, Z. E.   J. Invest. Dermat., 34:419, 1960.
565. Fukushiro, R., and others.   Press Méd., 65: 2142, 1957.
566. Iwata, K., and Wada, T.   Jap. J. Microbiol., 1:355, 1957.
567. Jaffé, R., and others.   Cited by Campins, H. Mycopath. and Mycol. Appl., 9:152, 1958.
568. King, A. B., and Collette, T. S.   Bull. Johns Hopkins Hosp., 91:298, 1952.
569. Lucasse, C., and others.   Ann. Soc. Belge Méd. Trop., 34:475, 1954.
570. McGill, H. C., Jr., and Breuck, J. W.   Arch. Path., 62:303, 1956.
571. Riley, O., Jr., and Mann, S. H.   Am. J. Clin. Path., 33:525, 1960.
572. Seeliger, H. P. R.   Zentr. Bakteriol. Parasitenk, Infek. Hyg., Abt I Orig., 167:396. 1957.
573. ——— and others.   Proc. 6th Inter. Congr. Trop. Med. Malaria, 4:636, 1959.
574. Shimazono, Y., and others.   Folia Psych. Neurol. Jap., 17:80, 1963.

80

Fungus Diseases Involving Skin and Subcutaneous Tissues

SPOROTRICHOSIS

Sporotrichosis, caused by *Sporotrichum schenckii,* is a chronic progressive infection of the skin and subcutaneous tissues characterized by a "sporotrichotic chancre" at the site of inoculation followed by the development and the formation of subcutaneous nodules along the lymphatics draining the primary lesions.

Schenck (47) in Baltimore isolated a fungus, *Sporotrichum* sp., from a patient with refractory subcutaneous abscesses on his arm. A second case in the United States was reported by Hektoen and Perkins (18), who named the fungus *Sporothrix schenckii.* Similar infections were found in France by de Beurmann and Ramond (2), and the fungus was named *Sporotrichum beurmanni* by Matruchot and Ramond (33). Several other species of *Sporotrichum* have been described from infections of man and animals, but they have been reduced to synonymy with *S. schenckii* by many investigators.

Morphology. *Sporotrichum schenckii* is rarely seen in human tissues or exudates unless stained by the Schiff-McManus technic (34). This Periodic Acid-Schiff stain for fungus in tissue stains the organisms red, and various background stains allow them to be seen easily (12). The organisms appear as fusiform bodies or round budding cells, 3 to 5 μ in diameter. Occasionally, asteroid bodies are seen (28). These are round, single budding cells, 5 to 10 μ in diameter, surrounded by an homogenous eosinophil-staining material. Infrequently, hyphal elements may be seen (28, 44). Cultures must be obtained, however, for a definitive diagnosis.

Cultural Characteristics. *S. schenckii* grows readily on Sabouraud's glucose agar at room temperature or on blood agar at 37° C. On Sabouraud's glucose agar, growth appears in four to five days as small, white to cream-colored colonies which rapidly enlarge, becoming smooth, leathery, and folded. Some strains remain cream colored, while other strains develop a brownish to black pigmentation (Fig. 1). Such colonies are very characteristic and diagnostic. Microscopically the mycelium is seen to be 1.5 to 2 μ in diameter with lateral branches of various lengths which support clusters (2 to 15) of pyriform conidia 2 to 4 by 2 to 6 μ in size (Fig. 2). Such spores also may be borne directly from the sides of hyphae in some strains.

When cultures are grown on cystine agar at 37° C. (5), they become soft, yeast-like and are composed of fusiform, round, oval, and budding cells similar to those seen in

Fig. 1. *Sporotrichum schenckii.* Colony on Sabouraud's glucose agar at room temperature for 12 days.

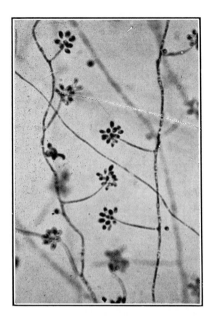

Fig. 2. *Sporotrichum schenckii.* Clusters of pyriform conidia from the ends of conidiophores. × 650. (From Conant and others. *Manual of Clinical Mycology,* 2nd ed., W. B. Saunders Co.)

lesions of infected animals (Fig. 3). The morphologic changes from mycelium to yeast have been studied in tissue culture (19).

Sugar fermentations are of no value in the differentiation of species (26, 36). In metabolic studies eight strains did not differ in their nitrogen metabolism; nitrogen of various amino acids, urea, and ammonium nitrate were utilized, and no single amino acid was essential for growth (25). However, Mariat and others (32) reported pyrimidine to be essential for growth. Previously, thiamine had been shown to be a requirement for growth (4).

Resistance. *S. schenckii* is killed at 56° C. for one hour. The growth of the fungus is inhibited by sulfanilamide and sodium sulfapyridine in concentrations of 500 to 1,000 mg. per 100 ml. of Sabouraud's agar (42), by Propamidine (11) in a concentration of 0.018 mg. per 20 ml. of agar, and by clavacin (23) and thiourea (10) but is not inhibited by penicillin (24). Streptomycin, from 0.01 to 2.5 mg. per milliliter of medium, stimulates growth of *S. schenckii* (6), while nystatin (31) inhibits growth of the yeast and mycelial phase of concentrations between 8 and 16 μg. per milliliter.

Fungus Metabolites. No endotoxins or exotoxins have been reported. Tyrosinase occurs in spore masses, and the black pigment which occurs in most strains is melanin in nature (41).

Antigenic Structure. Agglutinins can be demonstrated in the serums of human and experimental sporotrichosis (43). Lurie (27) has shown that different isolates of *Sporotrichum* are antigenically similar by agglutinin and agglutinin-absorption tests.

Kaden (21) has demonstrated precipitins to a carbohydrate extracted from yeast cells by an agar-gel diffusion technic.

Serologic studies in eleven human cases showed the precipitin test with autoclaved antigen to be positive in eight, the complement-fixation test to be positive in two, and the agglutination test to be positive in four (43).

Intracutaneous injections of saline suspensions of killed cultures (53) and carbohydrate obtained from cultures (14) elicit positive skin tests in 24 to 48 hours.

In experimental sporotrichosis, in mice soluble antigens from the peritoneal fluid and various tissues were found to precipitate in antisporotrichum rabbit serum (40). Also, capsules could be demonstrated on the

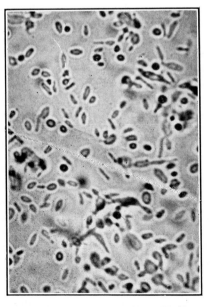

Fig. 3. *Sporotrichum schenckii.* Fusiform cells from cystine blood agar cultures at 37° C. × 762.

fungus cells recovered from infected mice (39).

Slight protection of mice against sporotrichosis follows immunization with formalin-killed antigen or preinfection with *S. schenckii* (17). The direct fluorescent antibody technic has been used for detecting *S. schenckii* in smears of exudates from animal and human lesions and in smears made from cultures (22).

Spontaneous Infections in Animals. Spontaneous infections have been found in horses (35, 45, 51) and dogs (15). Human infections may have resulted from contacts with infected animals or their products (35) and from the bite of an infected mouse (38) or rat (1).

Experimental Infections in Laboratory Animals. Mice, rats, guinea pigs, cats, and dogs may be infected experimentally by several routes of inoculation. The mouse and the rat show a marked orchitis in which the fungus may be seen in smears or may be cultured.

Sternberg and others (50) reported the localization of radioactive iodine (I^{131}) in sporotrichotic lesions in mice. Shintani and others (48) could not demonstrate a selective localization of radioactive iodine in any cellular zone of such lesions.

Howard and Orr (20) found that several strains isolated from nature were not pathogenic for laboratory animals, although they were morphologically identical and antigenically related to human pathogenic isolates.

Clinical Types of Infection in Man. In the monograph by de Beurmann and Gougerot (3), sporotrichosis was divided into six clinical types: lymphatic, disseminated, epidermal, mucosal, skeletal, and visceral. To these should be added the pseudoneoplastic form described by Smith (49). The localized lymphatic type of infection is seen most frequently in the United States. The primary lesion occurs on the hand or arm, where the fungus is introduced by trauma. The lesion begins as a hard inelastic nodule, which at first is pink but slowly changes to a purplish color and finally develops into a black necrotic ulcer. The lymphatics draining the area become cord-like, and chains of subcutaneous nodules develop along the lymphatic vessels. Such secondary nodules also may soften and ulcerate to become chronic ulcerating lesions. In contrast to tularemia, the patients with sporotrichosis have little if any fever and do not appear ill; the regional lymph nodes usually are not involved, with the possible exception of the epitrochlear gland.

The disseminated and visceral forms of the disease have been reported more frequently outside the United States (7, 8, 29).

However, sporotrichosis of the viscera, bones and joints should be considered in the differential diagnosis of infection of unknown etiology (30, 37). Not infrequently synovitis of the knee has been caused by *S. schenckii*.

Primary pulmonary sporotrichosis, caused by inhalation of infectious particles, must be more frequent than realized. Occasional reports of pulmonary infection (46) do not indicate the possible extent of self-limited infections. A suitable skin test antigen and its use in epidemiologic surveys, as for histoplasmosis and coccidioidomycosis, might provide the answer to the existence of benign infections.

Transmission. *Sporotrichum schenckii* occurs as a saprophyte in nature, where it can infect both man and animals. Man may become infected by wounds from plant materials, such as thorns and barbs, or by the handling of infected animals or contaminated dressings. Recently a number of infections acquired in the laboratory have come to our attention. Sporotrichosis occasionally assumes importance as an occupational disease (9, 13). The most remarkable epidemic of sporotrichosis, however, occurred in the gold mines in South Africa, where a total of 2,825 cases were reported (52). Males are infected more frequently than females, especially farmers, laborers, and horticulturists.

Biologic Products. Vaccines may be prepared from the tissue phase of *S. schenckii* from cystine agar cultures at 37° C. Heat-killed saline suspensions may be used for skin testing, agglutination reactions and for desensitization.

Treatment. Potassium iodide has a specific curative action in sporotrichosis. Large doses should be employed and continued for four to six weeks after apparent recovery. An occasional case may require supplementary vaccine therapy if a marked degree of hypersensitivity has developed during the infection. Successful treatment with stilbamidine and dihydroxystilbamidine has been reported (16, 37).

CHROMOBLASTOMYCOSIS

(Verrucous Dermatitis, Chromomycosis)

Chromoblastomycosis is an infection of the skin characterized by the development of warty or verrucous cutaneous lesions. The disease is caused by a variety of dematiaceous fungi: *Hormodendrum pedrosoi, H. compactum, H. dermatitidis, Cladosporium carrionii,* and *Phialophora verrucosa.*

Pedroso (84) in Brazil was the first to observe the disease; he noted characteristic dark brown bodies in a biopsy section. Although he isolated a darkly pigmented fungus and was aware of the fungus nature of the disease, he failed to report his observations (85). Lane (78) and Medlar (81) in Boston reported a new fungus, *Phialophora verrucosa,* which they isolated from lesions on the buttocks of an Italian patient in whose tissues they found spherical dark brown bodies. Pedroso and Gomes (85) then reported four Brazilian cases of "verrucous dermatitis" caused by *P. verrucosa.* Brumpt (61), however, renamed their fungus *Hormodendrum pedrosoi,* and Terra and others (93) named the disease "chromoblastomycosis." One of the fungi isolated from the four Brazilian cases, however, was found later to be *P. verrucosa* (83). The third etiologic agent to be identified with this disease was described from Puerto Rico as *Hormodendrum compactum* by Carrión (64).

Hormodendrum (Fonsecaea) *dermatitidis* has been reported from Japan (62) while *Cladosporium carrionii* has been reported from Venezuela, South Africa, and Australia (94).

Morphology. In spite of the variety of different fungi which have been isolated from chromoblastomycosis, they appear identical in clinical materials. They all appear in the pus, crusts, and in sections as thick-walled, dark brown, spherical bodies, 6 to 12 μ in diameter, which divide by septation rather than by budding (Fig. 4). The different

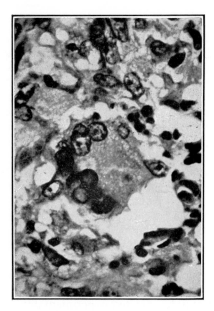

Fig. 4. *Hormodendrum pedrosoi.* Section of skin showing giant cell containing brown fungus bodies. × 736.

genera and species can be identified only in culture where typical spore formation occurs. Only three of the fungi which cause chromoblastomycosis will be discussed below; a full discussion of the known agents of this disease has been published by Carrión and Silva (65).

Cultural Characteristics. *Hormodendrum pedrosoi,* on Sabouraud's glucose agar at room temperature, is a slow-growing, flat colony covered with a felt-like, short aerial mycelium, dark green to brown or black in color (Fig. 5). Microscopically three types of spore formation are seen: (*a*) branching chains of ovoid olivaceous conidia from conidiophores of varying length, *Hormodendrum*-type (Fig. 6); (*b*) single ovoid conidia borne on the sides of swollen club-shaped ends of the conidiophores, *Acrotheca*-type (Fig. 7); and (*c*) small conidia borne from the cup-like tip of flask-shaped conidiophores, *Phialophora*-type (similar to Fig. 11). The prominence of each spore type varies with individual strains. Abortive perithecia have been reported in one strain (74).

The three types of spore production exhibited by *H. pedrosoi* in culture have caused confusion in the classification of this

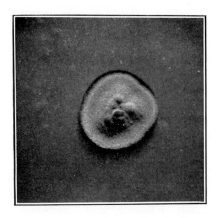

Fig. 5. *Hormodendrum pedrosoi.* Colony on Sabouraud's glucose agar at room temperature for 20 days.

fungus, and several attempts have been made to place *H. pedrosoi* in the single genus that would be acceptable (59, 63, 65, 83).

Hormodendrum compactum, on Sabouraud's glucose agar at room temperature, is a slow-growing, heaped, brittle colony covered with a coarse aerial mycelium, olive black in color (Fig. 8).Microscopically, subspherical conidia are borne in tight compact chain formation on the ends of conidio-

Fig. 6. *Hormodendrum pedrosoi.* Hormodendrum-type of conidiophore. × 400. (From Conant and others. *Manual of Clinical Mycology,* 2nd ed., W. B. Saunders Co.)

phores (Fig. 9), A *Phialophora* type of conidiophore also is developed by this fungus.

Phialophora verrucosa, on Sabouraud's glucose agar at room temperature, is a slow-growing, dark brown to black colony with olivaceous to gray aerial mycelium (Fig. 10). Microscopically the characteristic development of conidia from cup-like structures on the ends of flask-shaped conidiophores is diagnostic for this species (Fig. 11). Abortive perithecia also have been reported in one strain (54).

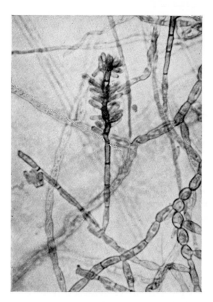

Fig. 7. *Hormodendrum pedrosoi.* Acrotheca type of conidiophore. × 400. (From Conant and others. *Manual of Clinical Mycology,* 2nd ed., W. B. Saunders Co.)

The biochemical activity of these fungi is of little help in their identification (37). Fuentes and Bosch (71) were able to show, however, that pathogenic strains in their biochemical activities differed from nonpathogenic saprophytic species of *Cladosporium;* the pathogenic strains did not liquefy gelatin or Löffler's medium, coagulate milk, digest starch, or utilize tributyrine and cellulose. The nonpathogenic strains were positive in all of these tests, except that they did not attack tributyrine or cellulose.

Resistance. All three fungi are killed at 56° C. for one hour. The tissue form of the fungus remains viable for 14 days in bi-

Fig. 8. *Hormodendrum compactum.* Colony on Sabouraud's glucose agar at room temperature for 41 days. (From Conant and others. *Manual of Clinical Mycology,* 2nd ed., W. B. Saunders Co.)

opsied tissue at 0° C. (9). Sodium sulfathiazole and sodium sulfamerazine were found to inhibit *H. pedrosoi* in a 100 mg. per cent concentration, but penicillin had no effect (75). Sodium caprylate and sodium undecylenate were found to be both fungistatic and fungicidal for *H. pedrosoi* (75).

Fungus Metabolites. No exotoxins or endotoxins have been reported for these fungi. A mixture of an ether-soluble and a water-soluble fraction from a culture of *H. pedrosoi* has been used as a skin-testing antigen (57). Ten patients with chromoblastomycosis gave positive delayed reactions, and 100 individuals, residents of the city of Havana, did not react to an intradermal injection of the antigen. The reaction was positive in 5 of 20 individuals who were residents of rural areas.

Antigenic Structure. Positive complement-fixation tests have been descibed by Martin and others (79). They found that several different fungus antigens and several serums from noninfected humans gave negative results in control tests and also that a close antigenic relationship existed between two morphologically different fungi, *H. pedrosoi* and *P. verrucosa,* in that a high titered serum from a patient with chromoblastomycosis caused by *H. pedrosoi* had complement-fixing antibodies for both fungi. Rabbits immunized with *H. pedrosoi, H. compactum,* and *P. verrucosa* produced complement-fixing antibodies for the homol-

ogous antigen; anti-*pedrosoi* rabbit serum also had complement-fixing antibodies for *H. compactum* and *P. verrucosa;* anti-*compactum* rabbit serum had complement-fixing antibodies for *H. pedrosoi* and *P. verrucosa;* but anti-*verrucosa* rabbit serum contained complement-fixing antibodies only for the homologous antigen (68).

Seeliger (88) and Seeliger and others (89) used agglutination, agglutinin-absorption, and precipitin tests for antigenic analyses of this group of fungi. Al-Doory and Gordon (56) used fluorescent antibody technics to distinguish *Cladosporium carrionii* from *Cladosporium bantianum.* Inaki (73) reported precipitin, precipitin-absorption, and agar-gel diffusion tests to give cross-reactions with antigens from 14 strains of these dematiaceous fungi.

Spontaneous Infections in Animals. As yet there have been no reports to indicate that these fungi cause natural infections in animals; chromoblastomycosis is a disease of humans.

Experimental Infection in Laboratory Animals. A chronic progressive disease similar to that seen clinically in humans has

Fig. 9. *Hormodendrum compactum.* Conidiophore with compact spore head. × 816. (From Conant and others. *Manual of Clinical Mycology,* 2nd ed., W. B. Saunders Co.)

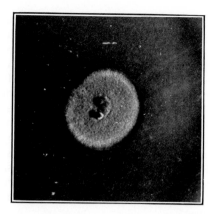

Fig. 10. *Phialophora verrucosa.* Colony on Sabouraud's glucose agar at room temperature for 20 days.

not been produced in animals, but local and systemic infections of a granulomatous type have resulted from experimental inoculations (65).

Duque (69) reported that *Cladosporium trichoides, Hormodendrum pedrosoi,* and *Hormodendrum compactum* produced extensive lesions in the brain of young mice following intracerebral inoculation. Only *C. trichoides,* however, produced brain lesions following intraperitoneal injection. Saprophytic strains were not pathogenic. Feliger and Friedman (70) reported similar results in experimental infections, with the exception that intraperitoneal inoculation resulted in dissemination to the brain. Experimental infections in man have been reported (58, 86, 87). These infections produced typical cutaneous chromoblastomycosis.

Clinical Types of Infection in Man. Chromoblastomycosis is a unilateral infection, usually of the foot and leg, caused by the introduction of the fungus by trauma. The lesion begins on the skin as a papule which evolves slowly over months or years and gradually develops into a verrucous, cauliflower-like growth with the development of numerous satellite lesions. Metastases have been reported in only two cases (63, 82). Early lesions which fail to show a typical verrucous appearance, or lesions which occur on the hand, arm, neck, or face, may not be suspected of fungus origin until the typical brownish bodies are seen in biopsy sections (96).

Other clinical entities are caused by dematiaceous fungi, some of which also cause true chromoblastomycosis. A very benign pigmented superficial infection of the skin on the palmar aspect of the hand, tinea nigra palmaris, is caused by *Cladosporium werneckii* (92).

Transmission. *Phialophora verrucosa* exists in nature as one of several fungi that cause staining of logs, lumber, and wood pulp, from which it has been isolated and identified under the name *Cadophora americana* (76, 77). The fungi isolated from chromoblastomycosis and those from nature have been shown to be both morphologically (67) and antigenically identical (80). *H. pedrosoi* (55) and *Cl. carrionii* (86) also have been isolated from nature.

Most cases follow injury to a foot, and the majority of infections are found in agricultural laborers. All races are susceptible, and males are infected more frequently than females.

Treatment. Small discrete lesions may be excised or treated by electrocoagulation. Extensive lesions are treated best with sodium iodide administered intravenously, potassium iodide by mouth, and x-ray therapy to the local lesions. Iontophoresis, using copper sulfate, has been used with some benefit (79). Sulfonamides and antibiotics may be

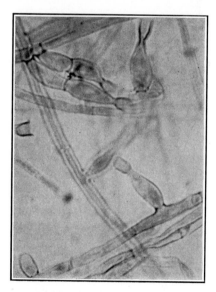

Fig. 11. *Phialophore verrucosa.* Typical conidiophore. × 1,500.

used to combat secondary bacterial infections, and sodium sulfamerazine should be tried, especially since Keeney and others (75) have shown this drug to be effective in vitro.

Gonzalez Ochoa (72) reported DDS and Bonilla (60) reported calciferol to be worthy of trial in the treatment of chromoblastomycosis. Van Vlierberghe and others (95) reported a favorable response to isoniazid in a tuberculous patient treated with this drug. Unless Amphotericin B (66) should prove effective, there is, as yet, no specific treatment for this disease.

MADUROMYCOSIS

Maduromycosis, caused by a variety of filamentous fungi, is a slowly progressive unilateral infection of the subcutaneous tissues of the foot, characterized by chronicity, tumefactions, and multiple sinus formation.

Colebrook (104), of the Madura Dispensary in India, used the term "Madura foot" for an infection of the feet commonly seen in India and previously described by Gill (109). Vandyke-Carter (125) established the fungus nature of the infection and

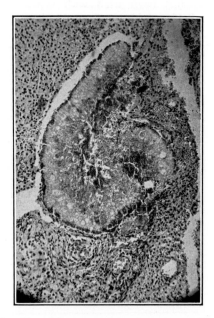

Fig. 12. *Monosporium apiospermum.* Section of tissue from foot showing granule. × 112. (From Fineberg. *Am. J. Clin. Path.,* 14:239, 1944.)

suggested the name "mycetoma" (fungus tumor). It became evident that species of *Nocardia* (*Actinomyces*) as well as species of typically filamentous fungi (molds) could be the etiologic agents of the disease. Pinoy (116) suggested that the infection be designated "actinomycosis" when the causative fungus was an *Actinomyces* and "true mycetoma" when the infection was caused by the higher fungi. Following this, Chalmers and Archibald (103) proposed the two divisions: actinomycotic mycetoma, and maduromycosis. This latter classification is now in general use.

Although maduromycosis usually is considered to be a disease of the tropics, 1,231 cases having been reported in the Sudan in a two-and-a-half-year period (97), several cases have been reported from temperate climates. In the United States the following fungi have been isolated from cases of this disease: *Monosporium apiospermum* (*Allescheria boydii*), *Madurella grisea* (114) and *Phialophora jeanselmei* (107, 110, 123). *Monosporium apiospermum,* which has been isolated from several cases of maduromycosis in the continental United States, will be described as one of the etiologic agents of the disease.

Morphology. *Monosporium apiospermum* occurs in the tissues or serosanguineous exudates from draining sinuses as a lobulated, yellowish white granule, 0.5 to 2 mm. in diameter. Microscopically the granule is composed of broad septate hyphae, 2 to 4 μ in diameter, with numerous chlamydospores, particularly around the periphery of the granule (Fig. 12).

Cultural Characteristics. On Sabouraud's glucose agar at room temperature the colony at first is white and cottony, but later the aerial mycelium becomes grayish in color (Fig. 13). Detailed nutritional studies for one strain have been reported (127). Microscopically the conidia appear singly on the ends of conidiosphores, occasionally from the sides of the hyphae or in small two to three clusters (Fig. 14). The spores are ovoid to clavate, with a truncate base at the point of attachment to the conidiophores, and are 5 to 7 by 8 to 10 μ in size.

Emmons (106) has shown that a Canadian strain of *M. apiospermum* not only

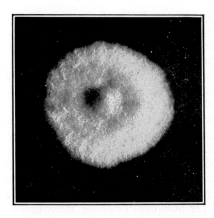

Fig. 13. *Monosporium apiospermum.* Colony on Sabouraud's glucose agar at room temperature for 15 days.

produced the imperfect spore form just described, but also produced cleistothecia and asci, allowing the strain to be identified as *Allescheria boydii,* which was isolated from maduromycosis by Boyd and Crutchfield (102) and described by Shear (122). According to the rules of botanical nomenclature, therefore, the name *M. apiospermum* should be discarded, as it represents merely the conidial stage of an ascomycetous fungus.

Resistance. *Monosporium apiospermum* is killed at 56° C. for one hour. It is not affected by sulfanilamide, sulfathiazole, sulfadiazine, or sulfaguanidine (126). The aromatic diamidine, diamidinodiphenylamine inhibits growth at 5-10 μg. while stilbamidine is effective only in concentrations greater than 200 μg. per milliliter of medium (112). Also 4,4' diaminodiphenylsufone (DDS) is effective only in concentrations greater than 200 μg. per milliliter of medium (112). Amphotericin B, however, partially inhibits growth at 100 μg. per milliliter of medium (113).

Fungus Metabolites. Neither exotoxins nor endotoxins have been reported.

Antigenic Structure. Reifferscheid and Seeliger (117) reported positive agglutinins, precipitins, and complement-fixing antibodies in the serum of a patient with chronic maduromycosis due to *M. apiospermum.* Skin tests with culture filtrate and a polysaccharide extract gave positive delayed, 48-hour, reactions.

Seeliger (119) reported several strains of *M. apiospermum,* two strains of *A. boydii,* and one strain each of *Acremoniella lutzi* and *Madurella americana* to be antigenically identical.

Spontaneous Infections in Animals. *M. apiospermum* has been isolated from mycetoma in a dog (120).

Experimental Infection in Laboratory Animals. Rabbits, mice, and guinea pigs have been inoculated intravenously, subcutaneously, and intraperitoneally with little or no reaction to the fungus. Gammel and Moritz (108) reported infection in rabbits by intraarticular inoculation of saline suspensions.

Clinical Types of Infection in Man. Infection follows the introduction of the fungus into the tissues by injury. A slowly progressing infection, taking weeks or months, evolves, with abscess formation, swelling, and the development of multiple-draining fistulae from which granules are discharged in a serosanguineous fluid. If the foot is infected, it becomes deformed or club-shaped, and the small bones often show proliferative changes and punched-out areas of destruction. The infection remains localized, with extension by direct invasion of tissue. There

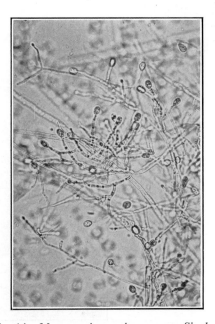

Fig. 14. *Monosporium apiospermum.* Single conidia on ends of conidiophores. × 305. (From Conant and others. *Manual of Clinical Mycology,* 2nd ed., W. B. Saunders Co.)

is no systemic reaction unless secondary bacterial infection takes place.

Transmission. Maduromycosis is a disease of the exposed parts of the body, particularly the feet and ocasionally the leg (121) and the hand (123). The source of the infection is exogenous, since more than half of the patients give a history of injury, such as a minor scratch, bruise, or introduction of foreign material into the skin. Four strains of *A. boydii* have been isolated from soil (98).

A. boydii (*M. apiospermum*) also has been isolated from the sputum of a patient with a chronic, suppurative lung disease (105, 111, 118, 124), from the blood of a patient with septicemia (128), from the spinal fluid of a patient with meningitis (100), and from patients with chronic otomycosis (99, 101).

Treatment. Maduromycosis does not respond to the sulfonamides or known antibiotics. Peters' (115) report of successful treatment with sulfadiazine refers to an infection caused by *Nocardia,* an aerobic actinomycete, and not to Madura foot caused by a filamentous fungus. An occasional patient with true maduromycosis may be bene-

fited temporarily by these drugs because of the elimination of superimposed bacterial infections. Seeliger and Reifferscheid (117) reported successful treatment of a patient by intramuscular and peroral therapy with 2'2 Dioxy-5'5 Dichlordiphenylsulfide. Neuhauser (114) reported favorable response to DDS when a patient with infection by *Madurella grisea* was treated for an extended period of time. Amphotericin B might also be used locally since *M. apiospermum* is sensitive at a level of 100 mg. per milliliter. Surgical intervention for removal of diseased tissue and for adequate drainage must accompany any form of drug therapy.

RHINOSPORIDIOSIS

Rhinosporidiosis, caused by *Rhinosporidium seeberii,* is an infection of man and domestic animals characterized by the formation of friable, sessile, or pedunculated polyps on the mucous membranes of the nose, nasopharynx, soft palate, and conjunctivas of the eyes, and, rarely, in the ear, in the vagina, on the penis, or on the skin.

Seeber (137) in Buenos Aires reported two cases of protozoan infection of the nose

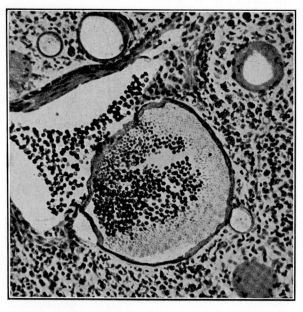

Fig. 15. *Rhinosporidium seeberii.* Section of nasal polyp showing mature and immature sporangia. × 175. (From Conant and others. *Manual of Clinical Mycology,* 2nd ed., W. B. Saunders Co.)

with polyp formation. The organism was named *Coccidium seeberi* by Wernicke (139) in 1903. O'Kinealy (135) in India reported the third case, and the organism was named *Rhinosporidium kinealyi* by Minchin and Fantham (133). Later, Seeber (138) reported the identity of these two organisms, and the name *R. seeberii* was established. Until Ashworth's (130) classic study of material from nasal polyps, the organism had been considered a protozoan. Although he was unable to obtain cultures, he demonstrated a morphologic similarity between the organism and rudimentary plants, such as those of the Chytridales. Until proved by culture, however, the position of *R. seeberii* must remain doubtful.

Of the many cases that have been reported in the United States, all have been infections of the conjunctivas.

Morphology. *R. seeberii* occurs in the polypoid masses as round, thick-walled sporangia, 40 to 300 μ in diameter. The mature sporangia are filled with hundreds or thousands of spores, 6 to 8 μ in diameter (Fig. 15).

Spontaneous Infections in Animals. Spontaneous infections have been reported in domestic animals such as cattle, horses, and mules (132).

Experimental Infection in Laboratory Animals. There have been no reports of successful animal inoculations.

Clinical Types of Infection in Man. The most prevalent infection in man occurs on the mucosa of the nose, with initial symptoms of painless itching, accompanied by a mucoid discharge. Sessile lesions develop into polypoid masses which bleed easily when traumatized. Such masses are pedunculate and may hang down from the nose or fall back into the posterior pharynx to cause obstruction. The polypoid masses are soft, nodular, pale pink to purplish red in color with minute, whitish, opaque areas (sporangia) scattered beneath the surface.

Infection of the conjunctivas may be minimal and not be detected by the patient, or the growths may be large enough to cause symptoms similar to those of foreign bodies. Granular, reddish, irregular masses may be seen on either the bulbar or palpebral conjunctiva (129).

Transmission. It is not known exactly how or where infection by *R. seeberii* is contracted. Epidemiologic studies of large numbers of cases in India suggest infection during contact with stagnant water (131, 134). However, an examination of water, silt, soil, and fish from stagnant waters did not reveal the organism. Inoculation of fish and snails with materials from human lesions was unsuccessful. Implantation of tissues on animals, cultures on a variety of media, serologic studies, and skin tests to demonstrate dermal sensitivity gave negative results (136). So far as is known, there is no transmission from man to man or from animal to man.

Treatment. Removal of the masses by dissection and cauterization usually is effective; recurrences are frequent when the masses are removed by snares. As an adjunct to surgical removal, Neostibosan may prove helpful (139).

REFERENCES

SPOROTRICHOSIS

1. Anderson, N. P., and Spector, B. K. J. Infect. Dis., 50:344, 1932.
2. de Beurmann, L., and Ramond, L. Ann. de dermat. et syph., 4:678, 1903.
3. ——— and Gougerot, H. Les Sporotrichoses, Paris, Librairie Felix Alcan, 1912, 825 pp.
4. Burkholder, R. R., and Moyer, R. Bull. Torrey Botanical Club, 70:372, 1943.
5. Campbell, C. C. J. Bact., 50:233, 1945.
6. ——— and Saslaw, S. Proc. Soc. Exper. Biol. & Med., 70:562, 1949.
7. Cawley, E. P. Ann. Int. Med., 30:1287, 1949.
8. Collins, W. T. Arch. Dermat. & Syph., 56:523, 1947.
9. Crevasse, L., and Ellner, P. D. J.A.M.A., 173:29, 1960.
10. Danowski, T. S., and Tager, M. J. Infect. Dis., 82:119, 1948.
11. Elson, W. O. J. Infect. Dis., 76:193, 1945.
12. Fetter, B. F. Arch. Path., 71:416, 1961.
13. Foerster, H. R. J.A.M.A., 87:1605, 1926.
14. Gonzalez-Ochoa, A., and Figueroa, E. S. Revista d. Inst. salub. y enferm. trop., 8:143, 1947.
15. Gougerot, H., and Caraven. Presse méd., 16:337, 1908.
16. Harrell, E. R., and others. Arch. Int. Med., 93:162, 1954.
17. Hasenclever, H. F., and Mitchell, W. J. Invest. Dermat., 33:145, 1959.
18. Hektoen, L., and Perkins, C. F. J. Exper. Med., 5:77, 1900.
19. Howard, D. H. J. Bact., 81:464, 1961.

20. Howard, D. H., and Orr, G. F.   J. Bact., 85: 816, 1963.
21. Kaden, R. Ztschr. f. Haut- und Geschlechtsk., 21:87, 1956.
22. Kaplan, W., and Ivens, M. S.   J. Invest. Dermat., 35:151, 1960.
23. Katzman, P. A., and others.   J. Biol. Chem., 154:475, 1944.
24. Keeney, E. L., and others.   Bull. Johns Hopkins Hosp., 75:410, 1944.
25. Lurie, H. I.   Mycologia, 43:117, 1951.
26. —— Mycologia, 42:624, 1950.
27. —— Mycologia, 40:106, 1948.
28. —— Arch. Path., 75:421, 1963.
29. —— Brit. J. Surg., 50:585, 1963.
30. Lynch, A. C., and others.   Proc. Staff Meet. Mayo Clin., 38:358, 1963.
31. Mariat, F.   Ann. Inst. Pasteur, 89:261, 1955.
32. —— and others.   Sabouraudia, 2:60, 1962.
33. Matruchot, L., and Ramond, L.   Compt. rend. Soc. de biol., 59:379, 1905.
34. McManus, J. F. A.   Stain Technol., 23:99, 1948.
35. Meyer, K. F.   J.A.M.A., 65:579, 1915.
36. —— and Aird, J. A.   J. Infect. Dis., 16:399, 1915.
37. Mikkelsen, W. M., and others.   Ann. Int. Med., 47:435, 1957.
38. Moore, J. J., and Davis, D. J.   J. Infect. Dis., 23:252, 1918.
39. Neill, J. M., and others.   J. Exper. Med., 89:93, 1949.
40. —— and Kapros, C. E.   Proc. Soc. Exper. Biol. & Med., 73:557, 1950.
41. Nickerson, W. J., ed.   Biology of Pathogenic Fungi, Waltham, Mass., Chronica Botanica Co., 1947, p. 157.
42. Noojin, R. O., and Callaway, J. L.   Arch. Dermat. & Syph., 49:305, 1944.
43. Norden, A.   Acta path. et microbiol. Scandin. (Suppl.). 89:1, 1951.
44. Okudaira, M., and others.   Tr. Soc. Path. Japan, 48:254, 1960.
45. Page, C. G., and others.   J. M. Research, 23:137, 1910.
46. Ridgeway, N. A., and others.   Am. J. Med., 32:153, 1962.
47. Schenck, B. R.   Bull. Johns Hopkins Hosp., 9:286, 1898.
48. Shintani, J., and others.   J. Invest. Dermat., 26:137, 1956.
49. Smith, L. M.   South. M. J., 38:505, 1945.
50. Sternberg, T., and others.   J. Invest. Dermat., 24:397, 1955.
51. Sutton, R. L.   Boston M. & S. J., 164:179, 1911.
52. Symposium: Sporotrichosis Infection on Mines of the Witwatersrand, Johannesburg, South Africa, Published by the Transvaal Chamber of Mines, 1947.
53. du Toit, C. J.   Transvaal Mine M. Off. A., 22:111, 1942.

CHROMOBLASTOMYCOSIS

54. Ajello, L., and Runyon, L.   Mycologia, 45:947, 1953.
55. —— Science, 123:876, 1956.
56. Al-Doory, Y., and Gordon, M. A.   J. Bact., 86:332, 1963.
57. Baquero, G. F.   Bol. Soc. Cubana Dermat. y Sifil., 16:90, 1959.
58. —— and others.   Bol. Soc. Cubana Dermat. y Sifil., 18:19, 1961.
59. Binford, C. H., and others.   Arch. Dermat. & Syph., 49:398, 1944.
60. Bonilla, E.   Arch. Dermat., 70:665, 1954.
61. Brumpt, E.   Précis de Parasitologie, 3rd ed., Paris, Masson et Cie., 1922, p. 1105.
62. Carrión, A. L.   Arch. Dermat. & Syph., 61:996, 1950.
63. —— and Koppisch, E.   Puerto Rico J. Pub. Health & Trop. Med., 9:169, 1933.
64. —— Puerto Rico J. Pub. Health & Trop. Med., 10:543, 1935.
65. —— and Silva, M.   In Nickerson, W. J. Biology of Pathogenic Fungi, Waltham, Mass., Chronica Botanica Co., 1947, chap. 3.
66. Castello, M. J., and others.   Arch. Dermat., 79:184, 1959.
67. Conant, N. F.   Mycologia, 29:597, 1937.
68. —— and Martin, D. S.   Am. J. Trop. Med., 17:553, 1937.
69. Duque, O.   Am. J. Clin. Path., 36:505, 1961.
70. Feliger, C. E., and Friedman, L.   J. Infect. Dis., 111:1, 1962.
71. Fuentes, C. A., and Bosch, Z. E.   J. Invest. Dermat., 34:419, 1960.
72. Gonzalez Ochoa, A.   Therapy of Fungus Diseases, ed. by T. H. Sternberg and V. D. Newcomer, Boston, Little, Brown and Co., 1955, p. 321.
73. Inaki, N.   Jap. J. Dermatol., 72:197, 1962.
74. Karrer, H., and Conant, N. F.   Mycologia, 45:693, 1953.
75. Keeney, E. L., and others.   Bull. Johns Hopkins Hosp., 75:377, 393, 410, 1944.
76. Kress, O., and others.   United States Department of Agriculture Bulletin, No. 1928, April, 1925, pp. 1-80.
77. Lagerberg, T., and others.   Svenska Skogsvards. Tidskr., 25:145, 1927.
78. Lane, C. G.   J. Cutan. Dis., 33:840, 1915.
79. Martin, D. S., and others.   Am. J. Trop. Med., 16:593, 1936.
80. —— Am. J. Trop. Med., 18:421, 1938.
81. Medlar, E. M.   J. M. Research, 32:507, 1915.
82. Montpellier, J., and Catanei, A.   Ann. de dermat. et syph., 8:626, 1927.
83. Moore, M., and Almeida, F. P.   Rev. de biol. e higiene, 6:94, 1935.
84. Pedroso, A.   1911, in Pedroso, A., and Gomes, J. M., Ann. paulist. de med. e cir., 11:53, 1920.
85. —— and Gomes, J. M.   Ann. paulist. de med. e cir., 11:53, 1920.
86. Ridley, M. F.   Australian J. Dermatol., 6:23, 1957.
87. Romero, J., and Borelli, D.   Dermat. Ve. nez., 3:267, 1962-1963.
88. Seeliger, H. P. R.   Zentr. Bakterial. Parasitenk. Abt. I Orig., 167:396, 1957.
89. —— and others.   Proc. 6th Intern. Congr. Trop. Med. Malaria, 4:636, 1959.
90. Silva, M.   Ann. New York Acad. Sc., 89:17, 1960.
91. Simson, F. W.   Mycologia, 38:432, 1946.
92. Spiller, W. F., and others.   J. Invest. Dermat., 27:187, 1956.
93. Terra, F., and others.   Brasil-med., 2:363, 1922.

94. Trejos, A.   Rev. Biol. Trop., 2:75, 1954.
95. Van Vlierberghe, R. G., and others.   Ann. Soc. Belge Méd. Trop., 37:965, 1957.
96. Weidman, F. D., and Rosenthal, L. H. Arch. Dermat. & Syph., 43:62, 1941.

MADUROMYCOSIS

97. Abbott, P.   Tr. Roy. Soc. Trop. Med. & Hyg., 50:11, 1956.
98. Ajello, L.   Am. J. Trop. Med., 1:227, 1952.
99. Belding, D. L., and Umanzio, C. B. Am. J. Path., 11:856, 1935.
100. Benham, R. W., and Georg, L. K.   J. Invest. Dermat., 10:99, 1948.
101. Blank, F., and Stuart, E. A.   Canad. M. A. J., 72:601, 1955.
102. Boyd, M. F., and Crutchfield, E. D. Am. J. Trop. Med., 1:215, 1921.
103. Chalmers, A. J., and Archibald, R. G. Ann. Trop. Med., 10:169, 1916.
104. Colebrook, L.   1864, in Chalmers, A. J., and Archibald, R. G., Ann. Trop. Med., 10: 169, 1916.
105. Creitz, J., and Harris, H. W. Am. Rev. Tuberc., 71:126, 1955.
106. Emmons, C. W.   Mycologia, 36:188, 1944.
107. ——— Arch. Path., 39:364, 1945.
108. Gammel, J. A., and Moritz, A. R.   Arch. Dermat. & Syph., 27:100, 1933.
109. Gill, 1842, in Chalmers, A. J., and Archibald, R. G., Ann. Trop. Med., 10:169, 1916.
110. Levin, N. E.   Calif. Med., 80:468, 1954.
111. Long, J. L., and others.   Am. Rev. Tuberc., 78:604, 1958.
112. Mackinnon, J. E., and others.   Tr. Roy. Soc. Trop. Med. & Hyg., 52:78, 1958.
113. ——— and Garcia-Zorron, N.   Tr. Roy. Soc. Trop. Med. & Hyg., 53:362, 1959.
114. Neuhauser, I.   Arch. Dermat., 72:550, 1955.
115. Peters, J. T.   Am. J. Trop. Med., 25:363, 1945.
116. Pinoy, E.   Bull. Inst. Pasteur, 11:929, 977, 1913.
117. Reifferscheid, M., and Seeliger, H.   Deutsche med. Wchnschr., 50:1841, 1955.
118. Scharyj, M., and others.   J. Infect. Dis., 106:141, 1960.

119. Seeliger, H. J.   Invest. Dermat., 26:81, 1956.
120. Seibold, H. R.   J. Am. Vet. M. A., 127:444, 1955.
121. Shaw, R. M., and Macgregor, J. W.   Canad. M. A. J., 33:23, 1935.
122. Shear, C. L.   Mycologia, 14:239, 1922.
123. Symmers, D., and Sporer, A.   Arch. Path., 37:309, 1944.
124. Travis, R. E., and others.   Ann. Int. Med., 54:141, 1961.
125. Vandyke-Carter, H.   1860, in Chalmers, A. J., and Archibald, R. G., Ann. Trop. Med., 10:169, 1916.
126. Wolf, F. T.   Mycologia, 38:213, 1946.
127. ——— and others.   Mycologia, 42:233, 1950.
128. Zaffiro, A.   Giron. Ital. Med. Milit., 86:636, 1938.

RHINOSPORIDIOSIS

129. Arnold, R., and Whildin, J.   Am. J. Ophth., 25:1227, 1942.
130. Ashworth, J. H.   Tr. Roy. Soc. Edinburgh, 53:301, 1932.
131. Mandlik, G. S.   Indian M. Gaz., 72:143, 1937.
132. Mello, M. T.   Estudos sobre o Rhinosporidium Seeber, Thesis, Escola Nacional Veterinaria, Rio de Janeiro, 1946.
133. Minchin, E. A., and Fantham, H. B.   Quat. J. Micr. Sc., 49:521, 1905.
134. Noronha, A. J.   J. Trop. Med., 36:115, 1933.
135. O'Kinealy, F.   Proc. Laryngol. Soc., London, 10:109, 1903; J. Laryng., Rhin. & Otol., 18: 375, 1903.
136. Reddy, D. G., and Lakshminarayana, C. S. Indian J. Med. Res., 50:363, 1962.
137. Seeber, G. R.   Un nuevo esporozoario parasito del hombre, Thesis, Universidad Nacional Buenos Aires, 1900.
138. ——— 1912, in Allen, F. R. W. K., and Dave, M. L., Indian M. Gaz., 71:376, 1936.
139. Wernicke, R.   1903, in Allen, F. R. W. K., and Dave, M. L., Indian M. Gaz., 71:376, 1936.

81

The Dermatomycoses

THE DERMATOPHYTES

The dermatophytes are parasites of man and animals which live in the superficial keratinized areas of the body: the skin, hair, and nails. They do not cause systemic infection and rarely invade the subcutaneous tissues.

Such infections are known to the layman as "athlete's foot," "jockey itch," and "ringworm," and although they do not kill, they are unsightly and often disabling and present a serious problem both to the private practitioner and to the public health authorities. *Microsporum audouinii* has caused extensive epidemics of ringworm among the school children in certain areas of this country (61), and *Trichophyton tonsurans* has been reported as the cause of epidemics in the adult and adolescent (34, 78).

The dermatophytes were the first of the pathogenic organisms to be discovered. *Achorion schoenleinii* was discovered by Schoenlein (83) in 1839; *Microsporum audouinii* by Gruby (47) in 1843; *Trichophyton tonsurans* by Malmsten (67) in 1845; *Epidermophyton inguinale* by Sabouraud (82) in 1907; and *Endodermophyton concentricum* by Castellani (15) in 1910. More and more species were named on the basis of minor cultural reactions, and the number had reached 45 by the time Sabouraud published his classic volume in 1910. This process of species-making continued unabated until 1930, at which time more than 100 species of *Trichophyton* had been described. Beginning at about this time, there was a concentrated effort to eliminate superfluous species (19, 24). The genera *Achorion* and *Endodermophyton* have been discarded and their species placed in the

genus *Trichophyton*. This genus now contains only 13 species. *Microsporum* contains only 7 species, and *Epidermophyton* possesses only a single species. After a technic for culturing keratinophilic fungi from soil was described by Vanbreuseghem (94) in 1952, many strains of *Microsporum gypseum* and *Microsporum cookei* (1) and a rare strain of *Microsporum nanum* (27) and *Trichophyton terrestre* (23) have been isolated from soil samples collected in various parts of the world. Also, a new genus and species of dermatophyte, *Keratomyces ajelloi,* was described (95) and has since been found to inhabit soil throughout the world.

Morphology. The dermatophytes present only rudimentary structures in their

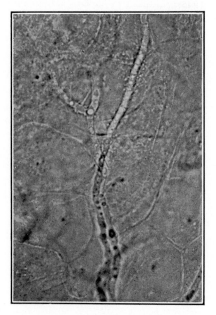

Fig. 1. Branching hypha seen in potassium hydroxide preparation of the skin. × 275.

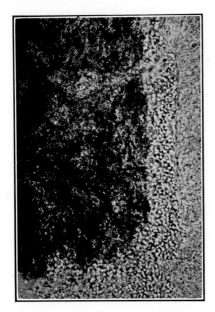

Fig. 2. Microsporum spore sheath around hair. × 350.

parasitic habitats of hair, skin, and nails. As seen in potassium hydroxide preparations, the fungi appear as mycelial fragments in the skin and nails (Fig. 1) or as arthrospores arranged inside or outside the hair (Figs. 2, 3, 4). To establish an identification of the fungus, however, it is necessary to culture the organism on artificial media in order to observe the type and arrangement of spore forms.

Cultural Characteristics. The dermatophytes grow on a variety of simple media, but they usually are cultivated on Sabouraud's glucose agar at room temperature. Both the appearance of the colonies and the microscopic morphology are necessary for generic and specific classification. The nutritional investigations of some of the dermatophytes by Benham (6), Bocobo and Benham (14), Georg (30, 31, 32), Hazen (48), Silva and Benham (84), and Swartz and Georg (89) have provided more satisfactory differential media upon which colony formation, pigmentation, and spore production are more consistent.

The isolation of dermatophytes from contaminated clinical materials is greatly facilitated by the use of Sabouraud's glucose agar (pH 5.5) with chloramphenicol (0.05 mg.

per milliliter) and cycloheximide (Actidione) in a concentration of 0.5 mg. per milliliter.

A brief description of the important genera and species as they appear in culture follows:

I. Genus *Epidermophyton*. This genus contains a single species which invades the **skin** and **nails** but **does not** invade the hair. The genus is characterized by numerous oval to broadly clavate (club-shaped) **macroconidia** produced in clusters or directly from the sides of hyphae. **No microconidia** are produced.

1. *E. floccosum* (Harz) Langeron and Milochevitch, 1930.

On Sabouraud's glucose agar the colony is powdery and greenish yellow and quickly develops a white, cottony aerial mycelium which spreads eventually to cover the surface (Fig. 5). Numerous clavate, two- to six-celled macroconidia, 7 to 12 by 20 to 40 μ in size, are produced from the sides of hyphae or in clusters (Fig. 6). Chlamydospores are numerous throughout the culture. This species is considered to be **anthropophilic** in that it affects only humans.

Fig. 3. Trichophyton hyphae and spores inside hair of endothrix type. × 170. (From Conant and others. *Manual of Clinical Mycology,* 2nd ed., W. B. Saunders Co.)

II. Genus *Microsporum*. This genus contains species which invade the hair and skin but rarely (65) the nails. The genus is characterized by numerous fusiform **macroconidia** produced singly from the ends of hyphae and by the occurrence of a few clavate **microconidia** produced along the sides of the hyphae.

1. *M. audouinii* Gruby, 1843.

On Sabouraud's glucose agar the colony is slow-growing, matted, and velvety, later developing radial grooves and producing an orange pigmentation in the agar (Fig. 7).

Fig. 5. *Epidermophyton floccosum.* Colony on Sabouraud's glucose agar at room temperature for 12 days.

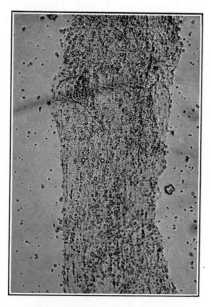

Fig. 4. Trichophyton hair of favus type with numerous hyphae and bubbles. × 305.

Macroconidia are **scarce** and when found usually are immature and appear as expanded ends of hyphae which have failed to develop fully. Sometimes a few bizarre forms may be found (Fig. 8). Microconidia may appear in primary cultures, but they become more numerous in subsequent transfers. Pectinate hyphae and raquette hyphae may be numerous. This species is considered **anthropophilic** in that it infects only humans. It is the cause of epidemic **tinea capitis** in children. Infected hairs exhibit a bright yellow-green fluorescence in Wood's light.

2. *M. canis* Bodin, 1902.

On Sabouraud's glucose agar the colony

is fast-growing, with a loose, white, aerial mycelium which becomes tan to brown in color and develops an orange pigmentation in the agar (Fig. 9). Macroconidia are **abundant** and appear as thick-walled, fusiform six- to 14-celled spores, 8 to 15 by 40 to 150 μ in size (Fig. 10). Microconidia become numerous on transfer. Raquette

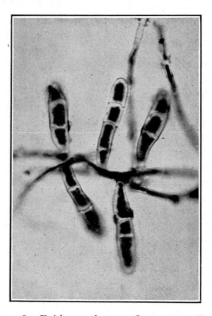

Fig. 6. *Epidermophyton floccosum.* Typical macroconidia borne laterally on the hyphae. × 736.

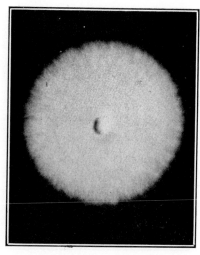

Fig. 7. *Microsporum audouinii.* Colony on Sabouraud's glucose agar at room temperature for 12 days.

hyphae and chlamydospores are numerous. This species is considered **zoophilic** in that it is primarily an animal parasite which causes sporadic infections in humans. When isolated from man, it generally was called *M. lanosum,* but if cultured from an animal, it generally was named after the animal; hence, such designations as *M. canis, M.*

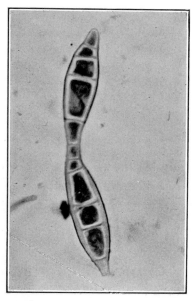

Fig. 8. *Microsporum audouinii.* Bizarre type of macroconidium. × 736.

felineum, and *M. equinum.* Infected hairs exhibit bright yellow-green fluorescence in the Wood's light.

3. *M. gypseum* (Bodin) Guiart and Grigorakis, 1928.

On Sabouraud's glucose agar the colony is fast-growing, powdery, and cinnamon-brown in color, with an orange pigmentation in the agar (Fig. 11). Macroconidia are abundant and appear as thin-walled, ellipsoid four- to six-celled spores, 8 to 12 by 30 to 50 μ in size (Fig. 12). Microconidia become numerous on transfer. Raquette hyphae and chlamydospores are produced.

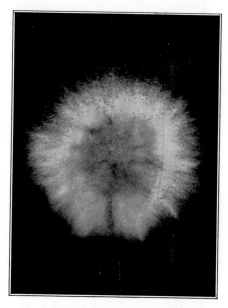

Fig. 9. *Microsporum canis.* Colony on Sabouraud's glucose agar at room temperature for seven days.

This species is considered to be **zoophilic** in that it is primarily an animal parasite which causes sporadic infection in humans (55). Infected hairs have no, or poor, fluorescence in the Wood's light. *M. gypseum* also has been isolated from soil throughout the world. It has an ascomycetous stage called *Nannizzia incurvata* Stockdale, 1961 (86).

Of the other species of *Microsporum* which have been described, some have been isolated from soil and are not known to cause infection in man, while others have been reported as an infrequent cause of infection in man and animals.

4. *M. distortum* Di Menna and Marples, 1954 (22).

This species was described as the cause of human infection in New Zealand. It has been found in an infected dog and in monkeys in this country (55). Humans become infected by handling these animals. Infected hairs exhibit bright yellow-green fluorescence in the Wood's light.

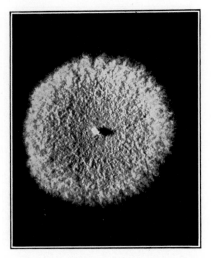

Fig. 11. *Microsporum gypseum.* Colony on Sabouraud's glucose agar at room temperature for seven days.

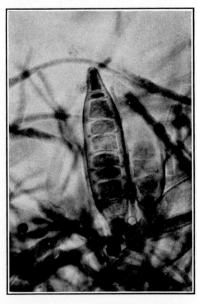

Fig. 10. *Microsporum canis.* Typical fusiform macroconidium. × 736.

throughout the world. Also, it has been isolated from animals without evidence of infection and is not infective for laboratory animals. Since it has characteristic spore forms of the genus *Microsporum,* it has been placed in this genus. It has an ascomycetous stage called *Nannizzia cajetana* Ajello, 1961 (2).

5. *M. vanbreuseghemii* Georg et al., 1961 (42).

This species has been isolated from infections in man (49), squirrel (41), and dog (42). It has an ascomycetous stage called *Nannizzia grubia* Georg et al., 1961 (42). Infected hairs have no, or poor, fluorescence in the Wood's light.

6. *M. nanum* Fuentes, 1956 (27).

This species was isolated from ringworm of the scalp in Cuba (28). It has been isolated from epidemic ringworm of pigs in Kenya and has an ascomycetous stage called *Nannizzia obtusa* Dawson and Gentles, 1961 (20). Infected hairs have no, or poor, fluorescence in the Wood's light.

7. *M. cookei* Ajello, 1959 (1).

This species has been cultured from soil

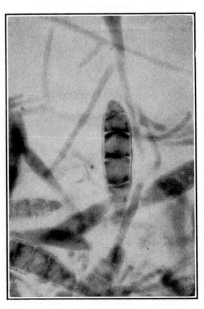

Fig. 12. *Microsporum gypseum.* Typical thin-walled macroconidium. × 736.

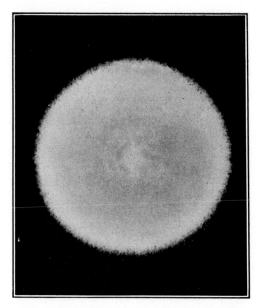

Fig. 13. *Trichophyton mentagrophytes*. Colony on Sabouraud's glucose agar (gypseum type) at room temperature for 10 days.

III. Genus *Keratinomyces*. This genus was described by Vanbreuseghem (95) after numerous isolations from the soil. It is characterized by long cylindro-fusiform, thick, smooth-walled, 5 to 12 septate macroconidia. An occasional isolate also will develop microconidia.

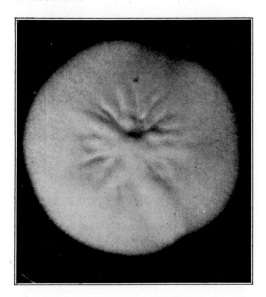

Fig. 14. *Trichophyton mentagrophytes*. Colony on Sabouraud's glucose agar (interdigitale type) at room temperature for eight days.

1. *Keratinomyces ajelloi* Vanbreuseghem, 1952 (95).

This species has been isolated from soil in many parts of the world. An occasional infection in horses has been reported (77, 79). Also, it has been possible to produce experimental infections in laboratory animals and man (25). It has an ascomycetous stage called *Arthroderma uncinatum* Dawson and Gentles, 1961 (20).

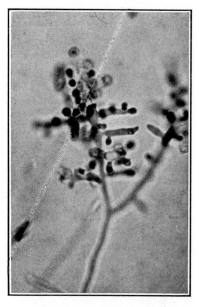

Fig. 15. *Trichophyton mentagrophytes*. Conidiophores from which clusters of microconidia (en grappe) develop. × 375. (From Conant and others. *Manual of Clinical Mycology,* 2nd ed., W. B. Saunders Co.)

IV. Genus *Trichophyton*. This genus contains several species which invade the **hair, skin,** and **nails.** The genus is more difficult to characterize than those previously described because spores are lacking in some forms, and it is necessary to resort to an artificial grouping of species by colony rather than by microscopic characteristics. The nutritional studies mentioned previously have aided greatly in the identification of certain species. When grown on suitable media containing accessory growth substances, better growth and sporulation is induced. When **macroconidia** are produced, they are few in number, elongated, thin-walled, clavate spores. The numerous **microconidia,** which

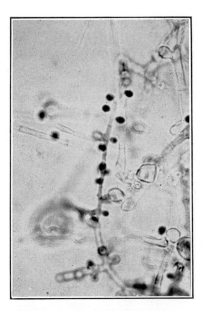

Fig. 16. *Trichophyton mentagrophytes.* Microconidia borne laterally on the hypha (en thyrses). × 375. (From Conant and others. *Manual of Clinical Mycology,* 2nd ed., W. B. Saunders Co.)

are subspherical, pyriform, or clavate, develop from the sides of hyphae, *en thyrses,* or in grape-like clusters, *en grappe.*

1. *T. mentagrophytes* (Robin) Blanchard, 1896.

On Sabouraud's glucose agar the colonies may be powdery and tan to buff in color, *gypseum* type; or the aerial hyphae may be compact, white and cottony, *interdigitale* type (Figs. 13, 14). Typical for this species is the development of numerous subspherical microconidia in grape-like clusters (Fig. 15) or along the sides of the hyphae (Fig. 16) and the coils of hyphae (Fig. 17). Macroconidia, when produced, are elongated, clavate, thin-walled spores, 4 to 6 by 10 to 50 μ in size (Fig. 18). This species is found in **ectothrix** infections of the hair and in infections of the beard.

2. *T. equinum* Gedoelst, 1904.

This species is very similar to *T. mentagrophytes,* above, and has been placed in synonymy with it by several investigators. However, Georg and others (40) have shown this species to differ in morphologic characteristics and in nutritional requirements for growth. *T. equinum* has an absolute requirement for nicotinic acid. *T.*

equinum has caused epizootic equine ringworm in the United States (5) and in other parts of the world (66), and man becomes infected by contact with these animals. This species causes **ectothrix** infections of the hair.

3. *T. verrucosum* Bodin, 1902.

On Sabouraud's glucose agar the colony is slow-growing, heaped, deeply folded, with smooth, waxy surface or with a fine white surface down. Better growth is obtained on Sabouraud's glucose agar with added thiamine (29).

On enriched thiamine medium both macroconidia and microconidia are produced (33).

This species produces ringworm in cattle and other domestic animals (8, 35) from which man becomes infected (39). It causes large-spored **ectothrix** infection of the hair.

4. *T. rubrum* (Castellani) Sabouraud, 1911.

On Sabouraud's glucose agar the colony at first is white, but it quickly develops a reddish to purplish pigmentation both in the aerial mycelium and in the agar (Fig. 19). Different strains will vary greatly in the amount of pigment produced and may re-

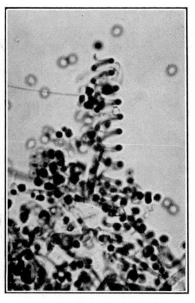

Fig. 17. *Trichophyton mentagrophytes.* Coiled hypha. × 375. (From Conant and others. *Manual of Clinical Mycology,* 2nd ed., W. B. Saunders Co.)

main cottony white, with the pigment confined to the reverse side of the colony in the agar. Consistent pigment formation is developed on cornmeal dextrose agar (14), and characteristic macroconidia are developed on heart infusion agar plus tryptose and "blood agar base" (6). Macroconidia are long, slender, and pencil-shaped; microconidia are more numerous, elongated, clavate, and single-celled. The appearance of these conidia helps distinguish this species from *T. mentagrophytes*. This species, which often is referred to as *T. purpureum*, causes recalcitrant lesions of the skin and nails.

Fig. 19. *Trichophyton rubrum.* Colony on Sabouraud's glucose agar at room temperature for 12 days.

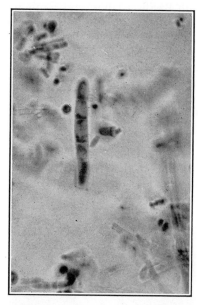

Fig. 18. *Trichophyton mentagrophytes.* Typical clavate macroconidium. × 736.

5. *T. tonsurans* Malmsten, 1845.

On Sabouraud's glucose agar the slow-growing velvety colony becomes heaped, folded, and cream to yellowish in color (Fig. 20). Some strains have a central crater (crateriform). Macroconidia are rare or lacking, but the microconidia are elongated, clavate spores attached to the sides of the hyphae. Characteristic macroscopic morphology of typical strains of this species is developed on the above medium. Microscopic morphology and spore production develop better on wort agar (37). Suspected atypical cultures can be identified by the requirement

of this species for thiamine (37, 89). There are many synonyms for this species because of the great variations in the gross colony characteristics of different strains (36). This species is found in endothrix infections of the hair and, like other endothrix fungi, is difficult to eradicate.

Whereas *M. audouinii* causes epidemic ringworm of the scalp only in children, epidemics caused by *T. tonsurans* are carried over into adult life or the fungus can directly infect the adult scalp.

6. *T. violaceum* Sabouraud, 1902.

On Sabouraud's glucose agar the slow-growing colony is folded, heaped, smooth and waxy, and develops a deep violet pig-

Fig. 20. *Trichophyton tonsurans.* Colony on Sabouraud's glucose agar at room temperature for 35 days.

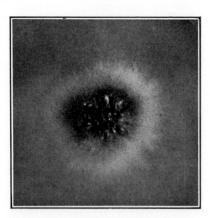

Fig. 21. *Trichophyton violaceum.* Colony on Sabouraud's glucose agar at room temperature for 27 days.

mentation (Fig. 21). On subsequent transfers a white aerial overgrowth may develop. Better colony formation is obtained by the addition of thiamine or pyrimidine to the medium (32). Microscopically, spore forms are lacking, and only swollen hyphae and chlamydospores are seen. This fungus is found in endothrix infections of the hair and causes lesions which are difficult to cure. This species infects the adult scalp.

7. *T. schoenleinii* (Lebert) Langeron and Milochevitch, 1930.

On Sabouraud's glucose agar the slow-growing colony becomes smooth, waxy, and folded (Fig. 22). A short aerial mycelium may develop in subsequent transfers. Except in special media, spore forms are lacking or scarce, but when present they are typical of the genus *Trichophyton*. Morphologically the fungus is composed of short-celled, swollen hyphae with numerous chlamydospores and "favic chandeliers," so called because they appear as antler-like processes on the ends of hyphae in the agar. The generic name *Achorion,* however, has been discarded because the fungus clearly belongs to the genus *Trichophyton,* species of which cause a variety of lesions. This fungus is isolated from typical **favus** lesions and causes a particular type of endothrix infection of the hair. This species infects the adult scalp.

Other species of *Trichophyton* which have been described occur in other parts of the world and are not encountered in ringworm infections in the United States.

8. *T. soudanense* Joyeux, 1912; the cause of epidemic endothrix-type ringworm in North Africa and the Congo (93).

9. *T. gourvilii* Catanei, 1933; the cause of epidemic endothrix-type ringworm in Africa (Algeria, Upper Volta, Chad) (16).

10. *T. yaoundei* Cochet and Doby-Dubois, 1957; the cause of epidemic endothrix-type ringworm in East Africa (Cameroun) and the Congo (17, 18).

11. *T. concentricum* Blanchard, 1896; the cause of tinea imbricata or tokelau. This is a striking widespread cutaneous infection characterized by concentric rings on the skin. Found in Central and South America, the South Pacific Islands, and southern Asia.

12. *T. megninii* Blanchard, 1896; the cause of large-spored ectothrix infections in Europe.

13. *T. gallinae* (Megnin) Silva and Benham, 1952; the cause of ringworm "white comb" in chickens and other birds. Only two human infections have been reported (92).

14. *T. terrestre* Durie and Frey, 1957; isolated from soil in many parts of the world. So far as known, it is not pathogenic for man and animals (22, 75). It has an

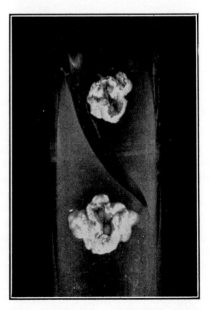

Fig. 22. *Trichophyton schoenleinii.* Colony on Sabouraud's glucose agar at room temperature for 28 days.

ascomycetous stage called *Arthroderma quadrifidum* Dawson and Gentles, 1961 (20).

Resistance. The dermatophytes are killed at 60° C. for one hour. Clinical materials such as infected hair or skin which remain in the laboratory for a year or more are capable of producing growth when inoculated on suitable media. It has been shown that *M. audouinii* and *T. tonsurans* can be cultured from the air on exposed plates during the time when specimens are being collected from patients in the clinic (26).

Many antibiotics, chemotherapeutic drugs, and members of the fatty acid series (C_1 to C_{11}) have been investigated over the years for their possible antifungal action. With the report by Gentles (43) in 1958 that griseofulvin was effective, when given by mouth, against experimental ringworm in guinea pigs, the search for an effective drug treatment for dermatophytosis had been culminated. All dermatophytes are sensitive to griseofulvin in low concentrations (46).

Fungus Metabolites. Neither endotoxins nor exotoxins are produced by the dermatophytes. Saline extracts of dried and powdered cultures (21), filtrates of a two to three months' culture mat ground up with its own liquid medium (87), and other such preparations have been shown to contain allergens which elicit positive skin tests in sensitized individuals. Such skin-testing material has been called "trichophytin." Studies have shown that the dermatophytes also may produce a penicillin-like substance (76). Protein and carbohydrate fractions have been isolated from synthetic media in which *T. mentagrophytes* and *T. rubrum* were grown (57). Since many of the dermatophytes produce pigments in culture, the nature of these substances has been the subject of numerous investigations. The isolation (13) and structure (53) of xanthomegnin from cultures of *T. megninii* have been reported. Pigment isolated from *T. rubrum, T. mentagrophytes,* and *T. megninii* was said to be an anthracene derivative (90, 91), an anthraquinone derivative (38, 73), a pH indicator (52, 90), and that from *T. rubrum* a mixture of several different compounds (97). Zussman and others (98) concluded the pigments of *T. rubrum* to be melanoid

in nature. Koehne and others (61) isolated bright yellow, pale yellow, and purple fractions, said to be identical with pigments in *T. rubrum,* from *M. cookei.* The bright yellow and purple pigments, by analysis, proved to be polyhydroxyl-methyl-anthraquinones. Blank (9) has shown the cell wall of dermatophytes to be chitin and a water-soluble fraction of the cell wall of *T. (granulosum) mentagrophytes* (12) to be a galactomannan containing D-galactose (16 per cent) and D-mannose (86 per cent).

Blank and others (11) identified brassicasterol and ergosterol from ether extracts of 14 different dermatophytes. The total lipids in the dermatophyte species studied was said to average 15.98 and 22.33 per cent for shake cultures and still cultures, respectively (4).

Antigenic Structure. The dermatophytes contain group-specific antigens which can be demonstrated by the Schultz-Dale technic in guinea pigs (50) or by the Prausnitz-Küstner technic in humans (68, 87). A protein fraction obtained from broth filtrates of *T. mentagrophytes* and *T. rubrum* gave positive precipitin reactions in serums of rabbits immunized by the homologous fungus. No cross-reactions occurred with these antigens in heterologous serums. Recently Kitamura (59) reported polysaccharide and protein fractions of *T. mentagrophytes* to give positive precipitin tests in the serum of rabbits inoculated intravenously with a suspension of live fungus.

The production of cutaneous infection in animals results in the development of a cellular antibody which can be demonstrated by the reaction to the intracutaneous injection of trichophytin. Such reactions become positive in 24 to 48 hours and may last for seven days. Animals infected and subsequently sensitized with one of the dermatophytes usually react to injections of products from other dermatophytes, indicating the presence of group antigens. Keeney and Huppert (57) induced hypersensitivity and increased resistance to infection by topical applications of a specially prepared antigen of *T. mentagrophytes.* A positive skin test in humans signifies past or present infection and cannot be used as a means of diagnosis.

Spontaneous Infection in Animals. Spontaneous dermatophytoses have been observed in the cat, dog, horse, calf, cow, sheep, squirrel, monkey, and rat (55, 56, 69, 70, 71). Many of these animal strains also are pathogenic for man.

Experimental Infection in Laboratory Animals. Experimental cutaneous infections can be established in a variety of laboratory animals. *M. audouinii,* however, seems to be primarily a parasite of man since infections in animals do not occur spontaneously or after experimental inoculations. Although guinea pigs infected experimentally with dermatophytes occasionally have positive blood cultures, they never show lesions of their internal organs. Dermatophytes are apparently adapted exclusively for growth in ectodermal structures. If the skin of a guinea pig is traumatized and spores are injected intravenously, no lesions of the internal organs occur, but characteristic cutaneous infections develop in the areas of trauma.

Occasional reports imply that some species can exist in and invade internal organs of experimentally infected animals (85).

Clinical Types of Infection in Man. The most prevalent type of dermatophytosis in man is that which occurs on the feet, particularly on the webs between the toes. This type of infection is known popularly as "athlete's foot" and usually is caused by species of *Trichophyton* or *E. floccosum.* Crops of small itching vesicles appear between the toes and, after being ruptured by trauma, discharge a thin serous fluid which causes maceration and peeling of the superficial layers of the skin, accompanied by the appearance of cracks and fissures. Even in the absence of secondary bacterial infection, the lesions persist as indolent infections for months or years, with occasional acute exacerbations. A secondary infection with bacteria often results in an acute inflammatory reaction, with lymphangitis and lymphadenitis. Many patients infected with species of *Trichophyton* become highly allergic to the fungi, which not only increases the intensity of the local reaction but often results in the appearance of vesicular lesions, indistinguishable from the primary infections, in other parts of the body. Such lesions, which are particularly common on the palms

of the hands, do not contain fungi and are referred to as **dermatophytids** (51).

Infections between the toes or on the feet may be followed by infection of the toenails known as **tinea unguium.** Usually only a few nails are affected, and these become opaque, lusterless, thickened and brittle. The nails of the hands also may become infected by contact with lesions of the feet.

A disease of the glabrous skin of the body, known as **tinea glabrosa,** occurs not uncommonly in children, either as the result of contact with infected animals or by autoinoculation with hairs from an infected scalp. Adults usually become infected by handling animals or infected children or by inoculating themselves from lesions on their own hands and feet. Although a variety of lesions may appear on the glabrous skin, in the typical case the infection starts as a tiny red pimple which spreads peripherally, leaving a scaly center and an active, erythematous vesiculopustular border. Involvement of deeper tissues may occur causing a nodular granulomatous perifolliculitis (96). Recalcitrant *T. rubrum* infections have been associated with increased glucose tolerance and with systemic lymphoblastoma (63, 80).

Ringworm of the scalp, known as **tinea capitis,** occurs in childhood and usually heals spontaneously at puberty. However, a few of the dermatophytes, such as *T. schoenleinii, T. violaceum,* and *T. tonsurans,* produce lesions which persist into adult life. Infections with *M. canis* are acquired by contact with infected cats and dogs and usually are sporadic. In contrast, infections with *M. audouinii* and *T. tonsurans* which are acquired by contact with other infected children, can occur in epidemic form.

In *Microsporum* infections the hair is broken off a short distance from the surface of the scalp, leaving grayish areas consisting of hair stubs surrounded by sheaths of spores. *M. canis* or *M. gypseum* also may cause an inflammatory reaction resulting in a boggy, tumor-like mass or **kerion** which resembles a pyodermia. Ectothrix species of *Trichophyton, T. (gypseum) mentagrophytes,* also may produce acute inflammatory reactions which result in **kerion** formation. Species of *Trichophyton* which invade the hair shaft (endothrix) cause small, scattered, scaly lesions with a thinning of the hair where they are broken off at the surface of the scalp, leaving follicles with a black center. This type is sometimes called **black-dot ringworm.** Another endothrix species, *T. schoenleinii,* causes a characteristic infection of the scalp known as **favus,** which is characterized by cup-like structures known as **scutula** which are formed by the infected hair follicles.

Infections of the bearded regions of man known as **tinea barbae** may be caused by *T. mentagrophytes, T. verrucosum,* and *M. gypseum* and are difficult to differentiate from infections caused by pyogenic bacteria except by microscopic examination of the hair and skin (7) and by culture.

Transmission. The dermatophytes cause infection of man and animals, and this group contains the only known pathogenic fungi for which there is a known transmission from man to man or animal to man. Hairs infected with *M. audouinii* cause epidemics of tinea capitis in children by direct contact, by the use of contaminated clippers in barber shops, and by contact with contaminated theater seats. **Tinea pedis,** or athlete's foot, is thought to be transmitted from man to man by the common use of shower bath facilities in clubs, schools, and colleges. Epidemics, such as the one due to *E. floccosum,* which involved a ship's crew (72), occasionally occur when extraordinary conditions favor the spread of a particular type of organism. Infections can be transmitted from cats, dogs, cows, and other animals to persons coming in contact with infected animals (10, 35). The infections usually are sporadic and can be traced to the animal with little difficulty.

Biologic Products. Skin-testing material, trichophytin, can be made in the laboratory or purchased from biologic supply companies. Occasionally the material can be used for desensitization as an adjunct to other forms of therapy.

Treatment. Since the discovery of Gentles (43, 44) that griseofulvin given by mouth cured experimental ringworm infections in guinea pigs, this antibiotic has been used extensively for the treatment of infection in humans (46, 58, 62, 74, 81).

Prevention. At least two dermatophytes, *Microsporum gypseum* (45) and *Trichophyton mentagrophytes* (64), have been isolated from the soil. Also, *T. mentagrophytes, T. rubrum,* and *Epidermophyton floccosum* have been isolated from used shoes and a shower stall (3). Individual prophylaxis is the best method of preventing epidemics of infection by the dermatophytes.

Sulzberger and Kanof (88) have reported excellent results in both treatment and prevention of infection by the daily use of foot powders (undecylenic acid and zinc undecylenate in talc or 1 per cent boric acid in talc). Such powders not only keep the feet dry but also contain fungistatic agents. The infection rate can be reduced by measures designed to prevent maceration of tissue and the collection of dead materials in which the fungi can become established.

Epidemics of tinea capitis among children can be prevented by quickly determining the extent of infection and instituting proper therapeutic measures. All children in the family should be examined under the Wood's light, which detects infected hairs by fluorescence. Surveys of school children with the Wood's light is an excellent method of detecting the infected individuals, allowing them to be placed under treatment early. Infection of children and adults by *T. tonsurans* cannot be detected by the Wood's light. Careful laboratory studies must be made of hair from individuals suspected of ringworm infection.

PIEDRA

Piedra is a term applied to two types of fungus infection of the hair. Black piedra, caused by *Piedraia hortai,* is characterized by hard black nodules which are adherent to the hair. White piedra, caused by *Trichosporon beigelii,* is distinguished by the soft and light-colored nodules which are detached easily from the hair.

Vuillemin (109) in France isolated a fungus from some light-colored nodules which occurred on the hair of a mustache. He named the fungus *Trichosporon beigelii* for Beigel (100), in Germany, who previously had described such nodules on the hair of wigs. Behrend (99) previously had described *T. ovoides,* which he had isolated from scalp hairs in Germany, and had compared it with material sent to him from Colombia. Since those early reports several

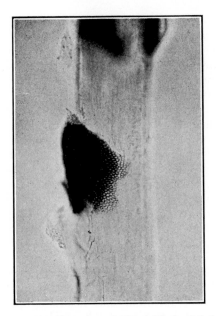

Fig. 23. *Piedraia hortai.* Hard black nodule on hair shaft. × 147.

species of *Trichosporon* have been described as the etiologic agents of white piedra found on hairs of the head, mustache, and beard of people in Central Europe, the Far East, and South America. Mackinnon and Schouten (107), however, studied the fungi which had been isolated and found them to be identical with *Trichosporon beigelii.*

Horta (103) in Brazil first described the fungus causing the hard black nodules on the hairs of the head, and Fonseca and Leão (102) named it *Piedraia hortai.* Like white piedra, several species of fungi had been described as etiologic agents of black piedra found on hairs of people in South America, Java, and Cochin China, but, according to Mackinnon and Schouten (107), they are all identical with *Piedraia hortai.*

Morphology. *Piedraia hortai* appears on hair as a discrete, hard, adherent, black, nodular mycelial mass composed of broad (4 to 12 μ), closely septate, dichotomously branched hyphae (Fig. 23). Scattered throughout the mycelial mass are numerous oval asci, 30 by 50 μ, which contain eight curved or fusiform ascospores, 10 by 30 μ, each with a single, terminal, cilia-like appendage.

Trichosporon beigelii appears on hair as

soft, gelatinous, easily detached, elongate sheaths of transparent mycelial masses composed of round, oval, and rectangular cells, from 2 to 4 μ to 10 μ in diameter (Fig. 24). The fungus reproduces both by arthrospore formation and by budding; the elements are held together in a gelatinous substance.

Cultural Characteristics. *Piedraia hortai* develops slowly on Sabouraud's glucose agar as an adherent, black to greenish black, glabrous, wrinkled colony. *Trichosporon beigelii* develops somewhat faster on Sabouraud's glucose agar as a soft, cream-colored, yeast-like, wrinkled colony.

For clinical purposes a diagnosis is based on the microscopic appearance of the fungus nodules on the hair in KOH preparations.

Spontaneous Infections in Animals. Black piedra has been reported on the pelts of chimpanzees (106). These museum pelts had been obtained from animals killed in the Cameroons. Kaplan (105), in a study of pelts from a wide variety of primates, reported black piedra in 195 of 438 specimens. These pelts had been obtained from primates of Asia, Africa, and the New World. Also, Kaplan (104) reported white piedra from a live monkey and Miguens (108) has reported this type of infection on a horse.

Transmission. *Piedraia hortai* infections are common in Brazil, where the fungus

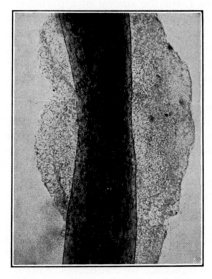

Fig. 24. *Trichosporon beigelii.* Soft white nodule on hair shaft. × 147.

causes epidemics more often among men than among women, probably because the latter take better care of their hair. It is not known where in nature the fungus may be located or how epidemics are established. Greasy hair preparations may have some significance, as their use is widespread in those areas where the infection is common.

Daly (101) has described a case seen in Vermont.

Trichosporon beigelii, which causes sporadic infections of the hair, is much less contagious, and the fungus is found more frequently on the hairs of the mustache and beard than on the scalp.

Treatment. Infected hairs should be cut or shaved off, and, after removal, the area should be treated by applications of a solution of bichloride of mercury (1:2000) or ammoniated mercury ointment (3 per cent).

TINEA VERSICOLOR

Tinea versicolor is an infection of the skin caused by *Malassezia furfur.*

The lesions usually appear on the trunk, but they may also occur on the neck, face, and arms. They appear as irregular, circumscribed brownish red, furfuraceous patches which fluoresce under the Wood's light. Cultures are not made; the clinical diagnosis can be confirmed by microscopic examination of the furfuraceous scales.

Morphology. In potassium hydroxide preparations or stained preparations of the scales, the fungus appears as clusters of round budding cells, 3 to 8 μ in diameter, intermixed with short fragments of hyphae (Fig. 25). Newer technics for obtaining scales for staining and microscopic examination have been described. Keddie and others (114, 116) have used cellulose tapes applied to the skin to remove the horny layer with its flora of yeast cells and hyphae characteristic for tinea versicolor. These tapes may be stained in a variety of ways or placed on suitable media for direct culture of the fungus. A particular tape, Eastman No. 910 Monomer, removes the layer of horny cells and hairs (117). Such preparations show the localization of *M. furfur* within follicles as well as in the surrounding stratum corneum.

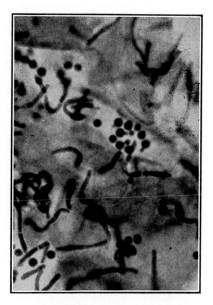

Fig. 25. *Malassezia furfur.* Clusters of round cells and short hyphal segments. $\times$ 736.

Cultural Characteristics. For a number of years it was not known with certainty if *M. furfur* had been or could be cultured from scales. In spite of the abundance of fungus elements seen in microscopic preparations of scrapings taken from the lesions, numerous negative reports attested to the difficulty of establishing cultures on a variety of media. Gordon (112, 113) in 1951, however, was able to grow a yeast-like fungus from the scales of normal skin and from tinea versicolor scales on Sabouraud's glucose slants overlaid with olive oil. Antibiotics, penicillin (20 units per milliliter) and streptomycin (40 units per milliliter) were added to the medium to prevent growth of contaminating bacteria. The culture obtained, *Pityrosporum obiculare,* was a white to cream-colored yeast-like growth on incubation at 30° to 37° C. The yeast cells are spherical with buds attached by a narrow isthmus, 2.8 to 3.8 μ in diameter. *P. obiculare* does not grow at 25° C. or at higher temperatures without oils or other fatty substances and is considered to be lipophilic.

Transmission. Tinea versicolor is rarely, if ever, transmitted from person to person. The rare report of conjugal infection and repeated failures to infect healthy skin with scales or cultures of *P. obiculare* have prevented epidemiologic investigations or studies concerning the pathogenesis of this disease. Burke (110) in 1961, however, was able to infect a patient with Cushing's syndrome, a patient on steroid therapy, and a patient with nutritional deficiency. These results would indicate biochemical or physiologic changes in the skin to be necessary predisposing factors for tinea versicolor. In a later study (111) an analysis of lipid level, fatty acid, and amino acid content of normal skin and skin of patients with tinea versicolor did not reveal significant differences. It is felt, however, that predisposition by one or many factors is necessary for infection.

Antigenic Structure. Sternberg and Keddie (118) and Keddie and Shadomy (115) have shown by immunofluorescent technics that *P. obiculare* and the fungus in scales are antigenically similar. These investigators also showed that a patient's serum would agglutinate cells of *P. obiculare* and, by the indirect immunofluorescent technic and by absorption tests, that antigenic similarity exists.

Spontaneous Infection in Animals. Tinea versicolor is a human disease. Moreover, all attempts to infect animals have failed.

Clinical Types of Infection in Man. The infection often is asymptomatic, with only an occasional complaint of pruritis. The lesions are superficial, furfuraceous, irregular or circumscribed brownish-red patches. Of diagnostic value is the ease with which the scales are scraped from the lesion either by curette or edge of a glass slide, or even by the fingernail.

The lesions fluoresce under the Wood's light; this characteristic aids in the management of the disease by locating and outlining areas for treatment.

Treatment. A weak keratolytic agent removes the fungus-laden scales.

REFERENCES

DERMATOPHYTES

1. Ajello, L. Mycologia, 51:69, 1959.
2. ———— Sabouraudia, 1:173, 1961.
3. ———— and Getz, M. E. J. Invest. Dermat., 22:17, 1954.
4. Al-Doory, Y., and Larsh, H. W. Applied Microbiol., 10:492, 1962.
5. Batte, E. G., and Miller, W. S. J. Am. Vet. Med. A., 123:111, 1953.

6. Benham, R. W. Mycologia, 40:232, 1948.
7. Birt, A. R., and Wilt, J. C. Arch. Dermat. & Syph., 69:441, 1954.
8. Blank, F. Canad. J. Comp. Med. Vet. Sci., 17:277, 1953.
9. ———— Biochem. et Biophys. Acta, 10:110, 1953.
10. ———— Am. J. M. Sc., 229:302, 1955.
11. ———— and others. J. Invest. Dermat., 39:91, 1962.
12. ———— and others. Canadian J. Chem., 40:1816, 1962.
13. ———— and others. J. Invest. Dermat., 40:133, 1963.
14. Bocobo, F. C., and Benham, R. W. Mycologia, 41:291, 1949.
15. Castellani, A. J. Trop. Med., 13:370, 1910.
16. Catanei, A. Arch. Inst. Pasteur Algérie, 11:341, 1933.
17. Cochet, G., and others. Ann. Parasit. Hum. & Comp., 32:580, 1957.
18. ———— and Doby-Dubois, M. Bull. Soc. Path. Exot., 49:418, 1956.
19. Conant, N. F. J. Invest. Dermat., 4:265, 1941.
20. Dawson, C. O., and Gentles, J. C. Sabouraudia, 1:49, 1961.
21. DeLamater, E. D., and Benham, R. W. J. Invest. Dermat., 1:469, 1938.
22. DiMenna, M., and Marples, M. J. Tr. Brit. Mycol. Soc., 37:372, 1954.
23. Durie, E. B., and Frey, D. Mycologia, 49:401, 1957.
24. Emmons, C. W. Arch. Dermat. & Syph., 30:337, 1934.
25. Evolceanu, E., and Alteras, I. Mycopath. & Mycol. Appl., 11:196, 1959.
26. Friedman, L., and others. J. Invest. Dermat., 35:3, 1960.
27. Fuentes, C. A. Mycologia, 48:613, 1956.
28. ———— and others. J. Invest. Dermat., 23:51, 1954.
29. Georg, L. K. Mycologia, 42:693, 1950.
30. ———— Ann. New York Acad. Sc., 50:1315, 1950.
31. ———— Mycologia, 42:693, 1950.
32. ———— Mycologia, 43:297, 1951.
33. ———— Mycologia, 43:536, 1951.
34. ———— Pub. Health Rep., 67:53, 1952.
35. ———— Vet. Med., 49:157, 1954.
36. ———— Mycologia, 48:65, 1956.
37. ———— Mycologia, 48:354, 1956.
38. ———— and Maechling, E. H. J. Invest. Dermat., 13:339, 1949.
39. ———— and others. J. Invest. Dermat., 27:335, 1956.
40. ———— and others. J. Invest. Dermat., 29:27, 1957.
41. ———— and others. J. Invest. Dermat., 32:539, 1959.
42. ———— and others. Sabouraudia, 1:189, 1961.
43. Gentles, J. C. Nature, London, 182:476, 1958.
44. ———— Brit. J. Dermat., 71:427, 1959.
45. Gordon, M. A. J. Invest. Dermat., 20:201, 1953.
46. Griseofulvin and Dermatomycoses. An International Symposium. Arch. Dermat., 81:5, 1960.
47. Gruby, M. Compt. rend. Acad. sc., 17:301, 1843.

48. Hazen, E. L.   Mycologia, 43:284, 1951.
49. Henington, V. M., and others.   Arch. Dermat. & Syph., 86:298, 1962.
50. Jadassohn, W., and others.   J. Immunol., 32:203, 1937.
51. Jillson, O. F., and Hoekelman, R. A.   Arch. Dermat. & Syph., 66:738, 1952.
52. Johnson, S. A., and Reedal, J. S.   J. Invest. Dermat., 16:275, 1951.
53. Just, G., and others.   Canadian J. Chem., 41:74, 1963.
54. Kaplan, W., and others.   J. Invest. Dermat., 28:449, 1957.
55. ———— and others.   Ann. N.Y. Acad. Sci., 70:636, 1958.
56. ———— and Ivens, M. S.   Sabouraudia, 1: 91, 1961.
57. Keeney, E. L., and Huppert, M.   J. Invest. Dermatol., 32:7, 1959.
58. Kirk, J., and Ajello, L.   Arch. Dermat., 80: 259, 1959.
59. Kitamura, J.   Bull. Pharm. Res. Inst., Osaka, No. 44, 1, 1963.
60. Koehne, G. W., and others.   J. Invest. Dermat., 39:189, 1962.
61. Lee, R. K. C.   Pub. Health Rep., 63:261, 1948.
62. Levin, H. B., and others.   Arch. Dermat., 81:827, 1960.
63. Lewis, G. M., and others.   Arch. Dermat. & Syph., 67:247, 1953.
64. Lurie, H. I., and Borok, R.   Mycologia, 47: 506, 1955.
65. Lyons, R. E.   Arch. Dermat. & Syph., 67: 460, 1953.
66. Mackinnon, J. E.   Arch. Uruguay Med. Cir. Esp., Montevideo, 8:498, 1936.
67. Malmsten, P. H.   Trans. by F. C. H. Creplin, Arch. f. Anat., Physiol. u. wissensch. Med., 1848, p. 1.
68. Marcussen, P. V.   Arch. Dermat. & Syph., 36:494, 1937.
69. McKeever, S., and others.   Am. J. Vet. Res., 19:969, 1958.
70. ———— and others.   Am. J. Vet. Res., 19: 973, 1958.
71. Menges, R. W., and Georg, L. K.   J. Am. Vet. Med. A., 128:395, 1956.
72. Mercer, S. T., and Farber, G. J.   Arch. Dermat. & Syph., 32:62, 1935.
73. Mier, P. D.   Nature, 179:1084, 1957.
74. Oral Treatment of Fungus Infections with Griseofulvin. An International Symposium. St. John's Hosp. Dermat. Soc., London, No. 45, 13-14, May 1960.
75. Otčenášek, M., and Dvořák, J.   Sabouraudia, 2:111, 1962.
76. Peck, S. M., and Hewitt, W. L.   Pub. Health Reports, 60:148, 1945.
77. Pier, A. C., and Hughes, J. P.   J. Am. Vet. Med. A., 138:484, 1961.
78. Pipkin, J. L.   Arch. Dermat. & Syph., 66:9, 1952.
79. Rieth, H., and El-Fiki, A. Y.   Bull. Pharm. Res. Inst. (Osaka) No. 21, 1, 1959.
80. Rothman, S.   Arch. Dermat. & Syph., 67: 259, 1953.
81. Russell, B., and others.   Lancet, May 28, p. 1141, 1960.
82. Sabouraud, R.   Arch. de méd. exper. et d'anat. path., 19:565, 1907.
83. Schoenlein, Prof.   Arch. f. Anat., Physiol. u. wissensch. Med., 1839, p. 82.
84. Silva, M., and Benham, R. W.   J. Invest. Dermat., 22:285, 1954.
85. Sternberg, T. H., and others.   J. Invest. Dermat., 19:373, 1952.
86. Stockdale, P. M.   Sabouraudia, 1:41, 1961.
87. Sulzberger, M. B.   J. Immunol., 23:73, 1932.
88. ———— and Kanof, A.   Arch. Dermat. & Syph., 55:391, 1947.
89. Swartz, H. E., and Georg, L. K.   Mycologia, 47:475, 1955.
90. Tate, P.   Biol. Rev., 4:41, 1929.
91. Thompson, K. W.   Report of the Conference on Dermatophytes, Div. Med. Sci., NRC, p. 13, Nov. 8, 1943.
92. Torres, G., and Georg, L. K.   Arch. Dermat., 74:191, 1956.
93. Vanbreuseghem, R.   Ann. Parasitol., 25: 493, 1950.
94. ———— Ann. Soc. Belge Méd. Trop., 32:173, 1952.
95. ———— Bull. Acad. Belg. Clin. Sci., 38:1068, 1952.
96. Wilson, J. W., and others.   Arch. Dermat. & Syph., 69:258, 1954.
97. Wirth, J. C., and others.   J. Invest. Dermat., 29:47, 1957.
98. Zussman, R. A.   J. Bact., 80:708, 1960.

PIEDRA

99. Behrend, G.   Berlin Klin. Wchnschr., 27: 464, 1890.
100. Beigel.   1865, in Fonseca, O., Rev., med.-cir. do Brasil, 38: 251, 1930.
101. Daly, J. F.   Arch. Dermat., 75:584, 1957.
102. Fonseca, O., and Leão, A. E.   Suppl. Mem. Inst. Oswaldo Cruz, 4:124, 1928.
103. Horta, P.   Mem. Inst. Oswaldo Cruz., 3:87, 1911.
104. Kaplan, W.   J. Am. Vet. Med. A., 134:113, 1959.
105. ———— Trop. Geograph. Med., 11:115, 1959.
106. Lochte, T.   Arch. Dermatol. u. Syphilis, 175:107, 1937.
107. Mackinnon, J. E., and Schouten, G. B.   Arch. Soc. de biol. de Montevideo, 10:227, 1942.
108. Miguens, M. P.   Actas Dermatosif. Santiago de Compostela, 6:1, 1952.
109. Vuillemin, P.   Arch. de parasitol., 5:38, 1902.

TINEA VERSICOLOR

110. Burke, R. C.   J. Invest. Dermat., 36:389, 1961.
111. ———— Yale J. Biol. & Med., 35:206, 1962.
112. Gordon, M. A.   J. Invest. Derm., 17:267, 1951.
113. ———— Mycologia, 43:524, 1951.
114. Keddie, F.   Arch. Dermat., 87:641, 1963.
115. ———— and Shadomy, S.   Sabouraudia, 3: 21, 1963.
116. ———— and others.   Sabouraudia, 1:108, 1961.
117. ———— and others.   J. Invest. Dermat., 41: 103, 1963.
118. Sternberg, T. H., and Keddie, F. M.   Arch. Dermat., 84:999, 1961.

82

Miscellaneous Mycoses

ASPERGILLOSIS

Aspergillosis, caused by *Aspergillus fumigatus* most frequently but by other species of *Aspergillus* as well, is an acute or chronic inflammatory granulomatous infection of the sinuses, bronchi, lungs, and occasionally other parts of the body.

Since species of *Aspergillus* are ubiquitous, it is difficult to ascribe pathogenicity to an isolate from any orifice in the body or from the sputums of patients with undiagnosed pulmonary infections. *A. fumigatus,* however, is a recognized pathogen of birds, both wild and domestic, as well as of animals and man. As early as 1856 Virchow (56) reported autopsy findings in human pulmonary aspergillosis, and Renon (41) in 1897 discussed aspergillosis in both human and animal infections. Aspergillosis has been recognized as an occupational disease occurring among those who handled and fed squabs and the handlers of furs and hair.

Morphology. *Aspergillus fumigatus,* in the sputum of patients with pulmonary aspergillosis, appears as broken fragments of hyphae, and occasionally conidia may be seen. When hyphal fragments or conidia are seen, cultures must be obtained for identification. Only repeated cultures from such materials are indicative of etiologic significance.

Aspergillus may appear as a hyphal mass or ball in a cyst or closed cavity in the lungs. This is referred to as an "aspergilloma." Mycelium and spore heads may be seen lining the wall of an open cavity or in bronchial casts seen in sputum in bronchitis. In tissues septate, twisted, dichotomously branching hyphae may be seen in gram-stained sections but are better stained with the PAS technic (periodic acid-Schiff stain) (Fig. 1).

Frequently the hyphae invade the wall of blood vessels, eventually their lumen, and cause infarction.

Cultural Characteristics. *Aspergillus fumigatus* grows rapidly on Sabouraud's glucose agar to form a white, cottony colony which becomes velvety (Fig. 2). As spores are produced, it attains a dark green powdery appearance. Microscopically the typical *Aspergillus* conidiophore is seen (Fig. 3). The vesicle is covered on the upper half with phialides which produce chains of dark green spherical conidia.

Resistance. The discovery by Fourneau and others (20) that sulfanilamide was the active ingredient of prontosil was based on the fungistatic activity of this material during in vitro studies on the growth of *Aspergillus niger, Aspergillus fumigatus, Aspergillus jeanselmei,* and *Lichtheimia italica.* It is interesting to note, therefore, that the first in vitro demonstration of the drug, from which so many important derivatives have been made, was based on fungistatic rather than bacteriostatic experiments.

Aspergillus niger is inhibited for 24 hours by 1:10,000, 8 to 10 days by 1:1,000 and for two months by 1:100 concentrations of sulfanilamide (20). Senturia and Wolf (47) showed that 20 to 30 mg. of sulfanilamide powdered over the surface of the culture inhibited *A. niger, A. fumigatus, A. glaucus,* and *A. sydowi,* while sulfathiazole, sulfadiazine, sulfaguanidine, and sulfamerazine were ineffective. Strains isolated from bronchopulmonary aspergillosis by Hinson and others (27) were insensitive to penicillin, streptomycin, chloramphenicol, and aureomycin. Amphotericin B, however, has inhibited some strains of *Aspergillus* in concentrations of 0.1 to 40 μg. per milliliter of medium (7, 21).

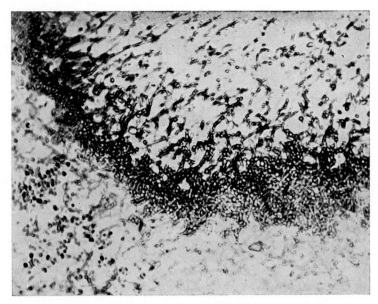

Fig. 1. *Aspergillus fumigatus.* Hyphae forming dense mass in section of lung. × 245. (From Weed and others. *Proc. Staff Meet., Mayo Clinic,* 24:463, 1949.)

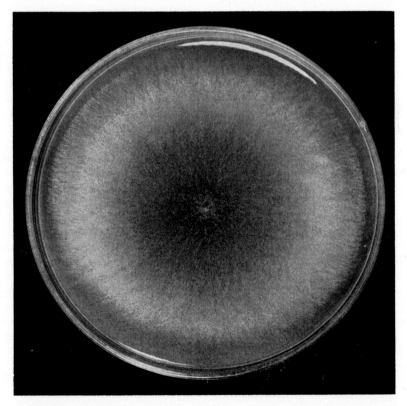

Fig. 2. *Aspergillus fumigatus.* Colony on Sabouraud's glucose agar at room temperature for six days. (From Conant and others. *Manual of Clinical Mycology,* 2nd ed., W. B. Saunders Co.)

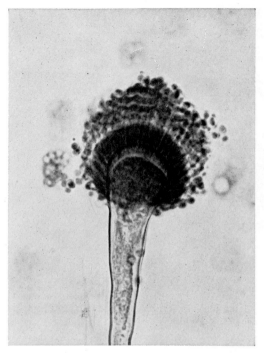

Fig. 3. *Aspergillus fumigatus.* Typical conidiophore. × 825. (From Conant and others. *Manual of Clinical Mycology,* 2nd ed., W. B. Saunders Co.)

Fungus Metabolites. Endotoxins have been demonstrated in *Aspergillus fumigatus* (25, 40, 49) and in *Aspergillus flavus* (53). A polysaccharide of low toxicity for the rabbit, and a lipoid which caused monocytosis and tubercle formation and which showed adjuvant properties have been reported (49, 50). From another pathogenic species, *A. nidulans,* extracted "cell sap" was found to be nontoxic for rabbits and guinea pigs but produced a delayed reaction on intracutaneous injection of previously infected rabbits (15). On the other hand, Bodin and Gauthier (10) found a toxic substance in filtrates of cultures of *A. fumigatus* which was lethal for rabbits but harmless for pigeons and guinea pigs. These various extracts from *A. fumigatus* may produce dermatonecrotic, hemolytic, or nephrotoxic reactions (53). A substance designated Aspergillin O has been extracted from filtrates of culture media of *A. oryzae.* This extract has proteolytic, fibrinolytic, and anticoagulant properties (30, 51).

Antigenic Structure. Henrici's (25) "cell sap" toxin on injection into rabbits resulted in the production of precipitins and antihemolysins. The polysaccharide isolated from *A. fumigatus* by Stanley (49) and the "cell sap" isolated from *A. nidulans* by Drake (15) were found to be antigenic in that precipitins could be demonstrated in the serums of previously inoculated rabbits. Immune serum from rabbits has been shown to prevent effects of toxins in experimental animals (25, 27). Henrici (25) was able to immunize rabbits actively against toxins of *A. fumigatus.*

Pepys and others (38) reported positive immediate wheal reactions and direct bronchial sensitivity tests in asthmatics. A peculiar delayed skin reaction, reaching its maximum in 24 hours, was considered to be an Arthus' type of reaction because of its eosinophilic nature. This reaction was said to be due to precipitating antibody in patients' serum. Complement-fixing antibodies to *Aspergillus* antigens have been reported by Junke and Theone (29) and Seeliger (44). Precipitation, hemagglutination, collodion, and latex particle agglutination tests have been described with a variety of antigens from species of *Aspergillus* and penicillium (28, 29, 54). The agar gel diffusion technic also has been used (16, 18, 24, 29). This test has shown common antigens to be shared by *Aspergillus* species and other saprophytic and pathogenic fungi (32, 39).

Spontaneous Disease in Animals. Species of *Aspergillus* cause a variety of diseases in many different animals: pulmonary infection in lambs (6), mycotic abortion in cattle (4, 5), and aspergillosis in chickens (11) and a variety of wild and captive birds (1, 2, 14, 26). The presence of *Aspergilli* in moldy substrates makes billions of spores readily available for inhalation infections (17, 22).

Experimental Infection in Laboratory Animals. Cattle, chickens, pigeons, rabbits, and guinea pigs may be infected by inoculating spores intravenously or intraperitoneally or by introducing them into the respiratory passages.

Clinical Types of Infection in Man. Otomycosis probably is secondary to bacterial infections of the ear with the fungus existing saprophytically on the macerated tissue or earwax. Hearing may be impaired by obstruction of the canal with a mycelial mass and epithelial débris. The symptoms are those of intense itching and edema, and not infrequently the pain may become unbearable (23, 52).

Involvement of the sinuses simulates infection by pyogenic bacteria.

Infection of the subcutaneous tissues of the foot produces the typical picture of maduromycosis.

Infection of the nails simulates infection by dermatophytes (36).

Bronchial infections simulate bronchitis caused by bacteria and may be associated with asthma (3).

Bronchiectasis complicated by infection with an *Aspergillus* may result in a so-called aspergilloma in which the mass of fungus distends and occupies a large area of cavitation. The fungus does not invade the bronchial wall. Repeated hemoptysis is the only symptom. The x-ray is characteristic and diagnostic (34, 45, 46).

Bronchopulmonary aspergillosis may be characterized by frequent pyrexial attacks associated with severe cough, purulent occasionally blood-tinged sputum with flecks of white or brownish material containing mycelium, and a high eosinophilia. Serial roentgenograms show shifting shadows appearing with pyrexial attacks (13, 27, 35, 43, 48, 55).

Systemic aspergillosis results from predisposing factors which, in the debilitated patient, interfere with humoral and tissue defense mechanisms. Patients with pre-existing leukemia, Hodgkin's disease, collagen diseases, malignancies, and so on, are frequently infected with *A. fumigatus*. The therapy, antibiotics and antimetabolites, available for the primary diseases may also predispose to secondary mycotic infections (8, 19, 21, 30, 31, 33).

Transmission. Species of *Aspergillus* are ubiquitous; they are found in the soil, water, and air, on foodstuffs and animal products, and may be cultured from almost any body orifice. Members of the genus are constant contaminants of clinical materials, such as sputum, pus, feces, wax from the ear, and exudates from open lesions. They may be cultured from the gastric contents, and at autopsy they frequently are seen and cultured from necrotic lesions of the lungs resulting from neoplasm or tuberculosis.

Conditions creating moisture and prolonged dampness are conducive to the growth of molds and a moldy environment predisposes to infection by *A. fumigatus*.

Treatment. Surgery has been effective in certain types of pulmonary aspergillosis (9, 37, 42). Demonstrated sensitivity in aspergillosis has been treated by desensitization with autogenous vaccines (12). Sodium iodide intravenously and potassium iodide by mouth may prove effective. Amphotericin B is, perhaps, the only antibiotic useful in drug therapy of aspergillosis.

PENICILLIOSIS

It is difficult to prove the etiologic relationship of species of *Penicillium* which may be isolated from a disease process. Like *Aspergillus,* species of *Penicillium* are ubiquitous and are constant contaminants of clinical materials. Wolf (59) lists the species of *Penicillium* that have been isolated from otomycosis. Aimé and others (57) reported a case of pulmonary infection and x-ray characteristics of pulmonary abscesses. Recently Huang and Harris (58) reported a case of acute disseminated penicilliosis and reviewed the pertinent literature.

MYCOTIC KERATITIS

Fungus infection of the cornea by a large variety of fungi follows trauma and bacterial infection. If recent concern, however, is the increasing incidence of mycotic infection of the diseased eye following antibiotic and topical cortisone treatment (60, 65, 66).

Leber (68) in 1879 described the first case of keratomycosis, proved its fungus etiology, and reproduced the disease in laboratory animals. For a number of years *A. fumigatus* has been responsible for the majority of cases proven by culture (72). Since the advent of antibiotics and corticosteroids, the list of fungi known to infect the cornea has increased to include many saprophytic as well as a few pathogenic fungi (62, 66, 72).

Morphology. In corneal scrapings the filamentous fungi appear as septate, branching, mycelial fragments (Fig. 4). Such a finding does not allow identification of the fungus. Cultures must be made and identified by their characteristic sporulating structures. Occasionally, budding yeast cells with pseudomycelium may be seen in microscopic preparations from the diseased eye. A tentative identification of *Candida* species may be made under these circumstances.

The fungi may not be visible in hematoxylin-eosin-stained sections of the eye. Sections should be stained by the Gridley, the PAS, or the Gomori methenamine silver stain. In the Gridley- and PAS-stained sections the fungus elements will appear red; in the Gomori-methenamine-silver-stained sections they will appear black.

Cultural Characteristics. The fungi are situated deep in the corneal stroma. Scrapings deep in the ulcer or at its edge must be made to obtain material for examination and culture. Sabouraud's glucose agar with chloramphenicol (0.05 mg. per milliliter) should

be used to avoid bacterial contamination. Pieces of the curetted materials are placed on the agar slant and the cultures held at room temperature.

Many different fungi have been isolated from the ulcerated cornea (60, 66). The diversity ranges from yeast-like species of *Candida* to any filamentous fungus that occurs as a saprophyte in nature. Cultures made from corneal scrapings may be identified as *Aspergillus* sp., *Fusarium* sp., *Penicillium* sp., *Scopulariopsis* sp., *Cephalosporium* sp., *Monosporium* sp., *Curvularia* sp., etc.

Fungus Metabolites. Little is known about the metabolites available that would allow saprophytic fungi to invade the corneal tissue. Injury seems to be necessary for invasion, but the continued growth and destructive abilities of the various fungi are probably dependent on products elaborated during growth. Burda and Fisher (61) reported that a crude mycelial extract of *Cephalosporium serrae* produced corneal destruction in the rabbit eye; further purification of this material allowed them to believe

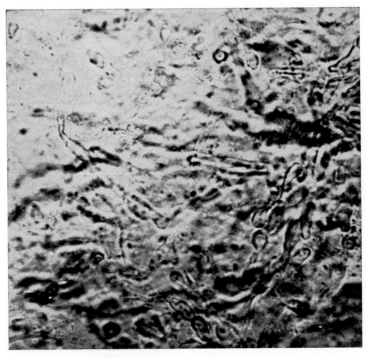

Fig. 4. Corneal scraping showing hyphae of invading fungus. (From Dr. E. W. Chick, Veterans' Administration Hospital, Durham. North Carolina.)

it to be a constitutive proteinase. Dudley and Chick (63) found a mycelial extract of *Fusarium moniliforme* to produce intracorneal necrosis in the rabbit eye.

Experimental Infection in Laboratory Animals. Many investigators have produced experimental corneal ulceration in laboratory animals. Primary pathogenicity can be demonstrated by inoculation following trauma (64, 71). Ley (69) produced corneal infections in rabbits by the use of cortisone and oxytetracycline.

Clinical Types of Infection in Man. Infection is initiated by trauma due to vegetable substances (twigs, corn stalks, etc.) or by wounds caused by foreign bodies which lodge in the cornea. The fungus spores carried into the wound germinate to produce a mycelial growth.

A white plaque develops at the site of trauma. The cornea usually is not vascularized, and ulceration develops in the corneal tissue surrounding these opacities.

Treatment. Nystatin and Amphotericin B drops have proved effective in some cases (60, 66, 67, 70). The drugs can reach the fungus only after removal of as much necrotic tissue as possible. All corticosteroids should be withdrawn from treatment.

REFERENCES

ASPERGILLOSIS

1. Ainsworth, G. C., and Austwick, P. K. C. Fungal Diseases of Animals, Farnham Royal, Bucks, England, Commonwealth Agriculture Bureau, 1959.
2. ——— and Rewell, R. E. J. Comp. Path. & Therapeutics, 59:213, 1949.
3. Argabrite, J. W., and others. Ann. Allergy, 2:283, 1963.
4. Austwick, P. K. C., and Venn, J. A. J. Vet. Record, 59:1, 1947.
5. ——— and Venn, J. A. J. Proc. 4th Internat. Congress on Animal Reproduction, The Hague, 1961.
6. ——— and others. Vet. Record, 72:19, 1960.
7. Bailey, J. C., and Fulmer, J. M. Am. J. Ophthal., 51:670, 1961.
8. Baker, R. D. Am. J. Clin. Path., 37:358, 1962.
9. Belcher, J. R., and Plummer, N. S. Brit. J. Dis. Chest, 54:335, 1960.
10. Bodin, E., and Gauthier, L. Ann. Inst. Pasteur, 20:209, 1906.
11. Brooksbank, N. H., and Austwick, P. K. C. Brit. Vet. J., 3:64, 1955.
12. Conant, N. F., and others. Manual of Clinical Mycology, 2nd ed., Philadelphia, W. B. Saunders Co., 1954, p. 203.
13. Davies, D. Canad. M. A. J., 89:392, 1963.
14. Davis, W. A., and McClung, L. S. J. Bact., 40:321, 1940.
15. Drake, C. H. Mycopathologia, 4:103, 1948.
16. Drouhet, E., and others. Ann. Inst. Pasteur, 105:597, 1963.
17. Emmons, C. W. Lab. Invest., 11:1026, 1962.
18. Fineberg, J. G., and Grayson, H. J. Gen. Microbiol., 18:1, 1958.
19. Finegold, S. M., and others. Am. J. Med., 27:463, 1959.
20. Fourneau, E., and others. Compt. rend. Soc. biol., 122:652, 1936.
21. Gold, W., and others. Antibiotics Annual, 1955-56, New York, Medical Encyclopedia, Inc., 1956, p. 579.
22. Gregory, P. H., and Lacey, M. E. Tr. Brit. Mycol. Soc., 46:73, 1963.
23. Haley, L. D. Arch. Otolaryng., 52:202, 208, 220, 1950.
24. Hayward, J., and others. Acta Allergol., 7:87, 1960.
25. Henrici, A. T. J. Immunol., 36:319, 1939.
26. Herman, C. M., and Sladen, W. J. L. Trans. 23rd North American Wildlife Conference, Washington, D.C., Wildlife Management Institute, 1958, p. 187.
27. Hinson, H. F. W., and others. Thorax, 7:317, 1952.
28. Horejsi, M., and others. Thorax, 15:212, 1960.
29. Janke, D., and Theone, J. Hautarzt, 13:145, 1962.
30. Karaca, M., and others. J. Lab. & Clin. Med., 59:799, 1962.
31. Keye, J. D., Jr., and Magee, W. E. Am. J. Clin. Path., 26:1235, 1956.
32. Longbottom, J. L., and Pepys, J. Internat. Arch. Allergy, 20:370, 1962.
33. Louria, D. B. Ann. New York Acad. Sc., 98:617, 1962.
34. Monod, O., and others. Presse méd., 59:1557, 1951.
35. Orie, N. G. M., and others. Am. Rev. Resp. Dis., 82:649, 1960.
36. Paldrok, H., and Hollstrom, E. Acta dermatvenereol., 32:255, 1952.
37. Pecora, D. V., and Toll, M. W. New England J. Med., 263:785, 1960.
38. Pepys, J., and others. Am. Rev. Resp. Dis., 80:167, 1959.
39. ——— and others. Nature, 184:1328, 1959.
40. Rau, E. M., and others. Mycopath. et Mycol. Appl., 14:347, 1961.
41. Renon, L. Etude sur l'Aspergillose chez les animaux et chez l'homme, Paris, Masson et Cie., 1897.
42. Schwarz, J., and others. Am. J. Med., 31:692, 1961.
43. Seabury, J. H., and Samuels, M. Am. J. Clin. Path., 4:21, 1963.
44. Seeliger, H. P. R. Serology of Fungi and Deep Fungous Infections, in Dalldorf, G., ed., Fungi and Fungous Diseases, Springfield, Ill., Charles C Thomas, 1962, p. 158.
45. Segretain, G. Fungous Diseases and Their Treatment, London, Butterworth & Co., 1959, p. 128.
46. ——— Lab. Invest., 11:1046, 1962.
47. Senturia, B. H., and Wolf, F. T. Arch. Otolaryng., 41:56, 1945.

48. Silver, M. D., and others. Canad. M. A. J., 87:579, 1962.
49. Stanley, N. F. Australian J. Exper. Biol. & Med. Sci., 28:109, 1950.
50. ———— Australian J. Exper. Biol. & Med. Sci., 28:99, 1950.
51. Stefanini, M., and Marin, H. Proc. Soc. Exper. Biol. & Med., 99:504, 1958.
52. Stuart, E. A., and Blank, F. Canad. M. A. J., 72:334, 1955.
53. Tilden, E. B., and others. Mycopath. et Mycol. Appl., 14:325, 1961.
54. Tomsikovar, A., and others. Ztschr. Immunitätsforsch., 120:40, 1960.
55. Utz, J. P., and others. New England J. Med., 260:264, 1959.
56. Virchow. Arch. f. path. Anat., 9:557, 1856.

PENICILLIOSIS

57. Aimé, P., and others. Presse méd., 41:761, 1933.
58. Huang, S., and Harris, L. S. Am. J. Clin. Path., 39:167, 1963.
59. Wolf, F. T. Arch. Otolaryng., 46:361, 1947.

MYCOTIC KERATITIS

60. Anderson, B., and others. Arch. Ophthal., 62:169, 1959.
61. Burda, C. D., and Fisher, E., Jr. Am. J. Ophthal., 50:926, 1960.
62. Chick, E. W., and Conant, N. F. Invest. Ophthal. (abstr.), 1:419, 1962.
63. Dudley, M. A., and Chick, E. W. Fed. Proc., 22:667, 1963.
64. Fazakas, A. Ophthalmologica, 126:91, 1953.
65. Fine, B. S., and Zimmerman, L. E. Am. J. Ophthal., 48:151, 1959.
66. Gingrich, W. D. J.A.M.A., 179:602, 1962.
67. Gordon, M. A. Arch. Ophthal., 62:758, 1959.
68. Leber, T. Arch. Ophthal. (Berlin), 25:285, 1879.
69. Ley, A. P. Am. J. Ophthal., 42:59, 1956.
70. Mangiaracine, A. B., and Liebman, S. D. Arch. Ophthal., 58:695, 1957.
71. Saubermann, G., and Scholer, H. J. Bibl. Ophthal. (Basel), 54:1, 1959.
72. Scholer, H. J., and Saubermann, G. Bibl. Ophthal. (Basel), 54:23, 1959.

MEDICAL PARASITOLOGY

83

Introduction to Medical Parasitology

Parasitology is the science or study of **parasitism**—that is, the relations between parasites and the organisms (hosts) that harbor them. In the fields of medicine and public health the subject matter of parasitology is limited to parasitism in man. In a **broad sense** this would involve the study of all organisms parasitic on or within the human body. However, this broad approach, including both **plant** and **animal** parasites, is not usually feasible for teaching purposes, since there are many specialized fields involved. Thus, it is customary to study parasites of the **plant kingdom** in medical bacteriology, virology, and mycology, while those of the **animal kingdom** are studied in **medical parasitology.** The most important species of animal parasites of man belong to **four** phyla of animals: the **Protozoa,** or single-celled animals; the **Nemathelminthes,** or roundworms; the **Platyhelminthes,** or flatworms; and the **Arthropoda,** which includes not only the true insects but ticks, mites, and others. While certain arthropods affect the health of man in many ways, their greatest importance in medicine and public health is the role played in **transmission of disease.** For this reason, and due to space limitations, they will be considered here only as transmitters of infectious agents.

In presenting the present material, an attempt will be made to coordinate the medical and biologic approaches to the subject—that is, to give proper attention to both the host and the parasite. The life cycle of the parasite will be given, followed by a brief consideration of the principal damage produced in the host and the striking signs and symptoms resulting therefrom. After these discussions of each infection, the laboratory diagnosis and treatment will be given. For the infections having **considerable** medical and public health importance in the United States the discussion will also include a brief account of certain factors dealing with the epidemiology and control. By relating the important **host-parasite relationships,** rather than emphasizing certain factors concerned only with the host or the parasite, it has been our experience that the student gains a better appreciation and understanding of these infections. In following this approach, however, it will be necessary to limit the space customarily given to details of classification, morphology of the parasite, pathology, and so forth. For those interested in more complete information, there are many excellent textbooks and journals available, including those listed below as general references.

It has not been practicable, for reasons of space, to cite bibliographic references, but the writer wishes to acknowledge the fact that this material is based on the published studies of others.

GENERAL REFERENCES

There are many excellent sources of information dealing with all phases of **medical parasitology.** The few references listed below are among the best as sources of information to supplement the material in these chapters.

TEXTBOOKS

Ash, J. E., and Spitz, S. Pathology of Tropical Diseases, Philadelphia, W. B. Saunders Company, 1945.
Belding, D. L. Textbook of Clinical Parasitology, 2nd ed., New York, Appleton-Century-Crofts, Inc., 1952.
——— Basic Clinical Parasitology, New York, Appleton-Century-Crofts, Inc., 1958.
Chandler, A. C., and Read, C. P. Introduction to Parasitology, 10th ed., New York, John Wiley & Sons, Inc., 1961.
Faust, E. C., Beaver, P. C., and Jung, R. C. Animal Agents and Vectors of Human Disease, 2nd ed., Philadelphia, Lea and Febiger, 1962.

Faust, E. C., and Russell, P. F.   Craig and Faust's Clinical Parasitology, Philadelphia, Lea and Febiger, 1957.

Herms, W. B., and James, M. T.   Medical Entomology, 5th ed., New York, The Macmillan Company, 1961.

Horsfall, W. R.   Medical Entomology, Arthropods and Human Disease, New York, The Ronald Press Company, 1962.

Hunter, G. W., III, Frye, W. W., and Swartzwelder, J. C.   A Manual of Tropical Medicine, 3rd ed., Philadelphia, W. B. Saunders Company, 1960.

Markell, E. K., and Voge, M.   Diagnostic Medical Parasitology, Philadelphia, W. B. Saunders Company, 1958.

Russell, P. F.   Malaria—Basic Principles Briefly Stated. Oxford, England, Blackwell Scientific Publications, 1952.

MANUALS

Brooke, M. M.   Amebiasis—Methods in Laboratory Diagnosis, Atlanta, U.S. Department of Health, Education and Welfare, Public Health Service, Bureau of State Services, Communicable Disease Center, 1958.

Wilcox, A.   Manual for the Microscopical Diagnosis of Malaria in Man, 2nd ed., Washington, D.C., Federal Security Agency, U.S. Public Health Service, National Institutes of Health Bulletin No. 180 (revised), U.S. Government Printing Office, 1950.

JOURNALS

Experimental Parasitology, Academic Press, Inc., New York.

The American Journal of Tropical Medicine and Hygiene, The Williams and Wilkins Company, Baltimore 2, Maryland.

The Journal of Infectious Diseases, George Banta Publishing Company, Menasha, Wisconsin.

The Journal of Parasitology, The Allen Press, Lawrence, Kansas.

Transactions of the Royal Society of Tropical Medicine and Hygiene, F. J. Parsons, Ltd., London.

Tropical Diseases Bulletin, The Eastern Press, Ltd., London.

84

Protozoa and Protozoan Infections

Protozoa are **unicellular animals** composed of a nucleus, or nuclei, and cytoplasm. The nucleus is concerned with reproduction. The cytoplasm is differentiated into an inner portion, the **endoplasm,** and an outer layer, the **ectoplasm.** The endoplasm is concerned mainly with nutrition, while the ectoplasm performs the functions of protection, ingestion of food, and so forth. Locomotion, if accomplished, is carried out by special ectoplasmic **organelles. Four** classes of Protozoa contain important parasites of man: 1, **rhizopoda** (amebae); 2, **ciliata** (ciliates); 3, **mastigophora** (flagellates); and 4, **sporozoa.** The amebae locomote by means of pseudopodia, the ciliates by cilia, and the flagellates by flagella, while the sporozoans lack definite organelles for locomotion. In addition to certain parasites included within these four classes, another of uncertain taxonomic affinities, *Toxoplasma gondii,* will be considered.

In the presentation of the material of this chapter, the protozoa will be grouped according to their usual location within the body of man. By so doing, there are two main groups to be considered: **the intestinal, oral, and genital protozoa,** and **the blood and tissue protozoa.**

INTESTINAL, ORAL, AND GENITAL PROTOZOA

This group will include **six** amebae, (rhizopoda), **one** organism in the class ciliata (*Balantidium coli*), and **five** flagellates (mastigophora). Most of these reside in the intestinal tract, but two occur in the mouth (an ameba and a flagellate) and one occurs in the genital organs (another flagellate). Emphasis will be placed on the agents of clinical importance, but it will be necessary to include information on the common so-called nonpathogenic agents, especially in relation to microscopic differentiation.

THE AMEBAE

Of the **six** amebae commonly found in man, only **one** (*Entamoeba gingivalis*) occurs in the **mouth;** the remaining **five** species (*Entamoeba histolytica, Entamoeba coli, Endolimax nana, Iodamoeba bütschlii,* and *Dientamoeba fragilis*) are located in the **large intestine.** Since *E. histolytica,* the cause of **amebiasis,** is the most important of the amebae, it will be given special attention. There is evidence that heavy infections with one or more of the other four amebae living in the large intestine may produce irritation resulting in certain cases of **diarrhea;** furthermore, there is some evidence that at least one of these so-called nonpathogenic amebae (*D. fragilis*) may exhibit pathogenicity in some individuals. Nevertheless, until more information becomes available, our main concern with these four amebae lies in the fact that one or more may coexist with *E. histolytica,* making differentiation necessary. For this reason, they will be mentioned only in connection with the laboratory diagnosis of *E. histolytica.* The remaining ameba, *E. gingivalis,* may be dismissed, since it is now considered a commensal organism. It is common in those with carious teeth and diseased gums and tonsils.

Morphology and Life Cycle of *E. histolytica.* There are **three** distinct stages in the life cycle: the trophozoite, the precyst, and the cyst (Fig. 1). The **trophozoites** vary considerably in size (8 to 60 μ). In warm smears prepared from fresh material they are active and exhibit progressive and directional motility by the action of ectoplasmic

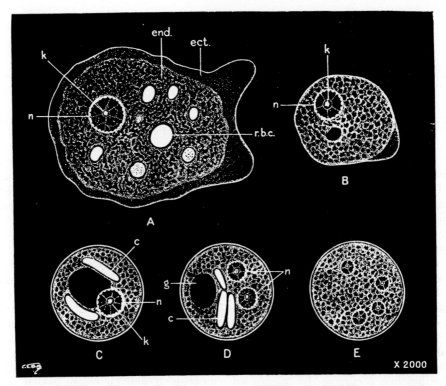

Fig. 1. Schematic representation of *Entamoeba histolytica.* A, trophozoite containing red blood cells undergoing digestion; B, precystic ameba devoid of cytoplasmic inclusions; C, young uninucleate cyst; D, binucleate cyst; E, mature quadrinucleate cyst; c, chromatoid bodies; ect., ectoplasm; end., endoplasm; g, glycogen vacuole; k, karyosome; n, nucleus; r.b.c., red blood cells. (From Belding. *Textbook of Clinical Parasitology,* 2nd ed., Appleton-Century-Crofts.)

pseudopodia. These are glass-like and are formed in explosive fashion. After extrusion of a pseudopodium, the remaining material of the cell is drawn toward it, tending to give a degree of polarity to the organism. The nucleus usually is not visible, so that the only inclusions noted are within the **food vacuoles,** where digestion takes place. If red blood cells are present in the material being examined, they often will be seen as well within the food vacuoles, but it should be emphasized that trophozoites from cases of **chronic amebiasis** usually **do not** contain these cells. The usual inclusions are indistinct, being presumably debris of tissue cells in various stages of digestion. When undergoing degeneration, the trophozoites become sluggish, and bacteria, as well as large vacuoles, can be seen within them.

In **stained** preparations the structure of the nucleus is distinctive. The nuclear membrane is delicate and has on its inner surface a single layer of minute chromatin **beads,** and the **karyosome** is small and usually located centrally. Again, when undergoing degeneration, changes occur in the nucleus, causing it to lose its characteristic appearance.

The **precystic stage** is intermediate between the trophozoite and cyst stages. The trophozoites become sluggish in action, and, after extrusion of food particles, there is a rounding of the cytoplasm. This results in a reduction in size compared with that of the motile amebae. Motility ceases and a cyst wall is secreted.

The **cyst stage** is more resistant than the other stages and is, under most conditions, the **infective** stage. Cysts range in size from 5 to 20 μ, are usually spherical, and contain one, two, or four nuclei with the same structure noted in the trophozoites. Also present in some are paired **chromatoid bars** with rounded ends and a **glycogen vacuole.** The chromatoid bars and the vacuole disappear gradually as the cyst reaches maturity by division of the nucleus to the quadrinucleate stage.

The life cycle of *E. histolytica* is comparatively simple. The parasite is passed in the stools of infected individuals. If the specimen is dysenteric or diarrheic, or has been obtained following purgation, **trophozoites** will predominate. Few cysts are observed in such specimens because, presumably, evacuation is too rapid for encystment. **Cysts,** therefore, usually are found only in normally passed stools that are formed, at least in part. Cysts will remain viable only if kept moist and if other favorable conditions exist, as they are readily destroyed by desiccation, sunlight, heat, and other factors. Reinfection of the same individual or infection of a new host(s) may occur **directly,** via contaminated fingers **(hand-to-mouth infection),** or **indirectly,** chiefly via contaminated food and/or fluids. The ingested cysts pass through the stomach and **excyst** in the **small intestine.** A metacystic ameba containing the four cystic nuclei emerges from each cyst. Cytoplasmic division takes place to form four small metacystic trophozoites, which feed and soon grow to full size. They pass along the intestinal canal until conditions are favorable for **colonization,** which occurs as the result of rapid and repeated transverse binary fission. This usually occurs first at the **cecal area** but may take place at a lower level of the large intestine. **Tissue invasion** is probably accomplished both by lytic and physical means. After entering the tissue, lytic digestion of host cells provides food for the ameba, allowing it to advance. Under certain conditions, some of the trophozoites may metastasize to the **liver** and other **extraintestinal sites.** When some of the trophozoites are extruded into the intestinal lumen, they begin their passage from the body. If this passage is not too rapid, they pass through the precystic stage and occur in the stool as cysts.

It should be added that many workers are of the opinion that the **small race(s)** of *E. histolytica* is a commensal organism living in the lumen of the intestine. However, it is known that geographic strains vary in pathogenicity, that the bacterial flora of the intestine, the resistance, and the nutritional status of the host all are factors in determining whether or not demonstrable pathology results from a given infection. Thus, it would seem wise, until final proof has been established, to consider all strains capable of damaging the host.

Pathology and Symptomatology of Amebiasis. The **intestinal pathology** of amebiasis is most commonly observed in the **cecal area,** followed by the **sigmoidorectal areas,** but lesions may occur at any point from the lower ileum downward. The process begins with a small lesion produced at the site of entry into the tissue. A minute cavity is formed from lytic necrosis. As viewed from the surface, these small lesions are surrounded by a raised yellowish ring and are separated by mucosa that appears normal. Usually showing no evidence of inflammatory reaction, these lesions fail to suggest the degree of subsurface damage that may be considerable. As the colony of amebae increases, a narrow channel often is formed to the base of the mucosa. There, due probably to the greater resistance of the muscularis mucosae, the lesion enlarges. This appears to be a critical stage determining whether or not extensive damage will be produced, and it may, therefore, be thought of as an expression of the degree of adaptation between the parasite and the host. If the organisms are unable to penetrate this layer, repair may keep pace with the damage, and in some cases the amebae may be eliminated. If, however, the organisms erode a passage through the muscularis mucosae into the submucosa, they usually spread out radially and produce an enlarged **flask-shaped ulcer.** The mucosa surrounding this usually is rolled and elevated due to the undermining. Secondary infections usually are not observed in these early lesions, despite extensive necrosis, and there is essentially no tissue reaction present. Later the surface of the ulcer sloughs off exposing **shaggy** overhanging edges. At this time secondary infections are common and the ulcer is infiltrated with neutrophilic leukocytes and other wandering cells, tending to thicken the overhanging edges. In severe cases the organisms may spread from the submucosa through the muscular coats into the serosa, where they are likely to cause perforation. Also, within the intestinal wall, the amebae may enter the portal venules or, less commonly, the lymphatics and be carried to the liver and other organs. **Liver involvement is most common,** followed by involvement of the lungs, which is by direct extension from the liver abscess. Lesions outside of the intestinal tract are always secondary to those in the intestine.

In intestinal amebiasis there often is no definite pattern of **symptoms;** in fact, the disease may manifest itself clinically in a deceiving fashion. In **acute amebiasis** (amebic dysentery) the individual usually is acutely ill, complains of general abdominal discomfort and tenderness, and passes numerous stools, which in most cases are dysenteric. The symptoms usually are referable to the cecal area and may resemble appendicitis and various other conditions. In **subacute infections,** the picture is similar but less striking. Considering the number of cases involved and the difficulty of diagnosis, **the major problem is chronic amebiasis.** The symptomatology in this case exhibits even greater latitude. Some may have periodic bouts of diarrhea or, less commonly, dysentery, but longer periods of constipation are characteristic. Others are without distinctive signs or symptoms and complain of a low fatigue threshold, moderate loss of weight, mental dullness, and the like. Still others found to be infected are entirely asymptomatic.

The pathology of amebic liver abscess results from the establishment and multiplication of **trophozoites** in that organ. Some recognize a preabscess stage known as **amebic hepatitis,** characterized by an enlarged and tender liver. The early abscess is small with a grayish brown matrix of necrosed hepatic cells. Connective tissue does not appear to be destroyed by the lytic property. As the abscess increases in size, the center liquefies, the wall thickens, and in most cases the contents become a viscid ("creamy") chocolate-colored mass. At all stages of abscess formation, the amebae are seen invading the **marginal** tissue. Abscesses occur more frequently in the **right lobe** than in the left and tend to be **solitary** rather than multiple. The latter are usually seen in those

with active dysentery, and these abscesses usually develop in a relatively brief period after the intestinal phase becomes acute. It is important to emphasize that liver abscess may be a sequela of **chronic** intestinal amebiasis as well as of the acute type (amebic dysentery). In fact, liver abscess without gross evidence of intestinal involvement and without organisms in the stool is not unusual.

The symptomatology of amebic liver abscess is characterized by hepatomegaly, tenderness over the liver, moderate leukocytosis, and a low-grade inconstant fever.

Laboratory Diagnosis of *E. histolytica.* In the diagnosis of **intestinal amebiasis,** various methods are used depending upon the type of specimen and other factors. If the fecal specimen is dysenteric or diarrheic, or has been obtained following purgation, it is likely to contain only **trophozoites.** If possible, it should be examined while still warm, because the trophozoites may soon lose their characteristic features. Two fecal smears should be prepared side-by-side, and about 1 mm. apart, on a microscope slide. One smear is made by emulsifying a bit of the specimen in a drop of tepid physiologic salt solution, and the other by emulsification in a drop of tepid **Quensel's supravital stain.** To avoid overstaining, the latter may require the addition of a small drop of tepid salt solution. Coverglasses are added to both preparations, and careful examinations are made under the low power and high dry power of a compound microscope. The salt solution smear is examined first and is most useful in permitting the observation of the characteristic locomotion of the trophozoites, and the Quensel-stained smear, viewed about five minutes after preparation, will permit the observation of the characteristic **stained nucleus.** Other supravital staining methods are available. It may be necessary to prepare and examine several dual preparations before making a species identification. If, in suspected cases of amebiasis, such direct examinations fail to reveal the organism, and especially if **Charcot-Leyden crystals** or other microscopic materials suggestive of amebiasis have been noted, it is worthwhile to **culture** some of the stool. By so doing, many cases, missed by direct examinations, may be diagnosed.

If it is not possible to examine the fresh specimen immediately, it may be preserved in **films** by the **PVA** or **Lawless technic** or in **bulk** by the **MIF technic.** Although usually not a part of routine diagnostic work, it is sometimes desirable to make **permanent,** stained films of the raw stool. Various methods are available.

If the fecal specimen is formed, or at least semiformed, it is likely to contain mostly **cysts** (Fig. 1). Again, direct examinations should be made of dual preparations. In this case, one smear is made in the salt solution, especially to observe the refractive chromatoid bars, and the other is made in **D'Antoni's iodine solution.** The latter stains the cyst, making visible the internal diagnostic characteristics. If direct examinations fail to reveal cysts, a **concentration method** should be employed. Also, a portion of the stool may be cultured, but success following the use of this method usually is not as likely as following attempts to culture trophozoites. Finally, a portion of the stool may be preserved for later study, and permanent stained films may be made.

The various technical procedures referred to above, and others, are explained fully in most of the standard textbooks (see list of references at end of Chapter 83, p. 1115).

Differentiation of *E. histolytica* from the other four intestinal amebae (p. 1117) must be made. Since all of these except *Dientamoeba fragilis* have a cyst stage, differentiation involves both stages, with this one exception. There are structural and other important differences between the various amebae, but limited space prohibits a discussion of all of these. The **single character** that is most diagnostic is the **structure of the nucleus** (Fig. 2). Two of the five intestinal amebae, *E. histolytica* and *E. coli,* have conspicuous peripheral chromatin on the inner surface of the nuclear membrane, while such material is lacking or is not conspicuous in the other three. In *E. histolytica* the nuclear membrane is delicate, and the chromatin on the inner surface appears as fine **beads;** the karyosome is small and usually central. In *E. coli* the membrane is thicker and the chromatin on the inner surface is in the form of coarse **plaques;** the karyosome is much larger than that of *E. histolytica* and is located eccentrically. The striking feature of the nucleus of *E. nana* is the large karyosome located in the center or slightly off-center.

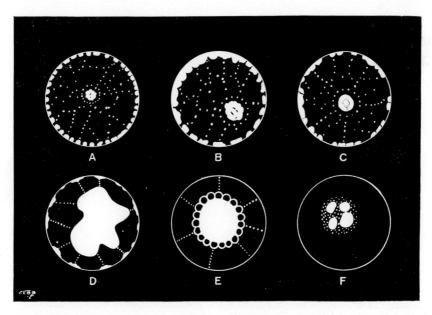

Fig. 2. Diagrammatic representation of the various types of nuclei in the amebae of man. A, *Entamoeba histolytica;* B, *Entamoeba coli;* C, *Entamoeba gingivalis;* D, *Endolimax nana;* E, *Iodamoeba bütschlii;* F, *Dientamoeba fragilis.* (From Belding. *Textbook of Clinical Parasitology,* 2nd ed., Appleton-Century-Crofts.)

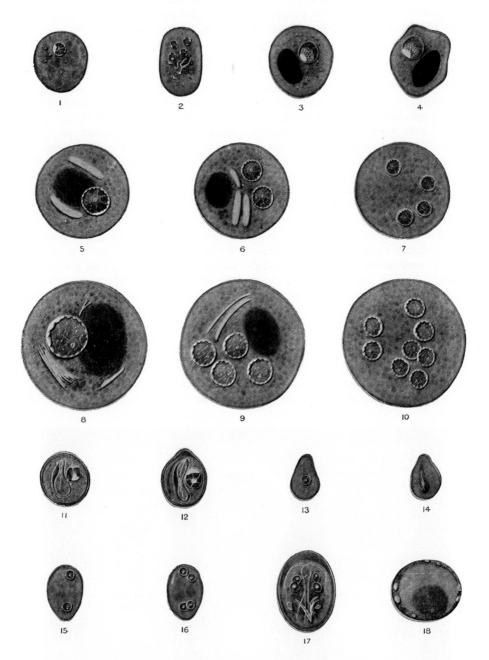

Plate I. Cysts of intestinal protozoa treated with iodine. × 2000. 1 and 2, *Endolimax nana;* 3 and 4, *Iodamoeba bütschlii;* 5, 6, and 7, *Entamoeba histolytica;* 8, 9, and 10, *Entamoeba coli;* 11 and 12, *Chilomastix mesnili;* 13 and 14, *Embadomonas intestinalis;* 15 and 16, *Enteromonas hominis;* 17, *Giardia lamblia;* 18, *Blastocystis hominis,* a yeast resembling a protozoan cyst. (From Belding. *Textbook of Clinical Parasitology,* 2nd ed., Appleton-Century-Crofts.)

In the case of *I. bütschlii,* the karyosome is also large but is surrounded by a ring of **achromatic granules,** giving a halo effect around the karyosome. *D. fragilis* usually has **two** nuclei, but organisms with a single nucleus are not rare. In all cases, the nucleus is composed of a central mass with four to six chromatin granules, one of which usually is larger and stains more deeply than the others. The characteristics of the amebae cysts after staining with iodine are shown in **Plate I.**

In addition to stool specimens, proctoscopic and other aspirates are sometimes submitted for direct examination. These should be examined immediately after being obtained in unstained preparations or in preparations stained with one of the supravital stains. Usually a variety of host tissue cells is present, so it is important to observe the typical motility of the trophozoites before deciding definitely on the diagnosis.

In the diagnosis of amebic liver abscess it is difficult to find typical trophozoites in aspirated contents. Nevertheless, such materials should be examined at once in unstained and stained preparations, and some should be cultured. It should be added that many have come to rely upon the **complement-fixation test** as one of the means of diagnosis.

It is important to emphasize that the laboratory diagnosis of **chronic amebiasis,** especially in children, often is difficult. Best results will be obtained following the use of a battery of tests, as described above, for examinations of a series of suitable specimens (e.g., one or more normally passed specimens, one following purgation, and one following administration of an enema). All should be free of urine, oil, magnesia, kaolin, barium, or bismuth and should be obtained, if possible, prior to the administration of medicants. Many drugs tend to suppress the growth of *E. histolytica* and/or alter the typical structure, making diagnosis more difficult. Finally, it should be added that recovery of the organism, difficult as it is at times, is only the initial step in diagnosis. The final and most difficult step is specific identification. This requires considerable experience.

Treatment of Amebiasis. For the treatment of **intestinal amebiasis,** a large number of effective antiamebic drugs are at hand. Excellent results have been obtained following the use of **Terramycin** alone, but many recommend combining the use of this antibiotic with **Diodoquin** (63.9 per cent iodine), using the full schedules and dosages recommended for each. For the treatment of **liver abscess, chloroquine** or **emetine hydrochloride** is the recommended drug.

Certain Factors in the Epidemiology and Control of Amebiasis. Although *E. histolytica* is found in certain **animal reservoirs** (monkeys, dogs, rats), they play a relatively unimportant role as sources of human infection. The only source of importance is man himself. This parasite has been shown to be present in man in all areas of the world where careful coprologic examinations have been made. The prevalence is higher in warm climates, but the disease may be a major public health problem in almost any area where persons live crowded together and where sanitation and hygiene are of a low order. In the **United States** many surveys have shown that the prevalence, while varying considerably in different geographic areas, **is more than 10 per cent.** In mental hospitals, prisons, children's homes, and other restricted communities the prevalence usually is very high, for the reasons mentioned above. This disease is typically **endemic,** but epidemics occur at intervals, especially as a result of gross contamination of drinking water with viable cysts of the ameba.

The viable cyst of *E. histolytica* probably is the only type of inoculum that produces human infection, and exposure is by the oral route. Whether exposure results in infection depends upon the number of viable cysts ingested, the pathogenicity of the strain of ameba, and the resistance of the host. Persons of all races and ages and of both sexes appear to be equally susceptible to infection. Differences in distribution usually can be explained by the degree of exposure. The modes of transmission are not understood fully, but most workers agree that person-to-person contamination; food contamination by filth flies, food handlers, and human excrement used as fertilizer; and polluted water are the most important.

Success in the **control** of amebiasis depends first upon its acceptance as a **major public health problem.** To determine the extent of the problem in a given community, a carefully planned survey must be made, using reliable diagnostic procedures. By studying the epidemiologic pattern—that is, the means by which the agent is propagated and maintained—the major cause(s) of the problem in the area, whether it be of an endemic, hyperendemic, or epidemic nature, may be determined. Careful studies must be made of the factors that may be responsible for transmission, such as person-to-person contact, filth flies, food handlers, water, etc. Once the important factor(s) has been determined, practical control methods must be instituted.

In restricted communities, such as mental hospitals, where responsible factors cannot be controlled satisfactorily **chemotherapeutic prophylaxis** has proved to be a practical control procedure. Mass therapy is administered to all persons, and all newcomers are required to take the treatment before joining the group.

THE CILIATED PROTOZOAN

Balantidium coli (Fig. 3) is the only ciliate parasitic in man and is by far the largest of the protozoa found in the human body. The **trophozoite** varies considerably in size (50 to 100 μ by 40 to 70 μ, or even larger), is ovoidal in shape, and covered entirely with short, constantly moving cilia. A funnel-shaped **peristome** ("mouth") leads into the **cytostome** ("gullet"), and a minute **cytopyge** is located at the posterior end. One or two **contractile vacuoles** may be seen within the cytoplasm, as well as **two** nuclei, a large, kidney-shaped **macronucleus** and, usually within the concavity, a small **micronucleus.** The **cyst,** observed less frequently than the trophozoite, is much smaller (45 to 65 μ in diameter), is almost spherical in shape, and is covered with a double transparent wall. Stained cysts reveal clearly the nuclear components.

This organism occurs usually in the **cecal area** but may be found at both higher and lower levels. The trophozoites feed upon bacteria and other substances in the lumen but take in host cells after they enter the tissues. They reproduce by transverse binary

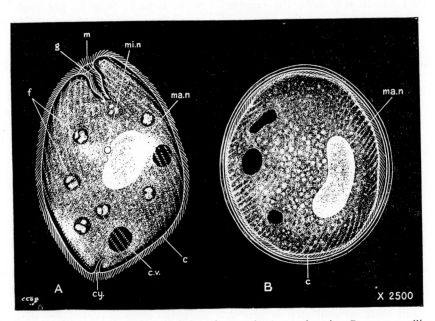

Fig. 3. Schematic representation of *Balantidium coli.* A, trophozoite; B, cyst; c, cilia; cy., cytopyge; c.v., contractile vacuole; f, food vacuole; g, "gullet"; m, "mouth"; ma.n, macronucleus; mi.n, micronucleus. (From Belding. *Textbook of Clinical Parasitology,* 2nd ed., Appleton-Century-Crofts.)

fission and in certain hosts they may become numerous. The mucosal layer appears to be penetrated mainly by boring action, and because of the size of the organism, the opening is much larger than that produced by *E. histolytica.* Having gained entrance into the mucosa, it appears to have little difficulty in passing through the muscularis mucosae into the submucosa, where it spreads out radially and may produce considerable destruction. Unlike *E. histolytica,* it apparently invades the muscular layers only on rare occasions, and although observed in lymphatics, it has not been found in extraintestinal sites. The ulcers produced may occur at all levels of the large intestine but are most common in the cecal and sigmoidorectal areas. They often resemble those produced by *E. histolytica,* especially after bacteria invade them. When this occurs, extensive inflammatory reactions are noted around the organisms as well as a diffuse infiltrate throughout the tissue.

Many harboring *B. coli* are asymptomatic, but others show symptoms ranging from mild to profuse diarrhea and even fulminating, fatal dysentery.

Laboratory diagnosis usually is made by finding the characteristic trophozoites in the stool. Because of their great size, they are easily detected. However, free-living ciliates may occur as contaminants of the stool or saline solution used in making the smear, resulting in a mistaken diagnosis. Cysts also may be found, depending somewhat upon the condition of the stool specimen.

Balantidiasis can be treated effectively with **Diodoquin** or **Terramycin.**

THE FLAGELLATED PROTOZOA

Morphology and Life Cycles. *Giardia lamblia* is found in the **small intestine;** it has a trophozoite and cyst stage. The **trophozoite** (10 to 18 μ by 6 to 11 μ) is bilaterally symmetrical with **two** nuclei and **four** pairs of flagella (Fig. 4). It has no oral opening, but on the ventral surface near the anterior end there is a characteristic **adhesive disc.** Two **axostyles** extend through the center

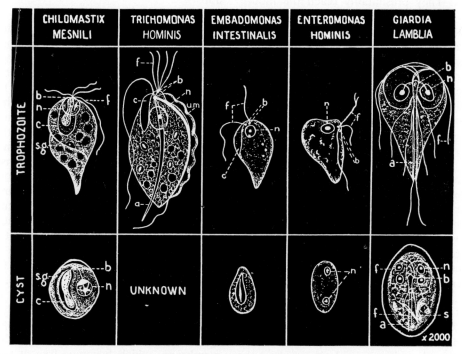

Fig. 4. Intestinal flagellates of man. a, axostyle; b, blepharoplasts; c, cytostome; f, flagella; n, nucleus; s, shields; s.g., spiral groove; u.m., undulating membrane. (From Belding. *Textbook of Clinical Parasitology,* 2nd ed., Appleton-Century-Crofts.)

portion to the posterior end, which is tapered and from which a pair of flagella emerges. Other structures, such as the **blepharoplasts** may be seen, but no food particles are evident. Since there is no cytostome, the food substances must be absorbed through the general surface of the body. The **cyst** (8 to 14 μ by 6 to 10 μ) is ovoid, and the wall is relatively thickened (Fig. 4; **Plate I**). When stained two, four, or occasionally more nuclei can be seen as well as curved fibrils.

The **trophozoites** usually are found in the intestinal crypts at the **duodenal level,** where they are **firmly attached** to the epithelial surface. At times they are also found at lower levels of the intestine and in the **common bile duct** and **gallbladder.** Multiplication is by longitudinal binary fission, which may result in myriads of organisms. Because of their location, trophozoites are not seen in the stool unless the individual has been given a saline cathartic or is extremely diarrheic. Therefore, only cysts usually are found in the stool. These occur intermittently and may be very numerous. Under moist conditions, the cysts may remain viable for long periods. They presumably reach the mouth of the same person or others by the avenues of transmission listed above for *E. histolytica.* They pass unharmed through the stomach and **excyst** in the upper intestine. **Two** trophozoites, or sometimes more, result from each cyst, hence this stage provides for reproduction as well as for transmission.

Chilomastix mesnili in the **trophozoite stage** (Fig. 4) is pear-shaped and ranges usually from 10 to 15 μ in length and from 3 to 4 μ in breadth. There are **three** anterior flagella and a **fourth** situated within the **cytostome.** A large spherical nucleus with one or more blocks of chromatin is located near the anterior end of the body. Numerous **food vacuoles,** filled mainly with bacteria, are crowded in the cytoplasm. The most characteristic features of this organism are the peripheral **spiral groove** and the **caudastyle,** a spine-like projection at the posterior end. The lemon-shaped **cysts** usually range from 7 to 9 μ in length and from 4 to 6 μ in width, have a thickened portion at the anterior end, and in stained smears show the nucleus and cytostomal structures (Fig. 4; **Plate I**).

The **trophozoites** live in the **lumen of the large intestine** and multiply by longitudinal binary fission. These may occur in large numbers in unformed stools, but usually only cysts are seen in formed stools. These are more resistant than most protozoan cysts as they have a thermal death point of 72° C. and may survive in clean water for longer than 200 days. Infection is acquired from swallowing viable cysts in fecal contaminated food and/or drink or from viable cysts introduced into the mouth from fecal contaminated fingers.

Three species of **trichomonads** are common in man and all are known only in the **trophozoite stage** (*Trichomonas tenax, T. hominis, T. vaginalis*). They have the following common characteristics: a pear-shaped appearance as a result of the rounded anterior end and a somewhat pointed posterior end, a slender rod-like **axostyle** that extrudes through the posterior tip, a small **cytostome,** a large spherical nucleus near the anterior end, and, the most characteristic structural feature, an **undulating membrane** (Fig. 5). Multiplication is by longitudinal binary fission.

Trichomonas tenax, 6 to 12 μ in length, has **four** anterior flagella, and the undulating membrane extends posteriorly about two-thirds the length of the body; the flagellum on its outer edge does not extend beyond the end of the membrane (Fig. 5). The normal habitat is the **mouth,** and the rate of infection is considerably higher in those with diseased gums and carious teeth than in those with normal mouths. Transmission, no doubt, usually occurs by the transfer of trophozoites during kissing, but contaminated dishes, glasses, and the like may be involved, especially during meals when those being used by an older person contain as well the food being given to an infant.

Trichomonas hominis lives in the **lumen of the large intestine** and is usually from 7 to 15 μ long and from 4 to 7 μ wide. There are usually **four** anterior flagella, but organisms with **three** or **five** are seen at times. In addition to these, there is a flagellum, attached to the outer edge of the undulating membrane, which becomes free at the posterior end of the body (Figs. 4, 5). The membrane, in this case, extends the full

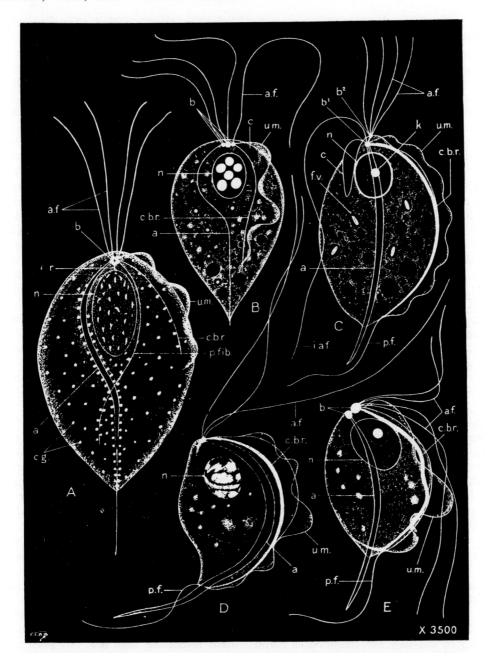

Fig. 5. Trichomonads of man. A, *Trichomonas vaginalis;* B, *Trichomonas tenax;* C, *Penta-trichomonas ardin delteili;* D, *Tritrichomonas fecalis;* E, *Trichomonas hominis;* a, axostyle; a.f., anterior flagella; b, b¹, b², blepharoplasts; c, cytostome; c.b.r., chromatoid basal rod; c.g., chromatin granules; f.v., food vacuole; i.a.f., inferior anterior flagellum; k, karyosome; n, nucleus; p.f., posterior flagellum; p.fib., parabasal fiber; r, rhizoplast; u.m., undulating membrane. (From Belding. *Textbook of Clinical Parasitology,* 2nd ed., Appleton-Century-Crofts.)

length of the body. Transmission occurs by the ingestion of trophozoites in contaminated food and/or drink. The organism can survive for many days in undiluted feces stored at temperatures ranging from 5 to 31° C., and there is evidence that house flies may play a role in transmission.

Trichomonas vaginalis (Fig. 5) is a normal inhabitant of the **human vagina** and of the **male genital tract** and is often found in the urine of infected subjects. It usually is much larger than the other two trichomonads, reaching 25 μ or more in length and 18 μ in breadth. It has **four** anterior flagella and one on the margin of the undulating membrane. The membrane in this case is very short, usually not extending below the upper half of the body, and the flagellum on its margin does not extend beyond the side of the body. Transmission in many cases is accomplished through sexual intercourse, but many infections cannot be explained on this basis. Some of these may have resulted from a transfer of organisms from female to female through the use of a common vaginal douche or a contaminated toilet seat, or from grossly contaminated clothing.

Pathology and Symptomatology. **Three** of these organisms are not important clinically, except in unusual cases. *T. tenax,* like *Entamoeba gingivalis,* is now considered a harmless organism that grows best in those who fail to practice good dental and oral hygiene. Also *C. mesnili* and *T. hominis* are considered to be nonpathogenic. However, there is some evidence that these organisms, when present alone or together in large numbers, may irritate the intestine and play a role in **diarrhea,** since the condition often subsides upon eradication of the parasite(s). The remaining **two** flagellates, *G. lamblia* and *T. vaginalis,* are important clinically whether or not they are classified as pathogenic. While many persons found to be infected with *G. lamblia* are entirely asymptomatic, others complain of periodic abdominal pain and show a history of recurrent or persistent mucous diarrhea, while others, mostly adults, may have symptoms referable to the **duodenum** and **gallbladder.** In some of the latter cases, the symptoms may approximate the typical syndrome of chronic cholecystitis. Many patients with a giardial infection, after a period when anorexia and diarrhea are pronounced, lose weight and may become dehydrated. *T. vaginalis* infection is not limited to females, as a large number of males with nongonorrheal urethral discharges are found to be infected. In the latter the symptoms usually are slight until the infection is aggravated by secondary bacterial invasion, after which the condition becomes a purulent urethritis and prostatovesiculitis. In the female, many infections do not result in a complaint of symptoms, but **the vaginal secretions are altered invariably.** In typical cases of *T. vaginalis* vaginitis, the normal pH of the vagina (3.8 to 4.4 during sexual maturity) becomes more alkaline, and the glycogen stores of the vaginal mucosa, especially in the superficial layers, are reduced greatly. The normal processes of cellular destruction make the glycogen available to the **Döderlein bacillus,** an inhabitant of the normal vagina, which metabolizes glycogen and excretes lactic acid. This maintains the normal acid state of the vagina. In the absence of normal stores of glycogen, the numbers of this organism are reduced, and in severe cases it may be eliminated. When these events occur, the physiologic protection offered by the normal vaginal acidity is altered, and the growth of *T. vaginalis* and other organisms is encouraged. Those with *T. vaginalis* have a profuse, watery leukorrheic discharge that produces a chafing of the vagina and vulva, and pruritus vulvae is distressing.

Laboratory Diagnosis. Fecal smears made from fresh material will reveal *G. lamblia, C. mesnili,* and *T. hominis.* If the specimen is formed, the cysts of *G. lamblia* and *C. mesnili* may be expected, but if liquid or semiformed, the trophozoites of all three forms may be seen. If cysts are difficult to find, indicating that few are present, they may be concentrated. Aside from the structural differences listed above, the trophozoites of each species exhibit characteristic movements. *G. lamblia* has a fluttery, "falling-leaf" movement, *C. mesnili* a graceful, progressive spiral movement, and *T. hominis* a nervous, jerky movement. *G. lamblia* trophozoites may also be obtained by duodenal aspiration and, if the gallbladder is involved, from bile aspirate.

T. tenax sometimes is difficult to demonstrate in smears but may be demonstrated by cultures.

T. vaginalis may be recovered in the urine, prostatic or urethral discharges of the male, and in the urine and vaginal discharges of the female.

Treatment. **Atabrine** is recommended for the removal of *G. lamblia;* **carbarsone** or **Diodoquin** for *C. mesnili* and *T. hominis.* Treatment for *T. tenax* is not necessary. The treatment of patients infected with *T. vaginalis* has not been satisfactory. Oral **aureomycin** has been used to treat males, and **Floraquin** (with **Diodoquin** as the trichomonacide, boric acid, dextrose, and lactose) has been popular for treating females (by use of powder insufflated through a speculum and/or use of tablets for insertion). Because of the high relapse rate in both males and females and the inherent difficulties of local therapy of females, there has been a great need for an effective systemic preparation for treating both sexes. Metronidazole **(Flagyl),** an oral drug, appears to meet this need and should be considered the present **drug of choice.**

BLOOD AND TISSUE PROTOZOA

Flagellated Protozoa

These flagellates differ greatly from those discussed above. Besides having an entirely different structure, the **blood and tissue flagellates** are found in different tissues in man and require a **bloodsucking arthropod** to complete their life cycle. **Six** species are involved, **three** in the genus *Trypanosoma* (*T. gambiense, T. rhodesiense,* and *T. cruzi*), and **three** in the genus *Leishmania* (*L. donovani, L. tropica,* and *L. brasiliensis*).

The Trypanosomal Parasites

Morphology and Life Cycles. *Trypanosoma gambiense* and *T. rhodesiense* (Fig. 6), agents of the **African trypanosomiases,** cannot be separated by morphologic characters. Both circulate primarily in the **blood stream** as the mature **trypanosomal stage.**

The most diagnostic feature of this stage is the long **undulating membrane** that originates near the posterior end of the body and extends along the margin of the body to the tip of the anterior end where the free flagellum may be seen (Fig. 7). These parasites are **polymorphic** in their appearance in the blood. Short and broad forms, long and slender forms, and intermediate forms ranging in length from 15 to 30 μ may be seen in the same stained preparation. When blood containing *T. rhodesiense* is injected into mice or other laboratory animals, forms with a nucleus located posteriorly may occur, permitting differentiation from *T. gambiense.* The trypanosomal stage in the blood of man is taken with a blood meal by the vector, one of the **tsetse flies.** *Glossina palpalis* is the most common vector for *T. gambiense,* while *G. morsitans* is the principal vector for *T. rhodesiense.* In the vector, the trypanosomal forms pass through the proventriculus into the midgut, where multiplication by longitudinal binary fission results in the production of elongated trypanosomes. These finally make their way into the **salivary glands,** where multiplication results in the production of **crithidial forms** (Fig. 7). These resemble the trypanosomal stage, but the undulating membrane is shorter, originating anterior to the nucleus. Later, these transform into **infective-stage trypanosomes,** which accumulate in the ducts of the salivary glands. The entire development within the fly requires about **two weeks** (*T. rhodesiense*) or **three weeks** (*T. gambiense*). Infection of man occurs when the fly, containing infective-stage trypanosomes, takes a blood meal.

T. cruzi, agent of **Chagas' disease** or **American trypanosomiasis,** differs from the other two trypanosomes in that it has an **intracellular phase** involving not only cells of the **lymphoid-macrophage system** but also those of the **myocardium, endocrine glands,** and the **glial cells** of the brain. In this phase, the parasite is a typical **leishmanial form** (Fig. 7), being ovoid in shape, 1.5 to 5 μ in the longer diameter, and having a large nucleus and a deeply staining **kinetoplast** composed of a **parabasal body** and a **blepharoplast.** A delicate axoneme may sometimes be seen arising from the blepharoplast. No

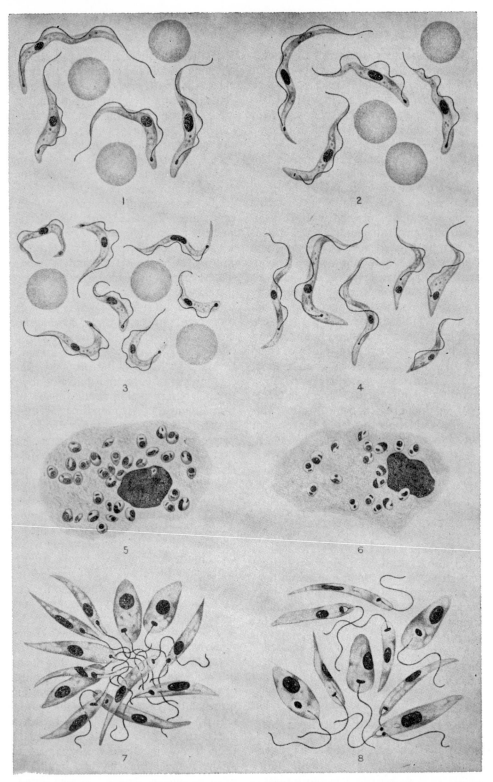

Fig. 6. Blood and tissue flagellates of man. × 1500. 1, *Trypanosoma gambiense* in blood; 2, *Trypanosoma rhodesiense* in blood; 3, *Trypanosoma cruzi* in blood; 4, *Trypanosoma gambiense*, developmental forms in *Glossina palpalis;* 5, *Leishmania donovani* in endothelial cell; 6, *Leishmania tropica* in large mononuclear cell; 7, *Leishmania donovani*, flagellated forms from culture; 8, *Leishmania tropica*, flagellated forms from culture. (From Belding. *Basic Clinical Parasitology,* Appleton-Century-Crofts).

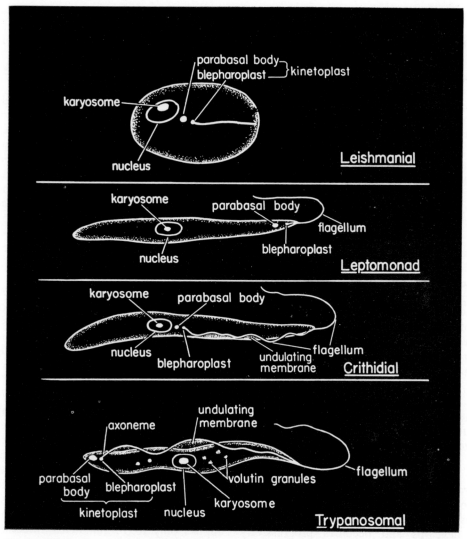

Fig. 7. Schematic representation of morphologic forms in the *Trypanosoma* and *Leishmania* genera. (From Mackie, Hunter, and Worth. *A Manual of Tropical Medicine,* 2nd ed., W. B. Saunders Co.)

true flagellum or undulating membrane is present. When freed from the host cell, this stage enters the blood stream where it transforms into a typical, or C-shaped, trypanosomal stage, about 20 μ long (Fig. 6), which is the stage taken by the vector. The vector, in this case, is a **triatomid** (cone-nosed) bug. Many species of these bugs have been found infected naturally with *T. cruzi,* but *Panstrongylus megistus, Triatoma infestans,* and *Rhodnius prolixus* appear to be the most important vectors. When taken into the bug,

the trypanosomal stage of the parasite is carried into the midgut, where it transforms into the crithidial stage (see above). Later, following multiplication in the hindgut, the **infective trypanosomes** are formed, which pass out in the liquid feces of the bug when it is taking a blood meal or immediately thereafter. This usually occurs at **night,** and the itching produced by the bite often results in an infection caused by rubbing into the wound, or nearby skin or mucous membrane, the excrement containing the infective parasites. The entire cycle in the bug requires about **two weeks.**

Pathology and Symptomatology. *T. rhodesiense* is much more likely than *T. gambiense* to run a rapid, fulminating course with a fatal outcome. In fact, it is rare for the patient to survive long enough for the trypanosomes to invade the **central nervous system.** In *T. gambiense* infections there usually are **three** progressive stages of tissue relationship: **parasitemia,** when the parasites are numerous in the blood; **lymphadenitis,** when they are concentrated in the lymph nodes, and **central nervous system involvement,** when the parasites are numerous in the brain substance and arachnoid spaces. In natives there are usually only **two** clinical stages. The **first** occurs when the parasites invade the lymph nodes. Febrile episodes occur, and, while the patient may complain of severe headache, weakness of the legs, and other conditions, the most characteristic feature is **lymphadenitis.** This is most pronounced in the posterior cervical triangle **(Winterbottom's sign).** Later anemia and other conditions may appear. The **second** stage is one characterized by **physical weakness** and **mental lethargy,** which follow invasion of the central nervous system. There is a generalized leptomeningitis composed of large histiocytes, lymphocytes, and other cells, and, paralleling the intensity of this infiltrate, there is a **perivascular infiltration of mononuclear cells,** near which there usually is an increase in neuroglial cells. Sleepiness develops and becomes progressively pronounced until, in the advanced stage, the patient sleeps continuously. Emaciation becomes extreme, convulsions occur, and then coma and death, which often results directly from pneumonia or other intercurrent infections.

An early, almost constant, sign of **acute** *T. cruzi* infection, especially in infants, is edema of the face and eyelids **(Romaña's sign).** Another early manifestation is enlargement of lymph nodes, especially the axillary and cervical. Soon after these events, the primary parasitemia occurs, which is accompanied by fever and often causes severe systemic toxemia. The acute form predominates in younger age groups, is usually of short duration, and has a high case-fatality rate in very young children. The **chronic** disease, usual among adults, follows the development of the parasite in several **visceral organs.** Here they multiply as leishmanial type organisms, destroying the host cells and bringing about inflammatory reactions in the involved tissues. Although the parasites may be found in any location or organ of the body, they have a definite predilection for **cardiac muscle, skeletal muscle,** and the **brain.** Therefore, it is not surprising that the principal pathologic changes are noted grossly in the heart and brain and the predominant symptoms are those of **cardiac failure.** The heart is enlarged and pale, and the muscle is soft and hemorrhagic. A large collection of organisms within a muscle fiber usually is surrounded by an interstitial infiltrate, chiefly of eosinophils, plasma cells, and histiocytes. The spleen and liver are enlarged and congested in relation to the degree of cardiac failure. The brain is congested and edematous, and often contains scattered petechial hemorrhages. Collections of organisms may be associated with glial nodules.

Laboratory Diagnosis. *T. gambiense* and *T. rhodesiense* occur in the **circulating blood** during febrile episodes and sometimes can be demonstrated in **thick** smear preparations. However, **lymph node aspirates** reveal more infections. After involvement of the central nervous system, examination of **spinal fluid** may yield positive results. For the reason explained above, this method applies only to *T. gambiense* infections. If these various methods fail to establish the diagnosis, susceptible laboratory animals (guinea pigs, white rats, and others) may be inoculated intraperitoneally with some of the patient's blood and later examined at intervals for the parasites.

T. cruzi also may be found in the **circulating blood** during febrile periods, but they are never numerous and therefore are often difficult to demonstrate even in thick film preparations. Laboratory animals may be inoculated with blood from suspected cases, and a widely used **xenodiagnostic test** is available. The latter involves the use of parasite-free, laboratory-raised triatomids, which are allowed to take blood from the patient. Examination of the feces or intestinal contents of the bugs after **eight** to **ten days** usually will reveal trypanosomes if they were present in the blood of the patient. The organisms also may be **cultivated** easily on various media (**N.N.N., Chang's,** and others) and in **tissue cultures,** all of which reveal the crithidial and trypanosomal forms. Finally, an excellent complement-fixation test devised recently should prove valuable, especially in diagnosing latent and chronic cases of the disease.

Treatment. Prompt treatment is vital, since delay reduces considerably the chances for recovery. For treating **early** cases (blood and lymph stages) of both *T. gambiense* and *T. rhodesiense,* **Suramin sodium** (Bayer 205) is the drug of choice. In the **late** stages (after invasion of the central nervous system) **Mel B** is the drug of choice. **Tryparsamide** also has been used widely. Finally, **Pentamidine isethionate,** an aromatic diamidine, is an excellent **chemoprophylactic** agent that has been used successfully in massive control programs.

T. cruzi infections are refractive to chemotherapy, leaving symptomatic relief as the only means of treatment. It should be noted, however, that a case of Chagas' disease diagnosed in Texas in 1955, the first authentic case reported as being **acquired in the United States,** was treated successfully with **Bayer 7602.** Perhaps this drug or related compounds will fill the great need for an effective chemotherapeutic agent against *T. cruzi.*

The Leishmanial Parasites

Morphology and Life Cycles. The size and other morphologic characters of *Leishmania donovani, L. tropica,* and *L. brasiliensis* are indistinguishable. In man they occur as typical leishmanial forms (2 to 3 μ long by 1 to 1.5 μ wide), often referred to as **"Leishman-Donovan bodies,"** with structures similar to those noted in this form during the tissue stage of *T. cruzi* (Figs. 6, 7). *L. donovani* causes **visceral** leishmaniasis, or **kala-azar,** and the organisms are usually numerous in the **endothelial cells** of the **blood and lymph capillaries** and in **leukocytes.** They have been described from almost all organs but occur especially in the **spleen, liver, bone marrow,** and **lymph nodes.** The

organisms probably are distributed throughout the body by the blood stream after reaching this site upon rupture of the host cells. They multiply, as do all members of the mastigophora, by longitudinal binary fission. *L. tropica* causes **cutaneous** leishmaniasis, or **oriental sore,** etc. There is no general dissemination of the parasites; only exposed **skin areas** are affected. The parasites often can be demonstrated within **endothelial macrophages.** *L. brasiliensis* causes **mucocutaneous** leishmaniasis, or **uta,** etc. The primary location of the organisms is in the **skin,** but in most cases they migrate to develop in secondary sites in **mucous membranes** near cutaneous junctions. The **nose** and/or **mouth** usually are involved, but extension into the **pharynx** may occur.

In the case of **all three** organisms, several species of small biting flies belonging to the genus *Phlebotomus* are mainly responsible for their transmission to **man and reservoirs.** The flies ingest the leishmanial form by direct ingestion from the infected skin or by ingestion of blood or tissue juices. After being ingested, the parasites develop into the **leptomonad stage** in the midgut (Fig. 7). This stage is characterized by having a free flagellum at the anterior end without having an undulating membrane. They multiply rapidly, and within **three** to **five days** many have migrated into the **proboscis.** In this location they are ready to be injected into the skin of the next individual when the fly takes another blood meal.

Pathology and Symptomatology. *L. donovani* infections cause hyperplasia of the cells of the lymphoid-macrophage system, especially of the **spleen, liver,** and **bone marrow.** Both the liver, with an increase in the number and size of Kupffer cells, and spleen become enlarged, and the bone marrow shows a reduction in the normal hematopoietic function. As a result of this reduced function, there is compensatory hematopoiesis in the fatty marrow, liver, and spleen. In the liver the Kupffer cells may be crowded with organisms without an associated inflammatory infiltrate. In fact, the **absence** of such an infiltrate is characteristic. In the spleen it is the large macrophages that usually contain the organisms. The usual signs and symptoms include an undulant type fever, loss of weight (which may be masked by edema), abdominal protuberance, visible pulsation of the carotid arteries, bleeding of the gums, lips, and nares, and hemorrhage from the intestinal mucosa. The usual blood picture shows a moderate erythropenia and an absolute monocytosis and neutropenia. The most important complication in children is bronchopneumonia. The case-fatality rate in some areas may be as high as **90 per cent** in untreated cases. *L. tropica* and *L. brasiliensis* infections produce **local** lesions that appear first as a **macule,** then a **papule** with a slightly raised center. Later the lesion opens at the center to discharge necrotic material. The lesion produced by *L. tropica* usually is **single.** Multiple lesions probably are the result of accidental **autoinoculation** but may also been seen as **satellite lesions** at the periphery of a healing ulcer or one healed and scarred. The lesions develop in a relatively sluggish fashion, usually not exceeding a few centimeters in diameter over a period of **several months.** Ulceration usually occurs late, after which rapid healing is the rule, always with the formation of a scar. However, secondary infections may occur, slowing healing and causing more extensive scarring. In the skin lesions the large histiocytes constitute the bulk of the material. The lesion produced by *L. brasiliensis,* on the other hand, **develops more rapidly,** and ulceration and secondary infection usually occur early in the disease. The lesions may reach a large size, and the duration of the disease tends to be more prolonged. After extension to the mucous membranes, destruction of tissue usually is considerable, and even if healing occurs, the scars are disfiguring to the extent of causing deformity of the face. The margins of old ulcers caused by both organisms tend to become irregular and indurated by infiltration of fibroblasts. It is a well-established fact that one attack of *L. tropica* confers **permanent immunity.** In endemic areas where *L. tropica* lesions are common on the face, this observation has led the natives to inoculate their children on an unexposed part of the body to prevent disfiguring scars.

Laboratory Diagnosis. *L. donovani* may be demonstrated sometimes in **stained blood smears,** but **cultivation** of the organisms by inoculating the blood into special media (N.N.N., Chang's, etc.) and incubating at **20 to 25° C.** is more likely to be successful. The leptomonad stage occurs in cultures (Figs. 6, 7). Many workers prefer to prepare **stained tissue smears** following removal of a specimen by **biopsy.** In the past spleen and liver specimens have been most often used, but today most workers favor the use of a **bone marrow specimen** from the iliac crest obtained by the **van den Bergh technic.** A portion of each sample should also be handled aseptically and **cultured.** If these various methods fail to reveal the parasites in suspect cases, hamsters may be inoculated. A complement-fixation test of great diagnostic value is available.

L. tropica and *L. brasiliensis* may be demonstrated in stained smears made from the crater of an early lesion or, less often, from material obtained from the indurated margin of older lesions. The material can also be cultured, but care must be taken to cleanse the area before taking a sample as the organisms **seldom will grow in the presence of bacteria.** A complement-fixation test and a skin test are available for diagnosis of both *L. tropica* and *L. brasiliensis,* but the skin test has been more widely used in clinics and in the field to diagnose *L. brasiliensis.*

Treatment. Neostibosan, a pentavalent organic antimonial, is the drug of choice for treating infections with *L. donovani,* except in the Egyptian Sudan and parts of East Africa, where the aromatic diamidine **Stilbamidine** is the choice. In other areas the latter, due to greater toxicity, is reserved for antimony-resistant cases. The drug of choice for treating *L. tropica* and *L. brasiliensis* is **Neostibosan.** After secondary bacterial infections of ulcers, sulfa drugs or antibiotics are used to destroy these agents before giving **Neostibosan.**

The Malarial Parasites

The malarial parasites belong to the **class** SPOROZOA, **order Haemosporidia,** and **genus** *Plasmodium,* and their life cycle involves both an asexual phase (**schizogony** in man as the **intermediate host**) and a sexual phase (**sporogony** in certain female anopheline mosquitoes as the **definitive host**). There are

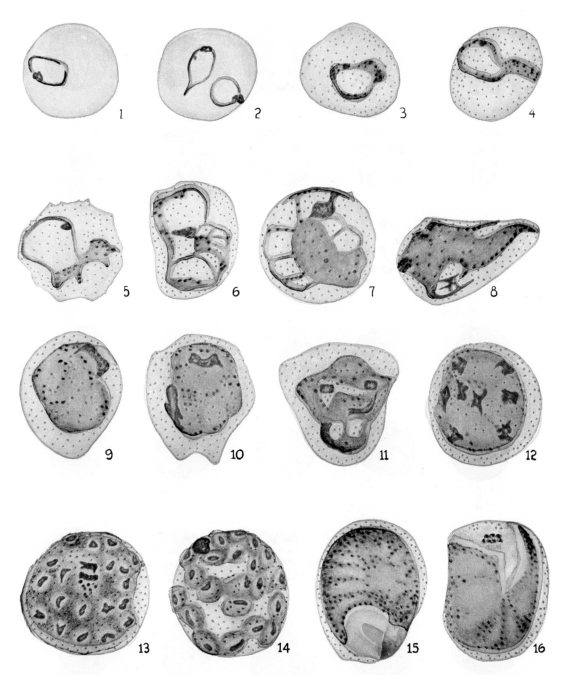

Plate II. *Plasmodium vivax*. Sexual and asexual developmental forms of the parasite within the red cells of man from a case of benign tertian malaria, as seen in dried blood films stained with Romanovsky stain. Approx. × 3200. 1 and 2, ring forms; 3-9, growth of trophozoite, enlargement and change in shape of red cell, formation of Schüffner's dots, and deposition of pigment in cytoplasm of parasite; 10-14, growth of schizont; 15, female gametocyte (macro-gametocyte); 16, male gametocyte (microgametocyte). (From Belding. *Textbook of Clinical Parasitology,* 2nd ed., Appleton-Century-Crofts.)

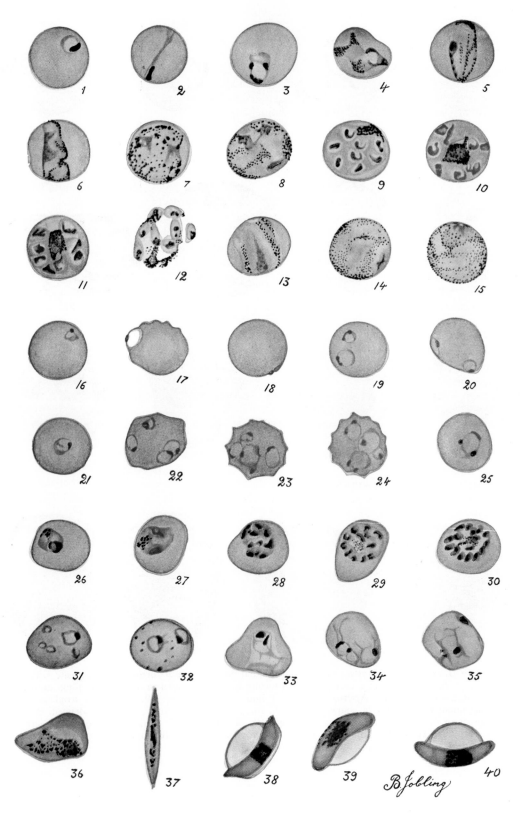

B. Jobling

three common species of human malarial parasites: (1) *Plasmodium vivax,* agent of **benign, tertian malaria,** is the most widely distributed and on a world-wide basis is the most prevalent species; (2) *P. falciparum,* agent of **malignant, subtertian malaria,** is as prevalent as *P. vivax* in subtropical and tropical regions but fails to establish in areas where there are long cold seasons; and (3) *P. malariae,* agent of **quartan malaria,** is limited almost entirely to tropical and subtropical areas where it is considerably less prevalent than *P. vivax* and *P. falciparum.* A fourth valid species, *P. ovale,* will not be included in this discussion. It has been reported sporadically from widely separated tropical and subtropical regions, but it is not the dominant type even in parts of Africa where it is well established. The parasite resembles *P. vivax* in certain characters and *P. malariae* in others.

General Asexual Cycle in Man. While there are striking morphologic differences between the three parasites selected for study, the general features of the cycles are the same. Specific differences will be considered below under laboratory diagnosis (**Plates II and III**). The cycle in man begins with the inoculation of infective **sporozoites** by a female anopheline mosquito. Within 30 minutes, the sporozoites disappear from the circulating blood, and no parasites can be demonstrated in red blood cells for many days. It is now known that during this negative phase the parasite is residing in **fixed tissue cells** (parenchyma cells of the **liver** and perhaps others). While the various stages of the parasite observed in **exo-erythrocytic foci** resemble those seen later within the red blood cells, the characteristic malarial pigment (**hemozoin**), derived from the breakdown of hemoglobin is, of course, not seen. After development in exo-erythrocytic foci for many days, the density of the parasites increases and certain of the progeny enter the blood stream and initiate erythrocytic infection. It should be added that the exo-erythrocytic forms of *P. vivax,* and probably those of *P. malariae* as well, may persist long after the eradication of the erythrocytic forms and thus are believed to be the cause of later episodes of parasitemia and clinical relapses. Following the use of **Giemsa** or other blood stains, **all** of the red blood cells stages are seen, with **the nucleus or chromatin red, the cytoplasm blue,** and **the malarial pigment** a **light brown** to **dense black,** depending upon the species. The first stage observed within the red blood cells is the **trophozoite.** The youngest trophozoite is referred to as a **ring,** which has a central vacuole and a ring of cytoplasm containing a chromatin dot. The growth of the parasite proceeds gradually, the vacuole disappears, and the cytoplasm increases in size. With the increase in volume of the cytoplasm, pigment may be observed within it. The pigment increases in amount with increasing age of the parasite, since it is a waste product of hemoglobin metabolism. When the single nucleus of the trophozoite stage divides to form two nuclei, the **schizont** stage is formed. The chromatin continues to divide until the number characteristic for the species is reached. At this point the **preseg-**

Plate III. *Plasmodium malariae* (1-15) and *Plasmodium falciparum* (16-40) as seen in dried blood films stained with Leishman stain. × 2,000. *Plasmodium malariae:* 1, young ring form; 2, young band form; 3, slightly older parasite with granule of pigment; 4-6, growth of trophozoite; 7-12, development of schizont; 13, older band form of nearly mature gametocyte; 14, female gametocyte (macrogametocyte); 15, male gametocyte (microgametocyte). *Plasmodium falciparum:* 16-24, ring forms; 25 and 26, growth of trophozoite and development of pigment; these forms usually occur in the internal organs, but are occasionally seen in the peripheral blood; 27-30, development of schizont; these forms occur rarely in the peripheral blood; 31 and 32, deeply stained cells containing ring forms and showing Stephens' and Christopher's or Maurer's dots on the surface of the cell; 33-35, irregular or ameboid young forms, showing tendency to fusion of one or more parasites (*"Plasmodium tenue"* of Stephens); 36 and 37, developing gametocytes; 38 and 40, female gametocytes (macrogametocytes) showing remains of host cell; 39, male gametocyte (microgametocyte). (From Wenyon. *Protozoology,* London, Baillière, Tindall and Cox, 1926. This plate was made from the original drawing now in the Museum of Medical Science, Wellcome Research Institution, obtained through the courtesy of Professor Wenyon and the Publishers. From Belding. *Textbook of Clinical Parasitology,* 2nd ed., Appleton-Century-Crofts.)

menter has been produced. The **segmenter** or mature schizont is observed soon thereafter, when each chromatin mass has been provided, after division of the cytoplasm, with an envelope of cytoplasm to form the **merozites.** By this time the **pigment,** scattered previously, has become clumped, usually near the center of the parasite. The red blood cell ruptures, and some of the merozoites enter new cells to begin again the asexual cycle. The length of this cycle, from entry of merozoite to the rupture of the host cell, varies with the species of parasite, being **48 hours** for *P. vivax* (although a **44-hour** strain has been demonstrated), **72 hours** for *P. malariae,* and **36** to **48 hours** for *P. falciparum.* The latter cycle, however, has considerably less synchronization than that of the other two species. In addition to trophozoites and schizonts, a third stage, **gametocyte,** is seen within the red blood cells. The gametocytes, male and female sex cells, nearly fill the red blood cell and have only a single chromatin mass. It is this stage that initiates the sporogenous cycle in the female anopheline. In summary, there are only three distinct stages within the red blood cells of man: the **trophozoite,** the **schizont,** and the **gametocyte.**

General Sexual Cycle in Anopheline Mosquito. After a susceptible female anopheline ingests a blood meal containing ripe gametocytes of both sexes, the sexual cycle begins. In the lumen of the midgut, the gametocytes escape from the host cells and soon undergo changes preparatory to fertilization. The female gametocyte (**macrogametocyte**) extrudes polar-like bodies, which some believe is indicative that the haploid condition is being assumed. The male gametocyte (**microgametocyte**), through a process known as **"exflagellation,"** forms a number of sperm-like bodies. Because these changes in both cells are noted within about **20 minutes** under favorable conditions, it is suggestive that the "lining-up" process within the nucleus of each actually begins in the human blood stream. In any event, fertilization occurs when a microgamete enters a macrogamete and a zygote is formed. Being motile, this form is referred to as the **ookinete.** The ookinete penetrates beneath the basement membrane lining the midgut and, after about **24 hours,** penetrates through the cells and becomes encysted on the **outside** wall of the midgut. Here the **oocyst** is formed, which when mature, contains large numbers of **sporozoites.** The oocyst ruptures into the body cavity (**haemocoel**) after about **two weeks,** and many of the sporozoites eventually find their way into the trilobed **salivary glands.** After a **few days** under optimum conditions, the sporozoites become infective and are capable of initiating an infection in a susceptible individual after being inoculated when the mosquito punctures the skin to take a blood meal.

Pathology and Symptomatology. The most characteristic features of the **pathology** of malaria are **anemia, pigmentation** of certain organs, and **hypertrophy** of the liver and, especially, the spleen. The **anemia,** a **microcytic, hypochromic type,** may be produced not only by the direct loss of red blood cells as a result of their destruction by the parasite but also from interference with hematopoiesis, by increased phagocytosis of red blood cells, and as the result of capillary hemorrhages. In **acute cases** *P. falciparum* produces the greatest degree of anemia, especially because of the marked loss of red blood cells by the growth of the parasite within them. In **chronic cases,** and especially during malarial **cachexia,** the anemia is particularly outstanding. During the latter cases leukopenia, with a 20 per cent or more monocytosis, is considered diagnostic of malaria. The pigmentation noted in the tissues of malaria victims is due to the phagocytosis of **hemozoin,** the true malarial pigment, released into the blood upon rupture of the host cells at the termination of each asexual cycle. It is taken in large amounts by cells of the lymphoid-macrophage system, especially by the macrophages in the spleen and bone marrow and the Kupffer cells in the liver. The pigmentation constantly increases with the age of the infection, so that it may be observed grossly in autopsied cases of chronic malaria. As would be expected from the massive blood destruction, there is also deposition of **hemosiderin** in the tissues. The **liver** is enlarged due to congestion during acute malaria, and it increases considerably in size during chronic infections. The **spleen,** the organ affected most seriously in malaria, is also enlarged, first as a result of congestion, following cavernous dilatation of the sinusoids, and later as a result of a great increase in macrophage elements, especially in Billroth's cords. With repeated attacks, the enlargement becomes progressively greater, and the organ may reach considerable size, especially in width, in chronic malaria. Fibrosis of the cords of Billroth is outstanding here. Splenomegaly in malaria is so characteristic that palpation of this organ has been used for a long time as a rapid and effective means of appraising the malaria problem in communities. Changes in the bone marrow, while much less striking, are similar in character to those in the spleen.

In addition to these changes that may be expected, to a degree, from any malarial infection, especially those of long standing, another important change, **capillary occlusions,** should be mentioned. These are most characteristic in *P. falciparum* infections and are most dangerous in the **brain.** The parasitized red blood cells become sticky, some believe as a result of a specific antibody-antigen reaction, and **agglutinate.** Such cells **marginate** at the periphery of the vessel lumen, probably as a result of centrifugal force, and later the capillary becomes **occluded.** Following this, hemorrhages occur about such vessels, exclusively in the subcortical and paraventricular white matter, producing a **ring** effect. The tissue immediately surrounding the vessel is necrotic, and the **ring hemorrhage** is somewhat removed from the vessel. Usually associated with ring hemorrhages are the so-called **malarial granulomas,** consisting essentially of a rosette of one or several layers of glial cells arranged around the necrotic zone. Anoxia with necrosis of tissue in the immediate vicinity must be the logical consequence of occluded vessels.

Blackwater fever should be mentioned, as it is associated with malarial infections, especially *P. falciparum* infections. The etiology is unknown. The disease is characterized by **intravascular hemolysis** with hemoglobinemia and hemoglobinuria. Hemoglobinuric casts occur in the distal convoluted tubules

in the kidney. Degeneration—and some regeneration—of the tubular epithelium is also seen.

The **symptomatology** of malaria differs between *P. viva* and *P. malariae* infections and that caused by *P. falciparum.* The typical **paroxysm** caused by the former two parasites involves, usually after a brief prodromal period, a **cold stage** (shaking chill), followed by a **fever stage** (a characteristic **remittent** type fever reaching suddenly a level of 104 to 105° F. and, after several hours, returning suddenly to near normal), and a marked terminal **sweating stage** resulting from the sudden fall in body temperature. *P. falciparum* paroxysms differ in many ways; the chill stage is less pronounced (there may be only a chilly sensation), the fever stage is more prolonged and intensified (fever tends to be a **continuous** type), and because the fever fails to remit sharply, the sweating stage is usually absent. *P. falciparum* infection is more **dangerous** than those of the other two species, since it often is accompanied by **pernicious** manifestations, such as coma, convulsions, and/or cardiac failure. *P. falciparum* parasites may localize in any organ, and those bearing the brunt of the attack will give rise to the most striking signs and symptoms. Therefore, the symptomatology of *P. falciparum* malaria may resemble that of many other diseases.

Laboratory Diagnosis. Stained blood smears are examined, under the oil immersion objective, for the presence of malarial parasites. For all uses, the most satisfactory procedure involves the preparation, on scrupulously clean microscope slides, of **thin and thick smears.** The latter involves the use of a large drop of blood covering, on one end of the slide, an area about the size of a dime. The **thin smear** usually is placed to the right and is streaked over about two-thirds of the slide. The **thick smear** is a **concentration method** and, as such, is advantageous for detecting a low concentration of parasites and for saving considerable time in conducting the examination. The main value of the thin smear is in the verification, if necessary, of parasites found in the thick smear. The thin smears also are valuable for studying the morphologic characters of the various stages of different parasites. After fixing the thin smear for **two to three minutes** in acetone-free absolute methyl alcohol, the entire slide is ready to be stained by one of several good staining technics. The **Giemsa method,** perhaps the most widely used procedure, involves staining for **45 minutes** in a 2 per cent solution of stain (one part stain to 49 parts neutral buffered water). Previous fixation of the thin smear prevents dehemoglobination, but this takes place simultaneously with staining of the parasites in the thick smear. For good differentiation, the thin smear is dipped quickly two or three times in neutral buffered water after removal from the stain, and the thick smear is left in the buffered water for a total of **three to five minutes.** After draining and drying in air (an electric fan is satisfactory), the smears are ready for examination. Considerable experi-

ence is necessary before an individual can make a reliable diagnosis of malaria from thick smears alone. Thus, this method, while of great advantage to those skilled in malaria diagnosis, especially during surveys, cannot be mastered in the brief time devoted to the subject by most students. For this reason and for the reason that familiarity with the morphology of the plasmodia is necessary before attempting to use the thick smear for diagnosis, emphasis should be placed in the beginning upon examination of thin smears. Comparative information on the **three** malarial parasites of man, including the most important differential diagnostic characters, is given in **Table 1** (see also **Plates II** and **III**).

Treatment. The modern approach to the treatment of malaria is based upon an understanding of the various stages of the parasite

Table 1. Differential Diagnosis of Malarial Parasites in Stained
Thin Blood Smears

Most Striking Differences	*Plasmodium vivax*	*Plasmodium malariae*	*Plasmodium falciparum*
Abundance of Parasites	More abundant than *P. malariae*	Least abundant	Most abundant
Stages of Parasite Usually Observed	Trophozoites, schizonts, gametocytes	As for *P. vivax*	Young trophozoites, gametocytes
Changes in Infected Red Blood Cells	*Enlarged, mal-shaped, blanched, Schüffner's dots	Changes not com mon	Changes not common
Trophozoites Ring Stage	Small and large (⅓ diameter of r.b.c.) with vacuole and usually one chromatin dot	Much like *P. vivax*	*Very small (⅙ diameter of r.b.c.) with vacuole, often with 2 chromatin dots, peripheral forms (accolé) common, multiple-infected cells very common
Half-grown	Ameboid, irregular with vacuoles, pigment yellow-brown rods	*Oval, band forms (25%), compact, pigment coarse black granules	Not usually seen
Schizonts (Mature)	*12-24 merozoites (usually 16-18)	*8-12 merozoites (usually 8-10) arranged in rosette	Not usually seen
Gametocytes	Spherical or oval (9-15 μ)	As for *P. vivax* (smaller)	*Kidney-bean shape, **round** or pointed ends

* Most diagnostic.

in man and the ways they are affected by the available drugs. Actually, there are **four** different antimalarial activities involved. **Prophylactic activity** is directed against the **sporozoites** and **primary tissue phases,** so that erythrocytic infection is prevented. While there are no known drugs in tolerated dosages that destroy sporozoites, some appear to exert a slight inhibitory effect against the primary tissue phases. Nevertheless, the use of this approach to prevent malaria is not yet practical. **Therapeutic (and suppressive) activity** is directed primarily against the **stages within the red blood cells.** Many effective drugs are available: **Atabrine** among the old antimalarials, and Aralen **(chloroquine),** Paludrine **(chlorguanide),** Daraprim **(pyrimethamine),** and others among the newer ones. The drugs in this group will terminate clinical attacks promptly. Also, when taken in suppressive amounts, they will usually prevent clinical attacks and, if continued long enough, will **cure** falciparum malaria. The newer compounds are more desirable than Atabrine in that less frequent and smaller dosages are required and they do not discolor the skin and eyes. Of the drugs exerting this type of activity **chloroquine,** a 4-aminoquinoline, is the most efficient and effective drug. **Curative activity** is directed primarily against the **persisting tissue stages** of vivax malaria. **Primaquine,** an 8-aminoquinoline, is a very effective curative agent. It is recommended that the acute attack be treated immediately with chloroquine, and concomitantly, or soon thereafter, primaquine treatment should be instituted. Chloroquine need not be included to cure vivax malaria in those not at present suffering an attack of the disease. The fourth type of antimalarial activity, **gametocidal activity,** is that directed against the **gametocytes. Plasmochin** (pamaquine) in low dosage destroys the gametocytes of **falciparum** malaria in man, and **Daraprim** prevents the development of mature **oocysts** of P. falciparum and P. vivax in susceptible anophelines. In summary, an ideal antimalarial is not yet available, but the intelligent use of available drugs, singly or in combination according to the activity desired, will result in a degree of chemotherapeutic control not dreamed possible prior to World War II.

THE TOXOPLASMA ORGANISM

In addition to the above protozoa belonging to the RHIZOPODA, CILIATA, MASTIGOPHORA, and SPOROZOA there is another of great importance whose taxonomic affinities are uncertain. *Toxoplasma gondii,* an obligate intracellular organism, is now known to be a cosmopolitan parasite of man, producing an infection known as **toxoplasmosis.** It has an amazing lack of host specificity, being found in various primates, carnivores, rodents, and birds.

Morphology and Life Cycle. The individual cells, 4 to 7 by 2 to 4 μ, usually are crescentic in shape with one end pointed and the other rounded (Fig. 8). They divide by binary fission. The body of the organism is made up of distinct cytoplasm and nuclear chromatin, but there are no flagella or other visible structures. The absence of inclusions, other than the nucleus, differentiates this organism from the leishmanial stage of *Leishmania* spp. and *Trypanosoma cruzi,* but its morphologic similarity to other organisms (*Histoplasma,* etc.) may confuse the diagnosis. *Toxoplasma* organisms may occur singly or in clusters, **usually** within **fixed** host cells. They may be found at times within wandering macrophages in exudates (peritoneal, pleural, or cerebral) and in circulating blood and technical preparations some may be extracellular (Fig. 8). The cells of the **lymphoid-macrophage system** are most often involved, but the parenchymal cells of the **liver, lungs, brain,** and other tissues may be parasitized. A peculiar **pseudocyst,** 5 to 100 μ, may be observed under certain conditions (Fig. 8). It is formed by aggregates of *Toxoplasma* and has a delicate, delimiting **argyrophilic** membrane. Tissue reaction seldom is associated with pseudocysts; hence they are believed by some to be the basis for the persistence of the organisms during **chronic** and **latent** infections. Little is known of the life cycle of the parasite because, despite extensive studies, the mode of transmission from host to host is still **unknown.**

Pathology and Symptomatology. These organisms may give rise to **four** types of infections: (1) a congenital infection with onset in utero; (2) an acquired encephalitic infection in older children; (3) an acute febrile illness, usually in adults, resembling typhus or spotted fevers and often producing pulmonary involvement (a typical diffuse interstitial pneumonitis), myocarditis, etc.; and (4) a latent infection, in children or adults, which usually can be recognized only by the presence of specific antibodies in the serum. In addition, there is recent evidence of an association between *Toxoplasma* organisms and granulomatous uveitis and chorioretinitis in adults. The congenital infection has been reported most frequently. With its onset in utero, it occurs as a fetal or neonatal encephalomyelitis, which often is fatal soon after birth but which may remain asymptomatic until much later. Marked lesions usually occur in the **central nervous system,** associated with **calcification** in the eyes and **viscera.** Chorioretinitis is very common. At times hydrocephaly or microcephaly and psychomotor disturbances are evident. In

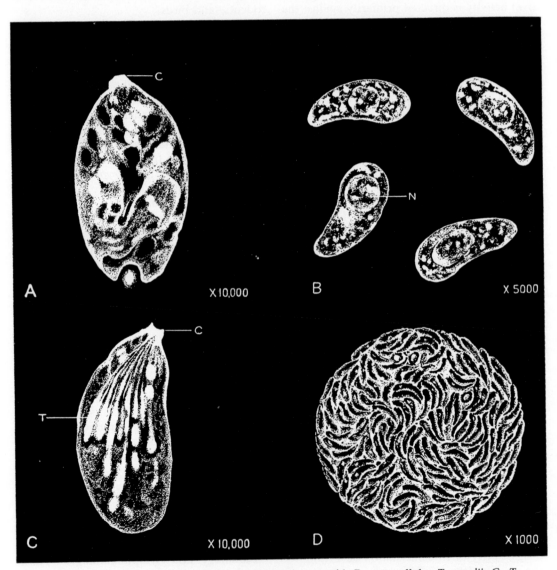

Fig. 8. *Toxoplasma gondii.* A, *T. gondii* showing conoid; B, extracellular *T. gondii;* C, *T. gondii* showing longitudinal toxonemes; D, pseudocyst; c, conoid; N, nucleus; T, toxonemes. (From Brown and Belding. *Basic Clinical Parasitology,* 2nd ed., Appleton-Century-Crofts.)

other types of infections lesions in the **viscera** are more common than those in the central nervous system. In summary, it may be stated that during toxoplasmic infections the organs most commonly attacked are the **brain, eyes, and lungs.**

Laboratory Diagnosis. **Three** approaches are available: direct examination, isolation of organisms, and serologic examination. For **direct examination** under the oil immersion objective, **impression films** of suspected tissues or fluids should be air dried and stained with Giemsa's stain. The preparations usually examined are tissues taken by **biopsy,** sputum, vaginal exudates, and the sediment of spinal, pleural, or peritoneal fluids. In an attempt to **isolate the organisms,** white mice or other susceptible laboratory animals should be inoculated intraperitoneally with fresh, untreated tissue or fluids most likely to contain the organisms. If present, a generalized infection will be produced in **five to ten days,** at which time the organisms usually can be demonstrated easily in the extensive peritoneal exudate. It should be added that this is an excellent source of organisms for serologic tests. The animals that die may be examined for *Toxoplasma* organisms by preparing films and/or sections of the peritoneal fluid, lungs, brain, and other tissues. Several **serologic tests** are available (complement fixation, etc.) to assist in the diagnosis, but the **dye test** is most widely used. This test is dependent on the fact that in the presence of specific antibodies the **cytoplasm** of the organism loses its affinity for **methylene blue.** Newer tests, such as the hemagglutination test, have been reported, and there is a good intracutaneous test available.

Treatment. Until recently there was no effective treatment available. There is now evidence that **triple sulfonamides** (equal parts of sulfadiazine, sulfamerazine, and Sulfamethazine) and **pyrimethamine** (Daraprim), acting synergistically, are effective and should be used as the treatment of choice for toxoplasmosis.

85

Helminths and Helminthic Infections

In addition to the **Protozoa,** or one-celled animals, there are a large number of many-celled animals, often referred to as **Metazoa,** that parasitize man. As stated above, the present discussion will deal with those that belong to **two** phyla of the animal kingdom, the Nemathelminthes (roundworms) and Platyhelminthes (flatworms). The species of medical and public health importance in the phylum Nemathelminthes belong to the class NEMATODA, or **roundworms;** those to the phylum Platyhelminthes belong to **two** classes: the CESTODA or **tapeworms,** and the TREMATODA or **flukes.** Collectively the parasitic worms are termed **helminths.** The most important members of the **three** separate groups will be discussed in the order listed: the **nematodes, cestodes,** and **trematodes.**

NEMATODES

The adult nematodes, or roundworms, are characterized by having an elongate, cylindrical body, which is **round** in cross-section. They are covered with a cuticle and have a complete digestive tract, with mouth and anus, as well as excretory, nervous, and reproductive systems. As in **all** parasitic worms the latter is the most conspicuous. The sexes are separate, and the males are almost invariably smaller than the females. Nematodes vary considerably in size, from forms difficult to see readily by the unaided eye to others many centimeters in length. They pass through a series of **molts,** or ecdyses, which are accomplished by shedding the cuticle. A complete series of stages in the life cycle include the ovum (unfertilized egg), egg, rhabditiform larva (larva of intestinal nematodes having an open mouth and conspicuous esophageal bulb), filariform larva (larva with a closed mouth and slender esophagus), and adult.

In presenting the material of this section, the nematodes will be grouped according to the usual location of the **adult** worms in man. This results in **two** main groups to be considered: the **intestinal nematodes** and the **tissue nematodes.** As an aid to the student, the intestinal nematodes will be divided into **two** groups: those **infective for man in the egg stage** and those **infective for man in a larval stage.**

INTESTINAL NEMATODES INFECTIVE FOR MAN IN THE EGG STAGE

Ascaris lumbricoides (the **Large Roundworm** of Man, Causing **Ascariasis**)

Life Cycle. These large nematodes (males 15 to 31 cm., females 20 to 35 cm. or more in length) usually live **unattached** in the lumen of the **small intestine** (Fig. 1). After reaching sexual maturity, copulation occurs and the females soon thereafter begin to **oviposit.** The daily egg production per female is phenomenal, averaging about 200,000. The **fertilized** eggs are still in the **one-cell** stage when they pass from the host in the feces (Fig. 2). **Infertile** eggs differing considerably in morphologic detail from the fertilized eggs, are sometimes seen (Fig. 2). If the stool containing the fertilized eggs is deposited in a warm, shady area, the eggs will develop. They have considerable resistance to cold and desiccation but lie dormant under these conditions. At temperatures between **22 and 33° C.,** the eggs develop to the infective stage within **two to three weeks.** By this time the first-stage **rhabditiform** larva within each egg has molted into the second-stage rhabditiform larva. These **infective eggs**

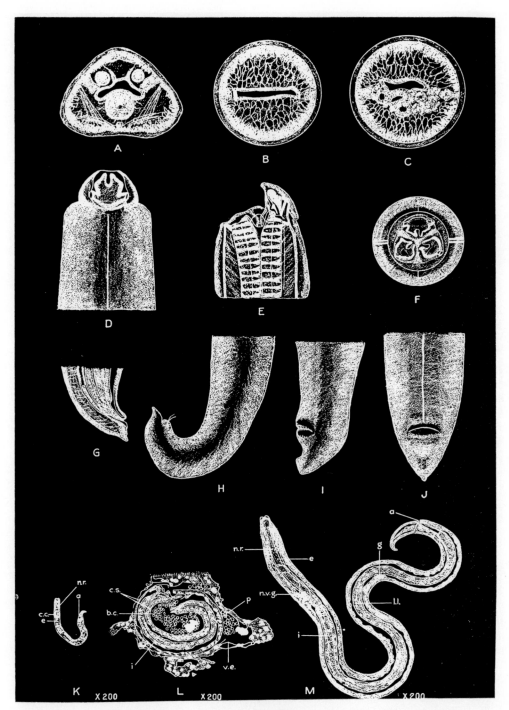

Fig. 1. *Ascaris lumbricoides.* A, cross section through posterior portion of male showing intestine, ejaculatory ducts, and spicules; B and C, cross sections showing longitudinal lines, musculature, and intestine; D, anterior end showing lips, dorsal view; E, longitudinal section of anterior end; F, papillated lips, front view; G, longitudinal section of posterior end of male, showing cloaca, ejaculatory duct, and spicular sheath; H, posterior end of male with extended spicules, lateral view; I, posterior end of female, lateral view; J, posterior end of female, ventral view; K, larva from liver of mouse; L, section of lung of rat showing larva in air vesicle; M, fully developed larva from lung of rat; a, anus; b.c., red blood cells; c.c., circumesophageal collar; c.s., cuticular surface; e, esophagus; g, gonads; i, intestine; l.l., lateral line; n.r., nerve ring; n.v.g., nucleus ventral gland; p, pigment; v.e., epithelium of air vesicle. (From Belding. *Basic Clinical Parasitology,* Appleton-Century-Crofts.)

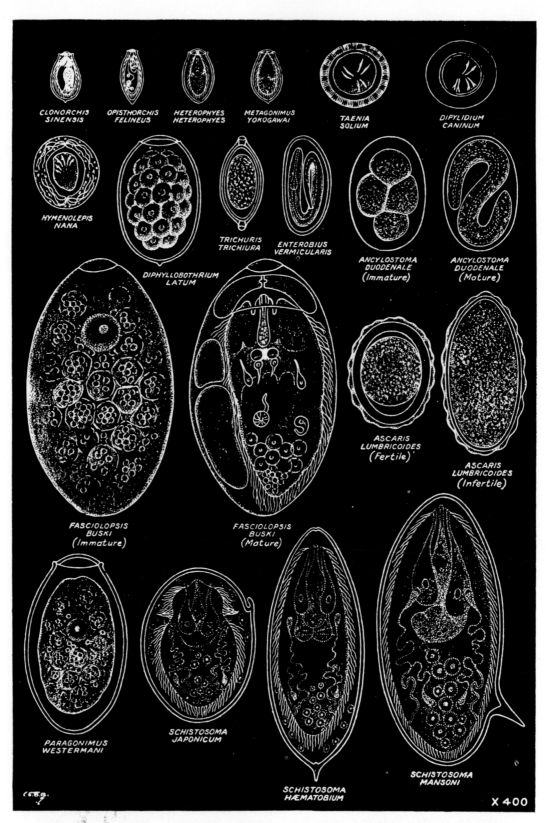

Fig. 2. Eggs of the common helminths of man. (From Belding. *Textbook of Clinical Parasitology*, 2nd ed., Appleton-Century-Crofts. The size of this illustration has been increased by ⅕.)

1146

may remain viable on the soil for many months, even years in some cases. Accidental ingestion of infective eggs results in infection. The eggs hatch in the duodenum, and the emerging larvae penetrate the intestinal wall, enter the circulatory system, and are carried to the right heart and thence to the lungs. They are filtered out of the lung capillaries and later penetrate into the alveoli (Fig. 1). After about **two weeks** in the lungs and after **two** additional molts have occurred, the fourth-stage larvae migrate up the respiratory tract to the epiglottis and are swallowed into the stomach. Upon reaching the **small intestine,** the final molt occurs, and the worms develop into adult males and females. The entire cycle, from infection to sexual maturity, requires from **eight** to **12 weeks.** The longevity of the adult worms is rarely more than **one year.** It should be emphasized that the lung migration is a **necessary** part of the cycle.

Pathology and Symptomatology. The principal damage produced by the **larvae** occurs in the **lungs.** Petechial hemorrhages are produced following entry into the alveoli. A

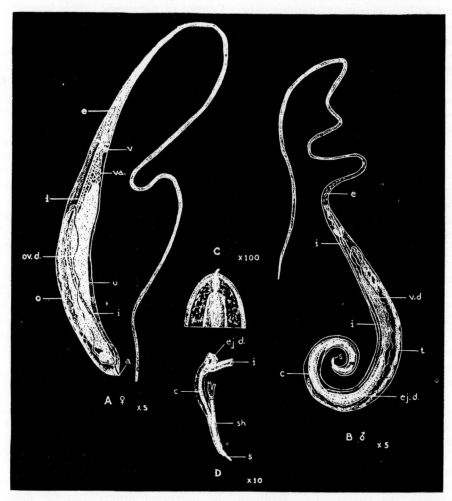

Fig. 3. *Trichuris trichiura.* A, female; B, male; C, anterior end showing spear; D, cloaca and copulatory organs of male; a, anus; c, cloaca; e, esophagus; ej.d., ejaculatory duct; i, intestine; o, ovary; ov.d., oviduct; s, spicule; sh., sheath of spicule; t, testis; u, uterus; v, vulva; va., vagina; v.d., vas deferens. (From Belding. *Textbook of Clinical Parasitology,* 2nd ed., Appleton-Century-Crofts.)

striking serocellular exudate collects, in which eosinophils are prominent. The cardinal signs and symptoms of this pneumonitis consist of dyspnea, dry cough, fever, and eosinophilia. X-ray findings show scattered mottling of the lungs suggestive of tuberculosis and other infections. The **adult worms** derive most of their nourishment from the semidigested food of the host, and if abundant, they may have a detrimental effect on the host's nutrition. However, most light infections produce little or no change in the host. Effects from the adult worms are more often noted in **children,** who often show loss of appetite and weight, intermittent intestinal colic, and various **nervous symptoms.** The **greatest danger** from the adult worms results from **abnormal migrations** within the body. They may enter the ampulla of Vater and block the common bile duct or penetrate into the liver parenchyma or the pancreas. They also have been found on rare occasions in other abnormal sites in the body. Sometimes they perforate the intestinal wall, but much more often, especially in young children, a mass of tangled worms causes an **acute obstruction** of the small intestine. There is evidence that absorption of the toxic and allergenic metabolites of the adult worms accounts for various referred symptoms, especially those of a **neurologic** nature.

Visceral Larva Migrans. This clinical condition, usually observed in **young children,** has been recognized only recently. It results from the larvae of *Toxocara canis* (the dog ascarid) or other nonhuman nematodes that hatch from eggs in the small intestine and migrate into the liver, lungs, or other organs. These larvae, not adapted to man, remain immature and eventually perish in the tissues. Outstanding characteristics of this condition are persistent eosinophilia, or hypereosinophilia, enlarged liver, pulmonary infiltration, fever, cough, and hyperglobulinemia. There is no specific treatment.

Laboratory Diagnosis. Except when only male worms are present (less than 5 per cent of infections), the characteristic fertilized eggs of *A. lumbricoides* are present in the stool in large numbers and can be found in smears by examination under low power of the microscope (Fig. 2). Concentration methods are not necessary. This egg is bluntly ovoid in shape, 45 to 70 by 35 to 50 μ, and has several layers between the single egg cell and the outside. The outer layer is coarsely mammillated. The various layers account for the **thick shell,** which is characteristic. The eggs usually are bile-stained by the time they are passed from the body and appear, usually, brown in color.

Treatment. The drug of choice for eliminating the **adult** worms is **Piperazine citrate** given by mouth in a syrup. When hookworms coexist with *A. lumbricoides,* **Hexylresorcinol** is advised (see below).

Certain Factors in the Epidemiology and Control of Ascariasis. This infection has a world-wide distribution. While the highest rates of infection occur in the tropics, the infection is common in most temperate regions, including parts of the southeastern United States. In most of our hyperendemic areas ascariasis is much more prevalent in young children, especially those of **preschool** age, than in the rest of the population. Promiscuous defecation in the **dooryard area** seeds the soil with the eggs. These are relatively resistant to desiccation and putrefaction, and embryonation occurs on hard clay soil as well as on loam, provided the soil is not reached by direct sunlight. Infective eggs remain viable for **weeks** or **months,** even surviving periods of freezing, and many are known to be carried into the houses. Infection occurs when infective eggs reach the mouth via contaminated hands, food, drink, or play objects, or as the result of dirt-eating. Thus, the **family** usually becomes the unit of *Ascaris* dissemination, although important community sources of infection occur in some areas.

Climatic limitations, so important in the distribution of many other parasitic infections, are **almost lacking** in the case of *Ascaris,* making it widespread and common. The determining factor in its distribution in most population groups is **human habit. Control,** therefore, centers around **health education** in the home and school. Mothers must be instructed properly in the methods of good household sanitation so that they in turn will teach the children. Toilet facilities must be provided and the children taught to use them.

Trichuris trichiura (Human **Whipworm,** Causing **Trichuriasis**)

Life Cycle. The anterior three-fifths of the adult whipworms are attenuated, while the posterior portion is more fleshy (Fig. 3). The male measures 35 to 45 mm. in length, the female 35 to 50 mm. The anterior end of the worm is **sewed** into the mucosa of the **large intestine,** typically of the cecum and appendix, and the posterior end swings freely in the lumen. After copulation, the females begin to oviposit, the daily egg production probably being 2,000 to 4,000. The characteristic barrel-shaped eggs occur in the stool while still in the **one-cell stage** (Fig. 2) Under favorable conditions (warm temperature, shade, moisture, sandy humus soil) the eggs **embryonate** and become **infective** after **three to five weeks.** They lack the great resistance of *Ascaris* eggs, and their survival is considered to be relatively brief. When infective eggs are ingested, they hatch in the duodenum. The freed larvae enter nearby intestinal crypts and penetrate into the glands and stroma. They leave these sites after about **10 days** and are found in the large intestine. The worms are sexually mature after approximately **90 days,** and they may live for **several years.**

Pathology and Symptomatology. The worms damage the tissues penetrated and may carry into these sites bacteria and other infectious agents. If the heads of the worms penetrate into blood capillaries, petechial hemorrhages are produced. The degree of damage corresponds to the number of worms involved. In light infections relatively little damage results, but in heavy infections the mucosa is hyperemic and eroded superficially and may be inflamed extensively. Extreme irritation in the wall of the lower colon and rectum may provoke **prolapse** of the rectum. Depending upon the degree of infection and reaction of the individual, the signs and symptoms vary from mild (epigastric discomfort, flatulence, loss of appetite and weight, etc.) to severe (nausea, vomiting, mucous diarrhea or dysentery, anemia, etc.).

Laboratory Diagnosis. This is dependent upon the demonstration of the characteristic eggs in the stool. These are about 20 by 50 μ in size, barrel-shaped, a golden brown color, and have a transparent prominence at each pole (Fig. 2). They may be few in number and difficult to find in fecal smears, in which cases it is of assistance to use the **simplified zinc sulfate concentration method.** This technical procedure and others referred to below are explained fully in the standard textbooks listed at the end of Chapter 83, page 1115.

Treatment. The most satisfactory treatment is with the new drug, **Dithiazanine,** which is taken orally. For those with heavy infections that cannot tolerate **Dithiazanine,** or cannot be exposed to the risks of toxic effects, **Hexylresorcinol,** given as a 0.3 per cent high-retention enema(s), is used.

Enterobius vermicularis (the **Pinworm** of Man, Causing **Enterobiasis**)

Life Cycle. These worms live usually in the **cecum** but may extend into other areas of the **large intestine.** They **attach** insecurely to the mucosa. The females, 8 to 13 mm. long, are considerably larger than the males, 2 to 5 mm. (Fig. 4). Both have a characteristic **cephalic swelling.** The males apparently disappear soon after copulation. The **gravid females** begin to migrate from the body after the uterus fills with eggs. This migration usually occurs at **night.** They cling temporarily to the rectal mucosa but soon pass out of the anus onto the perianal and perineal skin (in female subjects, especially young girls, they may reach the vulva and enter the vagina and may at times even reach the inner end of the Fallopian tubes). The female worms oviposit as they crawl about on the skin, and often the body wall ruptures, spilling all of the eggs (about 11,000 per female). These are fully developed, each containing a coiled first-stage larva (Fig. 2). The outer membrane of the eggs is albuminous, causing them to adhere to one another and to the skin and hairs. The **intense pruritus** produced by the crawling females and/or the eggs results in scratching of the affected part(s). In this way, eggs are transferred to the fingertips and may become lodged beneath the nails. Reinfection follows when the fingers, or food contaminated by the fingers, are placed in the mouth. Aside from this common type of **direct** transfer of eggs, often referred to as a **hand-to-mouth trans-fer,** the eggs may reach the mouth of the infected individual and/or others via one or more **indirect** routes. The eggs adhere to clothing and bed linen, and some get in air currents to settle later on objects. Thus, the household becomes contaminated, and all members sooner or later swallow some of the eggs. After the infective eggs are swallowed they hatch in the duodenum, freeing the contained first-stage larvae. These pass slowly toward the cecal area, undergoing the usual number of molts. Upon reaching the cecum, the worms attach and mating occurs to begin the cycle again. The complete life cycle may be as brief as **15 to 28 days.** However, it is now known that some of the eggs deposited on the perineum may hatch and the larvae may enter the anus, producing **retrofection.** When this occurs, the cycle may be lengthened considerably.

Pathology and Symptomatology. Inflammation, of an acute or chronic catarrhal nature, often is produced in the areas of worm attachment. Sometimes necrosis of the mucosa occurs and sympathetic nerve endings are exposed. This, and probably absorbed metabolites of the worms, is thought to be responsible for the commonly observed **reflex nervous symptoms.** In some cases the worms probably play a role in **appendicitis.** **Anal pruritus** is outstanding, and the scratching that follows may produce scarification, which is subject to invasion by bacteria and other infectious agents. In addition, especially in children, insomnia or restless sleep, low fatigue threshold, and especially **nervous symptoms** are common.

Laboratory Diagnosis. The characteristic eggs usually are **not** found in the stool but may be recovered easily from the **perianal area** by use of a simple **Scotch-tape, or other, swab.** These eggs are asymmetrical, being flattened on the ventral side, and range in size from 50 to 60 by 20 to 30 μ (Fig. 2). They are composed of two layers and contain the first-stage infective larva, which usually is active within the shell. Sometimes the diagnosis is made by finding the **female**

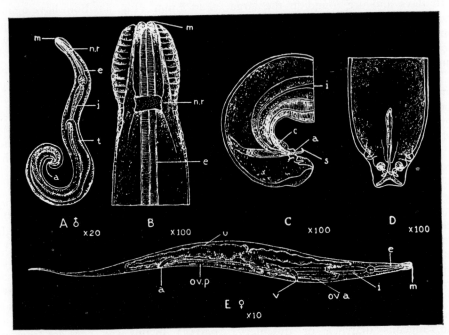

Fig. 4. *Enterobius vermicularis.* A, male; B, anterior end of worm; C, posterior end of male, lateral view; D, posterior end of male, ventral view; E, female; a, anus; c, cloaca; e, esophagus; i, intestine; m, mouth; n.r., nerve ring; ov.a., anterior ovary; ov.p., posterior ovary; s, spicule; t, testis; u, uterus; v, vulva. (From Belding. *Textbook of Clinical Parasitology,* 2nd ed., Appleton-Century-Crofts.)

worms on the perianal area or, less commonly, in a stool specimen, especially following an enema.

Treatment. The drug of choice is oral **Piperazine citrate,** or as a **single-dose** treatment, oral **Pyrvinium pamoate.**

Certain Factors in the Epidemiology and Control of Enterobiasis. This infection has a cosmopolitan distribution but is less common in tropical areas than in cool or temperate zones. It is much more common in **children** than in adults. Because of the peculiar life cycle of the worm, **crowding** is an important factor in the transmission. Thus, it follows that the infection rate is higher in large family groups, schools, asylums, and mental institutions than in the population at large. The eggs are sticky and adhere to various fomites, and some are known to be carried by air currents. In time the environment may become heavily contaminated with eggs. Cool, moist atmosphere with little or no ventilation is optimal for their survival. It is the rule that infected individuals constantly **reinfect** themselves, usually as a result of hand-to-mouth infection following scratching of the contaminated perianal and/or perineal skin. Also, the infection of others in the group **usually** follows. Individuals sleeping in the same bed or bedroom, or using the same toilet, may be exposed from fomites contaminated by the patient; others may become infected from ingesting eggs in contaminated food and/or drink or following the breathing in of eggs in air currents.

Good personal and group hygiene is necessary in attempts to **control** enterobiasis. Small children should be provided with closed sleeping garments to prevent contamination of the fingers by scratching, their fingernails should be kept short, and it should be seen that their hands are scrubbed thoroughly after each visit to the toilet and before meals. To prevent exposure of associates, sheets, night clothes, and undergarments of infected individuals should be **sterilized** frequently by boiling. Rugs, draperies, and the like should be vacuum-cleaned thoroughly and sunned on hot, dry days. Toilet seats should be sterilized regularly. It should be added that even the strictest hygienic measures often fail unless supplemented with **chemotherapy.** Once an infec-

tion is established, it can be eradicated only by persistent efforts directed toward the prevention of reinfection of the patient and the infection of others.

INTESTINAL NEMATODES INFECTIVE
FOR MAN IN A LARVAL STAGE

Hookworms

Four species are involved in human infections: **two** (*Necator americanus* and *Ancylostoma duodenale*) are **true human parasites** and **two** (*Ancylostoma braziliense* and *A. canimum*) are parasites of **cats and dogs.** The latter, especially *A. braziliense,* produce a dermatitis (**cutaneous larva migrans** or creeping eruption) **in man** following penetration of the skin by the **filariform** larvae (see below). All hookworms have certain common morphologic characteristics, the most striking being the umbrella-like copulatory **bursa** of the males, the twinned ovaries, oviducts, and uteri of the females, and the thin-shelled eggs (Figs. 2, 5, 6). *A. duodenale* males (8 to 11 mm. long) and females (10 to 13 mm. long) are somewhat larger than those of *N. americanus* (7 to 9 mm.; 9 to 11 mm. long), and the structures for attachment to the intestinal mucosa differ in the two species. In *A. duodenale,* the **buccal capsule** is provided with **paired tooth-like processes,** while **semilunar cutting plates** are present in *N. americanus* (Fig. 6). The females of *A. duodenale* produce more eggs per day (10,000 to 20,000) than those of *N. americanus* (5,000 to 10,000), and the *A. duodenale* infections usually are more severe and less amenable to treatment. *N. americanus,* **the American killer,** is the only human species of importance throughout the hookworm belt of the southern United States. It will be necessary, however, to be on the alert for *A. duodenale* as it is known that some veterans of World War II returned from other parts of the world with this species. The life cycles of these various hookworms are similar.

Life Cycle. The adult worms are usually **attached** to the upper levels of the **small intestine.** The head is anchored securely to the intestine, the tip of a villus usually being

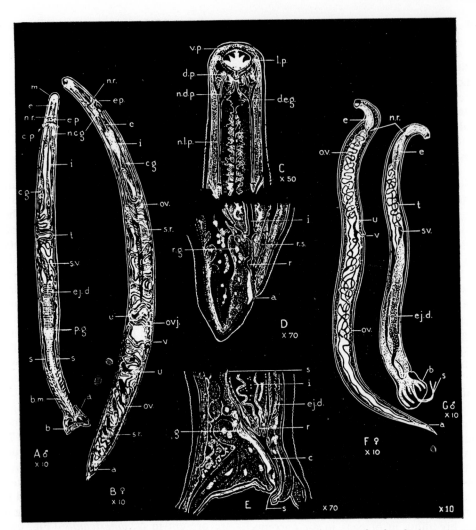

Fig. 5. Important hookworms of man. A, adult male *Ancylostoma duodenale* from ventral side; B, young adult female *A. duodenale* from right side; C, anterior end of *A. duodenale* from dorsal side; D, longitudinal section through end of female *A. duodenale,* somewhat diagrammatic; E, longitudinal section through end of male *A. duodenale,* not quite median; F, female *Necator americanus;* G, male *N. americanus;* a, anus; b, bursa; b.m., bursal muscles; c, cloaca; c.g., cervical gland; c.p., cervical papilla; d.e.g., dorsal esophageal gland; d.p., dorsal papilla; e, esophagus; e.p., excretory pore; ej.d., ejaculatory duct; g, gubernaculum; i, intestine; l.p., lateral papilla; m, mouth; n.c.g., nucleus of cephalic gland; n.d.p., nerve of dorsal papilla; n.l.p., nerve of lateral papilla; n.r., nerve ring; ov., ovary; ovj., ovejector; p.g., prostatic glands; r, rectum; r.g., rectal ganglion; r.s., rectal sphincter; s, spicules; s.r., seminal receptacle; s.v., seminal vesicle; t, testis; u, uterus; v, vulva; v.p., ventral papilla. (From Belding. *Textbook of Clinical Parasitology,* 2nd ed., Appleton-Century-Crofts.)

drawn into the mouth of the worm, and **blood is sucked from the capillaries.** After copulation, the females oviposit, and the eggs occur in the stool (Fig. 2). These usually are in the **four- to eight-cell stage,** but much further development is noted within eggs passed from constipated individuals.

Under **favorable** conditions (especially warm temperature, shade, and moist sandy-loam soil) the eggs will **embryonate** and hatch in the deposited feces within **24 to 48 hours.** The **first-stage** larvae, freed from the eggs, are typically **rhabditiform** and have a long **buccal chamber** (Fig. 7). They feed actively,

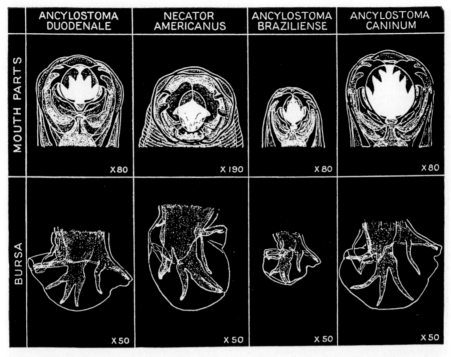

Fig. 6. Mouth parts and bursae of hookworms. (From Belding. *Textbook of Clinical Para-sitology,* 2nd ed., Appleton-Century-Crofts.)

especially on bacteria in the feces, and molt into the **second stage** after **two** or **three days.** This stage, also rhabditiform, continues to feed and grow for **two** or **three days,** when it molts into the **third stage.** The third-stage **filariform** larvae remain within the old cuticle (of the second molt) and thus **cannot** feed (Fig. 7). These larvae have sharply pointed tails and are the **infective** stage. Except under optimum conditions, most of the filariform larvae probably die **within a few weeks** in the absence of a suitable host. The usual means of human infection is penetration by these larvae, after escaping from the old cuticle, into the tender skin between the toes of barefooted individuals. After **many hours,** the larvae enter the cutaneous blood vessels and are carried through the right heart to the lungs. After a **few days,** they have succeeded in penetrating from the pulmonary capil-laries into the alveoli, have ascended the respiratory tract to the epiglottis and, after having been swallowed, have descended to the upper small intestine. During this time they undergo a third molt and acquire a temporary buccal capsule. After attaching to the villi, the young worms undergo a fourth molt and, in about **six weeks,** grow into sexually mature males and females. While some of the worms in man may live for **10 years,** most of them will have been lost from the host after **one to two years.**

Pathology and Symptomatology. At the site of entry of the filariform larvae into the skin, most individuals experience intense itching and burning, followed by edema and erythema. A **papule** may appear, which transforms into a **vesicle.** This condition, known as **ground itch,** is more serious in those sensitized by previous infections and in those developing secondary infections. The larvae reaching the lungs produce small focal hemorrhages as they penetrate from the capillaries into the alveoli, but usually only a subclinical pneumonitis is produced. The **greatest damage** results from the **adult worms** attached to the small intestine. The superficial mucosa within the buccal cavity of the worm becomes denuded, and the sur-rounding mucosa usually shows a mild in-

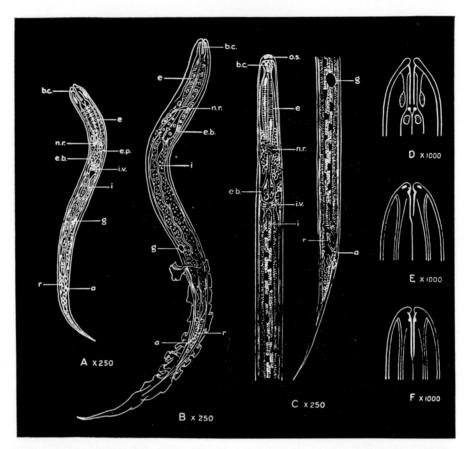

Fig. 7. Larvae of *Ancylostoma duodenale*. A, recently hatched rhabditiform larva, lateral view; B, rhabditiform larva during late stage of first ecdysis; C, filariform larva, lateral view; D, anterior end rhabditiform larva (schematic); E, anterior end filariform larva (schematic); F, anterior end filariform larva of *N. americanus* (schematic); a, anus; b.c., buccal cavity; e, esophagus; e.b., esophageal bulb; e.p., excretory pore; g, genital primordium; i, intestine; i.v., intestinal valve; n.r., nerve ring; o.s., old sheath; r, rectum. (From Belding. *Textbook of Clinical Parasitology,* 2nd ed., Appleton-Century-Crofts.)

flammatory infiltrate. More important is the **blood loss.** Blood is sucked from the capillaries of the villi, and it passes through the digestive tract of the worms. Apparently only highly refined products (amino acids, vitamins, etc.) are removed, the remainder being extruded through the anus in a wasteful fashion. Adding to this blood loss, which may vary from **0.1 to 0.67 ml.** per worm daily, is that occurring following a change(s) in site of attachment. The former wound continues to ooze blood for a time after the worm has released the tissue. **Blood loss** from the intestinal wall constitutes the greatest damage in hookworm infection. This loss, unless compensated adequately, will give rise to a **microcytic, hypochromic anemia.** Whether an individual with **hookworm infection** develops **hookworm disease** is dependent, in general, upon the number of worms harbored and his nutritional status. Even moderately heavy infections may fail to produce a significant anemia if the individual has been on an adequate, well-balanced diet rich in animal proteins, iron, and other minerals, and vitamins. However, in heavy infections, even with a highly fortified diet, the hematopoietic mechanism is unable to keep pace with the great loss of red blood cells.

In many endemic areas of hookworm, the natives are infected repeatedly from early childhood. Thus, **chronic hookworm disease** is most characteristic. Common signs and symptoms are anemia, epigastric burning, flatulence, hunger pains, sallow skin, tender abdomen, irritability, alternating diarrhea and constipation, dry skin, blurred vision, etc. When the condition finally produces marked physical weakness, the individual is not fit for any type of manual labor. This accounts for the early term **lazy disease.** Cardiac symptoms are evident in many, and, especially in severe cases, death may result from **cardiac failure.** Physical (including sexual) stunting is characteristic in **children,** and many are also retarded mentally.

Cutaneous Larva Migrans or Creeping Eruption. The **filariform** larvae of the dog and cat hookworms (*A. canimum* and, especially, *A. braziliense*) are the agents of this clinical condition, which is most often observed in **young children.** The condition is common along the sandy coastal areas from New Jersey to the Florida Keys and elsewhere. However, thus far the largest number of cases have been reported from the vicinity of Jacksonville, Florida. At each point of entry into the skin there is produced an itching, reddish **papule.** After a **few days,** the larvae have developed a **serpiginous tunnel** in the skin as they proceed (usually at the rate of several millimeters a day). Over a period of **weeks** or **months** this results in extensive skin involvement (Fig. 8). At

times severe systemic illness may result. These movements, limited to the skin of man, and the resulting tissue irritation produce an **intense pruritus.** This leads to scratching and often opens the lesions to pyogenic organisms. Some prefer to **treat** cases by **freezing** the lesions with **ethyl chloride spray;** others advocate the use of chemicals, such as **Mapharsen, Hetrazan,** and **Stibanose.**

Laboratory Diagnosis. To diagnose **human** hookworm infection, the characteristic eggs are demonstrated in the stool. These are bluntly ovoid in shape, 40 by 60 μ, have a **thin, transparent shell,** and usually are in the **four-cell stage** (Fig. 2). Simple fecal smears are sufficient in detecting most infections, but a concentration method (zinc sulfate, etc.) may be necessary to detect light infections. An estimate of the worm burden may be obtained by use of the **Stoll** or **Beaver technic.**

Treatment. Unless ascariasis is a complication, **tetrachlorethylene** is the drug of choice. In combined hookworm and *Ascaris* infections, this drug **should not be used** as it may cause dangerous migrations of the ascarids. In this case, **hexylresorcinol** (see above) should be employed. For individuals with low hemoglobin levels it is desirable to postpone administration of the drug until a fortified diet (see above) has been provided for a week or more. In addition, one

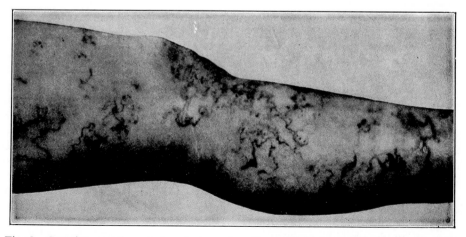

Fig. 8. Creeping eruption of *Ancylostoma braziliense.* Multiple, rapidly developing lesions of about two weeks' duration. (From Belding. *Textbook of Clinical Parasitology,* 2nd ed., Appleton-Century-Crofts.)

or more whole blood transfusions may be needed in some cases.

Certain Factors in the Epidemiology and Control of Hookworm Infection. This infection is endemic in the tropical and subtropical zones of the world mainly between 45° N. and 30° S. latitude. It is one of the **most common** of all helminthic parasitoses in these warm climates. Although *A. duodenale* has been reported from members of the American Armed Forces returning from the Pacific in World War II, the prevailing species throughout the hookworm belt of the southern United States is *N. americanus.*

Climatic and physiographic factors are **important** in the distribution of hookworms, since they affect the free stages of the parasites. Optimum conditions are provided by warm temperature, moderate to heavy rainfall, and a loose, well-shaded, sandy soil or loam or humus covered with vegetation. **Human habits** play a vital part in hookworm dissemination. **Soil pollution** by infected persons **away** from the house (e.g., in the garden area, barnyard, edge of cane field) seeds the soil with eggs. Provided favorable environmental conditions exist, the soil becomes **infested** with **filariform** larvae. **Human contact** with these areas, usually as the result of walking barefooted, produces **human infection** and begins again the cycle of dissemination. Often the cycle is associated intimately with occupational relations, such as coffee picking and working in cane fields. It is important to supplement data on the prevalence of hookworms in an area by an estimate of the prevalence and degree of soil infestation and the intensity of the infection —that is, the worm burden in those shown to be passing eggs.

The **control** of hookworm infection centers around anthelmintic treatment, especially those with a heavy worm burden, to reduce the sources of soil infestation, and sanitary disposal of human excreta. As to the latter, **health education** in the homes and schools is necessary to combat social customs, inertia, and other factors. While the eradication of this infection is desirable, it has not proved practical. Thus, the primary objective of public health authorities in recent years has been the detection, prevention, and control of **hookworm disease.** In

other words, there has been a concentration on those being debilitated by the worms to the point of showing definite clinical manifestations rather than upon all those infected. In this connection control also embodies improvement in the diet of hookworm communities, since infection of clinical grade is most prevalent in poorly nourished individuals.

Strongyloides stercoralis (Human Threadworm, Causing **Strongyloidiasis**)

Life Cycle. **Three** different cycles may be involved. The **direct cycle** is the most common. The parasitic females are slender filiform worms about 2 mm. in length. They usually reside among the epithelial and gland cells or in the tunica propria in the upper levels of the **small intestine.** Here, apparently in the absence of males, they lay several dozens of eggs daily (Fig. 9), at least during the **first few months** of infection. As the eggs filter through the mucosa toward the lumen they develop and hatch, freeing the first-stage **rhabditiform** larvae (Fig. 9). These make their way to the lumen and are passed in the stool. Under favorable conditions, the **filariform** larvae (Fig. 9) make their appearance within a **few days** and enter exposed human skin to initiate a new infection. Their migration to the lungs and thence to the small intestine is similar to that described above for hookworm larvae (p. 1153), but it should be noted that *S. stercoralis* larvae molt **twice,** rather than once, in the lungs. After reaching the tissue of the small intestine, the larvae develop into mature females in about **25 days,** and these worms may live for **several years.** They probably are **parthenogenetic.** This type of cycle is similar to that of the hookworm cycle, except that part of the early *S. stercoralis* cycle (embryonation and hatching of the eggs, and growth of the first-stage rhabditiform larvae) occurs **in man.** A **second** type of cycle, common only in the tropics, involves the interpolation of one or more **free-living** generations. This is the **indirect cycle.** In this case, the rhabditiform larvae in the stool retain the rhabditiform type of esophagus and develop into **free-living males and females.** Eventually some of the rhabditiform larvae produced

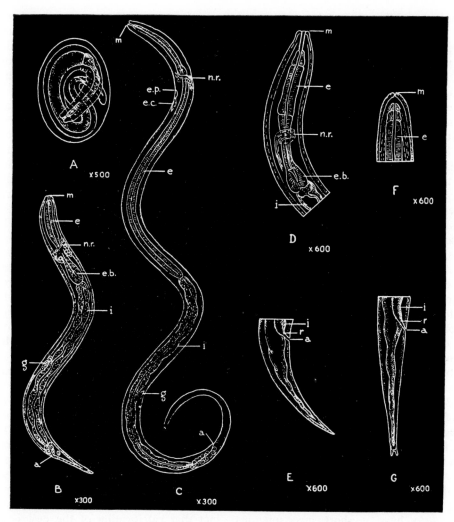

Fig. 9. Larvae of *Strongyloides stercoralis*. A, egg containing mature larva of *S. simiae;* B, rhabditiform larva; C, filariform larva; D, anterior end of rhabditiform larva; E, posterior end of rhabditiform larva; F, anterior end of filariform larva; G, posterior end of filariform larva; a, anus; e, esophagus; e.b., esophageal bulb; e.c., excretory cell; e.p., excretory pore; g, genital rudiment; i, intestine; m, mouth; n.r., nerve ring; r, rectum. (From Belding. *Textbook of Clinical Parasitology,* 2nd ed., Appleton-Century-Crofts.)

develop into filariform larvae to begin the parasitic cycle. The intrahuman cycle is the same as that of the direct cycle. The indirect cycle was, no doubt, the original cycle, from which the parasitic cycle evolved. Being able to live a free or parasitic existence suggests that *S. stercoralis* has become a parasite of man in comparatively recent times. The **third,** and perhaps least common, type of cycle is that known as **internal autoinfection,** or hyperinfection. In this case, the rhabditi-

form larvae, before leaving the inside of the body, metamorphose into the filariform larvae, which after entering the intestinal wall, migrate through the tissues of the body. Some reach the lungs, as in the other cycles, and return to the small intestine, but many find their way into various other tissues where considerable damage may result. This is most common in those with low tissue resistance, and it may produce a **fatal** outcome.

Pathology and Symptomatology. A pneumonitis may be produced by the **larvae** in the **lungs,** but the **main damage** is produced in the **wall of the small intestine** by the females, eggs, and rhabditiform larvae. Mechanical, and perhaps lytic, damage is produced, especially by the females, which move about considerably. Cellular infiltration, often striking, consists chiefly of eosinophils, lymphocytes, and epithelioid cells. This may be general throughout large areas of the mucosa and not limited to areas adjacent to the worms. The affected tissue becomes increasingly nonfunctional, and at times sloughing of the tissue occurs. There is evidence of systemic damage consisting of sensitization and, probably, toxic reactions. As stated above, autoinfection may produce severe damage in various tissues with striking signs and symptoms. The most characteristic **symptoms** of the **usual type** of infection are abdominal pain, a watery-mucus diarrhea, and eosinophilia.

Laboratory Diagnosis. This usually is made by finding the characteristic **rhabditiform** larvae in the stool (Fig. 9). These are about 200 by 15 μ in size. There usually is no confusion with hookworm, but it might be added that the structure of these larvae differs from that of hookworm. The difference in the **buccal chamber** alone is sufficient to differentiate the two. As mentioned above, the rhabditiform larvae of hookworm have a **long** buccal chamber, while those of *S. stercoralis* have a **short** inconspicuous chamber. The **filariform** larvae likewise may be differentiated by a single difference. Those of hookworm have a **sharply pointed tail,** those of *S. stercoralis* have a **notched tail** (Figs. 7, 9). Many times duodenal aspirates will reveal larvae when stools are negative, but at times the reverse is true. Sometimes the larvae can be recovered from urine, sputum, or aspirates from body cavities.

Treatment. Dithiazanine has been shown recently to be an effective drug against this parasite.

Trichinella spiralis (Cause of **Trichinosis**)

Life Cycle. Man is infected by ingesting **infective** larvae (Fig. 10) **encysted in striated muscles** of a **reservoir host, swine** being the most important. Gastric digestion frees most of the larvae. They soon enter the **small intestine** and penetrate into the mucosa. Within **two days** they have undergone the necessary molts to reach the adult stage (Fig. 10). The males measure 1.4 to 1.6 mm. in length and have a pair of characteristic **conical papillae** ("bursae") guarding the terminal cloaca. The females, more than twice the length of the males, have the vulvar opening at about one-fifth the body length from the anterior end. Copulation occurs and the females, after burrowing more deeply into the mucosa or even to lower levels, begin to **larvaposit.** This is thought to begin about **five days** after infection and may continue for **weeks,** during which time the total production of larvae is about 1,500 per female. The larvae released from the females are small, about 100 by 6 μ. They enter the circulation and are distributed throughout the body. However, only those entering **striated muscles** are capable of further development. Here, within **three weeks** after infection, **encapsulation** begins. This host reaction, initiated by infiltration mainly by round cells and eosinophils, results in the formation of a double-walled adventitious **capsule** (Fig. 10). The larvae within grow to about 0.8 mm. in length and become coiled tightly. The larvae are **infective** for a new host a few days after encapsulation has begun. Some remain viable within cysts for many years, despite the fact that **calcification** of the cyst is usually observed **after six months.** As noted, this parasite is **completely parasitic** as there is no free existence in its cycle.

Pathology and Symptomatology. Trichinosis has been confused with many other diseases, because the parasite may damage various tissues of the body. For a clear understanding of the disease, it is necessary to consider in turn the various stages involved. During the **first stage** the adult worms are becoming **established** in the mucosa of the small intestine. Due to extensive burrowing, tissue is destroyed, and an intense inflammatory reaction results. Nausea, vomiting, diarrhea, and fever may be experienced. These and other signs and symptoms resemble salmonellosis and other enteric infections. This stage usually lasts for about **10 days,**

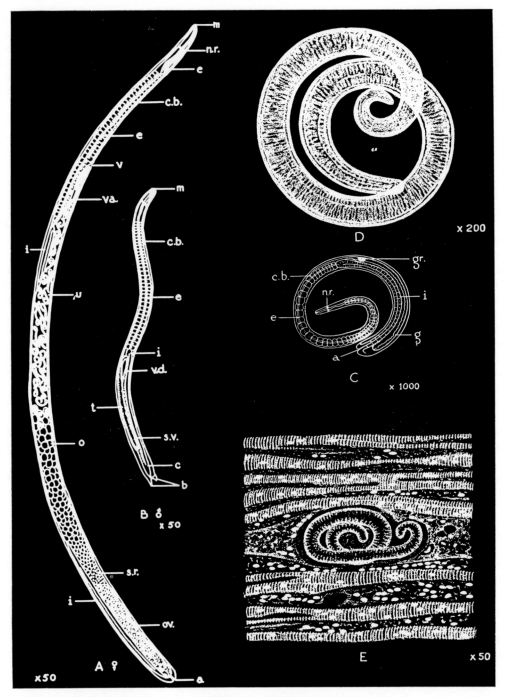

Fig. 10. *Trichinella spiralis.* A, adult female; B, adult male; C, young larva; D, mature larva from digested muscle; E, early encysted larva in muscle; a, anus; b, "bursa"; c, cloaca; c.b., cell bodies; e, esophagus; g. gonads (anlage); gr., granules; i, intestine; m, mouth; n.r., nerve ring; o, eggs; ov., ovary; s.r., seminal receptacle; s.v., seminal vesicle; t, testis; u, uterus; v, vulva; va., vagina; v.d., vas deferens. (From Brown and Belding. *Basic Clinical Parasitology,* 2nd ed., Appleton-Century-Crofts.)

thus it overlaps the second stage. The **second stage,** set arbitrarily between **seven and 14 days after infection,** involves the **initial** waves of larvae in the circulation. The fever usually reaches a peak (41° C.), and there is characteristic **edema** (especially of the face) and eosinophilia. In addition, dyspnea, difficulty in mastication and speech, and petechial hemorrhages, especially in the conjunctivae and retinal vessels, may be noted. **Cardiac** and **neurologic** signs and symptoms often are noted, and it should be remembered that **any** organ may be damaged by the migrating larvae. The features of this stage are most pronounced during the **second week** but continue throughout the period of larvaposition, which may last for **many weeks.** The **third stage, after 14 days,** is a culmination of the traumatic and toxic effects of the infection. Also **myositis** is outstanding, so that **muscular pains** are usually the chief complaint. Larvae entering muscle fibers cause a severe reaction. The infiltrate consists chiefly of plasma cells, lymphocytes, and especially, eosinophils. This host response results in the formation of the characteristic **cyst.** The edema, especially around the eyes, persists, as does the **hypereosinophilia,** which reaches a **peak** about **21 days after infection.** Cachexia may be profound. Many **fatal** cases show congestive heart failure, due to myocardial lesions, respiratory paralysis, and anaphylaxis. Those surviving usually are cured symptomatically **five to eight weeks** after infection, but a much longer period is required in some cases. Except during epidemics, most cases are relatively asymptomatic, due, presumably, to the consumption of small numbers of larvae. However, it should be kept in mind that death will result inevitably if large numbers are ingested simultaneously.

Laboratory Diagnosis. The most **specific** means of diagnosis is provided by **biopsy** of a small piece of the deltoid or other muscle. The larvae may be demonstrated by pressing the tissue firmly between two microscope slides prior to microscopic examination or by recovering the larvae following digestion in artificial gastric juice. To relate the presence of larvae to the present illness, it is important to consider the **stage** of cyst formation. For example, the finding of cal-

cified cysts only could not be related to an illness of recent origin. Various serologic tests are available, but the intradermal test has been most widely used as the indirect means of diagnosis. The degree of and changes in the eosinophilic response, while not specific and not always striking, are of assistance and should be charted.

Treatment. In general, only palliative and supportive measures are of value. However, **Cortisone** and related drugs are of great assistance during the larval encystment period. Allergic reactions to, or toxic effects from, the metabolites of the worms often show amelioration after use of **Cortisone,** and on ocasion this drug has appeared to be **life-saving.**

Certain Factors in the Epidemiology and Control of Trichinosis. This infection has a cosmopolitan distribution, but its importance as a human infection is much less in the tropics and the Orient than in Europe and the **United States.** The prevalence of human trichinosis is high in the United States, where about **one of every six individuals** is infected. One author has estimated that there are 350,000 new cases yearly, of which about 16,000 have detectable clinical manifestations. While there are many **reservoir hosts** for this parasite, most human cases result from consuming inadequately cooked or improperly processed **infected pork.** Garbage containing unsterilized pork scraps is the most common source of infection for hogs.

Most of the states in the United States now have laws prohibiting the feeding of raw garbage to hogs. If this measure is carried out consistently in all areas, it should protect many consumers by providing trichinella-free pork. However, such legislation is difficult to enforce on a large scale and may not prove to be the solution to the problem. In any event, the need will continue for the education of the public in methods of rendering pork safe for consumption. Two **practical** methods are **freezing** and **thorough cooking.** Thin cuts of pork stored at −18° C. (−0.4° F.) for at least 24 hours are rendered safe for consumption. Thorough cooking is always a safeguard, but the danger lies in failure to heat the interior sufficiently. Pork products eaten cus-

Table 1. Filariae and Dracunculus medinensis

Parasite	Disease	Location of Adults in Man	Location of Microfilariae in Man	Arthropod Intermediate Hosts
Wuchereria bancrofti	Bancroft's filariasis	Lymphatics	Blood	Mosquitoes; especially *Anopheles, Culex, Aëdes* spp.
W. malayi	Malayan filariasis	Lymphatics	Blood	Mosquitoes; *Mansonia, Anopheles* spp.
Onchocerca volvulus	Onchocerciasis	Subcutaneous nodules	Skin tissues	*Simulium* spp., black flies
Loa loa	Loasis	Subcutaneous tissues	Blood	*Chrysops* spp., deer flies
Acanthocheilonema perstans	Acanthocheilonemiasis	Body cavities, especially perirenal tissues	Blood	*Culicoides* spp., biting midges
Mansonella ozzardi	Ozzard's filariasis	Body cavities, especially mesentery fat	Blood	*Culicoides* spp., biting midges
Dracunculus medinensis	Dracontiasis	Visceral connective tissues, later in subcutaneous tissues	No microfilarial stage; female discharges rhabditiform larvae	*Cyclops* spp., small crustaceans

tomarily **without cooking,** such as wieners and cold cuts, should be purchased from companies whose abattoirs are under government inspection, since these plants are the only ones likely to process such meats adequately.

TISSUE NEMATODES

This group includes **six** species of **filariae** (Filaroidea) and *Dracunculus medinensis* (Dracunculoidea). Information regarding these parasites is given in **Table 1** (see also Fig. 11). Among those listed *Wuchereria bancrofti* is of the greatest interest and importance, hence it will be discussed in more detail.

Wuchereria bancrofti (Cause of **Bancroft's Filariasis**)

Life Cycle. The adults, usually coiled together, live within the **lymphatic system** of man. The males are about 40 mm. in length, and the females about 90 mm. Both sexes are thread-like, being no more than 0.3 mm. in diameter. Following copulation, the females give off living embryos, termed **microfilariae** (Fig. 11). These ultimately find their way into the **blood stream.** In most strains the larvae circulate in the blood in largest numbers at night and are said to have **nocturnal periodicity;** in certain other strains either no particular periodicity is noted or there is a tendency for the occurrence of largest numbers at dusk. The circulating microfilariae, 125 to 320 μ in length by 7 to 10 μ in cross-section, are active within a **sheath,** the retained transparent egg membranes that were stretched about the larvae during development *in utero.* These forms will develop only in certain mosquitoes; hence pathology will not result if blood containing them is transfused into a recipient. Female mosquitoes of various genera (espe-

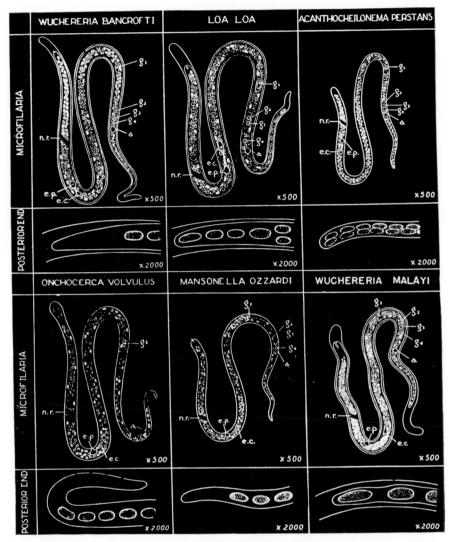

Fig. 11. Microfilariae. a, anal pore (tail spot); e.c., excretory cell; e.p., excretory pore (V spot); g_1, g_2, g_3, and g_4, second, third, and fourth genital cells; n.r., nerve ring. (From Belding. *Textbook of Clinical Parasitology,* 2nd ed., Appleton-Century-Crofts.)

cially *Culex, Aëdes,* and *Anopheles*) serve as **necessary intermediate hosts** for this parasite. When feeding upon an infected individual, they ingest the microfilariae from the peripheral blood stream. These pass into the midgut, and after escaping from their sheaths, many invade the intestinal wall. **Within 24 hours,** most of these find their way to the **thoracic muscles.** Under favorable conditions of temperature and humidity they undergo metamorphosis to an **infective** stage in **one to three weeks.** This stage is active and migrates to the tip of the **proboscis sheath,** from which it penetrates **onto** the skin of the human host at the time of the next blood meal. It probably enters the wound made by the mosquito. After entering the skin, these larvae pass to the lymphatic system and grow to maturity; in most cases this probably requires at least **one year.** The adult worms may live for **many years** in certain individuals.

Pathology and Symptomatology. In endemic areas, most of the natives are more or less **asymptomatic.** In these there appears to be an excellent host-parasite adjustment. The host experiences little or no disturbance, and the parasite is able to develop normally, which results in the release of large numbers of microfilariae. These individuals, therefore, are the main source of infection for the mosquito host, as man is the only known **definitive host.** In those showing clinical evidence of the infection, **two** distinct stages are evident. In the **acute stage** there is a characteristic, and often profound, lymphatic inflammation in response to trapped worms and/or their metabolites. Tissue changes tend eventually to constrict the wall of the lymphatic vessel or other affected parts of the system. This partial obstruction results in **lymph stasis** and **edema.** The cardinal manifestation is a recurrent **lymphangitis,** usually with an associated **lymphadenitis.** Some experience a low-grade fever, usually of short duration. The location of the obstruction determines the part of the body affected, the external genitalia of both sexes being the most common. In the absence of reinfections there usually is steady improvement in the individual, each relapse being milder than the former. Thus, even without specific therapy this condition is **self-limiting** and presumably will not become **chronic** in those acquiring the infection during a brief sojourn in an endemic area. It is of interest to note that microfilariae are difficult to demonstrate during the acute phase, indicating a pronounced disturbance in the host-parasite equilibrium. Lymph node **biopsy** (see below) has been used in special cases to demonstrate adult worms. Sectioning the tissues reveals the worms; the females are readily recognized by the microfilariae in utero. The characteristic reaction here consists of a necrotic zone around the worms and a palisaded area of foreign-body giant cells, epithelial cells, and eosinophils.

There is good evidence that the advanced **chronic type** of filariasis, known as **elephantiasis,** develops only in a small percentage of highly reactive individuals infected repeatedly for many years. Following lymphatic obstruction, striking proliferative changes occur, and the worms die and are absorbed or become calcified. The edema, soft at first, becomes fibrotic following the growth of connective tissue in the area. The redundant skin, being nourished poorly, cracks and becomes fissured and often is secondarily infected with pyogenic or mycotic organisms. This resemblance to elephant skin accounts for the term elephantiasis applied to this chronic, disfiguring condition. While microfilariae may appear in the blood of chronic cases, due to new active infections superimposed upon the older ones, they are not often demonstrated. Thus, it appears that the more reactive the host the less likely is the development of the worms and the release of larvae.

From this account, it is obvious that **undue emphasis** has been placed on the advanced chronic type of filariasis, which involves a relatively few individuals even in highly endemic areas.

Laboratory Diagnosis. A **final diagnosis** is made by demonstrating the microfilariae, usually in **thick** blood smears (Fig. 11). In most areas of the world, they are present in appreciable numbers only at **night,** usually with greatest frequency between 10 P.M. and 2 A.M. It should be remembered that microfilariae **cannot** be demonstrated during the incubation period and, usually, not during the acute phase of the infection. In the absence of microfilariae a **presumptive diagnosis** can be made on the basis of the history of exposure, clinical evidence of the disease, and positive serologic tests and/or a positive intradermal test. It may be added that lymph node **biopsy,** during clinical quiescence only, often will reveal adult or immature worms. This, however, is a research tool and should not be used except in unusual circumstances and then only by adhering to strict surgical technics.

Treatment. Acute cases resulting from recent primary exposure should be removed from the endemic area, if possible. Bed rest and supportive measures, such as hot and cold compresses, are of assistance in reducing the edema. **Psychotherapy** often is necessary, especially for young males with scrotal involvement.

The anthelmintic of choice is **Hetrazan,** an antimonial taken orally.

CESTODES

The adult cestodes, or tapeworms, are **strobilate;** i.e., they consist of a chain of units made up of the **scolex** (head), the **neck,** and a series of **proglottids** (segments). The scolex is adapted for attachment to the intestinal mucosa. It is provided with cupped suckers or sucking grooves according to the species. In some cases hooklets are also present. The delicate, unsegmented neck region, immediately behind the scolex, is a **budding zone** that gives rise to all of the more distal parts of the worm. Sexually immature proglottids arise directly from the neck, then mature units containing fully developed male and female reproductive organs, and distalmost the gravid units. The number of proglottids varies considerably among the different species. In contrast to the prominent male and female genital systems, tapeworms have simple nervous and excretory systems, and a digestive system is lacking.

In presenting the material of this section, the cestodes will be grouped according to their common habitat in the body, the intestinal tract and various tissues. The **intestinal cestodes** live as adults in man, while the **tissue cestodes** occur in a larval stage.

INTESTINAL CESTODES

This discussion will be limited to the **four** most common intestinal cestodes of man: *Diphyllobothrium latum* **(fish or broad tapeworm),** *Taenia saginata* **(beef tapeworm),** *T. sodium* **(pork tapeworm),** and *Hymenolepis nana* **(dwarf tapeworm).** The first three are very large, ranging in length from 3 to 10 m. or more, while the fourth is, by comparison, a dwarf, being 25 mm. or less in length. To conserve space, the four species will be considered together under each topic.

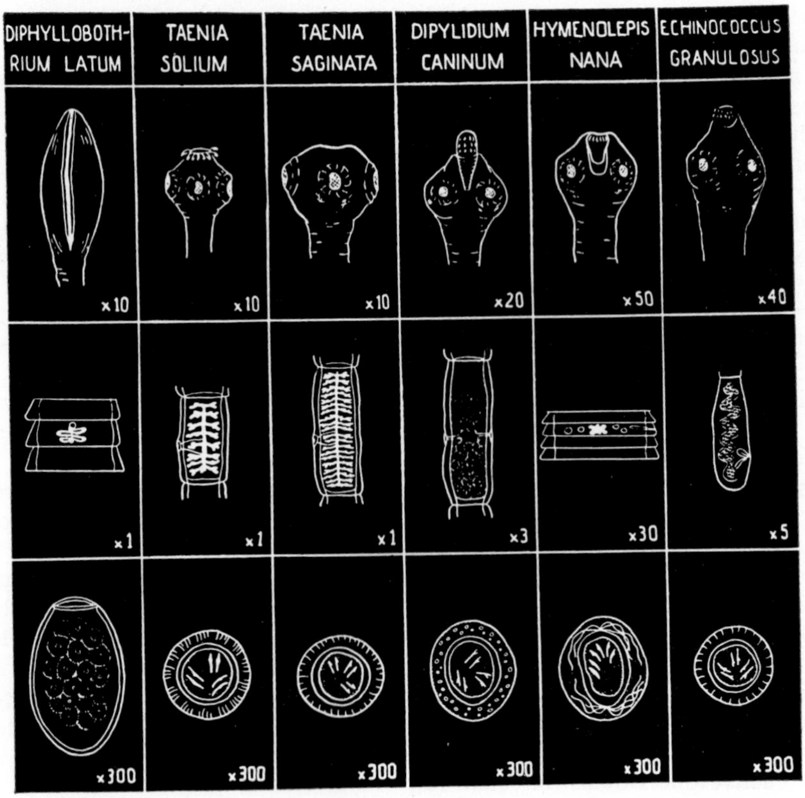

Fig. 12. Differential characteristics of common tapeworms of man. (Modified from Belding. *Textbook of Clinical Parasitology,* 2nd ed., Appleton-Century-Crofts.)

Life Cycles. *D. latum,* being a more **primitive form,** differs from the other species in many ways, both in structure and complexity of the life cycle. The scolex is spatulate and is provided with a median ventral and dorsal grooved sucker (Fig. 12). The proglottids are **broad,** and the centrally located uterus has a characteristic **rosette** arrangement. Eggs within the fully developed uterus are discharged continuously in large numbers from the uterine pore (Figs. 2, 12).

These are **undeveloped** when passed in the stool and will **embryonate** only upon reaching cool **fresh** water. Embryonation is completed after **two weeks** or more, and hatching occurs. A ciliated embryo **(coracidium)** escapes from the shell and swims about actively (Fig. 13). If this stage is ingested by one of the **first intermediate hosts (copepods** of the genus *Diaptomus* or *Cyclops*), the embryo, after losing the ciliated covering, burrows into the body cavity **(haemocoel)** and trans-

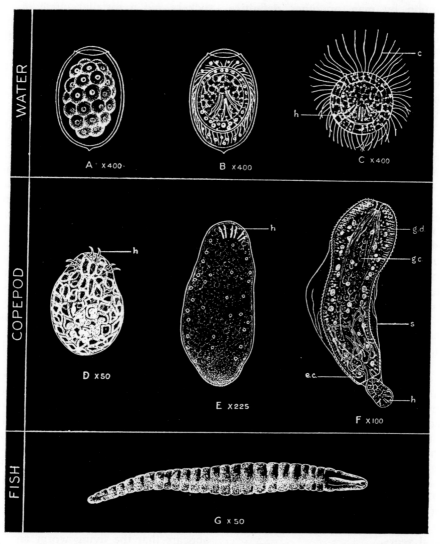

Fig. 13. Eggs and larval forms of *Diphyllobothrium latum.* A, undeveloped egg; B, hexacanth embryo in eggshell; C, ciliated coracidium; D, larva, seven days after infection of copepod; E, larva, 20 days; F, procercoid larva; G, plerocercoid larva; c, cilia; e.c., excretory cell; g.c., gland cells; g.d., ducts of glands; h, hooklets; s, old membrane of onchosphere. (From Belding. *Textbook of Clinical Parasitology,* 2nd ed., Appleton-Century-Crofts.)

forms, within **two to three weeks,** into a mature first larval stage **(procercoid,** Fig 13). Ingestion of the first intermediate host with these mature larvae by the **second intermediate host** (many different **fresh-water fishes**) continues the cycle. The larvae migrate into the **flesh** (often between the muscle fibers) of the fish and metamorphose, within **several weeks,** into a second larval stage **(plerocercoid,** Fig. 13). Larger (edible) fishes acquire the infection from eating their infected young or infected smaller species. Consumption by **man** or other **definitive hosts** (dog, bear, etc.) of fish flesh containing mature plerocercoid larvae completes the cycle. The worm, usually only one, develops to maturity in the **small intestine** in **three to five weeks,** and egg production begins. The worm may live for **many years.**

The scolex of *T. saginata* is rhomboidal and has cup-shaped suckers (Fig. 12). These are the sole means of attachment, since the rostellum is devoid of hooklets. The distal-most **gravid** proglottids (Fig. 12), each containing about 80,000 **mature** eggs (Fig. 12), become separated from the strobila and actively migrate out of the anus or are evacuated in the stool. If grazing **cattle,** the only **intermediate host,** ingest the proglottids or, more commonly, the eggs freed after disintegration of the proglottids on moist earth or in sewage, the cycle proceeds. The six-hooked embryos **(onchospheres)** escape from the eggs, following hatching in the duodenum, and penetrate into the intestinal tissue to reach, ultimately, the circulation. They are carried about, and most of them reach **skeletal muscles** or the **heart.** In these sites, they transform, in **60 to 75 days,** into a typical **cysticercus stage** (*Cysticercus bovis*), which contains a scolex, similar to that of the adult worm, invaginated into the fluid-filled bladder (Fig. 14). Man is infected by ingesting these larvae in beef, either raw or processed inadequately. The head of the larva attaches to the wall of the **ileum,** and the adult worm, usually only one, develops to maturity in **eight to ten weeks** and may live for **several years.**

The scolex of *T. solium* bears, in addition to the four cup-shaped suckers, 22 to 32 small hooklets on the rostellum (Fig. 12). The length of the worm is **shorter** than that of *T. saginata,* and the structure of the proglottids differs in the two species (Fig. 12). The life cycle of the two species is similar, except that the **hog** is the usual **intermediate host** for *T. solium.* The scolex of this larval stage (*Cysticercus cellulosae*) is provided with four suckers and a crown of hooklets. This stage may also occur in **man** and cause serious injury (see below). For this reason, *T. solium* has greater medical and public health importance than *T. saginata.*

The scolex of *H. nana* has four cup-shaped suckers and a rostellar circle of 20 to 30 hooklets (Fig. 12). Unlike the three large species that usually occur singly, the adults of *H. nana* may be **numerous.** The terminal gravid proglottids usually disintegrate before separation from the strobila, so that the **mature** eggs are passed in the stool (Figs. 2, 12). In the **direct cycle,** these eggs initiate infection upon ingestion. Such infections may be of a **direct** hand-to-mouth type or of an **indirect** type via contaminated food and/ or drink. The eggs hatch in the **duodenum,** and the liberated six-hooked embryos penetrate into nearby villi. The resulting larval stage **(cysticercoid),** mature in about **four days,** penetrates into the intestinal lumen, attaches to the mucosa, and develops in about **two weeks** into the adult worm. This cycle, with both the larval and adult stages in the same host, is **unique** for a cestode. In the **indirect cycle, insects,** especially certain beetles, serve as the **intermediate host.** Accidental ingestion of those containing the mature cysticercoids (Fig. 14) results in infection.

Pathology and Symptomatology. The adult stage of the **three** large cestodes usually causes little damage and gives rise only to vague signs and symptoms, such as epigastric distress, false hunger pains, and **nervous manifestations,** but there are **important exceptions** to this rule. The most important of these is the so-called **bothriocephalus anemia** exhibited by certain individuals infected with *D. latum.* This disease is a true symptomatic **pernicious anemia.** It appears that the living worm and the host compete for vitamin B_{12}. If the worm is in the proximal part of the small intestine, a deficiency in this substance may result, causing pernicious anemia. After a period of time, a poor supply of extrinsic factor and/or reduced production of intrinsic factor contribute to the development of this condition.

Heavy infections with *H. nana,* particularly in **children,** usually give rise to **serious** conditions, such as striking abdominal pain, bloody-mucus stools, and **exaggerated nervous disorders.**

Laboratory Diagnosis. This is based on the recovery of the species-characteristic eggs of *D. latum* and *H. nana* and gravid proglottids of *T. saginata* and *T. solium.* The eggs of *D. latum* are unembryonated, about 70 by 45 μ in size, have an **operculum** at one end and a thickened shell, often with a knob, at the opposite end (Fig. 2). Those of *H. nana* are nearly spherical, measure about 50 μ in diameter, and have **polar filaments** arising from the inner membranous shell that surrounds the embryo (Fig. 2). When the fresh proglottids of *T. saginata* are pressed gently between two microscope slides and held in front of a bright light, it is easy to see **15 to 20** main lateral arms of the uterus (Fig. 12). *T. solium* has only **seven to 13** of these arms (Fig. 12) making differentiation a simple procedure. Eggs of both *T. saginata* and *T. solium* are recovered occasionally from the stool, but they are **indistinguishable** (Figs. 2, 12).

Treatment. Recent evidence indicates that **Atabrine** is the drug of choice in **all four** infections, although hexylresorcinol crystoids are used by some to treat light infections with *H. nana.* Success with the Atabrine treatment depends, in large measure, upon **adequate preparation** of the patient. Most important is the administration of a saline purge the evening before treatment, since effective treatment depends on an empty intestine. The drug is given the following morning on an empty stomach as a single dose along with an equal amount of sodium bicarbonate or other substance to counteract nausea and vomiting. **Two hours later** a second saline purgation is employed to evacuate the worm(s), which usually is passed intact and stained a deep yellow.

TISSUE CESTODES

As noted above, **two** of the intestinal cestodes may have a tissue stage in man, *T. solium* and *H. nana.* In addition, there are two species of small cestodes in the genus *Echinococcus* that are **dangerous** tissue parasites of man, *E. granulosus* and *E. multilocularis.* Until 1951 there was general agreement that the various types of *Echinococcus* **larval** development in man were of the single species, *E. granulosus.* It is now clear that this species produces a larval cyst known as the **unilocular hydatid cyst** (see below), while the other species, *E. multilocularis* is responsible for a peculiar **branching-type** larval cyst, the **alveolar hydatid cyst.** Since space permits discussion of only one of these parasites, *E. multilocularis* will be omitted. However, to compare it with the **more common** and **widespread** *E. granulosus,* a few comments should be made.

E. multilocularis **adults (smaller** and morphologically differentiated from *E. granulosus*) occur in the **small intestine** of **wild canines,** the **fox** being the most important **definitive host (domestic dogs** may be involved in certain endemic areas). Infective eggs occur in the stool, and if ingested by an intermediate host (**wild mice** and **voles** are most important), the cycle continues. The embryos migrate to the **liver** (less often to other visceral sites) and grow by **exogenous** budding to form the larval stage, the **alveolar hydatid cyst.** Infected viscera with a mature cyst(s), if ingested by the **canine host,** completes the cycle when contained scolices develop into **adult worms. Man** serves accidentally as an **intermediate host** by **ingesting eggs,** usually on raw fruit, such as strawberries, **contaminated with feces** of the **definitive host.** The alveolar cyst in man lacks a strong **protective layer,** which appears to encourage branching formations of **cavities with little fluid.** The **liver** is most often involved, and the damage resembles that produced by a large **amebic liver abscess. The liver disease is almost always fatal. Skin** and **serologic tests** are used to make a **diagnosis** and **biotherapy** (see below) is the only known form of **treatment.**

The **most important** of the various **larval cestodes** in man are *Cysticercus cellulosae* (larval stage of *T. solium;* see above) and *Echinococcus granulosus.* They will be considered **together** for this discussion.

The Involvement of Man in the Life Cycle. The **egg** is the stage that infects man **in both**

cases. In the case of *C. cellulosae,* **three** means of infection are known. A patient harboring the adult worm may become infected by transferring mature eggs from the anus to the mouth on unclean finger tips **(external autoinfection),** or these eggs may be transferred **indirectly** to another person **(heteroinfection).** The **third** type, **internal autoinfection,** is thought to occur when detached gravid proglottids are regurgitated into the stomach and return to the intestine where some of the eggs become liberated. In the case of *E. granulosus,* the situation is entirely different in that man **does not** harbor the adult worms. These occur, usually in large numbers, in dogs and other **definitive hosts.** Many animals may serve as **intermediate hosts,** but the most important are sheep and hogs. **Man** serves in this capacity, but, as in trichinosis, he is a **blind alley** for the parasite. Human infection usually occurs by the accidental transfer of the mature eggs from

the fur of the dog to the human mouth. The eggs hatch in the small intestine, and the embryos penetrate into the circulatory system. They are filtered out in various tissues. Any organ or tissue may be involved, but the **liver and lungs** are the most common sites. By a remarkable process of asexual reproduction the embryos metamorphose into **hydatid cysts.** These **vacuolated** larval cestodes are called **unilocular hydatid cysts.** Cysts in soft tissues (**liver,** lungs, etc.) are somewhat similar, but the type in bone **(osseous)** tends to **elongate** as it flows into, and erodes, the bony canal. The unilocular hydatid cyst of the liver is the **most common** in man. It consists typically of a central, fluid-filled cavity lined with a **germinative** (protoplasmic) layer, surrounded by a **cuticular** (protective) layer that tends to become laminated. It usually requires **many years** for the cyst to reach a large size. In time it becomes covered with a fibrous host-

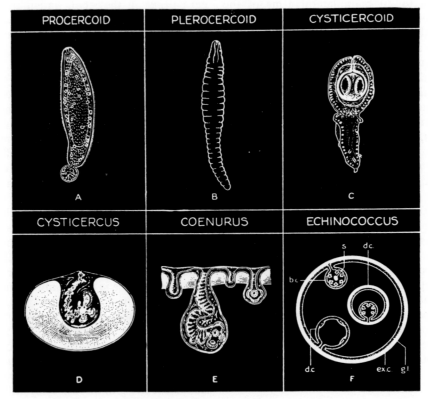

Fig. 14. Larval forms of tapeworms, b.c., brood capsule; d.c., daughter cyst; ex.c., external laminated cuticula; g.l., germinal or inner nucleated layer; s, scolex. (From Belding. *Textbook of Clinical Parasitology,* 2nd ed., Appleton-Century-Crofts.)

tissue capsule. Arising from the germinative layer, **internal buds** (brood capsules) are produced (Fig. 14). When full size, each forms **vesicles** along its **inner** margin. Typically, each vesicle (10 to 20 or more) develops into a small **scolex** (usually invaginated, which serves to protect the 20 to 30 rostellar **hooklets)** and a short "neck" region. Thus, a large mature cyst containing thousands of these scolices produces a heavy infection of adult worms when eaten by a definitive host. The optimum conditions for perpetuation of the parasite are provided in the **dog-sheep cycle.**

Pathology and Symptomatology. *C. cellulosae* may occur in various tissues of man, but of greatest concern is the common involvement of the **eyes and the brain. Ocular cysticercosis** may result in uveitis, dislocation of the retina, and other conditions. Pain, flashes of light and grotesque figures in the field of vision, and other complaints have been noted. **Cerebral cysticercosis** usually follows involvement of the **meninges,** with epilepsy as the most characteristic consequence, and the **fourth ventricle,** with hydrocephalus, headache, and diplopia being noteworthy.

The hydatid cysts of *E. granulosus* are usually **single,** but they may be multiple. Their size and contour depend upon the site of implantation and the age of the cysts. Because of the **slow growth** of cysts, vital processes usually are not disturbed sufficiently to be of concern to the patient until **many years** after infection. Ultimately, however, there may be great tissue destruction and striking signs and symptoms. The type and degree of this damage and the resulting clinical manifestations correspond to the exact location and size of the cyst(s). It should be added that systemic intoxication or **sensitization** often occurs in those with a unilocular hydatid cyst having a vascularized wall permitting leakage of sensitizing fluids. **Sensitized individuals** exhibit marked eosinophilia, and in some urticaria or angioneurotic edema is evident. **Anaphylaxis** may be precipitated by the sudden release of hydatid fluid, as in the case of spontaneous rupture of a large intraabdominal cyst or rupture following a severe blow to the area.

Laboratory Diagnosis. Both infections usually are diagnosed by **indirect** means, such as x-ray, intradermal, and precipitin tests.

Treatment. Surgery, in most instances, is the **only** therapeutic procedure of value in **both** infections. **In ocular cysticercosis** removal of the parasite while it is still alive usually prevents total loss of sight. **In cerebral cysticercosis,** procedures are well developed for extirpation of **solitary** cysts, and a majority of patients recover completely. However, operative technics are **not** recommended in cases with generalized cerebral infections. **In the case of hydatid cysts,** surgical intervention is limited to those with **unilocular** cysts in **operable** sites. **Meticulous care** must be taken to prevent spilling the cyst contents into the operative cavity for the reason mentioned above. For the treatment of cysts in **inoperable** sites or for treatment of **multiple** cysts in several anatomic locations, **biologic therapy** has been employed widely. This involves the use of sterile hydatid fluid, or only the protein component, to desensitize the host, which usually is followed in time by death and gradual absorption of the cyst.

TREMATODES

The exact form of **adult** digenetic trematodes is dependent upon the state of contraction, but they usually are flat, elongated, and leaf-shaped. They vary considerably in size, from less than 1 mm. to several centimeters. Characteristic **external** features include an oral and, in most species, a ventral sucker, the **acetabulum,** an excretory pore at the posterior extremity, and a genital pore near the anterior border of the ventral sucker. The principal **internal organs** include a blind, bifurcate intestinal tract, an excretory system, **prominent** male and/or female reproductive organs, and a primitive nervous system. The arrangement, shape, and size of these various structures are characteristic for different species.

Endoparasitic trematodes have complicated life cycles involving **alternation of generations and hosts.**

Information concerning the **most important** trematodes of man and the infections they cause is listed in **Table 2** (see also Figs.

Table 2. Important Trematodes of Man

Parasite	Disease	Location of Adults Where Eggs Are Laid	Stage Passed From Man	Second Intermediate Host (Certain Snails Are the First Intermediate Host)	Means of Human Infection	Laboratory Diagnosis
Fasciolopsis buski	Fasciolopsiasis	Small intestine	Undeveloped eggs in stool	Water caltrop, certain other fresh-water plants	Ingestion of metacercariae	Eggs in stool (140 x 80 μ)
Clonorchis sinensis	Clonorchiasis	Distal bile ducts of liver	Developed eggs in stool	Certain fresh-water fishes	Ingestion of metacercariae	Eggs in stool (30 x 16 μ)
Paragonimus westermani	Paragonimiasis	In lung capsules	Undeveloped eggs in stool and sputum	Certain fresh-water crabs and crayfishes	Ingestion of metacercariae	Eggs in stool and sputum (85 x 50 μ)
Schistosoma japonicum	Schistosomiasis japonica	Venules of superior and inferior mesenteric veins	Developed eggs in stool	None	Penetration of skin by cercariae	Eggs in stool (89 x 66 μ, with rudimentary lateral spine)
Schistosoma mansoni	Schistosomiasis mansoni	Venules of inferior (and, at times, superior) mesenteric vein	Developed eggs in stool, rarely in urine	None	Penetration of skin by cercariae	Eggs in stool or urine (150 x 60 μ, with large lateral spine)
Schistosoma haematobium	Schistosomiasis haematobia	Venules of vesical and pelvic plexuses	Developed eggs in urine, rarely in stool	None	Penetration of skin by cercariae	Eggs in urine or stool (150 x 60 μ, with large terminal spine)

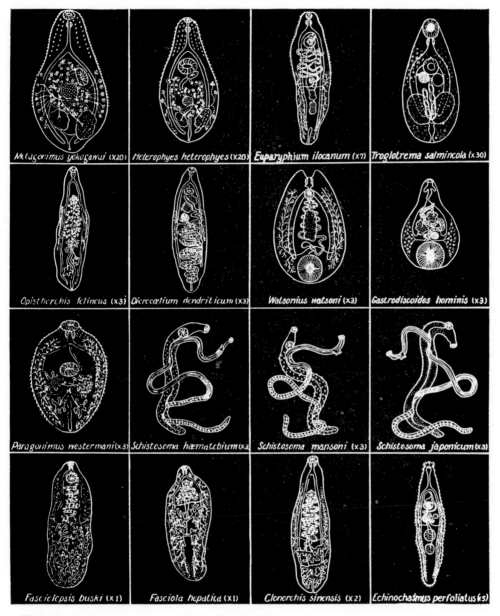

Fig. 15. Trematodes of man. (From Belding. *Textbook of Clinical Parasitology,* 2nd ed., Appleton-Century-Crofts. The size of this illustration has been increased by ⅒.)

2 and 15). **The schistosomes, or bloodflukes,** being of the greatest medical and public health importance, deserve further consideration.

THE SCHISTOSOMES

Schistosomes **differ** in many ways from the other digenetic trematodes. The important differences include the presence in schistosomes of separate sexes, nonoperculated eggs with spines, fork-tailed cercariae, and the absence of a true metacercarial stage in the life cycle. As noted in **Table 2** there are three species that occur commonly in man: *Schistosoma japonicum, S. mansoni,* and *S. haematobium.* While the other two species lack important **natural reservoirs,** *S. japonicum* has many mammalian reservoirs (cats, dogs, cattle, water buffaloes, etc.). However, it may be stated that **man** usually is the most important source of eggs of all three species. The adult worms occur characteristically **in pairs** in mesenteric veins (*S. japonicum* and *S. mansoni*) and vesical veins (*S. haematobium*). The male **attaches** to the wall of the blood vessel, holding the female in a ventrad groove, the **gynecophoral canal** (Fig. 15). The female is able to extend its anterior end into the smaller calibered venules where the eggs are discharged. As would be judged from the last two statements, the males are **stouter** (0.5 to 1.1 mm. being the range in breadth among the species) than the females (0.16 to 0.30 mm.). The females, on the other hand, are **longer** (14 to 20 mm. being the range among the species) than the males (10 to 15 mm.).

Life Cycles. The adults of *S. japonicum* and *S. mansoni* are found normally in the tributaries of the **superior and inferior mesenteric veins** respectively, while those of *S. haematobium* find the **vesical plexus** the optimum location. Although these are the usual locations, it should be remembered that the worms may be found in **other sites.** Perhaps most important in this connection is the well-known fact that following infection with *S. haematobium* a small percentage of the worms fail to reach the normal site and remain in the rectal vessels. Thus, some of the eggs released may occur in the stools rather than in the urine as expected in this infection. After copulation, the females give off a considerable number of eggs over a long period of time. These are **undeveloped** when laid but usually contain a fully developed ciliated larva **(miracidium)** after they have succeeded in passing through the wall of the intestine or bladder to occur in the stools or urine (Fig. 2). Upon reaching **fresh** water, hatching occurs through a tear in the shell and the miracidium swims about in the water. If appropriate **intermediate hosts** are present in the immediate vicinity, the miracidium will penetrate into the soft tissues. These hosts are certain **snails** (e.g., *Oncomelania quadrasi* for *S. japonicum* in the Philippines, *Australorbis glabratus* for

S. mansoni in the Americas, and *Bulinus contortus* for *S. haematobium* in Egypt). The **intrasnail cycle** lasts for **several weeks** and involves **three** distinct stages, the first **(mother)** and second **(daughter)** generation **sporocysts** and **cercariae.** The latter, with a characteristic **forked tail,** escape from the snail at intervals and swim about in the water. In contact with the skin of **man,** or other susceptible **definitive hosts,** they discard their tails and digest their way into the skin. They reach the blood stream and are carried through the right heart to the lungs. Here they pass the capillary filter and are carried to the left heart and thence into large arterial vessels. From the mesenteric artery, where most of them are carried, they pass through the capillaries into the **intrahepatic portal blood.** They feed and grow in this site, and **when sexual maturity approaches** (after about **16 days** of residence) they migrate against the portal blood flow to the areas where **oviposition** is to occur. *S. haematobium* is thought to pass from the rectal veins through anastomoses into hemorrhoidal and pudendal veins to reach ultimately the vesical venous system. **Several weeks** are required for the maturation of the adult worms (**four to five** for *S. japonicum,* **six to seven** for *S. mansoni,* and **ten to twelve weeks** after skin penetration in the case of *S. haematobium*), and they may live for **many years.** Thus, it can be seen that there is justification for the common statement that the life cycle of the schistosomes is a marvel of biology.

Pathology and Symptomatology. In the case of **all three** species, penetration of the skin by the cercariae produces small hemorrhages, and after the cercariae break out of the capillaries in the lungs they cause an acute inflammatory reaction predominated by eosinophils. Upon arrival in the intrahepatic portal blood an acute **hepatitis** may follow as well as systemic intoxication and **sensitization,** all due presumably to the toxic metabolites released. Many patients exhibit toxic manifestations, such as fever and sweats, epigastric distress, and pain in the back, groin, or legs. Some develop giant urticaria, and toxic diarrhea is common. These reactions may continue **long after** the worms have migrated to the area of oviposition. While the penetration of the cercariae and their migrations, and later the movements of the developing worms, usually produce detrimental effects, **the main agents of pathology in schistosomiasis are the eggs** released from the females.

The period of egg deposition and extrusion from the body usually is referred to as the **acute stage.** In the case of the **two** intestinal forms, *S. japonicum* and *S. mansoni,* the events of this stage are, in general, similar. However, it is important to add that the females of *S. japonicum* release considerably more eggs, hence the damage is proportionately greater. In both species the **intestinal tissue** is first to be damaged, usually the **small intestine** in the case of *S. japonicum* and the **colon** in the case of *S. mansoni.* Considerable trauma and hemorrhage is produced by the eggs as they are filtered through the perivascular tissues into the lumen. Eggs trapped in these sites are walled off, usually individually, by a **pseudoabscess,** which later transforms into a characteristic **pseudotubercle.** The egg, or its shell only, is usually surrounded by foreign body giant cells and epithelioid cells. The entire lesion often is surrounded by a peripheral ring of connective tissue, eosinophils, plasma cells, and lymphocytes. The acute stage is ushered in with diarrhea or dysentery and the appearance of eggs in the stools. Daily fever, anorexia, loss of weight, severe epigastric pain, and anemia are common. Many of the eggs are swept into the intrahepatic portal vessels where they provoke **pseudotubercle** formation. **Liver involvement** is more rapid and severe in *S. japonicum* infections. The liver becomes tender and enlarged. Coarse bands of dense connective tissue, chiefly about the large radicals of the portal vein, have been responsible for the term, **pipe-stem cirrhosis,** associated with schistosomiasis japonica and mansoni. It should be added that nests of *S. japonicum* eggs often occur also in **ectopic sites,** such as the **brain** and **heart.**

The **chronic stage** of schistosomiasis is one of tissue proliferation and repair. The intestinal wall becomes thickened by fibrosis, and the lumen may be reduced considerably. Anal polyps are common, as are papillomas

and fistulas; hemorrhoids may be the first indication of the infection, due to portal obstruction. The liver may become increasingly cirrhotic due to extensive periportal fibrosis, and there may be a compensatory congestive enlargement of the spleen, **especially** in *S. japonicum* infections. Thus, in many there is a rapidly developing dysfunction of the intestinal wall and periportal tissues. In the late stages of the disease in those with heavy infections, emaciation is severe and many die of exhaustion or a concurrent infection.

In the case of *S. haematobium,* the **acute stage** involves mainly the wall of the **urinary bladder,** but the **lungs** also may be involved. The latter involvement is due to eggs, and at times worms, which are probably carried via the inferior vena cava to reach the pulmonary arterioles. Here **pseudotubercles** are produced as described above. The damage produced in the wall of the urinary bladder is similar to that described above for the wall of the intestine. **Hematuria** usually is the first evidence of infection. As time passes, the bladder wall becomes thickened by dense fibrosis of the muscular and submucous coats, and multiple urinary polyps, papillomas, and fistulas are common. The superficial mucosa of the bladder may show metaplasia, an intense inflammatory infiltrate, and eggs (many calcified). Fever, suprapubic tenderness, and difficulty in urination are common. In addition to the bladder, **other parts of the genitourinary system** often become involved. Finally, it is worth noting that in some areas there is a close association between chronic schistosomiasis of the bladder and carcinoma, since eggs in capillaries are seen in the midst of an infiltrating carcinoma. In fact, the term **Egyptian irritation cancer** is well known.

Schistosome Dermatitis. In 1928 **Cort** demonstrated that **cercariae** of certain **non-human blood flukes** are the agents of an aggravating form of dermatitis. This condition, now known to be prevalent in certain areas of the United States and in many other parts of the world, usually results from infection during the warm months and is due to skin penetration of the cercariae. Most of the cercariae involved belong to species that develop into adults in various birds, but in a few instances mammals, such as cattle and rodents, are the **definitive hosts.** Once thought to be limited to contact with cercariae-infested fresh water, this condition is now also recognized along many **salt-water** beaches. **Marine snails** serve as the **intermediate hosts** in such cases. The dermatitis appears to be a **sensitization** reaction that is intensified by repeated exposure (Fig. 16). Upon entry of the cercariae, a prickly sensation is experienced and erythema soon appears. Local or generalized urticaria is common, especially in sensitive individuals exposed previously. A **macule** forms at each site of penetration, followed in a **few hours** by intense itching of the area, during which the macule transforms into a **papule.** The reaction reaches its maximum usually between the **second and third days,** after which it decreases gradually. **Treatment** consists in the topical application of palliatives, such as **calamine lotion,** to relieve the severe pruritus. Aside from the usually severe annoyance it produces in man, schistosome dermatitis poses an **economic problem,** especially in resort areas, where the condition may lead to the closing of beaches used for swimming and other recreation.

Laboratory Diagnosis. In a majority of cases, *S. haematobium* eggs can be demon-strated in the sediment that settles out of urine. In some instances, a small **bladder biopsy specimen** will reveal the eggs when they cannot be demonstrated in urine. If these measures fail in suspected cases, **stool** examinations and/or **rectal biopsies** should be considered, since these worms may involve the **rectum** as well. The **mature** eggs contain a miracidium, are rounded at the anterior pole, and have a **terminal** spine (Fig. 2). They range from 112 to 170 μ in length by 40 to 70 μ in breadth (**average, 150 by 60** μ). Intradermal and serologic tests, while available, usually are not needed to provide evidence of infection.

The eggs of *S. japonicum* and *S. mansoni* usually can be recovered from the stools of patients during the **acute stage,** but they tend to be released in clutches, making it necessary to perform repeated examinations at intervals for a period of **one month** before ruling out the infection. *S. japonicum* eggs are rotund, measure 70 to 100 μ by 50 to 70 μ (**average, 89 by 66** μ) and have a **rudimentary** lateral spine within a hook cavity (Fig. 2). Those of *S. mansoni* are rounded at both ends, measure 114 to 175 μ by 45 to 70 μ (**average, 150 by 60** μ), and have a conspicuous **lateral** spine near one pole (Fig. 2). The eggs of *S. japonicum* are more numerous and tend to be **mixed with the feces.** For this reason, a cross-section of the

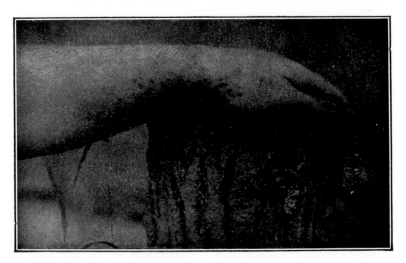

Fig. 16. Schistosomal dermatitis produced by cercariae of species parasitic in lower animals. (From Hegner, Root, Augustine, and Huff. *Parasitology,* D. Appleton-Century Company.)

bolus should be used for examination. On the other hand, eggs of *S. mansoni* tend to be concentrated **in the outer layer,** especially in mucus. In both infections, but especially in those with *S. mansoni,* simple fecal smears may fail to reveal the eggs, making it necessary to use a concentration technic. Sedimentation alone is helpful, but best results are obtained following the use of the **acid-ether-detergent method** or the **acid-sodium-sulfate-ether-detergent method.** In chronic cases, **rectal biopsy** often will reveal eggs when they have not been found in many different stool specimens. Intradermal and complement-fixation tests with schistosome antigen are available.

Treatment. Potassium (or sodium) **antimony tartrate** is the **only** effective drug against *S. japonicum.* For treating cases of *S. mansoni* and *S. haematobium,* **Fuadin (intramuscular)** or **Miracil D (oral)** is recommended. The latter is preferred by most clinicians treating cases **in the United States,** since it appears to be as effective as **Fuadin,** is less toxic, and is easier to administer, **especially** to **children.**

86

Arthropods

The **arthropods (phylum Arthropoda)** are the largest group of related organisms in the **animal kingdom.** They are **bilaterally symmetrical invertebrates** having a **segmented body,** a **firm exoskeleton,** and **paired jointed appendages.** Considering the large number of species, relatively few affect the health of man. However, many of these play a **vital role** in his welfare. They may be involved **directly,** in a variety of ways, as causal **agents of disease or discomfort.** Thus, they may be the basis of **morbid fear** (entomophobia), they may invade and **destroy tissues** (after accidental or deliberate contact), produce **envenomizations** (e.g., bites of centipedes, spiders; stings of scorpions, bees), or cause **dermatoses** (mites, fleas, lice, etc.). Because they serve as etiologic agents of various pathologic conditions, the responsible arthropods deserve careful attention. For an account of these, the student is referred to the textbooks listed at the end of Chapter 83, page 1115.

THE ROLE OF ARTHROPODS IN THE TRANSMISSION OF HUMAN DISEASES

In addition to their capacity to affect **directly** the health of man, arthropods play an even more important role in the transmission of infectious agents. In contrast to that above, this role may be considered to be an **indirect** one. In earlier chapters it has been noted that certain bacterial, spirochetal, rickettsial, and viral organisms depend for their dissemination upon various species of arthropods whose life cycles and behavior are involved intimately with the continued existence of the agents. Also, in the two previous chapters it has been noted that certain infections caused by animal parasites

can be classified as **arthropod-borne.** Therefore, it seems important to discuss **briefly** the orders of arthropods involved in the transmission of these various infectious agents. First, however, it is necessary to relate the **roles** played by arthropods in transmission.

Two main types of transmission by arthropods are recognized. The first, **mechanical,** results from a more or less **accidental** association between the arthropod and infectious agent. The classic example here is the house fly (*Musca domestica*)–enteric bacteria (e.g., *Salmonella* spp.) complex. The fly, by feeding upon or preparing to oviposit in human excreta, may become contaminated with viable organisms. This contamination may be limited to the mouth parts or body surfaces **(external),** or it may also involve the alimentary canal of the fly following ingestion of the organisms **(internal). In the former case** the viable organisms may be deposited on or within food or drink intended for human consumption when the fly rests and/or feeds upon such substances. **In the latter case** the organisms may be voided upon or within such substances in fecal dejecta and/or regurgitation drops of the fly. Perhaps the last named is more important, since there is better provision for protection of the organisms against adverse environmental factors. In any event, in these types of mechanical transmission, there is no **required** incubation of the infectious agent; frequently there is no multiplication involved. The efficiency of this type of transmission depends on the ability of the organisms to survive under the prevailing conditions, and usually, on the **rapidity** of the transfer.

The other type of transmission, **biologic,** involves a fundamental, and frequently an **obligate,** relationship to the life cycle of the organisms. **Three** types of biologic transmission will be noted in the discussions below: **cyclodevelopmental, cyclopropagative,** and **propagative.** In the **first** the agent undergoes a necessary cycle (development) in the arthropod but does not multiply. The best example of this is the microfilarial cycle in the mosquito. In the **second** there is both a necessary cycle and multiplication within the arthropod (e.g., the malarial cycle in anopheline mosquitoes). In the **propagative type** it is assumed that there is not a necessary cycle (change in form or type) within the arthropod, but the organisms are known to multiply (e.g., plague bacilli in fleas). This type will be excluded from future classifications of transmission, if as seems likely, slight changes in the form of the organisms in the arthropod host are revealed by studies with the electron microscope.

Two major groups (class ARACHNIDA and class INSECTA) of arthropods have species of importance in the transmission of infectious agents. Specifically, these are limited to the **order Acarina** (ticks and mites) of the class ARACHNIDA and to the following **orders** of the class INSECTA: **Siphonaptera** (fleas), **Anoplura** (bloodsucking lice), **Orthoptera** (cockroaches, etc.), **Hemiptera** (true bugs), and **Diptera** (flies, including mosquitoes). These will be presented in this order below. Space limits the material presented to: 1, **identification;** 2, **life cycle;** and 3, **diseases transmitted.** Under the topic of **identification** it will be possible to list only those gross features that characterize the group and, in some cases, those that assist in distinguishing members of the group. Under the life cycle heading, the stages will be listed. In some cases comments will be made concerning the particular stage involved in disease transmission. In presenting the section on **diseases transmitted,** no attempt will be made to include **all** diseases. The **main** purpose of this section is to bring together for the student a list of the important arthropod-borne diseases studied in this book, especially those of importance in this country. In most cases one or more of the most important arthropod transmitters will be listed.

This approach to the study of arthropods involved in the transmission of human diseases is intended only as a **brief introduction** to the subject. For detailed information concerning structure, classification (including the use of keys), and so forth, the student is urged to consult one or more of the textbooks listed at the end of Chapter 83, page 1115).

CLASS ARACHNIDA

Typical forms in this class have the head and thorax fused, forming a **cephalothorax,** and the adults normally possess **four pairs** of legs.

ORDER ACARINA (TICKS AND MITES)

The general **absence of body segmentation** is characteristic for members of this order. The body is more or less sac-like in appearance, since a head as such is lacking and in most members there is a strong fusion of the thorax and abdomen giving no **external** evidence of demarcation. Wings and antennae are absent. The sexes are separate.

TICKS

There are **two** main groups of ticks, families Ixodidae and Argasidae, referred to simply as **hard** and **soft** ticks, respectively. A single, easily recognized structure **(scutum or dorsal shield)** makes differentiation easy. The hard ticks possess this dorsal structure, while the soft ticks do not. In the **male** hard tick, the shield covers most of the dorsal surface, but in the **female** it is limited to the anterior portion.

Identification. **Ticks** are most likely to be confused with **mites.** The outstanding characteristics of assistance in identification are: 1, the much larger size of ticks (all ticks are macroscopic; many mites are microscopic); 2, the leathery integument of ticks (hairless or with only a few short hairs), in contrast with the membranous body of mites (covered with **long hairs**); and 3, the **hypostome.** The latter serves to anchor these arthropods to their hosts. **In ticks** it is covered characteristically with backward-pointing teeth and is a prominent structure, whereas **in mites** it is usually inconspicuous and unarmed.

Life Cycle. Both **ticks and mites** pass through **four** stages: egg, larva, nymph, and adult. The larva has only **three pairs** of legs. In the transmission of infectious agents to man, it is the **adult** stage of ticks and the **larval** stage of mites that are involved. Special mention should be made of **transovarial transmission,** which is especially common among the ticks and mites (and certain other arthropods to be considered below). In this case the infectious agent passes into the **eggs** of the infected arthropod (or into the **larvae** of mites) and is thus capable of being transmitted by succeeding generations. This has great epidemiologic significance, since the transmitting arthropod becomes also an important **reservoir** of the disease.

Diseases Transmitted. The important diseases transmitted by **hard ticks** in the United States are the rickettsial diseases, **Rocky Mountain spotted fever** (p. 799) and **Q fever** (p. 811), and the bacterial disease, **tularemia** (p. 657). Among the ticks incriminated in the spread of these diseases, *Dermacentor andersoni* (wood tick; western United States) and *D. variabilis* (dog tick; central and eastern United States; Fig. 1) deserve special attention. **Soft ticks** of the

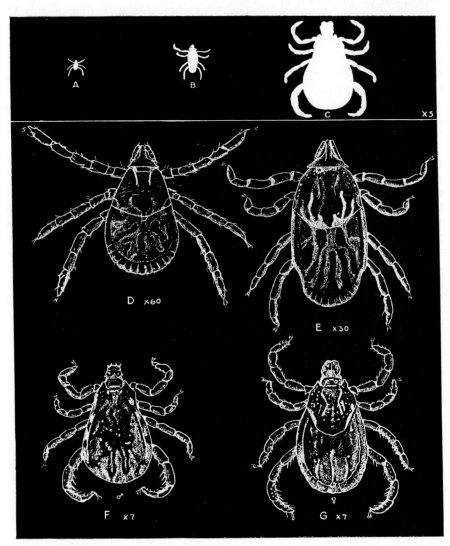

Fig. 1. *Dermacentor variabilis.* A to C, relative sizes of larva, nymph, and adult; D, larva; E, nymph; F, adult male; G, adult female. (From Belding. *Textbook of Clinical Parasitology,* 2nd ed., Appleton-Century-Crofts.)

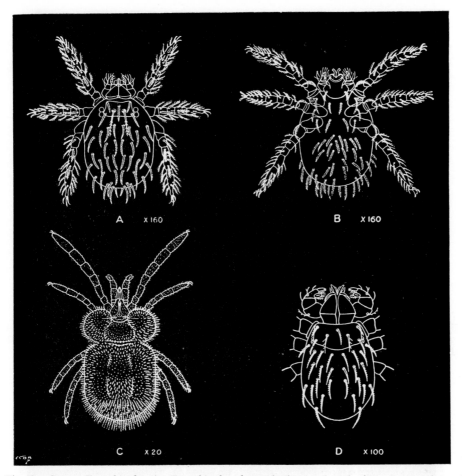

Fig. 2. Genus *Trombicula*. A, *Trombicula akamushi* larva, dorsal view; B, *T. akamushi* larva, ventral view; C, *Eutrombicula alfreddugèsi* (North American chigger) adult; D, *E. alfreddugèsi* larva, dorsal view (legs omitted). (From Belding. *Textbook of Clinical Parasitology,* 2nd ed., Appleton-Century-Crofts.)

genus *Ornithodoros* transmit a spirochetal disease, **endemic** (tick-borne) **relapsing fever** (p. 747).

MITES

Identification. See above under ticks.
Life Cycle. See above under ticks.
Diseases Transmitted. Larval trombiculid mites (*Trombicula akamushi, T. deliensis,* et al.; Fig. 2) transmit the rickettsial disease, **scrub typhus** (tsutsugamushi fever; p. 806). This disease is endemic in Japan, the Philippines, Malaya, South Pacific islands, and elsewhere. More than 6,000 cases were acquired by United States Army personnel in World War II. The **larval** stage of

a common mite parasite (*Allodermanyssus sanguineus*) of wild house mice (*Mus musculus*) transmits another rickettsial disease known as **rickettsialpox** (p. 802). This new disease, described in 1946, was discovered for the first time in New York City but now is being recognized in other parts of the country.

CLASS INSECTA

The body of true insects is divided into **three** distinct regions: the head, thorax, and abdomen. The head bears the mouth parts, a single pair of antennae, and, when present, the eyes. The **adults** possess **three pairs** of

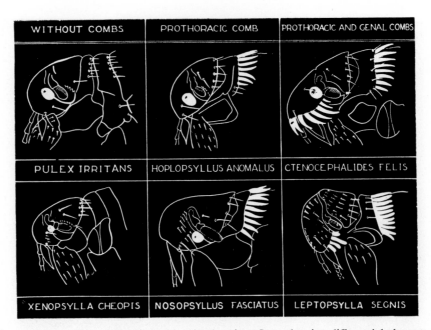

Fig. 3. Schematic representation of heads of various fleas, showing differential characteristics of shape, combs, eyes, and antennae. (From Belding. *Textbook of Clinical Parasitology,* 2nd ed., Appleton-Century-Crofts.)

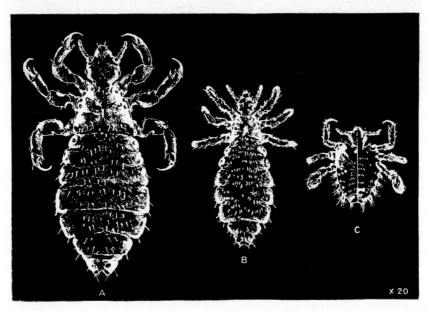

Fig. 4. Parasitic lice of man. A, *Pediculus humanus corporis,* female; B, *Pediculus humanus capitis,* female; C, *Phthirus pubis,* female. (From Belding. *Textbook of Clinical Parasitology,* 2nd ed., Appleton-Century-Crofts.)

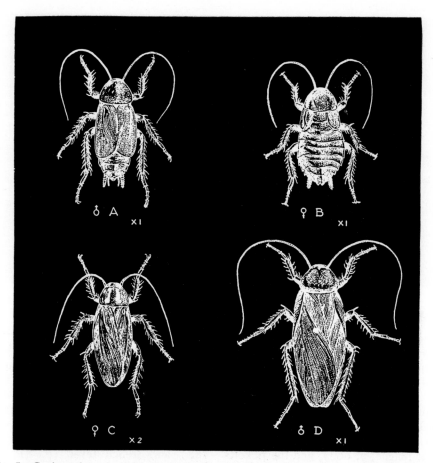

Fig. 5. Cockroaches. A, Oriental cockroach, *Blatta orientalis,* male; B, Oriental cockroach, *Blatta orientalis,* female; C, German cockroach, *Blatella germanica,* female; D, American cockroach, *Periplaneta americana,* male. (From Belding. *Textbook of Clinical Parasitology,* 2nd ed., Appleton-Century-Crofts.)

legs, one pair being borne by each of the three thoracic segments.

Members of **two** of the **orders** to be presented (**Siphonaptera,** fleas; **Anoplura,** blood-sucking lice) have piercing-sucking mouth parts and **do not** possess wings. In both cases the bodies are **compressed.** In the former, however, the compression is **lateral,** while in the lice it is **dorsoventral.** Members of **two** other **orders** to be presented (**Orthoptera,** cockroaches, etc.; **Hemiptera,** true bugs) commonly have **two pairs** of wings, but the mouth parts differ greatly. In the former prominent chewing mouth parts are seen, whereas in the true bugs the more delicate and less prominent piercing-sucking structures are present. The members of the last, and most important, order (**Diptera,** flies) possess only **one pair** of wings, the second pair being vestigial.

ORDER SIPHONAPTERA (FLEAS)

Identification. In addition to the above-mentioned characteristic features of fleas, the combs (**ctenidia**) possessed by some species should be mentioned. These backward-pointing rows of spines just above the mouth parts (**genal**), or located dorsally on the first thoracic segment (**pronotal**), are prominent structures. Their presence or absence in one or both sites is important in classification (Fig. 3). The common species of fleas range in length from 1.5 to 4.0 mm.

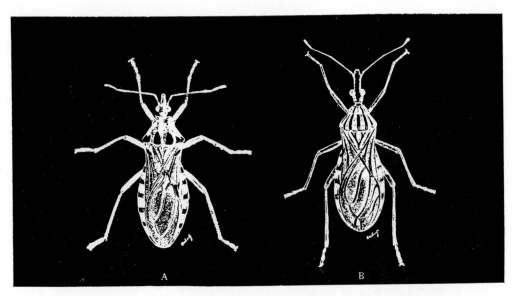

Fig. 6. A, adult male *Panstrongylus megistus;* B, adult male *Rhodnius prolixus.* (From Belding. *Textbook of Clinical Parasitology,* 2nd ed., Appleton-Century-Crofts.)

Life Cycle. Egg, larva **(chewing mouth parts)**, pupa **(in cocoon)**, adult. The adults, males and females, suck blood and are involved in the transmission of certain infectious agents.

Diseases Transmitted. Fleas transmit the important bacterial disease, **plague** (including sylvatic plague; p. 666), and the rickettsial disease, **endemic** (murine or flea-borne) **typhus** (p. 791). *Xenopsylla cheopis* (rat flea) is the most important transmitter of these diseases to man.

ORDER ANOPLURA
(BLOODSUCKING LICE)

Identification. In addition to the characteristics mentioned above, lice are unusual in having a single hook-like **claw** that, together with an opposing tibial process **(thumb)**, makes an effective grasping device (Fig. 4). The **three** parasitic lice of man range in length from 0.8 to 4.0 mm.

Life Cycle. Egg **(nit)**, nymph, adult. Both nymphs and adults take blood from man.

Diseases Transmitted. **Two** of the three types of lice found on man may be involved in the transmission of infectious agents. The **most important** is the **body louse** (*Pediculus*

humanus corporis, 2.0 to 4.0 mm. long), the other is the closely related **head louse** (*P. h. capitis,* 1.0 to 2.0 mm. long). The third louse, not involved in transmission, is the **pubic** (crab) **louse,** *Phthirus pubis* (0.8 to 1.2 mm. long). Lice transmit two rickettsial diseases, **epidemic** (louse-borne) **typhus** (p. 788) and **trench fever** (p. 811), and a spirochetal disease, **epidemic** (louse-borne) **relapsing fever** (p. 748).

ORDER ORTHOPTERA
(COCKROACHES, ETC.)

Identification. In addition to the above-listed characteristics, cockroaches have an oval-shaped body, long-slender antennae, and legs adapted for running. Those considered here range in length from about 1.3 to 3.8 cm.

Life Cycle. Egg (in **ootheca,** a purse-like rigid capsule), nymph, adult.

Diseases Transmitted. Because of their filthy habits, cockroaches have been under suspicion as **mechanical transmitters** of certain human diseases, especially of the **enteric group.** Some of these agents have been shown to pass unharmed through the intestinal tract of cockroaches. **Three** cockroaches commonly enter human dwellings in this country

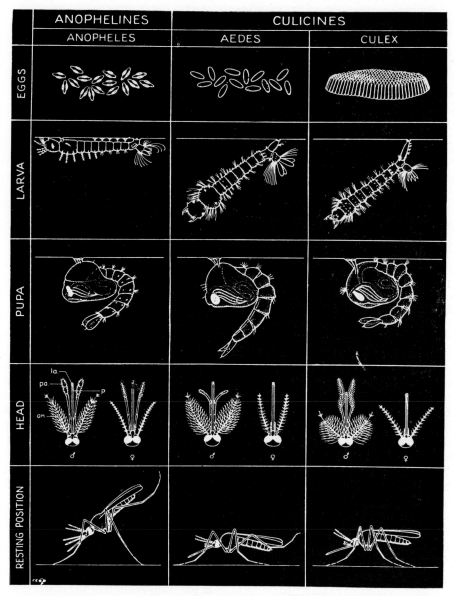

Fig. 7. Schematic representation of differential characteristics of anopheline and culicine mosquitoes. an., antenna; la., labella; p, proboscis; pa., palp. (From Belding. *Textbook of Clinical Parasitology,* 2nd ed., Appleton-Century-Crofts.)

(in order of size: the **American** cockroach, *Periplaneta americana,* about 3.8 cm. long; the **Oriental** cockroach, *Blatta orientalis,* about 2.5 cm. long; and the **German** cockroach, *Blatella germanica,* about 1.3 cm. long). The last-named is considered the **most important.** It can be differentiated from the other two by its smaller size and by the

pair of longitudinal stripes on the dorsal thorax (Fig. 5).

ORDER HEMIPTERA (TRUE BUGS)

Identification. The outstanding feature of this group, besides the features listed above, is the suctorial proboscis that is flexed be-

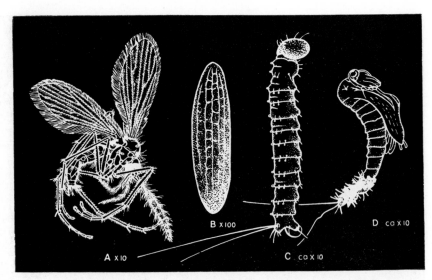

Fig. 8. The genus *Phlebotomus.* A, adult fly; B, egg of *P. papatasii;* C, larva of *P. papatasii;* D, pupa of *P. papatasii.* (From Belding. *Textbook of Clinical Parasitology,* 2nd ed., Appleton-Century-Crofts.)

neath the head and thorax when not in use.

Life Cycle. Egg, nymph, adult.

Disease Transmitted. Cone-nosed bugs (Fig. 6) of several **reduviid** genera, mainly *Triatoma, Rhodnius,* and *Panstrongylus,* transmit *Trypanosoma cruzi,* agent of **Chagas' disease** (p. 1129). The nymphs and adult bugs, of both sexes, may take blood from man. This usually occurs during the time he is sleeping; hence the origin of another common name for these bugs, **flying bedbugs.** Most of the important transmitters are large bugs. *Panstrongylus megistus,* for example, averages 3.0 cm. in length.

ORDER DIPTERA (FLIES)

Identification. All members have **one pair** of functional wings (the rudiments of a second pair are present in the form of knobbed organs, the **halteres).** Sucking mouth parts, either of a piercing or nonpiercing type, are possessed by all members. Within this group numerous structural modifications are seen. Some of these, such as the wings (especially the venation), antennae, external male genitalia, and others, are of value in distinguishing members of this large order.

Life Cycle. Egg, larva, pupa, adult.

Diseases Transmitted. *Mosquitoes* involved in transmission belong to **two** main groups and may for our purpose be referred to as **anophelines** and **culicines,** respectively. The former has only one genus of importance (*Anopheles*), while the latter has several (*Culex Aëdes, Mansonia,* etc.). The main differences between anophelines and culicines in the various stages are shown in Figure 7.

Certain anopheline mosquitoes are the only known transmitters of **malaria** (p. 1134), and certain species transmit *Wuchereria bancrofti* and *W. malayi* (Table 1 in Chap. 85, p. 1161).

Culicine mosquitoes may also be involved in the transmission of the above-listed filarial parasites. In addition, they transmit important **viral diseases** (Chapter 74, p. 782). In the case of **yellow fever** (urban and jungle) and **dengue** the principal transmitters are species of *Aëdes,* while in the case of the large group of the **encephalitides** members of both the *Aëdes* and *Culex* genera are involved. It should be added that members of other genera (e.g., *Mansonia, Haemagogus,* and even *Anopheles*) cannot be overlooked, as some are known to be involved in the transmission of one or more of these various diseases.

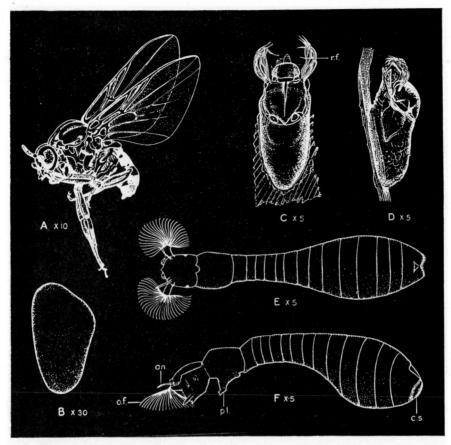

Fig. 9. The genus *Simulium*. A, adult fly; B, egg; C, cocoon and pupa of *S. mexicanum*, dorsal view; D, lateral view of same; E, larva, dorsal view; F, larva, lateral view; an., antenna; c.s., caudal sucker; pl., proleg of thorax; o.f., oral fan; r.f., respiratory filaments. (From Belding. *Textbook of Clinical Parasitology*, 2nd ed., Appleton-Century-Crofts.)

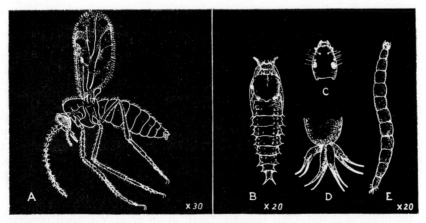

Fig. 10. The genus *Culicoides*. A, *Culicoides austeni*, adult female; B, pupa of *C. kiefferi*; C, head of larva of *C. kiefferi;* D, last segment of larva of *C. kiefferi* showing tracheal gills extruded; E, larva of *C. kiefferi*. (From Belding. *Textbook of Clinical Parasitology*, 2nd ed., Appleton-Century-Crofts.)

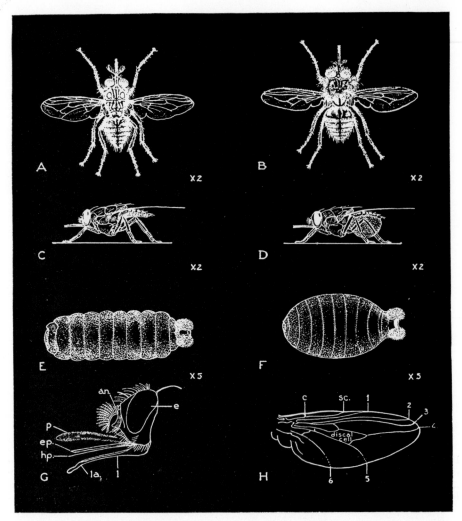

Fig. 11. Tsetse flies. A, *Glossina palpalis,* male; B, *G. morsitans,* female; C, *G. palpalis,* lateral view, before feeding; D, *G. palpalis,* lateral view, after blood meal; E, larva of *G. palpalis;* F, puparium of *G. pallidipes;* G, head and mouth parts of *G. palpalis;* H, wing of *G. palpalis,* showing venation; an., antenna; c, costal vein; sc., subcostal vein; e, eye; ep., epipharynx; hp., hypopharynx; 1, labium; la., labella; p, palps; 1 to 6, longitudinal veins. (From Belding. *Textbook of Clinical Parasitology,* 2nd ed., Appleton-Century-Crofts.)

Mosquitoes vary considerably in length; the North American species (females) range from 2.5 to 9.0 mm. Mosquitoes have wings with a characteristic venation (and conspicuous scales covering the wing veins and wing margins), and the head bears a conspicuous proboscis, which extends forward or downward when the insect is at rest. Only **females** are involved in bloodsucking. The biting activities of the numerous species vary considerably according to the age of the insect,

time of day (or night), and climatic conditions (especially temperature and humidity).

Phlebotomus spp. **(sandflies)** are transmitters of the three **leishmaniases** (p. 1133), **bartonellosis** (p. 722), and **pappataci** (sandfly) **fever** (p. 996). These small (3 to 5 mm.) hairy flies hold their wings, when at rest, in an erect V-shaped position over the back (Fig. 8). The **females** feed on blood at **night,** especially when conditions are warm and humid and there is no wind.

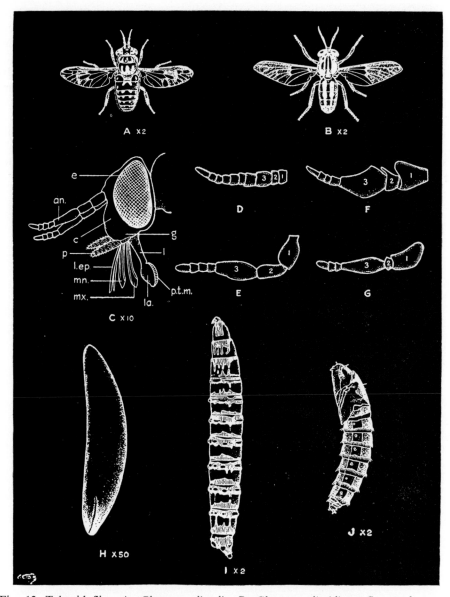

Fig. 12 Tabanid flies. A, *Chrysops discalis;* B, *Chrysops dimidiata;* C, mouth parts of *Chrysops discalis;* D, antenna of *Pangonia;* E, antenna of *Chrysops;* F, antenna of *Tabanus;* G, antenna of *Haematopota;* H, egg of *Tabanus;* I, larva of *Tabanus insignis;* J, pupa of *Tabanus variabilis;* an., antenna; c, clypeus; e, compound eye; g, gena; l, labium; la., labella; l.ep., labrum-epipharynx; mn., mandibles; mx., maxillae; p, palps. (From Belding. *Textbook of Clinical Parasitology,* 2nd ed., Appleton-Century-Crofts.)

Simulium spp. **(black flies)** transmit the filarial parasite, *Onchocerca volvulus* (Table 1 in Chapter 85, p. 1161). These small (1 to 5 mm.) flies are characterized by their hump-backed appearance and the presence of two or three very heavy veins in the anterior re-gion of the wings (Fig. 9). The **females** suck blood during the **daytime.**

Culicoides spp. **(biting midges)** transmit the filariae, *Acanthocheilonema perstans* and *Mansonella ozzardi* (Table 1 in Chapter 85, p. 1161). These small (2 to 3 mm.) flies may be recognized by their pubescent (with fine hairs) wings showing a characteristic iridescent spotting (Fig. 10). The **females** suck blood and are most active at **twilight** and during the **early morning** hours.

Glossina spp. **(tsetse flies)** transmit the two **African trypanosomiases** (p. 1129). The peculiar shape of the **discal cell** in the wings, resembling a butcher's cleaver, is diagnostic for this group of flies (Fig. 11). **Both sexes** (6 to 13 mm. long) take blood meals during **daylight** hours.

Chrysops spp. **(deer flies)** transmit a filarial parasite, *Loa loa* (Table 1 in Chapter 85, p. 1161) and a bacterial disease, **tularemia** (p. 657). These flies (7 to 9 mm.; Fig. 12) have a robust shape, a yellow-banded abdomen with dark stripes or spots, and clear wings with a dark band along the anterior margin and a broad crossband through the middle portion (some have also a spot at the tip of the wing). The **females** suck blood and attack man most actively in the **early morning** and **late afternoon.**

Index

Page numbers in **boldface type** refer to important sections.